UNDERSTANDING
Nutrition

UNDERSTANDING

Nutrition

Eleventh Edition

Ellie Whitney

Sharon Rady Rolfes

THOMSON

WADSWORTH

Australia • Canada • Mexico • Singapore • Spain
United Kingdom • United States

THOMSON
WADSWORTH

Understanding Nutrition, Eleventh Edition
Ellie Whitney, Sharon Rady Rolfes

Executive Editor: Peter Adams
Development Editor: Nedah Rose
Assistant Editor: Elesha Feldman, Kate Franco
Editorial Assistant: Jean Blomo
Technology Project Manager: Ericka Yeoman-Saler
Marketing Manager: Jennifer Somerville
Marketing Assistant: Catie Ronquillo
Marketing Communications Manager: Jessica Perry
Project Manager, Editorial Production: Cheryll Linthicum
Creative Director: Rob Hugel
Art Director: John Walker
Print Buyer: Becky Cross

Permissions Editor: Sarah D'Stair
Production Service: The Book Company, Dusty Friedman
Text Designer: Diane Beasley
Photo Researcher: Roman Barnes, Paul Forkner
Copy Editor: Mary Douglas
Illustrator: Imagineering, Lachina Publishing Services
Cover Designer: Dare Porter
Cover Image: © Masterfile Corporation
Cover Printer: China Translation & Printing Services Ltd.
Compositor: Lachina Publishing Services
Printer: China Translation & Printing Services Ltd.

Printed in China
2 3 4 5 6 7 11 10 09 08 07

Thomson Higher Education
10 Davis Drive
Belmont, CA 94002-3098
USA

For more information about our products, contact us at:
Thomson Learning Academic Resource Center
1-800-423-0563

For permission to use material from this text or product, submit a request online at:
http://www.thomsonrights.com

Any additional questions about permissions can be submitted by email to thomsonrights@thomson.com.

Library of Congress Control Number: 2007920597

Student Edition:
ISBN-13: 978-0-495-11669-1
ISBN-10: 0-495-11669-6
International Student Edition:
ISBN-13: 978-0-495-11682-0
ISBN-10: 0-495-11682-3

To the memory of
Gary Woodruff, the editor who
first encouraged me to write.
Ellie

To Ellie Whitney, my mentor,
partner, and friend, with much
appreciation for believing in
me, sharing your wisdom, and
giving me the opportunity to
pursue a career more challenging
and rewarding than any I could
have imagined.
Sharon

About the Authors

Ellie Whitney grew up in New York City and received her B.A. and Ph.D. degrees in English and Biology at Radcliffe/Harvard University and Washington University, respectively. She has lived in Tallahassee since 1970, has taught at both Florida State University and Florida A&M University, has written newspaper columns on environmental matters for the *Tallahassee Democrat*, and has authored almost a dozen college textbooks on nutrition, health, and related topics, many of which have been revised multiple times over the years. In addition to teaching and writing, she has spent the past three-plus decades exploring outdoor Florida and studying its ecology. Her latest book is *Priceless Florida: The Natural Ecosystems* (Pineapple Press, 2004).

Sharon Rady Rolfes received her M.S. in nutrition and food science from Florida State University. She is a founding member of Nutrition and Health Associates, an information resource center that maintains a research database on over 1000 nutrition-related topics. Her other publications include the college textbooks *Understanding Normal and Clinical Nutrition* and *Nutrition for Health and Health Care* and a multimedia CD-ROM called *Nutrition Interactive*. In addition to writing, she occasionally teaches at Florida State University and serves as a consultant for various educational projects. Her volunteer work includes coordinating meals for the hungry and homeless and serving on the steering committee of Working Well Leon County, a community initiative designed to help local businesses improve the health and well-being of their employees. She maintains her registration as a dietitian and membership in the American Dietetic Association.

Brief Contents

CHAPTER 1   An Overview of Nutrition   2
   HIGHLIGHT   Nutrition Information and Misinformation—On the Net and in the News   30

CHAPTER 2   Planning a Healthy Diet   36
   HIGHLIGHT   Vegetarian Diets   64

CHAPTER 3   Digestion, Absorption, and Transport   70
   HIGHLIGHT   Common Digestive Problems   92

CHAPTER 4   The Carbohydrates: Sugars, Starches, and Fibers   100
   HIGHLIGHT   Alternatives to Sugar   132

CHAPTER 5   The Lipids: Triglycerides, Phospholipids, and Sterols   138
   HIGHLIGHT   High-Fat Foods—Friend or Foe?   172

CHAPTER 6   Protein: Amino Acids   180
   HIGHLIGHT   Nutritional Genomics   207

CHAPTER 7   Metabolism: Transformations and Interactions   212
   HIGHLIGHT   Alcohol and Nutrition   238

CHAPTER 8   Energy Balance and Body Composition   248
   HIGHLIGHT   Eating Disorders   270

CHAPTER 9   Weight Management: Overweight, Obesity, and Underweight   280
   HIGHLIGHT   The Latest and Greatest Weight-Loss Diet—Again   315

CHAPTER 10   The Water-Soluble Vitamins: B Vitamins and Vitamin C   322
   HIGHLIGHT   Vitamin and Mineral Supplements   360

CHAPTER 11   The Fat-Soluble Vitamins: A, D, E, and K   368
   HIGHLIGHT   Antioxidant Nutrients in Disease Prevention   390

CHAPTER 12   Water and the Major Minerals   396
   HIGHLIGHT   Osteoporosis and Calcium   431

CHAPTER 13   The Trace Minerals   440
    HIGHLIGHT   Phytochemicals and Functional Foods   469

CHAPTER 14   Fitness: Physical Activity, Nutrients, and Body Adaptations   476
    HIGHLIGHT   Supplements as Ergogenic Aids   503

CHAPTER 15   Life Cycle Nutrition: Pregnancy and Lactation   508
    HIGHLIGHT   Fetal Alcohol Syndrome   543

CHAPTER 16   Life Cycle Nutrition: Infancy, Childhood, and Adolescence   546
    HIGHLIGHT   Childhood Obesity and the Early Development of Chronic Diseases   586

CHAPTER 17   Life Cycle Nutrition: Adulthood and the Later Years   592
    HIGHLIGHT   Nutrient-Drug Interactions   615

CHAPTER 18   Diet and Health   620
    HIGHLIGHT   Complementary and Alternative Medicine   652

CHAPTER 19   Consumer Concerns about Foods and Water   662
    HIGHLIGHT   Food Biotechnology   693

CHAPTER 20   Hunger and the Global Environment   700
    HIGHLIGHT   Progress toward Sustainable Food Production   716

APPENDIX A   Cells, Hormones, and Nerves   A-2
APPENDIX B   Basic Chemistry Concepts   B-1
APPENDIX C   Biochemical Structures and Pathways   C-1
APPENDIX D   Measures of Protein Quality   D-1
APPENDIX E   Nutrition Assessment   E-1
APPENDIX F   Physical Activity and Energy Requirements   F-1
APPENDIX G   United States: Exchange Lists   G-1
APPENDIX H   Table of Food Composition   H-1
APPENDIX I   WHO: Nutrition Recommendations
              Canada: Guidelines and Meal Planning   I-1
APPENDIX J   Healthy People 2010   J-1

Glossary   GL-1
Index   IN-1
Aids to Calculations   W

Dietary Reference Intakes (inside front covers)
Daily Values for Food Labels (inside back cover, left)
Glossary of Nutrient Measures (inside back cover, left)
Body Mass Index (BMI) (inside back cover, right)

Contents

CHAPTER 1

An Overview of Nutrition   2

Food Choices   3

The Nutrients   5
  Nutrients in Foods and in the Body   6
  The Energy-Yielding Nutrients: Carbohydrate, Fat, and Protein   7
  The Vitamins   10
  The Minerals   10
  Water   11

The Science of Nutrition   11
  Conducting Research   11
  Analyzing Research Findings   14
  Publishing Research   15

Dietary Reference Intakes   16
  Establishing Nutrient Recommendations   16
  Establishing Energy Recommendations   18
  Using Nutrient Recommendations   18
  Comparing Nutrient Recommendations   19

Nutrition Assessment   20
  Nutrition Assessment of Individuals   20
  Nutrition Assessment of Populations   22

Diet and Health   24
  Chronic Diseases   24
  Risk Factors for Chronic Diseases   24

HIGHLIGHT Nutrition Information and Misinformation—On the Net and in the News   30

CHAPTER 2

Planning a Healthy Diet   36

Principles and Guidelines   37
  Diet-Planning Principles   37
  Dietary Guidelines for Americans   39

Diet-Planning Guides   41
  USDA Food Guide   41
  Exchange Lists   47
  Putting the Plan into Action   48
  From Guidelines to Groceries   48

Food Labels   54
  The Ingredient List   55
  Serving Sizes   55
  Nutrition Facts   55
  The Daily Values   56
  Nutrient Claims   58
  Health Claims   59
  Structure-Function Claims   59
  Consumer Education   60

HIGHLIGHT Vegetarian Diets   64

CHAPTER 3

Digestion, Absorption, and Transport   70

Digestion   71
  Anatomy of the Digestive Tract   72
  The Muscular Action of Digestion   74
  The Secretions of Digestion   76
  The Final Stage   78

Absorption   80
  Anatomy of the Absorptive System   80
  A Closer Look at the Intestinal Cells   81

The Circulatory Systems   83
  The Vascular System   83
  The Lymphatic System   84

The Health and Regulation of the GI Tract   86
  Gastrointestinal Bacteria   86
  Gastrointestinal Hormones and Nerve Pathways   86
  The System at Its Best   88

HIGHLIGHT Common Digestive Problems   92

CHAPTER 4

The Carbohydrates: Sugars, Starches, and Fibers   100

The Chemist's View of Carbohydrates   101
The Simple Carbohydrates   102

Monosaccharides   102

Disaccharides   103

The Complex Carbohydrates   105

Glycogen   105

Starches   105

Fibers   106

Digestion and Absorption of Carbohydrates   107

Carbohydrate Digestion   108

Carbohydrate Absorption   108

Lactose Intolerance   110

Glucose in the Body   111

A Preview of Carbohydrate Metabolism   112

The Constancy of Blood Glucose   113

Health Effects and Recommended Intakes
of Sugars   117

Health Effects of Sugars   117

Controversies Surrounding Sugars   119

Recommended Intakes of Sugars   121

Health Effects and Recommended Intakes of Starch
and Fibers   122

Health Effects of Starch and Fibers   122

Recommended Intakes of Starch and Fibers   124

From Guidelines to Groceries   125

HIGHLIGHT   Alternatives to Sugar   132

CHAPTER 5

The Lipids: Triglycerides, Phospholipids, and Sterols   138

The Chemist's View of Fatty Acids and Triglycerides   139

Fatty Acids   140

Triglycerides   142

Degree of Unsaturation Revisited   142

The Chemist's View of Phospholipids and Sterols   145

Phospholipids   145

Sterols   146

Digestion, Absorption, and Transport of Lipids   147

Lipid Digestion   147

Lipid Absorption   149

Lipid Transport   150

Lipids in the Body   153

Roles of Triglycerides   153

Essential Fatty Acids   154

A Preview of Lipid Metabolism   155

Health Effects and Recommended Intakes of Lipids   156

Health Effects of Lipids   156

Recommended Intakes of Fat   160

From Guidelines to Groceries   161

HIGHLIGHT   High-Fat Foods—Friend or Foe?   172

CHAPTER 6

Protein: Amino Acids   180

The Chemist's View of Proteins   181

Amino Acids   181

Proteins   183

Digestion and Absorption of Protein   185

Protein Digestion   185

Protein Absorption   185

Proteins in the Body   187

Protein Synthesis   187

Roles of Proteins   189

A Preview of Protein Metabolism   193

Protein in Foods   195

Protein Quality   195

Protein Regulations for Food Labels   196

Health Effects and Recommended Intakes
of Protein   196

Protein-Energy Malnutrition   196

Health Effects of Protein   199

Recommended Intakes of Protein   201

Protein and Amino Acid Supplements   202

HIGHLIGHT   Nutritional Genomics   207

CHAPTER 7

Metabolism: Transformations and Interactions   212

Chemical Reactions in the Body   214

Breaking Down Nutrients for Energy   217

Glucose   219

Glycerol and Fatty Acids   222

Amino Acids   224

Breaking Down Nutrients for Energy—In Summary 226

The Final Steps of Catabolism   227

Energy Balance   230

Feasting—Excess Energy   232

The Transition from Feasting to Fasting   233

Fasting—Inadequate Energy   233

HIGHLIGHT   Alcohol and Nutrition   238

CHAPTER 8

Energy Balance and Body Composition 248

Energy Balance 249

Energy In: The kCalories Foods Provide 250

Food Composition 250

Food Intake 251

Energy Out: The kCalories the Body Expends 253

Components of Energy Expenditure 254

Estimating Energy Requirements 256

Body Weight, Body Composition, and Health 258

Defining Healthy Body Weight 258

Body Fat and Its Distribution 260

Health Risks Associated with Body Weight and Body Fat 263

HIGHLIGHT Eating Disorders 270

CHAPTER 9

Weight Management: Overweight, Obesity, and Underweight 280

Overweight and Obesity 281

Fat Cell Development 282

Fat Cell Metabolism 282

Set-Point Theory 283

Causes of Overweight and Obesity 283

Genetics 284

Environment 286

Problems of Overweight and Obesity 288

Health Risks 288

Perceptions and Prejudices 289

Dangerous Interventions 289

Aggressive Treatments for Obesity 292

Drugs 292

Surgery 292

Weight-Loss Strategies 294

Eating Plans 295

Physical Activity 299

Environmental Influences 302

Behavior and Attitude 303

Weight Maintenance 305

Prevention 306

Public Health Programs 306

Underweight 307

Problems of Underweight 307

Weight-Gain Strategies 307

HIGHLIGHT The Latest and Greatest Weight-Loss Diet—Again 315

CHAPTER 10

The Water Soluble Vitamins: B Vitamins and Vitamin C 322

The Vitamins—An Overview 323

The B Vitamins—As Individuals 326

Thiamin 327

Riboflavin 328

Niacin 331

Biotin 333

Pantothenic Acid 335

Vitamin B_6 336

Folate 338

Vitamin B_{12} 342

Non-B Vitamins 345

The B Vitamins—In Concert 346

B Vitamin Roles 347

B Vitamin Deficiencies 348

B Vitamin Toxicities 349

B Vitamin Food Sources 349

Vitamin C 350

Vitamin C Roles 351

Vitamin C Recommendations 352

Vitamin C Deficiency 353

Vitamin C Toxicity 353

Vitamin C Food Sources 354

HIGHLIGHT Vitamin and Mineral Supplements 360

CHAPTER 11

The Fat Soluble Vitamins: A, D, E, and K 368

Vitamin A and Beta-Carotene 369

Roles in the Body 370

Vitamin A Deficiency 372

Vitamin A Toxicity 374

Vitamin A Recommendations 374

Vitamin A in Foods 374

Vitamin D   377
   Roles in the Body   377
   Vitamin D Deficiency   378
   Vitamin D Toxicity   379
   Vitamin D Recommendations and Sources   379

Vitamin E   381
   Vitamin E as an Antioxidant   382
   Vitamin E Deficiency   382
   Vitamin E Toxicity   382
   Vitamin E Recommendations   382
   Vitamin E in Foods   383

Vitamin K   383
   Roles in the Body   384
   Vitamin K Deficiency   384
   Vitamin K Toxicity   385
   Vitamin K Recommendations and Sources   385

The Fat-Soluble Vitamins—In Summary   385

HIGHLIGHT Antioxidant Nutrients in
Disease Prevention   390

CHAPTER 12

Water and the Major Minerals   396

Water and the Body Fluids   397
   Water Balance and Recommended Intakes   398
   Blood Volume and Blood Pressure   401
   Fluid and Electrolyte Balance   402
   Fluid and Electrolyte Imbalance   406
   Acid-Base Balance   406

The Minerals—An Overview   408

Sodium   410

Chloride   413

Potassium   414

Calcium   416
   Calcium Roles in the Body   416
   Calcium Recommendations and Sources   418
   Calcium Deficiency   421

Phosphorus   422

Magnesium   423

Sulfate   425

HIGHLIGHT Osteoporosis and Calcium   431

CHAPTER 13

The Trace Minerals   440

The Trace Minerals—An Overview   441

Iron   442
   Iron Roles in the Body   442
   Iron Absorption and Metabolism   443
   Iron Deficiency   445
   Iron Toxicity   447
   Iron Recommendations and Sources   449
   Iron Contamination and Supplementation   450

Zinc   452
   Zinc Roles in the Body   452
   Zinc Absorption and Metabolism   452
   Zinc Deficiency   453
   Zinc Toxicity   454
   Zinc Recommendations and Sources   454
   Zinc Supplementation   455

Iodine   455

Selenium   457

Copper   458

Manganese   459

Fluoride   460

Chromium   461

Molybdenum   462

Other Trace Minerals   462

Contaminant Minerals   463

Closing Thoughts on the Nutrients   463

HIGHLIGHT Phytochemicals and Functional
Foods   469

CHAPTER 14

Fitness: Physical Activity, Nutrients, and Body Adaptations   476

Fitness   477
   Benefits of Fitness   478
   Developing Fitness   480
   Cardiorespiratory Endurance   482
   Weight Training   484

Energy Systems, Fuels, and Nutrients
to Support Activity 484
   The Energy Systems of Physical Activity—ATP and CP 484
   Glucose Use during Physical Activity 485
   Fat Use during Physical Activity 488
   Protein Use during Physical Activity—and between Times 490
   Vitamins and Minerals to Support Activity 491
   Fluids and Electrolytes to Support Activity 493
   Poor Beverage Choices: Caffeine and Alcohol 496

Diets for Physically Active People 496
   Choosing a Diet to Support Fitness 496
   Meals before and after Competition 497

HIGHLIGHT Supplements as Ergogenic Aids 503

CHAPTER 15

Life Cycle Nutrition: Pregnancy and Lactation 508

Nutrition prior to Pregnancy 509
Growth and Development during Pregnancy 510
   Placental Development 510
   Fetal Growth and Development 510
   Critical Periods 512

Maternal Weight 515
   Weight prior to Conception 516
   Weight Gain during Pregnancy 516
   Exercise during Pregnancy 518

Nutrition during Pregnancy 519
   Energy and Nutrient Needs during Pregnancy 520
   Vegetarian Diets during Pregnancy and Lactation 524
   Common Nutrition-Related Concerns of Pregnancy 524

High-Risk Pregnancies 525
   The Infant's Birthweight 525
   Malnutrition and Pregnancy 526
   Food Assistance Programs 527
   Maternal Health 527
   The Mother's Age 529
   Practices Incompatible with Pregnancy 530

Nutrition during Lactation 532
   Lactation: A Physiological Process 533
   Breastfeeding: A Learned Behavior 534
   Maternal Energy and Nutrient Needs during Lactation 534
   Maternal Health 536
   Practices Incompatible with Lactation 537

HIGHLIGHT Fetal Alcohol Syndrome 543

CHAPTER 16

Life Cycle Nutrition: Infancy, Childhood, and Adolescence 546

Nutrition during Infancy 547
   Energy and Nutrient Needs 547
   Breast Milk 550
   Infant Formula 552
   Special Needs of Preterm Infants 554
   Introducing Cow's Milk 554
   Introducing Solid Foods 555
   Mealtimes with Toddlers 557

Nutrition during Childhood 558
   Energy and Nutrient Needs 558
   Hunger and Malnutrition in Children 562
   The Malnutrition-Lead Connection 564
   Hyperactivity and "Hyper" Behavior 564
   Food Allergy and Intolerance 565
   Childhood Obesity 567
   Mealtimes at Home 571
   Nutrition at School 573

Nutrition during Adolescence 575
   Growth and Development 575
   Energy and Nutrient Needs 576
   Food Choices and Health Habits 577
   Problems Adolescents Face 578

HIGHLIGHT Childhood Obesity and the Early Development of Chronic Diseases 586

CHAPTER 17

Life Cycle Nutrition: Adulthood and the Later Years 592

Nutrition and Longevity 594
   Observation of Older Adults 595
   Manipulation of Diet 596

The Aging Process 597
   Physiological Changes 598
   Other Changes 600

Energy and Nutrient Needs of Older Adults 601
   Water 601
   Energy and Energy Nutrients 601
   Vitamins and Minerals 602
   Nutrient Supplements 603

Nutrition-Related Concerns of Older Adults   604
  Vision   604
  Arthritis   605
  The Aging Brain   606

Food Choices and Eating Habits
of Older Adults   607
  Food Assistance Programs   608
  Meals for Singles   609

HIGHLIGHT   Nutrient-Drug Interactions   615

CHAPTER 18

Diet and Health   620

Nutrition and Infectious Diseases   621
  The Immune System   622
  Nutrition and Immunity   623
  HIV and AIDS   623

Nutrition and Chronic Diseases   624

Cardiovascular Disease   626
  How Atherosclerosis Develops   626
  Risk Factors for Coronary Heart Disease   628
  Recommendations for Reducing Coronary Heart
  Disease Risk   630

Hypertension   632
  How Hypertension Develops   632
  Risk Factors for Hypertension   634
  Treatment of Hypertension   635

Diabetes Mellitus   637
  How Diabetes Develops   637
  Complications of Diabetes   639
  Recommendations for Diabetes   640

Cancer   642
  How Cancer Develops   642
  Recommendations for Reducing Cancer Risk   645

Recommendations for Chronic Diseases   646

HIGHLIGHT   Complementary and Alternative
Medicine   652

CHAPTER 19

Consumer Concerns about Foods
and Water   662

Foodborne Illnesses   664
  Foodborne Infections and Food Intoxications   664

Food Safety in the Marketplace   666
Food Safety in the Kitchen   667
Food Safety while Traveling   672
Advances in Food Safety   672

Nutritional Adequacy of Foods and Diets   673
  Obtaining Nutrient Information   673
  Minimizing Nutrient Losses   674

Environmental Contaminants   674
  Harmfulness of Environmental Contaminants   674
  Guidelines for Consumers   676

Natural Toxicants in Foods   677

Pesticides   678
  Hazards and Regulation of Pesticides   678
  Monitoring Pesticides   679
  Consumer Concerns   679

Food Additives   682
  Regulations Governing Additives   682
  Intentional Food Additives   683
  Indirect Food Additives   685

Consumer Concerns about Water   687
  Sources of Drinking Water   688
  Water Systems and Regulations   688

HIGHLIGHT   Food Biotechnology   693

CHAPTER 20

Hunger and the Global
Environment   700

Hunger in the United States   702
  Defining Hunger in the United States   702
  Relieving Hunger in the United States   703

World Hunger   705
  Food Shortages   705
  Malnutrition   706
  Diminishing Food Supply   707

Poverty and Overpopulation   707

Environmental Degradation and Hunger   709
  Environmental Limitations in Food Production   709
  Other Limitations in Food Production   710

Solutions   710
  Sustainable Development Worldwide   711
  Activism and Simpler Lifestyles at Home   711

HIGHLIGHT   Progress toward Sustainable Food
Production   716

APPENDIX A   Cells, Hormones, and Nerves A-2

APPENDIX B   Basic Chemistry Concepts B-1

APPENDIX C   Biochemical Structures
and Pathways C-1

APPENDIX D   Measures of Protein Quality D-1

APPENDIX E   Nutrition Assessment E-1

APPENDIX F   Physical Activity and Energy
Requirements F-1

APPENDIX G   United States: Exchange Lists G-1

APPENDIX H   Table of Food Composition H-1

APPENDIX I   WHO: Nutrition Recommendations
Canada: Guidelines and Meal Planning I-1

APPENDIX J   Healthy People 2010 J-1

Glossary GL-1
Index IN-1
Aids to Calculations W
Dietary Reference Intakes (Inside Front Covers)
Daily Values for Food Labels (Inside Back Cover, Left)
Glossary of Nutrient Measures (Inside Back Cover, Left)
Body Mass Index (BMI) (Inside Back Cover, Right)

Preface

Nutrition is a science. The details of a nutrient's chemistry or a cell's biology can be overwhelming and confusing to some, but it needn't be. When the science is explained step by step and the facts are connected one by one, the details become clear and understandable. By telling stories about fat mice, using analogies of lamps, and applying guidelines to groceries, we make the science of nutrition meaningful and memorable. That has been our goal since the first edition: to reveal the fascination of science and share the excitement of nutrition with readers. We have learned from the hundreds of professors and more than a million students who have used this book through the years that readers want to *understand* nutrition so that they can make healthy choices in their daily lives.

Because nutrition is an active science, staying current is paramount. To that end, this edition builds on the science of previous editions with the latest in nutrition research. Much has changed in the world of nutrition and in our daily lives since the first edition. The number of foods has increased dramatically—even as we spend less time than ever in the kitchen preparing meals. The connections between diet and disease have become more apparent—and our interest in making smart health choices has followed. More people are living longer and healthier lives. The science of nutrition has grown rapidly, with new "facts" emerging daily. In this edition, as with previous editions, every chapter has been substantially revised to reflect the many changes that have occurred in the field of nutrition and in our daily lives over the years. We hope that this book serves you well.

The Chapters *Understanding Nutrition* presents the core information of an introductory nutrition course. The early chapters introduce the nutrients and their work in the body, and the later chapters apply that information to people's lives—describing the role of foods and nutrients in energy balance and weight control, in physical activity, in the life cycle, in disease prevention, in food safety, and in hunger. Chapter 1 begins by exploring why we eat the foods we do and continues with a brief overview of the nutrients, the science of nutrition, recommended nutrient intakes, assessment, and important relationships between diet and health. Chapter 2 describes the diet-planning principles and food guides used to create diets that support good health and includes instructions on how to read a food label. In Chapter 3, readers follow the journey of digestion and absorption as the body transforms foods into nutrients. Chapters 4 through 6 describe carbohydrates, fats, and proteins—their chemistry, roles in the body, and places in the diet. Then Chapter 7 shows how the body derives energy from these three nutrients. Chapters 8 and 9 continue the story with a look at energy balance, the factors associated with overweight and underweight, and the benefits and dangers of weight loss and weight gain. Chapters 10 through 13 complete the introductory lessons by describing the vitamins, the minerals, and water—their roles in the body, deficiency and toxicity symptoms, and sources.

The next seven chapters weave that basic information into practical applications, showing how nutrition influences people's lives. Chapter 14 describes how physical activity and nutrition work together to support fitness. Chapters 15, 16, and 17 present the special nutrient needs of people through the life cycle—pregnancy and lactation; infancy, childhood, and adolescence; and adulthood and the later years. Chapter 18 focuses on the dietary risk factors and recommendations associated with chronic diseases, and Chapter 19 addresses consumer concerns about the safety of the food and water supply. Chapter 20 closes the book by examining hunger and the global environment and by exploring possible solutions for establishing sustainable foodways.

The Highlights Every chapter is followed by a highlight that provides readers with an in-depth look at a current, and often controversial, topic that relates to its companion chapter. This edition features a new highlight on nutritional genomics—the new field of study that explores how nutrients influence gene activity and how genes influence the activities of nutrients.

Special Features The art and layout in this edition have been carefully designed to be inviting while enhancing student learning. In addition, special features help readers identify key concepts and apply nutrition knowledge. For example, when a new term is introduced, it is printed in bold type and a **definition** is provided. These definitions often include pronunciations and derivations to facilitate understanding. The glossary at the end of the text includes all defined terms.

> **definition** (DEF-eh-NISH-en): the meaning of a word.
> • **de** = from
> • **finis** = boundary

Nutrition in Your Life

Each chapter begins with Nutrition in Your Life sections that introduce the essence of the chapter in a friendly and familiar scenario.

Nutrition Portfolio

At the end of the chapter, Nutrition Portfolio sections revisit that message and prompt readers to consider whether their personal choices are meeting the dietary goals introduced in the chapter.

IN SUMMARY

Each major section within a chapter concludes with a summary paragraph that reviews the key concepts. Similarly, summary tables cue readers to important reviews.

Also featured in this edition are the *Dietary Guidelines for Americans, 2005* recommendations, which are introduced in Chapter 2 and presented throughout the text whenever their subjects are discussed. Look for the following design.

Dietary Guidelines for Americans 2005

These guidelines provide science-based advice to promote health and to reduce the risk of chronic disease through diet and physical activity.

HOW TO

Many of the chapters include "How to" sections that guide readers through problem-solving tasks. For example, the "How to" in Chapter 1 takes students through the steps of calculating energy intake from the grams of carbohydrate, fat, and protein in a food; another "How to" in Chapter 20 describes how to plan healthy meals on a tight budget.

NUTRITION CALCULATIONS

ThomsonNOW

Several chapters close with a "Nutrition Calculation" section. These sections often reinforce the "How to" lessons and provide practice in doing nutrition-related calculations. The problems enable readers to apply their skills to hypothetical situations and then check their answers (found at the end of the chapter). Readers who successfully master these exercises will be well prepared for "real-life" nutrition-related problems.

NUTRITION ON THE NET

ThomsonNOW

Each chapter and many highlights conclude with Nutrition on the Net—a list of websites for further study of topics covered in the accompanying text. These lists do not imply an endorsement of the organizations or their programs. We have tried to provide reputable sources, but cannot be responsible for the content of these sites. (Read Highlight 1 to learn how to find reliable information on the Internet.)

STUDY QUESTIONS

ThomsonNOW

Each chapter ends with study questions in essay and multiple-choice format. Study questions offer readers the opportunity to review the major concepts presented in the chapters in preparation for exams. The page numbers after each essay question refer readers to discussions that answer the question; answers to the multiple-choice questions appear at the end of the chapter.

The Appendixes The appendixes are valuable references for a number of purposes. Appendix A summarizes background information on the hormonal and nervous systems, complementing Appendixes B and C on basic chemistry, the chemical structures of nutrients, and major metabolic pathways. Appendix D describes measures of protein quality. Appendix E provides detailed coverage of nutrition assessment, and Appendix F presents the estimated energy requirements for men and women at various levels of physical activity. Appendix G presents the 2003 U.S. Exchange System. Appendix H is an 8000-item food composition table compiled from the latest nutrient database assembled by Axxya Systems. Appendix I presents recommendations from the World Health Organization (WHO) and information for Canadians—the 2005 Beyond the Basics meal planning system and 2007 guidelines to healthy eating and physical activities. Appendix J presents the Healthy People 2010 nutrition-related objectives.

The Inside Covers The inside covers put commonly used information at your fingertips. The front covers (pp. A, B, and C) present the current nutrient recommendations; the inside back cover (p. Y on the left) features the Daily Values used on food labels and a glossary of nutrient measures; and the inside back cover (p. Z on the right) shows the suggested weight ranges for various heights. The pages just prior to the back cover (pp. W-X) assist readers with calculations and conversions.

Closing Comments We have taken great care to provide accurate information and have included many references at the end of each chapter and highlight. However, to keep the number of references manageable, many statements that appeared in previous editions with references now appear without them. All statements reflect current nutrition knowledge and the authors will supply references upon request. In addition to supporting text statements, the end-of-chapter references provide readers with resources for finding a good overview or more details on the subject. Nutrition is a fascinating subject, and we hope our enthusiasm for it comes through on every page.

Ellie Whitney
Sharon Rady Rolfes
April 2007

Acknowledgments

To produce a book requires the coordinated effort of a team of people—and, no doubt, each team member has another team of support people as well. We salute, with a big round of applause, everyone who has worked so diligently to ensure the quality of this book.

We thank our partners and friends, Linda DeBruyne and Fran Webb, for their valuable consultations and contributions; working together over the past 20+ years has been a most wonderful experience. We especially appreciate Linda's research assistance on several chapters. Special thanks to our colleagues Kathy Pinna for her insightful comments, Gail Hammond for her Canadian perspective, and Sylvia Crews for her revision of the Aids to Calculation section at the end of the book. A thousand thank yous to Beth Magana, Marni Jay Rolfes, and Alex Rodriguez for their careful attention to manuscript preparation and a multitude of other daily tasks.

We also thank the many people who have prepared the ancillaries that accompany this text: Harry Sitren for writing and enhancing the Test Bank; Gail Hammond, Melissa Langone, Sharon Stewart, Lori Turner, and Daryle Wane for contributing to the Instructor's Manual; Eugene Fenster for developing the WebTutor; and Lori Turner for organizing the Student Study Guide. Thanks also to Donna Kelly and to the folks at Axxya for their assistance in creating the food composition appendix and developing the computerized diet analysis program that accompanies this book.

Our special thanks to Peter Marshall, Beth Howe, and Sandra Craig for countless creative contributions to previous editions and to our new editorial team for stepping in with enthusiasm—Peter Adams for his leadership and support; Nedah Rose for her thoughtful suggestions and efficient analysis of reviews; Cheryll Linthicum for her artistic care of this project; Jean Blomo for her help with any and all requests; Dusty Friedman for her diligent attention to the innumerable details involved in production; Jennifer Somerville for her energetic efforts in marketing; Ericka Yeoman-Saler for her dedication in developing our online animations and study tools; Sarah D'Stair for her assistance in obtaining permissions; and Elesha Feldman for her competent coordination of ancillaries.

We also thank Diane Beasley for creatively designing these pages; Roman Barnes and Norman Baugher for selecting photographs and Matthew Farruggio for taking photographs that deliver nutrition messages beautifully; Mary Douglas for copyediting over 2000 manuscript pages; Debra Gates for proofreading close to 1000 final text pages; and Erin Taylor for composing a thorough and useful index. To the hundreds of others involved in production and sales, we tip our hats in appreciation.

We are especially grateful to our friends and families for their continued encouragement and support. We also thank our many reviewers for their comments and contributions to this edition and all previous editions.

Reviewers of *Understanding Nutrition*

Fernando Agudelo-Silva
Laney College

Nancy Amy
University of California, Berkeley

Melody Anacker
Montana State University

Janet Anderson
Utah State University

James Baily
University of Tennessee, Knoxville

Kathleen D. Bauer
Montclair State University

Eugenia Bearden
Clayton College and State University

Nancy Becker
Portland State University

Patricia Benarducci
Miami-Dade Community College

Margaret Ann Berry
University of Central Oklahoma

Sharleen J. Birkimer
University of Louisville

Debra Boardley
University of Toledo

Jeanne S. Boone
Palm Beach Community College

Ellen Brennan
San Antonio College

Judi Brooks
Eastern Michigan University

Dorothy A. Byrne
University of Texas at San Antonio

Nancy Canolty
University of Georgia

Leah Carter
Bakersfield College

Mary Ann Cessna
Indiana University of Pennsylvania

Jo Carol Chezum
Ball State University

Michele Ciccazzo
Florida International University

Donald D. Clarke
Fordham College of Fordham U.

Ava Craig
Sacramento City College

Tina Crook
University of Central Arkansas

Wendy Cunningham
California State University, Sacramento

Jim Daugherty
Glendale Community College

Robert Davidson
Brigham Young University

Beth Ellen DiLuglio
Palm Beach Community College

Robert DiSilvestro
Ohio State University

Marguerite Dunne
Marist College

Brenda Eissenstat
Pennsylvania State University

Eugene J. Fenster
Longview Community College

Cindy Fitch
West Virginia University

Pam Fletcher
Albuquerque Technical Vocational Institute

Mary Flynn
Brown University

Betty Forbes
West Virginia University

Eileen Ford
University of Pennsylvania

William Forsythe
University of Southern Mississippi

Coni Francis
University of Colorado Health Sciences Center

Jean Fremont
Simon Fraser University

Julie Rae Friedman
State University of New York, Farmingdale

Trish Froehlich
Palm Beach Community College

Patricia Garrett
University of Tennessee, Chattanooga

Francine Genta
Cabrillo College

Leonard E. Gerber
University of Rhode Island

Victoria Getty
Indiana University

Jill Golden
Orange Coast College

Gloria Gonzalez,
Pensacola Junior College

Kathleen Gould
Townson University

Sandra M. Gross
West Chester University

Bruce Grossie
Texas Woman's University

Deborah Gustafson
Utah State University

Leon Hageman
Burlington County College

Charlene Hamilton
University of Delaware

Shelley Hancock
The University of Alabama

Margaret Hedley
University of Guelph

Carol A. Heinz-Bennett
Mesa Community College

Kathryn Henry
Hood College

Nancy Hillquist
Elgin Community College

Sharon Himmelstein
Central New Mexico Community College

Carolyn Hoffman
Central Michigan University

Kim M. Hohol
Mesa Community College

Tracy Horton
University of Colorado Health Sciences Center

Andie Hsueh
Texas Woman's University

Eleanor B. Huang
Orange Coast College

Donna-Jean Hunt
Stephen F. Austin University

Bernadette Janas
Rutgers University

Michael Jenkins
Kent State University

Carol Johnston
Arizona State University

Connie Jones
Northwestern State University of Louisiana

Jayanthi Kandiah
Ball State University

Pramod Khosla
Wayne State University

Younghee Kim
Bowling Green State University

Beth Kitchin
University of Alabama, Birmingham

Kim Kline
University of Texas at Austin

Vicki Kloosterhouse
Oakland Community College

Susan M. Krueger
University of Wisconsin, Eau Claire

Joanne Kuchta
Texas A&M University

Michael LaFontaine
Central Connecticut State University

Betty Larson
Concordia College

Dale Larson
Johnson Community College

Chunhye Kim Lee
Northern Arizona University

Robert D. Lee
Central Michigan University

Anne Leftwich
University of Central Arkansas

Joseph Leichter
University of British Columbia

Alan Levine
Marywood University

Janet Levins
Pensacola Junior College

Lorraine Lewis
Viterbo University

Samantha Logan
University of Massachusetts, Amherst

Jack Logomarsino
Central Michigan University

Elaine M. Long
Boise State University

Kimberly Lower
Collin County Community College

Mary Maciolek
Middlesex County College

Swarna Mandali
Central Missouri State University

Laura McArthur
East Carolina University

Harriet McCoy
University of Arkansas, Fayetteville

Bruce McDonald
University of Manitoba

Lisa McKee
New Mexico State University

Kim McMahon
Utah State University

Mary Mead
University of California, Berkeley

Rhonda L. Meyers
Lower Columbia College

Lynn Monahan-Couch
West Chester University

Cynthia K. Moore
University of Montevallo

Cynthia Moore
University of Alabama

William Moore
Wytheville Community College

Edith Moran
Chicago State University

Mithia Mukutmoni
Sierra College

Yasmin Neggers
University of Alabama

Paula Netherton
Tulsa Junior College

Steven Nizielski
Grand Valley State University

Amy Olson
College of St. Benedict, St. John's University

Anna Page
Johnson County Community College

Sarah Panarello
Yakima Valley Community College

Marvin Parent
Oakland Community College

Roman Pawlak
East Carolina University

Linda Peck
University of Findlay

Susan S. Percival
University of Florida

Erwina Peterson
Yakima Valley Community College

Roseanne L. Poole
Tallahassee Community College

Julie Priday
Centralia College

Stephanie Raach
Rock Valley College

Ann Raymon
Chemeketa Community College

Nuha F. Rice
Portland Community College & Clackamas Community College

Ramona G. Rice
Georgia Military College

Robin R. Roach
The University of Memphis

Christian K. Roberts
University of California, Los Angeles

Sue Roberts
Walla Walla Community College

Janet Sass
Northern Virginia Community College

Tammy Sakanashi
Santa Rosa Junior College

Padmini Shankar
Georgia Southern University

Nancy Shearer
Cape Cod Community College

Linda Shelton
California State University, Fresno

Linda Shepherd
College of Saint Benedict, Saint John's University

Melissa Shock
University of Central Arkansas

Sandra Shortt
Cedarville University

Denise Signorelli
Community College of Southern Nevada

Brenda J. Smith
Oklahoma State University

Mollie Smith
California State University, Fresno

LuAnn Soliah
Baylor University

Diana-Marie Spillman
Miami University, Ohio

Karen Stammen
Chapman University

Tammy Stephenson
University of Kentucky

Sherry Stewart
Universtiy of Texas at Dallas

Wendy Stuhldreher
Slippery Rock University of Pennsylvania

Carla Taylor
University of Manitoba

Janet Thompson
University of Waterloo

Michele Trankina
Saint Mary's University

Josephine Umoren
Northern Illinois University

Anne VanBeber
Texas Christian University

Michelle L. Vineyard
University of Tennessee, Chattanooga

Eric Vlahov
University of Tampa

Ava Craig-Waite
Sacramento City College

Janelle Walter
Baylor University

Dana Wassmer
California State University, Sacramento

Suzy Weems
Stephen F. Austin University

D. Katie Wiedman
University of Saint Francis

Garrison Wilkes
University of Massachusetts, Boston

Richard A. Willis
University of Texas at Austin

Stacie Wing-Gaia
University of Utah

Shahla M. Wunderlich
Montclair State University

Lisa Young
New York University

Thomson™ NOW! Throughout this chapter, the ThomsonNOW logo indicates an opportunity for online self-study, linking you to interactive tutorials and videos based on your level of understanding.

www.thomsonedu.com/thomsonnow

How To: Practice Problems

Nutrition Portfolio Journal

Nutrition Calculations: Practice Problems

Nutrition in Your Life

Believe it or not, you have probably eaten at least 20,000 meals in your life. Without any conscious effort on your part, your body uses the nutrients from those foods to make all its components, fuel all its activities, and defend itself against diseases. How successfully your body handles these tasks depends, in part, on your food choices. Nutritious food choices support healthy bodies.

An Overview of Nutrition

CHAPTER OUTLINE

Food Choices

The Nutrients • Nutrients in Foods and in the Body • The Energy-Yielding Nutrients: Carbohydrate, Fat, and Protein • The Vitamins • The Minerals • Water

The Science of Nutrition • Conducting Research • Analyzing Research Findings • Publishing Research

Dietary Reference Intakes • Establishing Nutrient Recommendations • Establishing Energy Recommendations • Using Nutrient Recommendations • Comparing Nutrient Recommendations

Nutrition Assessment • Nutrition Assessment of Individuals • Nutrition Assessment of Populations

Diet and Health • Chronic Diseases • Risk Factors for Chronic Diseases

HIGHLIGHT 1 Nutrition Information and Misinformation—On the Net and in the News

Welcome to the world of **nutrition**. Although you may not always have been aware of it, nutrition has played a significant role in your life. And it will continue to affect you in major ways, depending on the **foods** you select.

Every day, several times a day, you make food choices that influence your body's health for better or worse. Each day's choices may benefit or harm your health only a little, but when these choices are repeated over years and decades, the rewards or consequences become major. That being the case, paying close attention to good eating habits now can bring you health benefits later. Conversely, carelessness about food choices can contribute to many chronic diseases ◆ prevalent in later life, including heart disease and cancer. Of course, some people will become ill or die young no matter what choices they make, and others will live long lives despite making poor choices. For the majority of us, however, the food choices we make each and every day will benefit or impair our health in proportion to the wisdom of those choices.

Although most people realize that their food habits affect their health, they often choose foods for other reasons. After all, foods bring to the table a variety of pleasures, traditions, and associations as well as nourishment. The challenge, then, is to combine favorite foods and fun times with a nutritionally balanced **diet**.

Food Choices

People decide what to eat, when to eat, and even whether to eat in highly personal ways, often based on behavioral or social motives rather than on an awareness of nutrition's importance to health. Many different food choices can support good health, and an understanding of nutrition helps you make sensible selections more often.

Personal Preference As you might expect, the number one reason people choose foods is taste—they like certain flavors. Two widely shared preferences are for the sweetness of sugar and the savoriness of salt. Liking high-fat foods also appears to be a universally common preference. Other preferences might be for the hot peppers

◆ In general, a **chronic** disease progresses slowly or with little change and lasts a long time. By comparison, an **acute** disease develops quickly, produces sharp symptoms, and runs a short course.
- **chronos** = time
- **acute** = sharp

nutrition: the science of foods and the nutrients and other substances they contain, and of their actions within the body (including ingestion, digestion, absorption, transport, metabolism, and excretion). A broader definition includes the social, economic, cultural, and psychological implications of food and eating.

foods: products derived from plants or animals that can be taken into the body to yield energy and nutrients for the maintenance of life and the growth and repair of tissues.

diet: the foods and beverages a person eats and drinks.

An enjoyable way to learn about other cultures is to taste their ethnic foods.

common in Mexican cooking or the curry spices of Indian cuisine. Some research suggests that genetics may influence people's food preferences.[1]

Habit People sometimes select foods out of habit. They eat cereal every morning, for example, simply because they have always eaten cereal for breakfast. Eating a familiar food and not having to make any decisions can be comforting.

Ethnic Heritage or Tradition

Among the strongest influences on food choices are ethnic heritage and tradition. People eat the foods they grew up eating. Every country, and in fact every region of a country, has its own typical foods and ways of combining them into meals. The "American diet" includes many ethnic foods from various countries, all adding variety to the diet. This is most evident when eating out: 60 percent of U.S. restaurants (excluding fast-food places) have an ethnic emphasis, most commonly Chinese, Italian, or Mexican.

Social Interactions Most people enjoy companionship while eating. It's fun to go out with friends for pizza or ice cream. Meals are social events, and sharing food is part of hospitality. Social customs invite people to accept food or drink offered by a host or shared by a group.

Availability, Convenience, and Economy People eat foods that are accessible, quick and easy to prepare, and within their financial means. Today's consumers value convenience and are willing to spend more than half of their food budget on meals that require little, if any, further preparation.[2] They frequently eat out, bring home ready-to-eat meals, or have food delivered. Even when they venture into the kitchen, they want to prepare a meal in 15 to 20 minutes, using less than a half dozen ingredients—and those "ingredients" are often semiprepared foods, such as canned soups. This emphasis on convenience limits food choices to the selections offered on menus and products designed for quick preparation. Whether decisions based on convenience meet a person's nutrition needs depends on the choices made. Eating a banana or a candy bar may be equally convenient, but the fruit offers more vitamins and minerals and less sugar and fat.

Positive and Negative Associations People tend to like particular foods associated with happy occasions—such as hot dogs at ball games or cake and ice cream at birthday parties. By the same token, people can develop aversions and dislike foods that they ate when they felt sick or that were forced on them.[3] By using foods as rewards or punishments, parents may inadvertently teach their children to like and dislike certain foods.

Emotional Comfort Some people cannot eat when they are emotionally upset. Others may eat in response to a variety of emotional stimuli—for example, to relieve boredom or depression or to calm anxiety.[4] A depressed person may choose to eat rather than to call a friend. A person who has returned home from an exciting evening out may unwind with a late-night snack. These people may find emotional comfort, in part, because foods can influence the brain's chemistry and the mind's response. Carbohydrates and alcohol, for example, tend to calm, whereas proteins and caffeine are more likely to activate. Eating in response to emotions can easily lead to overeating and obesity, but it may be appropriate at times. For example, sharing food at times of bereavement serves both the giver's need to provide comfort and the receiver's need to be cared for and to interact with others, as well as to take nourishment.

Values Food choices may reflect people's religious beliefs, political views, or environmental concerns. For example, many Christians forgo meat during Lent (the period prior to Easter), Jewish law includes an extensive set of dietary rules that govern the use of foods derived from animals, and Muslims fast between sunrise and sunset during Ramadan (the ninth month of the Islamic calendar). A concerned consumer may boycott fruit picked by migrant workers who have been exploited. People may buy vegetables from local farmers to save the fuel and environmental costs of foods shipped in from far away. They may also select foods packaged in containers that can be reused or recycled. Some consumers accept or reject foods that have been irradiated or genetically modified, depending on their approval of these processes (see Chapter and Highlight 19 for a complete discussion).

Body Weight and Image Sometimes people select certain foods and supplements that they believe will improve their physical appearance and avoid those they believe might be detrimental. Such decisions can be beneficial when based on sound nutrition and fitness knowledge, but decisions based on fads or carried to extremes undermine good health, as pointed out in later discussions of eating disorders (Highlight 8) and dietary supplements commonly used by athletes (Highlight 14).

Nutrition and Health Benefits Finally, of course, many consumers make food choices that will benefit health. Food manufacturers and restaurant chefs have responded to scientific findings linking health with nutrition by offering an abundant selection of health-promoting foods and beverages. Foods that provide health benefits beyond their nutrient contributions are called **functional foods.**[5] Whole foods—as natural and familiar as oatmeal or tomatoes—are the simplest functional foods. In other cases, foods have been modified to provide health benefits, perhaps by lowering the fat contents. In still other cases, manufacturers have fortified foods by adding nutrients or **phytochemicals** that provide health benefits (see Highlight 13). ◆ Examples of these functional foods include orange juice fortified with calcium to help build strong bones and margarine made with a plant sterol that lowers blood cholesterol.

Consumers typically welcome new foods into their diets, provided that these foods are reasonably priced, clearly labeled, easy to find in the grocery store, and convenient to prepare. These foods must also taste good—as good as the traditional choices. Of course, a person need not eat any of these "special" foods to enjoy a healthy diet; many "regular" foods provide numerous health benefits as well. In fact, "regular" foods such as whole grains; vegetables and legumes; fruits; meats, fish, and poultry; and milk products are among the healthiest choices a person can make.

© Ariel Skelley/CORBIS

To enhance your health, keep nutrition in mind when selecting foods.

◆ Functional foods may include whole foods, modified foods, or fortified foods.

IN SUMMARY

A person selects foods for a variety of reasons. Whatever those reasons may be, food choices influence health. Individual food selections neither make nor break a diet's healthfulness, but the balance of foods selected over time can make an important difference to health.[6] For this reason, people are wise to think "nutrition" when making their food choices.

The Nutrients

Biologically speaking, people eat to receive nourishment. Do you ever think of yourself as a biological being made of carefully arranged atoms, molecules, cells, tissues, and organs? Are you aware of the activity going on within your body even as you sit still? The atoms, molecules, and cells of your body continually move and change, even though the structures of your tissues and organs and your external appearance remain relatively constant. Your skin, which has covered you since your birth, is replaced entirely by new cells every seven years. The fat beneath your skin is not the

functional foods: foods that contain physiologically active compounds that provide health benefits beyond their nutrient contributions; sometimes called *designer foods* or *nutraceuticals.*

phytochemicals (FIE-toe-KEM-ih-cals): nonnutrient compounds found in plant-derived foods that have biological activity in the body.

• **phyto** = plant

Foods bring pleasure—and nutrients.

◆ As Chapter 5 explains, most lipids are fats.

same fat that was there a year ago. Your oldest red blood cell is only 120 days old, and the entire lining of your digestive tract is renewed every 3 to 5 days. To maintain your "self," you must continually replenish, from foods, the **energy** and the **nutrients** you deplete as your body maintains itself.

Nutrients in Foods and in the Body

Amazingly, our bodies can derive all the energy, structural materials, and regulating agents we need from the foods we eat. This section introduces the nutrients that foods deliver and shows how they participate in the dynamic processes that keep people alive and well.

Composition of Foods Chemical analysis of a food such as a tomato shows that it is composed primarily of water (95 percent). Most of the solid materials are carbohydrates, lipids, ◆ and proteins. If you could remove these materials, you would find a tiny residue of vitamins, minerals, and other compounds. Water, carbohydrates, lipids, proteins, vitamins, and some of the minerals found in foods are nutrients—substances the body uses for the growth, maintenance, and repair of its tissues.

This book focuses mostly on the nutrients, but foods contain other compounds as well—fibers, phytochemicals, pigments, additives, alcohols, and others. Some are beneficial, some are neutral, and a few are harmful. Later sections of the book touch on these compounds and their significance.

Composition of the Body A complete chemical analysis of your body would show that it is made of materials similar to those found in foods (see Figure 1-1). A healthy 150-pound body contains about 90 pounds of water and about 20 to 45 pounds of fat. The remaining pounds are mostly protein, carbohydrate, and the major minerals of the bones. Vitamins, other minerals, and incidental extras constitute a fraction of a pound.

FIGURE 1-1	Body Composition of Healthy-Weight Men and Women

The human body is made of compounds similar to those found in foods—mostly water (60 percent) and some fat (13 to 21 percent for young men, 23 to 31 percent for young women), with carbohydrate, protein, vitamins, minerals, and other minor constituents making up the remainder. (Chapter 8 describes the health hazards of too little or too much body fat.)

Key:
- % Carbohydrates, proteins, vitamins, minerals in the body
- % Fat in the body
- % Water in the body

© Photodisc/Getty Images

energy: the capacity to do work. The energy in food is chemical energy. The body can convert this chemical energy to mechanical, electrical, or heat energy.

nutrients: chemical substances obtained from food and used in the body to provide energy, structural materials, and regulating agents to support growth, maintenance, and repair of the body's tissues. Nutrients may also reduce the risks of some diseases.

Chemical Composition of Nutrients The simplest of the nutrients are the minerals. Each mineral is a chemical element; its atoms are all alike. As a result, its identity never changes. For example, iron may have different electrical charges, but the individual iron atoms remain the same when they are in a food, when a person eats the food, when the iron becomes part of a red blood cell, when the cell is broken down, and when the iron is lost from the body by excretion. The next simplest nutrient is water, a compound made of two elements—hydrogen and oxygen. Minerals and water are **inorganic** nutrients—which means they do not contain carbon.

The other four classes of nutrients (carbohydrates, lipids, proteins, and vitamins) are more complex. In addition to hydrogen and oxygen, they all contain carbon, an element found in all living things. They are therefore called **organic** ◆ compounds (meaning, literally, "alive"). Protein and some vitamins also contain nitrogen and may contain other elements as well (see Table 1-1).

Essential Nutrients The body can make some nutrients, but it cannot make all of them. Also, it makes some in insufficient quantities to meet its needs and, therefore, must obtain these nutrients from foods. The nutrients that foods must supply are **essential nutrients.** When used to refer to nutrients, the word *essential* means more than just "necessary"; it means "needed from outside the body"—normally, from foods.

The Energy-Yielding Nutrients: Carbohydrate, Fat, and Protein

In the body, three organic nutrients can be used to provide energy: carbohydrate, fat, and protein. ◆ In contrast to these **energy-yielding nutrients**, vitamins, minerals, and water do not yield energy in the human body.

Energy Measured in kCalories The energy released from carbohydrates, fats, and proteins can be measured in **calories**—tiny units of energy so small that a single apple provides tens of thousands of them. To ease calculations, energy is expressed in 1000-calorie metric units known as kilocalories (shortened to kcalories, but commonly called "calories"). When you read in popular books or magazines that an apple provides "100 calories," it actually means 100 kcalories. This book uses the term kcalorie and its abbreviation kcal throughout, as do other scientific books and journals. ◆ The "How to" on p. 8 provides a few tips on "thinking metric."

◆ In agriculture, *organic* farming refers to growing crops and raising livestock according to standards set by the U.S. Department of Agriculture (USDA). Chapter 19 presents details.

◆ Carbohydrate, fat, and protein are sometimes called **macronutrients** because the body requires them in relatively large amounts (many grams daily). In contrast, vitamins and minerals are **micronutrients**, required only in small amounts (milligrams or micrograms daily).

◆ The international unit for measuring food energy is the **joule**, a measure of *work* energy. To convert kcalories to kilojoules, multiply by 4.2; to convert kilojoules to kcalories, multiply by 0.24.

inorganic: not containing carbon or pertaining to living things.
- **in** = not

organic: in chemistry, a substance or molecule containing carbon-carbon bonds or carbon-hydrogen bonds. This definition excludes coal, diamonds, and a few carbon-containing compounds that contain only a single carbon and no hydrogen, such as carbon dioxide (CO_2), calcium carbonate ($CaCO_3$), magnesium carbonate ($MgCO_3$), and sodium cyanide (NaCN).

essential nutrients: nutrients a person must obtain from food because the body cannot make them for itself in sufficient quantity to meet physiological needs; also called **indispensable nutrients.** About 40 nutrients are currently known to be essential for human beings.

energy-yielding nutrients: the nutrients that break down to yield energy the body can use:
- Carbohydrate
- Fat
- Protein

calories: units by which energy is measured. Food energy is measured in **kilocalories** (1000 calories equal 1 kilocalorie), abbreviated **kcalories** or **kcal.** One kcalorie is the amount of heat necessary to raise the temperature of 1 kilogram (kg) of water 1°C. The scientific use of the term *kcalorie* is the same as the popular use of the term *calorie.*

| TABLE 1-1 | Elements in the Six Classes of Nutrients |

Notice that organic nutrients contain carbon.

	Carbon	Hydrogen	Oxygen	Nitrogen	Minerals
Inorganic nutrients					
Minerals					✓
Water		✓	✓		
Organic nutrients					
Carbohydrates	✓	✓	✓		
Lipids (fats)	✓	✓	✓		
Proteins[a]	✓	✓	✓	✓	
Vitamins[b]	✓	✓	✓		

[a] Some proteins also contain the mineral sulfur.
[b] Some vitamins contain nitrogen; some contain minerals.

HOW TO Think Metric

Like other scientists, nutrition scientists use metric units of measure. They measure food energy in kilocalories, people's height in centimeters, people's weight in kilograms, and the weights of foods and nutrients in grams, milligrams, or micrograms. For ease in using these measures, it helps to remember that the prefixes on the grams imply 1000. For example, a *kilo*gram is 1000 grams, a *milli*gram is 1/1000 of a gram, and a *micro*gram is 1/1000 of a milligram.

Most food labels and many recipe books provide "dual measures," listing both household measures, such as cups, quarts, and teaspoons, and metric measures, such as milliliters, liters, and grams. This practice gives people an opportunity to gradually learn to "think metric."

A person might begin to "think metric" by simply observing the measure—by noticing the amount of soda in a 2-liter bottle, for example. Through such experiences, a person can become familiar with a measure without having to do any conversions.

To facilitate communication, many members of the international scientific community have adopted a common system of measurement—the International System of Units (SI). In addition to using metric measures, the SI establishes common units of measurement. For example, the SI unit for measuring food energy is the joule (not the kcalorie). A joule is the amount of energy expended when 1 kilogram is moved 1 meter by a force of 1 newton. The joule is thus a measure of *work* energy, whereas the kcalorie is a measure of *heat* energy. While many scientists and journals report their findings in kilojoules (kJ), many others, particularly those in the United States, use kcalories (kcal). To convert energy measures from kcalories to kilojoules, multiply by 4.2. For example, a 50-kcalorie cookie provides 210 kilojoules:

$$50 \text{ kcal} \times 4.2 = 210 \text{ kJ}$$

Exact conversion factors for these and other units of measure are in the Aids to Calculation section on the last two pages of the book.

Volume: Liters (L)

1 L = 1000 milliliters (mL)
0.95 L = 1 quart
1 mL = 0.03 fluid ounces
240 mL = 1 cup

A liter of liquid is approximately one U.S. quart. (Four liters are only about 5 percent more than a gallon.)

One cup is about 240 milliliters; a half-cup of liquid is about 120 milliliters.

Weight: Grams (g)

1 g = 1000 milligrams (mg)
1 g = 0.04 ounce (oz)
1 oz = 28.35 g (or 30 g)
100 g = 3½ oz
1 kilogram (kg) = 1000 g
1 kg = 2.2 pounds (lb)
454 g = 1 lb

A kilogram is slightly more than 2 lb; conversely, a pound is about ½ kg.

A half-cup of vegetables weighs about 100 grams; one pea weighs about ½ gram.

A 5-pound bag of potatoes weighs about 2 kilograms, and a 176-pound person weighs 80 kilograms.

ThomsonNOW
To practice thinking metrically, log on to **www.thomsonedu.com/thomsonnow**, go to Chapter 1, then go to How To.

◆ Foods with a high energy density help with weight gain, whereas those with a low energy density help with weight loss.

energy density: a measure of the energy a food provides relative to the amount of food (kcalories per gram).

Energy from Foods The amount of energy a food provides depends on how much carbohydrate, fat, and protein it contains. When completely broken down in the body, a gram of carbohydrate yields about 4 kcalories of energy; a gram of protein also yields 4 kcalories; and a gram of fat yields 9 kcalories (see Table 1-2). Fat, therefore, has a greater **energy density** than either carbohydrate or protein. Figure 1-2 compares the energy density of two breakfast options, and later chapters describe how considering a food's energy density can help with weight management. ◆ The "How to" on p. 9 explains how to calculate the energy available from foods.

One other substance contributes energy—alcohol. Alcohol is not considered a nutrient because it interferes with the growth, maintenance, and repair of the body, but it does yield energy (7 kcalories per gram) when metabolized in the body. (Highlight 7 and Chapter 18 present the potential harms and possible benefits of alcohol consumption.)

FIGURE 1-2	Energy Density of Two Breakfast Options Compared

Gram for gram, ounce for ounce, and bite for bite, foods with a high energy density deliver more kcalories than foods with a low energy density. Both of these breakfast options provide 500 kcalories, but the cereal with milk, fruit salad, scrambled egg, turkey sausage, and toast with jam offers three times as much food as the doughnuts (based on weight); it has a lower energy density than the doughnuts. Selecting a variety of foods also helps to ensure nutrient adequacy.

LOWER ENERGY DENSITY	**HIGHER ENERGY DENSITY**
This 450-gram breakfast delivers 500 kcalories, for an energy density of 1.1 (500 kcal ÷ 450 g = 1.1 kcal/g).	This 144-gram breakfast delivers 500 kcalories, for an energy density of 3.5 (500 kcal ÷ 144 g = 3.5 kcal/g).

Most foods contain all three energy-yielding nutrients, as well as water, vitamins, minerals, and other substances. For example, meat contains water, fat, vitamins, and minerals as well as protein. Bread contains water, a trace of fat, a little protein, and some vitamins and minerals in addition to its carbohydrate. Only a few foods are exceptions to this rule, the common ones being sugar (pure carbohydrate) and oil (essentially pure fat).

Energy in the Body The body uses the energy-yielding nutrients to fuel all its activities. When the body uses carbohydrate, fat, or protein for energy, the bonds between

HOW TO	Calculate the Energy Available from Foods

To calculate the energy available from a food, multiply the number of grams of carbohydrate, protein, and fat by 4, 4, and 9, respectively. Then add the results together. For example, 1 slice of bread with 1 tablespoon of peanut butter on it contains 16 grams carbohydrate, 7 grams protein, and 9 grams fat:

16 g carbohydrate × 4 kcal/g =	64 kcal
7 g protein × 4 kcal/g =	28 kcal
9 g fat × 9 kcal/g =	81 kcal
Total =	173 kcal

From this information, you can calculate the percentage of kcalories each of the energy nutrients contributes to the total. To determine the percentage of kcalories from fat, for example, divide the 81 fat kcalories by the total 173 kcalories:

81 fat kcal ÷ 173 total kcal = 0.468 (rounded to 0.47)

Then multiply by 100 to get the percentage:

0.47 × 100 = 47%

Dietary recommendations that urge people to limit fat intake to 20 to 35 percent of kcalories refer to the day's total energy intake, not to individual foods. Still, if the proportion of fat in each food choice throughout a day exceeds 35 percent of kcalories, then the day's total surely will, too. Knowing that this snack provides 47 percent of its kcalories from fat alerts a person to the need to make lower-fat selections at other times that day.

ThomsonNOW™
To practice calculating the energy available from foods, log on to **www.thomsonedu.com/ thomsonnow**, go to Chapter 1, then go to How To.

TABLE 1-2	kCalorie Values

of Energy Nutrients[a]

Nutrients	Energy (kcal/g)
Carbohydrate	4
Fat	9
Protein	4

NOTE: Alcohol contributes 7 kcalories per gram that can be used for energy, but it is not considered a nutrient because it interferes with the body's growth, maintenance, and repair.

[a]For those using kilojoules: 1 g carbohydrate = 17 kJ; 1 g protein = 17 kJ; 1 g fat = 37 kJ; and 1 g alcohol = 29 kJ.

◆ The processes by which nutrients are broken down to yield energy or used to make body structures are known as **metabolism** (defined and described further in Chapter 7).

the nutrient's atoms break. As the bonds break, they release energy. ◆ Some of this energy is released as heat, but some is used to send electrical impulses through the brain and nerves, to synthesize body compounds, and to move muscles. Thus the energy from food supports every activity from quiet thought to vigorous sports.

If the body does not use these nutrients to fuel its current activities, it rearranges them into storage compounds (such as body fat), to be used between meals and overnight when fresh energy supplies run low. If more energy is consumed than expended, the result is an increase in energy stores and weight gain. Similarly, if less energy is consumed than expended, the result is a decrease in energy stores and weight loss.

When consumed in excess of energy needs, alcohol, too, can be converted to body fat and stored. When alcohol contributes a substantial portion of the energy in a person's diet, the harm it does far exceeds the problems of excess body fat. (Highlight 7 describes the effects of alcohol on health and nutrition.)

Other Roles of Energy-Yielding Nutrients In addition to providing energy, carbohydrates, fats, and proteins provide the raw materials for building the body's tissues and regulating its many activities. In fact, protein's role as a fuel source is relatively minor compared with both the other two nutrients and its other roles. Proteins are found in structures such as the muscles and skin and help to regulate activities such as digestion and energy metabolism.

The Vitamins

The **vitamins** are also organic, but they do not provide energy. Instead, they facilitate the release of energy from carbohydrate, fat, and protein and participate in numerous other activities throughout the body.

Each of the 13 different vitamins has its own special roles to play.* One vitamin enables the eyes to see in dim light, another helps protect the lungs from air pollution, and still another helps make the sex hormones—among other things. When you cut yourself, one vitamin helps stop the bleeding and another helps repair the skin. Vitamins busily help replace old red blood cells and the lining of the digestive tract. Almost every action in the body requires the assistance of vitamins.

Vitamins can function only if they are intact, but because they are complex organic molecules, they are vulnerable to destruction by heat, light, and chemical agents. This is why the body handles them carefully, and why nutrition-wise cooks do, too. The strategies of cooking vegetables at moderate temperatures for short times and using small amounts of water help to preserve the vitamins.

The Minerals

In the body, some **minerals** are put together in orderly arrays in such structures as bones and teeth. Minerals are also found in the fluids of the body, which influences fluid properties. Whatever their roles, minerals do not yield energy.

Only 16 minerals are known to be essential in human nutrition.** Others are being studied to determine whether they play significant roles in the human body. Still other minerals are environmental contaminants that displace the nutrient minerals from their workplaces in the body, disrupting body functions. The problems caused by contaminant minerals are described in Chapter 13.

Because minerals are inorganic, they are indestructible and need not be handled with the special care that vitamins require. Minerals can, however, be bound by substances that interfere with the body's ability to absorb them. They can also be lost during food-refining processes or during cooking when they leach into water that is discarded.

vitamins: organic, essential nutrients required in small amounts by the body for health.

minerals: inorganic elements. Some minerals are essential nutrients required in small amounts by the body for health.

* The water-soluble vitamins are vitamin C and the eight B vitamins: thiamin, riboflavin, niacin, vitamins B_6 and B_{12}, folate, biotin, and pantothenic acid. The fat-soluble vitamins are vitamins A, D, E, and K. The water-soluble vitamins are the subject of Chapter 10 and the fat-soluble vitamins, of Chapter 11.
** The major minerals are calcium, phosphorus, potassium, sodium, chloride, magnesium, and sulfate. The trace minerals are iron, iodine, zinc, chromium, selenium, fluoride, molybdenum, copper, and manganese. Chapters 12 and 13 are devoted to the major and trace minerals, respectively.

Water

Water, indispensable and abundant, provides the environment in which nearly all the body's activities are conducted. It participates in many metabolic reactions and supplies the medium for transporting vital materials to cells and carrying waste products away from them. Water is discussed fully in Chapter 12, but it is mentioned in every chapter. If you watch for it, you cannot help but be impressed by water's participation in all life processes.

IN SUMMARY

Foods provide nutrients—substances that support the growth, maintenance, and repair of the body's tissues. The six classes of nutrients include:

· Carbohydrates
· Lipids (fats)
· Proteins
· Vitamins
· Minerals
· Water

Foods rich in the energy-yielding nutrients (carbohydrates, fats, and proteins) provide the major materials for building the body's tissues and yield energy for the body's use or storage. Energy is measured in kcalories. Vitamins, minerals, and water facilitate a variety of activities in the body.

Water itself is an essential nutrient and naturally carries many minerals.

Without exaggeration, nutrients provide the physical and metabolic basis for nearly all that we are and all that we do. The next section introduces the science of nutrition with emphasis on the research methods scientists have used in uncovering the wonders of nutrition.

The Science of Nutrition

The science of nutrition is the study of the nutrients and other substances in foods and the body's handling of them. Its foundation depends on several other sciences, including biology, biochemistry, and physiology. As sciences go, nutrition is young, but as you can see from the size of this book, much has happened in nutrition's short life. And it is currently entering a tremendous growth spurt as scientists apply knowledge gained from sequencing the human **genome.** The integration of nutrition, genomics, and molecular biology has opened a whole new world of study called **nutritional genomics**—the science of how nutrients affect the activities of genes and how genes affect the interactions between diet and disease.[7] Highlight 6 describes how nutritional genomics is shaping the science of nutrition, and examples of nutrient–gene interactions appear throughout later sections of the book.

Conducting Research

Consumers may depend on personal experience or reports from friends ◆ to gather information on nutrition, but researchers use the scientific method to guide their work (see Figure 1-3 on p. 12). As the figure shows, research always begins with a problem or a question. For example, "What foods or nutrients might protect against the common cold?" In search of an answer, scientists make an educated guess (**hypothesis**), such as "foods rich in vitamin C reduce the number of common colds." Then they systematically conduct research studies to collect data that will test the hypothesis (see the glossary on p. 14 for definitions of research terms). Some examples of various types of research designs are presented in Figure 1-4 (p. 13). Each type of study has strengths and weaknesses (see Table 1-3 on p. 14). Consequently, some provide stronger evidence than others.

◆ A personal account of an experience or event is an **anecdote** and is not accepted as reliable scientific information.
• **anekdotos** = unpublished

genome (GEE-nome): the full complement of genetic material (DNA) in the chromosomes of a cell. In human beings, the genome consists of 46 chromosomes. The study of genomes is called **genomics.**

nutritional genomics: the science of how nutrients affect the activities of genes (**nutrigenomics**) and how genes affect the interactions between diet and disease (**nutrigenetics**).

FIGURE 1-3 The Scientific Method

Research scientists follow the scientific method. Note that most research generates new questions, not final answers. Thus the sequence begins anew, and research continues in a somewhat cyclical way.

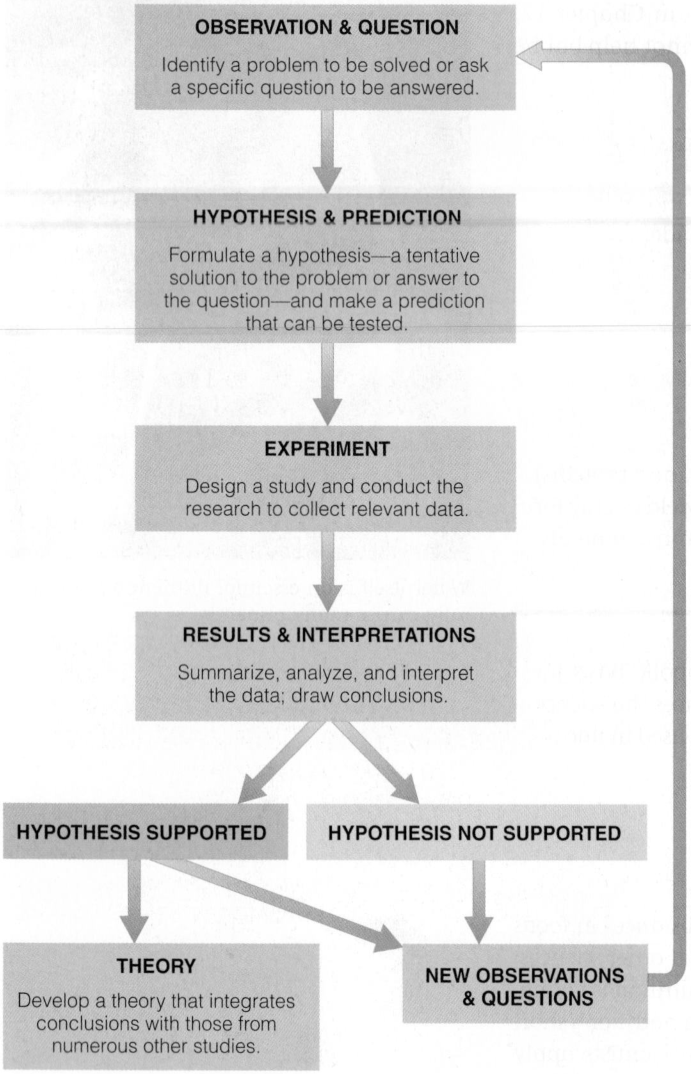

OBSERVATION & QUESTION

Identify a problem to be solved or ask a specific question to be answered.

HYPOTHESIS & PREDICTION

Formulate a hypothesis—a tentative solution to the problem or answer to the question—and make a prediction that can be tested.

EXPERIMENT

Design a study and conduct the research to collect relevant data.

RESULTS & INTERPRETATIONS

Summarize, analyze, and interpret the data; draw conclusions.

HYPOTHESIS SUPPORTED

HYPOTHESIS NOT SUPPORTED

THEORY

Develop a theory that integrates conclusions with those from numerous other studies.

NEW OBSERVATIONS & QUESTIONS

In attempting to discover whether a nutrient relieves symptoms or cures a disease, researchers deliberately manipulate one variable (for example, the amount of vitamin C in the diet) and measure any observed changes (perhaps the number of colds). As much as possible, all other conditions are held constant. The following paragraphs illustrate how this is accomplished.

Controls In studies examining the effectiveness of vitamin C, researchers typically divide the **subjects** into two groups. One group (the **experimental group**) receives a vitamin C supplement, and the other (the **control group**) does not. Researchers observe both groups to determine whether one group has fewer or shorter colds than the other. The following discussion describes some of the pitfalls inherent in an experiment of this kind and ways to avoid them.

In sorting subjects into two groups, researchers must ensure that each person has an equal chance of being assigned to either the experimental group or the control group. This is accomplished by **randomization;** that is, the subjects are chosen randomly from the same population by flipping a coin or some other method involving chance. Randomization helps to ensure that results reflect the treatment and not factors that might influence the grouping of subjects.

Importantly, the two groups of people must be similar and must have the same track record with respect to colds to rule out the possibility that observed differences in the rate, severity, or duration of colds might have occurred anyway. If, for example, the control group would normally catch twice as many colds as the experimental group, then the findings prove nothing.

In experiments involving a nutrient, the diets of both groups must also be similar, especially with respect to the nutrient being studied. If those in the experimental group were receiving less vitamin C from their usual diet, then any effects of the supplement may not be apparent.

Sample Size To ensure that chance variation between the two groups does not influence the results, the groups must be large. For example, if one member of a group of five people catches a bad cold by chance, he will pull the whole group's average toward bad colds; but if one member of a group of 500 catches a bad cold, she will not unduly affect the group average. Statistical methods are used to determine whether differences between groups of various sizes support a hypothesis.

Placebos If people who take vitamin C for colds *believe* it will cure them, their chances of recovery may improve. Taking anything believed to be beneficial may hasten recovery. This phenomenon, the result of expectations, is known as the **placebo effect.** In experiments designed to determine vitamin C's effect on colds, this mind-body effect must be rigorously controlled. Severity of symptoms is often a subjective measure, and people who believe they are receiving treatment may report less severe symptoms.

One way experimenters control for the placebo effect is to give pills to all participants. Those in the experimental group, for example, receive pills containing vitamin C, and those in the control group receive a **placebo**—pills of similar appearance and taste containing an inactive ingredient. This way, the expectations of both groups will be equal. It is not necessary to convince all subjects that they are receiving vitamin C, but the extent of belief or unbelief must be the same in both groups. A study conducted under these conditions is called a **blind exper-**

FIGURE 1-4 Examples of Research Designs

EPIDEMIOLOGICAL STUDIES

| CROSS-SECTIONAL | CASE-CONTROL | COHORT |

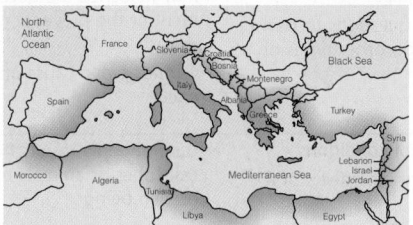

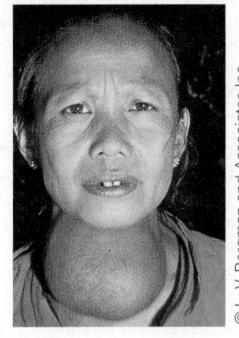

© L. V. Bergman and Associates Inc.

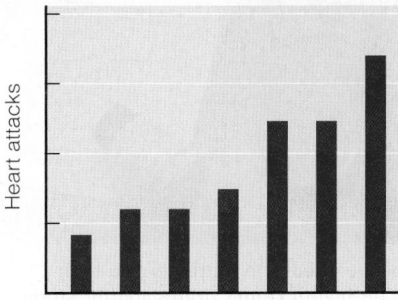

CROSS-SECTIONAL

Researchers observe how much and what kinds of foods a group of people eat and how healthy those people are. Their findings identify factors that might influence the incidence of a disease in various populations.

Example. The people of the Mediterranean region drink lots of wine, eat plenty of fat from olive oil, and have a lower incidence of heart disease than northern Europeans and North Americans.

CASE-CONTROL

Researchers compare people who do and do not have a given condition such as a disease, closely matching them in age, gender, and other key variables so that differences in other factors will stand out. These differences may account for the condition in the group that has it.

Example. People with goiter lack iodine in their diets.

COHORT

Researchers analyze data collected from a selected group of people (a cohort) at intervals over a certain period of time.

Example. Data collected periodically over the past several decades from over 5000 people randomly selected from the town of Framingham, Massachusetts, in 1948 have revealed that the risk of heart attack increases as blood cholesterol increases.

EXPERIMENTAL STUDIES

| LABORATORY-BASED ANIMAL STUDIES | LABORATORY-BASED IN VITRO STUDIES | HUMAN INTERVENTION (OR CLINICAL) TRIALS |

© R. Benali/Getty Images

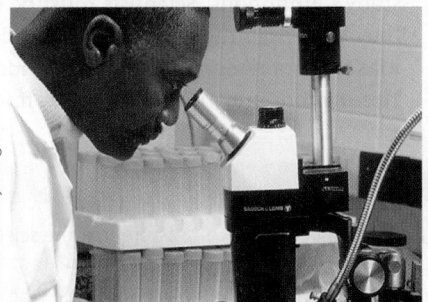

USDA Agricultural Research Service

© PhotoDisc/Getty Images

LABORATORY-BASED ANIMAL STUDIES

Researchers feed animals special diets that provide or omit specific nutrients and then observe any changes in health. Such studies test possible disease causes and treatments in a laboratory where all conditions can be controlled.

Example. Mice fed a high-fat diet eat less food than mice given a lower-fat diet, so they receive the same number of kcalories—but the mice eating the fat-rich diet become severely obese.

LABORATORY-BASED IN VITRO STUDIES

Researchers examine the effects of a specific variable on a tissue, cell, or molecule isolated from a living organism.

Example. Laboratory studies find that fish oils inhibit the growth and activity of the bacteria implicated in ulcer formation.

HUMAN INTERVENTION (OR CLINICAL) TRIALS

Researchers ask people to adopt a new behavior (for example, eat a citrus fruit, take a vitamin C supplement, or exercise daily). These trials help determine the effectiveness of such interventions on the development or prevention of disease.

Example. Heart disease risk factors improve when men receive fresh-squeezed orange juice daily for two months compared with those on a diet low in vitamin C—even when both groups follow a diet high in saturated fat.

iment—that is, the subjects do not know (are blind to) whether they are members of the experimental group (receiving treatment) or the control group (receiving the placebo).

Double Blind When both the subjects and the researchers do not know which subjects are in which group, the study is called a **double-blind experiment.** Being fallible human beings and having an emotional and sometimes financial investment

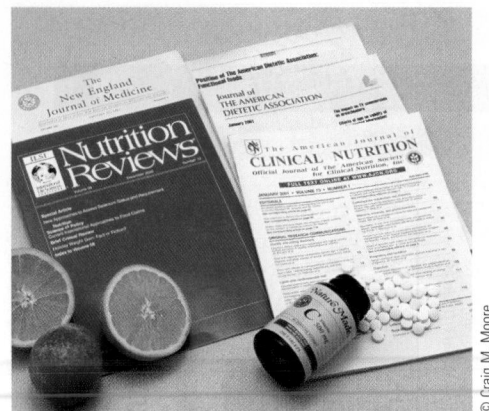

Knowledge about the nutrients and their effects on health comes from scientific study.

© Craig M. Moore

TABLE 1-3	Strengths and Weaknesses of Research Designs	
Type of Research	**Strengths**	**Weaknesses**
Epidemiological studies determine the incidence and distribution of diseases in a population. Epidemiological studies include cross-sectional, case-control, and cohort (see Figure 1-4).	• Can narrow down the list of possible causes • Can raise questions to pursue through other types of studies	• Cannot control variables that may influence the development or the prevention of a disease • Cannot prove cause and effect
Laboratory-based studies explore the effects of a specific variable on a tissue, cell, or molecule. Laboratory-based studies are often conducted in test tubes (in vitro) or on animals.	• Can control conditions • Can determine effects of a variable	• Cannot apply results from test tubes or animals to human beings
Human intervention or **clinical trials** involve human beings who follow a specified regimen.	• Can control conditions (for the most part) • Can apply findings to some groups of human beings	• Cannot generalize findings to all human beings • Cannot use certain treatments for clinical or ethical reasons

in a successful outcome, researchers might record and interpret results with a bias in the expected direction. To prevent such bias, the pills would be coded by a third party, who does not reveal to the experimenters which subjects were in which group until all results have been recorded.

Analyzing Research Findings

Research findings must be analyzed and interpreted with an awareness of each study's limitations. Scientists must be cautious about drawing any conclusions until they have accumulated a body of evidence from multiple studies that have used various types of research designs. As evidence accumulates, scientists begin to develop a **theory** that integrates the various findings and explains the complex relationships.

GLOSSARY OF RESEARCH TERMS

blind experiment: an experiment in which the subjects do not know whether they are members of the experimental group or the control group.

control group: a group of individuals similar in all possible respects to the experimental group except for the treatment. Ideally, the control group receives a placebo while the experimental group receives a real treatment.

correlation (CORE-ee-LAY-shun): the simultaneous increase, decrease, or change in two variables. If A increases as B increases, or if A decreases as B decreases, the correlation is **positive.** (This does not mean that A causes B or vice versa.) If A increases as B decreases, or if A decreases as B increases, the correlation is **negative.** (This does not mean that A prevents B

or vice versa.) Some third factor may account for both A and B.

double-blind experiment: an experiment in which neither the subjects nor the researchers know which subjects are members of the experimental group and which are serving as control subjects, until after the experiment is over.

experimental group: a group of individuals similar in all possible respects to the control group except for the treatment. The experimental group receives the real treatment.

hypothesis (hi-POTH-eh-sis): an unproven statement that tentatively explains the relationships between two or more variables.

peer review: a process in which a panel of scientists rigorously evaluates a research study to

assure that the scientific method was followed.

placebo (pla-SEE-bo): an inert, harmless medication given to provide comfort and hope; a sham treatment used in controlled research studies.

placebo effect: a change that occurs in reponse to expectations in the effectiveness of a treatment that actually has no pharmaceutical effects.

randomization (RAN-dom-ih-ZAY-shun): a process of choosing the members of the experimental and control groups without bias.

replication (REP-lih-KAY-shun): repeating an experiment and getting the same results. The skeptical scientist, on hearing of a new, exciting finding, will ask, "Has it been replicated yet?" If it hasn't, the scientist will

withhold judgment regarding the finding's validity.

subjects: the people or animals participating in a research project.

theory: a tentative explanation that integrates many and diverse findings to further the understanding of a defined topic.

validity (va-LID-ih-tee): having the quality of being founded on fact or evidence.

variables: factors that change. A variable may depend on another variable (for example, a child's height depends on his age), or it may be independent (for example, a child's height does not depend on the color of her eyes). Sometimes both variables correlate with a third variable (a child's height and eye color both depend on genetics).

Correlations and Causes Researchers often examine the relationships between two or more **variables**—for example, daily vitamin C intake and the number of colds or the duration and severity of cold symptoms. Importantly, researchers must be able to observe, measure, or verify the variables selected. Findings sometimes suggest no **correlation** between variables (regardless of the amount of vitamin C consumed, the number of colds remains the same). Other times, studies find either a **positive correlation** (the more vitamin C, the more colds) or a **negative correlation** (the more vitamin C, the fewer colds). Correlational evidence proves only that variables are associated, not that one is the cause of the other. People often jump to conclusions when they notice correlations, but their conclusions are often wrong. To actually prove that A causes B, scientists have to find evidence of the *mechanism*—that is, an explanation of how A might cause B.

Cautious Conclusions When researchers record and analyze the results of their experiments, they must exercise caution in their interpretation of the findings. For example, in an epidemiological study, scientists may use a specific segment of the population—say, men 18 to 30 years old. When the scientists draw conclusions, they are careful not to generalize the findings to all people. Similarly, scientists performing research studies using animals are cautious in applying their findings to human beings. Conclusions from any one research study are always tentative and take into account findings from studies conducted by other scientists as well. As evidence accumulates, scientists gain confidence about making recommendations that affect people's health and lives. Still, their statements are worded cautiously, such as "A diet high in fruits and vegetables *may* protect against *some* cancers."

Quite often, as scientists approach an answer to one research question, they raise several more questions, so future research projects are never lacking. Further scientific investigation then seeks to answer questions such as "What substance or substances within fruits and vegetables provide protection?" If those substances turn out to be the vitamins found so abundantly in fresh produce, then, "How much is needed to offer protection?" "How do these vitamins protect against cancer?" "Is it their action as antioxidant nutrients?" "If not, might it be another action or even another substance that accounts for the protection fruits and vegetables provide against cancer?" (Highlight 11 explores the answers to these questions and reviews recent research on antioxidant nutrients and disease.)

Publishing Research

The findings from a research study are submitted to a board of reviewers composed of other scientists who rigorously evaluate the study to assure that the scientific method was followed—a process known as **peer review.** The reviewers critique the study's hypothesis, methodology, statistical significance, and conclusions. If the reviewers consider the conclusions to be well supported by the evidence—that is, if the research has **validity**—they endorse the work for publication in a scientific journal where others can read it. This raises an important point regarding information found on the Internet: much gets published without the rigorous scrutiny of peer review. Consequently, readers must assume greater responsibility for examining the data and conclusions presented—often without the benefit of journal citations.

Even when a new finding is published or released to the media, it is still only preliminary and not very meaningful by itself. Other scientists will need to confirm or disprove the findings through **replication.** To be accepted into the body of nutrition knowledge, a finding must stand up to rigorous, repeated testing in experiments performed by several different researchers. What we "know" in nutrition results from years of replicating study findings. Communicating the latest finding in its proper context without distorting or oversimplifying the message is a challenge for scientists and journalists alike.

With each report from scientists, the field of nutrition changes a little—each finding contributes another piece to the whole body of knowledge. People who know how science works understand that single findings, like single frames in a movie, are just small parts of a larger story. Over years, the picture of what is "true" in nutrition gradually changes, and dietary recommendations change to reflect the current understanding of scientific research. Highlight 5 provides a detailed look at how dietary fat recommendations have evolved over the past several decades as researchers have uncovered the relationships between the various kinds of fat and their roles in supporting or harming health.

IN SUMMARY

Scientists learn about nutrition by conducting experiments that follow the protocol of scientific research. Researchers take care to establish similar control and experimental groups, large sample sizes, placebos, and blind treatments. Their findings must be reviewed and replicated by other scientists before being accepted as valid.

The characteristics of well-designed research have enabled scientists to study the actions of nutrients in the body. Such research has laid the foundation for quantifying how much of each nutrient the body needs.

Dietary Reference Intakes

Using the results of thousands of research studies, nutrition experts have produced a set of standards that define the amounts of energy, nutrients, other dietary components, and physical activity that best support health. These recommendations are called **Dietary Reference Intakes (DRI)**, and they reflect the collaborative efforts of researchers in both the United States and Canada.*[8] The inside front covers of this book provide a handy reference for DRI values.

Establishing Nutrient Recommendations

The DRI Committee consists of highly qualified scientists who base their estimates of nutrient needs on careful examination and interpretation of scientific evidence. These recommendations apply to healthy people and may not be appropriate for people with diseases that increase or decrease nutrient needs. The next several paragraphs discuss specific aspects of how the committee goes about establishing the values that make up the DRI:

- Estimated Average Requirements (EAR)
- Recommended Dietary Allowances (RDA)
- Adequate Intakes (AI)
- Tolerable Upper Intake Levels (UL)

Estimated Average Requirements (EAR) The committee reviews hundreds of research studies to determine the **requirement** for a nutrient—how much is needed in the diet. The committee selects a different criterion for each nutrient based on its various roles in performing activities in the body and in reducing disease risks.

An examination of all the available data reveals that each person's body is unique and has its own set of requirements. Men differ from women, and needs change as people grow from infancy through old age. For this reason, the committee clusters its recommendations for people into groups based on age and gender. Even so, the exact requirements for people of the same age and gender are likely to be different. For example, person A might need 40 units of a particular nutrient each day; person B might need 35; and person C, 57. Looking at enough people might reveal that their individual requirements fall into a symmetrical distribution,

Don't let the DRI "alphabet soup" of nutrient intake standards confuse you. Their names make sense when you learn their purposes.

Dietary Reference Intakes (DRI): a set of nutrient intake values for healthy people in the United States and Canada. These values are used for planning and assessing diets and include:
- Estimated Average Requirements (EAR)
- Recommended Dietary Allowances (RDA)
- Adequate Intakes (AI)
- Tolerable Upper Intake Levels (UL)

requirement: the lowest continuing intake of a nutrient that will maintain a specified criterion of adequacy.

* The DRI reports are produced by the Food and Nutrition Board, Institute of Medicine of the National Academies, with active involvement of scientists from Canada.

with most near the midpoint and only a few at the extremes (see the left side of Figure 1-5). Using this information, the committee determines an **Estimated Average Requirement (EAR)** for each nutrient—the average amount that appears sufficient for half of the population. In Figure 1-5, the Estimated Average Requirement is shown as 45 units.

Recommended Dietary Allowances (RDA) Once a nutrient *requirement* is established, the committee must decide what intake to *recommend* for everybody—the **Recommended Dietary Allowance (RDA).** As you can see by the distribution in Figure 1-5, the Estimated Average Requirement (shown in the figure as 45 units) is probably closest to everyone's need. However, if people consumed exactly the average requirement of a given nutrient each day, half of the population would develop deficiencies of that nutrient—in Figure 1-5, for example, person C would be among them. Recommendations are therefore set high enough above the Estimated Average Requirement to meet the needs of most healthy people.

Small amounts above the daily requirement do no harm, whereas amounts below the requirement may lead to health problems. When people's nutrient intakes are consistently **deficient** (less than the requirement), their nutrient stores decline, and over time this decline leads to poor health and deficiency symptoms. Therefore, to ensure that the nutrient RDA meet the needs of as many people as possible, the RDA are set near the top end of the range of the population's estimated requirements.

In this example, a reasonable RDA might be 63 units a day (see the right side of Figure 1-5). Such a point can be calculated mathematically so that it covers about 98 percent of a population. Almost everybody—including person C whose needs were higher than the average—would be covered if they met this dietary goal. Relatively few people's requirements would exceed this recommendation, and even then, they wouldn't exceed by much.

Adequate Intakes (AI) For some nutrients, there is insufficient scientific evidence to determine an Estimated Average Requirement (which is needed to set an RDA). In these cases, the committee establishes an **Adequate Intake (AI)** instead of an RDA. An AI reflects the average amount of a nutrient that a group of healthy people consumes. Like the RDA, the AI may be used as nutrient goals for individuals.

FIGURE 1-5 Estimated Average Requirements (EAR) and Recommended Dietary Allowances (RDA) Compared

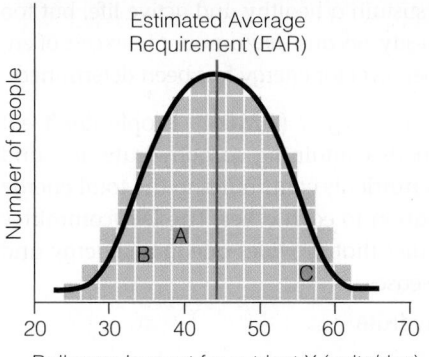
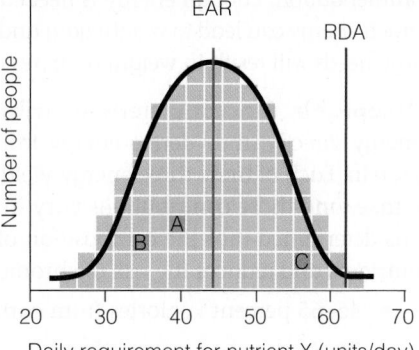

Each square in the graph above represents a person with unique nutritional requirements. (The text discusses three of these people—A, B, and C.) Some people require only a small amount of nutrient X and some require a lot. Most people, however, fall somewhere in the middle. This amount that covers half of the population is called the Estimated Average Requirement (EAR) and is represented here by the red line.

The Recommended Dietary Allowance (RDA) for a nutrient (shown here in purple) is set well above the EAR, covering about 98% of the population.

Estimated Average Requirement (EAR): the average daily amount of a nutrient that will maintain a specific biochemical or physiological function in half the healthy people of a given age and gender group.

Recommended Dietary Allowance (RDA): the average daily amount of a nutrient considered adequate to meet the known nutrient needs of practically all healthy people; a goal for dietary intake by individuals.

deficient: the amount of a nutrient below which almost all healthy people can be expected, over time, to experience deficiency symptoms.

Adequate Intake (AI): the average daily amount of a nutrient that appears sufficient to maintain a specified criterion; a value used as a guide for nutrient intake when an RDA cannot be determined.

FIGURE 1-6 Inaccurate versus Accurate View of Nutrient Intakes

The RDA or AI for a given nutrient represents a point that lies within a range of appropriate and reasonable intakes between toxicity and deficiency. Both of these recommendations are high enough to provide reserves in times of short-term dietary inadequacies, but not so high as to approach toxicity. Nutrient intakes above or below this range may be equally harmful.

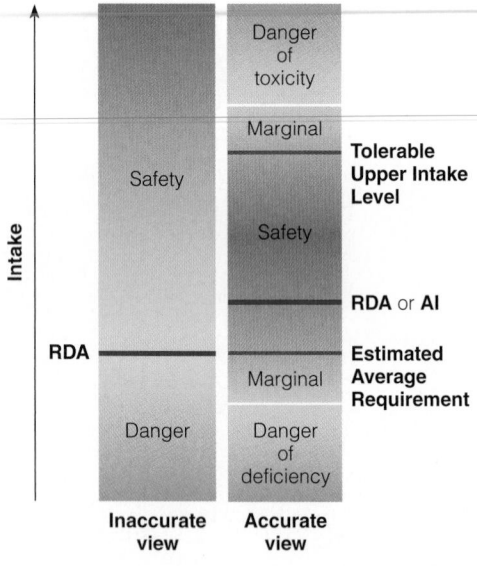

◆ Reference adults:
- Men: 19–30 yr, 5 ft 10 in., and 154 lb
- Women: 19–30 yr, 5 ft 4 in., and 126 lb

Tolerable Upper Intake Level (UL): the maximum daily amount of a nutrient that appears safe for most healthy people and beyond which there is an increased risk of adverse health effects.

Estimated Energy Requirement (EER): the average dietary energy intake that maintains energy balance and good health in a person of a given age, gender, weight, height, and level of physical activity.

Acceptable Macronutrient Distribution Ranges (AMDR): ranges of intakes for the energy nutrients that provide adequate energy and nutrients and reduce the risk of chronic diseases.

Although both the RDA and the AI serve as nutrient intake goals for individuals, their differences are noteworthy. An RDA for a given nutrient is based on enough scientific evidence to expect that the needs of almost all healthy people will be met. An AI, on the other hand, must rely more heavily on scientific judgments because sufficient evidence is lacking. The percentage of people covered by an AI is unknown; an AI is expected to exceed average requirements, but it may cover more or fewer people than an RDA would cover (if an RDA could be determined). For these reasons, AI values are more tentative than RDA. The table on the inside front cover identifies which nutrients have an RDA and which have an AI. Later chapters present the RDA and AI values for the vitamins and minerals.

Tolerable Upper Intake Levels (UL) As mentioned earlier, the recommended intakes for nutrients are generous, and they do not necessarily cover every individual for every nutrient. Nevertheless, it is probably best not to exceed these recommendations by very much or very often. Individual tolerances for high doses of nutrients vary, and somewhere above the recommended intake is a point beyond which a nutrient is likely to become toxic. This point is known as the **Tolerable Upper Intake Level (UL).** It is naive—and inaccurate—to think of recommendations as minimum amounts. A more accurate view is to see a person's nutrient needs as falling within a range, with marginal and danger zones both below and above it (see Figure 1-6).

Paying attention to upper levels is particularly useful in guarding against the overconsumption of nutrients, which may occur when people use large-dose supplements and fortified foods regularly. Later chapters discuss the dangers associated with excessively high intakes of vitamins and minerals, and the inside front cover (page C) presents tables that include the upper-level values for selected nutrients.

Establishing Energy Recommendations

In contrast to the RDA and AI values for nutrients, the recommendation for energy is not generous. Excess energy cannot be readily excreted and is eventually stored as body fat. These reserves may be beneficial when food is scarce, but they can also lead to obesity and its associated health consequences.

Estimated Energy Requirement (EER) The energy recommendation—called the **Estimated Energy Requirement (EER)**—represents the average dietary energy intake (kcalories per day) that will maintain energy balance in a person who has a healthy body weight and level of physical activity. ◆ Balance is key to the energy recommendation. Enough energy is needed to sustain a healthy and active life, but too much energy can lead to weight gain and obesity. Because *any* amount in excess of energy needs will result in weight gain, no upper level for energy has been determined.

Acceptable Macronutrient Distribution Ranges (AMDR) People don't eat energy directly; they derive energy from foods containing carbohydrate, fat, and protein. Each of these three energy-yielding nutrients contributes to the total energy intake, and those contributions vary in relation to each other. The DRI committee has determined that the composition of a diet that provides adequate energy and nutrients and reduces the risk of chronic diseases is:

- 45–65 percent kcalories from carbohydrate
- 20–35 percent kcalories from fat
- 10–35 percent kcalories from protein

These values are known as **Acceptable Macronutrient Distribution Ranges (AMDR).**

Using Nutrient Recommendations

Although the intent of nutrient recommendations seems simple, they are the subject of much misunderstanding and controversy. Perhaps the following facts will help put them in perspective:

1. Estimates of adequate energy and nutrient intakes apply to *healthy* people. They need to be adjusted for malnourished people or those with medical problems who may require supplemented or restricted intakes.

2. *Recommendations* are not minimum requirements, nor are they necessarily optimal intakes for all individuals. Recommendations can only target "most" of the people and cannot account for individual variations in nutrient needs—yet. Given the recent explosion of knowledge about genetics, the day may be fast approaching when nutrition scientists will be able to determine an individual's optimal nutrient needs.[9] Until then, registered dietitians ◆ and other qualified health professionals can help determine if recommendations should be adjusted to meet individual needs.

3. Most nutrient goals are intended to be met through diets composed of a variety of *foods* whenever possible. Because foods contain mixtures of nutrients and nonnutrients, they deliver more than just those nutrients covered by the recommendations. Excess intakes of vitamins and minerals are unlikely when they come from foods rather than supplements.

4. Recommendations apply to *average* daily intakes. Trying to meet the recommendations for every nutrient every day is difficult and unnecessary. The length of time over which a person's intake can deviate from the average without risk of deficiency or overdose varies for each nutrient, depending on how the body uses and stores the nutrient. For most nutrients (such as thiamin and vitamin C), deprivation would lead to rapid development of deficiency symptoms (within days or weeks); for others (such as vitamin A and vitamin B_{12}), deficiencies would develop more slowly (over months or years).

5. Each of the DRI categories serves a unique purpose. For example, the Estimated Average Requirements are most appropriately used to develop and evaluate nutrition programs for *groups* such as schoolchildren or military personnel. The RDA (or AI if an RDA is not available) can be used to set goals for *individuals*. Tolerable Upper Intake Levels serve as a reminder to keep nutrient intakes below amounts that increase the risk of toxicity—not a common problem when nutrients derive from foods, but a real possibility for some nutrients if supplements are used regularly.

With these understandings, professionals can use the DRI for a variety of purposes.

◆ A **registered dietitian** is a college-educated food and nutrition specialist who is qualified to evaluate people's nutritional health and needs. See Highlight 1 for more on what constitutes a nutrition expert.

Comparing Nutrient Recommendations

At least 40 different nations and international organizations have published nutrient standards similar to those used in the United States and Canada. Slight differences may be apparent, reflecting differences both in the interpretation of the data from which the standards were derived and in the food habits and physical activities of the populations they serve.

Many countries use the recommendations developed by two international groups: FAO (Food and Agriculture Organization) and WHO (World Health Organization). ◆ The FAO/WHO recommendations are considered sufficient to maintain health in nearly all healthy people worldwide.

◆ Nutrient recommendations from FAO/WHO are provided in Appendix I.

IN SUMMARY

The Dietary Reference Intakes (DRI) are a set of nutrient intake values that can be used to plan and evaluate diets for healthy people. The Estimated Average Requirement (EAR) defines the amount of a nutrient that supports a specific function in the body for half of the population. The Recommended Dietary Allowance (RDA) is based on the Estimated Average Requirement and establishes a goal for dietary intake that will meet the needs of almost all healthy people. An Adequate Intake (AI) serves a similar purpose when an RDA cannot be determined. The Estimated Energy Requirement (EER) defines the average amount of energy intake needed to maintain energy balance, and the Acceptable Macronutrient Distribution Ranges (AMDR) define the proportions contributed by carbohydrate, fat, and protein to a healthy diet. The Tolerable Upper Intake Level (UL) establishes the highest amount that appears safe for regular consumption.

Nutrition Assessment

What happens when a person doesn't get enough or gets too much of a nutrient or energy? If the deficiency or excess is significant over time, the person exhibits signs of **malnutrition**. With a deficiency of energy, the person may display the symptoms of **undernutrition** by becoming extremely thin, losing muscle tissue, and becoming prone to infection and disease. With a deficiency of a nutrient, the person may experience skin rashes, depression, hair loss, bleeding gums, muscle spasms, night blindness, or other symptoms. With an excess of energy, the person may become obese and vulnerable to diseases associated with **overnutrition** such as heart disease and diabetes. With a sudden nutrient overdose, the person may experience hot flashes, yellowing skin, a rapid heart rate, low blood pressure, or other symptoms. Similarly, over time, regular intakes in excess of needs may also have adverse effects.

Malnutrition symptoms—such as diarrhea, skin rashes, and fatigue—are easy to miss because they resemble the symptoms of other diseases. But a person who has learned how to use assessment techniques to detect malnutrition can identify when these conditions are caused by poor nutrition and can recommend steps to correct it. This discussion presents the basics of nutrition assessment; many more details are offered in later chapters and in Appendix E.

Nutrition Assessment of Individuals

To prepare a **nutrition assessment,** a registered dietitian or other trained health care professional uses:

- Historical information
- Anthropometric data
- Physical examinations
- Laboratory tests

Each of these methods involves collecting data in various ways and interpreting each finding in relation to the others to create a total picture.

Historical Information   One step in evaluating nutrition status is to obtain information about a person's history with respect to health status, socioeconomic status, drug use, and diet. The health history reflects a person's medical record and may reveal a disease that interferes with the person's ability to eat or the body's use of nutrients. The person's family history of major diseases is also noteworthy, especially for conditions such as heart disease that have a genetic tendency to run in families. Economic circumstances may show a financial inability to buy foods or inadequate kitchen facilities in which to prepare them. Social factors such as marital status, ethnic background, and educational level also influence food choices and nutrition status. A drug history, including all prescribed and over-the-counter medications as well as illegal substances, may highlight possible interactions that lead to nutrient deficiencies (as described in Highlight 17). A diet history that examines a person's intake

© Tom & Dee Ann McCarthy/CORBIS

A peek inside the mouth provides clues to a person's nutrition status. An inflamed tongue may indicate a B vitamin deficiency, and mottled teeth may reveal fluoride toxicity, for example.

malnutrition: any condition caused by excess or deficient food energy or nutrient intake or by an imbalance of nutrients.

- **mal** = bad

undernutrition: deficient energy or nutrients.

overnutrition: excess energy or nutrients.

nutrition assessment: a comprehensive analysis of a person's nutrition status that uses health, socioeconomic, drug, and diet histories; anthropometric measurements; physical examinations; and laboratory tests.

of foods, beverages, and supplements may reveal either a surplus or inadequacy of nutrients or energy.

To take a diet history, the assessor collects data about the foods a person eats. The data may be collected by recording the foods the person has eaten over a period of 24 hours, three days, or a week or more or by asking what foods the person typically eats and how much of each. The days in the record must be fairly typical of the person's diet, and portion sizes must be recorded accurately. To determine the amounts of nutrients consumed, the assessor usually enters the foods and their portion sizes into a computer using a diet analysis program. This step can also be done manually by looking up each food in a table of food composition such

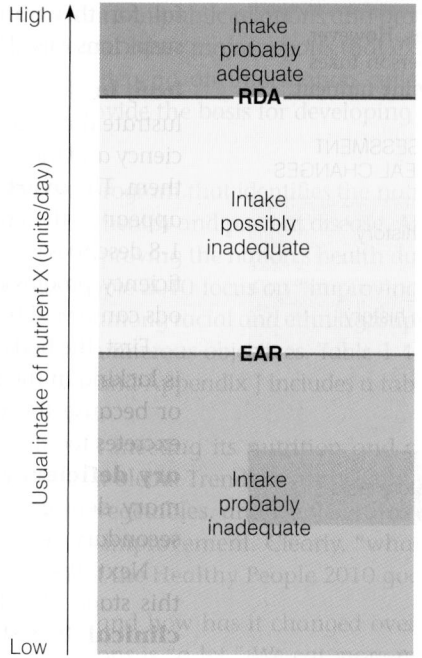

FIGURE 1-7 Using the DRI to Assess the Dietary Intake of a Healthy Individual

Usual intake of nutrient X (units/day)

High

Intake probably adequate

RDA

Intake possibly inadequate

EAR

Intake probably inadequate

Low

If a person's usual intake falls above the RDA, the intake is probably adequate because the RDA covers the needs of almost all people.

A usual intake that falls between the RDA and the EAR is more difficult to assess; the intake may be adequate, but the chances are greater or equal that it is inadequate.

If the usual intake falls below the EAR, it is probably inadequate.

as Appendix H in this book. The assessor then compares the calculated nutrient intakes with the DRI to determine the probability of adequacy (see Figure 1-7).[10] Alternatively, the diet history might be compared against standards such as the USDA Food Guide or *Dietary Guidelines* (described in Chapter 2).

An estimate of energy and nutrient intakes from a diet history, when combined with other sources of information, can help confirm or rule out the *possibility* of suspected nutrition problems. A sufficient intake of a nutrient does not guarantee adequacy, and an insufficient intake does not always indicate a deficiency. Such findings, however, warn of possible problems.

Anthropometric Data A second technique that may help to reveal nutrition problems is taking **anthropometric** measures such as height and weight. The assessor compares a person's measurements with standards specific for gender and age or with previous measures on the same individual. (Chapter 8 presents information on body weight and its standards.)

Measurements taken periodically and compared with previous measurements reveal patterns and indicate trends in a person's overall nutrition status, but they provide little information about specific nutrients. Instead, measurements out of line with expectations may reveal such problems as growth failure in children, wasting or swelling of body tissues in adults, and obesity—conditions that may reflect energy or nutrient deficiencies or excesses.

Physical Examinations A third nutrition assessment technique is a physical examination looking for clues to poor nutrition status. Every part of the body that can be inspected may offer such clues: the hair, eyes, skin, posture, tongue, fingernails, and others. The examination requires skill because many physical signs reflect more than one nutrient deficiency or toxicity—or even nonnutrition conditions. Like the other assessment techniques, a physical examination alone does not yield firm conclusions. Instead, physical examinations reveal possible imbalances that must be confirmed by other assessment techniques, or they confirm results from other assessment measures.

Laboratory Tests A fourth way to detect a developing deficiency, imbalance, or toxicity is to take samples of blood or urine, analyze them in the laboratory, and compare the results with normal values for a similar population. ◆ A goal of nutrition

◆ Assessment may one day depend on measures of how a nutrient influences genetic activity within the cells, instead of quantities in the blood or other tissues.

anthropometric (AN-throw-poe-MET-rick): relating to measurement of the physical characteristics of the body, such as height and weight.
• **anthropos** = human
• **metric** = measuring

3. The inorganic nutrients are:
   a. proteins and fats.
   b. vitamins and minerals.
   c. minerals and water.
   d. vitamins and proteins.

4. The energy-yielding nutrients are:
   a. fats, minerals, and water.
   b. minerals, proteins, and vitamins.
   c. carbohydrates, fats, and vitamins.
   d. carbohydrates, fats, and proteins.

5. Studies of populations that reveal correlations between dietary habits and disease incidence are:
   a. clinical trials.
   b. laboratory studies.
   c. case-control studies.
   d. epidemiological studies.

6. An experiment in which neither the researchers nor the subjects know who is receiving the treatment is known as:
   a. double blind.
   b. double control.
   c. blind variable.
   d. placebo control.

7. An RDA represents the:
   a. highest amount of a nutrient that appears safe for most healthy people.
   b. lowest amount of a nutrient that will maintain a specified criterion of adequacy.

c. average amount of a nutrient considered adequate to meet the known nutrient needs of practically all healthy people.
d. average amount of a nutrient that will maintain a specific biochemical or physiological function in half the people.

8. Historical information, physical examinations, laboratory tests, and anthropometric measures are:
   a. techniques used in diet planning.
   b. steps used in the scientific method.
   c. approaches used in disease prevention.
   d. methods used in a nutrition assessment.

9. A deficiency caused by an inadequate dietary intake is a(n):
   a. overt deficiency.
   b. covert deficiency.
   c. primary deficiency.
   d. secondary deficiency.

10. Behaviors such as smoking, dietary habits, physical activity, and alcohol consumption that influence the development of disease are known as:
   a. risk factors.
   b. chronic causes.
   c. preventive agents.
   d. disease descriptors.

REFERENCES

1. J. A. Mennella, M. Y. Pepino, and D. R. Reed, Genetic and environmental determinants of bitter perception and sweet preferences, *Pediatrics* 115 (2005): e216.
2. J. E. Tillotson, Our ready-prepared, ready-to-eat nation, *Nutrition Today* 37 (2002): 36-38.
3. D. Benton, Role of parents in the determination of the food preferences of children and the development of obesity, *International Journal of Obesity Related Metabolic Disorders* 28 (2004): 858-869.
4. L. Canetti, E. Bachar, and E. M. Berry, Food and emotion, *Behavioural Processes* 60 (2002): 157-164.
5. Position of the American Dietetic Association: Functional foods, *Journal of the American Dietetic Association* 104 (2004): 814-826.
6. Position of the American Dietetic Association: Total diet approach to communicating food and nutrition information, *Journal of the American Dietetic Association* 102 (2002): 100-108.
7. L. Afman and M. Müller, Nutrigenomics: From molecular nutrition to prevention of disease, *Journal of the American Dietetic Association* 106 (2006): 569-576; J. Ordovas and V. Mooser, Nutrigenomics and nutrigenetics, *Current Opinion in Lipidology* 15 (2005): 101-108; D. Shattuck, Nutritional genomics, *Journal of the American Dietetic Association* 103 (2003): 16, 18; P. Trayhurn,

Nutritional genomics-"Nutrigenomics," *British Journal of Nutrition* 89 (2003): 1-2.
8. Committee on Dietary Reference Intakes, *Dietary Reference Intakes for Water, Potassium, Sodium, Chloride, and Sulfate* (Washington, D.C.: National Academies Press, 2005); Committee on Dietary Reference Intakes, *Dietary Reference Intakes for Energy, Carbohydrate, Fiber, Fat, Fatty Acids, Cholesterol, Protein, and Amino Acids* (Washington, D.C.: National Academies Press, 2005); Committee on Dietary Reference Intakes, *Dietary Reference Intakes for Vitamin A, Vitamin K, Arsenic, Boron, Chromium, Copper, Iodine, Iron, Manganese, Molybdenum, Nickel, Silicon, Vanadium, and Zinc* (Washington, D.C.: National Academy Press, 2001); Committee on Dietary Reference Intakes, *Dietary Reference Intakes for Vitamin C, Vitamin E, Selenium, and Carotenoids* (Washington, D.C.: National Academy Press, 2000); Committee on Dietary Reference Intakes, *Dietary Reference Intakes for Thiamin, Riboflavin, Niacin, Vitamin B6, Folate, Vitamin B12, Pantothenic Acid, Biotin, and Choline* (Washington, D.C.: National Academy Press, 1998); Committee on Dietary Reference Intakes, *Dietary Reference Intakes for Calcium, Phosphorus, Magnesium, Vitamin D, and Fluoride* (Washington, D.C.: National Academy Press, 1997).
10. S. P. Murphy, S. I. Barr, and M. I. Poos, Using the new Dietary Reference Intakes to

assess diets: A map to the maze, *Nutrition Reviews* 60 (2002): 267-275.
12. J. Dwyer and coauthors, Collection of food and dietary supplement intake data: What we eat in America-NHANES, *Journal of Nutrition* 133 (2003): 590S-600S.
13. S. J. Crockett and coauthors, Nutrition monitoring application in the food industry, *Nutrition Today* 37 (2002): 130-135.
15. R. R. Briefel and C. L. Johnson, Secular trends in dietary intake in the United States, *Annual Review of Nutrition* 24 (2004): 401-431.
16. B. M. Popkin, Global nutrition dynamics: The world is shifting rapidly toward a diet linked with noncommunicable diseases, *American Journal of Clinical Nutrition* 84 (2006): 289-298; D. Yach and coauthors, The global burden of chronic diseases: Overcoming impediments to prevention and control, *Journal of the American Medical Association* 291 (2004): 2616-2622.
17. A. Jemal and coauthors, Trends in the leading causes of death in the United States, 1970-2002, *Journal of the American Medical Association* 294 (2005): 1255-1259.
18. A. H. Mokdad and coauthors, Actual causes of death in the United States, 2000, *Journal of the American Medical Association* 291 (2004): 1238-1245.

ANSWERS

Nutrition Calculations

1. a.   5 g protein $\times$ 4 kcal/g = 20 kcal protein
   30 g carbohydrate $\times$ 4 kcal/g = 120 kcal carbohydrate
   11 g fat $\times$ 9 kcal/g = 99 kcal fat
   Total = 239 kcal

   b.   20 kcal $\div$ 239 kcal $\times$ 100 = 8.4% kcal from protein
   120 kcal $\div$ 239 kcal $\times$ 100 = 50.2% kcal from carbohydrate
   99 kcal $\div$ 239 kcal $\times$ 100 = 41.4% kcal from fat
   Total = 100%.

   c.   1 g protein = 4 kcal protein
   13 g carbohydrate = 52 kcal carbohydrate
   146 total kcal − 56 kcal (protein + carbohydrate)
   = 90 kcal alcohol
   90 kcal alcohol $\div$ 7 g/kcal = 12.9 g alcohol

2. No. 15 g protein $\times$ 4 kcal/g = 60 kcal

Study Questions (multiple choice)

1. d   2. b   3. c   4. d   5. d   6. a   7. c   8. d
9. c   10. a

Nutrition Information and Misinformation—On the Net and in the News

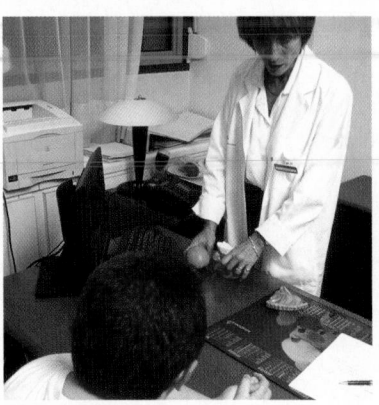

© Laurent/Jessy/© BSIP/Phototake

How can people distinguish valid nutrition information from misinformation? One excellent approach is to notice *who* is providing the information. The "who" behind the information is not always evident, though, especially in the world of electronic media. Keep in mind that *people* develop CD-ROMs and create websites on the Internet, just as people write books and report the news. In all cases, consumers need to determine whether the person is qualified to provide nutrition information.

This highlight begins by examining the unique potential as well as the problems of relying on the Internet and the media for nutrition information. It continues with a discussion of how to identify reliable nutrition information that applies to all resources, including the Internet and the news. (The glossary on p. 32 defines related terms.)

Nutrition on the Net

Got a question? The **Internet** has an answer. The Internet offers endless opportunities to obtain high-quality information, but it also delivers an abundance of incomplete, misleading, or inaccurate information.[1] Simply put: anyone can publish anything.

With hundreds of millions of **websites** on the **World Wide Web,** searching for nutrition information can be an overwhelming experience—much like walking into an enormous bookstore with millions of books, magazines, newspapers, and videos. And like a bookstore, the Internet offers no guarantees of the accuracy of the information found there—much of which is pure fiction.

When using the Internet, keep in mind that the quality of health-related information available covers a broad range.[2] You must evaluate websites for their accuracy, just like every other source. The accompanying "How to" provides tips for determining whether a website is reliable.

One of the most trustworthy sites used by scientists and others is the National Library of Medicine's PubMed, which provides free access to over 10 million abstracts (short descriptions) of research papers published in scientific journals around the world. Many abstracts provide links to websites where full articles are available. Figure H1-1 introduces this valuable resource.

Did you receive the e-mail warning about Costa Rican bananas causing the disease "necrotizing fasciitis"? If so, you've been scammed by Internet misinformation. When nutrition information arrives in unsolicited e-mails, be suspicious if:

- The person sending it to you didn't write it and you cannot determine who did or if that person is a nutrition expert
- The phrase "Forward this to everyone you know" appears
- The phrase "This is not a hoax" appears; chances are that it is
- The news is sensational and you've never heard about it from legitimate sources
- The language is emphatic and the text is sprinkled with capitalized words and exclamation marks
- No references are given or, if present, are of questionable validity when examined
- The message has been debunked on websites such as **www.quackwatch.org** or **www.urbanlegends.com**

Nutrition in the News

Consumers get much of their nutrition information from television news and magazine reports, which have heightened awareness of how diet influences the development of diseases. Consumers benefit from news coverage of nutrition when they learn to make lifestyle changes that will improve their health. Sometimes, however, when magazine articles or television programs report nutrition trends, they mislead consumers and create confusion. They often tell a lopsided story based on a few testimonials instead of presenting the results of research studies or a balance of expert opinions.

Tight deadlines and limited understanding sometimes make it difficult to provide a thorough report. Hungry for the latest news, the media often report scientific findings prematurely—without benefit of careful interpretation, replication, and peer review.[3] Usually, the reports present findings from a single, recently released study, making the news current and controversial. Consequently, the public receives diet and health news quickly, but not always in perspective. Reporters may twist inconclusive findings into "meaningful discoveries" when pressured to write catchy headlines and sensational stories.

As a result, "surprising new findings" seem to contradict one another, and consumers feel frustrated and betrayed. Occasionally, the reports are downright false, but more often the apparent contradictions are simply the normal result of science at work. A single study contributes to the big picture, but when viewed alone, it can easily distort the image. To be meaningful, the conclusions of any study must be presented cautiously within the context of other research findings.

Identifying Nutrition Experts

Regardless of whether the medium is electronic, print, or video, consumers need to ask whether the person behind the information is qualified to speak on nutrition. If the creator of an Internet website recommends eating three pineapples a day to lose weight, a trainer at the gym praises a high-protein diet, or a health-store clerk suggests an herbal supplement, should you believe these people? Can you distinguish between accurate news reports and infomercials on television? Have you noticed that many televised nutrition messages are presented by celebrities, fitness experts, psychologists, food editors, and chefs—that is, almost anyone except a **dietitian?** When you are confused or need sound dietary advice, whom should you ask?

Physicians and Other Health Care Professionals

Many people turn to physicians or other health care professionals for dietary advice, expecting them to know about all health-related matters. But are they the best sources of accurate and current information on nutrition? Only about 30 percent of all medical schools in the United States require students to take a separate nutrition course; less than half require the minimum 25 hours of nutrition instruction recommended by the National Academy of Sciences.[4] By comparison, most students reading this text are taking a nutrition class that provides an average of 45 hours of instruction.

The **American Dietetic Association (ADA)** asserts that standardized nutrition education should be included

| HOW TO | Determine Whether a Website Is Reliable |

To determine whether a website offers reliable nutrition information, ask the following questions:

- **Who?** Who is responsible for the site? Is it staffed by qualified professionals? Look for the authors' names and credentials. Have experts reviewed the content for accuracy?
- **When?** When was the site last updated? Because nutrition is an ever-changing science, sites need to be dated and updated frequently.
- **Where?** Where is the information coming from? The three letters following the dot in a Web address identify the site's affiliation. Addresses ending in "gov" (government), "edu" (educational institute), and "org" (organization) generally provide reliable information; "com" (commercial) sites represent businesses and, depending on their qualifications and integrity, may or may not offer dependable information.
- **Why?** Why is the site giving you this information? Is the site providing a public service or selling a product? Many commercial sites provide accurate information, but some do not. When money is the prime motivation, be aware that the information may be biased.

If you are satisfied with the answers to all of the questions above, then ask this final question:

- **What?** What is the message, and is it in line with other reliable sources? Information that contradicts common knowledge should be questioned. Many reliable sites provide links to other sites to facilitate your quest for knowledge, but this provision alone does not guarantee a reputable intention. Be aware that any site can link to any other site without permission.

in the curricula for all health care professionals: physicians, nurses, physician's assistants, dental hygienists, physical and occupational therapists, social workers, and all others who provide services directly to clients. When these professionals understand the relevance of nutrition in the treatment and prevention of disease and have command of reliable nutrition information, then all the people they serve will also be better informed.

| FIGURE H1-1 | PUBMED (www.pubmed.gov): Internet Resource for Scientific Nutrition References |

The U.S. National Library of Medicine's PubMed website offers tutorials to help teach beginners to use the search system effectively. Often, simply visiting the site, typing a query in the "Search for" box, and clicking "Go" will yield satisfactory results.

For example, to find research concerning calcium and bone health, typing "calcium bone" nets over 30,000 results. Try setting limits on dates, types of articles, languages, and other criteria to obtain a more manageable number of abstracts to peruse.

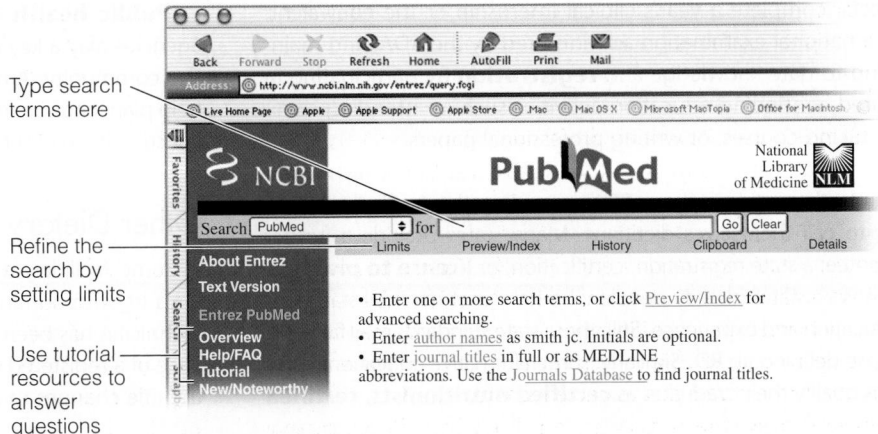

Type search terms here

Refine the search by setting limits

Use tutorial resources to answer questions

GLOSSARY

accredited: approved; in the case of medical centers or universities, certified by an agency recognized by the U.S. Department of Education.

American Dietetic Association (ADA): the professional organization of dietitians in the United States. The Canadian equivalent is Dietitians of Canada, which operates similarly.

certified nutritionists or **certified nutritional consultants** or **certified nutrition therapists:** a person who has been granted a document declaring his or her authority as a nutrition professional; see also nutritionalist.

correspondence schools: schools that offer courses and degrees by mail. Some correspondence schools are accredited; others are not.

dietetic technician: a person who has completed a minimum of an associate's degree from an accredited university or college and an approved dietetic

technician program that includes a supervised practice experience. See also dietetic technician, registered (DTR).

dietetic technician, registered (DTR): a dietetic technician who has passed a national examination and maintains registration through continuing professional education.

dietitian: a person trained in nutrition, food science, and diet planning. See also registered dietitian.

DTR: see dietetic technician, registered.

fraudulent: the promotion, for financial gain, of devices, treatments, services, plans, or products (including diets and supplements) that alter or claim to alter a human condition without proof of safety or effectiveness. (The word quackery comes from the term quacksalver, meaning a person who quacks loudly about a miracle product—a lotion or a salve.)

Internet (the net): a worldwide network of millions of computers linked together to share information.

license to practice: permission under state or federal law, granted on meeting specified criteria, to use a certain title (such as dietitian) and offer certain services. **Licensed dietitians** may use the initials **LD** after their names.

misinformation: false or misleading information.

nutritionist: a person who specializes in the study of nutrition. Note that this definition does not specify qualifications and may apply not only to registered dietitians but also to self-described experts whose training is questionable. Most states have licensing laws that define the scope of practice for those calling themselves nutritionists.

public health dietitians: dietitians who specialize in providing nutrition services

through organized community efforts.

RD: see registered dietitian.

registered dietitian (RD): a person who has completed a minimum of a bachelor's degree from an accredited university or college, has completed approved course work and a supervised practice program, has passed a national examination, and maintains registration through continuing professional education.

registration: listing; with respect to health professionals, listing with a professional organization that requires specific course work, experience, and passing of an examination.

websites: Internet resources composed of text and graphic files, each with a unique URL (Uniform Resource Locator) that names the site (for example, www.usda.gov).

World Wide Web (the web, commonly abbreviated www): a graphical subset of the Internet.

Most health care professionals appreciate the connections between health and nutrition. Those who have specialized in clinical nutrition are especially well qualified to speak on the subject. Few, however, have the time or experience to develop diet plans and provide detailed diet instructions for clients. Often they wisely refer clients to a qualified nutrition expert—a **registered dietitian (RD).**

Registered Dietitians (RD)

A registered dietitian (RD) has the educational background necessary to deliver reliable nutrition advice and care.[5] To become an RD, a person must earn an undergraduate degree requiring about 60 semester hours in nutrition, food science, and other related subjects; complete a year's clinical internship or the equivalent; pass a national examination administered by the ADA; and maintain up-to-date knowledge and **registration** by participating in required continuing education activities such as attending seminars, taking courses, or writing professional papers.

Some states allow anyone to use the title dietitian or **nutritionist,** but others allow only an RD or people with specified qualifications to call themselves dietitians. Many states provide a further guarantee: a state registration, certification, or **license to practice.** In this way, states identify people who have met minimal standards of education and experience. Still, these state standards may fall short of those defining an RD. Similarly, some alternative educational programs qualify their graduates as **certified nutritionists, certified**

nutritional consultants, or **certified nutrition therapists**—terms that sound authoritative but lack the credentials of an RD.[6]

Dietitians perform a multitude of duties in many settings in most communities. They work in the food industry, pharmaceutical companies, home health agencies, long-term care institutions, private practice, public health departments, research centers, education settings, fitness centers, and hospitals. Depending on their work settings, dietitians can assume a number of different job responsibilities and positions. In hospitals, administrative dietitians manage the foodservice system; clinical dietitians provide client care; and nutrition support team dietitians coordinate nutrition care with other health care professionals. In the food industry, dietitians conduct research, develop products, and market services.

Public health dietitians who work in government-funded agencies play a key role in delivering nutrition services to people in the community. Among their many roles, public health dietitians help plan, coordinate, and evaluate food assistance programs; act as consultants to other agencies; manage finances; and much more.

Other Dietary Employees

In some facilities, a **dietetic technician** assists registered dietitians in both administrative and clinical responsibilities. A dietetic technician has been educated and trained to work under the guidance of a registered dietitian; upon passing a national examination, the title changes to **dietetic technician, registered (DTR).**

In addition to the dietetic technician, other dietary employees may include clerks, aides, cooks, porters, and other assistants. These dietary employees do not have extensive formal training in nutrition, and their ability to provide accurate information may be limited.

Identifying Fake Credentials

In contrast to registered dietitians, thousands of people obtain fake nutrition degrees and claim to be nutrition consultants or doctors of "nutrimedicine." These and other such titles may sound meaningful, but most of these people lack the established credentials and training of an ADA-sanctioned dietitian. If you look closely, you can see signs of their fake expertise.

Consider educational background, for example. The minimum standards of education for a dietitian specify a bachelor of science (BS) degree in food science and human nutrition or related fields from an **accredited** college or university.* Such a degree generally requires four to five years of study. In contrast, a fake nutrition expert may display a degree from a six-month correspondence course. Such a degree simply falls short. In some cases, businesses posing as legitimate **correspondence schools** offer even less—they sell certificates to anyone who pays the fees. To obtain these "degrees," a candidate need not attend any classes, read any books, or pass any examinations.

To safeguard educational quality, an accrediting agency recognized by the U.S. Department of Education (DOE) certifies that certain schools meet criteria established to ensure that an institution provides complete and accurate schooling. Unfortunately, fake nutrition degrees are available from schools "accredited" by more than 30 phony accrediting agencies. Acquiring false credentials is especially easy today, with **fraudulent** businesses operating via the Internet.

Knowing the qualifications of someone who provides nutrition information can help you determine whether that person's advice might be harmful or helpful. Don't be afraid to ask for credentials. The accompanying "How to" lists credible sources of nutrition information.

Red Flags of Nutrition Quackery

Figure H1-2 (p. 34) features eight red flags consumers can use to identify nutrition **misinformation.** Sales of unproven and

HOW TO Find Credible Sources of Nutrition Information

Government agencies, volunteer associations, consumer groups, and professional organizations provide consumers with reliable health and nutrition information. Credible sources of nutrition information include:

- Nutrition and food science departments at a university or community college
- Local agencies such as the health department or County Cooperative Extension Service
- Government health agencies such as:
  - Department of Agriculture (USDA)   **www.usda.gov**
  - Department of Health and Human Services (DHHS)   **www.os.dhhs.gov**
  - Food and Drug Administration (FDA)   **www.fda.gov**
  - Health Canada   **www.hc-sc.gc.ca/nutrition**
- Volunteer health agencies such as:
  - American Cancer Society   **www.cancer.org**
  - American Diabetes Association   **www.diabetes.org**
  - American Heart Association   **www.americanheart.org**
- Reputable consumer groups such as:
  - American Council on Science and Health   **www.acsh.org**
  - Federal Citizen Information Center   **www.pueblo.gsa.gov**
  - International Food Information Council   **ific.org**
- Professional health organizations such as:
  - American Dietetic Assocation   **www.eatright.org**
  - American Medical Association   **www.ama-assn.org**
  - Dietitians of Canada   **www.dietitians.ca**
- Journals such as:
  - *American Journal of Clinical Nutrition*   **www.ajcn.org**
  - *New England Journal of Medicine*   **www.nejm.org**
  - *Nutrition Reviews*   **www.ilsi.org**

dangerous products have always been a concern, but the Internet now provides merchants with an easy and inexpensive way to reach millions of customers around the world. Because of the difficulty in regulating the Internet, fraudulent and illegal sales of medical products have hit a bonanza. As is the case with the air, no one owns the Internet, and similarly, no one has control over the pollution. Countries have different laws regarding sales of drugs, dietary supplements, and other health products, but applying these laws to the Internet marketplace is almost impossible. Even if illegal activities could be defined and identified, finding the person responsible for a particular website is not always possible. Websites can open and close in a blink of a cursor. Now, more than ever, consumers must heed the caution "Buyer beware."

In summary, when you hear nutrition news, consider its source. Ask yourself these two questions: Is the person providing the information qualified to speak on nutrition? Is the information based on valid scientific research? If not, find a better source. After all, your health depends on it.

---

* To ensure the quality and continued improvement of nutrition and dietetics education programs, an ADA agency known as the Commission on Accreditation for Dietetics Education (CADE) establishes and enforces eligibility requirements and accreditation standards for programs preparing students for careers as registered dietitians or dietetic technicians. Programs meeting those standards are accredited by CADE.

FIGURE H1-2 Red Flags of Nutrition Quackery

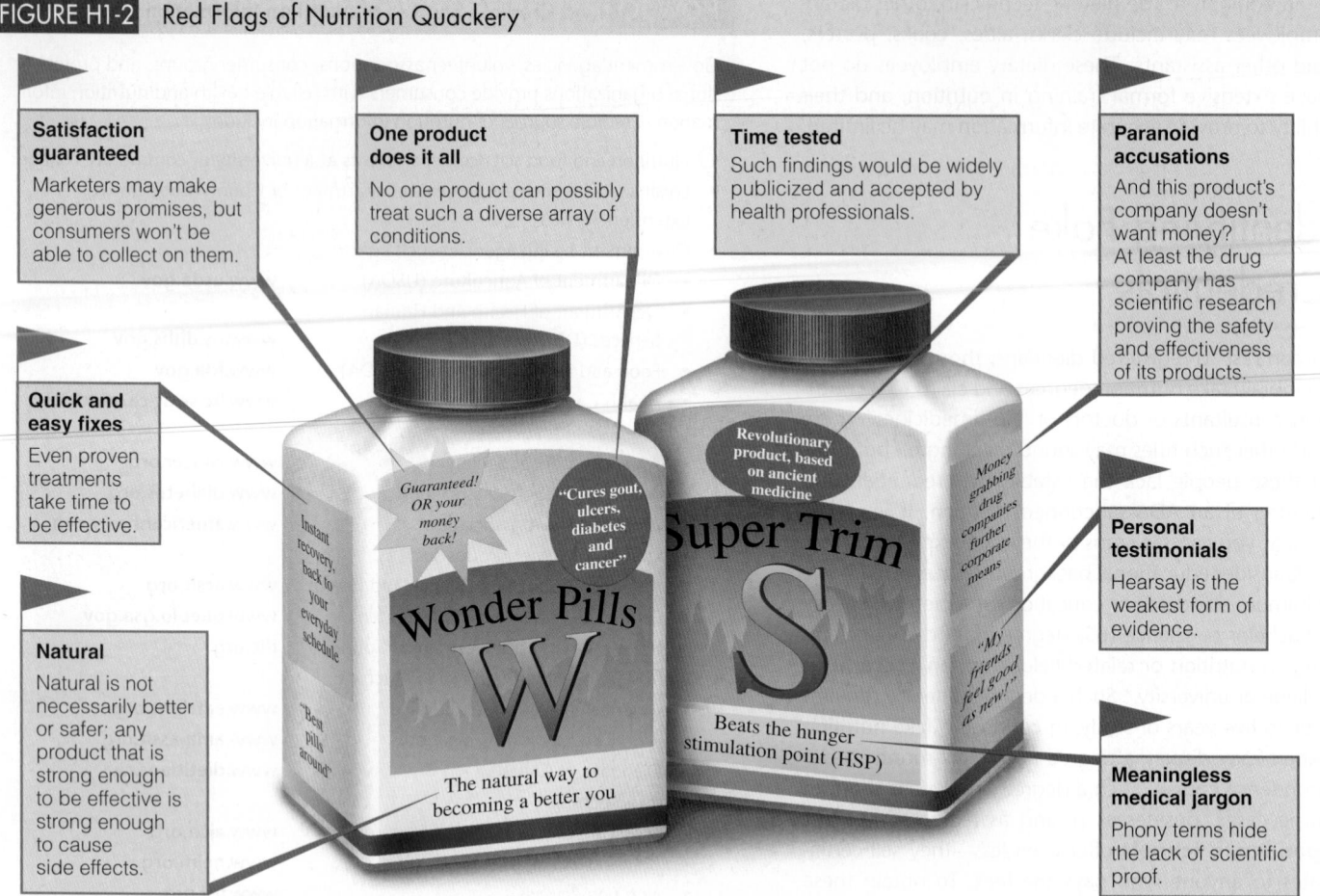

Satisfaction guaranteed
Marketers may make generous promises, but consumers won't be able to collect on them.

One product does it all
No one product can possibly treat such a diverse array of conditions.

Time tested
Such findings would be widely publicized and accepted by health professionals.

Paranoid accusations
And this product's company doesn't want money? At least the drug company has scientific research proving the safety and effectiveness of its products.

Quick and easy fixes
Even proven treatments take time to be effective.

Natural
Natural is not necessarily better or safer; any product that is strong enough to be effective is strong enough to cause side effects.

Personal testimonials
Hearsay is the weakest form of evidence.

Meaningless medical jargon
Phony terms hide the lack of scientific proof.

NUTRITION ON THE NET

- Visit the National Council Against Health Fraud: **www.ncahf.org**
- Find a registered dietitian in your area from the American Dietetic Association: **www.eatright.org**
- Find a nutrition professional in Canada from the Dietitians of Canada: **www.dietitians.ca**
- Find out whether a correspondence school is accredited from the Distance Education and Training Council's Accrediting Commission: **www.detc.org**
- Find useful and reliable health information from the Health on the Net Foundation: **www.hon.ch**

- Find out whether a school is properly accredited for a dietetics degree from the American Dietetic Association: **www.eatright.org/cade**
- Obtain a listing of accredited institutions, professionally accredited programs, and candidates for accreditation from the American Council on Education: **www.acenet.edu**
- Learn more about quackery from Stephen Barrett's Quackwatch: **www.quackwatch.org**
- Check out health-related hoaxes and urban legends: **www.cdc.gov/hoax_rumors.htm** and **www.urbanlegends.com/**
- Find reliable research articles: **www.pubmed.gov**

REFERENCES

1. Position of the American Dietetic Association: Food and nutrition misinformation, *Journal of the American Dietetic Association* 106 (2006): 601-607.
2. G. Eysenbach and coauthors, Empirical studies assessing the quality of health information for consumers on the World Wide Web: A systematic review, *Journal of the American Medical Association* 287 (2002): 2691-2700.
3. L. M. Schwartz, S. Woloshin, and L. Baczek, Media coverage of scientific meetings: Too much, too soon? *Journal of the American Medical Association* 287 (2002): 2859-2863.
4. K. M. Adams and coauthors, Status of nutrition education in medical schools, *American Journal of Clinical Nutrition* 83 (2006): 941S-944S.
5. Position of the American Dietetic Association: The roles of registered dieticians and dietetic technicians, registered in health promotion and disease prevention, *Journal of the American Dietetic Association* 106 (2006): 1875-1884.
6. Nutritionist imposters and how to spot them, *Nutrition and the M.D.*, September 2004, pp. 4-6.

Nutrition in Your Life

You make food choices—deciding what to eat and how much to eat—more than 1000 times every year. We eat so frequently that it's easy to choose a meal without giving any thought to its nutrient contributions or health consequences. Even when we want to make healthy choices, we may not know which foods to select or how much to consume. With a few tools and tips, you can learn to plan a healthy diet.

Planning a Healthy Diet

CHAPTER OUTLINE

Principles and Guidelines • Diet-Planning Principles • Dietary Guidelines for Americans

Diet-Planning Guides • USDA Food Guide • Exchange Lists • Putting the Plan into Action • From Guidelines to Groceries

Food Labels • The Ingredient List • Serving Sizes • Nutrition Facts • The Daily Values • Nutrient Claims • Health Claims • Structure-Function Claims • Consumer Education

HIGHLIGHT 2 Vegetarian Diets

Chapter 1 explained that the body's many activities are supported by the nutrients delivered by the foods people eat. Food choices made over years influence the body's health, and consistently poor choices increase the risks of developing chronic diseases. This chapter shows how a person can select from the tens of thousands of available foods to create a diet that supports health. Fortunately, most foods provide several nutrients, so one trick for wise diet planning is to select a combination of foods that deliver a full array of nutrients. This chapter begins by introducing the diet-planning principles and dietary guidelines that assist people in selecting foods that will deliver nutrients without excess energy (kcalories).

Principles and Guidelines

How well you nourish yourself does not depend on the selection of any one food. Instead, it depends on the selection of many different foods at numerous meals over days, months, and years. Diet-planning principles and dietary guidelines are key concepts to keep in mind whenever you are selecting foods—whether shopping at the grocery store, choosing from a restaurant menu, or preparing a home-cooked meal.

Diet-Planning Principles

Diet planners have developed several ways to select foods. Whatever plan or combination of plans they use, though, they keep in mind the six basic diet-planning principles ◆ listed in the margin.

Adequacy **Adequacy** means that the diet provides sufficient energy and enough of all the nutrients to meet the needs of healthy people. Take the essential nutrient iron, for example. Because the body loses some iron each day, people have to replace it by eating foods that contain iron. A person whose diet fails to provide enough iron-rich foods may develop the symptoms of iron-deficiency anemia: the person may feel weak, tired, and listless; have frequent headaches; and find that even the smallest amount of muscular work brings disabling fatigue. To prevent these deficiency symptoms, a person must include foods that supply adequate iron. The same is true for all the other essential nutrients introduced in Chapter 1.

◆ Diet-planning principles:
- **A**dequacy
- **B**alance
- k**C**alorie (energy) control
- Nutrient **D**ensity
- **M**oderation
- **V**ariety

adequacy (dietary): providing all the essential nutrients, fiber, and energy in amounts sufficient to maintain health.

To ensure an adequate and balanced diet, eat a variety of foods daily, choosing different foods from each group.

Balance The art of balancing the diet involves consuming enough—but not too much—of each type of food. The essential minerals calcium and iron, taken together, illustrate the importance of dietary **balance**. Meats, fish, and poultry are rich in iron but poor in calcium. Conversely, milk and milk products are rich in calcium but poor in iron. Use some meat or meat alternates for iron; use some milk and milk products for calcium; and save some space for other foods, too, because a diet consisting of milk and meat alone would not be adequate. ◆ For the other nutrients, people need whole grains, vegetables, and fruits.

kCalorie (Energy) Control Designing an adequate diet without overeating requires careful planning. Once again, balance plays a key role. The amount of energy coming into the body from foods should balance with the amount of energy being used by the body to sustain its metabolic and physical activities. Upsetting this balance leads to gains or losses in body weight. The discussion of energy balance and weight control in Chapters 8 and 9 examines this issue in more detail, but the key to **kcalorie control** is to select foods of high **nutrient density**.

Nutrient Density To eat well without overeating, select foods that deliver the most nutrients for the least food energy. Consider foods containing calcium, for example. You can get about 300 milligrams of calcium from either 1½ ounces of cheddar cheese or 1 cup of fat-free milk, but the cheese delivers about twice as much food energy (kcalories) as the milk. The fat-free milk, then, is twice as calcium dense as the cheddar cheese; it offers the same amount of calcium for half the kcalories. Both foods are excellent choices for adequacy's sake alone, but to achieve adequacy while controlling kcalories, ◆ the fat-free milk is the better choice. (Alternatively, a person could select a low-fat cheddar cheese.) The many bar graphs that appear in Chapters 10 through 13 highlight the most nutrient-dense choices, and the accompanying "How to" describes how to compare foods based on nutrient density.

◆ Balance in the diet helps to ensure adequacy.

◆ Nutrient density promotes adequacy and kcalorie control.

balance (dietary): providing foods in proportion to each other and in proportion to the body's needs.

kcalorie (energy) control: management of food energy intake.

nutrient density: a measure of the nutrients a food provides relative to the energy it provides. The more nutrients and the fewer kcalories, the higher the nutrient density.

HOW TO Compare Foods Based on Nutrient Density

One way to evaluate foods is simply to notice their nutrient contribution *per serving:* 1 cup of milk provides about 300 milligrams of calcium, and ½ cup of fresh, cooked turnip greens provides about 100 milligrams. Thus a serving of milk offers three times as much calcium as a serving of turnip greens. To get 300 milligrams of calcium, a person could choose either 1 cup of milk or 1½ cups of turnip greens.

Another valuable way to evaluate foods is to consider their nutrient density—their nutrient contribution *per kcalorie*. Fat-free milk delivers about 85 kcalories with its 300 milligrams of calcium. To calculate the nutrient density, divide milligrams by kcalories:

$$\frac{300 \text{ mg calcium}}{85 \text{ kcal}} = 3.5 \text{ mg per kcal}$$

Do the same for the fresh turnip greens, which provide 15 kcalories with the 100 milligrams of calcium:

$$\frac{100 \text{ mg calcium}}{15 \text{ kcal}} = 6.7 \text{ mg per kcal}$$

The more milligrams per kcalorie, the greater the nutrient density. Turnip greens are more calcium dense than milk. They provide more calcium *per kcalorie* than milk, but milk offers more calcium *per serving*. Both approaches offer valuable information, especially when combined with a realistic appraisal. What matters most is which are you more likely to consume—1½ cups of turnip greens or 1 cup of milk? You can get 300 milligrams of calcium from either, but the greens will save you about 40 kcalories (the savings would be even greater if you usually use whole milk).

Keep in mind, too, that calcium is only one of the many nutrients that foods provide. Similar calculations for protein, for example, would show that fat-free milk provides more protein both *per kcalorie* and *per serving* than turnip greens—that is, milk is more protein dense. Combining variety with nutrient density helps to ensure the adequacy of all nutrients.

Just like a person who has to pay for rent, food, clothes, and tuition on a limited budget, we have to obtain iron, calcium, and all the other essential nutrients on a limited energy allowance. Success depends on getting many nutrients for each kcalorie "dollar." For example, a can of cola and a handful of grapes may both provide about the same number of kcalories, but the grapes deliver many more nutrients. A person who makes nutrient-dense choices, such as fruit instead of cola, can meet daily nutrient needs on a lower energy budget. Such choices support good health.

Foods that are notably low in nutrient density—such as potato chips, candy, and colas—are sometimes called **empty-kcalorie foods**. The kcalories these foods provide are called "empty" because they deliver energy (from sugar, fat, or both) with little, or no, protein, vitamins, or minerals.

Moderation Foods rich in fat and sugar provide enjoyment and energy but relatively few nutrients. In addition, they promote weight gain when eaten in excess. A person practicing **moderation** ◆ eats such foods only on occasion and regularly selects foods low in solid fats and added sugars, a practice that automatically improves nutrient density. Returning to the example of cheddar cheese versus fat-free milk, the fat-free milk not only offers the same amount of calcium for less energy, but it also contains far less fat than the cheese.

◆ Moderation contributes to adequacy, balance, and kcalorie control.

Variety A diet may have all of the virtues just described and still lack **variety**, if a person eats the same foods day after day. People should select foods from each of the food groups daily and vary their choices within each food group from day to day for several reasons. First, different foods within the same group contain different arrays of nutrients. Among the fruits, for example, strawberries are especially rich in vitamin C while apricots are rich in vitamin A. Variety improves nutrient adequacy.[1] Second, no food is guaranteed entirely free of substances that, in excess, could be harmful. The strawberries might contain trace amounts of one contaminant, the apricots another. By alternating fruit choices, a person will ingest very little of either contaminant. (Contamination of foods is discussed in Chapter 19.) Third, as the adage goes, variety is the spice of life. A person who eats beans frequently can enjoy pinto beans in Mexican burritos today, garbanzo beans in Greek salad tomorrow, and baked beans with barbecued chicken on the weekend. Eating nutritious meals need never be boring.

Dietary Guidelines for Americans

What should a person eat to stay healthy? The answers can be found in the *Dietary Guidelines for Americans 2005*. These guidelines provide science-based advice to promote health and to reduce risk of chronic diseases through diet and physical activity.[2] Table 2-1 presents the nine *Dietary Guidelines* topics with their key recommendations. These key recommendations, along with additional recommendations for specific population groups, also appear throughout the text as their subjects are discussed. The first three topics focus on choosing nutrient-dense foods within energy needs, maintaining a healthy body weight, and engaging in regular physical activity. The fourth topic, "Food Groups to Encourage," focuses on the selection of a variety of fruits and vegetables, whole grains, and milk. The next four topics advise people to choose sensibly in their use of fats, carbohydrates, salt, and alcoholic beverages (for those who partake). Finally, consumers are reminded to keep foods safe. Together, the *Dietary Guidelines* point the way toward better health. Table 2-2 presents Canada's *Guidelines for Healthy Eating*.

Some people might wonder why *dietary* guidelines include recommendations for physical activity. The simple answer is that most people who maintain a healthy body weight do more than eat right. They also exercise—the equivalent of 60 minutes or more of moderately intense physical activity daily. As you will see repeatedly throughout this text, food and physical activity choices are integral partners in supporting good health.

empty-kcalorie foods: a popular term used to denote foods that contribute energy but lack protein, vitamins, and minerals.

moderation (dietary): providing enough but not too much of a substance.

variety (dietary): eating a wide selection of foods within and among the major food groups.

TABLE 2-1 Key Recommendations of the *Dietary Guidelines for Americans 2005*

Adequate Nutrients within Energy Needs

- Consume a variety of nutrient-dense foods and beverages within and among the basic food groups; limit intakes of saturated and *trans* fats, cholesterol, added sugars, salt, and alcohol.
- Meet recommended intakes within energy needs by adopting a balanced eating pattern, such as the USDA Food Guide (see pp. 41–47).

Weight Management

- To maintain body weight in a healthy range, balance kcalories from foods and beverages with kcalories expended (see Chapters 8 and 9).
- To prevent gradual weight gain over time, make small decreases in food and beverage kcalories and increase physical activity.

Physical Activity

- Engage in regular physical activity and reduce sedentary activities to promote health, psychological well-being, and a healthy body weight.
- Achieve physical fitness by including cardiovascular conditioning, stretching exercises for flexibility, and resistance exercises or calisthenics for muscle strength and endurance.

Food Groups to Encourage

- Consume a sufficient amount of fruits, vegetables, milk and milk products, and whole grains while staying within energy needs.
- Select a variety of fruits and vegetables each day, including selections from all five vegetable subgroups (dark green, orange, legumes, starchy vegetables, and other vegetables) several times a week. Make at least half of the grain selections whole grains. Select fat-free or low-fat milk products.

Fats

- Consume less than 10 percent of kcalories from saturated fats and less than 300 milligrams of cholesterol per day, and keep *trans* fats consumption as low as possible (see Chapter 5).
- Keep total fat intake between 20 and 35 percent of kcalories; choose from mostly polyunsaturated and monounsaturated fat sources such as fish, nuts, and vegetable oils.
- Select and prepare foods that are lean, low fat, or fat-free and low in saturated and/or *trans* fats.

Carbohydrates

- Choose fiber-rich fruits, vegetables, and whole grains often.
- Choose and prepare foods and beverages with little added sugars (see Chapter 4).
- Reduce the incidence of dental caries by practicing good oral hygiene and consuming sugar- and starch-containing foods and beverages less frequently.

Sodium and Potassium

- Choose and prepare foods with little salt (less than 2300 milligrams sodium or approximately 1 teaspoon salt daily). At the same time, consume potassium-rich foods, such as fruits and vegetables (see Chapter 12).

Alcoholic Beverages

- Those who choose to drink alcoholic beverages should do so sensibly and in moderation (up to one drink per day for women and up to two drinks per day for men).
- Some individuals should not consume alcoholic beverages (see Highlight 7).

Food Safety

- To avoid microbial foodborne illness, keep foods safe: clean hands, food contact surfaces, and fruits and vegetables; separate raw, cooked, and ready-to-eat foods; cook foods to a safe internal temperature; chill perishable food promptly; and defrost food properly.
- Avoid unpasteurized milk and products made from it; raw or undercooked eggs, meat, poultry, fish, and shellfish; unpasteurized juices; raw sprouts.

NOTE: These guidelines are intended for adults and healthy children ages 2 and older.
SOURCE: The *Dietary Guidelines for Americans 2005*, available at **www.healthierus.gov/dietaryguidelines**.

TABLE 2-2 Canada's *Guidelines for Healthy Eating*

- Enjoy a variety of foods.
- Emphasize cereals, breads, other grain products, vegetables, and fruits.
- Choose lower-fat dairy products, leaner meats, and foods prepared with little or no fat.
- Achieve and maintain a healthy body weight by enjoying regular physical activity and healthy eating.
- Limit salt, alcohol, and caffeine.

SOURCE: These guidelines derive from *Action Towards Healthy Eating—Canada's Guidelines for Healthy Eating and Recommended Strategies for Implementation.*

IN SUMMARY

A well-planned diet delivers adequate nutrients, a balanced array of nutrients, and an appropriate amount of energy. It is based on nutrient-dense foods, moderate in substances that can be detrimental to health, and varied in its selections. The 2005 *Dietary Guidelines* apply these principles, offering practical advice on how to eat for good health.

Diet-Planning Guides

To plan a diet that achieves all of the dietary ideals just outlined, a person needs tools as well as knowledge. Among the most widely used tools for diet planning are **food group plans** that build a diet from clusters of foods that are similar in nutrient content. Thus each group represents a set of nutrients that differs somewhat from the nutrients supplied by the other groups. Selecting foods from each of the groups eases the task of creating an adequate and balanced diet.

USDA Food Guide

The 2005 *Dietary Guidelines* encourage consumers to adopt a balanced eating plan, such as the USDA's Food Guide (see Figure 2-1 on pp. 42–43). The USDA Food Guide assigns foods to five major groups ◆ and recommends daily amounts of foods from each group to meet nutrient needs. In addition to presenting the food groups, the figure lists the most notable nutrients of each group, the serving equivalents, and the foods within each group sorted by nutrient density. Chapter 16 provides a food guide for young children, and Appendix I presents Canada's food group plan, the *Food Guide to Healthy Eating*.

◆ Five food groups:
  • Fruits
  • Vegetables
  • Grains
  • Meat and legumes
  • Milk

Dietary Guidelines for Americans 2005

Meet recommended intakes within energy needs by adopting a balanced eating pattern, such as the USDA Food Guide or the DASH eating plan. (The DASH eating plan is presented in Chapter 12.)

◆ Chapter 8 explains how to determine energy needs. For an approximation, turn to the DRI Estimated Energy Requirement (EER) on the inside front cover.

Recommended Amounts All food groups offer valuable nutrients, and people should make selections from each group daily. Table 2-3 specifies the amounts of foods from each group needed daily to create a healthful diet for several energy (kcalorie) levels. ◆ Estimated daily kcalorie needs for sedentary and active men and

food group plans: diet-planning tools that sort foods into groups based on nutrient content and then specify that people should eat certain amounts of foods from each group.

TABLE 2-3	Recommended Daily Amounts from Each Food Group							
	1600 kcal	1800 kcal	2000 kcal	2200 kcal	2400 kcal	2600 kcal	2800 kcal	3000 kcal
Fruits	1½ c	1½ c	2 c	2 c	2 c	2 c	2½ c	2½ c
Vegetables	2 c	2½ c	2½ c	3 c	3 c	3½ c	3½ c	4 c
Grains	5 oz	6 oz	6 oz	7 oz	8 oz	9 oz	10 oz	10 oz
Meat and legumes	5 oz	5 oz	5½ oz	6 oz	6½ oz	6½ oz	7 oz	7 oz
Milk	3 c	3 c	3 c	3 c	3 c	3 c	3 c	3 c
Oils	5 tsp	5 tsp	6 tsp	6 tsp	7 tsp	8 tsp	8 tsp	10 tsp
Discretionary kcalorie allowance	132 kcal	195 kcal	267 kcal	290 kcal	362 kcal	410 kcal	426 kcal	512 kcal

FIGURE 2-1 USDA Food Guide, 2005

Key:
- ● Foods generally high in nutrient density (choose most often)
- ▲ Foods lower in nutrient density (limit selections)

FRUITS

© Polara Studios, Inc.

Consume a variety of fruits and no more than one-third of the recommended intake as fruit juice.

These foods contribute folate, vitamin A, vitamin C, potassium, and fiber.

> ½ c fruit is equivalent to ½ c fresh, frozen, or canned fruit; 1 small fruit; ¼ c dried fruit; ½ c fruit juice.

- ● Apples, apricots, avocados, bananas, blueberries, cantaloupe, cherries, grapefruit, grapes, guava, kiwi, mango, oranges, papaya, peaches, pears, pineapples, plums, raspberries, strawberries, watermelon; dried fruit (dates, figs, raisins); unsweetened juices.

- ▲ Canned or frozen fruit in syrup; juices, punches, ades, and fruit drinks with added sugars; fried plantains.

VEGETABLES

© Polara Studios, Inc.

Choose a variety of vegetables from all five subgroups several times a week.

These foods contribute folate, vitamin A, vitamin C, vitamin K, vitamin E, magnesium, potassium, and fiber.

> ½ c vegetables is equivalent to ½ c cut-up raw or cooked vegetables; ½ c cooked legumes; ½ c vegetable juice; 1 c raw, leafy greens.

- ● Dark green vegetables: Broccoli and leafy greens such as arugula, beet greens, bok choy, collard greens, kale, mustard greens, romaine lettuce, spinach, and turnip greens.

- ● Orange and deep yellow vegetables: Carrots, carrot juice, pumpkin, sweet potatoes, and winter squash (acorn, butternut).

- ● Legumes: Black beans, black-eyed peas, garbanzo beans (chickpeas), kidney beans, lentils, navy beans, pinto beans, soybeans and soy products such as tofu, and split peas.

- ● Starchy vegetables: Cassava, corn, green peas, hominy, lima beans, and potatoes.

- ● Other vegetables: Artichokes, asparagus, bamboo shoots, bean sprouts, beets, brussels sprouts, cabbages, cactus, cauliflower, celery, cucumbers, eggplant, green beans, iceberg lettuce, mushrooms, okra, onions, peppers, seaweed, snow peas, tomatoes, vegetable juices, zucchini.

- ▲ Baked beans, candied sweet potatoes, coleslaw, French fries, potato salad, refried beans, scalloped potatoes, tempura vegetables.

GRAINS

© Polara Studios, Inc.

Make at least half of the grain selections whole grains.

These foods contribute folate, niacin, riboflavin, thiamin, iron, magnesium, selenium, and fiber.

> 1 oz grains is equivalent to 1 slice bread; ½ c cooked rice, pasta, or cereal; 1 oz dry pasta or rice; 1 c ready-to-eat cereal; 3 c popped popcorn.

- ● Whole grains (amaranth, barley, brown rice, buckwheat, bulgur, millet, oats, quinoa, rye, wheat) and whole-grain, low-fat breads, cereals, crackers, and pastas; popcorn.

- ● Enriched bagels, breads, cereals, pastas (couscous, macaroni, spaghetti), pretzels, rice, rolls, tortillas.

- ▲ Biscuits, cakes, cookies, cornbread, crackers, croissants, doughnuts, French toast, fried rice, granola, muffins, pancakes, pastries, pies, presweetened cereals, taco shells, waffles.

FIGURE 2-1 USDA Food Guide, 2005, continued

MEAT, POULTRY, FISH, LEGUMES, EGGS, AND NUTS

Make lean or low-fat choices. Prepare them with little, or no, added fat.

Meat, poultry, fish, and eggs contribute protein, niacin, thiamin, vitamin B_6, vitamin B_{12}, iron, magnesium, potassium, and zinc; legumes and nuts are notable for their protein, folate, thiamin, vitamin E, iron, magnesium, potassium, zinc, and fiber.

> 1 oz meat is equivalent to 1 oz cooked lean meat, poultry, or fish; 1 egg; $\frac{1}{4}$ c cooked legumes or tofu; 1 tbs peanut butter; $\frac{1}{2}$ oz nuts or seeds.

- Poultry (no skin), fish, shellfish, legumes, eggs, lean meat (fat-trimmed beef, game, ham, lamb, pork); low-fat tofu, tempeh, peanut butter, nuts (almonds, filberts, peanuts, pistachios, walnuts) or seeds (flaxseeds, pumpkin seeds, sunflower seeds).

△ Bacon; baked beans; fried meat, fish, poultry, eggs, or tofu; refried beans; ground beef; hot dogs; luncheon meats; marbled steaks; poultry with skin; sausages; spare ribs.

© Polara Studios, Inc.

MILK, YOGURT, AND CHEESE

Make fat-free or low-fat choices. Choose lactose-free products or other calcium-rich foods if you don't consume milk.

These foods contribute protein, riboflavin, vitamin B_{12}, calcium, magnesium, potassium, and, when fortified, vitamin A and vitamin D.

> 1 c milk is equivalent to 1 c fat-free milk or yogurt; $1\frac{1}{2}$ oz fat-free natural cheese; 2 oz fat-free processed cheese.

- Fat-free milk and fat-free milk products such as buttermilk, cheeses, cottage cheese, yogurt; fat-free fortified soy milk.

△ 1% low-fat milk, 2% reduced-fat milk, and whole milk; low-fat, reduced-fat, and whole-milk products such as cheeses, cottage cheese, and yogurt; milk products with added sugars such as chocolate milk, custard, ice cream, ice milk, milk shakes, pudding, sherbet; fortified soy milk.

© Polara Studios, Inc.

OILS

Select the recommended amounts of oils from among these sources.

These foods contribute vitamin E and essential fatty acids (see Chapter 5), along with abundant kcalories.

> 1 tsp oil is equivalent to 1 tbs low-fat mayonnaise; 2 tbs light salad dressing; 1 tsp vegetable oil; 1 tsp soft margarine.

- Liquid vegetable oils such as canola, corn, flaxseed, nut, olive, peanut, safflower, sesame, soybean, and sunflower oils; mayonnaise, oil-based salad dressing, soft *trans*-free margarine.

- Unsaturated oils that occur naturally in foods such as avocados, fatty fish, nuts, olives, seeds (flaxseeds, sesame seeds), and shellfish.

Matthew Farruggio

SOLID FATS AND ADDED SUGARS

Limit intakes of food and beverages with solid fats and added sugars.

Solid fats deliver saturated fat and *trans* fat, and intake should be kept low. Solid fats and added sugars contribute abundant kcalories but few nutrients, and intakes should not exceed the discretionary kcalorie allowance—kcalories to meet energy needs after all nutrient needs have been met with nutrient-dense foods. Alcohol also contributes abundant kcalories but few nutrients, and its kcalories are counted among discretionary kcalories. See Table 2-3 for some discretionary kcalorie allowances.

△ Solid fats that occur in foods naturally such as milk fat and meat fat (see △ in previous lists).

△ Solid fats that are often added to foods such as butter, cream cheese, hard margarine, lard, sour cream, and shortening.

△ Added sugars such as brown sugar, candy, honey, jelly, molasses, soft drinks, sugar, and syrup.

△ Alcoholic beverages include beer, wine, and liquor.

Matthew Farruggio

TABLE 2-4	Estimated Daily kCalorie Needs for Adults	
	Sedentary[a]	Active[b]
Women		
19–30 yr	2000	2400
31–50 yr	1800	2200
51+ yr	1600	2100
Men		
19–30 yr	2400	3000
31–50 yr	2200	2900
51+ yr	2000	2600

[a]Sedentary describes a lifestyle that includes only the activities typical of day-to-day life.
[b]Active describes a lifestyle that includes physical activity equivalent to walking more than 3 miles per day at a rate of 3 to 4 miles per hour, in addition to the activities typical of day-to-day life. kCalorie values for active people reflect the midpoint of the range appropriate for age and gender, but within each group, older adults may need fewer kcalories and younger adults may need more.
NOTE: In addition to gender, age, and activity level, energy needs vary with height and weight (see Chapter 8 and Appendix F).

◆ Reminder: *Phytochemicals* are the nonnutrient compounds found in plant-derived foods that have biological activity in the body.

◆ The USDA nutrients of concern are fiber, vitamin A, vitamin C, vitamin E, and the minerals calcium, magnesium, and potassium.

legumes (lay-GYOOMS, LEG-yooms): plants of the bean and pea family, with seeds that are rich in protein compared with other plant-derived foods.

women are shown in Table 2-4. A sedentary young women needing 2000 kcalories a day, for example, would select 2 cups of fruit; $2^1/_2$ cups of vegetables (dispersed among the vegetable subgroups); 6 ounces of grain foods (with at least half coming from whole grains); $5^1/_2$ ounces of meat, poultry, or fish, or the equivalent of **legumes**, eggs, seeds, or nuts; and 3 cups of milk or yogurt, or the equivalent amount of cheese or fortified soy products. Additionally, a small amount of unsaturated oil, such as vegetable oil, or the oils of nuts, olives, or fatty fish, is required to supply needed nutrients.

All vegetables provide an array of vitamins, fiber, and the mineral potassium, but some vegetables are especially good sources of certain nutrients and beneficial phytochemicals. ◆ For this reason, the USDA Food Guide sorts the vegetable group into five subgroups. The dark green vegetables deliver the B vitamin folate; the orange vegetables provide vitamin A; legumes supply iron and protein; the starchy vegetables contribute carbohydrate energy; and the other vegetables fill in the gaps and add more of these same nutrients.

In a 2000-kcalorie diet, then, the recommended $2^1/_2$ cups of daily vegetables should be varied among the subgroups over a week's time, as shown in Table 2-5. In other words, consuming $2^1/_2$ cups of potatoes or even nutrient-rich spinach every day for seven days does *not* meet the recommended vegetable intakes. Potatoes and spinach make excellent choices when consumed in balance with vegetables from other subgroups. Intakes of vegetables are appropriately averaged over a week's time—it is not necessary to include every subgroup every day.

Notable Nutrients As Figure 2-1 notes, each food group contributes key nutrients. This feature provides flexibility in diet planning because a person can select any food from a food group and receive similar nutrients. For example, a person can choose milk, cheese, or yogurt and receive the same key nutrients. Importantly, foods provide not only these key nutrients, but small amounts of other nutrients and phytochemicals as well.

Because legumes contribute the same key nutrients—notably, protein, iron, and zinc—as meats, poultry, and fish, they are included in the same food group. For this reason, legumes are useful as meat alternatives, and they are also excellent sources of fiber and the B vitamin folate. To encourage frequent consumption, the USDA Food Guide also includes legumes as a subgroup of the vegetable group. Thus legumes count in either the vegetable group or the meat and legume group. In general, people who regularly eat meat, poultry, and fish count legumes as a vegetable, and vegetarians and others who seldom eat meat, poultry, or fish count legumes in the meat and legumes group.

The USDA Food Guide encourages greater consumption from certain food groups to provide the nutrients most often lacking ◆ in the diets of Americans. In general, most people need to eat:

• *More* dark green vegetables, orange vegetables, legumes, fruits, whole grains, and low-fat milk and milk products

TABLE 2-5	Recommended Weekly Amounts from the Vegetable Subgroups

Table 2-3 specifies the recommended amounts of total vegetables per *day*. This table shows those amounts dispersed among five vegetable subgroups per *week*.

Vegetable Subgroups	1600 kcal	1800 kcal	2000 kcal	2200 kcal	2400 kcal	2600 kcal	2800 kcal	3000 kcal
Dark green	2 c	3 c	3 c	3 c	3 c	3 c	3 c	3 c
Orange and deep yellow	1½ c	2 c	2 c	2 c	2 c	2½ c	2½ c	2½ c
Legumes	2½ c	3 c	3 c	3 c	3 c	3½ c	3½ c	3½ c
Starchy	2½ c	3 c	3 c	6 c	6 c	7 c	7 c	9 c
Other	5½ c	6½ c	6½ c	7 c	7 c	8½ c	8½ c	10 c

- *Less* refined grains, total fats (especially saturated fat, *trans* fat, and cholesterol), added sugars, and total kcalories

Nutrient Density   The USDA Food Guide provides a foundation for a healthy diet by emphasizing nutrient-dense options within each food group. By consistently selecting nutrient-dense foods, a person can obtain all the nutrients needed and still keep kcalories under control. In contrast, eating foods that are low in nutrient density makes it difficult to get enough nutrients without exceeding energy needs and gaining weight. For this reason, consumers should select low-fat foods from each group and foods without added fats or sugars—for example, fat-free milk instead of whole milk, baked chicken without the skin instead of hot dogs, green beans instead of French fries, orange juice instead of fruit punch, and whole-wheat bread instead of biscuits. Notice that the key in Figure 2-1 indicates which foods *within each group* are high or low in nutrient density. Oil is a notable exception: even though oil is pure fat and therefore rich in kcalories, a small amount of oil from sources such as nuts, fish, or vegetable oils is necessary every day to provide nutrients lacking from other foods. Consequently these high-fat foods are listed among the nutrient-dense foods (see Highlight 5 to learn why).

Dietary Guidelines for Americans 2005

Consume a variety of nutrient-dense foods and beverages within and among the basic food groups while choosing foods that limit the intake of saturated and *trans* fats, cholesterol, added sugars, salt, and alcohol.

Discretionary kCalorie Allowance   At each kcalorie level, people who consistently choose nutrient-dense foods may be able to meet their nutrient needs without consuming their full allowance of kcalories. The difference between the kcalories needed to supply nutrients and those needed for energy—known as the **discretionary kcalorie allowance**—is illustrated in Figure 2-2. Table 2-3 (p. 41) includes the discretionary kcalorie allowance for several kcalorie levels. A person with discretionary kcalories available might choose to:

- Eat additional nutrient-dense foods, such as an extra serving of skinless chicken or a second ear of corn.
- Select a few foods with fats or added sugars, such as reduced-fat milk or sweetened cereal.
- Add a little fat or sugar to foods, such as butter or jelly on toast.
- Consume some alcohol. (Highlight 7 explains why this may not be a good choice for some individuals.)

Alternatively, a person wanting to lose weight might choose to:

- *Not* use the kcalories available from the discretionary kcalorie allowance.

Added fats and sugars are always counted as discretionary kcalories. The kcalories from the fat in higher-fat milks and meats are also counted among discretionary kcalories. It helps to think of fat-free milk as "milk" and whole milk or reduced-fat milk as "milk with added fat." Similarly, "meats" should be the leanest; other cuts are "meats with added fat." Puddings and other desserts made from whole milk provide discretionary kcalories from both the sugar added to sweeten them and the naturally occurring fat in the whole milk they contain. Even fruits, vegetables, and grains can carry discretionary kcalories into the diet in the form of peaches canned in syrup, scalloped potatoes, or high-fat crackers.

Discretionary kcalories must be counted separately from the kcalories of the nutrient-dense foods of which they may be a part. A fried chicken leg, for example, provides discretionary kcalories from two sources: the naturally occurring fat of the chicken skin and the added fat absorbed during frying. The kcalories of the skinless chicken underneath are not discretionary kcalories—they are necessary to provide the nutrients of chicken.

FIGURE 2-2   Discretionary kCalorie Allowance for a 2000-kCalorie Diet Plan

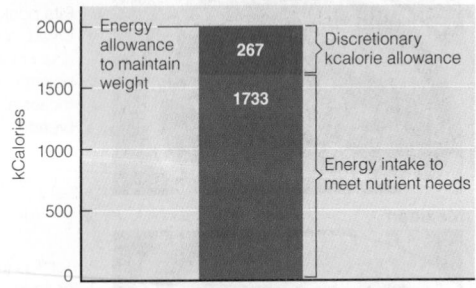

discretionary kcalorie allowance: the kcalories remaining in a person's energy allowance after consuming enough nutrient-dense foods to meet all nutrient needs for a day.

◆ For quick and easy estimates, visualize each portion as being about the size of a common object:
- 1 c fruit or vegetables = a baseball
- $1/4$ c dried fruit = a golf ball
- 3 oz meat = a deck of cards
- 2 tbs peanut butter = a marshmallow
- $1^{1}/_{2}$ oz cheese = 6 stacked dice
- $1/2$ c ice cream = a racquetball
- 4 small cookies = 4 poker chips

Serving Equivalents Recommended serving amounts for fruits, vegetables, and milk are measured in cups and those for grains and meats, in ounces. Figure 2-1 provides equivalent measures among the foods in each group specifying, for example, that 1 ounce of grains is equivalent to 1 slice of bread or $1/2$ cup of cooked rice.

A person using the USDA Food Guide can become more familiar with measured portions by determining the answers to questions such as these: ◆ What portion of a cup is a small handful of raisins? Is a "helping" of mashed potatoes more or less than a half-cup? How many ounces of cereal do you typically pour into the bowl? How many ounces is the steak at your favorite restaurant? How many cups of milk does your glass hold? Figure 2-1 (pp. 42–43) includes the serving sizes and equivalent amounts for foods within each group.

Mixtures of Foods Some foods—such as casseroles, soups, and sandwiches—fall into two or more food groups. With a little practice, users can learn to see these mixtures of foods as items from various food groups. For example, from the USDA Food Guide point of view, a taco represents four different food groups: the taco shell from the grains group; the onions, lettuce, and tomatoes from the "other vegetables" group; the ground beef from the meat group; and the cheese from the milk group.

Vegetarian Food Guide Vegetarian diets rely mainly on plant foods: grains, vegetables, legumes, fruits, seeds, and nuts. Some vegetarian diets include eggs, milk products, or both. People who do not eat meats or milk products can still use the USDA Food Guide to create an adequate diet.[3] ◆ The food groups are similar, and the amounts for each serving remain the same. Highlight 2 defines vegetarian terms and provides details on planning healthy vegetarian diets.

Ethnic Food Choices People can use the USDA Food Guide and still enjoy a diverse array of culinary styles by sorting ethnic foods into their appropriate food groups. For example, a person eating Mexican foods would find tortillas in the grains group, jicama in the vegetable group, and guava in the fruit group. Table 2-6 features ethnic food choices.

TABLE 2-6 Ethnic Food Choices	Grains	Vegetables	Fruits	Meats and legumes	Milk
Asian 	Rice, noodles, millet	Amaranth, baby corn, bamboo shoots, chayote, bok choy, mung bean sprouts, sugar peas, straw mushrooms, water chestnuts, kelp	Carambola, guava, kumquat, lychee, persimmon, melons, mandarin orange	Soybeans and soy products such as soy milk and tofu, squid, duck eggs, pork, poultry, fish and other seafood, peanuts, cashews	Usually excluded
Mediterranean 	Pita pocket bread, pastas, rice, couscous, polenta, bulgur, focaccia, Italian bread	Eggplant, tomatoes, peppers, cucumbers, grape leaves	Olives, grapes, figs	Fish and other seafood, gyros, lamb, chicken, beef, pork, sausage, lentils, fava beans	Ricotta, provolone, parmesan, feta, mozzarella, and goat cheeses; yogurt
Mexican 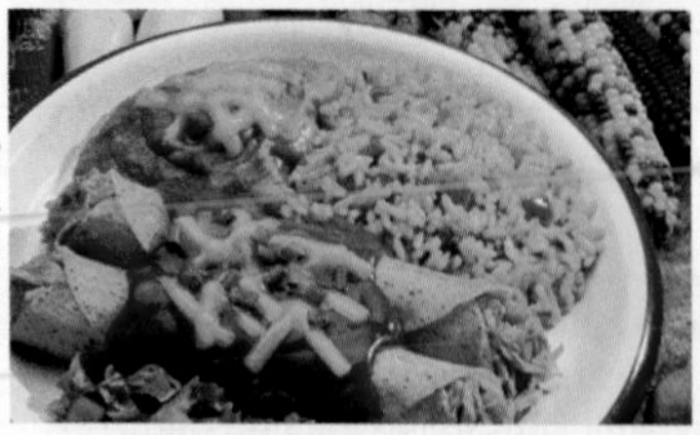	Tortillas (corn or flour), taco shells, rice	Chayote, corn, jicama, tomato salsa, cactus, cassava, tomatoes, yams, chilies	Guava, mango, papaya, avocado, plantain, bananas, oranges	Refried beans, fish, chicken, chorizo, beef, eggs	Cheese, custard

© Becky Luigart-Stayner/Corbis

© Photo Disc/Getty Images

© Photo Disc/Getty Images

MyPyramid—Steps to a Healthier You The USDA created an educational tool called MyPyramid to illustrate the concepts of the *Dietary Guidelines* and the USDA Food Guide. Figure 2-3 presents a graphic image of MyPyramid, which was designed to encourage consumers to make healthy food and physical activity choices every day.

The abundant materials that support MyPyramid help consumers choose the kinds and amounts of foods to eat each day (**MyPyramid.gov**). In addition to creating a personal plan, consumers can find tips to help them improve their diet and lifestyle by "taking small steps each day."

◆ **MyPyramid.gov** offers information on vegetarian diets in its Tips & Resources section.

Exchange Lists

Food group plans are particularly well suited to help a person achieve dietary adequacy, balance, and variety. **Exchange lists** provide additional help in achieving kcalorie control and moderation. Originally developed for people with diabetes, exchange systems have proved useful for general diet planning as well.

Unlike the USDA Food Guide, which sorts foods primarily by their vitamin and mineral contents, the exchange system sorts foods according to their energy-nutrient contents. Consequently, foods do not always appear on the exchange list where you might first expect to find them. For example, cheeses are grouped with meats because, like meats, cheeses contribute energy from protein and fat but provide negligible carbohydrate. (In the USDA Food Guide presented earlier, cheeses are grouped with milk because they are milk products with similar calcium contents.)

exchange lists: diet-planning tools that organize foods by their proportions of carbohydrate, fat, and protein. Foods on any single list can be used interchangeably.

FIGURE 2-3 MyPyramid: Steps to a Healthier You

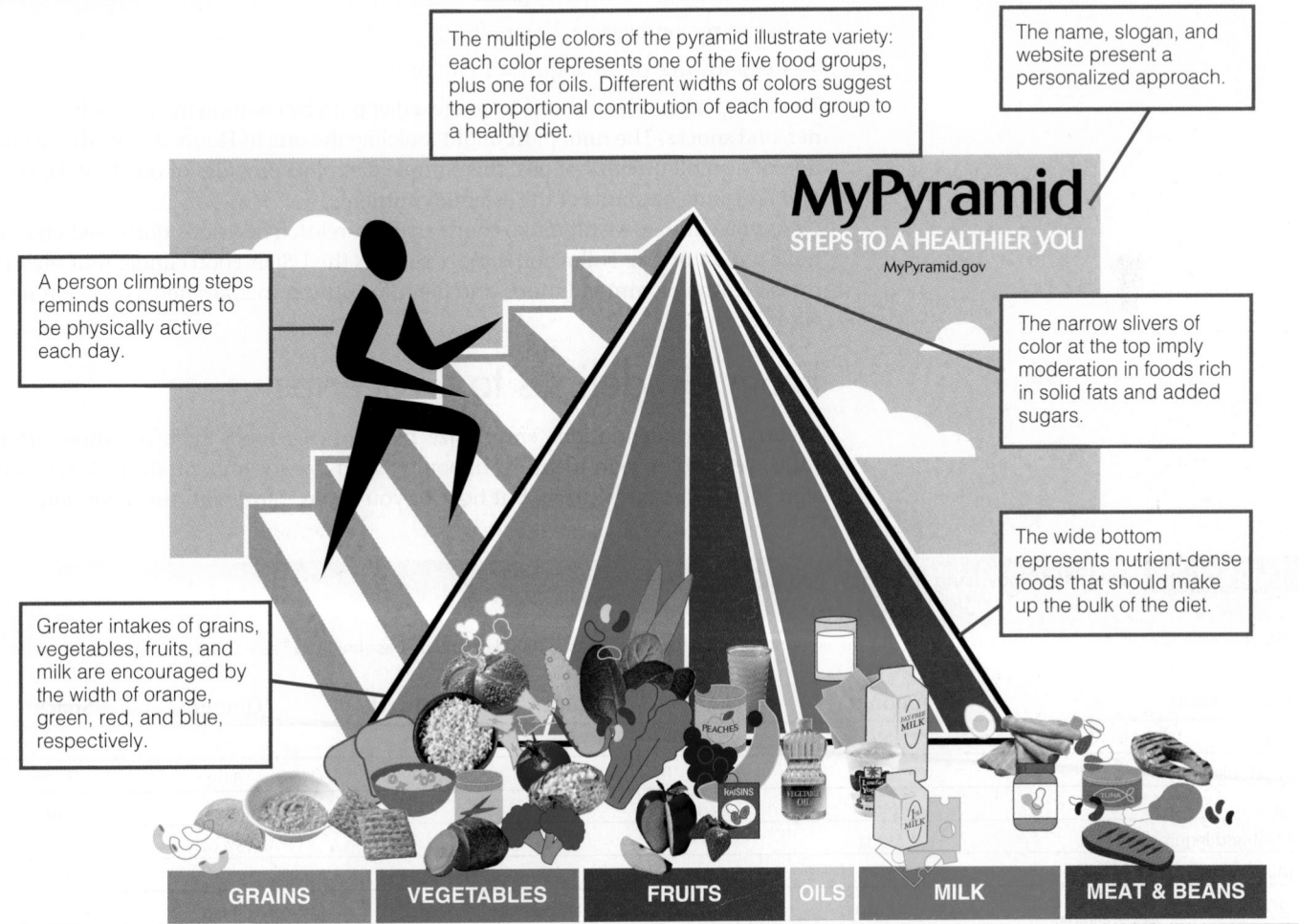

The multiple colors of the pyramid illustrate variety: each color represents one of the five food groups, plus one for oils. Different widths of colors suggest the proportional contribution of each food group to a healthy diet.

The name, slogan, and website present a personalized approach.

A person climbing steps reminds consumers to be physically active each day.

The narrow slivers of color at the top imply moderation in foods rich in solid fats and added sugars.

The wide bottom represents nutrient-dense foods that should make up the bulk of the diet.

Greater intakes of grains, vegetables, fruits, and milk are encouraged by the width of orange, green, red, and blue, respectively.

MyPyramid
STEPS TO A HEALTHIER YOU
MyPyramid.gov

GRAINS | VEGETABLES | FRUITS | OILS | MILK | MEAT & BEANS

SOURCE: USDA, 2005

Most bagels today weigh in at 4 ounces or more—meaning that a person eating one of these large bagels for breakfast is actually getting four or more grain servings, not one.

For similar reasons, starchy vegetables such as corn, green peas, and potatoes are listed with grains on the starch list in the exchange system, rather than with the vegetables. Likewise, olives are not classed as a "fruit" as a botanist would claim; they are classified as a "fat" because their fat content makes them more similar to oil than to berries. Bacon and nuts are also on the fat list to remind users of their high fat content. These groupings highlight the characteristics of foods that are significant to energy intake. To learn more about this useful diet-planning tool, study Appendix G, which gives details of the exchange system used in the United States, and Appendix I, which provides details of *Beyond the Basics,* a similar diet-planning system used in Canada.

Putting the Plan into Action

Familiarizing yourself with each of the food groups is the first step in diet planning. Table 2-7 shows how to use the USDA Food Guide to plan a 2000-kcalorie diet. The amounts listed from each of the food groups (see the second column of the table) were taken from Table 2-3 (p. 41). The next step is to assign the food groups to meals (and snacks), as in the remaining columns of Table 2-7.

Now, a person can begin to fill in the plan with real foods to create a menu. For example, the breakfast calls for 1 ounce grain, $^1/_2$ cup fruit, and 1 cup milk. A person might select a bowl of cereal with banana slices and milk:

1 cup cereal = 1 ounce grain

1 small banana = $^1/_2$ cup fruit

1 cup fat-free milk = 1 cup milk

Or $^1/_2$ bagel and a bowl of cantaloupe pieces topped with yogurt:

$^1/_2$ small bagel = 1 ounce grain

$^1/_2$ cup melon pieces = $^1/_2$ cup fruit

1 cup fat-free plain yogurt = 1 cup milk

Then the person can continue to create a diet plan by creating menus for lunch, dinner, and snacks. The final plan might look like the one in Figure 2-4. With the addition of a small amount of oils, this sample diet plan provides about 1850 kcalories and adequate amounts of the essential nutrients.

As you can see, we all make countless food-related decisions daily—whether we have a plan or not. Following a plan, such as the USDA Food Guide, that incorporates health recommendations and diet-planning principles helps a person make wise decisions.

From Guidelines to Groceries

Dietary recommendations emphasize nutrient-rich foods such as whole grains, fruits, vegetables, lean meats, fish, poultry, and low-fat milk products. You can design such a diet for yourself, but how do you begin? Start with the foods you enjoy

TABLE 2-7	Diet Planning Using the USDA Food Guide

This diet plan is one of many possibilities. It follows the amounts of foods suggested for a 2000-kcalorie diet as shown in Table 2-3 on p. 41 (with an extra ½ cup of vegetables).

Food Group	Amounts	Breakfast	Lunch	Snack	Dinner	Snack
Fruits	2 c	½ c		½ c	1 c	
Vegetables	2½ c		1 c		1½ c	
Grains	6 oz	1 oz	2 oz	½ oz	2 oz	½ oz
Meat and legumes	5½ oz		2 oz		3½ oz	
Milk	3 c	1 c		1 c		1 c
Oils	5½ tsp		1½ tsp		4 tsp	
Discretionary kcalorie allowance	267 kcal					

FIGURE 2-4 A Sample Diet Plan and Menu

This sample menu provides about 1850 kcalories and meets dietary recommendations to provide 45 to 65 percent of its kcalories from carbohydrate, 20 to 35 percent from fat, and 10 to 35 percent from protein. Some discretionary kcalories were spent on the fat in the low-fat cheese and in the sugar added to the graham crackers; about 150 discretionary kcalories remain available in this 2000-kcalorie diet plan.

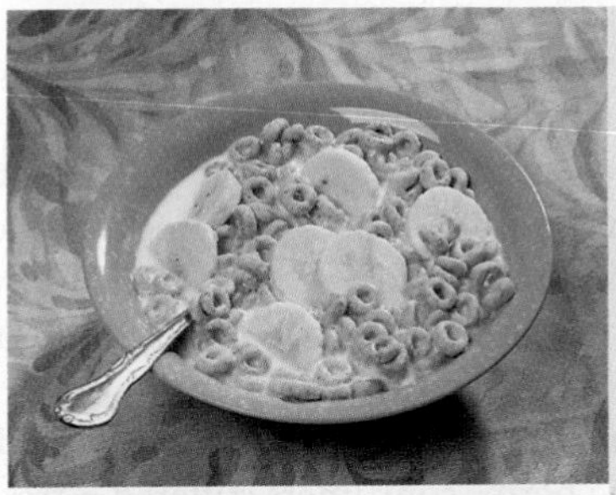

© Polara Studios, Inc.

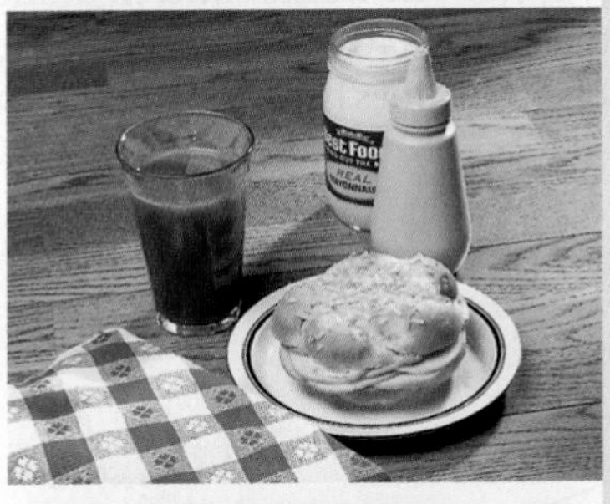

© Polara Studios, Inc.

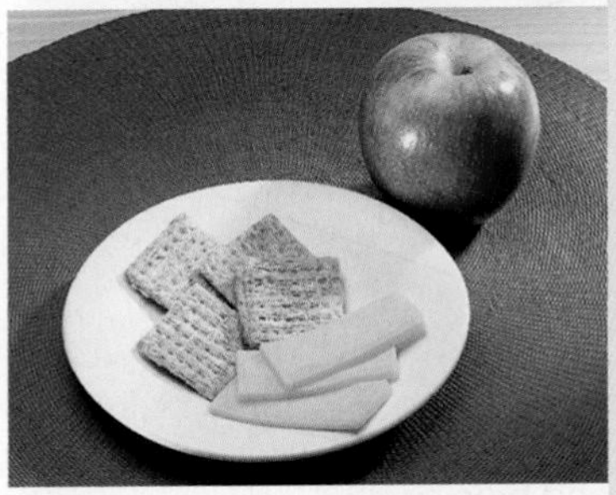

© Polara Studios, Inc.

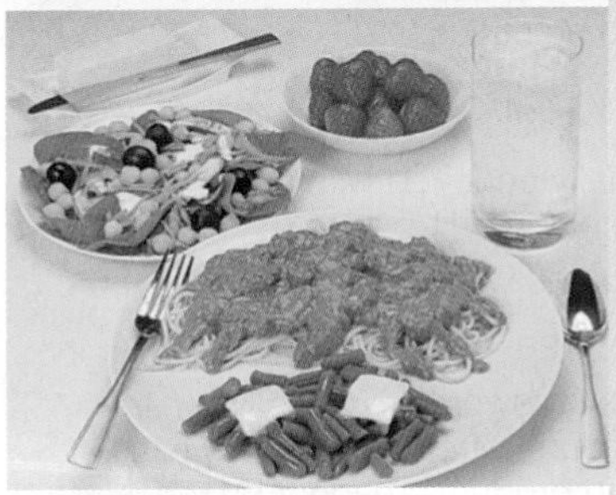

© Quest

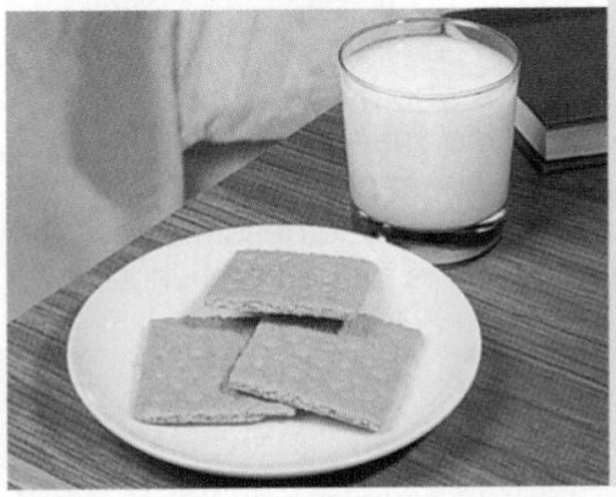

© Quest

Amounts	SAMPLE MENU	Energy (kcal)
	Breakfast	
1 oz whole grains	1 c whole-grain cereal	108
1 c milk	1 c fat-free milk	83
$\frac{1}{2}$ c fruit	1 small banana (sliced)	105
	Lunch	
2 oz whole grains, 2 oz meats	1 turkey sandwich on roll	272
$1\frac{1}{2}$ tsp oils	$1\frac{1}{2}$ tbs low-fat mayonnaise	75
1 c vegetables	1 c vegetable juice	53
	Snack	
$\frac{1}{2}$ oz whole grains	4 whole-wheat, reduced-fat crackers	86
1 c milk	$1\frac{1}{2}$ oz low-fat cheddar cheese	74
$\frac{1}{2}$ c fruit	1 small apple	72
	Dinner	
$\frac{1}{2}$ c vegetables	1 c salad	8
1 oz meats	$\frac{1}{4}$ c garbanzo beans	71
2 tsp oils	2 tbs oil-based salad dressing and olives	81
$\frac{1}{2}$ c vegetables, $2\frac{1}{2}$ oz meats, 2 oz enriched grains	Spaghetti with meat sauce	425
$\frac{1}{2}$ c vegetables	$\frac{1}{2}$ c green beans	22
2 tsp oils	2 tsp soft margarine	67
1 c fruit	1 c strawberries	49
	Snack	
$\frac{1}{2}$ oz whole grains	3 graham crackers	90
1 c milk	1 c fat-free milk	83

eating. Then try to make improvements, little by little. When shopping, think of the food groups, and choose nutrient-dense foods within each group.

Be aware that many of the 50,000 food options available today are **processed foods** that have lost valuable nutrients and gained sugar, fat, and salt as they were transformed from farm-fresh foods to those found in the bags, boxes, and cans that line grocery-store shelves. Their value in the diet depends on the starting food and how it was prepared or processed. Sometimes these foods have been **fortified** to improve their nutrient contents.

Grains When shopping for grain products, you will find them described as *refined, enriched,* or *whole grain.* These terms refer to the milling process and the making of grain products, and they have different nutrition implications (see Figure 2-5). **Refined** foods may have lost many nutrients during processing; **enriched** products may have had some nutrients added back; and **whole-grain** products may be rich in fiber and all the nutrients found in the original grain. As such, whole-grain products support good health and should account for at least half of the grains daily.

When it became a common practice to refine the wheat flour used for bread by milling it and throwing away the bran and the germ, consumers suffered a tragic loss of many nutrients.[4] As a consequence, in the early 1940s Congress passed legislation requiring that all grain products that cross state lines be enriched with iron,

processed foods: foods that have been treated to change their physical, chemical, microbiological, or sensory properties.

fortified: the addition to a food of nutrients that were either not originally present or present in insignificant amounts. Fortification can be used to correct or prevent a widespread nutrient deficiency or to balance the total nutrient profile of a food.

refined: the process by which the coarse parts of a food are removed. When wheat is refined into flour, the bran, germ, and husk are removed, leaving only the endosperm.

enriched: the addition to a food of nutrients that were lost during processing so that the food will meet a specified standard.

whole grain: a grain milled in its entirety (all but the husk), not refined.

FIGURE 2-5 A Wheat Plant

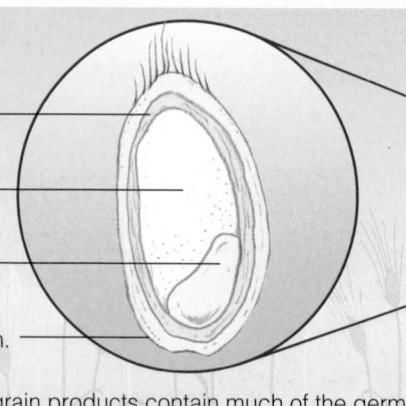
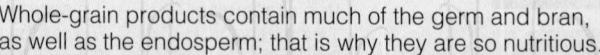
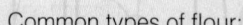

The protective coating of **bran** around the kernel of grain is rich in nutrients and fiber.

The **endosperm** contains starch and proteins.

The **germ** is the seed that grows into a wheat plant, so it is especially rich in vitamins and minerals to support new life.

The outer **husk** (or **chaff**) is the inedible part of a grain.

Whole-grain products contain much of the germ and bran, as well as the endosperm; that is why they are so nutritious.

Common types of flour:
- *Refined flour*—finely ground endosperm that is usually enriched with nutrients and bleached for whiteness; sometimes called *white flour.*
- *Wheat flour*—any flour made from the endosperm of the wheat kernel.
- *Whole-wheat flour*—any flour made from the entire wheat kernel.

The difference between *white flour* and *white wheat* is noteworthy. Typically, *white flour* refers to refined flour (as defined above). Most flour—whether refined, white, or whole wheat—is made from red wheat. Whole-grain products made from red wheat are typically brown and full flavored.

To capture the health benefits of whole grains for consumers who prefer white bread, manufacturers have been experimenting with an albino variety of wheat called *white wheat.* Whole-grain products made from white wheat provide the nutrients and fiber of a whole grain with a light color and natural sweetness. Read labels carefully—white bread is a whole-grain product only if it is made from whole white wheat.

Refined grain products contain only the endosperm. Even with nutrients added back, they are not as nutritious as whole-grain products, as the next figure shows.

Dietary Guidelines for Americans 2005

Consume 3 or more ounce-equivalents of whole-grain products per day, with the rest of the recommended grains coming from enriched or whole-grain products. In general, at least half the grains should come from whole grains.

thiamin, riboflavin, and niacin. In 1996, this legislation was amended to include folate, a vitamin considered essential in the prevention of some birth defects. Most grain products that have been refined, such as rice, wheat pastas like macaroni and spaghetti, and cereals (both cooked and ready-to-eat types), have subsequently been enriched, ◆ and their labels say so.

Enrichment doesn't make a slice of bread rich in these added nutrients, but people who eat several slices a day obtain significantly more of these nutrients than they would from unenriched bread. Even though the enrichment of flour helps to prevent deficiencies of these nutrients, it fails to compensate for losses of many other nutrients and fiber. As Figure 2-6 shows, whole-grain items still outshine the enriched ones. Only *whole-grain* flour contains all of the nutritive portions of the grain. Whole-grain products, such as brown rice or oatmeal, provide more nutrients and fiber and contain less salt and sugar than flavored, processed rice or sweetened cereals.

Speaking of cereals, ready-to-eat breakfast cereals are the most highly fortified foods on the market. Like an enriched food, a *fortified* food has had nutrients added during processing, but in a fortified food, the added nutrients may not have been present in the original product. (The terms *fortified* and *enriched* may be used interchangeably.[5]) Some breakfast cereals made from refined flour and fortified with high doses of vitamins and minerals are actually more like supplements disguised

◆ Grain enrichment nutrients:
- Iron
- Thiamin
- Riboflavin
- Niacin
- Folate

FIGURE 2-6 Nutrients in Bread

Whole-grain bread is more nutritious than other breads, even enriched bread. For iron, thiamin, riboflavin, niacin, and folate, enriched bread provides about the same quantities as whole-grain bread and significantly more than unenriched bread. For fiber and the other nutrients (those shown here as well as those not shown), enriched bread provides less than whole-grain bread.

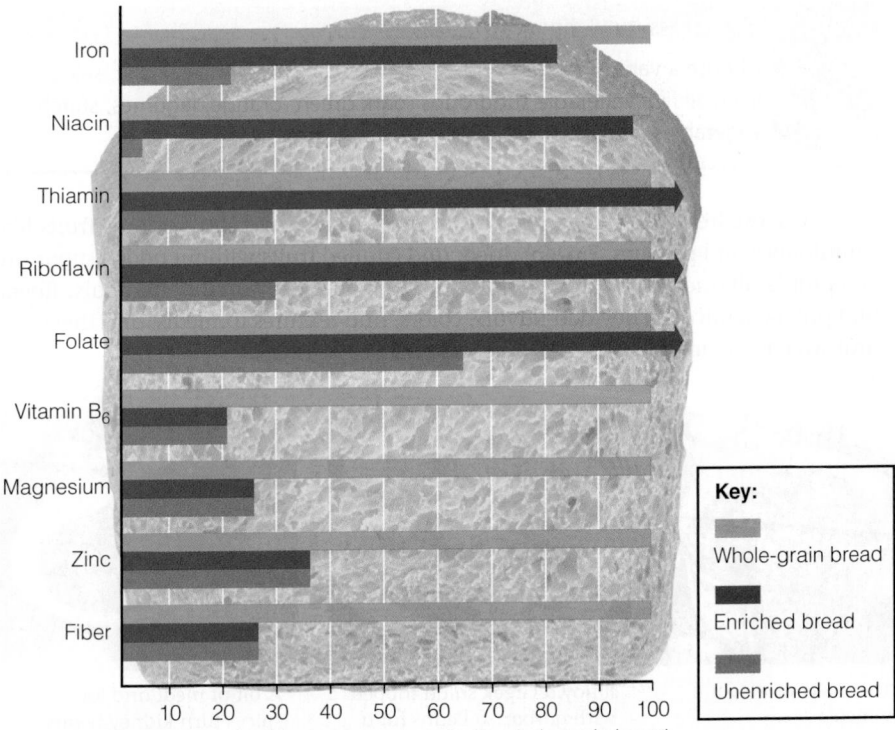

Key:
- Whole-grain bread
- Enriched bread
- Unenriched bread

Percentage of nutrients as compared with whole-grain bread

When shopping for bread, look for the descriptive words *whole grain* or *whole wheat* and check the fiber contents on the Nutrition Facts panel of the label—the more fiber, the more likely the bread is a whole-grain product.

FIGURE 2-7 Eat 5 to 9 a Day for Better Health

The "5 to 9 a Day" campaign (**www.5aday.gov**) encourages consumers to eat a variety of fruits and vegetables. Because "everyone benefits from eating more," the campaign's slogan and messages are being revised to say *Fruits and Veggies—More Matters.*

as cereals than they are like whole grains. They may be nutritious—with respect to the nutrients added—but they still may fail to convey the full spectrum of nutrients that a whole-grain food or a mixture of such foods might provide. Still, fortified foods help people meet their vitamin and mineral needs.[6]

Vegetables Posters in the produce section of grocery stores encourage consumers to "eat 5 a day." Such efforts are part of a national educational campaign to increase fruit and vegetable consumption to 5 to 9 servings every day (see Figure 2-7). To help consumers remember to eat a variety of fruits and vegetables, the campaign provides practical tips, such as selecting from each of five colors.

Choose fresh vegetables often, especially dark green leafy and yellow-orange vegetables like spinach, broccoli, and sweet potatoes. Cooked or raw, vegetables are good sources of vitamins, minerals, and fiber. Frozen and canned vegetables without added salt are acceptable alternatives to fresh. To control fat, energy, and sodium intakes, limit butter and salt on vegetables.

Choose often from the variety of legumes available. ◆ They are an economical, low-fat, nutrient- and fiber-rich food choice.

◆ Legumes include a variety of beans and peas:

- Adzuki beans
- Black beans
- Black-eyed peas
- Fava beans
- Garbanzo beans
- Great northern beans
- Kidney beans
- Lentils
- Lima beans
- Navy beans
- Peanuts
- Pinto beans
- Soybeans
- Split peas

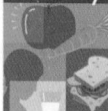

Dietary Guidelines for Americans 2005

Choose a variety of fruits and vegetables each day. In particular, select from all five vegetable subgroups (dark green, orange, legumes, starchy vegetables, and other vegetables) several times a week.

Fruit Choose fresh fruits often, especially citrus fruits and yellow-orange fruits like cantaloupes and peaches. Frozen, dried, and canned fruits without added sugar are acceptable alternatives to fresh. Fruits supply valuable vitamins, minerals, fibers, and phytochemicals. They add flavors, colors, and textures to meals, and their natural sweetness makes them enjoyable as snacks or desserts.

© 1998 Photo Disc Inc.

Combining legumes with foods from other food groups creates delicious meals.

© 1998 Photo Disc Inc.

Add rice to red beans for a hearty meal.

© Felicia Martinez Newman/PhotoEdit

Enjoy a Greek salad topped with garbanzo beans for a little ethnic diversity.

© Michael Newman/PhotoEdit

A bit of meat and lots of spices turn kidney beans into chili con carne.

Fruit juices are healthy beverages but contain little dietary fiber compared with whole fruits. Whole fruits satisfy the appetite better than juices, thereby helping people to limit food energy intakes. For people who need extra food energy, though, juices are a good choice. Be aware that sweetened fruit "drinks" or "ades" contain mostly water, sugar, and a little juice for flavor. Some may have been fortified with vitamin C or calcium but lack any other significant nutritional value.

Dietary Guidelines for Americans 2005

Consume a sufficient amount of fruits and vegetables while staying within energy needs.

Meat, Fish, and Poultry Meat, fish, and poultry provide essential minerals, such as iron and zinc, and abundant B vitamins as well as protein. To buy and prepare these foods without excess energy, fat, and sodium takes a little knowledge and planning. When shopping in the meat department, choose fish, poultry, and lean cuts of beef and pork named "round" or "loin" (as in top round or pork tenderloin). As a guide, "prime" and "choice" cuts generally have more fat than "select" cuts. Restaurants usually serve prime cuts. Ground beef, even "lean" ground beef, derives most of its food energy from fat. Have the butcher trim and grind a lean round steak instead. Alternatively, **textured vegetable protein** can be used instead of ground beef in a casserole, spaghetti sauce, or chili, saving fat kcalories.

Weigh meat after it is cooked and the bones and fat are removed. In general, 4 ounces of raw meat is equal to about 3 ounces of cooked meat. Some examples of 3-ounce portions of meat include 1 medium pork chop, $1/2$ chicken breast, or 1 steak or hamburger about the size of a deck of cards. To keep fat intake moderate, bake, roast, broil, grill, or braise meats (but do not fry them in fat); remove the skin from poultry after cooking; trim visible fat before cooking; and drain fat after cooking. Chapter 5 offers many additional strategies for moderating fat intake.

Milk Shoppers find a variety of fortified foods in the dairy case. Examples are milk, to which vitamins A and D have been added, and soy milk, ◆ to which calcium, vitamin D, and vitamin B_{12} have been added. In addition, shoppers may find **imitation foods** (such as cheese products), **food substitutes** (such as egg substitutes), and functional foods ◆ (such as margarine with added plant sterols). As food technology advances, many such foods offer alternatives to traditional choices that may help people who want to reduce their fat and cholesterol intakes. Chapter 5 gives other examples.

When shopping, choose fat-free ◆ or low-fat milk, yogurt, and cheeses. Such selections help consumers meet their vitamin and mineral needs within their energy and fat allowances.[7] Milk products are important sources of calcium, but can provide too much sodium and fat if not selected with care.

◆ Be aware that not all soy milks have been fortified. Read labels carefully.

◆ Reminder: *Functional foods* contain physiologically active compounds that provide health benefits beyond basic nutrition.

◆ Milk descriptions:
- **Fat-free** milk may also be called **non-fat**, **skim**, **zero-fat**, or **no-fat.**
- **Low-fat** milk refers to 1% milk.
- **Reduced-fat** milk refers to 2% milk; it may also be called **less-fat.**

Dietary Guidelines for Americans 2005

Consume 3 cups per day of fat-free or low-fat milk or equivalent milk products.

IN SUMMARY

Food group plans such as the USDA Food Guide help consumers select the types and amounts of foods to provide adequacy, balance, and variety in the diet. They make it easier to plan a diet that includes a balance of grains, vegetables, fruits, meats, and milk products. In making any food choice, remember to view the food in the context of your total diet. The combination of many different foods provides the abundance of nutrients that is so essential to a healthy diet.

textured vegetable protein: processed soybean protein used in vegetarian products such as soy burgers.

imitation foods: foods that substitute for and resemble another food, but are nutritionally inferior to it with respect to vitamin, mineral, or protein content. If the substitute is not inferior to the food it resembles and if its name provides an accurate description of the product, it need not be labeled "imitation."

food substitutes: foods that are designed to replace other foods.

Food Labels

Many consumers read food labels to help them make healthy choices.[8] Food labels appear on virtually all processed foods, and posters or brochures provide similar nutrition information for fresh meats, fruits, and vegetables (see Figure 2-8). A few foods need not carry nutrition labels: those contributing few nutrients, such as plain coffee, tea, and spices; those produced by small businesses; and those prepared and sold in the same establishment. Producers of some of these items, however, voluntarily use labels. Even markets selling nonpackaged items voluntarily present nutrient information, either in brochures or on signs posted at the point of purchase. Restaurants need not supply complete nutrition information for menu items unless claims such as "low fat" or "heart healthy" have been made. When ordering such items, keep in mind that restaurants tend to serve extra-large portions—two to three times standard serving sizes. A "low-fat" ice cream, for example, may have only 3 grams of fat per 1/2 cup, but you may be served 2 cups for a total of 12 grams of fat and all their accompanying kcalories.

FIGURE 2-8 Example of a Food Label

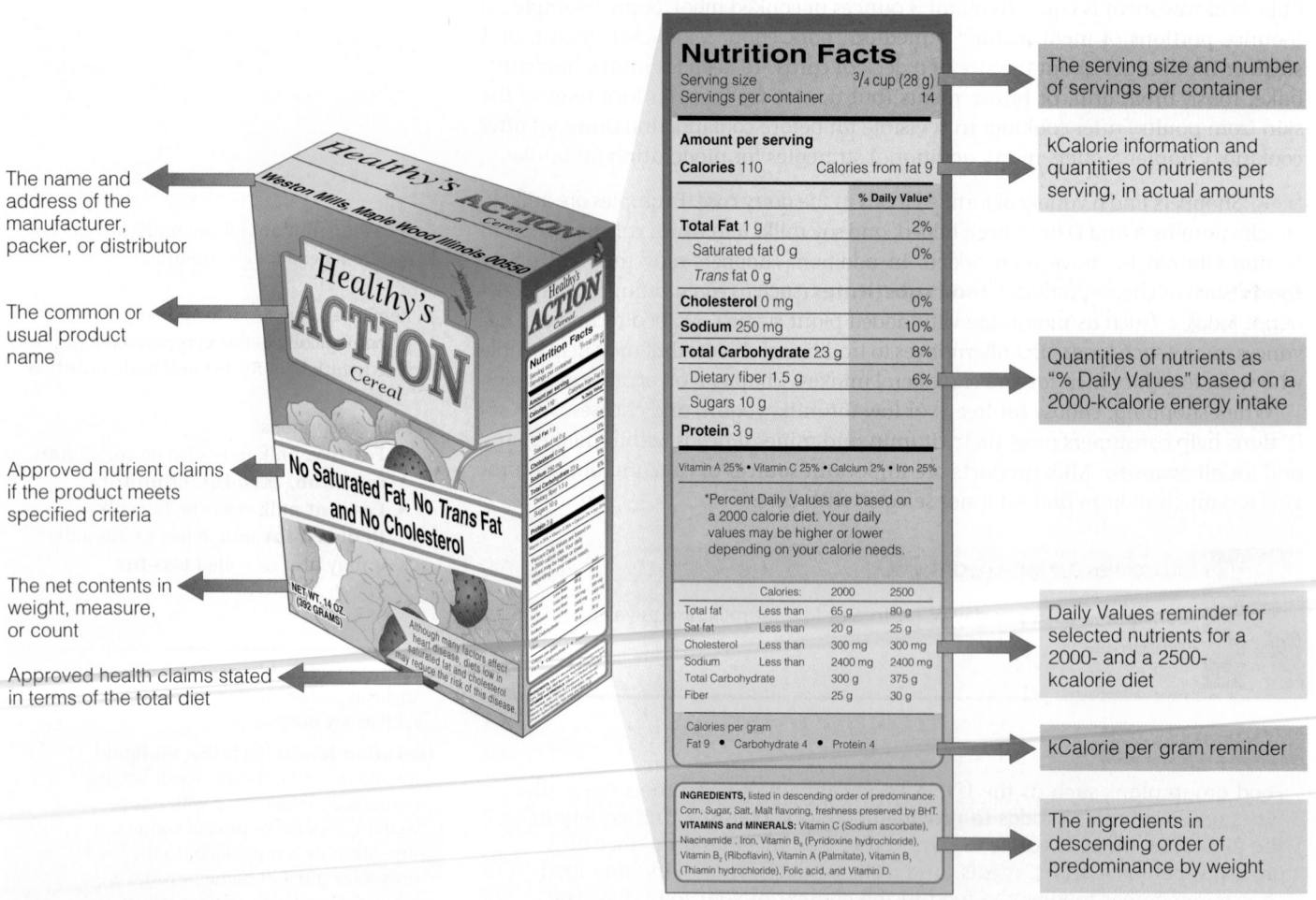

The name and address of the manufacturer, packer, or distributor

The common or usual product name

Approved nutrient claims if the product meets specified criteria

The net contents in weight, measure, or count

Approved health claims stated in terms of the total diet

Nutrition Facts

Serving size   3/4 cup (28 g)
Servings per container   14

Amount per serving

Calories 110   Calories from fat 9

	% Daily Value*
Total Fat 1 g	2%
Saturated fat 0 g	0%
Trans fat 0 g	
Cholesterol 0 mg	0%
Sodium 250 mg	10%
Total Carbohydrate 23 g	8%
Dietary fiber 1.5 g	6%
Sugars 10 g	
Protein 3 g	

Vitamin A 25% • Vitamin C 25% • Calcium 2% • Iron 25%

*Percent Daily Values are based on a 2000 calorie diet. Your daily values may be higher or lower depending on your calorie needs.

	Calories:	2000	2500
Total fat	Less than	65 g	80 g
Sat fat	Less than	20 g	25 g
Cholesterol	Less than	300 mg	300 mg
Sodium	Less than	2400 mg	2400 mg
Total Carbohydrate		300 g	375 g
Fiber		25 g	30 g

Calories per gram

Fat 9 • Carbohydrate 4 • Protein 4

INGREDIENTS, listed in descending order of predominance: Corn, Sugar, Salt, Malt flavoring, freshness preserved by BHT. **VITAMINS and MINERALS:** Vitamin C (Sodium ascorbate), Niacinamide , Iron, Vitamin B₆ (Pyridoxine hydrochloride), Vitamin B₂ (Riboflavin), Vitamin A (Palmitate), Vitamin B₁ (Thiamin hydrochloride), Folic acid, and Vitamin D.

The serving size and number of servings per container

kCalorie information and quantities of nutrients per serving, in actual amounts

Quantities of nutrients as "% Daily Values" based on a 2000-kcalorie energy intake

Daily Values reminder for selected nutrients for a 2000- and a 2500-kcalorie diet

kCalorie per gram reminder

The ingredients in descending order of predominance by weight

The Ingredient List

All packaged foods must list all ingredients on the label in descending order of predominance by weight. Knowing that the first ingredient predominates by weight, consumers can glean much information. Compare these products, for example:

- A beverage powder that contains "sugar, citric acid, natural flavors . . ." versus a juice that contains "water, tomato concentrate, concentrated juices of carrots, celery . . ."
- A cereal that contains "puffed milled corn, sugar, corn syrup, molasses, salt . . ." versus one that contains "100 percent rolled oats"
- A canned fruit that contains "sugar, apples, water" versus one that contains simply "apples, water"

In each of these comparisons, consumers can see that the second product is the more nutrient dense.

Serving Sizes

Because labels present nutrient information *per serving,* they must identify the size of the serving. The Food and Drug Administration (FDA) has established specific serving sizes for various foods and requires that all labels for a given product use the same serving size. For example, the serving size for all ice creams is $1/2$ cup and for all beverages, 8 fluid ounces. This facilitates comparison shopping. Consumers can see at a glance which brand has more or fewer kcalories or grams of fat, for example. Standard serving sizes are expressed in both common household measures, such as cups, and metric measures, such as milliliters, to accommodate users of both types of measures (see Table 2-8).

When examining the nutrition facts on a food label, consumers need to compare the serving size on the label with how much they actually eat and adjust their calculations accordingly. For example, if the serving size is four cookies and you only eat two, then you need to cut the nutrient and kcalorie values in half; similarly, if you eat eight cookies, then you need to double the values. Notice, too, that small bags or individually wrapped items, such as chips or candy bars, may contain more than a single serving. The number of servings per container is listed just below the serving size.

Be aware that serving sizes on food labels are not always the same as those of the USDA Food Guide.[9] For example, a serving of rice on a food label is 1 cup, whereas in the USDA Food Guide it is $1/2$ cup. Unfortunately, this discrepancy, coupled with each person's own perception (oftentimes misperception) of standard serving sizes, sometimes creates confusion for consumers trying to follow recommendations.

Nutrition Facts

In addition to the serving size and the servings per container, the FDA requires that the "Nutrition Facts" panel on food labels present nutrient information in two ways—in quantities (such as grams) and as percentages of standards called the **Daily Values.** The Nutrition Facts panel must provide the nutrient amount, percent Daily Value, or both for the following:

- Total food energy (kcalories)
- Food energy from fat (kcalories)
- Total fat (grams and percent Daily Value)
- Saturated fat (grams and percent Daily Value)
- *Trans* fat (grams)
- Cholesterol (milligrams and percent Daily Value)
- Sodium (milligrams and percent Daily Value)

TABLE 2-8   Household and Metric Measures

- 1 teaspoon (tsp) = 5 milliliters (mL)
- 1 tablespoon (tbs) = 15 mL
- 1 cup (c) = 240 mL
- 1 fluid ounce (fl oz) = 30 mL
- 1 ounce (oz) = 28 grams (g)

NOTE: The Aids to Calculation section at the back of the book provides additional weights and measures.

Daily Values (DV): reference values developed by the FDA specifically for use on food labels.

Consumers read food labels to learn about the nutrient contents of a food or to compare similar foods.

- Total carbohydrate, which includes starch, sugar, and fiber (grams and percent Daily Value)
- Dietary fiber (grams and percent Daily Value)
- Sugars, which includes both those naturally present in and those added to the food (grams)
- Protein (grams)

The labels must also present nutrient content information as a percentage of the Daily Values for the following vitamins and minerals:

- Vitamin A
- Vitamin C
- Iron
- Calcium

The Daily Values

The FDA developed the Daily Values for use on food labels because comparing nutrient amounts against a standard helps make the numbers more meaningful to consumers. Table 2-9 presents the Daily Value standards for nutrients that are required to provide this information. Food labels list the amount of a nutrient in a product as a percentage of its Daily Value. A person reading a food label might wonder, for example, whether 1 milligram of iron or calcium is a little or a lot. As Table 2-9 shows, the Daily Value for iron is 18 milligrams, so 1 milligram of iron is enough to notice—it is more than 5 percent, and that is what the food label will say. But because the Daily Value for calcium on food labels is 1000 milligrams, 1 milligram of calcium is insignificant, and the food label will read "0%."

The Daily Values reflect dietary recommendations for nutrients and dietary components that have important relationships with health. The "% Daily Value" column on a label provides a ballpark estimate of how individual foods contribute to the total diet. It compares key nutrients in a serving of food with the goals of a person consuming 2000 kcalories per day. A 2000-kcalorie diet is considered about right for sedentary younger women, active older women, and sedentary older men.

TABLE 2-9 Daily Values for Food Labels

Food labels must present the "% Daily Value" for these nutrients.

Food Component	Daily Value	Calculation Factors
Fat	65 g	30% of kcalories
Saturated fat	20 g	10% of kcalories
Cholesterol	300 mg	—
Carbohydrate (total)	300 g	60% of kcalories
Fiber	25 g	11.5 g per 1000 kcalories
Protein	50 g	10% of kcalories
Sodium	2400 mg	—
Potassium	3500 mg	—
Vitamin C	60 mg	—
Vitamin A	1500 µg	—
Calcium	1000 mg	—
Iron	18 mg	—

NOTE: Daily Values were established for adults and children over 4 years old. The values for energy-yielding nutrients are based on 2000 kcalories a day. For fiber, the Daily Value was rounded up from 23.

Young children and sedentary older women may need fewer kcalories. Most labels list, at the bottom, Daily Values for both a 2000-kcalorie and a 2500-kcalorie diet, but the "% Daily Value" column on all labels applies only to a 2000-kcalorie diet. A 2500-kcalorie diet is considered about right for many men, teenage boys, and active younger women. People who are exceptionally active may have still higher energy needs. Labels may also provide a reminder of the kcalories in a gram of carbohydrate, fat, and protein just below the Daily Value information (review Figure 2-8).

People who consume 2000 kcalories a day can simply add up all of the "% Daily Values" for a particular nutrient to see if their diet for the day fits recommendations. People who require more or less than 2000 kcalories daily must do some calculations to see how foods compare with their personal nutrition goals. They can use the calculation column in Table 2-9 or the suggestions presented in the accompanying "How to" feature.

Daily Values help consumers see easily whether a food contributes "a little" or "a lot" of a nutrient. ◆ For example, the "% Daily Value" column on a label of macaroni and cheese may say 20 percent for fat. This tells the consumer that each serving of this food contains about 20 percent of the day's allotted 65 grams of fat. A person consuming 2000 kcalories a day could simply keep track of the percentages of Daily Values from foods eaten in a day and try not to exceed 100 percent. Be aware that for some nutrients (such as fat and sodium) you will want to select foods with a low "% Daily Value" and for others (such as calcium and fiber) you will want a high "% Daily Value." To determine whether a particular food is a wise choice, a consumer needs to consider its place in the diet among all the other foods eaten during the day.

Daily Values also make it easy to compare foods. For example, a consumer might discover that frozen macaroni and cheese has a Daily Value for fat of 20 percent, whereas macaroni and cheese prepared from a boxed mix has a Daily Value of 15 percent. By comparing labels, consumers who are concerned about their fat intakes can make informed decisions.

The Daily Values used on labels are based in part on values from the 1968 Recommended Dietary Allowances. Since 1997, Dietary Reference Intakes that reflect scientific research on diet and health have been released. Efforts to update the Daily Values based on these current recommendations and to make labels more effective and easier to understand are underway.[10]

◆ % Daily Values:
- ≥ 20% = high or excellent source
- 10-19% = good source
- ≤ 5% = low

HOW TO Calculate Personal Daily Values

The Daily Values on food labels are designed for a 2000-kcalorie intake, but you can calculate a personal set of Daily Values based on your energy allowance. Consider a 1500-kcalorie intake, for example. To calculate a daily goal for fat, multiply energy intake by 30 percent:

1500 kcal × 0.30 kcal from fat
= 450 kcal from fat

The "kcalories from fat" are listed on food labels, so you can add all the "kcalories from fat" values for a day, using 450 as an upper limit. A person who prefers to count grams of fat can divide this 450 kcalories from fat by 9 kcalories per gram to determine the goal in grams:

450 kcal from fat ÷ 9 kcal/g
= 50 g fat

Alternatively, a person can calculate that 1500 kcalories is 75 percent of the 2000-kcalorie intake used for Daily Values:

1500 kcal ÷ 2000 kcal = 0.75
0.75 × 100 = 75%

Then, instead of trying to achieve 100 percent of the Daily Value, a person consuming 1500 kcalories will aim for 75 percent. Similarly, a person consuming 2800 kcalories would aim for 140 percent:

2800 kcal ÷ 2000 kcal = 1.40 or 140%

Table 2-9 includes a calculation column that can help you estimate your personal daily value for several nutrients.

ThomsonNOW™
To calculate your personal daily values, log on to **www.thomsonedu.com/thomsonnow,** then go to Chapter 2, then go to How To.

Nutrient Claims

Have you noticed phrases such as "good source of fiber" on a box of cereal or "rich in calcium" on a package of cheese? These and other **nutrient claims** may be used on labels as long as they meet FDA definitions, which include the conditions under which each term can be used. For example, in addition to having less than 2 milligrams of cholesterol, a "cholesterol-free" product may not contain more than 2 grams of saturated fat and *trans* fat combined per serving. The accompanying glossary defines nutrient terms on food labels, including criteria for foods described as "low," "reduced," and "free."

Some descriptions *imply* that a food contains, or does not contain, a nutrient. Implied claims are prohibited unless they meet specified criteria. For example, a claim that a product "contains no oil" *implies* that the food contains no fat. If the product is truly fat-free, then it may make the no-oil claim, but if it contains another source of fat, such as butter, it may not.

> **nutrient claims:** statements that characterize the quantity of a nutrient in a food.

GLOSSARY OF TERMS ON FOOD LABELS

GENERAL TERMS

free: "nutritionally trivial" and unlikely to have a physiological consequence; synonyms include "without," "no," and "zero." A food that does not contain a nutrient naturally may make such a claim, but only as it applies to all similar foods (for example, "applesauce, a fat-free food").

good source of: the product provides between 10 and 19% of the Daily Value for a given nutrient per serving.

healthy: a food that is low in fat, saturated fat, cholesterol, and sodium and that contains at least 10% of the Daily Values for vitamin A, vitamin C, iron, calcium, protein, or fiber.

high: 20% or more of the Daily Value for a given nutrient per serving; synonyms include "rich in" or "excellent source."

less: at least 25% less of a given nutrient or kcalories than the comparison food (see individual nutrients); synonyms include "fewer" and "reduced."

light or **lite:** one-third fewer kcalories than the comparison food; 50% or less of the fat or sodium than the comparison food; any use of the term other than as defined must specify what it is referring to (for example, "light in color" or "light in texture").

low: an amount that would allow frequent consumption of a food without exceeding the Daily Value for the nutrient. A food that is naturally low in a nutrient may make such a claim, but only as it applies to all similar foods (for example, "fresh cauliflower, a low-sodium food"); synonyms include "little," "few," and "low source of."

more: at least 10% more of the Daily Value for a given nutrient than the comparison food; synonyms include "added" and "extra."

organic: on food labels, that at least 95% of the product's ingredients have been grown and processsed according to USDA regulations defining the use of fertilizers, herbicides, insecticides, fungicides, preservatives, and other chemical ingredients (see Chapter 19).

ENERGY

kcalorie-free: fewer than 5 kcal per serving.

low kcalorie: 40 kcal or less per serving.

reduced kcalorie: at least 25% fewer kcalories per serving than the comparison food.

FAT AND CHOLESTEROL[a]

percent fat-free: may be used only if the product meets the definition of *low fat* or *fat-free* and must reflect the amount of fat in 100 g (for example, a food that contains 2.5 g of fat per 50 g can claim to be "95 percent fat free").

fat-free: less than 0.5 g of fat per serving (and no added fat or oil); synonyms include "zero-fat," "no-fat," and "nonfat."

low fat: 3 g or less fat per serving.

less fat: 25% or less fat than the comparison food.

saturated fat-free: less than 0.5 g of saturated fat and 0.5 g of *trans* fat per serving.

low saturated fat: 1 g or less saturated fat and less than 0.5 g of *trans* fat per serving.

less saturated fat: 25% or less saturated fat and *trans* fat combined than the comparison food.

***trans* fat-free:** less than 0.5 g of *trans* fat and less than 0.5 g of saturated fat per serving.

cholesterol-free: less than 2 mg cholesterol per serving and 2 g or less saturated fat and *trans* fat combined per serving.

low cholesterol: 20 mg or less cholesterol per serving and 2 g or less saturated fat and *trans* fat combined per serving.

less cholesterol: 25% or less cholesterol than the comparison food (reflecting a reduction of at least 20 mg per serving), and 2 g or less saturated fat and *trans* fat combined per serving.

extra lean: less than 5 g of fat, 2 g of saturated fat and *trans* fat combined, and 95 mg of cholesterol per serving and per 100 g of meat, poultry, and seafood.

lean: less than 10 g of fat, 4.5 g of saturated fat and *trans* fat combined, and 95 mg of cholesterol per serving and per 100 g of meat, poultry, and seafood.

CARBOHYDRATES: FIBER AND SUGAR

high fiber: 5 g or more fiber per serving. A high-fiber claim made on a food that contains more than 3 g fat per serving and per 100 g of food must also declare total fat.

sugar-free: less than 0.5 g of sugar per serving.

SODIUM

sodium-free and **salt-free:** less than 5 mg of sodium per serving.

low sodium: 140 mg or less per serving.

very low sodium: 35 mg or less per serving.

[a] Foods containing more than 13 grams total fat per serving or per 50 grams of food must indicate those contents immediately after a cholesterol claim. As you can see, all cholesterol claims are prohibited when the food contains more than 2 grams saturated fat and *trans* fat combined per serving.

Health Claims

Until 2003, the FDA held manufacturers to the highest standards of scientific evidence before approving **health claims** on food labels. Consumers reading "Diets low in sodium may reduce the risk of high blood pressure," for example, knew that the FDA had examined enough scientific evidence to establish a clear link between diet and health. Such reliable health claims make up the FDA's "A" list (see Table 2-10). The FDA refers to these health claims as "unqualified"—not that they lack the necessary qualifications, but that they can stand alone without further explanation or qualification.

These reliable health claims still appear on some food labels, but finding them may be difficult now that the FDA has created three additional categories of claims based on scientific evidence that is less conclusive (see Table 2-11). These categories were added after a court ruled: "Holding only the highest scientific standard for claims interferes with commercial free speech." Food manufacturers had argued that they should be allowed to inform consumers about possible benefits based on less than clear and convincing evidence. The FDA must allow manufacturers to provide information about nutrients and foods that show preliminary promise in preventing disease. These health claims are "qualified"—not that they meet the necessary qualifications, but that they require a qualifying explanation. For example, "Very limited and preliminary research suggests that eating one-half to one cup of tomatoes and/or tomato sauce a week may reduce the risk of prostate cancer. FDA concludes that there is little scientific evidence supporting the claim." Consumer groups argue that such information is confusing. Even with required disclaimers for health claims graded "B," "C," or "D," distinguishing "A" claims from others is difficult, as the next section shows. (Health claims on supplement labels are presented in Highlight 10.)

TABLE 2-10 Food Label Health Claims—The "A" List
• Calcium and reduced risk of osteoporosis
• Sodium and reduced risk of hypertension
• Dietary saturated fat and cholesterol and reduced risk of coronary heart disease
• Dietary fat and reduced risk of cancer
• Fiber-containing grain products, fruits, and vegetables and reduced risk of cancer
• Fruits, vegetables, and grain products that contain fiber, particularly soluble fiber, and reduced risk of coronary heart disease
• Fruits and vegetables and reduced risk of cancer
• Folate and reduced risk of neural tube defects
• Sugar alcohols and reduced risk of tooth decay
• Soluble fiber from whole oats and from psyllium seed husk and reduced risk of heart disease
• Soy protein and reduced risk of heart disease
• Whole grains and reduced risk of heart disease and certain cancers
• Plant sterol and plant stanol esters and heart disease
• Potassium and reduced risk of hypertension and stroke

Structure-Function Claims

Unlike health claims, which require food manufacturers to collect scientific evidence and petition the FDA, **structure-function claims** can be made without any FDA approval. Product labels can claim to "slow aging," "improve memory," and "build strong bones" without any proof. The only criterion for a structure-function claim is that it must not mention a disease or symptom. Unfortunately, structure-function claims can be deceptively similar to health claims. Consider these statements:

- "May reduce the risk of heart disease."
- "Promotes a healthy heart."

Most consumers do not distinguish between these two types of claims.[11] In the statements above, for example, the first is a health claim that requires FDA approval and the second is an unproven, but legal, structure-function claim. Table 2-12 lists examples of structure-function claims.

health claims: statements that characterize the relationship between a nutrient or other substance in a food and a disease or health-related condition.

structure-function claims: statements that characterize the relationship between a nutrient or other substance in a food and its role in the body.

TABLE 2-11	The FDA's Health Claims Report Card	
Grade	**Level of Confidence in Health Claim**	**Required Label Disclaimers**
A	High: Significant scientific agreement	These health claims do not require disclaimers; see Table 2-10 for examples.
B	Moderate: Evidence is supportive but not conclusive	"[Health claim.] Although there is scientific evidence supporting this claim, the evidence is not conclusive."
C	Low: Evidence is limited and not conclusive	"Some scientific evidence suggests [health claim]. However, FDA has determined that this evidence is limited and not conclusive."
D	Very low: Little scientific evidence supporting this claim	"Very limited and preliminary scientific research suggests [health claim]. FDA concludes that there is little scientific evidence supporting this claim."

TABLE 2-12	Examples of Structure-Function Claims

- Builds strong bones
- Promotes relaxation
- Improves memory
- Boosts the immune system
- Supports heart health
- Defends your health
- Slows aging
- Guards against colds
- Lifts your spirits

NOTE: Structure-function claims cannot make statements about diseases. See Table 2-10 on p. 59 for examples of health claims.

Consumer Education

Because labels are valuable only if people know how to use them, the FDA has designed several programs to educate consumers. Consumers who understand how to read labels are best able to apply the information to achieve and maintain healthful dietary practices.

Table 2-13 shows how the messages from the 2005 *Dietary Guidelines,* the USDA Food Guide, and food labels coordinate with each other. To promote healthy eating and physical activity, the "Healthier US Initiative" coordinates the efforts of national educational programs developed by government agencies.[12] The mission of this initiative is to deliver simple messages that will motivate consumers to make small changes in their eating and physical activity habits to yield big rewards.

TABLE 2-13	From Guidelines to Groceries	
Dietary Guidelines	**USDA Food Guide/MyPyramid**	**Food Labels**
Adequate nutrients within energy needs	Select the recommended amounts from each food group at the energy level appropriate for your energy needs.	Look for foods that describe their vitamin, mineral, or fiber contents as a *good source* or *high.*
Weight management	Select nutrient-dense foods and beverages within and among the food groups. Limit high-fat foods and foods and beverages with added fats and sugars. Use appropriate portion sizes.	Look for foods that describe their kcalorie contents as *free, low, reduced, light,* or *less.*
Physical activity	Be phyisically active for at least 30 minutes most days of the week. Children and teenagers should be physically active for 60 minutes every day, or most days.	
Food groups to encourage	Select a variety of fruits each day. Include vegetables from all five subgroups (dark green, orange, legumes, starchy vegetables, and other vegetables) several times a week. Make at least half of the grain selections whole grains. Select fat-free or low-fat milk products.	Look for foods that describe their fiber contents as *good source* or *high.* Look for foods that provide at least 10% of the Daily Value for fiber, vitamin A, vitamin C, iron, and calcium from a variety of sources.
Fats	Choose foods within each group that are lean, low fat, or fat-free. Choose foods within each group that have little added fat.	Look for foods that describe their fat, saturated fat, *trans* fat, and cholesterol contents as *free, less, low, light, reduced, lean,* or *extra lean.* Look for foods that provide no more than 5% of the Daily Value for fat, saturated fat, and cholesterol.
Carbohydrates	Choose fiber-rich fruits, vegetables, and whole grains often. Choose foods and beverages within each group that have little added sugars.	Look for foods that describe their sugar contents as *free* or *reduced.* A food may be high in sugar if its ingredients list begins with or contains several of the following: *sugar, sucrose, fructose, maltose, lactose, honey, syrup, corn syrup, high-fructose corn syrup, molasses, evaporated cane juice,* or *fruit juice concentrate.*
Sodium and potassium	Choose foods within each group that are low in salt or sodium. Choose potassium-rich foods such as fruits and vegetables.	Look for foods that describe their salt and sodium contents as *free, low,* or *reduced.* Look for foods that provide no more than 5% of the Daily Value for sodium. Look for foods that provide at least 10% of the Daily Value for potassium.
Alcoholic beverages	Use sensibly and in moderation (no more than one drink a day for women and two drinks a day for men).	*Light* beverages contain fewer kcalories and less alcohol than regular versions.
Food safety		Follow the *safe handling instructions* on packages of meat and other safety instructions, such as *keep refrigerated,* on packages of perishable foods.

IN SUMMARY

Food labels provide consumers with information they need to select foods that will help them meet their nutrition and health goals. When labels contain relevant information presented in a standardized, easy-to-read format, consumers are well prepared to plan and create healthful diets.

This chapter provides the links to go from dietary guidelines to buying groceries and offers helpful tips for selecting nutritious foods. For additional information on foods, including organic foods, irradiated foods, genetically modified foods, and more, turn to Chapter 19.

 Nutrition Portfolio

ThomsonNOW
www.thomsonedu.com/thomsonnow

The secret to making healthy food choices is learning to incorporate the 2005 *Dietary Guidelines* and the USDA Food Guide into your decision-making process.

■ Compare the foods you typically eat daily with the USDA Food Guide recommendations for your energy needs (see Table 2-3 on p. 41 and Table 2-4 on p. 44), making note of which food groups are usually over- or underrepresented.

■ Describe your choices within each food group from day to day and include realistic suggestions for enhancing the variety in your diet.

■ Write yourself a letter describing the dietary changes you can make to improve your chances of enjoying good health.

NUTRITION ON THE NET

ThomsonNOW
For further study of topics covered in this chapter, log on to **www.thomsonedu .com/thomsonnow**. Go to Chapter 2, then to Nutrition on the Net.

• Search for "diet" and "food labels" at the U.S. Government health information site: **www.healthfinder.gov**

• Learn more about the *Dietary Guidelines for Americans:* **www.healthierus.gov/dietaryguidelines**

• Find Canadian information on nutrition guidelines and food labels at: **www.hc-sc.gc.ca**

• Learn more about the USDA Food Guide and MyPyramid: **mypyramid.gov**

• Visit the USDA Food Guide section (including its ethnic/cultural pyramids) of the U.S. Department of Agriculture: **www.nal.usda.gov/fnic**

• Visit the Traditional Diet Pyramids for various ethnic groups at Oldways Preservation and Exchange Trust: **www.oldwayspt.org**

• Search for "exchange lists" at the American Diabetes Association: **www.diabetes.org**

• Learn more about food labeling from the Food and Drug Administration: **www.cfsan.fda.gov**

• Search for "food labels" at the International Food Information Council: **www.ific.org**

• Assess your diet at the CNPP Interactive Healthy Eating Index: **www.usda.gov/cnpp**

• Get healthy eating tips from the "5 a day" programs: **www.5aday.gov** or **www.5aday.org**

NUTRITION CALCULATIONS

ThomsonNOW For additional practice log on to **www.thomsonedu.com/thomsonnow**. Go to Chapter 2, then to Nutrition Calculations.

These problems will give you practice in doing simple nutrition-related calculations. Although the situations are hypothetical, the numbers are real, and calculating the answers (check them on p. 63) provides a valuable nutrition lesson. Be sure to show your calculations for each problem.

1. *Read a food label.* Look at the cereal label in Figure 2-8 and answer the following questions:
   a. What is the size of a serving of cereal?
   b. How many kcalories are in a serving?
   c. How much fat is in a serving?
   d. How many kcalories does this represent?
   e. What percentage of the kcalories in this product comes from fat?
   f. What does this tell you?
   g. What is the % Daily Value for fat?
   h. What does this tell you?
   i. Does this cereal meet the criteria for a low-fat product (refer to the glossary on p. 58)?
   j. How much fiber is in a serving?
   k. Read the Daily Value chart on the lower section of the label. What is the Daily Value for fiber?
   l. What percentage of the Daily Value for fiber does a serving of the cereal contribute? Show the calculation the label-makers used to come up with the % Daily Value for fiber.
   m. What is the predominant ingredient in the cereal?
   n. Have any nutrients been added to this cereal (is it fortified)?

2. *Calculate a personal Daily Value.* The Daily Values on food labels are for people with a 2000-kcalorie intake.
   a. Suppose a person has a 1600-kcalorie energy allowance. Use the calculation factors listed in Table 2-9 to calculate a set of personal "Daily Values" based on 1600 kcalories. Show your calculations.
   b. Revise the % Daily Value chart of the cereal label in Figure 2-8 based on your "Daily Values" for a 1600-kcalorie diet.

STUDY QUESTIONS

These questions will help you review this chapter. You will find the answers in the discussions on the pages provided.

1. Name the diet-planning principles and briefly describe how each principle helps in diet planning. (pp. 37–39)
2. What recommendations appear in the *Dietary Guidelines for Americans*? (pp. 39–40)
3. Name the five food groups in the USDA Food Guide and identify several foods typical of each group. Explain how such plans group foods and what diet-planning principles the plans best accommodate. How are food group plans used, and what are some of their strengths and weaknesses? (pp. 41–47)
4. Review the *Dietary Guidelines.* What types of grocery selections would you make to achieve those recommendations? (pp. 40, 48–53)
5. What information can you expect to find on a food label? How can this information help you choose between two similar products? (pp. 54–57)
6. What are the Daily Values? How can they help you meet health recommendations? (pp. 55–57)
7. Describe the differences between nutrient claims, health claims, and structure-function claims. (pp. 58–59)

These multiple choice questions will help you prepare for an exam. Answers can be found on p. 63.

1. The diet-planning principle that provides all the essential nutrients in sufficient amounts to support health is:
   a. balance.
   b. variety.
   c. adequacy.
   d. moderation.
2. A person who chooses a chicken leg that provides 0.5 milligram of iron and 95 kcalories instead of two tablespoons of peanut butter that also provide 0.5 milligram of iron but 188 kcalories is using the principle of nutrient:
   a. control.
   b. density.
   c. adequacy.
   d. moderation.
3. Which of the following is consistent with the *Dietary Guidelines for Americans*?
   a. Choose a diet restricted in fat and cholesterol.
   b. Balance the food you eat with physical activity.
   c. Choose a diet with plenty of milk products and meats.
   d. Eat an abundance of foods to ensure nutrient adequacy.
4. According to the USDA Food Guide, added fats and sugars are counted as:
   a. meats and grains.
   b. nutrient-dense foods.
   c. discretionary kcalories.
   d. oils and carbohydrates.
5. Foods within a given food group of the USDA Food Guide are similar in their contents of:
   a. energy.
   b. proteins and fibers.
   c. vitamins and minerals.
   d. carbohydrates and fats.
6. In the exchange system, each portion of food on any given list provides about the same amount of:
   a. energy.
   b. satiety.
   c. vitamins.
   d. minerals.
7. Enriched grain products are fortified with:
   a. fiber, folate, iron, niacin, and zinc.
   b. thiamin, iron, calcium, zinc, and sodium.
   c. iron, thiamin, riboflavin, niacin, and folate.
   d. folate, magnesium, vitamin B_6, zinc, and fiber.

8. Food labels list ingredients in:
   a. alphabetical order.
   b. ascending order of predominance by weight.
   c. descending order of predominance by weight.
   d. manufacturer's order of preference.

9. "Milk builds strong bones" is an example of a:
   a. health claim.
   b. nutrition fact.
   c. nutrient content claim.
   d. structure-function claim.

10. Daily Values on food labels are based on a:
   a. 1500-kcalorie diet.
   b. 2000-kcalorie diet.
   c. 2500-kcalorie diet.
   d. 3000-kcalorie diet.

REFERENCES

1. S. P. Murphy and coauthors, Simple measures of dietary variety are associated with improved dietary quality, *Journal of the American Dietetic Association* 106 (2006): 425–429.
2. U.S. Department of Agriculture and U.S. Department of Health and Human Services, *Dietary Guidelines for Americans, 2005*, available at www.healthierus.gov/dietaryguidelines.
3. Position of the American Dietetic Association and Dietitians of Canada: Vegetarian diets, *Journal of the American Dietetic Association* 103 (2003): 748–765.
4. J. R. Backstrand, The history and future of food fortification in the United States: A public health perspective, *Nutrition Reviews* 60 (2002): 15–26.
5. As cited in 21 Code of Federal Regulations—Food and Drugs, Section 104.20, 45 *Federal Register* 6323, January 25, 1980, as amended in 58 *Federal Register* 2228, January 6, 1993.
6. Position of the American Dietetic Association: Food fortification and nutritional supple-

ments, *Journal of the American Dietetic Association* 105 (2005): 1300–1311.
7. R. Ranganathan and coauthors, The nutritional impact of dairy product consumption on dietary intakes of adults (1995–1996): The Bogalusa Heart Study, *Journal of the American Dietetic Association* 105 (2005): 1391–1400; L. G. Weinberg, L. A. Berner, and J. E. Groves, Nutrient contributions of dairy foods in the United States, Continuing Survey of Food Intakes by Individuals, 1994–1996, 1998, *Journal of the American Dietetic Association* 104 (2004): 895–902.
8. L. LeGault and coauthors, 2000–2001 Food Label and Package Survey: An update on prevalence of nutrition labeling and claims on processed, packaged foods, *Journal of the American Dietetic Association* 104 (2004): 952–958.
9. D. Herring and coauthors, Serving sizes in the Food Guide Pyramid and on the nutrition facts label: What's different and why? *Family*

Economics and Nutrition Review 14 (2002): 71–73.
10. Dietary Reference Intakes (DRIs) for food labeling, *American Journal of Clinical Nutrition* 83 (2006): suppl; T. Philipson, Government perspective: Food labeling, *American Journal of Clinical Nutrition* 82 (2005): 262S–264S; The National Academy of Sciences, Dietary Reference Intakes: Guiding principles for nutrition labeling and fortification (2004), http://www.nap.edu/openbook/0309091438/html/R1.html.
11. P. Williams, Consumer understanding and use of health claims for foods, *Nutrition Reviews* 63 (2005): 256–264.
12. K. A. Donato, National health education programs to promote healthy eating and physical activity, *Nutrition Reviews* 64 (2006): S65–S70.

ANSWERS

Nutrition Calculations

1. a. ¾ cup (28 g)
   b. 110 kcalories
   c. 1 g fat
   d. 9 kcalories
   e. 9 kcal ÷ 110 kcal = 0.08
      0.08 × 100 = 8%
   f. This cereal derives 8 percent of its kcalories from fat
   g. 2%
   h. A serving of this cereal provides 2 percent of the 65 grams of fat recommended for a 2000-kcalorie diet
   i. Yes
   j. 1.5 g fiber
   k. 25 g
   l. 1.5 g ÷ 25 g = 0.06
      0.06 × 100 = 6%
   m. Corn
   n. Yes

2. a. Daily Values for 1600-kcalorie diet:
      Fat: 1600 kcal × 0.30 = 480 kcal from fat
         480 kcal ÷ 9 kcal/g = 53 g fat

Saturated fat: 1600 kcal × 0.10 = 160 kcal from saturated fat
   160 kcal ÷ 9 kcal/g = 18 g saturated fat
Cholesterol: 300 mg
Carbohydrate: 1600 kcal × 0.60 = 960 kcal from carbohydrate
   960 kcal ÷ 4 kcal/g = 240 g carbohydrate
Fiber: 1600 kcal ÷ 1000 kcal = 1.6
   1.6 × 11.5 g = 18.4 g fiber
Protein: 1600 kcal × 0.10 = 160 kcal from protein
   160 kcal ÷ 4 kcal/g = 40 g protein
Sodium: 2400 mg
Potassium: 3500 mg

b.

Total fat	2%	(1 g ÷ 53 g)
Saturated fat	0%	(0 g ÷ 18 g)
Cholesterol	0%	(no calculation needed)
Sodium	10%	(no calculation needed)
Total carbohydrate	10%	(23 g ÷ 240 g)
Dietary fiber	8%	(1.5 g ÷ 18.4 g)

Study Questions (multiple choice)

1. c 2. b 3. b 4. c 5. c 6. a 7. c 8. c
9. d 10. b

Vegetarian Diets

© Polora Studios, Inc.

The waiter presents this evening's specials: a fresh spinach salad topped with mandarin oranges, raisins, and sunflower seeds, served with a bowl of pasta smothered in a mushroom and tomato sauce and topped with grated parmesan cheese. Then this one: a salad made of chopped parsley, scallions, celery, and tomatoes mixed with bulgur wheat and dressed with olive oil and lemon juice, served with a spinach and feta cheese pie. Do these meals sound good to you? Or is something missing . . . a pork chop or ribeye, perhaps?

Would vegetarian fare be acceptable to you some of the time? Most of the time? Ever? Perhaps it is helpful to recognize that dietary choices fall along a continuum—from one end, where people eat no meat or foods of animal origin, to the other end, where they eat generous quantities daily. Meat's place in the diet has been the subject of much research and controversy, as this highlight will reveal. One of the missions of this highlight, in fact, is to identify the *range* of meat intakes most compatible with health. The health benefits of a primarily vegetarian diet seem to have encouraged many people to eat more vegetarian meals. The popular press refers to these "part-time vegetarians" who eat small amounts of meat from time to time as "flexitarians."

People who choose to exclude meat and other animal-derived foods from their diets today do so for many of the same reasons the Greek philosopher Pythagoras cited in the sixth century B.C.: physical health, ecological responsibility, and philosophical concerns. They might also cite world hunger issues, economic reasons, ethical concerns, or religious beliefs as motivating factors. Whatever their reasons—and even if they don't have a particular reason—people who exclude meat will be better prepared to plan well-balanced meals if they understand the nutrition and health implications of vegetarian diets.

Vegetarians generally are categorized, not by their motivations, but by the foods they choose to exclude (see the glossary below). Some people exclude red meat only; some also exclude chicken or fish; others also exclude eggs; and still others exclude milk and milk products as well. In fact, finding agreement on the definition of the term *vegetarian* is a challenge.[1]

As you will see, though, the foods a person *excludes* are not nearly as important as the foods a person *includes* in the diet. Vegetarian diets that include a variety of whole grains, vegetables, legumes, nuts, and fruits offer abundant complex carbohydrates and fibers, an assortment of vitamins and minerals, a mixture of phytochemicals, and little fat—characteristics that reflect current dietary recommendations aimed at promoting health and reducing obesity. Each of these foods—whole grains, vegetables, legumes, nuts, and fruits—independently reduces the risk for several chronic diseases.[2] This highlight examines the health benefits and potential problems of vegetarian diets and shows how to plan a well-balanced vegetarian diet.

GLOSSARY

lactovegetarians: people who include milk and milk products, but exclude meat, poultry, fish, seafood, and eggs from their diets.
• **lacto** = milk

lacto-ovo-vegetarians: people who include milk, milk products, and eggs, but exclude meat, poultry, fish, and seafood from their diets.
• **ovo** = egg

macrobiotic diets: extremely restrictive diets limited to a few grains and vegetables; based on metaphysical beliefs and not on nutrition. A macrobiotic diet might consist of brown rice, miso soup, and sea vegetables, for example.

meat replacements: products formulated to look and taste like meat, fish, or poultry; usually made of textured vegetable protein.

omnivores: people who have no formal restriction on the eating of any foods.
• **omni** = all
• **vores** = to eat

tempeh (TEM-pay): a fermented soybean food, rich in protein and fiber.

textured vegetable protein: processed soybean protein used in vegetarian products such as soy burgers; see also *meat replacements*.

tofu (TOE-foo): a curd made from soybeans, rich in protein and often fortified with calcium; used in many Asian and vegetarian dishes in place of meat.

vegans (VEE-gans): people who exclude all animal-derived foods (including meat, poultry, fish, eggs, and dairy products) from their diets; also called **pure vegetarians, strict vegetarians,** or **total vegetarians.**

vegetarians: a general term used to describe people who exclude meat, poultry, fish, or other animal-derived foods from their diets.

Health Benefits of Vegetarian Diets

Research on the health implications of vegetarian diets would be relatively easy if vegetarians differed from other people only in not eating meat. Many vegetarians, however, have also adopted lifestyles that may differ from many **omnivores**: they typically use no tobacco or illicit drugs, use little (if any) alcohol, and are physically active. Researchers must account for these lifestyle differences before they can determine which aspects of health correlate just with diet. Even then, *correlations* merely reveal what health factors *go with* the vegetarian diet, not what health effects may be *caused by* the diet. Despite these limitations, research findings suggest that well-planned vegetarian diets offer sound nutrition and health benefits to adults.[3] Dietary patterns that include very little, if any, meat may even increase life expectancy.[4]

Weight Control

In general, vegetarians maintain a lower and healthier body weight than nonvegetarians.[5] Vegetarians' lower body weights correlate with their high intakes of fiber and low intakes of fat. Because obesity impairs health in a number of ways, this gives vegetarians a health advantage.

Blood Pressure

Vegetarians tend to have lower blood pressure and lower rates of hypertension than nonvegetarians. Appropriate body weight helps to maintain a healthy blood pressure, as does a diet low in total fat and saturated fat and high in fiber, fruits, vegetables, and soy protein.[6] Lifestyle factors also influence blood pressure: smoking and alcohol intake raise blood pressure, and physical activity lowers it.

Heart Disease

The incidence of heart disease and related deaths is much lower for vegetarians than for meat eaters. The dietary factor most directly related to heart disease is saturated animal fat, and in general, vegetarian diets are lower in total fat, saturated fat, and cholesterol than typical meat-based diets.[7] The fats common in plant-based diets—the monounsaturated fats of olives, seeds, and nuts and the polyunsaturated fats of vegetable oils—are associated with a decreased risk of heart disease.[8] Furthermore, vegetarian diets are generally higher in dietary fiber, antioxidant vitamins, and phytochemicals—all factors that help control blood lipids and protect against heart disease.[9]

Many vegetarians include soy products such as **tofu** in their diets. Soy products may help to protect against heart disease because they contain polyunsaturated fats, fiber, vitamins, and minerals, and little saturated fat.[10] Even when intakes of energy, protein, carbohydrate, total fat, saturated fat, unsaturated fat, alcohol, and fiber are the same, people eating meals based on tofu have lower blood cholesterol and triglyceride levels than those eating meat. Some research suggests that soy protein and phytochemicals may be responsible for some of these health benefits (as Highlight 13 explains in greater detail).[11]

Cancer

Vegetarians have a significantly lower rate of cancer than the general population. Their low cancer rates may be due to their high intakes of fruits and vegetables (as Highlight 11 explains). In fact, the ratio of vegetables to meat may be the most relevant dietary factor responsible for cancer prevention.[12]

Some scientific findings indicate that vegetarian diets are associated not only with lower cancer mortality in general, but also with lower incidence of cancer at specific sites as well, most notably, colon cancer.[13] People with colon cancer seem to eat more meat, more saturated fat, and fewer vegetables than do people without colon cancer. High-protein, high-fat, low-fiber diets create an environment in the colon that promotes the development of cancer in some people. A high-meat diet has been associated with stomach cancer as well.[14]

Other Diseases

In addition to obesity, hypertension, heart disease, and cancer, vegetarian diets may help prevent diabetes, osteoporosis, diverticular disease, gallstones, and rheumatoid arthritis.[15] These health benefits of a vegetarian diet depend on wise diet planning.

Vegetarian Diet Planning

The vegetarian has the same meal-planning task as any other person—using a variety of foods to deliver all the needed nutrients within an energy allowance that maintains a healthy body weight (as discussed in Chapter 2). Vegetarians who include milk products and eggs can meet recommendations for most nutrients about as easily as nonvegetarians. Such diets provide enough energy, protein, and other nutrients to support the health of adults and the growth of children and adolescents.

Vegetarians who exclude milk products and eggs can select legumes, nuts, and seeds and products made from them, such as peanut butter, **tempeh,** and tofu, from the meat group. Those who do not use milk can use soy "milk"—a product made from soybeans that provides similar nutrients if fortified with calcium, vitamin D, and vitamin B_{12}.

The MyPyramid resources include tips for planning vegetarian diets using the USDA Food Guide. In addition, several food guides have been developed specifically for vegetarian diets.[16] They all address the particular nutrition concerns of vegetarians, but differ slightly. Figure H2-1 presents one version. When selecting from the vegetable and fruit groups, vegetarians should emphasize particularly good sources of calcium and iron, respectively. Green leafy vegetables, for example, provide almost five times as much calcium per serving as other vegetables. Similarly, dried fruits deserve special notice in the fruit group because they deliver six

FIGURE H2-1 An Example of a Vegetarian Food Pyramid

Review Figure 2–1 and Table 2–3 to find recommended daily amounts from each food group, serving size equivalents, examples of common foods within each group, and the most notable nutrients for each group. Tips for planning a vegetarian diet can be found at **MyPyramid.gov.**

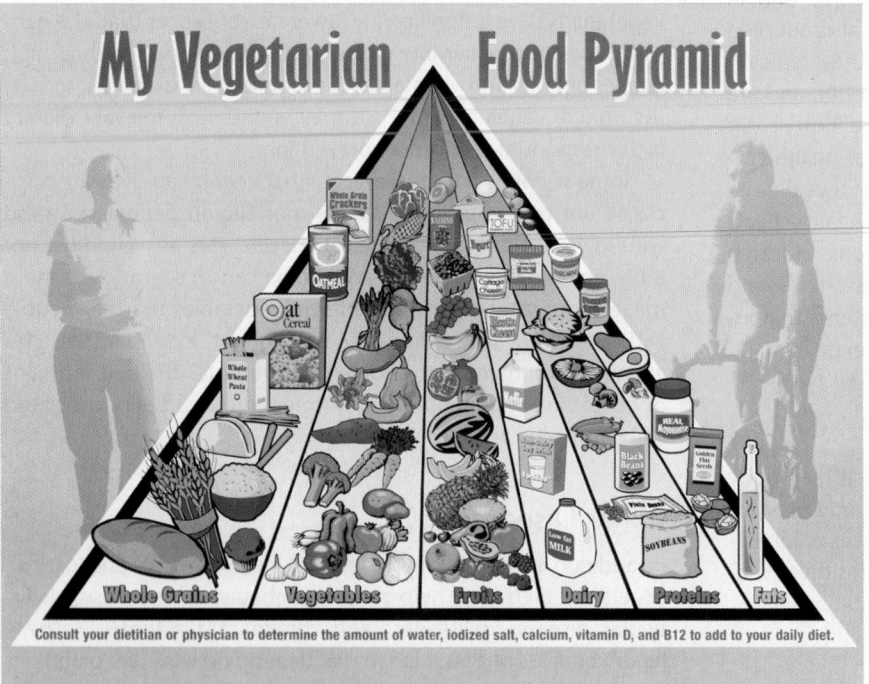

Consult your dietitian or physician to determine the amount of water, iodized salt, calcium, vitamin D, and B12 to add to your daily diet.

SOURCE: © GC Nutrition Council, 2006, adapted from USDA 2005 Dietary Guidelines and www.mypyramid.gov. Copies can be ordered from 301-680-6717.

times as much iron as other fruits. The milk group features fortified soy milks for those who do not use milk, cheese, or yogurt. The meat group is called "proteins" and includes legumes, soy products, nuts, and seeds. A group for oils encourages the use of vegetable oils, nuts, and seeds rich in unsaturated fats and omega-3 fatty acids. To ensure adequate intakes of vitamin B_{12}, vitamin D, and calcium, vegetarians need to select fortified foods or take supplements daily. The vegetarian food pyramid is flexible enough that a variety of people can use it: people who have adopted various vegetarian diets, those who want to make the transition to a vegetarian diet, and those who simply want to include more plant-based meals in their diet. Like MyPyramid, this vegetarian food pyramid also encourages physical activity.

Most vegetarians easily obtain large quantities of the nutrients that are abundant in plant foods: thiamin, folate, and vitamins B_6, C, A, and E. Vegetarian food guides help to ensure adequate intakes of the main nutrients vegetarian diets might otherwise lack: protein, iron, zinc, calcium, vitamin B_{12}, vitamin D, and omega-3 fatty acids.

Protein

The protein RDA for vegetarians is the same as for others, although some have suggested that it should be higher because of the lower digestibility of plant proteins.[17] **Lacto-ovo-vegetarians,** who use animal-derived foods such as milk and eggs, receive high-quality proteins and are likely to meet their protein needs. Even those

who adopt only plant-based diets are likely to meet protein needs provided that their energy intakes are adequate and the protein sources varied.[18] The proteins of whole grains, legumes, seeds, nuts, and vegetables can provide adequate amounts of all the amino acids. An advantage of many vegetarian sources of protein is that they are generally lower in saturated fat than meats and are often higher in fiber and richer in some vitamins and minerals.

Vegetarians sometimes use **meat replacements** made of **textured vegetable protein** (soy protein). These foods are formulated to look and taste like meat, fish, or poultry. Many of these products are fortified to provide the vitamins and minerals found in animal sources of protein. A wise vegetarian learns to use a variety of whole, unrefined foods often and commercially prepared foods less frequently. Vegetarians may also use soy products such as tofu to bolster protein intake.

Iron

Getting enough iron can be a problem even for meat eaters, and those who eat no meat must pay special attention to their iron intake. The iron in plant foods such as legumes, dark green leafy vegetables, iron-fortified cereals, and whole-grain breads and cereals is poorly absorbed.[19] Because iron absorption from a vegetarian diet is low, the iron RDA for vegetarians is higher than for others (see Chapter 13 for more details).

Fortunately, the body seems to adapt to a vegetarian diet by absorbing iron more efficiently. Furthermore, iron absorption is enhanced by vitamin C, and vegetarians typically eat many vitamin C–rich fruits and vegetables. Consequently, vegetarians suffer no more iron deficiency than other people do.[20]

Zinc

Zinc is similar to iron in that meat is its richest food source, and zinc from plant sources is not well absorbed.[21] In addition, soy, which is commonly used as a meat alternative in vegetarian meals, interferes with zinc absorption. Nevertheless, most vegetarian adults are not zinc deficient. Perhaps the best advice to vegetarians regarding zinc is to eat a variety of nutrient-dense foods; include whole grains, nuts, and legumes such as black-eyed peas, pinto beans, and kidney beans; and maintain an adequate energy intake. For those who include seafood in their diets, oysters, crabmeat, and shrimp are rich in zinc.

Calcium

The calcium intakes of **lactovegetarians** are similar to those of the general population, but people who use no milk products risk deficiency. Careful planners select calcium-rich foods, such as calcium-fortified juices, soy milk, and breakfast cereals, in ample quantities regularly. This advice is especially important for children and adolescents. Soy formulas for infants are fortified with calcium and can be used in cooking, even for adults. Other good calcium sources include figs, some legumes, some green vegetables such as broccoli and turnip greens, some nuts such as almonds, certain seeds such as sesame seeds, and calcium-set tofu.* The choices should be varied because calcium absorption from some plant foods may be limited (as Chapter 12 explains).

Vitamin B$_{12}$

The requirement for vitamin B$_{12}$ is small, but this vitamin is found only in animal-derived foods. Consequently, vegetarians, in general, and **vegans** who eat no foods of animal original, in particular, may not get enough vitamin B$_{12}$ in their diets.[22] Fermented soy products such as tempeh may contain some vitamin B$_{12}$ from the bacteria, but unfortunately, much of the vitamin B$_{12}$ found in these products may be an inactive form. Seaweeds such as nori and chlorella supply some vitamin B$_{12}$, but not much, and excessive intakes of these foods can lead to iodine toxicity. To defend against vitamin B$_{12}$ deficiency, vegans must rely on vitamin B$_{12}$-fortified sources (such as soy milk or breakfast cereals) or supplements. Without vitamin B$_{12}$, the nerves suffer damage, leading to such health consequences as loss of vision.

Vitamin D

People who do not use vitamin D–fortified foods and do not receive enough exposure to sunlight to synthesize adequate vitamin D may need supplements to defend against bone loss. This is particularly important for infants, children, and older adults. In northern climates during winter months, young children on vegan diets can readily develop rickets, the vitamin D–deficiency disease.

Omega-3 Fatty Acids

Both Chapter 5 and Highlight 5 describe the health benefits of unsaturated fats, most notably the omega-3 fatty acids com-

*Calcium salts are often added during processing to coagulate the tofu.

monly found in fatty fish. To obtain sufficient amounts of omega-3 fatty acids, vegetarians need to consume flaxseed, walnuts, soybeans, and their oils.

Healthy Food Choices

In general, adults who eat vegetarian diets have lowered their risks of mortality and several chronic diseases, including obesity, high blood pressure, heart disease, and cancer. But there is nothing mysterious or magical about the vegetarian diet; vegetarianism is not a religion like Buddhism or Hinduism, but merely an eating plan that selects plant foods to deliver needed nutrients. The quality of the diet depends not on whether it includes meat, but on whether the other food choices are nutritionally sound. A diet that includes ample fruits, vegetables, whole grains, legumes, nuts, and seeds is higher in fiber, antioxidant vitamins, and phytochemicals, and lower in saturated fats than meat-based diets. Variety is key to nutritional adequacy in a vegetarian diet. Restrictive plans, such as **macrobiotic diets,** that limit selections to a few grains and vegetables cannot possibly deliver a full array of nutrients.

If not properly balanced, any diet—vegetarian or otherwise—can lack nutrients. Poorly planned vegetarian diets typically lack iron, zinc, calcium, vitamin B$_{12}$, and vitamin D; without planning, the meat eater's diet may lack vitamin A, vitamin C, folate, and fiber, among others. Quite simply, the negative health aspects of any diet, including vegetarian diets, reflect poor diet planning. Careful attention to energy intake and specific problem nutrients can ensure adequacy.

Keep in mind, too, that diet is only one factor influencing health. Whatever a diet consists of, its context is also important: no smoking, alcohol consumption in moderation (if at all), regular physical activity, adequate rest, and medical attention when needed all contribute to a healthy life. Establishing these healthy habits early in life seems to be the most important step one can take to reduce the risks of later diseases (as Highlight 16 explains).

REFERENCES

1. S. I. Barr and G. E. Chapman, Perceptions and practices of self-defined current vegetarian, former vegetarian, and nonvegetarian women, *Journal of the American Dietetic Association* 102 (2002): 354-360.

2. J. Sabate, The contribution of vegetarian diets to human health, *Forum of Nutrition* 56 (2003): 218-220.

3. Position of the American Dietetic Association and Dietitians of Canada: Vegetarian diets, *Journal of the American Dietetic Association* 103 (2003): 748-765; J. Sabaté, The contribution of vegetarian diets to health and disease: A paradigm shift? *American Journal of Clinical Nutrition* 78 (2003): 502S-507S.

4. P. N. Singh, J. Sabaté, and G. E. Fraser, Does low meat consumption increase life expectancy in humans? *American Journal of Clinical Nutrition* 78 (2003): 526S-532S.

5. P. K. Newby, K. L. Tucker, and A. Wolk, Risk of overweight and obesity among semivegetarian, lactovegetarian, and vegan women, *American Journal of Clinical Nutrition* 81 (2005): 1267-1274; N. Brathwaite and coauthors, Obesity, diabetes, hypertension, and vegetarian status among Seventh-Day Adventists in Barbados, *Ethnicity and Disease* 13 (2003): 34-39; E. H. Haddad and J. S. Tanzman, What do vegetarians in the United States eat? *American Journal of Clinical Nutrition* 78 (2003): 626S-632S.

6. S. E. Berkow and N. D. Barnard, Blood pressure regulation and vegetarian diets, *Nutrition Reviews* 63 (2005): 1-8; L. J. Appel, The effects of protein intake on blood pressure and cardiovascular disease, *Current Opinion in Lipidology* 14 (2003): 55-59.

7. J. E. Cade and coauthors, The UK Women's Cohort Study: Comparison of vegetarians, fish-eaters, and meat-eaters, *Public Health Nutrition* 7 (2004): 871-878; E. H. Haddad and J. S. Tanzman, What do vegetarians in the United States eat? *American Journal of Clinical Nutrition* 78 (2003): 626S-632S.

8. *Third Report of the National Cholesterol Education Program (NCEP) Expert Panel on Detection, Evaluation, and Treatment of High Blood Cholesterol in Adults (Adult Treatment Panel III)*, NIH publication no. 02-5215 (Bethesda, Md.: National Heart, Lung, and Blood Institute, 2002).

9. F. B. Hu, Plant-based foods and prevention of cardiovascular disease: An overview, *American Journal of Clinical Nutrition* 78 (2003): 544S-551S.

10. F. M. Sacks and coauthors, Soy protein, isoflavones, and cardiovascular health: An American Heart Association Science Advisory for professionals from the Nutrition Committee, *Circulation* 113 (2006): 1034-1044.

11. B. L. McVeigh and coauthors, Effect of soy protein varying in isoflavone content on serum lipids in healthy young men, *American Journal of Clinical Nutrition* 83 (2006): 244-251; D. Lukaczer and coauthors, Effect of a low glycemic index diet with soy protein and phytosterols on CVD risk factors in postmenopausal women, *Nutrition* 22 (2006): 104-113; M. S. Rosell and coauthors, Soy intake and blood cholesterol concentrations: A cross-sectional study of 1033 pre- and postmenopausal women in the Oxford arm of the European Prospective Investigation into Cancer and Nutrition, *American Journal of Clinical Nutrition* 80 (2004): 1391-1396; S. Tonstad, K. Smerud, and L. Hoie, A comparison of the effects of 2 doses of soy protein or casein on serum lipids, serum lipoproteins, and plasma total homocysteine in hypercholesterolemic subjects, *American Journal of Clinical Nutrition* 76 (2002): 78-84.

12. M. Kapiszewska, A vegetable to meat consumption ratio as a relevant factor determining cancer preventive diet: The Mediterranean versus other European countries, *Forum of Nutrition* 59 (2006): 130–153.

13. M. H. Lewin and coauthors, Red meat enhances the colonic formation of the DNA adduct O6-carboxymethyl guanine: Implications for colorectal cancer risk, *Cancer Research* 66 (2006): 1859-1865.

14. H. Chen and coauthors, Dietary patterns and adenocarcinoma of the esophagus and distal stomach, *American Journal of Clinical Nutrition* 75 (2002): 137-144.

15. C. Leitzmann, Vegetarian diets: What are the advantages? *Forum of Nutrition* 57 (2005): 147-156.

16. M. Virginia, V. Melina, and A. R. Mangels, A new food guide for North American vegetarians, *Journal of the American Dietetic Association* 103 (2003): 771-775; C. A. Venti and C. S. Johnston, Modified food guide pyramid for lactovegetarians and vegans, *Journal of Nutrition* 132 (2002): 1050-1054.

17. Venti and Johnston, 2002; V. Messina and A. R. Mangels, Considerations in planning vegan diets: Children, *Journal of the American Dietetic Association* 101 (2001): 661-669.

18. Position of the American Dietetic Association and Dietitians of Canada, 2003.

19. J. R. Hunt, Moving toward a plant-based diet: Are iron and zinc at risk? *Nutrition Reviews* 60 (2002): 127-134.

20. C. L. Larsson and G. K. Johansson, Dietary intake and nutritional status of young vegans and omnivores in Sweden, *American Journal of Clinical Nutrition* 76 (2002): 100-106.

21. Hunt, 2002.

22. W. Herrmann and coauthors, Vitamin B12 status, particularly holotranscobalamin II and methylmalonic acid concentrations, and hyperhomocysteinemia in vegetarians, *American Journal of Clinical Nutrition* 78 (2003): 131-136.

Foodcollection/Getty Images

Thomson NOW! Throughout this chapter, the ThomsonNOW logo indicates an opportunity for online self-study, linking you to interactive tutorials and videos based on your level of understanding.

www.thomsonedu.com/thomsonnow

Figure 3.8: Animated! The Digestive Fate of a Sandwich

Figure 3.11: Animated! The Vascular System

Nutrition Portfolio Journal

Nutrition in Your Life

Have you ever wondered what happens to the food you eat after you swallow it? Or how your body extracts nutrients from food? Have you ever marveled at how it all just seems to happen? Follow foods as they travel through the digestive system. Learn how a healthy digestive system transforms whatever food you give it—whether sirloin steak and potatoes or tofu and brussels sprouts—into the nutrients that will nourish the cells of your body.

Digestion, Absorption, and Transport

CHAPTER OUTLINE

Digestion • Anatomy of the Digestive Tract • The Muscular Action of Digestion • The Secretions of Digestion • The Final Stage

Absorption • Anatomy of the Absorptive System • A Closer Look at the Intestinal Cells

The Circulatory Systems • The Vascular System • The Lymphatic System

The Health and Regulation of the GI Tract • Gastrointestinal Bacteria • Gastrointestinal Hormones and Nerve Pathways • The System at Its Best

HIGHLIGHT 3 Common Digestive Problems

This chapter takes you on the journey that transforms the foods you eat into the nutrients featured in the later chapters. Then it follows the nutrients as they travel through the intestinal cells and into the body to do their work. This introduction presents a general overview of the processes common to all nutrients; later chapters discuss the specifics of digesting and absorbing individual nutrients.

Digestion

Digestion is the body's ingenious way of breaking down foods into nutrients in preparation for **absorption.** In the process, it overcomes many challenges without any conscious effort on your part. Consider these challenges:

1. Human beings breathe, eat, and drink through their mouths. Air taken in through the mouth must go to the lungs; food and liquid must go to the stomach. The throat must be arranged so that swallowing and breathing don't interfere with each other.

2. Below the lungs lies the diaphragm, a dome of muscle that separates the upper half of the major body cavity from the lower half. Food must pass through this wall to reach the stomach.

3. The materials within the digestive tract should be kept moving forward, slowly but steadily, at a pace that permits all reactions to reach completion.

4. To move through the system, food must be lubricated with fluids. Too much would form a liquid that would flow too rapidly; too little would form a paste too dry and compact to move at all. The amount of fluids must be regulated to keep the intestinal contents at the right consistency to move smoothly along.

5. When the digestive enzymes break food down, they need it in a finely divided form, suspended in enough liquid so that every particle is accessible. Once digestion is complete and the needed nutrients have been absorbed out of the tract and into the body, the system must excrete the remaining residue. Excreting all the water along with the solid residue, however, would be both wasteful and messy. Some water must be withdrawn to leave a paste just solid enough to be smooth and easy to pass.

6. The enzymes of the digestive tract are designed to digest carbohydrate, fat, and protein. The walls of the tract, composed of living cells, are also made of

digestion: the process by which food is broken down into absorbable units.
• **digestion** = take apart

absorption: the uptake of nutrients by the cells of the small intestine for transport into either the blood or the lymph.
• **absorb** = suck in

The process of digestion transforms all kinds of *foods* into *nutrients*.

◆ The process of chewing is called **mastication** (mass-tih-KAY-shun).

gastrointestinal (GI) tract: the digestive tract. The principal organs are the stomach and intestines.
• **gastro** = stomach
• **intestinalis** = intestine

carbohydrate, fat, and protein. These cells need protection against the action of the powerful digestive juices that they secrete.

7. Once waste matter has reached the end of the tract, it must be excreted, but it would be inconvenient and embarrassing if this function occurred continuously. Provision must be made for periodic, voluntary evacuation.

The following sections show how the body elegantly and efficiently handles these challenges.

Anatomy of the Digestive Tract

The **gastrointestinal (GI) tract** is a flexible muscular tube that extends from the mouth, through the esophagus, stomach, small intestine, large intestine, and rectum to the anus. Figure 3-1 traces the path followed by food from one end to the other. In a sense, the human body surrounds the GI tract. The inner space within the GI tract, called the **lumen**, is continuous from one end to the other. (GI anatomy terms appear in boldface type and are defined in the accompanying glossary.) Only when a nutrient or other substance finally penetrates the GI tract's wall does it enter the body proper; many materials pass through the GI tract without being digested or absorbed.

Mouth The process of digestion begins in the **mouth.** As you chew, ◆ your teeth crush large pieces of food into smaller ones, and fluids from foods, beverages, and salivary glands blend with these pieces to ease swallowing. Fluids also help dissolve the food so that you can taste it; only particles in solution can react with taste buds. When stimulated, the taste buds detect one, or a combination, of the four basic taste sensations: sweet, sour, bitter, and salty. Some scientists also include the flavor associated with monosodium glutamate, sometimes called *savory* or its Asian name, *umami* (oo-MOM-ee). In addition to these chemical triggers, aroma, texture, and temperature also affect a food's flavor. In fact, the sense of smell is thousands of times more sensitive than the sense of taste.

The tongue allows you not only to taste food, but also to move food around the mouth, facilitating chewing and swallowing. When you swallow a mouthful of

GLOSSARY OF GI ANATOMY TERMS

These terms are listed in order from start to end of the digestive system.

lumen (LOO-men): the space within a vessel, such as the intestine.

mouth: the oral cavity containing the tongue and teeth.

pharynx (FAIR-inks): the passageway leading from the nose and mouth to the larynx and esophagus, respectively.

epiglottis (epp-ih-GLOTT-iss): cartilage in the throat that guards the entrance to the trachea and prevents fluid or food from entering it when a person swallows.
• **epi** = upon (over)
• **glottis** = back of tongue

esophagus (ee-SOFF-ah-gus): the food pipe; the conduit from the mouth to the stomach.

sphincter (SFINK-ter): a circular muscle surrounding, and able to close, a body opening. Sphincters are found at specific points along the GI tract and regulate the flow of food particles.
• **sphincter** = band (binder)

esophageal (ee-SOF-ah-GEE-al) **sphincter:** a sphincter muscle at the upper or lower end of the esophagus. The *lower esophageal sphincter* is also called the *cardiac sphincter.*

stomach: a muscular, elastic, saclike portion of the digestive tract that grinds and churns swallowed food, mixing it with acid and enzymes to form chyme.

pyloric (pie-LORE-ic) **sphincter:** the circular muscle that separates the stomach from the small intestine and regulates the flow of partially digested food into the small intestine; also called *pylorus* or *pyloric valve.*
• **pylorus** = gatekeeper

small intestine: a 10-foot length of small-diameter intestine that is the major site of digestion of

food and absorption of nutrients. Its segments are the duodenum, jejunum, and ileum.

gallbladder: the organ that stores and concentrates bile. When it receives the signal that fat is present in the duodenum, the gallbladder contracts and squirts bile through the bile duct into the duodenum.

pancreas: a gland that secretes digestive enzymes and juices into the duodenum. (The pancreas also secretes hormones into the blood that help to maintain glucose homeostasis.)

duodenum (doo-oh-DEEN-um, doo-ODD-num): the top portion of the small intestine (about "12 fingers' breadth" long in ancient terminology).
• **duodecim** = twelve

jejunum (je-JOON-um): the first two-fifths of the small intestine beyond the duodenum.

ileum (ILL-ee-um): the last segment of the small intestine.

ileocecal (ill-ee-oh-SEEK-ul) **valve:** the sphincter separating the small and large intestines.

large intestine or **colon** (COAL-un): the lower portion of intestine that completes the digestive process. Its segments are the ascending colon, the transverse colon, the descending colon, and the sigmoid colon.
• **sigmoid** = shaped like the letter S (sigma in Greek)

appendix: a narrow blind sac extending from the beginning of the colon that stores lymph cells.

rectum: the muscular terminal part of the intestine, extending from the sigmoid colon to the anus.

anus (AY-nus): the terminal outlet of the GI tract.

digestive system: all the organs and glands associated with the ingestion and digestion of food.

FIGURE 3–1 The Gastrointestinal Tract

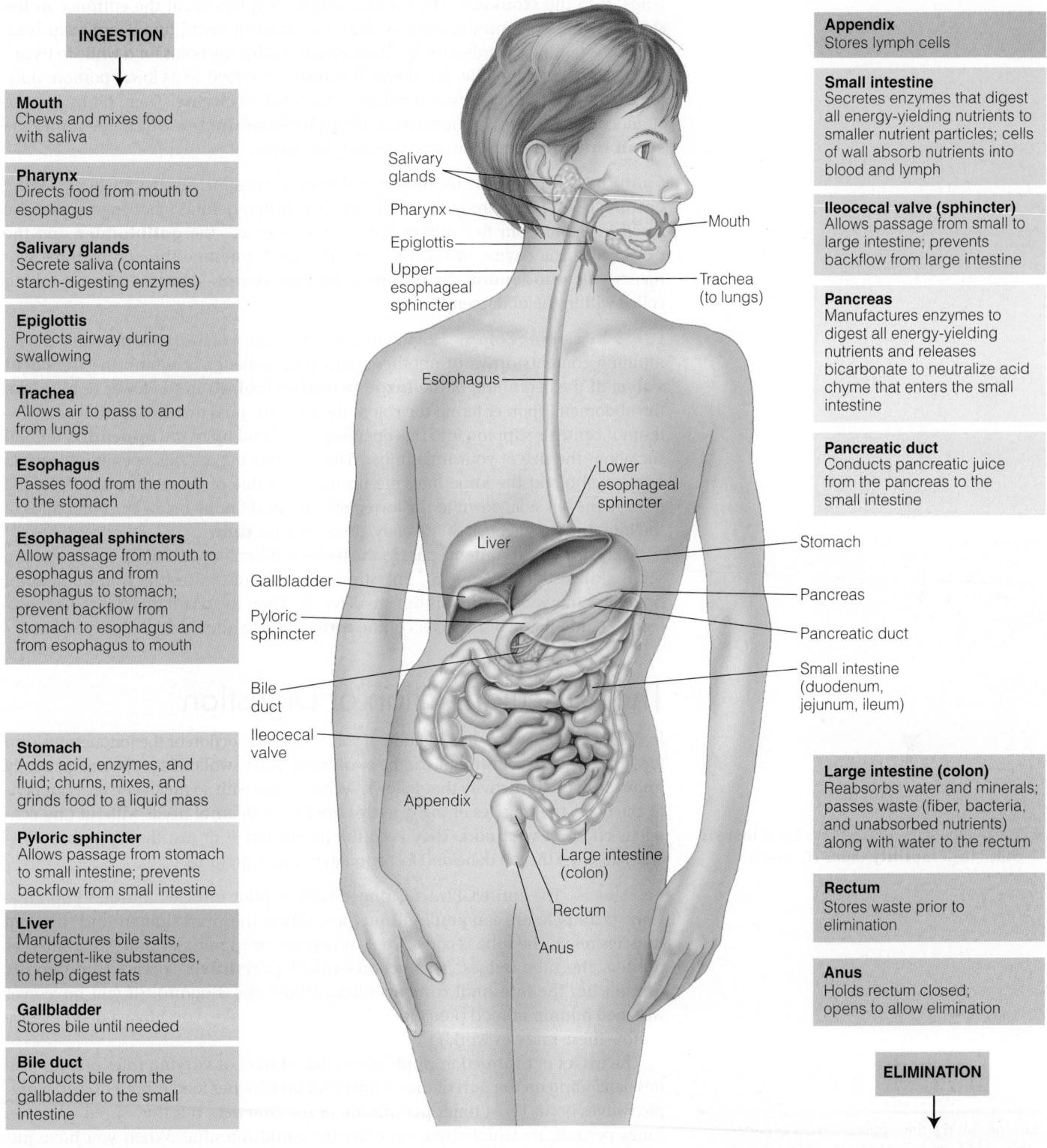

INGESTION

Mouth
Chews and mixes food with saliva

Pharynx
Directs food from mouth to esophagus

Salivary glands
Secrete saliva (contains starch-digesting enzymes)

Epiglottis
Protects airway during swallowing

Trachea
Allows air to pass to and from lungs

Esophagus
Passes food from the mouth to the stomach

Esophageal sphincters
Allow passage from mouth to esophagus and from esophagus to stomach; prevent backflow from stomach to esophagus and from esophagus to mouth

Stomach
Adds acid, enzymes, and fluid; churns, mixes, and grinds food to a liquid mass

Pyloric sphincter
Allows passage from stomach to small intestine; prevents backflow from small intestine

Liver
Manufactures bile salts, detergent-like substances, to help digest fats

Gallbladder
Stores bile until needed

Bile duct
Conducts bile from the gallbladder to the small intestine

Appendix
Stores lymph cells

Small intestine
Secretes enzymes that digest all energy-yielding nutrients to smaller nutrient particles; cells of wall absorb nutrients into blood and lymph

Ileocecal valve (sphincter)
Allows passage from small to large intestine; prevents backflow from large intestine

Pancreas
Manufactures enzymes to digest all energy-yielding nutrients and releases bicarbonate to neutralize acid chyme that enters the small intestine

Pancreatic duct
Conducts pancreatic juice from the pancreas to the small intestine

Large intestine (colon)
Reabsorbs water and minerals; passes waste (fiber, bacteria, and unabsorbed nutrients) along with water to the rectum

Rectum
Stores waste prior to elimination

Anus
Holds rectum closed; opens to allow elimination

ELIMINATION

Labels on figure:
Salivary glands
Pharynx
Epiglottis
Upper esophageal sphincter
Mouth
Trachea (to lungs)
Esophagus
Lower esophageal sphincter
Liver
Gallbladder
Pyloric sphincter
Bile duct
Ileocecal valve
Appendix
Stomach
Pancreas
Pancreatic duct
Small intestine (duodenum, jejunum, ileum)
Large intestine (colon)
Rectum
Anus

food, it passes through the **pharynx,** a short tube that is shared by both the **digestive system** and the respiratory system. To bypass the entrance to your lungs, the **epiglottis** closes off your air passages so that you don't choke when you swallow, thus resolving the first challenge. (Choking is discussed on pp. 92–93.) After a mouthful of food has been swallowed, it is called a **bolus**.

bolus (BOH-lus): a portion; with respect to food, the amount swallowed at one time.
• **bolos** = lump

Esophagus to the Stomach The **esophagus** has a **sphincter** muscle at each end. During a swallow, the upper **esophageal sphincter** opens. The bolus then slides down the esophagus, which passes through a hole in the diaphragm (challenge 2) to the **stomach.** The lower esophageal sphincter at the entrance to the stomach closes behind the bolus so that it proceeds forward and doesn't slip back into the esophagus (challenge 3). The stomach retains the bolus for a while in its upper portion. Little by little, the stomach transfers the food to its lower portion, adds juices to it, and grinds it to a semiliquid mass called **chyme.** Then, bit by bit, the stomach releases the chyme through the **pyloric sphincter,** which opens into the **small intestine** and then closes behind the chyme.

Small Intestine At the beginning of the small intestine, the chyme bypasses the opening from the common bile duct, which is dripping fluids (challenge 4) into the small intestine from two organs outside the GI tract—the **gallbladder** and the **pancreas.** The chyme travels on down the small intestine through its three segments—the **duodenum,** the **jejunum,** and the **ileum**—almost 10 feet of tubing coiled within the abdomen.*

Large Intestine (Colon) Having traveled the length of the small intestine, the remaining contents arrive at another sphincter (challenge 3 again): the **ileocecal valve,** at the beginning of the **large intestine (colon)** in the lower right side of the abdomen. Upon entering the colon, the contents pass another opening. Any intestinal contents slipping into this opening would end up in the **appendix,** a blind sac about the size of your little finger. The contents bypass this opening, however, and travel along the large intestine up the right side of the abdomen, across the front to the left side, down to the lower left side, and finally below the other folds of the intestines to the back of the body, above the **rectum.**

As the intestinal contents pass to the rectum, the colon withdraws water, leaving semisolid waste (challenge 5). The strong muscles of the rectum and anal canal hold back this waste until it is time to defecate. Then the rectal muscles relax (challenge 7), and the two sphincters of the **anus** open to allow passage of the waste.

The Muscular Action of Digestion

In the mouth, chewing, the addition of saliva, and the action of the tonguetransform food into a coarse mash that can be swallowed. After swallowing, you are generally unaware of all the activity that follows. As is the case with so much else that happens in the body, the muscles of the digestive tract meet internal needs without any conscious effort on your part. They keep things moving ◆ at just the right pace, slow enough to get the job done and fast enough to make progress.

◆ The ability of the GI tract muscles to move is called their **motility** (moh-TIL-ih-tee).

Peristalsis The entire GI tract is ringed with circular muscles. Surrounding these rings of muscle are longitudinal muscles. When the rings tighten and the long muscles relax, the tube is constricted. When the rings relax and the long muscles tighten, the tube bulges. This action—called **peristalsis**—occurs continuously and pushes the intestinal contents along (challenge 3 again). (If you have ever watched a lump of food pass along the body of a snake, you have a good picture of how these muscles work.)

The waves of contraction ripple along the GI tract at varying rates and intensities depending on the part of the GI tract and on whether food is present. For example, waves occur three times per minute in the stomach, but they speed up to ten times per minute when chyme reaches the small intestine. When you have just eaten a meal, the waves are slow and continuous; when the GI tract is empty, the intestine is quiet except for periodic bursts of powerful rhythmic waves. Peristalsis,

chyme (KIME): the semiliquid mass of partly digested food expelled by the stomach into the duodenum.
• **chymos** = juice
peristalsis (per-ih-STALL-sis): wavelike muscular contractions of the GI tract that push its contents along.
• **peri** = around
• **stellein** = wrap

* The small intestine is almost 2½ times shorter in living adults than it is at death, when muscles are relaxed and elongated.

along with sphincter muscles located at key places, keeps things moving along.

Stomach Action The stomach has the thickest walls and strongest muscles of all the GI tract organs. In addition to the circular and longitudinal muscles, it has a third layer of diagonal muscles that also alternately contract and relax (see Figure 3-2). These three sets of muscles work to force the chyme downward, but the pyloric sphincter usually remains tightly closed, preventing the chyme from passing into the duodenum of the small intestine. As a result, the chyme is churned and forced down, hits the pyloric sphincter, and remains in the stomach. Meanwhile, the stomach wall releases gastric juices. When the chyme is completely liquefied, the pyloric sphincter opens briefly, about three times a minute, to allow small portions of chyme to pass through. At this point, the chyme no longer resembles food in the least.

Segmentation The circular muscles of the intestines rhythmically contract and squeeze their contents (see Figure 3-3). These contractions,

FIGURE 3–2 Stomach Muscles

The stomach has three layers of muscles.

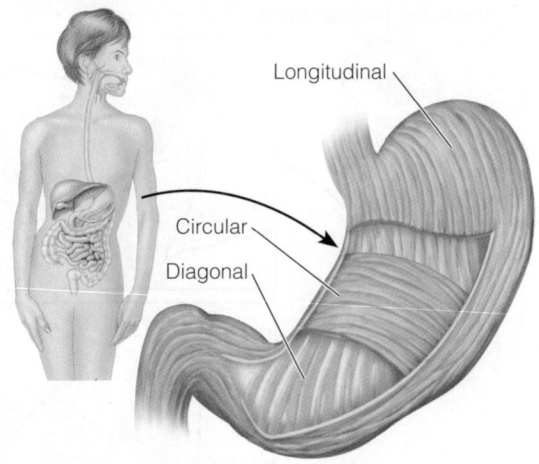

Longitudinal

Circular

Diagonal

FIGURE 3–3 Peristalsis and Segmentation

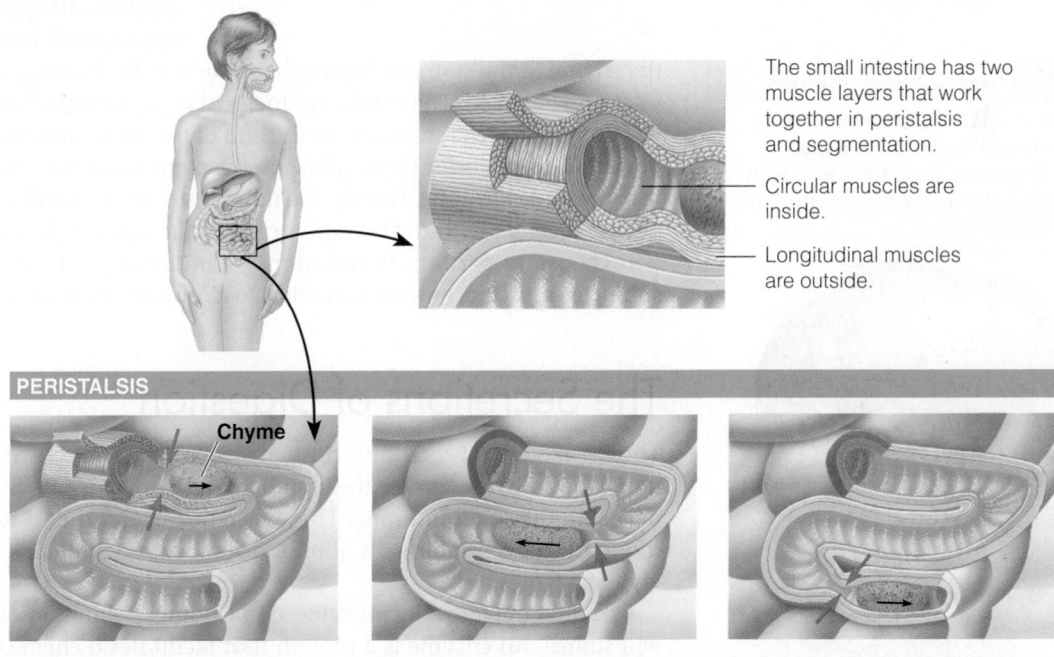

The small intestine has two muscle layers that work together in peristalsis and segmentation.

Circular muscles are inside.

Longitudinal muscles are outside.

PERISTALSIS

Chyme

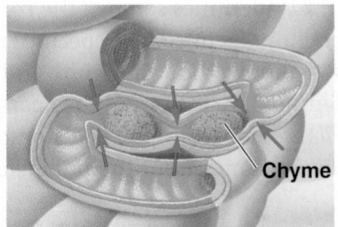

The inner circular muscles contract, tightening the tube and pushing the food forward in the intestine.

When the circular muscles relax, the outer longitudinal muscles contract, and the intestinal tube is loose.

As the circular and longitudinal muscles tighten and relax, the chyme moves ahead of the constriction.

SEGMENTATION

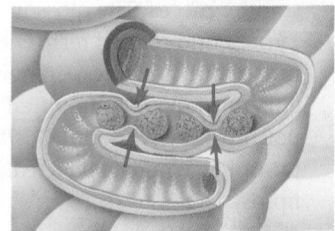

Chyme

Circular muscles contract, creating segments within the intestine.

As each set of circular muscles relaxes and contracts, the chyme is broken up and mixed with digestive juices.

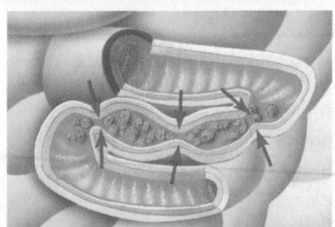

These alternating contractions, occurring 12 to 16 times per minute, continue to mix the chyme and bring the nutrients into contact with the intestinal lining for absorption.

FIGURE 3–4 An Example of a Sphincter Muscle

When the circular muscles of a sphincter contract, the passage closes; when they relax, the passage opens.

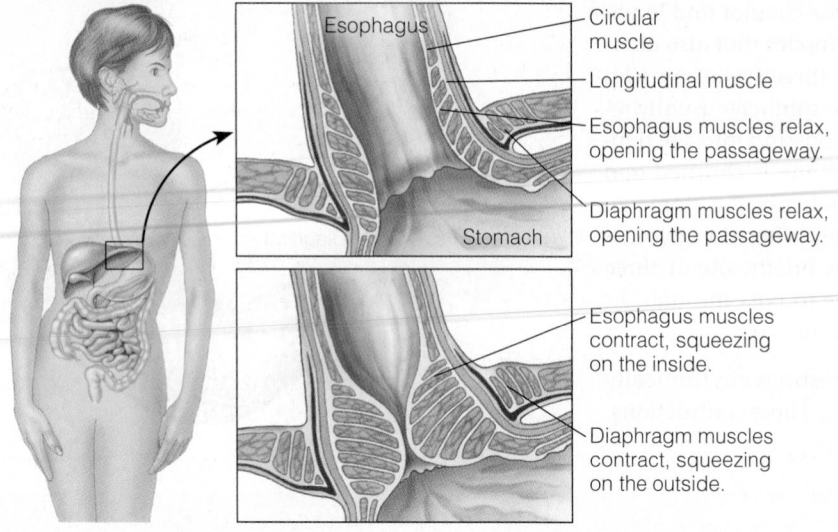

Esophagus

Circular muscle

Longitudinal muscle

Esophagus muscles relax, opening the passageway.

Diaphragm muscles relax, opening the passageway.

Stomach

Esophagus muscles contract, squeezing on the inside.

Diaphragm muscles contract, squeezing on the outside.

FIGURE 3–5 The Salivary Glands

The salivary glands secrete saliva into the mouth and begin the digestive process. Given the short time food is in the mouth, salivary enzymes contribute little to digestion.

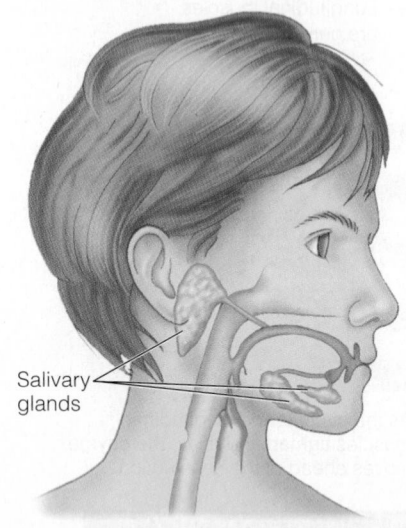

Salivary glands

segmentation (SEG-men-TAY-shun): a periodic squeezing or partitioning of the intestine at intervals along its length by its circular muscles.

reflux: a backward flow.
- **re** = back
- **flux** = flow

catalyst (CAT-uh-list): a compound that facilitates chemical reactions without itself being changed in the process.

called **segmentation**, mix the chyme and promote close contact with the digestive juices and the absorbing cells of the intestinal walls before letting the contents move slowly along. Figure 3-3 illustrates peristalsis and segmentation.

Sphincter Contractions Sphincter muscles periodically open and close, allowing the contents of the GI tract to move along at a controlled pace (challenge 3 again). At the top of the esophagus, the upper esophageal sphincter opens in response to swallowing. At the bottom of the esophagus, the lower esophageal sphincter (sometimes called the cardiac sphincter because of its proximity to the heart) prevents **reflux** of the stomach contents. At the bottom of the stomach, the pyloric sphincter, which stays closed most of the time, holds the chyme in the stomach long enough for it to be thoroughly mixed with gastric juice and liquefied. The pyloric sphincter also prevents the intestinal contents from backing up into the stomach. At the end of the small intestine, the ileocecal valve performs a similar function, allowing the contents of the small intestine to empty into the large intestine. Finally, the tightness of the rectal muscle is a kind of safety device; together with the two sphincters of the anus, it prevents elimination until you choose to perform it voluntarily (challenge 7). Figure 3-4 illustrates how sphincter muscles contract and relax to close and open passageways.

The Secretions of Digestion

The breakdown of food into nutrients requires secretions from five different organs: the salivary glands, the stomach, the pancreas, the liver (via the gallbladder), and the small intestine. These secretions enter the GI tract at various points along the way, bringing an abundance of water (challenge 3 again) and a variety of enzymes.

Enzymes are formally introduced in Chapter 6, but for now a simple definition will suffice. An enzyme is a protein that facilitates a chemical reaction—making a molecule, breaking a molecule apart, changing the arrangement of a molecule, or exchanging parts of molecules. As a **catalyst,** the enzyme itself remains unchanged. The enzymes involved in digestion facilitate a chemical reaction known as **hydrolysis**—the addition of water *(hydro)* to break *(lysis)* a molecule into smaller pieces. The glossary (p. 77) identifies some of the common **digestive enzymes** and related terms; later chapters introduce specific enzymes. When learning about enzymes, it helps to know that the word ending *-ase* denotes an enzyme. Enzymes are often identified by the organ they come from and the compounds they work on. *Gastric lipase*, for example, is a stomach enzyme that acts on lipids, whereas *pancreatic lipase* comes from the pancreas (and also works on lipids).

Saliva The **salivary glands**, shown in Figure 3-5, squirt just enough **saliva** to moisten each mouthful of food so that it can pass easily down the esophagus (challenge 4). (Digestive **glands** and their secretions are defined in the glossary on

p. 78.) The saliva contains water, salts, mucus, and enzymes that initiate the digestion of carbohydrates. Saliva also protects the teeth and the linings of the mouth, esophagus, and stomach from attack by substances that might harm them.

Gastric Juice In the stomach, **gastric glands** secrete **gastric juice,** a mixture of water, enzymes, and **hydrochloric acid,** which acts primarily in protein digestion. The acid is so strong that it causes the sensation of heartburn if it happens to reflux into the esophagus. Highlight 3, following this chapter, discusses heartburn, ulcers, and other common digestive problems.

The strong acidity of the stomach prevents bacterial growth and kills most bacteria that enter the body with food. It would destroy the cells of the stomach as well, but for their natural defenses. To protect themselves from gastric juice, the cells of the stomach wall secrete **mucus,** a thick, slippery, white substance that coats the cells, protecting them from the acid, enzymes, and disease-causing bacteria that might otherwise harm them (challenge 6).

Figure 3-6 shows how the strength of acids is measured—in **pH** ◆ units. Note that the acidity of gastric juice registers below "2" on the pH scale—stronger than vinegar. The stomach enzymes work most efficiently in the stomach's strong acid, but the salivary enzymes, which are swallowed with food, do not work in acid this strong. Consequently, the salivary digestion of carbohydrate gradually ceases when the stomach acid penetrates each newly swallowed bolus of food. When they enter the stomach, salivary enzymes become just other proteins to be digested.

Pancreatic Juice and Intestinal Enzymes By the time food leaves the stomach, digestion of all three energy nutrients (carbohydrates, fats, and proteins) has begun, and the action gains momentum in the small intestine. There the pancreas contributes digestive juices by way of ducts leading into the duodenum. The **pancreatic juice** contains enzymes that act on all three energy nutrients, and the cells of the intestinal wall also possess digestive enzymes on their surfaces.

In addition to enzymes, the pancreatic juice contains sodium **bicarbonate,** which is basic or alkaline—the opposite of the stomach's acid (review Figure 3-6). The pancreatic juice thus neutralizes the acidic chyme arriving in the small intestine from the stomach. From this point on, the chyme remains at a neutral or slightly alkaline pH. The enzymes of both the intestine and the pancreas work best in this environment.

Bile **Bile** also flows into the duodenum. The **liver** continuously produces bile, which is then concentrated and stored in the gallbladder. The gallbladder squirts

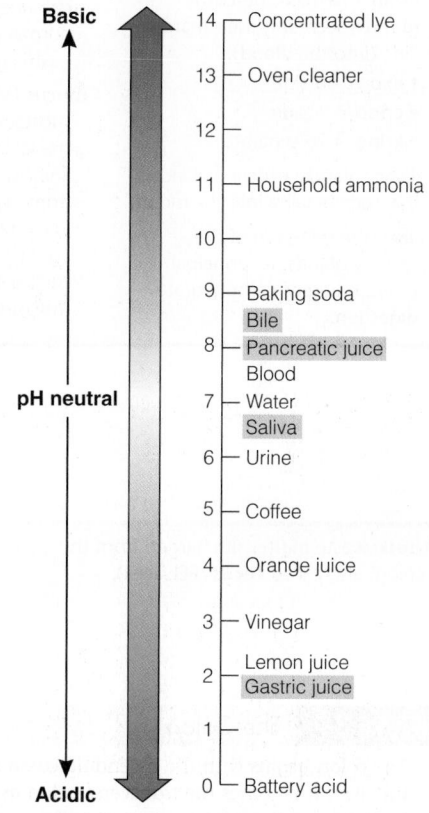

FIGURE 3–6 The pH Scale

A substance's acidity or alkalinity is measured in pH units. The pH is the negative logarithm of the hydrogen ion concentration. Each increment represents a tenfold increase in concentration of hydrogen particles. This means, for example, that a pH of 2 is 1000 times stronger than a pH of 5.

pH of common substances:

Basic

14 — Concentrated lye
13 — Oven cleaner
12 —
11 — Household ammonia
10 —
9 — Baking soda
     Bile
8 — Pancreatic juice
     Blood
7 — Water
     Saliva
6 — Urine
5 — Coffee
4 — Orange juice
3 — Vinegar
     Lemon juice
2 — Gastric juice
1 —
0 — Battery acid

pH neutral

Acidic

◆ The lower the pH, the higher the H⁺ ion concentration and the stronger the acid. A pH above 7 is alkaline, or base (a solution in which OH⁻ ions predominate).

GLOSSARY OF DIGESTIVE ENZYMES

digestive enzymes: proteins found in digestive juices that act on food substances, causing them to break down into simpler compounds.

-ase (ACE): a word ending denoting an enzyme. The word beginning often identifies the compounds the enzyme works on. Examples include:

• **carbohydrase** (KAR-boe-HIGH-drase), an enzyme that hydrolyzes carbohydrates.

• **lipase** (LYE-pase), an enzyme that hydrolyzes lipids (fats).

• **protease** (PRO-tee-ase), an enzyme that hydrolyzes proteins.

hydrolysis (high-DROL-ih-sis): a chemical reaction in which a major reactant is split into two products, with the addition of a hydrogen atom (H) to one and a hydroxyl group (OH) to the other (from water, H_2O). (The noun is **hydrolysis**; the verb is **hydrolyze**.)

• **hydro** = water

• **lysis** = breaking

pH: the unit of measure expressing a substance's acidity or alkalinity.

GLOSSARY OF DIGESTIVE GLANDS AND THEIR SECRETIONS

These terms are listed in order from start to end of the digestive tract.

glands: cells or groups of cells that secrete materials for special uses in the body. Glands may be **exocrine** (EKS-oh-crin) **glands,** secreting their materials "out" (into the digestive tract or onto the surface of the skin), or **endocrine** (EN-doe-crin) **glands,** secreting their materials "in" (into the blood).

• **exo** = outside
• **endo** = inside
• **krine** = to separate

salivary glands: exocrine glands that secrete saliva into the mouth.

saliva: the secretion of the salivary glands. Its principal enzyme begins carbohydrate digestion.

gastric glands: exocrine glands in the stomach wall that secrete gastric juice into the stomach.
• **gastro** = stomach

gastric juice: the digestive secretion of the gastric glands of the stomach.

hydrochloric acid: an acid composed of hydrogen and chloride atoms (HCl) that is normally produced by the gastric glands.

mucus (MYOO-kus): a slippery substance secreted by cells of the GI lining (and other body linings) that protects the cells from exposure to digestive juices (and other destructive agents). The lining of the GI tract with its coat of mucus is a **mucous membrane.** (The noun

is **mucus;** the adjective is **mucous.**)

liver: the organ that manufactures bile. (The liver's many other functions are described in Chapter 7.)

bile: an emulsifier that prepares fats and oils for digestion; an exocrine secretion made by the liver, stored in the gallbladder, and released into the small intestine when needed.

emulsifier (ee-MUL-sih-fire): a substance with both water-soluble and fat-soluble portions that promotes the mixing of oils and fats in a watery solution.

pancreatic (pank-ree-AT-ic) **juice:** the exocrine secretion of the pancreas, containing enzymes for the digestion of carbohydrate,

fat, and protein as well as bicarbonate, a neutralizing agent. The juice flows from the pancreas into the small intestine through the pancreatic duct. (The pancreas also has an endocrine function, the secretion of insulin and other hormones.)

bicarbonate: an alkaline compound with the formula HCO_3 that is secreted from the pancreas as part of the pancreatic juice. (Bicarbonate is also produced in all cell fluids from the dissociation of carbonic acid to help maintain the body's acid-base balance.)

---

stools: waste matter discharged from the colon; also called **feces** (FEE-seez).

the bile into the duodenum of the small intestine when fat arrives there. Bile is not an enzyme; it is an **emulsifier** that brings fats into suspension in water so that enzymes can break them down into their component parts. Thanks to all these secretions, the three energy-yielding nutrients are digested in the small intestine (the summary on p. 80 provides a table of digestive secretions and their actions).

The Final Stage

At this point, the three energy-yielding nutrients—carbohydrate, fat, and protein—have been disassembled and are ready to be absorbed. Most of the other nutrients—vitamins, minerals, and water—need no such disassembly; some vitamins and minerals are altered slightly during digestion, but most are absorbed as they are. Undigested residues, such as some fibers, are not absorbed. Instead, they continue through the digestive tract, providing a semisolid mass that helps exercise the muscles and keep them strong enough to perform peristalsis efficiently. Fiber also retains water, accounting for the pasty consistency of **stools,** and thereby carries some bile acids, some minerals, and some additives and contaminants with it out of the body.

By the time the contents of the GI tract reach the end of the small intestine, little remains but water, a few dissolved salts and body secretions, and undigested materials such as fiber. These enter the large intestine (colon).

In the colon, intestinal bacteria ferment some fibers, producing water, gas, and small fragments of fat that provide energy for the cells of the colon. The colon itself retrieves all materials that the body can recycle—water and dissolved salts (see Figure 3-7). The waste that is finally excreted has little or nothing of value left in it. The body has extracted all that it can use from the food. Figure 3-8 summarizes digestion by following a sandwich through the GI tract and into the body.

FIGURE 3–7 The Colon

The colon begins with the ascending colon rising upward toward the liver. It becomes the transverse colon as it turns and crosses the body toward the spleen. The descending colon turns downward and becomes the sigmoid colon, which extends to the rectum. Along the way, the colon mixes the intestinal contents, absorbs water and salts, and forms stools.

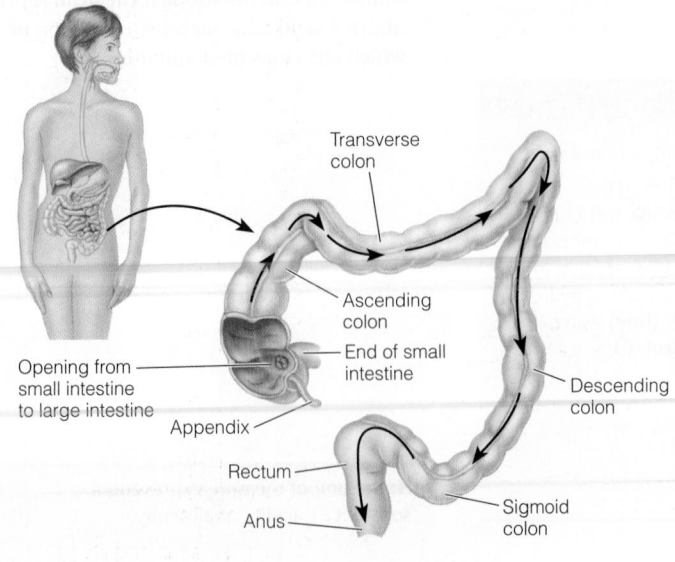

Transverse colon

Ascending colon

End of small intestine

Opening from small intestine to large intestine

Appendix

Rectum

Anus

Descending colon

Sigmoid colon

FIGURE 3–8 | *Animated!* The Digestive Fate of a Sandwich

To review the digestive processes, follow a peanut butter and banana sandwich on whole-wheat, seasame seed bread through the GI tract. As the graph on the right illustrates, digestion of the energy nutrients begins in different parts of the GI tract, but all are ready for absorption by the time they reach the end of the small intestine.

ThomsonNOW™
To test your understanding of these concepts, log on to **www**.thomsonedu.com/login

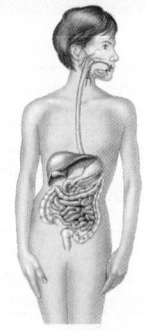

MOUTH: CHEWING AND SWALLOWING, WITH LITTLE DIGESTION

Carbohydrate digestion begins as the salivary enzyme starts to break down the starch from bread and peanut butter.
Fiber covering on the sesame seeds is crushed by the teeth, which exposes the nutrients inside the seeds to the upcoming digestive enzymes.

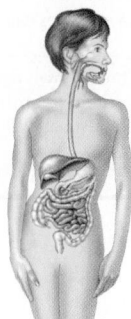

STOMACH: COLLECTING AND CHURNING, WITH SOME DIGESTION

Carbohydrate digestion continues until the mashed sandwich has been mixed with the gastric juices; the stomach acid of the gastric juices inactivates the salivary enzyme, and carbohydrate digestion ceases.
Proteins from the bread, seeds, and peanut butter begin to uncoil when they mix with the gastric acid, making them available to the gastric protease enzymes that begin to digest proteins.
Fat from the peanut butter forms a separate layer on top of the watery mixture.

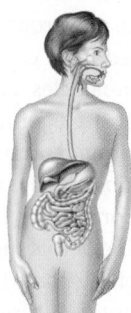

SMALL INTESTINE: DIGESTING AND ABSORBING

Sugars from the banana require so little digestion that they begin to traverse the intestinal cells immediately on contact.
Starch digestion picks up when the pancreas sends pancreatic enzymes to the small intestine via the pancreatic duct. Enzymes on the surfaces of the small intestinal cells complete the process of breaking down starch into small fragments that can be absorbed through the intestinal cell walls and into the hepatic portal vein.
Fat from the peanut butter and seeds is emulsified with the watery digestive fluids by bile. Now the pancreatic and intestinal lipases can begin to break down the fat to smaller fragments that can be absorbed through the cells of the small intestinal wall and into the lymph.
Protein digestion depends on the pancreatic and intestinal proteases. Small fragments of protein are liberated and absorbed through the cells of the small intestinal wall and into the hepatic portal vein.
Vitamins and minerals are absorbed.

Note: Sugars and starches are members of the carbohydrate family.

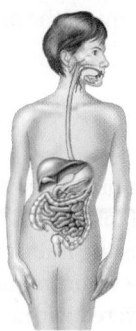

LARGE INTESTINE: REABSORBING AND ELIMINATING

Fluids and some minerals are absorbed.
Some fibers from the seeds, whole-wheat bread, peanut butter, and banana are partly digested by the bacteria living there, and some of these products are absorbed.
Most fibers pass through the large intestine and are excreted as feces; some fat, cholesterol, and minerals bind to fiber and are also excreted.

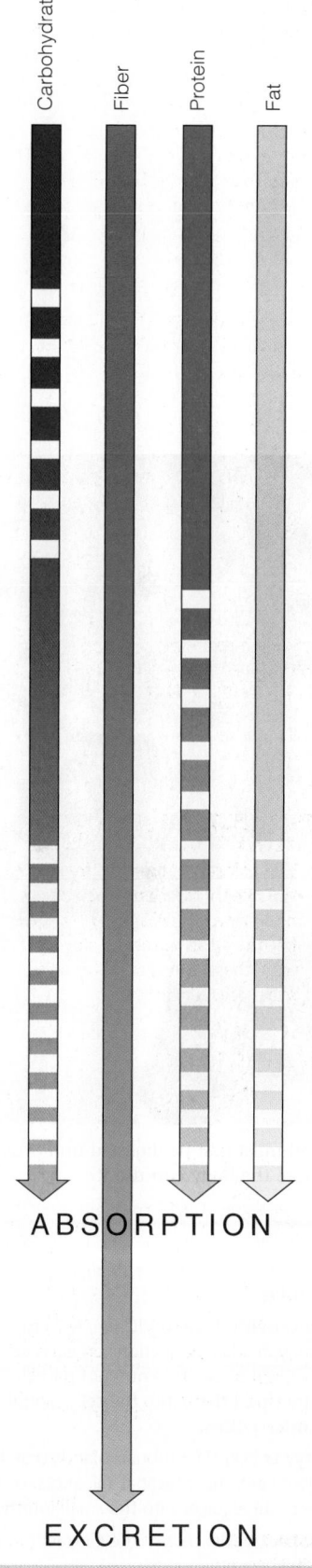

Carbohydrate

Fiber

Protein

Fat

ABSORPTION

EXCRETION

IN SUMMARY

As Figure 3-1 shows, food enters the mouth and travels down the esophagus and through the upper and lower esophageal sphincters to the stomach, then through the pyloric sphincter to the small intestine, on through the ileocecal valve to the large intestine, past the appendix to the rectum, ending at the anus. The wavelike contractions of peristalsis and the periodic squeezing of segmentation keep things moving at a reasonable pace. Along the way, secretions from the salivary glands, stomach, pancreas, liver (via the gallbladder), and small intestine deliver fluids and digestive enzymes.

Summary of Digestive Secretions and Their Major Actions

Organ or Gland	Target Organ	Secretion	Action
Salivary glands	Mouth	Saliva	Fluid eases swallowing; salivary enzyme breaks down **carbohydrate.***
Gastric glands	Stomach	Gastric juice	Fluid mixes with bolus; hydrochloric acid uncoils **proteins**; enzymes break down proteins; mucus protects stomach cells.*
Pancreas	Small intestine	Pancreatic juice	Bicarbonate neutralizes acidic gastric juices; pancreatic enzymes break down **carbohydrates, fats**, and **proteins**.
Liver	Gallbladder	Bile	Bile stored until needed.
Gallbladder	Small intestine	Bile	Bile emulsifies **fat** so enzymes can attack.
Intestinal glands	Small intestine	Intestinal juice	Intestinal enzymes break down **carbohydrate, fat**, and **protein** fragments; mucus protects the intestinal wall.

* Saliva and gastric juices also contain lipases, but most fat breakdown occurs in the small intestines.

Food must first be digested and absorbed before the body can use it.

Absorption

Within three or four hours after you have eaten a dinner of beans and rice (or spinach lasagna, or steak and potatoes) with vegetable, salad, beverage, and dessert, your body must find a way to absorb the molecules derived from carbohydrate, protein, and fat digestion—and the vitamin and mineral molecules as well. Most absorption takes place in the small intestine, one of the most elegantly designed organ systems in the body. Within its 10-foot length, which provides a surface area equivalent to a tennis court, the small intestine engulfs and absorbs the nutrient molecules. To remove the molecules rapidly and provide room for more to be absorbed, a rush of circulating blood continuously washes the underside of this surface, carrying the absorbed nutrients away to the liver and other parts of the body. Figure 3-9 describes how nutrients are absorbed by simple diffusion, facilitated diffusion, or active transport. Later chapters provide details on specific nutrients. Before following nutrients through the body, we must look more closely at the anatomy of the absorptive system.

Anatomy of the Absorptive System

The inner surface of the small intestine looks smooth and slippery, but when viewed through a microscope, it turns out to be wrinkled into hundreds of folds. Each fold is contoured into thousands of fingerlike projections, as numerous as the hairs on velvet fabric. These small intestinal projections are the **villi**. A single villus, magnified still more, turns out to be composed of hundreds of cells, each covered with its own microscopic hairs, the **microvilli** (see Figure 3-10 on p. 82). In the crevices between the villi lie the **crypts**—tubular glands that secrete the intestinal juices into the small intestine. Nearby **goblet cells** secrete mucus.

villi (VILL-ee, VILL-eye): fingerlike projections from the folds of the small intestine; singular **villus.**

microvilli (MY-cro-VILL-ee, MY-cro-VILL-eye): tiny, hairlike projections on each cell of every villus that can trap nutrient particles and transport them into the cells; singular **microvillus.**

crypts (KRIPTS): tubular glands that lie between the intestinal villi and secrete intestinal juices into the small intestine.

goblet cells: cells of the GI tract (and lungs) that secrete mucus.

Foodcollection/Getty Images

| FIGURE 3–9 | Absorption of Nutrients |

Absorption of nutrients into intestinal cells typically occurs by simple diffusion, facilitated diffusion, or active transport.

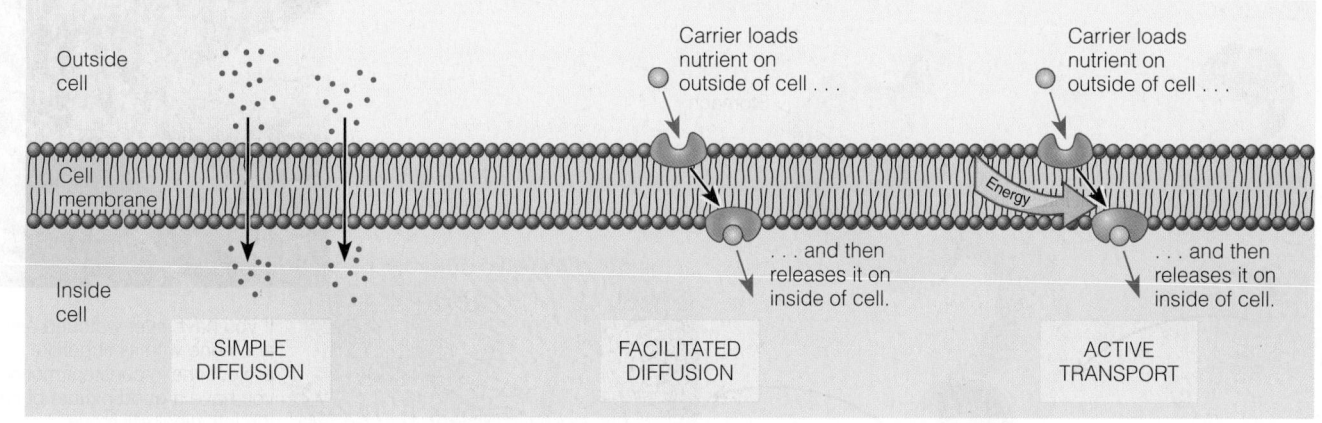

Some nutrients (such as water and small lipids) are absorbed by simple diffusion. They cross into intestinal cells freely.

Some nutrients (such as the water-soluble vitamins) are absorbed by facilitated diffusion. They need a specific carrier to transport them from one side of the cell membrane to the other. (Alternatively, facilitated diffusion may occur when the carrier changes the cell membrane in such a way that the nutrients can pass through.)

Some nutrients (such as glucose and amino acids) must be absorbed actively. These nutrients move against a concentration gradient, which requires energy.

The villi are in constant motion. Each villus is lined by a thin sheet of muscle, so it can wave, squirm, and wriggle like the tentacles of a sea anemone. Any nutrient molecule small enough to be absorbed is trapped among the microvilli that coat the cells and then drawn into the cells. Some partially digested nutrients are caught in the microvilli, digested further by enzymes there, and then absorbed into the cells.

A Closer Look at the Intestinal Cells

The cells of the villi are among the most amazing in the body, for they recognize and select the nutrients the body needs and regulate their absorption. ◆ As already described, each cell of a villus is coated with thousands of microvilli, which project from the cell's membrane (review Figure 3-10). In these microvilli, and in the membrane, lie hundreds of different kinds of enzymes and "pumps," which recognize and act on different nutrients. Descriptions of specific enzymes and "pumps" for each nutrient are presented in the following chapters where appropriate; the point here is that the cells are equipped to handle all kinds and combinations of foods and nutrients.

◆ The problem of food contaminants, which may be absorbed defenselessly by the body, is the subject of Chapter 19.

Specialization in the GI Tract A further refinement of the system is that the cells of successive portions of the intestinal tract are specialized to absorb different nutrients. The nutrients that are ready for absorption early are absorbed near the top of the tract; those that take longer to be digested are absorbed farther down. Registered dietitians and medical professionals who treat digestive disorders learn the specialized absorptive functions of different parts of the GI tract so that if one part becomes dysfunctional, the diet can be adjusted accordingly.

The Myth of "Food Combining" The idea that people should not eat certain food combinations (for example, fruit and meat) at the same meal, because the digestive system cannot handle more than one task at a time, is a myth. The art of "food combining" (which actually emphasizes "food separating") is based on this idea, and it represents faulty logic and a gross underestimation of the body's capabilities. In fact, the contrary is often true; foods eaten together can enhance each

FIGURE 3–10 The Small Intestinal Villi

Absorption of nutrients into intestinal cells typically occurs by simple diffusion or active transport.

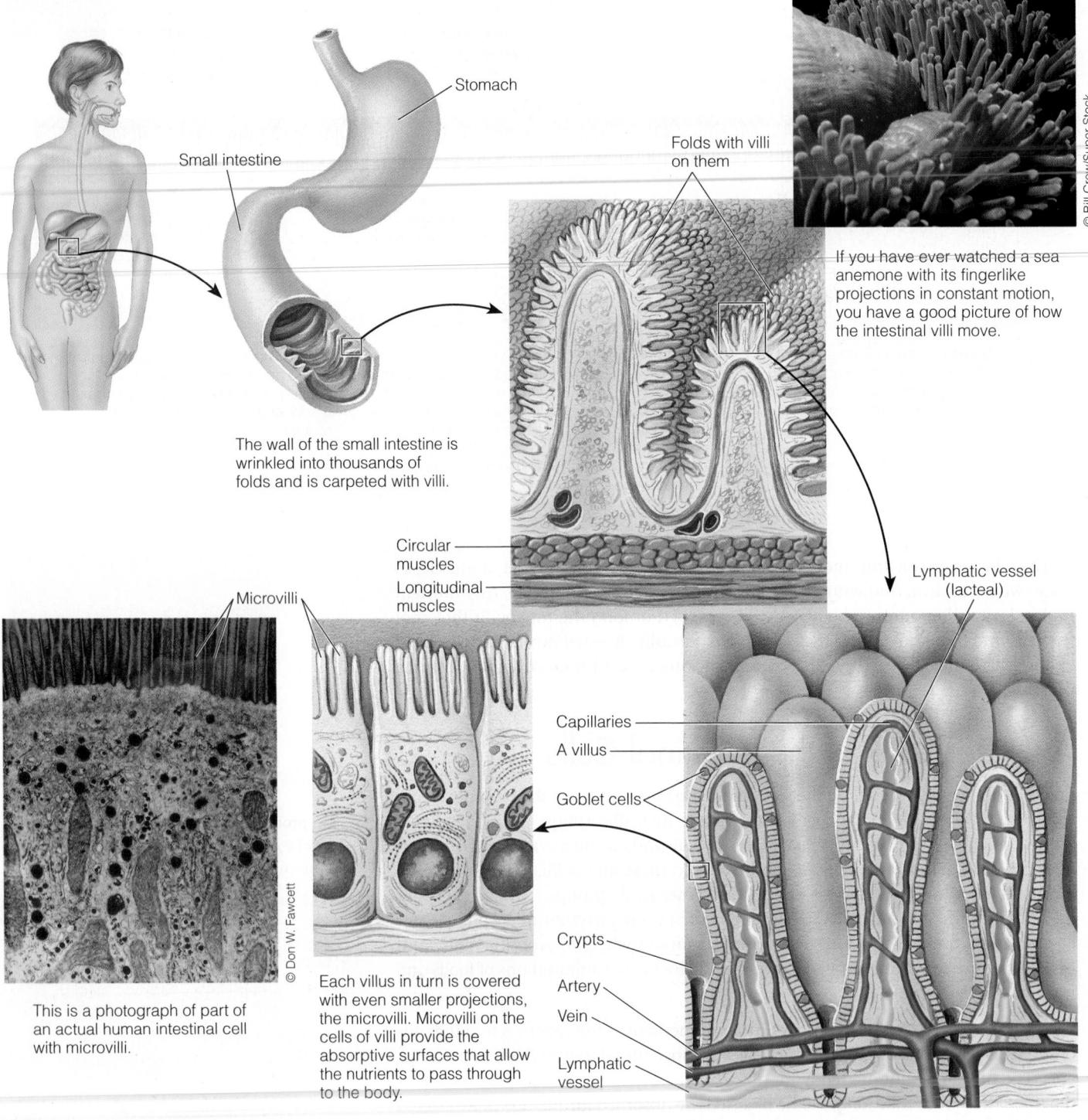

Stomach

Small intestine

Folds with villi on them

© Bill Crew/Super Stock

If you have ever watched a sea anemone with its fingerlike projections in constant motion, you have a good picture of how the intestinal villi move.

The wall of the small intestine is wrinkled into thousands of folds and is carpeted with villi.

Circular muscles

Longitudinal muscles

Lymphatic vessel (lacteal)

Microvilli

Capillaries

A villus

Goblet cells

© Don W. Fawcett

Crypts

Artery

Vein

Lymphatic vessel

This is a photograph of part of an actual human intestinal cell with microvilli.

Each villus in turn is covered with even smaller projections, the microvilli. Microvilli on the cells of villi provide the absorptive surfaces that allow the nutrients to pass through to the body.

other's use by the body. For example, vitamin C in a pineapple or other citrus fruit can enhance the absorption of iron from a meal of chicken and rice or other iron-containing foods. Many other instances of mutually beneficial interactions are presented in later chapters.

Preparing Nutrients for Transport When a nutrient molecule has crossed the cell of a villus, it enters either the bloodstream or the lymphatic system. Both transport systems supply vessels to each villus, as shown in Figure 3-10. The water-soluble nutrients and the smaller products of fat digestion are released directly into the bloodstream and guided directly to the liver where their fate and destination will be determined.

The larger fats and the fat-soluble vitamins are insoluble in water, however, and blood is mostly water. The intestinal cells assemble many of the products of fat digestion into larger molecules. These larger molecules cluster together with special proteins, forming chylomicrons. ◆ Because these chylomicrons cannot pass into the capillaries, they are released into the lymphatic system instead; the chylomicrons move through the lymph and later enter the bloodstream at a point near the heart, thus bypassing the liver at first. Details follow.

◆ Chylomicrons (kye-lo-MY-cronz) are described in Chapter 5.

IN SUMMARY

The many folds and villi of the small intestine dramatically increase its surface area, facilitating nutrient absorption. Nutrients pass through the cells of the villi and enter either the blood (if they are water soluble or small fat fragments) or the lymph (if they are fat soluble).

The Circulatory Systems

Once a nutrient has entered the bloodstream, it may be transported to any of the cells in the body, from the tips of the toes to the roots of the hair. The circulatory systems deliver nutrients wherever they are needed.

The Vascular System

The vascular, or blood circulatory, system is a closed system of vessels through which blood flows continuously, with the heart serving as the pump (see Figure 3-11, p. 84). As the blood circulates through this system, it picks up and delivers materials as needed.

All the body tissues derive oxygen and nutrients from the blood and deposit carbon dioxide and other wastes back into the blood. The lungs exchange carbon dioxide (which leaves the blood to be exhaled) and oxygen (which enters the blood to be delivered to all cells). The digestive system supplies the nutrients to be picked up. In the kidneys, wastes other than carbon dioxide are filtered out of the blood to be excreted in the urine.

Blood leaving the right side of the heart circulates through the lungs and then back to the left side of the heart. The left side of the heart then pumps the blood out of the **aorta** through **arteries** to all systems of the body. The blood circulates in the **capillaries,** where it exchanges material with the cells and then collects into **veins,** which return it again to the right side of the heart. In short, blood travels this simple route:

- Heart to arteries to capillaries to veins to heart

The routing of the blood leaving the digestive system has a special feature. The blood is carried to the digestive system (as to all organs) by way of an artery, which (as in all organs) branches into capillaries to reach every cell. Blood leaving the digestive system, however, goes by way of a vein. The **hepatic portal vein** directs blood not back to the heart, but to another organ—the liver. This vein *again* branches into *capillaries* so that every cell of the liver has access to the blood. Blood leaving the liver then *again* collects into a vein, called the **hepatic vein,** which returns blood to the heart.

The route is:

- Heart to arteries to capillaries (in intestines) to hepatic portal vein to capillaries (in liver) to hepatic vein to heart

aorta (ay-OR-tuh): the large, primary artery that conducts blood from the heart to the body's smaller arteries.

arteries: vessels that carry blood from the heart to the tissues.

capillaries (CAP-ill-aries): small vessels that branch from an artery. Capillaries connect arteries to veins. Exchange of oxygen, nutrients, and waste materials takes place across capillary walls.

veins (VANES): vessels that carry blood to the heart.

hepatic portal vein: the vein that collects blood from the GI tract and conducts it to capillaries in the liver.
- **portal** = gateway

hepatic vein: the vein that collects blood from the liver capillaries and returns it to the heart.
- **hepatic** = liver

FIGURE 3–11   *Animated!* The Vascular System

ThomsonNOW™
To test your understanding of
these concepts, log on to **www**
.thomsonedu.com/login

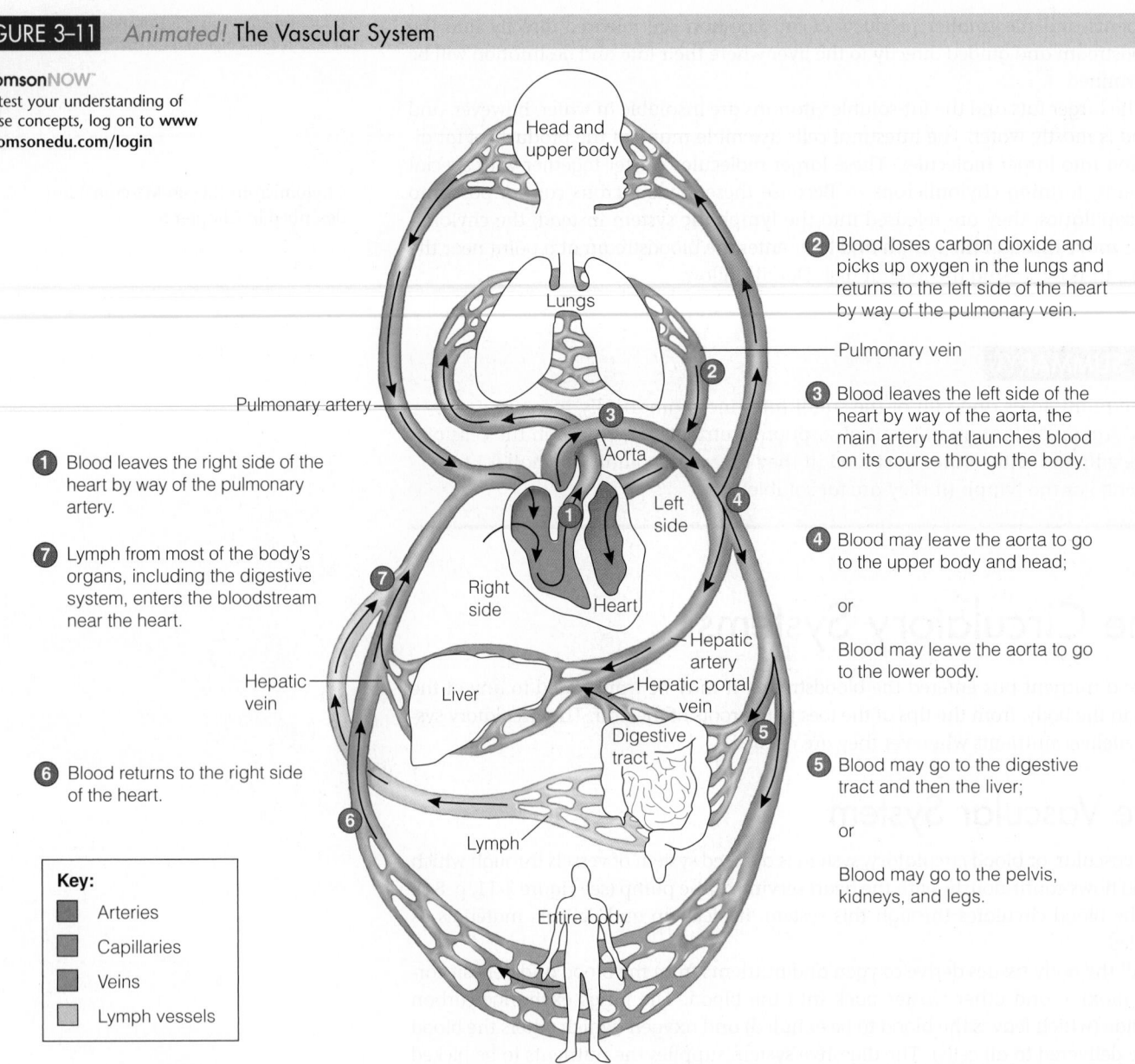

2 Blood loses carbon dioxide and picks up oxygen in the lungs and returns to the left side of the heart by way of the pulmonary vein.

Pulmonary vein

3 Blood leaves the left side of the heart by way of the aorta, the main artery that launches blood on its course through the body.

4 Blood may leave the aorta to go to the upper body and head;

or

Blood may leave the aorta to go to the lower body.

5 Blood may go to the digestive tract and then the liver;

or

Blood may go to the pelvis, kidneys, and legs.

1 Blood leaves the right side of the heart by way of the pulmonary artery.

7 Lymph from most of the body's organs, including the digestive system, enters the bloodstream near the heart.

6 Blood returns to the right side of the heart.

Key:

■ Arteries

■ Capillaries

■ Veins

■ Lymph vessels

Figure 3-12 shows the liver's key position in nutrient transport. An anatomist studying this system knows there must be a reason for this special arrangement. The liver's placement ensures that it will be first to receive the nutrients absorbed from the GI tract. In fact, the liver has many jobs to do in preparing the absorbed nutrients for use by the body. It is the body's major metabolic organ.

You might guess that, in addition, the liver serves as a gatekeeper to defend against substances that might harm the heart or brain. This is why, when people ingest poisons that succeed in passing the first barrier (the intestinal cells), the liver quite often suffers the damage—from viruses such as hepatitis, from drugs such as barbiturates or alcohol, from toxins such as pesticide residues, and from contaminants such as mercury. Perhaps, in fact, you have been undervaluing your liver, not knowing what heroic tasks it quietly performs for you.

The Lymphatic System

The **lymphatic system** provides a one-way route for fluid from the tissue spaces to enter the blood. Unlike the vascular system, the lymphatic system has

lymphatic (lim-FAT-ic) **system:** a loosely organized system of vessels and ducts that convey fluids toward the heart. The GI part of the lymphatic system carries the products of fat digestion into the bloodstream.

FIGURE 3–12 The Liver

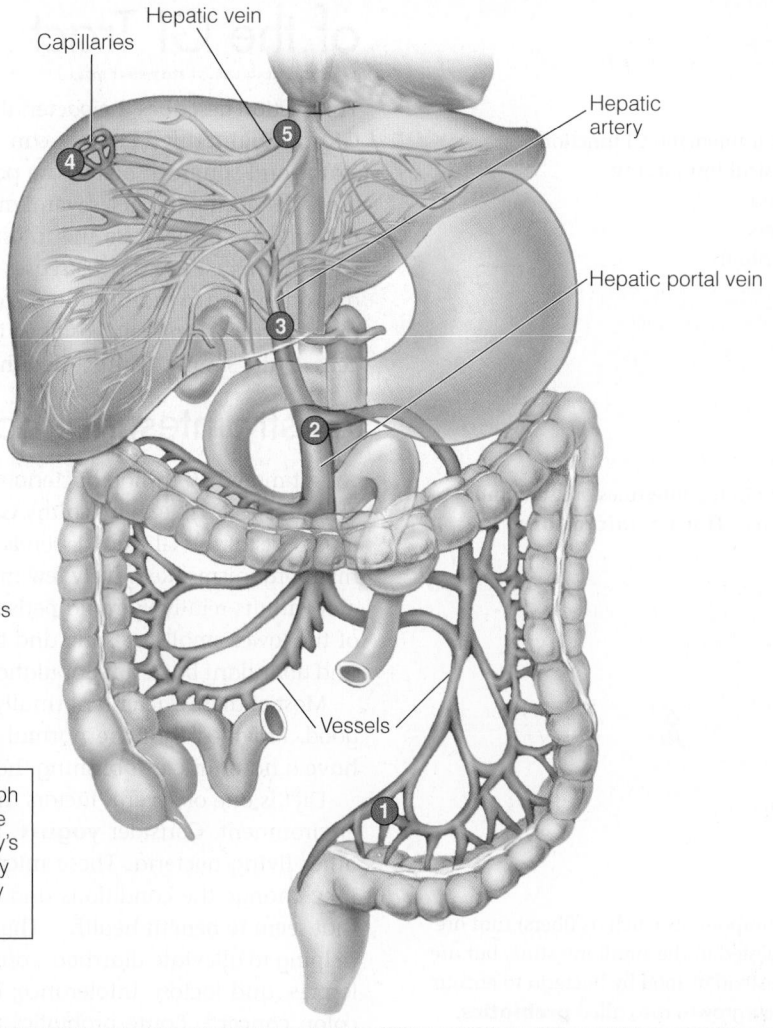

1. Vessels gather up nutrients and reabsorbed water and salts from all over the digestive tract.

   Not shown here:
   Parallel to these vessels (veins) are other vessels (arteries) that carry oxygen-rich blood from the heart to the intestines.

2. The vessels merge into the hepatic portal vein, which conducts all absorbed materials to the liver.

3. The hepatic artery brings a supply of freshly oxygenated blood (not loaded with nutrients) from the lungs to supply oxygen to the liver's own cells.

4. Capillaries branch all over the liver, making nutrients and oxygen available to all its cells and giving the cells access to blood from the digestive system.

5. The hepatic vein gathers up blood in the liver and returns it to the heart.

   In contrast, nutrients absorbed into lymph do not go to the liver first. They go to the heart, which pumps them to all the body's cells. The cells remove the nutrients they need, and the liver then has to deal only with the remnants.

Labels on figure: Hepatic vein, Capillaries, Hepatic artery, Hepatic portal vein, Vessels

no pump; instead, **lymph** circulates *between* the cells of the body and collects into tiny vessels. The fluid moves from one portion of the body to another as muscles contract and create pressure here and there. Ultimately, much of the lymph collects in the **thoracic duct** behind the heart. The thoracic duct opens into the **subclavian vein**, where the lymph enters the bloodstream. Thus nutrients from the GI tract that enter lymphatic vessels ◆ (large fats and fat-soluble vitamins) ultimately enter the bloodstream, circulating through arteries, capillaries, and veins like the other nutrients, with a notable exception—they bypass the liver at first.

Once inside the vascular system, the nutrients can travel freely to any destination and can be taken into cells and used as needed. What becomes of them is described in later chapters.

◆ The lymphatic vessels of the intestine that take up nutrients and pass them to the lymph circulation are called **lacteals** (LACK-tee-als).

lymph (LIMF): a clear yellowish fluid that is similar to blood except that it contains no red blood cells or platelets. Lymph from the GI tract transports fat and fat-soluble vitamins to the bloodstream via lymphatic vessels.

thoracic (thor-ASS-ic) **duct**: the main lymphatic vessel that collects lymph and drains into the left subclavian vein.

subclavian (sub-KLAY-vee-an) **vein**: the vein that provides passageway from the lymphatic system to the vascular system.

IN SUMMARY

Nutrients leaving the digestive system via the blood are routed directly to the liver before being transported to the body's cells. Those leaving via the lymphatic system eventually enter the vascular system but bypass the liver at first.

The Health and Regulation of the GI Tract

This section describes the bacterial conditions and hormonal regulation of a healthy GI tract, but many factors ◆ can influence normal GI function. For example, peristalsis and sphincter action are poorly coordinated in newborns, so infants tend to "spit up" during the first several months of life. Older adults often experience constipation, in part because the intestinal wall loses strength and elasticity with age, which slows GI motility. Diseases can also interfere with digestion and absorption and often lead to malnutrition. Lack of nourishment, in general, and lack of certain dietary constituents such as fiber, in particular, alter the structure and function of GI cells. Quite simply, GI tract health depends on adequate nutrition.

◆ Factors influencing GI function:
- Physical immaturity
- Aging
- Illness
- Nutrition

Gastrointestinal Bacteria

An estimated 10 trillion bacteria ◆ representing some 400 or more different species and subspecies live in a healthy GI tract. The prevalence of different bacteria in various parts of the GI tract depends on such factors as pH, peristalsis, diet, and other microorganisms. Relatively few microorganisms can live in the low pH of the stomach with its relatively rapid peristalsis, whereas the neutral pH and slow peristalsis of the lower small intestine and the large intestine permit the growth of a diverse and abundant bacterial population.[1]

◆ Bacteria in the intestines are sometimes referred to as **flora** or **microflora.**

Most of these bacteria normally do the body no harm and may actually do some good. Provided that the normal intestinal flora are thriving, infectious bacteria have a hard time establishing themselves to launch an attack on the system.

Diet is one of several factors that influence the body's bacterial population and environment. Consider **yogurt,** for example.[2] Yogurt contains *Lactobacillus* and other living bacteria. These microorganisms are considered **probiotics** because they change the conditions and native bacterial colonies in the GI tract in ways that seem to benefit health.[3] The potential GI health benefits of probiotics include helping to alleviate diarrhea, constipation, inflammatory bowel disease, ulcers, allergies, and lactose intolerance; enhance immune function; and protect against colon cancer.[4] Some probiotics may have adverse effects under certain circumstances.[5] Research studies continue to explore how diet influences GI bacteria and which foods—with their probiotics—affect GI health.

◆ Food components (such as fibers) that are not digested in the small intestine, but are used instead as food by bacteria to encourage their growth are called **prebiotics.**

GI bacteria also digest fibers and complex proteins.[6] ◆ In doing so, the bacteria produce nutrients such as short fragments of fat that the cells of the colon use for energy. Bacteria in the GI tract also produce several vitamins, ◆ including a significant amount of vitamin K, although the amount is insufficient to meet the body's total need for that vitamin.

◆ Vitamins produced by bacteria include:
- Biotin
- Folate
- Vitamin B_6
- Vitamin B_{12}
- Vitamin K

yogurt: milk product that results from the fermentation of lactic acid in milk by *Lactobacillus bulgaricus* and *Streptococcus thermophilus.*

probiotics: living microorganisms found in foods that, when consumed in sufficient quantities, are beneficial to health.
- **pro** = for
- **bios** = life

homeostasis (HOME-ee-oh-STAY-sis): the maintenance of constant internal conditions (such as blood chemistry, temperature, and blood pressure) by the body's control systems. A homeostatic system is constantly reacting to external forces to maintain limits set by the body's needs.
- **homeo** = the same
- **stasis** = staying

Gastrointestinal Hormones and Nerve Pathways

The ability of the digestive tract to handle its ever-changing contents routinely illustrates an important physiological principle that governs the way all living things function—the principle of **homeostasis.** Simply stated, survival depends on body conditions staying about the same; if they deviate too far from the norm, the body must "do something" to bring them back to normal. The body's regulation of digestion is one example of homeostatic regulation. The body also regulates its temperature, its blood pressure, and all other aspects of its blood chemistry in similar ways.

Two intricate and sensitive systems coordinate all the digestive and absorptive processes: the hormonal (or endocrine) system and the nervous system. Even before the first bite of food is taken, the mere thought, sight, or smell of food can trigger a response from these systems. Then, as food travels through the GI tract, it either stimulates or inhibits digestive secretions by way of messages that are carried from one section of the GI tract to another by both **hormones** ◆ and nerve pathways. (Appendix A presents a brief summary of the body's hormonal system and nervous system.)

Notice that the kinds of regulation described next are all examples of *feedback* mechanisms. A certain condition demands a response. The response changes that condition, and the change then cuts off the response. Thus the system is self-correcting. Examples follow:

- *The stomach normally maintains a pH between 1.5 and 1.7. How does it stay that way?* Food entering the stomach stimulates cells in the stomach wall to release the hormone **gastrin.** Gastrin, in turn, stimulates the stomach glands to secrete the components of hydrochloric acid. When pH 1.5 is reached, the acid itself turns off the gastrin-producing cells. They stop releasing gastrin, and the glands stop producing hydrochloric acid. Thus the system adjusts itself.

  Nerve receptors in the stomach wall also respond to the presence of food and stimulate the gastric glands to secrete juices and the muscles to contract. As the stomach empties, the receptors are no longer stimulated, the flow of juices slows, and the stomach quiets down.

- *The pyloric sphincter opens to let out a little chyme, then closes again. How does it know when to open and close?* When the pyloric sphincter relaxes, acidic chyme slips through. The cells of the pyloric muscle on the intestinal side sense the acid, causing the pyloric sphincter to close tightly. Only after the chyme has been neutralized by pancreatic bicarbonate and the juices surrounding the pyloric sphincter have become alkaline can the muscle relax again. This process ensures that the chyme will be released slowly enough to be neutralized as it flows through the small intestine. This is important because the small intestine has less of a mucous coating than the stomach does and so is not as well protected from acid.

- *As the chyme enters the intestine, the pancreas adds bicarbonate to it so that the intestinal contents always remain at a slightly alkaline pH. How does the pancreas know how much to add?* The presence of chyme stimulates the cells of the duodenum wall to release the hormone **secretin** into the blood. When secretin reaches the pancreas, it stimulates the pancreas to release its bicarbonate-rich juices. Thus, whenever the duodenum signals that acidic chyme is present, the pancreas responds by sending bicarbonate to neutralize it. When the need has been met, the cells of the duodenum wall are no longer stimulated to release secretin, the hormone no longer flows through the blood, the pancreas no longer receives the message, and it stops sending pancreatic juice. Nerves also regulate pancreatic secretions.

- *Pancreatic secretions contain a mixture of enzymes to digest carbohydrate, fat, and protein. How does the pancreas know how much of each type of enzyme to provide?* This is one of the most interesting questions physiologists have asked. Clearly, the pancreas does know what its owner has been eating, and it secretes enzyme mixtures tailored to handle the food mixtures that have been arriving recently (over the last several days). Enzyme activity changes proportionately in response to the amounts of carbohydrate, fat, and protein in the diet. If a person has been eating mostly carbohydrates, the pancreas makes and secretes mostly carbohydrases; if the person's diet has been high in fat, the pancreas produces more lipases; and so forth. Presumably, hormones from the GI tract, secreted in response to meals, keep the pancreas informed as to its digestive tasks. The day or two lag between the time a person's diet changes dramatically and the time digestion of the new diet becomes efficient explains why dietary changes can "upset digestion" and should be made gradually.

◆ In general, any gastrointestinal hormone may be called an **enterogastrone** (EN-ter-oh-GAS-trone), but the term refers specifically to any hormone that slows motility and inhibits gastric secretions.

hormones: chemical messengers. Hormones are secreted by a variety of glands in response to altered conditions in the body. Each hormone travels to one or more specific target tissues or organs, where it elicits a specific response to maintain homeostasis.

gastrin: a hormone secreted by cells in the stomach wall. Target organ: the glands of the stomach. Response: secretion of gastric acid.

secretin (see-CREET-in): a hormone produced by cells in the duodenum wall. Target organ: the pancreas. Response: secretion of bicarbonate-rich pancreatic juice.

◆ The inactive precursor of an enzyme is called a **proenzyme** or **zymogen** (ZYE-mo-jen).
- **pro** = before
- **zym** = concerning enzymes
- **gen** = to produce

- *Why don't the digestive enzymes damage the pancreas?* The pancreas protects itself from harm by producing an inactive form of the enzymes. ◆ It releases these proteins into the small intestine where they are activated to become enzymes. In pancreatitis, the digestive enzymes become active within the infected pancreas, causing inflammation and damaging the delicate pancreatic tissues.

- *When fat is present in the intestine, the gallbladder contracts to squirt bile into the intestine to emulsify the fat. How does the gallbladder get the message that fat is present?* Fat in the intestine stimulates cells of the intestinal wall to release the hormone **cholecystokinin (CCK).** This hormone, traveling by way of the blood to the gallbladder, stimulates it to contract, releasing bile into the small intestine. Cholescystokinin also travels to the pancreas, stimulates it to secrete its juices, releasing bicarbonate and enzymes into the small intestine. Once the fat in the intestine is emulsified and enzymes have begun to work on it, the fat no longer provokes release of the hormone, and the message to contract is canceled. (By the way, fat emulsification can continue even after a diseased gallbladder has been surgically removed because the liver can deliver bile directly to the small intestine.)

- *Fat and protein take longer to digest than carbohydrate does. When fat or protein is present, intestinal motility slows to allow time for its digestion. How does the intestine know when to slow down?* Cholecystokinin is released in response to fat or protein in the small intestine. In addition to its role in fat emulsification and digestion, cholecystokinin slows GI tract motility. Slowing the digestive process helps to maintain a pace that allows all reactions to reach completion. Hormonal and nervous mechanisms like these account for much of the body's ability to adapt to changing conditions.

Table 3-1 summarizes the actions of these GI hormones.

Once a person has started to learn the answers to questions like these, it may be hard to stop. Some people devote their whole lives to the study of physiology. For now, however, these few examples illustrate how all the processes throughout the digestive system are precisely and automatically regulated without any conscious effort.

IN SUMMARY

A diverse and abundant bacteria population support GI health. The regulation of GI processes depends on the coordinated efforts of the hormonal system and the nervous system; together, digestion and absorption transform foods into nutrients.

cholecystokinin (COAL-ee-SIS-toe-KINE-in), or **CCK:** a hormone produced by cells of the intestinal wall. Target organ: the gallbladder. Response: release of bile and slowing of GI motility.

The System at Its Best

This chapter describes the anatomy of the digestive tract on several levels: the sequence of digestive organs, the cells and structures of the villi, and the selective ma-

TABLE 3-1	The Primary Actions of GI Hormones			
Hormone:	Responds to:	Secreted from:	Stimulates:	Response:
Gastrin	Food in the stomach	Stomach wall	Stomach glands	Hydrochloric acid secreted into the stomach
Secretin	Acidic chyme in the small intestine	Duodenal wall	Pancreas	Bicarbonate-rich juices secreted into the small intestine
Cholecystokinin	Fat or protein in the small intestine	Intestinal wall	Gallbladder	Bile secreted into the duodenum
			Pancreas	Bicarbonate- and enzyme-rich juices secreted into the small intestine

chinery of the cell membranes. The intricate architecture of the digestive system makes it sensitive and responsive to conditions in its environment. Several different kinds of GI tract cells confer specific immunity against intestinal diseases such as inflammatory bowel disease. In addition, secretions from the GI tract—saliva, mucus, gastric acid, and digestive enzymes—not only help with digestion, but also defend against foreign invaders. Together the GI's team of bacteria, cells, and secretions defend the body against numerous challenges.[7] Knowing the optimal conditions will help you to make choices that promote the best functioning of the system.

One indispensable condition is good health of the digestive tract itself. This health is affected by such lifestyle factors as sleep, physical activity, and state of mind. Adequate sleep allows for repair and maintenance of tissue and removal of wastes that might impair efficient functioning. Activity promotes healthy muscle tone. Mental state influences the activity of regulatory nerves and hormones; for healthy digestion, you should be relaxed and tranquil at mealtimes.

Nourishing foods and pleasant conversations support a healthy digestive system.

Another factor in GI health is the kind of meals you eat. Among the characteristics of meals that promote optimal absorption of nutrients are those mentioned in Chapter 2: balance, moderation, variety, and adequacy. Balance and moderation require having neither too much nor too little of anything. For example, too much fat can be harmful, but some fat is beneficial in slowing down intestinal motility and providing time for absorption of some of the nutrients that are slow to be absorbed.

Variety is important for many reasons, but one is that some food constituents interfere with nutrient absorption. For example, some compounds common in high-fiber foods such as whole-grain cereals, certain leafy green vegetables, and legumes bind with minerals. To some extent, then, the minerals in those foods may become unavailable for absorption. These high-fiber foods are still valuable, but they need to be balanced with a variety of other foods that can provide the minerals.

As for adequacy—in a sense, this entire book is about dietary adequacy. But here, at the end of this chapter, is a good place to underline the interdependence of the nutrients. It could almost be said that every nutrient depends on every other. All the nutrients work together, and all are present in the cells of a healthy digestive tract. To maintain health and promote the functions of the GI tract, you should make balance, moderation, variety, and adequacy features of every day's menus.

Nutrition Portfolio

ThomsonNOW™
www.thomsonedu.com/login

A healthy digestive system can adjust to almost any diet and can handle any combination of foods with ease.

■ Describe the physical and emotional environment that typically surrounds your meals, including how it affects you and how it might be improved.

■ Detail any GI discomforts you may experience regularly and include suggestions to alleviate or prevent their occurrence (see Highlight 3).

■ List any changes you can make in your eating habits to promote overall GI health.

NUTRITION ON THE NET

ThomsonNOW™
For further study of topics covered in this chapter, log on to www.thomsonedu
.com/thomsonnow. Go to Chapter 3, then to Nutrition on the Net.

- Visit the Center for Digestive Health and Nutrition: www.gihealth.com

- Visit the patient information section of the American College of Gastroenterology: www.acg.gi.org

STUDY QUESTIONS

ThomsonNOW™
To assess your understanding of chapter topics, take the Student Practice Test and explore the modules recommended in your Personalized Study Plan. Log onto www.thomsonedu.com/thomsonnow.

These questions will help you review this chapter. You will find the answers in the discussions on the pages provided.

1. Describe the challenges associated with digesting food and the solutions offered by the human body. (pp. 71–80)

2. Describe the path food follows as it travels through the digestive system. Summarize the muscular actions that take place along the way. (pp. 72–76)

3. Name five organs that secrete digestive juices. How do the juices and enzymes facilitate digestion? (pp. 76–78)

4. Describe the problems associated with absorbing nutrients and the solutions offered by the small intestine. (pp. 80–83)

5. How is blood routed through the digestive system? Which nutrients enter the bloodstream directly? Which are first absorbed into the lymph? (pp. 83–85)

6. Describe how the body coordinates and regulates the processes of digestion and absorption. (pp. 86–88)

7. How does the composition of the diet influence the functioning of the GI tract? (p. 89)

8. What steps can you take to help your GI tract function at its best? (p. 89)

These multiple choice questions will help you prepare for an exam. Answers can be found on p. 91.

1. The semiliquid, partially digested food that travels through the intestinal tract is called:
   a. bile.
   b. lymph.
   c. chyme.
   d. secretin.

2. The muscular contractions that move food through the GI tract are called:
   a. hydrolysis.
   b. sphincters.
   c. peristalsis.
   d. bowel movements.

3. The main function of bile is to:
   a. emulsify fats.
   b. catalyze hydrolysis.
   c. slow protein digestion.
   d. neutralize stomach acidity.

4. The pancreas neutralizes stomach acid in the small intestine by secreting:
   a. bile.
   b. mucus.
   c. enzymes.
   d. bicarbonate.

5. Which nutrient passes through the GI tract mostly undigested and unabsorbed?
   a. fat
   b. fiber
   c. protein
   d. carbohydrate

6. Absorption occurs primarily in the:
   a. mouth.
   b. stomach.
   c. small intestine.
   d. large intestine.

7. All blood leaving the GI tract travels first to the:
   a. heart.
   b. liver.
   c. kidneys.
   d. pancreas.

8. Which nutrients leave the GI tract by way of the lymphatic system?
   a. water and minerals
   b. proteins and minerals
   c. all vitamins and minerals
   d. fats and fat-soluble vitamins

9. Digestion and absorption are coordinated by the:
   a. pancreas and kidneys.
   b. liver and gallbladder.
   c. hormonal system and the nervous system.
   d. vascular system and the lymphatic system.

10. Gastrin, secretin, and cholecystokinin are examples of:
    a. crypts.
    b. enzymes.
    c. hormones.
    d. goblet cells.

REFERENCES

1. P. B. Eckburg and coauthors, Diversity of the human intestinal microbial flora, *Science* 308 (2005): 1635-1638; W. L. Hao and Y. K. Lee, Microflora of the gastrointestinal tract: A review, *Methods in Molecular Biology* 268 (2004): 491-502.

2. O. Adolfsson, S. N. Meydani, and R. M. Russell, Yogurt and gut function, *American Journal of Clinical Nutrition* 80 (2004): 245-256.

3. C. C. Chen and W. A. Walker, Probiotics and prebiotics: Role in clinical disease states, *Advances in Pediatrics* 52 (2005): 77-113; M. E. Sanders, Probiotics: Considerations for human health, *Nutrition Reviews* 61 (2003): 91-99; M. H. Floch and J. Hong-Curtiss, Probiotics and functional foods in gastrointestinal disorders, *Current Gastroenterology Reports* 3 (2001): 343-350; Probiotics and prebiotics, *American Journal of Clinical Nutrition (supp.)* 73 (2001): entire issue.

4. S. Santosa, E. Farnworth, P. J. H. Jones, Probiotics and their potential health claims, *Nutrition Reviews* 64 (2006): 265-274; S. J. Salminen, M. Gueimonde, and E. Isolauri, Probiotics that modify disease risk, *American Society for Nutritional Sciences* 135 (2005): 1294-1298; F. Guarner and coauthors, Should yoghurt cultures be considered probiotic? *British Journal of Nutrition* 93 (2005): 783-786; J. M. Saavedra and A. Tschernia, Human studies with probiotics and prebiotics: Clinical implications, *British Journal of Nutrition* 87 (2002): S241-S246; P. Marteau and M. C. Boutron-Ruault, Nutritional advantages of probiotics and prebiotics, *British Journal of Nutrition* 87 (2002): S153-S157; G. T. Macfarlane and J. H. Cummings, Probiotics, infection and immunity, *Current Opinion in Infectious Diseases* 15 (2002): 501-506; L. Kopp-Hoolihan, Prophylactic and therapeutic uses of probiotics: A review, *Journal of the American Dietetic Association* 101 (2001): 229-238; M. B. Roberfroid, Prebiotics and probiotics: Are they functional foods? *American Journal of Clinical Nutrition* 71 (2000): 1682S-1687S.

5. J. Ezendam and H. van Loveren, Probiotics: Immunomodulation and evaluation of safety and efficacy, *Nutrition Reviews* 64 (2006): 1-14.

6. J. M. Wong and coauthors, Colonic health: Fermentation and short chain fatty acids, *Journal of Clinical Gastroenterology* 40 (2006): 235-243; S. Bengmark, Colonic food: Pre- and probiotics, *American Journal of Gastroenterology* 95 (2000): S5-S7.

7. P. Bourlioux and coauthors, The intestine and its microflora are partners for the protection of the host: Report on the Danone Symposium "The Intelligent Intestine," held in Paris, June 14, 2002, *American Journal of Clinical Nutrition* 78 (2003): 675-683.

ANSWERS

Study Questions (multiple choice)

1. c   2. c   3. a   4. d   5. b   6. c   7. b   8. d
9. c   10. c

Common Digestive Problems

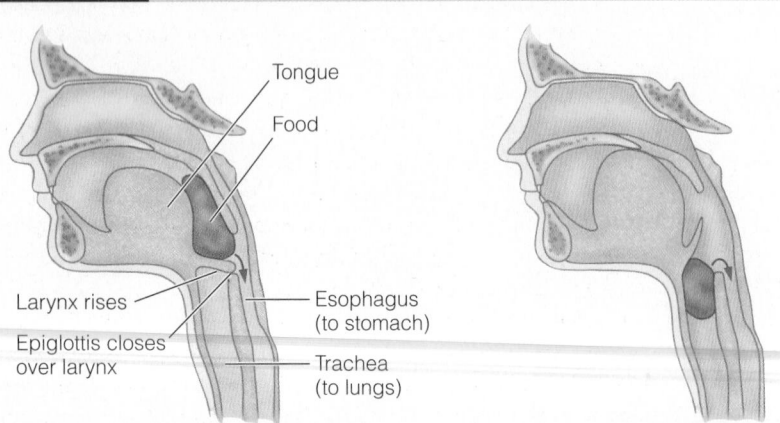

The facts of anatomy and physiology presented in Chapter 3 permit easy understanding of some common problems that occasionally arise in the digestive tract. Food may slip into the air passages instead of the esophagus, causing choking. Bowel movements may be loose and watery, as in diarrhea, or painful and hard, as in constipation. Some people complain about belching, while others are bothered by intestinal gas. Sometimes people develop medical problems such as an ulcer. This highlight describes some of the symptoms of these common digestive problems and suggests strategies for preventing them (the glossary on p. 94 defines the relevant terms).

Choking

A person chokes when a piece of food slips into the **trachea** and becomes lodged so securely that it cuts off breathing (see Figure H3-1). Without oxygen, the person may suffer brain damage or die. For this reason, it is imperative that everyone learns to recognize a person grabbing his or her own throat as the international signal for choking (shown in Figure H3-2) and act promptly.

The choking scenario might read like this. A person is dining in a restaurant with friends. A chunk of food, usually meat, becomes lodged in his trachea so firmly that he cannot make a sound. No sound can be made because the **larynx** is in the trachea and makes sounds only when air is pushed across it. Often he chooses to suffer alone rather than "make a scene in public." If he tries to communicate distress to his friends, he must depend on pantomime. The friends are bewildered by his antics and become terribly worried when he "faints" after a few minutes without air. They call for an ambulance, but by the time it arrives, he is dead from suffocation.

To help a person who is choking, first ask this critical question: "Can you make any sound at all?" If so, relax. You have time to decide what you can do to help. Whatever you do, *do not* hit him on the back—the particle may become lodged more firmly in his air passage. If the person cannot make a sound, shout for help and perform the **Heimlich maneuver** (described in Figure H3-2). You would do well to take a life-saving course and practice these techniques because you will have no time for hesitation if you are called upon to perform this death-defying act.

Almost any food can cause choking, although some are cited more often than others: chunks of meat, hot dogs, nuts, whole grapes, raw carrots, marshmallows, hard or sticky candies, gum, popcorn, and peanut butter. These foods are particularly difficult for young children to safely chew and swallow. In 2000, more than 17,500 children (under 15 years old) in the United States choked; most of them choked on food, and 160 of them choked to death.[1] Always remain alert to the dangers of choking whenever young children are eating. To prevent choking, cut food into small pieces, chew thoroughly before swallowing, don't talk or laugh with food in your mouth, and don't eat when breathing hard.

Vomiting

Another common digestive mishap is **vomiting.** Vomiting can be a symptom of many different diseases or may arise in situations that upset the body's equilibrium, such as air or sea travel. For whatever reason, the contents of the stomach are propelled up through the esophagus to the mouth and expelled.

FIGURE H3-1 Normal Swallowing and Choking

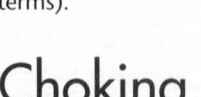

Tongue

Food

Larynx rises

Epiglottis closes over larynx

Esophagus (to stomach)

Trachea (to lungs)

Swallowing. The epiglottis closes over the larynx, blocking entrance to the lungs via the trachea. The red arrow shows that food is heading down the esophagus normally.

Choking. A choking person cannot speak or gasp because food lodged in the trachea blocks the passage of air. The red arrow points to where the food should have gone to prevent choking.

FIGURE H3-2 First Aid for Choking

The first-aid strategy most likely to succeed is abdominal thrusts, sometimes called the Heimlich maneuver. Only if all else fails, open the person's mouth by grasping both his tongue and lower jaw and lifting. Then, and *only if* you can see the object, use your finger to sweep it out and begin rescue breathing.

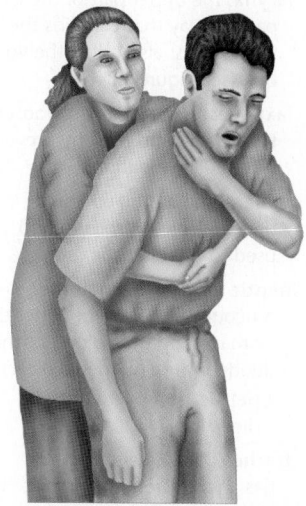

The universal signal for choking is when a person grabs his throat. It alerts others to the need for assistance. If this happens, stand behind the person, and wrap your arms around him. Place the thumb side of one fist snugly against his body, slightly above the navel and below the rib cage. Grasp your fist with your other hand and give him a sudden strong hug inward and upward. Repeat thrusts as necessary.

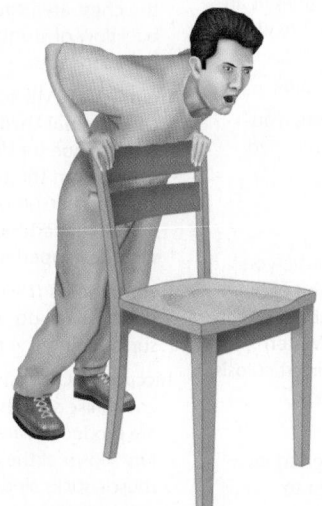

If you are choking and need to self-administer first aid, place the thumb side of one fist slightly above your navel and below your rib cage, grasp the fist with your other hand, and then press inward and upward with a quick motion. If this is unsuccessful, quickly press your upper abdomen over any firm surface such as the back of a chair, a countertop, or a railing.

If vomiting continues long enough or is severe enough, the muscular contractions will extend beyond the stomach and carry the contents of the duodenum, with its green bile, into the stomach and then up the esophagus. Although certainly unpleasant and wearying for the nauseated person, vomiting such as this is no cause for alarm. Vomiting is one of the body's adaptive mechanisms to rid itself of something irritating. The best advice is to rest and drink small amounts of liquids as tolerated until the nausea subsides.

A physician's care may be needed, however, when large quantities of fluid are lost from the GI tract, causing dehydration. With massive fluid loss from the GI tract, all of the body's other fluids redistribute themselves so that, eventually, fluid is taken from every cell of the body. Leaving the cells with the fluid are salts that are absolutely essential to the life of the cells, and they must be replaced. Replacement is difficult if the vomiting continues, and intravenous feedings of saline and glucose may be necessary while the physician diagnoses the cause of the vomiting and begins corrective therapy.

In an infant, vomiting is likely to become serious early in its course, and a physician should be contacted soon after onset. Infants have more fluid between their body cells than adults do, so more fluid can move readily into the digestive tract and be lost from the body. Consequently, the body water of infants becomes depleted and their body salt balance upset faster than in adults.

Self-induced vomiting, such as occurs in bulimia nervosa, also has serious consequences. In addition to fluid and salt imbalances, repeated vomiting can cause irritation and infection of the pharynx, esophagus, and salivary glands; erosion of the teeth and gums; and dental caries. The esophagus may rupture or tear, as may the stomach. Sometimes the eyes become red from pressure during vomiting. Bulimic behavior reflects underlying psychological problems that require intervention. (Bulimia nervosa is discussed fully in Highlight 8.)

Projectile vomiting is also serious. The contents of the stomach are expelled with such force that they leave the mouth in a wide arc like a bullet leaving a gun. This type of vomiting requires immediate medical attention.

Diarrhea

Diarrhea is characterized by frequent, loose, watery stools. Such stools indicate that the intestinal contents have moved too quickly through the intestines for fluid absorption to take place, or that water has been drawn from the cells lining the intestinal tract and added to the food residue. Like vomiting, diarrhea can lead to considerable fluid and salt losses, but the composition of the fluids is different. Stomach fluids lost in vomiting are highly acidic, whereas intestinal fluids lost in diarrhea are nearly neutral. When fluid losses require medical attention, correct replacement is crucial.

Diarrhea is a symptom of various medical conditions and treatments. It may occur abruptly in a healthy person as a result of infections (such as food poisoning) or as a side effect of medications. When used in large quantities, food ingredients such as the sugar alternative sorbitol and the fat alternative olestra may also cause diarrhea in some people. If a food is responsible, then that food must be omitted from the diet, at least temporarily. If medication is responsible, a different medicine, when possible, or a different form (injectable versus oral, for example) may alleviate the problem.

Diarrhea may also occur as a result of disorders of the GI tract, such as irritable bowel syndrome or colitis. **Irritable bowel syndrome** is one of the most common GI disorders and is characterized by a disturbance in the motility of the GI tract.[2] In most cases, GI contractions are stronger and last longer than normal, forcing intestinal contents through quickly and causing gas, bloating, and diarrhea. In some cases, however, GI contractions are weaker than normal, slowing the passage of intestinal contents and causing constipation. The exact cause of irritable bowel syndrome is not known, but researchers believe nerves and hormones are involved. The condition seems to worsen for some

GLOSSARY

acid controllers: medications used to prevent or relieve indigestion by suppressing production of acid in the stomach; also called **H2 blockers.** Common brands include Pepcid AC, Tagamet HB, Zantac 75, and Axid AR.

antacids: medications used to relieve indigestion by neutralizing acid in the stomach. Common brands include Alka-Seltzer, Maalox, Rolaids, and Tums.

belching: the expulsion of gas from the stomach through the mouth.

colitis (ko-LYE-tis): inflammation of the colon.

colonic irrigation: the popular, but potentially harmful practice of "washing" the large intestine with a powerful enema machine.

constipation: the condition of having infrequent or difficult bowel movements.

defecate (DEF-uh-cate): to move the bowels and eliminate waste.
- **defaecare** = to remove dregs

diarrhea: the frequent passage of watery bowel movements.

diverticula (dye-ver-TIC-you-la): sacs or pouches that develop in the weakened areas of the intestinal wall (like bulges in an inner tube where the tire wall is weak).
- **divertir** = to turn aside

diverticulitis (DYE-ver-tic-you-LYE-tis): infected or inflamed diverticula.
- **itis** = infection or inflammation

diverticulosis (DYE-ver-tic-you-LOH-sis): the condition of having diverticula. About one in every six people in Western countries develops diverticulosis in middle or later life.
- **osis** = condition

enemas: solutions inserted into the rectum and colon to stimulate a bowel movement and empty the lower large intestine.

gastroesophageal reflux: the backflow of stomach acid into the esophagus, causing damage to the cells of the esophagus and the sensation of heartburn. **Gastroesophageal reflux disease (GERD)** is characterized by symptoms of reflux occurring two or more times a week.

heartburn: a burning sensation in the chest area caused by backflow of stomach acid into the esophagus.

Heimlich (HIME-lick) **maneuver (abdominal thrust maneuver):** a technique for dislodging an object from the trachea of a choking person (see Figure H3-2); named for the physician who developed it.

hemorrhoids (HEM-oh-royds): painful swelling of the veins surrounding the rectum.

hiccups (HICK-ups): repeated cough-like sounds and jerks that are produced when an involuntary spasm of the diaphragm muscle sucks air down the windpipe; also spelled *hiccoughs*.

indigestion: incomplete or uncomfortable digestion, usually accompanied by pain, nausea, vomiting, heartburn, intestinal gas, or belching.
- **in** = not

irritable bowel syndrome: an intestinal disorder of unknown cause. Symptoms include abdominal discomfort and cramping, diarrhea, constipation, or alternating diarrhea and constipation.

larynx: the upper part of the air passageway that contains the vocal cords; also called the voice box (see Figure H3-1).

laxatives: substances that loosen the bowels and thereby prevent or treat constipation.

mineral oil: a purified liquid derived from petroleum and used to treat constipation.

peptic ulcer: a lesion in the mucous membrane of either the stomach (a gastric ulcer) or the duodenum (a duodenal ulcer).
- **peptic** = concerning digestion

trachea (TRAKE-ee-uh): the air passageway from the larynx to the lungs; also called the *windpipe*.

ulcer: a lesion of the skin or mucous membranes characterized by inflammation and damaged tissues. See also *peptic ulcer*.

vomiting: expulsion of the contents of the stomach up through the esophagus to the mouth.

---

people when they eat certain foods or during stressful events. These triggers seem to aggravate symptoms but not cause them. Dietary treatment hinges on identifying and avoiding individual foods that aggravate symptoms; small meals may also be beneficial. People with **colitis,** an inflammation of the large intestine, may also suffer from severe diarrhea. They often benefit from complete bowel rest and medication. If treatment fails, surgery to remove the colon and rectum may be necessary.

Treatment for diarrhea depends on cause and severity, but it always begins with rehydration.[3] Mild diarrhea may subside with simple rest and extra liquids (such as clear juices and soups) to replace fluid losses. However, call a physician if diarrhea is bloody or if it worsens or persists—especially in an infant, young child, elderly person, or person with a compromised immune system. Severe diarrhea can be life threatening.

Constipation

Like diarrhea, **constipation** describes a symptom, not a disease. Each person's GI tract has its own cycle of waste elimination, which depends on its owner's health, the type of food eaten, when it was eaten, and when the person takes time to **defecate.** What's normal for some people may not be normal for others. Some people have bowel movements three times a day; others

may have them three times a week. The symptoms of constipation include straining during bowel movements, hard stools, and infrequent bowel movements (fewer than three per week).[4] Ab-

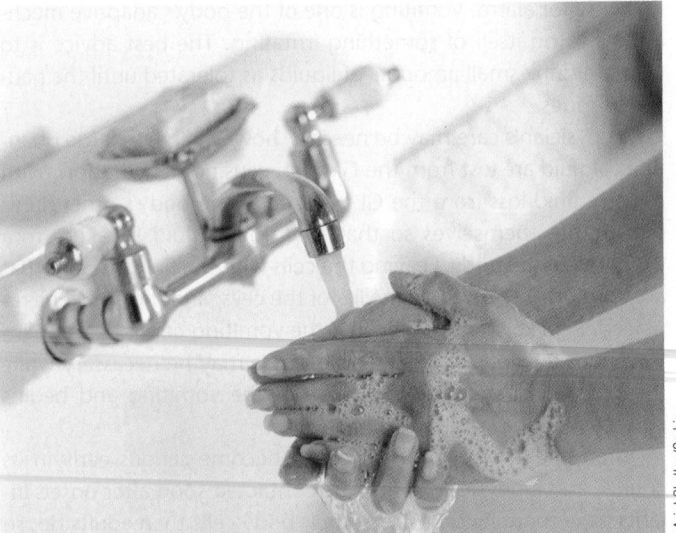

Personal hygiene (such as regular hand washing with soap and water) and safe food preparation (as described in Chapter 19) are easy and effective steps to take in preventing diarrheal diseases.

dominal discomfort, headaches, backaches, and the passing of gas sometimes accompany constipation.

Often a person's lifestyle may cause constipation. Being too busy to respond to the defecation signal is a common complaint. If a person receives the signal to defecate and ignores it, the signal may not return for several hours. In the meantime, water continues to be withdrawn from the fecal matter, so when the person does defecate, the stools are dry and hard. In such a case, a person's daily regimen may need to be revised to allow time to have a bowel movement when the body sends its signal. One possibility is to go to bed earlier in order to rise earlier, allowing ample time for a leisurely breakfast and a movement.

Although constipation usually reflects lifestyle habits, in some cases it may be a side effect of medication or may reflect a medical problem such as tumors that are obstructing the passage of waste. If discomfort is associated with passing fecal matter, seek medical advice to rule out disease. Once this has been done, dietary or other measures for correction can be considered.

One dietary measure that may be appropriate is to increase dietary fiber to 20 to 25 grams per day over the course of a week or two. Fibers found in fruits, vegetables, and whole grains help to prevent constipation by increasing fecal mass. In the GI tract, fiber attracts water, creating soft, bulky stools that stimulate bowel contractions to push the contents along. These contractions strengthen the intestinal muscles. The improved muscle tone, together with the water content of the stools, eases elimination, reducing the pressure in the rectal veins and helping to prevent **hemorrhoids.** Chapter 4 provides more information on fiber's role in maintaining a healthy colon and reducing the risks of colon cancer and diverticulosis. **Diverticulosis** is a condition in which the intestinal walls develop bulges in weakened areas, most commonly in the colon (see Figure H3-3). These bulging pockets, known as **diverticula,** can worsen constipation, entrap feces, and become painfully infected and inflamed **(diverticulitis).** Treatment may require hospitalization, antibiotics, or surgery.

FIGURE H3-3 Diverticula in the Colon

Diverticula may develop anywhere along the GI tract, but they are most common in the colon.

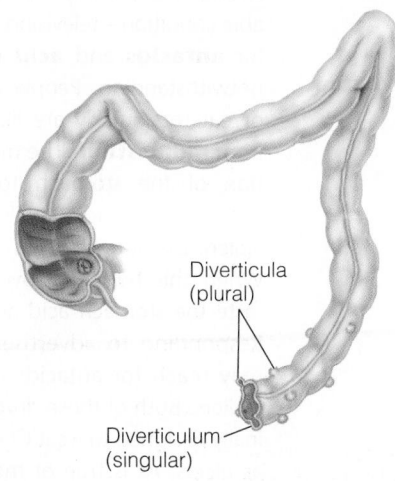

Diverticula (plural)

Diverticulum (singular)

Drinking plenty of water in conjunction with eating high-fiber foods also helps to prevent constipation. The increased bulk physically stimulates the upper GI tract, promoting peristalsis throughout. Similarly, physical activity improves the muscle tone and motility of the digestive tract. As little as 30 minutes of physical activity a day can help prevent or alleviate constipation.

Eating prunes—or "dried plums" as some have renamed them—can also be helpful. Prunes are high in fiber and also contain a laxative substance.* If a morning defecation is desired, a person can drink prune juice at bedtime; if the evening is preferred, the person can drink prune juice with breakfast.

These suggested changes in lifestyle or diet should correct chronic constipation without the use of **laxatives, enemas,** or **mineral oil,** although television commercials often try to persuade people otherwise. One of the fallacies often perpetrated by advertisements is that one person's successful use of a product is a good recommendation for others to use that product.

As a matter of fact, diet changes that relieve constipation for one person may increase the constipation of another. For instance, increasing fiber intake stimulates peristalsis and helps the person with a sluggish colon. Some people, though, have a spastic type of constipation, in which peristalsis promotes strong contractions that close off a segment of the colon and prevent passage; for these people, increasing fiber intake would be exactly the wrong thing to do.

A person who seems to need products such as laxatives frequently should seek a physician's advice. One potentially harmful but currently popular practice is **colonic irrigation**—the internal washing of the large intestine with a powerful enema machine. Such an extreme cleansing is not only unnecessary, but it can be hazardous, causing illness and death from equipment contamination, electrolyte depletion, and intestinal perforation. Less extreme practices can cause problems, too. Frequent use of laxatives and enemas can lead to dependency; upset the body's fluid, salt, and mineral balances; and, in the case of mineral oil, interfere with the absorption of fat-soluble vitamins. (Mineral oil dissolves the vitamins but is not itself absorbed. Instead, it leaves the body, carrying the vitamins with it.)

Belching and Gas

Many people complain of problems that they attribute to excessive gas. For some, **belching** is the complaint. Others blame intestinal gas for abdominal discomforts and embarrassment. Most people believe that the problems occur after they eat certain foods. This may be the case with intestinal gas, but belching results from swallowing air. The best advice for belching seems to be to eat slowly, chew thoroughly, and relax while eating.

Everyone swallows a little bit of air with each mouthful of food, but people who eat too fast may swallow too much air and then have to belch. Ill-fitting dentures, carbonated beverages, and chewing gum can also contribute to the swallowing of air with resultant belching. Occasionally, belching can be a sign of a more serious disorder, such as gallbladder disease or a peptic ulcer.

---

* This substance is dihydroxyphenyl isatin.

People troubled by gas need to determine which foods bother them and then eat those foods in moderation.

People who eat or drink too fast may also trigger **hiccups,** the repeated spasms that produce a cough-like sound and jerky movement. Normally, hiccups soon subside and are of no medical significance, but they can be bothersome. The most effective cure is to hold the breath for as long as possible, which helps to relieve the spasms of the diaphragm.

Although expelling gas can be a humiliating experience, it is quite normal. (People who experience painful bloating from mal-

absorption diseases, however, require medical treatment.) Healthy people expel several hundred milliliters of gas several times a day. Almost all (99 percent) of the gases expelled—nitrogen, oxygen, hydrogen, methane, and carbon dioxide—are odorless. The remaining "volatile" gases are the infamous ones.

Foods that produce gas usually must be determined individually. The most common offenders are foods rich in the carbohydrates—sugars, starches, and fibers. When partially digested carbohydrates reach the large intestine, bacteria digest them, giving off gas as a by-product. People can test foods suspected of forming gas by omitting them individually for a trial period to see if there is any improvement.

Heartburn and "Acid Indigestion"

Almost everyone has experienced **heartburn** at one time or another, usually soon after eating a meal. Medically known as **gastroesophageal reflux,** heartburn is the painful sensation a person feels behind the breastbone when the lower esophageal sphincter allows the stomach contents to reflux into the esophagus (see Figure H3-4). This may happen if a person eats or drinks too much (or both). Tight clothing and even changes of position (lying down, bending over) can cause it, too, as can some medications and smoking. Weight gain and overweight increase the frequency, severity, and duration of heartburn symptoms.[5] A defect of the sphincter muscle itself is a possible, but less common, cause.

If the heartburn is not caused by an anatomical defect, treatment is fairly simple. To avoid such misery in the future, the person needs to learn to eat less at a sitting, chew food more thoroughly, and eat it more slowly. Additional strategies are presented in Table H3-1 at the end of this highlight.

As far as "acid indigestion" is concerned, recall from Chapter 3 that the strong acidity of the stomach is a desirable condition—television commercials for **antacids** and **acid controllers** notwithstanding. People who overeat or eat too quickly are likely to suffer from **indigestion.** The muscular reaction of the stomach to unchewed lumps or to being overfilled may be so violent that it upsets normal peristalsis. When this happens, overeaters may taste the stomach acid and feel pain. Responding to advertisements, they may reach for antacids or acid controllers. Both of these drugs were originally designed to treat GI illnesses such as ulcers. As is true of most over-the-counter medicines, antacids and acid

FIGURE H3-4   Gastroesophageal Reflux

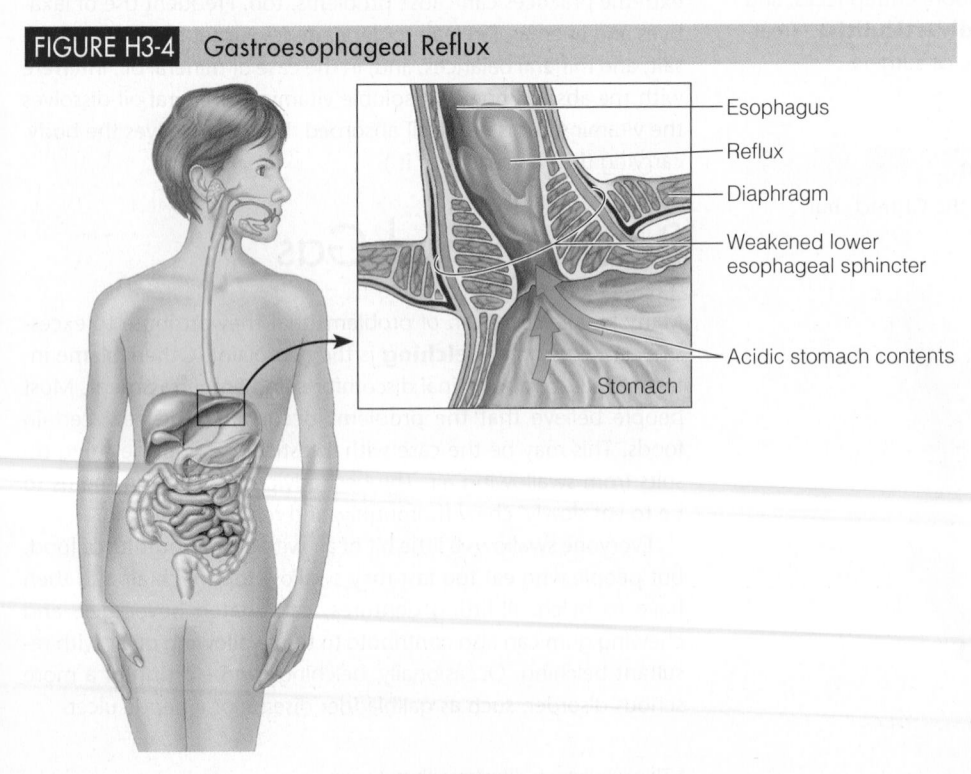

- Esophagus
- Reflux
- Diaphragm
- Weakened lower esophageal sphincter
- Acidic stomach contents
- Stomach

controllers should be used only infrequently for occasional heart-burn; they may mask or cause problems if used regularly. Acid-blocking drugs weaken the defensive mucous barrier of the GI tract, thereby increasing the risks of infections such as pneumo-nia, especially in vulnerable populations like the elderly.[6] Instead of self-medicating, people who suffer from frequent and regular bouts of heartburn and indigestion should try the strategies presented in the table below. If problems continue, they may need to see a physician, who can prescribe specific medication to control gastroesophageal reflux. Without treatment, the re-peated splashes of acid can severely damage the cells of the esophagus, creating a condition known as Barrett's esophagus.[7] At that stage, the risk of cancer in the throat or esophagus in-creases dramatically. To repeat, if symptoms persist, see a doc-tor—don't self-medicate.

Ulcers

Ulcers are another common digestive problem. An **ulcer** is a le-sion (a sore) and a **peptic ulcer** is a lesion in the lining of the stomach (gastric ulcers) or the duodenum of the small intestine (duodenal ulcers). The compromised lining is left unprotected and exposed to gastric juices, which can be painful. In some cases, ulcers can cause internal bleeding. If GI bleeding is exces-sive, iron deficiency may develop. Ulcers that perforate the GI lin-ing can pose life-threatening complications.

Many people naively believe that an ulcer is caused by stress or spicy foods, but this is not the case. The stomach lining in a healthy person is well protected by its mucous coat. What, then, causes ulcers to form?

Three major causes of ulcers have been identified: bacterial in-fection with *Helicobacter pylori* (commonly abbreviated *H. pylori);*

the use of certain anti-inflammatory drugs such as aspirin, ibupro-fen, and naproxen; and disorders that cause excessive gastric acid secretion. Most commonly, ulcers develop in response to *H. pylori* infection.[8] The cause of the ulcer dictates the type of medication used in treatment. For example, people with ulcers caused by in-fection receive antibiotics, whereas those with ulcers caused by medicines discontinue their use. In addition, all treatment plans aim to relieve pain, heal the ulcer, and prevent recurrence.

The regimen for ulcer treatment is to treat for infection, elimi-nate any food that routinely causes indigestion or pain, and avoid coffee and caffeine- and alcohol-containing beverages. Both reg-ular and decaffeinated coffee stimulate acid secretion and so ag-gravate *existing* ulcers.

Ulcers and their treatments highlight the importance of not self-medicating when symptoms persist. People with *H. pylori* in-fection often take over-the-counter acid controllers to relieve the pain of their ulcers when, instead, they need physician-prescribed antibiotics. Suppressing gastric acidity not only fails to heal the ul-cer, but it also actually worsens inflammation during an *H. pylori* infection. Furthermore, *H. pylori* infection has been linked with stomach cancer, making prompt diagnosis and appropriate treat-ment essential.[9]

Table H3-1 summarizes strategies to prevent or alleviate common GI problems. Many of these problems reflect hurried lifestyles. For this reason, many of their remedies require that people slow down and take the time to eat leisurely; chew food thoroughly to prevent choking, heartburn, and acid indigestion; rest until vom-iting and diarrhea subside; and heed the urge to defecate. In ad-dition, people must learn how to handle life's day-to-day problems and challenges without overreacting and becoming up-set; learn how to relax, get enough sleep, and enjoy life. Remem-ber, "what's eating you" may cause more GI distress than what you eat.

TABLE H3-1	Strategies to Prevent or Alleviate Common GI Problems		
GI Problem	**Strategies**	**GI Problem**	**Strategies**
Choking	• Take small bites of food. • Chew thoroughly before swallowing. • Don't talk or laugh with food in your mouth. • Don't eat when breathing hard.	Heartburn	• Eat small meals. • Drink liquids between meals. • Sit up while eating; elevate your head when lying down. • Wait 3 hours after eating before lying down. • Wait 2 hours after eating before exercising. • Refrain from wearing tight-fitting clothing. • Avoid foods, beverages, and medications that aggravate your heartburn. • Refrain from smoking cigarettes or using tobacco products. • Lose weight if overweight.
Diarrhea	• Rest. • Drink fluids to replace losses. • Call for medical help if diarrhea persists.		
Constipation	• Eat a high-fiber diet. • Drink plenty of fluids. • Exercise regularly. • Respond promptly to the urge to defecate.		
Belching	• Eat slowly. • Chew thoroughly. • Relax while eating.	Ulcer	• Take medicine as prescribed by your physician. • Avoid coffee and caffeine- and alcohol-containing beverages. • Avoid foods that aggravate your ulcer. • Minimize aspirin, ibuprofen, and naproxen use. • Refrain from smoking cigarettes.
Intestinal gas	• Eat bothersome foods in moderation.		

NUTRITION ON THE NET

- Search for "choking," "vomiting," "diarrhea," "constipation," "heartburn," "indigestion," and "ulcers" at the U.S.
  Government health information site:
  www.healthfinder.gov

- Visit the Center for Digestive Health and Nutrition:
  www.gihealth.com

- Visit the Digestive Diseases section of the National Institute of Diabetes, Digestive, and Kidney Diseases:
  www.niddk.nih.gov/health/health.htm

- Visit the patient information section of the American
  College of Gastroenterology: **www.acg.gi.org**

- Learn more about *H. pylori* from the Helicobacter Foundation: **www.helico.com**

REFERENCES

1. K. Gotsch, J. L. Annest, and P. Holmgreen,
   Nonfatal choking-related episodes among
   children-United States, 2001, *Morbidity and
   Mortality Weekly Report* 51 (2002): 945-948.
2. B. J. Horwitz and R. S. Fisher, The irritable
   bowel syndrome, *New England Journal of
   Medicine* 344 (2001): 1846-1850.
3. N. M. Thielman and R. L. Guerrant, Acute
   infectious diarrhea, *New England Journal of
   Medicine* 350 (2004): 38-47.
4. A. Lembo and M. Camilleri, Chronic constipation, *New England Journal of Medicine* 349
   (2003): 1360-1368.

5. B. C. Jacobson and coauthors, Body-mass
   index and symptoms of gastroesophageal
   reflux in women, *New England Journal of
   Medicine* 354 (2006): 2340-2348.
6. R. J. F. Laheij and coauthors, Risk of commu-
   nity-acquired pneumonia and use of gastric
   acid-suppressive drugs, *Journal of the American
   Medical Association* 292 (2004): 1955-1960.
7. N. Shaheen and D. F. Ransohoff, Gastroesophageal reflux, Barrett's esophagus, and
   esophageal cancer: Scientific review, *Journal
   of the American Medical Association* 287
   (2002): 1972-1981.

8. S. Suerbaum and P. Michetti, Helicobacter
   pylori infection, *New England Journal of
   Medicine* 347 (2002): 1175-1186.
9. N. Uemura and coauthors, Helicobacter
   pylori infection and the development of
   gastric cancer, *New England Journal of Medicine* 345 (2001): 784-789.

Thomson™ NOW! Throughout this chapter, the ThomsonNOW logo indicates an opportunity for online self-study, linking you to interactive tutorials and videos based on your level of understanding.

www.thomsonedu.com/thomsonnow

Figure 4.10: Animated! Carbohydrate Digestion in the GI Tract

Nutrition Portfolio Journal

Nutrition Calculations: Practice Problems

Nutrition in Your Life

Whether you are cramming for an exam or daydreaming about your next vacation, your brain needs carbohydrate to power its activities. Your muscles need carbohydrate to fuel their work, too, whether you are racing up the stairs to class or moving on the dance floor to your favorite music. Where can you get carbohydrate? And are some foods healthier choices than others? As you will learn from this chapter, whole grains, vegetables, legumes, and fruits naturally deliver ample carbohydrate and fiber with valuable vitamins and minerals and little or no fat. Milk products typically lack fiber, but they also provide carbohydrate along with an assortment of vitamins and minerals.

The Carbohydrates: Sugars, Starches, and Fibers

CHAPTER OUTLINE

The Chemist's View of Carbohydrates

The Simple Carbohydrates • Monosaccharides • Disaccharides

The Complex Carbohydrates • Glycogen • Starches • Fibers

Digestion and Absorption of Carbohydrates • Carbohydrate Digestion • Carbohydrate Absorption • Lactose Intolerance

Glucose in the Body • A Preview of Carbohydrate Metabolism • The Constancy of Blood Glucose

Health Effects and Recommended Intakes of Sugars • Health Effects of Sugars • Controversies Surrounding Sugars • Recommended Intakes of Sugars

Health Effects and Recommended Intakes of Starch and Fibers • Health Effects of Starch and Fibers • Recommended Intakes of Starch and Fibers • From Guidelines to Groceries

HIGHLIGHT 4 Alternatives to Sugar

A student, quietly studying a textbook, is seldom aware that within his brain cells, billions of glucose molecules are splitting to provide the energy that permits him to learn. Yet glucose provides nearly all of the energy the human brain uses daily. Similarly, a marathon runner, bursting across the finish line in an explosion of sweat and triumph, seldom gives credit to the glycogen fuel her muscles have devoured to help her finish the race. Yet, together, these two **carbohydrates**—glucose and its storage form glycogen—provide about half of all the energy muscles and other body tissues use. The other half of the body's energy comes mostly from fat.

People don't eat glucose and glycogen directly. When they eat foods rich in carbohydrates, their bodies receive glucose for immediate energy and into glycogen for reserve energy. All plant foods—whole grains, vegetables, legumes, and fruits—provide ample carbohydrate. Milk also contains carbohydrates.

Many people mistakenly think of carbohydrates as "fattening" and avoid them when trying to lose weight. Such a strategy may be helpful if the carbohydrates are the simple sugars of soft drinks, candy, and cookies, but it is counterproductive if the carbohydrates are the complex carbohydrates of whole grains, vegetables, and legumes. As the next section explains, not all carbohydrates are created equal.

The Chemist's View of Carbohydrates

The dietary carbohydrate family includes the **simple carbohydrates** (the sugars) and the **complex carbohydrates** (the starches and fibers). The simple carbohydrates are those that chemists describe as:

- Monosaccharides—single sugars
- Disaccharides—sugars composed of pairs of monosaccharides

The complex carbohydrates are:

- Polysaccharides—large molecules composed of chains of monosaccharides

carbohydrates: compounds composed of carbon, oxygen, and hydrogen arranged as monosaccharides or multiples of monosaccharides. Most, but not all, carbohydrates have a ratio of one carbon molecule to one water molecule: $(CH_2O)_n$.
- **carbo** = carbon (C)
- **hydrate** = with water (H_2O)

simple carbohydrates (sugars): monosaccharides and disaccharides.

complex carbohydrates (starches and fibers): polysaccharides composed of straight or branched chains of monosaccharides.

FIGURE 4-1 Atoms and Their Bonds

The four main types of atoms found in nutrients are hydrogen (H), oxygen (O), nitrogen (N), and carbon (C).

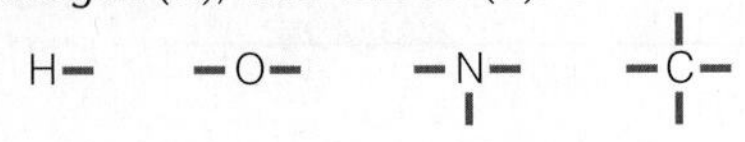

$$H- \quad -O- \quad -\overset{\displaystyle |}{\underset{\displaystyle |}{N}}- \quad -\overset{\displaystyle |}{\underset{\displaystyle |}{C}}-$$

$$1 \qquad 2 \qquad 3 \qquad 4$$

Each atom has a characteristic number of bonds it can form with other atoms.

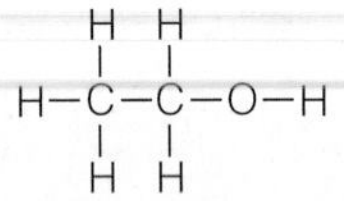

$$H-\overset{\displaystyle \overset{H}{|}}{\underset{\displaystyle \underset{H}{|}}{C}}-\overset{\displaystyle \overset{H}{|}}{\underset{\displaystyle \underset{H}{|}}{C}}-O-H$$

Notice that in this simple molecule of ethyl alcohol, each H has one bond, O has two, and each C has four.

◆ Most of the monosaccharides important in nutrition are **hexoses,** simple sugars with six atoms of carbon and the formula $C_6H_{12}O_6$.
- **hex** = six

FIGURE 4-2 Chemical Structure of Glucose

On paper, the structure of glucose has to be drawn flat, but in nature the five carbons and oxygen are roughly in a plane. The atoms attached to the ring carbons extend above and below the plane.

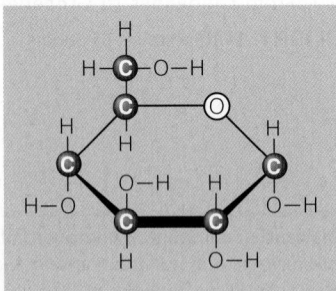

---

monosaccharides (mon-oh-SACK-uh-rides): carbohydrates of the general formula $C_nH_{2n}O_n$ that typically form a single ring. See Appendix C for the chemical structures of the monosaccharides.
- **mono** = one
- **saccharide** = sugar

glucose (GLOO-kose): a monosaccharide; sometimes known as blood sugar or **dextrose.**
- **ose** = carbohydrate
- ⬡ = glucose

To understand the structure of carbohydrates, look at the units of which they are made. The monosaccharides most important in nutrition ◆ each contain 6 carbon atoms, 12 hydrogens, and 6 oxygens (written in shorthand as $C_6H_{12}O_6$).

Each atom can form a certain number of chemical bonds with other atoms:

- Carbon atoms can form four bonds
- Nitrogen atoms, three
- Oxygen atoms, two
- Hydrogen atoms, only one

Chemists represent the bonds as lines between the chemical symbols (such as C, N, O, and H) that stand for the atoms (see Figure 4-1).

Atoms form molecules in ways that satisfy the bonding requirements of each atom. Figure 4-1 includes the structure of ethyl alcohol, the active ingredient of alcoholic beverages, as an example. The two carbons each have four bonds represented by lines; the oxygen has two; and each hydrogen has one bond connecting it to other atoms. Chemical structures bond according to these rules as dictated by nature.

IN SUMMARY

The carbohydrates are made of carbon (C), oxygen (O), and hydrogen (H). Each of these atoms can form a specified number of chemical bonds: carbon forms four, oxygen forms two, and hydrogen forms one.

The Simple Carbohydrates

The following list of the most important simple carbohydrates in nutrition symbolizes them as hexagons and pentagons of different colors.* Three are monosaccharides:

- Glucose ⬡
- Fructose ⬠
- Galactose ⬡

Three are disaccharides:

- Maltose (glucose + glucose) ⬡⬡
- Sucrose (glucose + fructose) ⬡⬠
- Lactose (glucose + galactose) ⬡⬡

Monosaccharides

The three **monosaccharides** important in nutrition all have the same numbers and kinds of atoms, but in different arrangements. These chemical differences account for the differing sweetness of the monosaccharides. A pinch of purified glucose on the tongue gives only a mild sweet flavor, and galactose hardly tastes sweet at all. Fructose, however, is as intensely sweet as honey and, in fact, is the sugar primarily responsible for honey's sweetness.

Glucose Chemically, **glucose** is a larger and more complicated molecule than the ethyl alcohol shown in Figure 4-1, but it obeys the same rules of chemistry: each carbon atom has four bonds; each oxygen, two bonds; and each hydrogen, one bond. Figure 4-2 illustrates the chemical structure of a glucose molecule.

The diagram of a glucose molecule shows all the relationships between the atoms and proves simple on examination, but chemists have adopted even simpler ways to depict chemical structures. Figure 4-3 presents the chemical structure

---

* Fructose is shown as a pentagon, but like the other monosaccharides, it has six carbons (as you will see in Figure 4-4).

FIGURE 4-3 Simplified Diagrams of Glucose

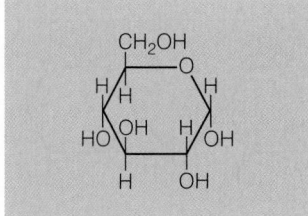 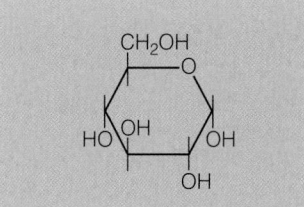 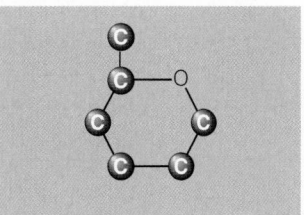 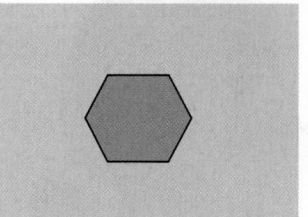

The lines representing some of the bonds and the carbons at the corners are not shown.

Now the single hydrogens are not shown, but lines still extend upward or downward from the ring to show where they belong.

Another way to look at glucose is to notice that its six carbon atoms are all connected.

In this and other illustrations throughout this book, glucose is represented as a blue hexagon.

of glucose in a more simplified way by combining or omitting several symbols— yet it conveys the same information.

Commonly known as blood sugar, glucose serves as an essential energy source for all the body's activities. Its significance to nutrition is tremendous. Later sections explain that glucose is one of the two sugars in every disaccharide and the unit from which the polysaccharides are made almost exclusively. One of these polysaccharides, starch, is the chief food source of energy for all the world's people; another, glycogen, is an important storage form of energy in the body. Glucose reappears frequently throughout this chapter and all those that follow.

Fructose **Fructose** is the sweetest of the sugars. Curiously, fructose has exactly the same chemical *formula* as glucose—$C_6H_{12}O_6$—but its *structure* differs (see Figure 4-4). The arrangement of the atoms in fructose stimulates the taste buds on the tongue to produce the sweet sensation. Fructose occurs naturally in fruits and honey; other sources include products such as soft drinks, ready-to-eat cereals, and desserts that have been sweetened with high-fructose corn syrup (defined on p. 118).

Galactose The monosaccharide **galactose** occurs naturally as a single sugar in only a few foods. Galactose has the same numbers and kinds of atoms as glucose and fructose in yet another arrangement. Figure 4-5 shows galactose beside a molecule of glucose for comparison.

Disaccharides

The **disaccharides** are pairs of the three monosaccharides just described. Glucose occurs in all three; the second member of the pair is either fructose, galactose, or

fructose (FRUK-tose or FROOK-tose): a monosaccharide; sometimes known as fruit sugar or **levulose**. Fructose is found abundantly in fruits, honey, and saps.
- **fruct** = fruit
- ⬡ = fructose

galactose (ga-LAK-tose): a monosaccharide; part of the disaccharide lactose.
- ⬡ = galactose

disaccharides (dye-SACK-uh-rides): pairs of monosaccharides linked together. See Appendix C for the chemical structures of the disaccharides.
- **di** = two

FIGURE 4-4 Two Monosaccharides: Glucose and Fructose

Can you see the similarities? If you learned the rules in Figure 4-3, you will be able to "see" 6 carbons (numbered), 12 hydrogens (those shown plus one at the end of each single line), and 6 oxygens in both these compounds.

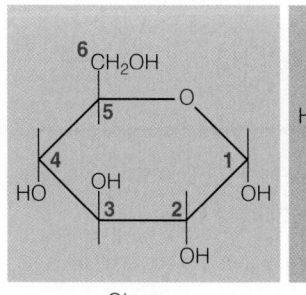

Glucose

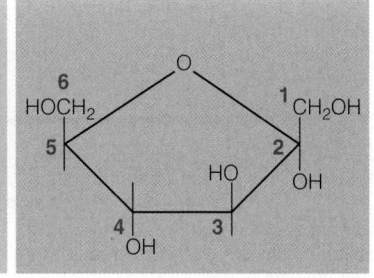

Fructose

FIGURE 4-5 Two Monosaccharides: Glucose and Galactose

Notice the similarities and the difference (highlighted in red) between glucose and galactose. Both have 6 carbons, 12 hydrogens, and 6 oxygens, but the position of one OH group differs slightly.

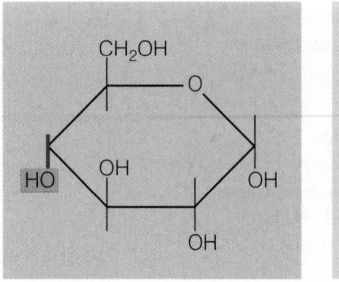

Glucose

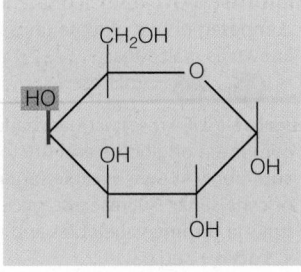

Galactose

Fruits package their simple sugars with fibers, vitamins, and minerals, making them a sweet and healthy snack.

◆ Reminder: A *hydrolysis* reaction splits a molecule into two, with H added to one and OH to the other (from water); Chapter 3 explained that hydrolysis reactions break down molecules during digestion.

condensation: a chemical reaction in which two reactants combine to yield a larger product.

maltose (MAWL-tose): a disaccharide composed of two glucose units; sometimes known as malt sugar.
• ⬡⬡ = maltose

sucrose (SUE-krose): a disaccharide composed of glucose and fructose; commonly known as table sugar, beet sugar, or cane sugar. Sucrose also occurs in many fruits and some vegetables and grains.
• **sucro** = sugar
• ⬡⬡ = sucrose

FIGURE 4-6 Condensation of Two Monosaccharides to Form a Disaccharide

H_2O Water

H_2O Water

Glucose + glucose ⟶ Maltose

An OH group from one glucose and an H atom from another glucose combine to create a molecule of H_2O.

The two glucose molecules bond together with a single O atom to form the disaccharide maltose.

---

another glucose. These carbohydrates—and all the other energy nutrients—are put together and taken apart by similar chemical reactions: condensation and hydrolysis.

Condensation To make a disaccharide, a chemical reaction known as **condensation** links two monosaccharides together (see Figure 4-6). A hydroxyl (OH) group from one monosaccharide and a hydrogen atom (H) from the other combine to create a molecule of water (H_2O). The two originally separate monosaccharides link together with a single oxygen (O).

Hydrolysis To break a disaccharide in two, a chemical reaction known as hydrolysis ◆ occurs (see Figure 4-7). A molecule of water splits to provide the H and OH needed to complete the resulting monosaccharides. Hydrolysis reactions commonly occur during digestion.

Maltose The disaccharide **maltose** consists of two glucose units. Maltose is produced whenever starch breaks down—as happens in human beings during carbohydrate digestion. It also occurs during the fermentation process that yields alcohol. Maltose is only a minor constituent of a few foods, most notably barley.

Sucrose Fructose and glucose together form **sucrose.** Because the fructose is accessible to the taste receptors, sucrose tastes sweet, accounting for some of the natural sweetness of fruits, vegetables, and grains. To make table sugar, sucrose is refined from the juices of sugarcane and sugar beets, then granulated. Depending on the extent to which it is refined, the product becomes the familiar brown, white, and powdered sugars available at grocery stores.

FIGURE 4-7 Hydrolysis of a Disaccharide

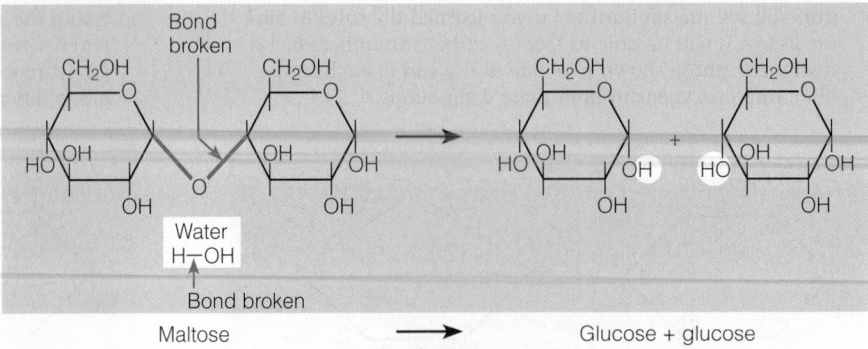

Bond broken

Water
H—OH

Bond broken

Maltose ⟶ Glucose + glucose

The disaccharide maltose splits into two glucose molecules with H added to one and OH to the other (from the water molecule).

Lactose The combination of galactose and glucose makes the disaccharide **lactose,** the principal carbohydrate of milk. Known as milk sugar, lactose contributes half of the energy (kcalories) provided by fat-free milk.

Major sources of starch include grains (such as rice, wheat, millet, rye, barley, and oats), legumes (such as kidney beans, black-eyed peas, pinto beans, navy beans, and garbanzo beans), tubers (such as potatoes), and root crops (such as yams and cassava).

IN SUMMARY

Six simple carbohydrates, or sugars, are important in nutrition. The three monosaccharides (glucose, fructose, and galactose) all have the same chemical formula ($C_6H_{12}O_6$), but their structures differ. The three disaccharides (maltose, sucrose, and lactose) are pairs of monosaccharides, each containing a glucose paired with one of the three monosaccharides. The sugars derive primarily from plants, except for lactose and its component galactose, which come from milk and milk products. Two monosaccharides can be linked together by a condensation reaction to form a disaccharide and water. A disaccharide, in turn, can be broken into its two monosaccharides by a hydrolysis reaction using water.

The Complex Carbohydrates

The simple carbohydrates are the sugars just mentioned—the monosaccharides glucose, fructose, and galactose and the disaccharides maltose, sucrose, and lactose. In contrast, the complex carbohydrates contain many glucose units and, in some cases, a few other monosaccharides strung together as **polysaccharides.** Three types of polysaccharides are important in nutrition: glycogen, starches, and fibers.

Glycogen is a storage form of energy in the animal body; starches play that role in plants; and fibers provide structure in stems, trunks, roots, leaves, and skins of plants. Both glycogen and starch are built of glucose units; fibers are composed of a variety of monosaccharides and other carbohydrate derivatives.

Glycogen

Glycogen is found to only a limited extent in meats and not at all in plants.* For this reason, food is not a significant source of this carbohydrate. However, glycogen does perform an important role in the body. The human body stores glucose as glycogen—many glucose molecules linked together in highly branched chains (see the left side of Figure 4-8 on p. 106). This arrangement permits rapid hydrolysis. When the hormonal message "release energy" arrives at the glycogen storage sites in a liver or muscle cell, enzymes respond by attacking the many branches of glycogen simultaneously, making a surge of glucose available.**

Starches

The human body stores glucose as glycogen, but plant cells store glucose as **starches**—long, branched or unbranched chains of hundreds or thousands of glucose molecules linked together (see the middle and right side of Figure 4-8). These giant starch molecules are packed side by side in grains such as wheat or rice, in root crops and tubers such as yams and potatoes, and in legumes such as peas and beans. When you eat the plant, your body hydrolyzes the starch to glucose and uses the glucose for its own energy purposes.

All starchy foods come from plants. Grains are the richest food source of starch, providing much of the food energy for people all over the world—rice in Asia;

lactose (LAK-tose): a disaccharide composed of glucose and galactose; commonly known as milk sugar.
- **lact** = milk
- ⬡〰⬡ = lactose

polysaccharides: compounds composed of many monosaccharides linked together. An intermediate string of three to ten monosaccharides is an **oligosaccharide.**
- **poly** = many
- **oligo** = few

glycogen (GLY-ko-jen): an animal polysaccharide composed of glucose; manufactured and stored in the liver and muscles as a storage form of glucose. Glycogen is not a significant food source of carbohydrate and is not counted as one of the complex carbohydrates in foods.
- **glyco** = glucose
- **gen** = gives rise to

starches: plant polysaccharides composed of glucose.

---

* Glycogen in animal muscles rapidly hydrolyzes after slaughter.
** Normally, only liver cells can produce glucose from glycogen to be sent *directly* to the blood; muscle cells can also produce glucose from glycogen, but must use it themselves. Muscle cells can restore the blood glucose level *indirectly,* however, as Chapter 7 explains.

| FIGURE 4-8 | Glycogen and Starch Molecules Compared (Small Segments) |

Notice the more highly branched the structure, the greater the number of ends from which glucose can be released. (These units would have to be magnified millions of times to appear at the size shown in this figure. For details of the chemical structures, see Appendix C.)

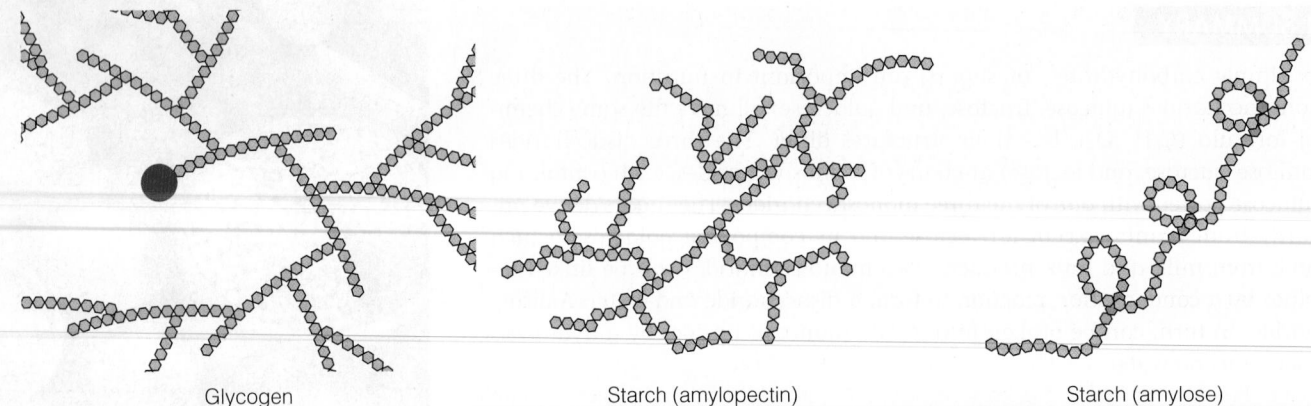

Glycogen

Starch (amylopectin)

Starch (amylose)

A glycogen molecule contains hundreds of glucose units in highly branched chains. Each new glycogen molecule needs a special protein for the attachment of the first glucose (shown here in red).

A starch molecule contains hundreds of glucose molecules in either occasionally branched chains (amylopectin) or unbranched chains (amylose).

wheat in Canada, the United States, and Europe; corn in much of Central and South America; and millet, rye, barley, and oats elsewhere. Legumes and tubers are also important sources of starch.

Fibers

Dietary fibers are the structural parts of plants and thus are found in all plant-derived foods—vegetables, fruits, whole grains, and legumes. Most dietary fibers are polysaccharides. As mentioned earlier, starches are also polysacharides, but dietary fibers differ from starches in that the bonds between their monosaccharides cannot be broken down by digestive enzymes in the body. For this reason, dietary fibers are often described as *nonstarch polysaccharides.** Figure 4-9 illustrates the difference in the bonds that link glucose molecules together in starch with those found in the fiber cellulose. Because dietary fibers pass through the body, they contribute no monosaccharides, and therefore little or no energy.

Even though most foods contain a variety of fibers, researchers often sort dietary fibers into two groups according to their solubility. Such distinctions help to explain their actions in the body.

Soluble Fibers Some dietary fibers dissolve in water (**soluble fibers**), form gels (**viscous**), and are easily digested by bacteria in the colon (**fermentable**). Commonly found in oats, barley, legumes, and citrus fruits, soluble fibers are most often associated with protecting against heart disease and diabetes by lowering blood cholesterol and glucose levels, respectively.[1]

Insoluble Fibers Other fibers do not dissolve in water (**insoluble fibers**), do not form gels (nonviscous), and are less readily fermented. Found mostly in whole grains (bran) and vegetables, insoluble fibers promote bowel movements and alleviate constipation.

Fiber Sources As mentioned, dietary fibers occur naturally in plants. When these fibers have been extracted from plants or manufactured and then added to foods or used in supplements they are called *functional fibers*—if they have beneficial health

dietary fibers: in plant foods, the *nonstarch polysaccharides* that are not digested by human digestive enzymes, although some are digested by GI tract bacteria. Dietary fibers include cellulose, hemicelluloses, pectins, gums, and mucilages and the nonpolysaccharides lignins, cutins, and tannins.

soluble fibers: indigestible food components that dissolve in water to form a gel. An example is pectin from fruit, which is used to thicken jellies.

viscous: a gel-like consistency.

fermentable: the extent to which bacteria in the GI tract can break down fibers to fragments that the body can use.**

insoluble fibers: indigestible food components that do not dissolve in water. Examples include the tough, fibrous structures found in the strings of celery and the skins of corn kernels.

---

*The nonstarch polysaccharide fibers include cellulose, hemicelluloses, pectins, gums, and mucilages. Fibers also include some *nonpolysaccharides* such as lignins, cutins, and tannins.
**Dietary fibers are fermented by bacteria in the colon to short-chain fatty acids, which are absorbed and metabolized by cells in the GI tract and liver (Chapter 5 describes fatty acids).

effects. Cellulose in cereals, for example, is a dietary fiber, but when consumed as a supplement to alleviate constipation, cellulose is considered a functional fiber. *Total fiber* refers to the sum of dietary fibers and functional fibers. These terms ◆ were created by the DRI committee to accommodate products that may contain new fiber sources, but consumers may find them too confusing to be used on food labels.[2]

Resistant Starches A few starches are classified as dietary fibers. Known as **resistant starches**, these starches escape digestion and absorption in the small intestine. Starch may resist digestion for several reasons, including the individual's efficiency in digesting starches and the food's physical properties. Resistant starch is common in whole legumes, raw potatoes, and unripe bananas.

Phytic Acid Although not classified as a dietary fiber, **phytic acid** is often found accompanying them in the same foods. Because of this close association, researchers have been unable to determine whether it is the dietary fiber, the phytic acid, or both, that binds with minerals, preventing their absorption. This binding presents a risk of mineral deficiencies, but the risk is minimal when total fiber intake is reasonable and mineral intake adequate. The nutrition consequences of such mineral losses are described further in Chapters 12 and 13.

FIGURE 4-9 Starch and Cellulose Molecules Compared (Small Segments)

The bonds that link the glucose molecules together in cellulose are different from the bonds in starch (and glycogen). Human enzymes cannot digest cellulose. See Appendix C for chemical structures and descriptions of linkages.

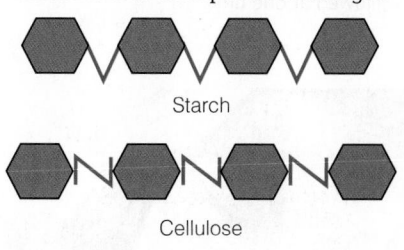

Starch

Cellulose

◆ *Dietary fibers* occur naturally in intact plants. *Functional fibers* have been extracted from plants or manufactured and have beneficial effects in human beings. *Total fiber* is the sum of dietary fibers and functional fibers.

IN SUMMARY

The complex carbohydrates are the polysaccharides (chains of monosaccharides): glycogen, starches, and dietary fibers. Both glycogen and starch are storage forms of glucose—glycogen in the body, and starch in plants—and both yield energy for human use. The dietary fibers also contain glucose (and other monosaccharides), but their bonds cannot be broken by human digestive enzymes, so they yield little, if any, energy. The accompanying table summarizes the carbohydrate family of compounds.

The Carbohydrate Family

Simple Carbohydrates (Sugars)	Complex Carbohydrates
• Monosaccharides:	• Polysaccharides:
Glucose	Glycogen[a]
Fructose	Starches
Galactose	Fibers
• Disaccharides:	
Maltose	
Sucrose	
Lactose	

[a]Glycogen is a complex carbohydrate (a polysaccharide) but not a *dietary* source of carbohydrate.

Digestion and Absorption of Carbohydrates

The ultimate goal of digestion and absorption of sugars and starches is to break them into small molecules—chiefly glucose—that the body can absorb and use. The large starch molecules require extensive breakdown; the disaccharides need only be broken once and the monosaccharides not at all. The initial splitting begins in the mouth; the final splitting and absorption occur in the small intestine; and conversion to a common energy currency (glucose) takes place in the liver. The details follow.

resistant starches: starches that escape digestion and absorption in the small intestine of healthy people.

phytic (FYE-tick) **acid:** a nonnutrient component of plant seeds; also called **phytate** (FYE-tate). Phytic acid occurs in the husks of grains, legumes, and seeds and is capable of binding minerals such as zinc, iron, calcium, magnesium, and copper in insoluble complexes in the intestine, which the body excretes unused.

◆ The short chains of glucose units that result from the breakdown of starch are known as **dextrins**. The word sometimes appears on food labels because dextrins can be used as thickening agents in processed foods.

◆ Reminder: A *bolus* is a portion of food swallowed at one time.

When a person eats carbohydrate-rich foods, the body receives a valuable commodity—glucose.

◆ Reminder: In general, the word ending *–ase* identifies an enzyme, and the beginning of the word identifies the molecule that the enzyme works on.

◆ Starches and sugars are called **available carbohydrates** because human digestive enzymes break them down for the body's use. In contrast, fibers are called **unavailable carbohydrates** because human digestive enzymes cannot break their bonds.

---

amylase (AM-ih-lace): an enzyme that hydrolyzes amylose (a form of starch). Amylase is a *carbohydrase,* an enzyme that breaks down carbohydrates.

satiety (sah-TIE-eh-tee): the feeling of fullness and satisfaction that occurs after a meal and inhibits eating until the next meal. Satiety determines how much time passes between meals.
• **sate** = to fill

maltase: an enzyme that hydrolyzes maltose

sucrase: an enzyme that hydrolyzes sucrose

lactase: an enzyme that hydrolyzes lactose

Carbohydrate Digestion

Figure 4-10 traces the digestion of carbohydrates through the GI tract. When a person eats foods containing starch, enzymes hydrolyze the long chains to shorter chains, ◆ the short chains to disaccharides, and, finally, the disaccharides to monosaccharides. This process begins in the mouth.

In the Mouth In the mouth, thoroughly chewing high-fiber foods slows eating and stimulates the flow of saliva. The salivary enzyme **amylase** starts to work, hydrolyzing starch to shorter polysaccharides and to the disaccharide maltose. In fact, you can taste the change if you hold a piece of starchy food like a cracker in your mouth for a few minutes without swallowing it—the cracker begins tasting sweeter as the enzyme acts on it. Because food is in the mouth for only a short time, very little carbohydrate digestion takes place there; it begins again in the small intestine.

In the Stomach The swallowed bolus ◆ mixes with the stomach's acid and protein-digesting enzymes, which inactivate salivary amylase. Thus the role of salivary amylase in starch digestion is relatively minor. To a small extent, the stomach's acid continues breaking down starch, but its juices contain no enzymes to digest carbohydrate. Fibers linger in the stomach and delay gastric emptying, thereby providing a feeling of fullness and **satiety.**

In the Small Intestine The small intestine performs most of the work of carbohydrate digestion. A major carbohydrate-digesting enzyme, pancreatic amylase, enters the intestine via the pancreatic duct and continues breaking down the polysaccharides to shorter glucose chains and maltose. The final step takes place on the outer membranes of the intestinal cells. There specific enzymes ◆ break down specific disaccharides:

- **Maltase** breaks maltose into two glucose molecules.
- **Sucrase** breaks sucrose into one glucose and one fructose molecule.
- **Lactase** breaks lactose into one glucose and one galactose molecule.

At this point, all polysaccharides and disaccharides have been broken down to monosaccharides—mostly glucose molecules, with some fructose and galactose molecules as well.

In the Large Intestine Within one to four hours after a meal, all the sugars and most of the starches have been digested. ◆ Only the fibers remain in the digestive tract. Fibers in the large intestine attract water, which softens the stools for passage without straining. Also, bacteria in the GI tract ferment some fibers. This process generates water, gas, and short-chain fatty acids (described in Chapter 5).* The colon uses these small fat molecules for energy. Metabolism of short-chain fatty acids also occurs in the cells of the liver. Fibers, therefore, can contribute some energy (1.5 to 2.5 kcalories per gram), depending on the extent to which they are broken down by bacteria and the fatty acids are absorbed.

Carbohydrate Absorption

Glucose is unique in that it can be absorbed to some extent through the lining of the mouth, but for the most part, nutrient absorption takes place in the small intestine. Glucose and galactose traverse the cells lining the small intestine by active transport; fructose is absorbed by facilitated diffusion, which slows its entry and produces a smaller rise in blood glucose. Likewise, unbranched chains of starch are digested slowly and produce a smaller rise in blood glucose than branched chains, which have many more places for enzymes to attack and release glucose rapidly.

As the blood from the intestines circulates through the liver, cells there take up fructose and galactose and convert them to other compounds, most often to glu-

---

* The short-chain fatty acids produced by GI bacteria are primarily acetic acid, propionic acid, and butyric acid.

FIGURE 4-10 *Animated!* Carbohydrate Digestion in the GI Tract

ThomsonNOW™
To test your understanding of these concepts, log on to
www.thomsonedu.com/login

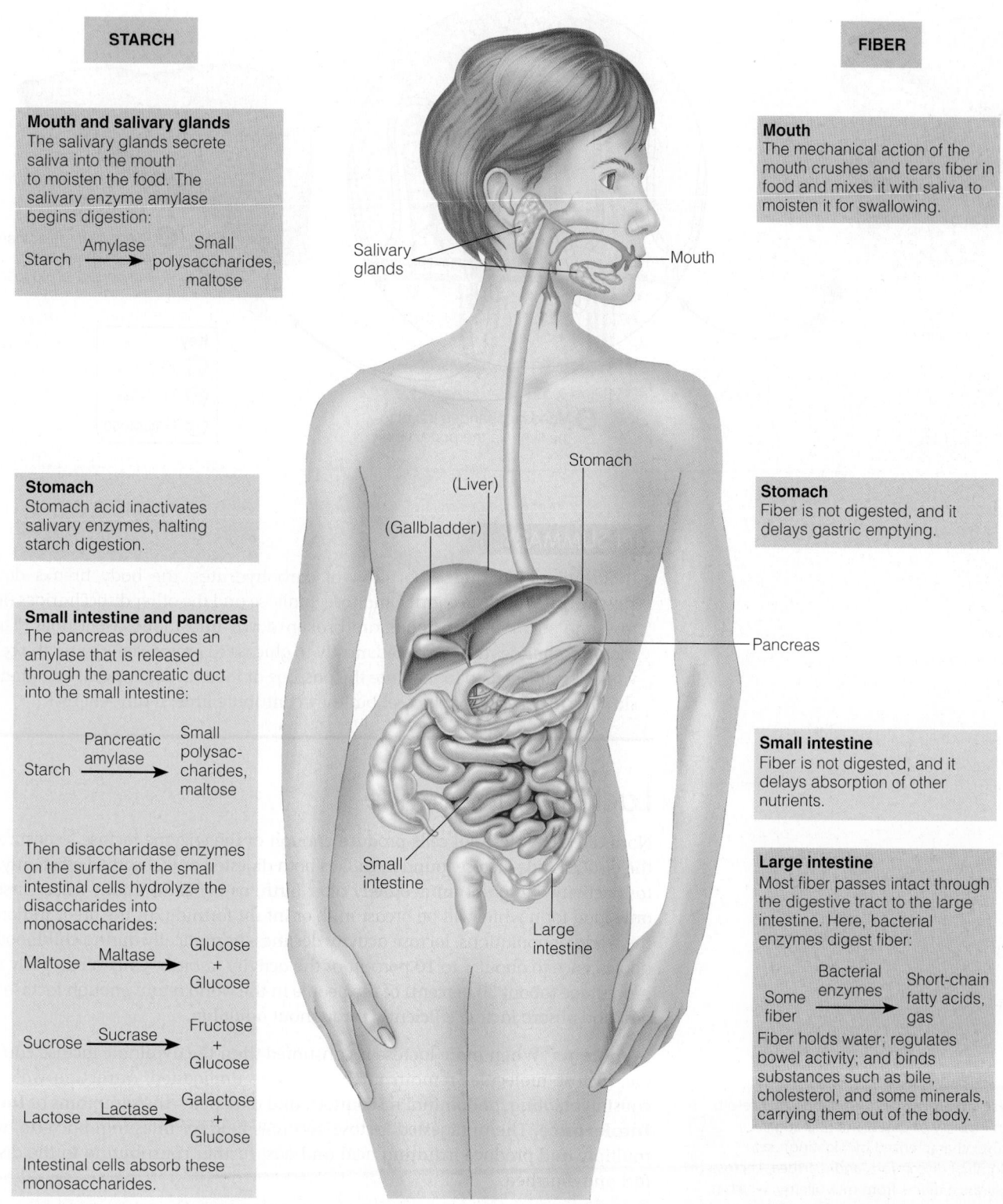

STARCH

Mouth and salivary glands
The salivary glands secrete saliva into the mouth to moisten the food. The salivary enzyme amylase begins digestion:

Starch $\xrightarrow{\text{Amylase}}$ Small polysaccharides, maltose

Stomach
Stomach acid inactivates salivary enzymes, halting starch digestion.

Small intestine and pancreas
The pancreas produces an amylase that is released through the pancreatic duct into the small intestine:

Starch $\xrightarrow{\substack{\text{Pancreatic} \\ \text{amylase}}}$ Small polysac-charides, maltose

Then disaccharidase enzymes on the surface of the small intestinal cells hydrolyze the disaccharides into monosaccharides:

Maltose $\xrightarrow{\text{Maltase}}$ Glucose + Glucose

Sucrose $\xrightarrow{\text{Sucrase}}$ Fructose + Glucose

Lactose $\xrightarrow{\text{Lactase}}$ Galactose + Glucose

Intestinal cells absorb these monosaccharides.

FIBER

Mouth
The mechanical action of the mouth crushes and tears fiber in food and mixes it with saliva to moisten it for swallowing.

Stomach
Fiber is not digested, and it delays gastric emptying.

Small intestine
Fiber is not digested, and it delays absorption of other nutrients.

Large intestine
Most fiber passes intact through the digestive tract to the large intestine. Here, bacterial enzymes digest fiber:

Some fiber $\xrightarrow{\substack{\text{Bacterial} \\ \text{enzymes}}}$ Short-chain fatty acids, gas

Fiber holds water; regulates bowel activity; and binds substances such as bile, cholesterol, and some minerals, carrying them out of the body.

Labels on figure: Salivary glands, Mouth, Stomach, (Liver), (Gallbladder), Pancreas, Small intestine, Large intestine

cose, as shown in Figure 4-11 (p. 110). Thus all disaccharides provide at least one glucose molecule directly, and they can provide another one indirectly—through the conversion of fructose and galactose to glucose.

FIGURE 4-11   Absorption of Monosaccharides

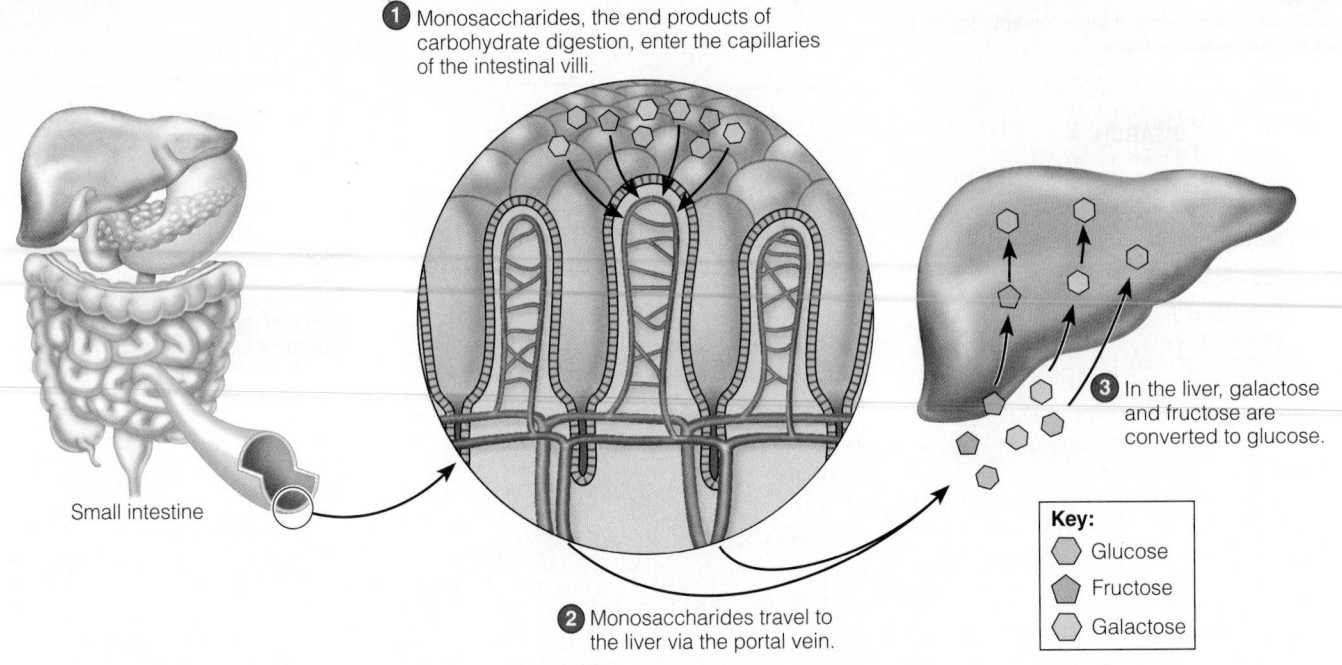

1 Monosaccharides, the end products of carbohydrate digestion, enter the capillaries of the intestinal villi.

Small intestine

2 Monosaccharides travel to the liver via the portal vein.

3 In the liver, galactose and fructose are converted to glucose.

Key:
- Glucose
- Fructose
- Galactose

IN SUMMARY

In the digestion and absorption of carbohydrates, the body breaks down starches into the disaccharide maltose. Maltose and the other disaccharides (lactose and sucrose) from foods are broken down into monosaccharides. Then monosaccharides are converted mostly to glucose to provide energy for the cells' work. The fibers help to regulate the passage of food through the GI system and slow the absorption of glucose, but they contribute little, if any, energy.

Lactose Intolerance

Normally, the intestinal cells produce enough of the enzyme lactase to ensure that the disaccharide lactose found in milk is both digested and absorbed efficiently. Lactase activity is highest immediately after birth, as befits an infant whose first and only food for a while will be breast milk or infant formula. In the great majority of the world's populations, lactase activity declines dramatically during childhood and adolescence to about 5 to 10 percent of the activity at birth. Only a relatively small percentage (about 30 percent) of the people in the world retain enough lactase to digest and absorb lactose efficiently throughout adult life.

Symptoms When more lactose is consumed than the available lactase can handle, lactose molecules remain in the intestine undigested, attracting water and causing bloating, abdominal discomfort, and diarrhea—the symptoms of **lactose intolerance.** The undigested lactose becomes food for intestinal bacteria, which multiply and produce irritating acid and gas, further contributing to the discomfort and diarrhea.

Causes As mentioned, lactase activity commonly declines with age. **Lactase deficiency** may also develop when the intestinal villi are damaged by disease, certain medicines, prolonged diarrhea, or malnutrition. Depending on the extent of the intestinal damage, lactose malabsorption may be temporary or permanent. In extremely rare cases, an infant is born with a lactase deficiency.

lactose intolerance: a condition that results from inability to digest the milk sugar lactose; characterized by bloating, gas, abdominal discomfort, and diarrhea. Lactose intolerance differs from milk allergy, which is caused by an immune reaction to the protein in milk.

lactase deficiency: a lack of the enzyme required to digest the disaccharide lactose into its component monosaccharides (glucose and galactose).

Prevalence The prevalence ◆ of lactose intolerance varies widely among ethnic groups, indicating that the trait is genetically determined. The prevalence of lactose intolerance is lowest among Scandinavians and other northern Europeans and highest among native North Americans and Southeast Asians.

Dietary Changes Managing lactose intolerance requires some dietary changes, although total elimination of milk products usually is not necessary. Excluding all milk products from the diet can lead to nutrient deficiencies because these foods are a major source of several nutrients, notably the mineral calcium, vitamin D, and the B vitamin riboflavin. Fortunately, many people with lactose intolerance can consume foods containing up to 6 grams of lactose (1/2 cup milk) without symptoms. The most successful strategies are to increase intake of milk products gradually, take them with other foods in meals, and spread their intake throughout the day. A change in the GI bacteria, not the reappearance of the missing enzyme, accounts for the ability to adapt to milk products. Importantly, most lactose-intolerant individuals need to *manage* their dairy consumption rather than *restrict* it.[3]

In many cases, lactose-intolerant people can tolerate fermented milk products such as yogurt and **kefir**.[4] The bacteria in these products digest lactose for their own use, thus reducing the lactose content. Even when the lactose content is equivalent to milk's, yogurt produces fewer symptoms. Hard cheeses, such as cheddar, and cottage cheese are often well tolerated because most of the lactose is removed with the whey during manufacturing. Lactose continues to diminish as cheese ages.

Many lactose-intolerant people use commercially prepared milk products that have been treated with an enzyme that breaks down the lactose. Alternatively, they take enzyme tablets with meals or add enzyme drops to their milk. The enzyme hydrolyzes much of the lactose in milk to glucose and galactose, which lactose-intolerant people can absorb without ill effects.

Because people's tolerance to lactose varies widely, lactose-restricted diets must be highly individualized. A completely lactose-free diet can be difficult because lactose appears not only in milk and milk products but also as an ingredient in many nondairy foods ◆ such as breads, cereals, breakfast drinks, salad dressings, and cake mixes. People on strict lactose-free diets need to read labels and avoid foods that include milk, milk solids, whey (milk liquid), and casein (milk protein, which may contain traces of lactose). They also need to check all medications with the pharmacist because 20 percent of prescription drugs and 5 percent of over-the-counter drugs contain lactose as a filler.

People who consume few or no milk products must take care to meet riboflavin, vitamin D, and calcium needs. Later chapters on the vitamins and minerals offer help with finding good nonmilk sources of these nutrients.

◆ Estimated prevalence of lactose intolerance:
>80% Southeast Asians
80% Native Americans
75% African Americans
70% Mediterranean peoples
60% Inuits
50% Hispanics
20% Caucasians
<10% Northern Europeans

◆ Lactose in selected foods:

Whole-wheat bread, 1 slice	0.5 g
Dinner roll, 1	0.5 g
Cheese, 1 oz	
Cheddar or American	0.5 g
Parmesan or cream	0.8 g
Doughnut (cake type), 1	1.2 g
Chocolate candy, 1 oz	2.3 g
Sherbet, 1 c	4.0 g
Cottage cheese (low-fat), 1 c	7.5 g
Ice cream, 1 c	9.0 g
Milk, 1 c	12.0 g
Yogurt (low-fat), 1 c	15.0 g

Note: Yogurt is often enriched with nonfat milk solids, which increase its lactose content to a level higher than milk's.

IN SUMMARY

Lactose intolerance is a common condition that occurs when there is insufficient lactase to digest the disaccharide lactose found in milk and milk products. Symptoms include GI distress. Because treatment requires limiting milk intake, other sources of riboflavin, vitamin D, and calcium must be included in the diet.

Glucose in the Body

The primary role of the available carbohydrates in human nutrition is to supply the body's cells with glucose for energy. Starch contributes most to the body's glucose supply, but as explained earlier, any of the monosaccharides can also provide glucose.

kefir (keh-FUR): a fermented milk created by adding *Lactobacillus acidophilus* and other bacteria that break down lactose to glucose and galactose, producing a sweet, lactose-free product.

◆ The study of sugars is known as *glycobiology.*

◆ These combination molecules are known as *glycoproteins* and *glycolipids,* respectively.

Scientists have long known that providing energy is glucose's primary role in the body, but they have only recently uncovered additional roles that glucose and other sugars perform in the body.[5] ◆ Sugar molecules dangle from many of the body's protein and fat molecules, with dramatic consequences. Sugars attached to a protein change the protein's shape and function; when they bind to lipids in a cell's membranes, sugars alter the way cells recognize each other.[6] ◆ Cancer cells coated with sugar molecules, for example, are able to sneak by the cells of the immune system. Armed with this knowledge, scientists are now trying to use sugar molecules to create an anticancer vaccine. Further advances in knowledge are sure to reveal numerous ways these simple, yet remarkable, sugar molecules influence the health of the body.

A Preview of Carbohydrate Metabolism

Glucose plays the central role in carbohydrate metabolism. This brief discussion provides just enough information about carbohydrate metabolism to illustrate that the body needs and uses glucose as a chief energy nutrient. Chapter 7 provides a full description of energy metabolism.

The carbohydrates of grains, vegetables, fruits, and legumes supply most of the energy in a healthful diet.

Storing Glucose as Glycogen The liver stores about one-third of the body's total glycogen and releases glucose into the bloodstream as needed. After a meal, blood glucose rises, and liver cells link the excess glucose molecules by condensation reactions into long, branching chains of glycogen. When blood glucose falls, the liver cells break glycogen by hydrolysis reactions into single molecules of glucose and release them into the bloodstream. Thus glucose becomes available to supply energy to the brain and other tissues regardless of whether the person has eaten recently. Muscle cells can also store glucose as glycogen (the other two-thirds), but they hoard most of their supply, using it just for themselves during exercise. The brain maintains a small amount of glycogen, which is thought to provide an emergency energy reserve during times of severe glucose deprivation.[7]

Glycogen holds water and, therefore, is rather bulky. The body can store only enough glycogen to provide energy for relatively short periods of time—less than a day during rest and a few hours at most during exercise. For its long-term energy reserves, for use over days or weeks of food deprivation, the body uses its abundant, water-free fuel, fat, as Chapter 5 describes.

Using Glucose for Energy Glucose fuels the work of most of the body's cells. Inside a cell, enzymes break glucose in half. These halves can be put back together to make glucose, or they can be further broken down into even smaller fragments (never again to be reassembled to form glucose). The small fragments can yield energy when broken down completely to carbon dioxide and water (see Chapter 7).

As mentioned, the liver's glycogen stores last only for hours, not for days. To keep providing glucose to meet the body's energy needs, a person has to eat dietary carbohydrate frequently. Yet people who do not always attend faithfully to their bodies' carbohydrate needs still survive. How do they manage without glucose from dietary carbohydrate? Do they simply draw energy from the other two energy-yielding nutrients, fat and protein? They do draw energy from them, but not simply.

Making Glucose from Protein Glucose is the preferred energy source for brain cells, other nerve cells, and developing red blood cells. Body protein can be converted to glucose to some extent, but protein has jobs of its own that no other nutrient can do. Body fat cannot be converted to glucose to any significant extent. Thus, when a person does not replenish depleted glycogen stores by eating carbohydrate, body proteins are broken down to make glucose to fuel these special cells.

The conversion of protein to glucose is called **gluconeogenesis**—literally, the making of new glucose. Only adequate dietary carbohydrate can prevent this use of protein for energy, and this role of carbohydrate is known as its **protein-sparing action.**

gluconeogenesis (gloo-ko-nee-oh-JEN-ih-sis): the making of glucose from a noncarbohydrate source (described in more detail in Chapter 7).
- **gluco** = glucose
- **neo** = new
- **genesis** = making

protein-sparing action: the action of carbohydrate (and fat) in providing energy that allows protein to be used for other purposes.

Making Ketone Bodies from Fat Fragments An inadequate supply of carbohydrate can shift the body's energy metabolism in a precarious direction. With less carbohydrate providing glucose to meet the brain's energy needs, fat takes an alternative metabolic pathway; instead of entering the main energy pathway, fat fragments combine with each other, forming **ketone bodies.** Ketone bodies provide an alternate fuel source during starvation, but when their production exceeds their use, they accumulate in the blood, causing **ketosis,** a condition that disturbs the body's normal **acid-base balance,** as Chapter 7 describes. (Highlight 9 explores ketosis and the health consequences of low-carbohydrate diets further.)

To spare body protein and prevent ketosis, the body needs at least 50 to 100 grams of carbohydrate a day. Dietary recommendations urge people to select abundantly from carbohydrate-rich foods to provide for considerably more.

Using Glucose to Make Fat After meeting its energy needs and filling its glycogen stores to capacity, the body must find a way to handle any extra glucose. At first, energy metabolism shifts to use more glucose instead of fat. If that isn't enough to restore glucose balance, the liver breaks glucose into smaller molecules and puts them together into the more permanent energy-storage compound—fat. Thus when carbohydrate is abundant, fat is either conserved or created. The fat then travels to the fatty tissues of the body for storage. Unlike the liver cells, which can store only enough glycogen to meet less than a day's energy needs, fat cells can store seemingly unlimited quantities of fat.

The Constancy of Blood Glucose

Every body cell depends on glucose for its fuel to some extent, and the cells of the brain and the rest of the nervous system depend almost exclusively on glucose for their energy. The activities of these cells never cease, and they have limited ability to store glucose. Day and night, they continually draw on the supply of glucose in the fluid surrounding them. To maintain the supply, a steady stream of blood moves past these cells bringing more glucose from either the intestines (food) or the liver (via glycogen breakdown or gluconeogenesis).

Maintaining Glucose Homeostasis To function optimally, the body must maintain blood glucose within limits that permit the cells to nourish themselves. If blood glucose falls below normal, ◆ a person may become dizzy and weak; if it rises above normal, a person may become fatigued. Left untreated, fluctuations to the extremes—either high or low—can be fatal.

The Regulating Hormones Blood glucose homeostasis ◆ is regulated primarily by two hormones: *insulin*, which moves glucose from the blood into the cells, and *glucagon*, which brings glucose out of storage when necessary. Figure 4-12 (p. 114) depicts these hormonal regulators at work.

After a meal, as blood glucose rises, special cells of the pancreas respond by secreting **insulin** into the blood.* In general, the amount of insulin secreted corresponds with the rise in glucose. As the circulating insulin contacts the receptors on the body's other cells, the receptors respond by ushering glucose from the blood into the cells. Most of the cells take only the glucose they can use for energy right away, but the liver and muscle cells can assemble the small glucose units into long, branching chains of glycogen for storage. The liver cells can also convert glucose to fat for export to other cells. Thus elevated blood glucose returns to normal levels as excess glucose is stored as glycogen and fat.

When blood glucose falls (as occurs between meals), other special cells of the pancreas respond by secreting **glucagon** into the blood.** Glucagon raises blood glucose by signaling the liver to break down its glycogen stores and release glucose into the blood for use by all the other body cells.

---

* The *beta* (BAY-tuh) *cells*, one of several types of cells in the pancreas, secrete insulin in response to elevated blood glucose concentration.
** The *alpha cells* of the pancreas secrete glucagon in response to low blood glucose.

◆ Normal blood glucose (fasting): 70 to 100 mg/dL (published values vary slightly).

◆ Reminder: *Homeostasis* is the maintenance of constant internal conditions by the body's control systems.

ketone (KEE-tone) **bodies:** the product of the incomplete breakdown of fat when glucose is not available in the cells.

ketosis (kee-TOE-sis): an undesirably high concentration of ketone bodies in the blood and urine.

acid-base balance: the equilibrium in the body between acid and base concentrations (see Chapter 12).

insulin (IN-suh-lin): a hormone secreted by special cells in the pancreas in response to (among other things) increased blood glucose concentration. The primary role of insulin is to control the transport of glucose from the bloodstream into the muscle and fat cells.

glucagon (GLOO-ka-gon): a hormone that is secreted by special cells in the pancreas in response to low blood glucose concentration and elicits release of glucose from liver glycogen stores.

FIGURE 4-12 Maintaining Blood Glucose Homeostasis

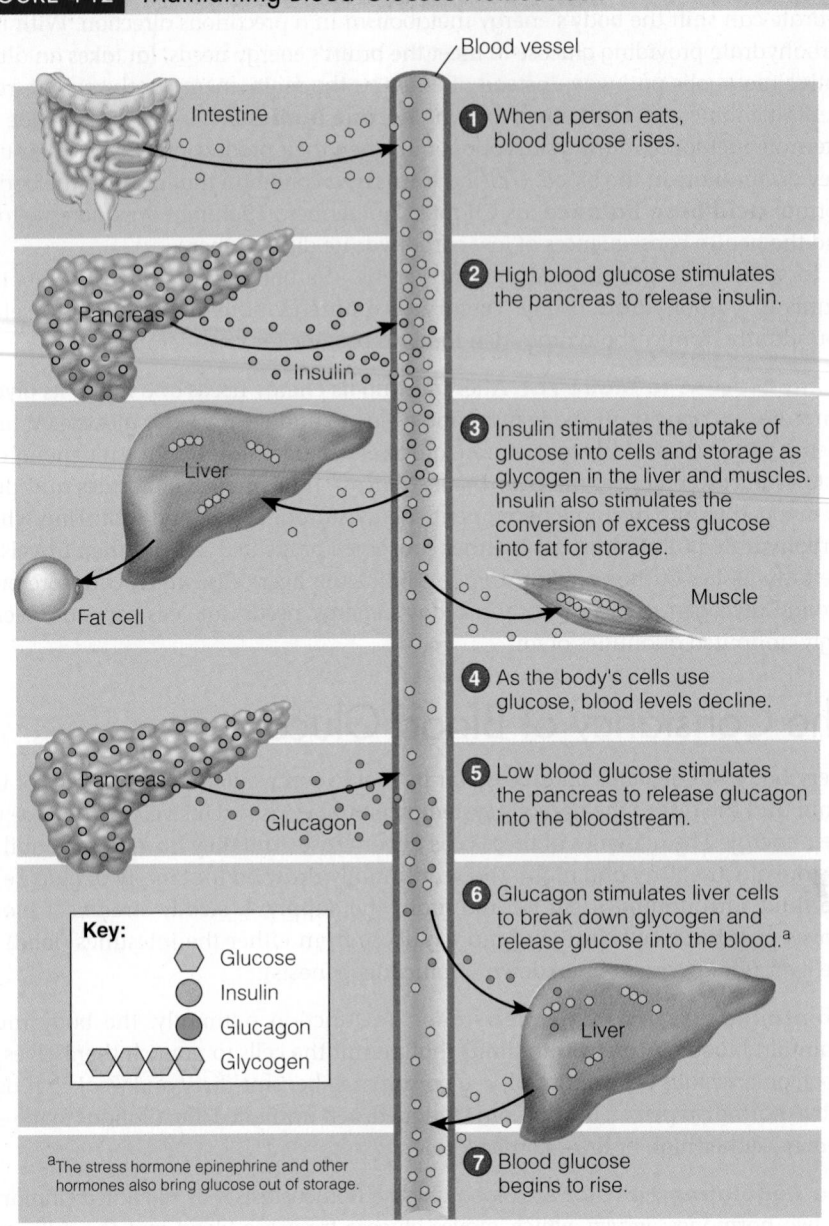

Blood vessel

Intestine

1 When a person eats, blood glucose rises.

Pancreas

Insulin

2 High blood glucose stimulates the pancreas to release insulin.

Liver

3 Insulin stimulates the uptake of glucose into cells and storage as glycogen in the liver and muscles. Insulin also stimulates the conversion of excess glucose into fat for storage.

Fat cell

Muscle

4 As the body's cells use glucose, blood levels decline.

Pancreas

Glucagon

5 Low blood glucose stimulates the pancreas to release glucagon into the bloodstream.

6 Glucagon stimulates liver cells to break down glycogen and release glucose into the blood.[a]

Liver

Key:
⬡ Glucose
○ Insulin
● Glucagon
⬡⬡⬡⬡ Glycogen

7 Blood glucose begins to rise.

[a]The stress hormone epinephrine and other hormones also bring glucose out of storage.

Another hormone that signals the liver cells to release glucose is the "fight-or-flight" hormone, **epinephrine.** When a person experiences stress, epinephrine acts quickly, ensuring that all the body cells have energy fuel in emergencies. Among its many roles in the body, epinephrine works to release glucose from liver glycogen to the blood.

Balancing within the Normal Range The maintenance of normal blood glucose ordinarily depends on two processes. When blood glucose falls below normal, food can replenish it, or in the absence of food, glucagon can signal the liver to break down glycogen stores. When blood glucose rises above normal, insulin can signal the cells to take in glucose for energy. Eating balanced meals at regular intervals helps the body maintain a happy medium between the extremes. Balanced meals that provide abundant complex carbohydrates, including fibers and a little fat, help to slow down the digestion and absorption of carbohydrate so that glucose enters the blood gradually, providing a steady, ongoing supply.

epinephrine (EP-ih-NEFF-rin): a hormone of the adrenal gland that modulates the stress response; formerly called **adrenaline.** When administered by injection, epinephrine counteracts anaphylactic shock by opening the airways and maintaining heartbeat and blood pressure.

Falling outside the Normal Range The influence of foods on blood glucose has given rise to the oversimplification that foods *govern* blood glucose concentrations. Foods do not; the body does. In some people, however, blood glucose regulation fails. When this happens, either of two conditions can result: diabetes or hypoglycemia. People with these conditions often plan their diets to help maintain their blood glucose within a normal range.

Diabetes In **diabetes,** blood glucose surges after a meal and remains above normal levels ◆ because insulin is either inadequate or ineffective. Thus *blood* glucose is central to diabetes, but *dietary* carbohydrates do not cause diabetes.

There are two main types of diabetes. In **type 1 diabetes,** the less common type, the pancreas fails to produce insulin. Although the exact cause is unclear, some research suggests that in genetically susceptible people, certain viruses activate the immune system to attack and destroy cells in the pancreas as if they were foreign cells. In **type 2 diabetes,** the more common type of diabetes, the cells fail to respond to insulin. ◆ This condition tends to occur as a consequence of obesity. As the incidence of obesity in the United States has risen in recent decades, the incidence of diabetes has followed. This trend is most notable among children and adolescents, as obesity among the nation's youth reaches epidemic proportions. Because obesity can precipitate type 2 diabetes, the best preventive measure is to maintain a healthy body weight. Concentrated sweets are not strictly excluded from the diabetic diet as they once were; they can be eaten in limited amounts with meals as part of a healthy diet. Chapter 15 describes the type of diabetes that develops in some women during pregnancy (gestational diabetes), and Chapter 18 gives full coverage to type 1 and type 2 diabetes and their associated problems.

Hypoglycemia In healthy people, blood glucose rises after eating and then gradually falls back into the normal range. The transition occurs without notice. Should blood glucose drop below normal, a person would experience the symptoms of **hypoglycemia:** weakness, rapid heartbeat, sweating, anxiety, hunger, and trembling. Most commonly, hypoglycemia is a consequence of poorly managed diabetes. Too much insulin, strenuous physical activity, inadequate food intake, or illness that causes blood glucose levels to plummet.

Hypoglycemia in healthy people is rare. Most people who experience hypoglycemia need only adjust their diets by replacing refined carbohydrates with fiber-rich carbohydrates and ensuring an adequate protein intake. In addition, smaller meals eaten more frequently may help. Hypoglycemia caused by certain medications, pancreatic tumors, overuse of insulin, alcohol abuse, uncontrolled diabetes, or other illnesses requires medical intervention.

The Glycemic Response The **glycemic response** refers to how quickly glucose is absorbed after a person eats, how high blood glucose rises, and how quickly it returns to normal. Slow absorption, a modest rise in blood glucose, and a smooth return to normal are desirable (a low glycemic response). Fast absorption, a surge in blood glucose, and an overreaction that plunges glucose below normal are less desirable (a high glycemic response). Different foods have different effects on blood glucose.

The rate of glucose absorption is particularly important to people with diabetes, who may benefit from limiting foods that produce too great a rise, or too sudden a fall, in blood glucose. To aid their choices, they may be able to use the **glycemic index,** a method of classifying foods according to their potential to raise blood glucose. ◆ Figure 4-13 (p. 116) ranks selected foods by their glycemic index. [8] Some studies have shown that selecting foods with a low glycemic index is a practical way to improve glucose control. [9]

Lowering the glycemic index of the *diet* may improve blood lipids and reduce the risk of heart disease as well.[10] A low glycemic diet may also help with weight management, although research findings are mixed.[11] Fibers and other slowly digested

◆ Blood glucose (fasting):
  • Prediabetes: 100 to 125 mg/dL
  • Diabetes: ≥ 126 mg/dL

◆ The condition of having blood glucose levels higher than normal, but below the diagnosis of diabetes, is sometimes called **prediabetes.**

◆ A related term, **glycemic load**, reflects both the glycemic index and the amount of carbohydrate.

diabetes (DYE-uh-BEET-eez)**:** a chronic disorder of carbohydrate metabolism, usually resulting from insufficient or ineffective insulin.

type 1 diabetes: the less common type of diabetes in which the pancreas fails to produce insulin.

type 2 diabetes: the more common type of diabetes in which the cells fail to respond to insulin.

hypoglycemia (HIGH-po-gly-SEE-me-ah)**:** an abnormally low blood glucose concentration.

glycemic (gly-SEEM-ic) **response:** the extent to which a food raises the blood glucose concentration and elicits an insulin response.

glycemic index: a method of classifying foods according to their potential for raising blood glucose.

FIGURE 4-13 Glycemic Index of Selected Foods

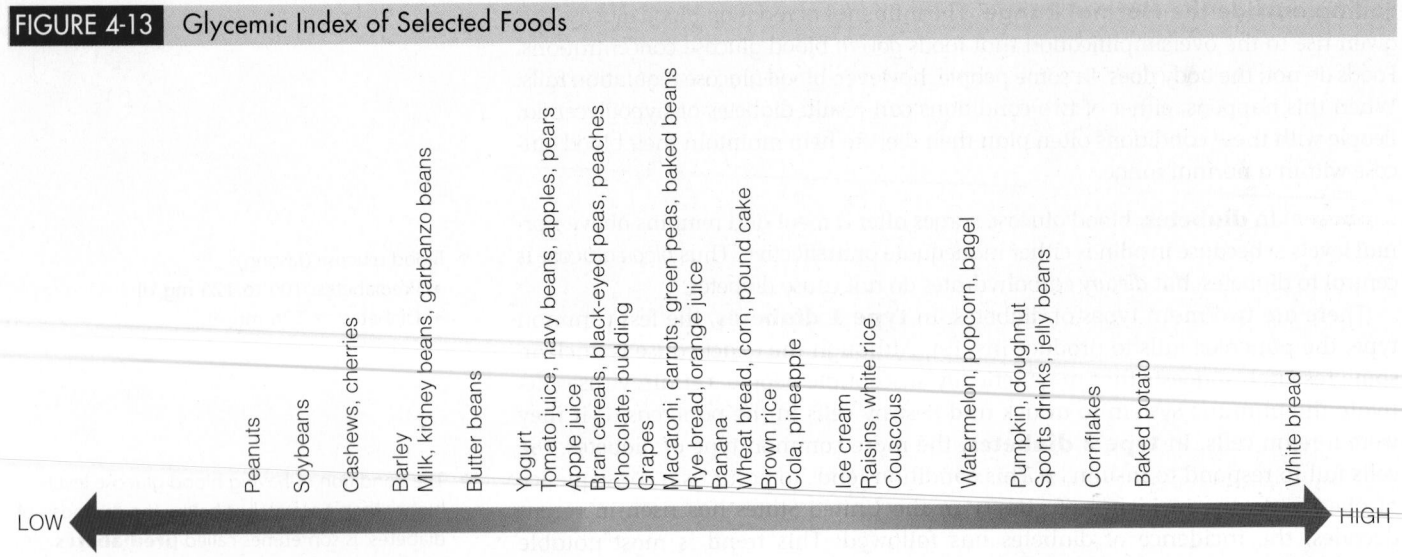

carbohydrates prolong the presence of foods in the digestive tract, thus providing greater satiety and diminishing the insulin response, which can help with weight control.[12] In contrast, the rapid absorption of glucose from a high glycemic diet seems to increase the risk of heart disease and promote overeating in some overweight people.[13]

Despite these possible benefits, the usefulness of the glycemic index is surrounded by controversy as researchers debate whether selecting foods based on the glycemic index is practical or offers any real health benefits.[14] Those opposing the use of the glycemic index argue that it is not sufficiently supported by scientific research.[15] The glycemic index has been determined for relatively few foods, and when the glycemic index has been established, it is based on an average of multiple tests with wide variations in their results. Values vary because of differences in the physical and chemical characteristics of foods, testing methods of laboratories, and digestive processes of individuals.

Furthermore, the practical utility of the glycemic index is limited because this information is neither provided on food labels nor intuitively apparent. Indeed, a food's glycemic index is not always what one might expect. Ice cream, for example, is a high-sugar food but produces less of a glycemic response than baked potatoes, a high-starch food. This effect is most likely because the fat in the ice cream slows GI motility and thus the rate of glucose absorption. Mashed potatoes produce more of a response than honey, probably because the fructose content of honey has little effect on blood glucose. In fact, sugars such as fructose generally have a moderate to low glycemic index.[16] Perhaps most relevant to real life, a food's glycemic effect differs depending on plant variety, food processing, cooking method, and whether it is eaten alone or with other foods.[17] Most people eat a variety of foods, cooked and raw, that provide different amounts of carbohydrate, fat, and protein—all of which influence the glycemic index of a meal.

Paying attention to the glycemic index may not be necessary because current guidelines already suggest many low glycemic index choices: whole grains, legumes, vegetables, fruits, and milk products. In addition, eating frequent, small meals spreads glucose absorption across the day and thus offers similar metabolic advantages to eating foods with a low glycemic response. People wanting to follow a low glycemic diet should be careful not to adopt a low carbohydrate diet as well. The problems associated with a low carbohydrate diet are addressed in Highlight 9.

IN SUMMARY

Dietary carbohydrates provide glucose that can be used by the cells for energy, stored by the liver and muscles as glycogen, or converted into fat if intakes exceed needs. All of the body's cells depend on glucose; those of the central nervous system are especially dependent on it. Without glucose, the body is forced to break down its protein tissues to make glucose and to alter energy metabolism to make ketone bodies from fats. Blood glucose regulation depends primarily on two pancreatic hormones: insulin to move glucose from the blood into the cells when levels are high and glucagon to free glucose from glycogen stores and release it into the blood when levels are low. The glycemic index measures how blood glucose responds to foods.

Health Effects and Recommended Intakes of Sugars

Ever since people first discovered honey and dates, they have enjoyed the sweetness of sugars. In the United States, the natural sugars of milk, fruits, vegetables, and grains account for about half of the sugar intake; the other half consists of sugars that have been refined and added to foods for a variety of purposes. ◆ The use of **added sugars** has risen steadily over the past several decades, both in the United States and around the world, with soft drinks and sugared fruit drinks accounting for most of the increase.[18] These added sugars assume various names on food labels: sucrose, invert sugar, corn sugar, corn syrups and solids, high-fructose corn syrup, and honey. A food is likely to be high in added sugars if its ingredient list starts with any of the sugars named in the glossary (p. 118) or if it includes several of them.

◆ As an additive, sugar:
- Enhances flavor
- Supplies texture and color to baked goods
- Provides fuel for fermentation, causing bread to rise or producing alcohol
- Acts as a bulking agent in ice cream and baked goods
- Acts as a preservative in jams
- Balances the acidity of tomato- and vinegar-based products

Health Effects of Sugars

In moderate amounts, sugars add pleasure to meals without harming health. In excess, however, they can be detrimental in two ways. One, sugars can contribute to nutrient deficiencies by supplying energy (kcalories) without providing nutrients. Two, sugars contribute to tooth decay.

Nutrient Deficiencies Empty-kcalorie foods that contain lots of added sugar such as cakes, candies, and sodas deliver glucose and energy with few, if any, other nutrients. By comparison, foods such as whole grains, vegetables, legumes, and fruits that contain some natural sugars and lots of starches and fibers deliver protein, vitamins, and minerals along with their glucose and energy.

A person spending 200 kcalories of a day's energy allowance on a 16-ounce soda gets little of value for those kcaloric "dollars." In contrast, a person using 200 kcalories on three slices of whole-wheat bread gets 9 grams of protein, 6 grams of fiber, plus several of the B vitamins with those kcalories. For the person who wants something sweet, a reasonable compromise might be two slices of bread with a teaspoon of jam on each. The amount of sugar a person can afford to eat depends on how many kcalories are available beyond those needed to deliver indispensable vitamins and minerals.

With careful food selections, a typical adult can obtain all the needed nutrients within an allowance of about 1500 kcalories. Some people have more generous energy allowances with which to "purchase" nutrients. For example, an active teenage boy may need as many as 3000 kcalories a day. If he eats mostly nutritious foods, then the "empty kcalories" of cola beverages

Over half of the added sugars in our diet come from soft drinks and table sugar, but baked goods, fruit drinks, ice cream, candy, and breakfast cereals also make substantial contributions.

added sugars: sugars and syrups used as an ingredient in the processing and preparation of foods such as breads, cakes, beverages, jellies, and ice cream as well as sugars eaten separately or added to foods at the table.

GLOSSARY OF ADDED SUGARS

brown sugar: refined white sugar crystals to which manufacturers have added molasses syrup with natural flavor and color; 91 to 96% pure sucrose.

confectioners' sugar: finely powdered sucrose, 99.9% pure.

corn sweeteners: corn syrup and sugars derived from corn.

corn syrup: a syrup made from cornstarch that has been treated with acid, high temperatures, and enzymes that produce glucose, maltose, and dextrins. See also *high-fructose corn syrup (HFCS)*.

dextrose: an older name for glucose.

granulated sugar: crystalline sucrose; 99.9% pure.

high-fructose corn syrup (HFCS): a syrup made from cornstarch that has been treated with an enzyme that converts some of the glucose to the sweeter fructose; made especially for use in processed foods and beverages, where it is the predominant sweetener. With a chemical structure similar to sucrose, HFCS has a fructose content of 42, 55, or 90%, with glucose making up the remainder.

honey: sugar (mostly sucrose) formed from nectar gathered by bees. An enzyme splits the sucrose into glucose and fructose. Composition and flavor vary, but honey always contains a mixture of sucrose, fructose, and glucose.

invert sugar: a mixture of glucose and fructose formed by the hydrolysis of sucrose in a chemical process; sold only in liquid form and sweeter than sucrose. Invert sugar is used as a food additive to help preserve freshness and prevent shrinkage.

levulose: an older name for fructose.

maple sugar: a sugar (mostly sucrose) purified from the concentrated sap of the sugar maple tree.

molasses: the thick brown syrup produced during sugar refining. Molasses retains residual sugar and other by-products and a few minerals; blackstrap molasses contains significant amounts of calcium and iron.

raw sugar: the first crop of crystals harvested during sugar processing. Raw sugar cannot be sold in the United States because it contains too much filth (dirt, insect fragments, and the like). Sugar sold as "raw sugar" domestically has actually gone through over half of the refining steps.

turbinado (ter-bih-NOD-oh) **sugar:** sugar produced using the same refining process as white sugar, but without the bleaching and anti-caking treatment. Traces of molasses give turbinado its sandy color.

white sugar: pure sucrose or "table sugar," produced by dissolving, concentrating, and recrystallizing raw sugar.

---

may be an acceptable addition to his diet. In contrast, an inactive older woman who is limited to fewer than 1500 kcalories a day can afford to eat only the most nutrient-dense foods.

Some people believe that because honey is a natural food, it is nutritious—or, at least, more nutritious than sugar.* A look at their chemical structures reveals the truth. Honey, like table sugar, contains glucose and fructose. The primary difference is that in table sugar the two monosaccharides are bonded together as a disaccharide, whereas in honey some of them are free. Whether a person eats monosaccharides individually, as in honey, or linked together, as in table sugar, they end up the same way in the body: as glucose and fructose.

Honey does contain a few vitamins and minerals, but not many, as Table 4-1 shows. Honey is denser than crystalline sugar, too, so it provides more energy per spoonful.

---

* Honey should never be fed to infants because of the risk of botulism. Chapters 16 and 19 provide more details.

TABLE 4-1   Sample Nutrients in Sugar and Other Foods

The indicated portion of any of these foods provides approximately 100 kcalories. Notice that for a similar number of kcalories and grams of carbohydrate, milk, legumes, fruits, grains, and vegetables offer more of the other nutrients than do the sugars.

	Size of 100 kcal Portion	Carbohydrate (g)	Protein (g)	Calcium (mg)	Iron (mg)	Vitamin A (µg)	Vitamin C (mg)
Foods							
Milk, 1% low-fat	1 c	12	8	300	0.1	144	2
Kidney beans	½ c	20	7	30	1.6	0	2
Apricots	6	24	2	30	1.1	554	22
Bread, whole-wheat	1½ slices	20	4	30	1.9	0	0
Broccoli, cooked	2 c	20	12	188	2.2	696	148
Sugars							
Sugar, white	2 tbs	24	0	trace	trace	0	0
Molasses, blackstrap	2½ tbs	28	0	343	12.6	0	0.1
Cola beverage	1 c	26	0	6	trace	0	0
Honey	1½ tbs	26	trace	2	0.2	0	trace

This is not to say that all sugar sources are alike, for some are more nutritious than others. Consider a fruit, say, an orange. The fruit may give you the same amounts of fructose and glucose and the same number of kcalories as a dose of sugar or honey, but the packaging is more valuable nutritionally. The fruit's sugars arrive in the body diluted in a large volume of water, packaged in fiber, and mixed with essential vitamins, minerals, and phytochemicals.

As these comparisons illustrate, the significant difference between sugar sources is not between "natural" honey and "purified" sugar but between concentrated sweets and the dilute, naturally occurring sugars that sweeten foods. You can suspect an exaggerated nutrition claim when someone asserts that one product is more nutritious than another because it contains honey.

Sugar can contribute to nutrient deficiencies only by displacing nutrients. For nutrition's sake, the appropriate attitude to take is not that sugar is "bad" and must be avoided, but that nutritious foods must come first. If nutritious foods crowd sugar out of the diet, that is fine—but not the other way around. As always, the goals to seek are balance, variety, and moderation.

Dental Caries Sugars from foods and from the breakdown of starches in the mouth can contribute to tooth decay. Bacteria in the mouth ferment the sugars and, in the process, produce an acid that erodes tooth enamel (see Figure 4-14), causing **dental caries**, or tooth decay. People can eat sugar without this happening, though, for much depends on how long foods stay in the mouth. Sticky foods stay on the teeth longer and continue to yield acid longer than foods that are readily cleared from the mouth. For that reason, sugar in a juice consumed quickly, for example, is less likely to cause dental caries than sugar in a pastry. By the same token, the sugar in sticky foods such as dried fruits can be more detrimental than its quantity alone would suggest.

Another concern is how often people eat sugar. Bacteria produce acid for 20 to 30 minutes after each exposure. If a person eats three pieces of candy at one time, the teeth will be exposed to approximately 30 minutes of acid destruction. But, if the person eats three pieces at half-hour intervals, the time of exposure increases to 90 minutes. Likewise, slowly sipping a sugary sports beverage may be more harmful than drinking quickly and clearing the mouth of sugar. Nonsugary foods can help remove sugar from tooth surfaces; hence, it is better to eat sugar with meals than between meals.[19] Foods such as milk and cheese may be particularly helpful in minimizing the effects of the acids and in restoring the lost enamel.[20]

Beverages such as soft drinks, orange juice, and sports drinks not only contain sugar but also have a low pH. These acidic drinks can erode tooth enamel and may explain why dental erosion is highly prevalent today.[21]

The development of caries depends on several factors: the bacteria that reside in **dental plaque,** the saliva that cleanses the mouth, the minerals that form the teeth, and the foods that remain after swallowing. For most people, good oral hygiene will prevent ◆ dental caries. In fact, regular brushing (twice a day, with a fluoride toothpaste) and flossing may be more effective in preventing dental caries than restricting sugary foods.

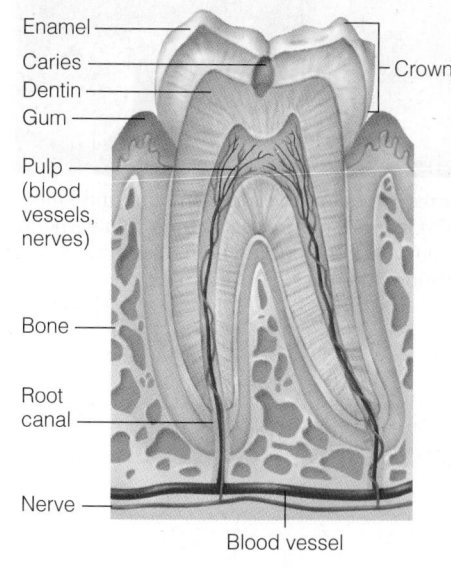

FIGURE 4-14 Dental Caries

Dental caries begins when acid dissolves the enamel that covers the tooth. If not repaired, the decay may penetrate the dentin and spread into the pulp of the tooth, causing inflammation, abscess, and possible loss of the tooth.

Enamel
Caries
Dentin
Gum
Crown
Pulp (blood vessels, nerves)
Bone
Root canal
Nerve
Blood vessel

◆ To prevent dental caries:
- Limit between-meal snacks containing sugars and starches.
- Brush and floss teeth regularly.
- If brushing and flossing are not possible, at least rinse with water.

Dietary Guidelines for Americans 2005

Reduce the incidence of dental caries by practicing good oral hygiene and consuming sugar- and starch-containing foods and beverages less frequently.

Controversies Surrounding Sugars

Sugars have been blamed for a variety of other health problems.[22] The following paragraphs evaluate some of these controversies.

dental caries: decay of teeth.
- **caries** = rottenness

dental plaque: a gummy mass of bacteria that grows on teeth and can lead to dental caries and gum disease.

You receive about the same amount and kinds of sugars from an orange as from a tablespoon of honey, but the packaging makes a big nutrition difference.

Controversy: Does Sugar Cause Obesity? Over the past three decades, obesity rates have risen sharply in the United States. During the same period, consumption of added sugars has reached an all-time high—much of it because of the dramatic rise in high-fructose corn syrup used in beverages. Between 1977 and 2001, as people grew fatter, their intake of kcalories from fruit drinks and punches doubled and kcalories from soft drinks nearly tripled.[23] Although the use of this sweetener parallels unprecedented gains of body fatness, does it mean that the increasing sugar intakes are responsible for the increase in obesity?[24]

When eaten in excess of need, energy from added sugars contributes to body fat stores, just as excess energy from other sources does. Added sugars provide excess kcalories, raising the risk of weight gain and type 2 diabetes.[25] When total kcalorie intakes are controlled, however, *moderate* amounts of sugar do not cause obesity.[26]

People with diets *high* in added sugars often consume more kcalories each day than people with lower sugar intakes. Adolescents, for example, who drink as much as 26 ounces or more (about two cans) of sugar-sweetened soft drinks daily, consume 400 more kcalories a day than teens who don't. Overweight children and adolescents increase their risk of becoming obese by 60 percent with each additional syrup-sweetened drink they add to their daily diet. The liquid form of sugar in soft drinks makes it especially easy to overconsume kcalories.[27] Investigators are evaluating these and other possible links between fructose in the syrupy sweeteners of soft drinks and weight gain.[28] Research suggests that fructose from these added sugars favors the fat-making pathways.[29]

Limiting selections of foods and beverages high in added sugars can be an effective weight-loss strategy, especially for people whose excess kcalories come primarily from added sugars.[30] Replacing a can of cola with a glass of water every day, for example, can help a person lose a pound (or at least not gain a pound) in one month. That may not sound like much, but it adds up to more than 10 pounds a year, for very little effort.

Controversy: Does Sugar Cause Heart Disease? A diet high in added sugars can alter blood lipids to favor heart disease.[31] (Lipids include fats and cholesterol, as Chapter 5 explains.) This effect is most dramatic in people who respond to sucrose with abnormally high insulin secretions, which promote the making of excess fat.[32] For most people, though, moderate sugar intakes do *not* elevate blood lipids. To keep these findings in perspective, consider that heart disease correlates most closely with factors that have nothing to do with nutrition, such as smoking and genetics. Among dietary risk factors, several—such as saturated fats, *trans* fats, and cholesterol—have much stronger associations with heart disease than do sugar intakes.

Controversy: Does Sugar Cause Misbehavior in Children and Criminal Behavior in Adults? Sugar has been blamed for the misbehaviors of hyperactive children, delinquent adolescents, and lawbreaking adults. Such speculations have been based on personal stories and have not been confirmed by scientific research. No scientific evidence supports a relationship between sugar and hyperactivity or other misbehaviors. Chapter 16 provides accurate information on diet and children's behavior.

Controversy: Does Sugar Cause Cravings and Addictions? Foods in general, and carbohydrates and sugars more specifically, are not physically addictive in the ways that drugs are. Yet some people describe themselves as having "carbohydrate cravings" or being "sugar addicts." One frequently noted theory is that people seek carbohydrates as a way to increase their levels of the brain neurotransmitter **serotonin**, which elevates mood. Interestingly, when those with self-described carbohydrate cravings indulge, they tend to eat more of everything, but the percentage of energy from carbohydrates remains unchanged.[33] Alcohol also raises serotonin levels, and alcohol-dependent people who crave carbohydrates seem to handle sobriety better when given a high-carbohydrate diet.

One reasonable explanation for the carbohydrate cravings that some people experience involves the self-imposed labeling of a food as both "good" and "bad"—that is, one that is desirable but should be eaten with restraint. Chocolate is a familiar ex-

serotonin (SER-oh-TONE-in): a neurotransmitter important in sleep regulation, appetite control, intestinal motility, obsessive-compulsive behaviors, and mood disorders.

ample. Restricting intake heightens the desire further (a "craving"). Then "addiction" is used to explain why resisting the food is so difficult and, sometimes, even impossible. But the "addiction" is not pharmacological; a capsule of the psychoactive substances commonly found in chocolate, for example, does not satisfy the craving.

Recommended Intakes of Sugars

Because added sugars deliver kcalories but few or no nutrients, the 2005 *Dietary Guidelines* urge consumers to "choose and prepare foods and beverages with little added sugars." The USDA Food Guide counts these sugar kcalories (and those from solid fats and alcohol) as discretionary kcalories. Most people need to limit their use of added sugars. ◆ Estimates indicate that, on average, each person in the United States consumes about 105 pounds (almost 50 kilograms) of added sugar per year, or about 30 teaspoons (about 120 grams) of added sugar a day, an amount that exceeds these guidelines.[34]

◆ USDA Food Guide amounts of added sugars that can be included as discretionary kcalories when food choices are nutrient dense and fat ≤ 30% total kcal:
- 3 tsp for 1600 kcal diet
- 5 tsp for 1800 kcal diet
- 8 tsp for 2000 kcal diet
- 9 tsp for 2200 kcal diet
- 12 tsp for 2400 kcal diet

Dietary Guidelines for Americans 2005

Choose and prepare foods and beverages with little added sugars.

Estimating the *added* sugars in a diet is not always easy for consumers. Food labels list the total grams of sugar a food provides, but this total reflects both added sugars and those occurring naturally in foods. To help estimate sugar and energy intakes accurately, the list in the margin ◆ shows the amounts of concentrated sweets that are equivalent to 1 teaspoon of white sugar. These sugars all provide *about* 5 grams of carbohydrate and about 20 kcalories per teaspoon. Some are lower (16 kcalories for table sugar), and others are higher (22 kcalories for honey), but a 20-kcalorie average is an acceptable approximation. For a person who uses catsup liberally, it may help to remember that 1 tablespoon of catsup supplies about 1 teaspoon of sugar.

The DRI committee did not set an upper level for sugar, but as mentioned, excessive intakes can interfere with sound nutrition and dental health. Few people can eat lots of sugary treats and still meet all of their nutrient needs without exceeding their kcalorie allowance. Specifically, the DRI suggests that added sugars should account for no more than 25 percent of the day's total energy intake.[35] When added sugars occupy this much of a diet, however, intakes from the five food groups fall below recommendations. For a person consuming 2000 kcalories a day, 25 percent represents 500 kcalories (that is, 125 grams, or 31 teaspoons) from concentrated sugars—and that's a lot of sugar. ◆ Perhaps an athlete in training whose energy needs are high can afford the added sugars from sports drinks without compromising nutrient intake, but most people do better by limiting their use of added sugars. The World Health Organization (WHO) and the Food and Agriculture Organization (FAO) suggest restricting consumption of added sugars to less than 10 percent of total energy.

◆ 1 tsp white sugar =
- 1 tsp brown sugar
- 1 tsp candy
- 1 tsp corn sweetener or corn syrup
- 1 tsp honey
- 1 tsp jam or jelly
- 1 tsp maple sugar or maple syrup
- 1 tsp molasses
- 1^1/$_2$ oz carbonated soda
- 1 tbs catsup

◆ For perspective, each of these concentrated sugars provides about 500 kcal:
- 40 oz cola
- ^{1}/$_2$ c honey
- 125 jelly beans
- 23 marshmallows
- 30 tsp sugar

How many kcalories from sugar does your favorite beverage or snack provide?

IN SUMMARY

Sugars pose no major health threat except for an increased risk of dental caries. Excessive intakes, however, may displace needed nutrients and fiber and may contribute to obesity when energy intake exceeds needs. A person deciding to limit daily sugar intake should recognize that not all sugars need to be restricted, just concentrated sweets, which are relatively empty of other nutrients and high in kcalories. Sugars that occur naturally in fruits, vegetables, and milk are acceptable.

Foods rich in starch and fiber offer many health benefits.

◆ Consuming 5 to 10 g of soluble fiber daily reduces blood cholesterol by 3 to 5%. For perspective, $^1/_2$ c dry oat bran provides 8 g of fiber, and 1 c cooked barley or $^1/_2$ c cooked legumes provides about 6 g of fiber.

Health Effects and Recommended Intakes of Starch and Fibers

Carbohydrates and fats are the two major sources of energy in the diet. When one is high, the other is usually low—and vice versa. A diet that provides abundant carbohydrate (45 to 65 percent of energy intake) and some fat (20 to 35 percent of energy intake) within a reasonable energy allowance best supports good health. To increase carbohydrate in the diet, focus on whole grains, vegetables, legumes, and fruits— foods noted for their starch, fibers, and naturally occurring sugars.

Health Effects of Starch and Fibers

In addition to starch, fibers, and natural sugars, whole grains, vegetables, legumes, and fruits supply valuable vitamins and minerals and little or no fat. The following paragraphs describe some of the health benefits of diets that include a variety of these foods daily.

Heart Disease High-carbohydrate diets, especially those rich in whole grains, may protect against heart disease and stroke, although sorting out the exact reasons why can be difficult.[36] Such diets are low in animal fat and cholesterol and high in fibers, vegetable proteins, and phytochemicals—all factors associated with a lower risk of heart disease. (The role of animal fat and cholesterol in heart disease is discussed in Chapter 5. The role of vegetable proteins in heart disease is presented in Chapter 6. The benefits of phytochemicals in disease prevention are featured in Highlight 13.)

Foods rich in soluble fibers (such as oat bran, barley, and legumes) lower blood cholesterol ◆ by binding with bile acids and thereby increasing their excretion. Consequently, the liver must use its cholesterol to make new bile acids. In addition, the bacterial by-products of fiber fermentation in the colon also inhibit cholesterol synthesis in the liver. The net result is lower blood cholesterol.[37]

Several researchers have speculated that fiber may also exert its effect by displacing fats in the diet. Whereas this is certainly helpful, even when dietary fat is low, high intakes of fibers exert a separate and significant cholesterol-lowering effect. In other words, a high-fiber diet helps to decrease the risk of heart disease independent of fat intake.[38]

Diabetes High-fiber foods—especially whole grains—play a key role in reducing the risk of type 2 diabetes.[39] When soluble fibers trap nutrients and delay their transit through the GI tract, glucose absorption is slowed, which helps to prevent the glucose surge and rebound that seem to be associated with diabetes onset.

GI Health Dietary fibers enhance the health of the large intestine. The healthier the intestinal walls, the better they can block absorption of unwanted constituents. Fibers such as cellulose (as in cereal brans, fruits, and vegetables) increase stool weight, easing passage, and reduce transit time. In this way, the fibers help to alleviate or prevent constipation.

Taken with ample fluids, fibers help to prevent several GI disorders. Large, soft stools ease elimination for the rectal muscles and reduce the pressure in the lower bowel, making it less likely that rectal veins will swell (hemorrhoids). Fiber prevents compaction of the intestinal contents, which could obstruct the appendix and permit bacteria to invade and infect it (appendicitis). In addition, fiber stimulates the GI tract muscles so that they retain their strength and resist bulging out into pouches known as diverticula (illustrated in Figure H3-3 on p. 95).[40]

Cancer Many, but not all, research studies suggest that increasing dietary fiber protects against colon cancer.[41] When the largest study of diet and cancer to date examined the diets of over a half million people in ten countries for four and a half

© Rita Mass/The Image Bank/Getty Images

years, the researchers found an inverse association between dietary fiber and colon cancer.[42] People who ate the most dietary fiber (35 grams per day) reduced their risk of colon cancer by 40 percent compared with those who ate the least fiber (15 grams per day). Importantly, the study focused on dietary fiber, not fiber supplements or additives, which lack valuable nutrients and phytochemicals that also help protect against cancer. Plant foods—vegetables, fruits, and whole-grain products—reduce the risks of colon and rectal cancers.[43]

Fibers may help prevent colon cancer by diluting, binding, and rapidly removing potential cancer-causing agents from the colon. In addition, soluble fibers stimulate bacterial fermentation of resistant starch and fiber in the colon, a process that produces short-chain fatty acids that lower the pH. These small fat molecules activate cancer-killing enzymes and inhibit inflammation in the colon.[44]

Weight Management High-fiber and whole-grain foods help a person to maintain a healthy body weight.[45] Foods rich in complex carbohydrates tend to be low in fat and added sugars and can therefore promote weight loss by delivering less energy ◆ per bite. In addition, as fibers absorb water from the digestive juices, they swell, creating feelings of fullness and delaying hunger.

Many weight-loss products on the market today contain bulk-inducing fibers such as methylcellulose, but buying pure fiber compounds like this is neither necessary nor advisable. Most experts agree that the health and weight management benefits attributed to fiber may come from other constituents of fiber-containing foods, and not from fiber alone.[46] For this reason, consumers should select whole grains, legumes, fruits, and vegetables instead of fiber supplements. High-fiber foods not only add bulk to the diet but are economical and nutritious as well. Table 4-2 summarizes fibers and their health benefits.

Harmful Effects of Excessive Fiber Intake Despite fibers' benefits to health, a diet high in fiber also has a few drawbacks. A person who has a small capacity and eats mostly high-fiber foods may not be able to take in enough food to meet energy or nutrient needs. The malnourished, the elderly, and young children adhering to all-plant (vegan) diets are especially vulnerable to this problem.

Launching suddenly into a high-fiber diet can cause temporary bouts of abdominal discomfort, gas, and diarrhea and, more seriously, can obstruct the GI tract. To

◆ Reminder:
- Carbohydrate: 4 kcal/g
- Fat: 9 kcal/g

TABLE 4-2 Dietary Fibers: Their Characteristics, Food Sources, and Health Effects in the Body

Fiber Characteristics	Major Food Sources	Actions in the Body	Health Benefits
Soluble, viscous, more fermentable • Gums and mucilages • Pectins • Psyllium[a] • Some hemicelluloses	Whole-grain products (barley, oats, oat bran, rye), fruits (apples, citrus), legumes, seeds and husks, vegetables; also extracted and used as food additives	• Lower blood cholesterol by binding bile • Slow glucose absorption • Slow transit of food through upper GI tract • Hold moisture in stools, softening them • Yield small fat molecules after fermentation that the colon can use for energy	• Lower risk of heart disease • Lower risk of diabetes
Insoluble, nonviscous, less fermentable • Cellulose • Lignins • Psyllium[a] • Resistant starch • Many hemicelluloses	Brown rice, fruits, legumes, seeds, vegetables (cabbage, carrots, brussels sprouts), wheat bran, whole grains; also extracted and used as food additives	• Increase fecal weight and speed fecal passage through colon • Provide bulk and feelings of fullness	• Alleviate constipation • Lower risks of diverticulosis, hemorrhoids, and appendicitis • May help with weight management

[a]Psyllium, a fiber laxative and cereal additive, has both soluble and insoluble properties.

prevent such complications, a person adopting a high-fiber diet can take the following precautions:

- Increase fiber intake gradually over several weeks to give the GI tract time to adapt.
- Drink plenty of liquids to soften the fiber as it moves through the GI tract.
- Select fiber-rich foods from a variety of sources—fruits, vegetables, legumes, and whole-grain breads and cereals.

Some fibers can limit the absorption of nutrients by speeding the transit of foods through the GI tract and by binding to minerals. When mineral intake is adequate, however, a reasonable intake of high-fiber foods does not seem to compromise mineral balance.

Clearly, fiber is like all the nutrients in that "more" is "better" only up to a point. Again, the key words are balance, moderation, and variety.

IN SUMMARY

Adequate intake of fiber:
- Fosters weight management
- Lowers blood cholesterol
- May help prevent colon cancer
- Helps prevent and control diabetes
- Helps prevent and alleviate hemorrhoids
- Helps prevent appendicitis
- Helps prevent diverticulosis

Excessive intake of fiber:
- Displaces energy- and nutrient-dense foods
- Causes intestinal discomfort and distention
- May interfere with mineral absorption

Recommended Intakes of Starch and Fibers

Dietary recommendations suggest that carbohydrates provide about half (45 to 65 percent) of the energy requirement. A person consuming 2000 kcalories a day should therefore have 900 to 1300 kcalories of carbohydrate, or about 225 to 325 grams. ◆ This amount is more than adequate to meet the RDA ◆ for carbohydrate, which is set at 130 grams per day, based on the average minimum amount of glucose used by the brain.[47]

When it established the Daily Values that appear on food labels, the Food and Drug Administration (FDA) used a 60 percent of kcalories guideline in setting the Daily Value ◆ for carbohydrate at 300 grams per day. For most people, this means increasing total carbohydrate intake. To this end, the *Dietary Guidelines* encourage people to choose a variety of whole grains, vegetables, fruits, and legumes daily.

Dietary Guidelines for Americans 2005

Choose fiber-rich fruits, vegetables, and whole grains often.

Recommendations for fiber ◆ suggest the same foods just mentioned: whole grains, vegetables, fruits, and legumes, which also provide minerals and vitamins. The FDA set the Daily Value ◆ for fiber at 25 grams, rounding up from the recom-

---

◆ The Aids to Calculations section at the end of this book explains how to solve such problems.

◆ RDA for carbohydrate:
- 130 g/day
- 45 to 65% of energy intake

◆ Daily Value:
- 300 g carbohydrate (based on 60% of 2000 kcal diet)

◆ To increase your fiber intake:
- Eat whole-grain cereals that contain ≥ 5 g fiber per serving for breakfast.
- Eat raw vegetables.
- Eat fruits (such as pears) and vegetables (such as potatoes) with their skins.
- Add legumes to soups, salads, and casseroles.
- Eat fresh and dried fruit for snacks.

◆ Daily Value:
- 25 g fiber (based on 11.5 g/1000 kcal)

TABLE 4-3	Fiber in Selected Foods

Grains

Whole-grain products provide about 1 to 2 grams (or more) of fiber per serving:

- 1 slice whole-wheat, pumpernickel, rye bread
- 1 oz ready-to-eat cereal (100% bran cereals contain 10 grams or more)
- ½ c cooked barley, bulgur, grits, oatmeal

Vegetable

Most vegetables contain about 2 to 3 grams of fiber per serving:

- 1 c raw bean sprouts
- ½ c cooked broccoli, brussels sprouts, cabbage, carrots, cauliflower, collards, corn, eggplant, green beans, green peas, kale, mushrooms, okra, parsnips, potatoes, pumpkin, spinach, sweet potatoes, swiss chard, winter squash
- ½ c chopped raw carrots, peppers

Fruit

Fresh, frozen, and dried fruits have about 2 grams of fiber per serving:

- 1 medium apple, banana, kiwi, nectarine, orange, pear
- ½ c applesauce, blackberries, blueberries, raspberries, strawberries
- Fruit juices contain very little fiber

Legumes

Many legumes provide about 6 to 8 grams of fiber per serving:

- ½ c cooked baked beans, black beans, black-eyed peas, kidney beans, navy beans, pinto beans

Some legumes provide about 5 grams of fiber per serving:

- ½ c cooked garbanzo beans, great northern beans, lentils, lima beans, split peas

NOTE: Appendix H provides fiber grams for over 2000 foods.

mended 11.5 grams per 1000-kcalories for a 2000-kcalorie intake. The DRI recommendation is slightly higher, at 14 grams per 1000-kcalorie intake. Similarly, the American Dietetic Association suggests 20 to 35 grams of dietary fiber daily, which is about two times higher than the average intake in the United States.[48] An effective way to add fiber while lowering fat is to substitute plant sources of proteins (legumes) for animal sources (meats). Table 4-3 presents a list of fiber sources.

As mentioned earlier, too much fiber is no better than too little. The World Health Organization recommends an upper limit of 40 grams of dietary fiber a day.

From Guidelines to Groceries

A diet following the USDA Food Guide, which includes several servings of fruits, vegetables, and grains daily, can easily supply the recommended amount of carbohydrates and fiber. In selecting high-fiber foods, keep in mind the principle of variety. The fibers in oats lower cholesterol, whereas those in bran help promote GI tract health. (Review Table 4-2 to see the diverse health effects of various fibers.)

Grains An ounce-equivalent of most foods in the grain group provides about 15 grams of carbohydrate, mostly as starch. Be aware that some foods in this group, especially snack crackers and baked goods such as biscuits, croissants, and muffins, contain added sugars, added fat, or both. When selecting from the grain group, be sure to include at least half as whole-grain products (see Figure 4-15, p. 126). The "3 are Key" message may help consumers to remember to choose a whole-grain cereal for breakfast, a whole-grain bread for lunch, and a whole-grain pasta or rice for dinner.

FIGURE 4-15 Bread Labels Compared

Food labels list the quantities of total carbohydrate, dietary fiber, and sugars. Total carbohydrate and dietary fiber are also stated as "% Daily Values." A close look at these two labels reveals that bread made from whole wheat-flour provides almost three times as much fiber as the one made mostly from refined wheat flour. When the words whole wheat or whole grain appear on the label, the bread inside contains all of the nutrients that bread can provide.

Nutrition Facts	
Serving size 1 slice (30g)	
Servings Per Container 15	
Amount per serving	
Calories 90	Calories from Fat 14
	% Daily Value*
Total Fat 1.5g	2%
Sodium 135mg	6%
Total Carbohydrate 15g	5%
Dietary fiber 2g	8%
Sugars 2g	
Protein 4g	

MADE FROM: UNBROMATED STONE GROUND 100% WHOLE WHEAT FLOUR, WATER, CRUSHED WHEAT, HIGH FRUCTOSE CORN SYRUP, PARTIALLY HYDROGENATED VEGETABLE SHORTENING (SOYBEAN AND COTTONSEED OILS), RAISIN JUICE CONCENTRATE, WHEAT GLUTEN, YEAST, WHOLE WHEAT FLAKES, UNSULPHURED MOLASSES, SALT, HONEY, VINEGAR, ENZYME MODIFIED SOY LECITHIN, CULTURED WHEY, UNBLEACHED WHEAT FLOUR AND SOY LECITHIN.

Nutrition Facts	
Serving size 1 slice (30g)	
Servings Per Container 15	
Amount per serving	
Calories 90	Calories from Fat 14
	% Daily Value*
Total Fat 1.5g	2%
Sodium 220mg	9%
Total Carbohydrate 15g	5%
Dietary fiber less than 1g	2%
Sugars 2g	
Protein 4g	

INGREDIENTS: UNBLEACHED ENRICHED WHEAT FLOUR [MALTED BARLEY FLOUR, NIACIN, REDUCED IRON, THIAMIN MONONITRATE (VITAMIN B1), RIBOFLAVIN (VITAMIN B2), FOLIC ACID], WATER, HIGH FRUCTOSE CORN SYRUP, MOLASSES, PARTIALLY HYDROGENATED SOYBEAN OIL, YEAST, CORN FLOUR, SALT, GROUND CARAWAY, WHEAT GLUTEN, CALCIUM PROPIONATE (PRESERVATIVE), MONOGLYCERIDES, SOY LECITHIN.

Vegetables The amount of carbohydrate a serving of vegetables provides depends primarily on its starch content. Starchy vegetables—a half-cup of cooked corn, peas, or potatoes—provide about 15 grams of carbohydrate per serving. A serving of most other *nonstarchy* vegetables—such as a half-cup of broccoli, green beans, or tomatoes—provides about 5 grams.

Fruits A typical fruit serving—a small banana, apple, or orange or a half-cup of most canned or fresh fruit—contains an average of about 15 grams of carbohydrate, mostly as sugars, including the fruit sugar fructose. Fruits vary greatly in their water and fiber contents and, therefore, in their sugar concentrations.

Milks and Milk Products A serving (a cup) of milk or yogurt provides about 12 grams of carbohydrate. Cottage cheese provides about 6 grams of carbohydrate per cup, but most other cheeses contain little, if any, carbohydrate.

Meats and Meat Alternates With two exceptions, foods in the meats and meat alternates group deliver almost no carbohydrate to the diet. The exceptions are nuts, which provide a little starch and fiber along with their abundant fat, and legumes, which provide an abundance of both starch and fiber. Just a half-cup serving of legumes provides about 20 grams of carbohydrate, a third from fiber.

Read Food Labels Food labels list the amount, in grams, of *total* carbohydrate—including starch, fibers, and sugars—per serving (review Figure 4-15). Fiber grams are also listed separately, as are the grams of sugars. (With this information, you can calculate starch grams ◆ by subtracting the grams of fibers and sugars from the total carbohydrate.) Sugars reflect both added sugars and those that occur naturally in foods. Total carbohydrate and dietary fiber are also expressed as "% Daily Values" for a person consuming 2000 kcalories; there is no Daily Value for sugars.

◆ To calculate starch grams using the first label in Figure 4-15:
15 g total − 4 g (dietary fiber + sugars) = 11 g starch

IN SUMMARY

Clearly, a diet rich in complex carbohydrates—starches and fibers—supports efforts to control body weight and prevent heart disease, cancer, diabetes, and GI disorders. For these reasons, recommendations urge people to eat plenty of whole grains, vegetables, legumes, and fruits—enough to provide 45 to 65 percent of the daily energy intake from carbohydrate.

In today's world, there is one other reason why plant foods rich in complex carbohydrates and natural sugars are a better choice than animal foods or foods high in concentrated sweets: in general, less energy and fewer resources are required to grow and process plant foods than to produce sugar or foods derived from animals. Chapter 20 takes a closer look at the environmental impacts of food production and use.

Nutrition Portfolio

ThomsonNOW
www.thomsonedu.com/thomsonnow

Foods that derive from plants—whole grains, vegetables, legumes, and fruits—naturally provide ample carbohydrates and fiber with little or no fat. Refined foods often contain added sugars and fat.

■ List the types and amounts of grain products you eat daily, making note of which are whole-grain or refined foods and how your choices could include more whole-grain options.

■ List the types and amounts of fruits and vegetables you eat daily, making note of how many are dark-green, orange, or deep yellow, how many are starchy or legumes, and how your choices could include more of these options.

■ Describe choices you can make in selecting and preparing foods and beverages to lower your intake of added sugars.

NUTRITION ON THE NET

- Search for "lactose intolerance" at the U.S. Government health information site: **www.healthfinder.gov**

- Search for "sugars" and "fiber" at the International Food Information Council site: **www.ific.org**

- Learn more about dental caries from the American Dental Association and the National Institute of Dental and

Craniofacial Research: **www.ada.org** and **www.nidcr.nih.gov**

- Learn more about diabetes from the American Diabetes Association, the Canadian Diabetes Association, and the National Institute of Diabetes and Digestive and Kidney Diseases: **www.diabetes.org**, **www.diabetes.ca**, and **www.niddk.nih.gov**

NUTRITION CALCULATIONS

ThomsonNOW™ For additional practice log on to www.thomsonedu.com/thomsonnow. Go to Chapter 4, then to Nutrition Calculations.

These problems will give you practice in doing simple nutrition-related calculations. Although the situations are hypothetical, the numbers are real, and calculating the answers (check them on p. 131) provides a valuable lesson. Be sure to show your calculations for each problem.

Health recommendations suggest that 45 to 65 percent of the daily energy intake come from carbohydrates. Stating recommendations in terms of percentage of energy intake is meaningful only if energy intake is known. The following exercises illustrate this concept.

1. Calculate the carbohydrate intake (in grams) for a student who has a high carbohydrate intake (70 percent of energy intake) and a moderate energy intake (2000 kcalories a day).

    How does this carbohydrate intake compare to the Daily Value of 300 grams? To the 45 to 65 percent recommendation?

2. Now consider a professor who eats half as much carbohydrate as the student (in grams) and has the same energy intake. What percentage does carbohydrate contribute to the daily intake?

    How does carbohydrate intake compare to the Daily Value of 300 grams? To the 45 to 65 percent recommendation?

3. Now consider an athlete who eats twice as much carbohydrate (in grams) as the student and has a much higher energy intake (6000 kcalories a day). What percentage does carbohydrate contribute to this person's daily intake?

    How does carbohydrate intake compare to the Daily Value of 300 grams? To the 45 to 65 percent recommendation?

4. One more example. In an attempt to lose weight, a person adopts a diet that provides 150 grams of carbohydrate per day and limits energy intake to 1000 kcalories. What percentage does carbohydrate contribute to this person's daily intake?

    How does this carbohydrate intake compare to the Daily Value of 300 grams? To the 45 to 65 percent recommendation?

These exercises should convince you of the importance of examining actual intake as well the percentage of energy intake.

STUDY QUESTIONS

ThomsonNOW™
To assess your understanding of chapter topics, take the Student Practice Test and explore the modules recommended in your Personalized Study Plan. Log onto www.thomsonedu.com/thomsonnow.

These questions will help you review this chapter. You will find the answers in the discussions on the pages provided.

1. Which carbohydrates are described as simple and which are complex? (p. 101)

2. Describe the structure of a monosaccharide and name the three monosaccharides important in nutrition. Name the three disaccharides commonly found in foods and their component monosaccharides. In what foods are these sugars found? (pp. 102–105)

3. What happens in a condensation reaction? In a hydrolysis reaction? (p. 104)

4. Describe the structure of polysaccharides and name the ones important in nutrition. How are starch and glycogen similar, and how do they differ? How do the fibers differ from the other polysaccharides? (pp. 105–107)

5. Describe carbohydrate digestion and absorption. What role does fiber play in the process? (pp. 107–110)

6. What are the possible fates of glucose in the body? What is the protein-sparing action of carbohydrate? (pp. 111–113)

7. How does the body maintain its blood glucose concentration? What happens when the blood glucose concentration rises too high or falls too low? (pp. 113–117)

8. What are the health effects of sugars? What are the dietary recommendations regarding concentrated sugar intakes? (pp. 117–121)

9. What are the health effects of starches and fibers? What are the dietary recommendations regarding these complex carbohydrates? (pp. 122–125)

10. What foods provide starches and fibers? (pp. 125–126)

These multiple choice questions will help you prepare for an exam. Answers can be found on p. 131.

1. Carbohydrates are found in virtually all foods except:
    a. milks.
    b. meats.
    c. breads.
    d. fruits.

2. Disaccharides include:
    a. starch, glycogen, and fiber.
    b. amylose, pectin, and dextrose.
    c. sucrose, maltose, and lactose.
    d. glucose, galactose, and fructose.

3. The making of a disaccharide from two monosaccharides is an example of:
    a. digestion.
    b. hydrolysis.
    c. condensation.
    d. gluconeogenesis.

4. The storage form of glucose in the body is:
   a. insulin.
   b. maltose.
   c. glucagon.
   d. glycogen.

5. The significant difference between starch and cellulose is that:
   a. starch is a polysaccharide, but cellulose is not.
   b. animals can store glucose as starch, but not as cellulose.
   c. hormones can make glucose from cellulose, but not from starch.
   d. digestive enzymes can break the bonds in starch, but not in cellulose.

6. The ultimate goal of carbohydrate digestion and absorption is to yield:
   a. fibers.
   b. glucose.
   c. enzymes.
   d. amylase.

7. The enzyme that breaks a disaccharide into glucose and galactose is:
   a. amylase.
   b. maltase.
   c. sucrase.
   d. lactase.

8. With insufficient glucose in metabolism, fat fragments combine to form:
   a. dextrins.
   b. mucilages.
   c. phytic acids.
   d. ketone bodies.

9. What does the pancreas secrete when blood glucose rises? When blood glucose falls?
   a. insulin; glucagon
   b. glucagon; insulin
   c. insulin; glycogen
   d. glycogen; epinephrine

10. What percentage of the daily energy intake should come from carbohydrates?
    a. 15 to 20
    b. 25 to 30
    c. 45 to 50
    d. 45 to 65

REFERENCES

1. N. R. Sahyoan and coauthors, Whole-grain intake is inversely associated with metabolic syndrome and mortality in older adults, *American Journal of Clinical Nutrition* 83 (2006): 124-131; B. M. Davy and C. L. Melby, The effect of fiber-rich carbohydrates on features of Syndrome X, *Journal of the American Dietetic Association* 103 (2003): 86-96.
2. J. R. Jones, D. M. Lineback, and M. J. Levine, Dietary Reference Intakes: Implications for fiber labeling and consumption: A summary of the International Life Sciences Institute North America Fiber Workshop, June 1-2, 2004, Washington, DC, *Nutrition Reviews* 64 (2006): 31-38.
3. D. Savaiano, Lactose intolerance: A self-fulfilling prophecy leading to osteoporosis? *Nutrition Reviews* 61 (2003): 221-223.
4. S. R. Hertzler and S. M. Clancy, Kefir improves lactose digestion and tolerance in adults with lactose maldigestion, *Journal of the American Dietetic Association* 103 (2003): 582-587.
5. R. S. Haltiwanger and J. B. Lowe, Role of glycosylation in development, *Annual Review of Biochemistry* 73 (2004): 491-537; T. Maeder, Sweet medicines, *Scientific American* 287 (2002): 40-47; J. Travis, The true sweet science-Researchers develop a taster for the study of sugars, *Science News* 161 (2002): 232-233.
6. R. L. Schnaar, Glycolipid-mediated cell-cell recognition in inflammation and nerve regeneration, *Archives of Biochemistry and Biophysics* 426 (2003): 163-172.
7. R. Gruetter, Glycogen: The forgotten cerebral energy store, *Journal of Neuroscience Research* 74 (2003): 179-183.
8. K. Foster-Powell, S. H. A. Holt, and J. C. Brand-Miller, International table of glycemic index and glycemic load values: 2002, *American Journal of Clinical Nutrition* 76 (2002): 5-56.
9. A. M. Opperman and coauthors, Meta-analysis of the health effects of using the glycaemic index in meal-planning, *British Journal of Nutrition* 92 (2004): 367-381.
10. C. B. Ebbeling and coauthors, Effects of an ad libitum low-glycemic load diet on cardiovascular disease risk factors in obese young adults, *American Journal of Clinical Nutrition* 81 (2005): 976-982; S. Dickinson and J. Brand-Miller, Glycemic index, postprandial glycemia and cardiovascular disease, *Current Opinion in Lipidology* 16 (2005): 69-75; A. M. Opperman and coauthors, Meta-analysis of the health effects of using the glycaemic index in meal-planning, *British Journal of Nutrition* 92 (2004): 367-381; M. A. Pereira and coauthors, Effects of a low-glycemic load diet on resting energy expenditure and heart disease risk factors during weight loss, *Journal of the American Medical Association* 292 (2004): 2482-2490; T. M. S. Wolever, Carbohydrate and the regulation of blood glucose and metabolism, *Nutrition Reviews* 61 (2003): S40-S48; D. J. A. Jenkins and coauthors, Glycemic index: Overview of implications in health and disease, *American Journal of Clinical Nutrition* 76 (2002): 266S-273S.
11. G. Livesey, Low-glycemic diets and health: Implications for obesity, *Proceedings of the Nutrition Society* 64 (2005): 105-113; B. Sloth and coauthors, No difference in body weight decrease between a low-glycemic-index and a high-glycemic-index diet but reduced LDL cholesterol after 10-wk ad libitum intake of the low-glycemic-index diet, *American Journal of Clinical Nutrition* 80 (2004): 337-347; C. Bouché and coauthors, Five-week, low-glycemic index diet decreases total fat mass and improves plasma lipid profile in moderately overweight nondiabetic men, *Diabetes Care* 25 (2002): 822-828.
12. S. D. Ball and coauthors, Prolongation of satiety after low versus moderately high glycemic index meals in obese adolescents, *Pediatrics* 111 (2003): 488-494; S. B. Roberts, Glycemic index and satiety, *Nutrition in Clinical Care* 6 (2003): 20-26.
13. S. Liu and coauthors, Relation between a diet with a high glycemic load and plasma concentrations of high-sensitivity C-reactive protein in middle-aged women, *American Journal of Clinical Nutrition* 75 (2002): 492-498.
14. D. S. Ludwig, The glycemic index—Physiological mechanisms relating to obesity, diabetes, and cardiovascular disease, *Journal of the American Medical Association* 287 (2002): 2414-2423.
15. F. X. Pi-Sunyer, Glycemic index and disease, *American Journal of Clinical Nutrition* 76 (2002): 290S-298S.
16. D. R. Lineback and J. M. Jones, Sugars and health workshop: Summary and conclusions, *American Journal of Clinical Nutrition* 78 (2003): 893S-897S.
17. G. Fernandes, A. Velangi, and T. M. S. Wolever, Glycemic index of potatoes commonly consumed in North America, *Journal of the American Dietetic Association* 105 (2005): 557-562; E. M. Y. Chan and coauthors, Postprandial glucose response to Chinese foods in patients with type 2 diabetes, *Journal of the American Dietetic Association* 104 (2004): 1854-1858.
18. B. M. Popkin and S. J. Nielsen, The sweetening of the world's diet, *Obesity Research* 11 (2003): 1325-1332.

19. R. Touger-Decker and C. van Loveren, Sugars and dental caries, *American Journal of Clinical Nutrition* 78 (2003): 881S-892S.

20. S. Kashket and D. P. DePaola, Cheese consumption and the development and progression of dental caries, *Nutrition Reviews* 60 (2002): 97-103; Department of Health and Human Services, *Oral Health in America: A Report of the Surgeon General* (Rockville, Md.: National Institutes of Health, 2000), pp. 250-251.

21. S. Wongkhantee and coauthors, Effect of acidic food and drinks on surface hardness of enamel, dentine, and tooth-coloured filling materials, *Journal of Dentistry* 34 (2006): 214-220; W. K. Seow and K. M. Thong, Erosive effects of common beverages on extracted premolar teeth, *Australian Dental Journal* 50 (2005): 173-178.

22. J. M. Jones and K. Elam, Sugars and health: Is there an issue? *Journal of the American Dietetic Association* 103 (2003): 1058-1060.

23. G. A. Bray, S. J. Nielsen, and B. M. Popkin, Consumption of high-fructose corn syrup in beverages may play a role in the epidemic of obesity, *American Journal of Clinical Nutrition* 79 (2004): 537-543; S. J. Nielsen and B. M. Popkin, Changes in beverage intake between 1977 and 2001, *American Journal of Preventive Medicine* 27 (2004): 205-210.

24. A. M. Coulston and R. K. Johnson, Sugar and sugars: Myths and realities, *Journal of the American Dietetic Association* 102 (2002): 351-353.

25. M. B. Schulze and coauthors, Sugar-sweetened beverages, weight gain, and incidence of type 2 diabetes in young and middle-aged women, *Journal of the American Medical Association* 292 (2004): 927-934; L. S. Gross and coauthors, Increased consumption of refined carbohydrates and the epidemic of type 2 diabetes in the United States: An ecologic assessment, *American Journal of Clinical Nutrition* 79 (2004): 774-779.

26. Joint WHO/FAO Expert Consultation, 2003, pp. 57-58; S. H. F. Vermunt and coauthors, Effects of sugar intake on body weight: A review, *Obesity Reviews* 4 (2003): 91-99.

27. M. K. Hellerstein, Carbohydrate-induced hypertriglyceridemia: Modifying factors and implications for cardiovascular risk, *Current Opinion in Lipidology* 13 (2002): 33-40.

28. Bray, 2004; S. S. Elliott and coauthors, Fructose, weight gain, and the insulin resistance syndrome, *American Journal of Clinical Nutrition* 76 (2002): 911-922.

29. P. J. Havel, Dietary fructose: Implications for dysregulation of energy homeostasis and lipid/carbohydrate metabolism, *Nutrition Reviews* 63 (2005): 133-157; J. Wylie-Rosett, C. J. Segal-Isaacson, and A. Segal-Isaacson, Carbohydrates and increases in obesity: Does the type of carbohydrate make a difference? *Obesity Research* 12 (2004): 124S-129S; Elliott and coauthors, 2002.

30. J. James and coauthors, Preventing childhood obesity by reducing consumption of carbonated drinks: Cluster randomised controlled trial, *British Medical Journal* 10 (2004): 1136-1141.

31. S. K. Fried and S. P. Rao, Sugars, hypertriglyceridemia, and cardiovascular disease, *American Journal of Clinical Nutrition* 78 (2003): 873S-880S; B. V. Howard and J. Wylie-Rosett, AHA Scientific Statement: Sugar and cardiovascular disease, *Circulation* 106 (2002): 523.

32. J. M. Schwarz and coauthors, Hepatic de novo lipogenesis in normoinsulinemic and hyperinsulinemic subjects consuming high-fat, low-carbohydrate and low-fat, high-carbohydrate isoenergetic diets, *American Journal of Clinical Nutrition* 77 (2003): 43-50.

33. S. Yanovski, Sugar and fat: Cravings and aversions, *Journal of Nutrition* 133 (2003): 835S-837S.

34. J. Putnam and S. Haley, Estimating consumption of caloric sweeteners, *Economic Research Service, Farm Service Agency, and Foreign Agricultural Service, USDA*, 2004.

35. Committee on Dietary Reference Intakes, *Dietary Reference Intakes: Energy, Carbohydrate, Fiber, Fat, Fatty Acids, Cholesterol, Protein, and Amino Acids* (Washington, D.C.: National Academies Press, 2005).

36. M. K. Jenson and coauthors, Whole grains, bran, and germ in relation to homocysteine and markers of glycemic control, lipids, and inflammation, *American Journal of Clinical Nutrition* 83 (2006): 275-283; M. K. Jensen and coauthors, Intakes of whole grains, bran, and germ and the risk of coronary heart disease in men, *American Journal of Clinical Nutrition* 80 (2004): 1492-1499; F. B. Hu and W. C. Willett, Optimal diets for prevention of coronary heart disease, *Journal of the American Medical Association* 288 (2002): 2569-2578; N. M. McKeown and coauthors, Whole-grain intake is favorably associated with metabolic risk factors for type 2 diabetes and cardiovascular disease in the Framingham Offspring Study, *American Journal of Clinical Nutrition* 76 (2002): 390-398; S. Liu, Intake of refined carbohydrates and whole grain foods in relation to risk of type 2 diabetes mellitus and coronary heart disease, *Journal of the American College of Nutrition* 21 (2002): 298-306.

37. K. M. Behall, D. J. Scholfield, and J. Hallfrisch, Diets containing barley significantly reduce lipids in mildly hypercholesterolemic men and women, *American Journal of Clinical Nutrition* 80 (2004): 1185-1193; B. M. Davy and coauthors, High-fiber oat cereal compared with wheat cereal consumption favorably alters LDL-cholesterol subclass and particle numbers in middle-aged and older men, *American Journal of Clinical Nutrition* 76 (2002): 351-358; D. J. A. Jenkins and coauthors, Soluble fiber intake at a dose approved by the US Food and Drug Administration for a claim of health benefits: Serum lipid risk factors for cardiovascular disease assessed in a randomized controlled crossover trial, *American Journal of Clinical Nutrition* 75 (2002): 834-839.

38. U. A. Ajani, E. S. Ford, and A. H. Mokdad, Dietary fiber and C-reactive protein: Findings from National Health and Nutrition Examination Survey Data, *Journal of Nutrition* 134 (2004): 1181-1185.

39. M. K. Jenson and coauthors, Whole grains, bran and germ in relation to homocysteine and markers of glycemic control, lipids, and inflammation, *American Journal of Clinical Nutrition* 83 (2006): 275-283; T. T. Fung and coauthors, Whole-grain intake and the risk of type 2 diabetes: A prospective study in men, *American Journal of Clinical Nutrition* 76 (2002): 535-540.

40. W. Aldoori and M. Ryan-Harshman, Preventing diverticular disease: Review of recent evidence on high-fibre diets, *Canadian Family Physician* 48 (2002): 1632-1637.

41. Y. Park and coauthors, Dietary fiber intake and risk of colorectal cancer, *Journal of the American Medical Association* 294 (2005): 2849-2857; T. Asano and R. S. McLeod, Dietary fibre for the prevention of colorectal adenomas and carcinomas, *Cochrane Database of Systematic Reviews* 2 (2002): CD003430.

42. S. A. Bingham and coauthors, Dietary fibre in food and protection against colorectal cancer in the European Prospective Investigation into Cancer and Nutrition (EPIC): An observational study, *Lancet* 361 (2003): 1496-1501.

43. M. L. Slattery and coauthors, Plant foods, fiber, and rectal cancer, *American Journal of Clinical Nutrition* 79 (2004): 274-281.

44. L. McMillan and coauthors, Opposing effects of butyrate and bile acids on apoptosis of human colon adenoma cells: Differential activation of PKC and MAP kinases, *British Journal of Cancer* 88 (2003): 748-753; M. E. Rodriguez-Cabezas and coauthors, Dietary fiber down-regulates colonic tumor necrosis factor alpha and nitric oxide production in trinitrobenzenesulfonic acid-induced colitic rats, *Journal of Nutrition* 11 (2002): 3263-3271.

45. S. Liu and coauthors, Relation between changes in intakes of dietary fiber and grain products and changes in weight and development of obesity among middle-aged women, *American Journal of Clinical Nutrition* 78 (2003): 920-927.

46. P. Koh-Banerjee, Changes in whole-grain, bran, and cereal fiber consumption in relation to 8-y weight gain among men, *American Journal of Clinical Nutrition* 80 (2004): 1237-1245; Committee on Dietary Reference Intakes, 2002/2005, pp. 342-344.

47. Committee on Dietary Reference Intakes, 2005.

48. Position of the American Dietetic Association: Health implications of dietary fiber, *Journal of the American Dietetic Association* 102 (2002): 993-999.

ANSWERS

Nutrition Calculations

1. 0.7×2000 total kcal/day $= 1400$ kcal from carbohydrate/day

    1400 kcal from carbohydrate $\div$ 4 kcal/g $= 350$ g carbohydrate

This carbohydrate intake is higher than the Daily Value and higher than the 45 to 65 percent recommendation.

2. 350 g carbohydrate $\div$ 2 $= 175$ g carbohydrate/day

    175 g carbohydrate $\times$ 4 kcal/g $= 700$ kcal from carbohydrate

    700 kcal from carbohydrate $\div$ 2000 total kcal/day $= 0.35$

    $0.35 \times 100 = 35\%$ kcal from carbohydrate

This carbohydrate intake is lower than the Daily Value and lower than the 45 to 65 percent recommendation.

3. 350 g carbohydrate $\times$ 2 $= 700$ g carbohydrate/day

    700 g carbohydrate $\times$ 4 kcal/g $= 2800$ kcal from carbohydrate

    2800 kcal from carbohydrate $\div$ 6000 total kcal/day $= 0.47$

    $0.47 \times 100 = 47\%$ kcal from carbohydrate

This carbohydrate intake is higher than the Daily Value and meets the 45 to 65 percent recommendation.

4. 150 g carbohydrate $\times$ 4 kcal/g $= 600$ kcal from carbohydrate

    600 kcal from carbohydrate $\div$ 1000 total kcal/day $= 0.60$

    $0.60 \times 100 = 60\%$ kcal from carbohydrate

This carbohydrate intake is lower than the Daily Value and meets the 45 to 65 percent recommendation.

Study Questions (multiple choice)

1. b 2. c 3. c 4. d 5. d
6. b 7. d 8. d 9. a 10. d

Alternatives to Sugar

Funnette Division, Hoechst Celenese Corp.

Almost everyone finds pleasure in sweet foods—after all, the taste preference for sweets is inborn. To a child, the sweeter the food, the better. In adults, this preference is somewhat diminished, but most adults still enjoy an occasional sweet food or beverage. Because they want to control weight gain, blood glucose, and dental caries, many consumers turn to alternative sweeteners to help them limit kcalories and minimize sugar intake. In doing so, they encounter two sets of alternative sweeteners: **artificial sweeteners** and **sugar replacers.**

Artificial Sweeteners

The Food and Drug Administration (FDA) has approved the use of several artificial sweeteners—saccharin, aspartame, acesulfame potassium (acesulfame-K), sucralose, and neotame. Two others are awaiting FDA approval—alitame and cyclamate. Another— tagatose—did not need approval because it is generally recognized as a safe ingredient. These artificial sweeteners are sometimes called **nonnutritive sweeteners** because they provide virtually no energy. Table H4-1 and the accompanying glossary provide general

details about each of these sweeteners.

Saccharin, acesulfame-K, and sucralose are not metabolized in the body; in contrast, the body digests aspartame as a protein. In fact, aspartame yields energy (4 kcalories per gram, as does protein), but because so little is used, its energy contribution is negligible.

Some consumers have challenged the safety of using artificial sweeteners. Considering that all substances are toxic at some dose, it is little surprise that large doses of artificial sweeteners (or their components or metabolic by-products) have toxic effects. The question to ask is whether their ingestion is safe for human beings in quantities people normally use (and potentially abuse).

Saccharin

Saccharin, used for over 100 years in the United States, is currently used by some 50 million people—primarily in soft drinks, secondarily as a tabletop sweetener. Saccharin is rapidly excreted in the urine and does not accumulate in the body.

Questions about saccharin's safety surfaced in 1977, when experiments suggested that large doses of saccharin (equivalent to

TABLE H4-1	Sweeteners

Sweeteners	Relative Sweetness[a]	Energy (kcal/g)	Acceptable Daily Intake	Average Amount to Replace 1 tsp Sugar	Approved Uses
Approved Sweeteners (Trade Name)					
Saccharin (Sweet 'n Low)	450	0	5 mg/kg body weight	12 mg	Tabletop sweeteners, wide range of foods, beverages, cosmetics, and pharmaceutical products
Aspartame (Nutrasweet, Equal, NutraTaste)	200	4[b]	50 mg/kg body weight[c]	18 mg	General purpose sweetener in all foods and beverages Warning to people with PKU: Contains phenylalanine
Acesulfame potassium or Acesulfame-K (Sunette, Sweet One, Sweet 'n Safe)	200	0	15 mg/kg body weight[d]	25 mg	Tabletop sweeteners, puddings, gelatins, chewing gum, candies, baked goods, desserts, beverages
Sucralose (Splenda)	600	0	5 mg/kg body weight	6 mg	General purpose sweetener for all foods
Neotame	8000	0	18 mg/day	0.5 μg	Baked goods, nonalcoholic beverages, chewing gum, candies, frostings, frozen desserts, gelatins, puddings, jams and jellies, syrups
Tagatose (Nutralose)	0.8	1.5	7.5 g/day	1 tsp	Baked goods, beverages, cereals, chewing gum, confections, dairy products, dietary supplements, health bars, tabletop sweetener
Sweeteners with Approval Pending					**Proposed Uses**
Alitame	2000	4[e]	—		Beverages, baked goods, tabletop sweeteners, frozen desserts
Cyclamate	30	0	—		Tabletop sweeteners, baked goods

[a] Relative sweetness is determined by comparing the approximate sweetness of a sugar substitute with the sweetness of pure sucrose, which has been defined as 1.0. Chemical structure, temperature, acidity, and other flavors of the foods in which the substance occurs all influence relative sweetness.

[b] Aspartame provides 4 kcalories per gram, as does protein, but because so little is used, its energy contribution is negligible. In powdered form, it is sometimes mixed with lactose, however, so a 1-gram packet may provide 4 kcalories.

[c] Recommendations from the World Health Organization and in Europe and Canada limit aspartame intake to 40 milligrams per kilogram of body weight per day.

[d] Recommendations from the World Health Organization limit acesulfame-K intake to 9 milligrams per kilogram of body weight per day.

[e] Alitame provides 4 kcalories per gram, as does protein, but because so little is used, its energy contribution is negligible.

hundreds of cans of diet soda daily for a lifetime) increased the risk of bladder cancer in rats. The FDA proposed banning saccharin as a result. Public outcry in favor of saccharin was so loud, however, that Congress imposed a moratorium on the ban while additional safety studies were conducted. Products containing saccharin were required to carry a warning label until 2001, when studies concluded that saccharin did not cause cancer in humans.

Does saccharin cause cancer? The largest population study to date, involving 9000 men and women, showed that overall saccharin use did not increase the risk of cancer. Among certain small groups of the population, however, such as those who both smoked heavily and used saccharin, the risk of bladder cancer was slightly greater. Other studies involving more than 5000 people with bladder cancer showed no association between bladder cancer and saccharin use. In 2000, saccharin was removed from the list of suspected cancer-causing substances. Warning labels are no longer required.

Common sense dictates that consuming large amounts of any substance is probably not wise, but at current, moderate intake levels, saccharin appears to be safe for most people. It has been approved for use in more than 100 countries.

Aspartame

Aspartame is a simple chemical compound made of components common to many foods: two amino acids (phenylalanine and aspartic acid) and a methyl group (CH_3). Figure H4-1 (p. 134) shows its chemical structure. The flavors of the components give no clue to the combined effect; one of them tastes bitter, and the other is tasteless, but the combination creates a product that is 200 times sweeter than sucrose.

In the digestive tract, enzymes split aspartame into its three component parts. The body absorbs the two amino acids and uses them just as if they had come from food protein, which is made entirely of amino acids, including these two.

Because this sweetener contributes phenylalanine, products containing aspartame must bear a warning label for people with the inherited disease phenylketonuria (PKU). People with PKU are unable to dispose of any excess phenylalanine. The accumulation of phenylalanine and its by-products is toxic to the developing nervous system, causing irreversible brain damage. For this reason, all newborns in the United States are screened for PKU. The treatment for PKU is a special diet that must strike a balance, pro-

FIGURE H4-1 Structure of Aspartame

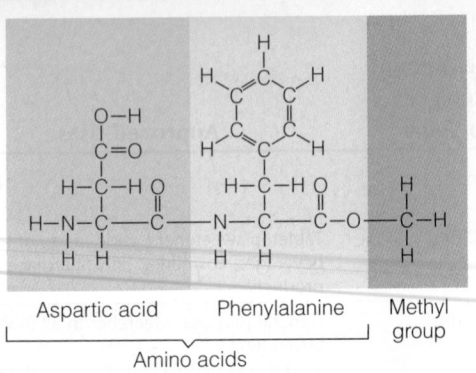

Aspartic acid   Phenylalanine   Methyl group

Amino acids

FIGURE H4-2 Metabolism of Aspartame

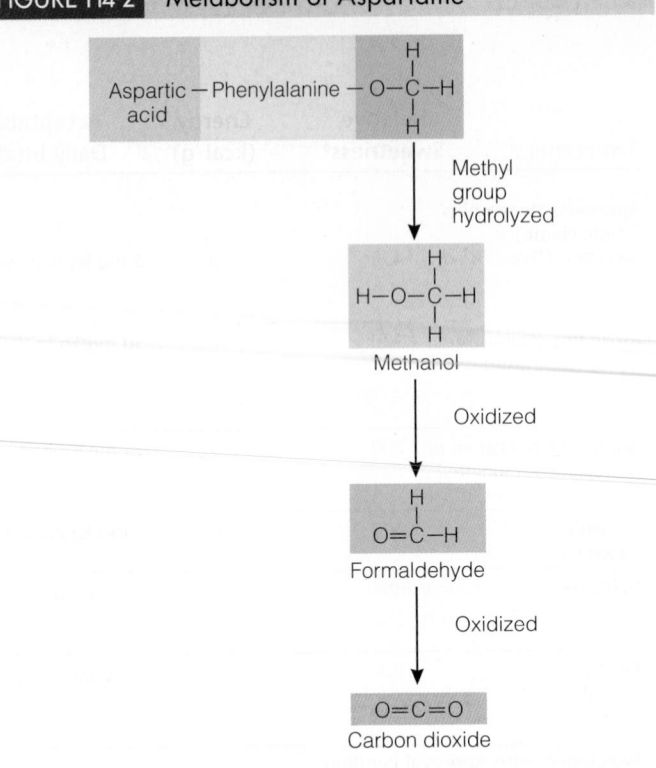

Aspartic acid — Phenylalanine — O—C—H

Methyl group hydrolyzed

Methanol

Oxidized

Formaldehyde

Oxidized

Carbon dioxide

viding enough phenylalanine to support normal growth and health but not enough to cause harm. The little extra phenylalanine from aspartame poses only a small risk, even in heavy users, but children with PKU need to get all their required phenylalanine from foods instead of from an artificial sweetener. The PKU diet excludes such protein- and nutrient-rich foods as milk, meat, fish, poultry, cheese, eggs, nuts, legumes, and many bread products. Consequently, these children have difficulty obtaining the many essential nutrients—such as calcium, iron, and the B vitamins—found along with phenylalanine in these foods. Children with PKU cannot afford to squander their limited phenylalanine allowance on the phenylalanine of aspartame, which contributes none of the associated vitamins or minerals essential for good health and normal growth.

During metabolism, the methyl group momentarily becomes methyl alcohol (methanol)—a potentially toxic compound (see Figure H4-2). This breakdown also occurs when aspartame-sweetened beverages are stored at warm temperatures over time. The amount of methanol produced may be safe to consume, but a person may not want to, considering that the beverage has lost its sweetness. In the body, enzymes convert methanol to formaldehyde, another toxic compound. Finally, formaldehyde is broken down to carbon dioxide. Before aspartame could be approved, the quantities of these products generated during metabolism had to be determined, and they were found to fall below the threshold at which they would cause harm. In fact, ounce for ounce, tomato juice yields six times as much methanol as a diet soda.

A recent Italian study found that aspartame caused cancer in female rats and fueled the controversies surrounding aspartame's safety.[1] Statements from the FDA and others, however, indicate that such a conclusion is not supported by the data.[2] The only valid scientific concern is that for people with epilepsy, excessive intake of aspartame may decrease their threshold for seizures; this does not appear to be a problem when intakes are within recommended amounts.[3]

Acesulfame-K

Because **acesulfame potassium (acesulfame-K)** passes through the body unchanged, it does not provide any energy nor does it increase the intake of potassium. Acesulfame-K is ap-

proved for use in the United States, Canada, and more than 60 other countries.

Sucralose

Sucralose is unique among the artificial sweeteners in that it is made from sugar that has had three of its hydroxyl (OH) groups replaced by chlorine atoms. The result is an exceptionally stable molecule that is much sweeter than sugar. Because the body does not recognize sucralose as a carbohydrate, it passes through the GI tract undigested and unabsorbed.

Neotame

Like aspartame, **neotame** also contains the amino acids phenylalanine and aspartic acid and a methyl group. Unlike aspartame, however, neotame has an additional side group attached. This simple difference makes all the difference to people with PKU because it blocks the digestive enzymes that normally separate phenylalanine and aspartic acid. Consequently, the amino acids are not absorbed and neotame need not carry a warning for people with PKU.

Tagatose

The FDA granted the fructose relative **tagatose** the status of "generally recognized as safe," making it available as a low-kcalorie sweetener for a variety of foods and beverages. This monosaccharide is naturally found in only a few foods, but it can be derived from lactose. Unlike fructose or lactose, however, 80 percent of tagatose remains unabsorbed until it reaches the large intestine. There, bacteria ferment tagatose, releasing gases and short chain fatty acids that are absorbed. As a result, tagatose provides 1.5 kcalories per gram. At high doses, tagatose causes flatulence, rumbling, and loose stools; otherwise, no adverse side effects have been noted. In fact, tagatose is a prebiotic that may benefit GI health. Unlike other sugars, tagatose does not promote dental caries and may carry a dental caries health claim.

Alitame and Cyclamate

FDA approval for **alitame** and **cyclamate** is still pending. To date, no safety issues have been raised for alitame, and it has been approved for use in other countries. In contrast, cyclamate has been battling safety issues for 50 years. Approved by the FDA in 1949, cyclamate was banned in 1969 principally on the basis of one study indicating that it caused bladder cancer in rats.

The National Research Council has reviewed dozens of studies on cyclamate and concluded that neither cyclamate nor its metabolites cause cancer. The council did, however, recommend further research to determine if heavy or long-term use poses risks. Although cyclamate does not *initiate* cancer, it may *promote* cancer development once it is started. The FDA currently has no policy on substances that enhance the cancer-causing activities of other substances, but it is unlikely to approve cyclamate soon, if at all. Agencies in more than 50 other countries, including Canada, have approved cyclamate.

Acceptable Daily Intake

The amount of artificial sweetener considered safe for daily use is called the **Acceptable Daily Intake (ADI).** The ADI represents the level of consumption that, if maintained every day throughout a person's life, would still be considered safe by a wide margin. It usually reflects an amount 100 times less than the level at which no observed effects occur in animal research studies.

The ADI for aspartame, for example, is 50 milligrams per kilogram of body weight. That is, the FDA approved aspartame based on the assumption that no one would consume more than 50 milligrams per kilogram of body weight in a day. This maximum daily intake is indeed high: for a 150-pound adult, it adds up to 97 packets of Equal or 20 cans of soft drinks sweetened only with aspartame. The company that produces aspartame estimates that if all the sugar and saccharin in the U.S. diet were replaced with aspartame, 1 percent of the population would be consuming the FDA maximum. Most people who use aspartame consume less than 5 milligrams per kilogram of body weight per day. But a young child who drinks four glasses of aspartame-sweetened beverages on a hot day and has five servings of other products with aspartame that day (such as pudding, chewing gum, cereal, gelatin, and frozen desserts) consumes the FDA maximum level. Although this intake presents no proven hazard, it seems wise to offer children other foods so as not to exceed the limit. Table H4-2 lists the average amounts of aspartame in some common foods.

For persons choosing to use artificial sweeteners, the American Dietetic Association wisely advises that they be used in moderation and only as part of a well-balanced nutritious diet.[4] The dietary principles of moderation and variety help to reduce the possible risks associated with any food.

Artificial Sweeteners and Weight Control

The rate of obesity in the United States has been rising for decades. Foods and beverages sweetened with artificial sweeteners were among the first products developed to help people control their weight. Ironically, a few studies have reported that intense sweeteners, such as aspartame, may stimulate appetite, which could lead to weight gain. Contradicting these reports, most studies find no change in feelings of hunger and no change in food intakes or body weight. Adding to the confusion, some studies report lower energy intakes and greater weight losses when people eat or drink artificially sweetened products.[5]

When studying the effects of artificial sweeteners on food intake and body weight, researchers ask different questions and take different approaches. It matters, for example, whether the people used in a study are of a healthy weight and whether they are following a weight-loss diet. Motivations for using sweeteners differ, too, and this influences a person's actions. For example, one person might drink an artificially sweetened beverage now so as to be able to eat a high-kcalorie food later. This person's energy intake might stay the same or increase. A person trying to control food energy intake might drink an artificially sweetened beverage now and choose a low-kcalorie food later. This plan would help reduce the person's total energy intake.

In designing experiments on artificial sweeteners, researchers have to distinguish between the effects of sweetness and the effects of a particular substance. If a person is hungry shortly after eating an artificially sweetened snack, is that because the sweet taste (of all sweeteners, including sugars) stimulates appetite? Or is it because the artificial sweetener itself stimulates appetite? Research must also distinguish between the effects of food energy and the effects of the substance. If a person is hungry shortly after eating an artificially sweetened snack, is that because less food energy was available to satisfy hunger? Or is it because the artificial sweetener itself triggers hunger? Furthermore, if appetite is stimulated and a person feels hungry, does that actually lead to increased food intake?

Whether a person compensates for the energy reduction of artificial sweeteners either partially or fully depends on several factors. Using artificial sweeteners will not automatically lower energy intake; to control energy intake successfully, a person needs to make informed diet and activity decisions throughout the day (as Chapter 9 explains).

TABLE H4-2 Average Aspartame Contents of Selected Foods

Food	Aspartame (mg)
12 oz diet soft drink	170
8 oz powdered drink	100
8 oz sugar-free fruit yogurt	124
4 oz gelatin dessert	80
1 packet sweetener	35

Stevia—An Herbal Alternative

The FDA has backed its approval or denial of artificial sweeteners with decades of extensive research. Such research is lacking for the herb **stevia,** a shrub whose leaves have long been used by the people of South America to sweeten their beverages. In the United States, stevia is sold in health-food stores as a dietary supplement. The FDA has reviewed the limited research on the use of stevia as an alternative to artificial sweeteners and found concerns regarding its effect on reproduction, cancer development, and energy metabolism. Used sparingly, stevia may do little harm, but the FDA could not approve its extensive and widespread use in the U.S. market. Canada, the European Union, and the United Nations have reached similar conclusions. In Canada, provisional guidelines have been adopted for the use of stevia as a medicinal ingredient and as a sweetening agent. That stevia can be sold as a dietary supplement but not used as a food additive in the United States, highlights key differences in FDA regulations. Food additives must prove their safety and effectiveness before receiving FDA approval, whereas dietary supplements are not required to submit to any testing or receive any approval. (See Highlight 10 for information on dietary supplements and Highlight 18 for more on herbs.)

Sugar Replacers

Some "sugar-free" or reduced-kcalorie products contain sugar replacers.* The term *sugar replacers* describes the sugar alcohols—familiar examples include erythritol, mannitol, sorbitol, xylitol, maltitol, isomalt, and lactitol—that provide bulk and sweetness in cookies, hard candies, sugarless gums, jams, and jellies. These products claim to be "sugar-free" on their labels, but in this case, "sugar-free" does not mean free of kcalories. Sugar replacers do provide kcalories, but fewer than their carbohydrate cousins, the sugars. Because sugar replacers yield energy, they are sometimes referred to as **nutritive sweeteners**. Table H4-3 includes their energy values, but a simple estimate can help consumers: divide grams by 2. Sugar alcohols occur naturally in fruits and vegetables; manufacturers also use sugar alcohols as a low-energy bulk ingredient in many processed foods.

* To minimize confusion, the American Diabetes Association prefers the term sugar replacers instead of "sugar alcohols" (which connotes alcohol), "bulk sweeteners" (which connotes fiber), or "sugar substitutes" (which connotes aspartame and saccharin).

TABLE H4-3 Sugar Replacers

Sugar Alcohols	Relative Sweetness[a]	Energy (kcal/g)	Approved Uses
Erythritol	0.7	0.4	Beverages, frozen dairy desserts, baked goods, chewing gum, candies
Isomalt	0.5	2.0	Candies, chewing gum, ice cream, jams and jellies, frostings, beverages, baked goods
Lactitol	0.4	2.0	Candies, chewing gum, frozen dairy desserts, jams and jellies, frostings, baked goods
Maltitol	0.9	2.1	Particularly good for candy coating
Mannitol	0.7	1.6	Bulking agent, chewing gum
Sorbitol	0.5	2.6	Special dietary foods, candies, gums
Xylitol	1.0	2.4	Chewing gum, candies, pharmaceutical and oral health products

[a] Relative sweetness is determined by comparing the approximate sweetness of a sugar replacer with the sweetness of pure sucrose, which has been defined as 1.0. Chemical structure, temperature, acidity, and other flavors of the foods in which the substance occurs all influence relative sweetness.

Sugar alcohols evoke a low glycemic response. The body absorbs sugar alcohols slowly; consequently, they are slower to enter the bloodstream than other sugars. Side effects such as gas, abdominal discomfort, and diarrhea, however, make them less attractive than the artificial sweeteners. For this reason, regulations require food labels to state "Excess consumption may have a laxative effect" if reasonable consumption of that food could result in the daily ingestion of 50 grams of a sugar alcohol.

The real benefit of using sugar replacers is that they do not contribute to dental caries. Bacteria in the mouth cannot metabolize sugar alcohols as rapidly as sugar. They are therefore valuable in chewing gums, breath mints, and other products that people keep in their mouths for a while. Figure H4-3 presents labeling information for products using sugar alternatives.

The sugar replacers, like the artificial sweeteners, can occupy a place in the diet, and provided they are used in moderation, they will do no harm. In fact, they can help, both by providing an alternative to sugar for people with diabetes and by inhibiting caries-causing bacteria. People may find it appropriate to use all three sweeteners at times: artificial sweeteners, sugar replacers, and sugar itself.

FIGURE H4-3 Sugar Alternatives on Food Labels

Products containing sugar replacers may claim to "not promote tooth decay" if they meet FDA criteria for dental plaque activity.

Products containing aspartame must carry a warning for people with phenylketonuria.

© Craig Moore

This ingredient list includes both sugar alcohols and artificial sweetenters.

INGREDIENTS: SORBITOL, MALTITOL, GUM BASE, MANNITOL, ARTIFICIAL AND NATURAL FLAVORING, ACACIA, SOFTENERS, TITANIUM DIOXIDE (COLOR), ASPARTAME, ACESULFAME POTASSIUM AND CANDELILLA WAX.
PHENYLKETONURICS: CONTAINS PHENYLALANINE.

35% FEWER CALORIES THAN SUGARED GUM.

Nutrition Facts	Amount per serving	% DV*
	Total Fat 0g	0%
Sodium 0mg		0%
Serving Size 2 pieces (3g)	**Total Carb.** 2g	1%
Servings 6	Sugars 0g	
Calories 5	Sugar Alcohol 2g	
	Protein 0g	
*Percent Daily Values (DV) are based on a 2,000 calorie diet.	Not a significant source of other nutrients.	

Products containing less than 0.5 g of sugar per serving can claim to be "sugarless" or "sugar-free."

Products that claim to be "reduced kcalories" must provide at least 25% fewer kcalories per serving than the comparison item.

NUTRITION ON THE NET

ThomsonNOW™
For furthur study of topics covered in this Highlight, log on to **www .thomsonedu.com/thomsonnow**. Go to Chapter 4, then to Highlights Nutrition on the Net.

- Search for "artificial sweeteners" at the U.S. Government health information site: **www.healthfinder.gov**

- Search for "sweeteners" at the International Food Information Council site: **www.ific.org**

REFERENCES

1. M. Soffritti and coauthors, Aspartame induces lymphomas and leukaemias in rats, *European Journal of Oncology* 10 (2005): 107-116.
2. U.S. Food and Drug Administration, FDA statement on European aspartame study, posted May 8, 2006, www.fda.gov; M. R. Weihrauch and V. Diehl, Artificial sweeteners—Do they bear a carcinogenic risk? *Annals of Oncology* 15 (2004): 1460-1465.
3. S. M. Jankovic, Controversies with aspartame, *Medicinski Pregled* 56 (2003): 27-29.
4. Position of the American Dietetic Association: Use of nutritive and nonnutritive sweeteners, *Journal of the American Dietetic Association* 104 (2004): 255-275.
5. S. H. F. Vermunt and coauthors, Effects of sugar intake on body weight: A review, *Obesity Reviews* 4 (2003): 91-99.

Michael Paul/Getty Images

Nutrition in Your Life

Most likely, you know what you don't like about body fat, but do you appreciate how it insulates you against the cold or powers your hike around a lake? And what about food fat? You're right to credit fat for providing the delicious flavors and aromas of buttered popcorn and fried chicken—and to criticize it for contributing to the weight gain and heart disease so common today. The challenge is to strike a healthy balance of enjoying some fat, but not too much. Learning which kinds of fats are most harmful will help you make wise decisions.

The Lipids: Triglycerides, Phospholipids, and Sterols

CHAPTER OUTLINE

The Chemist's View of Fatty Acids and Triglycerides • Fatty Acids • Triglycerides • Degree of Unsaturation Revisited

The Chemist's View of Phospholipids and Sterols • Phospholipids • Sterols

Digestion, Absorption, and Transport of Lipids • Lipid Digestion • Lipid Absorption • Lipid Transport •

Lipids in the Body • Roles of Triglycerides • Essential Fatty Acids • A Preview of Lipid Metabolism

Health Effects and Recommended Intakes of Lipids • Health Effects of Lipids • Recommended Intakes of Fat • From Guidelines to Groceries

HIGHLIGHT 5 High-Fat Foods—Friend or Foe?

Most people are surprised to learn that fat has some virtues. Only when people consume either too much or too little fat, or too much of some kinds of fat, does poor health develop. It is true, though, that in our society of abundance, people are likely to consume too much fat.

Fat refers to the class of nutrients known as **lipids.** The lipid family includes triglycerides (**fats** and **oils**), phospholipids, and sterols. The triglycerides ◆ predominate, both in foods and in the body.

The Chemist's View of Fatty Acids and Triglycerides

Like carbohydrates, fatty acids and triglycerides are composed of carbon (C), hydrogen (H), and oxygen (O). Because these lipids have many more carbons and hydrogens in proportion to their oxygens, however, they can supply more energy per gram than carbohydrates can (Chapter 7 provides details).

The many names and relationships in the lipid family can seem overwhelming—like meeting a friend's extended family for the first time. To ease the introductions, this chapter first presents each of the lipids from a chemist's point of view using both words and diagrams. Then the chapter follows the lipids through digestion and absorption and into the body to examine their roles in health and disease. For people who think more easily in words than in chemical symbols, this *preview* of the upcoming chemistry may be helpful:

1. Every triglyceride contains one molecule of glycerol and three fatty acids (basically, chains of carbon atoms).

2. Fatty acids may be 4 to 24 (even numbers of) carbons long, the 18-carbon ones being the most common in foods and especially noteworthy in nutrition.

3. Fatty acids may be saturated or unsaturated. Unsaturated fatty acids may have one or more points of unsaturation. (That is, they may be monounsaturated or polyunsaturated.)

4. Of special importance in nutrition are the polyunsaturated fatty acids whose *first* point of unsaturation is next to the third carbon (known as omega-3 fatty acids) or next to the sixth carbon (omega-6).

5. The 18-carbon fatty acids that fit this description are linolenic acid (omega-3) and linoleic acid (omega-6). Each is the primary member of a family of longer-chain

◆ Of the lipids in foods, 95% are fats and oils (triglycerides); of the lipids stored in the body, 99% are triglycerides.

lipids: a family of compounds that includes triglycerides, phospholipids, and sterols. Lipids are characterized by their insolubility in water. (Lipids also include the fat-soluble vitamins, described in Chapter 11.)

fats: lipids that are solid at room temperature (77°F or 25°C).

oils: lipids that are liquid at room temperature (77°F or 25°C).

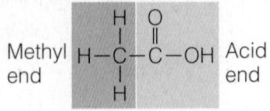

Acetic acid is a two-carbon organic acid.

fatty acids that help to regulate blood pressure, blood clotting, and other body functions important to health.

The paragraphs, definitions, and diagrams that follow present this information again in much more detail.

Fatty Acids

A **fatty acid** is an organic acid—a chain of carbon atoms with hydrogens attached—that has an acid group (COOH) at one end and a methyl group (CH$_3$) at the other end. The organic acid shown in Figure 5-1 is acetic acid, the compound that gives vinegar its sour taste. Acetic acid is the shortest such acid, with a "chain" only two carbon atoms long.

The Length of the Carbon Chain   Most naturally occurring fatty acids contain even numbers of carbons in their chains—up to 24 carbons in length. This discussion begins with the 18-carbon fatty acids, which are abundant in our food supply. Stearic acid is the simplest of the 18-carbon fatty acids; the bonds between its carbons are all alike:

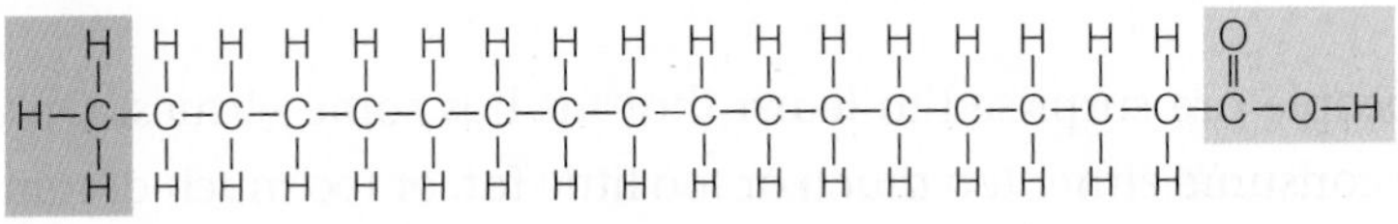

Stearic acid, an 18-carbon saturated fatty acid

As you can see, stearic acid is 18 carbons long, and each atom meets the rules of chemical bonding described in Figure 4-1 on p. 102. The following structure also depicts stearic acid, but in a simpler way, with each "corner" on the zigzag line representing a carbon atom with two attached hydrogens:

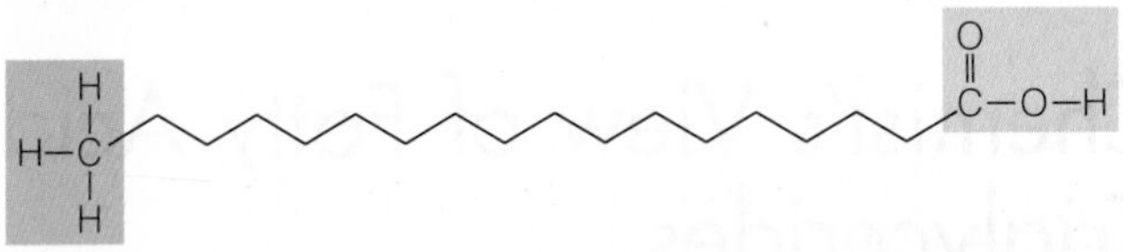

Stearic acid (simplified structure)

As mentioned, the carbon chains of fatty acids vary in length. The long-chain (12 to 24 carbons) fatty acids of meats, fish, and vegetable oils are most common in the diet. Smaller amounts of medium-chain (6 to 10 carbons) and short-chain (fewer than 6 carbons) fatty acids also occur, primarily in dairy products. (Tables C-1 and C-2 in Appendix C provide the names, chain lengths, and sources of fatty acids commonly found in foods.)

The Degree of Unsaturation   Stearic acid is a **saturated fatty acid**, (terms that describe the saturation of fatty acids are defined in the accompanying glossary). A saturated fatty acid is fully loaded with hydrogen atoms and contains only single bonds between its carbon atoms. If two hydrogens were missing from the middle of the carbon chain, the remaining structure might be:

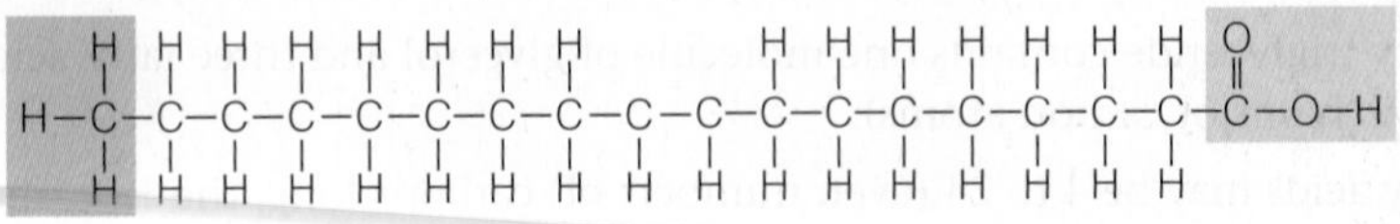

An impossible chemical structure

Such a compound cannot exist, however, because two of the carbons have only three bonds each, and nature requires that every carbon have four bonds. The two carbons therefore form a double bond:

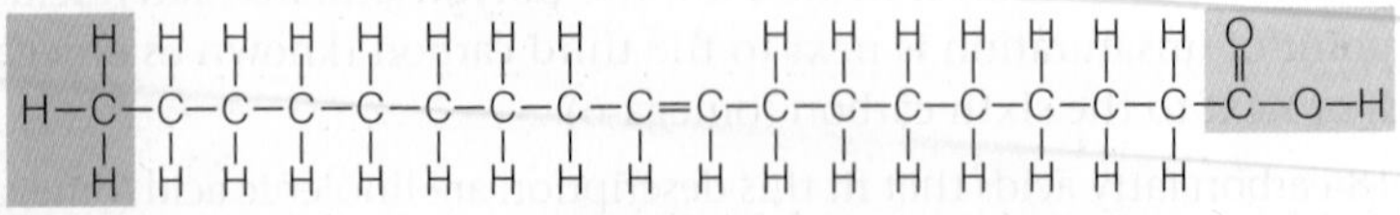

Oleic acid, an 18-carbon monounsaturated fatty acid

GLOSSARY OF FATTY ACID TERMS

fatty acid: an organic compound composed of a carbon chain with hydrogens attached and an acid group (COOH) at one end and a methyl group (CH_3) at the other end.

monounsaturated fatty acid (MUFA): a fatty acid that lacks two hydrogen atoms and has one double bond between carbons—for example, oleic acid. A **monounsaturated fat** is composed of triglycerides in which most of the fatty acids are monounsaturated.

• **mono** = one

point of unsaturation: the double bond of a fatty acid, where hydrogen atoms can easily be added to the structure.

polyunsaturated fatty acid (PUFA): a fatty acid that lacks four or more hydrogen atoms and has two or more double bonds between carbons—for

example, linoleic acid (two double bonds) and linolenic acid (three double bonds). A **polyunsaturated fat** is composed of triglycerides in which most of the fatty acids are polyunsaturated.

• **poly** = many

saturated fatty acid: a fatty acid carrying the maximum possible number of hydrogen atoms—for example, stearic acid. A

saturated fat is composed of triglycerides in which most of the fatty acids are saturated.

unsaturated fatty acid: a fatty acid that lacks hydrogen atoms and has at least one double bond between carbons (includes monounsaturated and polyunsaturated fatty acids). An **unsaturated fat** is composed of triglycerides in which most of the fatty acids are unsaturated.

The same structure drawn more simply looks like this: ◆

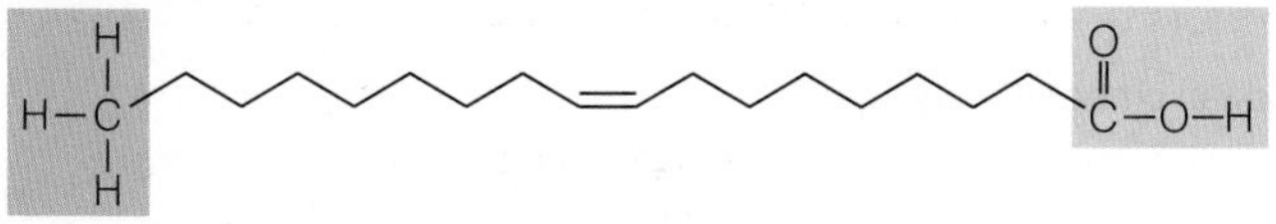

The double bond is a **point of unsaturation.** Hence, a fatty acid like this—with two hydrogens missing and a double bond—is an **unsaturated fatty acid.** This one is the 18-carbon **monounsaturated fatty acid** oleic acid, which is abundant in olive oil and canola oil.

A **polyunsaturated fatty acid** has two or more carbon-to-carbon double bonds. **Linoleic acid,** the 18-carbon fatty acid common in vegetable oils, lacks four hydrogens and has two double bonds:

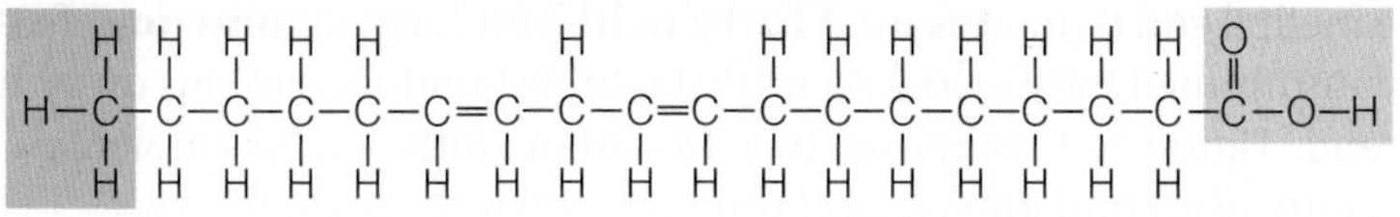

Drawn more simply, linoleic acid looks like this (though the actual shape would kink at the double bonds):

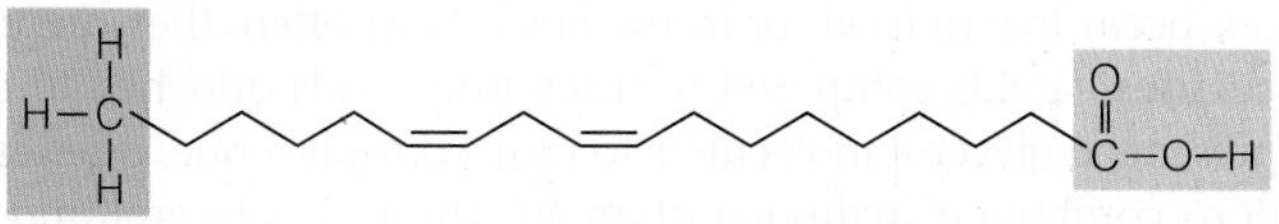

A fourth 18-carbon fatty acid is **linolenic acid,** which has three double bonds. Table 5-1 presents the 18-carbon fatty acids. ◆

The Location of Double Bonds Fatty acids differ not only in the length of their chains and their degree of saturation, but also in the locations of their double bonds. Chemists identify polyunsaturated fatty acids by the position of the double bond nearest the methyl (CH_3) end of the carbon chain, which is described by an **omega** number. A polyunsaturated fatty acid with its first double bond three carbons away

Oleic acid (simplified structure)

◆ Remember that each "corner" on the zigzag line represents a carbon atom with two attached hydrogens. In addition, although drawn straight here, the actual shape kinks at the double bonds (as shown in the left side of Figure 5-8).

Linoleic acid, an 18-carbon polyunsaturated fatty acid

Linoleic acid (simplified structure)

◆ Chemists use a shorthand notation to describe fatty acids. The first number indicates the number of carbon atoms; the second, the number of the double bonds. For example, the notation for stearic acid is 18:0.

TABLE 5-1 18-Carbon Fatty Acids

Name	Number of Carbon Atoms	Number of Double Bonds	Saturation	Common Food Sources
Stearic acid	18	0	Saturated	Most animal fats
Oleic acid	18	1	Monounsaturated	Olive, canola oils
Linoleic acid	18	2	Polyunsaturated	Sunflower, safflower, corn, and soybean oils
Linolenic acid	18	3	Polyunsaturated	Soybean and canola oils, flaxseed, walnuts

linoleic (lin-oh-LAY-ick) **acid:** an essential fatty acid with 18 carbons and two double bonds.

linolenic (lin-oh-LEN-ick) **acid:** an essential fatty acid with 18 carbons and three double bonds.

omega: the last letter of the Greek alphabet (ω), used by chemists to refer to the position of the first double bond from the methyl (CH_3) end of a fatty acid.

FIGURE 5-2 Omega-3 and Omega-6 Fatty Acids Compared

The omega number indicates the position of the first double bond in a fatty acid, counting from the methyl (CH_3) end. Thus an omega-3 fatty acid's first double bond occurs three carbons from the methyl end, and an omega-6 fatty acid's first double bond occurs six carbons from the methyl end. The members of an omega family may have different lengths and different numbers of double bonds, but the first double bond occurs at the same point in all of them. These structures are drawn linearly here to ease counting carbons and locating double bonds, but their shapes actually bend at the double bonds, as shown in Figure 5-8 (p. 145).

Linolenic acid, an omega-3 fatty acid

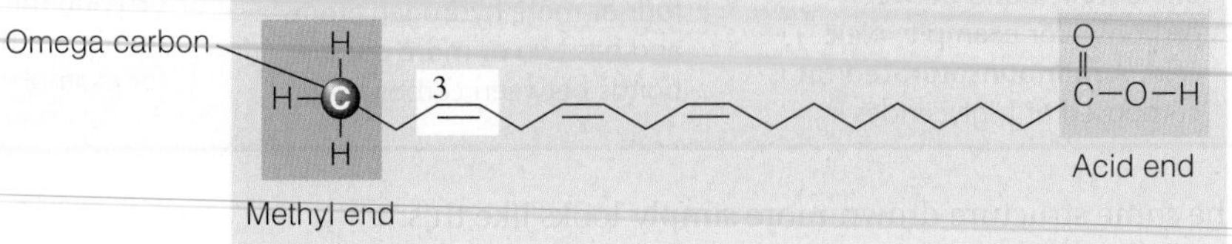

Linoleic acid, an omega-6 fatty acid

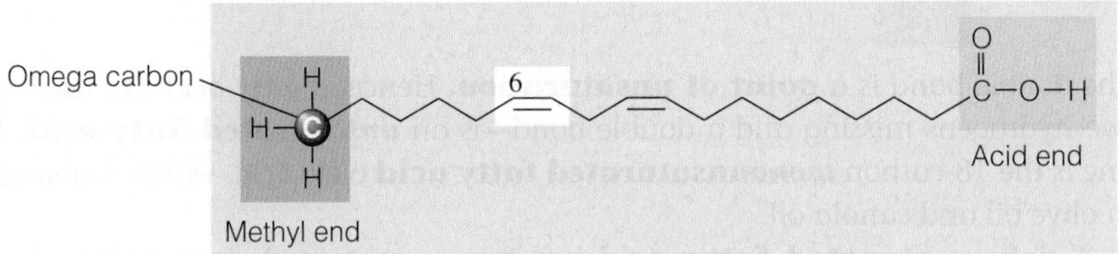

FIGURE 5-3 Glycerol

When glycerol is free, an OH group is attached to each carbon. When glycerol is part of a triglyceride, each carbon is attached to a fatty acid by a carbon-oxygen bond.

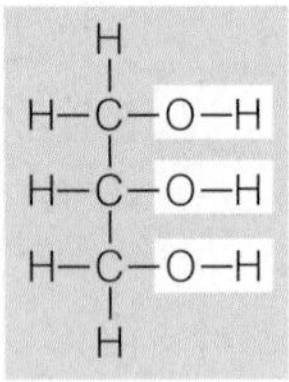

◆ The food industry often refers to these saturated vegetable oils as the "tropical oils."

omega-3 fatty acid: a polyunsaturated fatty acid in which the first double bond is three carbons away from the methyl (CH_3) end of the carbon chain.

omega-6 fatty acid: a polyunsaturated fatty acid in which the first double bond is six carbons from the methyl (CH_3) end of the carbon chain.

triglycerides (try-GLISS-er-rides): the chief form of fat in the diet and the major storage form of fat in the body; composed of a molecule of glycerol with three fatty acids attached; also called **triacylglycerols** (try-ay-seel-GLISS-er-ols).*
- **tri** = three
- **glyceride** = of glycerol
- **acyl** = a carbon chain

glycerol (GLISS-er-ol): an alcohol composed of a three-carbon chain, which can serve as the backbone for a triglyceride.
- **ol** = alcohol

from the methyl end is an **omega-3 fatty acid.** Similarly, an **omega-6 fatty acid** is a polyunsaturated fatty acid with its first double bond six carbons away from the methyl end. Figure 5-2 compares two 18-carbon fatty acids—linolenic acid (an omega-3 fatty acid) and linoleic acid (an omega-6 fatty acid).

Triglycerides

Few fatty acids occur free in foods or in the body. Most often, they are incorporated into **triglycerides**—lipids composed of three fatty acids attached to a **glycerol.** (Figure 5-3 presents a glycerol molecule.) To make a triglyceride, a series of condensation reactions combine a hydrogen atom (H) from the glycerol and a hydroxyl (OH) group from a fatty acid, forming a molecule of water (H_2O) and leaving a bond between the other two molecules (see Figure 5-4). Most triglycerides contain a mixture of more than one type of fatty acid (see Figure 5-5).

Degree of Unsaturation Revisited

The chemistry of a fatty acid—whether it is short or long, saturated or unsaturated, with its first double bond here or there—influences the characteristics of foods and the health of the body. A section later in this chapter explains how these features affect health; this section describes how the degree of unsaturation influences the fats and oils in foods.

Firmness The degree of unsaturation influences the firmness of fats at room temperature. Generally speaking, the polyunsaturated vegetable oils are liquid at room temperature, and the more saturated animal fats are solid. Not all vegetable oils are polyunsaturated, however. Cocoa butter, palm oil, palm kernel oil, and coconut oil ◆ are saturated even though they are of vegetable origin; they are firmer than most vegetable oils because of their saturation, but softer than most animal fats because of their shorter carbon chains (8 to 14 carbons long). Generally, the shorter the car-

* Research scientists commonly use the term *triacylglycerols;* this book continues to use the more familiar term *triglycerides,* as do many other health and nutrition books and journals.

FIGURE 5-4 Condensation of Glycerol and Fatty Acids to Form a Triglyceride

To make a triglyceride, three fatty acids attach to glycerol in condensation reactions.

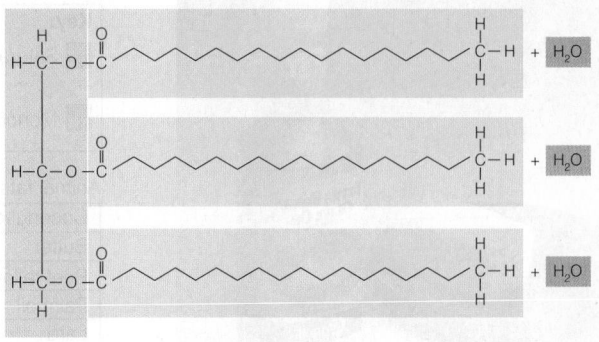

Glycerol + 3 fatty acids ⟶ Triglyceride + 3 water molecules

An H atom from glycerol and an OH group from a fatty acid combine to create water, leaving the O on the glycerol and the C at the acid end of each fatty acid to form a bond.

Three fatty acids attached to a glycerol form a triglyceride and yield water. In this example, all three fatty acids are stearic acid, but most often triglycerides contain mixtures of fatty acids (as shown in Figure 5-5).

---

bon chain, the softer the fat is at room temperature. Fatty acid compositions of selected fats and oils are shown in Figure 5-6 (p. 144), and Appendix H provides the fat and fatty acid contents of many other foods.

Stability Saturation also influences stability. All fats become spoiled when exposed to oxygen. Polyunsaturated fats spoil most readily because their double bonds are unstable; monounsaturated fats are slightly less susceptible. Saturated fats are most resistant to **oxidation** and thus least likely to become rancid. The oxidation of fats produces a variety of compounds that smell and taste rancid; other types of spoilage can occur due to microbial growth.

Manufacturers can protect fat-containing products against rancidity in three ways—none of them perfect. First, products may be sealed in air-tight, nonmetallic containers, protected from light, and refrigerated—an expensive and inconvenient storage system. Second, manufacturers may add **antioxidants** to compete for the oxygen and thus protect the oil (examples are the additives BHA and BHT and vitamin E).* The advantages and disadvantages of antioxidants in food processing are presented in Chapter 19. Third, manufacturers may saturate some or all of the points of unsaturation by adding hydrogen molecules—a process known as hydrogenation.

Hydrogenation **Hydrogenation** offers two advantages. First, it protects against oxidation (thereby prolonging shelf life) by making polyunsaturated fats more saturated (see Figure 5-7, p. 144). Second, it alters the texture of foods by making liquid vegetable oils more solid (as in margarine and shortening). Hydrogenated fats make margarine spreadable, pie crusts flaky, and puddings creamy.

Trans-Fatty Acids Figure 5-7 illustrates the total hydrogenation of a polyunsaturated fatty acid to a saturated fatty acid, which rarely occurs during food processing. Most often, a fat is partially hydrogenated, and some of the double bonds that remain after processing change from *cis* to *trans*. In nature, most double bonds are *cis*—meaning that the hydrogens next to the double bonds are on the same side of the carbon chain. Only a few fatty acids (notably a small percentage of those found in milk and meat products) are ***trans*-fatty acids**—meaning that the hydrogens next to the double bonds are on opposite sides of the carbon chain (see Figure 5-8, p. 145).** These arrangements result in different configurations for the fatty acids, and this difference affects function: in the body, *trans*-fatty acids that derive from hydrogenation behave more like saturated fats than like unsaturated fats. The relationship between *trans*-fatty acids and heart disease has been the subject of much

---

* BHA is butylated hydroxyanisole; BHT is butylated hydroxytoluene.
** For example, most dairy products contain less than 0.5 grams *trans* fat per serving.

FIGURE 5-5 A Mixed Triglyceride

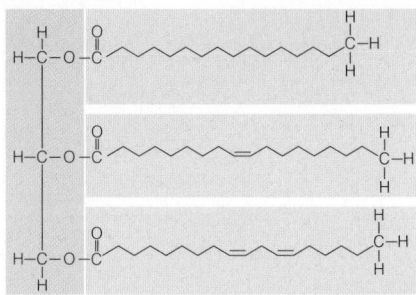

This mixed triglyceride includes a saturated fatty acid, a monounsaturated fatty acid, and a polyunsaturated fatty acid, respectively.

oxidation (OKS-ee-day-shun): the process of a substance combining with oxygen; oxidation reactions involve the loss of electrons.

antioxidants: as a food additive, preservatives that delay or prevent rancidity of fats in foods and other damage to food caused by oxygen.

hydrogenation (HIGH-dro-jen-AY-shun or high-DROJ-eh-NAY-shun): a chemical process by which hydrogens are added to monounsaturated or polyunsaturated fatty acids to reduce the number of double bonds, making the fats more saturated (solid) and more resistant to oxidation (protecting against rancidity). Hydrogenation produces *trans*-fatty acids.

***trans*-fatty acids:** fatty acids with hydrogens on opposite sides of the double bond.

At room temperature, saturated fats (such as those commonly found in butter and other animal fats) are solid, whereas unsaturated fats (such as those found in vegetable oils) are usually liquid.

© Polara Studios Inc.

FIGURE 5-6 Comparison of Dietary Fats

Most fats are a mixture of saturated, monounsaturated, and polyunsaturated fatty acids.

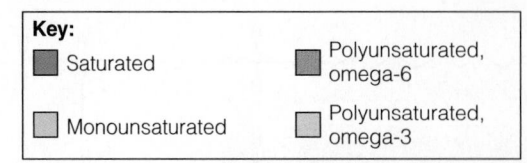

Key:

■ Saturated	■ Polyunsaturated, omega-6	
▢ Monounsaturated	▢ Polyunsaturated, omega-3	

Animal fats and the tropical oils of coconut and palm are mostly **saturated** fatty acids.

Coconut oil
Butter
Beef tallow
Palm oil
Lard

Some vegetable oils, such as olive and canola, are rich in **monounsaturated** fatty acids.

Olive oil
Canola oil
Peanut oil

Many vegetable oils are rich in **polyunsaturated** fatty acids.

Safflower oil
Flaxseed oil
Walnut oil
Sunflower oil
Corn oil

recent research, as a later section describes. In contrast, naturally occurring fatty acids, such as **conjugated linoleic acid**, that have a *trans* configuration may have health benefits.[1]

IN SUMMARY

The predominant lipids both in foods and in the body are triglycerides: glycerol backbones with three fatty acids attached. Fatty acids vary in the length of their carbon chains, their degrees of unsaturation, and the location of their double bond(s). Those that are fully loaded with hydrogens are saturated; those that are missing hydrogens and therefore have double bonds are unsaturated (monounsaturated or polyunsaturated). The vast majority of triglycerides contain more than one type of fatty acid. Fatty acid saturation affects fats' physical characteristics and storage properties. Hydrogenation, which makes polyunsaturated fats more saturated, gives rise to *trans*-fatty acids, altered fatty acids that may have health effects similar to those of saturated fatty acids.

FIGURE 5-7 Hydrogenation

Double bonds carry a slightly negative charge and readily accept positively charged hydrogen atoms, creating a saturated fatty acid. Most often, fat is partially hydrogenated, creating a *trans*-fatty acid (shown in Figure 5-8).

Polyunsaturated fatty acid   Hydrogenated (saturated) fatty acid

conjugated linoleic acid: a collective term for several fatty acids that have the same chemical formula as linoleic acid (18 carbons, two double bonds) but with different configurations.

| FIGURE 5-8 | *Cis-* and *Trans*-Fatty Acids Compared |

This example shows the *cis* configuration for an 18-carbon monounsaturated fatty acid (oleic acid) and its corresponding *trans* configuration (elaidic acid).

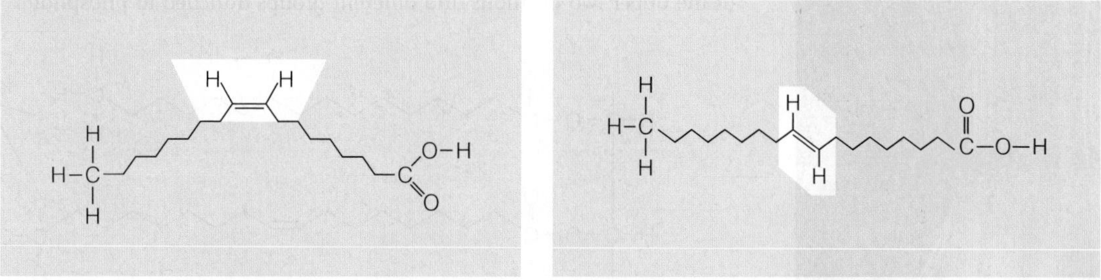

cis-fatty acid

A *cis*-fatty acid has its hydrogens on the same side of the double bond; *cis* molecules fold back into a U-like formation. Most naturally occuring unsaturated fatty acids in foods are *cis*.

trans-fatty acid

A *trans*-fatty acid has its hydrogens on the opposite sides of the double bond; *trans* molecules are more linear. The *trans* form typically occurs in partially hydrogenated foods when hydrogen atoms shift around some double bonds and change the configuration from *cis* to *trans*.

The Chemist's View of Phospholipids and Sterols

The preceding pages have been devoted to one of the three classes of lipids, the triglycerides, and their component parts, the fatty acids. The other two classes of lipids, the phospholipids and sterols, make up only 5 percent of the lipids in the diet.

Phospholipids

The best-known **phospholipid** is **lecithin.** A diagram of a lecithin molecule is shown in Figure 5-9 (p. 146). Notice that lecithin has a backbone of glycerol with two of its three attachment sites occupied by fatty acids like those in triglycerides. The third site is occupied by a phosphate group and a molecule of **choline.** The fatty acids make phospholipids soluble in fat; the phosphate group allows them to dissolve in water. Such versatility enables the food industry to use phospholipids as emulsifiers ◆ to mix fats with water in such products as mayonnaise and candy bars.

Phospholipids in Foods In addition to the phospholipids used by the food industry as emulsifiers, phospholipids are also found naturally in foods. The richest food sources of lecithin are eggs, liver, soybeans, wheat germ, and peanuts.

Roles of Phospholipids The lecithins and other phospholipids are important constituents of cell membranes (see Figure 5-10, p. 146). Because phospholipids are soluble in both water and fat, they can help lipids move back and forth across the cell membranes into the watery fluids on both sides. Thus they enable fat-soluble substances, including vitamins and hormones, to pass easily in and out of cells. The phospholipids also act as emulsifiers in the body, helping to keep fats suspended in the blood and body fluids.

Lecithin periodically receives attention in the popular press. Its advocates claim that it is a major constituent of cell membranes (true), that cell membranes are essential to the integrity of cells (true), and that consumers must therefore take lecithin supplements (false). The liver makes from scratch all the lecithin a person needs. As for lecithin taken as a supplement, the digestive enzyme lecithinase ◆ in the intestine hydrolyzes most of it before it passes into the body, so little lecithin reaches the tissues intact. In other words, lecithin is *not an essential nutrient;* it is just another

◆ Reminder: *Emulsifiers* are substances with both water-soluble and fat-soluble portions that promote the mixing of oils and fats in watery solutions.

◆ Reminder: The word ending *-ase* denotes an enzyme. Hence, lecithinase is an enzyme that works on lecithin.

phospholipid (FOS-foe-LIP-id): a compound similar to a triglyceride but having a phosphate group (a phosphorus-containing salt) and choline (or another nitrogen-containing compound) in place of one of the fatty acids.

lecithin (LESS-uh-thin): one of the phospholipids. Both nature and the food industry use lecithin as an emulsifier to combine water-soluble and fat-soluble ingredients that do not ordinarily mix, such as water and oil.

choline (KOH-leen): a nitrogen-containing compound found in foods and made in the body from the amino acid methionine. Choline is part of the phospholipid lecithin and the neurotransmitter acetylcholine.

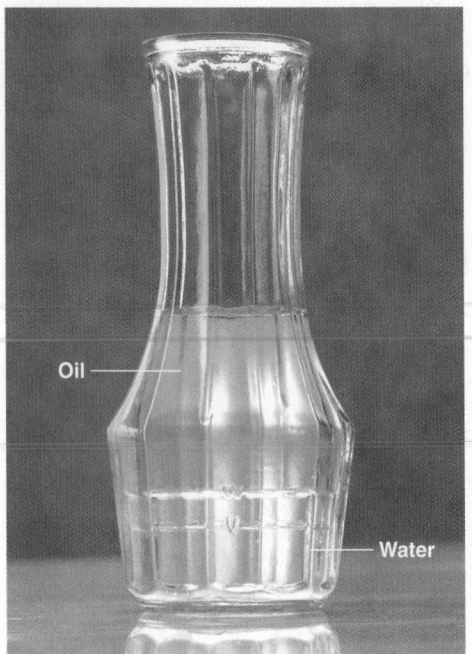

Without help from emulsifiers, fats and water don't mix.

FIGURE 5-10 Phospholipids of a Cell Membrane

A cell membrane is made of phospholipids assembled into an orderly formation called a bilayer. The fatty acid "tails" orient themselves away from the watery fluid inside and outside of the cell. The glycerol and phosphate "heads" are attracted to the watery fluid.

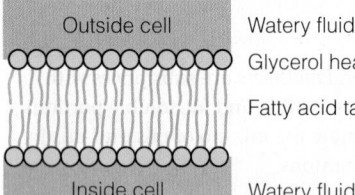

Outside cell	Watery fluid
	Glycerol heads
	Fatty acid tails
Inside cell	Watery fluid

◆ The chemical structure is the same, but cholesterol that is made in the body is called **endogenous** (en-DOGDE-eh-nus), whereas cholesterol from outside the body (from foods) is called **exogenous** (eks-ODGE-eh-nus).

- **endo** = within
- **gen** = arising
- **exo** = outside (the body)

sterols (STARE-ols or STEER-ols): compounds containing a four ring carbon structure with any of a variety of side chains attached.

cholesterol (koh-LESS-ter-ol): one of the sterols containing a four ring carbon structure with a carbon side chain.

FIGURE 5-9 Lecithin

Lecithin is one of the phospholipids. Notice that a molecule of lecithin is similar to a triglyceride but contains only two fatty acids. The third position is occupied by a phosphate group and a molecule of choline. Other phospholipids have different fatty acids at the upper two positions and different groups attached to phosphate.

From 2 fatty acids

The plus charge on the N is balanced by a negative ion— usually chloride.

From choline

From glycerol   From phosphate

lipid. Like other lipids, lecithin contributes 9 kcalories per gram—an unexpected "bonus" many people taking lecithin supplements fail to realize. Furthermore, large doses of lecithin may cause GI distress, sweating, and loss of appetite. Perhaps these symptoms can be considered beneficial—if they serve to warn people to stop self-dosing with lecithin.

IN SUMMARY

Phospholipids, including lecithin, have a unique chemical structure that allows them to be soluble in both water and fat. In the body, phospholipids are part of cell membranes; the food industry uses phospholipids as emulsifiers to mix fats with water.

Sterols

In addition to triglycerides and phospholipids, the lipids include the **sterols**, compounds with a multiple-ring structure.* The most famous sterol is **cholesterol**; Figure 5-11 (p. 147) shows its chemical structure.

Sterols in Foods Foods derived from both plants and animals contain sterols, but only those from animals contain significant amounts of cholesterol—meats, eggs, fish, poultry, and dairy products. Some people, confused about the distinction between dietary ◆ and blood cholesterol, have asked which foods contain the "good" cholesterol. "Good" cholesterol is not a type of cholesterol found in foods, but it refers to the way the body transports cholesterol in the blood, as explained later (p. 152).

Sterols other than cholesterol are naturally found in all plants. Being structurally similar to cholesterol, these plant sterols interfere with cholesterol absorption, thus lowering blood cholesterol levels.[2] Food manufacturers have fortified foods such as margarine with plant sterols, creating a functional food that helps to reduce blood cholesterol.

---

* The four-ring core structure identifies a steroid; sterols are alcohol derivatives with a steroid ring structure.

Roles of Sterols Many vitally important body compounds are sterols. Among them are bile acids, the sex hormones (such as testosterone), the adrenal hormones (such as cortisol), and vitamin D, as well as cholesterol itself. Cholesterol in the body can serve as the starting material for the synthesis of these compounds ◆ or as a structural component of cell membranes; more than 90 percent of all the body's cholesterol resides in the cells. Despite popular impressions to the contrary, cholesterol is not a villain lurking in some evil foods—it is a compound the body makes and uses. Right now, as you read, your liver is manufacturing cholesterol from fragments of carbohydrate, protein, and fat. In fact, the liver makes about 800 to 1500 milligrams of cholesterol per day, ◆ thus contributing much more to the body's total than does the diet.

Cholesterol's harmful effects in the body occur when it forms deposits in the artery walls. These deposits lead to **atherosclerosis,** a disease that causes heart attacks and strokes. (Chapter 18 provides many more details.)

IN SUMMARY

Sterols have a multiple-ring structure that differs from the structure of other lipids. In the body, sterols include cholesterol, bile, vitamin D, and some hormones. Animal-derived foods contain cholesterol. To summarize, the members of the lipid family include:

- **Triglycerides** (fats and oils), which are made of:
  - Glycerol (1 per triglyceride) and
  - Fatty acids (3 per triglyceride); depending on the number of double bonds, fatty acids may be:
    - *Saturated* (no double bonds)
    - *Monounsaturated* (one double bond)
    - *Polyunsaturated* (more than one double bond); depending on the location of the double bonds, polyunsaturated fatty acids may be:
      - *Omega-3* (first double bond 3 carbons away from methyl end)
      - *Omega-6* (first double bond 6 carbons away from methyl end)
- **Phospholipids** (such as lecithin)
- **Sterols** (such as cholesterol)

Digestion, Absorption, and Transport of Lipids

Each day, the GI tract receives, on average from the food we eat, 50 to 100 grams of triglycerides, 4 to 8 grams of phospholipids, and 200 to 350 milligrams of cholesterol. The body faces a challenge in digesting and absorbing these lipids: getting at them. Fats are **hydrophobic**—that is, they tend to separate from the watery fluids of the GI tract—whereas the enzymes for digesting fats are **hydrophilic.** The challenge is keeping the fats mixed in the watery fluids of the GI tract.

Lipid Digestion

The goal of fat digestion is to dismantle triglycerides into small molecules that the body can absorb and use—namely, **monoglycerides,** fatty acids, and glycerol. Figure 5-12 (p. 148) traces the digestion of triglycerides through the GI tract, and the following paragraphs provide the details.

In the Mouth Fat digestion starts off slowly in the mouth, with some hard fats beginning to melt when they reach body temperature. A salivary gland at the base of the tongue releases an enzyme (lingual lipase) ◆ that plays a minor role in fat

FIGURE 5-11 Cholesterol

The fat-soluble vitamin D is synthesized from cholesterol; notice the many structural similarities. The only difference is that cholesterol has a closed ring (highlighted in red), whereas vitamin D's is open, accounting for its vitamin activity. Notice, too, how different cholesterol is from the triglycerides and phospholipids.

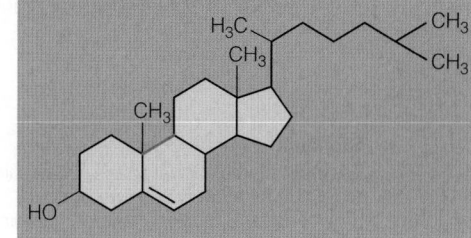

Cholesterol

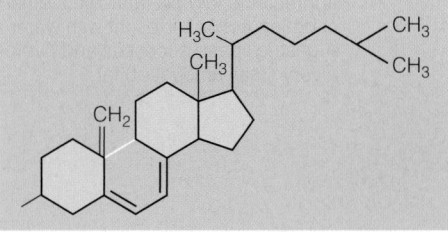

Vitamin D_3

◆ Compounds made from cholestrol:
- Bile acids
- Steroid hormones (testosterone, androgens, estrogens, progesterones, cortisol, cortisone, and aldosterone)
- Vitamin D

◆ For perspective, the Daily Value for cholesterol is 300 mg/day.

◆ Reminder: An enzyme that hydrolyzes lipids is called a *lipase; lingual* refers to the tongue.

atherosclerosis (ATH-er-oh-scler-OH-sis): a type of artery disease characterized by placques (accumulations of lipid-containing material) on the inner walls of the arteries (see Chapter 18).

hydrophobic (high-dro-FOE-bick): a term referring to water-fearing, or non-water-soluble, substances; also known as **lipophilic** (fat loving).
- **hydro** = water
- **phobia** = fear
- **lipo** = lipid
- **phile** = love

hydrophilic (high-dro-FIL-ick): a term referring to water-loving, or water-soluble, substances.

monoglycerides: molecules of glycerol with one fatty acid attached. A molecule of glycerol with two fatty acids attached is a **diglyceride.**
- **mono** = one
- **di** = two

FIGURE 5-12 Fat Digestion in the GI Tract

FAT

Mouth and salivary glands
Some hard fats begin to melt as they reach body temperature. The sublingual salivary gland in the base of the tongue secretes lingual lipase.

Stomach
The acid-stable lingual lipase initiates lipid digestion by hydrolyzing one bond of triglycerides to produce diglycerides and fatty acids. The degree of hydrolysis by lingual lipase is slight for most fats but may be appreciable for milk fats. The stomach's churning action mixes fat with water and acid. A gastric lipase accesses and hydrolyzes (only a very small amount of) fat.

Small intestine
Bile flows in from the gallbladder (via the common bile duct):

$$\text{Fat} \xrightarrow{\text{Bile}} \text{Emulsified fat}$$

Pancreatic lipase flows in from the pancreas (via the pancreatic duct):

$$\text{Emulsified fat} \xrightarrow{\substack{\text{Pancreatic} \\ \text{(and intestinal)} \\ \text{lipase}}} \substack{\text{Monoglycerides,} \\ \text{glycerol, fatty} \\ \text{acids (absorbed)}}$$
(triglycerides)

Large intestine
Some fat and cholesterol, trapped in fiber, exit in feces.

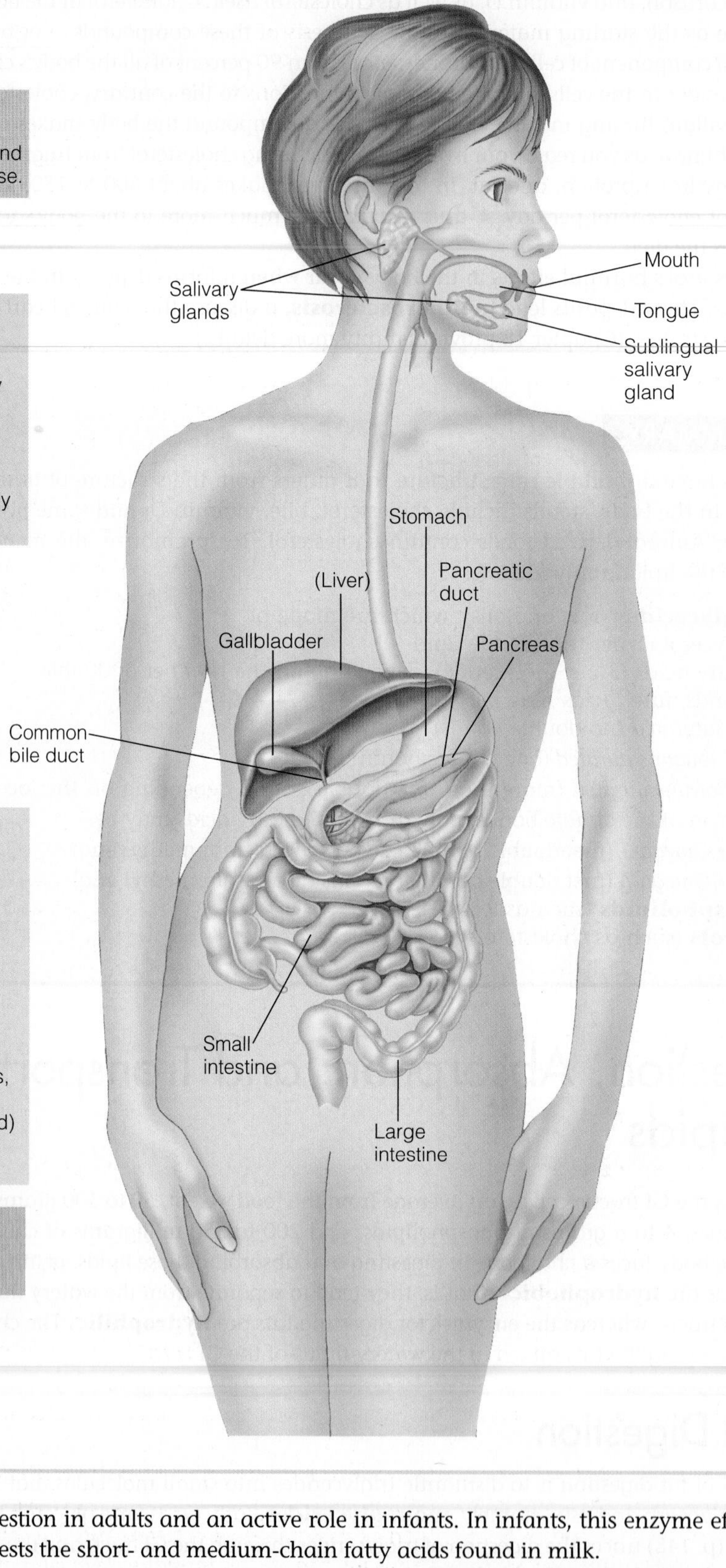

Mouth
Tongue
Sublingual salivary gland
Salivary glands
Stomach
Pancreatic duct
(Liver)
Gallbladder
Pancreas
Common bile duct
Small intestine
Large intestine

digestion in adults and an active role in infants. In infants, this enzyme efficiently digests the short- and medium-chain fatty acids found in milk.

In the Stomach In a quiet stomach, fat would float as a layer above the other components of swallowed food. But the strong muscle contractions of the stomach propel the stomach contents toward the pyloric sphincter. Some chyme passes through the pyloric sphincter periodically, but the remaining partially digested food is propelled back into the body of the stomach. This churning grinds the solid pieces to finer particles, mixes the chyme, and disperses the fat into smaller droplets. These actions help to expose the fat for attack by the gastric lipase enzyme—an enzyme that performs best in the acidic environment of the stomach. Still, little fat digestion takes place in the stomach; most of the action occurs in the small intestine.

In the Small Intestine When fat enters the small intestine, it triggers the release of the hormone cholecystokinin (CCK), which signals the gallbladder to release its stores of bile. (Remember that the liver makes bile, and the gallbladder stores it until it is needed.) Among bile's many ingredients ◆ are bile acids, which are made in the liver from cholesterol and have a similar structure. In addition, they often pair up with an amino acid (a building block of protein). The amino acid end is attracted to water, and the sterol end is attracted to fat (see Figure 5-13, p. 150). This structure improves bile's ability to act as an emulsifier, drawing fat molecules into the surrounding watery fluids. There, the fats are fully digested as they encounter lipase enzymes from the pancreas and small intestine. The process of emulsification is diagrammed in Figure 5-14 (p. 150).

Most of the hydrolysis of triglycerides occurs in the small intestine. The major fat-digesting enzymes are pancreatic lipases; some intestinal lipases are also active. These enzymes remove one, then the other, of each triglyceride's outer fatty acids, leaving a monoglyceride. Occasionally, enzymes remove all three fatty acids, leaving a free molecule of glycerol. Hydrolysis of a triglyceride is shown in Figure 5-15 (p. 151).

Phospholipids are digested similarly—that is, their fatty acids are removed by hydrolysis. The two fatty acids and the remaining phospholipid fragment are then absorbed. Most sterols can be absorbed as is; if any fatty acids are attached, they are first hydrolyzed off.

Bile's Routes After bile enters the small intestine and emulsifies fat, it has two possible destinations, illustrated in Figure 5-16 (p. 151). Most of the bile is reabsorbed from the intestine and recycled. The other possibility is that some of the bile can be trapped by dietary fibers in the large intestine and carried out of the body with the feces. Because cholesterol is needed to make bile, the excretion of bile effectively reduces blood cholesterol. As Chapter 4 explains, the dietary fibers most effective at lowering blood cholesterol this way are the soluble fibers commonly found in fruits, whole grains, and legumes.

◆ In addition to bile acids and bile salts, bile contains cholesterol, phospholipids (especially lecithin), antibodies, water, electrolytes, and bilirubin and biliverdin (pigments resulting from the breakdown of heme).

Lipid Absorption

Figure 5-17 (p. 152) illustrates the absorption of lipids. Small molecules of digested triglycerides (glycerol and short- and medium-chain fatty acids) can diffuse easily into the intestinal cells; they are absorbed directly into the bloodstream. Larger molecules (the monoglycerides and long-chain fatty acids) merge into spherical complexes, known as **micelles.** Micelles are emulsified fat droplets formed by molecules of bile surrounding monoglycerides and fatty acids. This configuration permits solubility in the watery digestive fluids and transportation to the intestinal cells. Upon arrival, the lipid contents of the micelles diffuse into the intestinal cells. Once inside, the monoglycerides and long-chain fatty acids are reassembled into new triglycerides.

Within the intestinal cells, the newly made triglycerides and other lipids (cholesterol and phospholipids) are packed with protein into transport vehicles known as **chylomicrons.** The intestinal cells then release the chylomicrons into the lymphatic system. The chylomicrons glide through the lymph until they reach a point of entry into the bloodstream at the thoracic duct near the heart. (Recall from Chapter 3 that nutrients from the GI tract that enter the lymph system bypass the liver at first.) The blood carries these lipids to the rest of the body for immediate use

micelles (MY-cells): tiny spherical complexes of emulsified fat that arise during digestion; most contain bile salts and the products of lipid digestion, including fatty acids, monoglycerides, and cholesterol.

chylomicrons (kye-lo-MY-cronz): the class of lipoproteins that transport lipids from the intestinal cells to the rest of the body.

FIGURE 5-13 A Bile Acid

This is one of several bile acids the liver makes from cholesterol. It is then bound to an amino acid to improve its ability to form micelles, spherical complexes of emulsified fat. Most bile acids occur as bile salts, usually in association with sodium, but sometimes with potassium or calcium.

Bile acid made from cholesterol (hydrophobic)	Bound to an amino acid from protein (hydrophilic)

CH_3

HO — CH — CH_2 — CH_2 — C — NH — CH_2 — $COOH$

O

HO OH

H

or storage. A look at these lipids in the body reveals the kinds of fat the diet has been delivering.[3] The fat stores and muscle cells of people who eat a diet rich in unsaturated fats, for example, contain more unsaturated fats than those of people who select a diet high in saturated fats.

IN SUMMARY

The body makes special arrangements to digest and absorb lipids. It provides the emulsifier bile to make them accessible to the fat-digesting lipases that dismantle triglycerides, mostly to monoglycerides and fatty acids, for absorption by the intestinal cells. The intestinal cells assemble freshly absorbed lipids into chylomicrons, lipid packages with protein escorts, for transport so that cells all over the body may select needed lipids from them.

lipoproteins (LIP-oh-PRO-teenz): clusters of lipids associated with proteins that serve as transport vehicles for lipids in the lymph and blood.

Lipid Transport

The chylomicrons are only one of several clusters of lipids and proteins that are used as transport vehicles for fats. As a group, these vehicles are known as **lipoproteins**,

FIGURE 5-14 Emulsification of Fat by Bile

Like bile, detergents are emulsifiers and work the same way, which is why they are effective in removing grease spots from clothes. Molecule by molecule, the grease is dissolved out of the spot and suspended in the water, where it can be rinsed away.

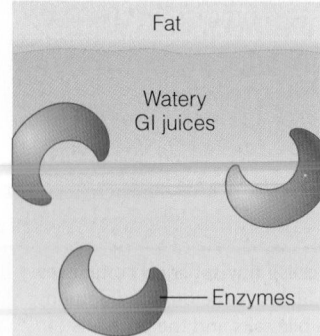
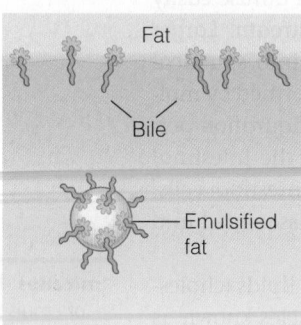
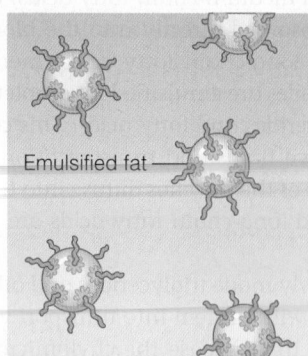
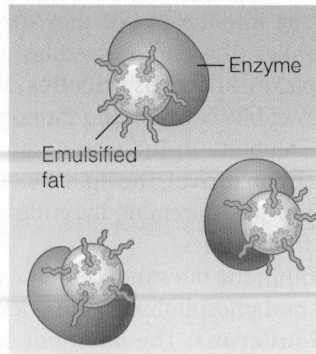

In the stomach, the fat and watery GI juices tend to separate. The enzymes in the GI juices can't get at the fat.

When fat enters the small intestine, the gallbladder secretes bile. Bile has an affinity for both fat and water, so it can bring the fat into the water.

Bile's emulsifying action converts large fat globules into small droplets that repel each other.

After emulsification, more fat is exposed to the enzymes, making fat digestion more efficient.

FIGURE 5-15 Digestion (Hydrolysis) of a Triglyceride

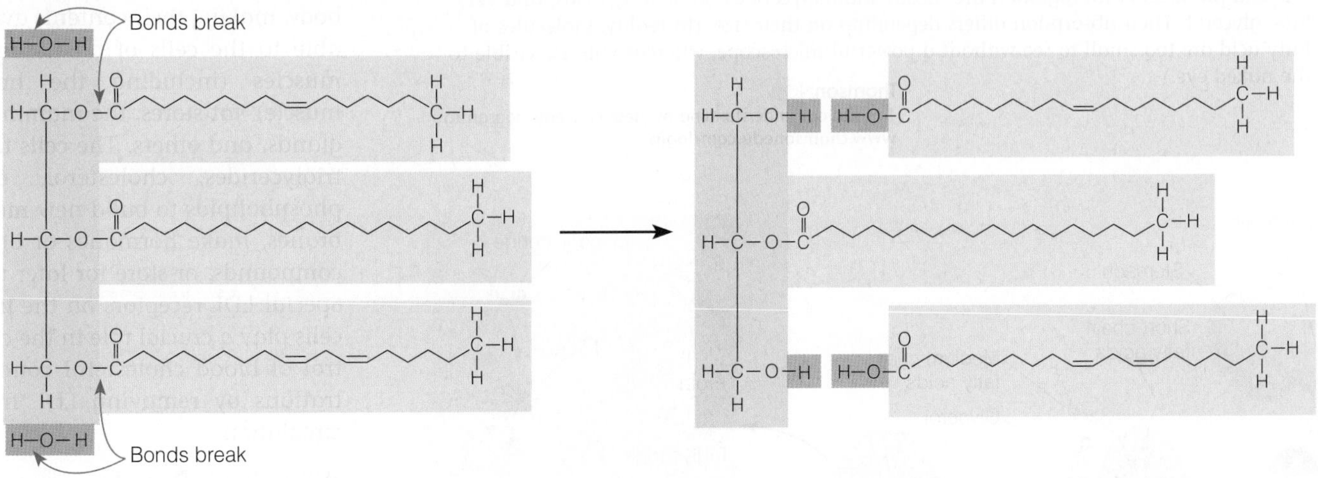

Bonds break

H—O—H

Triglyceride

The triglyceride and two molecules of water are split. The H and OH from water complete the structures of two fatty acids and leave a monoglyceride.

Bonds break

H—O—H

Monoglyceride + 2 fatty acids

These products may pass into the intestinal cells, but sometimes the monoglyceride is split with another molecule of water to give a third fatty acid and glycerol. Fatty acids, monoglycerides, and glycerol are absorbed into intestinal cells.

and they solve the body's problem of transporting fat through the watery bloodstream. The body makes four main types of lipoproteins, distinguished by their size and density.* Each type contains different kinds and amounts of lipids and proteins. ◆ Figure 5-18 (p. 153) shows the relative compositions and sizes of the lipoproteins.

Chylomicrons The chylomicrons are the largest and least dense of the lipoproteins. They transport *diet*-derived lipids (mostly triglycerides) from the intestine (via the lymph system) to the rest of the body. Cells all over the body remove triglycerides from the chylomicrons as they pass by, so the chylomicrons get smaller and smaller. Within 14 hours after absorption, most of the triglycerides have been depleted, and only a few remnants of protein, cholesterol, and phospholipid remain. Special protein receptors on the membranes of the liver cells recognize and remove these chylomicron remnants from the blood. After collecting the remnants, the liver cells first dismantle them and then either use or recycle the pieces.

VLDL (Very-Low-Density Lipoproteins) Meanwhile, in the liver—the most active site of lipid synthesis—cells are synthesizing other lipids. The liver cells use fatty acids arriving in the blood to make cholesterol, other fatty acids, and other compounds. At the same time, the liver cells may be making lipids from carbohydrates, proteins, or alcohol. Ultimately, the lipids made in the liver and those collected from chylomicron remnants are packaged with proteins as **VLDL (very-low-density lipoprotein)** and shipped to other parts of the body.

As the VLDL travel through the body, cells remove triglycerides, causing the VLDL to shrink. As a VLDL loses triglycerides, the proportion of lipids shifts, and the lipoprotein density increases. The remaining cholesterol-rich lipoprotein eventually becomes an **LDL (low-density lipoprotein).**** This transformation explains why LDL contain few triglycerides but are loaded with cholesterol.

---

* Chemists can identify the various lipoproteins by their density. They place a blood sample below a thick fluid in a test tube and spin the tube in a centrifuge. The most buoyant particles (highest in lipids) rise to the top and have the lowest density; the densest particles (highest in proteins) remain at the bottom and have the highest density. Others distribute themselves in between.

** Before becoming LDL, the VLDL are first transformed into intermediate-density lipoproteins (IDL), sometimes called VLDL remnants. Some IDL may be picked up by the liver and rapidly broken down; those IDL that remain in circulation continue to deliver triglycerides to the cells and eventually become LDL. Researchers debate whether IDL are simply transitional particles or a separate class of lipoproteins; normally, IDL do not accumulate in the blood. Measures of blood lipids include IDL with LDL.

FIGURE 5-16 Enterohepatic Circulation

Most of the bile released into the small intestine is reabsorbed and sent back to the liver to be reused. This cycle is called the **enterohepatic circulation** of bile. Some bile is excreted.
- **enteron** = intestine
- **hepat** = liver

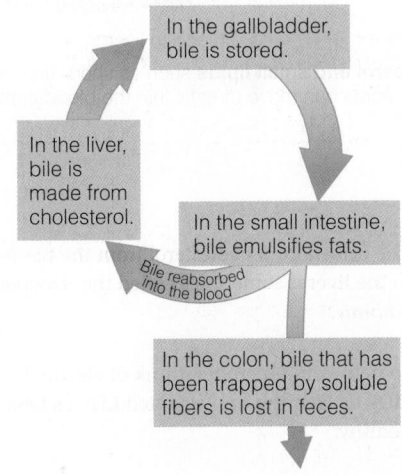

In the gallbladder, bile is stored.

In the liver, bile is made from cholesterol.

In the small intestine, bile emulsifies fats.

Bile reabsorbed into the blood

In the colon, bile that has been trapped by soluble fibers is lost in feces.

◆ The more lipids, the lower the density; the more proteins, the higher the density.

VLDL (very-low-density lipoprotein): the type of lipoprotein made primarily by liver cells to transport lipids to various tissues in the body; composed primarily of triglycerides.

LDL (low-density lipoprotein): the type of lipoprotein derived from very-low-density lipoproteins (VLDL) as VLDL triglycerides are removed and broken down; composed primarily of cholesterol.

FIGURE 5-17 *Animated!* Absorption of Fat

The end products of fat digestion are mostly monoglycerides, some fatty acids, and very little glycerol. Their absorption differs depending on their size. (In reality, molecules of fatty acid are too small to see without a powerful microscope, whereas villi are visible to the naked eye.)

ThomsonNOW™
To test your understanding of these concepts, log on to
www.thomsonedu.com/login

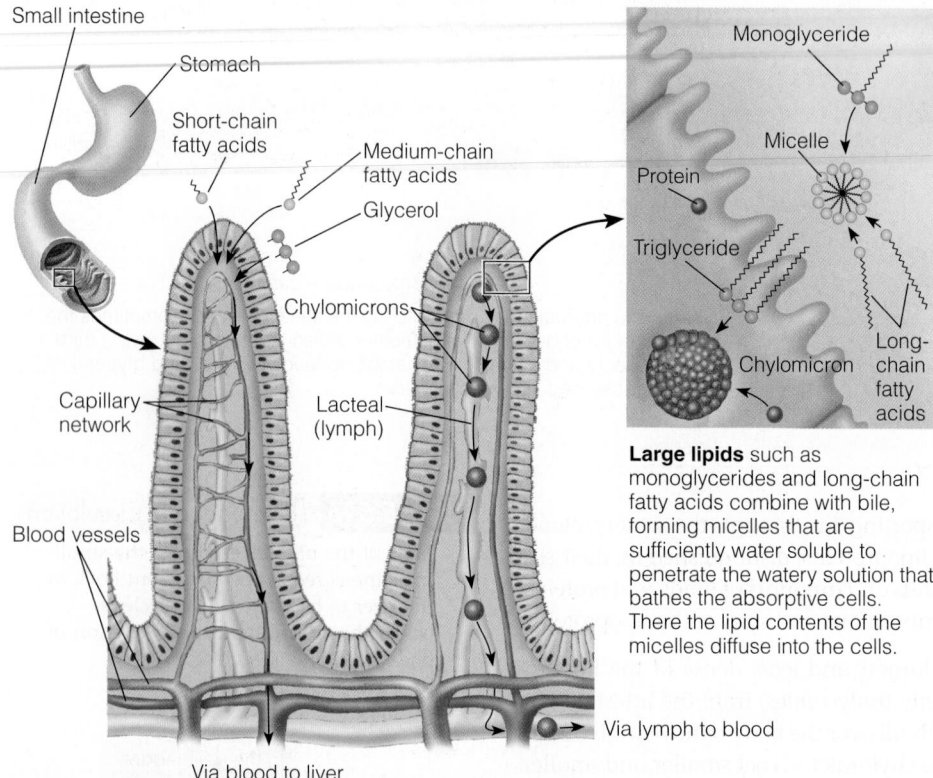

Large lipids such as monoglycerides and long-chain fatty acids combine with bile, forming micelles that are sufficiently water soluble to penetrate the watery solution that bathes the absorptive cells. There the lipid contents of the micelles diffuse into the cells.

Glycerol and small lipids such as short- and medium-chain fatty acids can move directly into the bloodstream.

LDL (Low-Density Lipoproteins)

The LDL circulate throughout the body, making their contents available to the cells of all tissues—muscles (including the heart muscle), fat stores, the mammary glands, and others. The cells take triglycerides, cholesterol, and phospholipids to build new membranes, make hormones or other compounds, or store for later use. Special LDL receptors on the liver cells play a crucial role in the control of blood cholesterol concentrations by removing LDL from circulation.

HDL (High-Density Lipoproteins)

Fat cells may release glycerol, fatty acids, cholesterol, and phospholipids to the blood. The liver makes **HDL (high-density lipoprotein)** to carry cholesterol from the cells back to the liver for recycling or disposal.

Health Implications

The distinction between LDL and HDL has implications for the health of the heart and blood vessels. The blood cholesterol linked to heart disease is LDL cholesterol. HDL also carry cholesterol, but elevated HDL represent cholesterol returning ◆ from the rest of the body to the liver for breakdown and excretion. High LDL cholesterol is associated with a high risk of heart attack, whereas high HDL cholesterol seems to have a protective effect. This is why some people refer to LDL as "bad," and HDL as "good," cholesterol. ◆ Keep in mind that the cholesterol itself is the same, and that the differences between LDL and HDL reflect the *proportions* and *types* of lipids and proteins within them—not the type of cholesterol. The margin ◆ lists factors that influence LDL and HDL, and Chapter 18 provides many more details.

Not too surprisingly, numerous genes influence how the body handles the uptake, synthesis, transport, and degradation of the lipoproteins. Much current research is focused on how nutrient-gene interactions may direct the progression of heart disease.

◆ The transport of cholesterol from the tissues to the liver is sometimes called the *scavenger pathway*.

◆ To help you remember, think of elevated **H**DL as **H**ealthy and elevated **L**DL as **L**ess healthy.

◆ Factors that lower LDL or raise HDL:
• Weight control
• Monounsaturated or polyunsaturated, instead of saturated, fat in the diet
• Soluble, viscous fibers (see Chapter 4)
• Phytochemicals (see Highlight 13)
• Moderate alcohol consumption
• Physical activity

HDL (high-density lipoprotein): the type of lipoprotein that transports cholesterol back to the liver from the cells; composed primarily of protein.

IN SUMMARY

The liver assembles lipids and proteins into lipoproteins for transport around the body. All four types of lipoproteins carry all classes of lipids (triglycerides, phospholipids, and cholesterol), but the chylomicrons are the largest and the highest in triglycerides; VLDL are smaller and are about half triglycerides; LDL are smaller still and are high in cholesterol; and HDL are the smallest and are rich in protein.

FIGURE 5-18 Sizes and Compositions of the Lipoproteins

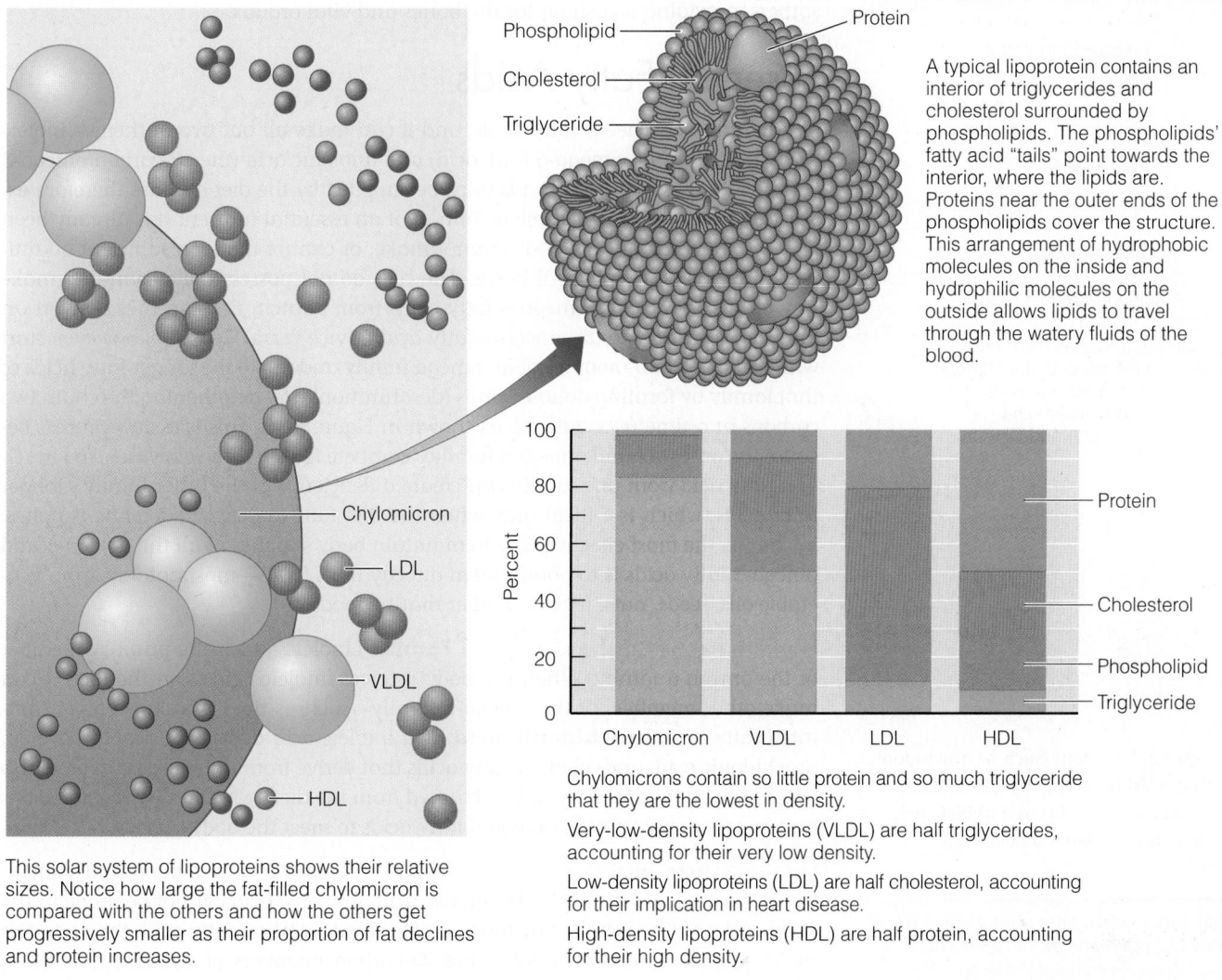

A typical lipoprotein contains an interior of triglycerides and cholesterol surrounded by phospholipids. The phospholipids' fatty acid "tails" point towards the interior, where the lipids are. Proteins near the outer ends of the phospholipids cover the structure. This arrangement of hydrophobic molecules on the inside and hydrophilic molecules on the outside allows lipids to travel through the watery fluids of the blood.

This solar system of lipoproteins shows their relative sizes. Notice how large the fat-filled chylomicron is compared with the others and how the others get progressively smaller as their proportion of fat declines and protein increases.

Chylomicrons contain so little protein and so much triglyceride that they are the lowest in density.

Very-low-density lipoproteins (VLDL) are half triglycerides, accounting for their very low density.

Low-density lipoproteins (LDL) are half cholesterol, accounting for their implication in heart disease.

High-density lipoproteins (HDL) are half protein, accounting for their high density.

Lipids in the Body

The blood carries lipids to various sites around the body. Once lipids arrive at their destinations, they can get to work providing energy, insulating against temperature extremes, protecting against shock, and maintaining cell membranes. This section provides an overview of the roles of triglycerides and fatty acids and then of the metabolic pathways they can follow within the body's cells.

Roles of Triglycerides

First and foremost, the triglycerides—either from food or from the body's fat stores—provide the body with energy. When a person dances all night, her dinner's triglycerides provide some of the fuel that keeps her moving. When a person loses his appetite, his stored triglycerides fuel much of his body's work until he can eat again.

Efficient energy metabolism depends on the energy nutrients—carbohydrate, fat, and protein—supporting each other. Glucose fragments combine with fat fragments during energy metabolism, and fat and carbohydrate help spare protein, providing energy so that protein can be used for other important tasks.

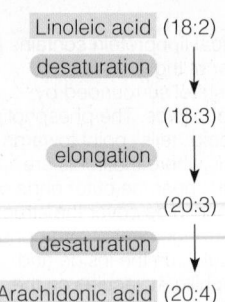

FIGURE 5-19 The Pathway from One Omega-6 Fatty Acid to Another

Linoleic acid (18:2)
desaturation ↓
(18:3)
elongation ↓
(20:3)
desaturation ↓
Arachidonic acid (20:4)

The first number indicates the number of carbons and the second, the number of double bonds. Similar reactions occur when the body makes the omega-3 fatty acids EPA and DHA from linolenic acid.

◆ A nonessential nutrient (such as arachidonic acid) that must be supplied by the diet in special circumstances (as in a linoleic acid deficiency) is considered *conditionally essential.*

essential fatty acids: fatty acids needed by the body but not made by it in amounts sufficient to meet physiological needs.

arachidonic (a-RACK-ih-DON-ic) **acid:** an omega-6 polyunsaturated fatty acid with 20 carbons and four double bonds; present in small amounts in meat and other animal products and synthesized in the body from linoleic acid.

eicosapentaenoic (EYE-cossa-PENTA-ee-NO-ick) **acid (EPA):** an omega-3 polyunsaturated fatty acid with 20 carbons and five double bonds; present in fish and synthesized in limited amounts in the body from linolenic acid.

docosahexaenoic (DOE-cossa-HEXA-ee-NO-ick) **acid (DHA):** an omega-3 polyunsaturated fatty acid with 22 carbons and six double bonds; present in fish and synthesized in limited amounts in the body from linolenic acid.

eicosanoids (eye-COSS-uh-noyds): derivatives of 20-carbon fatty acids; biologically active compounds that help to regulate blood pressure, blood clotting, and other body functions. They include *prostaglandins* (PROS-tah-GLAND-ins), *thromboxanes* (throm-BOX-ains), and *leukotrienes* (LOO-ko-TRY-eens).

Fat also insulates the body. Fat is a poor conductor of heat, so the layer of fat beneath the skin helps keep the body warm. Fat pads also serve as natural shock absorbers, providing a cushion for the bones and vital organs.

Essential Fatty Acids

The human body needs fatty acids, and it can make all but two of them—linoleic acid (the 18-carbon omega-6 fatty acid) and linolenic acid (the 18-carbon omega-3 fatty acid). These two fatty acids must be supplied by the diet and are therefore **essential fatty acids.** A simple definition of an essential nutrient has already been given: a nutrient that the body cannot make, or cannot make in sufficient quantities to meet its physiological needs. The cells do not possess the enzymes to make any of the omega-6 or omega-3 fatty acids from scratch, nor can they convert an omega-6 fatty acid to an omega-3 fatty acid or vice versa. Cells *can,* however, start with the 18-carbon member of an omega family and make the longer fatty acids of that family by forming double bonds (desaturation) and lengthening the chain two carbons at a time (elongation), as shown in Figure 5-19. This is a slow process because the omega-3 and omega-6 families compete for the same enzymes. Too much of a fatty acid from one family can create a deficiency of the other family's longer fatty acids, which is critical only when the diet fails to deliver adequate supplies. Therefore, the most effective way to maintain body supplies of all the omega-6 and omega-3 fatty acids is to obtain them directly from foods—most notably, from vegetable oils, seeds, nuts, fish, and other marine foods.

Linoleic Acid and the Omega-6 Family Linoleic acid is the primary member of the omega-6 family. When the body receives linoleic acid from the diet, it can make other members of the omega-6 family—such as the 20-carbon polyunsaturated fatty acid, **arachidonic acid.** If a linoleic acid deficiency should develop, arachidonic acid, and all other fatty acids that derive from linoleic acid, would also become essential and have to be obtained from the diet. ◆ Normally, vegetable oils and meats supply enough omega-6 fatty acids to meet the body's needs.

Linolenic Acid and the Omega-3 Family Linolenic acid is the primary member of the omega-3 family.* Like linoleic acid, linolenic acid cannot be made in the body and must be supplied by foods. Given this 18-carbon fatty acid, the body can make small amounts of the 20- and 22-carbon members of the omega-3 series, **eicosapentaenoic acid (EPA)** and **docosahexaenoic acid (DHA)**. These omega-3 fatty acids are essential for normal growth and development, especially in the eyes and brain.[4] They may also play an important role in the prevention and treatment of heart disease.

Eicosanoids The body uses arachidonic acid and EPA to make substances known as **eicosanoids.** Eicosanoids are a diverse group of compounds that are sometimes described as "hormonelike," but they differ from hormones in important ways. For one, hormones are secreted in one location and travel to affect cells all over the body, whereas eicosanoids appear to affect only the cells in which they are made or nearby cells in the same localized environment. For another, hormones elicit the same response from all their target cells, whereas eicosanoids often have different effects on different cells.

The actions of various eicosanoids sometimes oppose each other. For example, one causes muscles to relax and blood vessels to dilate, whereas another causes muscles to contract and blood vessels to constrict. Certain eicosanoids participate in the immune response to injury and infection, producing fever, inflammation, and pain. One of the ways aspirin relieves these symptoms is by slowing the synthesis of these eicosanoids.

---

* This omega-3 linolenic acid is known as alpha-linolenic acid and is the fatty acid referred to in this chapter. Another fatty acid, also with 18 carbons and three double bonds, belongs to the omega-6 family and is known as gamma-linolenic acid.

Eicosanoids that derive from EPA differ from those that derive from arachidonic acid, with those from EPA providing greater health benefits.[5] The EPA eicosanoids help lower blood pressure, prevent blood clot formation, protect against irregular heartbeats, and reduce inflammation. Because the omega-6 and omega-3 fatty acids compete for the same enzymes to make arachidonic acid and EPA and to make the eicosanoids, the body needs these long-chain polyunsaturated fatty acids from the diet to make eicosanoids in sufficient quantities.[6]

Fatty Acid Deficiencies Most diets in the United States and Canada meet the minimum essential fatty acid requirement adequately. Historically, deficiencies have developed only in infants and young children who have been fed fat-free milk and low-fat diets or in hospital clients who have been mistakenly fed formulas that provided no polyunsaturated fatty acids for long periods of time. Classic deficiency symptoms include growth retardation, reproductive failure, skin lesions, kidney and liver disorders, and subtle neurological and visual problems.

Interestingly, a deficiency of omega-3 fatty acids (EPA and DHA) may be associated with depression.[7] Some neurochemical pathways in the brain become more active and others become less active.[8] It is unclear, however, which comes first—whether inadequate intake alters brain activity or depression alters fatty acid metabolism. To find the answers, researchers must untangle a multitude of confounding factors.

Double thanks: The body's fat stores provide energy for a walk, and the heel's fat pads cushion against the hard pavement.

IN SUMMARY

In the body, triglycerides:
- Provide an energy reserve when stored in the body's fat tissue
- Insulate against temperature extremes
- Protect against shock
- Help the body use carbohydrate and protein efficiently

Linoleic acid (18 carbons, omega-6) and linolenic acid (18 carbons, omega-3) are essential nutrients. They serve as structural parts of cell membranes and as precursors to the longer fatty acids that can make eicosanoids—powerful compounds that participate in blood pressure regulation, blood clot formation, and the immune response to injury and infection, among other functions. Because essential fatty acids are common in the diet and stored in the body, deficiencies are unlikely.

FIGURE 5-20 An Adipose Cell

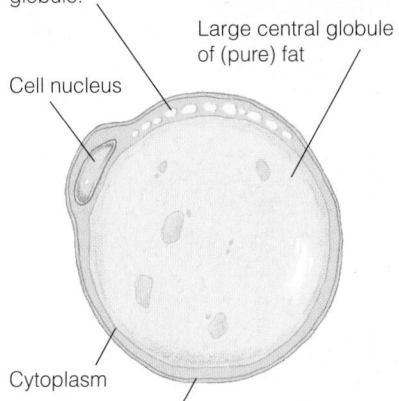

Newly imported triglycerides first form small droplets at the periphery of the cell, then merge with the large, central globule.

Large central globule of (pure) fat

Cell nucleus

Cytoplasm

As the central globule enlarges, the fat cell membrane expands to accommodate its swollen contents.

A Preview of Lipid Metabolism

The blood delivers triglycerides to the cells for their use. This is a preview of how the cells store and release energy from fat; Chapter 7 provides details.

Storing Fat as Fat The triglycerides, familiar as the fat in foods and as body fat, serve the body primarily as a source of fuel. Fat provides more than twice the energy of carbohydrate and protein, ◆ making it an extremely efficient storage form of energy. Unlike the liver's glycogen stores, the body's fat stores have virtually unlimited capacity, thanks to the special cells of the **adipose tissue.** Unlike most body cells, which can store only limited amounts of fat, the fat cells of the adipose tissue readily take up and store fat. An adipose cell is depicted in Figure 5-20.

To convert food fats to body fat, the body simply breaks them down, absorbs the parts, and puts them (and others) together again in storage. It requires very little energy to do this. An enzyme—**lipoprotein lipase (LPL)**—hydrolyzes triglycerides from lipoproteins, producing glycerol, fatty acids, and monoglycerides that enter the adipose cells. Inside the cells, other enzymes reassemble the pieces into triglycerides again for storage. Earlier, Figure 5-4 (p. 143) showed how the body can make a triglyceride from glycerol and fatty acids. Triglycerides fill the adipose cells, storing a lot of energy in a relatively small space. Adipose cells store fat

◆ Reminder: Gram for gram, fat provides more than twice as much energy (9 kcal) as carbohydrate or protein (4 kcal).

adipose (ADD-ih-poce) **tissue:** the body's fat tissue; consists of masses of triglyceride-storing cells.

lipoprotein lipase (LPL): an enzyme that hydrolyzes triglycerides passing by in the bloodstream and directs their parts into the cells, where they can be metabolized for energy or reassembled for storage.

Fat supplies most of the energy during a long-distance run.

◆ 1 lb body fat = 3500 kcal

◆ Desirable blood lipid profile:
  • Total cholesterol: <200 mg/dL
  • LDL cholesterol: <100 mg/dL
  • HDL cholesterol: ≥60 mg/dL
  • Triglycerides: <150 mg/dL

hormone-sensitive lipase: an enzyme inside adipose cells that responds to the body's need for fuel by hydrolyzing triglycerides so that their parts (glycerol and fatty acids) escape into the general circulation and thus become available to other cells for fuel. The signals to which this enzyme responds include epinephrine and glucagon, which oppose insulin (see Chapter 4).

blood lipid profile: results of blood tests that reveal a person's total cholesterol, triglycerides, and various lipoproteins.

after meals when a heavy traffic of chylomicrons and VLDL loaded with triglycerides passes by; they release it later whenever the other cells need replenishing.

Using Fat for Energy Fat supplies 60 percent of the body's ongoing energy needs during rest. During prolonged light to moderately intense exercise or extended periods of food deprivation, fat stores may make a slightly greater contribution to energy needs.

When cells demand energy, an enzyme **(hormone-sensitive lipase)** inside the adipose cells responds by dismantling stored triglycerides and releasing the glycerol and fatty acids directly into the blood. Energy-hungry cells anywhere in the body can then capture these compounds and take them through a series of chemical reactions to yield energy, carbon dioxide, and water.

A person who fasts (drinking only water) will rapidly metabolize body fat. A pound of body fat provides 3500 kcalories, ◆ so you might think a fasting person who expends 2000 kcalories a day could lose more than half a pound of body fat each day.* Actually, the person has to obtain some energy from lean tissue because the brain, nerves, and red blood cells need glucose. Also, the complete breakdown of fat requires carbohydrate or protein. Even on a total fast, a person cannot lose more than half a pound of pure fat per day. Still, in conditions of enforced starvation—say, during a siege or a famine—a fatter person can survive longer than a thinner person thanks to this energy reserve.

Although fat provides energy during a fast, it can provide very little glucose to give energy to the brain and nerves. Only the small glycerol molecule can be converted to glucose; fatty acids cannot be. (Figure 7-12 on p. 224 illustrates how only 3 of the 50 or so carbon atoms in a molecule of fat can yield glucose.) After prolonged glucose deprivation, brain and nerve cells develop the ability to derive about two-thirds of their minimum energy needs from the ketone bodies that the body makes from fat fragments. Ketone bodies cannot sustain life by themselves, however. As Chapter 7 explains, fasting for too long will cause death, even if the person still has ample body fat.

IN SUMMARY

The body can easily store unlimited amounts of fat if given excesses, and this body fat is used for energy when needed. (Remember that the liver can also convert excess carbohydrate and protein into fat.) Fat breakdown requires simultaneous carbohydrate breakdown for maximum efficiency; without carbohydrate, fats break down to ketone bodies.

Health Effects and Recommended Intakes of Lipids

Of all the nutrients, fat is most often linked with heart disease, some types of cancer, and obesity. Fortunately, the same recommendation can help with all of these health problems: choose a diet that is low in saturated fats, *trans* fats, and cholesterol and moderate in total fat.

Health Effects of Lipids

Hearing a physician say, "Your blood lipid profile looks fine," is reassuring. The **blood lipid profile** ◆ reveals the concentrations of various lipids in the blood,

---

* The reader who knows that 1 pound = 454 grams and that 1 gram of fat = 9 kcalories may wonder why a pound of body fat does not equal 4086 (9 × 454) kcalories. The reason is that body fat contains some cell water and other materials; it is not quite pure fat.

notably triglycerides and cholesterol, and their lipoprotein carriers (VLDL, LDL, and HDL). This information alerts people to possible disease risks and perhaps to a need for changing their exercise and eating habits. Both the amounts and types of fat in the diet influence people's risk for disease.[9]

Heart Disease Most people realize that elevated blood cholesterol is a major risk factor for **cardiovascular disease.** Cholesterol accumulates in the arteries, restricting blood flow and raising blood pressure. The consequences are deadly; in fact, heart disease is the nation's number one killer of adults. Blood cholesterol level is often used to predict the likelihood of a person's suffering a heart attack or stroke; the higher the cholesterol, the earlier and more likely the tragedy. Much of the effort to prevent heart disease focuses on lowering blood cholesterol.

Commercials advertise products that are low in cholesterol, and magazine articles tell readers how to cut the cholesterol from their favorite recipes. What most people don't realize, though, is that *food* cholesterol does not raise *blood* cholesterol as dramatically as *saturated fat* does.

Risks from Saturated Fats As mentioned earlier, LDL cholesterol raises the risk of heart disease. Saturated fats are most often implicated in raising LDL cholesterol. In general, the more saturated fat in the diet, the more LDL cholesterol in the body. Not all saturated fats have the same cholesterol-raising effect, however. Most notable among the saturated fatty acids that raise blood cholesterol are lauric, myristic, and palmitic acids (12, 14, and 16 carbons, respectively). In contrast, stearic acid (18 carbons) does not seem to raise blood cholesterol. However, making such distinctions may be impractical in diet planning because these saturated fatty acids typically appear together in the same foods.

Fats from animal sources are the main sources of saturated fats ◆ in most people's diets (see Figure 5-21). Some vegetable fats (coconut and palm) and hydrogenated fats provide smaller amounts of saturated fats. Selecting poultry or fish and fat-free milk products helps to lower saturated fat intake and heart disease risk. Using nonhydrogenated margarine and unsaturated cooking oil is another simple change that can dramatically lower saturated fat intake.

Risks from Trans Fats Research also suggests an association between dietary *trans*-fatty acids and heart disease.[10] In the body, *trans*-fatty acids alter blood cholesterol the same way some saturated fats do: they raise LDL cholesterol and, at high intakes, lower HDL cholesterol.[11] *Trans*-fatty acids also appear to increase inflammation and insulin resistance.[12] Limiting the intake of *trans*-fatty acids can improve blood cholesterol and lower the risk of heart disease. The estimated average intake of *trans*-fatty acids in the United States is about 5 grams per day—mostly from products that have been hydrogenated.[13] ◆

Reports on *trans*-fatty acids have raised consumer doubts about whether margarine is, after all, a better choice than butter for heart health. The American Heart Association has stated that because butter is rich in both saturated fat and cholesterol whereas margarine is made from vegetable fat with no dietary cholesterol, margarine is still preferable to butter. Be aware that soft margarines (liquid or tub) ◆ are less hydrogenated and relatively lower in *trans*-fatty acids; consequently, they do not raise blood cholesterol as much as the saturated fats of butter or the *trans* fats of hard (stick) margarines do. Some manufacturers are now offering nonhydrogenated margarines that are "*trans* fat free." The last section of this chapter describes how to read food labels and compares butter and margarines. Whichever you decide to use, remember to use them sparingly.

Risks from Cholesterol Although its effect is not as strong as that of saturated fat or *trans* fat, dietary cholesterol also raises blood cholesterol and increases the risk of heart disease. To maximize the effect on blood cholesterol, limit dietary cholesterol as well.

Recall that cholesterol is found in all foods derived from animals. Consequently, eating less fat from meats, eggs, and milk products helps lower dietary cholesterol intake ◆ (as well as total and saturated fat intakes). Figure 5-22 (p. 158) shows the

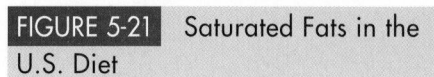

FIGURE 5-21 Saturated Fats in the U.S. Diet

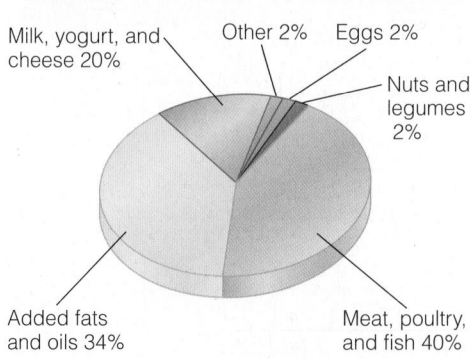

Milk, yogurt, and cheese 20%
Other 2%
Eggs 2%
Nuts and legumes 2%
Added fats and oils 34%
Meat, poultry, and fish 40%

Note that fruits, grains, and vegetables are insignificant sources, unless saturated fats are intentionally added to them during preparation.

◆ Major sources of saturated fats:
  • Whole milk, cream, butter, cheese
  • Fatty cuts of beef and pork
  • Coconut, palm, and palm kernel oils (and products containing them such as candies, pastries, pies, doughnuts, and cookies)

◆ Major sources of *trans* fats:
  • Deep-fried foods (vegetable shortening)
  • Cakes, cookies, doughnuts, pastry, crackers
  • Snack chips
  • Margarine
  • Imitation cheese
  • Meat and dairy products

◆ When selecting margarine, look for:
  • Soft (liquid or tub) instead of hard (stick)
  • ≤2 g saturated fat
  • Liquid vegetable oil (not hydrogenated or partially hydrogenated) as first ingredient
  • "*Trans* fat free"

◆ Major sources of cholesterol:
  • Eggs
  • Milk products
  • Meat, poultry, shellfish

cardiovascular disease (CVD): a general term for all diseases of the heart and blood vessels. Atherosclerosis is the main cause of CVD. When the arteries that carry blood to the heart muscle become blocked, the heart suffers damage known as **coronary heart disease (CHD).**
• **cardio** = heart
• **vascular** = blood vessels

cholesterol contents of selected foods. Many more foods, with their cholesterol contents, appear in Appendix H. For most people trying to lower blood cholesterol, however, limiting saturated fat is more effective than limiting cholesterol intake.

Most foods that are high in cholesterol are also high in saturated fat, but eggs are an exception. An egg contains only 1 gram of saturated fat but just over 200 milligrams of cholesterol—roughly two-thirds of the recommended daily limit. For people with a healthy lipid profile, eating one egg a day is not detrimental. People with high blood cholesterol, however, may benefit from limiting daily cholesterol intake to less that 200 milligrams.[14] When eggs are included in the diet, other sources of cholesterol may need to be limited on that day. Eggs are a valuable part of the diet because they are inexpensive, useful in cooking, and a source of high-quality protein and other nutrients. Low saturated fat, high omega-3 fat eggs are now available, and food manufacturers have produced several fat-free, cholesterol-free egg substitutes.

◆ Sources of monounsaturated fats:
  • Olive oil, canola oil, peanut oil
  • Avocados

◆ Sources of polyunsaturated fats:
  • Vegetable oils (safflower, sesame, soy, corn, sunflower)
  • Nuts and seeds

Benefits from Monounsaturated Fats and Polyunsaturated Fats Replacing both saturated and *trans* fats with monounsaturated ◆ and polyunsaturated ◆ fats may be the most effective dietary strategy in preventing heart disease. The lower rate of heart disease among people in the Mediterranean region of the world is often attributed to their liberal use of olive oil, a rich source of monounsaturated fatty acids. Olive oil also delivers valuable phytochemicals that help to protect against heart disease.[15] Replacing saturated fats with the polyunsaturated fatty acids of other vegetable oils also lowers blood cholesterol.[16] Highlight 5 examines various types of fats and their roles in supporting or harming heart health.

◆ Major sources of omega-3 fats:
  • Vegetable oils (canola, soybean, flaxseed)
  • Walnuts, flaxseeds
  • Fatty fish (mackerel, salmon, sardines)

Benefits from Omega-3 Fats Research on the different types of fats has spotlighted the beneficial effects of the omega-3 ◆ polyunsaturated fatty acids in reducing the risks of heart disease and stroke.[17] Regular consumption of omega-3 fatty acids helps to prevent blood clots, protect against irregular heartbeats, and lower blood pressure, especially in people with hypertension or atherosclerosis.[18]

Fatty fish are among the best sources of omega-3 fatty acids, and Highlight 5 features their role in supporting heart health. Chapter 19 discusses the adverse con-

FIGURE 5-22 Cholesterol in Selected Foods

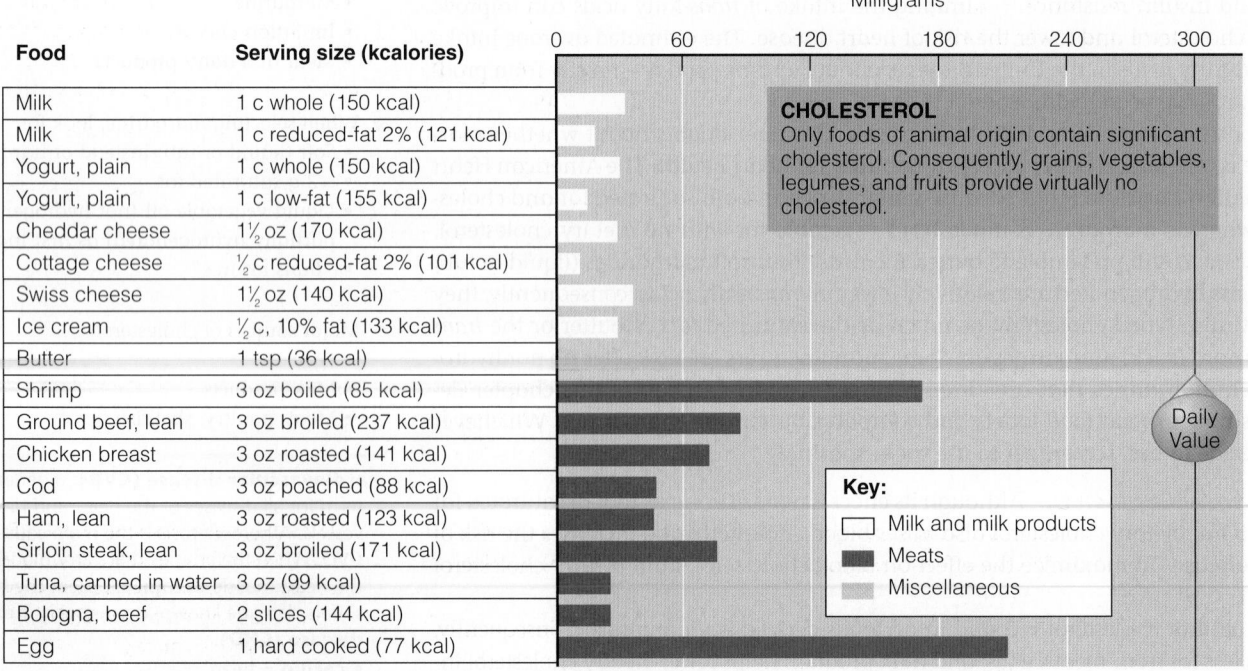

TABLE 5-2	Sources of Omega-3 and Omega-6 Fatty Acids
Omega-6	
Linoleic acid	Vegetable oils (corn, sunflower, safflower, soybean, cottonseed), poultry fat, nuts, seeds
Arachidonic acid	Meats, poultry, eggs (or can be made from linoleic acid)
Omega-3	
Linolenic acid	Oils (flaxseed, canola, walnut, wheat germ, soybean) Nuts and seeds (butternuts, flaxseeds, walnuts, soybean kernels) Vegetables (soybeans)
EPA and DHA	Human milk Pacific oysters and fish[a] (mackerel, salmon, bluefish, mullet, sablefish, menhaden, anchovy, herring, lake trout, sardines, tuna) (or can be made from linolenic acid)

[a]All fish contain some EPA and DHA; the amounts vary among species and within a species depending on such factors as diet, season, and environment. The fish listed here, except tuna, provide at least 1 gram of omega-3 fatty acids in 100 grams of fish (3.5 ounces). Tuna provides fewer omega-3 fatty acids, but because it is commonly consumed, its contribution can be significant.

sequences of mercury, ◆ an environmental contaminant common in some fish. To maximize the benefits and minimize the risks, most healthy people should eat two servings of fish a week.[19]

Balance Omega-6 and Omega-3 Intakes Table 5-2 provides sources of omega-6 and omega-3 fatty acids. To obtain sufficient intakes and the right balance between omega-6 and omega-3 fatty acids, ◆ most people need to eat more fish and less meat.[20] The American Heart Association recommends two servings of fish a week, with an emphasis on fatty fish (salmon, herring, and mackerel, for example).[21] Eating fish instead of meat supports heart health, especially when combined with physical activity. Even one fish meal a month may be enough to make a difference.[22] When preparing fish, grill, bake, or broil, but do not fry. Fried fish from fast-food restaurants and frozen fried fish products are often low in omega-3 fatty acids and high in *trans-* and saturated fatty acids. Fish provides many minerals (except iron) and vitamins and is leaner than most other animal-protein sources. When used in a weight-loss program, eating fish improves blood lipids even more effectively than can be explained by losing weight or eating fish alone.

In addition to fish, other functional foods ◆ are being developed to help consumers improve their omega-3 fatty acid intake. For example, hens fed flaxseed produce eggs rich in omega-3 fatty acids. Including even one enriched egg in the diet daily can significantly increase a person's intake of omega-3 fatty acids. Another option may be to select wild game or pasture-fed cattle, which provide more omega-3 fatty acids and less saturated fat than grain-fed cattle.[23]

Omega-3 fatty acids are also available in capsules of fish oil supplements. Routine supplementation, however, is not recommended. High intakes of omega-3 polyunsaturated fatty acids may increase bleeding time, interfere with wound healing, raise LDL cholesterol, and suppress immune function.* [24] Such findings reinforce the concept that too much of a good thing can sometimes be harmful. People with heart disease, however, may benefit from doses greater than can be achieved through diet alone. They should always consult a physician first because including supplements as part of a treatment plan may be contraindicated for some patients.[25] Supplements may also provide relief for people with rheumatoid arthritis or asthma.[26]

Cancer The evidence for links between dietary fats and cancer ◆ is less convincing than for heart disease, but it does suggest possible associations between some types

◆ Fish relatively high in mercury:
  • Tilefish (also called golden snapper or golden bass), swordfish, king mackerel, shark
  Fish relatively low in mercury:
  • Cod, haddock, pollock, salmon, sole, tilapia
  • Most shellfish

◆ Recommended omega-6 to omega-3 ratio: 6 to 1

◆ Reminder: *Functional foods* contain physiologically active compounds that provide health benefits beyond basic nutrition (see Highlight 13 for a full discussion).

◆ Other risk factors for cancer include smoking, alcohol, and environmental contaminants. Chapter 18 provides many more details about these risk factors and the development of cancer.

* Suppressed immune function is seen with daily intake of 0.9 to 9.4 grams EPA and 0.6 to 6.0 grams DHA for 3 to 24 weeks.

of fat and some types of cancers.[27] Dietary fat does not seem to *initiate* cancer development but, instead, may *promote* cancer once it has arisen.

The relationship between dietary fat and the risk of cancer differs for various types of cancers. In the case of breast cancer, evidence has been weak and inconclusive. Some studies indicate little or no association between dietary fat and breast cancer; others find that total *energy* intake and obesity contribute to the risk.[28] In the case of prostate cancer, some studies indicate a harmful association with total and saturated fat, although a specific type fatty acid has not yet been implicated.[29]

The relationship between dietary fat and the risk of cancer differs for various types of fats as well. The association between cancer and fat appears to be due primarily to saturated fats or dietary fat from meats (which is mostly saturated). Fat from milk or fish has not been implicated in cancer risk.[30] In fact, the omega-3 fatty acids of fish may protect against some cancers, although evidence does not support supplementation.[31] Thus dietary advice to reduce cancer risks parallels that given to reduce heart disease risks: reduce saturated fats and increase omega-3 fatty acids.

Obesity Fat contributes more than twice as many kcalories ◆ per gram as either carbohydrate or protein. Consequently, people who eat high-fat diets regularly may exceed their energy needs and gain weight, especially if they are inactive.[32] Because fat boosts energy intake, cutting fat from the diet can be an effective strategy in cutting kcalories. In some cases, though, choosing a fat-free food offers no kcalorie savings. Fat-free frozen desserts, for example, often have so much sugar added that the kcalorie count can be as high as in the regular-fat product. In this case, therefore, cutting fat and adding carbohydrate offers no kcalorie savings or weight-loss advantage. In fact, it may even raise energy intake and exacerbate weight problems. Later chapters revisit the role of dietary fat in the development of obesity.

◆ Fat is a more concentrated energy source than the other energy nutrients: 1 g carbohydrate or protein = 4 kcal, but 1 g fat = 9 kcal

IN SUMMARY

High blood LDL cholesterol poses a risk of heart disease, and high intakes of saturated and *trans* fats, specifically, contribute most to high LDL. Cholesterol in foods presents less of a risk. Omega-3 fatty acids appear to be protective.

Recommended Intakes of Fat

Some fat in the diet is essential for good health, but too much fat, especially saturated fat, increases the risks for chronic diseases. Defining the exact amount of fat, saturated fat, or cholesterol that benefits health or begins to harm health, however, is not possible. For this reason, no RDA or upper limit has been set. Instead, the DRI and 2005 *Dietary Guidelines* suggest a diet that is low in saturated fat, *trans* fat, and cholesterol and provides 20 to 35 percent of the daily energy intake from fat. ◆ The top end of this range is slightly higher than previous recommendations. This revision recognizes that diets with up to 35 percent of kcalories from fat can be compatible with good health if energy intake is reasonable and saturated fat intake is low. When total fat exceeds 35 percent, saturated fat increases to unhealthy levels.[33] For a 2000-kcalorie diet, 20 to 35 percent represents 400 to 700 kcalories from fat (roughly 45 to 75 grams). Part of this fat allowance should provide for the essential fatty acids—linoleic acid and linolenic acid. For this reason, an Adequate Intake (AI) has been established for these two fatty acids. Recommendations suggest that linoleic acid ◆ provide 5 to 10 percent of the daily energy intake and linolenic acid ◆ 0.6 to 1.2 percent.[34]

To help consumers meet the dietary fat goals, the Food and Drug Administration (FDA) established Daily Values ◆ on food labels using 30 percent of energy intake as the guideline for fat and 10 percent for saturated fat. The Daily Value for choles-

◆ DRI and 2005 *Dietary Guidelines* for fat:
  • 20 to 35% of energy intake (from mostly polyunsaturated and monounsaturated fat sources such as fish, nuts, and vegetable oils)

◆ Linoleic acid (omega-6) AI:
  Men:
  • 19–50 yr: 17 g/day
  • 51+ yr: 14 g/day
  Women:
  • 19–50 yr: 12 g/day
  • 51+ yr: 11 g/day

◆ Linolenic acid (omega-3) AI:
  • Men: 1.6 g/day
  • Women: 1.1 g/day

◆ Daily Values:
  • 65 g fat (based on 30% of 2000 kcal diet)
  • 20 g saturated fat (based on 10% of 2000 kcal diet)
  • 300 mg cholesterol

terol is 300 milligrams regardless of energy intake. There is no Daily Value for *trans* fat, but consumers should try to keep intakes as low as possible and within the 10 percent allotted for saturated fat. According to surveys, adults in the United States receive about 33 percent of their total energy from fat, with saturated fat contributing about 11 percent of the total. Cholesterol intakes in the United States average 190 milligrams a day for women and 290 for men. [35]

> **Dietary Guidelines for Americans 2005**
>
> Consume less than 10 percent of kcalories from saturated fatty acids and less than 300 mg/day of cholesterol, and keep *trans* fatty acid consumption as low as possible.

The fats of fish, nuts, and vegetable oils are not counted as discretionary kcalories because they provide valuable omega-3 fatty acids, essential fatty acids, and vitamin E. In contrast, solid fats ◆ deliver an abundance of saturated fatty acids; the USDA Food Guide counts them as discretionary kcalories. Discretionary kcalories may be used to add fats in cooking or at the table or to select higher fat items from the food groups. ◆

Although it is very difficult to do, some people actually manage to eat too little fat—to their detriment. Among them are people with eating disorders, described in Highlight 8, and athletes. Athletes following a diet too low in fat (less than 20 percent of total kcalories) fall short on energy, vitamins, minerals, and essential fatty acids as well as on performance.[36] As a practical guideline, it is wise to include the equivalent of at least a teaspoon of fat in every meal—a little peanut butter on toast or mayonnaise on tuna, for example. Dietary recommendations that limit fat were developed for healthy people over age two; Chapter 16 discusses the fat needs of infants and young children.

As the photos in Figure 5-23 show (p. 162), fat accounts for much of the energy in foods, and removing the fat from foods cuts energy and saturated fat intakes dramatically. To reduce dietary fat, eliminate fat as a seasoning and in cooking; remove the fat from high-fat foods; replace high-fat foods with low-fat alternatives; and emphasize whole grains, fruits, and vegetables. The remainder of this chapter identifies sources of fat in the diet, food group by food group.

From Guidelines to Groceries

Fats accompany protein in foods derived from animals, such as meat, fish, poultry, and eggs, and fats accompany carbohydrate in foods derived from plants, such as avocados and coconuts. Fats carry with them the four fat-soluble vitamins—A, D, E, and K—together with many of the compounds that give foods their flavor, texture, and palatability. Fat is responsible for the delicious aromas associated with sizzling bacon and hamburgers on the grill, onions being sautéed, or vegetables in a stir-fry. Of course, these wonderful characteristics lure people into eating too much from time to time. With careful selections, a diet following the USDA Food Guide can support good health and still meet fat recommendations (see the "How to" feature on p. 163).

Meats and Meat Alternates Many meats and meat alternates ◆ contain fat, saturated fat, and cholesterol but also provide high-quality protein and valuable vitamins and minerals. They can be included in a healthy diet if a person makes lean choices and prepares them using the suggestions outlined in the box on p. 163. Selecting "free-range" meats from grass-fed instead of grain-fed livestock offers the nutrient advantages of being lower in fat, and the fat has more polyunsaturated fatty acids, including the omega-3 type. Another strategy to lower blood cholesterol is to prepare meals using soy protein instead of animal protein.[37]

◆ Solid fats include meat and poultry fats (as in poultry skin, luncheon meats, sausage); milk fat (as in whole milk, cheese, butter); shortening (as in fried foods and baked goods); and hard margarines.

◆ The USDA Food Guide amounts of fats that can be included as discretionary kcalories when most food choices are nutrient dense and fat < 30% total kcal:
- 11 g for 1600 kcal diet
- 15 g for 1800 kcal diet
- 18 g for 2000 kcal diet
- 19 g for 2200 kcal diet
- 22 g for 2400 kcal diet

For perspective, 1 tsp oil = 5 g fat and provides about 45 kcal

◆ Very lean options:
- Chicken (white meat, no skin); cod, flounder, trout; tuna (canned in water); legumes

Lean options:
- Beef or pork "round" or "loin" cuts; chicken (dark meat, no skin); herring or salmon; tuna (canned in oil)

Medium-fat options:
- Ground beef, eggs, tofu

High-fat options:
- Sausage, bacon, luncheon meats, hot dogs, peanut butter, nuts

REFERENCES

1. M. A. Zulet and coauthors, Inflammation and conjugated linoleic acid: Mechanisms of action and implications for human health, *Journal of Physiology and Biochemistry* 61 (2005): 483-494; M. A. Belury, Dietary conjugated linoleic acid in health: Physiological effects and mechanisms of action, *Annual Review of Nutrition* 22 (2002): 505-531.

2. K. A. Varady and coauthors, Plant sterols and endurance training combine to favorably alter plasma lipid profiles in previously sedentary hypercholesterolemic adults after 8 wk, *American Journal of Clinical Nutrition* 80 (2004): 1159-1166; M. Richelle and coauthors, Both free and esterified plant sterols reduce cholesterol absorption and the bioavailability of β-carotene and α-tocopherol in normocholesterolemic humans, *American Journal of Clinical Nutrition* 80 (2004): 171-177.

3. A. Andersson and coauthors, Fatty acid composition of skeletal muscle reflects dietary fat composition in humans, *American Journal of Clinical Nutrition* 76 (2002): 1222-1229; A. Baylin and coauthors, Adipose tissue biomarkers of fatty acid intake, *American Journal of Clinical Nutrition* 76 (2002): 750-757.

4. R. Uauy and A. D. Dangour, Nutrition in brain development and aging: Role of essential fatty acids, *Nutrition Reviews* 64 (2006): S24-S33; W. C. Heird and A. Lapillonne, The role of essential fatty acids in development, *Annual Review of Nutrition* 25 (2005): 549-571; J. M. Alessandri and coauthors, Polyunsaturated fatty acids in the central nervous system: Evolution of concepts and nutritional implications throughout life, *Reproduction, Nutrition, Development* 6 (2004): 509-538.

5. H. Tapiero and coauthors, Polyunsaturated fatty acids (PUFA) and eicosanoids in human health and pathologies, *Biomedicine and Pharmacotherapy* 56 (2002): 215-222.

6. M. T. Nakamura and T. Y. Nara, Structure, function, and dietary regulation of Δ6, Δ5, and Δ9 desaturases, *Annual Review of Nutrition* 24 (2004): 345-376.

7. J. R. Hibbeln, Seafood consumption, the DHA content of mothers' milk and prevalence rates of postpartum depression: A cross-national, ecological analysis, *Journal of Affective Disorders* 69 (2002): 15-29.

8. L. Zimmer and coauthors, The dopamine mesocorticolimbic pathway is affected by deficiency in n-3 polyunsaturated fatty acids, *American Journal of Clinical Nutrition* 75 (2002): 662-667.

9. P. J. Nestel and coauthors, Relation of diet to cardiovascular disease risk factors in subjects with cardiovascular disease in Australia and New Zealand: Analysis of the Long-Term Intervention with Pravastatin in Ischaemic Disease trial, *American Journal of Clinical Nutrition* 81 (2005): 1322-1329.

10. D. Mozaffarian and coauthors, Trans fatty acids and cardiovascular disease, *New England Journal of Medicine* 354 (2006): 1601-1613.

11. J. Dyerberg and coauthors, Effects of trans- and n-3 unsaturated fatty acids on cardiovascular risk markers in healthy males: An 8 weeks dietary intervention study, *European Journal of Clinical Nutrition* 58 (2004): 1062-1070; P. M. Clifton, J. B. Keogh, and M. Noakes, Trans fatty acids in adipose tissue and the food supply are associated with myocardial infarction, *Journal of Nutrition* 134 (2004): 874-879; N. M. deRoos, E. G. Schouten, and M. B. Katan, *Trans* fatty acids, HDL-cholesterol, and cardiovascular disease: Effects of dietary changes on vascular reactivity, *European Journal of Medical Research* 8 (2003): 355-357.

12. D. Mozaffarian and coauthors, *Trans* fatty acids and systemic inflammation in heart failure, *American Journal of Clinical Nutrition* 80 (2004): 1521-1525; D. J. Baer and coauthors, Dietary fatty acids affect plasma markers of inflammation in healthy men fed controlled diets: A randomized crossover study, *American Journal of Clinical Nutrition* 79 (2004): 969-973; D. Mozaffarian and coauthors, Dietary intake of *trans* fatty acids and systemic inflammation in women, *American Journal of Clinical Nutrition* 79 (2004): 606-612; G. A. Bray and coauthors, The influence of different fats and fatty acids on obesity, insulin resistance and inflammation, *Journal of Nutrition* 132 (2002): 2488-2491.

13. Federal Register 68, July 11, 2003, p. 41444.

14. Expert Panel on Detection, Evaluation, and Treatment of High Blood Cholesterol in Adults (Adult Treatment Panel III), *Third Report of the National Cholesterol Education Program (NCEP)*, NIH publication no. 02-5215 (Bethesda, Md.: National Heart, Lung, and Blood Institute, 2002), p. V-10.

15. A. H. Stark and Z. Madar, Olive oil as a functional food: Epidemiology and nutritional approaches, *Nutrition Reviews* 60 (2002): 170-176.

16. P. M. Kris-Etherton, K. D. Hecker, and A. E. Binkoski, Polyunsaturated fatty acids and cardiovascular health, *Nutrition Reviews* 62 (2004): 414-426.

17. J. L. Breslow, n-3 Fatty acids and cardiovascular disease, *American Journal of Clinical Nutrition* 83 (2006): 1477S-1482S; F. B. Hu and coauthors, Fish and omega-3 fatty acid intake and risk of coronary heart disease in women, *Journal of the American Medical Association* 287 (2002): 1815-1821; C. M. Albert and coauthors, Blood levels of long-chain n-3 fatty acids and the risk of sudden death, *New England Journal of Medicine* 346 (2002): 1113-1118.

18. Breslow, 2006; P. J. H. Jones and V. W. Y. Lau, Effect of n-3 polyunsaturated fatty acids on risk reduction of sudden death, *Nutrition Reviews* 60 (2002): 407-413.

19. M. C. Nesheim and A. L. Yaktine, eds., Seafood, *Seafood Choices: Balancing Benefits and Risks* (National Academies Press, Washington, D. C.: 2007), p. 12; C. W. Levenson and D. M. Axelrad, Too much of a good thing? Update on fish consumption and murcury exposure, *Nutrition Reviews* 64 (2006): 139-145; E. Guallar and coauthors, Mercury, fish oils, and the risk of myocardial infarction, *New England Journal of Medicine* 347 (2002): 1747-1754.

20. V. Wijendran and K. C. Hayes, Dietary n-6 and n-3 fatty acid balance and cardiovascular health, *Annual Review of Nutrition* 24 (2004): 597-615.

21. AHA Scientific statement: Diet and lifestyle recommendations revision 2006, *Circulation* 114 (2006): 82-96

22. K. He and coauthors, Fish consumption and risk of stroke in men, *Journal of the American Medical Association* 288 (2002): 3130-3136.

23. L. Cordain and coauthors, Fatty acid analysis of wild ruminant tissues: Evolutionary implications for reducing diet-related chronic disease, *European Journal of Clinical Nutrition* 56 (2002): 181-191.

24. S. Bechoua and coauthors, Influence of very low dietary intake of marine oil on some functional aspects of immune cells in healthy elderly people, *British Journal of Nutrition* 89 (2003): 523-532.

25. M. H. Raitt and coauthors, Fish oil supplementation and risk of ventricular tachycardia and ventricular fibrillation in patients with implantable defibrillators: A randomized control study, *Journal of the American Medical Association* 293 (2005): 2884-2891; P. M. Kris-Etherton and coauthors, AHA Scientific Statement: Fish consumption, fish oil, omega-3 fatty acids, and cardiovascular disease, *Circulation* 106 (2002): 2747-2757.

26. C. B. Stephensen, Fish oil and inflammatory disease: Is asthma the next target for n-3 fatty acid supplements? *Nutrition Reviews* 62 (2004): 486-489.

27. G. L. Khor, Dietary fat quality: A nutritional epidemiologist's view, *Asia Pacific Journal of Clinical Nutrition* 13 (2004): S22; R. Stoeckli and U. Keller, Nutritional fats and the risk of type 2 diabetes and cancer, *Physiology and Behavior* 83 (2004): 611-615.

28. M. D. Holmes and W. C. Willett, Does diet affect breast cancer risk? *Breast Cancer Research* 6 (2004): 170-178.

29. L. K. Dennis and coauthors, Problems with the assessment of dietary fat in prostate cancer studies, *American Journal of Epidemiology* 160 (2004): 436-444.

30. P. W. Parodi, Dairy product consumption and the risk of breast cancer, *Journal of the American College of Nutrition* 24 (2005): 556S-568S; J. Zhang and H. Kesteloot, Milk consumption in relation to incidence of prostate, breast, colon, and rectal cancers: Is there an independent effect? *Nutrition and Cancer* 53 (2005): 65-72.

31. C. H. MacLean and coauthors, Effects of omega-3 fatty acids on cancer risk-A systematic review, *Journal of the American Medical Association* 295 (2006): 403-415; W. E. Hardman, (n-3) Fatty acids and cancer therapy, *Journal of Nutrition* 134 (2004): 3427S-3430S; M. F. Leitzmann and coauthors, Dietary intake of n-3 and n-6 fatty acids and the risk of prostate cancer, *American Journal of Clinical Nutrition* 80 (2004): 204-216; S. C. Larsson and coauthors, Dietary long-chain n-3 fatty acids for the prevention of cancer: A review of potential mechanisms, *American Journal of Clinical Nutrition* 79 (2004): 935-945.

32. Committee on Dietary Reference Intakes, *Dietary Reference Intakes for Energy, Carbohydrate, Fiber, Fat, Fatty Acids, Cholesterol, Protein, and Amino Acids* (Washington, D.C.: National Academies Press, 2002/2005).

33. Committee on Dietary Reference Intakes, 2002/2005.

34. Committee on Dietary Reference Intakes, 2002/2005.
35. National Center for Health Statistics, *Chartbook on Trends in the Health of Americans, 2005*, www.cdc.gov/nchs, site visited on January 18, 2006; Committee on Dietary Reference Intakes, 2002/2005.
36. Position of the American Dietetic Association, Dietitians of Canada, and the American College of Sports Medicine: Nutrition and athletic performance, *Journal of the American Dietetic Association* 100 (2000): 1543-1556.
37. S. Tonstad, K. Smerud, and L. Høie, A comparison of the effects of 2 doses of soy protein or casein on serum lipids, serum lipoproteins, and plasma total homocysteine in hypercholesterolemic subjects, *American Journal of Clinical Nutrition* 76 (2002): 78-84.
38. B. M. Davy and coauthors, High-fiber oat cereal compared with wheat cereal consumption favorably alters LDL-cholesterol subclass and particle numbers in middle-aged and older men, *American Journal of Clinical Nutrition* 76 (2002): 351-358; D. J. A. Jenkins and coauthors, Soluble fiber intake at a dose approved by the U.S. Food and Drug Administration for a claim of health benefits: Serum lipid risk factors for cardiovascular disease assessed in a randomized controlled crossover trial, *American Journal of Clinical Nutrition* 75 (2002): 834-839.
39. C. S. Patch, L. C. Tapsell, and P. G. Williams, Plant sterol/stanol prescription is an effective treatment strategy for managing hypercholesterolemia in outpatient clinical practice, *Journal of the American Dietetic Association* 105 (2005): 46-52.
40. Position of the American Dietetic Association: Fat replacers, *Journal of the American Dietetic Association* 105 (2005): 266-275.

ANSWERS

Nutrition Calculations

1. a. Milk A: 8 g fat ÷ 244 g total = 0.03; 0.03 × 100 = 3%

    Milk B: 5 g fat ÷ 244 g total = 0.02; 0.02 × 100 = 2%

    Milk C: 3 g fat ÷ 244 g total = 0.01; 0.01 × 100 = 1%

    Milk D: 0 g fat ÷ 244 g total = 0.00; 0.00 × 100 = 0%

    b. Milk A: 8 g fat × 9 kcal/g = 72 kcal from fat

    Milk B: 5 g fat × 9 kcal/g = 45 kcal from fat

    Milk C: 3 g fat × 9 kcal/g = 27 kcal from fat

    Milk D: 0 g fat × 9 kcal/g = 0 kcal from fat

    c. Milk A: (8 g fat × 9 kcal/g) + (8 g prot × 4 kcal/g) + (12 g carb × 4 kcal/g) = 152 kcal

    Milk B: (5 g fat × 9 kcal/g) + (8 g prot × 4 kcal/g) + (12 g carb × 4 kcal/g) = 125 kcal

    Milk C: (3 g fat × 9 kcal/g) + (8 g prot × 4 kcal/g) + (12 g carb × 4 kcal/g) = 107 kcal

    Milk D: (0 g fat × 9 kcal/g) + (8 g prot × 4 kcal/g) + (12 g carb × 4 kcal/g) = 80 kcal

    d. Milk A: 72 kcal from fat ÷ 152 total kcal = 0.47; 0.47 × 100 = 47%

    Milk B: 45 kcal from fat ÷ 125 total kcal = 0.36; 0.36 × 100 = 36%

    Milk C: 27 kcal from fat ÷ 107 total kcal = 0.25; 0.25 × 100 = 25%

    Milk D: 0 kcal from fat ÷ 80 total kcal = 0.00; 0.00 × 100 = 0%

    e. Milk A: whole

    Milk B: reduced-fat, 2%, or less-fat

    Milk C: low-fat or 1%

    Milk D: fat-free, nonfat, skim, zero-fat, or no-fat

2. a. 6.5 g ÷ 65 g = 0.1; 0.1 × 100 = 10%; a Daily Value of 10% means that one serving of this food contributes about ¹⁄₁₀ of the day's fat allotment

    b. 6.5 g × 9 kcal/g = 58.5, rounded to 59 kcal from fat

    c. (59 kcal from fat ÷ 200 kcal) × 100 = 30% kcalories from fat

3. (30 g fat ÷ 65 g fat) × 100 = 46% of the Daily Value for fat; this means that almost half of the day's fat allotment would be used in this one dessert

Study Questions (multiple choice)

1. c   2. c   3. d   4. c   5. d   6. b   7. c   8. a

9. d   10. b

High-Fat Foods—Friend or Foe?

© Philip Salverry/FoodPix/Jupiter Images

Eat less fat. Eat more fatty fish. Give up butter. Use margarine. Give up margarine. Use olive oil. Steer clear of saturated. Seek out omega-3. Stay away from *trans*. Stick with mono- and polyunsaturated. Keep fat intake moderate. Today's fat messages seem to be forever multiplying and changing. No wonder people feel confused about dietary fat. The confusion stems in part from the complexities of fat and in part from the nature of recommendations. As Chapter 5 explained, "dietary fat" refers to several kinds of fats. Some fats support health whereas others damage it, and foods typically provide a mixture of fats in varying proportions. Researchers have spent decades sorting through the relationships among the various kinds of fat and their roles in supporting or harming health. Translating these research findings into dietary recommendations is challenging. Too little information can mislead consumers, but too much detail can overwhelm them. As research findings accumulate, recommendations slowly evolve and become more refined. Fortunately, that's where we are with fat recommendations today—refining them from the general to the specific. Though they may seem to be "forever multiplying and changing," in fact, they are becoming more meaningful.

This highlight begins with a look at the dietary guidelines for fat intake. It continues by identifying which foods provide which fats and presenting the Mediterranean diet, an example of a food plan that embraces the heart-healthy fats. It closes with strategies to help consumers choose the right amounts of the right kinds of fats for a healthy diet.

Guidelines for Fat Intake

Dietary recommendations for fat have changed in recent years, shifting the emphasis from lowering total fat, in general, to limiting saturated and *trans* fat, specifically. For decades, health experts advised limiting intakes of total fat to 30 percent or less of energy intake. They recognized that saturated fats and *trans* fats are the fats that raise blood cholesterol but reasoned that by limiting total fat intake, saturated and *trans* fat intake would decline as well. People were simply advised to cut back on all fat and thereby they would cut back on saturated and *trans* fat. Such advice may have oversimplified the message and unnecessarily restricted total fat.

Low-fat diets have a place in treatment plans for people with elevated blood lipids or heart disease, but some researchers question the wisdom of such diets for healthy people as a means of controlling weight and preventing diseases. Several problems accompany low-fat diets. For one, many people find low-fat diets difficult to maintain over time. For another, low-fat diets are not necessarily low-kcalorie diets. If energy intake exceeds energy needs, weight gain follows, and obesity brings a host of health problems, including heart disease. For still another, diets extremely low in fat may exclude fatty fish, nuts, seeds, and vegetable oils—all valuable sources of many essential fatty acids, phytochemicals, vitamins, and minerals. Importantly, the fats from these sources protect against heart disease, as later sections of this highlight explain.

Instead of urging people to cut back on all fats, current recommendations suggest carefully replacing the "bad" saturated fats with the "good" unsaturated fats and enjoying them in moderation.[1] The goal is to create a diet moderate in kcalories that provides enough of the fats that support good health, but not too much of those that harm health. (Turn to pp. 156–160 for a review of the health consequences of each type of fat.)

With these findings and goals in mind, the DRI committee suggests a healthy range of 20 to 35 percent of energy intake from fat. This range appears to be compatible with low rates of heart disease, diabetes, obesity, and cancer.[2] Heart-healthy recommendations suggest that within this range, consumers should try to minimize their intakes of saturated fat, *trans* fat, and cholesterol and use monounsaturated and polyunsaturated fats instead.[3]

Asking consumers to limit their total fat intake was less than perfect advice, but it was straightforward—find the fat and cut back. Asking consumers to keep their intakes of saturated fats, *trans* fats, and cholesterol low and to use monounsaturated and polyunsaturated fats instead may be more on target with heart health, but it also makes diet planning more complicated. To make appropriate selections, consumers must first learn which foods contain which fats.

High-Fat Foods and Heart Health

Avocados, bacon, walnuts, potato chips, and mackerel are all high-fat foods, yet some of these foods have detrimental effects on heart health when consumed in excess, whereas others seem neutral or even beneficial. This section presents some of the accumulating evidence that helped to distinguish which high-fat foods belong in a healthy diet and which ones need to be kept to a minimum. As you will see, a little more fat in the diet may be compatible with heart health, but only if the great majority of it is the unsaturated kind.

Cook with Olive Oil

As it turns out, the traditional diets of Greece and other countries in the Mediterranean region offer an excellent example of eating patterns that use "good" fats liberally. Often, these diets are rich in olives and their oil. A classic study of the world's people, the Seven Countries Study, found that death rates from heart disease were strongly associated with diets high in saturated fats but only weakly linked with total fat.[4] In fact, the two countries with the highest fat intakes, Finland and the Greek island of Crete, had the highest (Finland) and lowest (Crete) rates of heart disease deaths. In both countries, the people consumed 40 percent or more of their kcalories from fat. Clearly, a high-fat diet was not the primary problem, so researchers refocused their attention on the *type* of fat. They began to notice the benefits of olive oil.

A diet that uses olive oil instead of other cooking fats, especially butter, stick margarine, and meat fats, may offer numerous health benefits.[5] Olive oil and other oils rich in mono- unsaturated fatty acids help to protect against heart disease by:

- Lowering total and LDL cholesterol and not lowering HDL cholesterol or raising triglycerides[6]
- Lowering LDL cholesterol susceptibility to oxidation[7]
- Lowering blood-clotting factors[8]
- Providing phytochemicals that act as antioxidants (see Highlight 11)[9]
- Lowering blood pressure[10]

When compared with other fats, olive oil seems to be a wise choice, but controlled clinical trials are too scarce to support population-wide recommendations to switch to a high-fat diet rich in olive oil. Importantly, olive oil is not a magic potion; drizzling it on foods does not make them healthier. Like other fats, olive oil delivers 9 kcalories per gram, which can contribute to weight gain in people who fail to balance their energy intake with their energy output. Its role in a healthy diet is to *replace* the saturated fats. Other vegetable oils, such as canola or safflower oil, are also generally low in saturated fats and high in unsaturated fats. For this reason, heart-healthy diets use these unsaturated vegetable oils as substitutes for the more saturated fats of butter, hydrogenated stick margarine, lard, or shortening. (Remember that the tropical oils—coconut, palm, and palm kernel—are too saturated to be included with the heart-healthy vegetable oils.)

Nibble on Nuts

Tree nuts and peanuts are traditionally excluded from low-fat diets, and for good reasons. Nuts provide up to 80 percent of their kcalories from fat, and a quarter cup (about an ounce) of mixed nuts provides over 200 kcalories. In a recent review of the literature, however, researchers found that people who ate a one-ounce serving of nuts on five or more days a week had a reduced risk of heart disease compared with people who consumed no nuts.[11] A smaller positive association was noted for

Olives and their oil may benefit heart health.

any amount greater than one serving of nuts a week. The nuts in this study were those commonly eaten in the United States: almonds, Brazil nuts, cashews, hazelnuts, macadamia nuts, pecans, pistachios, walnuts, and even peanuts. On average, these nuts contain mostly monounsaturated fat (59 percent), some polyunsaturated fat (27 percent), and little saturated fat (14 percent).

Research has shown a benefit from walnuts and almonds in particular. In study after study, walnuts, when substituted for other fats in the diet, produce favorable effects on blood lipids—even in people with elevated total and LDL cholesterol.[12] Results are similar for almonds. In one study, researchers gave men and women one of three kinds of snacks, all of equal kcalories: whole-wheat muffins, almonds (about 2½ ounces), or half muffins and half almonds.[13] At the end of a month, people receiving the full almond snack had the greatest drop in blood LDL cholesterol; those eating the half almond snack had a lesser, but still significant, drop in blood lipids; and those eating the muffin only snack had no change.

Studies on peanuts, macadamia nuts, pecans, and pistachios follow suit, indicating that including nuts may be a wise strategy against heart disease. Nuts may protect against heart disease because they provide:

- Monounsaturated and polyunsaturated fats in abundance, but few saturated fats
- Fiber, vegetable protein, and other valuable nutrients, including the antioxidant vitamin E (see Highlight 11)
- Phytochemicals that act as antioxidants (see Highlight 13)

Before advising consumers to include nuts in their diets, a caution is in order. As mentioned, most of the energy nuts provide comes from fats. Consequently, they deliver many kcalories per bite. In studies examining the effects of nuts on heart disease, researchers carefully adjust diets to make room for the nuts without

Matthew Farruggio

For heart health, snack on a few nuts instead of potato chips. Because nuts are energy dense (high in kcalories per ounce), it is especially important to keep portion size in mind when eating them.

increasing the total kcalories—that is, they use nuts *instead of, not in addition to,* other foods (such as meats, potato chips, oils, margarine, and butter). Consumers who do not make similar replacements could end up gaining weight if they simply add nuts on top of their regular diets. Weight gain, in turn, elevates blood lipids and raises the risks of heart disease.

Feast on Fish

Research into the health benefits of the long-chain omega-3 polyunsaturated fatty acids began with a simple observation: the native peoples of Alaska, northern Canada, and Greenland, who eat a diet rich in omega-3 fatty acids, notably EPA and DHA, have a remarkably low rate of heart disease even though their diets are relatively high in fat.[14] These omega-3 fatty acids help to protect against heart disease by:[15]

- Reducing blood triglycerides
- Preventing blood clots
- Protecting against irregular heartbeats
- Lowering blood pressure
- Defending against inflammation
- Serving as precursors to eicosanoids

For people with hypertension or atherosclerosis, these actions can be life saving.

Research studies have provided strong evidence that increasing omega-3 fatty acids in the diet supports heart health and lowers the rate of deaths from heart disease.[16] For this reason, the American Heart Association recommends including fish in a heart-healthy diet. People who eat some fish each week can lower their risks of heart attack and stroke. Table 5-2 on p. 159 lists fish that provide at least 1 gram of omega-3 fatty acids per serving.

Fish is the best source of EPA and DHA in the diet, but it is also a major source of mercury, an environmental contaminant. Most fish contain at least trace amounts of mercury, but tilefish (also known as

golden snapper or golden bass), swordfish, king mackerel, marlin, and shark have especially high levels. For this reason, the FDA advises pregnant and lactating women, women of childbearing age who may become pregnant, and young children to avoid:

- Tilefish (also called golden snapper or golden bass), swordfish, king mackeral, marlin, and shark

And to limit average weekly consumption of:

- A variety of fish and shellfish to 12 ounces (cooked or canned)
- White (albacore) tuna to 6 ounces (cooked or canned)

Commonly eaten seafood relatively low in mercury include shrimp, catfish, pollock, salmon, and canned light tuna.

In addition to the direct toxic effects of mercury, some (but not all) research suggests that mercury may diminish the health benefits of omega-3 fatty acids.[17] Such findings serve as a reminder that our health depends on the health of our planet. The protective effect of fish in the diet is available, provided that the fish and their surrounding waters are not heavily contaminated. (Chapter 19 discusses the adverse consequences of mercury, and Chapter 20 presents the relationships between diet and the environment in more detail.)

In an effort to limit exposure to pollutants, some consumers choose farm-raised fish. Compared with fish caught in the wild, farm-raised fish tend to be lower in mercury, but they are also lower in omega-3 fatty acids. When selecting fish, keep the diet strategies of variety and moderation in mind. Varying choices and eating moderate amounts helps to limit the intake of contaminants such as mercury.

© www.comstock.com

Fish is a good source of the omega-3 fatty acids.

High-Fat Foods and Heart Disease

The number one dietary determinant of LDL cholesterol is saturated fat. Figure H5-1 shows that each 1 percent increase in energy from saturated fatty acids in the diet may produce a 2 percent jump in heart disease risk by elevating blood LDL cholesterol. Conversely, reducing saturated fat intake by 1 percent can be expected to produce a 2 percent drop in heart disease risk by the same mechanism. Even a 2 percent drop in LDL represents a significant improvement for the health of the heart.[18] Like saturated fats, *trans* fats also raise heart disease risk by elevating LDL cholesterol. A heart-healthy diet limits foods rich in these two types of fat.

Limit Fatty Meats, Whole-Milk Products, and Tropical Oils

The major sources of saturated fats in the U.S. diet are fatty meats, whole milk products, tropical oils, and products made from any of these foods. To limit saturated fat intake, consumers must choose carefully among these high-fat foods. Over a third of the fat in most meats is saturated. Similarly, over half of the fat is saturated in whole milk and other high-fat dairy products, such as cheese, butter, cream, half-and-half, cream cheese, sour cream, and ice cream. The tropical oils of palm, palm kernel, and coconut, which are rarely used by consumers in the kitchen, are used heavily by food manufacturers, and are commonly found in many commercially prepared foods.

When choosing meats, milk products, and commercially prepared foods, look for those lowest in saturated fat. Labels provide a useful guide for comparing products in this regard, and Appendix H lists the saturated fat in several thousand foods.

Even with careful selections, a nutritionally adequate diet will provide some saturated fat. Zero saturated fat is not possible even when experts design menus with the mission to keep saturated fat as low as possible.[19] Because most saturated fats come from animal foods, vegetarian diets can, and usually do, deliver fewer saturated fats than mixed diets.

Limit Hydrogenated Foods

Chapter 5 explained that solid shortening and margarine are made from vegetable oil that has been hardened through hydrogenation. This process both saturates some of the unsaturated fatty acids and introduces *trans*-fatty acids. Many convenience foods contain *trans* fats, including:

- Fried foods such as French fries, chicken, and other commercially fried foods
- Commercial baked goods such as cookies, doughnuts, pastries, breads, and crackers
- Snack foods such as chips
- Imitation cheeses

To keep *trans* fat intake low, use these foods sparingly as an occasional taste treat.

Table H5-1 (p. 176) summarizes which foods provide which fats. Substituting unsaturated fats for saturated fats at each meal and snack can help protect against heart disease. Figure H5-2 (p. 176) compares two meals and shows how such substitutions can lower saturated fat and raise unsaturated fat—even when total fat and kcalories remain unchanged.

The Mediterranean Diet

The links between good health and traditional Mediterranean diets of the mid-1900s were introduced earlier with regard to olive

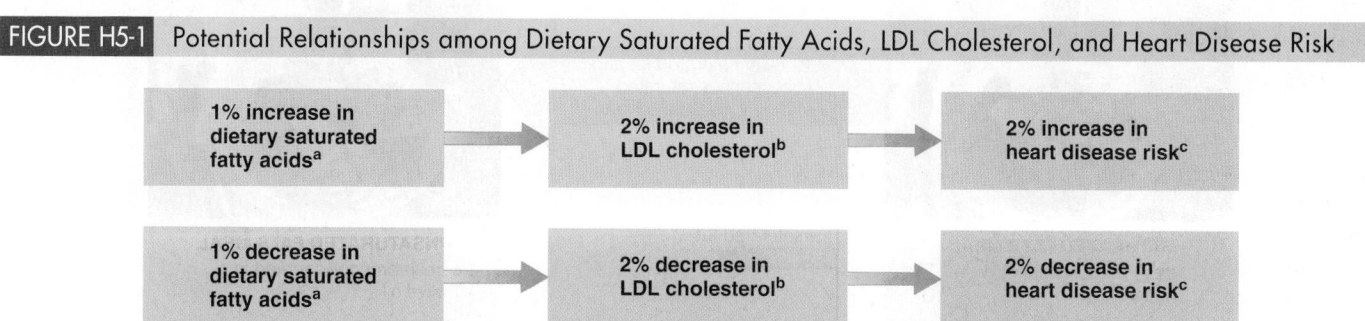

FIGURE H5-1 Potential Relationships among Dietary Saturated Fatty Acids, LDL Cholesterol, and Heart Disease Risk

[a]Percentage of change in total dietary energy from saturated fatty acids.
[b]Percentage of change in blood LDL cholesterol.
[c]Percentage of change in an individual's risk of heart disease; the percentage of change in risk may increase when blood lipid changes are sustained over time.

SOURCE: *Third Report of the National Cholesterol Education Program (NCEP) Expert Panel on Detection, Evaluation, and Treatment of High Blood Cholesterol in Adults (Adult Treatment Panel III)*, NIH publication no. 02-5215 (Bethesda, Md.: National Heart, Lung, and Blood Institute, 2002), p. V-8 and II-4.

TABLE H5-1   Major Sources of Various Fatty Acids

Healthful Fatty Acids

Monounsaturated	Omega-6 Polyunsaturated	Omega-3 Polyunsaturated
Avocado	Margarine (nonhydrogenated)	Fatty fish (herring, mackerel, salmon, tuna)
Oils (canola, olive, peanut, sesame)	Oils (corn, cottonseed, safflower, soybean)	Flaxseed
Nuts (almonds, cashews, filberts, hazelnuts, macadamia nuts, peanuts, pecans, pistachios)	Nuts (pine nuts, walnuts)	Nuts (walnuts)
	Mayonnaise	
Olives	Salad dressing	
Peanut butter	Seeds (pumpkin, sunflower)	
Seeds (sesame)		

Harmful Fatty Acids

Saturated	Trans
Bacon	Fried foods (hydrogenated shortening)
Butter	Margarine (hydrogenated or partially hydrogenated)
Chocolate	Nondairy creamers
Coconut	Many fast foods
Cream cheese	Shortening
Cream, half-and-half	Commercial baked goods (including doughnuts, cakes, cookies)
Lard	Many snack foods (including microwave popcorn, chips, crackers)
Meat	
Milk and milk products (whole)	
Oils (coconut, palm, palm kernel)	
Shortening	
Sour cream	

NOTE: Keep in mind that foods contain a mixture of fatty acids.

FIGURE H5-2   Two Meals Compared: Replacing Saturated Fat with Unsaturated Fat

Examples of ways to replace saturated fats with unsaturated fats include sautéing vegetables in olive oil instead of butter, garnishing salads with avocado and sunflower seeds instead of bacon and blue cheese, and eating salmon instead of steak. Each of these meals provides roughly the same number of kcalories and grams of fat, but the one on the left has almost four times as much saturated fat and only half as many omega-3 fatty acids.

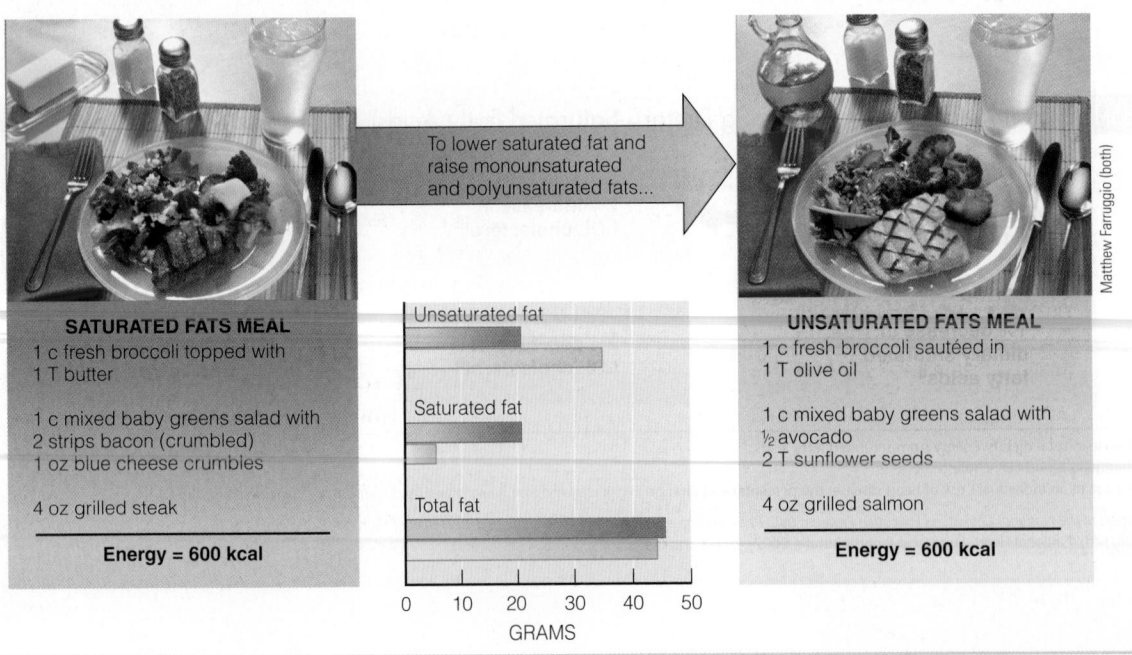

To lower saturated fat and raise monounsaturated and polyunsaturated fats...

SATURATED FATS MEAL

1 c fresh broccoli topped with 1 T butter

1 c mixed baby greens salad with 2 strips bacon (crumbled) 1 oz blue cheese crumbles

4 oz grilled steak

Energy = 600 kcal

UNSATURATED FATS MEAL

1 c fresh broccoli sautéed in 1 T olive oil

1 c mixed baby greens salad with ½ avocado 2 T sunflower seeds

4 oz grilled salmon

Energy = 600 kcal

Unsaturated fat

Saturated fat

Total fat

0   10   20   30   40   50
GRAMS

Matthew Farruggio (both)

oil. For people who eat these diets, the incidence of heart disease, some cancers, and other chronic diseases is low, and life expectancy is high.[20]

Although each of the many countries that border the Mediterranean Sea has its own culture, traditions, and dietary habits, their similarities are much greater than the use of olive oil alone. In fact, according to a recent study, no one factor alone can be credited with reducing disease risks—the association holds true only when the overall diet pattern is present.[21] Apparently, each of the foods contributes small benefits that harmonize to produce either a substantial cumulative or a synergistic effect.

The Mediterranean people focus their diets on crusty breads, whole grains, potatoes, and pastas; a variety of vegetables (including wild greens) and legumes; feta and mozzarella cheeses and yogurt; nuts; and fruits (especially grapes and figs). They eat some fish, other seafood, poultry, a few eggs, and little meat. Along with olives and olive oil, their principal sources of fat are nuts and fish; they rarely use butter or encounter hydrogenated fats. Consequently, traditional Mediterranean diets are:

- Low in saturated fat
- Very low in *trans* fat
- Rich in unsaturated fat
- Rich in complex carbohydrate and fiber
- Rich in nutrients and phytochemicals that support good health

People following the traditional Mediterranean diet can receive as much as 40 percent of a day's kcalories from fat, but their limited consumption of dairy products and meats provides less than 10 percent from saturated fats. In addition, because the animals in the Mediterranean region graze, the meat, dairy products, and eggs are richer in omega-3 fatty acids than those from animals fed grain. Other foods typical of the Mediterranean, such as wild plants and snails, provide omega-3 fatty acids as well. All in all, the traditional Mediterranean diet has gained a reputation for its health benefits as well as its delicious flavors, but beware of the typical Mediterranean-style cuisine available in U.S. restaurants. It has been adjusted to popular tastes, meaning that it is often much higher in saturated fats and meats—and much lower in the potentially beneficial constituents—than the traditional fare. Unfortunately, it appears that people in the Mediterranean region who are replacing some of their traditional dietary habits with those of the United States are losing the health benefits previously enjoyed.[22]

Conclusion

Are some fats "good," and others "bad" from the body's point of view? The saturated and *trans* fats indeed seem mostly bad for the health of the heart. Aside from providing energy, which unsaturated fats can do equally well, saturated and *trans* fats bring no indispensable benefits to the body. Furthermore, no harm can come from consuming diets low in them. Still, foods rich in these fats are often delicious, giving them a special place in the diet.

In contrast, the unsaturated fats are mostly good for the health of the heart when consumed in moderation. To date, their one proven fault seems to be that they, like all fats, provide abundant energy to the body and so may promote obesity if they drive kcalorie intakes higher than energy needs.[23] Obesity, in turn, often begets many body ills, as Chapter 8 makes clear.

When judging foods by their fatty acids, keep in mind that the fat in foods is a mixture of "good" and "bad," providing both saturated and unsaturated fatty acids. Even predominantly monounsaturated olive oil delivers some saturated fat. Consequently, even when a person chooses foods with mostly unsaturated fats, saturated fat can still add up if total fat is high. For this reason, fat must be kept below 35 percent of total kcalories if the diet is to be moderate in saturated fat. Even experts run into difficulty when attempting to create nutritious diets from a variety of foods that are low in saturated fats when kcalories from fat exceed 35 percent of the total.[24]

Does this mean that you must forever go without favorite cheeses, ice cream cones, or a grilled steak? The famous chef Julia Child made this point about moderation:

> An imaginary shelf labeled INDULGENCES is a good idea. It contains the best butter, jumbo-size eggs, heavy cream, marbled steaks, sausages and pâtés, hollandaise and butter sauces, French butter-cream fillings, gooey chocolate cakes, and all those lovely items that demand disciplined rationing. Thus, with these items high up and almost out of reach, we are ever conscious that they are not everyday foods. They are for special occasions, and when that occasion comes we can enjoy every mouthful.
> Julia Child, *The Way to Cook,* 1989

Additionally, food manufacturers have come to the assistance of consumers who wish to avoid the health threats from saturated and *trans* fats. Some margarine makers no longer offer products containing *trans* fats, and many snack manufacturers have reduced the saturated and *trans* fats in some products and now offer snack foods in 100-kcalorie packages. Other companies are following as consumers respond favorably.

Adopting some of the Mediterranean eating habits may serve those who enjoy a little more fat in the diet. Including vegetables, fruits, and legumes as part of a balanced daily diet is a good idea, as is *replacing* saturated fats such as butter, shortening, and meat fat with unsaturated fats like olive oil and the oils from nuts and fish. These foods provide vitamins, minerals, and phytochemicals—all valuable in protecting the body's health. The authors of this book do not stop there, however. They urge you to reduce fats from convenience foods and fast foods; choose small portions of meats, fish, and poultry; and include fresh foods from all the food groups each day. Take care to select portion sizes that will best meet your energy needs. Also, exercise daily.

REFERENCES

1. *Third Report of the National Cholesterol Education Program (NCEP) Expert Panel on Detection, Evaluation, and Treatment of High Blood Cholesterol in Adults (Adult Treatment Panel III)*, publication NIH no. 02-5215 (Bethesda, Md.: National Heart, Lung, and Blood Institute, 2002); Committee on Dietary Reference Intakes, *Dietary Reference Intakes for Energy, Carbohydrate, Fiber, Fat, Fatty Acids, Cholesterol, Protein, and Amino Acids* (Washington, D.C.: National Academies Press, 2002/2005).

2. Committee on Dietary Reference Intakes, 2002/2005, p. 769.

3. American Heart Association Scientific statement: Diet and lifestyle recommendations revision 2006, *Circulation* 114 (2006): 82-96; *Third Report of the National Cholesterol Education Program (NCEP) Expert Panel on Detection, Evaluation, and Treatment of High Blood Cholesterol in Adults (Adult Treatment Panel III)*, publication NIH no. 02-5215 (Bethesda, Md.: National Heart, Lung, and Blood Institute, 2002); Committee on Dietary Reference Intakes, *Dietary Reference Intakes for Energy, Carbohydrate, Fiber, Fat, Fatty Acids, Cholesterol, Protein, and Amino Acids* (Washington, D.C.: National Academies Press, 2002/2005).

4. A. Keys, *Seven Countries: A Multivariate Analysis of Death and Coronary Heart Disease* (Cambridge: Harvard University Press, 1980).

5. A. H. Stark and Z. Madar, Olive oil as a functional food: Epidemiology and nutritional approaches, *Nutrition Reviews* 60 (2002): 170–176.

6. M. I. Covas and coauthors, The effect of polyphenols in olive oil on heart disease risk factors, *Annals of Internal Medicine* 145 (2006): 333-341.

7. F. Visioli and coauthors, Virgin Olive Oil Study (VOLOS): Vasoprotective potential of extra virgin olive oil in mildly dislipidemic patients, *European Journal of Nutrition* 44 (2005): 121-127.

8. J. López-Miranda, Monounsaturated fat and cardiovascular risk, *Nutrition Reviews* 64 (2006): S2-S12.

9. F. Visioli and C. Galli, Biological properties of olive oil phytochemicals, *Critical Reviews in Food Science and Nutrition* 42 (2002): 209-221; M. N. Vissers and coauthors, Olive oil phenols are absorbed in humans, *Journal of Nutrition* 132 (2002): 409-417.

10. B. M. Rasmussen and coauthors, Effects of dietary saturated, monounsaturated, and n-3 fatty acids on blood pressure in healthy subjects, *American Journal of Clinical Nutrition* 83 (2006): 221-226; T. Psaltopoulou and coauthors, Olive oil, the Mediterranean diet, and arterial blood pressure: The Greek European Prospective Investigation into Cancer and Nutrition (EPIC) study, *American Journal of Clinical Nutrition* 80 (2004): 1012-1018.

11. J. H. Kelly and J. Sabate, Nuts and coronary heart disease: An epidemiological perspective, *British Journal of Nutrition* 96 (2006): S61-S67.

12. E. B. Feldman, The scientific evidence for a beneficial health relationship between walnuts and coronary heart disease, *Journal of Nutrition* 132 (2002): 1062S–1101S.

13. D. J. Jenkins and coauthors, Dose response of almonds on coronary heart disease risk factors: Blood lipids, oxidized low-density lipoproteins, lipoprotein (a), homocysteine, and pulmonary nitric oxide: A randomized, controlled, crossover trial, *Circulation* 106 (2002): 1327–1332.

14. E. Dewailly and coauthors, Cardiovascular disease risk factors and n-3 fatty acid status in the adult population of James Bay Cree, *American Journal of Clinical Nutrition* 76 (2002): 85–92.

15. J. L. Breslow, n-3 fatty acids and cardiovascular disease, *American Journal of Clinical Nutrition* 83 (2006): 1477S-1482S; P. J. H. Jones and V. W. Y. Lau, Effect of n-3 polyunsaturated fatty acids on risk reduction of sudden death, *Nutrition Reviews* 60 (2002): 407–413.

16. Breslow, 2006; F. B. Hu and coauthors, Fish and omega-3 fatty acid intake and risk of coronary heart disease in women, *Journal of the American Medical Association* 287 (2002): 1815–1821.

17. E. Guallar and coauthors, Mercury, fish oils, and the risk of myocardial infarction, *New England Journal of Medicine* 347 (2002): 1747–1754; K. Yoshizawa and coauthors, Mercury and the risk of coronary heart disease in man, *New England Journal of Medicine* 347 (2002): 1755–1760.

18. *Third Report of the National Cholesterol Education Program (NCEP) Expert Panel on Detection, Evaluation, and Treatment of High Blood Cholesterol in Adults (Adult Treatment Panel III)*, 2002, p.V-8.

19. Committee on Dietary Reference Intakes, 2002/2005, p. 835.

20. L. Serra-Majem, B. Roman, and R. Estruch, Scientific evidence of interventions using the Mediterranean diet: A systematic review, *Nutrition Reviews* 64 (2006): S27–S47; C. Pitsavos and coauthors, Adherence to the Mediterranean diet is associated with total antioxidant capacity in healthy adults: The ATTICA study, *American Journal of Clinical Nutrition* 82 (2005): 694–699; M. Meydani, A Mediterranean-style diet and metabolic syndrome, *Nutrition Reviews* 63 (2005): 312–314; D. B. Panagiotakos and coauthors, Can a Mediterranean diet moderate the development and clinical progression of coronary heart disease? A systematic review, *Medical Science Monitor* 10 (2004): RA193–RA198; K. T. B. Knoops and coauthors, Mediterranean diet, lifestyle factors, and 10-year mortality in elderly European men and women, *Journal of the American Medical Association* 292 (2004): 1433–1439; K. Esposito and coauthors, Effect of a Mediterranean-style diet on endothelial dysfunction and markers of vascular inflammation in the metabolic syndrome: A randomized study, *Journal of the American Medical Association* 292 (2004): 1440–1446.

21. A. Trichopoulou and coauthors, Adherence to a Mediterranean diet and survival in a Greek population, *New England Journal of Medicine* 348 (2003): 2599–2608.

22. F. Sofi and coauthors, Dietary habits, lifestyle, and cardiovascular risk factors in a clinically healthy Italian population: The "Florence" diet is not Mediterranean, *European Journal of Clinical Nutrition* 59 (2005): 584–591.

23. Committee on Dietary Reference Intakes, 2002/2005, pp. 796-797.

24. Committee on Dietary Reference Intakes, 2002/2005, pp. 799-802.

Nutrition in Your Life

Figure 6.6: Animated! Protein Digestion in the GI Tract

Figure 6.7: Animated! Protein Synthesis

Figure 6.10: Animated! An Example of Protein Transport

How to: Practice Problems

Nutrition Portfolio Journal

Nutrition Calculations: Practice Problems

Their versatility in the body is impressive. They help your muscles to contract, your blood to clot, and your eyes to see. They keep you alive and well by facilitating chemical reactions and defending against infections. Without them, your bones, skin, and hair would have no structure. No wonder they were named *proteins,* meaning "of prime importance." Does that mean proteins deserve top billing in your diet as well? Are the best sources of protein beef, beans, or broccoli? Learn which foods will supply you with enough, but not too much, high-quality protein.

Protein: Amino Acids

CHAPTER OUTLINE

The Chemist's View of Proteins •
Amino Acids • Proteins

**Digestion and Absorption of
Protein** • Protein Digestion • Protein
Absorption

Proteins in the Body • Protein Synthesis • Roles of Proteins • A Preview of
Protein Metabolism

Protein in Foods • Protein Quality •
Protein Regulations for Food Labels

**Health Effects and Recommended
Intakes of Protein** • Protein-Energy
Malnutrition • Health Effects of Protein •
Recommended Intakes of Protein •
Protein and Amino Acid Supplements

HIGHLIGHT 6 Nutritional Genomics

A few misconceptions surround the roles of protein in the body and the importance of protein in the diet. For example, people who associate meat with protein and protein with strength may eat steak to build muscles. Their thinking is only partly correct, however. Protein is a vital structural and working substance in all cells—not just muscle cells. To build strength, muscles cells need physical activity and all the nutrients—not just protein. Furthermore, protein is found in milk, eggs, legumes, and many grains and vegetables—not just meat. By overvaluing protein and overemphasizing meat in the diet, a person may mistakenly crowd out other, equally important nutrients and foods. As this chapter describes the various roles of protein in the body and food sources in the diet, keep in mind that protein is one of many nutrients needed to maintain good health.

The Chemist's View of Proteins

Chemically, **proteins** contain the same atoms as carbohydrates and lipids—carbon (C), hydrogen (H), and oxygen (O)—but proteins also contain nitrogen (N) atoms. These nitrogen atoms give the name *amino* (nitrogen containing) to the amino acids—the links in the chains of proteins.

Amino Acids

All **amino acids** have the same basic structure—a central carbon (C) atom with a hydrogen atom (H), an amino group (NH_2), and an acid group (COOH) attached to it. However, carbon atoms need to form four bonds, ◆ so a fourth attachment is necessary. This fourth site distinguishes each amino acid from the others. Attached to the carbon atom at the fourth bond is a distinct atom, or group of atoms, known as the *side group* or *side chain* (see Figure 6-1).

Unique Side Groups The side groups on amino acids vary from one amino acid to the next, making proteins more complex than either carbohydrates or lipids. A polysaccharide (starch, for example) may be several thousand units long, but each unit is a glucose molecule just like all the others. A protein, on the other hand, is

◆ Reminder:
- H forms 1 bond
- O forms 2 bonds
- N forms 3 bonds
- C forms 4 bonds

proteins: compounds composed of carbon, hydrogen, oxygen, and nitrogen atoms, arranged into amino acids linked in a chain. Some amino acids also contain sulfur atoms.

amino (a-MEEN-oh) **acids:** building blocks of proteins. Each contains an amino group, an acid group, a hydrogen atom, and a distinctive side group, all attached to a central carbon atom.
- **amino** = containing nitrogen

FIGURE 6-1   Amino Acid Structure

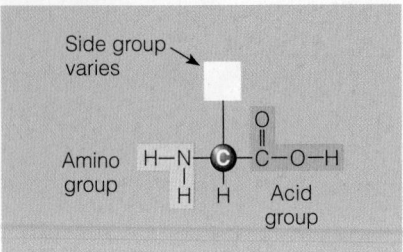

All amino acids have a carbon (known as the alpha-carbon), with an amino group (NH_2), an acid group (COOH), a hydrogen (H), and a side group attached. The side group is a unique chemical structure that differentiates one amino acid from another.

TABLE 6-1   Amino Acids

Proteins are made up of about 20 common amino acids. The first column lists the essential amino acids for human beings (those the body cannot make—that must be provided in the diet). The second column lists the nonessential amino acids. In special cases, some nonessential amino acids may become conditionally essential (see the text). In a newborn, for example, only five amino acids are truly nonessential; the other nonessential amino acids are conditionally essential until the metabolic pathways are developed enough to make those amino acids in adequate amounts.

Essential Amino Acids		Nonessential Amino Acids	
Histidine	(HISS-tuh-deen)	Alanine	(AL-ah-neen)
Isoleucine	(eye-so-LOO-seen)	Arginine	(ARJ-ih-neen)
Leucine	(LOO-seen)	Asparagine	(ah-SPAR-ah-geen)
Lysine	(LYE-seen)	Aspartic acid	(ah-SPAR-tic acid)
Methionine	(meh-THIGH-oh-neen)	Cysteine	(SIS-teh-een)
Phenylalanine	(fen-il-AL-ah-neen)	Glutamic acid	(GLU-tam-ic acid)
Threonine	(THREE-oh-neen)	Glutamine	(GLU-tah-meen)
Tryptophan	(TRIP-toe-fan,	Glycine	(GLY-seen)
	TRIP-toe-fane)	Proline	(PRO-leen)
Valine	(VAY-leen)	Serine	(SEER-een)
		Tyrosine	(TIE-roe-seen)

made up of about 20 different amino acids, each with a different side group. Table 6-1 lists the amino acids most common in proteins.*

The simplest amino acid, glycine, has a hydrogen atom as its side group. A slightly more complex amino acid, alanine, has an extra carbon with three hydrogen atoms. Other amino acids have more complex side groups (see Figure 6-2 for examples). Thus, although all amino acids share a common structure, they differ in size, shape, electrical charge, and other characteristics because of differences in these side groups.

Nonessential Amino Acids   More than half of the amino acids are *nonessential,* meaning that the body can synthesize them for itself. Proteins in foods usually deliver these amino acids, but it is not essential that they do so. The body can make all **nonessential amino acids,** given nitrogen to form the amino group and fragments from carbohydrate or fat to form the rest of the structure.

---

*Besides the 20 common amino acids, which can all be components of proteins, others do not occur in proteins, but can be found individually (for example, taurine and ornithine). Some amino acids occur in related forms (for example, proline can acquire an OH group to become hydroxyproline).

FIGURE 6-2   Examples of Amino Acids

Note that all amino acids have a common chemical structure but that each has a different side group. Appendix C presents the chemical structures of the 20 amino acids most common in proteins.

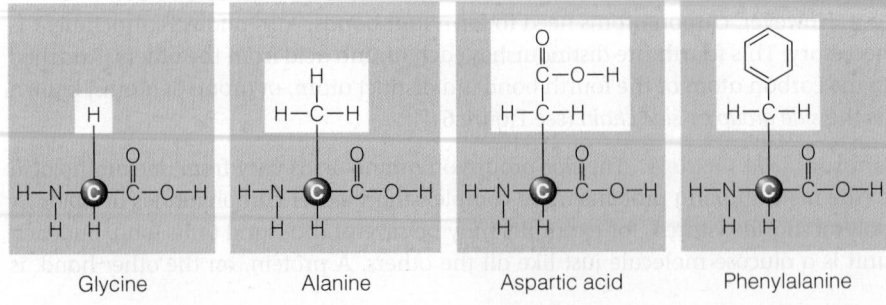

Glycine   Alanine   Aspartic acid   Phenylalanine

nonessential amino acids: amino acids that the body can synthesize (see Table 6-1).

Essential Amino Acids There are nine amino acids that the human body either cannot make at all or cannot make in sufficient quantity to meet its needs. These nine amino acids must be supplied by the diet; they are *essential.* ◆ The first column in Table 6-1 presents the **essential amino acids.**

Conditionally Essential Amino Acids Sometimes a nonessential amino acid becomes essential under special circumstances. For example, the body normally uses the essential amino acid phenylalanine to make tyrosine (a nonessential amino acid). But if the diet fails to supply enough phenylalanine, or if the body cannot make the conversion for some reason (as happens in the inherited disease phenylketonuria), then tyrosine becomes a **conditionally essential amino acid.**

◆ Some researchers refer to essential amino acids as **indispensable** and to nonessential amino acids as **dispensable.**

Proteins

Cells link amino acids end-to-end in a variety of sequences to form thousands of different proteins. A **peptide bond** unites each amino acid to the next.

Amino Acid Chains Condensation reactions connect amino acids, just as they combine monosaccharides to form disaccharides and fatty acids with glycerol to form triglycerides. Two amino acids bonded together form a **dipeptide** (see Figure 6-3). By another such reaction, a third amino acid can be added to the chain to form a **tripeptide.** As additional amino acids join the chain, a **polypeptide** is formed. Most proteins are a few dozen to several hundred amino acids long. Figure 6-4 (p. 184) provides an example—insulin.

Amino Acid Sequences If a person could walk along a carbohydrate molecule like starch, the first stepping stone would be a glucose. The next stepping stone would also be a glucose, and it would be followed by a glucose, and yet another glucose. But if a person were to walk along a polypeptide chain, each stepping stone would be one of 20 different amino acids. The first stepping stone might be the amino acid methionine. The second might be an alanine. The third might be a glycine, and the fourth a tryptophan, and so on. Walking along another polypeptide path, a person might step on a phenylalanine, then a valine, and a glutamine. In other words, amino acid sequences within proteins vary.

The amino acids can act somewhat like the letters in an alphabet. If you had only the letter G, all you could write would be a string of Gs: G–G–G–G–G–G–G. But with 20 different letters available, you can create poems, songs, and novels. Similarly, the 20 amino acids can be linked together in a variety of sequences—even more than are possible for letters in a word or words in a sentence. Thus the variety of possible sequences for polypeptide chains is tremendous.

essential amino acids: amino acids that the body cannot synthesize in amounts sufficient to meet physiological needs (see Table 6-1 on p. 182).

conditionally essential amino acid: an amino acid that is normally nonessential, but must be supplied by the diet in special circumstances when the need for it exceeds the body's ability to produce it.

peptide bond: a bond that connects the acid end of one amino acid with the amino end of another, forming a link in a protein chain.

dipeptide (dye-PEP-tide): two amino acids bonded together.
- **di** = two
- **peptide** = amino acid

tripeptide: three amino acids bonded together.
- **tri** = three

polypeptide: many (ten or more) amino acids bonded together.
- **poly** = many

FIGURE 6-3 Condensation of Two Amino Acids to Form a Dipeptide

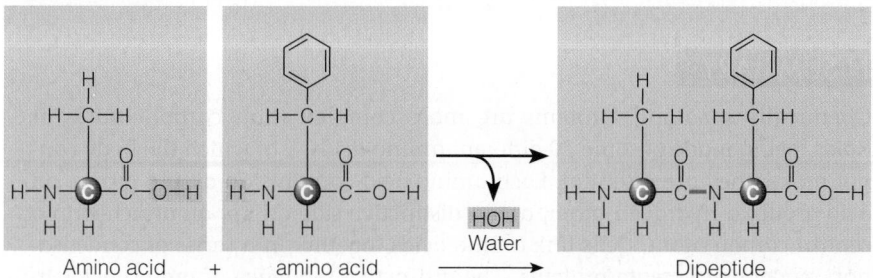

An OH group from the acid end of one amino acid and an H atom from the amino group of another join to form a molecule of water.

A peptide bond (highlighted in red) forms between the two amino acids, creating a dipeptide.

FIGURE 6-4 Amino Acid Sequence of Human Insulin

Human insulin is a relatively small protein that consists of 51 amino acids in two short polypeptide chains. (For amino acid abbreviations, see Appendix C.) Two bridges link the two chains. A third bridge spans a section within the short chain. Known as *disulfide bridges,* these links always involve the amino acid cysteine (Cys), whose side group contains sulfur (S). Cysteines connect to each other when bonds form between these side groups.

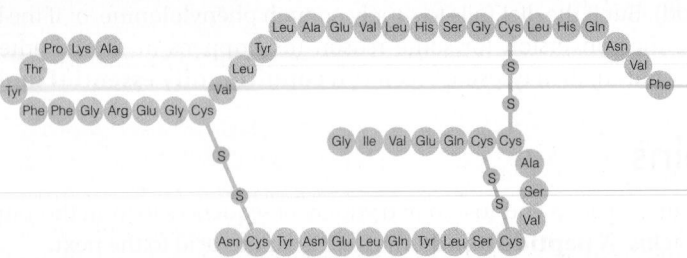

FIGURE 6-5 The Structure of Hemoglobin

Four highly folded polypeptide chains form the globular hemoglobin protein.

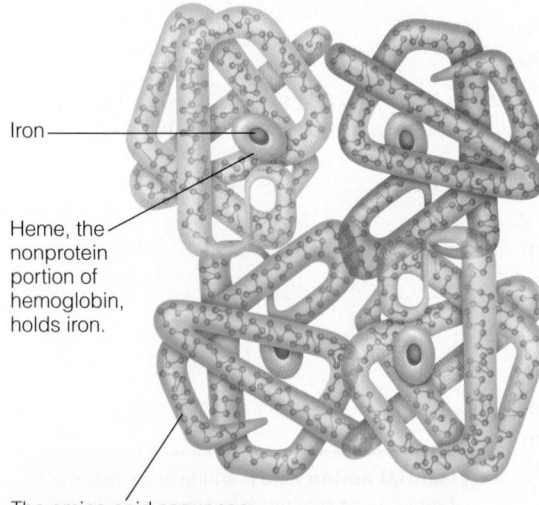

Iron

Heme, the nonprotein portion of hemoglobin, holds iron.

The amino acid sequence determines the shape of the polypeptide chain.

Protein Shapes Polypeptide chains twist into a variety of complex, tangled shapes, depending on their amino acid sequences. The unique side group of each amino acid gives it characteristics that attract it to, or repel it from, the surrounding fluids and other amino acids. Some amino acid side groups carry electrical charges that are attracted to water molecules; they are *hydrophilic*. Other side groups are neutral and are repelled by water; they are *hydrophobic*. As amino acids are strung together to make a polypeptide, the chain folds so that its charged hydrophilic side groups are on the outer surface near water; the neutral hydrophobic groups tuck themselves inside, away from water. The intricate, coiled shape the polypeptide finally assumes gives it maximum stability.

Protein Functions The extraordinary and unique shapes of proteins enable them to perform their various tasks in the body. Some form hollow balls that can carry and store materials within them, and some, such as those of tendons, are more than ten times as long as they are wide, forming strong, rod-like structures. Some polypeptides are functioning proteins just as they are; others need to associate with other polypeptides to form larger working complexes. Some proteins require minerals to activate them. One molecule of **hemoglobin**—the large, globular protein molecule that, by the billions, packs the red blood cells and carries oxygen—is made of four associated polypeptide chains, each holding the mineral iron (see Figure 6-5).

Protein Denaturation When proteins are subjected to heat, acid, or other conditions that disturb their stability, they undergo **denaturation**—that is, they uncoil and lose their shapes and, consequently, also lose their ability to function. Past a certain point, denaturation is irreversible. Familiar examples

hemoglobin (HE-moh-GLO-bin): the globular protein of the red blood cells that carries oxygen from the lungs to the cells throughout the body.

• **hemo** = blood

• **globin** = globular protein

denaturation (dee-NAY-chur-AY-shun): the change in a protein's shape and consequent loss of its function brought about by heat, agitation, acid, base, alcohol, heavy metals, or other agents.

IN SUMMARY

Chemically speaking, proteins are more complex than carbohydrates or lipids, being made of some 20 different amino acids, 9 of which the body cannot make; they are essential. Each amino acid contains an amino group, an acid group, a hydrogen atom, and a distinctive side group, all attached to a central carbon atom. Cells link amino acids together in a series of condensation reactions to create proteins. The distinctive sequence of amino acids in each protein determines its unique shape and function.

of denaturation include the hardening of an egg when it is cooked, the curdling of milk when acid is added, and the stiffening of egg whites when they are whipped.

Digestion and Absorption of Protein

Proteins in foods do not become body proteins directly. Instead, they supply the amino acids from which the body makes its own proteins. When a person eats foods containing protein, enzymes break the long polypeptide strands into shorter strands, the short strands into tripeptides and dipeptides, and, finally, the tripeptides and dipeptides into amino acids.

Protein Digestion

Figure 6-6 (p. 186) illustrates the digestion of protein through the GI tract. Proteins are crushed and moistened in the mouth, but the real action begins in the stomach.

In the Stomach The major event in the stomach is the partial breakdown (hydrolysis) of proteins. Hydrochloric acid uncoils (denatures) each protein's tangled strands so that digestive enzymes can attack the peptide bonds. The hydrochloric acid also converts the inactive form ◆ of the enzyme pepsinogen to its active form, **pepsin.** Pepsin cleaves proteins—large polypeptides—into smaller polypeptides and some amino acids.

In the Small Intestine When polypeptides enter the small intestine, several pancreatic and intestinal **proteases** hydrolyze them further into short peptide chains, ◆ tripeptides, dipeptides, and amino acids. Then **peptidase** enzymes on the membrane surfaces of the intestinal cells split most of the dipeptides and tripeptides into single amino acids. Only a few peptides escape digestion and enter the blood intact. Figure 6-6 includes names of the digestive enzymes for protein and describes their actions.

Protein Absorption

A number of specific carriers transport amino acids (and some dipeptides and tripeptides) into the intestinal cells. Once inside the intestinal cells, amino acids may be used for energy or to synthesize needed compounds. Amino acids that are not used by the intestinal cells are transported across the cell membrane into the surrounding fluid where they enter the capillaries on their way to the liver.

Consumers lacking nutrition knowledge may fail to realize that most proteins are broken down to amino acids before absorption. They may be mislead by advertisements urging them to "Eat enzyme A. It will help you digest your food." Or "Don't eat food B. It contains enzyme C, which will digest cells in your body." In reality, though, enzymes in foods are digested, just as all proteins are. Even the digestive enzymes—which function optimally at their specific pH—are denatured and digested when the pH of their environment changes. (For example, the enzyme pepsin, which works best in the low pH of the stomach becomes inactive and digested when it enters the higher pH of the small intestine.)

Another misconception is that eating predigested proteins (amino acid supplements) saves the body from having to digest proteins and keeps the digestive system from "overworking." Such a belief grossly underestimates the body's abilities. As a matter of fact, the digestive system handles whole proteins *better* than predigested ones because it dismantles and absorbs the amino acids at rates that are optimal for the body's use. (The last section of this chapter discusses amino acid supplements further.)

◆ The inactive form of an enzyme is called a **proenzyme** or a **zymogen** (ZYE-moh-jen).

◆ A string of four to nine amino acids is an **oligopeptide** (OL-ee-go-PEP-tide).
• **oligo** = few

pepsin: a gastric enzyme that hydrolyzes protein. Pepsin is secreted in an inactive form, **pepsinogen,** which is activated by hydrochloric acid in the stomach.

proteases (PRO-tee-aces): enzymes that hydrolyze protein.

peptidase: a digestive enzyme that hydrolyzes peptide bonds. *Tripeptidases* cleave tripeptides; *dipeptidases* cleave dipeptides. *Endopeptidases* cleave peptide bonds within the chain to create smaller fragments, whereas *exopeptidases* cleave bonds at the ends to release free amino acids.
• **tri** = three
• **di** = two
• **endo** = within
• **exo** = outside

FIGURE 6-6 *Animated!* Protein Digestion in the GI Tract

ThomsonNOW™
To test your understanding of these concepts, log on to www.thomsonedu.com/thomsonnow

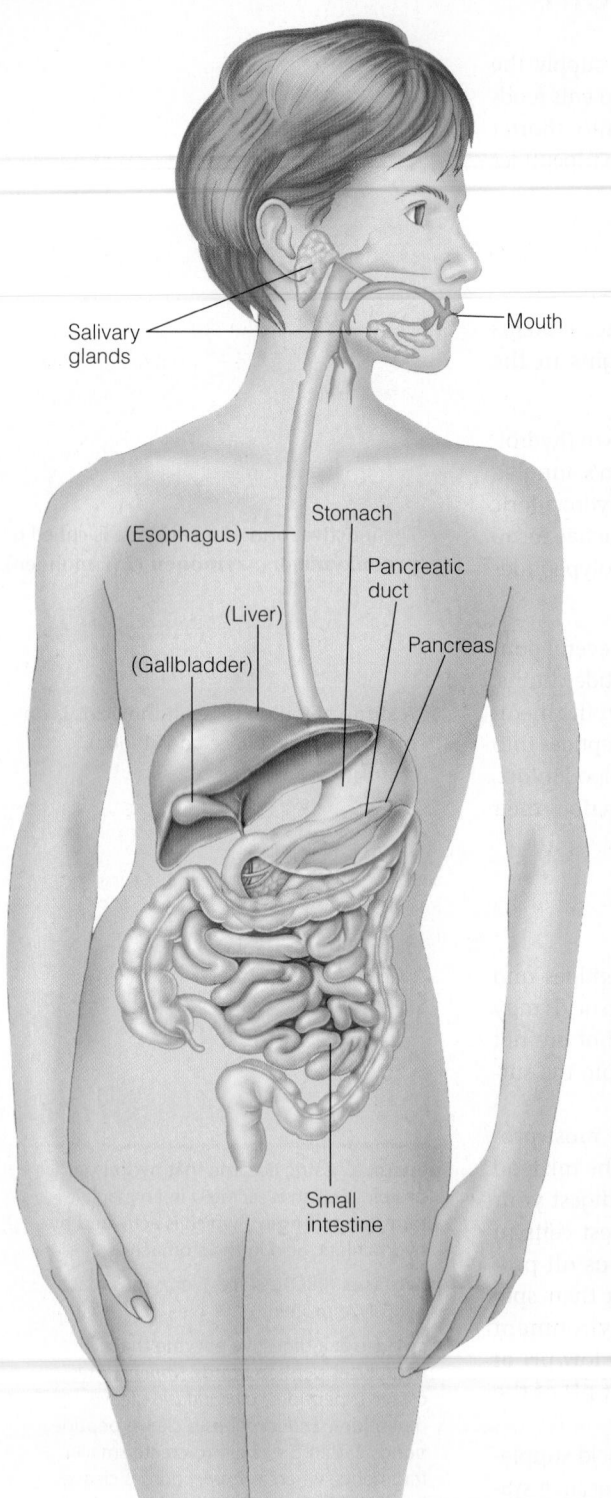

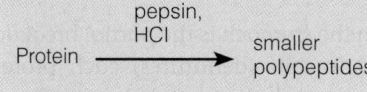

PROTEIN

Mouth and salivary glands

Chewing and crushing moisten protein-rich foods and mix them with saliva to be swallowed

Stomach

Hydrochloric acid (HCl) uncoils protein strands and activates stomach enzymes:

Protein $\xrightarrow{\text{pepsin, HCl}}$ smaller polypeptides

Small intestine and pancreas

Pancreatic and small intestinal enzymes split polypeptides further:

Poly-peptides $\xrightarrow{\text{pancreatic and intestinal proteases}}$ tripeptides, dipeptides, amino acids

Then enzymes on the surface of the small intestinal cells hydrolyze these peptides and the cells absorb them:

Peptides $\xrightarrow{\text{intestinal tripeptidases and dipeptidases}}$ amino acids (absorbed)

HYDROCHLORIC ACID AND THE DIGESTIVE ENZYMES

In the stomach:

Hydrochloric acid (HCl)
• Denatures protein structure
• Activates pepsinogen to pepsin

Pepsin
• Cleaves proteins to smaller polypeptides and some free amino acids
• Inhibits pepsinogen synthesis

In the small intestine:

Enteropeptidase[a]
• Converts pancreatic trypsinogen to trypsin

Trypsin
• Inhibits trypsinogen synthesis
• Cleaves peptide bonds next to the amino acids lysine and arginine
• Converts pancreatic procarboxypeptidases to carboxypeptidases
• Converts pancreatic chymotrypsinogen to chymotrypsin

Chymotrypsin
• Cleaves peptide bonds next to the amino acids phenylalanine, tyrosine, tryptophan, methionine, asparagine, and histidine

Carboxypeptidases
• Cleave amino acids from the acid (carboxyl) ends of polypeptides

Elastase and collagenase
• Cleave polypeptides into smaller polypeptides and tripeptides

Intestinal tripeptidases
• Cleave tripeptides to dipeptides and amino acids

Intestinal dipeptidases
• Cleave dipeptides to amino acids

Intestinal aminopeptidases
• Cleave amino acids from the amino ends of small polypeptides (oligopeptides)

[a]Enteropeptidase was formerly known as *enterokinase*.

IN SUMMARY

Digestion is facilitated mostly by the stomach's acid and enzymes, which first denature dietary proteins, then cleave them into smaller polypeptides and some amino acids. Pancreatic and intestinal enzymes split these polypeptides further, to oligo-, tri-, and dipeptides, and then split most of these to single amino acids. Then carriers in the membranes of intestinal cells transport the amino acids into the cells, where they are released into the bloodstream.

Proteins in the Body

The human body contains an estimated 30,000 different kinds of proteins. Of these, about 3000 have been studied, ◆ although with the recent surge in knowledge gained from sequencing the human genome, ◆ this number is growing rapidly. Only about 10 are described in this chapter—but these should be enough to illustrate the versatility, uniqueness, and importance of proteins. As you will see, each protein has a specific function, and that function is determined during protein synthesis.

◆ The study of the body's proteins is called **proteomics.**

◆ Reminder: The *human genome* is the full set of chromosomes, including all of the genes and associated DNA.

Protein Synthesis

Each human being is unique because of small differences in the body's proteins. These differences are determined by the amino acid sequences of proteins, which, in turn, are determined by genes. The following paragraphs describe in words the ways cells synthesize proteins; Figure 6-7 (p. 188) provides a pictorial description.

The instructions for making every protein in a person's body are transmitted by way of the genetic information received at conception. This body of knowledge, which is filed in the DNA (deoxyribonucleic acid) within the nucleus of every cell, never leaves the nucleus.

Delivering the Instructions Transforming the information in DNA into the appropriate sequence of amino acids needed to make a specific protein requires two major steps. In the first step, ◆ a stretch of DNA is used as a template to make a strand of RNA (ribonucleic acid) known as messenger RNA. Messenger RNA then carries the code across the nuclear membrane into the body of the cell. There it seeks out and attaches itself to one of the ribosomes (a protein-making machine, which is itself composed of RNA and protein), where the second step ◆ takes place. Situated on a ribosome, messenger RNA specifies the sequence in which the amino acids line up for the synthesis of a protein.

◆ This process of messenger RNA being made from a template of DNA is known as **transcription.**

◆ This process of messenger RNA directing the sequence of amino acids and synthesis of proteins is known as **translation.**

Lining Up the Amino Acids Other forms of RNA, called transfer RNA, collect amino acids from the cell fluid and bring them to the messenger. Each of the 20 amino acids has a specific transfer RNA. Thousands of transfer RNAs, each carrying its amino acid, cluster around the ribosomes, awaiting their turn to unload. When the messenger's list calls for a specific amino acid, the transfer RNA carrying that amino acid moves into position. Then the next loaded transfer RNA moves into place and then the next and the next. In this way, the amino acids line up in the sequence that is called for, and enzymes bind them together. Finally, the completed protein strand is released, and the transfer RNAs are freed to return for other loads of amino acids.

Sequencing Errors The sequence of amino acids in each protein determines its shape, which supports a specific function. If a genetic error alters the amino acid sequence of a protein, or if a mistake is made in copying the sequence, an altered protein will result, sometimes with dramatic consequences. The protein hemoglobin

FIGURE 6-7 *Animated!* Protein Synthesis

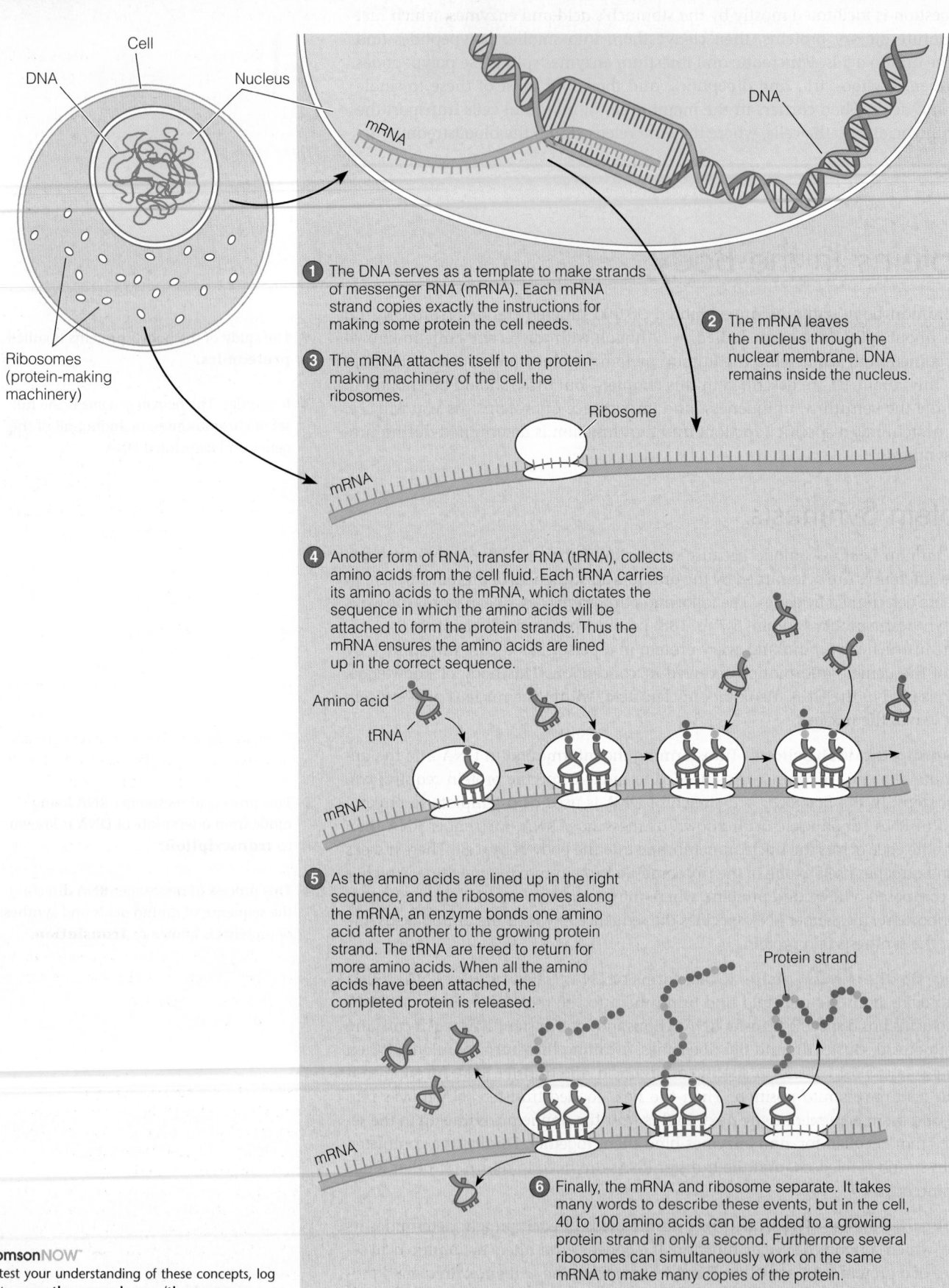

Cell

DNA

Nucleus

DNA

mRNA

Ribosomes (protein-making machinery)

1 The DNA serves as a template to make strands of messenger RNA (mRNA). Each mRNA strand copies exactly the instructions for making some protein the cell needs.

2 The mRNA leaves the nucleus through the nuclear membrane. DNA remains inside the nucleus.

3 The mRNA attaches itself to the protein-making machinery of the cell, the ribosomes.

Ribosome

mRNA

4 Another form of RNA, transfer RNA (tRNA), collects amino acids from the cell fluid. Each tRNA carries its amino acids to the mRNA, which dictates the sequence in which the amino acids will be attached to form the protein strands. Thus the mRNA ensures the amino acids are lined up in the correct sequence.

Amino acid

tRNA

mRNA

5 As the amino acids are lined up in the right sequence, and the ribosome moves along the mRNA, an enzyme bonds one amino acid after another to the growing protein strand. The tRNA are freed to return for more amino acids. When all the amino acids have been attached, the completed protein is released.

Protein strand

mRNA

6 Finally, the mRNA and ribosome separate. It takes many words to describe these events, but in the cell, 40 to 100 amino acids can be added to a growing protein strand in only a second. Furthermore several ribosomes can simultaneously work on the same mRNA to make many copies of the protein.

offers one example of such a genetic variation. In a person with **sickle-cell anemia,** ◆ two of hemoglobin's four polypeptide chains (described earlier on p. 184) have the normal sequence of amino acids, but the other two chains do not—they have the amino acid valine in a position that is normally occupied by glutamic acid (see Figure 6-8). This single alteration in the amino acid sequence changes the characteristics and shape of hemoglobin so much that it loses its ability to carry oxygen effectively. The red blood cells filled with this abnormal hemoglobin stiffen into elongated sickle, or crescent, shapes instead of maintaining their normal pliable disc shape—hence the name, sickle-cell anemia. Sickle-cell anemia raises energy needs, causes many medical problems, and can be fatal.[1] Caring for children with sickle-cell anemia includes diligent attention to their water needs; dehydration can trigger a crisis.

Nutrients and Gene Expression When a cell makes a protein as described earlier, scientists say that the gene for that protein has been "expressed." Cells can regulate **gene expression** to make the type of protein, in the amounts and at the rate, they need. Nearly all of the body's cells possess the genes for making all human proteins, but each type of cell makes only the proteins it needs. For example, cells of the pancreas express the gene for insulin; in other cells, that gene is idle. Similarly, the cells of the pancreas do not make the protein hemoglobin, which is needed only by the red blood cells.

Recent research has unveiled some of the fascinating ways nutrients regulate gene expression and protein synthesis (see Highlight 6). ◆ Because diet plays an ongoing role in our lives from conception to death, it has a major influence on gene expression and disease development.[2] The benefits of polyunsaturated fatty acids in defending against heart disease, for example, are partially explained by their role in influencing gene expression for lipid enzymes. Later chapters provide additional examples of relationships among nutrients, genes, and disease development.

FIGURE 6-8 Sickle Cell Compared with Normal Red Blood Cell

Normally, red blood cells are disc-shaped, but in the inherited disorder sickle-cell anemia, red blood cells are sickle- or crescent-shaped. This alteration in shape occurs because valine replaces glutamic acid in the amino acid sequence of two of hemoglobin's polypeptide chains. As a result of this one alteration, the hemoglobin has a diminished capacity to carry oxygen.

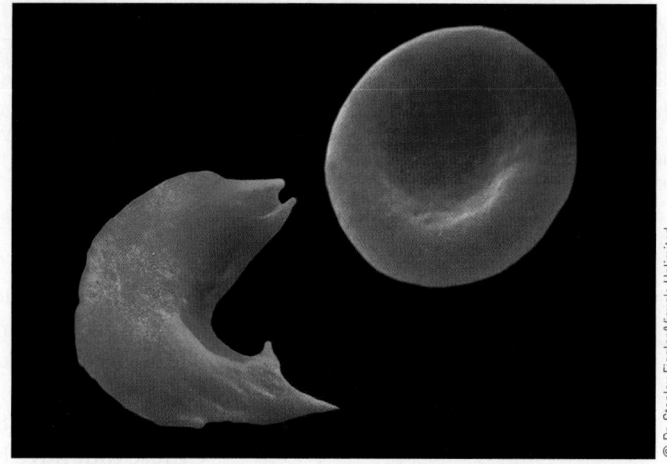

© Dr. Stanley Flegler/Visuals Unlimited

Sickle-shaped blood cell   Normal red blood cell

Amino acid sequence of normal hemoglobin:
Val —His —Leu — Thr — Pro — Glu —Glu

Amino acid sequence of sickle-cell hemoglobin:
Val —His —Leu — Thr — Pro — Val —Glu

◆ Anemia is not a disease, but a symptom of various diseases. In the case of sickle-cell anemia, a defect in the hemoglobin molecule changes the shape of the red blood cells. Later chapters describe the anemias of vitamin and mineral deficiencies. In all cases, the abnormal blood cells are unable to meet the body's oxygen demands.

◆ Nutrients can play key roles in activating or silencing genes. Switching genes on and off, without changing the genetic sequence itself, is known as **epigenetics**.
  • **epi** = among

sickle-cell anemia: a hereditary form of anemia characterized by abnormal sickle- or crescent-shaped red blood cells. Sickled cells interfere with oxygen transport and blood flow. Symptoms are precipitated by dehydration and insufficient oxygen (as may occur at high altitudes) and include hemolytic anemia (red blood cells burst), fever, and severe pain in the joints and abdomen.

gene expression: the process by which a cell converts the genetic code into RNA and protein.

IN SUMMARY

Cells synthesize proteins according to the genetic information provided by the DNA in the nucleus of each cell. This information dictates the order in which amino acids must be linked together to form a given protein. Sequencing errors occasionally occur, sometimes with significant consequences.

Roles of Proteins

Whenever the body is growing, repairing, or replacing tissue, proteins are involved. Sometimes their role is to facilitate or to regulate; other times it is to become part of a structure. Versatility is a key feature of proteins.

FIGURE 6-9 Enzyme Action

Each enzyme facilitates a specific chemical reaction. In this diagram, an enzyme enables two compounds to make a more complex structure, but the enzyme itself remains unchanged.

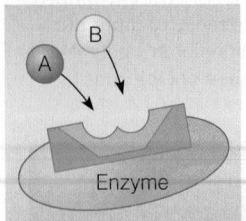
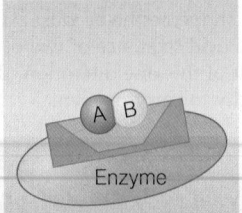
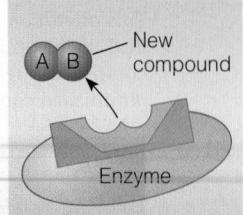

The separate compounds, A and B, are attracted to the enzyme's active site, making a reaction likely.

The enzyme forms a complex with A and B.

The enzyme is unchanged, but A and B have formed a new compound, AB.

As Building Materials for Growth and Maintenance From the moment of conception, proteins form the building blocks of muscles, blood, and skin—in fact, of most body structures. For example, to build a bone or a tooth, cells first lay down a **matrix** of the protein **collagen** and then fill it with crystals of calcium, phosphorus, magnesium, fluoride, and other minerals.

Collagen also provides the material of ligaments and tendons and the strengthening glue between the cells of the artery walls that enables the arteries to withstand the pressure of the blood surging through them with each heartbeat. Also made of collagen are scars that knit the separated parts of torn tissues together.

Proteins are also needed for replacing dead or damaged cells. The life span of a skin cell is only about 30 days. As old skin cells are shed, new cells made largely of protein grow from underneath to replace them. Cells in the deeper skin layers synthesize new proteins to go into hair and fingernails. Muscle cells make new proteins to grow larger and stronger in response to exercise. Cells of the GI tract are replaced every few days. Both inside and outside, then, the body continuously deposits protein into the new cells that replace those that have been lost.

As Enzymes Some proteins act as **enzymes.** Digestive enzymes have appeared in every chapter since Chapter 3, but digestion is only one of the many processes facilitated by enzymes. Enzymes not only break down substances, but they also build substances (such as bone) ◆ and transform one substance into another (amino acids into glucose, for example). Figure 6-9 diagrams a synthesis reaction.

◆ Breaking down reactions are **catabolic,** whereas building up reactions are **anabolic.** (Chapter 7 provides more details.)

An analogy may help to clarify the role of enzymes. Enzymes are comparable to the clergy and judges who make and dissolve marriages. When a minister marries two people, they become a couple, with a new bond between them. They are joined together—but the minister remains unchanged. The minister represents enzymes that synthesize large compounds from smaller ones. One minister can perform thousands of marriage ceremonies, just as one enzyme can perform billions of synthetic reactions.

Similarly, a judge who lets married couples separate may decree many divorces before retiring. The judge represents enzymes that hydrolyze larger compounds to smaller ones; for example, the digestive enzymes. The point is that, like the minister and the judge, enzymes themselves are not altered by the reactions they facilitate. They are catalysts, permitting reactions to occur more quickly and efficiently than if substances depended on chance encounters alone.

As Hormones The body's many hormones are messenger molecules, and *some* hormones are proteins. ◆ Various endocrine glands in the body release hormones in response to changes that challenge the body. The blood carries the hormones from these glands to their target tissues, where they elicit the appropriate responses to restore and maintain normal conditions.

◆ Recall from Chapter 5 that some hormones, such as estrogen and testosterone, derive from cholesterol.

The hormone insulin provides a familiar example. When blood glucose rises, the pancreas releases its insulin. Insulin stimulates the transport proteins of the muscles and adipose tissue to pump glucose into the cells faster than it can leak out. (After acting on the message, the cells destroy the insulin.) Then, as blood glucose falls, the pancreas slows its release of insulin. Many other proteins act as hormones, regulating a variety of actions in the body (see Table 6-2 for examples).

matrix (MAY-tricks): the basic substance that gives form to a developing structure; in the body, the formative cells from which teeth and bones grow.

collagen (KOL-ah-jen): the protein from which connective tissues such as scars, tendons, ligaments, and the foundations of bones and teeth are made.

enzymes: proteins that facilitate chemical reactions without being changed in the process; protein catalysts.

fluid balance: maintenance of the proper types and amounts of fluid in each compartment of the body fluids (see also Chapter 12).

As Regulators of Fluid Balance Proteins help to maintain the body's **fluid balance.** Figure 12-1 in Chapter 12 illustrates a cell and its associated fluids. As the figure explains, the body's fluids are contained inside the cells (intracellular) or outside the cells (extracellular). Extracellular fluids, in turn, can be found either in the spaces between the cells (interstitial) or within the blood vessels (intravascular). The fluid within the intravascular spaces is called plasma (essentially blood without its red blood cells). Fluids can flow freely between these compartments, but being large, proteins cannot. Proteins are trapped primarily within the cells and to a lesser extent in the plasma.

The exchange of materials between the blood and the cells takes place across the capillary walls, which allow the passage of fluids and a variety of materials—but usually not plasma proteins. Still some plasma proteins leak out of the capillaries into the interstitial fluid between the cells. These proteins cannot be reabsorbed back into the plasma; they normally reenter circulation via the lymph system. If plasma proteins enter the interstitial spaces faster than they can be cleared, fluid accumulates (because plasma proteins attract water) and causes swelling. Swelling due to an excess of interstitial fluid is known as **edema.** The protein-related causes of edema include:

- Excessive protein losses caused by kidney disease or large wounds (such as extensive burns)

- Inadequate protein synthesis caused by liver disease

- Inadequate dietary intake of protein

Whatever the cause of edema, the result is the same: a diminished capacity to deliver nutrients and oxygen to the cells and to remove wastes from them. As a consequence, cells fail to function adequately.

As Acid-Base Regulators Proteins also help to maintain the balance between **acids** and **bases** within the body fluids. Normal body processes continually produce acids and bases, which the blood carries to the kidneys and lungs for excretion. The challenge is to do this without upsetting the blood's acid-base balance.

In an acid solution, hydrogen ions (H^+) abound; the more hydrogen ions, the more concentrated the acid. Proteins, which have negative charges on their surfaces, attract hydrogen ions, which have positive charges. By accepting and releasing hydrogen ions, ◆ proteins maintain the acid-base balance of the blood and body fluids.

The blood's acid-base balance is tightly controlled. The extremes of **acidosis** and **alkalosis** lead to coma and death, largely because they denature working proteins. Disturbing a protein's shape renders it useless. To give just one example, denatured hemoglobin loses its capacity to carry oxygen.

As Transporters Some proteins move about in the body fluids, carrying nutrients and other molecules. The protein hemoglobin carries oxygen from the lungs to the cells. The lipoproteins transport lipids around the body. Special transport proteins carry vitamins and minerals.

The transport of the mineral iron provides an especially good illustration of these proteins' specificity and precision. When iron enters an intestinal cell after a meal has been digested and absorbed, it is captured by a protein. Before leaving the intestinal cell, iron is attached to another protein that carries it though the bloodstream to the cells. Once iron enters a cell, it is attached to a storage protein that will hold the iron until it is needed. When it is needed, iron is incorporated into proteins in the red blood cells and muscles that assist in oxygen transport and use. (Chapter 13 provides more details on how these protein carriers transport and store iron.)

Some transport proteins reside in cell membranes and act as "pumps," picking up compounds on one side of the membrane and releasing them on the other as needed. Each transport protein is specific for a certain compound or group of related compounds. Figure 6-10 (p. 192) illustrates how a membrane-bound transport protein helps to maintain the sodium and potassium concentrations in the fluids inside and outside cells. The balance of these two minerals is critical to nerve transmissions and muscle contractions; imbalances can cause irregular heartbeats, muscular weakness, kidney failure, and even death.

TABLE 6-2	Examples of Hormones and Their Actions
Hormones	**Actions**
Growth hormone	Promotes growth
Insulin and glucagon	Regulate blood glucose (see Chapter 4)
Thyroxin	Regulates the body's metabolic rate (see Chapter 8)
Calcitonin and parathyroid hormone	Regulate blood calcium (see Chapter 12)
Antidiuretic hormone	Regulates fluid and electrolyte balance (see Chapter 12)

NOTE: *Hormones* are chemical messengers that are secreted by endocrine glands in response to altered conditions in the body. Each travels to one or more specific target tissues or organs, where it elicits a specific response. For descriptions of many hormones important in nutrition, see Appendix A.

◆ Compounds that help keep a solution's acidity or alkalinity constant are called **buffers.**

edema (eh-DEEM-uh): the swelling of body tissue caused by excessive amounts of fluid in the interstitial spaces; seen in protein deficiency (among other conditions).

acids: compounds that release hydrogen ions in a solution.

bases: compounds that accept hydrogen ions in a solution.

acidosis (assi-DOE-sis): above-normal acidity in the blood and body fluids.

alkalosis (alka-LOE-sis): above-normal alkalinity (base) in the blood and body fluids.

FIGURE 6-10 *Animated!* An Example of Protein Transport

This transport protein resides within a cell membrane and acts as a two-door passageway. Molecules enter on one side of the membrane and exit on the other, but the protein doesn't leave the membrane. This example shows how the transport protein moves sodium and potassium in opposite directions across the membrane to maintain a high concentration of potassium and a low concentration of sodium within the cell. This active transport system requires energy.

ThomsonNOW™
To test your understanding of these concepts, log on to
www.thomsonedu.com/thomsonnow

Key:
- Sodium
- Potassium

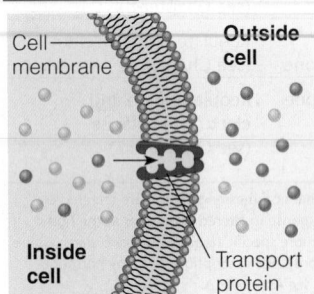
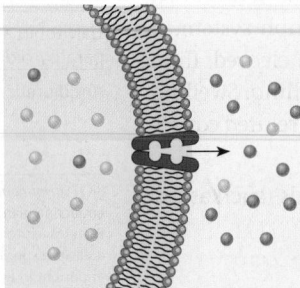
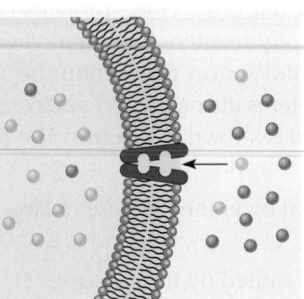
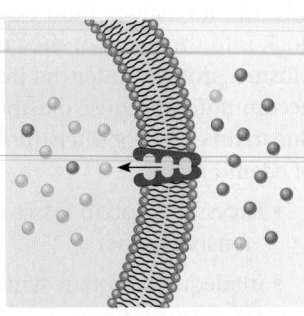

The transport protein picks up sodium from inside the cell.

The protein changes shape and releases sodium outside the cell.

The transport protein picks up potassium from outside the cell.

The protein changes shape and releases potassium inside the cell.

◆ Reminder: Protein provides 4 kcal/g. Return to p. 9 for a refresher on how to calculate the protein kcalories from foods.

◆ Reminder: The making of glucose from non-carbohydrate sources such as amino acids is *gluconeogenesis.*

antigens: substances that elicit the formation of antibodies or an inflammation reaction from the immune system. A bacterium, a virus, a toxin, and a protein in food that causes allergy are all examples of antigens.

antibodies: large proteins of the blood and body fluids, produced by the immune system in response to the invasion of the body by foreign molecules (usually proteins called *antigens*). Antibodies combine with and inactivate the foreign invaders, thus protecting the body.

immunity: the body's ability to defend itself against diseases (see also Chapter 18).

As Antibodies Proteins also defend the body against disease. A virus—whether it is one that causes flu, smallpox, measles, or the common cold—enters the cells and multiplies there. One virus may produce 100 replicas of itself within an hour or so. Each replica can then burst out and invade 100 different cells, soon yielding 10,000 virus particles, which invade 10,000 cells. Left free to do their worst, they will soon overwhelm the body with disease.

Fortunately, when the body detects these invading **antigens,** it manufactures **antibodies,** giant protein molecules designed specifically to combat them. The antibodies work so swiftly and efficiently that in a normal, healthy individual, most diseases never have a chance to get started. Without sufficient protein, though, the body cannot maintain its army of antibodies to resist infectious diseases.

Each antibody is designed to destroy a specific antigen. Once the body has manufactured antibodies against a particular antigen (such as the measles virus), it "remembers" how to make them. Consequently, the next time the body encounters that same antigen, it produces antibodies even more quickly. In other words, the body develops a molecular memory, known as **immunity.** (Chapter 16 describes food allergies—the immune system's response to food antigens.)

As a Source of Energy and Glucose Without energy, cells die; without glucose, the brain and nervous system falter. Even though proteins are needed to do the work that only they can perform, they will be sacrificed to provide energy ◆ and glucose ◆ during times of starvation or insufficient carbohydrate intake. The body will break down its tissue proteins to make amino acids available for energy or glucose production. In this way, protein can maintain blood glucose levels, but at the expense of losing lean body tissue. Chapter 7 provides many more details on energy metabolism.

Other Roles As mentioned earlier, proteins form integral parts of most body structures such as skin, muscles, and bones. They also participate in some of the body's most amazing activities such as blood clotting and vision. When a tissue is injured, a rapid chain of events leads to the production of fibrin, a stringy, insoluble mass of protein fibers that forms a solid clot from liquid blood. Later, more slowly, the protein collagen forms a scar to replace the clot and permanently heal the wound. The light-sensitive pigments in the cells of the eye's retina are molecules of the protein opsin. Opsin responds to light by changing its shape, thus initiating the nerve impulses that convey the sense of sight to the brain.

The protein functions discussed here are summarized in the accompanying table. They are only a few of the many roles proteins play, but they convey some sense of the immense variety of proteins and their importance in the body.

Growth and maintenance	Proteins form integral parts of most body structures such as skin, tendons, membranes, muscles, organs, and bones. As such, they support the growth and repair of body tissues.
Enzymes	Proteins facilitate chemical reactions.
Hormones	Proteins regulate body processes. (Some, but not all, hormones are proteins.)
Fluid balance	Proteins help to maintain the volume and composition of body fluids.
Acid-base balance	Proteins help maintain the acid-base balance of body fluids by acting as buffers.
Transportation	Proteins transport substances, such as lipids, vitamins, minerals, and oxygen, around the body.
Antibodies	Proteins inactivate foreign invaders, thus protecting the body against diseases.
Energy and glucose	Proteins provide some fuel, and glucose if needed, for the body's energy needs.

Growing children end each day with more bone, blood, muscle, and skin cells than they had at the beginning of the day.

A Preview of Protein Metabolism

This section previews protein metabolism; Chapter 7 provides a full description. Cells have several metabolic options, depending on their protein and energy needs.

Protein Turnover and the Amino Acid Pool Within each cell, proteins are continually being made and broken down, a process known as **protein turnover.** When proteins break down, they free amino acids. ◆ These amino acids mix with amino acids from dietary protein to form an **"amino acid pool"** within the cells and circulating blood. The rate of protein degradation and the amount of protein intake may vary, but the pattern of amino acids within the pool remains fairly constant. Regardless of their source, any of these amino acids can be used to make body proteins or other nitrogen-containing compounds, or they can be stripped of their nitrogen and used for energy (either immediately or stored as fat for later use).

Nitrogen Balance Protein turnover and **nitrogen balance** go hand in hand. In healthy adults, protein synthesis balances with degradation, and protein intake from food balances with nitrogen excretion in the urine, feces, and sweat. When nitrogen intake equals nitrogen output, the person is in nitrogen equilibrium, ◆ or zero nitrogen balance. Researchers use nitrogen balance studies to estimate protein requirements.[3]

If the body synthesizes more than it degrades and adds protein, nitrogen status becomes positive. ◆ Nitrogen status is positive in growing infants, children, adolescents, pregnant women, and people recovering from protein deficiency or illness; their nitrogen intake exceeds their nitrogen output. They are retaining protein in new tissues as they add blood, bone, skin, and muscle cells to their bodies.

If the body degrades more than it synthesizes and loses protein, nitrogen status becomes negative. ◆ Nitrogen status is negative in people who are starving or suffering other severe stresses such as burns, injuries, infections, and fever; their nitrogen

◆ Amino acids (or proteins) that derive from within the body are **endogenous** (en-DODGE-eh-nus). In contrast, those that derive from foods are **exogenous** (eks-ODGE-eh-nus).
- **endo** = within
- **gen** = arising
- **exo** = outside (the body)

◆ Nitrogen balance:
- Nitrogen equilibrium (zero nitrogen balance): N in = N out.
- Positive nitrogen: N in > N out.
- Negative nitrogen: N in < N out.

protein turnover: the degradation and synthesis of protein.

amino acid pool: the supply of amino acids derived from either food proteins or body proteins that collect in the cells and circulating blood and stand ready to be incorporated in proteins and other compounds or used for energy.

nitrogen balance: the amount of nitrogen consumed (N in) as compared with the amount of nitrogen excreted (N out) in a given period of time.*

---

* The genetic materials DNA and RNA contain nitrogen, but the quantity is insignificant compared with the amount in protein. Protein is 16 percent nitrogen. Said another way, the average protein weighs about 6.25 times as much as the nitrogen it contains, so scientists can estimate the amount of protein in a sample of food, body tissue, or other material by multiplying the weight of the nitrogen in it by 6.25.

output exceeds their nitrogen intake. During these times, the body loses nitrogen as it breaks down muscle and other body proteins for energy.

Using Amino Acids to Make Proteins or Nonessential Amino Acids As mentioned, cells can assemble amino acids into the proteins they need to do their work. If a particular nonessential amino acid is not readily available, cells can make it from another amino acid. If an essential amino acid is missing, the body may break down some of its own proteins to obtain it.

Using Amino Acids to Make Other Compounds Cells can also use amino acids to make other compounds. For example, the amino acid tyrosine is used to make the **neurotransmitters** norepinephrine and epinephrine, which relay nervous system messages throughout the body. Tyrosine can also be made into the pigment melanin, which is responsible for brown hair, eye, and skin color, or into the hormone thyroxin, which helps to regulate the metabolic rate. For another example, the amino acid tryptophan serves as a precursor for the vitamin niacin and for serotonin, a neurotransmitter important in sleep regulation, appetite control, and sensory perception.

Using Amino Acids for Energy and Glucose As mentioned earlier, when glucose or fatty acids are limited, cells are forced to use amino acids for energy and glucose. The body does not make a specialized storage form of protein as it does for carbohydrate and fat. Glucose is stored as glycogen in the liver and fat as triglycerides in adipose tissue, but protein in the body is available only from the working and structural components of the tissues. When the need arises, the body breaks down its tissue proteins and uses their amino acids for energy or glucose. Thus, over time, energy deprivation (starvation) always causes wasting of lean body tissue as well as fat loss. An adequate supply of carbohydrates and fats spares amino acids from being used for energy and allows them to perform their unique roles.

Deaminating Amino Acids When amino acids are broken down (as occurs when they are used for energy), they are first deaminated—stripped of their nitrogen-containing amino groups. **Deamination** produces ammonia, which the cells release into the bloodstream. The liver picks up the ammonia, converts it into urea (a less toxic compound), and returns the urea to the blood. The production of urea increases as dietary protein increases, until production hits its maximum rate at intakes approaching 250 grams per day. (Urea metabolism is described in Chapter 7.) The kidneys filter urea out of the blood; thus the amino nitrogen ends up in the urine. The remaining carbon fragments of the deaminated amino acids may enter a number of metabolic pathways—for example, they may be used for energy or for the production of glucose, ketones, cholesterol, or fat.[†]

Using Amino Acids to Make Fat Amino acids may be used to make fat when energy and protein intakes exceed needs and carbohydrate intake is adequate. The amino acids are deaminated, the nitrogen is excreted, and the remaining carbon fragments are converted to fat and stored for later use. In this way, protein-rich foods can contribute to weight gain.

IN SUMMARY

Proteins are constantly being synthesized and broken down as needed. The body's assimilation of amino acids into proteins and its release of amino acids via protein degradation and excretion can be tracked by measuring nitrogen balance, which should be positive during growth and steady in adulthood. An energy deficit or an inadequate protein intake may force the body to use amino acids as fuel, creating a negative nitrogen balance. Protein eaten in excess of need is degraded and stored as body fat.

neurotransmitters: chemicals that are released at the end of a nerve cell when a nerve impulse arrives there. They diffuse across the gap to the next cell and alter the membrane of that second cell to either inhibit or excite it.

deamination (dee-AM-ih-NAY-shun): removal of the amino (NH_2) group from a compound such as an amino acid.

[†] Chemists sometimes classify amino acids according to the destinations of their carbon fragments after deamination. If the fragment leads to the production of glucose, the amino acid is called *glucogenic;* if it leads to the formation of ketone bodies, fats, and sterols, the amino acid is called *ketogenic.* There is no sharp distinction between glucogenic and ketogenic amino acids, however. A few are both, most are considered glucogenic, only one (leucine) is clearly ketogenic.

Protein in Foods

In the United States and Canada, where nutritious foods are abundant, most people eat protein in such large quantities that they receive all the amino acids they need. In countries where food is scarce and the people eat only marginal amounts of protein-rich foods, however, the *quality* of the protein becomes crucial.

Protein Quality

The protein quality of the diet determines, in large part, how well children grow and how well adults maintain their health. Put simply, **high-quality proteins** provide enough of all the essential amino acids needed to support the body's work, and low-quality proteins don't. Two factors influence protein quality—the protein's digestibility and its amino acid composition.

Digestibility As explained earlier, proteins must be digested before they can provide amino acids. **Protein digestibility** depends on such factors as the protein's source and the other foods eaten with it. The digestibility of most animal proteins is high (90 to 99 percent); plant proteins are less digestible (70 to 90 percent for most, but over 90 percent for soy and legumes).

Amino Acid Composition To make proteins, a cell must have all the needed amino acids available simultaneously. The liver can produce any nonessential amino acid that may be in short supply so that the cells can continue linking amino acids into protein strands. If an essential amino acid is missing, though, a cell must dismantle its own proteins to obtain it. Therefore, to prevent protein breakdown, dietary protein must supply at least the nine essential amino acids plus enough nitrogen-containing amino groups and energy for the synthesis of the others. If the diet supplies too little of any essential amino acid, protein synthesis will be limited. The body makes whole proteins only; if one amino acid is missing, the others cannot form a "partial" protein. An essential amino acid supplied in less than the amount needed to support protein synthesis is called a **limiting amino acid.**

Reference Protein The quality of a food protein is determined by comparing its amino acid composition with the essential amino acid requirements of preschool-age children. Such a standard is called a **reference protein.** ◆ The rationale behind using the requirements of this age group is that if a protein will effectively support a young child's growth and development, then it will meet or exceed the requirements of older children and adults.

High-Quality Proteins As mentioned earlier, a high-quality protein contains all the essential amino acids in relatively the same amounts and proportions that human beings require; it may or may not contain all the nonessential amino acids. Proteins that are low in an essential amino acid cannot, by themselves, support protein synthesis. Generally, foods derived from animals (meat, fish, poultry, cheese, eggs, yogurt, and milk) provide high-quality proteins, although gelatin is an exception. (It lacks tryptophan and cannot support growth and health as a diet's sole protein.) Proteins from plants (vegetables, nuts, seeds, grains, and legumes) have more diverse amino acid patterns and tend to be limiting in one or more essential amino acids. Some plant proteins are notoriously low quality (for example, corn protein). A few others are high quality (for example, soy protein).

Researchers have developed several methods for evaluating the quality of food proteins and identifying high-quality proteins. Appendix D provides details.

Complementary Proteins In general, plant proteins are lower quality than animal proteins, and plants also offer less protein (per weight or measure of food). For this reason, many vegetarians improve the quality of proteins in their diets by combining plant-protein foods that have different but complementary amino acid patterns. This strategy yields **complementary proteins** that together contain all the

Black beans and rice, a favorite Hispanic combination, together provide a balanced array of amino acids.

◆ In the past, egg protein was commonly used as the reference protein. Table D-1 in Appendix D presents the amino acid profile of egg. As the reference protein, egg was assigned the value of 100; Table D-3 includes scores of other food proteins for comparison.

high-quality proteins: dietary proteins containing all the essential amino acids in relatively the same amounts that human beings require. They may also contain nonessential amino acids.

protein digestibility: a measure of the amount of amino acids absorbed from a given protein intake.

limiting amino acid: the essential amino acid found in the shortest supply relative to the amounts needed for protein synthesis in the body. Four amino acids are most likely to be limiting:
- Lysine
- Methionine
- Threonine
- Tryptophan

reference protein: a standard against which to measure the quality of other proteins.

complementary proteins: two or more dietary proteins whose amino acid assortments complement each other in such a way that the essential amino acids missing from one are supplied by the other.

FIGURE 6-11 Complementary Proteins

In general, legumes provide plenty of isoleucine (Ile) and lysine (Lys) but fall short in methionine (Met) and tryptophan (Trp). Grains have the opposite strengths and weaknesses, making them a perfect match for legumes.

	Ile	Lys	Met	Trp
Legumes				
Grains				
Together				

◆ Daily Value:
 • 50 g protein (based on 10% of 2000 kcal diet)

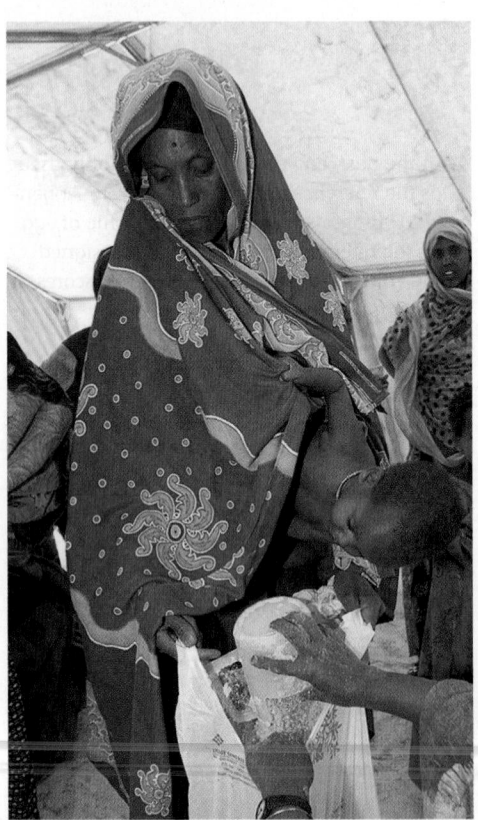

Donated food saves some people from starvation, but it is usually insufficient to meet nutrient needs or even to defend against hunger.

protein-energy malnutrition (PEM), also called **protein-kcalorie malnutrition (PCM):** a deficiency of protein, energy, or both, including kwashiorkor, marasmus, and instances in which they overlap (see p. 198).

essential amino acids in quantities sufficient to support health. The protein quality of the combination is greater than for either food alone (see Figure 6-11).

Many people have long believed that combining plant proteins at every meal is critical to protein nutrition. For most healthy vegetarians, though, it is not necessary to balance amino acids at each meal if protein intake is varied and energy intake is sufficient.[4] Vegetarians can receive all the amino acids they need over the course of a day by eating a variety of whole grains, legumes, seeds, nuts, and vegetables. Protein deficiency will develop, however, when fruits and certain vegetables make up the core of the diet, severely limiting both the *quantity* and *quality* of protein. Highlight 2 describes how to plan a nutritious vegetarian diet.

IN SUMMARY

A diet that supplies all of the essential amino acids in adequate amounts ensures protein synthesis. The best guarantee of amino acid adequacy is to eat foods containing high-quality proteins or mixtures of foods containing complementary proteins that can each supply the amino acids missing in the other. In addition to its amino acid content, the quality of protein is measured by its digestibility and its ability to support growth. Such measures are of great importance in dealing with malnutrition worldwide, but in the United States and Canada, where protein deficiency is not common, protein quality scores of individual foods deserve little emphasis.

Protein Regulations for Food Labels

All food labels must state the quantity of protein in grams. The "% Daily Value" ◆ for protein is not mandatory on all labels but is required whenever a food makes a protein claim or is intended for consumption by children under four years old.[‡] Whenever the Daily Value percentage is declared, researchers must determine the quality of the protein. Thus, when a % Daily Value is stated for protein, it reflects both quantity and quality.

Health Effects and Recommended Intakes of Protein

As you know by now, protein is indispensable to life. It should come as no surprise that protein deficiency can have devastating effects on people's health. But, like the other nutrients, protein in excess can also be harmful. This section examines the health effects and recommended intakes of protein.

Protein-Energy Malnutrition

When people are deprived of protein, energy, or both, the result is **protein-energy malnutrition (PEM).** Although PEM touches many adult lives, it most often strikes early in childhood. It is one of the most prevalent and devastating forms of malnutrition in the world, afflicting one of every four children worldwide. Most of the 33,000 children who die each day are malnourished.[5]

Inadequate food intake leads to poor growth in children and to weight loss and wasting in adults. Children who are thin for their height may be suffering from

[‡] For labeling purposes, the Daily Values for protein are as follows: for infants, 14 grams; for children under age four, 16 grams; for older children and adults, 50 grams; for pregnant women, 60 grams; and for lactating women, 65 grams.

acute PEM (recent severe food deprivation), whereas children who are short for their age have experienced **chronic PEM** (long-term food deprivation). Poor growth due to PEM is easy to overlook because a small child may look quite normal, but it is the most common sign of malnutrition.

PEM is most prevalent in Africa, Central America, South America, and East and Southeast Asia. In the United States, homeless people and those living in substandard housing in inner cities and rural areas have been diagnosed with PEM. In addition to those living in poverty, elderly people who live alone and adults who are addicted to drugs and alcohol are frequently victims of PEM. PEM can develop in young children when parents mistakenly provide "health-food beverages" ◆ that lack adequate energy or protein instead of milk, most commonly because of nutritional ignorance, perceived milk intolerance, or food faddism. Adult PEM is also seen in people hospitalized with infections such as AIDS or tuberculosis; these infections deplete body proteins, demand extra energy, induce nutrient losses, and alter metabolic pathways. Furthermore, poor nutrient intake during hospitalization worsens malnutrition and impairs recovery, whereas nutrition intervention often improves the body's response to other treatments and the chances of survival. PEM is also common in those suffering from the eating disorder anorexia nervosa (discussed in Highlight 8). Prevention emphasizes frequent, nutrient-dense, energy-dense meals and, equally important, resolution of the underlying causes of PEM—poverty, infections, and illness.

Classifying PEM PEM occurs in two forms: marasmus and kwashiorkor, which differ in their clinical features (see Table 6-3). The following paragraphs present three clinical syndromes—marasmus, kwashiorkor, and the combination of the two.

Marasmus Appropriately named from the Greek word meaning "dying away," **marasmus** reflects a severe deprivation of food over a long time (chronic PEM). Put simply, the person is starving and suffering from an inadequate energy *and* protein intake (and inadequate essential fatty acids, vitamins, and minerals as well). Marasmus occurs most commonly in children from 6 to 18 months of age in all the overpopulated and impoverished areas of the world. Children in impoverished nations simply do not have enough to eat and subsist on diluted cereal drinks that supply scant energy and protein of low quality; such food can barely sustain life, much less support growth. Consequently, marasmic children look like little old people—just skin and bones.

◆ Rice drinks are often sold as milk alternatives, but they fail to provide adequate protein, vitamins, and minerals.

acute PEM: protein-energy malnutrition caused by recent severe food restriction; characterized in children by thinness for height (wasting).

chronic PEM: protein-energy malnutrition caused by long-term food deprivation; characterized in children by short height for age (stunting).

marasmus (ma-RAZ-mus): a form of PEM that results from a severe deprivation, or impaired absorption, of energy, protein, vitamins, and minerals.

TABLE 6-3   Features of Marasmus and Kwashiorkor in Children

Separating PEM into two classifications oversimplifies the condition, but at the extremes, marasmus and kwashiorkor exhibit marked differences. Marasmus-kwashiorkor mix presents symptoms common to both marasmus and kwashiorkor. In all cases, children are likely to develop diarrhea, infections, and multiple nutrient deficiencies.

Marasmus	Kwashiorkor
Infancy (less than 2 yr)	Older infants and young children (1 to 3 yr)
Severe deprivation, or impaired absorption, of protein, energy, vitamins, and minerals	Inadequate protein intake or, more commonly, infections
Develops slowly; chronic PEM	Rapid onset; acute PEM
Severe weight loss	Some weight loss
Severe muscle wasting, with no body fat	Some muscle wasting, with retention of some body fat
Growth: <60% weight-for-age	Growth: 60 to 80% weight-for-age
No detectable edema	Edema
No fatty liver	Enlarged fatty liver
Anxiety, apathy	Apathy, misery, irritability, sadness
Good appetite possible	Loss of appetite
Hair is sparse, thin, and dry; easily pulled out	Hair is dry and brittle; easily pulled out; changes color; becomes straight
Skin is dry, thin, and easily wrinkles	Skin develops lesions

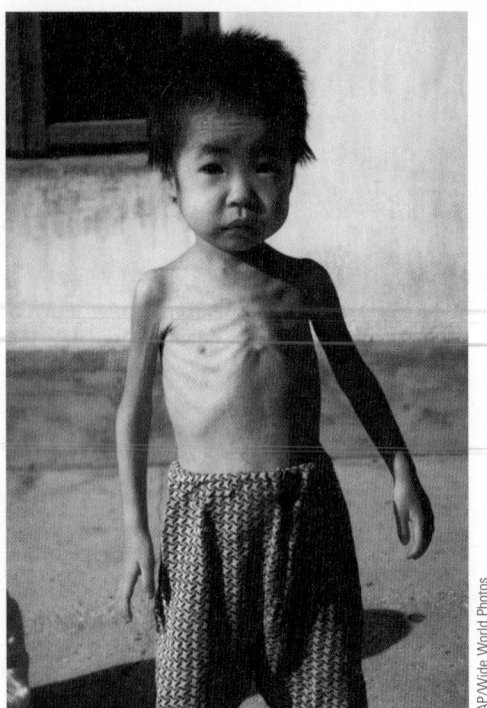

AP/Wide World Photos

The extreme loss of muscle and fat characteristic of marasmus is apparent in this child's "matchstick" arms.

Without adequate nutrition, muscles, including the heart, waste and weaken. Because the brain normally grows to almost its full adult size within the first two years of life, marasmus impairs brain development and learning ability. Reduced synthesis of key hormones slows metabolism and lowers body temperature. There is little or no fat under the skin to insulate against cold. Hospital workers find that children with marasmus need to be clothed, covered, and kept warm. Because these children often suffer delays in their mental and behavioral development, they also need loving care, a stimulating environment, and parental attention.

The starving child faces this threat to life by engaging in as little activity as possible—not even crying for food. The body musters all its forces to meet the crisis, so it cuts down on any expenditure of energy not needed for the functioning of the heart, lungs, and brain. Growth ceases; the child is no larger at age four than at age two. Enzymes are in short supply and the GI tract lining deteriorates. Consequently, the child can't digest and absorb what little food is eaten.

Kwashiorkor **Kwashiorkor** typically reflects a sudden and recent deprivation of food (acute PEM). Kwashiorkor is a Ghanaian word that refers to the birth position of a child and is used to describe the illness a child develops when the next child is born. When a mother who has been nursing her first child bears a second child, she weans the first child and puts the second one on the breast. The first child, suddenly switched from nutrient-dense, protein-rich breast milk to a starchy, protein-poor cereal, soon begins to sicken and die. Kwashiorkor typically sets in between 18 months and two years.

Kwashiorkor usually develops rapidly as a result of protein deficiency or, more commonly, is precipitated by an illness such as measles or other infection. Other factors, such as aflatoxins (a contaminant sometimes found in moldy grains), may also contribute to the development of, or symptoms that accompany, kwashiorkor.[6]

◆ For this reason, kwashiorkor is sometimes referred to as "wet" PEM and marasmus as "dry" PEM.

The loss of weight and body fat is usually not as severe in kwashiorkor as in marasmus, but some muscle wasting may occur. Proteins and hormones that previously maintained fluid balance diminish, and fluid leaks into the interstitial spaces. The child's limbs and abdomen become swollen with edema, a distinguishing feature of kwashiorkor. ◆ A fatty liver develops due to a lack of the protein carriers that transport fat out of the liver. The fatty liver lacks enzymes to clear metabolic toxins from the body, so their harmful effects are prolonged. Inflammation in response to these toxins and to infections further contributes to the edema that accompanies kwashiorkor. Without sufficient tyrosine to make melanin, the child's hair loses its color, and inadequate protein synthesis leaves the skin patchy and scaly, often with sores that fail to heal. The lack of proteins to carry or store iron leaves iron free. Unbound iron is common in children with kwashiorkor and may contribute to their illnesses and deaths by promoting bacterial growth and free-radical damage. (Free-radical damage is discussed fully in Highlight 11.)

Marasmus-Kwashiorkor Mix The combination of marasmus and kwashiorkor is characterized by the edema of kwashiorkor with the wasting of marasmus. Most often, the child suffers the effects of both malnutrition and infections. Some researchers believe that kwashiorkor and marasmus are two stages of the same disease. They point out that kwashiorkor and marasmus often exist side by side in the same community where children consume the same diet. They note that a child who has marasmus can later develop kwashiorkor. Some research indicates that marasmus represents the body's adaptation to starvation and that kwashiorkor develops when adaptation fails.

Infections In PEM, antibodies to fight off invading bacteria are degraded to provide amino acids for other uses, leaving the malnourished child vulnerable to infections. Blood proteins, including hemoglobin, are no longer synthesized, so the child becomes anemic and weak. **Dysentery,** an infection of the digestive tract, causes diarrhea, further depleting the body of nutrients and fluids. In the marasmic child, once infection sets in, kwashiorkor often follows, and the immune response weakens further.[7]

kwashiorkor (kwash-ee-OR-core, kwash-ee-or-CORE): a form of PEM that results either from inadequate protein intake or, more commonly, from infections.

dysentery (DISS-en-terry): an infection of the digestive tract that causes diarrhea.

The combination of infections, fever, fluid imbalances, and anemia often leads to heart failure and occasionally sudden death. Infections combined with malnutrition are responsible for two-thirds of the deaths of young children in developing countries. Measles, which might make a healthy child sick for a week or two, kills a child with PEM within two or three days.

Rehabilitation If caught in time, the life of a starving child may be saved with nutrition intervention. In severe cases, diarrhea will have incurred dramatic fluid and mineral losses that need to be replaced during the first 24 to 48 hours to help raise the blood pressure and strengthen the heartbeat. After that, protein and food energy may be given in *small* quantities, with intakes *gradually* increased as tolerated. Severely malnourished people, especially those with edema, recover better with an initial diet that is relatively low in protein (10 percent kcalories from protein).

Experts assure us that we possess the knowledge, technology, and resources to end hunger. Programs that tailor interventions to the local people and involve them in the process of identifying problems and devising solutions have the most success. To win the war on hunger, those who have the food, technology, and resources must make fighting hunger a priority (see Chapter 20 for more on hunger).

Health Effects of Protein

While many of the world's people struggle to obtain enough food energy and protein, in developed countries both are so abundant that problems of excess are seen. Overconsumption of protein offers no benefits and may pose health risks. High-protein diets have been implicated in several chronic diseases, including heart disease, cancer, osteoporosis, obesity, and kidney stones, but evidence is insufficient to establish an upper level.[8]

Researchers attempting to clarify the relationships between excess protein and chronic diseases face several obstacles. Population studies have difficulty determining whether diseases correlate with animal proteins or with their accompanying saturated fats, for example. Studies that rely on data from vegetarians must sort out the many lifestyle factors, in addition to a "no-meat diet," that might explain relationships between protein and health.

Heart Disease A high-protein diet may contribute to the progression of heart disease. As Chapter 5 mentioned, foods rich in animal protein also tend to be rich in saturated fats. Consequently, it is not surprising to find a correlation between animal-protein intake (red meats and dairy products) and heart disease.[9] On the other hand, substituting vegetable protein for animal protein improves blood lipids and decreases heart disease mortality.[10]

Research suggests that elevated levels of the amino acid homocysteine may be an independent risk factor for heart disease, heart attacks, and sudden death in patients with heart disease.[11] Researchers do not yet fully understand the many factors—including a high protein diet—that can raise homocysteine in the blood or whether elevated levels are a cause or an effect of heart disease.[12] Until they can determine the exact role homocysteine plays in heart disease, researchers are following several leads in pursuit of the answers. Coffee's role in heart disease has been controversial, but research suggests it is among the most influential factors in raising homocysteine, which may explain some of the adverse health effects of heavy consumption.[13] Elevated homocysteine levels are among the many adverse health consequences of smoking cigarettes and drinking alcohol as well.[14] Homocysteine is also elevated with inadequate intakes of B vitamins and can usually be lowered with fortified foods or supplements of vitamin B_{12}, vitamin B_6, and folate.[15] Lowering homocysteine, however, may not help in preventing heart attacks.[16] Supplements of the B vitamins do not always benefit those with heart disease and in fact, may actually increase the risks.[17]

In contrast to homocysteine, the amino acid arginine may help protect against heart disease by lowering blood pressure and homocysteine levels.[18] Additional research is needed to confirm the benefits of arginine.[19] In the meantime, it is unwise

The edema characteristic of kwashiorkor is apparent in this child's swollen belly. Malnourished children commonly have an enlarged abdomen from parasites as well.

for consumers to use supplements of arginine, or any other amino acid for that matter (as pp. 202–203 explain). Physicians, however, may find it beneficial to add arginine supplements to their heart patients' treatment plan.[20]

Cancer As in heart disease, the effects of protein and fats on cancers cannot be easily separated. Population studies suggest a correlation between high intakes of animal proteins and some types of cancer (notably, cancer of the colon, breast, kidneys, pancreas, and prostate).

Adult Bone Loss (Osteoporosis) Chapter 12 presents calcium metabolism, and Highlight 12 elaborates on the main factors that influence osteoporosis. This section briefly describes the relationships between protein intake and bone loss. When protein intake is high, calcium excretion increases. Whether excess protein depletes the bones of their chief mineral may depend upon the ratio of calcium intake to protein intake. After all, bones need both protein and calcium. An ideal ratio has not been determined, but a young woman whose intake meets recommendations for both nutrients has a calcium-to-protein ratio of more than 20 to 1 (milligrams to grams), which probably provides adequate protection for the bones. For most women in the United States, however, average calcium intakes are lower and protein intakes are higher, yielding a 9-to-1 ratio, which may produce calcium losses significant enough to compromise bone health. In other words, the problem may reflect too little calcium, not too much protein.[21] In establishing recommendations, the DRI Committee considered protein's effect on calcium metabolism and bone health, but it did not find sufficient evidence to warrant an adjustment for calcium or an upper level for protein.[22]

Some (but not all) research suggests that animal protein may be more detrimental to calcium metabolism and bone health than vegetable protein.[23] A review of the topic, however, concludes that excess protein—whether from animal or vegetable sources—increases calcium excretion and, perhaps more importantly, that the other nutrients in the protein source may be equally, if not more, responsible for the effects on bone health.[24]

Inadequate intakes of protein may also compromise bone health.[25] Osteoporosis is particularly common in elderly women and in adolescents with anorexia nervosa—groups who typically receive less protein than they need. For these people, increasing protein intake may be just what they need to protect their bones.[26]

Weight Control Dietary protein may play a role in increasing body weight.[27] Protein-rich foods are often fat-rich foods that contribute to weight gain with its accompanying health risks. As Highlight 9 explains, weight-loss gimmicks that encourage a high-protein, low-carbohydrate diet may be temporarily effective, but only because they are low-kcalorie diets. Diets that provide adequate protein, moderate fat, and sufficient energy from carbohydrates can better support weight loss and good health. Including protein at each meal may help with weight loss by providing satiety.[28] Selecting too many protein-rich foods, such as meat and milk, may crowd out fruits, vegetables, and whole grains, making the diet inadequate in other nutrients.

Kidney Disease Excretion of the end products of protein metabolism depends, in part, on an adequate fluid intake and healthy kidneys. A high protein intake increases the work of the kidneys, but does not appear to diminish kidney function or cause kidney disease.[29] Restricting dietary protein, however, may help to slow the progression of kidney disease and limit the formation of kidney stones in people who have these conditions.

IN SUMMARY

Protein deficiencies arise from both energy-poor and protein-poor diets and lead to the devastating diseases of marasmus and kwashiorkor. Together, these diseases are known as PEM (protein-energy malnutrition), a major form of malnutrition causing death in children worldwide. Excesses of protein offer no advantage; in fact, overconsumption of protein-rich foods may incur health problems as well.

Recommended Intakes of Protein

As mentioned earlier, the body continuously breaks down and loses some protein and cannot store amino acids. To replace protein, the body needs dietary protein for two reasons. First, food protein is the only source of the *essential* amino acids, and second, it is the only practical source of *nitrogen* with which to build the nonessential amino acids and other nitrogen-containing compounds the body needs.

Given recommendations that people's fat intakes should contribute 20 to 35 percent of total food energy and carbohydrate intakes should contribute 45 to 65 percent, that leaves 10 to 35 percent for protein. In a 2000-kcalorie diet, that represents 200 to 700 kcalories from protein, or 50 to 175 grams. Average intakes in the United States and Canada fall within this range.

Protein RDA The protein RDA ◆ for adults is 0.8 grams per kilogram of healthy body weight per day. For infants and children, the RDA is slightly higher. The table on the inside front cover lists the RDA for males and females at various ages in two ways—grams per day based on reference body weights and grams per kilogram body weight per day.

The RDA generously covers the needs for replacing worn-out tissue, so it increases for larger people; it also covers the needs for building new tissue during growth, so it increases for infants, children, and pregnant women. The protein RDA is the same for athletes as for others, although some fitness authorities recommend a slightly higher intake, as Chapter 14 explains.[30] The accompanying "How to" explains how to calculate your RDA for protein.

In setting the RDA, the DRI Committee assumes that people are healthy and do not have unusual metabolic needs for protein, that the protein eaten will be of mixed quality (from both high- and low-quality sources), and that the body will use the protein efficiently. In addition, the committee assumes that the protein is consumed along with sufficient carbohydrate and fat to provide adequate energy and that other nutrients in the diet are adequate.

Adequate Energy Note the qualification "adequate energy" in the preceding statement, and consider what happens if energy intake falls short of needs. An intake of 50 grams of protein provides 200 kcalories, which represents 10 percent of the total energy from protein, if the person receives 2000 kcalories a day. But if the person cuts energy intake drastically—to, say, 800 kcalories a day—then an intake of 200 kcalories from protein is suddenly 25 percent of the total; yet it's still the same amount of protein (number of grams). The protein intake is reasonable, but the energy intake is not. The low energy intake forces the body to use the protein to meet energy needs rather than to replace lost body protein. Similarly, if the person's energy intake is high—say, 4000 kcalories—the 50-gram protein intake represents only 5 percent of the total; yet it *still* is a reasonable protein intake. Again, the energy intake is unreasonable for most people, but in this case, it permits the protein to be used to meet the body's needs.

Be careful when judging protein (or carbohydrate or fat) intake as a percentage of energy. Always ascertain the number of grams as well, and compare it with the RDA or another standard stated in grams. A recommendation stated as a percentage of energy intake is useful only if the energy intake is within reason.

Protein in Abundance Most people in the United States and Canada receive more protein than they need. Even athletes in training typically don't need to increase their protein intakes because the additional foods they eat to meet their high energy needs deliver protein as well. (Chapter 14 provides full details on the energy and protein needs of athletes.) That protein intake is high is not surprising considering the abundance of food eaten and the central role meats hold in the North American diet. A single ounce of meat (or $1/2$ cup legumes) delivers about 7 grams of protein, so 8 ounces of meat alone supplies more than the RDA for an average-size person. Besides meat, well-fed people eat many other nutritious foods, many of which also provide protein. A cup of milk provides 8 grams of protein. Grains and

---

HOW TO Calculate Recommended Protein Intakes

To figure your protein RDA:

- Look up the healthy weight for a person of your height (inside back cover). If your present weight falls within that range, use it for the following calculations. If your present weight falls outside the range, use the midpoint of the healthy weight range as your reference weight.
- Convert pounds to kilograms, if necessary (pounds divided by 2.2 equals kilograms).
- Multiply kilograms by 0.8 to get your RDA in grams per day. (Older teens 14 to 18 years old, multiply by 0.85.) Example:

Weight = 150 lb

150 lb ÷ 2.2 lb/kg = 68 kg (rounded off)

68 kg × 0.8 g/kg = 54 g protein (rounded off)

ThomsonNOW
To calculate recommended protein intakes, log on to **www.thomsonedu.com/thomsonnow,** go to Chapter 6, then go to How To.

◆ RDA for protein:
- 0.8 g/kg/day
- 10 to 35% of energy intake

For many people, this 5-ounce steak provides almost all of the meat and much of the protein recommended for a day's intake.

Vegetarians obtain their protein from whole grains, legumes, nuts, vegetables, and, in some cases, eggs and milk products.

◆ Use of amino acids as dietary supplements is *inappropriate*, especially for:
- All women of childbearing age
- Pregnant or lactating women
- Infants, children, and adolescents
- Elderly people
- People with inborn errors of metabolism that affect their bodies' handling of amino acids
- Smokers
- People on low-protein diets
- People with chronic or acute mental or physical illnesses who take amino acids without medical supervision

whey protein: a by-product of cheese production; falsely promoted as increasing muscle mass. Whey is the watery part of milk that separates from the curds.

vegetables provide small amounts of protein, but they can add up to significant quantities; fruits and fats provide no protein.

To illustrate how easy it is to overconsume protein, consider the amounts recommended by the USDA Food Guide for a 2000-kcalorie diet. Six ounces of grains provide about 18 grams of protein; 2½ cups of vegetables deliver about 10 grams; 3 cups of milk offer 24 grams; and 5½ ounces of meat supply 38 grams. This totals 90 grams of protein—higher than recommendations for most people and yet still lower than the average intake of people in the United States.

People in the United States and Canada get more protein than they need. If they have an adequate *food* intake, they have a more-than-adequate protein intake. The key diet-planning principle to emphasize for protein is moderation. Even though most people receive plenty of protein, some feel compelled to take supplements as well, as the next section describes.

IN SUMMARY

The optimal diet is adequate in energy from carbohydrate and fat and delivers 0.8 grams of protein per kilogram of healthy body weight each day. U.S. and Canadian diets are typically more than adequate in this respect.

Protein and Amino Acid Supplements

Websites, health-food stores, and popular magazine articles advertise a wide variety of protein supplements, and people take these supplements for many different reasons. Athletes take protein powders to build muscle. Dieters take them to spare their bodies' protein while losing weight. Women take them to strengthen their fingernails. People take individual amino acids, too—to cure herpes, to make themselves sleep better, to lose weight, and to relieve pain and depression.* Like many other magic solutions to health problems, protein and amino acid ◆ supplements don't work these miracles. Furthermore, they may be harmful.

Protein Powders Because the body builds muscle protein from amino acids, many athletes take protein powders with the false hope of stimulating muscle growth. Muscle work builds muscle; protein supplements do not, and athletes do not need them. Taking protein supplements does not improve athletic performance.[31] (Highlight 14 presents more information on other supplements athletes commonly use.) Protein powders can supply amino acids to the body, but nature's protein sources—lean meat, milk, eggs, and legumes—supply all these amino acids and more.

Whey protein appears to be particularly popular among athletes hoping to achieve greater muscle gains. A waste product of cheese manufacturing, whey protein is a common ingredient in many low-cost protein powders. When combined with strength training, whey supplements may increase protein synthesis slightly, but they do not seem to enhance athletic performance.[32] To build stronger muscles, athletes need to eat food with adequate energy and protein to support the weight-training work that does increase muscle mass. Those who still think they need more whey should pour a glass of milk; one cup provides 1.5 grams of whey.

Purified protein preparations contain none of the other nutrients needed to support the building of muscle, and the protein they supply is not needed by athletes who eat food. It is excess protein, and the body dismantles it and uses it for energy or stores it as body fat. The deamination of excess amino acids places an extra burden on the kidneys to excrete unused nitrogen.

Amino Acid Supplements Single amino acids do not occur naturally in foods and offer no benefit to the body; in fact, they may be harmful. The body was not designed to handle the high concentrations and unusual combinations of amino acids

* Canada only allows single amino acid supplements to be sold as drugs or used as food additives.

found in supplements. An excess of one amino acid can create such a demand for a carrier that it limits the absorption of another amino acid, presenting the possibility of a deficiency. Those amino acids winning the competition enter in excess, creating the possibility of toxicity. Toxicity of single amino acids in animal studies raises concerns about their use in human beings. Anyone considering taking amino acid supplements should check with a registered dietitian or physician first.

Most healthy athletes eating well-balanced diets do not need amino acid supplements. Advertisers point to research that identifies the **branched-chain amino acids** ◆ as the main ones used as fuel by exercising muscles. What the ads leave out is that compared to glucose and fatty acids, branched-chain amino acids provide very little fuel and that ordinary foods provide them in abundance anyway. Large doses of branched-chain amino acids can raise plasma ammonia concentrations, which can be toxic to the brain. Branched-chain amino acid supplements may be useful in conditions such as advanced liver failure, but otherwise, they are not routinely recommended.[33]

In two cases, recommendations for single amino acid supplements have led to widespread public use—lysine to prevent or relieve the infections that cause herpes cold sores on the mouth or genital organs, and tryptophan to relieve pain, depression, and insomnia. In both cases, enthusiastic popular reports preceded careful scientific experiments and health recommendations. Research is insufficient to determine whether lysine suppresses herpes infections, but it appears safe (up to 3 grams per day) when taken in divided doses with meals.[34]

Tryptophan may be effective with respect to pain and sleep, but its use for these purposes is experimental. About 20 years ago, more than 1500 people who elected to take tryptophan supplements developed a rare blood disorder known as eosinophilia-myalgia syndrome (EMS). EMS is characterized by severe muscle and joint pain, extremely high fever, and, in over three dozen cases, death. Treatment for EMS usually involves physical therapy and low doses of corticosteroids to relieve symptoms temporarily. The Food and Drug Administration implicated impurities in the supplements, issued a recall of all products containing manufactured tryptophan, and warned that high-dose supplements of tryptophan might provoke EMS even in the absence of impurities.

◆ The branched-chain amino acids are leucine, isoleucine, and valine.

IN SUMMARY

Normal, healthy people never need protein or amino acid supplements. It is safest to obtain lysine, tryptophan, and all other amino acids from protein-rich foods, eaten with abundant carbohydrate and some fat to facilitate their use in the body. With all that we know about science, it is hard to improve on nature.

Nutrition Portfolio

ThomsonNOW
www.thomsonedu.com/thomsonnow

Foods that derive from animals—meats, fish, poultry, eggs, and milk products—provide plenty of protein but are often accompanied by fat. Those that derive from plants—whole grains, vegetables, and legumes—may provide less protein but also less fat.

- Calculate your daily protein needs and compare them with your protein intake. Consider whether you receive enough, but not too much, protein daily.

- Describe your dietary sources of proteins and whether you use mostly plant-based or animal-based protein foods in your diet.

- Debate the risks and benefits of taking protein or amino acid supplements.

branched-chain amino acids: the essential amino acids leucine, isoleucine, and valine, which are present in large amounts in skeletal muscle tissue; falsely promoted as fuel for exercising muscles.

NUTRITION ON THE NET

For further study of topics covered in this chapter, log on to **www.thomsonedu.com/thomsonnow**. Go to Chapter 6, then to Nutrition on the Net.

- Learn more about sickle-cell anemia from the National Heart, Lung, and Blood Institute or the Sickle Cell Disease Association of America: **www.nhlbi.nih.gov** or **www.sicklecelldisease.org**

- Learn more about protein-energy malnutrition and world hunger from the World Health Organization Nutrition

Programme or the National Institute of Child Health and Human Development: **www.who.int/nut** or **www.nichd.nih.gov**

- Chapter 20 offers many more websites on malnutrition and world hunger.

NUTRITION CALCULATIONS

For additional practice, log on to **www.thomsonedu.com/thomsonnow**. Go to Chapter 6, then to Nutrition Calculations.

These problems will give you practice in doing simple nutrition-related calculations using hypothetical situations (see p. 206 for answers). Once you have mastered these examples, you will be prepared to examine your own protein needs. Be sure to show your calculations for each problem.

1. Compute recommended protein intakes for people of different sizes. Refer to the "How to" on p. 201 and compute the protein recommendation for the following people. The intake for a woman who weighs 144 pounds is computed for you as an example.

$$144 \text{ lb} \div 2.2 \text{ lb/kg} = 65 \text{ kg}$$

$$0.8 \text{ g/kg} \times 65 \text{ kg} = 52 \text{ g protein per day}$$

   a. a woman who weighs 116 pounds
   b. a man (18 years) who weighs 180 pounds

2. The chapter warns that recommendations based on percentage of energy intake are not always appropriate. Consider a woman 26 years old who weighs 165 pounds. Her diet provides 1500 kcalories/day with 50 grams carbohydrate and 100 grams fat.
   a. What is this woman's protein intake? Show your calculations.
   b. Is her protein intake appropriate? Justify your answer.
   c. Are her carbohydrate and fat intakes appropriate? Justify your answer.

This exercise should help you develop a perspective on protein recommendations.

STUDY QUESTIONS

To assess your understanding of chapter topics, take the Student Practice Test and explore the modules recommended in your Personalized Study Plan. Log onto **www.thomsonedu.com/thomsonnow**.

These questions will help you review the chapter. You will find the answers in the discussions on the pages provided.

1. How does the chemical structure of proteins differ from the structures of carbohydrates and fats? (pp. 181–184)

2. Describe the structure of amino acids, and explain how their sequence in proteins affects the proteins' shapes. What are essential amino acids? (pp. 181–184)

3. Describe protein digestion and absorption. (pp. 185–186)

4. Describe protein synthesis. (pp. 187–189)

5. Describe some of the roles proteins play in the human body. (pp. 189–192)

6. What are enzymes? What roles do they play in chemical reactions? Describe the differences between enzymes and hormones. (p. 190)

7. How does the body use amino acids? What is deamination? Define nitrogen balance. What conditions are associated with zero, positive, and negative balance? (pp. 193–194)

8. What factors affect the quality of dietary protein? What is a high-quality protein? (pp. 195–196)

9. How can vegetarians meet their protein needs without eating meat? (pp. 195–196)

10. What are the health consequences of ingesting inadequate protein and energy? Describe marasmus and kwashiorkor. How can the two conditions be distinguished, and in what ways do they overlap? (pp. 196–199)

11. How might protein excess, or the type of protein eaten, influence health? (pp. 199–200)

12. What factors are considered in establishing recommended protein intakes? (pp. 201–202)

13. What are the benefits and risks of taking protein and amino acid supplements? (p. 202–203)

These multiple choice questions will help you prepare for an exam. Answers can be found on p. 206.

1. Which part of its chemical structure differentiates one amino acid from another?
   a. its side group
   b. its acid group
   c. its amino group
   d. its double bonds

2. Isoleucine, leucine, and lysine are:
   a. proteases.
   b. polypeptides.
   c. essential amino acids.
   d. complementary proteins.

3. In the stomach, hydrochloric acid:
   a. denatures proteins and activates pepsin.
   b. hydrolyzes proteins and denatures pepsin.
   c. emulsifies proteins and releases peptidase.
   d. condenses proteins and facilitates digestion.

4. Proteins that facilitate chemical reactions are:
   a. buffers.
   b. enzymes.
   c. hormones.
   d. antigens.

5. If an essential amino acid that is needed to make a protein is unavailable, the cells must:
   a. deaminate another amino acid.
   b. substitute a similar amino acid.
   c. break down proteins to obtain it.
   d. synthesize the amino acid from glucose and nitrogen.

6. Protein turnover describes the amount of protein:
   a. found in foods and the body.
   b. absorbed from the diet.
   c. synthesized and degraded.
   d. used to make glucose.

7. Which of the following foods provides the highest quality protein?
   a. egg
   b. corn
   c. gelatin
   d. whole grains

8. Marasmus develops from:
   a. too much fat clogging the liver.
   b. megadoses of amino acid supplements.
   c. inadequate protein and energy intake.
   d. excessive fluid intake causing edema.

9. The protein RDA for a healthy adult who weighs 180 pounds is:
   a. 50 milligrams/day.
   b. 65 grams/day.
   c. 180 grams/day.
   d. 2000 milligrams/day.

10. Which of these foods has the least protein per $^1/_2$ cup?
    a. rice
    b. broccoli
    c. pinto beans
    d. orange juice

REFERENCES

1. M. S. Buchowski and coauthors, Equation to estimate resting energy expenditure in adolescents with sickle cell anemia, *American Journal of Clinical Nutrition* 76 (2002): 1335-1344; Committee on Genetics, Health supervision for children with sickle cell disease, *Pediatrics* 109 (2002): 526-535.
2. J. M. Ordovas and D. Corella, Nutritional genomics, *Annual Review of Genomics and Human Genetics* 5 (2004): 71-118.
3. W. M. Rand, P. L. Pellett, and V. R. Young, Meta-analysis of nitrogen balance studies for estimating protein requirements in healthy adults, *American Journal of Clinical Nutrition* 77 (2003): 109-127.
4. Position of the American Dietetic Association and Dietitians of Canada: Vegetarian diets, *Journal of the American Dietetic Association* 103 (2003): 748-765.
5. Data from www.unicef.org, posted April 2005 and May 2006.
6. M. Krawinkel, Kwashiorkor is still not fully understood, *Bulletin of the World Health Organization* 81 (2003): 910-911.
7. M. Reid and coauthors, The acute-phase protein response to infection in edematous and nonedematous protein-energy malnutrition, *American Journal of Clinical Nutrition* 76 (2002): 1409-1415.
8. Committee on Dietary Reference Intakes, *Dietary Reference Intakes for Energy, Carbohydrate, Fiber, Fat, Fatty Acids, Cholesterol, Protein, and Amino Acids* (Washington, D.C.: National Academies Press, 2002/2005), p. 694.

9. L. E. Kelemen and coauthors, Associations of dietary protein with disease and mortality in a prospective study of postmenopausal women, *American Journal of Epidemiology* 161 (2005): 239-249.
10. B. L. McVeigh and coauthors, Effect of soy protein varying in isoflavone content on serum lipids in healthy young men, *American Journal of Clinical Nutrition* 83 (2006): 244-251; L. E. Kelemen and coauthors, Associations of dietary protein with disease and mortality in a prospective study of postmenopausal women, *American Journal of Epidemiology* 161 (2005): 239-249; S. Tonstad, K. Smerud, and L. Høie, A comparison of the effects of 2 doses of soy protein or casein on serum lipids, serum lipoproteins, and plasma total homocysteine in hypercholesterolemic subjects, *American Journal of Clinical Nutrition* 76 (2002): 78-84.
11. M. Haim and coauthors, Serum homocysteine and long-term risk of myocardial infarction and sudden death in patients with coronary heart disease, *Cardiology* 107 (2006): 52-56; M. B. Kazemi and coauthors, Homocysteine level and coronary artery disease, *Angiology* 57 (2006): 9-14; D. S. Wald, M. Law, and J. K. Morris, Homocysteine and cardiovascular disease: Evidence on causality from a meta-analysis, *British Medical Journal* 325 (2002): 1202-1217; The Homocysteine Studies Collaboration, Homocysteine and risk of ischemic heart

disease and stroke, *Journal of the American Medical Association* 288 (2002): 2015-2022.
12. J. Selhub, The many facets of hyperhomocysteinemia: Studies from the Framingham cohorts, *Journal of Nutrition* 136 (2006): 1726S-1730S; P. Verhoef and coauthors, A high-protein diet increases postprandial but not fasting plasma total homocysteine concentrations: A dietary controlled, crossover trial in healthy volunteers, *American Journal of Clinical Nutrition* 82 (2005): 553-558.
13. S. E. Chiuve and coauthors, Alcohol intake and methylenetetrahydrofolate reductase polymorphism modify the relation of folate intake to plasma homocysteine, *American Journal of Clinical Nutrition* 82 (2005): 155-162; P. Verhoef and coauthors, Contribution of caffeine to the homocysteine-raising effect of coffee: A randomized controlled trial in humans, *American Journal of Clinical Nutrition* 76 (2002): 1244-1248.
14. J. A. Troughton and coauthors, Homocysteine and coronary heart disease risk in the PRIME study, *Atherosclerosis* (2006); S. E. Chiuve and coauthors, Alcohol intake and methylenetetrahydrofolate reductase polymorphism modify the relation of folate intake to plasma homocysteine, *American Journal of Clinical Nutrition* 82 (2005): 155-162.
15. D. Genser and coauthors, Homocysteine, folate and vitamin B(12) in patients with coronary heart disease, *Annals of Nutrition &*

Metabolism 50 (2006): 413-419; Ø. Bleie and coauthors, Changes in basal and postmethionine load concentrations of total homocysteine and cystathionine after B vitamin intervention, *American Journal of Clinical Nutrition* 80 (2004): 641-648; E. Nurk and coauthors, Changes in lifestyle and plasma total homocysteine: The Hordaland Homocysteine Study, *American Journal of Clinical Nutrition* 79 (2004): 812-819; K. L. Tucker and coauthors, Breakfast cereal fortified with folic acid, vitamin B-6, and vitamin B-12 increases vitamin concentrations and reduces homocysteine concentrations: A randomized trial, *American Journal of Clinical Nutrition* 79 (2004): 805-811; J. F. Toole and coauthors, Lowering homocysteine in patients with ischemic stroke to prevent recurrent stroke, myocardial infarction, and death: The Vitamin Intervention for Stroke Prevention (VISP) randomized controlled trial, *Journal of the American Medical Association* 291 (2004): 565-575.

16. B-Vitamin Treatment Trialists' Collaboration, Homocysteine-lowering trials for prevention of cardiovascular events: A review of the design and power of the large randomized trials, *American Heart Journal* 151 (2006): 282-287.

17. E. Lonn and coauthors, Homocysteine lowering with folic acid and B vitamins in vascular disease, *New England Journal of Medicine* 354 (2006): 1567-1577; K. H. Bonaa and coauthors, Homocysteine lowering and cardiovascular events after acute myocardial infarction, *New England Journal of Medicine* 354 (2006): 1578-1588; G. Schnyder and coauthors, Effect of homocysteine-lowering therapy with folic acid, vitamin B12, and vitamin B6 on clinical outcome after percutaneous coronary intervention-The Swiss Heart Study: A randomized controlled trial, *Journal of the American Medical Association* 288 (2002): 973-979; B. J. Venn and coauthors, Dietary counseling to increase natural folate intake: A randomized, placebo-controlled trial in free-living subjects to assess effects on serum folate and plasma total homocysteine, *American Journal of Clinical Nutrition* 76 (2002): 758-765.

18. S. G. West and coauthors, Oral L-arginine improves hemodynamic responses to stress and reduces plasma homocysteine in hypercholesterolemic men, *Journal of Nutrition* 135 (2005): 212-217.

19. N. Gokce, L-arginine and hypertension, *Journal of Nutrition* 134 (2004): 2807S-2811S.

20. B. S. Kendler, Supplemental conditionally essential nutrients in cardiovascular disease therapy, *Journal of Cardiovascular Nursing* 21 (2006): 9-16.

21. B. Dawson-Hughes, Interaction of dietary calcium and protein in bone health in humans, *Journal of Nutrition* 133 (2003): 852S-854S.

22. Committee on Dietary Reference Intakes, 2002/2005, p. 841; Committee on Dietary Reference Intakes, *Dietary Reference Intakes for Calcium, Phosphorus, Magnesium, Vitamin D, and Fluoride* (Washington, D.C.: National Academy Press, 1997), pp. 75-76.

23. J. P. Bonjour, Dietary protein: An essential nutrient for bone health, *Journal of the American College of Nutrition* 24 (2005): 526S-536S; C. Weikert and coauthors, The relation between dietary protein, calcium and bone health in women: Results from the EPIC-Potsdam cohort, *Annals of Nutrition & Metabolism* 49 (2005): 312-318.

24. L. K. Massey, Dietary animal and plant protein and human bone health: A whole foods approach, *Journal of Nutrition* 133 (2003): 862S-865S.

25. F. Ginty, Dietary protein and bone health, *The Proceedings of the Nutrition Society* 62 (2003): 867-876; J. E. Kerstetter, K. O. O'Brien, and K. L. Insogna, Low protein intake: The impact on calcuim and bone homeostasis in humans, *Journal of Nutrition* 133 (2003): 855S-861S.

26. A. Devine and coauthors, Protein consumption is an important predictor of lower limb bone mass in elderly women, *American Journal of Clinical Nutrition* 81 (2005): 1423-1428; J. Bell and S. J. Whiting, Elderly women need dietary protein to maintain bone mass, *Nutrition Reviews* 60 (2002): 337-341; M. T. Munoz and J. Argente, Anorexia nervosa in female adolescents: Endocrine and bone mineral density disturbances, *European Journal of Endocrinology* 147 (2002): 275-286.

27. A. Trichopoulou and coauthors, Lipid, protein and carbohydrate intake in relation to body mass index, *European Journal of Clinical Nutrition* 56 (2002): 37-43.

28. A. Astrup, The satiating power of protein—a key to obesity prevention? *American Journal of Clinical Nutrition* 82 (2005): 1-2; D. S. Weigle and coauthors, A high-protein diet induces sustained reductions in appetite, ad libitum caloric intake, and body weight despite compensatory changes in diurnal plasma leptin and ghrelin concentrations, *American Journal of Clinical Nutrition* 82 (2005): 41-48.

29. E. L. Knight and coauthors, The impact of protein intake on renal function decline in women with normal renal function or mild renal insufficiency, *Annals of Internal Medicine* 138 (2003): 460-467.

30. Position of the American Dietetic Association, Dietitians of Canada, and the American College of Sports Nutrition, Nutrition and athletic performance, *Journal of the American Dietetic Association* 100 (2000): 1543-1556.

31. L. L. Andersen and coauthors, The effect of resistance training combined with timed ingestion of protein on muscle fiber size and muscle strength, *Metabolism: Clinical and Experimental* 54 (2005): 151-156.

32. K. D. Tipton, Ingestion of casein and whey proteins result in muscle anabolism after resistance exercise, *Medicine and Science in Sports and Exercise* 36 (2004): 2073-2081.

33. R. Mascarenhas and S. Mobarhan, New support for branched-chain amino acid supplementation in advanced hepatic failure, *Nutrition Reviews* 62 (2004): 33-38.

34. M. M. Perfect and coauthors, Use of complementary and alternative medicine for the treatment of genital herpes, *Herpes* 12 (2005): 38-41.

ANSWERS

Nutrition Calculations

1. a. 116 lb ÷ 2.2 lb/kg = 53 kg

   0.8 g/kg × 53 kg = 42 g protein per day

   b. 180 lb ÷ 2.2 lb/kg = 82 kg

   He is 18 years old, so use 0.85 g/kg.

   0.85 g/kg × 82 kg = 70 g protein per day

2. a. 50 g carbohydrate × 4 kcal/g = 200 kcal from carbohydrate

   100 g fat × 9 kcal/g = 900 kcal from fat

   1500 kcal − (200 + 900 kcal) = 400 kcal from protein

   400 kcal ÷ 4 kcal/g = 100 g protein

   b. Using the RDA guideline of 0.8 g/kg, an appropriate protein intake for this woman would be 60 g protein/day (165 lb ÷ 2.2 lb/kg = 75 kg; 0.8 g/kg × 75 = 60 g/day). Her intake is higher than her RDA. Using the guideline that protein should contribute 10 to 35% of energy intake, her intake of 100 g protein on a 1500 kcal diet falls within the suggested range (400 kcal protein ÷ 1500 total kcal = 27%).

   c. Using the guideline that carbohydrate should contribute 45 to 65% and fat should contribute 20 to 35% of energy intake, her intake of 50 g carbohydrate is low (200 kcal carbohydrate ÷ 1500 total kcal = 13%), and her intake of 100 g fat is high (900 kcal fat ÷ 1500 total kcal = 60%).

Study Questions (multiple choice)

1. a 2. c 3. a 4. b 5. c 6. c 7. a
8. c 9. b 10. d

Nutritional Genomics

© Science VU/Visuals Unlimited

Imagine this scenario: A physician scrapes a sample of cells from inside your cheek and submits it to a **genomics** lab. The lab returns a report based on your genetic profile that reveals which diseases you are most likely to develop and makes recommendations for specific diet and lifestyle changes that can help you maintain good health. You may also be given a prescription for a dietary supplement that will best meet your personal nutrient requirements. Such a scenario may one day become reality as scientists uncover the genetic relationships between diet and disease. (Until then, however, consumers need to know that current genetic test kits commonly available on the Internet are unproven and quite likely fraudulent.)

How nutrients influence gene activity and how **genes** influence the activities of nutrients is the focus of a new field of study called **nutritional genomics** (see the accompanying glossary). Unlike sciences in the 20th century, nutritional genomics takes a comprehensive approach in analyzing information from several fields of study, providing an integrated understanding of the findings.[1] Consider how multiple disciplines contributed to our understanding of vitamin A over the past several decades, for example. Biochemistry revealed vitamin A's three chemical structures. Immunology identified the anti-infective properties of one

of these structures while physiology focused on another structure and it's role in vision. Epidemiology has reported improvements in the death rates and vision of malnourished children given vitamin A supplements, and biology has explored how such effects might be possible. The process was slow as researchers collected information on one gene, one action, and one nutrient at a time. Today's research in nutritional genomics involves all of the sciences, coordinating their multiple findings, and explaining their interactions among several genes, actions, and nutrients in relatively little time. As a result, nutrition knowledge is growing at an incredibly fast pace.

The recent surge in genomics research grew from the Human Genome Project, an international effort by industry and government scientists to identify and describe all of the genes in the **human genome**—that is, all the genetic information contained within a person's cells. Completed in 2003, this project developed many of the research technologies needed to study genes and genetic variation. Scientists are now working to identify the individual proteins made by the genes, the genes associated with diseases, and the dietary and lifestyle choices that most influence the expression of those genes. Such information will have major implications for society in general, and for health care in particular.[2]

GLOSSARY

chromosomes: structures within the nucleus of a cell made of DNA and associated proteins. Human beings have 46 chromosomes in 23 pairs. Each chromosome has many genes.

DNA (deoxyribonucleic acid): the double helix molecules of which genes are made.

epigenetics: the study of heritable changes in gene function that occur without a change in the DNA sequence.

gene expression: the process by which a cell converts the genetic code into RNA and protein.

genes: sections of chromosomes that contain the instructions

needed to make one or more proteins.

genetics: the study of genes and inheritance.

genomics: the study of all the genes in an organism and their interactions with environmental factors.

human genome (GEE-nome): the full complement of genetic material in the chromosomes of a person's cells.

microarray technology: research tools that analyze the expression of thousands of genes simultaneously and search for particular gene changes associated with a disease. DNA microarrays are also called *DNA chips.*

mutations: a permanent change in the DNA that can be inherited.

nucleotide bases: the nitrogen-containing building blocks of DNA and RNA—cytosine (C), thymine (T), uracil (U), guanine (G), and adenine (A). In DNA, the base pairs are A–T and C–G and in RNA, the base pairs are A–U and C–G.

nucleotides: the subunits of DNA and RNA molecules, composed of a phosphate group, a 5-carbon sugar (deoxyribose for DNA and ribose for RNA), and a nitrogen-containing base.

nutritional genomics: the science of how food (and its components) interacts with the

genome. The study of how nutrients affect the activities of genes is called *nutrigenomics.* The study of how genes affect the activities of nutrients is called *nutrigenetics.*

phenylketonuria (FEN-il-KEY-toe-NEW-ree-ah) or **PKU:** an inherited disorder characterized by failure to metabolize the amino acid phenylalanine to tyrosine.

RNA (ribonucleic acid): a compound similar to DNA, but RNA is a single strand with a ribose sugar instead of a deoxyribose sugar and uracil instead of thymine as one of its bases.

A Genomics Primer

Figure H6-1 shows the relationships among the materials that comprise the genome. As Chapter 6's discussion of protein synthesis pointed out, genetic information is encoded in DNA molecules within the nucleus of cells. The DNA molecules and associated proteins are packed within 46 **chromosomes.** The genes are segments of a DNA strand that can eventually be translated into one or more proteins. The sequence of **nucleotide bases** within each gene determines the amino acid sequence of a particular protein. Scientists currently estimate that there are between 20,000 and 25,000 genes in the human genome.

As Figure 6-7 (p. 188) explained, when cells make proteins, a **DNA** sequence is used to make messenger **RNA.** The **nucleotide** sequence in messenger RNA then determines the amino acid sequence to make a protein. This process—from genetic information to protein synthesis—is known as **gene expression.** Gene expression can be determined by measuring the amounts of messenger RNA in a tissue sample. **Microarray technology** (see photo on p. 207) allows researchers to detect messenger RNA and analyze the expression of thousands of genes simultaneously.

Simply having a certain gene does not determine that its associated trait will be expressed; the gene has to be activated. (Similarly,

owning lamps does not ensure you will have light in your home unless you turn them on.) Nutrients are among many environmental factors that play key roles in either activating or silencing genes. Switching genes on and off does not change the DNA itself, but it can have dramatic consequences for a person's health.

The area of study that examines how environmental factors influence gene expression without changing the DNA is known as **epigenetics.** To turn genes on, enzymes attach proteins near the beginning of a gene. If enzymes attach a methyl group (CH_3) instead, the protein is blocked from binding to the gene and the gene remains switched off. Other factors influence gene expression as well, but methyl groups are currently the most well understood. They also are known to have dietary connections.

The accompanying photo of two mice illustrates epigenetics and how diet can influence genetic traits such as hair color and body weight. Both mice have a gene that tends to produce fat, yellow pups, but their mothers were given different diets. The mother of the mouse on the right was given a dietary supplement containing the B vitamins folate and vitamin B_{12}. These nutrients silenced the gene for "yellow and fat," resulting in brown pups with normal appetites. As Chapter 10 explains, one of the main roles of these B vitamins is to transfer methyl groups. In the case of the supplemented mice, methyl groups migrated onto DNA and shut off several genes, thus producing brown coats and protecting against the development of

FIGURE H6-1 The Human Genome

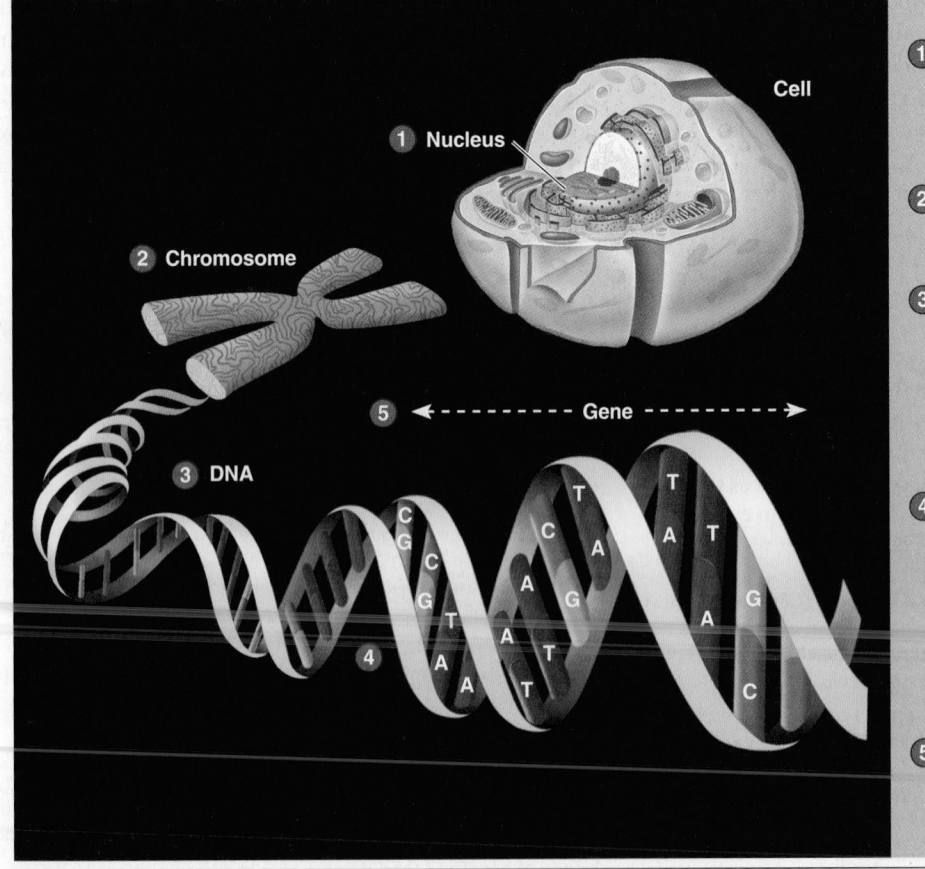

1. The human genome is a complete set of genetic material organized into 46 chromosomes, located within the nucleus of a cell.

2. A chromosome is made of DNA and associated proteins.

3. The double helical structure of a DNA molecule is made up of two long chains of nucleotides. Each nucleotide is composed of a phosphate group, a 5-carbon sugar, and a base.

4. The sequence of nucleotide bases (C, G, A, T) determines the amino acid sequence of proteins. These bases are connected by hydrogen bonding to form base pairs—adenine (A) with thymine (T) and guanine (G) with cytosine (C).

5. A gene is a segment of DNA that includes the information needed to synthesize one or more proteins.

Adapted from "A Primer: From DNA to Life," Human Genome Project, U.S. Department of Energy Office of Science; http://www.orn.gov/sci/techresources/Human_Genome/primer-pic.shtml.

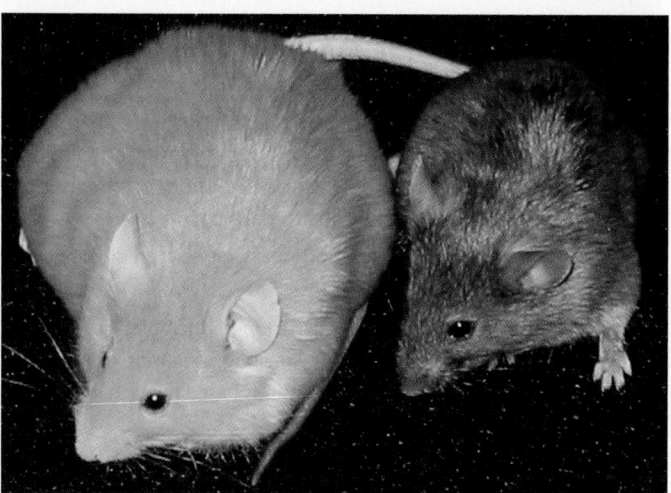

Both of these mice have the gene that tends to produce fat, yellow pups, but their mothers had different diets. The mother of the mouse on the right received a dietary supplement, which silenced the gene, resulting in brown pups with normal appetites.

© Jirtle and Waterland

obesity and some related diseases. Keep in mind that these changes occurred epigenetically. In other words, the DNA sequence within the genes of the mice remained the same.

Whether silencing or activating a gene is beneficial or harmful depends on what the gene does. Silencing a gene that stimulates cancer growth, for example, would be beneficial, but silencing a gene that suppresses cancer growth would be harmful. Similarly, activating a gene that defends against obesity would be beneficial, but activating a gene that promotes obesity would be harmful. Much research is under way to determine which nutrients activate or silence which genes.

Genetic Variation and Disease

Except for identical twins, no two persons are genetically identical. The variation in the genomes of any two persons, however, is only about 0.1 percent, a difference of only one nucleotide base in every 1000. Yet it is this incredibly small difference that makes each of us unique and explains why, given the same environmental influences, some of us develop certain diseases and others do not. Similarly, genetic variation explains why some of us respond to interventions such as diet and others do not. For example, following a diet low in saturated fats will significantly lower LDL cholesterol for most people, but the degree of change varies dramatically among individuals, with some people having only a small decrease or even a slight increase.[3] In other words, dietary factors may be more helpful or more harmful depending on a person's particular genetic variations.[4] (Such findings help to explain some of the conflicting results from research studies.) The goal of nutritional genomics is to custom design *specific* recommendations that fit the needs of *each* individual. Such personalized recommendations are expected to provide more effective disease prevention and treatment solutions.

Diseases characterized by a single-gene disorder are genetically predetermined, usually exert their effects early in life, and greatly affect those touched by them, but are relatively rare. The cause and effect of single-gene disorders is clear—those with the genetic defect get the disease and those without it don't. In contrast, the more common diseases, such as heart disease and cancer, are influenced by many genes and typically develop over several decades. These chronic diseases have multiple genetic components that *predispose* the prevention or development of a disease, depending on a variety of environmental factors (such as smoking, diet, and physical activity).[5] Both types are of interest to researchers in nutritional genomics.

Single-Gene Disorders

Some disorders are caused by **mutations** in single genes that are inherited at birth. The consequences of a missing or malfunctioning protein can seriously disrupt metabolism and may require significant dietary or medical intervention. A classic example of a diet-related, single-gene disorder is **phenylketonuria,** or **PKU**.

Approximately one in every 15,000 infants in the United States is born with PKU. PKU arises from mutations in the gene that codes for the enzyme that converts the essential amino acid phenylalanine to the amino acid tyrosine. Without this enzyme, phenylalanine and its metabolites accumulate and damage the nervous system, resulting in mental retardation, seizures, and behavior abnormalities. At the same time, the body cannot make tyrosine or compounds made from it (such as the neurotransmitter epinephrine). Consequently, tyrosine becomes an essential amino acid: because the body cannot make it, the diet must supply it.

Although the most debilitating effect is on brain development, other symptoms of PKU become evident if the condition is left untreated. Infants with PKU may have poor appetites and grow slowly. They may be irritable or have tremors or seizures. Their bodies and urine may have a musty odor. Their skin coloring may be unusually pale, and they may develop skin rashes.

The effect of nutrition intervention in PKU is remarkable. In fact, the only current treatment for PKU is a diet that restricts phenylalanine and supplies tyrosine to maintain blood levels of these amino acids within safe ranges. Because all foods containing protein provide phenylalanine, the diet must depend on a formula to supply a phenylalanine-free source of energy, protein, vitamins, and minerals. If the restricted diet is conscientiously followed, the symptoms can be prevented. Because phenylalanine is an essential amino acid, the diet cannot exclude it completely. Children with PKU need phenylalanine to grow, but they cannot handle excesses without detrimental effects. Therefore, their diets must provide enough phenylalanine to support normal growth and health but not enough to cause harm. The diet must also provide tyrosine. To ensure that blood concentrations of phenylalanine and tyrosine are close to normal, children and adults who have PKU must have blood tests periodically and adjust their diets as necessary.

Multigene Disorders

In multigene disorders, each of the genes can influence the progression of a disease, but no single gene causes the disease on its own. For this reason, genomics researchers must study the expression and interactions of *multiple* genes. Because multigene disorders are often sensitive to interactions with environmental influences, they are not as straightforward as single-gene disorders. Heart disease provides an example of a chronic disease with multiple gene and environmental influences. Consider that major risk factors for heart disease include elevated blood cholesterol levels, obesity, diabetes, and hypertension, yet the underlying genetic and environmental causes of any of these individual risk factors is not completely understood. Genomic research can reveal details about each of these risk factors. For example, tests could determine whether blood cholesterol levels are high due to increased cholesterol absorption or production or because of decreased cholesterol degradation.[6] This information could then guide physicians and dietitians to prescribe the most appropriate medical and dietary interventions from among many possible solutions.[7] Today's dietary recommendations advise a low-fat diet, which helps people with a small type of LDL but not those with the large type. In fact, a low-fat diet is actually more harmful for people with the large type. Finding the best option for each person will be a challenge given the many possible interactions between genes and environmental factors and the millions of possible gene variations in the human genome that make each individual unique.[8]

The results of genomic research are helping to explain findings from previous nutrition research. Consider dietary fat and heart disease, for example. As Highlight 5 explained, epidemiological and clinical studies have found that a diet high in unsaturated fatty acids often helps to maintain a healthy blood lipid profile. Now genetic studies offer an underlying explanation of this relationship: diets rich in polyunsaturated fatty acids activate genes responsible for making enzymes that break down fats and silence genes responsible for making enzymes that make fats.[9] Both actions change fat metabolism in the direction of lowering blood lipids.

To learn more about how individuals respond to diet, researchers examine the genetic differences between people. The most common genetic differences involve a change in a single nucleotide base located in a particular region of a DNA strand—thymine replacing cytosine, for example. Such variations are called single nucleotide polymorphisms (SNPs), and they commonly occur throughout the genome. Many SNPs (commonly pronounced "snips") have no effect on cell activity. In fact, SNPs are significant only if they affect the amino acid sequence of a protein in a way that alters its function *and* if that function is critical to the body's well-being. Research on a gene that plays a key role in lipid metabolism reveals differences in a person's response to diet depending on whether the gene has a common SNP. People with the SNP have lower LDL when eating a diet rich in polyunsaturated fatty acids—and higher LDL with a low intake—than those without the SNP.[10] These findings clearly show how diet (in this case, polyunsaturated fat) interacts with a gene (in this case, a fat metabolism gene with a SNP) to influence the development of a disease (changing blood lipids implicated in heart disease). The quest now is to identify the genetic characteristics that predict various responses to dietary recommendations.[11]

Clinical Concerns

Because multigene, chronic diseases are common, an understanding of the human genome will have widespread ramifications for health care. This new understanding of the human genome is expected to change health care by:

- Providing knowledge of an individual's genetic predisposition to specific diseases.

- Allowing physicians to develop "designer" therapies—prescribing the most effective schedule of screening, behavior changes (including diet), and medical interventions based on each individual's genetic profile.

- Enabling manufacturers to create new medications for each genetic variation so that physicians can prescribe the best medicine in the exact dose and frequency to enhance effectiveness and minimize the risks of side effects.

- Providing a better understanding of the nongenetic factors that influence disease development.

Enthusiasm surrounding genomic research needs to be put into perspective, however, in terms of the present status of clinical medicine as well as people's willingness to make difficult lifestyle choices. Critics have questioned whether genetic markers for disease would be more useful than simple clinical measurements, which reflect both genetic *and* environmental influences. In other words, knowing that a person is genetically predisposed to have high blood cholesterol is not necessarily more useful than knowing the person's actual blood cholesterol level.[12] Furthermore, if a disease has many genetic risk factors, each gene that contributes to susceptibility may have little influence on its own, so the benefits of identifying an individual genetic marker might be small. The long-range possibility is that many genetic markers will eventually be identified, and the hope is that the combined information will be a useful and accurate predictor of disease.

Having the knowledge to prevent disease and actually taking action do not always coincide. Despite the abundance of current dietary recommendations, people seem unwilling to make behavior changes known to improve their health. For example, it has been estimated that heart disease and type 2 diabetes are 90 percent preventable when people adopt an appropriate diet, maintain a healthy body weight, and exercise regularly.[13] Yet these two diseases remain among the leading causes of death. Given the difficulty that people have with current recommendations, it may be unrealistic to expect that many of them will enthusiastically adopt an even more detailed list of lifestyle modifications. Then again, compliance may be better when it is supported by information based on a person's own genetic profile.

The debate over nature versus nurture—whether genes or the environment are more influential—has quieted. The focus has shifted. Scientists acknowledge the important roles of each and understand the real answers lie within the myriad interactions. Current research is sorting through how nutrients (and other dietary factors) and genes confer health benefits or risks. Answers from genomic research may not become apparent for years to come, but the opportunities and rewards may prove well worth the efforts.[14]

NUTRITION ON THE NET

- Get information about human genomic discoveries and
  how they can be used to improve health from the Genomics and Disease Prevention site of the Centers for
  Disease Control: **www.cdc.gov/genomics**

REFERENCES

1. G. T. Keusch, What do –omics mean for the science and policy of the nutritional sciences? *American Journal of Clinical Nutrition* 83 (2006): 520S–522S.
2. N. Fogg-Johnson and J. Kaput, Nutrigenomics: An emerging scientific discipline, *Food Technology* 57 (2003): 60–67; R. Weinshilboum, Inheritance and drug response, *New England Journal of Medicine* 348 (2003): 529–537; A. E. Guttmacher and F. S. Collins, Genomic medicine—A primer, *New England Journal of Medicine* 347 (2002): 1512–1520.
3. D. Corella and J. M. Ordovas, Single nucleotide polymorphisms that influence lipid metabolism: Interaction with dietary factors, *Annual Review of Nutrition* 25 (2005): 341–390.
4. E. Trujillo, C. Davis, and J. Milner, Nutrigenomics, proteomics, metabolomics, and the practice of dietetics, *Journal of the American Dietetic Association* 106 (2006): 403–413.
5. J. Kaput and coauthors, The case for strategic international alliances to harness nutritional genomics for public and personal health, *British Journal of Nutrition* 94 (2005): 623–632; J. Kaput and R. L. Rodriguez, Nutritional genomics: The next frontier in the postgenome era, *Physiological Genomics* 16 (2004): 166–177.
6. J. B. German, M. A. Roberts, and S. M. Watkins, Personal metabolomics as a next generation nutritional assessment, *Journal of Nutrition* 133 (2003): 4260–4266.
7. R. M. DeBusk and coauthors, Nutritional genomics in practice: Where do we begin? *Journal of the American Dietetic Association* 105 (2005): 589–597.
8. J. M. Ordovas, Nutrigenetics, plasma lipids, and cardiovascular risk, *Journal of the American Dietetic Association* 106 (2006): 1074–1081.
9. H. Sampath and J. M. Ntambi, Polyunsaturated fatty acid regulation of genes of lipid metabolism, *Annual Review of Nutrition* 25 (2005): 317–340.
10. E. S. Tai and coauthors, Polyunsaturated fatty acids interact with PPARA–L162V polymorphism to affect plasma triglyceride apolipoprotein C-III concentrations in the Framingham Heart Study, *Journal of Nutrition* 135 (2005): 397–403.
11. J. M. Ordovas, The quest for cardiovascular health in the genomic era: Nutrigenetics and plasma lipoproteins, *Proceedings of the Nutrition Society* 63 (2004): 145–152.
12. W. C. Willett, Balancing life-style and genomics research for disease prevention, *Science* 296 (2002): 695–698.
13. S. Yusut and coauthors, Effect of potentially modifiable risk factors associated with myocardial infarction in 52 countries (the INTERHEART Study): Case-control study, *Lancet* 364 (2004): 937–952; Willett, 2002.
14. A. E. Guttmacher and F. S. Collins, Realizing the promise of genomics in biomedical research, *Journal of the American Medical Association* 294 (2005): 1399–1402; P. J. Stover, Nutritional genomics, *Physiological Genomics* 16 (2004): 161–165.

Thomson NOW! Throughout this chapter, the ThomsonNOW logo indicates an opportunity for online self-study, linking you to interactive tutorials and videos based on your level of understanding.

www.thomsonedu.com/login

Figure 7.5: Animated! Glycolysis: Glucose-to-Pyruvate

Figure 7.10: Animated! Fatty Acid-to-Acetyl CoA

Figure 7.18: Animated! The TCA Cycle

Figure 7.19: Animated! Electron Transport Chain and ATP Synthesis

Nutrition Portfolio Journal

Nutrition in Your Life

You eat breakfast and hustle off to class. After lunch, you study for tomorrow's exam. Dinner is followed by an evening of dancing. Do you ever think about how the food you eat powers the activities of your life? What happens when you don't eat—or when you eat too much? Learn how the cells of your body transform carbohydrates, fats, and proteins into energy—and what happens when you give your cells too much or too little of any of these nutrients. Discover the metabolic pathways that lead to body fat and those that support physical activity. It's really quite fascinating.

Metabolism: Transformations and Interactions

CHAPTER OUTLINE

Chemical Reactions in the Body

Breaking Down Nutrients for Energy • Glucose • Glycerol and Fatty Acids • Amino Acids • Breaking Down Nutrients for Energy—In Summary • The Final Steps of Catabolism

Energy Balance • Feasting—Excess Energy • The Transition from Feasting to Fasting • Fasting—Inadequate Energy

HIGHLIGHT 7 Alcohol and Nutrition

Energy makes it possible for people to breathe, ride bicycles, compose music, and do everything else they do. All the energy that sustains human life initially comes from the sun—the ultimate source of energy. As Chapter 1 explained, *energy* is the capacity to do work. Although every aspect of our lives depends on energy, the concept of energy can be difficult to grasp because it cannot be seen or touched, and it manifests in various forms, including heat, mechanical, electrical, and chemical energy. In the body, heat energy maintains a constant body temperature, and electrical energy sends nerve impulses. Energy is stored in foods and in the body as chemical energy.

During **photosynthesis**, plants make simple sugars from carbon dioxide and capture the sun's light energy in the chemical bonds of those sugars. Then human beings eat either the plants or animals that have eaten the plants. These foods provide energy, but how does the body obtain that energy from foods? This chapter answers that question by following the nutrients that provide the body with **fuel** through a series of reactions that release energy from their chemical bonds. As the bonds break, they release energy in a controlled version of the same process by which wood burns in a fire. Both wood and food have the potential to provide energy. When wood burns in the presence of oxygen, it generates heat and light (energy), steam (water), and some carbon dioxide and ash (waste). Similarly, during **metabolism**, the body releases energy, water, and carbon dioxide.

By studying metabolism, you will understand how the body uses foods to meet its needs and why some foods meet those needs better than others. Readers who are interested in weight control will discover which foods contribute most to body fat and which to select when trying to gain or lose weight safely. Physically active readers will discover which foods best support endurance activities and which to select when trying to build lean body mass.

photosynthesis: the process by which green plants use the sun's energy to make carbohydrates from carbon dioxide and water.
  • **photo** = light
  • **synthesis** = put together (making)

fuel: compounds that cells can use for energy. The major fuels include glucose, fatty acids, and amino acids; other fuels include ketone bodies, lactate, glycerol, and alcohol.

metabolism: the sum total of all the chemical reactions that go on in living cells. Energy metabolism includes all the reactions by which the body obtains and expends the energy from food.
  • **metaballein** = change

Chemical Reactions in the Body

Earlier chapters introduced some of the body's chemical reactions: the making and breaking of the bonds in carbohydrates, lipids, and proteins. Metabolism is the sum of these and all the other chemical reactions that go on in living cells; *energy metabolism* includes all the ways the body obtains and uses energy from food.

The Site of Metabolic Reactions—Cells The human body is made up of trillions of cells, and each cell busily conducts its metabolic work all the time. (Appendix A presents a brief summary of the structure and function of the cell.) Figure 7-1 depicts a typical cell and shows where the major reactions of energy metabolism take place. The type and extent of metabolic activities vary depending on the type of cell, but of all the body's cells, the liver cells are the most versatile and metabolically active. Table 7-1 offers insights into the liver's work.

The Building Reactions—Anabolism Earlier chapters described how condensation reactions combine the basic units of energy-yielding nutrients to build body compounds. Glucose molecules may be joined together to make glycogen chains. Glycerol and fatty acids may be assembled into triglycerides. Amino acids may be linked together to make proteins. Each of these reactions starts with small, simple compounds and uses them as building blocks to form larger, more complex structures. Because such reactions involve doing work, they require energy. The building up of body compounds is known as **anabolism.** Anabolic reactions are represented in this book, wherever possible, with "up" arrows in chemical diagrams (such as those shown in Figure 7-2).

> **anabolism** (an-AB-o-lism): reactions in which small molecules are put together to build larger ones. Anabolic reactions require energy.
> • **ana** = up

FIGURE 7-1 A Typical Cell (Simplified Diagram)

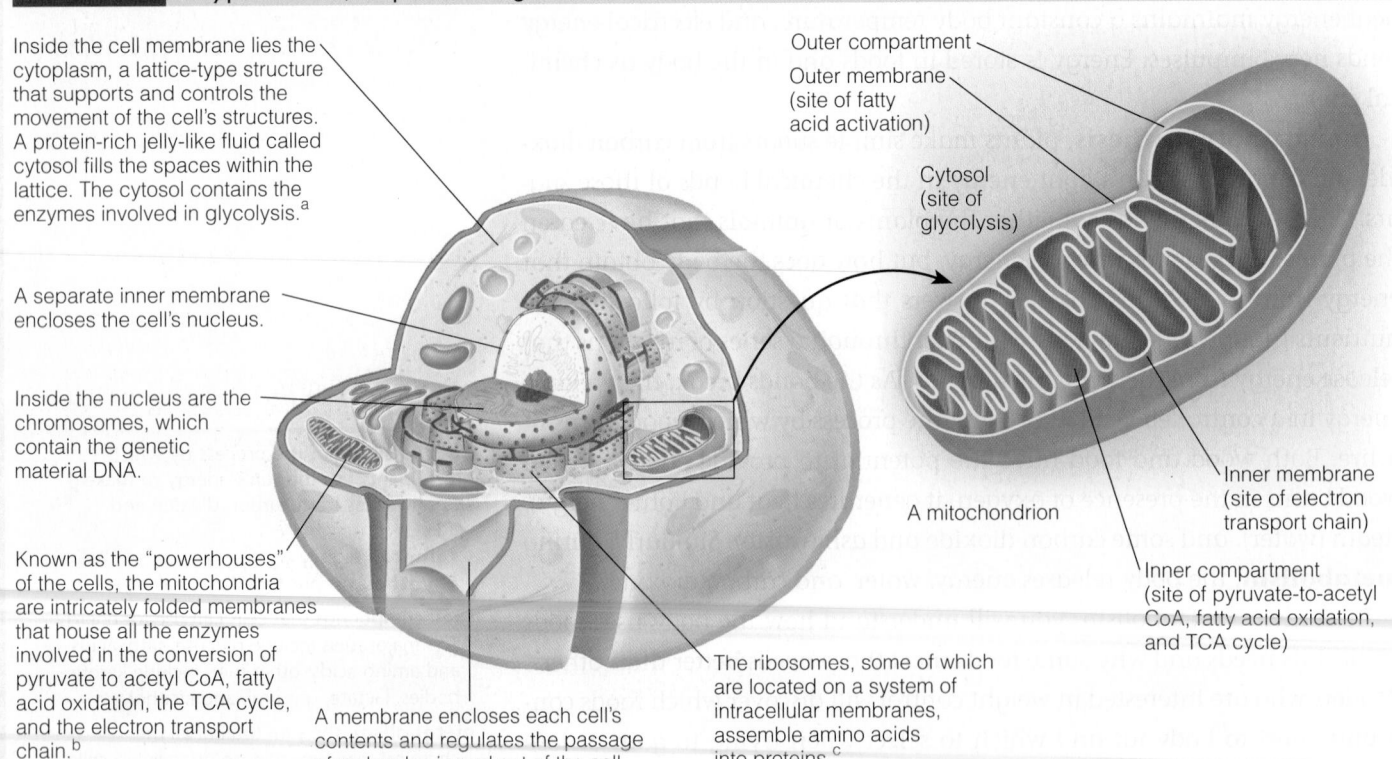

Inside the cell membrane lies the cytoplasm, a lattice-type structure that supports and controls the movement of the cell's structures. A protein-rich jelly-like fluid called cytosol fills the spaces within the lattice. The cytosol contains the enzymes involved in glycolysis.[a]

A separate inner membrane encloses the cell's nucleus.

Inside the nucleus are the chromosomes, which contain the genetic material DNA.

Known as the "powerhouses" of the cells, the mitochondria are intricately folded membranes that house all the enzymes involved in the conversion of pyruvate to acetyl CoA, fatty acid oxidation, the TCA cycle, and the electron transport chain.[b]

A membrane encloses each cell's contents and regulates the passage of molecules in and out of the cell.

The ribosomes, some of which are located on a system of intracellular membranes, assemble amino acids into proteins.[c]

Outer compartment

Outer membrane (site of fatty acid activation)

Cytosol (site of glycolysis)

A mitochondrion

Inner membrane (site of electron transport chain)

Inner compartment (site of pyruvate-to-acetyl CoA, fatty acid oxidation, and TCA cycle)

[a]Glycolysis is introduced on p. 219.
[b]The conversion of pyruvate to acetyl CoA, fatty acid oxidation, the TCA cycle, and the electron transport chain are described later in the chapter..
[c]Figure 6-7 on p. 188 describes protein synthesis.

TABLE 7-1 Metabolic Work of the Liver

The liver is the most active processing center in the body. When nutrients enter the body from the digestive tract, the liver receives them first; then it metabolizes, packages, stores, or ships them out for use by other organs. When alcohol, drugs, or poisons enter the body, they are also sent directly to the liver; here they are detoxified and their by-products shipped out for excretion. An enthusiastic anatomy and physiology professor once remarked that given the many vital activities of the liver, we should express our feelings for others by saying, "I love you with all my liver," instead of "with all my heart." Granted, this declaration lacks romance, but it makes a valid point. Here are just some of the many jobs performed by the liver. To renew your appreciation for this remarkable organ, review Figure 3-12 on p. 85.

Carbohydrates:

- Converts fructose and galactose to glucose
- Makes and stores glycogen
- Breaks down glycogen and releases glucose
- Breaks down glucose for energy when needed
- Makes glucose from some amino acids and glycerol when needed
- Converts excess glucose to fatty acids

Lipids:

- Builds and breaks down triglycerides, phospholipids, and cholesterol as needed
- Breaks down fatty acids for energy when needed
- Packages extra lipids in lipoproteins for transport to other body organs
- Manufactures bile to send to the gallbladder for use in fat digestion
- Makes ketone bodies when necessary

Proteins:

- Manufactures nonessential amino acids that are in short supply
- Removes from circulation amino acids that are present in excess of need and converts them to other amino acids or deaminates them and converts them to glucose or fatty acids
- Removes ammonia from the blood and converts it to urea to be sent to the kidneys for excretion
- Makes other nitrogen-containing compounds the body needs (such as bases used in DNA and RNA)
- Makes plasma proteins such as clotting factors

Other:

- Detoxifies alcohol, other drugs, and poisons; prepares waste products for excretion
- Helps dismantle old red blood cells and captures the iron for recycling
- Stores most vitamins and many minerals

FIGURE 7-2 Anabolic and Catabolic Reactions Compared

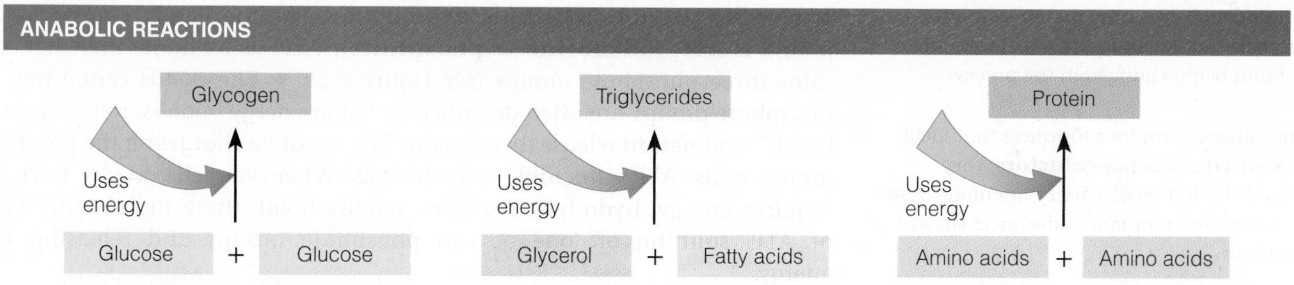

ANABOLIC REACTIONS

Anabolic reactions include the making of glycogen, triglycerides, and protein; these reactions require differing amounts of energy.

CATABOLIC REACTIONS

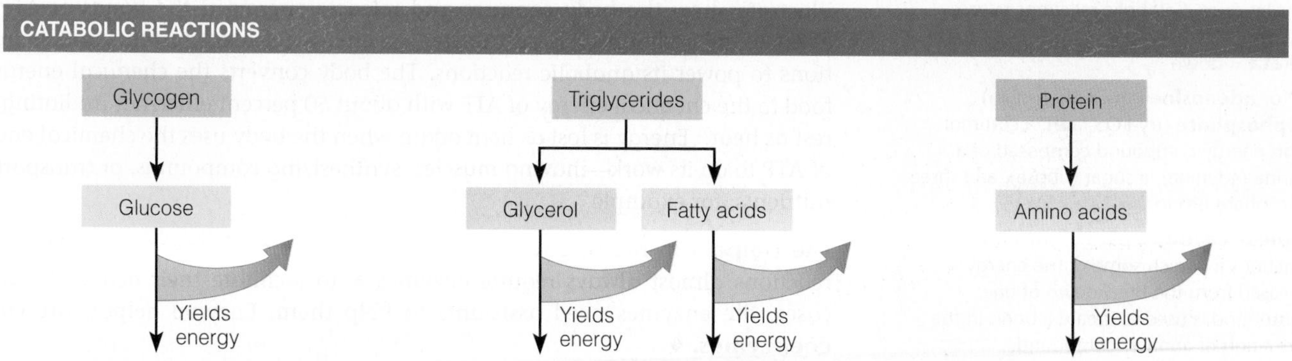

Catabolic reactions include the breakdown of glycogen, triglycerides, and protein; the further catabolism of glucose, glycerol, fatty acids, and amino acids releases differing amounts of energy. Much of the energy released is captured in the bonds of adenosine triphosphate (ATP).

NOTE: You need not memorize a color code to understand the figures in this chapter, but you may find it helpful to know that blue is used for carbohydrates, yellow for fats, and red for proteins.

FIGURE 7-3 ATP (Adenosine Triphosphate)

ATP is one of the body's high-energy molecules. Notice that the bonds connecting the three phosphate groups have been drawn as wavy lines, indicating a high-energy bond. When these bonds are broken, energy is released.

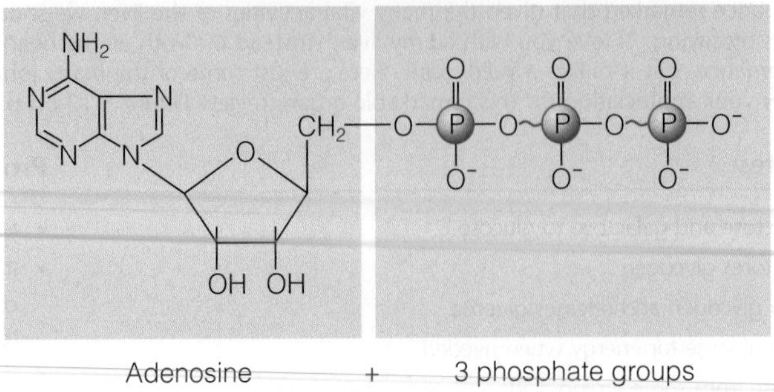

Adenosine   +   3 phosphate groups

◆ ATP = A-P~P~P.
(Each ~ denotes a "high-energy" bond.)

◆ Reminder: *Enzymes* are protein catalysts—proteins that facilitate chemical reactions without being changed in the process.

◆ The general term for substances that facilitate enzyme action is **cofactors**; they include both organic coenzymes made from vitamins and inorganic substances such as minerals.

catabolism (ca-TAB-o-lism): reactions in which large molecules are broken down to smaller ones. Catabolic reactions release energy.
• **kata** = down

ATP or **adenosine** (ah-DEN-oh-seen) **triphosphate** (try-FOS-fate): a common high-energy compound composed of a purine (adenine), a sugar (ribose), and three phosphate groups.

coupled reactions: pairs of chemical reactions in which some of the energy released from the breakdown of one compound is used to create a bond in the formation of another compound.

coenzymes: complex organic molecules that work with enzymes to facilitate the enzymes' activity. Many coenzymes have B vitamins as part of their structures (Figure 10-1 on p. 327 in Chapter 10 illustrates coenzyme action).
• **co** = with

The Breakdown Reactions—Catabolism The breaking down of body compounds is known as **catabolism;** catabolic reactions release energy and are represented, wherever possible, by "down" arrows in chemical diagrams (as in Figure 7-2, p. 215). Earlier chapters described how hydrolysis reactions break down glycogen to glucose, triglycerides to fatty acids and glycerol, and proteins to amino acids. When the body needs energy, it breaks down any or all of these four basic units into even smaller units, as described later.

The Transfer of Energy in Reactions—ATP High-energy storage compounds in the body capture some of the energy released during the breakdown of glucose, glycerol, fatty acids, and amino acids from foods. One such compound is **ATP (adenosine triphosphate).** ATP, as its name indicates, contains three phosphate groups (see Figure 7-3). ◆ The bonds connecting the phosphate groups are often described as "high-energy" bonds, referring to the bonds' readiness to release their energy. The negative charges on the phosphate groups make ATP vulnerable to hydrolysis. Whenever cells do any work that requires energy, hydrolytic reactions readily break these high-energy bonds of ATP, splitting off one or two phosphate groups and releasing their energy.

Quite often, the hydrolysis of ATP occurs simultaneously with reactions that will use that energy—a metabolic duet known as **coupled reactions.** Figure 7-4 illustrates how the body captures and releases energy in the bonds of ATP. In essence, the body uses ATP to transfer the energy released during catabolic reactions to power its anabolic reactions. The body converts the chemical energy of food to the chemical energy of ATP with about 50 percent efficiency, radiating the rest as heat.[1] Energy is lost as heat again when the body uses the chemical energy of ATP to do its work—moving muscles, synthesizing compounds, or transporting nutrients, for example.

The Helpers in Metabolic Reactions—Enzymes and Coenzymes Metabolic reactions almost always require enzymes ◆ to facilitate their action. In many cases, the enzymes need assistants to help them. Enzyme helpers are called **coenzymes.** ◆

Coenzymes are complex organic molecules that associate closely with most enzymes but are not proteins themselves. The relationships between various coenzymes and their respective enzymes may differ in detail, but one thing is true of all: without its coenzyme, an enzyme cannot function. Some of the B vitamins serve as coenzymes that participate in the energy metabolism of glucose, glycerol, fatty acids, and amino acids (Chapter 10 provides more details).

FIGURE 7-4 Transfer of Energy by ATP—A Coupled Reaction

The breakdown of ATP (adenosine triphosphate) to ADP (adenosine diphosphate) releases energy that can be used to power another reaction (such as the synthesis of a needed compound). The simultaneous occurrence of one reaction releasing energy and another reaction using the energy is called a coupled reaction.

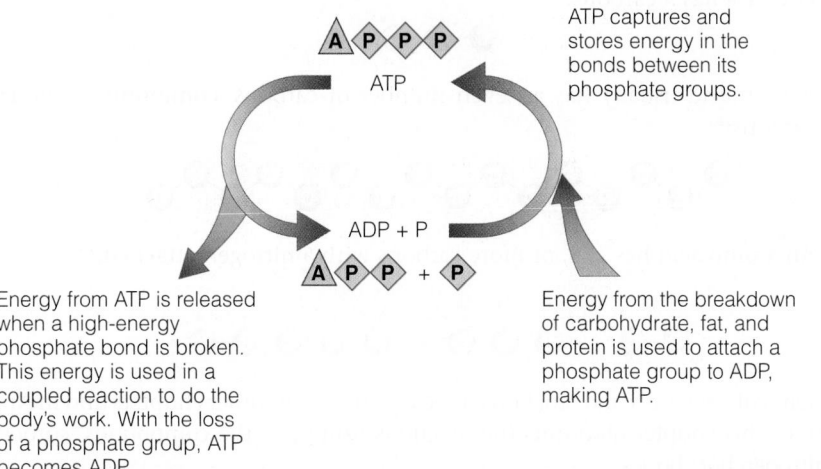

ATP captures and stores energy in the bonds between its phosphate groups.

Energy from ATP is released when a high-energy phosphate bond is broken. This energy is used in a coupled reaction to do the body's work. With the loss of a phosphate group, ATP becomes ADP.

Energy from the breakdown of carbohydrate, fat, and protein is used to attach a phosphate group to ADP, making ATP.

IN SUMMARY

During digestion the energy-yielding nutrients—carbohydrates, lipids, and proteins—are broken down to glucose (and other monosaccharides), glycerol, fatty acids, and amino acids. Aided by enzymes and coenzymes, the cells use these products of digestion to build more complex compounds (anabolism) or break them down further to release energy (catabolism). High-energy compounds such as ATP may capture the energy released during catabolism.

Breaking Down Nutrients for Energy

Chapters 4, 5, and 6 laid the groundwork for the study of metabolism; a brief review may be helpful. During digestion, the body breaks down the three energy-yielding nutrients—carbohydrates, lipids, and proteins—into four basic units that can be absorbed into the blood:

- From carbohydrates—glucose (and other monosaccharides)
- From fats (triglycerides)—glycerol and fatty acids
- From proteins—amino acids

The body uses carbohydrates and fats for most of its energy needs. Amino acids are used primarily as building blocks for proteins, but they also enter energy pathways, contributing about 10 to 15 percent of the day's energy use. Look for these four basic units—glucose, glycerol, fatty acids, and amino acids—to appear again and again in the metabolic reactions described in this chapter. Alcohol also enters many of the metabolic pathways; Highlight 7 focuses on how alcohol disrupts metabolism and how the body handles it.

Glucose, glycerol, fatty acids, and amino acids are the basic units derived from food, but a molecule of each of these compounds is made of still smaller units, the atoms—carbons, nitrogens, oxygens, and hydrogens. During catabolism, the body

All the energy used to keep the heart beating, the brain thinking, and the legs running comes from the carbohydrates, fats, and proteins in foods.

© Chris Cole/The Image Bank/Getty Images

◆ A healthy diet provides:
- 45–65% kcalories from carbohydrate
- 10–35% kcalories from protein
- 20–35% kcalories from fat

pyruvate (PIE-roo-vate): a 3-carbon compound that plays a key role in energy metabolism.

$$CH_3$$
$$|$$
$$C=O$$
$$|$$
$$COOH$$

acetyl CoA (ASS-eh-teel, or ah-SEET-il, coh-AY): a 2-carbon compound (**acetate,** or **acetic acid,** shown in Figure 5-1 on p. 140) to which a molecule of CoA is attached.

CoA (coh-AY): coenzyme A; the coenzyme derived from the B vitamin pantothenic acid and central to energy metabolism.

TCA cycle or **tricarboxylic** (try-car-box-ILL-ick) **acid cycle:** a series of metabolic reactions that break down molecules of acetyl CoA to carbon dioxide and hydrogen atoms; also called the **Kreb's cycle** after the biochemist who elucidated its reactions.

electron transport chain: the final pathway in energy metabolism that transports electrons from hydrogen to oxygen and captures the energy released in the bonds of ATP.

separates these atoms from one another. To follow this action, recall how many carbons are in the "backbones" of these compounds:

- Glucose has 6 carbons:

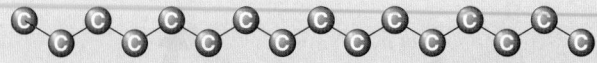

- Glycerol has 3 carbons:

- A fatty acid usually has an even number of carbons, commonly 16 or 18 carbons:*

- An amino acid has 2, 3, or more carbons with a nitrogen attached:**

Full chemical structures and reactions appear both in the earlier chapters and in Appendix C; this chapter diagrams the reactions using just the compounds' carbon and nitrogen backbones.

As you will see, each of the compounds—glucose, glycerol, fatty acids, and amino acids—starts down a different path. Along the way, two new names appear—**pyruvate** (a 3-carbon structure) and **acetyl CoA** (a 2-carbon structure with a coenzyme, **CoA,** attached)—and the rest of the story falls into place around them.[†] Two major points to notice in the following discussion:

- Pyruvate can be used to make glucose.
- Acetyl CoA cannot be used to make glucose.

A key to understanding these metabolic pathways is learning which fuels can be converted to glucose and which cannot. The parts of protein and fat that can be converted to pyruvate *can* provide glucose for the body, whereas the parts that are converted to acetyl CoA *cannot* provide glucose but can readily provide fat. The body must have glucose to fuel the activities of the central nervous system and red blood cells. Without glucose from food, the body will devour its own lean (protein-containing) tissue to provide the amino acids to make glucose. Therefore, to keep this from happening, the body needs foods that can provide glucose—primarily carbohydrate. Giving the body only fat, which delivers mostly acetyl CoA, puts it in the position of having to break down protein tissue to make glucose. Giving the body only protein puts it in the position of having to convert protein to glucose. Clearly, the best diet ◆ provides ample carbohydrate, adequate protein, and some fat.

Eventually, all of the energy-yielding nutrients can enter the common pathways of the **TCA cycle** and the **electron transport chain.** (Similarly, people from three different cities can all enter an interstate highway and travel to the same destination.) The TCA cycle and electron transport chain have central roles in energy metabolism and receive full attention later in the chapter. First, the text describes how each of the energy-yielding nutrients is broken down to acetyl CoA and other compounds in preparation for their entrance into these final energy pathways.

---

* The figures in this chapter show 16- or 18-carbon fatty acids. Fatty acids may have 4 to 20 or more carbons, with chain lengths of 16 and 18 carbons most prevalent.
** The figures in this chapter usually show amino acids as compounds of 2, 3, or 5 carbons arranged in a straight line, but in reality amino acids may contain other numbers of carbons and assume other structural shapes (see Appendix C).
† The term *pyruvate* means a salt of *pyruvic acid.* (Throughout this book, the ending *–ate* is used interchangeably with *–ic acid;* for our purposes they mean the same thing.)

Glucose

What happens to glucose, glycerol, fatty acids, and amino acids during energy metabolism can best be understood by starting with glucose. This discussion features glucose because of its central role in carbohydrate metabolism and because liver cells can convert the other monosaccharides (fructose and galactose) to compounds that enter the same energy pathways.

Glucose-to-Pyruvate The first pathway glucose takes on its way to yield energy is called **glycolysis** (glucose splitting).* Figure 7-5 shows a simplified drawing of glycolysis. (This pathway actually involves several steps and several enzymes, which

* Glycolysis takes place in the cytosol of the cell (see Figure 7-1, p. 214).

glycolysis (gly-COLL-ih-sis): the metabolic breakdown of glucose to pyruvate. Glycolysis does not require oxygen (anaerobic).
• **glyco** = glucose
• **lysis** = breakdown

FIGURE 7-5 *Animated!* Glycolysis: Glucose-to-Pyruvate

This simplified overview of glycolysis illustrates the steps in the process of converting glucose to pyruvate. Appendix C provides more details.

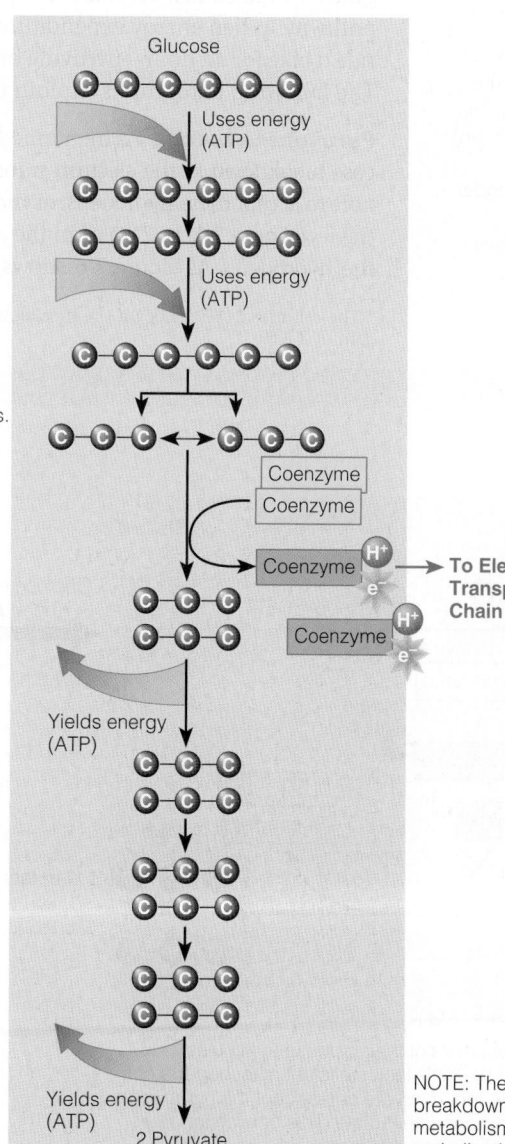

A little ATP is used to start glycolysis.

Galactose and fructose enter glycolysis at different places, but all continue on the same pathway.

In a series of reactions, the 6-carbon glucose is converted to other 6-carbon compounds, which eventually split into two interchangeable 3-carbon compounds.

A little ATP is produced, and coenzymes carry the hydrogens and their electrons to the electron transport chain.

These 3-carbon compounds are converted to pyruvate. Glycolysis of one molecule of glucose produces two molecules of pyruvate.

NOTE: These arrows point down indicating the breakdown of glucose to pyruvate during energy metabolism. (Alternatively, the arrows could point up indicating the making of glucose from pyruvate, but that is not the focus of this discussion.)

are shown in Appendix C.) In a series of reactions, the 6-carbon glucose is converted to similar 6-carbon compounds before being split in half, forming two 3-carbon compounds. These 3-carbon compounds continue along the pathway until they are converted to pyruvate. Thus the net yield of one glucose molecule is two pyruvate molecules. The net yield of energy at this point is small; to start glycolysis, the cell uses a little energy and then produces only a little more than it had to invest initially.* In addition, as glucose breaks down to pyruvate, hydrogen atoms with their electrons are released and carried to the electron transport chain by coenzymes made from the B vitamin niacin. A later section of the chapter explains how oxygen accepts the electrons and combines with the hydrogens to form water and how the process captures energy in the bonds of ATP.

This discussion focuses primarily on the breakdown of glucose for energy, but if needed, cells in the liver (and to some extent, the kidneys) can make glucose again from pyruvate in a process similar to the reversal of glycolysis. Making glucose requires energy, however, and a few different enzymes. Still, glucose can be made from pyruvate, so the arrows between glucose and pyruvate could point up as well as down. ◆

Glucose

↕

Pyruvate

◆ Glucose may go "down" to make pyruvate, or pyruvate may go "up" to make glucose, depending on the cell's needs.

anaerobic (AN-air-ROE-bic): not requiring oxygen.
• **an** = not

aerobic (air-ROE-bic): requiring oxygen.

mitochondria (my-toh-KON-dree-uh): the cellular organelles responsible for producing ATP; made of membranes (lipid and protein) with enzymes mounted on them.
• **mitos** = thread (referring to their slender shape)
• **chondros** = cartilage (referring to their external appearance)

Pyruvate's Options Pyruvate may enter either an **anaerobic** or an **aerobic** energy pathway. When the body needs energy quickly—as occurs when you run a quarter mile as fast as you can—pyruvate is converted to lactate in an anaerobic pathway. When energy expenditure proceeds at a slower pace—as occurs when you ride a bike for an hour—pyruvate breaks down to acetyl CoA in an aerobic pathway. The following paragraphs explain these pathways.

Pyruvate-to-Lactate As mentioned earlier, coenzymes carry the hydrogens from glucose breakdown to the electron transport chain. If the electron transport chain is unable to accept these hydrogens, as may occur when cells lack sufficient **mitochondria** (review Figure 7-1, p. 214) or in the absence of sufficient oxygen, pyruvate can accept the hydrogens. As Figure 7-6 shows, by accepting the hydrogens, pyruvate becomes

---

* The cell uses 2 ATP to begin the breakdown of glucose to pyruvate, but it then gains 4 ATP for a net gain of 2 ATP.

FIGURE 7-6 Pyruvate-to-Lactate

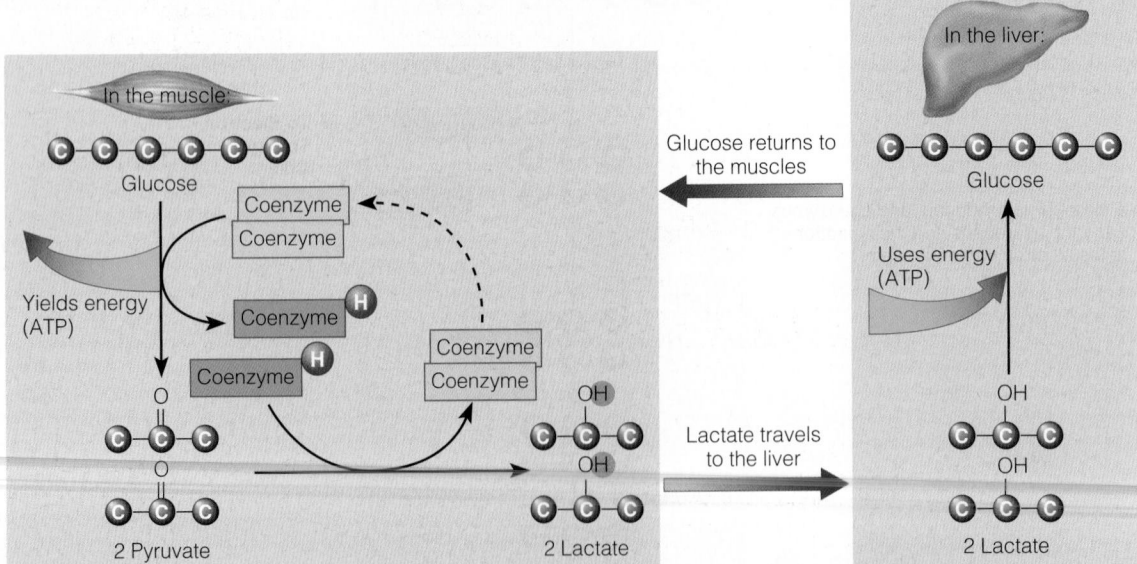

Working muscles break down most of their glucose molecules anaerobically to pyruvate. If the cells lack sufficient mitochondria or in the absence of sufficient oxygen, pyruvate can accept the hydrogens from glucose breakdown and become lactate. This conversion frees the coenzymes so that glycolysis can continue.

Liver enzymes can convert lactate to glucose, but this reaction requires energy. The process of converting lactate from the muscles to glucose in the liver that can be returned to the muscles is known as the Cori cycle.

lactate, and the coenzymes are freed to return to glycolysis to pick up more hydrogens. In this way, glucose can continue providing energy anaerobically for a while (see the left side of Figure 7-6).

The production of lactate occurs to a limited extent even at rest. During high-intensity exercise, however, the muscles rely heavily on anaerobic glycolysis to produce ATP quickly and the concentration of lactate increases dramatically. The rapid rate of glycolysis produces abundant pyruvate and releases hydrogen-carrying coenzymes more rapidly than the mitochondria can handle them. To enable exercise to continue at this intensity, pyruvate is converted to lactate and coenzymes are released, which allows glycolysis to continue (as mentioned earlier). The accumulation of lactate in the muscles coincides with—but is not the cause of—the subsequent drop in blood pH, burning pain, and fatigue that are commonly associated with intense exercise.[2] In fact, making lactate from pyruvate consumes two hydrogen ions, which actually diminishes acidity and improves the performance of tired muscles.[3] A person performing the same exercise following endurance training actually experiences less discomfort—in part because the number of mitochondria in the muscle cells have increased. This adaptation improves the mitochondria's ability to keep pace with the muscles' demand for energy.

One possible fate of lactate is to be transported from the muscles to the liver. There the liver can convert the lactate produced in muscles to glucose, which can then be returned to the muscles. This recycling process is called the **Cori cycle** (see Figure 7-6). (Muscle cells cannot recycle lactate to glucose because they lack a necessary enzyme.)

Whenever carbohydrates, fats, or proteins are broken down to provide energy, oxygen is always ultimately involved in the process. The role of oxygen in metabolism is worth noticing, for it helps our understanding of physiology and metabolic reactions. Chapter 14 describes the body's use of the energy nutrients to fuel physical activity, but the facts just presented offer a sneak preview. The breakdown of glucose-to-pyruvate-to-lactate proceeds without oxygen—it is anaerobic. This anaerobic pathway yields energy quickly, but it cannot be sustained for long—a couple of minutes at most. Conversely, the aerobic pathways produce energy more slowly, but because they can be sustained for a long time, their total energy yield is greater.

Pyruvate-to-Acetyl CoA If the cell needs energy and oxygen is available, pyruvate molecules enter the mitochondria of the cell (review Figure 7-1, p. 214). There a carbon group (COOH) from the 3-carbon pyruvate is removed to produce a 2-carbon compound that bonds with a molecule of CoA, becoming acetyl CoA. The carbon group from pyruvate becomes carbon dioxide, which is released into the blood, circulated to the lungs, and breathed out. Figure 7-7 diagrams the pyruvate-to-acetyl CoA reaction.

The step from pyruvate to acetyl CoA is metabolically irreversible: a cell cannot retrieve the shed carbons from carbon dioxide to remake pyruvate and then glucose. It is a one-way step and is therefore shown with only a "down" arrow in Figure 7-8.

© Jim Cummins/Taxi/Getty Images

The anaerobic breakdown of glucose-to-pyruvate-to-lactate is the major source of energy for short, intense exercise.

FIGURE 7-7 Pyruvate-to-Acetyl CoA

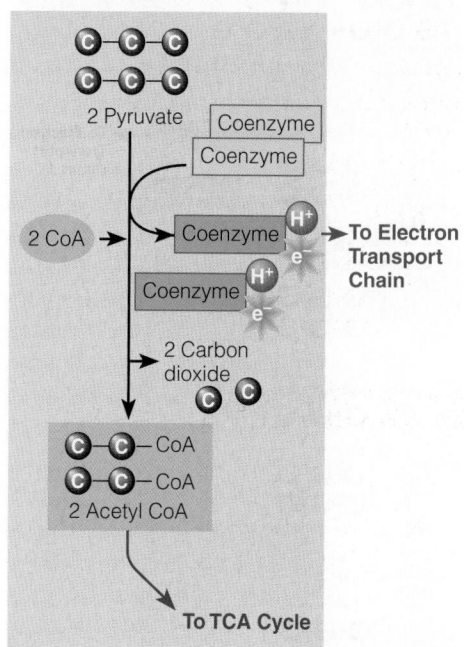

Each pyruvate loses a carbon as carbon dioxide and picks up a molecule of CoA, becoming acetyl CoA. The arrow goes only one way (down) because the step is not reversible. Result: 1 glucose yields 2 pyruvate, which yield 2 carbon dioxide and 2 acetyl CoA.

FIGURE 7-8 The Paths of Pyruvate and Acetyl CoA

Pyruvate may follow several reversible paths, but the path from pyruvate to acetyl CoA is irreversible.

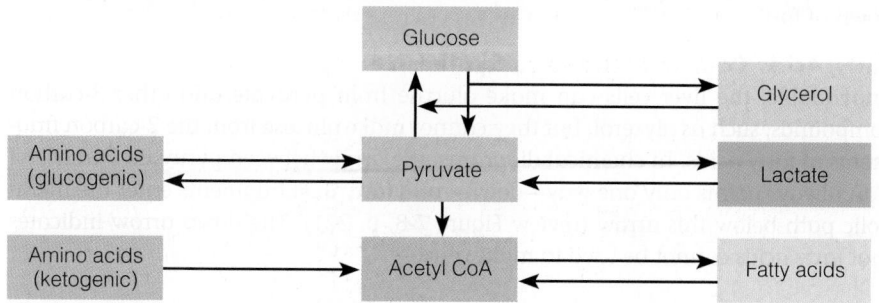

NOTE: Amino acids that can be used to make glucose are called *glucogenic;* amino acids that are converted to acetyl CoA are called *ketogenic.*

lactate: a 3-carbon compound produced from pyruvate during anaerobic metabolism.

Cori cycle: the path from muscle glycogen to glucose to pyruvate to lactate (which travels to the liver) to glucose (which can travel back to the muscle) to glycogen; named after the scientist who elucidated this pathway.

FIGURE 7-9 Glucose Enters the Energy Pathway

This figure combines Figure 7-5 and Figure 7-7 to show the breakdown of glucose-to-pyruvate-to-acetyl CoA. Details of the TCA cycle and the electron transport chain are given later and in Appendix C.

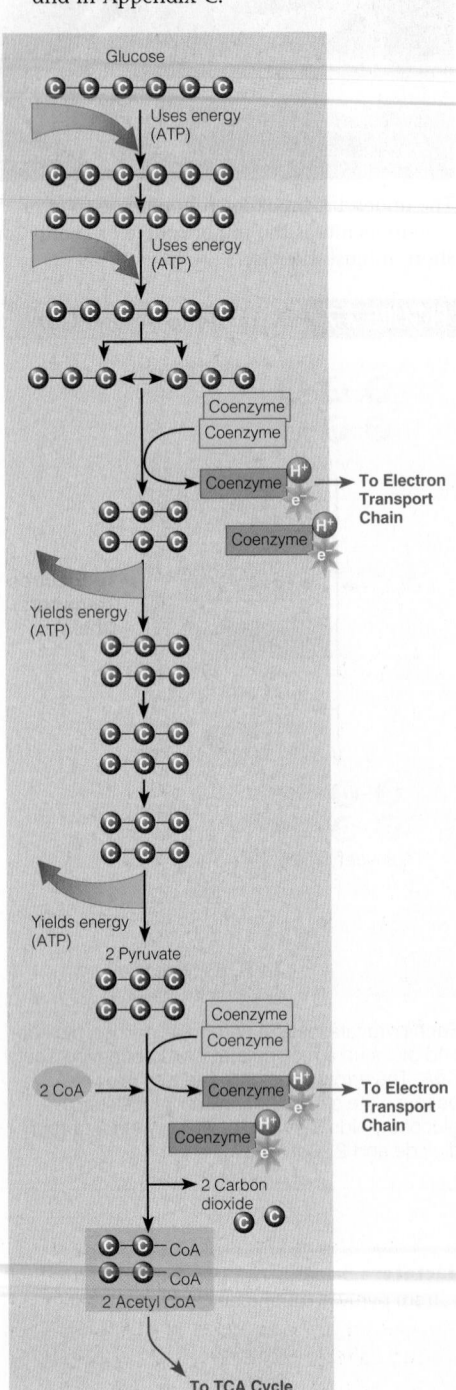

Acetyl CoA's Options Acetyl CoA has two main functions—it may be used to synthesize fats or to generate ATP. When ATP is abundant, acetyl CoA makes fat, the most efficient way to store energy for later use when energy may be needed. Thus any molecule that can make acetyl CoA—including glucose, glycerol, fatty acids, and amino acids—can make fat. In reviewing Figure 7-8, notice that acetyl CoA can be used as a building block for fatty acids, but it cannot be used to make glucose or amino acids.

When ATP is low and the cell needs energy, acetyl CoA may proceed through the TCA cycle, releasing hydrogens, with their electrons, to the electron transport chain. The story of acetyl CoA continues on p. 227 after a discussion of how fat and protein arrive at the same crossroads. For now, know that when acetyl CoA from the breakdown of glucose enters the aerobic pathways of the TCA cycle and electron transport chain, much more ATP is produced than during glycolysis. The role of glycolysis is to provide energy for short bursts of activity and to prepare glucose for later energy pathways.

IN SUMMARY

The breakdown of glucose to energy begins with glycolysis, a pathway that produces pyruvate. Keep in mind that glucose can be synthesized only from pyruvate or compounds earlier in the pathway. Pyruvate may be converted to lactate anaerobically or to acetyl CoA aerobically. Once the commitment to acetyl CoA is made, glucose is not retrievable; acetyl CoA cannot go back to glucose. Figure 7-9 summarizes the breakdown of glucose.

Glycerol and Fatty Acids

Once glucose breakdown is understood, fat and protein breakdown are easily learned, for all three eventually enter the same metabolic pathways. Recall that triglycerides can break down to glycerol and fatty acids.

Glycerol-to-Pyruvate Glycerol is a 3-carbon compound like pyruvate but with a different arrangement of H and OH on the C. As such, glycerol can easily be converted to another 3-carbon compound that can go either "up" the pathway to form glucose or "down" to form pyruvate and then acetyl CoA (review Figure 7-8, p. 221).

Fatty Acids-to-Acetyl CoA Fatty acids are taken apart 2 carbons at a time in a series of reactions known as **fatty acid oxidation.*** Figure 7-10 illustrates fatty acid oxidation and shows that in the process, each 2-carbon fragment splits off and combines with a molecule of CoA to make acetyl CoA. As each 2-carbon fragment breaks off from a fatty acid during oxidation, hydrogens and their electrons are released and carried to the electron transport chain by coenzymes made from the B vitamins riboflavin and niacin. Figure 7-11 (p. 224) summarizes the breakdown of fats.

Fatty Acids Cannot Be Used to Synthesize Glucose When carbohydrate is unavailable, the liver cells can make glucose from pyruvate and other 3-carbon compounds, such as glycerol, but they cannot make glucose from the 2-carbon fragments of fatty acids. In chemical diagrams, the arrow between pyruvate and acetyl CoA always points only one way—down—and fatty acid fragments enter the metabolic path below this arrow (review Figure 7-8, p. 221). The down arrow indicates that fatty acids cannot be used to make glucose.

---

fatty acid oxidation: the metabolic breakdown of fatty acids to acetyl CoA; also called **beta oxidation.**

---

* Oxidation of fatty acids occurs in the mitochondria of the cells (see Figure 7-1, p. 214).

FIGURE 7-10 *Animated!* Fatty Acid-to-Acetyl CoA

Fatty acids are broken apart into 2-carbon fragments that combine with CoA to make acetyl CoA.

ThomsonNOW™
To test your understanding of these concepts, log on to **www.thomsonedu.com/thomsonnow**

The fatty acid is first activated by coenzyme A.

As each carbon-carbon bond is cleaved, hydrogens and their electrons are released, and coenzymes pick them up.

Another CoA joins the chain, and the bond at the second carbon (the beta-carbon) weakens. Acetyl CoA splits off, leaving a fatty acid that is two carbons shorter.

The shorter fatty acid enters the pathway and the cycle repeats, releasing more hydrogens with their electrons and more acetyl CoA. The molecules of acetyl CoA enter the TCA cycle, and the coenzymes carry the hydrogens and their electrons to the electron transport chain.

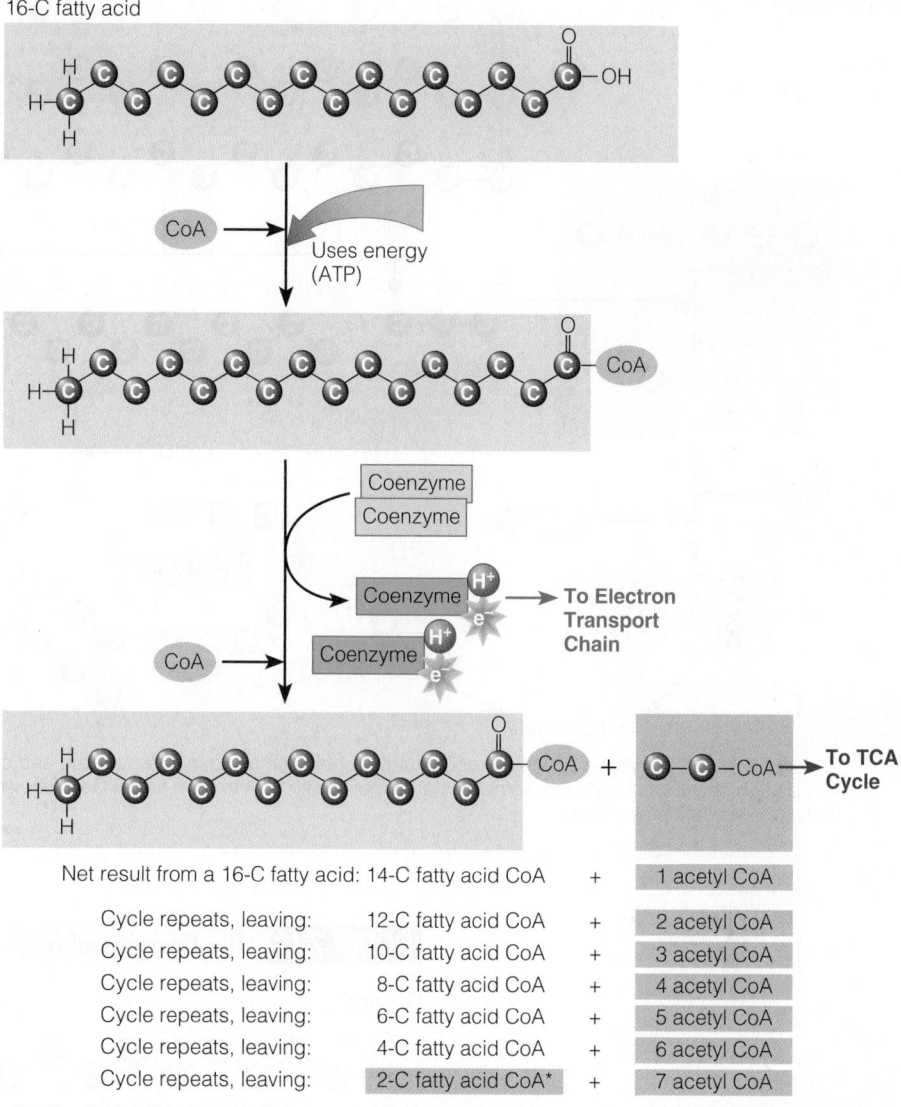

16-C fatty acid

Net result from a 16-C fatty acid: 14-C fatty acid CoA + 1 acetyl CoA

Cycle repeats, leaving:	12-C fatty acid CoA	+	2 acetyl CoA
Cycle repeats, leaving:	10-C fatty acid CoA	+	3 acetyl CoA
Cycle repeats, leaving:	8-C fatty acid CoA	+	4 acetyl CoA
Cycle repeats, leaving:	6-C fatty acid CoA	+	5 acetyl CoA
Cycle repeats, leaving:	4-C fatty acid CoA	+	6 acetyl CoA
Cycle repeats, leaving:	2-C fatty acid CoA*	+	7 acetyl CoA

*Notice that 2-C fatty acid CoA = acetyl CoA, so that the final yield from a 16-C fatty acid is 8 acetyl CoA.

The significance of fatty acids not being able to make glucose is that red blood cells and the brain and nervous system depend primarily on glucose as fuel. Remember that almost all dietary fats are triglycerides and that triglycerides contain only one small molecule of glycerol with three fatty acids. The glycerol can yield glucose, ◆ but that represents only 3 of the 50 or so carbon atoms in a triglyceride—about 5 percent of its weight (see Figure 7-12). The other 95 percent cannot be converted to glucose.

◆ Reminder: The making of glucose from non-carbohydrate sources is called *gluconeogenesis*. The glycerol portion of a triglyceride and most amino acids can be used to make glucose (review Figure 7-8, p. 221). The liver is the major site of gluconeogenesis, but the kidneys become increasingly involved under certain circumstances, such as starvation.

IN SUMMARY

The body can convert the small glycerol portion of a triglyceride to either pyruvate (and then glucose) or acetyl CoA. The fatty acids of a triglyceride, on the other hand, cannot make glucose, but they can provide abundant acetyl CoA. Acetyl CoA may then enter the TCA cycle to release energy or combine with other molecules of acetyl CoA to make body fat.

FIGURE 7-11   *Animated!* Fats Enter the Energy Pathway

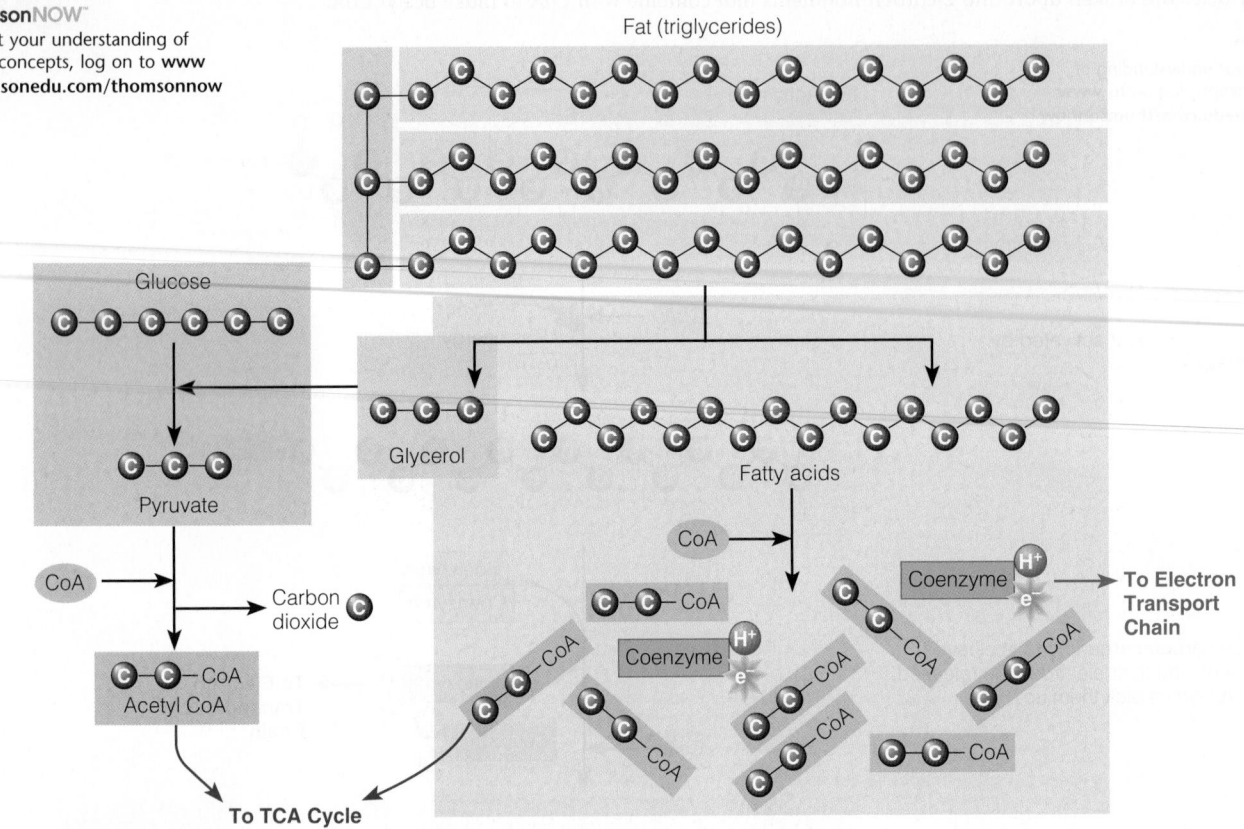

Glycerol enters the glycolysis pathway about midway between glucose and pyruvate and can be converted to either. Fatty acids are broken down into 2-carbon fragments that combine with CoA to form acetyl CoA (shown in Figure 7-10). Result: a 16-carbon fatty acid yields 8 acetyl CoA.

FIGURE 7-12   The Carbons of a Typical Triglyceride

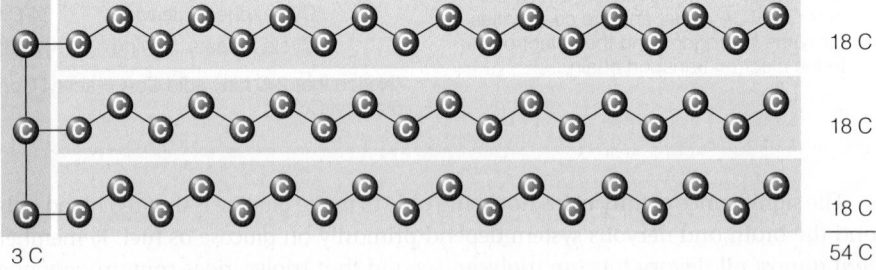

A typical triglyceride contains only one small molecule of glycerol (3 C) but has three fatty acids (each commonly 16 C or 18 C, or about 48 C to 54 C in total). Only the glycerol portion of a triglyceride can yield glucose.

Amino Acids

The preceding two sections have described how the breakdown of carbohydrate and fat produces acetyl CoA, which can enter the pathways that provide energy for the body's use. One energy-yielding nutrient remains: protein or, rather, the amino acids of protein.

FIGURE 7-13 Amino Acids Enter the Energy Pathway

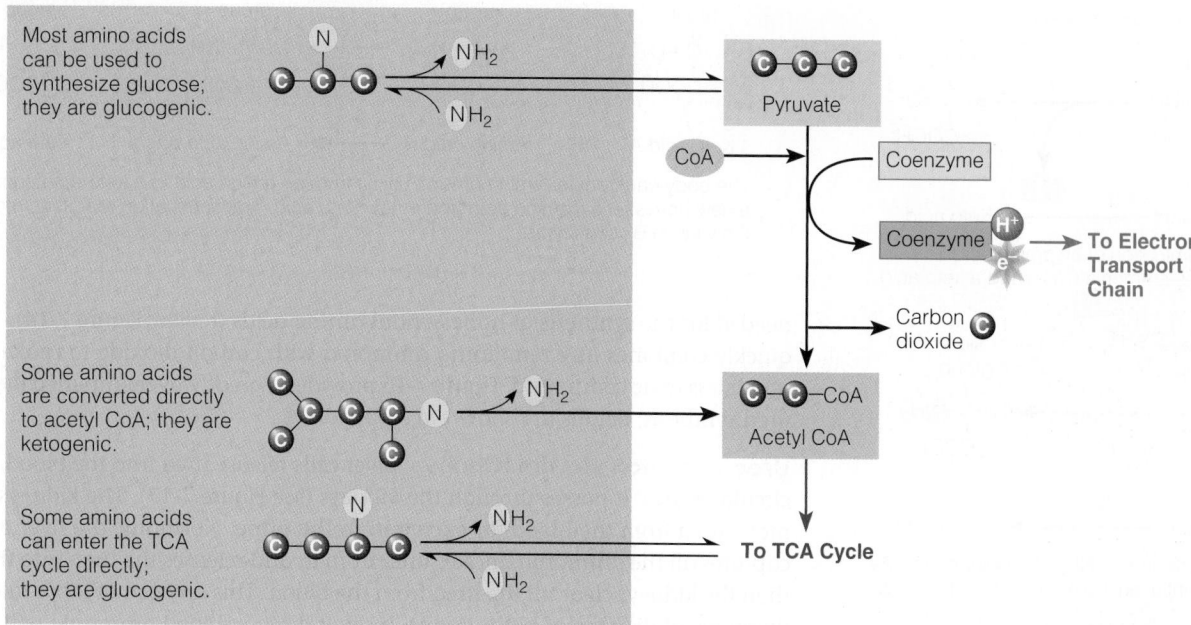

Amino acids

Most amino acids can be used to synthesize glucose; they are glucogenic.

Pyruvate

CoA

Coenzyme

Coenzyme H^+

To Electron Transport Chain

Carbon dioxide

Some amino acids are converted directly to acetyl CoA; they are ketogenic.

—CoA
Acetyl CoA

Some amino acids can enter the TCA cycle directly; they are glucogenic.

To TCA Cycle

NOTE: The arrows from pyruvate and the TCA cycle to amino acids are possible only for *nonessential* amino acids; remember, the body cannot make essential amino acids.

Amino Acids-to-Acetyl CoA Before entering the metabolic pathways, amino acids are deaminated (that is, they lose their nitrogen-containing amino group) and then they are catabolized in a variety of ways. As Figure 7-13 illustrates, some amino acids can be converted to pyruvate, others are converted to acetyl CoA, and still others enter the TCA cycle directly as compounds other than acetyl CoA.

Amino Acids-to-Glucose As you might expect, amino acids that are used to make pyruvate can provide glucose, whereas those used to make acetyl CoA can provide additional energy or make body fat but cannot make glucose. ◆ Amino acids entering the TCA cycle directly can continue in the cycle and generate energy; alternatively, they can generate glucose.[4] Thus protein, unlike fat, is a fairly good source of glucose when carbohydrate is not available.

Deamination When amino acids are metabolized for energy or used to make glucose or fat, they must be deaminated first. Two products result from deamination. One is the carbon structure without its amino group—often a **keto acid** (see Figure 7-14, p. 226). The other product is **ammonia** (NH_3), a toxic compound chemically identical to the strong-smelling ammonia in bottled cleaning solutions. Ammonia is a base, and if the body produces larger quantities than it can handle, the blood's critical acid-base balance becomes upset.

Transamination As the discussion of protein in Chapter 6 pointed out, only some amino acids are essential; others can be made in the body, given a source of nitrogen. By transferring an amino group from one amino acid to its corresponding keto acid, cells can make a new amino acid and a new keto acid, as shown in Figure 7-15 (p. 226). Through many such **transamination** reactions, involving many different keto acids, the liver cells can synthesize the nonessential amino acids.

Ammonia-to-Urea in the Liver The liver continuously produces small amounts of ammonia in deamination reactions. Some of this ammonia provides the nitrogen

◆ Amino acids that can make glucose via either pyruvate or TCA cycle intermediates are *glucogenic;* amino acids that are degraded to acetyl CoA are *ketogenic.*

keto (KEY-toe) **acid:** an organic acid that contains a carbonyl group (C=O).

ammonia: a compound with the chemical formula NH_3; produced during the deamination of amino acids.

transamination (TRANS-am-ih-NAY-shun): the transfer of an amino group from one amino acid to a keto acid, producing a new nonessential amino acid and a new keto acid.

FIGURE 7-14 Deamination and Synthesis of a Nonessential Amino Acid

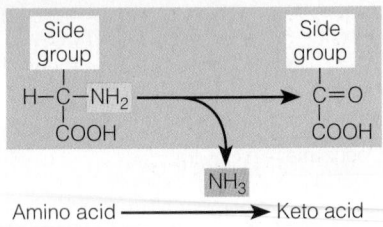

The deamination of an amino acid produces ammonia (NH_3) and a keto acid.

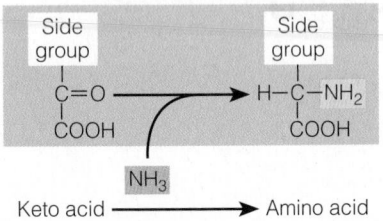

Given a source of NH_3, the body can make nonessential amino acids from keto acids.

FIGURE 7-16 Urea Synthesis

When amino acids are deaminated, ammonia is produced. The liver detoxifies ammonia before releasing it into the bloodstream by combining it with another waste product, carbon dioxide, to produce urea. See Appendix C for details.

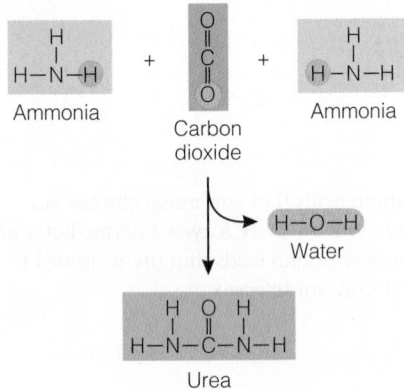

FIGURE 7-15 Transamination and Synthesis of a Nonessential Amino Acid

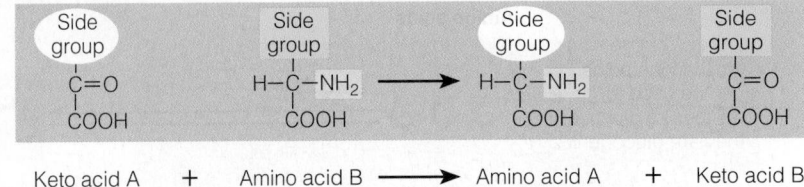

Keto acid A + Amino acid B ⟶ Amino acid A + Keto acid B

The body can transfer amino groups (NH_2) from an amino acid to a keto acid, forming a new *nonessential* amino acid and a new keto acid. Transamination reactions require the vitamin B_6 coenzyme.

needed for the synthesis of nonessential amino acids (review Figure 7-14). The liver quickly combines any remaining ammonia with carbon dioxide to make **urea**, a much less toxic compound. Figure 7-16 provides a greatly oversimplified diagram of urea synthesis; details are shown in Appendix C.

Urea Excretion via the Kidneys Liver cells release urea into the blood, where it circulates until it passes through the kidneys (see Figure 7-17). The kidneys then remove urea from the blood for excretion in the urine. Normally, the liver efficiently captures all the ammonia, makes urea from it, and releases the urea into the blood; then the kidneys clear all the urea from the blood. This division of labor allows easy diagnosis of diseases of both organs. In liver disease, blood ammonia will be high; in kidney disease, blood urea will be high.

Urea is the body's principal vehicle for excreting unused nitrogen, and the amount of urea produced increases with protein intake. To keep urea in solution, the body needs water. For this reason, a person who regularly consumes a high-protein diet (say, 100 grams a day or more) must drink plenty of water to dilute and excrete urea from the body. Without extra water, a person on a high-protein diet risks dehydration because the body uses its water to rid itself of urea. This explains some of the water loss that accompanies high-protein diets. Such losses may make high-protein diets *appear* to be effective, but water loss, of course, is of no value to the person who wants to lose body fat (as Highlight 9 explains).

IN SUMMARY

The body can use some amino acids to produce glucose, whereas others can be used either to generate energy or to make fat. Before an amino acid enters any of these metabolic pathways, its nitrogen-containing amino group must be removed through deamination. Deamination, which produces ammonia (NH_3), may be used to make nonessential amino acids and other nitrogen-containing compounds; the rest is cleared from the body via urea synthesis in the liver and excretion via the kidneys.

Breaking Down Nutrients for Energy— In Summary

To review the ways the body can use the energy-yielding nutrients, see the summary table (p. 227). To obtain energy, the body uses glucose and fatty acids as its primary fuels and amino acids to a lesser extent. To make glucose, the body can use all carbohydrates and most amino acids, but it can convert only 5 percent of fat (the glycerol portion) to glucose. To make proteins, the body needs amino acids. It can use glucose to make some nonessential amino acids when nitrogen is available; it cannot use fats to make body proteins. Finally, when energy is consumed beyond the body's needs, all three energy-yielding nutrients can contribute to body fat stores.

urea (you-REE-uh): the principal nitrogen-excretion product of protein metabolism. Two ammonia fragments are combined with carbon dioxide to form urea.

IN SUMMARY

Nutrient	Yields Energy?	Yields Glucose?	Yields Amino Acids and Body Proteins?	Yields Fat Stores?[a]
Carbohydrates (glucose)	Yes	Yes	Yes—when nitrogen is available, can yield *nonessential* amino acids	Yes
Lipids (fatty acids)	Yes	No	No	Yes
Lipids (glycerol)	Yes	Yes—when carbohydrate is unavailable	Yes—when nitrogen is available, can yield *nonessential* amino acids	Yes
Proteins (amino acids)	Yes	Yes—when carbohydrate is unavailable	Yes	Yes

[a]When energy intake exceeds needs, any of the energy-yielding nutrients can contribute to body fat stores.

The Final Steps of Catabolism

Thus far the discussion has followed each of the energy-yielding nutrients down three different pathways. All lead to the point where acetyl CoA enters the TCA cycle. The TCA cycle reactions take place in the inner compartment of the mitochondria. Examine the structure of the mitochondria shown in Figure 7-1 (p. 214). The significance of its structure will become evident as details unfold.

The TCA Cycle Acetyl CoA enters the TCA cycle, a busy metabolic traffic center. The TCA cycle is called a cycle, but that doesn't mean it regenerates acetyl CoA. Acetyl CoA goes one way only—down to two carbon dioxide molecules and a coenzyme (CoA). The TCA cycle is a circular path, though, in the sense that a 4-carbon compound known as **oxaloacetate** is needed in the first step and synthesized in the last step.

Oxaloacetate's role in replenishing the TCA cycle is critical. When oxaloacetate is insufficient, the TCA cycle slows down, and the cells face an energy crisis. Oxaloacetate is made primarily from pyruvate, although it can also be made from certain amino acids. Importantly, oxaloacetate cannot be made from fat. That oxaloacetate must be available for acetyl CoA to enter the TCA cycle underscores the importance of carbohydrates in the diet. A diet that provides ample carbohydrate ensures an adequate supply of oxaloacetate (because glucose produces pyruvate during glycolysis). (Highlight 9 presents more information on the consequences of low-carbohydrate diets.)

As Figure 7-18 shows, oxaloacetate is the first 4-carbon compound to enter the TCA cycle. Oxaloacetate picks up acetyl CoA (a 2-carbon compound), drops off one carbon (as carbon dioxide), then another carbon (as carbon dioxide), and returns to pick up another acetyl CoA. As for the acetyl CoA, its carbons go only one way—to carbon dioxide (see Appendix C for additional details).*

---

* Actually, the carbons that enter the cycle in acetyl CoA may not be the exact ones that are given off as carbon dioxide. In one of the steps of the cycle, a 6-carbon compound of the cycle becomes symmetrical, both ends being identical. Thereafter it loses carbons to carbon dioxide at one end or the other. Thus only half of the carbons from acetyl CoA are given off as carbon dioxide in any one turn of the cycle; the other half become part of the compound that returns to pick up another acetyl CoA. It is true to say, though, that for each acetyl CoA that enters the TCA cycle, 2 carbons are given off as carbon dioxide. It is also true that with each turn of the cycle, the energy equivalent of one acetyl CoA is released.

FIGURE 7-17 Urea Excretion

The liver and kidneys both play a role in disposing of excess nitrogen. Can you see why the person with liver disease has high blood ammonia, whereas the person with kidney disease has high blood urea? (Figure 12-2 provides details of how the kidneys work.)

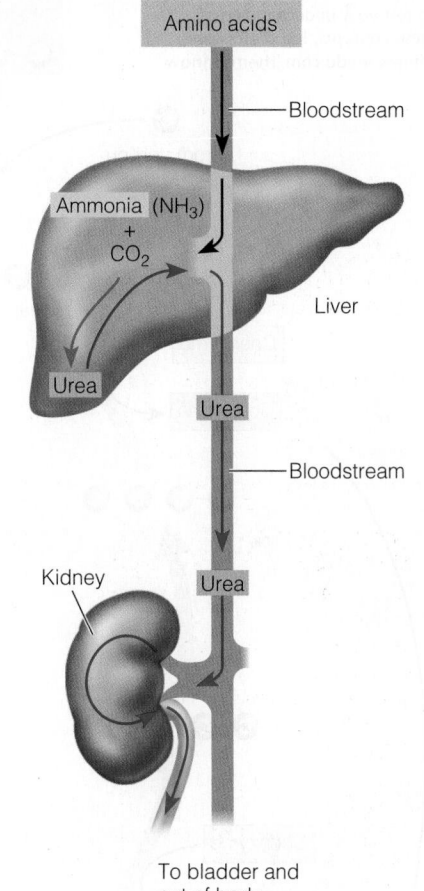

oxaloacetate (OKS-ah-low-AS-eh-tate): a carbohydrate intermediate of the TCA cycle.

FIGURE 7-18 Animated! The TCA Cycle

Oxaloacetate, a compound made primarily from pyruvate, starts the TCA cycle. The 4-carbon oxaloacetate joins with the 2-carbon acetyl CoA to make a 6-carbon compound. This compound is changed a little to make a new 6-carbon compound, which releases carbons as carbon dioxide, becoming a 5- and then a 4-carbon compound. Each reaction changes the structure slightly until finally the original 4-carbon oxaloacetate forms again and picks up another acetyl CoA—from the breakdown of glucose, glycerol, fatty acids, and amino acids—and starts the cycle over again. The breakdown of acetyl CoA releases hydrogens with their electrons, which are carried by coenzymes made from the B vitamins niacin and riboflavin to the electron transport chain. (For more details, see Appendix C.)

ThomsonNOW
To test your understanding of these concepts, log on to **www.thomsonedu.com/thomsonnow**

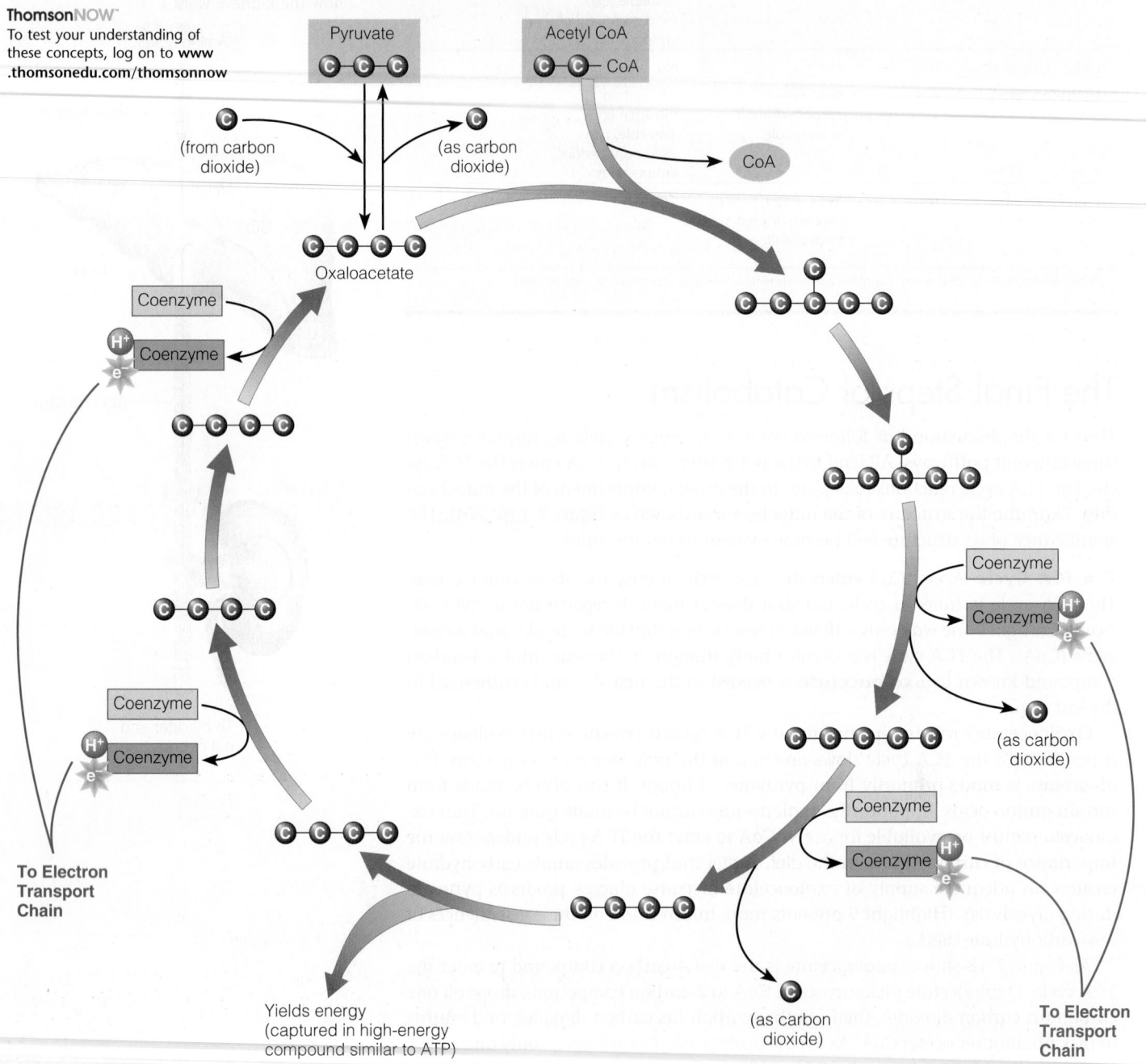

NOTE: Knowing that glucose produces pyruvate during glycolysis and that oxaloacetate must be available to start the TCA cycle, you can understand why the complete oxidation of fat requires carbohydrate.

As acetyl CoA molecules break down to carbon dioxide, hydrogen atoms with their electrons are removed from the compounds in the cycle. Each turn of the TCA cycle releases a total of eight electrons. Coenzymes made from the B vitamins niacin and riboflavin receive the hydrogens and their electrons from the TCA cycle and transfer them to the electron transport chain—much like a taxi cab that picks up passengers in one location and drops them off in another.

The Electron Transport Chain In the final pathway, the electron transport chain, energy is captured in the high-energy bonds of ATP. The electron transport chain consists of a series of proteins that serve as electron "carriers." These carriers are mounted in sequence on the inner membrane of the mitochondria (review Figure 7-1 on p. 214). As the coenzymes deliver their electrons from the TCA cycle, glycolysis, and fatty acid oxidation to the electron transport chain, each carrier receives the electrons and passes them on to the next carrier. These electron carriers continue passing the electrons down until they reach oxygen at the end of the chain. Oxygen (O) accepts the electrons and combines with hydrogen atoms (H) to form water (H_2O). ◆ That oxygen must be available for energy metabolism explains why it is essential to life.

As electrons are passed from carrier to carrier, enough energy is released to pump hydrogen ions across the membrane to the outer compartment of the mitochondria. The rush of hydrogen ions back into the inner compartment powers the synthesis of ATP. In this way, energy is captured in the bonds of ATP. The ATP leaves the mitochondria and enters the cytoplasm, where it can be used for energy. Figure 7-19 provides a simple diagram of the electron transport chain (see Appendix C for details).

The kCalories-per-Gram Secret Revealed Of the three energy-yielding nutrients, fat provides the most energy per gram. ◆ The reason may be apparent in Figure 7-20 (p. 230), which compares a fatty acid with a glucose molecule. Notice that nearly all the bonds in the fatty acid are between carbons and hydrogens. Oxygen can be added to all of them (forming carbon dioxide with the carbons and water with the hydrogens). As this happens, hydrogens are released to coenzymes heading

◆ The results of the electron transport chain:
- O_2 consumed
- H_2O and CO_2 produced
- Energy captured in ATP

◆ Fat = 9 kcal/g
Carbohydrate = 4 kcal/g
Protein = 4 kcal/g

FIGURE 7-19 *Animated!* Electron Transport Chain and ATP Synthesis

ThomsonNOW™
To test your understanding of these concepts, log on to **www .thomsonedu.com/thomsonnow**

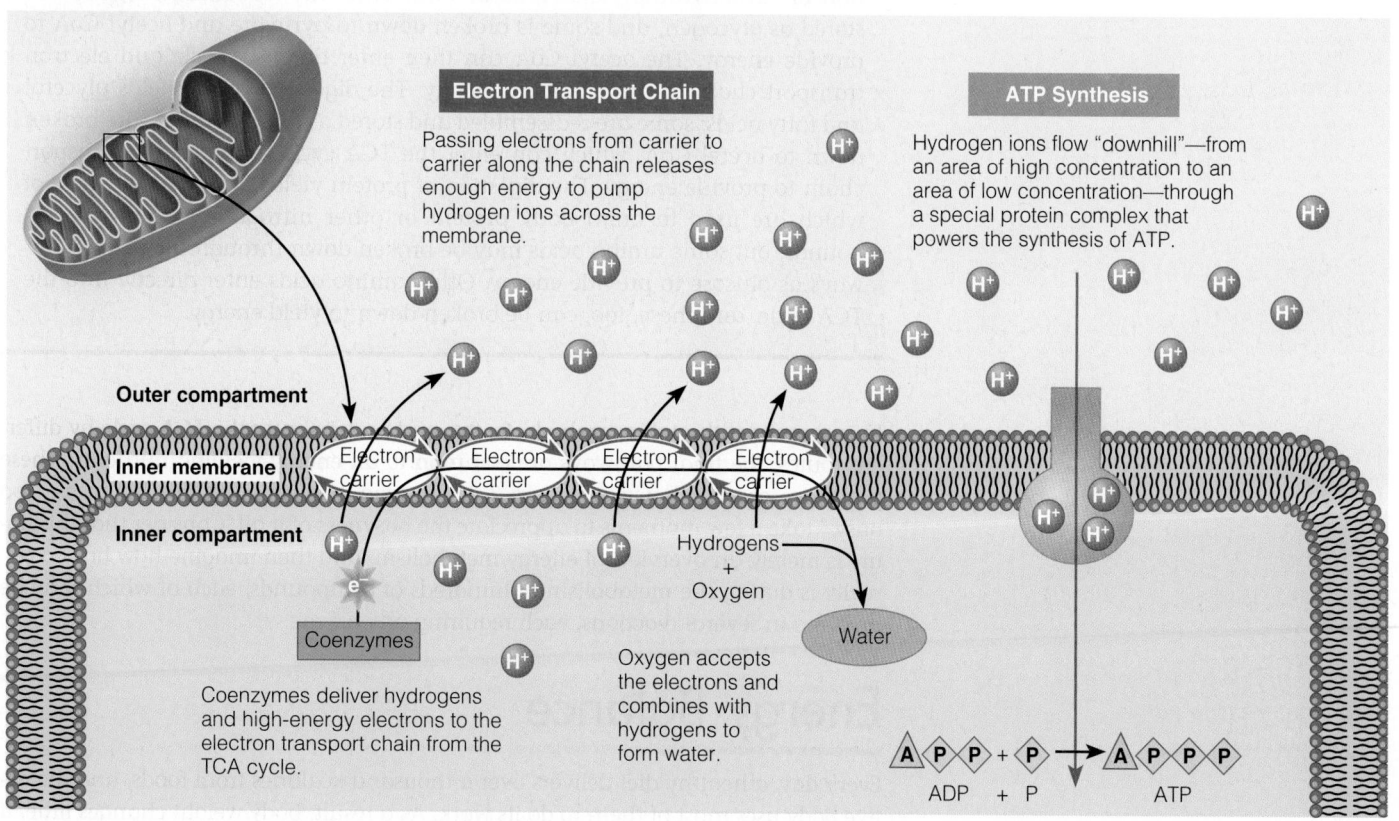

Electron Transport Chain

Passing electrons from carrier to carrier along the chain releases enough energy to pump hydrogen ions across the membrane.

ATP Synthesis

Hydrogen ions flow "downhill"—from an area of high concentration to an area of low concentration—through a special protein complex that powers the synthesis of ATP.

Outer compartment

Inner membrane — Electron carrier | Electron carrier | Electron carrier | Electron carrier

Inner compartment

Coenzymes

Coenzymes deliver hydrogens and high-energy electrons to the electron transport chain from the TCA cycle.

Hydrogens + Oxygen

Oxygen accepts the electrons and combines with hydrogens to form water.

Water

ADP + P → ATP

FIGURE 7-20 Chemical Structures of a Fatty Acid and Glucose Compared

To ease comparison, the structure shown here for glucose is not the ring structure shown in Chapter 4, but an alternative way of drawing its chemical structure.

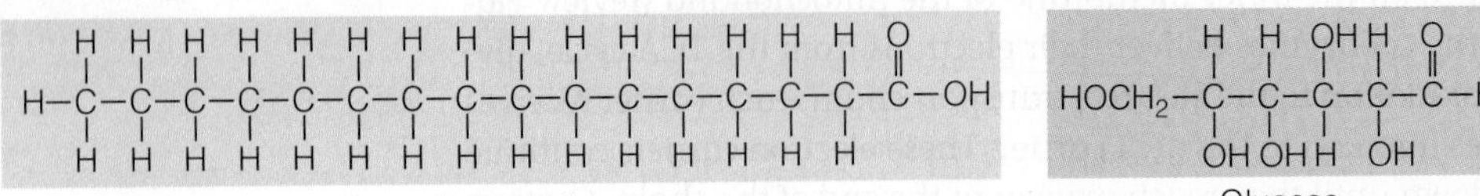

Fatty acid   Glucose

for the electron transport chain. In glucose, on the other hand, an oxygen is already bonded to each carbon. Thus there is less potential for oxidation, and fewer hydrogens are released when the remaining bonds are broken.

Because fat contains many carbon-hydrogen bonds that can be readily oxidized, it sends numerous coenzymes with their hydrogens and electrons to the electron transport chain where that energy can be captured in the bonds of ATP. This explains why fat yields more kcalories per gram than carbohydrate or protein. (Remember that each ATP holds energy and that kcalories measure energy; thus the more ATP generated, the more kcalories have been collected.) For example, one glucose molecule will yield 30 to 32 ATP when completely oxidized.[5] In comparison, one 16-carbon fatty acid molecule will yield 129 ATP when completely oxidized. Fat is a more efficient fuel source. Gram for gram, fat can provide much more energy than either of the other two energy-yielding nutrients, making it the body's preferred form of energy storage. (Similarly, you might prefer to fill your car with a fuel that provides 130 miles per gallon versus one that provides 30 miles per gallon.)

IN SUMMARY

After a balanced meal, the body handles the nutrients as follows. The digestion of carbohydrate yields glucose (and other monosaccharides); some is stored as glycogen, and some is broken down to pyruvate and acetyl CoA to provide energy. The acetyl CoA can then enter the TCA cycle and electron transport chain to provide more energy. The digestion of fat yields glycerol and fatty acids; some are reassembled and stored as fat, and others are broken down to acetyl CoA, which can enter the TCA cycle and electron transport chain to provide energy. The digestion of protein yields amino acids, most of which are used to build body protein or other nitrogen-containing compounds, but some amino acids may be broken down through the same pathways as glucose to provide energy. Other amino acids enter directly into the TCA cycle, and these, too, can be broken down to yield energy.

In summary, although carbohydrate, fat, and protein enter the TCA cycle by different routes, the final pathways are common to all energy-yielding nutrients. These pathways are all shown in Figure 7-21. Instead of dismissing this figure as "too busy," take a few moments to appreciate the busyness of it all. Consider that this figure is merely an overview of energy metabolism, and then imagine how busy a cell really is during the metabolism of hundreds of compounds, each of which may be involved in several reactions, each requiring an enzyme.

Energy Balance

Every day, a healthy diet delivers over a thousand kcalories from foods, and the active body uses most of them to do its work. As a result, body weight changes little, if at all. Maintaining body weight reflects that the body's energy budget is balanced.

FIGURE 7-21   The Central Pathways of Energy Metabolism

In reviewing these pathways, notice that:

- All of the energy-yielding nutrients—protein, carbohydrates, and fat—can be broken down to acetyl CoA, which can enter the TCA cycle.
- Many of these reactions release hydrogen atoms with their electrons, which are carried by coenzymes to the electron transport chain, where ATP is synthesized.
- In the end, oxygen is consumed, water and carbon dioxide are produced, and energy is captured in ATP.

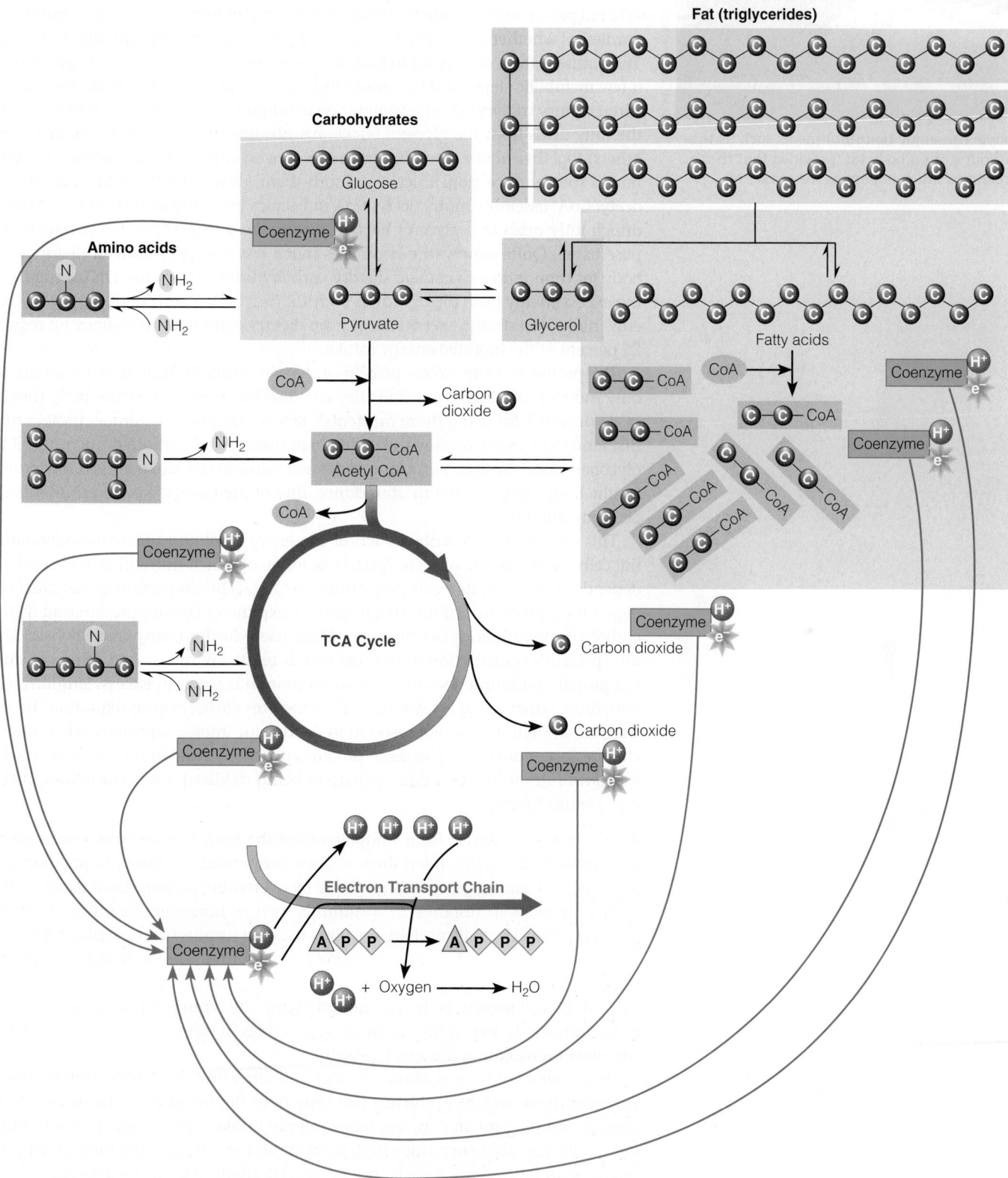

People can enjoy bountiful meals such as this without storing body fat, provided that they expend as much energy as they take in.

Some people, however, eat too much or exercise too little and get fat; others eat too little or exercise too much and get thin. The metabolic details have already been described; the next sections review them from the perspective of the body fat gained or lost. The possible reasons why people gain or lose weight are explored in Chapter 8.

Feasting—Excess Energy

When a person eats too much, metabolism favors fat formation. Fat cells enlarge regardless of whether the excess in kcalories derives from protein, carbohydrate, or fat. The pathway from dietary fat to body fat, however, is the most direct (requiring only a few metabolic steps) and the most efficient (costing only a few kcalories). To convert a dietary triglyceride to a triglyceride in adipose tissue, the body removes two of the fatty acids from the glycerol backbone, absorbs the parts, and puts them (and others) together again. By comparison, to convert a molecule of sucrose, the body has to split glucose from fructose, absorb them, dismantle them to pyruvate and acetyl CoA, assemble many acetyl CoA molecules into fatty acid chains, and finally attach fatty acids to a glycerol backbone to make a triglyceride for storage in adipose tissue. Quite simply, the body uses much less energy to convert dietary fat to body fat than it does to convert dietary carbohydrate to body fat. On average, storing excess energy from dietary fat as body fat uses only 5 percent of the ingested energy intake, but storing excess energy from dietary carbohydrate as body fat requires 25 percent of the ingested energy intake.

The pathways from excess protein and excess carbohydrate to body fat are not only indirect and inefficient, but they are also less preferred by the body (having other priorities for using these nutrients). Before entering fat storage, protein must first tend to its many roles in the body's lean tissues, and carbohydrate must fill the glycogen stores. Simply put, using these two nutrients to make fat is a low priority for the body. Still, if eaten in abundance, any of the energy-yielding nutrients can be made into fat.

This chapter has described each of the energy-yielding nutrients individually, but cells use a mixture of these fuels. How much of which nutrient is in the fuel mix depends, in part, on its availability from the diet. (The proportion of each fuel also depends on physical activity, as Chapter 14 explains.) Dietary protein and dietary carbohydrate influence the mixture of fuel used during energy metabolism. Usually, protein's contribution to the fuel mix is relatively minor and fairly constant, but protein oxidation does increase when protein is eaten in excess. Similarly, carbohydrate eaten in excess significantly enhances carbohydrate oxidation. In contrast, fat oxidation does *not* respond to dietary fat intake, especially when dietary changes occur abruptly. The more protein or carbohydrate in the fuel mix, the less fat contributes to the fuel mix. Instead of being oxidized, fat accumulates in storage. Details follow.

Excess Protein Recall from Chapter 6 that the body cannot store excess amino acids as such; it has to convert them to other compounds. Contrary to popular opinion, a person cannot grow muscle simply by overeating protein. Lean tissue such as muscle develops in response to a stimulus such as hormones or physical activity. When a person overeats protein, the body uses the surplus first by replacing normal daily losses and then by increasing protein oxidation. The body achieves protein balance this way, but any increase in protein oxidation displaces fat in the fuel mix. Any additional protein is then deaminated and the remaining carbons are used to make fatty acids, which are stored as triglycerides in adipose tissue. Thus a person can grow fat by eating too much protein.

People who eat huge portions of meat and other protein-rich foods may wonder why they have weight problems. Not only does the fat in those foods lead to fat storage, but the protein can, too, when energy intake exceeds energy needs. Many fad weight-loss diets encourage high protein intakes based on the false assumption that protein builds only muscle, not fat (see Highlight 9 for more details).

Excess Carbohydrate Compared with protein, the proportion of carbohydrate in the fuel mix changes more dramatically when a person overeats. The body handles abundant carbohydrate by first storing it as glycogen, but glycogen storage areas are limited and fill quickly. Because maintaining glucose balance is critical, the body uses glucose frugally when the diet provides only small amounts and freely when stores are abundant. In other words, glucose oxidation rapidly adjusts to the dietary intake of carbohydrate.

Excess glucose can also be converted to fat directly, but this is a minor pathway.[6] As mentioned earlier, converting glucose to fat is energetically expensive and does not occur until after glycogen stores have been filled. Even then, only a little, if any, new fat is made from carbohydrate.[7]

Nevertheless, excess dietary carbohydrate can lead to weight gain when it displaces fat in the fuel mix. When this occurs, carbohydrate spares both dietary fat and body fat from oxidation—an effect that may be more pronounced in overweight people than in lean people.[8] The net result: excess carbohydrate contributes to obesity or at least to the maintenance of an overweight body.

Excess Fat Unlike excess protein and carbohydrate, which both enhance their own oxidation, eating too much fat does not promote fat oxidation.[9] Instead, excess dietary fat moves efficiently into the body's fat stores; almost all of the excess is stored.

IN SUMMARY

If energy intake exceeds the body's energy needs, the result will be weight gain—regardless of whether the excess intake is from protein, carbohydrate, or fat. The difference is that the body is much more efficient at storing energy when the excess derives from dietary fat.

The Transition from Feasting to Fasting

Figure 7-22 (p. 234) shows the metabolic pathways operating in the body as it shifts from feasting (part A) to fasting (parts B and C). After a meal, glucose, glycerol, and fatty acids from foods are used as needed and then stored. Later, as the body shifts from a fed state to a fasting one, it begins drawing on these stores. Glycogen and fat are released from storage to provide more glucose, glycerol, and fatty acids for energy.

Energy is needed all the time. Even when a person is asleep and totally relaxed, the cells of many organs are hard at work. In fact, this work—the cells' work that maintains all life processes ◆ without any conscious effort—represents about two-thirds of the total energy a person spends in a day. The small remainder is the work that a person's muscles perform voluntarily during waking hours.

The body's top priority is to meet the cells' needs for energy, and it normally does this by periodic refueling—that is, by eating several times a day. When food is not available, the body turns to its own tissues for other fuel sources. If people choose not to eat, we say they are fasting; if they have no choice, we say they are starving. The body makes no such distinction. In either case, the body is forced to draw on its reserves of carbohydrate and fat and, within a day or so, on its vital protein tissues as well.

◆ The cells' work that maintains all life processes refers to the body's *basal metabolism*, which is described in Chapter 8.

Fasting—Inadequate Energy

During fasting, carbohydrate, fat, and protein are all eventually used for energy—fuel must be delivered to every cell. As the fast begins, glucose from the liver's stored glycogen and fatty acids from the adipose tissue's stored fat are both flowing into

FIGURE 7-22 Feasting and Fasting

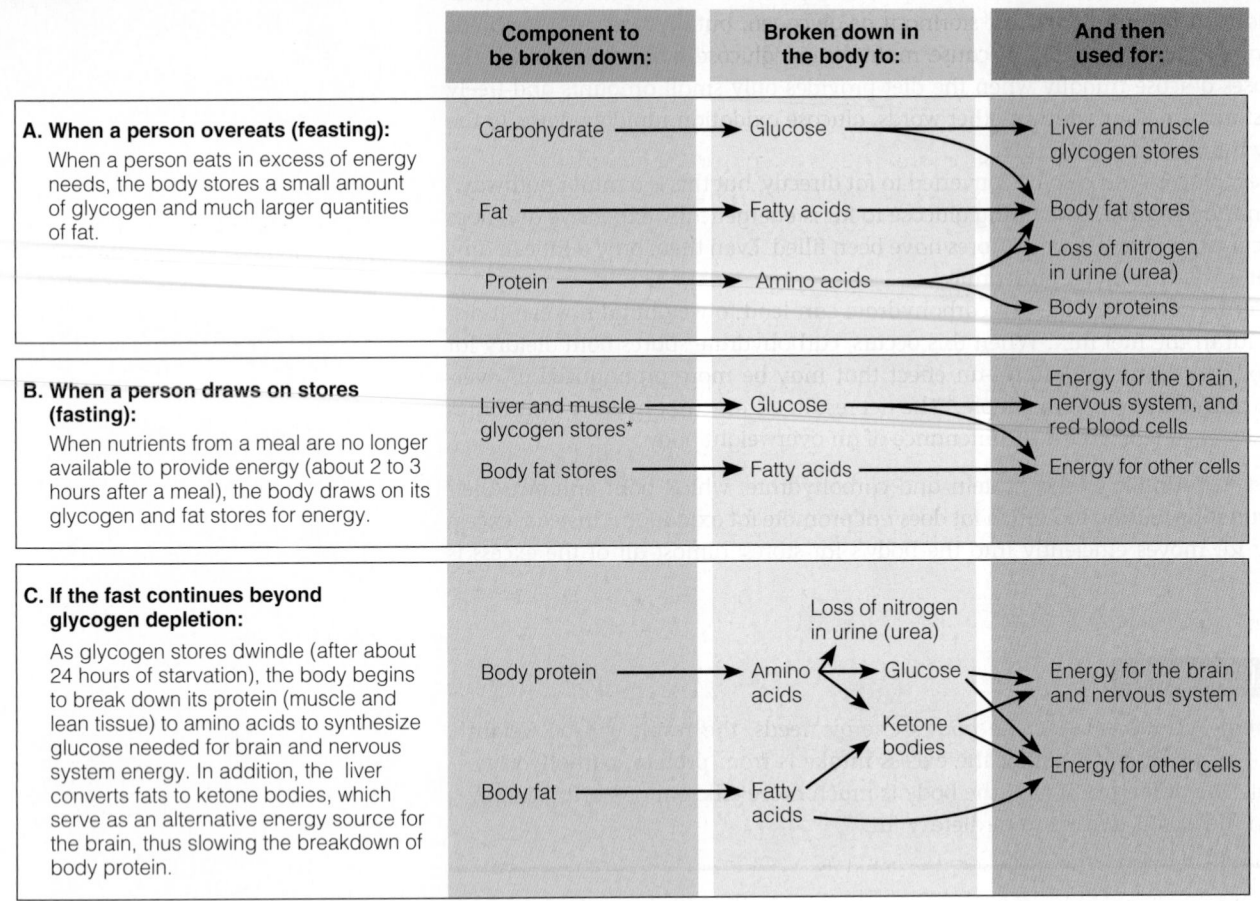

	Component to be broken down:	Broken down in the body to:	And then used for:
A. When a person overeats (feasting): When a person eats in excess of energy needs, the body stores a small amount of glycogen and much larger quantities of fat.	Carbohydrate → Fat → Protein →	Glucose Fatty acids Amino acids	Liver and muscle glycogen stores Body fat stores Loss of nitrogen in urine (urea) Body proteins
B. When a person draws on stores (fasting): When nutrients from a meal are no longer available to provide energy (about 2 to 3 hours after a meal), the body draws on its glycogen and fat stores for energy.	Liver and muscle glycogen stores* → Body fat stores →	Glucose Fatty acids	Energy for the brain, nervous system, and red blood cells Energy for other cells
C. If the fast continues beyond glycogen depletion: As glycogen stores dwindle (after about 24 hours of starvation), the body begins to break down its protein (muscle and lean tissue) to amino acids to synthesize glucose needed for brain and nervous system energy. In addition, the liver converts fats to ketone bodies, which serve as an alternative energy source for the brain, thus slowing the breakdown of body protein.	Body protein → Body fat →	Amino acids → Glucose → Ketone bodies ← Fatty acids Loss of nitrogen in urine (urea)	Energy for the brain and nervous system Energy for other cells

*The muscles' stored glycogen provides glucose only for the muscle in which the glycogen is stored.

cells, then breaking down to yield acetyl CoA, and finally delivering energy to power the cells' work. Several hours later, however, most of the glucose is used up—liver glycogen is exhausted and blood glucose begins to fall. Low blood glucose serves as a signal that promotes further fat breakdown and release of amino acids from muscles.

Glucose Needed for the Brain At this point, most of the cells are depending on fatty acids to continue providing their fuel. But red blood cells and the cells of the nervous system need glucose. Glucose is their primary energy fuel, and even when other energy fuels are available, glucose must be present to permit the energy-metabolizing machinery of the nervous system to work. Normally, the brain and nerve cells—which weigh only about three pounds—consume about half of the total *glucose* used each day (about 500 kcalories' worth). About one-fourth of the *energy* the adult body uses when it is at rest is spent by the brain; in children, it can be up to one-half.

Protein Meets Glucose Needs The red blood cells' and brain's special requirements for glucose pose a problem for the fasting body. The body can use its stores of fat, which may be quite generous, to furnish most of its cells with energy, but the red blood cells are completely dependent on glucose, ◆ and the brain and nerves prefer energy in the form of glucose. Amino acids that yield pyruvate can be used to make glucose, and to obtain the amino acids, body proteins must be broken down. For this reason, body protein tissues such as muscle and liver always break down to some extent during fasting. The amino acids that can't be used to make glucose are used as an energy source for other body cells.

The breakdown of body protein is an expensive way to obtain glucose. In the first few days of a fast, body protein provides about 90 percent of the needed glu-

◆ Red blood cells contain no mitochondria. Review Figure 7-1 (p. 214) to fully appreciate why red blood cells must depend on glucose for energy.

cose; glycerol, about 10 percent. If body protein losses were to continue at this rate, death would ensue within three weeks, regardless of the quantity of fat a person had stored. Fortunately, fat breakdown also increases with fasting—in fact, fat breakdown almost doubles, providing energy for other body cells and glycerol for glucose production.

The Shift to Ketosis As the fast continues, the body finds a way to use its fat to fuel the brain. It adapts by combining acetyl CoA fragments derived from fatty acids to produce an alternate energy source, ketone bodies (Figure 7-23). Normally produced and used only in small quantities, ketone bodies ◆ can provide fuel for some brain cells. Ketone body production rises until, after about ten days of fasting, it is meeting much of the nervous system's energy needs. Still, many areas of the brain rely exclusively on glucose, and to produce it, the body continues to sacrifice protein—albeit at a slower rate than in the early days of fasting.

◆ Reminder: *Ketone bodies* are compounds produced during the incomplete breakdown of fat when glucose is not available.

When ketone bodies contain an acid group (COOH), they are called keto acids. Small amounts of keto acids are a normal part of the blood chemistry, but when their concentration rises, the pH of the blood drops. This is ketosis, a sign that the body's chemistry is going awry. Elevated blood ketones (ketonemia) are excreted in the urine (ketonuria). A fruity odor on the breath (known as acetone breath) develops, reflecting the presence of the ketone acetone.

Suppression of Appetite Ketosis also induces a loss of appetite. As starvation continues, this loss of appetite becomes an advantage to a person without access to food, because the search for food would be a waste of energy. When the person finds food and eats again, the body shifts out of ketosis, the hunger center gets the message that food is again available, and the appetite returns. Highlight 9 includes a discussion of the risks of ketosis-producing diets in its review of popular weight-loss diets.

Slowing of Metabolism In an effort to conserve body tissues for as long as possible, the hormones of fasting slow metabolism. As the body shifts to the use of ketone bodies, it simultaneously reduces its energy output and conserves both its fat and its lean tissue. Still the lean (protein-containing) organ tissues shrink in mass and perform less metabolic work, reducing energy expenditures. As the muscles waste, they can do less work and so demand less energy, reducing expenditures further. Although fasting may promote dramatic *weight* loss, a low-kcalorie diet better supports *fat* loss while retaining lean tissue.

FIGURE 7-23 Ketone Body Formation

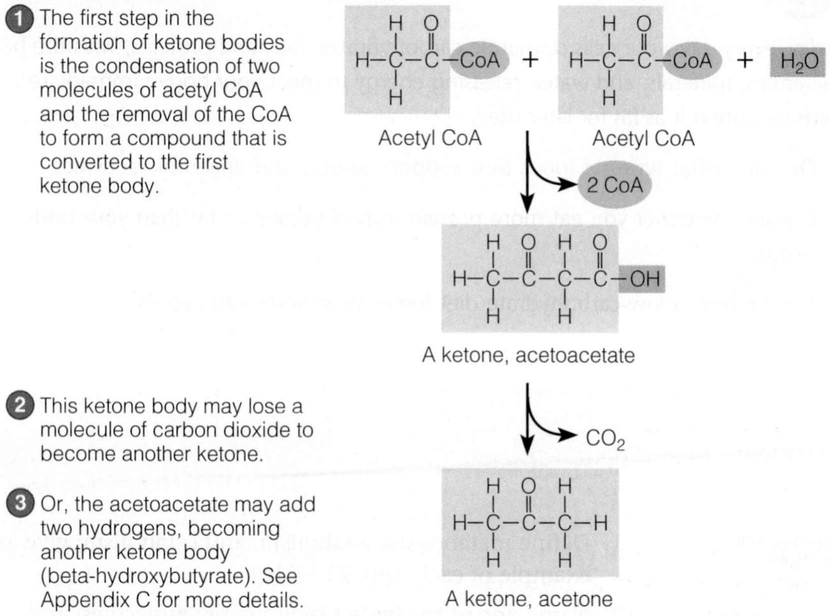

1 The first step in the formation of ketone bodies is the condensation of two molecules of acetyl CoA and the removal of the CoA to form a compound that is converted to the first ketone body.

Acetyl CoA   Acetyl CoA

2 CoA

A ketone, acetoacetate

2 This ketone body may lose a molecule of carbon dioxide to become another ketone.

CO_2

3 Or, the acetoacetate may add two hydrogens, becoming another ketone body (beta-hydroxybutyrate). See Appendix C for more details.

A ketone, acetone

Symptoms of Starvation The adaptations just described—slowing of energy output and reduction in fat loss—occur in the starving child, the hungry homeless adult, the fasting religious person, the adolescent with anorexia nervosa, and the malnourished hospital patient. Such adaptations help to prolong their lives and explain the physical symptoms of starvation: wasting; slowed heart rate, respiration, and metabolism; lowered body temperature; impaired vision; organ failure; and reduced resistance to disease.[10] Psychological effects of food deprivation include depression, anxiety, and food-related dreams.

The body's adaptations to fasting are sufficient to maintain life for a long time—up to two months. Mental alertness need not be diminished, and even some physical energy may remain unimpaired for a surprisingly long time. These remarkable adaptations, however, should not prevent anyone from recognizing the very real hazards that fasting presents.

IN SUMMARY

When fasting, the body makes a number of adaptations: increasing the breakdown of fat to provide energy for most of the cells, using glycerol and amino acids to make glucose for the red blood cells and central nervous system, producing ketones to fuel the brain, suppressing the appetite, and slowing metabolism. All of these measures conserve energy and minimize losses.

This chapter has probed the intricate details of metabolism at the level of the cells, exploring the transformations of nutrients to energy and to storage compounds. Several chapters and highlights build on this information. The highlight that follows this chapter shows how alcohol disrupts normal metabolism. Chapter 8 describes how a person's intake and expenditure of energy are reflected in body weight and body composition. Chapter 9 examines the consequences of unbalanced energy budgets—overweight and underweight. Chapter 10 shows the vital roles the B vitamins play as coenzymes assisting all the metabolic pathways described here. And Chapter 14 revisits metabolism to show how it supports the work of physically active people and how athletes can best apply that information in their choices of foods to eat.

ThomsonNOW
www.thomsonedu.com/thomsonnow

 Nutrition Portfolio

All day, every day, your cells dismantle carbohydrates, fats, and proteins, with the help of vitamins, minerals, and water, releasing energy to meet your body's immediate needs or storing it as fat for later use.

- Describe what types of foods best support aerobic and anaerobic activities.

- Consider whether you eat more protein, carbohydrate, or fat than your body needs.

- Explain how a low-carbohydrate diet forces your body into ketosis.

STUDY QUESTIONS

ThomsonNOW
To assess your understanding of chapter topics, take the Student Practice Test and explore the modules recommended in your Personalized Study Plan. Log onto **www.thomsonedu.com/thomsonnow**.

These questions will help you review the chapter. You will find the answers in the discussions on the pages provided.

1. Define metabolism, anabolism, and catabolism; give an example of each. (pp. 213–216)

2. Name one of the body's high-energy molecules, and describe how it is used. (pp. 216–217)

3. What are coenzymes, and what service do they provide in metabolism? (p. 216)

4. Name the four basic units, derived from foods, that are used by the body in metabolic transformations. How many carbons are in the "backbones" of each? (pp. 217–218)

5. Define aerobic and anaerobic metabolism. How does insufficient oxygen influence metabolism? (pp. 220–221)

6. How does the body dispose of excess nitrogen? (pp. 225–227)

7. Summarize the main steps in the metabolism of glucose, glycerol, fatty acids, and amino acids. (pp. 226–228)

8. Describe how a surplus of the three energy nutrients contributes to body fat stores. (pp. 219–226)

9. What adaptations does the body make during a fast? What are ketone bodies? Define ketosis. (pp. 233–236)

10. Distinguish between a loss of *fat* and a loss of *weight,* and describe how each might happen. (pp. 235–236)

These multiple choice questions will help you prepare for an exam. Answers can be found below.

1. Hydrolysis is an example of a(n):
    a. coupled reaction.
    b. anabolic reaction.
    c. catabolic reaction.
    d. synthesis reaction.

2. During metabolism, released energy is captured and transferred by:
    a. enzymes.
    b. pyruvate.
    c. acetyl CoA.
    d. adenosine triphosphate.

3. Glycolysis:
    a. requires oxygen.
    b. generates abundant energy.
    c. converts glucose to pyruvate.
    d. produces ammonia as a by-product.

4. The pathway from pyruvate to acetyl CoA:
    a. produces lactate.
    b. is known as gluconeogenesis.
    c. is metabolically irreversible.
    d. requires more energy than it produces.

5. For complete oxidation, acetyl CoA enters:
    a. glycolysis.
    b. the TCA cycle.
    c. the Cori cycle.
    d. the electron transport chain.

6. Deamination of an amino acid produces:
    a. vitamin B$_6$ and energy.
    b. pyruvate and acetyl CoA.
    c. ammonia and a keto acid.
    d. carbon dioxide and water.

7. Before entering the TCA cycle, each of the energy-yielding nutrients is broken down to:
    a. ammonia.
    b. pyruvate.
    c. electrons.
    d. acetyl CoA.

8. The body stores energy for future use in:
    a. proteins.
    b. acetyl CoA.
    c. triglycerides.
    d. ketone bodies.

9. During a fast, when glycogen stores have been depleted, the body begins to synthesize glucose from:
    a. acetyl CoA.
    b. amino acids.
    c. fatty acids.
    d. ketone bodies.

10. During a fast, the body produces ketone bodies by:
    a. hydrolyzing glycogen.
    b. condensing acetyl CoA.
    c. transaminating keto acids.
    d. converting ammonia to urea.

REFERENCES

1. R. H. Garrett and C. M. Grisham, *Biochemistry* (Belmont, Calif.: Thomson Brooks/Cole, 2005), p. 73.
2. R. A. Robergs, F. Ghiasvand, and D. Parker, Biochemistry of exercise-induced metabolic acidosis, *American Journal of Physiology-Regulatory, Integrative and Comparative Physiology* 287 (2004): R502-R516.
3. T. H. Pederson and coauthors, Intracellular acidosis enhances the excitability of working muscle, *Science* 305 (2004): 1144-1147.
4. S. S. Gropper, J. L. Smith, and J. L. Groff, *Advanced Nutrition and Human Metabolism* (Belmont, Calif.: Wadsworth/Thomson Learning, 2005), p. 198.
5. Garrett and Grisham, 2005, p. 669.
6. M. K. Hellerstein, No common energy currency: De novo lipogenesis as the road less traveled, *American Journal of Clinical Nutrition* 74 (2001): 707-708.
7. R. M. Devitt and coauthors, De novo lipogenesis during controlled overfeeding with sucrose or glucose in lean and obese women, *American Journal of Clinical Nutrition* 74 (2001): 707-708.
8. I. Marques-Lopes and coauthors, Postprandial de novo lipogenesis and metabolic changes induced by a high-carbohydrate, low-fat meal in lean and overweight men, *American Journal of Clinical Nutrition* 73 (2001): 253-261.
9. E. J. Parks, Macronutrient Metabolism Group Symposium on "Dietary fat: How low should we go?" Changes in fat synthesis influenced by dietary macronutrient content, *Proceedings of the Nutrition Society* 61 (2002): 281-286.
10. C. A. Jolly, Dietary restriction and immune function, *Journal of Nutrition* 134 (2004): 1853-1856.

ANSWERS

Study Questions (multiple choice)

1. c   2. d   3. c   4. c   5. b   6. c   7. d   8. c
9. b   10. b

Alcohol and Nutrition

Richard Dunkley/Getty Images

With the understanding of metabolism gained from Chapter 7, you are in a position to understand how the body handles alcohol, how alcohol interferes with metabolism, and how alcohol impairs health and nutrition. Before examining alcohol's damaging effects, it may be appropriate to mention that drinking alcohol in *moderation* may have some health benefits, including reduced risks of heart attacks, strokes, dementia, diabetes, and osteoporosis.[1] Moderate alcohol consumption may lower mortality from all causes, but only in adults age 35 and older.[2] No health benefits are evident before middle age.[3] Importantly, any benefits of alcohol must be weighed against the many harmful effects described in this highlight, as well as the possibility of alcohol abuse.

Alcohol in Beverages

To the chemist, **alcohol** refers to a class of organic compounds containing hydroxyl (OH) groups (the accompanying glossary defines alcohol and related terms). The glycerol to which fatty acids are attached in triglycerides is an example of an alcohol to a chemist. To most people, though, *alcohol* refers to the intoxicating ingredient in **beer, wine,** and **distilled liquor (hard liquor).** The chemist's name for this particular alcohol is *ethyl alcohol,* or **ethanol.** Glycerol has 3 carbons with 3 hydroxyl groups attached; ethanol has only 2 carbons and 1 hydroxyl group (see Figure H7-1). The remainder of this highlight talks about the particular alcohol, ethanol, but refers to it simply as *alcohol.*

Alcohols affect living things profoundly, partly because they act as lipid solvents. Their ability to dissolve lipids out of cell membranes allows alcohols to penetrate rapidly into cells, destroying cell structures and thereby killing the cells. For this reason, most alcohols are toxic in relatively small amounts; by the same token, because they kill microbial cells, they are useful as disinfectants.

Ethanol is less toxic than the other alcohols. Sufficiently diluted and taken in small enough doses, its action in the brain produces an effect that people seek—not with zero risk, but with a low enough risk (if the doses are low enough) to be tolerable. Used in this way, alcohol is a **drug**—that is, a substance that modifies body functions. Like all drugs, alcohol both offers benefits and poses hazards. The 2005 *Dietary Guidelines* advise "those who choose to drink alcoholic beverages to do so sensibly and in moderation."

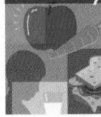

Dietary Guidelines for Americans 2005

- Those who choose to drink alcoholic beverages should do so sensibly and in moderation: up to one drink per day for women and two drinks per day for men.

- Alcoholic beverages should not be consumed by some individuals, including those who cannot restrict their alcohol intake, women of childbearing age who may become pregnant, pregnant and lactating women, children and adolescents, individuals taking medications that can interact with alcohol, and those with specific medical conditions.

- Alcoholic beverages should be avoided by individuals engaging in activities that require attention, skill, or coordination, such as driving or operating machinery.

The term **moderation** is important when describing alcohol use. How many drinks constitute moderate use, and how much is "a drink"? First, a **drink** is any alcoholic beverage that delivers $1/2$ ounce of *pure ethanol:*

- 5 ounces of wine
- 10 ounces of wine cooler
- 12 ounces of beer
- $1^1/2$ ounces of distilled liquor (80 proof whiskey, scotch, rum, or vodka)

Beer, wine, and liquor deliver different amounts of alcohol. The amount of alcohol in distilled liquor is stated as **proof:** 100 proof liquor is 50 percent alcohol, 80 proof is 40 percent alcohol, and so forth. Wine and beer have less alcohol than distilled liquor, although some fortified wines and beers have more alcohol than the regular varieties (see photo caption on p. 239).

FIGURE H7-1 Two Alcohols: Glycerol and Ethanol

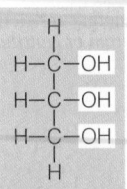
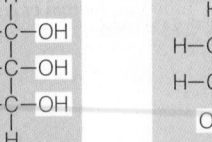

Glycerol is the alcohol used to make triglycerides.

Ethanol is the alcohol in beer, wine, and distilled liquor.

GLOSSARY

acetaldehyde (ass-et-AL-duh-hide): an intermediate in alcohol metabolism.

alcohol: a class of organic compounds containing hydroxyl (OH) groups.

alcohol abuse: a pattern of drinking that includes failure to fulfill work, school, or home responsibilities; drinking in situations that are physically dangerous (as in driving while intoxicated); recurring alcohol-related legal problems (as in aggravated assault charges); or continued drinking despite ongoing social problems that are caused by or worsened by alcohol.

alcohol dehydrogenase (dee-high-DROJ-eh-nayz): an enzyme active in the stomach and the liver that converts ethanol to acetaldehyde.

alcoholism: a pattern of drinking that includes a strong craving for alcohol, a loss of control and an inability to stop drinking once begun, withdrawal symptoms (nausea, sweating, shakiness, and anxiety) after heavy drinking, and the need for increasing amounts of alcohol to feel "high."

antidiuretic hormone (ADH): a hormone produced by the pituitary gland in response to dehydration (or a high sodium concentration in the blood). It stimulates the kidneys to reabsorb more water and therefore prevents water loss in urine (also called *vasopressin*). (This ADH should not be confused with the enzyme alcohol dehydrogenase, which is also sometimes abbreviated ADH.)

beer: an alcoholic beverage brewed by fermenting malt and hops.

cirrhosis (seer-OH-sis): advanced liver disease in which liver cells turn orange, die, and harden, permanently losing their function; often associated with alcoholism.

• **cirrhos** = an orange

distilled liquor or **hard liquor:** an alcoholic beverage made by fermenting and distilling grains; sometimes called *distilled spirits.*

drink: a dose of any alcoholic beverage that delivers ½ oz of pure ethanol:
• 5 oz of wine
• 10 oz of wine cooler
• 12 oz of beer

• 1½ oz of hard liquor (80 proof whiskey, scotch, rum, or vodka)

drug: a substance that can modify one or more of the body's functions.

ethanol: a particular type of alcohol found in beer, wine, and distilled liquor; also called *ethyl alcohol* (see Figure H7-1). Ethanol is the most widely used—and abused—drug in our society. It is also the only legal, nonprescription drug that produces euphoria.

fatty liver: an early stage of liver deterioration seen in several diseases, including kwashiorkor and alcoholic liver disease. Fatty liver is characterized by an accumulation of fat in the liver cells.

fibrosis (fye-BROH-sis): an intermediate stage of liver deterioration seen in several diseases, including viral hepatitis and alcoholic liver disease. In fibrosis, the liver cells lose their function and assume the characteristics of connective tissue cells (fibers).

MEOS or **microsomal** (my-krow-SO-mal) **ethanol-oxidizing system:** a system of enzymes in the liver that oxidize not only

alcohol but also several classes of drugs.

moderation: in relation to alcohol consumption, not more than two drinks a day for the average-size man and not more than one drink a day for the average-size woman.

NAD (nicotinamide adenine dinucleotide): the main coenzyme form of the vitamin niacin. Its reduced form is NADH.

narcotic (nar-KOT-ic): a drug that dulls the senses, induces sleep, and becomes addictive with prolonged use.

proof: a way of stating the percentage of alcohol in distilled liquor. Liquor that is 100 proof is 50% alcohol; 90 proof is 45%, and so forth.

Wernicke-Korsakoff (VER-nee-key KORE-sah-kof) **syndrome:** a neurological disorder typically associated with chronic alcoholism and caused by a deficiency of the B vitamin thiamin; also called *alcohol-related dementia.*

wine: an alcoholic beverage made by fermenting grape juice.

12 oz beer

10 oz wine cooler

1½ oz liquor (80 proof whiskey, gin, brandy, rum, vodka)

5 oz wine

© Polara Studios, Inc.

Each of these servings equals one drink.

Matthew Farruggio

Wines contain 7 to 24 percent alcohol by volume; those containing 14 percent or more must state their alcohol content on the label, whereas those with less than 14 percent may simply state "table wine" or "light wine." Beers typically contain less than 5 percent alcohol by volume and malt liquors, 5 to 8 percent; regulations vary, with some states requiring beer labels to show the alcohol content and others prohibiting such statements.

Second, because people have different tolerances for alcohol, it is impossible to name an exact daily amount of alcohol that is appropriate for everyone. Authorities have attempted to identify amounts that are acceptable for most healthy people. An accepted definition of moderation is up to two drinks per day for men and up to one

drink per day for women. (Pregnant women are advised to abstain from alcohol, as Highlight 15 explains.) Notice that this advice is stated as a maximum, not as an average; seven drinks one night a week would not be considered moderate, even though one a day would be. Doubtless some people could consume slightly more; others could not handle nearly so much without risk. The amount a person can drink safely is highly individual, depending on genetics, health, gender, body composition, age, and family history.

Alcohol in the Body

From the moment an alcoholic beverage enters the body, alcohol is treated as if it has special privileges. Unlike foods, which require time for digestion, alcohol needs no digestion and is quickly absorbed across the walls of an empty stomach, reaching the brain within a few minutes. Consequently, a person can immediately feel euphoric when drinking, especially on an empty stomach.

When the stomach is full of food, alcohol has less chance of touching the walls and diffusing through, so its influence on the brain is slightly delayed. This information leads to a practical tip: eat snacks when drinking alcoholic beverages. Carbohydrate snacks slow alcohol absorption and high-fat snacks slow peristalsis, keeping the alcohol in the stomach longer. Salty snacks make a person thirsty; to quench thirst, drink water instead of more alcohol.

The stomach begins to break down alcohol with its **alcohol dehydrogenase** enzyme. Women produce less of this stomach enzyme than men; consequently, more alcohol reaches the intestine for absorption into the bloodstream. As a result, women absorb more alcohol than men of the same size who drink the same amount of alcohol. Consequently, they are more likely to become more intoxicated on less alcohol than men. Such differences between men and women help explain why women have a lower alcohol tolerance and a lower recommendation for moderate intake.

In the small intestine, alcohol is rapidly absorbed. From this point on, alcohol receives priority treatment: it gets absorbed and metabolized before most nutrients. Alcohol's priority status helps to ensure a speedy disposal and reflects two facts: alcohol cannot be stored in the body, and it is potentially toxic.

Alcohol Arrives in the Liver

The capillaries of the digestive tract merge into veins that carry the alcohol-laden blood to the liver. These veins branch and rebranch into capillaries that touch every liver cell. Liver cells are the only other cells in the body that can make enough of the alcohol dehydrogenase enzyme to oxidize alcohol at an appreciable rate. The routing of blood through the liver cells gives them the chance to dispose of some alcohol before it moves on.

Alcohol affects every organ of the body, but the most dramatic evidence of its disruptive behavior appears in the liver. If liver cells could talk, they would describe alcohol as demanding, egocentric, and disruptive of the liver's efficient way of running its business. For example, liver cells normally prefer fatty acids as their fuel, and they like to package excess fatty acids into triglycerides and ship them out to other tissues. When alcohol is present, however, the liver cells are forced to metabolize alcohol and let the fatty acids accumulate, sometimes in huge stockpiles. Alcohol metabolism can also permanently change liver cell structure, impairing the liver's ability to metabolize fats. As a result, heavy drinkers develop fatty livers.

The liver is the primary site of alcohol metabolism.[4] It can process about $1/2$ ounce of *ethanol* per hour (the amount in a typical drink), depending on the person's body size, previous drinking experience, food intake, and general health. This maximum rate of alcohol breakdown is set by the amount of alcohol dehydrogenase available. If more alcohol arrives at the liver than the enzymes can handle, the extra alcohol travels to all parts of the body, circulating again and again until liver enzymes are finally available to process it. Another practical tip derives from this information: drink slowly enough to allow the liver to keep up—no more than one drink per hour.

The amount of alcohol dehydrogenase enzyme present in the liver varies with individuals, depending on the genes they have inherited and on how recently they have eaten. Fasting for as little as a day forces the body to degrade its proteins, including the alcohol-processing enzymes, and this can slow the rate of alcohol metabolism by half. Drinking after not eating all day thus causes the drinker to feel the effects more promptly for two reasons: rapid absorption and slowed breakdown. By maintaining higher blood alcohol concentrations for longer times, alcohol can anesthetize the brain more completely (as described later in this highlight).

The alcohol dehydrogenase enzyme breaks down alcohol by removing hydrogens in two steps. (Figure H7-2 provides a simplified diagram of alcohol metabolism; Appendix C provides the chemical details.) In the first step, alcohol dehydrogenase oxidizes alcohol to **acetaldehyde.** High concentrations of acetaldehyde in the brain and other tissues are responsible for many of the damaging effects of **alcohol abuse.**

FIGURE H7-2 Alcohol Metabolism

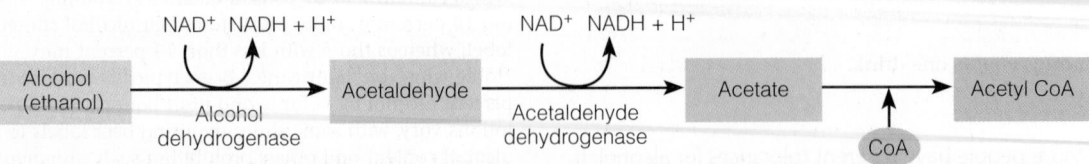

The conversion of alcohol to acetyl CoA requires the B vitamin niacin in its role as the coenzyme NAD. When the enzymes oxidize alcohol, they remove H atoms and attach them to NAD. Thus NAD is used up and NADH accumulates. (Note: More accurately, NAD^+ is converted to $NADH + H^+$.)

FIGURE H7-3   Alternate Route for Acetyl CoA: To Fat

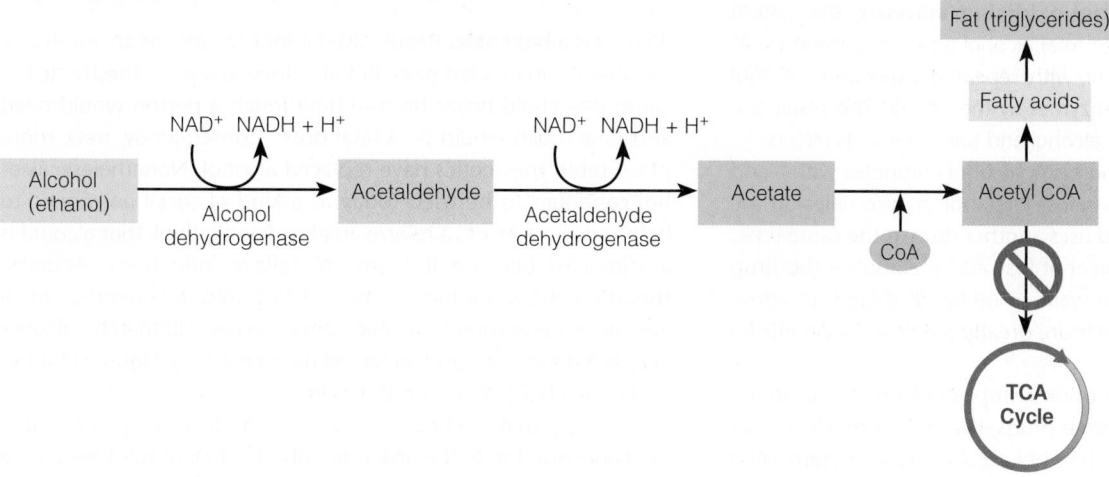

Acetyl CoA molecules are blocked from getting into the TCA cycle by the high level of NADH. Instead of being used for energy, the acetyl CoA molecules become building blocks for fatty acids.

In the second step, a related enzyme, acetaldehyde dehydrogenase, converts acetaldehyde to acetate, which is then converted to acetyl CoA—the "crossroads" compound introduced in Chapter 7 that can enter the TCA cycle to generate energy. These reactions produce hydrogen ions (H+). The B vitamin niacin, in its role as the coenzyme **NAD (nicotinamide adenine dinucleotide),** helpfully picks up these hydrogen ions (becoming NADH). Thus, whenever the body breaks down alcohol, NAD diminishes and NADH accumulates. (Chapter 10 presents information on NAD and the other coenzyme roles of the B vitamins.)

Alcohol Disrupts the Liver

During alcohol metabolism, the multitude of other metabolic processes for which NAD is required, including glycolysis, the TCA cycle, and the electron transport chain, falter. Its presence is sorely missed in these energy pathways because it is the chief carrier of the hydrogens that travel with their electrons along the electron transport chain. Without adequate NAD, these energy pathways cannot function. Traffic either backs up, or an alternate route is taken. Such changes in the normal flow of energy pathways have striking physical consequences.

For one, the accumulation of hydrogen ions during alcohol metabolism shifts the body's acid-base balance toward acid. For another, the accumulation of NADH slows the TCA cycle, so pyruvate and acetyl CoA build up. Excess acetyl CoA then takes the route to fatty acid synthesis (as Figure H7-3 illustrates), and fat clogs the liver.

As you might expect, a liver overburdened with fat cannot function properly. Liver cells become less efficient at performing a number of tasks. Much of this inefficiency impairs a person's nutritional health in ways that cannot be corrected by diet alone. For example, the liver has difficulty activating vitamin D, as well as producing and releasing bile. To overcome such problems, a person needs to stop drinking alcohol.

The synthesis of fatty acids accelerates with exposure to alcohol. Fat accumulation can be seen in the liver after a single night of heavy drinking. **Fatty liver,** the first stage of liver deterioration seen in heavy drinkers, interferes with the distribution of nutrients and oxygen to the liver cells. Fatty liver is reversible with abstinence from alcohol. If fatty liver lasts long enough, however, the liver cells will die and form fibrous scar tissue. This second stage of liver deterioration is called **fibrosis.** Some liver cells can regenerate with good nutrition and abstinence from alcohol, but in the most advanced stage, **cirrhosis,** damage is the least reversible.

The fatty liver has difficulty generating glucose from protein. Without gluconeogenesis, blood glucose can plummet, leading to irreversible damage to the central nervous system.

The lack of glucose together with the overabundance of acetyl CoA sets the stage for ketosis. The body uses the acetyl CoA to make ketone bodies; their acidity pushes the acid-base balance further toward acid and suppresses nervous system activity.

Excess NADH also promotes the making of lactate from pyruvate. The conversion of pyruvate to lactate uses the hydrogens from NADH and restores some NAD, but a lactate buildup has serious consequences of its own—it adds still further to the body's acid burden and interferes with the excretion of another acid, uric acid, causing inflammation of the joints.

Alcohol alters both amino acid and protein metabolism. Synthesis of proteins important in the immune system slows down, weakening the body's defenses against infection. Protein deficiency can develop, both from a diminished synthesis of protein and from a poor diet. Normally, the cells would at least use the amino acids from the protein foods a person eats, but the drinker's liver deaminates the amino acids and uses the carbon fragments primarily to make fat or ketones. Eating well does not protect the drinker from protein depletion; a person has to stop drinking alcohol.

The liver's priority treatment of alcohol affects its handling of drugs as well as nutrients. In addition to the dehydrogenase enzyme already described, the liver possesses an enzyme system that metabolizes *both* alcohol and several other types of drugs. Called the **MEOS (microsomal ethanol-oxidizing system)**, this system handles about one-fifth of the total alcohol a person consumes. At high blood concentrations or with repeated exposures, alcohol stimulates the synthesis of enzymes in the MEOS. The result is a more efficient metabolism of alcohol and tolerance to its effects.

As a person's blood alcohol rises, alcohol competes with—and wins out over—other drugs whose metabolism also relies on the MEOS. If a person drinks and uses another drug at the same time, the MEOS will dispose of alcohol first and metabolize the drug more slowly. While the drug waits to be handled later, the dose may build up so that its effects are greatly amplified—sometimes to the point of being fatal.

In contrast, once a heavy drinker stops drinking and alcohol is no longer competing with other drugs, the enhanced MEOS metabolizes drugs much faster than before. As a result, determining the correct dosages of medications can be challenging.

This discussion has emphasized the major way that the blood is cleared of alcohol—metabolism by the liver—but there is another way. About 10 percent of the alcohol leaves the body through the breath and in the urine. This is the basis for the breath and urine tests for drunkenness. The amounts of alcohol in the breath and in the urine are in proportion to the amount still in the bloodstream and brain. In nearly all states, legal drunkenness is set at 0.10 percent or less, reflecting the relationship between alcohol use and traffic and other accidents.

Alcohol Arrives in the Brain

Alcohol is a **narcotic.** People used it for centuries as an anesthetic because it can deaden pain. But alcohol was a poor anesthetic because one could never be sure how much a person would need and how much would be a fatal dose. Consequently, new, more predictable anesthetics have replaced alcohol. Nonetheless, alcohol continues to be used today as a kind of social anesthetic to help people relax or to relieve anxiety. People think that alcohol is a stimulant because it seems to relieve inhibitions. Actually, though, it accomplishes this by sedating *inhibitory* nerves, which are more numerous than excitatory nerves. Ultimately, alcohol acts as a depressant and affects all the nerve cells. Figure H7-4 describes alcohol's effects on the brain.

It is lucky that the brain centers respond to a rising blood alcohol concentration in the order described in Figure H7-4 because a person usually passes out before managing to drink a lethal dose. It is possible, though, to drink so fast that the effects of alcohol continue to accelerate after the person has passed out. Occasionally, a person dies from drinking enough to stop the heart before passing out. Table H7-1 shows the blood alcohol levels that correspond to progressively greater intoxication, and Table H7-2 shows the brain responses that occur at these blood levels.

Like liver cells, brain cells die with excessive exposure to alcohol. Liver cells may be replaced, but not all brain cells can regenerate. Thus some heavy drinkers suffer permanent brain damage.

FIGURE H7-4 Alcohol's Effects on the Brain

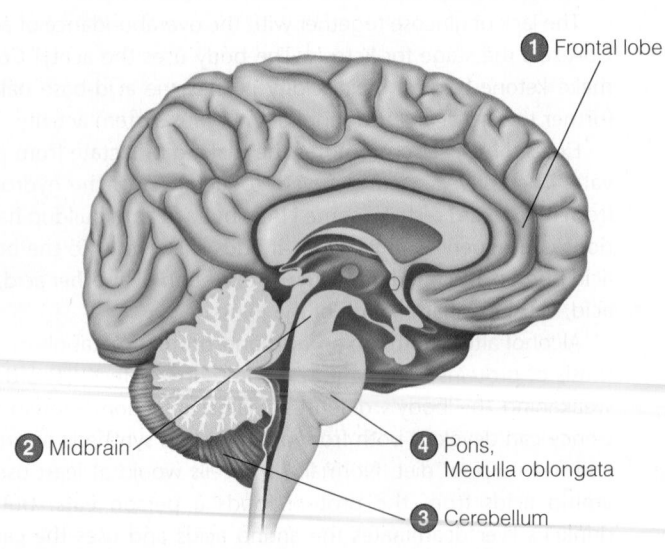

1 Frontal lobe

2 Midbrain

3 Cerebellum

4 Pons, Medulla oblongata

1 Judgment and reasoning centers are most sensitive to alcohol. When alcohol flows to the brain, it first sedates the frontal lobe, the center of all conscious activity. As the alcohol molecules diffuse into the cells of these lobes, they interfere with reasoning and judgment.

2 Speech and vision centers in the midbrain are affected next. If the drinker drinks faster than the rate at which the liver can oxidize the alcohol, blood alcohol concentrations rise: the speech and vision centers of the brain become sedated.

3 Voluntary muscular control is then affected. At still higher concentrations, the cells in the cerebellum responsible for coordination of voluntary muscles are affected, including those used in speech, eye-hand coordination, and limb movements. At this point people under the influence stagger or weave when they try to walk, or they may slur their speech.

4 Respiration and heart action are the last to be affected. Finally, the conscious brain is completely subdued, and the person passes out. Now the person can drink no more; this is fortunate because higher doses would anesthetize the deepest brain centers that control breathing and heartbeat, causing death.

TABLE H7-1 Alcohol Doses and Approximate Blood Level Percentages for Men and Women

Drinks[a] — Body Weight in Pounds—Men

Drinks[a]	100	120	140	160	180	200	220	240	
	00	00	00	00	00	00	00	00	ONLY SAFE DRIVING LIMIT
1	.04	.03	.03	.02	.02	.02	.02	.02	IMPAIRMENT BEGINS
2	.08	.06	.05	.05	.04	.04	.03	.03	
3	.11	.09	.08	.07	.06	.06	.05	.05	DRIVING SKILLS SIGNIFICANTLY AFFECTED
4	.15	.12	.11	.09	.08	.08	.07	.06	
5	.19	.16	.13	.12	.11	.09	.09	.08	
6	.23	.19	.16	.14	.13	.11	.10	.09	
7	.26	.22	.19	.16	.15	.13	.12	.11	
8	.30	.25	.21	.19	.17	.15	.14	.13	LEGALLY INTOXICATED
9	.34	.28	.24	.21	.19	.17	.15	.14	
10	.38	.31	.27	.23	.21	.19	.17	.16	

Drinks[a] — Body Weight in Pounds—Women

Drinks[a]	90	100	120	140	160	180	200	220	240	
	00	00	00	00	00	00	00	00	00	ONLY SAFE DRIVING LIMIT
1	.05	.05	.04	.03	.03	.03	.02	.02	.02	IMPAIRMENT BEGINS
2	.10	.09	.08	.07	.06	.05	.05	.04	.04	
3	.15	.14	.11	.10	.09	.08	.07	.06	.06	DRIVING SKILLS SIGNIFICANTLY AFFECTED
4	.20	.18	.15	.13	.11	.10	.09	.08	.08	
5	.25	.23	.19	.16	.14	.13	.11	.10	.09	
6	.30	.27	.23	.19	.17	.15	.14	.12	.11	
7	.35	.32	.27	.23	.20	.18	.16	.14	.13	LEGALLY INTOXICATED
8	.40	.36	.30	.26	.23	.20	.18	.17	.15	
9	.45	.41	.34	.29	.26	.23	.20	.19	.17	
10	.51	.45	.38	.32	.28	.25	.23	.21	.19	

NOTE: In some states, driving under the influence is proved when an adult's blood contains 0.08 percent alcohol, and in others, 0.10. Many states have adopted a "zero-tolerance" policy for drivers under age 21, using 0.02 percent as the limit.

[a]Taken within an hour or so; each drink equivalent to ½ ounce pure ethanol.

SOURCE: National Clearinghouse for Alcohol and Drug Information

TABLE H7-2 Alcohol Blood Levels and Brain Responses

Blood Alcohol Concentration	Effect on Brain
0.05	Impaired judgment, relaxed inhibitions, altered mood, increased heart rate
0.10	Impaired coordination, delayed reaction time, exaggerated emotions, impaired peripheral vision, impaired ability to operate a vehicle
0.15	Slurred speech, blurred vision, staggered walk, seriously impaired coordination and judgment
0.20	Double vision, inability to walk
0.30	Uninhibited behavior, stupor, confusion, inability to comprehend
0.40 to 0.60	Unconsciousness, shock, coma, death (cardiac or respiratory failure)

NOTE: Blood alcohol concentration depends on a number of factors, including alcohol in the beverage, the rate of consumption, the person's gender, and body weight. For example, a 100-pound female can become legally drunk (≥0.10 concentration) by drinking three beers in an hour, whereas a 220-pound male consuming that amount at the same rate would have a 0.05 blood alcohol concentration.

Whether alcohol impairs cognition in moderate drinkers is unclear.[5]

People who drink alcoholic beverages may notice that they urinate more, but they may be unaware of the vicious cycle that results. Alcohol depresses production of **antidiuretic hormone (ADH),** a hormone produced by the pituitary gland that retains water—consequently, with less ADH, more water is lost. Loss of body water leads to thirst, and thirst leads to more drinking. Water will relieve dehydration, but the thirsty drinker may drink alcohol instead, which only worsens the problem. Such information provides another practical tip: drink water when thirsty and before each alcoholic drink. Drink an extra glass or two before going to bed. This strategy will help lessen the effects of a hangover.

Water loss is accompanied by the loss of important minerals. As Chapters 12 and 13 explain, these minerals are vital to the body's fluid balance and to many chemical reactions in the cells, including muscle action. Detoxification treatment includes restoration of mineral balance as quickly as possible.

Alcohol and Malnutrition

For many moderate drinkers, alcohol does not suppress food intake and may actually stimulate appetite. Moderate drinkers usually consume alcohol as *added* energy—on top of their normal food intake. In addition, alcohol in moderate doses is efficiently metabolized. Consequently, alcohol can contribute to body fat and weight gain—either by inhibiting oxidation or by being converted to fat.[6] Metabolically, alcohol is almost as efficient as fat in promoting obesity; each ounce of alcohol represents about a half-ounce of fat. Alcohol's contribution to body fat is most evident in the central obesity that commonly accompanies alcohol consumption, popularly—and appropriately—known as the "beer belly."[7] Alcohol in heavy doses, though, is not efficiently metabolized, generating more heat than fat. Heavy drinkers usually consume alcohol as *substituted* energy—instead of their normal food intake. They tend to eat poorly and suffer malnutrition.

Alcohol is rich in energy (7 kcalories per gram), but as with pure sugar or fat, the kcalories are empty of nutrients. The more alcohol people drink, the less likely that they will eat enough food to obtain adequate nutrients. The more kcalories spent on alcohol, the fewer kcalories available to spend on nutritious foods. Table H7-3 (p. 244) shows the kcalorie amounts of typical alcoholic beverages.

Chronic alcohol abuse not only displaces nutrients from the diet, but it also interferes with the body's metabolism of nutrients. Most dramatic is alcohol's effect on the B vitamin folate. The liver loses its ability to retain folate, and the kidneys increase their excretion of it. Alcohol abuse creates a folate deficiency that devastates digestive

TABLE H7-3 kCalories in Alcoholic Beverages and Mixers

Beverage	Amount (oz)	Energy (kcal)
Beer		
Regular	12	150
Light	12	78–131
Nonalcoholic	12	32–82
Distilled liquor (gin, rum, vodka, whiskey)		
80 proof	1½	100
86 proof	1½	105
90 proof	1½	110
Liqueurs		
Coffee liqueur, 53 proof	1½	175
Coffee and cream liqueur, 34 proof	1½	155
Crème de menthe, 72 proof	1½	185
Mixers		
Club soda	12	0
Cola	12	150
Cranberry juice cocktail	8	145
Diet drinks	12	2
Ginger ale or tonic	12	125
Grapefruit juice	8	95
Orange juice	8	110
Tomato or vegetable juice	8	45
Wine		
Dessert	3½	110–135
Nonalcoholic	8	14
Red or rosé	3½	75
White	3½	70
Wine cooler	12	170

system function. The intestine normally releases and retrieves folate continuously, but it becomes damaged by folate deficiency and alcohol toxicity, so it fails to retrieve its own folate and misses any that may trickle in from food as well. Alcohol also interferes with the action of folate in converting the amino acid homocysteine to methionine. The result is an excess of homocysteine, which has been linked to heart disease, and an inadequate supply of methionine, which slows the production of new cells, especially the rapidly dividing cells of the intestine and the blood. The combination of poor folate status and alcohol consumption has also been implicated in promoting colorectal cancer.

The inadequate food intake and impaired nutrient absorption that accompany chronic alcohol abuse frequently lead to a deficiency of another B vitamin—thiamin. In fact, the cluster of thiamin-deficiency symptoms commonly seen in chronic **alcoholism** has its own name—the **Wernicke-Korsakoff syndrome.** This syndrome is characterized by paralysis of the eye muscles, poor muscle coordination, impaired memory, and damaged nerves; it and other alcohol-related memory problems may respond to thiamin supplements.

Acetaldehyde, an intermediate in alcohol metabolism (review Figure H7-2, p. 240), interferes with nutrient use, too. For example, acetaldehyde dislodges vitamin B_6 from its protective binding protein so that it is destroyed, causing a vitamin B_6 deficiency and, thereby, lowered production of red blood cells.

Malnutrition occurs not only because of lack of intake and altered metabolism but because of direct toxic effects as well. Alcohol causes stomach cells to oversecrete both gastric acid and histamine, an immune system agent that produces inflammation. Beer in particular stimulates gastric acid secretion, irritating the linings of the stomach and esophagus and making them vulnerable to ulcer formation.

Overall, nutrient deficiencies are virtually inevitable in alcohol abuse, not only because alcohol displaces food but also because alcohol directly interferes with the body's use of nutrients, making them ineffective even if they are present. Intestinal cells fail to absorb B vitamins, notably, thiamin, folate, and vitamin B_{12}. Liver cells lose efficiency in activating vitamin D. Cells in the retina of the eye, which normally process the alcohol form of vitamin A (retinol) to its aldehyde form needed in vision (retinal), find themselves processing ethanol to acetaldehyde instead. Likewise, the liver cannot convert the aldehyde form of vitamin A to its acid form (retinoic acid), which is needed to support the growth of its (and all) cells.

Regardless of dietary intake, excessive drinking over a lifetime creates deficits of all the nutrients mentioned in this discussion and more. No diet can compensate for the damage caused by heavy alcohol consumption.

Alcohol's Short-Term Effects

The effects of abusing alcohol may be apparent immediately, or they may not become evident for years to come. Among the immediate consequences, all of the following involve alcohol use:[8]

- One-quarter of all emergency-room admissions
- One-third of all suicides
- One-half of all homicides
- One-half of all domestic violence incidents
- One-half of all traffic fatalities
- One-half of all fire victim fatalities

These statistics are sobering. The consequences of heavy drinking touch all races and all segments of society—men and women, young and old, rich and poor. One group particularly hard hit by heavy drinking is college students—not because they are prone to alcoholism, but because they live in an environment and are in a developmental stage of life in which heavy drinking is considered acceptable.[9]

Heavy drinking or binge drinking (defined as at least four drinks in a row for women and five drinks in a row for men) is widespread on college campuses and poses serious health and social consequences to drinkers and nondrinkers alike.*[10] In fact, binge drinking can kill: the respiratory center of the brain becomes anesthetized, and breathing stops. Acute alcohol intoxication can cause coronary artery spasms, leading to heart attacks.

Binge drinking is especially common among college students who live in a fraternity or sorority house, attend parties frequently, engage in other risky behaviors, and have a history of binge drinking in high school. Compared with nondrinkers or moderate drinkers, people who frequently binge drink (at least three times within two weeks) are more likely to engage in unpro-

* This definition of binge drinking, without specification of time elapsed, is consistent with standard practice in alcohol research.

tected sex, have multiple sex partners, damage property, and assault others.[11] On average, *every day* alcohol is involved in the:[12]

- Death of 5 college students
- Sexual assault of 266 college students
- Injury of 1641 college students
- Assault of 1907 college students

Binge drinkers skew the statistics on college students' alcohol use. The median number of drinks consumed by college students is 1.5 per week, but for binge drinkers, it is 14.5. Nationally, only 20 percent of all students are frequent binge drinkers; yet they account for two-thirds of all the alcohol students report consuming and most of the alcohol-related problems.

Binge drinking is not limited to college campuses, of course, but it is most common among 18 to 24 year-olds.[13] That age group and environment seem most accepting of such behavior despite its problems. Social acceptance may make it difficult for binge drinkers to recognize themselves as problem drinkers. For this reason, interventions must focus both on educating individuals and on changing the campus social environment.[14] The damage alcohol causes only becomes worse if the pattern is not broken. Alcohol abuse sets in much more quickly in young people than in adults. Those who start drinking at an early age more often suffer from alcoholism than people who start later on. Table H7-4 lists the key signs of alcoholism.

Alcohol's Long-Term Effects

The most devastating long-term effect of alcohol is the damage done to a child whose mother abused alcohol during pregnancy. The effects of alcohol on the unborn and the message that pregnant women should not drink alcohol are presented in Highlight 15.

For nonpregnant adults, a drink or two sets in motion many destructive processes in the body, but the next day's abstinence reverses them. As long as the doses are moderate, the time between them is ample, and nutrition is adequate, recovery is probably complete.

If the doses of alcohol are heavy and the time between them short, complete recovery cannot take place. Repeated onslaughts of alcohol gradually take a toll on all parts of the body (see Table H7-5, p. 246). Compared with nondrinkers and moderate drinkers, heavy drinkers have significantly greater risks of dying from all causes.[15] Excessive alcohol consumption is the third leading preventable cause of death in the United States.[16]

Personal Strategies

One obvious option available to people attending social gatherings is to enjoy the conversation, eat the food, and drink nonalcoholic beverages. Several nonalcoholic beverages are available that mimic the look and taste of their alcoholic counterparts. For those who enjoy champagne or beer, sparkling ciders and beers without alcohol are available. Instead of drinking a cocktail, a person can sip tomato juice with a slice of lime and a stalk of celery or just a plain cola beverage. Any of these drinks can ease conversation.

The person who chooses to drink alcohol should sip each drink slowly with food. The alcohol should arrive at the liver cells slowly enough that the enzymes can handle the load. It is best to space drinks, too, allowing about an hour or so to metabolize each drink.

If you want to help sober up a friend who has had too much to drink, don't bother walking arm in arm around the block. Walking muscles have to work harder, but muscle cells can't metabolize alcohol; only liver cells can. Remember that each person has a limited amount of the alcohol dehydrogenase enzyme that clears the blood at a steady rate. Time alone will do the job.

Nor will it help to give your friend a cup of coffee. Caffeine is a stimulant, but it won't speed up alcohol metabolism. The police say ruefully, "If you give a drunk a cup of coffee, you'll just have a wide-awake drunk on your hands." Table H7-6 (p. 246) presents other alcohol myths.

People who have passed out from drinking need 24 hours to sober up completely. Let them sleep, but watch over them. Encourage them to lie on their sides, instead of their backs. That way, if they vomit, they won't choke.

Don't drive too soon after drinking. The lack of glucose for the brain's function and the length of time needed to clear the blood of alcohol make alcohol's adverse effects linger long after its blood concentration has fallen. Driving coordination is still impaired the morning *after* a night of drinking, even if the drinking was moderate. Responsible aircraft pilots know that they must allow 24 hours for their bodies to clear alcohol completely, and they refuse to fly any sooner. The Federal Aviation Administration and major airlines enforce this rule.

TABLE H7-4 Signs of Alcoholism

- Tolerance—the person needs higher and higher intakes of alcohol to achieve intoxication
- Withdrawal—the person who stops drinking experiences anxiety, agitation, increased blood pressure, or seizures, or seeks alcohol to relieve these symptoms
- Impaired control—the person intends to have 1 or 2 drinks, but has 9 or 10 instead, or the person tries to control or quit drinking, but fails
- Disinterest—the person neglects important social, family, job, or school activities because of drinking
- Time—the person spends a great deal of time obtaining and drinking alcohol or recovering from excessive drinking
- Impaired ability—the person's intoxication or withdrawal symptoms interfere with work, school, or home
- Problems—the person continues drinking despite physical hazards or medical, legal, psychological, family, employment, or school problems

The presence of three or more of these conditions is required to make a diagnosis.

SOURCE: Adapted from *Diagnostic and Statistical Manual of Mental Disorders*, 4th ed. (Washington, D.C.: American Psychiatric Association, 1994).

TABLE H7-5 Health Effects of Heavy Alcohol Consumption

Health Problem	Effects of Alcohol
Arthritis	Increases the risk of inflamed joints
Cancer	Increases the risk of cancer of the liver, pancreas, rectum, and breast; increases the risk of cancer of the lungs, mouth, pharynx, larynx, and esophagus, where alcohol interacts synergistically with tobacco
Fetal alcohol syndrome	Causes physical and behavioral abnormalities in the fetus (see Highlight 15)
Heart disease	In heavy drinkers, raises blood pressure, blood lipids, and the risk of stroke and heart disease; when compared with those who abstain, heart disease risk is generally lower in light-to-moderate drinkers (see Chapter 18)
Hyperglycemia	Raises blood glucose
Hypoglycemia	Lowers blood glucose, especially in people with diabetes
Infertility	Increases the risks of menstrual disorders and spontaneous abortions (in women); suppresses luteinizing hormone (in women) and testosterone (in men)
Kidney disease	Enlarges the kidneys, alters hormone functions, and increases the risk of kidney failure
Liver disease	Causes fatty liver, alcoholic hepatitis, and cirrhosis
Malnutrition	Increases the risk of protein-energy malnutrition; low intakes of protein, calcium, iron, vitamin A, vitamin C, thiamin, vitamin B_6, and riboflavin; and impaired absorption of calcium, phosphorus, vitamin D, and zinc
Nervous disorders	Causes neuropathy and dementia; impairs balance and memory
Obesity	Increases energy intake, but is not a primary cause of obesity
Psychological disturbances	Causes depression, anxiety, and insomnia

NOTE: This list is by no means all-inclusive. Alcohol has direct toxic effects on all body systems.

TABLE H7-6 Myths and Truths Concerning Alcohol

Myth: Hard liquors such as rum, vodka, and tequila are more harmful than wine and beer.
Truth: The damage caused by alcohol depends largely on the *amount* consumed. Compared with hard liquor, beer and wine have relatively low percentages of alcohol, but they are often consumed in larger quantities.

Myth: Consuming alcohol with raw seafood diminishes the likelihood of getting hepatitis.
Truth: People have eaten contaminated oysters while drinking alcoholic beverages and not gotten as sick as those who were not drinking. But do not be misled: hepatitis is too serious an illness for anyone to depend on alcohol for protection.

Myth: Alcohol stimulates the appetite.
Truth: For some people, alcohol may stimulate appetite, but it seems to have the opposite effect in heavy drinkers. Heavy drinkers tend to eat poorly and suffer malnutrition.

Myth: Drinking alcohol is healthy.
Truth: Moderate alcohol consumption is associated with a lower risk for heart disease (see Chapter 18 for more details). Higher intakes, however, raise the risks for high blood pressure, stroke, heart disease, some cancers, accidents, violence, suicide, birth defects, and deaths in general. Furthermore, excessive alcohol consumption damages the liver, pancreas, brain, and heart. No authority recommends that nondrinkers begin drinking alcoholic beverages to obtain health benefits.

Myth: Wine increases the body's absorption of minerals.
Truth: Wine may increase the body's absorption of potassium, calcium, phosphorus, magnesium, and zinc, but the alcohol in wine also promotes the body's excretion of these minerals, so no benefit is gained.

Myth: Alcohol is legal and, therefore, not a drug.
Truth: Alcohol is legal for adults 21 years old and older, but it is also a drug—a substance that alters one or more of the body's functions.

Myth: A shot of alcohol warms you up.
Truth: Alcohol diverts blood flow to the skin making you *feel* warmer, but it actually cools the body.

Myth: Wine and beer are mild; they do not lead to alcoholism.
Truth: Alcoholism is not related to the kind of beverage, but rather to the quantity and frequency of consumption.

Myth: Mixing different types of drinks gives you a hangover.
Truth: Too much alcohol in any form produces a hangover.

Myth: Alcohol is a stimulant.
Truth: People think alcohol is a stimulant because it seems to relieve inhibitions, but it does so by depressing the activity of the brain. Alcohol is medically defined as a depressant drug.

Myth: Beer is a great source of carbohydrate, vitamins, minerals, and fluids.
Truth: Beer does provide some carbohydrate, but most of its kcalories come from alcohol. The few vitamins and minerals in beer cannot compete with rich food sources. And the diuretic effect of alcohol causes the body to lose more fluid in urine than is provided by the beer.

Look again at the drawing of the brain in Figure H7-4, and note that when someone drinks, judgment fails first. Judgment might tell a person to limit alcohol consumption to two drinks at a party, but if the first drink takes judgment away, many more drinks may follow. The failure to stop drinking as planned, on repeated occasions, is a danger sign warning that the person should not drink at all. The accompanying Nutrition on the Net provides websites for organizations that offer information about alcohol and alcohol abuse.

Ethanol interferes with a multitude of chemical and hormonal reactions in the body—many more than have been enumerated here. With heavy alcohol consumption, the potential for harm is great. The best way to escape the harmful effects of alcohol is, of course, to refuse alcohol altogether. If you do drink alcoholic beverages, do so with care, and in moderation.

NUTRITION ON THE NET

ThomsonNOW
For furthur study of topics covered in this Highlight, log on to **www .thomsonedu.com/thomsonnow**, Go to Chapter 7, then to Highlights Nutrition on the Net.

- Search for "alcohol" at the U.S. Government health site: **www.healthfinder.gov**

- Gather information on alcohol and drug abuse from the National Clearinghouse for Alcohol and Drug Information (NCADI): **ncadi.samhsa.gov**

- Learn more about alcoholism and drug dependence from the National Council on Alcoholism and Drug Dependence (NCADD): **www.ncadd.org**

- Visit the National Institute on Alcohol Abuse and Alcoholism: **www.collegedrinkingprevention.gov**

- Find help for a family alcohol problem from Alateen and Al-Anon Family support groups: **www.al-anon.alateen.org**

- Find help for an alcohol or drug problem from Alcoholics Anonymous (AA) or Narcotics Anonymous: **www.aa.org** or **www.wsoinc.com**

- Search for "party" to find tips for hosting a safe party from Mothers Against Drunk Driving (MADD): **www.madd.org**

REFERENCES

1. D. J. Meyerhoff and coauthors, Health risks of chronic moderate and heavy alcohol consumption: How much is too much? *Alcoholism, Clinical and Experimental Research* 29 (2005): 1334-1340; J. B. Standridge, R. G. Zylstra, and S. M. Adams, Alcohol consumption: An overview of benefits and risks, *Southern Medical Journal* 97 (2004): 664-672.
2. V. Arndt and coauthors, Age, alcohol consumption, and all-cause mortality, *Annals of Epidemiology* 14 (2004): 750-753.
3. J. Connor and coauthors, The burden of death, disease, and disability due to alcohol in New Zealand, *New Zealand Medical Journal* 118 (2005): U1412.
4. L. E. Nagy, Molecular aspects of alcohol metabolism: Transcription factors involved in early ethanol-induced liver injury, *Annual Review of Nutrition* 24 (2004): 55-78.
5. D. Krahn and coauthors, Alcohol use and cognition at mid-life: The importance of adjusting for baseline cognitive ability and educational attainment, *Alcoholism: Clinical and Experimental Research* 27 (2003): 1162-1166.
6. R. A. Breslow and B. A. Smothers, Drinking patterns and body mass index in never smokers: National Health Interview Survey, 1997-2001, *American Journal of Epidemiology* 161 (2005): 368-376; M. R. Yeomans, Effects of alcohol on food and energy intake in human subjects: Evidence for passive and active over-consumption of energy, *British Journal of Nutrition* 92 (2004): S31-S34; S. G.

Wannamethee and A. G. Shaper, Alcohol, body weight, and weight gain in middle-aged men, *American Journal of Clinical Nutrition* 77 (2003): 1312-1317; E. Jequier, Pathways to obesity, *International Journal of Obesity and Related Metabolic Disorders* 26 (2002): S12-S17.
7. S. G. Wannamethee, A. G. Shaper, and P. H. Whincup, Alcohol and adiposity: Effects of quantity and type of drink and time relation with meals, *International Journal of Obesity and Related Metabolic Disorders* 29 (2005): 1436-1444; J. M. Dorn and coauthors, Alcohol drinking patterns differentially affect central adiposity as measured by abdominal height in women and men, *Journal of Nutrition* 133 (2003): 2655-2662.
8. Position paper on drug policy: Physician Leadership on National Drug Policy (PLNDP), Brown University Center for Alcohol and Addiction Studies, 2000.
9. A. M. Brower, Are college students alcoholics? *Journal of American College Health* 50 (2002): 253-255.
10. R. D. Brewer and M. H. Swahn, Binge drinking and violence, *Journal of the American Medical Association* 294 (2005): 616-618; H. Wechsler and coauthors, Trends in college binge drinking during a period of increased prevention efforts—Findings from Harvard School of Public Health College Alcohol Study Surveys: 1993-2001, *Journal of American College Health* 50 (2002): 203-217.
11. Wechsler and coauthors, 2002.

12. R. W. Hingson and coauthors, Magnitude of alcohol-related mortality and morbidity among U.S. college students ages 18-24: Changes from 1998 to 2001, *Annual Review of Public Health* 26 (2005): 259-279.
13. National Center for Health Statistics, *Chartbook on Trends in the Health of Americans,* Alcohol consumption by adults 18 years of age and over, according to selected characteristics: United States, selected years 1997-2003, (2005): 264-266.
14. A. Ziemelis, R. B. Bucknam, and A. M. Elfessi, Prevention efforts underlying decreases in binge drinking at institutions of higher learning, *Journal of American College Health* 50 (2002): 238-252.
15. A. Y. Strandberg and coauthors, Alcohol consumption, 29-y total mortality, and quality of life in men in old age, *American Journal of Clinical Nutrition* 80 (2004): 1366-1371; I. R. White, D. R. Altmann, and K. Nanchahal, Alcohol consumption and mortality: Modeling risks for men and women at different ages, *British Medical Journal* 325 (2002): 191-197.
16. Centers for Disease Control, Alcohol-attributable deaths and years of potential life lost-United States, 2001, *Morbidity and Mortality Weekly Report* 53 (2004): 866-870.

Thomson Throughout this chapter, the
NOW! ThomsonNOW logo indicates
an opportunity for online
self-study, linking you to interactive tutorials and
videos based on your level of understanding.
www.thomsonedu.com/thomsonnow

How To: Practice Problems

Nutrition Portfolio Journal

Nutrition Calculations: Practice Problems

Nutrition in Your Life

It's a simple mathematical equation: energy in + energy out = energy balance.

The reality, of course, is much more complex. One day you may devour a

dozen doughnuts at midnight and sleep through your morning workout—

tipping the scales toward weight gain. Another day you may snack on veggies

and train for this weekend's 10K race—shifting the balance toward weight loss.

Your body weight—especially as it relates to your body fat—and your level of

fitness have consequences for your health. So, how are you doing? Are you

ready to see how your "energy in" and "energy out" balance and whether

your body weight and fat measures are consistent with good health?

Energy Balance and Body Composition

CHAPTER OUTLINE

Energy Balance

Energy In: The kCalories Foods Provide • Food Composition • Food Intake

Energy Out: The kCalories the Body Expends • Components of Energy Expenditure • Estimating Energy Requirements

Body Weight, Body Composition, and Health • Defining Healthy Body Weight • Body Fat and Its Distribution • Health Risks Associated with Body Weight and Body Fat

HIGHLIGHT 8 Eating Disorders

The body's remarkable machinery can cope with many extremes of diet. As Chapter 7 explained, both excess carbohydrate (glucose) and excess protein (amino acids) can contribute to body fat. To some extent, amino acids can be used to make glucose. To a very limited extent, even fat (the glycerol portion) can be used to make glucose. But a grossly unbalanced diet imposes hardships on the body. If energy intake is too low or if too little carbohydrate or protein is supplied, the body must degrade its own lean tissue to meet its glucose and protein needs. If energy intake is too high, the body stores fat.

Both excessive and deficient body fat result from an energy imbalance budgets. The simple picture is as follows. People who have consumed more food energy than they have expended bank the surplus as body fat. To reduce body fat, they need to expend more energy than they take in from food. In contrast, people who have consumed too little food energy to support their bodies' activities have relied on their bodies' fat stores and possibly some of their lean tissues as well. To gain weight, these people need to take in more food energy than they expend. As you will see, though, the details of the body's weight regulation are quite complex.[1] This chapter describes energy balance and body composition and examines the health problems associated with having too much or too little body fat. The next chapter presents strategies toward resolving these problems.

Energy Balance

People expend energy continuously and eat periodically to refuel. Ideally, their energy intakes cover their energy expenditures without too much excess. Excess energy is stored as fat, and stored fat is used for energy between meals. The amount of body fat a person deposits in, or withdraws from, "storage" on any given day depends on the energy balance for that day—the amount consumed (energy in) versus the amount expended (energy out). When a person is maintaining weight, energy in equals energy out. When the balance shifts, weight changes. For each 3500 kcalories eaten in excess, a pound of body fat is stored; similarly, a pound of fat is lost for

When energy in balances with energy out, a person's body weight is stable.

◆ 1 lb body fat = 3500 kcal
Body fat, or adipose tissue, is composed of a mixture of mostly fat, some protein, and water. A pound of body fat (454 g) is approximately 87% fat, or (454 × 0.87) 395 g, and 395g × 9 kcal/g = 3555 kcal.

each 3500 kcalories expended beyond those consumed. ◆ The fat stores of even a healthy-weight adult represent an ample reserve of energy—50,000 to 200,000 kcalories.

Quick changes in body weight are not simple changes in fat stores. Weight gained or lost rapidly includes some fat, large amounts of fluid, and some lean tissues such as muscle proteins and bone minerals. (Because water constitutes about 60 percent of an adult's body weight, retention or loss of water can greatly influence body weight.) Even over the long term, the composition of weight gained or lost is normally about 75 percent fat and 25 percent lean. During starvation, losses of fat and lean are about equal. (Recall from Chapter 7 that without adequate carbohydrate, protein-rich lean tissues break down to provide glucose.) Invariably, though, *fat* gains and losses are gradual. The next two sections examine the two sides of the energy-balance equation: energy in and energy out.

IN SUMMARY

When the energy consumed equals the energy expended, a person is in energy balance and body weight is stable. If more energy is taken in than is expended, a person gains weight. If more energy is expended than is taken in, a person loses weight.

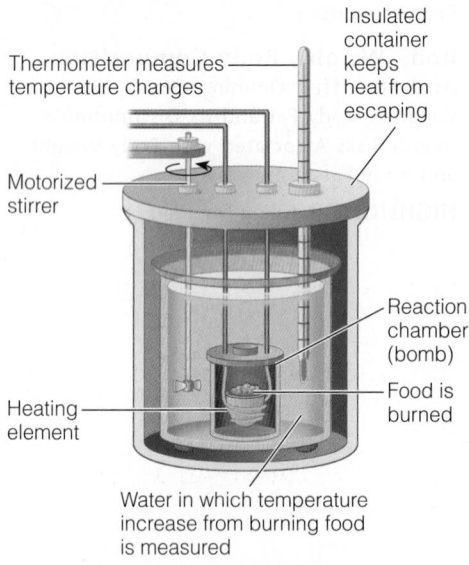

FIGURE 8-1 Bomb Calorimeter

When food is burned, energy is released in the form of heat. Heat energy is measured in kcalories.

Thermometer measures temperature changes

Insulated container keeps heat from escaping

Motorized stirrer

Reaction chamber (bomb)

Heating element

Food is burned

Water in which temperature increase from burning food is measured

◆ Food energy values can be determined by:
- **Direct calorimetry**, which measures the amount of heat released
- **Indirect calorimetry**, which measures the amount of oxygen consumed

◆ The number of kcalories that the body derives from a food, in contrast to the number of kcalories determined by calorimetry, is the **physiological fuel value.**

bomb calorimeter (KAL-oh-RIM-eh-ter): an instrument that measures the heat energy released when foods are burned, thus providing an estimate of the potential energy of the foods.
- **calor** = heat
- **metron** = measure

Energy In: The kCalories Foods Provide

Foods and beverages provide the "energy in" part of the energy-balance equation. How much energy a person receives depends on the composition of the foods and beverages and on the amount the person eats and drinks.

Food Composition

To find out how many kcalories a food provides, a scientist can burn the food in a **bomb calorimeter** (see Figure 8-1). When the food burns, energy is released in the form of heat. The amount of heat given off provides a *direct* measure of the food's energy value (remember that kcalories are units of heat energy). In addition to releasing heat, these reactions generate carbon dioxide and water—just as the body's cells do when they metabolize the energy-yielding nutrients. When the food burns and the chemical bonds break, the carbons (C) and hydrogens (H) combine with oxygens (O) to form carbon dioxide (CO_2) and water (H_2O). The amount of oxygen consumed gives an *indirect* measure ◆ of the amount of energy released.

A bomb calorimeter measures the available energy in foods but overstates the amount of energy that the human body ◆ derives from foods. The body is less efficient than a calorimeter and cannot metabolize all of the energy-yielding nutrients in a food completely. Researchers can correct for this discrepancy mathematically to create useful tables of the energy values of foods (such as Appendix H). These values provide reasonable estimates, but they do not reflect the *precise* amount of energy a person will derive from the foods consumed.

The energy values of foods can also be computed from the amounts of carbohydrate, fat, and protein (and alcohol, if present) in the foods.* For example, a food
◆ containing 12 grams of carbohydrate, 5 grams of fat, and 8 grams of protein will provide 48 carbohydrate kcalories, 45 fat kcalories, and 32 protein kcalories, for a total of 125 kcalories. (To review how to calculate the energy available from foods, turn to p. 9.)

Food Intake

To achieve energy balance, the body must meet its needs without taking in too much or too little energy. Somehow the body decides how much and how often to eat—when to start eating and when to stop. As you will see, many signals initiate or delay eating. **Appetite** refers to the sensations of hunger, satiation, and satiety that prompt a person to eat or not eat.[2]

Hunger People eat for a variety of reasons, most obviously (although not necessarily most commonly) because they are hungry. Most people recognize **hunger** as an irritating feeling that prompts thoughts of food and motivates them to start eating. In the body, hunger is the physiological response to a need for food triggered by chemical messengers originating and acting in the brain, primarily in the **hypothalamus.**[3] Hunger can be influenced by the presence or absence of nutrients in the bloodstream, the size and composition of the preceding meal, customary eating patterns, climate (heat reduces food intake; cold increases it), exercise, hormones, and physical and mental illnesses. Hunger determines what to eat, when to eat, and how much to eat.

The stomach is ideally designed to handle periodic batches of food, and people typically eat meals at roughly four-hour intervals. Four hours after a meal, most, if not all, of the food has left the stomach. Most people do not feel like eating again until the stomach is either empty or almost so. Even then, a person may not feel hungry for quite a while.

Satiation During the course of a meal, as food enters the GI tract and hunger diminishes, **satiation** develops. As receptors in the stomach stretch and hormones such as cholecystokinin increase, the person begins to feel full.[4] The response: satiation occurs and the person stops eating.

Satiety After a meal, the feeling of **satiety** continues to suppress hunger and allows a person to not eat again for a while. Whereas *satiation* tells us to "stop eating," *satiety* reminds us to "not start eating again." Figure 8-2 (p. 252) summarizes the relationships among hunger, satiation, and satiety. Of course, people can override these signals, especially when presented with stressful situations or favorite foods.

Overriding Hunger and Satiety Not surprisingly, eating can be triggered by signals other than hunger, even when the body does not need food. Some people experience food cravings when they are bored or anxious. In fact, they may eat in response to any kind of stress, ◆ negative or positive. ("What do I do when I'm grieving? Eat. What do I do when I'm celebrating? Eat!") Many people respond to external cues such as the time of day ("It's time to eat") or the availability, sight, and taste of food ("I'd love a piece of chocolate even though I'm stuffed"). Environmental influences such as large portion sizes, favorite foods, or an abundance or variety of foods stimulate eating and increase energy intake.[5] These cognitive influences ◆ can easily lead to weight gain.

Eating can also be suppressed by signals other than satiety, even when a person is hungry. People with the eating disorder anorexia nervosa, for example, use

---

◆ Reminder:
  • 1 g carbohydrate = 4 kcal
  • 1 g fat = 9 kcal
  • 1 g protein = 4 kcal
  • 1 g alcohol = 7 kcal
As Chapter 1 mentioned, many scientists measure food energy in kilojoules instead. Conversion factors for these and other measures are in the Aids to Calculation section on the last two pages of the book.

◆ Eating in response to arousal is called **stress eating.**

◆ Cognitive influences include perceptions, memories, intellect, and social interactions.

appetite: the integrated response to the sight, smell, thought, or taste of food that initiates or delays eating.

hunger: the painful sensation caused by a lack of food that initiates food-seeking behavior.

hypothalamus (high-po-THAL-ah-mus): a brain center that controls activities such as maintenance of water balance, regulation of body temperature, and control of appetite.

satiation (say-she-AY-shun): the feeling of satisfaction and fullness that occurs during a meal and halts eating. Satiation determines how much food is consumed during a meal.

satiety: the feeling of fullness and satisfaction that occurs after a meal and inhibits eating until the next meal is called. Satiety determines how much time passes between meals.

---

* Some of the food energy values in the table of food composition in Appendix H were derived by bomb calorimetry, and many were calculated from their energy-yielding nutrient contents.

FIGURE 8-2 Hunger, Satiation, and Satiety

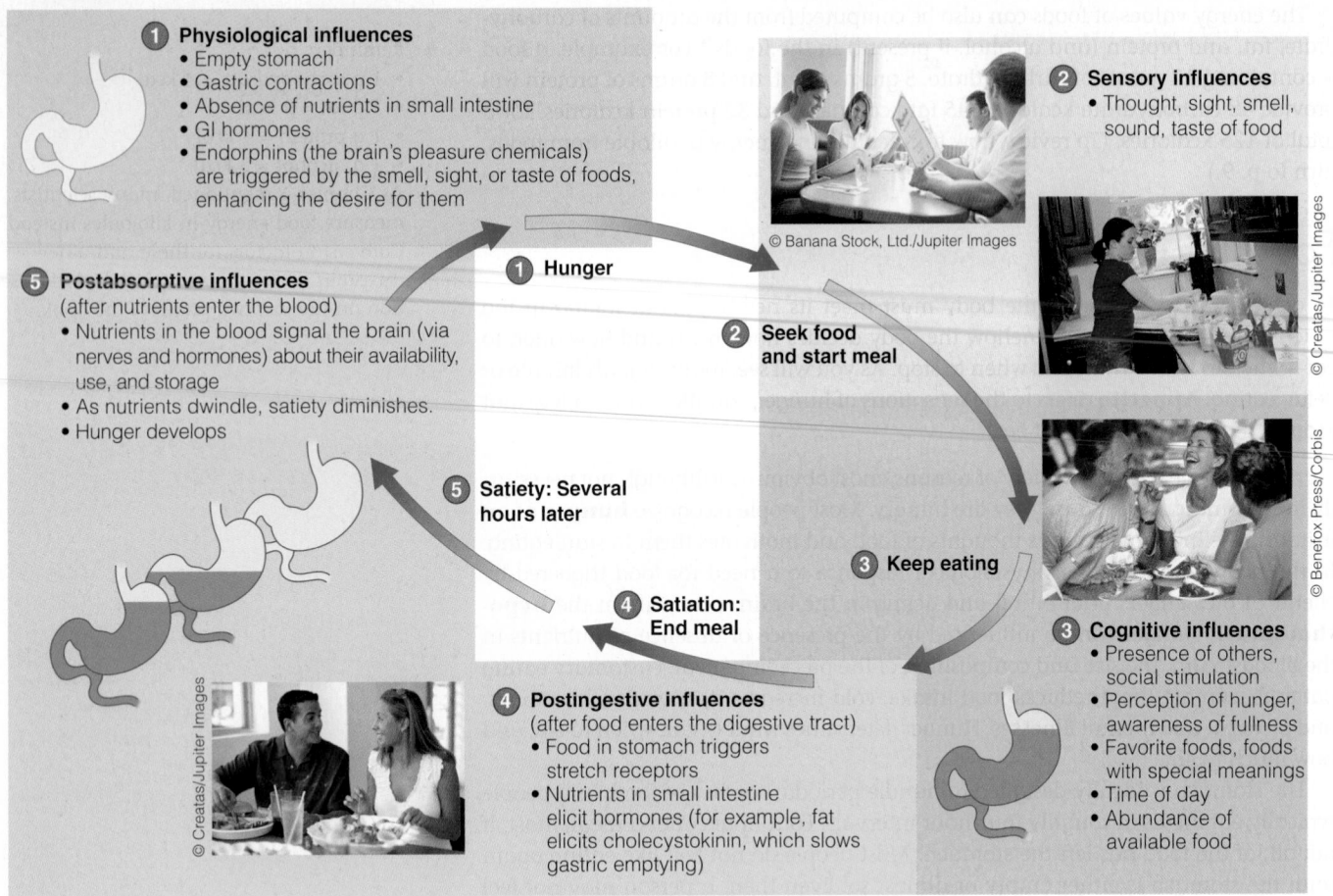

① Physiological influences
- Empty stomach
- Gastric contractions
- Absence of nutrients in small intestine
- GI hormones
- Endorphins (the brain's pleasure chemicals) are triggered by the smell, sight, or taste of foods, enhancing the desire for them

⑤ Postabsorptive influences
(after nutrients enter the blood)
- Nutrients in the blood signal the brain (via nerves and hormones) about their availability, use, and storage
- As nutrients dwindle, satiety diminishes.
- Hunger develops

① Hunger

② Seek food and start meal

⑤ Satiety: Several hours later

③ Keep eating

④ Satiation: End meal

④ Postingestive influences
(after food enters the digestive tract)
- Food in stomach triggers stretch receptors
- Nutrients in small intestine elicit hormones (for example, fat elicits cholecystokinin, which slows gastric emptying)

② Sensory influences
- Thought, sight, smell, sound, taste of food

③ Cognitive influences
- Presence of others, social stimulation
- Perception of hunger, awareness of fullness
- Favorite foods, foods with special meanings
- Time of day
- Abundance of available food

© Banana Stock, Ltd./Jupiter Images

© Creatas/Jupiter Images

© Benefox Press/Corbis

© Creatas/Jupiter Images

tremendous discipline to ignore the pangs of hunger. Some people simply cannot eat during times of stress, negative or positive. ("I'm too sad to eat." "I'm too excited to eat!") Why some people overeat in response to stress and others cannot eat at all remains a bit of a mystery, although researchers are beginning to understand the connections between stress hormones, brain activity, and "comfort foods."[6] Factors that appear to be involved include how the person perceives the stress and whether usual eating behaviors are restrained. (Highlight 8 features anorexia nervosa and other eating disorders.)

Sustaining Satiation and Satiety The extent to which foods produce satiation and sustain satiety depends in part on the nutrient composition of a meal.[7] Of the three energy-yielding nutrients, protein is considered the most **satiating**. Foods low in energy density are also more satiating.[8] High-fiber foods effectively provide satiation by filling the stomach and delaying the absorption of nutrients. For this reason, eating a large salad as a first course helps a person eat less during the meal.[9] In contrast, fat has a weak effect on satiation; consequently, eating high-fat foods may lead to passive overconsumption. High-fat foods are flavorful, which stimulates the appetite and entices people to eat more. High-fat foods are also energy dense; consequently, they deliver more kcalories per bite. (Chapter 1 introduced the concept of energy density, and Chapter 9 describes how considering a food's energy density can help with weight management.) Although fat provides little satiation during a meal, it produces strong satiety signals once it enters the intestine. Fat in the intestine triggers the release of cholecystokinin—a hormone that signals satiety and inhibits food intake.[10]

Eating high-fat foods while trying to limit energy intake requires small portion sizes, which can leave a person feeling unsatisfied. Portion size correlates directly with a food's satiety. Instead of eating small portions of high-fat foods and feeling

satiating: having the power to suppress hunger and inhibit eating.

deprived, a person can feel satisfied by eating large portions of high-protein and high-fiber foods. Figure 8-3 illustrates how fat influences portion size.

Message Central—The Hypothalamus As you can see, eating is a complex behavior controlled by a variety of psychological, social, metabolic, and physiological factors. The hypothalamus appears to be the control center, integrating messages about energy intake, expenditure, and storage from other parts of the brain and from the mouth, GI tract, and liver. Some of these messages influence satiation, which helps control the size of a meal; others influence satiety, which helps determine the frequency of meals.

Dozens of chemicals in the brain participate in appetite control and energy balance. By understanding the action of these brain chemicals, researchers may one day be able to control appetite. The greatest challenge now is to sort out the many actions of these brain chemicals. For example, one of these chemicals, **neuropeptide Y,** causes carbohydrate cravings, initiates eating, decreases energy expenditure, and increases fat storage—all factors favoring a positive energy balance and weight gain.

Regardless of hunger, people typically overeat when offered the abundance and variety of an "all you can eat" buffet.

IN SUMMARY

A mixture of signals governs a person's eating behaviors. Hunger and appetite initiate eating, whereas satiation and satiety stop and delay eating, respectively. Each responds to messages from the nervous and hormonal systems. Superimposed on these signals are complex factors involving emotions, habits, and other aspects of human behavior.

Energy Out: The kCalories the Body Expends

Chapter 7 explained that heat is released whenever the body breaks down carbohydrate, fat, or protein for energy and again when that energy is used to do work. The generation of heat, known as **thermogenesis,** can be measured to determine the amount of energy expended. ◆ The total energy a body expends reflects three main categories of thermogenesis:

- Energy expended for basal metabolism
- Energy expended for physical activity

◆ Energy expenditure, like food energy, can be determined by:
  - **Direct calorimetry,** which measures the amount of heat released
  - **Indirect calorimetry,** which measures the amount of oxygen consumed and carbon dioxide expelled

neuropeptide Y: a chemical produced in the brain that stimulates appetite, diminishes energy expenditure, and increases fat storage.

thermogenesis: the generation of heat; used in physiology and nutrition studies as an index of how much energy the body is expending.

FIGURE 8-3 How Fat Influences Portion Sizes

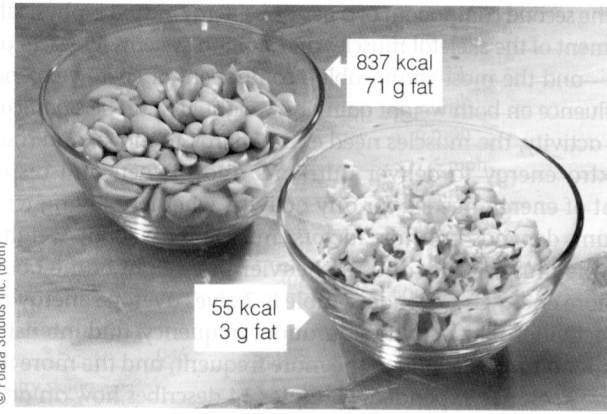

837 kcal
71 g fat

55 kcal
3 g fat

For the same size portion, peanuts deliver more than 15 times the kcalories and 20 times the fat of popcorn.

100 kcal
9 g fat

100 kcal
5 g fat

For the same number of kcalories, a person can have a few high-fat peanuts or almost 2 cups of high-fiber popcorn. (This comparison used oil-based popcorn; using air-popped popcorn would double the amount of popcorn in this example.)

◆ Thermic effect of foods:
- Carbohydrate: 5–10%
- Fat: 0–5%
- Protein: 20–30%
- Alcohol: 15–20%

The percentages are calculated by dividing the energy expended during digestion and absorption (above basal) by the energy content of the food.

◆ Note that Table 8-1 (p. 255) lists these factors among those that influence BMR and consequently energy expenditure.

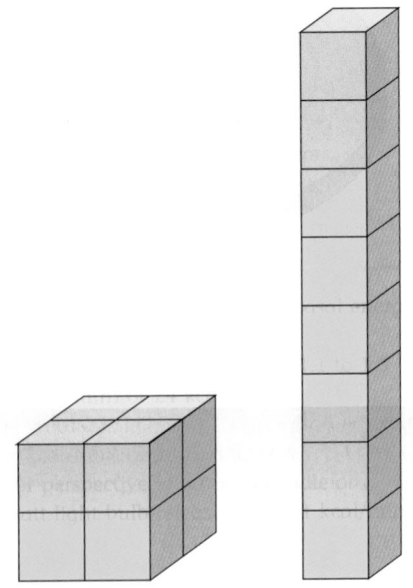

◆ Each of these structures is made of 8 blocks. They weigh the same, but they are arranged differently. The short, wide structure has 24 sides and the tall, thin one has 34. Because the tall, thin structure has a greater surface area, it will lose more heat (expend more energy) than the short, wide one. Similarly, two people of different heights might weigh the same, but the taller, thin one will have a higher BMR (expending more energy) because of the greater skin surface.

---

thermic effect of food (TEF): an estimation of the energy required to process food (digest, absorb, transport, metabolize, and store ingested nutrients); also called the **specific dynamic effect (SDE)** of food or the **specific dynamic activity (SDA)** of food. The sum of the TEF and any increase in the metabolic rate due to overeating is known as **diet-induced thermogenesis (DIT).**

adaptive thermogenesis: adjustments in energy expenditure related to changes in environment such as extreme cold and to physiological events such as overfeeding, trauma, and changes in hormone status.

---

begin their tasks, and some nutrients are absorbed by active transport. This acceleration of activity requires energy and produces heat; it is known as the **thermic effect of food (TEF).**

The thermic effect of food is proportional to the food energy taken in and is usually estimated at 10 percent of energy intake. Thus a person who ingests 2000 kcalories probably expends about 200 kcalories on the thermic effect of food. The proportions vary for different foods, however, and are also influenced by factors such as meal size and frequency. In general, the thermic effect of food is greater for high-protein foods than for high-fat foods ◆ and for a meal eaten all at once rather than spread out over a couple of hours. Some research suggests that the thermic effect of food is reduced in obese people and may contribute to their efficient storage of fat.[11] For most purposes, however, the thermic effect of food can be ignored when estimating energy expenditure because its contribution to total energy output is smaller than the probable errors involved in estimating overall energy intake and output.

Adaptive Thermogenesis Some additional energy is spent when a person must adapt to dramatically changed circumstances **(adaptive thermogenesis).** When the body has to adapt to physical conditioning, extreme cold, overfeeding, starvation, trauma, or other types of stress, it has extra work to do, building the tissues and producing the enzymes and hormones necessary to cope with the demand. In some circumstances, this energy makes a considerable difference in the total energy expended. Because this component of energy expenditure is so variable and specific to individuals, it is not included when calculating energy requirements.

Estimating Energy Requirements

In estimating energy requirements, the DRI Committee developed equations that consider how the following factors influence energy expenditure: ◆

- *Gender.* In general, women have a lower BMR than men, in large part because men typically have more lean body mass. Two sets of energy equations—one for men and one for women—were developed to accommodate the influence of gender on energy expenditure.

- *Growth.* The BMR is high in people who are growing. For this reason, pregnant women, infants, children, and adolescents have their own sets of energy equations (see Appendix F).

- *Age.* The BMR declines during adulthood as lean body mass diminishes. This change in body composition occurs, in part, because some hormones that influence appetite, body weight, and metabolism become more, or less, active with age.[12] Physical activities tend to decline as well, bringing the average reduction in energy expenditure to about 5 percent per decade. The decline in the BMR that occurs when a person becomes less active reflects the loss of lean body mass and may be minimized with ongoing physical activity. Because age influences energy expenditure, it is also factored into the energy equations.

- *Physical activity.* Using individual values for various physical activities (as in Table 8-2) is time-consuming and impractical for estimating the energy needs of a population. Instead, various activities are clustered according to the typical intensity of a day's efforts. Energy equations include a physical activity factor for various levels of intensity for each gender.

- *Body composition and body size.* The BMR is high in people who are tall and so have a large surface area. ◆ Similarly, the more a person weighs, the more energy is expended on basal metabolism. For these reasons, the energy equations include a factor for both height and weight.

As just explained, energy needs vary between individuals depending on such factors as gender, growth, age, physical activity, and body size and composition.

Even when two people are similarly matched, however, their energy needs still differ because of genetic differences. Perhaps one day genetic research will reveal how to estimate requirements for each individual. For now, the accompanying "How to" provides instructions on calculating your estimated energy requirements using the DRI equations and physical activity factors. ◆

It feels like work and it may make you tired, but studying requires only one or two kcalories per minute.

IN SUMMARY

A person in energy balance takes in energy from food and expends much of it on basal metabolic activities, some of it on physical activities, and a little on the thermic effect of food. Because energy requirements vary from person to person, such factors as gender, age, weight, and height as well as the intensity and duration of physical activity must be considered when estimating energy requirements.

HOW TO Estimate Energy Requirements

To determine your estimated energy requirements (EER), use the appropriate equation, inserting your age in years, weight (wt) in kilograms, height (ht) in meters, and physical activity (PA) factor from the accompanying table. (To convert pounds to kilograms, divide by 2.2; to convert inches to meters, divide by 39.37.)

- For men 19 years and older:
EER = [662 − (9.53 × age)] + PA × [(15.91 × wt) + (539.6 × ht)]
- For women 19 years and older:
EER = [354 − (6.91 × age)] + PA × [(9.36 × wt) + (726 × ht)]

For example, consider an active 30-year-old male who is 5 feet 11 inches tall and weighs 178 pounds. First, he converts his weight from pounds to kilograms and his height from inches to meters, if necessary:

178 lb ÷ 2.2 = 80.9 kg
71 in ÷ 39.37 = 1.8 m

Next, he considers his level of daily physical activity and selects the appropriate PA factor from the accompanying table. (In this example, 1.25 for an active male.)

Then, he inserts his age, PA factor, weight, and height into the appropriate equation:

EER = [662 − (9.53 × 30)] + 1.25 × [(15.91 × 80.9) + (539.6 × 1.8)]

(A reminder: Do calculations within the parentheses first.) He calculates:

EER = [662 − 286] + 1.25 × [1287 + 971]

(Another reminder: Do calculations within the brackets next.)

EER = 376 + 1.25 × 2258

(One more reminder: Do multiplication before addition.)

EER = 376 + 2823
EER = 3199

The estimated energy requirement for an active 30-year-old male who is 5 feet 11 inches tall and weighs 178 pounds is about 3200 kcalories/day. His actual requirement probably falls within a range ◆ of 200 kcalories above and below this estimate.

NOTE: Appendix F provides EER equations for infants, children, adolescents, and pregnant women.

◆ Appendix F presents DRI tables that provide a shortcut to estimating total energy expenditure and instructions to help you determine the appropriate physical activity factor to use in the equation.

◆ For *most* people, the actual energy requirement falls within these ranges:
- For men, EER ± 200 kcal
- For women, EER ± 160 kcal
For *almost all* people, the actual energy requirement falls within these ranges:
- For men, EER ± 400 kcal
- For women, EER ± 320 kcal

Physical Activity (PA) Factors for EER Equations

	Men	Women	Physical Activity
Sedentary	1.0	1.0	Typical daily living activities
Low active	1.11	1.12	Plus 30–60 min moderate activity
Active	1.25	1.27	Plus ≥ 60 min moderate activity
Very active	1.48	1.45	Plus ≥ 60 min moderate activity and 60 min vigorous or 120 min moderate activity

Note: Moderate activity is equivalent to walking at 3 to 4½ mph.

ThomsonNOW
To practice estimating energy requirements, log on to **www.thomsonedu.com/thomsonnow**, go to Chapter 8, then go to How To.

At 6 feet 4 inches tall and 250 pounds (1.93 meters and 113 kilograms), this runner would be considered overweight by most standards. Yet he is clearly not overfat.

◆ In metric terms, a person 1.78 meters tall who weighs 68 kilograms may carry only about 14 of those kilograms as fat.

Body Weight, Body Composition, and Health

A person 5 feet 10 inches tall who weighs 150 pounds ◆ may carry only about 30 of those pounds as fat. The rest is mostly water and lean tissues—muscles, organs such as the heart and liver, and the bones of the skeleton. Direct measures of **body composition** are impossible in living human beings; instead, researchers assess body composition indirectly based on the following assumption:

body weight = fat + lean tissue (including water)

Weight gains and losses tell us nothing about how the body's composition may have changed, yet weight is the measure most people use to judge their "fatness." For many people, overweight means overfat, but this is not always the case. Athletes with dense bones and well-developed muscles may be overweight by some standards but have little body fat. Conversely, inactive people may seem to have acceptable weights, when, in fact, they may have too much body fat.

Defining Healthy Body Weight

How much should a person weigh? How can a person know if her weight is appropriate for her height? How can a person know if his weight is jeopardizing his health? Such questions seem so simple, yet the answers can be complex—and quite different depending on whom you ask.

The Criterion of Fashion In asking what is ideal, people often mistakenly turn to fashion for the answer. No doubt our society sets unrealistic ideals for body weight, especially for women. Miss America, our nation's icon of beauty, has never been overweight, and until recently, she has grown progressively thinner over the years (see Figure 8-5). Magazines, movies, and television all convey the message that to be thin is to be beautiful and happy. As a result, the media have a great influence on the weight concerns and dieting patterns of people of all ages, but most tragically on young, impressionable children and adolescents.[13] One-half of preteen girls and one-third of preteen boys are dissatisfied with their body weight and shape.[14]

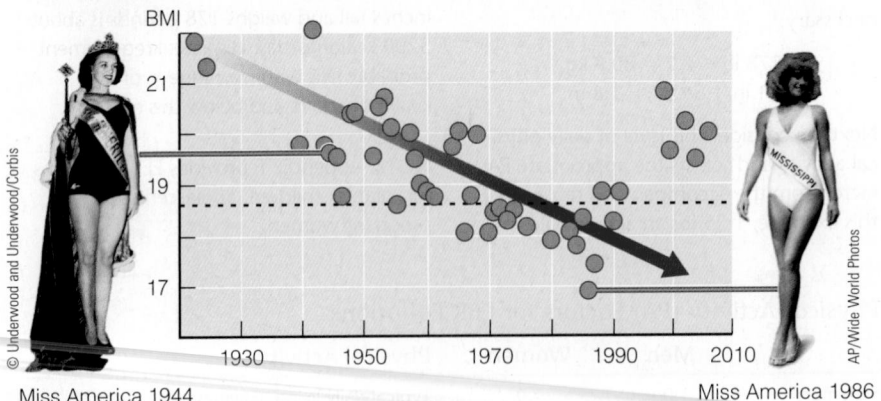

FIGURE 8-5 The Declining Weight of Miss America

Miss America 1944

Miss America 1986

As explained on p. 259, the body mass index (BMI) describes relative weight for height. Over the years, the BMI of Miss America has declined steadily. Since the mid-1960s, most have fallen below 18.5, the cutoff point indicating underweight with its associated health problems.

SOURCE: S. Rubenstein and B. Caballero, Is Miss America an undernourished role model? *Journal of the American Medical Association* 283 (2000): 1569.

body composition: the proportions of muscle, bone, fat, and other tissue that make up a person's total body weight.

TABLE 8-3 Tips for Accepting a Healthy Body Weight

- Value yourself and others for human attributes other than body weight. Realize that prejudging people by weight is as harmful as prejudging them by race, religion, or gender.
- Use positive, nonjudgmental descriptions of your body.
- Accept positive comments from others.
- Focus on your whole self including your intelligence, social grace, and professional and scholastic achievements.
- Accept that no magic diet exists.
- Stop dieting to lose weight. Adopt a lifestyle of healthy eating and physical activity permanently.

- Follow the USDA Food Guide. Never restrict food intake below the minimum levels that meet nutrient needs.
- Become physically active, not because it will help you get thin but because it will make you feel good and enhance your health.
- Seek support from loved ones. Tell them of your plan for a healthy life in the body you have been given.
- Seek professional counseling, *not* from a weight-loss counselor, but from someone who can help you make gains in self-esteem without weight as a factor.

Importantly, perceived body image has little to do with actual body weight or size. People of all shapes, sizes, and ages—including extremely thin fashion models with anorexia nervosa and fitness instructors with ideal body composition—have learned to be unhappy with their "overweight" bodies. Such dissatisfaction can lead to damaging behaviors, such as starvation diets, diet pill abuse, and health care avoidance.[15] The first step toward making healthy changes may be self-acceptance. Keep in mind that fashion is fickle; the body shapes valued by our society change with time. Furthermore, body shapes valued by our society differ from those of other societies. The standards defining "ideal" are subjective and frequently have little in common with health. Table 8-3 offers some tips for adopting health as an ideal, rather than society's misconceived image of beauty.

The Criterion of Health Even if our society were to accept fat as beautiful, obesity would still be a major risk factor for several life-threatening diseases. For this reason, the most important criterion for determining how much a person should weigh and how much body fat a person needs is not appearance but good health and longevity. Ideally, a person has enough fat to meet basic needs but not so much as to incur health risks. This range of healthy body weights has been identified using a common measure of weight and height—the body mass index.

Body Mass Index The **body mass index (BMI)** describes relative weight for height: ◆

$$\text{BMI} = \frac{\text{weight (kg)}}{\text{height (m)}^2} \quad \text{or} \quad \frac{\text{weight (lb)} \times 703}{\text{height (in)}^2}$$

Weight classifications based on BMI are presented in Figure 8-6 (p. 260). Notice that healthy weight falls between a BMI of 18.5 and 24.9, with **underweight** below 18.5, **overweight** above 25, and **obese** above 30. Well over half of adults in the United States have a BMI greater than 25, as Figure 8-7 (p. 260) shows.[16]

A BMI of 25 for adults represents a healthy target for overweight people to achieve or for others not to exceed. Obesity-related diseases and increased mortality become evident beyond a BMI of 25. The lower end of the healthy range may be a reasonable target for severely underweight people. BMI values slightly below the healthy range may be compatible with good health if food intake is adequate, but signs of illness, reduced work capacity, and poor reproductive function become apparent when BMI is below 17. The inside back cover presents weights and visual images associated with various BMI values. The "How to" on p. 261 describes how to determine an appropriate body weight based on BMI.

Keep in mind that BMI reflects height and weight measures and not body composition. Consequently, muscular athletes may be classified as over*weight* by BMI standards and not be over*fat*.[17] At the peak of his bodybuilding career, Arnold Schwarzenegger won the Mr. Olympia competition with a BMI of 31; the runner on p. 258 also has a BMI greater than 30. Yet neither would be considered obese. Striking differences in body composition are also apparent among people of various ethnic and racial groups, making standard BMI guidelines inappropriate for some

A healthy body contains enough lean tissue to support health and the right amount of fat to meet body needs.

◆ To convert pounds to kilograms:
lb × 2.2 lb/kg = kg
To convert inches to meters:
in × 39.37 in/m = m

body mass index (BMI): an index of a person's weight in relation to height; determined by dividing the weight (in kilograms) by the square of the height (in meters).

underweight: body weight below some standard of acceptable weight that is usually defined in relation to height (such as BMI); BMI below 18.5.

overweight: body weight above some standard of acceptable weight that is usually defined in relation to height (such as BMI); BMI 25 to 29.9.

obese: overweight with adverse health effects; BMI 30 or higher.

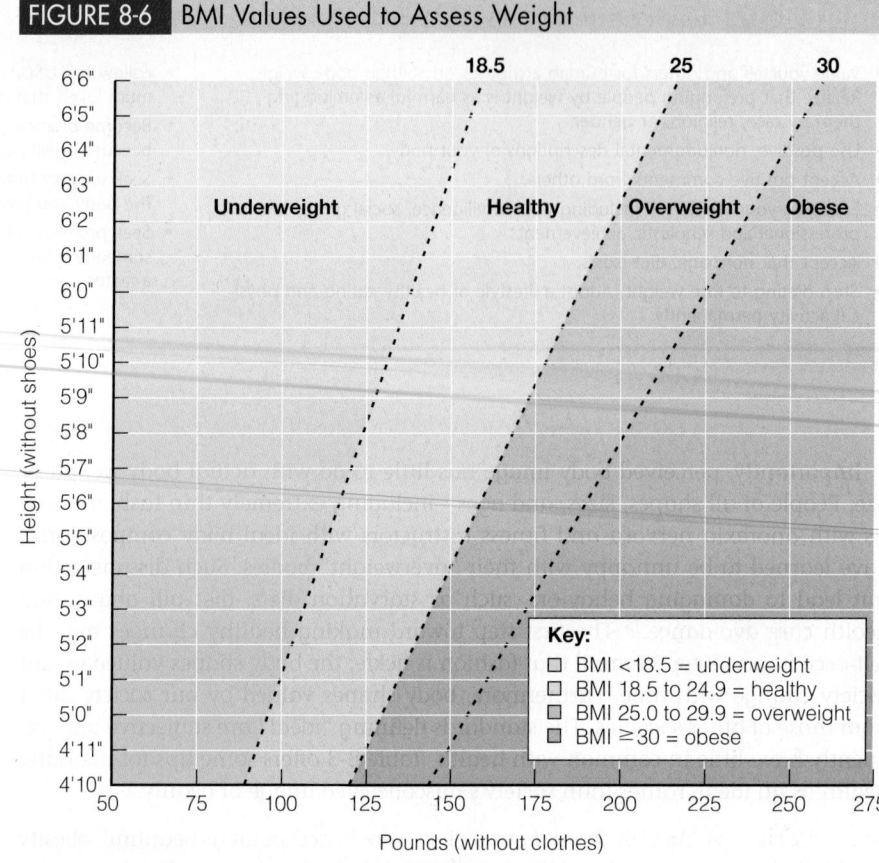

FIGURE 8-6 BMI Values Used to Assess Weight

Underweight   Healthy   Overweight   Obese

Height (without shoes)

Pounds (without clothes)

Key:
- BMI <18.5 = underweight
- BMI 18.5 to 24.9 = healthy
- BMI 25.0 to 29.9 = overweight
- BMI ≥30 = obese

NOTE: Chapter 16 presents BMI values for children and adolescents age 2 to 20.
SOURCE: U.S. Department of Agriculture and U.S. Department of Health and Human Services, *Nutrition and Your Health: Dietary Guidelines for Americans* (Washington, D.C.: 2000), p. 7.

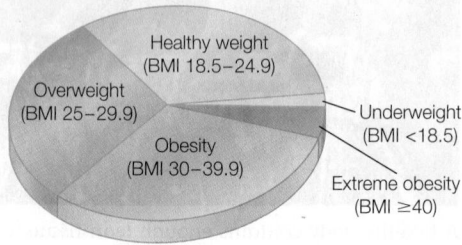

FIGURE 8-7 Distribution of Body Weights in U.S. Adults

Healthy weight (BMI 18.5–24.9)

Overweight (BMI 25–29.9)

Obesity (BMI 30–39.9)

Underweight (BMI <18.5)

Extreme obesity (BMI ≥40)

populations.[18] For example, blacks tend to have a greater bone density and protein content than whites; consequently, using BMI as the standard may overestimate the prevalence of obesity among blacks.

IN SUMMARY

Current standards for body weight are based on a person's weight in relation to height, called the body mass index (BMI), and reflect disease risks. To its disadvantage, BMI does not reflect body fat, and it may misclassify very muscular people as overweight.

Body Fat and Its Distribution

Although weight measures are inexpensive, easy to take, and highly accurate, they fail to reveal two valuable pieces of information in assessing disease risk: how much of the weight is fat and where the fat is located. The ideal amount of body fat depends partly on the person. A normal-weight man may have from 13 to 21 percent body fat; a woman, because of her greater quantity of essential fat, 23 to 31 percent. In general, health problems typically develop when body fat exceeds 22 percent in young men, 25 percent in men over age 40, 32 percent in young women, and 35 percent in women over age 40. Body fat may contribute as much as 70 percent in excessively obese adults. Figure 8-8 compares the body composition of healthy weight men and women.

HOW TO Determine Body Weight Based on BMI

A person whose BMI reflects an unacceptable health risk can choose a desired BMI and then calculate an appropriate body weight. For example, a woman who is 5 feet 5 inches (1.65 meters) tall and weighs 180 pounds (82 kilograms) has a BMI of 30:

$$BMI = \frac{82 \text{ kg}}{1.65 \text{ m}^2} = 30$$

or

$$BMI = \frac{180 \text{ lb} \times 703}{65 \text{ in}^2} = 30$$

A reasonable target for most overweight people is a BMI 2 units below their current one. To determine a desired goal weight based on a BMI of 28, for example, the woman could divide the desired BMI by the factor appropriate for her height from the table below:

desired BMI ÷ factor = goal weight

28 ÷ 0.166 = 169 lb

To reach a BMI of 28, this woman would need to lose 11 pounds. Such a calculation can help a person to determine realistic weight goals using health risk as a guide. Alternatively, a person could search the table on the inside back cover for the weight that corresponds to his or her height and the desired BMI.

ThomsonNOW
To determine BMI, log on to **www.thomsonedu.com/thomsonnow**, go to Chapter 8, then go to How To.

Height	Factor	Height	Factor	Height	Factor
4'7" (1.40 m)	0.232	5'3" (1.60 m)	0.177	5'11" (1.80 m)	0.139
4'8" (1.42 m)	0.224	5'4" (1.63 m)	0.172	6'0" (1.83 m)	0.136
4'9" (1.45 m)	0.216	5'5" (1.65 m)	0.166	6'1" (1.85 m)	0.132
4'10" (1.47 m)	0.209	5'6" (1.68 m)	0.161	6'2" (1.88 m)	0.128
4'11" (1.50 m)	0.202	5'7" (1.70 m)	0.157	6'3" (1.90 m)	0.125
5'0" (1.52 m)	0.195	5'8" (1.73 m)	0.152	6'4" (1.93 m)	0.122
5'1" (1.55 m)	0.189	5'9" (1.75 m)	0.148	6'5" (1.96 m)	0.119
5'2" (1.57 m)	0.183	5'10" (1.78 m)	0.143	6'6" (1.98 m)	0.116

SOURCE: R. P. Abernathy, Body mass index: Determination and use, *Journal of the American Dietetic Association* 91 (1991): 843.

Some People Need Less Body Fat For many athletes, a lower percentage of body fat may be ideal—just enough fat to provide fuel, insulate and protect the body, assist in nerve impulse transmissions, and support normal hormone activity,

FIGURE 8-8 Male and Female Body Compositions Compared

The differences between male and female body compositions become apparent during adolescence. Lean body mass (primarily muscle) increases more in males than in females. Fat assumes a larger percentage of female body composition as essential body fat is deposited in the mammary glands and pelvic region in preparation for childbearing. Both men and women have essential fat associated with the bone marrow, the central nervous system, and the internal organs.

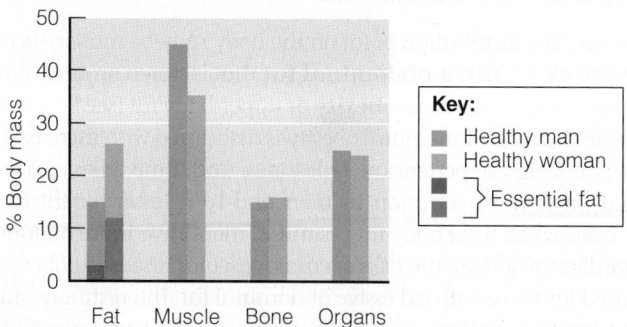

SOURCE: R. E. C. Wildman and D. M. Medeiros, *Advanced Human Nutrition* (Boca Raton, Fla.: CRC Press, 2000), pp. 321–323. Used with permission.

FIGURE 8-9   Abdominal Fat

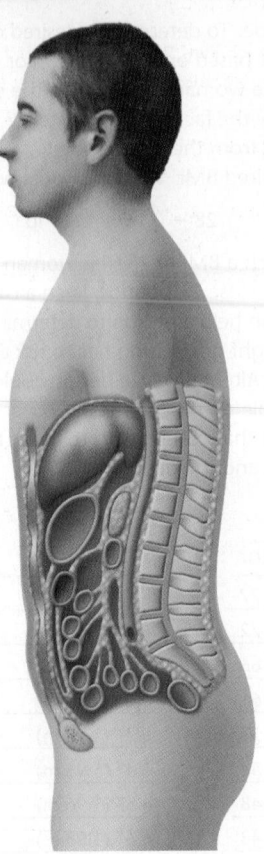
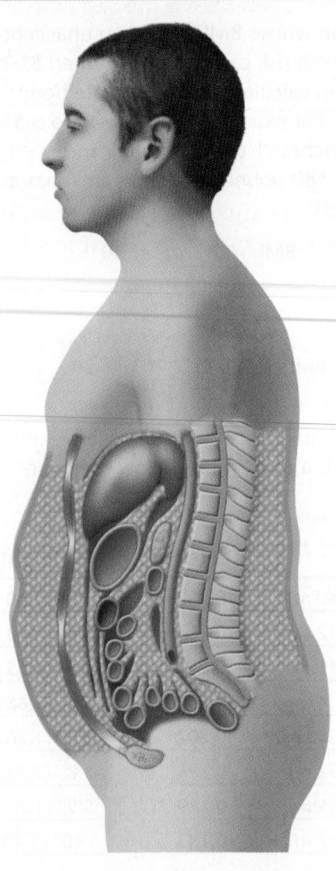

In healthy weight people, some fat is stored around the organs of the abdomen.

In overweight people, excess abdominal fat increases the risks of diseases.

but not so much as to burden the body with excess bulk. For some athletes, then, ideal body fat might be 5 to 10 percent for men and 15 to 20 percent for women. (Review the photo on p. 258 to appreciate what 8 percent body fat looks like.)

Some People Need More Body Fat   For an Alaska fisherman, a higher percentage of body fat is probably beneficial because fat provides an insulating blanket to prevent excessive loss of body heat in cold climates. A woman starting a pregnancy needs sufficient body fat to support conception and fetal growth. Below a certain threshold for body fat, hormone synthesis falters, and individuals may become infertile, develop depression, experience abnormal hunger regulation, or become unable to keep warm. These thresholds differ for each function and for each individual; much remains to be learned about them.

Fat Distribution   The distribution of fat on the body may be more critical than the total amount of fat alone. **Intra-abdominal fat** that is stored around the organs of the abdomen is referred to as **central obesity** or upper-body fat (see Figure 8-9). Independently of BMI or total body fat, central obesity is associated with increased risks of heart disease, stroke, diabetes, hypertension, gallstones, and some types of cancer.[19]

Abdominal fat is most common in men and to a lesser extent in women past menopause. Even when total body fat is similar, men have more abdominal fat than women. Regardless of gender, the risks of cardiovascular disease, diabetes, and mortality are increased for those with excessive abdominal fat. Interestingly, smokers tend to have more abdominal fat than nonsmokers even though they have lower BMI.[20]

Fat around the hips and thighs, sometimes referred to as lower-body fat, is most common in women during their reproductive years and seems relatively harmless. In fact, overweight people who do not have abdominal fat are less susceptible to

intra-abdominal fat: fat stored within the abdominal cavity in association with the internal abdominal organs, as opposed to the fat stored directly under the skin (subcutaneous fat).

central obesity: excess fat around the trunk of the body; also called **abdominal fat** or **upper-body fat.**

health problems than overweight people with abdominal fat. Figure 8-10 compares the body shapes of people with upper-body fat and lower-body fat.

Waist Circumference A person's **waist circumference** is the most practical indicator of fat distribution and central obesity. [21] In general, women with a waist circumference of greater than 35 inches (88 centimeters) and men with a waist circumference of greater than 40 inches (102 centimeters) have a high risk of central obesity-related health problems, such as diabetes and cardiovascular disease.[22] As waist circumference increases, disease risks increase.[23] Appendix E includes instructions for measuring waist circumference and assessing abdominal fat.

Some researchers use the waist-to-hip ratio when studying disease risks. The ratio requires another step or two (measuring the hips and comparing that measure to the waist measure), but it does not provide any additional information. Therefore, waist circumference alone is the preferred method for assessing abdominal fat in a clinical setting.*

Other Measures of Body Composition Health care professionals commonly use BMI and waist circumference measures because they are relatively easy and inexpensive. Together, these two measures prove most valuable in assessing a person's health risks and monitoring changes over time.[24] Researchers needing more precise measures of body composition may choose any of several other techniques to estimate body fat and its distribution (see Figure 8-11 on p. 264). Mastering these techniques requires proper instruction and practice to ensure reliability. In addition to the methods shown in Figure 8-11, researchers sometimes estimate body composition using these methods: total body water, radioactive potassium count, near-infrared spectrophotometry, ultrasound, computed tomography, and magnetic resonance imaging. Each method has advantages and disadvantages with respect to cost, technical difficulty, and precision of estimating body fat (see Appendix E for a comparison). Appendix E provides additional details and includes many of the tables and charts routinely used in assessment procedures.

IN SUMMARY

The ideal amount of body fat varies from person to person, but researchers have found that body fat in excess of 22 percent for young men and 32 percent for young women (the levels rise slightly with age) poses health risks. Central obesity, in which excess abdominal fat is distributed around the trunk of the body, presents greater health risks than excess fat distributed on the lower body.

Health Risks Associated with Body Weight and Body Fat

Body weight and fat distribution correlate with disease risks and life expectancy.[25] They indicate a greater *likelihood* of developing a chronic disease and shortening life expectancy. Not all overweight and underweight people will get sick and die before their time nor will all normal-weight people live long healthy lives. *Correlations* are not *causes*. For the most part, people with a BMI between 18.5 and 24.9 have relatively few health risks; risks increase as BMI falls below or rises above this range, indicating that both too little and too much body fat impair health.[26] Epidemiological data show a J- or U-shaped relationship between body weights and mortality (see Figure 8-12, p. 264).[27] People who are extremely underweight or extremely obese carry higher risks of early deaths than those whose weights fall within the acceptable range; these mortality risks decline with age.[28]

* The National Heart, Lung, and Blood Institute recommends using the waist circumference instead of the waist-to-hip ratio to assess obesity health risks.

FIGURE 8-10 **"Apple" and "Pear" Body Shapes Compared**

Popular articles sometimes call bodies with upper-body fat "apples" and those with lower-body fat, "pears." Researchers sometimes refer to upper-body fat as "android" (manlike) obesity and to lower-body fat as "gynoid" (womanlike) obesity.

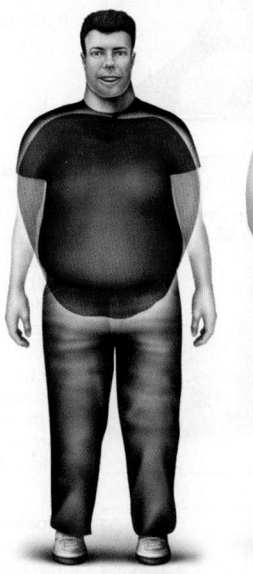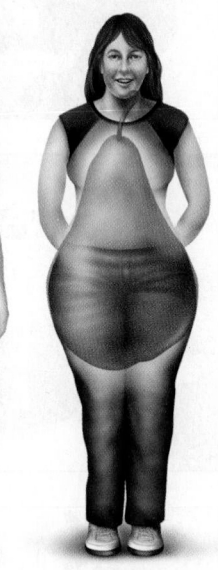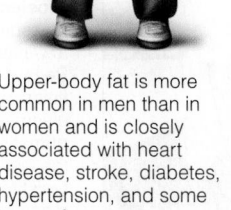

Upper-body fat is more common in men than in women and is closely associated with heart disease, stroke, diabetes, hypertension, and some types of cancer.

Lower body fat is more common in women than in men and is not usually associated with chronic diseases.

waist circumference: an anthropometric measurement used to assess a person's abdominal fat.

FIGURE 8-11 Common Methods Used to Assess Body Fat

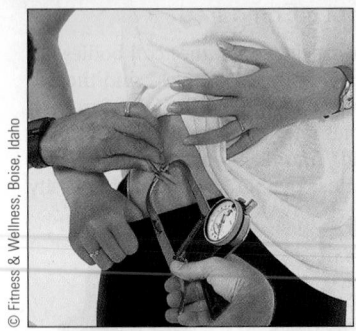

Skinfold measures estimate body fat by using a caliper to gauge the thickness of a fold of skin on the back of the arm (over the triceps), below the shoulder blade (subscapular), and in other places (including lower-body sites) and then comparing these measurements with standards.

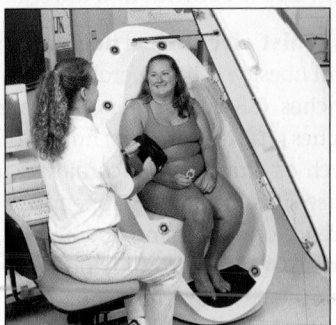

Air displacement plethysmography estimates body composition by having a person sit inside a chamber while computerized sensors determine the amount of air displaced by the person's body.

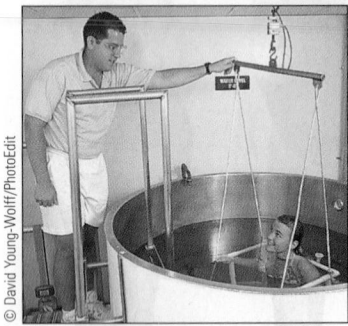

Hydrodensitometry measures body density by weighing the person first on land and then again while submerged in water. The difference between the person's actual weight and underwater weight provides a measure of the body's volume. A mathematical equation using the two measurements (volume and actual weight) determines body density, from which the percentage of body fat can be estimated.

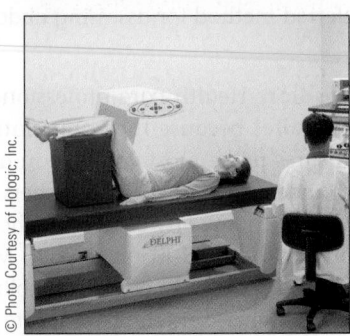

Dual energy X-ray absorptiometry (DEXA) uses two low-dose X-rays that differentiate among fat-free soft tissue (lean body mass), fat tissue, and bone tissue, providing a precise measurement of total fat and its distribution in all but extremely obese subjects.

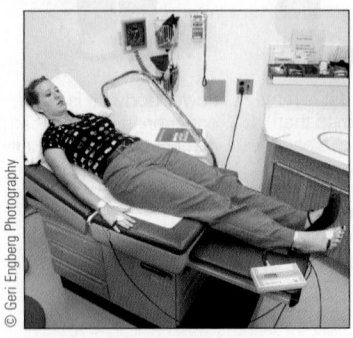

Bioelectrical impedance measures body fat by using a low-intensity electrical current. Because electrolyte-containing fluids, which readily conduct an electrical current, are found primarily in lean body tissues, the leaner the person, the less resistance to the current. The measurement of electrical resistance is then used in a mathematical equation to estimate the percentage of body fat.

FIGURE 8-12 BMI and Mortality

This J-shaped curve describes the relationship between body mass index (BMI) and mortality and shows that both underweight and overweight present risks of a premature death.

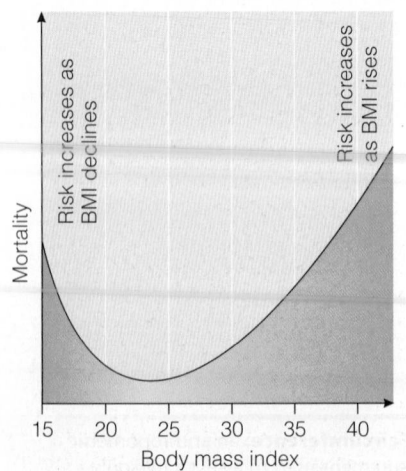

Independently of BMI, factors such as smoking habits raise health risks, and physical fitness lowers them.[29] A man with a BMI of 22 who smokes two packs of cigarettes a day is jeopardizing his health, whereas a woman with a BMI of 32 who walks briskly for an hour a day is improving her health.

Health Risks of Underweight Some underweight people enjoy an active, healthy life, but others are underweight because of malnutrition, smoking habits, substance abuse, or illnesses. Weight and fat measures alone would not reveal these underlying causes, but a complete assessment that includes a diet and medical history, physical examination, and biochemical analysis would.

An underweight person, especially an older adult, may be unable to preserve lean tissue during the fight against a wasting disease such as cancer or a digestive disorder, especially when the disease is accompanied by malnutrition. Without adequate nutrient and energy reserves, an underweight person will have a particularly tough battle against such medical stresses. Underweight women develop menstrual irregularities and become infertile. Exactly how infertility develops is unclear, but contributing factors include body weight as well as restricted energy and fat intake and depleted body fat stores. Those who do conceive may give birth to unhealthy infants. An underweight woman can improve her chances of having a healthy infant by gaining weight prior to conception, during pregnancy, or both. Underweight and significant weight loss are also associated with osteoporosis and bone fractures. For all these reasons, underweight people may benefit from enough of a weight gain to provide an energy reserve and protective amounts of all the nutrients that can be stored.

Health Risks of Overweight As for excessive body fat, the health risks are so many that it has been designated a disease—obesity. Among the health risks associated with obesity are diabetes, hypertension, cardiovascular disease, sleep apnea (abnormal ceasing of breathing during sleep), osteoarthritis, some cancers, gallbladder disease, kidney stones, respiratory problems (including Pickwickian syndrome, a breathing blockage linked with sudden death), and complications in pregnancy and surgery. Each year, these obesity-related illnesses cost our nation billions of dollars—in fact, as much as the medical costs of smoking.[30]

The cost in terms of lives is also great: an estimated 300,000 people die each year from obesity-related diseases. In fact, obesity is second only to tobacco in causing preventable illnesses and premature deaths. Mortality increases as excess weight increases; people with a BMI greater than 35 are more than twice as likely to die prematurely as others.[31] The risks associated with a high BMI appear to be greater for whites than for blacks; in fact, the health risks associated with obesity do not become apparent in black women until a BMI of 37.[32]

Equally important, both central obesity and weight gains of more than 20 pounds (9 kilograms) between early and middle adulthood correlate with increased disease risks.[33] Fluctuations in body weight, as typically occur with "yo-yo" dieting, may also increase the risks of chronic diseases and premature death. In contrast, sustained weight loss improves physical well-being, reduces disease risks, and increases life expectancy.

Cardiovascular Disease The relationship between obesity and cardiovascular disease risk is strong, with links to both elevated blood cholesterol and hypertension. Central obesity may raise the risk of heart attack and stroke as much as the three leading risk factors (high LDL cholesterol, hypertension, and smoking) do. ◆ In addition to body fat and its distribution, weight gain also increases the risk of cardiovascular disease. Weight loss, on the other hand, can effectively lower both blood cholesterol and blood pressure in obese people. Of course, lean and normal-weight people may also have high blood cholesterol and blood pressure, and these factors are just as dangerous in lean people as in obese people.

Diabetes Most adults with type 2 diabetes are overweight or obese.[34] Diabetes (type 2) is three times more likely to develop in an obese person than in a nonobese person. Furthermore, the person with type 2 diabetes often has central obesity. Central-body fat cells appear to be larger and more insulin-resistant than lower-body fat cells.[35] The association between **insulin resistance** and obesity is strong. Both are major risk factors for the development of type 2 diabetes.

Diabetes appears to be influenced by weight gains as well as by body weight. A weight gain of more than 10 pounds (4.5 kilograms) after the age of 18 doubles the risk of developing diabetes, even in women of average weight. In contrast, weight loss is effective in improving glucose tolerance and insulin resistance.[36]

Inflammation and the Metabolic Syndrome Chronic **inflammation** accompanies obesity, and inflammation contributes to chronic diseases.[37] As a person grows fatter, lipids first fill the adipose tissue and then migrate into other tissues such as the muscles and liver.[38] This accumulation of fat, especially in the abdominal region, changes the body's metabolism, resulting in insulin resistance, low HDL, high triglycerides, and high blood pressure.[39] This cluster of symptoms—collectively known as the metabolic syndrome—increases the risks for diabetes, hypertension, and atherosclerosis.◆ Fat accumulation, especially in the abdominal region, also activates genes that code for proteins ◆ involved in inflammation.[40] Furthermore, although relatively few immune cells are commonly found in adipose tissue, weight gain significantly increases their number and their role in inflammation.[41] Elevated blood lipids—whether due to obesity or to a high-fat diet—also promote inflammation.[42] Together, these factors help to explain why chronic inflammation accompanies obesity and how obesity contributes to the metabolic syndrome and the progression of

◆ Cardiovascular disease risk factors associated with obesity:
- High LDL cholesterol
- Low HDL cholesterol
- High blood pressure (hypertension)
- Diabetes

Chapter 18 provides many more details.

◆ Metabolic syndrome is a cluster of at least three of the following risk factors:
- High blood pressure
- High blood glucose
- High blood triglycerides
- Low HDL cholesterol
- High waist circumference

◆ Proteins released from adipose tissue signal changes in the body's fat and energy status and are called **adipokines**. Over 50 adipokines have been identified, some of which play a role in inflammation.

insulin resistance: the condition in which a normal amount of insulin produces a subnormal effect in muscle, adipose, and liver cells, resulting in an elevated fasting glucose; a metabolic consequence of obesity that precedes type 2 diabetes.

inflammation: an immunological response to cellular injury characterized by an increase in white blood cells.

Being active—even if overweight—is healthier than being sedentary. With a BMI of 36, aerobics instructor Jennifer Portnick is considered obese, but her daily workout routine helps to keep her in good health.

ThomsonNOW
www.thomsonedu.com/thomsonnow

chronic diseases.[43] Even in healthy youngsters, body fat correlates positively with chronic inflammation.[44] As might be expected, weight loss reduces the number of immune cells in adipose tissue and changes gene expression to reduce inflammation.[45]

Cancer

The risk of some cancers increases with both body weight and weight gain, but researchers do not fully understand the relationships. One possible explanation may be that obese people have elevated levels of hormones that could influence cancer development.[46] For example, adipose tissue is the major site of estrogen synthesis in women, obese women have elevated levels of estrogen, and estrogen has been implicated in the development of cancers of the female reproductive system—cancers that account for half of all cancers in women.

Fit and Fat versus Sedentary and Slim Importantly, BMI and weight gains and losses do not tell the whole story. Cardiorespiratory fitness also plays a major role in health and longevity, independently of BMI.[47] Normal-weight people who are fit have a lower risk of mortality than normal-weight people who are unfit. Furthermore, overweight but fit people have lower risks than normal-weight, unfit ones.[48] Clearly, a healthy body weight is good, but it may not be good enough. Fitness, in and of itself, offers many health benefits, as Chapter 14 confirms. The next chapter explores weight management and the benefits of achieving and maintaining a healthy weight.

IN SUMMARY

The weight appropriate for an individual depends largely on factors specific to that individual, including body fat distribution, family health history, and current health status. At the extremes, both overweight and underweight carry clear risks to health.

Nutrition Portfolio

When combined with fitness, a healthy body weight will help you to defend against chronic diseases.

■ Describe how your daily food intake and physical activity balance with each other.

■ Calculate your estimated energy requirements.

■ Describe any health risks that may be of concern for a person of your BMI and waist circumference.

NUTRITION ON THE NET

• Obtain food composition data from the USDA Nutrient Data Laboratory: www.ars.usda.gov/ba/bhnrc/ndl

• Learn about the 10,000 Steps Program at Shape Up America: www.shapeup.org

• Visit the special web pages and interactive applications for Healthy Weight: www.nhlbi.nih.gov/subsites/index.htm

NUTRITION CALCULATIONS

ThomsonNOW™ For additional practice log on to www.thomsonedu.com/thomsonnow. Go to Chapter 8, then to Nutrition Calculations.

These problems give you practice in estimating energy needs. Once you have mastered these examples, you will be prepared to examine your own energy intakes and energy expenditures. Be sure to show your calculations for each problem and check p. 269 for answers.

1. Compare the energy a person might spend on various physical activities. Refer to Table 8-2 on p. 255, and compute how much energy a person who weighs 142 pounds (64.4 kilograms) would spend doing each of the following. You may want to compare various activities based on your weight.

   30 min vigorous aerobic dance:

   0.062 kcal/lb/min $\times$ 142 lb = 8.8 kcal/min
   (or 0.136 kcal/kg/min x 64.5 kg = 8.8 kcal/min)

   8.8 kcal/min $\times$ 30 min = 264 kcal

   a. 2 hours golf, carrying clubs
   b. 20 minutes running at 9 mph
   c. 45 minutes swimming at 20 yd/min
   d. 1 hour walking at 3.5 mph

2. Consider the effect of age on BMR. An infant who weighs 20 pounds (9.1 kilograms) has a BMR of 500 kcalories/day; an adult who weighs 170 pounds (77.3 kilograms) has a BMR of about 1500. Based on body weight, who has the faster BMR?

3. Compute daily energy needs for a woman, age 20, who is 5 feet 6 inches tall (1.68 meters), weighs 130 pounds (59 kilograms), and is lightly active.

4. Discover what weight is needed to achieve a desired BMI. Refer to the table on p. 261 and consider a person who is 5 feet 4 inches (1.63 meters) tall. Suppose this person wants to have a BMI of 21. What should this person weigh? Does this agree with the table on the inside back cover?

STUDY QUESTIONS

ThomsonNOW™
To assess your understanding of chapter topics, take the Student Practice Test and explore the modules recommended in your Personalized Study Plan. Log onto www.thomsonedu.com/thomsonnow.

These questions will help you review the chapter. You will find the answers in the discussions on the pages provided.

1. What are the consequences of an unbalanced energy budget? (pp. 249–250)

2. Define hunger, appetite, satiation, and satiety and describe how each influences food intake. (pp. 251–253)

3. Describe each component of energy expenditure. What factors influence each? How can energy expenditure be estimated? (pp. 253–257)

4. Distinguish between body weight and body composition. What assessment techniques are used to measure each? (pp. 258–264)

5. What problems are involved in defining "ideal" body weight? (pp. 258–259)

6. What is central obesity, and what is its relationship to disease? (pp. 262–265)

7. What risks are associated with excess body weight and excess body fat? (pp. 265–266)

These multiple choice questions will help you prepare for an exam. Answers can be found on p. 269.

1. A person who consistently consumes 1700 kcalories a day and spends 2200 kcalories a day for a month would be expected to:
   a. lose ½ to 1 pound.
   b. gain ½ to 1 pound.
   c. lose 4 to 5 pounds.
   d. gain 4 to 5 pounds.

2. A bomb calorimeter measures:
   a. physiological fuel.
   b. energy available from foods.
   c. kcalories a person derives from foods.
   d. heat a person releases in basal metabolism.

3. The psychological desire to eat that accompanies the sight, smell, or thought of food is known as:
   a. hunger.
   b. satiety.
   c. appetite.
   d. palatability.

4. A person watching television after dinner reaches for a snack during a commercial in response to:
   a. external cues.
   b. hunger signals.
   c. stress arousal.
   d. satiety factors.

5. The largest component of energy expenditure is:
   a. basal metabolism.
   b. physical activity.
   c. indirect calorimetry.
   d. thermic effect of food.

6. A major factor influencing BMR is:
   a. hunger.
   b. food intake.
   c. body composition.
   d. physical activity.

7. The thermic effect of an 800-kcalorie meal is about:
   a. 8 kcalories
   b. 80 kcalories
   c. 160 kcalories
   d. 200 kcalories

8. For health's sake, a person with a BMI of 21 might want to:
   a. lose weight
   b. maintain weight
   c. gain weight

9. Which of the following reflects height and weight?
   a. body mass index
   b. central obesity
   c. waist circumference
   d. body composition

10. Which of the following increases disease risks?
   a. BMI 19–21
   b. BMI 22–25
   c. lower-body fat
   d. central obesity

REFERENCES

1. G. A. Bray and C. M. Champagne, Beyond energy balance: There is more to obesity than kilocalories, *Journal of the American Dietetic Association* 105 (2005): S17-S23.
2. R. D. Mattes and coauthors, Appetite: Measurement and manipulation misgivings, *Journal of the American Dietetic Association* 105 (2005): S87-S97.
3. A. Del Parigi and coauthors, Sex differences in the human brain's response to hunger and satiation, *American Journal of Clinical Nutrition* 75 (2002): 1017-1022.
4. C. de Graaf and coauthors, Biomarkers of satiation and satiety, *American Journal of Clinical Nutrition* 79 (2004): 946-961; S. C. Woods, Gastrointestinal satiety signals: An overview of gastrointestinal signals that influence food intake, *American Journal of Physiology: Gastrointestinal and Liver Physiology* 286 (2004): G7-G13; T. H. Moran and K. P. Kinzig, Gastrointestinal satiety signals: Cholecystokinin, *American Journal of Physiology: Gastrointestinal and Liver Physiology* 286 (2004): G183-G188.
5. E. Kennedy, Dietary diversity, diet quality, and body weight regulation, *Nutrition Reviews* 62 (2004): S78-S81; B. Wansink, Environmental factors that increase the food intake and consumption volume of unknowing consumers, *Annual Review of Nutrition* 24 (2004): 455-479; B. J. Rolls, E. L. Morris, and L. S. Roe, Portion size of food affects energy intake in normal-weight and overweight men and women, *American Journal of Clinical Nutrition* 76 (2002): 1207-1213.
6. M. F. Dallman and coauthors, Chronic stress and obesity: A new view of "comfort food," *The Proceedings of the National Academy of Sciences* 100 (2003): 11696-11701.
7. D. E. Gerstein and coauthors, Clarifying concepts about macronutrients' effects on satiation and satiety, *Journal of the American Dietetic Association* 104 (2004): 1151-1153.
8. A. Drewnowski and coauthors, Dietary energy density and body weight: Is there a relationship? *Nutrition Reviews* 62 (2004): 403-413.
9. B. J. Rolls, L. S. Roe, and J. S. Meengs, Salad and satiety: Energy density and portion size of a first-course salad affect energy intake at lunch, *Journal of the American Dietetic Association* 104 (2004): 1570-1576.
10. B. Burton-Freeman, P. A. Davis, and B. O. Schneeman, Interaction of fat availability and sex on postprandial satiety and cholecystokinin after mixed-food meals, *American Journal of Clinical Nutrition* 80 (2004): 1207-1214.
11. G. P. Granata and L. J. Brandon, The thermic effect of food and obesity: Discrepant results and methodological variations, *Nutrition Reviews* 60 (2002): 223-233; L. Jonge and G. A. Bray, The thermic effect of food is reduced in obesity, *Nutrition Reviews* 60 (2002): 295-297.
12. N. Meunier and coauthors, Basal metabolic rate and thyroid hormones of late-middle-aged and older human subjects: The ZENITH study, *European Journal of Clinical Nutrition* 59 (2005): S53-S57; B. A. Parker and I. M. Chapman, Food intake and ageing—The role of the gut, *Mechanisms of Ageing and Development* 125 (2004): 859-866; I. M. Chapman, Endocrinology of anorexia of ageing, *Clinical Endocrinology and Metabolism* 18 (2004): 437-452.
13. J. Wardle, J. Waller, and E. Fox, Age of onset and body dissatisfaction in obesity, *Addictive Behaviors* 27 (2002): 561-573.
14. H. Truby and S. J. Paxton, Development of the Children's Body Image Scale, *British Journal of Clinical Psychology* 41 (2002): 185-203; H. A. Hausenblas and coauthors, Body image in middle school children, *Eating and Weight Disorders* 7 (2002): 244-248.
15. C. A. Drury and M. Louis, Exploring the association between body weight, stigma of obesity, and health care avoidance, *Journal of the American Academy of Nurse Practitioners* 14 (2002): 554-561.
16. K. M. Flegal and coauthors, Prevalence and trends in obesity among US adults, *Journal of the American Medical Association* 288 (2002): 1723-1727.
17. K. A. Witt and E. A. Bush, College athletes with an elevated body mass index often have a high upper arm muscle area, but not elevated triceps and subscapular skinfolds, *Journal of the American Dietetic Association* 105 (2005): 599-602.
18. R. P. Wildman and coauthors, Appropriate body mass index and waist circumference cutoffs for categorization of overweight and central adiposity among Chinese adults, *American Journal of Clinical Nutrition* 80 (2004): 1129-1136.
19. G. R. Dagenais and coauthors, Prognostic impact of body weight and abdominal obesity in women and men with cardiovascular disease, *American Heart Journal* 149 (2005): 54-60; Y. Wang and coauthors, Comparison of abdominal adiposity and overall obesity in predicting risk of type 2 diabetes among men, *American Journal of Clinical Nutrition* 81 (2005): 555-563; C. J. Tsai and coauthors, Prospective study of abdominal adiposity and gallstone disease in US men, *American Journal of Clinical Nutrition* 80 (2004): 38-44; T. B. Nguyen-Duy and coauthors, Visceral fat and liver fat are independent predictors of metabolic risk factors for men, *American Journal of Physiology: Endocrinology and Metabolism* (2003); G. Davì and coauthors, Platelet activation in obese women—Role of inflammation and oxidant stress, *Journal of the American Medical Association* 288 (2002): 2008-2014; J. M. Oppert and coauthors, Anthropometric estimates of muscle and fat mass in relation to cardiac and cancer mortality in men: The Paris Prospective Study, *American Journal of Clinical Nutrition* 75 (2002): 1107-1113.
20. D. Canoy and coauthors, Cigarette smoking and fat distribution in 21,828 British men and women: A population-based study, *Obesity Research* 13 (2005): 1466-1475.
21. Y. Wang and coauthors, Comparison of abdominal adiposity and overall obesity in predicting risk of type 2 diabetes among men, *American Journal of Clinical Nutrition* 81 (2005): 555-563; I. Janssen and coauthors, Body mass index and waist circumference independently contribute to the prediction of nonabdominal, abdominal subcutaneous, and visceral fat, *American Journal of Clinical Nutrition* 75 (2002): 683-688.
22. I. Lofgren and coauthors, Waist circumference is a better predictor than body mass index of coronary heart disease risk in overweight premenopausal women, *Journal of Nutrition* 134 (2004): 1071-1076; S. K. Zhu and coauthors, Waist circumference and obesity-associated risk factors among whites in the third National Health and Nutrition Examination Survey: Clinical action thresholds, *American Journal of Clinical Nutrition* 76 (2002): 743-749.
23. I. Janssen, P. T. Katzmarzyk, and R. Ross, Waist circumference and not body mass index explains obesity-related health risk, *American Journal of Clinical Nutrition* 79 (2004): 379-384.
24. G. A. Bray, Don't throw the baby out with the bath water, *American Journal of Clinical Nutrition* 79 (2004): 347-349.
25. A. H. Mokdad and coauthors, Prevalence of obesity, diabetes, and obesity-related health risk factors, 2001, *Journal of the American Medical Association* 289 (2003): 76-79; K. R. Fontaine and coauthors, Years of life lost due to obesity, *Journal of the American Medical Association* 289 (2003): 187-193.
26. D. M. Freedman and coauthors, Body mass index and all-cause mortality in a nationwide US cohort, *International Journal of Obesity* 30 (2006): 822-829; A. Thorogood and coauthors, Relation between body mass index and mortality in an unusually slim cohort, *Journal of Epidemiology and Community Health* 57 (2003) 130-133.
27. R. G. Rogers, R. A. Hummer, and P. M. Krueger, The effect of obesity on overall, circulatory disease- and diabetes-specific mortality, *Journal of Biosocial Science* 35 (2003): 107-129; D. B. Allison and coauthors, Differential associations of body mass index and adiposity with all-cause mortality among men in the first and second National Health and Nutrition Examination Surveys (NHANES I and NHANES II) follow-up studies, *International Journal of Obesity and*

Related Metabolic Disorders 26 (2002): 410-416; H. E. Meyer and coauthors, Body mass index and mortality: The influence of physical activity and smoking, *Medicine and Science in Sports and Exercise* 34 (2002): 1065-1070.

28. G. M. Price and coauthors, Weight, shape, and mortality risk in older persons: Elevated waist-hip ratio, not high body mass index, is associated with a greater risk of death, *American Journal of Clinical Nutrition* 84 (2006): 449-460; K. M. Flegal and coauthors, Excess deaths associated with underweight, overweight, and obesity, *Journal of the American Medical Association* 293 (2005): 1861-1867.

29. A. Peeters and coauthors, Obesity in adulthood and its consequences for life expectancy: A life-table analysis, *Annals of Internal Medicine* 138 (2003): 24-32.

30. E. A. Finkelstein, I. C. Fiebelkorn, and G. Wang, National medical expenditures attributable to overweight and obesity: How much, and who's paying? 2003, available at www.healthaffairs.org/WebExclusives/Finkelstein_Web_Excl_051403.htm.

31. K. M. Flegal and coauthors, Excess deaths associated with underweight, overweight, and obesity, *Journal of the American Medical Association* 293 (2005): 1861-1867.

32. J. E. Manson and S. S. Bassuk, Obesity in the United States: A fresh look at its high toll, *Journal of the American Medical Association* 289 (2003): 229-230; J. Stevens and coauthors, The effect of decision rules on the choice of a body mass index cutoff for obesity: Examples from African American and white women, *American Journal of Clinical Nutrition* 75 (2002): 986-992.

33. A. Schienkiewitz and coauthors, Body mass index history and risk of type 2 diabetes: Results from the European Prospective Investigation into Cancer and Nutrition (EPIC)—Potsdam Study, *American Journal of Clinical Nutrition* 84 (2006): 427-433.

34. Prevalence of overweight and obesity among adults with diagnosed diabetes-United States, 1988-1994 and 1999-2002, *Morbidity and Mortality Weekly Report* 53 (2004): 1066-1068.

35. E. H. Livingston, Lower body subcutaneous fat accumulation and diabetes mellitus risk, *Surgery for Obesity and Related Diseases* 2 (2006): 362-368.

36. G. M. Reaven, The insulin resistance syndrome: Definition and dietary approaches to treatment, *Annual Review of Nutrition* 25 (2005): 391-406; S. Klein and coauthors, Weight management through lifestyle modification for the prevention and management of type 2 diabetes: Rationale and strategies. A statement of the American Diabetes Association, the North American Association for the Study of Obesity, and the American Society for Clinical Nutrition, *American Journal of Clinical Nutrition* 80 (2004): 257-263.

37. R. DeCaterina and coauthors, Nutritional mechanisms that influence cardiovascular disease, *American Journal of Clinical Nutrition* 83 (2006): 421S-426S.

38. E. N. Hansen, A. Torquati, and N. N. Abumrad, Results of bariatric surgery, *Annual Review of Nutrition* 26 (2006): 481-511.

39. J. P. Despres, Is visceral obesity the cause of the metabolic syndrome, *Annals of Medicine* 38 (2006): 52-63.

40. P. Trayhurn, C. Bing, and I. S. Wood, Adipose tissue and adipokines—Energy regulation from the human perspective, *Journal of Nutrition* 136 (2006): 1935S-1939S; B. E. Wisse, The inflammatory syndrome: The role of adipose tissue cytokines in metabolic disorders linked to obesity, *Journal of the American Society of Nephrology* 15 (2004): 2792-2800.

41. A. H. Berg and P. E. Scherer, Adipose tissue, inflammation, and cardiovascular disease, *Circulation Research* 96 (2005): 939-968.

42. G. Boden, Fatty acid-induced inflammation and insulin resistance in skeletal muscle and liver, *Current Diabetes Reports* 6 (2006): 177-181.

43. D. C. W. Lau and coauthors, Adipokines: Molecular links between obesity and atherosclerosis, *American Journal of Physiology-Heart and Circulatory Physiology* 288 (2005): H2031-H2041.

44. A. Sbarbati and coauthors, Obesity and inflammation: Evidence for an elementary lesion, *Pediatrics* 117 (2006): 220-223; J. Warnberg and coauthors, Inflammatory proteins are related to total and abdominal adiposity in a healthy adolescent population: The AVENA Study, *American Journal of Clinical Nutrition* 84 (2006): 505-512.

45. J. P. Bastard and coauthors, Recent advances in the relationship between obesity, inflammation, and insulin resistance, *European Cytokine Network* 17 (2006): 4-12.

46. G. A. Bray, The underlying basis for obesity: Relationship to cancer, *Journal of Nutrition* 132 (2002): 3451S-3455S.

47. T. R. Wessel and coauthors, Relationship of physical fitness vs body mass index with coronary artery disease and cardiovascular events in women, *Journal of the American Medical Association* 292 (2004): 1179-1187; T. S. Church and coauthors, Exercise capacity and body composition as predictors of mortality among men with diabetes, *Diabetes Care* 27 (2004): 83-88; S. W. Farrell and coauthors, The relation of body mass index, cardiorespiratory fitness, and all-cause mortality in women, *Obesity Research* 10 (2002): 417-423; C. D. Lee and S. N. Blair, Cardiorespiratory fitness and smoking-related and total cancer mortality in men, *Medicine and Science in Sports and Exercise* 34 (2002): 735-739; C. D. Lee and S. N. Blair, Cardiorespiratory fitness and stroke mortality in men, *Medicine and Science in Sports and Exercise* 34 (2002): 592-595.

48. F. B. Hu and coauthors, Adiposity as compared with physical activity in predicting mortality among women, *New England Journal of Medicine* 351 (2004): 2694-2703.

ANSWERS

Nutrition Calculations

1. a. 0.045 kcal/lb/min × 142 lb = 6.4 kcal/min

   6.4 kcal/min × 120 min = 768 kcal

   b. 0.103 kcal/lb/min × 142 lb = 14.6 kcal/min

   14.6 kcal/min × 20 min = 292 kcal

   c. 0.032 kcal/lb/min × 142 lb = 4.5 kcal/min

   4.5 kcal/min × 45 min = 203 kcal

   d. 0.035 kcal/lb/min × 142 lb = 5 kcal/min

   5 kcal/min × 60 min = 300 kcal

2. The infant has the faster BMR (500 kcal/day ÷ 20 lb = 25 kcal/lb/day and 1500 kcal/day ÷ 170 lb = 8.8 kcal/lb/day). Because the infant has a BMR of 25 kcal/lb, whereas the adult has a BMR of 8.8 kcal/lb, the infant's BMR is almost 3 times faster than the adult's based on body weight.

3. EER = [354 − (6.91 × 20)] + 1.12 × [(9.36 × 59) + (726 × 1.68)]

   EER = (354 − 138.2) + 1.12 (552.24 + 1219.68)

   EER = (354 − 138.2) + 1.12 × 1771.9

   EER = 215.8 + 1984.6 = 2200 kcal/day

4. 21 ÷ 0.172 = 122 lb., yes

Study Questions (multiple choice)

1. c 2. b 3. c 4. a 5. a 6. c 7. b 8. b

9. a 10. d

Eating Disorders

© Steve Niedorf Photography/The Image Bank/Getty Images

For some people, low body weight becomes an obsessive goal, and they begin to view normal healthy body weight as being too fat. Their efforts to lose weight progress to a dangerously unhealthy point. An estimated 5 million people in the United States, primarily girls and young women, suffer from the **eating disorders** anorexia nervosa and bulimia nervosa (the accompanying glossary defines these and related terms).[1] Many more suffer from binge-eating disorders or other unspecified conditions that, even though they do not meet the strict criteria for anorexia nervosa or bulimia nervosa, imperil a person's well-being.

Why do so many people in our society suffer from eating disorders? Most experts agree that the causes include multiple factors: sociocultural, psychological, and perhaps neurochemical. Excessive pressure to be thin is at least partly to blame. Young people who attempt extreme weight loss may have learned to identify discomforts such as anger, jealousy, or disappointment with "feeling fat." They may also be depressed or suffer social anxiety. As weight loss becomes more of a focus, psychological problems worsen, and the likelihood of developing eating disorders intensifies. Athletes are among those most likely to develop eating disorders.

The Female Athlete Triad

At age 14, Suzanne was a top contender for a spot on the state gymnastics team. Each day her coach reminded team members

that they must weigh no more than their assigned weights to qualify for competition. The coach chastised gymnasts who gained weight, and Suzanne was terrified of being singled out. Convinced that the less she weighed the better she would perform, Suzanne weighed herself several times a day to confirm that she had not exceeded her 80-pound limit. Driven to excel in her sport, Suzanne kept her weight down by eating very little and training very hard. Unlike many of her friends, Suzanne never began to menstruate. A few months before her fifteenth birthday, Suzanne's coach dropped her back to the second-level team. Suzanne blamed her poor performance on a slow-healing stress fracture. Mentally stressed and physically exhausted, she quit gymnastics and began overeating between periods of self-starvation. Suzanne had developed the dangerous combination of problems that characterize the **female athlete triad**—disordered eating, amenorrhea, and osteoporosis (see Figure H8-1).[2]

Disordered Eating

Part of the reason many athletes engage in **disordered eating** behaviors may be that they and their coaches have embraced unsuitable weight standards. An athlete's body must be heavier for a given height than a nonathlete's body because the athlete's body is dense, containing more healthy bone and muscle and less fat. When athletes rely only on the scales, they may mistakenly believe they are too fat because weight standards, such as the BMI, do not provide adequate information about body composition.

GLOSSARY

amenorrhea (ay-MEN-oh-REE-ah): the absence of or cessation of menstruation. **Primary amenorrhea** is menarche delayed beyond 16 years of age. **Secondary amenorrhea** is the absence of three to six consecutive menstrual cycles.

anorexia (an-oh-RECK-see-ah) **nervosa**: an eating disorder characterized by a refusal to maintain a minimally normal body weight and a distortion in perception of body shape and weight.
• **an** = without

• **orex** = mouth
• **nervos** = of nervous origin

binge-eating disorder: an eating disorder with criteria similar to those of bulimia nervosa, excluding purging or other compensatory behaviors.

bulimia (byoo-LEEM-ee-ah) **nervosa**: an eating disorder characterized by repeated episodes of binge eating usually followed by self-induced vomiting, misuse of laxatives or diuretics, fasting, or excessive exercise.
• **buli** = ox

cathartic (ka-THAR-tik): a strong laxative.

disordered eating: eating behaviors that are neither normal nor healthy, including restrained eating, fasting, binge eating, and purging.

eating disorders: disturbances in eating behavior that jeopardize a person's physical or psychological health.

emetic (em-ETT-ic): an agent that causes vomiting.

female athlete triad: a potentially fatal combination of three medical problems—

disordered eating, amenorrhea, and osteoporosis.

muscle dysmorphia (dis-MORE-fee-ah): a psychiatric disorder characterized by a preoccupation with building body mass.

stress fractures: bone damage or breaks caused by stress on bone surfaces during exercise.

unspecified eating disorders: eating disorders that do not meet the defined criteria for specific eating disorders.

FIGURE H8-1 The Female Athlete Triad

Eating Disorder
- Restrictive dieting (inadequate energy and nutrient intake)
- Overexercising
- Weight loss
- Lack of body fat

Osteoporosis
- Loss of calcium from bones

Amenorrhea
- Diminished hormones

Many young athletes severely restrict energy intakes to improve performance, enhance the aesthetic appeal of their performance, or meet the weight guidelines of their specific sports. They fail to realize that the loss of lean tissue that accompanies energy restriction actually impairs their physical performance. The increasing incidence of abnormal eating habits among athletes is cause for concern. Male athletes, especially wrestlers and gymnasts, are affected by these disorders as well, but females are most vulnerable. Risk factors for eating disorders among athletes include:

- Young age (adolescence)
- Pressure to excel at a chosen sport
- Focus on achieving or maintaining an "ideal" body weight or body fat percentage
- Participation in sports or competitions that emphasize a lean appearance or judge performance on aesthetic appeal such as gymnastics, wrestling, figure skating, or dance[3]
- Weight-loss dieting at an early age
- Unsupervised dieting

A few years ago, this Olympic gold medalist was weak and malnourished from anorexia nervosa. However, she recovered and set a world record in the cycling road race.

Amenorrhea

The prevalence of **amenorrhea** among premenopausal women in the United States is about 2 to 5 percent overall, but among female athletes, it may be as high as 66 percent. Contrary to previous notions, amenorrhea is *not* a normal adaptation to strenuous physical training: it is a symptom of something going wrong.[4] Amenorrhea is characterized by low blood estrogen, infertility, and often bone mineral losses. Excessive training, depleted body fat, low body weight, and inadequate nutrition all contribute to amenorrhea. However amenorrhea develops, it threatens the integrity of the bones. Bone losses remain significant even after recovery. (Women with bulimia frequently have menstrual irregularities, but because they rarely cease menstruating, they may be spared this loss of bone integrity.[5])

Osteoporosis

For most people, weight-bearing physical activity, dietary calcium, and (for women) the hormone estrogen protect against the bone loss of osteoporosis. For young women with disordered eating and amenorrhea, strenuous activity can impair bone health. Vigorous training combined with inadequate food intake disrupts metabolic and hormonal balances.[6] These disturbances compromise bone health, greatly increasing the risks of **stress fractures** today and of osteoporosis in later life. Stress fractures, a serious form of bone injury, commonly occur among dancers and other athletes with amenorrhea, low calcium intakes, and disordered eating. Many underweight young athletes have bones like those of postmenopausal women, and they may never recover their lost bone even after diagnosis and treatment—which makes prevention critical. Young athletes should be encouraged to consume 1300 milligrams of calcium each day, to eat nutrient-dense foods, and to obtain enough energy to support both weight gain and the energy expended in physical activity.

Other Dangerous Practices of Athletes

Only females face the threats of the female athlete triad, of course, but many male athletes face pressure to achieve a certain body weight and may develop eating disorders. Each week throughout the season, David drastically restricts his food and fluid intake before a wrestling match in an effort to "make weight." Wrestlers and their coaches believe that competing in a lower weight class will give them a competitive advantage over smaller opponents. To that end, David practices in rubber suits, sits in saunas, and takes diuretics to lose 4 to 6 pounds. He hopes to replenish the lost fluids, glycogen, and lean tissue during the hours between his weigh-in and competition, but the body needs days to correct this metabolic mayhem. Reestablishing fluid and electrolyte balances may take a day or two, replenishing glycogen stores may take two to three days, and replacing lean tissue may take even longer.

Ironically, the combination of food deprivation and dehydration impairs physical performance by reducing muscle strength, decreasing anaerobic power, and reducing endurance capacity. For optimal performance, wrestlers need to first achieve their competitive weight during the off-season and then eat well-balanced meals and drink plenty of fluids during the competitive season.

Some athletes go to extreme measures to bulk up and *gain* weight. People afflicted with **muscle dysmorphia** eat high-protein diets, take dietary supplements, weight train for hours at a time, and often abuse steroids in an attempt to bulk up. Their bodies are large and muscular, yet they see themselves as puny 90-pound weaklings. They are preoccupied with the idea that their bodies are too small or inadequately muscular. Like others with distorted body images, people with muscle dysmorphia weigh themselves frequently and center their lives on diet and exercise. Paying attention to diet and pumping iron for fitness is admirable, but obsessing over it can cause serious social, occupational, and physical problems.

Preventing Eating Disorders in Athletes

To prevent eating disorders in athletes and dancers, the performers, their coaches, and their parents must learn about inappropriate body weight ideals, improper weight-loss techniques, eating disorder development, proper nutrition, and safe weight-control methods. Young people naturally search for identity and will often follow the advice of a person in authority without question. Therefore, coaches and dance instructors should never encourage unhealthy weight loss to qualify for competition or to conform to distorted artistic ideals. Athletes who truly need to lose weight should try to do so during the off-season and under the supervision of a health care professional. Frequent weighings can push young people who are striving to lose weight into a cycle of starving to confront the scale, then bingeing uncontrollably afterward. The erosion of self-esteem that accompanies these events can interfere with normal psychological development and set the stage for serious problems later on.

Table H8-1 includes suggestions to help athletes and dancers protect themselves against developing eating disorders. The remaining sections describe eating disorders that anyone, athlete or nonathlete, may experience.

Anorexia Nervosa

Julie, 18 years old, is a superachiever in school. She watches her diet with great care, and she exercises daily, maintaining a rigorous schedule of self-discipline. She is thin, but she is determined to lose more weight. She is 5 feet 6 inches tall and weighs 85 pounds (roughly 1.68 meters and 39 kilograms). She has **anorexia nervosa.**

TABLE H8-1	Tips for Combating Eating Disorders

General Guidelines

- Never restrict food amounts to below those suggested for adequacy by the USDA Food Guide (see Table 2-3 on p. 41).

- Eat frequently. Include healthy snacks between meals. The person who eats frequently never gets so hungry as to allow hunger to dictate food choices.

- If not at a healthy weight, establish a reasonable weight goal based on a healthy body composition.

- Allow a reasonable time to achieve the goal. A reasonable loss of excess fat can be achieved at the rate of about 10 percent of body weight in six months.

- Establish a weight-maintenance support group with people who share interests.

Specific Guidelines for Athletes and Dancers

- Replace weight-based goals with performance-based goals.

- Restrict weight-loss activities to the off-season.

- Remember that eating disorders impair physical performance. Seek confidential help in obtaining treatment if needed.

- Focus on proper nutrition as an important facet of your training, as important as proper technique.

Characteristics of Anorexia Nervosa

Julie is unaware that she is undernourished, and she sees no need to obtain treatment. She developed amenorrhea several months ago and has become moody and chronically depressed. She insists that she is too fat, although her eyes are sunk in deep hollows in her face. Julie denies that she is ever tired, although she is close to physical exhaustion and no longer sleeps easily. Her family is concerned, and though reluctant to push her, they have finally insisted that she see a psychiatrist. Julie's psychiatrist has diagnosed anorexia nervosa (see Table H8-2) and prescribed group therapy as a start. If she does not begin to gain weight soon, she may need to be hospitalized.

As mentioned in the introduction, most anorexia nervosa victims are females; males account for only about 1 in 20 reported cases. Central to the diagnosis of anorexia nervosa is a distorted body image that overestimates personal body fatness. When Julie looks at herself in the mirror, she sees a "fat" 85-pound body. The more Julie overestimates her body size, the more resistant she is to treatment, and the more unwilling to examine her faulty values and misconceptions. Malnutrition is known to affect brain functioning and judgment in this way, causing lethargy, confusion, and delirium.

Anorexia nervosa cannot be self-diagnosed. Many people in our society are engaged in the pursuit of thinness, and denial runs high among people with anorexia nervosa. Some women have all the attitudes and behaviors associated with the condition, but without the dramatic weight loss.

Self-Starvation How can a person as thin as Julie continue to starve herself? Julie uses tremendous discipline against her hunger to strictly limit her portions of low-kcalorie foods. She will deny her hunger, and having adapted to so little food, she feels full af-

TABLE H8-2 Criteria for Diagnosis of Anorexia Nervosa

A person with anorexia nervosa demonstrates the following:

A. Refusal to maintain body weight at or above a minimal normal weight for age and height (e.g., weight loss leading to maintenance of body weight less than 85 percent of that expected; or failure to make expected weight gain during period of growth, leading to body weight less than 85 percent of that expected).

B. Intense fear of gaining weight or becoming fat, even though underweight.

C. Disturbance in the way in which one's body weight or shape is experienced, undue influence of body weight or shape on self-evaluation, or denial of the seriousness of the current low body weight.

D. In females past puberty, amenorrhea, i.e., the absence of at least three consecutive menstrual cycles. (A woman is considered to have amenorrhea if her periods occur only following hormone, e.g., estrogen, administration.)

Two types:

- *Restricting type:* During the episode of anorexia nervosa, the person does not regularly engage in binge eating or purging behavior (i.e., self-induced vomiting or the misuse of laxatives, diuretics, or enemas).

- *Binge eating/purging type:* During the episode of anorexia nervosa, the person regularly engages in binge eating or purging behavior (i.e., self-induced vomiting or the misuse of laxatives, diuretics, or enemas).

SOURCE: Reprinted with permission from American Psychiatric Association, *Diagnostic and Statistical Manual of Mental Disorders,* 4th ed. Text Revision. (Washington, D.C.: American Psychiatric Association, 2000).

ter eating only a half-dozen carrot sticks. She knows the kcalorie contents of dozens of foods and the kcalorie costs of as many exercises. If she feels that she has gained an ounce of weight, she runs or jumps rope until she is sure she has exercised it off. If she fears that the food she has eaten outweighs the exercise, she may take laxatives to hasten the passage of food from her system. She drinks water incessantly to fill her stomach, risking dangerous mineral imbalances. She is desperately hungry. In fact, she is starving, but she doesn't eat because her need for self-control dominates.

Many people, on learning of this disorder, say they wish they had "a touch" of it to get thin. They mistakenly think that people with anorexia nervosa feel no hunger. They also fail to recognize the pain of the associated psychological and physical trauma.

Physical Consequences The starvation of anorexia nervosa damages the body just as the starvation of war and poverty does. In fact, after a few months, most people with anorexia nervosa have protein-energy malnutrition (PEM) that is similar to marasmus (described in Chapter 6).[7] Their bodies have been depleted of both body fat and protein.[8] Victims are dying to be thin—quite literally. In young people, growth ceases and normal development falters. They lose so much lean tissue that basal metabolic rate slows. In addition, the heart pumps inefficiently and irregularly, the heart muscle becomes weak and thin, the chambers diminish in size, and the blood pressure falls.[9] Minerals that help to regulate heartbeat become unbalanced. Many deaths occur due to multiple organ system failure when the heart, kidneys, and liver cease to function.

Starvation brings other physical consequences as well, such as loss of brain tissue, impaired immune response, anemia, and a loss of digestive functions that worsens malnutrition. Peristalsis becomes sluggish, the stomach empties slowly, and the lining of the intestinal tract atrophies. The deteriorated GI tract fails to provide sufficient digestive enzymes and absorptive surfaces for handling any food that is eaten. The pancreas slows its production of digestive enzymes. The person may suffer from diarrhea, further worsening malnutrition.

Other effects of starvation include altered blood lipids, high blood vitamin A and vitamin E, low blood proteins, dry thin skin, abnormal nerve functioning, reduced bone density, low body temperature, low blood pressure, and the development of fine body hair (the body's attempt to keep warm). The electrical activity of the brain becomes abnormal, and insomnia is common. Both women and men lose their sex drives.

Women with anorexia nervosa develop amenorrhea. (It is one of the diagnostic criteria.) In young girls, the onset of menstruation is delayed. Menstrual periods typically resume with recovery, although some women never restart even after they have gained weight. Should an underweight woman with anorexia nervosa become pregnant, she is likely to give birth to an underweight baby—and low-birthweight babies face many health problems (as Chapter 15 explains). Mothers with anorexia nervosa may underfeed their children who then fail to grow and may also suffer the other consequences of starvation.

Treatment of Anorexia Nervosa

Treatment of anorexia nervosa requires a multidisciplinary approach.[10] Teams of physicians, nurses, psychiatrists, family therapists, and dietitians work together to resolve two sets of issues and behaviors: those relating to food and weight and those involving relationships with oneself and others. The first dietary objective is to stop weight loss while establishing regular eating patterns. Appropriate diet is crucial to recovery and must be tailored to individual client's needs. Because body weight is low and fear of weight gain is high, initial food intake may be small—perhaps only 1200 kcalories per day.[11] As eating becomes more comfortable, clients should gradually increase energy intake. Initially, clients may be unwilling to eat for themselves. Those who do eat will have a good chance of recovering without additional interventions. Even after recovery, however, energy intakes and eating behaviors may not fully return to normal.[12] Furthermore, weight gains may be slow because energy needs may be slightly elevated due to anxiety, abdominal pain, and cigarette smoking.[13]

Because anorexia nervosa is like starvation physically, health care professionals classify clients based on indicators of PEM.* Low-risk clients need nutrition counseling. Intermediate-risk clients may need supplements such as high-kcalorie, high-protein formulas in addition to regular meals. High-risk clients may require hospitalization and may need to be fed by tube at first to prevent death. This step may cause psychological trauma. Although drugs are commonly prescribed, they play a limited role in treatment.

---

* Indicators of protein-energy malnutrition: a low percentage of body fat, low serum albumin, low serum transferrin, and impaired immune reactions.

Denial runs high among those with anorexia nervosa. Few seek treatment on their own. About half of the women who are treated can maintain their body weight at 85 percent or more of a healthy weight, and at that weight, many of them begin menstruating again.[14] The other half have poor to fair treatment outcomes, relapse into abnormal eating behaviors, or die. Anorexia nervosa has one of the highest mortality rates among psychiatric disorders.[15] An estimated 1000 women die each year of anorexia nervosa—most commonly from cardiac complications due to malnutrition or by suicide.[16]

Before drawing conclusions about someone who is extremely thin or who eats very little, remember that diagnosis requires professional assessment. Several national organizations offer information for people who are seeking help with anorexia nervosa, either for themselves or for others.*

Bulimia Nervosa

Kelly is a charming, intelligent, 30-year-old flight attendant of normal weight who thinks constantly about food. She alternates between starving herself and secretly bingeing, and when she has eaten too much, she makes herself vomit. Most readers recognize these symptoms as those of **bulimia nervosa.**

Characteristics of Bulimia Nervosa

Bulimia nervosa is distinct from anorexia nervosa and is more prevalent, although the true incidence is difficult to establish because bulimia nervosa is not as physically apparent. More men suffer from bulimia nervosa than from anorexia nervosa, but bulimia nervosa is still more common in women than in men. The secretive nature of bulimic behaviors makes recognition of the problem difficult, but once it is recognized, diagnosis is based on the criteria listed in Table H8-3.

Like the typical person with bulimia nervosa, Kelly is single, female, and white. She is well educated and close to her ideal body weight, although her weight fluctuates over a range of 10 pounds or so every few weeks. She prefers to weigh less than the weight that her body maintains naturally.

Kelly seldom lets her eating disorder interfere with work or other activities, although a third of all bulimics do. From early childhood, she has been a high achiever and emotionally dependent on her parents. As a young teen, Kelly frequently followed severely restricted diets but could never maintain the weight loss. Kelly feels anxious at social events and cannot easily establish close personal relationships. She is usually depressed, is often impulsive, and has low self-esteem. When crisis hits, Kelly responds by replaying events, worrying excessively, and blaming herself but never asking for help—behaviors that interfere with effective coping.

Binge Eating Like the person with anorexia nervosa, the person with bulimia nervosa spends much time thinking about body weight and food. The preoccupation with food manifests itself in

| TABLE H8-3 | Criteria for Diagnosis of Bulimia Nervosa |

A person with bulimia nervosa demonstrates the following:

A. Recurrent episodes of binge eating. An episode of binge eating is characterized by both of the following:

  1. Eating, in a discrete period of time (e.g., within any two-hour period), an amount of food that is definitely larger than most people would eat during a similar period of time and under similar circumstances.

  2. A sense of lack of control over eating during the episode (e.g., a feeling that one cannot stop eating or control what or how much one is eating).

B. Recurrent inappropriate compensatory behavior to prevent weight gain, such as self-induced vomiting; misuse of laxatives, diuretics, enemas, or other medications; fasting; or excessive exercise.

C. Binge eating and inappropriate compensatory behaviors both occur, on average, at least twice a week for three months.

D. Self-evaluation unduly influenced by body shape and weight.

E. The disturbance does not occur exclusively during episodes of anorexia nervosa.

Two types:

- *Purging type:* The person regularly engages in self-induced vomiting or the misuse of laxatives, diuretics, or enemas.

- *Nonpurging type:* The person uses other inappropriate compensatory behaviors, such as fasting or excessive exercise, but does not regularly engage in self-induced vomiting or the misuse of laxatives, diuretics, or enemas.

SOURCE: Reprinted with permission from American Psychiatric Association, *Diagnostic and Statistical Manual of Mental Disorders,* 4th ed. Text Revision. (Washington, D.C.: American Psychiatric Association, 2000).

secret binge-eating episodes, which usually progress through several emotional stages: anticipation and planning, anxiety, urgency to begin, rapid and uncontrollable consumption of food, relief and relaxation, disappointment, and finally shame or disgust.

A bulimic binge is characterized by a sense of lacking control over eating. During a binge, the person consumes food for its emotional comfort and cannot stop eating or control what or how much is eaten. A typical binge occurs periodically, in secret, usually at night, and lasts an hour or more. Because a binge frequently follows a period of rigid dieting, eating is accelerated by intense hunger. Energy restriction followed by bingeing can set in motion a pattern of weight cycling, which may make weight loss and maintenance more difficult over time.

During a binge, Kelly consumes thousands of kcalories of easy-to-eat, low-fiber, high-fat, and, especially, high-carbohydrate foods. Typically, she chooses cookies, cakes, and ice cream—and she eats the entire bag of cookies, the whole cake, and every last spoonful in a carton of ice cream. After the binge, Kelly pays the price with swollen hands and feet, bloating, fatigue, headache, nausea, and pain.

Purging To purge the food from her body, Kelly may use a **cathartic**—a strong laxative that can injure the lower intestinal tract. Or she may induce vomiting, with or without the use of an **emetic**—a drug intended as first aid for poisoning. These purging behaviors are often accompanied by feelings of shame or guilt. Hence a vicious cycle develops: negative self-perceptions

---

* Internet sites are listed at the end of this highlight.

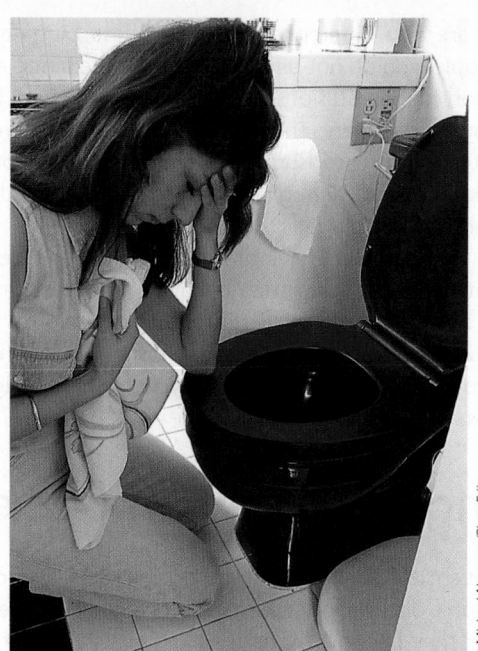

Bulimic binges are often followed by self-induced vomiting and feelings of shame or disgust.

followed by dieting, bingeing, and purging, which in turn lead to negative self-perceptions (see Figure H8-2).

On first glance, purging seems to offer a quick and easy solution to the problems of unwanted kcalories and body weight. Many people perceive such behavior as neutral or even positive, when, in fact, binge eating and purging have serious physical consequences. Signs of subclinical malnutrition are evident in a compromised immune system. Fluid and mineral imbalances caused by vomiting or diarrhea can lead to abnormal heart rhythms and injury to the kidneys. Urinary tract infections can lead to kidney failure. Vomiting causes irritation and infection of the pharynx, esophagus, and salivary glands; erosion of the teeth; and dental caries. The esophagus may rupture or tear, as may the

FIGURE H8-2 The Vicious Cycle of Restrictive Dieting and Binge Eating

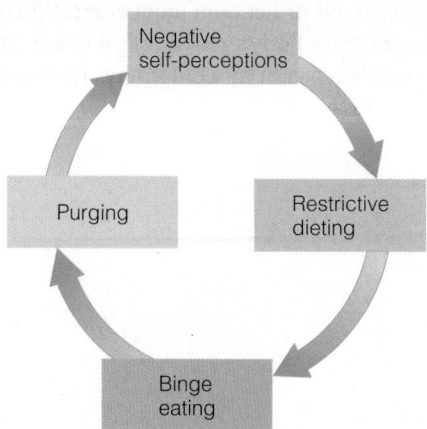

stomach. Sometimes the eyes become red from pressure during vomiting. The hands may be calloused or cut by the teeth while inducing vomiting. Overuse of emetics depletes potassium concentrations and can lead to death by heart failure.

Unlike Julie, Kelly is aware that her behavior is abnormal, and she is deeply ashamed of it. She wants to recover, and this makes recovery more likely for her than for Julie, who clings to denial. Feeling inadequate ("I can't even control my eating"), Kelly tends to be passive and to look to others for confirmation of her sense of worth. When she experiences rejection, either in reality or in her imagination, her bulimia nervosa becomes worse. If Kelly's depression deepens, she may seek solace in drug or alcohol abuse or in other addictive behaviors. Clinical depression is common in people with bulimia nervosa, and the rates of substance abuse are high.[17]

Treatment of Bulimia Nervosa

Kelly needs to establish regular eating patterns. She may also benefit from a regular exercise program.[18] Weight maintenance, rather than cyclic weight gains and losses, is the treatment goal. Major steps toward recovery include discontinuing purging and restrictive dieting habits and learning to eat three meals a day plus snacks.[19] Initially, energy intake should provide enough food to satisfy hunger and maintain body weight. Table H8-4 offers diet strategies to correct the eating problems of bulimia nervosa. About half of the women diagnosed with bulimia nervosa recover

TABLE H8-4 Diet Strategies for Combating Bulimia Nervosa

Planning Principles

- Plan meals and snacks; record plans in a food diary prior to eating.
- Plan meals and snacks that require eating at the table and using utensils.
- Refrain from finger foods.
- Refrain from "dieting" or skipping meals.

Nutrition Principles

- Eat a well-balanced diet and regularly timed meals consisting of a variety of foods.
- Include raw vegetables, salad, or raw fruit at meals to prolong eating times.
- Choose whole-grain, high-fiber breads, pasta, rice, and cereals to increase bulk.
- Consume adequate fluid, particularly water.

Other Tips

- Choose foods that provide protein and fat for satiety and bulky, fiber-rich carbohydrates for immediate feelings of fullness.
- Try including soups and other water-rich foods for satiety.
- Choose portions that meet the definition of "a serving" according to the Daily Food Guide (pp. 42–43).
- For convenience (and to reduce temptation) select foods that naturally divide into portions. Select one potato, rather than rice or pasta that can be overloaded onto the plate; purchase yogurt and cottage cheese in individual containers; look for small packages of precut steak or chicken; choose frozen dinners with measured portions.
- Include 30 minutes of physical activity every day—exercise may be an important tool in defeating bulimia.

completely after five to ten years, with or without treatment, but treatment probably speeds the recovery process.

A mental health professional should be on the treatment team to help clients with their depression and addictive behaviors. Some physicians prescribe the antidepressant drug fluoxetine in the treatment of bulimia nervosa.* Another drug that may be useful in the management of bulimia nervosa is naloxone, an opiate antagonist that suppresses the consumption of sweet and high-fat foods in binge-eaters.

Anorexia nervosa and bulimia nervosa are distinct eating disorders, yet they sometimes overlap in important ways. Anorexia victims may purge, and victims of both disorders may be overly concerned with body weight and have a tendency to drastically undereat. Many perceive foods as "forbidden" and "give in" to an eating binge. The two disorders can also appear in the same person, or one can lead to the other. Treatment is challenging and relapses are not unusual. Other people have **unspecified eating disorders** that fall short of the criteria for anorexia nervosa or bulimia nervosa but share some of their features. One such condition is binge-eating disorder.

Binge-Eating Disorder

Charlie is a 40-year-old schoolteacher who has been overweight all his life. His friends and family are forever encouraging him to lose weight, and he has come to believe that if he only had more willpower, dieting would work. He periodically gives dieting his best shot—restricting energy intake for a day or two only to succumb to uncontrollable cravings, especially for high-fat foods. Like Charlie, up to half of the obese people who try to lose weight periodically binge; unlike people with bulimia nervosa, however, they typically do not purge. Such an eating disorder does not meet the criteria for either anorexia nervosa or bulimia nervosa—yet such compulsive overeating is a problem and occurs in people of normal weight as well as those who are severely overweight. Table H8-5 lists criteria for unspecified eating disorders, including binge eating. Obesity alone is not an eating disorder.

Clinicians note differences between people with bulimia nervosa and those with binge-eating disorder.[20] People with **binge-eating disorder** consume less during a binge, rarely purge, and exert less restraint during times of dieting. Similarities also exist, including feeling out of control, disgusted, depressed, embarrassed, guilty, or distressed because of their self-perceived gluttony.[21]

---

* Fluoxetine is marketed under the trade name Prozac.

There are also differences between obese binge-eaters and obese people who do not binge. Those with the binge-eating disorder report higher rates of self-loathing, disgust about body size, depression, and anxiety. Their eating habits differ as well. Obese binge-eaters tend to consume more kcalories and more dessert and snack-type foods during regular meals and binges than obese people who do not binge.

Binge eating is a behavioral disorder that can be resolved with treatment. Resolving such behavior may not bring weight loss, but it may make participation in weight-control programs easier. It also improves physical health, mental health, and the chances of success in breaking the cycle of rapid weight losses and gains.

Eating Disorders in Society

Proof that society plays a role in eating disorders is found in their demographic distribution—they are known only in developed nations, and they become more prevalent as wealth increases and food becomes plentiful. Some people point to the vomitoriums of ancient times and claim that bulimia nervosa is not new, but the two are actually distinct. Ancient people were eating for pleasure, without guilt, and in the company of others; they vomited so that they could rejoin the feast. Bulimia nervosa is a disorder of isolation and is often accompanied by low self-esteem.

Chapter 8 described how our society sets unrealistic ideals for body weight, especially in women, and devalues those who do not conform to them. Anorexia nervosa and bulimia nervosa are not a form of rebellion against these unreasonable expectations, but rather an exaggerated acceptance of them. In fact, body dissatisfaction is a primary factor in the development of eating disorders.[22] Not everyone who is dissatisfied will develop an eating disorder, but everyone with an eating disorder is dissatisfied.

Characteristics of disordered eating such as restrained eating, fasting, binge eating, purging, fear of fatness, and distortion of body image are extraordinarily common among young girls. Most are "on diets," and many are poorly nourished. Some eat too little food to support normal growth; thus they miss out on their adolescent growth spurts and may never catch up. Many eat so little that hunger propels them into binge-purge cycles.

Perhaps a person's best defense against these disorders is to learn to appreciate his or her own uniqueness. When people discover and honor their body's real physical needs, they become unwilling to sacrifice health for conformity. To respect and value oneself may be lifesaving.

TABLE H8-5 Unspecified Eating Disorders, Including Binge-Eating Disorder

Criteria for Diagnosis of Unspecified Eating Disorders, in General

Many people have eating disorders but do not meet all the criteria to be classified as having anorexia nervosa or bulimia nervosa. Some examples include those who:

A. Meet all of the criteria for anorexia nervosa, except irregular menses.

B. Meet all of the criteria for anorexia nervosa, except that their current weights fall within the normal ranges.

C. Meet all of the criteria for bulimia nervosa, except that binges occur less frequently than stated in the criteria.

D. Are of normal body weight and who compensate inappropriately for eating small amounts of food (example: self-induced vomiting after eating two cookies).

E. Repeatedly chew food but spit it out without swallowing.

F. Have recurrent episodes of binge eating but do not compensate as do those with bulimia nervosa.

Criteria for Diagnosis of Binge-Eating Disorder, Specifically

A person with a binge-eating disorder demonstrates the following:

A. Recurrent episodes of binge eating. An episode of binge eating is characterized by both of the following:

1. Eating, in a discrete period of time (e.g., within any two-hour period) an amount of food that is definitely larger than most people would eat in a similar period of time under similar circumstances.

2. A sense of lack of control over eating during the episode (e.g., a feeling that one cannot stop eating or control what or how much one is eating).

B. Binge-eating episodes are associated with at least three of the following:

1. Eating much more rapidly than normal.

2. Eating until feeling uncomfortably full.

3. Eating large amounts of food when not feeling physically hungry.

4. Eating alone because of being embarrassed by how much one is eating.

5. Feeling disgusted with oneself, depressed, or very guilty after overeating.

C. The binge eating causes marked distress.

D. The binge eating occurs, on average, at least twice a week for six months.

E. The binge eating is not associated with the regular use of inappropriate compensatory behaviors (e.g., purging, fasting, excessive exercise) and does not occur exclusively during the course of anorexia nervosa or bulimia nervosa.

SOURCE: Reprinted with permission from American Psychiatric Association, *Diagnostic and Statistical Manual of Mental Disorders*, 4th ed. Text Revision. (Washington, D.C.: American Psychiatric Association, 2000).

NUTRITION ON THE NET

ThomsonNOW
For furthur study of topics covered in this Highlight, log on to www.thomsonedu.com/thomsonnow. Go to Chapter 8, then to Highlights Nutrition on the Net.

• Search for "anorexia," "bulimia," and "eating disorders" at the U.S. Government health information site: **www.healthfinder.gov**

• Learn more about anorexia nervosa and related eating disorders from Anorexia Nervosa and Related Eating Disorders or the Academy of Eating Disorders: **www.anred.com** or **www.aedweb.org**

• Get facts about eating disorders from the National Institute of Mental Health: **www.nimh.nih.gov/publicat/eatingdisorders.cfm**

REFERENCES

1. Position of the American Dietetic Association: Nutrition intervention in the treatment of anorexia nervosa, bulimia nervosa, and eating disorders not otherwise specified (EDNOS), *Journal of the American Dietetic Association* 101 (2001): 810-819.

2. K. Kazis and E. Iglesias, The female athlete triad, *Adolescent Medicine* 14 (2003): 87-95; S. Sabatini, The female athlete triad, *American Journal of the Medical Sciences* 322 (2001): 193-195; Committee on Sports Medicine and Fitness, Medical concerns in the female athlete, *Pediatrics* 106 (2000): 610-613.

3. M. F. Reinking and L. E. Alexander, Prevalence of disordered-eating behaviors in undergraduate female collegiate athletes and nonathletes, *Journal of Athletic Training* 40 (2005): 47-51; M. K. Torstveit and J. Sundgot-Borgen, The female athlete triad: Are elite athletes at increased risk? *Medicine & Science in Sports & Exercise* 37 (2005): 184-193.

4. N. H. Golden, A review of the female athlete triad (amenorrhea, osteoporosis and disordered eating), *International Journal of Adolescent Medicine and Health* 14 (2002): 9-17.

5. S. J. Crow and coauthors, Long-term menstrual and reproductive function in patients with bulimia nervosa, *American Journal of Psychiatry* 159 (2002): 1048-1050.

6. C. L. Zanker and C. B. Cooke, Energy balance, bone turnover, and skeletal health in physically active individuals, *Medicine & Science in Sports & Exercise* 36 (2004): 1372-1381.

7. M. P. Fuhrman, P. Charney, and C. M. Mueller, Hepatic proteins and nutrition assessment, *Journal of the American Dietetic Association* 104 (2004): 1258-1264.

8. K. P. Kerruish and coauthors, Body composition in adolescents with anorexia nervosa, *American Journal of Clinical Nutrition* 75 (2002): 31-37.

9. C. Romano and coauthors, Reduced hemodynamic load and cardiac hypotrophy in patients with anorexia nervosa, *American Journal of Clinical Nutrition* 77 (2003): 308-312.

10. Committee on Adolescence, Identifying and treating eating disorders, *Pediatrics* 111 (2003): 204-211.

11. J. Yager and A. E. Andersen, Anorexia nervosa, *New England Journal of Medicine* 353 (2005): 1481-1488.

12. R. Sysko and coauthors, Eating behavior among women with anorexia nervosa, *American Journal of Clinical Nutrition* 82 (2005): 296-301; B. R. Carruth and J. D. Skinner, Dietary and physical activity patterns of young females with histories of eating disorders, *Topics in Clinical Nutrition* 16 (2000): 13-23.

13. V. van Wymelbeke and coauthors, Factors associated with the increase in resting energy expenditure during refeeding in malnourished anorexia nervosa patients, *American Journal of Clinical Nutrition* 80 (2004): 1469-1477.

14. H. C. Steinhausen, The outcome of anorexia nervosa in the 20th century, *American Journal of Psychiatry* 159 (2002): 1284-1293;

B. Lowe and coauthors, Long-term outcome of anorexia nervosa in a prospective 21-year follow-up study, *Psychological Medicine* 31 (2001): 881-890.

15. P. K. Keel and coauthors, Predictors of mortality in eating disorders, *Archives of General Psychiatry* 60 (2003): 179-183.

16. M. B. Tamburrino and R. A. McGinnis, Anorexia nervosa: A review, *Panminerva Medica* 44 (2002): 301-311.

17. C. M. Bulik and coauthors, Alcohol use disorder comorbidity in eating disorders: A multicenter study, *Journal of Clinical Psychiatry* 65 (2004): 1000-1006.

18. J. Sundgot-Borgen and coauthors, The effect of exercise, cognitive therapy, and nutritional counseling in treating bulimia nervosa, *Medicine and Science in Sports and Exercise* 34 (2002): 190-195.

19. Position of the American Dietetic Association, 2001.

20. A. E. Dingemans, M. J. Bruna, and E. F. van Furth, Binge eating disorder: A review, *International Journal of Obesity and Related Metabolic Disorders* 26 (2002): 299-307.

21. D. M. Ackard and coauthors, Overeating among adolescents: Prevalence and associations with weight-related characteristics and psychological health, *Pediatrics* 111 (2003): 67-74.

22. J. Polivy and C. P. Herman, Causes of eating disorders, *Annual Review of Psychology* 53 (2002): 187-213.

 **NOW!** Throughout this chapter, the ThomsonNOW logo indicates an opportunity for online self-study, linking you to interactive tutorials and videos based on your level of understanding.

www.thomsonedu.com/thomsonnow

Figure 9-1: Animated! Increasing Prevalence of Obesity among U.S. Adults

Figure 9-8: Animated! Influence of Physical Activity on Discretionary kCalorie Allowance

How To: Practice Problems

Nutrition Portfolio Journal

Nutrition Calculations: Practice Problems

Nutrition in Your Life

Are you pleased with your body weight? If so, you are a rare individual. Most people in our society think they should weigh more or less (mostly less) than they do. Usually, their primary concern is appearance, but they often understand that physical health is also somehow related to body weight.

One does not necessarily cause the other—that is, an ideal body weight does not ensure good health. Instead, both depend on diet and physical activity.

A well-balanced diet and active lifestyle support good health—and help maintain body weight within a reasonable range.

Weight Management: Overweight, Obesity, and Underweight

CHAPTER OUTLINE

Overweight and Obesity • Fat Cell Development • Fat Cell Metabolism • Set-Point Theory

Causes of Overweight and Obesity • Genetics • Environment

Problems of Overweight and Obesity • Health Risks • Perceptions and Prejudices • Dangerous Interventions

Aggressive Treatments for Obesity • Drugs • Surgery

Weight-Loss Strategies • Eating Plans • Physical Activity • Environmental Influences • Behavior and Attitude • Weight Maintenance • Prevention • Public Health Programs

Underweight • Problems of Underweight • Weight-Gain Strategies

HIGHLIGHT 9 The Latest and Greatest Weight-Loss Diet—Again

The previous chapter described how body weight is stable when energy in equals energy out. Weight gains occur when energy intake exceeds energy expended, and conversely, weight losses occur when energy expended exceeds energy intake. At the extremes, both overweight and underweight present health risks. **Weight management** is a key component of good health.

This chapter emphasizes overweight, partly because it has been more intensively studied and partly because it is a major health problem in the United States and a growing concern worldwide. Information on underweight is presented wherever appropriate. The highlight that follows this chapter examines fad diets.

Overweight and Obesity

Despite our preoccupation with body image and weight loss, the prevalence of overweight and obesity in the United States continues to rise dramatically.[1] In the past two decades, obesity increased in every state, in both genders, and across all ages, races, and educational levels (see Figure 9-1, p. 282). An estimated 66 percent of the adults in the United States are now considered overweight or obese, as defined by a BMI of 25 or greater.[2] ◆ The prevalence of overweight is especially high among women, the poor, blacks, and Hispanics.

The prevalence of overweight among children in the United States has also risen at an alarming rate. An estimated 33 percent of children and adolescents ages 2 to 19 years are either overweight or "at risk for overweight."[3] Chapter and Highlight 16 present information on overweight during childhood and adolescence.

◆ BMI:
• Underweight: <18.5
• Healthy weight: 18.5–24.9
• Overweight: 25.0–29.9
• Obese: ≥30

weight management: maintaining body weight in a healthy range by preventing gradual weight gain over time and losing weight if overweight.

FIGURE 9-1 *Animated!* Increasing Prevalence of Obesity (BMI ≥ 30) among U.S. Adults

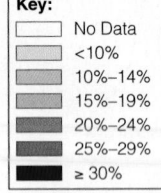

Key:
- No Data
- <10%
- 10%–14%
- 15%–19%
- 20%–24%
- 25%–29%
- ≥ 30%

ThomsonNOW
To test your understanding of these concepts, log on to www .thomsonedu.com/thomsonnow

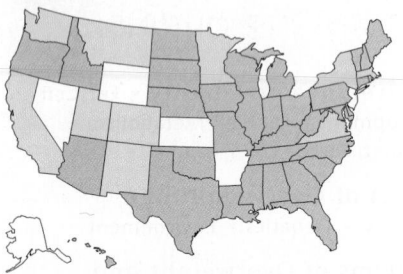

1990: No state had prevalence rates greater than or equal to 15 percent.

1995: Over half the states had prevalence rates greater than or equal to 15 percent, but no state had prevalence rates greater than or equal to 20 percent.

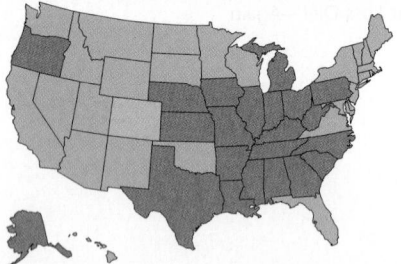

2000: Only one state had prevalence rates less than 15 percent, almost half of the states had prevalence rates greater than or equal to 20 percent, and no state had prevalence rates greater than or equal to 25 percent.

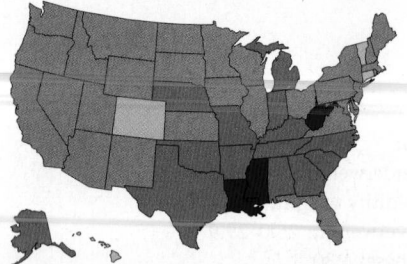

2005: Only four states had prevalence rates less than 20 percent, about one-third of the states had prevalence rates greater than or equal to 25 percent, with three states having prevalence rates greater than or equal to 30 percent.

SOURCE: www.cdc.nccdphp/dnpa/obesity/trend/maps/index.htm

Obesity is so widespread and its prevalence is rising so rapidly that many refer to it as an **epidemic.**[4] According to the World Health Organization, this epidemic of obesity has spread worldwide, affecting over 300 million adults. Contrary to popular opinion, obesity is not limited to industrialized nations; over 115 million people in developing countries suffer from obesity-related problems. Before examining the suspected causes of obesity and the various strategies used to treat it, it is helpful to understand the development and metabolism of body fat.

Fat Cell Development

When more energy is consumed than is expended, much of the excess energy is stored in the fat cells of adipose tissue. The amount of fat in a person's body reflects both the *number* and the *size* of the fat cells. The number of fat cells increases most rapidly during the growing years of late childhood and early puberty. After growth ceases, fat cell number may continue to increase whenever energy balance is positive. Obese people have more fat cells than healthy-weight people; their fat cells are also larger.

When energy intake exceeds expenditure, the fat cells accumulate triglycerides and expand in size (review Figure 5-20, p. 155). When the cells enlarge, they stimulate cell proliferation so that their numbers increase again.[5] Thus obesity develops ◆ when a person's fat cells increase in number, in size, or quite often both. Figure 9-2 illustrates fat cell development.

When energy out exceeds energy in, the size of fat cells dwindles, but not their number. People with extra fat cells tend to regain lost weight rapidly; with weight gain, their many fat cells readily fill. In contrast, people with an average number of enlarged fat cells may be more successful in maintaining weight losses; when their cells shrink, both cell size and number are normal. Prevention of obesity is most critical, then, during the growing years when fat cells increase in number.

As mentioned, excess fat is typically stored in adipose tissue. This stored fat may be well tolerated, but fat accumulation in organs such as the heart or liver clearly plays a key role in the development of diseases such as heart failure or fatty liver.[6] ◆

Fat Cell Metabolism

The enzyme lipoprotein lipase (LPL) ◆ promotes fat storage in both adipose and muscle cells. Obese people generally have much more LPL activity in their fat cells than lean people do (their muscle cell LPL activity is similar, though). This high LPL activity makes fat storage especially efficient. Consequently, even modest excesses in energy intake have a more dramatic impact on obese people than on lean people.

The activity of LPL is partially regulated by gender-specific hormones—estrogen in women and testosterone in men. In women, fat cells in the breasts, hips, and thighs produce abundant LPL, putting fat away in those body sites; in men, fat cells in the abdomen produce abundant LPL. This enzyme activity explains why men tend to develop central obesity around the abdomen (apple-shaped) whereas women more readily develop lower-body fat around the hips and thighs (pear-shaped).

Gender differences are also apparent in the activity of the enzymes controlling the release and breakdown of fat in various parts of the body. The release of lower-body fat is less active in women than in men, whereas the release of upper-body fat is similar. Furthermore, the rate of fat breakdown is lower in women than in men. Consequently, women may have a more difficult time losing fat in general, and from the hips and thighs in particular.

Enzyme activity may also explain why some people who lose weight regain it so easily. After weight loss, LPL activity increases, and it does so most dramatically in people who were fattest prior to weight loss. Apparently, weight loss serves as a signal to the gene that produces the LPL enzyme, saying "Make more of the enzyme that stores fat." People easily regain weight after having lost it because they are bat-

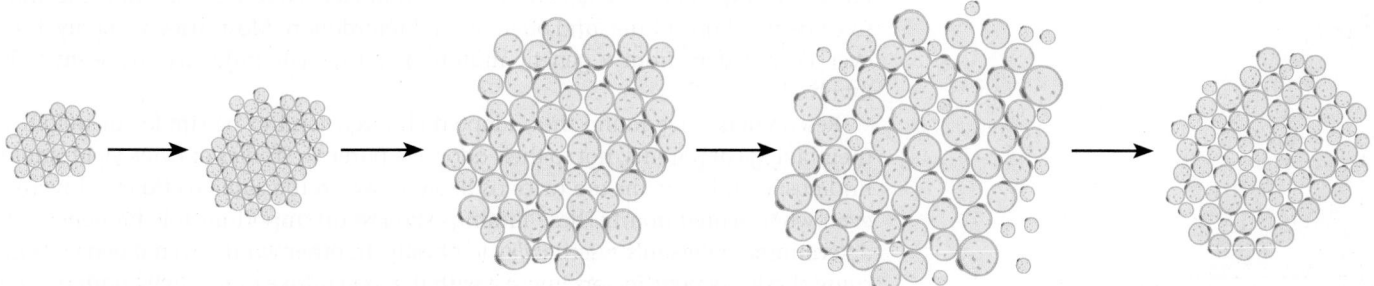

FIGURE 9-2 Fat Cell Development

Fat cells are capable of increasing their size by 20-fold and their number by several thousandfold.

During growth, fat cells increase in number.

When energy intake exceeds expenditure, fat cells increase in size.

When fat cells have enlarged and energy intake continues to exceed energy expenditure, fat cells increase in number again.

With fat loss, the size of the fat cells shrinks but not the number.

tling against enzymes that want to store fat. The activities of these and other proteins provide an explanation for the observation that some inner mechanism seems to set a person's weight or body composition at a fixed point; the body will adjust to restore that **set point** if the person tries to change it.

Set-Point Theory

Many internal physiological variables, such as blood glucose, blood pH, and body temperature, remain fairly stable under a variety of conditions. The hypothalamus and other regulatory centers constantly monitor and delicately adjust conditions to maintain homeostasis. The stability of such complex systems may depend on set-point regulators that maintain variables within specified limits.

Researchers have confirmed that after weight gains or losses, the body adjusts its metabolism to restore the original weight. Energy expenditure increases after weight gain and decreases after weight loss. These changes in energy expenditure differ from those that would be expected based on body composition alone, and they help to explain why it is so difficult for an underweight person to maintain weight gains and an overweight person to maintain weight losses.

- Obesity due to an increase in the *number* of fat cells is **hyperplastic obesity.** Obesity due to an increase in the *size* of fat cells is **hypertrophic obesity.**

- The adverse effects of fat in nonadipose tissues are known as **lipotoxicity.**

- Reminder: *Lipoprotein lipase (LPL)* is an enzyme that hydrolyzes triglycerides passing by in the bloodstream and directs their parts into the cells, where they can be metabolized or reassembled for storage.

IN SUMMARY

Fat cells develop by increasing in number and size. Prevention of excess weight gain depends on maintaining a reasonable number of fat cells. With weight gains or losses, the body adjusts in an attempt to return to its previous status.

Causes of Overweight and Obesity

Why do people accumulate excess body fat? The obvious answer is that they take in more food energy than they expend. But that answer falls short of explaining why they do this. Is it genetic? Environmental? Cultural? Behavioral? Socioeconomic? Psychological? Metabolic? All of these? Most likely, obesity has many interrelated causes. Why an imbalance between energy intake and energy expenditure occurs remains a bit of a mystery; the next sections summarize possible explanations.

epidemic (ep-ih-DEM-ick): the appearance of a disease (usually infectious) or condition that attacks many people at the same time in the same region.
- **epi** = upon
- **demos** = people

set point: the point at which controls are set (for example, on a thermostat). The set-point theory that relates to body weight proposes that the body tends to maintain a certain weight by means of its own internal controls.

Genetics

Genetics plays a true causative role in relatively few cases of obesity, for example, in Prader-Willi syndrome—a genetic disorder characterized by excessive appetite, massive obesity, short stature, and often mental retardation. Most cases of obesity, however, do not stem from a genetic mutation, yet genetic influences do seem to be involved.

Researchers have found that adopted children tend to be similar in weight to their biological parents, not to their adoptive parents. Studies of twins yield similar findings: identical twins are twice as likely to weigh the same as fraternal twins—even when reared apart. These findings suggest an important role for genetics in determining a person's *susceptibility* to obesity. In other words, even if genes do not *cause* obesity, genetic factors interact with the food intake and activity patterns that lead to it and the metabolic pathways that maintain it.[7]

Clearly, something genetic makes a person more or less likely to gain or lose weight when overeating or undereating.[8] Some people gain more weight than others on comparable energy intakes. Given an extra 1000 kcalories a day for 100 days, some pairs of identical twins gain less than 10 pounds while others gain up to 30 pounds. Within each pair, the amounts of weight gained, percentages of body fat, and locations of fat deposits are similar. Similarly, some people lose more weight than others following comparable exercise routines.

Researchers have been examining several genes in search of answers to obesity questions. As the section on protein synthesis in Chapter 6 described, each cell expresses only the genes for the proteins it needs, and each protein performs a unique function. The following paragraphs describe some recent research involving proteins that might help explain appetite control, energy regulation, and obesity development.[9]

Leptin Researchers have identified an obesity gene, called *ob*, which is expressed primarily in the adipose tissue and codes for the protein **leptin**. Leptin acts as a hormone, primarily in the hypothalamus. Research suggests that leptin from adipose tissue signals sufficient energy stores and promotes a negative energy balance by suppressing appetite and increasing energy expenditure. Changes in energy expenditure primarily reflect changes in basal metabolism but may also include changes in physical activity patterns. Leptin is also released from stomach cells in response to the presence of food, suggesting a role for both short-term and long-term satiety regulation.[10]

Mice with a defective *ob* gene do not produce leptin and can weigh up to three times as much as normal mice and have five times as much body fat (see Figure 9-3). When injected with a synthetic form of leptin, the mice rapidly lose body fat. (Because leptin is a protein, it would be destroyed during digestion if given orally; consequently, it must be given by injection.) The fat cells not only lose fat, but they self-destruct (reducing cell number), which may explain why weight gains are delayed when the mice are fed again.

Although extremely rare, a genetic deficiency of leptin has been identified in human beings as well. An error in the gene that codes for leptin has been discovered in a few extremely obese children with barely detectable blood levels of leptin. Without leptin, the children have little appetite control; they are constantly hungry and eat considerably more than their siblings or peers. Given daily injections of leptin, these children lost a substantial amount of weight, confirming leptin's role in regulating appetite and body weight.[11]

Not too surprisingly, leptin injections are effective in suppressing appetite and supporting weight loss only when overeating and obesity are the result of a leptin deficiency. Very few obese people have a leptin deficiency, however. In fact, obese people generally have high leptin levels, and weight gain increases leptin concentrations. Researchers speculate that in obesity, leptin rises in an effort to overcome an insensitivity or resistance to leptin.

leptin: a protein produced by fat cells under direction of the *ob* gene that decreases appetite and increases energy expenditure; sometimes called the ***ob* protein.**

• *leptos* = thin

FIGURE 9-3 Mice with and without Leptin Compared

Both of these mice have a defective *ob* gene. Consequently, they do not produce leptin. They both became obese, but the one on the right received daily injections of leptin, which suppressed food intake and increased energy expenditure, resulting in weight loss.

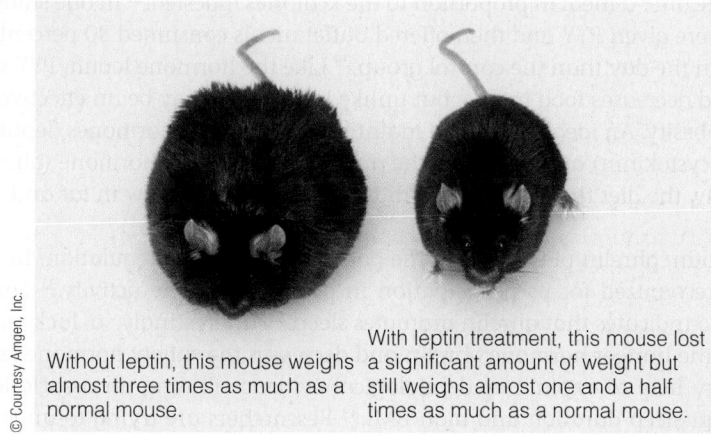

© Courtesy Amgen, Inc.

Without leptin, this mouse weighs almost three times as much as a normal mouse.

With leptin treatment, this mouse lost a significant amount of weight but still weighs almost one and a half times as much as a normal mouse.

Some researchers have reexamined the evidence on leptin from another point of view—one of undernutrition. Instead of focusing on leptin's role as a satiety signal that might help prevent obesity by regulating food intake, they view leptin as a starvation hormone that signals energy deficits.[12] When energy intake is low, leptin levels decline, and metabolism slows in an effort to reduce energy demands. Clearly, leptin plays a major role in energy regulation, but additional research is needed to clarify its actions when intake is either excessive or deficient.

In addition to its involvement in energy regulation, leptin plays several other roles in the body.[13] For example, leptin may inform the female reproductive system about body fat reserves; stimulate growth of new blood vessels, especially in the cornea of the eye; enhance the maturation of bone marrow cells; promote formation of red blood cells; and help support a normal immune response.[14] Elevated leptin levels may be partially responsible for the early maturation that commonly occurs in obese children.[15]

Ghrelin Leptin interacts with another protein that also acts as a hormone primarily in the hypothalamus.[16] Known as **ghrelin,** this protein is secreted primarily by the stomach cells and promotes a positive energy balance by stimulating appetite and promoting efficient energy storage.[17] The role ghrelin plays in regulating food intake and body weight is currently the subject of much intense research.[18]

Ghrelin triggers the desire to eat. Blood levels of ghrelin typically rise before and fall after a meal in proportion to the kcalories ingested—reflecting the hunger and satiety that precede and follow eating.[19] In general, fasting blood levels correlate inversely with body weight: lean people have high ghrelin levels and obese people have low levels.[20] Interestingly, although ghrelin levels are high in underweight people, they are exceptionally high in anorexia nervosa and return to normal with nutrition intervention—indicating that both body weight and nutrition status influence ghrelin levels.[21] Also noteworthy, ghrelin levels in Prader-Willi syndrome are markedly high and remain elevated even after a meal, which helps to explain the excessive appetite commonly seen in this disorder.[22] Similarly, ghrelin levels do not seem to decline as much after a meal in obese people or in people with binge-eating disorders as they do for lean people.[23]

Ghrelin fights to maintain a stable body weight.[24] In fact, some researchers speculate that its role is to maximize fat stores during times of famine.[25] On average, ghrelin levels are high whenever the body is in negative energy balance, as occurs during low-kcalorie diets, for example. This response may help explain why weight

ghrelin (GRELL-in): a protein produced by the stomach cells that enhances appetite and decreases energy expenditure.
• **ghre** = growth

loss is so difficult to maintain. Weight loss is more successful following gastric bypass surgery, in part because ghrelin levels are abnormally low. (Why this is so remains unknown.)[26] Ghrelin levels decline again whenever the body is in positive energy balance, as occurs with weight gains.[27]

Ghrelin levels also decline in response to high levels of PYY, a peptide that the GI cells secrete after a meal in proportion to the kcalories ingested.[28] In one study, people who were given PYY and then offered buffet meals consumed 30 percent fewer kcalories in the day than the control group.[29] Like the hormone leptin, PYY signals satiety and decreases food intake, but unlike leptin, PYY may be an effective treatment for obesity. An ideal diet would maintain the satiating hormones (leptin, PYY, and cholecystokinin) and minimize the appetite stimulating hormone (ghrelin).[30] Fortunately, the diet that seems to do that best is one that is low in fat and rich in fiber.

Like leptin, ghrelin plays roles in the body beyond energy regulation. In fact, it was first recognized for its participation in growth hormone activity.[31] Some research also indicates that ghrelin promotes sleep.[32] Interestingly, a lack of sleep increases the hunger hormone ghrelin and decreases the satiety hormone leptin—which may help to explain epidemiological evidence finding an association between short sleep duration and high BMI.[33] Researchers are trying to understand the relationships among genes, sleep disorders, eating habits, and other related factors that may influence body weight and weight gain.[34]

Uncoupling Proteins Other genes code for proteins involved in energy metabolism. These proteins may influence the storing or expending of energy with different efficiencies or in different types of fat. The body has two types of fat: white and **brown adipose tissue**.[35] White adipose tissue stores fat for other cells to use for energy; brown adipose tissue releases stored energy as heat. Recall from Chapter 7 that when fat is oxidized, some of the energy is released in heat and some is captured in ATP. In brown adipose tissue, oxidation may be uncoupled ◆ from ATP formation, producing heat only.[36] By radiating energy away as heat, the body expends, rather than stores, energy. Brown fat and heat production is particularly important in newborns and in animals exposed to cold weather, especially those that hibernate.[37] They have plenty of brown adipose tissue. In contrast, most human adults have little brown fat—less than 1 percent of all fat cells and interspersed among the white fat cells.[38] The role of brown fat in body weight regulation, though probably minimal, is not yet understood.[39]

Uncoupling proteins are active not only in brown fat, but also in white fat and many other tissues. Their actions seem to influence the basal metabolic rate (BMR) and oppose the development of obesity. Animals with abundant amounts of these uncoupling proteins resist weight gain, whereas those with minimal amounts gain weight easily. Similarly, people with a genetic variant of an uncoupling protein have lower metabolic rates and are more overweight than others.[40] Whether the body dissipates the energy from an ice cream sundae as heat or stores it in body fat has major consequences for a person's body weight.

Environment

Although genetic studies indicate that body weight may be at least partially heritable, they do not fully explain obesity. In contrast to the studies mentioned earlier that found similar weights between identical twins, some identical twins have dramatically different body weights. With obesity rates rising over the past three decades and the **gene pool** remaining relatively unchanged, environment must also play a role in obesity. The *environment* includes all of the circumstances that we encounter daily that push us toward fatness or thinness. Keep in mind that genetic and environmental factors are not mutually exclusive; genes can influence eating behaviors, for example, and numerous eating behaviors influence body weight. A simple behavior, such as regularly skipping breakfast, for example, can contribute to obesity.[41]

◆ Reminder: In *coupled reactions,* the energy released from the breakdown of one compound is used to create a bond in the formation of another compound. In *uncoupled reactions,* the energy is released as heat.

brown adipose tissue: masses of specialized fat cells packed with pigmented mitochondria that produce heat instead of ATP.

gene pool: all the genetic information of a population at a given time.

Overeating One explanation for obesity is that overweight people overeat, although diet histories may not always reflect high intakes. Diet histories are not always accurate records of actual intakes; both normal-weight and obese people commonly misreport their dietary intakes.[42] Most importantly, current dietary intakes may not reflect the eating habits that led to obesity. Obese people who had a positive energy-balance for years and accumulated excess body fat may not currently have a positive energy balance. This reality highlights an important point: the energy-balance equation must consider time. Both present *and* past eating and activity patterns influence current body weight.

We live in an environment that exposes us to an abundance of high-kcalorie, high-fat foods that are readily available, relatively inexpensive, heavily advertised, and reasonably tasty.[43] Food is available everywhere, all the time—thanks largely to fast food. Our highways are lined with fast-food restaurants, and convenience stores and service stations offer fast food as well. Fast food is available in our schools, malls, and airports. It's convenient and it's available morning, noon, and night—and all times in between.

◆ The food industry spends $30 billion a year on advertising. The message? "Eat more."

Most alarming are the extraordinarily large serving sizes and ready-to-go meals that offer supersize ◆ combinations. People buy the large sizes and combinations, perceiving them to be a good value, but then they eat more than they need—a bad deal. Large package or portion sizes can increase consumption—even when the food is not particularly appealing. Moviegoers given stale popcorn ate more when eating from a huge container than from a large container (both sizes were greater than anyone could finish).[44] Simply put, large portion sizes deliver more kcalories.[45] And portion sizes of virtually all foods and beverages have increased markedly in the past several decades, most notably at fast-food restaurants.[46] Not only have portion sizes increased over time, but they are now two to eight times larger than standard serving sizes.[47] The trend toward large portion sizes parallels the increasing prevalence of overweight and obesity in the United States, beginning in the 1970s, increasing sharply in the 1980s, and continuing today.[48]

◆ "Want fries with that?" A supersize portion delivers over 600 kcalories.

Restaurant food, especially fast food, is a major player in the development of obesity.[49] Fast food is often high in fat.[50] Fat's 9 kcalories per gram quickly add up, amplifying people's energy intakes and enlarging their body fat stores. The combination of large portions and energy-dense foods is a double whammy.[51] Reducing portion sizes is somewhat helpful, but the real kcalorie savings come from lowering the energy density.[52] After all, large portions of foods with low energy density such as lean meats, fruits, and vegetables can help with weight loss. Unfortunately, these foods may not be as inexpensive, flavorful, and convenient as energy dense foods.[53] Restaurants can help their customers eat healthfully by reducing portion sizes and offering more fruits, vegetables, legumes, and whole grains.[54]

Physical Inactivity Our environment fosters physical inactivity as well.[55] Life requires little exertion—escalators carry us up stairs, automobiles take us across town, buttons roll down windows, and remote controls change television channels from a distance. Modern technology has replaced physical activity at home, at work, and in transportation. Inactivity contributes to weight gain and poor health.[56] In turn, watching television, playing video games, and using the computer may contribute most to physical inactivity. The more time people spend in these sedentary activities, the more likely they are to be overweight.[57]

These sedentary activities contribute to weight gain in several ways. First, they require little energy beyond the resting metabolic rate. Second, they replace time spent in more vigorous activities. Third, watching television influences food purchases and correlates with between-meal snacking on the high-kcalorie, high-fat foods most heavily advertised.

People may be obese, therefore, not because they eat too much, but because they move too little—both in purposeful exercise and in the routines of daily life. One study reports that the differences in the time obese and lean people spent lying, sitting, standing, and moving accounts for about 350 kcalories a day.[58] Some obese people are so extraordinarily inactive that even when they eat less than lean people,

Lack of physical activity fosters obesity.

© Stockbyte/Jupiter Images

they still have an energy surplus. Reducing their food intake further would jeopardize health and incur nutrient deficiencies. Physical activity is a necessary component of nutritional health. People must be physically active if they are to eat enough food to deliver all the nutrients they need without unhealthy weight gain. In fact, to prevent weight gain, the DRI ◆ suggests an accumulation of 60 minutes of moderately intense physical activities every day in addition to the less intense activities of daily living.

◆ DRI for physical activity: 60 min/day (moderate intensity)

IN SUMMARY

Obesity has many causes and different combinations of causes in different people. Some causes, such as overeating and physical inactivity, may be within a person's control, and some, such as genetics, may be beyond it.

Problems of Overweight and Obesity

An estimated 35 to 45 percent of all U.S. women (and 20 to 30 percent of U.S. men) are trying to lose weight at any given time, spending up to $40 billion each year to do so.[59] Some of these people do not even need to lose weight. Others may benefit from weight loss, but they are not successful. Relatively few people succeed in losing weight, and even fewer succeed permanently. Whether an overweight person needs to lose weight is a question of health.

Health Risks

Chapter 8 described some of the health problems that commonly accompany obesity. In evaluating the risks to health from obesity, health care professionals use three indicators:[60]

◆ BMI 25.0-29.9 = overweight
BMI ≥30 = obese

◆ Men: >40 in (>102 cm)
Women: >35 in (>88 cm)

- Body mass index ◆ (BMI, as described in Chapter 8)
- Waist circumference ◆ (also described in Chapter 8)
- Disease risk profile, taking into account family history, life-threatening diseases, and common risk factors for chronic diseases[61]

The higher the BMI, the greater the waist circumference and the more risk factors—the greater the urgency to treat obesity.

People can best decide whether weight loss might be beneficial by considering their health status and motivation. People who are overweight by BMI standards, but otherwise in good health, might not benefit from losing weight; they might focus on preventing further weight gains instead. In contrast, those who are obese and suffering from a life-threatening disease such as diabetes might improve their health substantially by adopting a diet and exercise plan that supports weight loss. Motivation is a key component; to lose weight, a person needs to be ready and willing to make lifestyle changes for a lifetime.

◆ For reference, a woman with a BMI of 26 might be:
- 5 ft 3 in, 146 lb (1.60 m, 66.2 kg)
- 5 ft 5 in, 156 lb (1.65 m, 70.8 kg)
- 5 ft 7 in, 166 lb (1.70 m, 75.3 kg)

◆ Obese people and overweight people with two or more of these risk factors require aggressive treatment:
- Hypertension
- Cigarette smoking
- High LDL
- Low HDL
- Impaired glucose tolerance
- Family history of heart disease
- Men ≥45 yr; women ≥55 yr

Overweight in Good Health Often a person's motivations for weight loss have nothing to do with health. A healthy young woman with a BMI of 26 ◆ might want to lose a few pounds for spring break, but doing so might not improve her health. In fact, if she opts for a starvation diet or diet pills, she would be healthier *not* trying to lose weight.

Obese or Overweight with Risk Factors Weight loss is recommended for people who are obese and those who are overweight (or who have a high waist circumference) with two or more risk factors for chronic diseases. ◆ A 50-year-old man with a BMI of 28 ◆ who has high blood pressure and a family history of heart disease can

◆ For reference, a man with a BMI of 28 might be:
- 5 ft 8 in, 184 lb (1.73 m, 83.5 kg)
- 5 ft 10 in, 195 lb (1.78m, 88.5 kg)
- 6 ft, 206 lb (1.83 m, 93.4 kg)

improve his health by adopting a diet low in saturated fat and a regular exercise plan.

Obese or Overweight with Life Threatening Condition Weight loss is also recommended for a person who is either overweight or obese and suffering from a life-threatening condition such as heart disease, diabetes, or sleep apnea. ◆ The health benefits of weight loss are clear. For example, a 30-year-old man with a BMI of 40 ◆ might be able to prevent or control the diabetes that runs in his family by losing 75 pounds. Although the effort required to do so may be great, it may be no greater than the effort and consequences of living with diabetes.

Perceptions and Prejudices

Many people assume that every obese person can achieve slenderness and should pursue that goal. First consider that most obese people do not—for whatever reason—successfully lose weight and maintain their losses. Then consider the prejudice involved in that assumption. People come with varying weight tendencies, just as they come with varying potentials for height and degrees of health, yet we do not expect tall people to shrink or healthy people to get sick in an effort to become "normal."

Social Consequences Large segments of our society place such enormous value on thinness that obese people face prejudice and discrimination on the job, at school, and in social situations: they are judged on their appearance more than on their character.[62] Socially, obese people are stereotyped as lazy and lacking in self-control. Such a critical view of overweight is not prevalent in many other cultures, including segments of our own society. Instead, overweight is simply accepted or even embraced as a sign of robust health and beauty. Many overweight people today are tired of the obsession with weight control and simply want to be accepted as they are. To free society of its obsession with body weight and prejudice against obesity, people must first learn to judge others for who they are and not for what they weigh.

Psychological Problems Psychologically, obese people may suffer embarrassment when others treat them with hostility and contempt, and some have even come to view their own bodies as grotesque and loathsome. Parents and friends may scold them for lacking the discipline to resolve their weight problems. Health care professionals, including dietitians, are among the chief offenders. Criticism from others hurts self-esteem. Feelings of rejection, shame, or depression are common among obese people.

Most weight-loss programs assume that the problem can be solved simply by applying willpower and hard work. If determination were the only factor involved, though, the success rate would be far greater than it is. Overweight people may readily assume blame for failure to lose weight and maintain the losses when, in fact, it is the programs that have failed. Ineffective treatment and its associated sense of failure add to a person's psychological burden. Figure 9-4 illustrates how the devastating psychological effects of obesity and dieting perpetuate themselves.

Dangerous Interventions

People attach so many dreams of happiness to weight loss that they willingly risk huge sums of money for the slightest chance of success. As a result, weight-loss schemes flourish. Of the tens of thousands of claims, treatments, and theories for losing weight, few are effective—and many are downright dangerous. The negative effects must be carefully considered before embarking on any weight-loss program. Some interventions ◆ entail greater dangers than the risk of being overweight. Physical problems may arise from fad diets, "yo-yo" dieting, and drug use, and psychological problems may emerge from repeated "failures."

◆ Obese people and overweight people with any of these diseases require aggressive treatment:
- Heart disease
- Diabetes (type 2)
- Sleep apnea (a disturbance of breathing during sleep, including temporarily stopping)

◆ For reference, a man with a BMI of 40 might be:
- 5 ft 8 in, 265 lb (1.73 m, 120.2 kg)
- 5 ft 10 in, 280 lb (1.78 m, 127 kg)
- 6 ft, 295 lb (1.83 m, 133.8 kg)

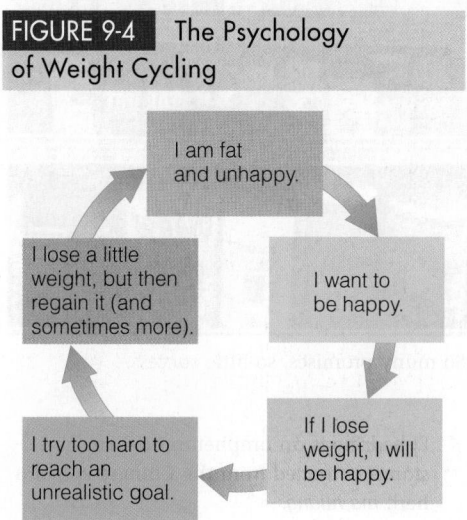

FIGURE 9-4 The Psychology of Weight Cycling

◆ Scrutinize fad diets, magic potions, and wonder gizmos with a healthy dose of skepticism.

TABLE 9-1	Weight-Loss Consumer Bill of Rights (An Example)

1. *WARNING:* Rapid weight loss may cause serious health problems. Rapid weight loss is weight loss of more than 1½ to 2 pounds per week or weight loss of more than 1 percent of body weight per week after the second week of participation in a weight-loss program.

2. Consult your personal physician before starting any weight-loss program.

3. Only permanent lifestyle changes, such as making healthful food choices and increasing physical activity, promote long-term weight loss and successful maintenance.

4. Qualifications of this provider are available upon request.

5. *YOU HAVE A RIGHT TO:*

   • Ask questions about the potential health risks of this program and its nutritional content, psychological support, and educational components.

   • Receive an itemized statement of the actual or estimated price of the weight-loss program, including extra products, services, supplements, examinations, and laboratory tests.

   • Know the actual or estimated duration of the program.

   • Know the name, address, and qualifications of the dietitian or nutritionist who has reviewed and approved the weight-loss program.

Some of the nation's most popular diet books and weight-loss programs have misled consumers with unsubstantiated claims and deceptive testimonials. Furthermore, they fail to provide an assessment of the short- and long-term results of their treatment plans, even though such evaluations are possible and would permit consumers to make informed decisions. Of course, some weight-loss programs are better than others in terms of cost, approach, and customer satisfaction, but few are particularly successful in helping people keep lost weight off. Clients can expect reputable programs to abide by a consumer bill of rights that explains the risks associated with weight-loss programs and provides honest predictions of success (see Table 9-1).

Fad Diets **Fad diets** often sound good, but they typically fall short of delivering on their promises. They espouse exaggerated or false theories of weight loss and advise consumers to follow inadequate diets. Some fad diets are hazardous to health as Highlight 9 explains. Adverse reactions can be as minor as headaches, nausea, and dizziness or as serious as death. Table H9-4 (on p. 320) offers guidelines for identifying unsound weight-loss schemes and fad diets.

Weight-Loss Products Millions of people in the United States use nonprescription weight-loss products. Most of them are women, especially young overweight women, but almost 10 percent are of normal weight.

In their search for weight-loss magic, some consumers turn to "natural" herbal products and dietary supplements, even though few have proved to be effective. St. John's wort, for example, contains substances that inhibit the uptake of **serotonin** and thus suppress appetite. In addition to the many cautions that accompany the use of all herbal remedies, consumers should be aware that St. John's wort is often prepared in combination with the herbal stimulant ephedrine. ◆ Ephedrine-containing supplements promote modest short-term weight loss (about 2 pounds a month), but the associated risks are high.[63] These supplements have been implicated in several cases of heart attacks and seizures and have been linked to about 100 deaths. For this reason, the FDA has banned the sale of dietary supplements containing ephedra, but they are readily available on the Internet.* Table 9-2 presents the claims and the dangers behind ephedrine and several other common dietary supplements used for weight loss.[64]

Herbal laxatives containing senna, aloe, rhubarb root, cascara, castor oil, and buckthorn (or various combinations) are commonly sold as "dieter's tea." Such concoctions commonly cause nausea, vomiting, diarrhea, cramping, and fainting and may have contributed to the deaths of four women who had drastically reduced their food intakes. Consumers mistakenly believe that laxatives will diminish nutrient absorption and reduce kcalorie intake, but remember that absorption

So many promises, so little success.

◆ Ephedrine is an amphetamine-like substance extracted from the Chinese ephedra herb *ma huang*.

fad diets: popular eating plans that promise quick weight loss. Most fad diets severely limit certain foods or overemphasize others (for example, never eat potatoes or pasta or eat cabbage soup daily).

serotonin (ser-oh-TONE-in): a neurotransmitter important in sleep regulation, appetite control, and sensory perception, among other roles. Serotonin is synthesized in the body from the amino acid tryptophan with the help of vitamin B_6.

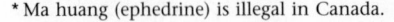

* Ma huang (ephedrine) is illegal in Canada.

TABLE 9-2	Selected Herbal and Other Dietary Supplements Marketed for Weight Loss		
Product	**Manufacturers' Claims**	**Research Findings**	**Adverse Effects**
Bitter orange[a] (*Citrus aurantium,* a natural flavoring that contains synephrine, a compound structurally similiar to epinephrine)	Stimulates weight loss; provides an alternative to ephedra	Little evidence available	May increase blood pressure; may interact with drugs
Chitosan[b] (pronounced KITE-oh-san; derived from chitin, the substance that forms the hard shells of lobsters, crabs, and other crustaceans)	Binds to dietary fat, preventing digestion and absorption	Ineffective	Impaired absorption of fat-soluble vitamins
Chromium (trace mineral)	Eliminates body fat	Ineffective; weight gain reported when not accompanied by exercise	Headaches, sleep disturbances, and mood swings; hexavalent form is toxic and carcinogenic
Conjugated linoleic acid (CLA; a group of fatty acids related to linoleic acid, but with different *cis-* and *trans*-configurations)	Reduces body fat and suppresses appetite	Some evidence in animal studies, but ineffective in human studies	None known
Ephedrine[c] (amphetamine-like substance derived from the Chinese ephedra herb ma huang)	Speeds body's metabolism	Short-term weight loss and dangerous side effects	Insomnia, tremors, heart attacks, strokes, and death; FDA has banned the sale of these products
Hydroxycitric acid[d] (active ingredient derived from the rind of the tropical fruit *garcinia cambogia*)	Inhibits the enzyme that converts citric acid to fat; suppresses appetite	Ineffective	Toxicity symptoms reported in animal studies; headaches, respiratory and gastrointestinal distress in humans
Pyruvate[e] (3-carbon compound produced during glycolysis)	Speeds body's metabolism	Modest weight loss with high doses	GI distress
Yohimbine (derived from the bark of a West African tree)	Promotes weight loss	Ineffective	Nervousness, insomnia, anxiety, dizziness, tremors, headaches, nausea, vomiting, hypertension

NOTE: The FDA has not approved the use of any of these products; most products are used in conjunction with a 1000- to 1800-kcalorie diet.
[a] Marketed under the trade names Xenadrine EFX, Metabolife Ultra, NOW Diet Support.
[b] Marketed under the trade names Chitorich, Exofat, Fat Breaker, Fat Blocker, Fat Magnet, Fat Trapper, and Fatsorb.
[c] Marketed under the trade names Diet Fuel, Metabolife, and Nature's Nutrition Formula One.
[d] Marketed under the trade names Ultra Burn, Citralean, CitriMax, Citrin, Slim Life, Brindleslim, Medislim, and Beer Belly Busters.
[e] Marketed under the trade names Exercise in a Bottle, Pyruvate Punch, Pyruvate-c, and Provate.

occurs primarily in the small intestine and these laxatives act on the large intestine. Highlight 18 explores the possible benefits and potential dangers of herbal products and other alternative therapies. As it explains, current laws do not require manufacturers of dietary supplements to test the safety or effectiveness of any product. Consumers cannot assume that an herb or supplement of any kind is safe or effective just because it is available on the market. Supplements may contain contaminants and may not contain the amounts of active ingredients listed on the labels.[65] Anyone using dietary supplements for weight loss should first consult with a physician.

Other Gimmicks Other gimmicks don't help with weight loss either. Hot baths do not speed up metabolism so that pounds can be lost in hours. Steam and sauna baths do not melt the fat off the body, although they may dehydrate people so that they lose water weight. Brushes, sponges, wraps, creams, and massages intended to move, burn, or break up **"cellulite"** do nothing of the kind because there is no such thing as cellulite.

IN SUMMARY

The question of whether a person should lose weight depends on many factors: among them are the extent of overweight, age, health, and genetic makeup. Not all obesity will cause disease or shorten life expectancy. Just as there are unhealthy, normal-weight people, there are healthy, obese people. Some people may risk more in the process of losing weight than in remaining overweight. Fad diets and weight-loss supplements can be physically and psychologically damaging.

cellulite (SELL-you-light or SELL-you-leet): supposedly, a lumpy form of fat; actually, a fraud. Fatty areas of the body may appear lumpy when the strands of connective tissue that attach the skin to underlying muscles pull tight where the fat is thick. The fat itself is the same as fat anywhere else in the body. If the fat in these areas is lost, the lumpy appearance disappears.

Aggressive Treatments for Obesity

The appropriate strategies for weight reduction depend on the degree of obesity and the risk of disease. An overweight person in good health may need only to improve eating habits and increase physical activity, but someone with **clinically severe obesity** may need more aggressive treatment ◆ options—drugs or surgery.[66] Drugs appear to be modestly effective and safe, at least in the short term; surgery appears to be dramatically effective but can have severe complications, at least for some people.[67]

Drugs

Based on new understandings of obesity's genetic basis and its classification as a chronic disease, much research effort has focused on drug treatments for obesity. Experts reason that if obesity is a chronic disease, it should be treated as such—and the treatment of most chronic diseases includes drugs. The challenge, then, is to develop an effective drug that can be used over time without adverse side effects or the potential for abuse.

Several drugs for weight loss have been tried over the years. When used as part of a long-term, comprehensive weight-loss program, drugs can help obese people to lose weight. Because weight regain commonly occurs with the discontinuation of drug therapy, treatment must be long term. Yet the long-term use of drugs poses risks. We don't yet know whether a person would be harmed more from maintaining a 100-pound excess or from taking a drug for a decade to keep the 100 pounds off. Physicians must prescribe drugs appropriately, inform consumers of the potential risks, and monitor side effects carefully. Two prescription drugs are currently on the market: sibutramine and orlistat. One reduces food intake; the other reduces nutrient absorption.[68]

Sibutramine **Sibutramine** suppresses appetite.* The drug is most effective when used in combination with a reduced-kcalorie diet and increased physical activity. Side effects include dry mouth, headache, constipation, rapid heart rate, and high blood pressure. The FDA warns those with high blood pressure not to use sibutramine and advises others to monitor their blood pressure.

Orlistat **Orlistat** takes a different approach to weight control.** It inhibits pancreatic lipase activity in the GI tract, thus blocking dietary fat digestion and absorption by about 30 percent. The drug is taken with meals and is most effective when accompanied by a reduced-kcalorie, low-fat diet. Side effects include gas, frequent bowel movements, and reduced absorption of fat-soluble vitamins. The FDA is recently approved† the over-the-counter sale of a low-dose version of orlistat.

Other Drugs Some physicians prescribe drugs that have not been approved for weight loss, a practice known as "off-label" use. These drugs have been approved for other conditions (such as seizures) and incidentally cause modest weight loss.[69] Physicians using off-label drugs must be well-informed of the drugs' use and effects and monitor their patients' responses closely.

Surgery

Surgery ◆ as an approach to weight loss is justified in some specific cases of clinically severe obesity. Over 100,000 such surgeries are performed annually.[70] As Figure 9-5 shows, surgical procedures effectively limit food intake by reducing the capacity of the stomach. In addition, they suppress hunger by reducing production of the hormone ghrelin.[71] The results are dramatic: most people achieve a lasting weight loss of more than 50 percent of their excess body weight.[72] Importantly, most of them experience dramatic improvements in their diabetes, blood lipids, and blood pressure.[73]

* Sibutramine is marketed under the trade name Meridia.
** Orlistat is marketed under the trade name Xenical.
† The low-dose, over-the-counter version of orlistat is marketed under the trade name Alli (AL-eye).

◆ The field of medicine that specializes in treating obesity is called **bariatrics.**
  • **bar** = weight

◆ Surgery may be an option for people with all of the following conditions:
  • Have tried diet and exercise programs without success
  • Remain obese (BMI > 35)
  • Have weight-related health problems

clinically severe obesity: a BMI of 40 or greater or a BMI of 35 or greater with additional medical problems. A less preferred term used to describe the same condition is *morbid obesity.*

sibutramine (sigh-BYOO-tra-mean): a drug used in the treatment of obesity that slows the reabsorption of serotonin in the brain, thus suppressing appetite and creating a feeling of fullness.

orlistat (OR-leh-stat): a drug used in the treatment of obesity that inhibits the absorption of fat in the GI tract, thus limiting kcaloric intake.

FIGURE 9-5 Gastric Surgery Used in the Treatment of Severe Obesity

Both of these surgical procedures limit the amount of food that can be comfortably eaten.

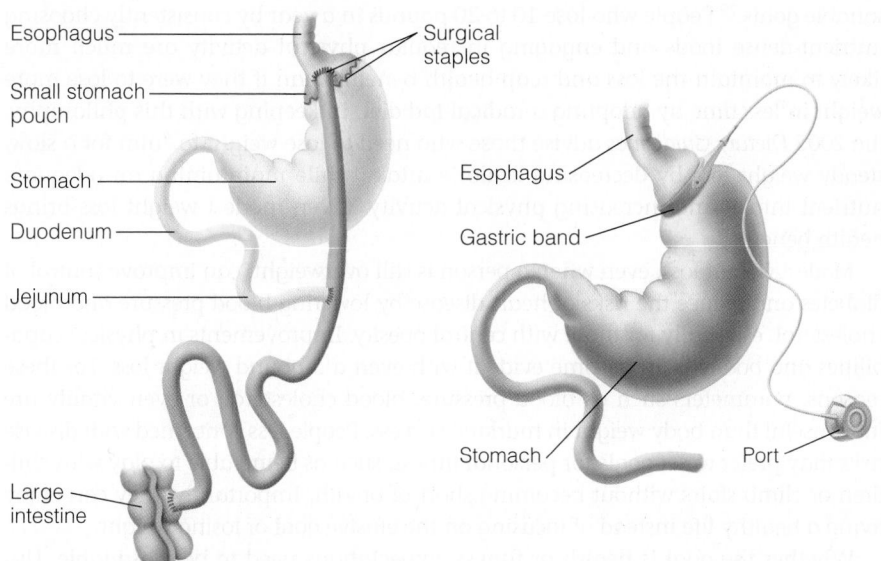

Esophagus

Small stomach pouch

Stomach

Duodenum

Jejunum

Large intestine

Surgical staples

Esophagus

Gastric band

Stomach

Port

In gastric bypass, the surgeon constructs a small stomach pouch and creates an outlet directly to the small intestine, bypassing most of the stomach, the entire duodenum, and some of the jejunum. (Dark areas highlight the flow of food through the GI tract; pale areas indicate bypassed sections.)

In gastric banding, the surgeon uses a gastric band to reduce the opening from the esophagus to the stomach. The size of the opening can be adjusted by inflating or deflating the band by way of a port placed in the abdomen just beneath the skin.

Whether surgery is a reasonable option for obese teens is the subject of much debate among pediatricians and bariatric surgeons.[74] In addition to the criteria listed in the margin (p. 292) for adults considering surgery, teens must have a BMI greater than 40, and they must have attained skeletal maturity.[75] Considerations of the adolescent's physical growth, emotional development, family support, and ability to comply with dietary instructions weigh heavily in the decision.

The long-term safety and effectiveness of gastric surgery depend, in large part, on compliance with dietary instructions. Common immediate postsurgical complications include infections, nausea, vomiting, and dehydration. In the long term, deficiencies of iron, vitamin B_{12}, folate, calcium, and vitamin D are common.[76] Weight regain and psychological problems may also occur. Lifelong medical supervision is necessary for those who choose the surgical route, but in suitable candidates, the health benefits of weight loss may prove worth the risks.[77]

Another surgical procedure is used, not to treat obesity, but to remove the evidence. Plastic surgeons can extract some fat deposits by suction lipectomy, or "liposuction." This cosmetic procedure has little effect on body weight, but can alter body shape slightly in specific areas. Liposuction is a popular procedure in part because of its perceived safety, but, in fact, serious complications can occasionally result in death. Furthermore, removing adipose tissue by way of liposuction does not provide the health benefits that typically accompany weight loss.[78]

IN SUMMARY

Obese people with high risks of medical problems may need aggressive treatment, including drugs or surgery. Others may benefit most from improving eating and exercise habits.

Weight-Loss Strategies

Successful weight-loss strategies embrace small changes, moderate losses, and reasonable goals.[79] People who lose 10 to 20 pounds in a year by consistently choosing nutrient-dense foods and engaging in regular physical activity are much more likely to maintain the loss and reap health benefits than if they were to lose more weight in less time by adopting a radical fad diet. In keeping with this philosophy, the 2005 *Dietary Guidelines* advise those who need to lose weight to "aim for a slow, steady weight loss by decreasing kcalorie intake while maintaining an adequate nutrient intake and increasing physical activity." Even modest weight loss brings health benefits.

Modest weight loss, even when a person is still overweight, can improve control of diabetes and reduce the risks of heart disease by lowering blood pressure and blood cholesterol, especially for those with central obesity. Improvements in physical capabilities and bodily pain become evident with even a 5-pound weight loss. For these reasons, parameters such as blood pressure, blood cholesterol, or even vitality are more useful than body weight in marking success. People less concerned with disease risks may prefer to set goals for personal fitness, such as being able to play with children or climb stairs without becoming short of breath. Importantly, they can enjoy living a healthy life instead of focusing on the elusive goal of losing weight.

Whether the goal is health or fitness, expectations need to be reasonable. Unreachable targets ensure frustration and failure. When goals are achieved or exceeded, people enjoy rewards instead of finding disappointment.

Research findings highlight the great disparity between lofty expectations and reasonable success.[80] Before beginning a weight-loss program, obese women identified the weights they would describe as "dream," "happy," "acceptable," and "disappointing" (see Figure 9-6). All of these weights were below their starting weight. Their goal weights far exceeded the 5 to 10 percent recommended by experts, or even the 15 percent reported by the most successful weight-loss studies. Even their "disappointing" weights exceeded recommended goals. Close to a year later, and after an average loss of 35 pounds, almost half of the women did not achieve even their "disappointing" weights. They did, however, experience more physical, social, and psychological benefits than they had predicted for that weight. Still, in a cul-

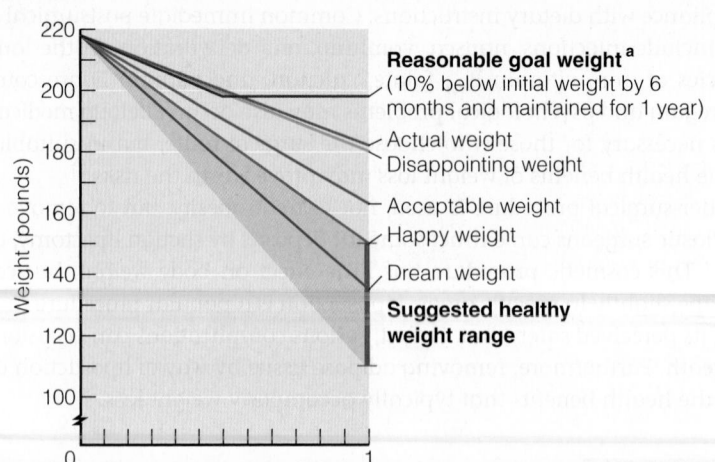

| FIGURE 9-6 | Reasonable Weight Goals and Expectations Compared |

Reasonable goal weight [a]
(10% below initial weight by 6 months and maintained for 1 year)

Actual weight
Disappointing weight

Acceptable weight
Happy weight
Dream weight

Suggested healthy weight range

[a]Reasonable goal weights reflect pounds lost over time. Given more time, reasonable goals may eventually fall within the suggested healthy-weight range.
SOURCE: Adapted from G. D. Foster and coauthors, What is a reasonable weight loss? Patients' expectations and evaluations of obesity treatment outcomes, *Journal of Consulting and Clinical Psychology* 65 (1997): 79–85.

ture that overvalues thinness, these women were not satisfied with a 16 percent reduction in weight—not because their efforts were unsuccessful, but because their expectations were unrealistic.

Depending on initial body weight, a reasonable rate of weight loss for overweight people is $1/2$ to 2 pounds a week, ◆ or 10 percent of body weight over six months.[81] For a person weighing 250 pounds, a 10 percent loss is 25 pounds, or about 1 pound a week for six months. Such gradual weight losses are more likely to be maintained than rapid losses. Keep in mind that pursuing good health is a lifelong journey. Most adults are keenly aware of their body weights and shapes and realize that what they eat and what they do can make a difference to some extent. Those who are most successful at weight management seem to have fully incorporated healthful eating and physical activity into their daily lives.[82] Such advice—to reduce energy intake and increase physical activity—would hardly surprise anyone, yet relatively few people trying to control their weight follow these recommendations.

◆ Safe rate for weight loss:
- $1/2$ to 2 lb/week (0.2 to 0.9 kg)
- 10% body weight/6 mo
- For a person weighing 110 kg, a 10% loss is 11 kg, or about 0.5 kg a week for six months

Eating Plans

Contrary to the claims of fad diets, no single food plan is magical, and no specific food must be included or avoided in a weight-management program. In designing a plan, people need only consider foods that they like or can learn to like, that are available, and that are within their means.

Be Realistic about Energy Intake The main characteristic of a weight-loss diet is that it provides less energy than the person needs to maintain present body weight. If food energy is restricted too severely, dieters may not receive sufficient nutrients and may lose lean tissue. Rapid weight loss usually means excessive loss of lean tissue, a lower BMR, and a rapid weight gain to follow. In addition, restrictive eating may set in motion the unhealthy behaviors of eating disorders as previously described in Highlight 8.

Table 9-3 outlines the recommendations of a weight-loss diet. Energy intake should provide nutritional adequacy without excess—that is, somewhere between

TABLE 9-3	Recommendations for a Weight-Loss Diet
Nutrient	**Recommended Intake**
kCalories	
For people with BMI ≥ 35	Approximately 500 to 1000 kcalories per day reduction from usual intake
For people with BMI between 27 and 35	Approximately 300 to 500 kcalories per day reduction from usual intake
Total fat	30% or less of total kcalories
Saturated fatty acids[a]	8 to 10% of total kcalories
Monounsaturated fatty acids	Up to 15% of total kcalories
Polyunsaturated fatty acids	Up to 10% of total kcalories
Cholesterol[a]	300 mg or less per day
Protein[b]	Approximately 15% of total kcalories
Carbohydrate[c]	55% or more of total kcalories
Sodium chloride	No more than 2400 mg of sodium or approximately 6 g of sodium chloride (salt) per day
Calcium	1000 to 1500 mg per day
Fiber[c]	20 to 30 g per day

[a]People with high blood cholesterol should aim for less than 7 percent kcalories from saturated fat and 200 milligrams of cholesterol per day.
[b]Protein should be derived from plant sources and lean sources of animal protein.
[c]Carbohydrates and fiber should be derived from vegetables, fruits, and whole grains.
SOURCE: National Institutes of Health Obesity Education Initiative, *The Practical Guide: Identification, Evaluation, and Treatment of Overweight and Obesity in Adults* (Washington, D.C.: U.S. Department of Health and Human Services, 2000), p. 27.

deprivation and complete freedom to eat whatever, whenever. A reasonable suggestion is that an adult needs to increase activity and reduce food intake enough to create a deficit of 500 kcalories per day. Such a deficit produces a weight loss of about 1 pound per week—a rate that supports the loss of fat efficiently while retaining lean tissue. In general, weight-loss diets provide 1000 to 1200 kcalories per day for women and 1200 to 1600 kcalories a day for men.[83] Table 9-4 specifies the amounts of foods from each food group for these kcalorie levels.

Emphasize Nutritional Adequacy Nutritional adequacy is difficult to achieve on fewer than 1200 kcalories a day, and most healthy adults need never consume any less. A plan that provides an adequate intake supports a healthier and more successful weight loss than a restrictive plan that creates feelings of starvation and deprivation, which can lead to an irresistible urge to binge.

Table 9-4 includes the recommended amounts for diets providing 1000 to 1600 kcalories. Such an intake would allow most people to lose weight and still meet their nutrient needs with careful, nutrient-dense food selections. (Women might need iron supplements.) Keep in mind, too, that well-balanced diets that emphasize fruits, vegetables, whole grains, lean meats or meat alternates, and low-fat milk products offer many health rewards even when they don't result in weight loss. A supplement providing vitamins and minerals at or below 100 percent of the Daily Values can help people following low-kcalorie diets to achieve nutrient adequacy.[84]

Eat Small Portions As mentioned earlier, portion sizes at markets, at restaurants, and even at home have increased dramatically over the years.[85] We have come to expect large portions, and we have learned to clean our plates. Many of us pay more attention to these external cues defining how much to eat than to our internal cues of hunger and satiety.[86] For health's sake, we may need to learn to eat less food at each meal—one piece of chicken for dinner instead of two, a teaspoon of butter on vegetables instead of a tablespoon, and one cookie for dessert instead of six. The goal is to eat enough food for adequate energy, abundant vitamins and minerals, and some pleasure, but not more. This amount should leave a person feeling satisfied—not stuffed.

Keep in mind that even fat-free and low-fat foods can deliver a lot of kcalories when a person eats large quantities. A low-fat cookie or two can be a sweet treat even on a weight-loss diet, but larger portions defeat the savings.

Lower Energy Density Most people take their cues about how much to eat based on portion sizes, and the larger the portion size, the more they eat—even when the food is not particularly tasty.[87] To lower energy intake, a person can either reduce the portion size or reduce the energy density.[88] Selecting low-energy-dense foods seems to be more a successful strategy than restricting portion sizes.[89] Figure 9-7 illustrates how water, fiber, and fat influence energy density, and the accompanying "How to" feature compares foods based on their energy density. Foods containing water, those rich in fiber, and those low in fat help to lower energy density, providing more satiety for

TABLE 9-4 Daily Amounts from Each Food Group for 1000- to 1600-kCalorie Diets

Food Group	1000 kcalories	1200 kcalories	1400 kcalories	1600 kcalories
Fruit	1 c	1 c	1 1/2 c	1 1/2 c
Vegetables	1 c	1 1/2 c	1 1/2 c	2 c
Grains	3 oz	4 oz	5 oz	5 oz
Meat and Legumes	2 oz	3 oz	4 oz	5 oz
Milk	3 c	3 c	3 c	3 c
Oils	3 tsp	3 tsp	3 tsp	4 tsp

NOTE: The USDA Food Guide patterns for 1000-, 1200-, and 1400-kcalories were designed for children and provided 2 cups milk. They were modified here to include an additional cup of milk, as 3 cups per day is recommended for all adults. The discretionary kcalorie allowance for these patterns is about 100 kcalories.

FIGURE 9-7	Energy Density

Decreasing the energy density (kcal/g) of foods allows a person to eat satisfying portions while still reducing energy intake. To lower energy density, select foods high in water or fiber and low in fat.

Selecting grapes with their high water content instead of raisins increases the volume and cuts the energy intake in half.

Even at the same weight and similar serving sizes, the fiber-rich broccoli delivers twice the fiber of the potatoes for about one-fourth the energy.

By selecting the water-packed tuna (on the right) instead of the oil-packed tuna (on the left), a person can enjoy the same amount for fewer kcalories.

fewer kcalories.[90] Because a low-energy-density diet is a low-fat, high-fiber diet rich in many vitamins and minerals, it supports good health in addition to weight loss.[91]

Remember Water Water helps with weight management in several ways. For one, foods with high water content (such as broth-based soups) increase fullness, reduce hunger, and consequently reduce energy intake. For another, drinking water fills the stomach between meals and satisfies thirst without adding kcalories. The average U.S. diet delivers an estimated 75 to 150 kcalories a day from sweetened beverages.[92] Simply replacing nutrient-poor, energy-dense beverages with water could save a person up to 15 pounds a year. Water also helps the GI tract adapt to a high-fiber diet.

Focus on Fiber Healthy meals and snacks center on high-fiber foods. Fresh fruits, vegetables, legumes, and whole grains offer abundant vitamins, minerals, and fiber but little fat. Consequently, high-carbohydrate diets rich in fiber tend to be relatively low in energy and high in nutrients.[93]

High-fiber foods also require effort to eat—an added bonus. Eating fiber-rich fruits and vegetables reduces energy density, lowers kcalorie intake, and promotes

HOW TO	Compare Foods Based on Energy Density

Chapter 2 described how to evaluate foods based on their nutrient density—their nutrient contribution per kcalorie. Another way to evaluate foods is to consider their energy density—their energy contribution per gram. This example compares carrot sticks with french fries. The conclusion is no surprise, but understanding the mathematics may offer valuable insight into the concept of energy density. A carrot weighing 72 grams delivers 31 kcalories. To calculate the energy density, divide kcalories by grams:

$$\frac{31 \text{ kcal}}{72 \text{ g}} = 0.43 \text{ kcal/g}$$

Do the same for french fries weighing 50 grams and contributing 167 kcalories:

$$\frac{167 \text{ kcal}}{50 \text{ g}} = 3.34 \text{ kcal/g}$$

The more kcalories per gram, the greater the energy density. French fries are more energy dense than carrots. They provide more energy per gram—and per bite. Considering a food's energy density is especially useful in planning diets for weight management. Foods with a high energy density help with weight gain, whereas foods with a low energy density help with weight loss.

ThomsonNOW
To practice comparing foods based on energy density, log on **www.thomsonedu.com/thomsonnow**, then go to Chapter 9, then go to How To.

© Corbis

If you want to lose weight, steer clear of the empty kcalories in fancy coffee drinks. A 16-oz café mocha delivers 400 kcalories—half of them from fat.

satiety.[94] The satiety signal indicating fullness is sent after a 20-minute lag, so a person who slows down and savors each bite eats less before the signal reaches the brain. Of course, much depends on whether the person pays attention to internal satiety signals and stops eating or, instead, responds to external cognitive influences and continues.

Choose Fats Sensibly Ideally, a weight-loss diet is both high in fiber and low in fat. Lowering the fat content of a food lowers its energy density—for example, selecting fat-free milk instead of whole milk. That way, a person can consume the usual amount (say, a cup of milk) at a lower energy intake (85 instead of 150 kcalories).

Fat has a weak satiating effect, and satiation plays a key role in determining food intake during a meal. Consequently, a person eating a high-fat meal raises energy intake by adding more food and more fat kcalories. For these reasons, measure fat with extra caution. Less fat in the diet means less fat in the body (review p. 163 for strategies to lower fat in the diet). Be careful not to take this advice to extremes, however; too little fat in the diet or in the body carries health risks as well, as Chapter 5 explained.

Whether a low-fat diet is the best option for weight loss is the subject of some controversy and much debate. An important point to notice in any discussion on weight-loss diets is total energy intake. *Low fat* simply means the energy derived from fat is relatively low compared with the total energy intake; it does not mean total energy intake is low. And reducing energy intake to less than expended is essential for weight loss. One way to lower energy intake is to lower fat intake. In these cases, adopting a low-fat diet can help with weight loss.[95]

Another currently popular way to lower energy intake is to lower carbohydrate intake. The highlight that follows this chapter discusses these diets fully, but findings from a recent study are worth mentioning here as well.[96] In this study, people were randomly assigned to one of two diets—either a low-carbohydrate diet or a low-fat diet. They were given descriptions of the diets and then fed themselves, as would be typical of many dieters. Both groups lost weight, but those on the low-carbohydrate diet lost more weight during the first six months; their diets produced a greater energy deficit. Interestingly, the differences in weight loss between the two groups disappeared by the end of one year. Between six months and one year, weight remained fairly stable in the low-fat group, but regains were evident in the low-carbohydrate group, suggesting that adhering to a low-carbohydrate diet for an extended length of time may be difficult. These findings highlight an important point: weight loss requires a commitment to long-term changes in food choices. They also confirm another critical point: weight loss depends on a low energy intake—not the proportion of energy nutrients.[97]

Watch for Other Empty kCalories A person trying to achieve or maintain a healthy weight needs to pay attention not only to fat, but to sugar and alcohol, too.[98] Using sugar or alcohol for pleasure on occasion is compatible with health as long as most daily choices are of nutrient-dense foods. Not only does alcohol add kcalories, but accompanying mixers can also add both kcalories and fat, especially in creamy drinks such as piña coladas (review Table H7-3 on p. 244). Furthermore, drinking alcohol reduces a person's inhibitions, which can sabotage weight-control efforts—at least temporarily.

IN SUMMARY

A person who adopts a lifelong "eating plan for good health" rather than a "diet for weight loss" will be more likely to keep the lost weight off. Table 9-5 provides several tips for successful weight management.

TABLE 9-5	Weight-Management Strategies

In General

- Focus on healthy eating and activity habits, not on weight losses or gains.
- Adopt reasonable expectations about health and fitness goals and about how long it will take to achieve them.
- Make nutritional adequacy a high priority.
- Learn, practice, and follow a healthful eating plan for the rest of your life.
- Participate in some form of physical activity regularly.
- Adopt permanent lifestyle changes to achieve and maintain a healthy weight.

For Weight Loss

- Energy out should exceed energy in by about 500 kcalories/day. Increase your physical activity enough to spend more energy than you consume from foods.
- Emphasize foods with a low energy density and a high nutrient density.
- Eat small portions. Share a restaurant meal with a friend or take home half for lunch tomorrow.
- Eat slowly.
- Limit high-fat foods. Make legumes, whole grains, vegetables, and fruits central to your diet plan.
- Limit low-fat treats to the serving size on the label.
- Limit concentrated sweets and alcoholic beverages.
- Drink a glass of water before you begin to eat and another while you eat. Drink plenty of water throughout the day (8 glasses or more a day).
- Keep a record of diet and exercise habits; it reveals problem areas, the first step toward improving behaviors.
- Learn alternative ways to deal with emotions and stresses.
- Attend support groups regularly or develop supportive relationships with others.

For Weight Gain

- Energy in should exceed energy out by at least 500 kcalories/day. Increase your food intake enough to store more energy than you spend in exercise. Exercise and eat to build muscles.
- Expect weight gain to take time (1 pound per month would be reasonable).
- Emphasize energy-dense foods.
- Eat at least three meals a day.
- Eat large portions of foods and expect to feel full.
- Eat snacks between meals.
- Drink plenty of juice and milk.

Physical Activity

The best approach to weight management includes physical activity.[99] Yet among people trying to lose weight, only half are physically active and only half of the active group meet minimal recommendations.[100] To prevent weight gains and support weight losses, current recommendations advise 60 minutes of moderately intense physical activity a day in addition to activities of daily life.[101] People who combine diet and exercise typically lose more fat, retain more muscle, and regain less weight than those who only follow a weight-loss diet. Even when people who include physical activity in their weight-management program do not lose more weight, they seem to follow their diet plans more closely and maintain their losses better than those who do not exercise. Consequently, they benefit from taking in a little less energy as well as from expending a little more energy in physical activity. Importantly, those who exercise reduce abdominal obesity and improve their blood pressure, insulin resistance, and cardiorespiratory fitness, regardless of weight loss.[102] Chapter 14 presents the many health benefits of physical activity; the focus here is on its role in weight management.

The key to good health is to combine sensible eating with regular exercise.

Dietary Guidelines for Americans 2005

To help manage body weight and prevent gradual, unhealthy body weight gain in adulthood, engage in approximately 60 minutes of moderate- to vigorous-intensity activity on most days of the week while not exceeding kcaloric intake requirements.

Activity and Energy Expenditure Table 8-2 (p. 255) shows how much energy each of several activities uses. The number of kcalories spent in an activity depends on body weight, intensity, and duration. For example, a person who weighs 150 pounds and walks $3^1/_2$ miles in 60 minutes expends about 315 kcalories. That same person running 3 miles in 30 minutes uses a similar amount. By comparison, a 200-pound person running 3 miles in 30 minutes expends an additional 100 kcalories or so. The goal is to expend as much energy as your time allows. The greater the energy deficit created by exercise, the greater the fat loss. And be careful not to compensate for the energy spent in exercise by eating more food. Otherwise, energy balance won't shift and fat loss will be less significant.

Activity and Discretionary kCalorie Allowance Chapter 2 introduced the discretionary kcalorie allowance as the difference between the kcalories needed to supply nutrients and those needed to maintain energy balance. Because exercise expends energy, the energy allowance to maintain balance increases with increased physical activity—yet the energy needed to deliver needed nutrients remains about the same. In this way, physical activity increases the discretionary kcalorie allowance (see Figure 9-8). Having a larger discretionary kcalorie allowance puts a little more wiggle room in a weight-loss diet for such options as second helpings, sweet treats, or alcoholic beverages on occasion. Of course, selecting nutrient-dense foods and *not* using discretionary kcalories will maximize weight loss.

Activity and Metabolism Activity also contributes to energy expenditure in an indirect way—by speeding up metabolism. It does this both immediately and over the long term. On any given day, metabolism remains slightly elevated for several hours after intense and prolonged exercise. ◆ Over the long term, a person who engages in daily vigorous activity gradually develops more lean tissue. Metabolic rate rises accordingly, and this supports continued weight loss or maintenance.

◆ This postexercise effect raises the energy expenditure of exercise by about 15 percent.

Activity and Body Composition Physically active people have less body fat than sedentary people do—even if they have the same BMI. Physical activity, even

FIGURE 9-8   *Animated!* Influence of Physical Activity on Discretionary kCalorie Allowance

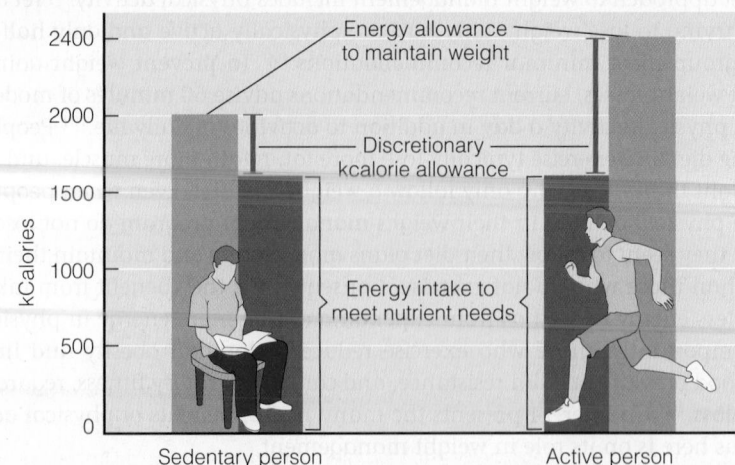

without weight loss, changes body composition: body fat decreases and lean body mass increases. Furthermore, exercise specifically decreases abdominal fat.[103]

Activity and Appetite Control Many people think that exercising will make them eat more, but this is not entirely true. Active people do have healthy appetites, but *immediately* after an intense workout, most people do not feel like eating. They may be thirsty and want to shower, but they are not hungry. The body has released fuels from storage to support the exercise, so glucose and fatty acids are abundant in the blood. At the same time, the body has suppressed its digestive functions. Hard physical work and eating are not compatible. A person must calm down, put energy fuels back in storage, and relax before eating. At that time, a physically active person may eat more than a sedentary person, but not so much as so fully compensate for the kcalories expended in exercise.[104]

Exercise may help curb the inappropriate appetite that accompanies boredom, anxiety, or depression. Weight-management programs encourage people who feel the urge to eat when not hungry to go out and exercise instead. The activity passes time, relieves anxiety, and prevents inappropriate eating.

Activity and Psychological Benefits Activity also helps reduce stress. Because stress itself cues inappropriate eating for many people, activity can help here, too. In addition, the fit person looks and feels healthy and, as a result, gains self-esteem. High self-esteem motivates a person to persist in seeking good health and fitness, which keeps the beneficial ◆ cycle going.

Choosing Activities Clearly, physical activity is a plus in a weight-management program. What kind of physical activity is best? People should choose activities that they enjoy and are willing to do regularly. What schedule of physical activity is best? ◆ It doesn't matter; whether a person chooses several short bouts of exercise or one continuous workout, the fitness and weight-loss benefits are the same—and any activity is better than being sedentary.

Health care professionals frequently advise people to engage in activities of low-to-moderate intensity for a long duration, such as an hour-long, fast-paced walk. The reasoning behind such advice is that people exercising at low-to-moderate intensity are more likely to stick with their activity for longer times and are less likely to injure themselves. A person who stays with an activity routine long enough to enjoy the rewards will be less inclined to give it up and will, over the long term, reap many health benefits. Activity of low-to-moderate intensity ◆ that expends at least 2000 kcalories per week is especially helpful for weight management. Higher levels produce even greater losses.[105]

In addition to exercise, a person can incorporate hundreds of energy-expending activities into daily routines: take the stairs instead of the elevator, walk to the neighbor's apartment instead of making a phone call, and rake the leaves instead of using a blower. Remember that sitting uses more kcalories than lying down, standing uses more kcalories than sitting, and moving uses more kcalories than standing. A 175-pound person who replaces a 30-minute television program with a 2-mile walk a day can expend enough energy to lose (or at least not gain) 18 pounds in a year. Meeting an activity goal of 10,000 steps a day helps to support a healthy BMI.[106] By wearing a pedometer, a person can easily track a day's activities without measuring miles or watching the clock. The point is to be active. Walk. Run. Swim. Dance. Cycle. Climb. Skip. Do whatever you enjoy doing—and do it often.

Spot Reducing People sometimes ask about "spot reducing." Unfortunately, muscles do not "own" the fat that surrounds them. Fat cells all over the body release fat in response to the demand of physical activity for use by whatever muscles are active. No exercise can remove the fat from any particular area.

Exercise can help with trouble spots in another way, though. The "trouble spot" for most men is the abdomen, their primary site of fat storage. During aerobic exercise, abdominal fat readily releases its stores, providing fuel to the physically active body. With regular exercise and weight loss, men will deplete these abdominal

◆ Benefits of physical activity in a weight-management program:
  • Short-term increase in energy expenditure (from exercise and from a slight rise in metabolism)
  • Long-term increase in BMR (from an increase in lean tissue)
  • Improved body composition
  • Appetite control
  • Stress reduction and control of stress eating
  • Physical, and therefore psychological, well-being
  • Improved self-esteem
Chapter 14 presents additional benefits of physical activity.

◆ For an active life, limit sedentary activities, engage in strength and flexibility activities, enjoy leisure activities often, engage in vigorous activities regularly, and be as active as possible every day (see the activity pyramid in Chapter 14).

◆ Estimated energy expended when walking at a moderate pace = 1 kcal/mi/kg body wt.

fat stores before those in the lower body. Women may also deplete abdominal fat with exercise, but their "trouble spots" are more likely to be their hips and thighs.

In addition to aerobic activity, strength training can help to improve the tone of muscles in a trouble area, and stretching to gain flexibility can help with associated posture problems. A combination of aerobic, strength, and flexibility workouts best improves fitness and physical appearance.

IN SUMMARY

Physical activity should be an integral part of a weight-control program. Physical activity can increase energy expenditure, improve body composition, help control appetite, reduce stress and stress eating, and enhance physical and psychological well-being.

Environmental Influences

Chapter 8 described how hormones regulate hunger, satiety, and satiation, but people don't always pay close attention to such internal signals. Instead, their eating behaviors are often dictated by environmental factors. Environmental factors include those surrounding the eating experience as well as those pertaining to the food itself.[107] Changing any of these factors can influence how much a person eats.[108]

Atmosphere The environment surrounding a meal or snack influences its duration. When the lighting, décor, aromas, and sounds of an environment are pleasant and comfortable, people tend to spend more time eating and thus eat more. A person needn't eat under neon lights with offensive music to eat less, of course. Instead, after completing a meal, remove food from the table and enjoy the ambience—without the presence of visual cues to stimulate additional eating.

Accessibility Among the strongest influences on how much we eat is the accessibility, ease, and convenience of obtaining food. In general, the less effort needed to obtain food, the more likely food will be eaten. Are you more likely to eat if half a leftover pizza is in your refrigerator or if you have to drive to the grocery store, buy a frozen pizza, and bake it for 45 minutes? Having food nearby and visible encourages eating. In one study, secretaries ate more chocolates when the candy was on their desks than when they had to walk six feet.[109] Interestingly, the secretaries underestimated the amount of chocolates they had eaten when the candy was on their desk and overestimated when it was a short distance away. The message is clear for people wanting to eat less candy (or any other tempting item)—keep it out of sight and in an inconvenient place (or don't even buy it).

Socializing People tend to eat more when socializing with others. Pleasant conversations extend the duration of a meal, allowing a person more time to eat more, and research confirms that the longer the meal, the greater the consumption.[110] In addition, by taking a visual cue from companions, a person might eat more when others at the table, clean their plates, or go to the buffet line for seconds. One way to eat less is to pace yourself with the person who seems to be eating the least and slowest. Social interactions also distract a person from paying attention to how much has been eaten. In some cases, socializing with friends during a meal may provide comfort and lower a person's motivation to limit consumption. In other cases, socializing with unfamiliar people during a meal—during a job interview or blind date, for example—may create stress and reduce food consumption. To eat less while socializing, pay attention to portion sizes.

Distractions Distractions influence food intake by initiating eating, interfering with internal controls to stop eating, and extending the duration of eating. Some people start eating dinner when a favorite television program comes on, regardless of hunger. Other people continue eating breakfast until they finish reading the newspaper. Such mindless eating can easily become overeating.

In addition to influencing the start and stop of a meal, distractions interfere with a person's ability to monitor and regulate how much is consumed.[111] Do you eat more popcorn when you are engrossed in a movie or if you are paying attention to how much popcorn you are eating? If distractions are a part of the eating experience, extra care is needed to control portion sizes.

Eating from the package while distracted by television is a weight-gaining combination.

Presence The mere sight (or smell, or even thought) of a food can prompt a person to start eating—regardless of hunger. The chocolates in the clear candy dishes on the secretaries' desks were eaten much faster than those in opaque containers.[112]

Variety When offered a variety of foods, or a variety of flavors of the same food, people tend to eat more. Interestingly, they tend to eat more even when variety is only *perceived.* Given six flavors of jelly beans, people will eat more when offered an assorted mixture than when presented with the exact same flavors and quantities sorted in a sectioned container.[113]

Variety is pleasing and distracting—two factors that slow the eating experience and delay satiation.[114] To limit intake, then, focus on a limited number of foods per meal. Be careful not to misunderstand and abandon variety in diet planning. Eating a variety of foods from each of the food groups is still a healthy plan—just not all at one meal.

Package and Portion Sizes As noted earlier, the sizes of packages in grocery stores and portion sizes at restaurants and at home have increased dramatically in recent decades, contributing to the increase in obesity in the United States.[115] Put simply, we tend to clean our plates and finish the package. The larger the bag of potato chips, the greater the intake.[116] To keep from overeating, repackage snacks into smaller containers and eat them from a plate, not directly from the package.

Serving Containers We often use plates, utensils, and glasses as visual cues to guide our decisions on how much to eat and drink.[117] If you plan to eat a bowl of ice cream, it matters whether the bowl you select holds 8 ounces or 24 ounces. Even the size of the serving container matters. Students took more—and ate more—snacks when serving from two large bowls instead of from four medium bowls.[118]

Large dinner plates and wide glasses create illusions and misperceptions about quantities consumed. A scoop of mashed potatoes on a small plate looks larger than the same-size scoop on a large plate, leading a person to underestimate the amount of food eaten.[119] To control portion sizes, use small bowls and plates, small serving spoons, and tall, narrow glasses.[120]

Behavior and Attitude

Behavior and attitude play important roles in supporting efforts to achieve and maintain appropriate body weight and composition. **Behavior modification** focuses on how to change behaviors to increase energy expenditure and decrease energy intake.[121] A person must commit to taking action.

Adopting a positive, matter-of-fact attitude helps to ensure success. Healthy eating and activity choices are an essential part of healthy living and should simply be incorporated into the day—much like brushing one's teeth or wearing a safety belt.

Become Aware of Behaviors To solve a problem, a person must first identify all the behaviors that created the problem. Keeping a record will help to identify eating and exercise behaviors that may need changing (see Figure 9-9, p. 304). It will also establish a baseline against which to measure future progress.

Change Behaviors Strategies ◆ focus on learning desired eating and exercise behaviors and eliminating unwanted behaviors. With so many possible behavior changes, a person can choose where to begin. Start simply and don't try to master

◆ Examples of behavioral strategies to support weight change:
- Do not grocery shop when hungry.
- Eat slowly (pause during meals, chew thoroughly, put down utensils between bites).
- Exercise when watching television.

behavior modification: the changing of behavior by the manipulation of antecedents (cues or environmental factors that trigger behavior), the behavior itself, and consequences (the penalties or rewards attached to behavior).

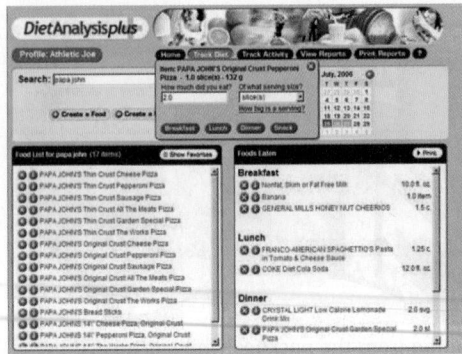

Diet analysis programs help people identify high-kcalorie foods and monitor their eating habits.

FIGURE 9-9 Food Record

The entries in a food record should include the times and places of meals and snacks, the types and amounts of foods eaten, and a description of the individual's feelings when eating. The diary should also record physical activities: the kind, the intensity level, the duration, and the person's feelings about them.

Time	Place	Activity or food eaten	People present	Mood
10:30–10:40	School vending machine	6 peanut butter crackers and 12 oz. cola	by myself	starved
12:15–12:30	Restaurant	Sub sandwich and 12 oz. cola	friends	relaxed & friendly
3:00–3:45	Gym	Weight training	work out partner	tired
4:00–4:10	Snack bar	Small frozen yogurt	by myself	OK

them all at once. Attempting too many changes at one time can be overwhelming. Pick one trouble area that is manageable and start there. Practice a desired behavior until it becomes routine. Then select another trouble area to work on, and so on. Another bit of advice along the same lines: don't try to tackle major changes during a particularly stressful time of life.

Personal Attitude For many people, overeating and being overweight have become an integral part of their identity. Those who fully understand their personal relationships with food are best prepared to make healthful changes in eating and exercise behaviors.

Sometimes habitual behaviors that are hazardous to health, such as smoking or drinking alcohol, contribute positively by helping people adapt to stressful situations. Similarly, many people overeat to cope with the stresses of life. To break out of that pattern, they must first identify the particular stressors that trigger the urge to overeat. Then, when faced with these situations, they must learn and practice problem-solving skills that will help them to respond appropriately.[122]

All this is not to imply that psychological therapy holds the magic answer to a weight problem. Still, efforts to improve one's general well-being may result in healthy eating and activity habits even when weight loss is not the primary goal. When the problems that trigger the urge to overeat are resolved in alternative ways, people may find they eat less. They may begin to respond appropriately to internal cues of hunger rather than inappropriately to external cues of stress. Sound emotional health supports a person's ability to take care of physical health in all ways—including nutrition, weight management, and fitness.

Support Groups Group support can prove helpful when making life changes. Some people find it useful to join a group such as Take Off Pounds Sensibly (TOPS), Weight Watchers (WW), Overeaters Anonymous (OA), or others. Some dieters prefer to form their own self-help groups or find support online. The Internet offers numerous opportunities for weight-loss education and counseling that may be effective alternatives to face-to-face programs.[123] As always, consumers need to choose wisely and avoid rip-offs.

IN SUMMARY

A surefire remedy for obesity has yet to be found, although many people find a combination of the approaches just described to be most effective. Diet and exercise shift energy balance so that more energy is being expended than is taken in. Physical activity increases energy expenditure, builds lean tissue, and improves health. Energy intake should be reduced by 500 to 1000 kcalories per day, depending on starting body weight and usual food intake. Behavior modification retrains habits to support a healthy eating and exercise plan. This treatment package requires time, individualization, and sometimes the assistance of a registered dietitian.

Weight Maintenance

People who are successful often experience much of their weight loss within half a year and then reach a plateau. This slowdown can be disappointing, but it should be recognized as an opportunity for the body to adjust to its new weight. Reaching a plateau provides a little relief from the distraction of weight-loss dieting. An appropriate goal at this point is to continue the eating and activity behaviors that will maintain weight. Attempting to lose additional weight at this point would require major effort and would almost certainly meet with failure.

The prevalence of **successful weight-loss maintenance** is difficult to determine, in part because researchers have used different criteria. Some look at success after one year and others after five years; some quantify success as 10 or more pounds lost and others as 5 or 10 percent of initial body weight lost. Furthermore, most research studies examine the success of one episode of weight loss in a structured program, but this scenario does not necessarily reflect the experiences of the general population. In reality, most people have lost weight several times in their lifetimes and did so on their own, not in a formal program. Almost 50 percent of people who intentionally lost weight have successfully maintained the loss for at least a year.[124]

Those who are successful in maintaining their weight loss have established vigorous exercise regimens and careful eating patterns, taking in less energy and a lower percentage of kcalories from fat than the national average.[125] Because these people are more efficient at storing fat, they do not have the same flexibility in their food and activity habits as their friends who have never been overweight. With weight loss, metabolism shifts downward so that formerly overweight people require less energy than might be expected given their current body weight and body composition. Consequently, to keep weight off, they must either eat less or exercise more than people the same size who have never been obese.

Physical activity plays a key role in maintaining weight.[126] Those who exercise vigorously are far more successful than those who are inactive. On average, weight maintenance requires a person to expend about 2000 kcalories in physical activity per week.[127] To accomplish this, a person might exercise either moderately (such as brisk walking) for 60 minutes a day or vigorously (such as fast bicycling) for 35 minutes a day, for example. Being active during both work hours and leisure time also helps a person to maintain weight loss.[128]

© Rick Gomez/Masterfile

Maintaining a healthy body weight requires maintaining the vigorous physical activities and careful eating habits that supported weight loss.

Dietary Guidelines for Americans 2005

To sustain weight loss in adulthood, participate in at least 60 to 90 minutes of moderately intense physical activity daily while not exceeding kcaloric intake requirements. Some people may need to consult with a healthcare provider before participating in this level of activity.

successful weight-loss maintenance: achieving a weight loss of at least 10 percent of initial body weight and maintaining the loss for at least one year.

In addition to limiting energy intake and exercising regularly, one other strategy may help with weight maintenance: frequent self-monitoring. People who weigh themselves periodically and monitor their eating and exercise habits regularly can detect weight gains in the early stages and promptly initiate changes to prevent relapse.[129]

Losing weight and maintaining the loss may not be as easy as gaining the weight in the first place, but it is possible. Those who have been successful find that it gets easier with time—the changes in diet and activity patterns become permanent.[130]

Prevention

Given the information presented up to this point in the chapter, the adage "An ounce of prevention is worth a pound of cure" seems particularly apropos. Preventing weight gain would benefit almost everybody.[131] Obesity is a major risk factor for numerous diseases, and losing weight is challenging and often temporary. Strategies for preventing weight gain ◆ are very similar to those for losing weight, with one exception: they begin early. Over the years, they become an integral part of a person's life. It is much easier for a person to resist doughnuts for breakfast if he rarely eats them. Similarly, a person will have little trouble walking each morning if she has always been active.

◆ To prevent weight gain:
- Eat regular meals and limit snacking.
- Drink water instead of high-kcalorie beverages.
- Select sensible portion sizes and limit daily energy intake to no more than energy expended.
- Become physically active and limit sedentary activities.

Dietary Guidelines for Americans 2005

To prevent gradual weight gain over time, make small decreases in food and beverage kcalories and increase physical activity.

Public Health Programs

Has anyone in the United States *not* heard the message that obesity raises the risks of chronic diseases and that overweight people should aim for a healthy weight by eating sensibly and becoming physically active? Not likely. Yet implementing such advice is difficult in an environment of abundant food and physical inactivity. To successfully treat obesity, we may have to change the environment in which we live through public health law.[132] Table 9-6 provides examples of public health strategies that have been suggested to improve our nation's nutrition environment. Some of these strate-

TABLE 9-6	Suggested Public Health Strategies	
Strategies	Examples of Suggested Nutritional Strategies	Examples of Successful Nonnutritional Strategies
Impose safety standards to reduce the potential for harm.	• Regulate the energy or fat density of foods. • Regulate the size of packages of high-fat foods.	• Mandate safety glass in automobiles. • Regulate the lead content of paint.
Control commercial advertising to limit the influence of harmful products.	• Improve nutrition labeling and product packaging. • Restrict the promotion of high-fat foods (especially when directed at children).	• Restrict cigarette advertising (especially when directed at children). • Add health warnings to alcoholic beverages.
Control the conditions under which products are sold to limit exposure to hazardous substances.	• Remove high-fat, low–nutrient density foods from school vending machines. • Restrict the number of vendors licensed to sell high-fat foods.	• Mandate minimum-age laws for the use of tobacco, alcohol, and automobiles. • Restrict the number of vendors licensed to sell alcohol.
Control prices to reduce consumption.	• Tax soft drinks and other foods high in kcalories, fat, or sugar.	• Tax alcohol and tobacco.

SOURCES: Adapted from L. O. Gostin, Law as a tool to facilitate healthier lifestyles and prevent obesity, *Journal of the American Medical Association* 297 (2007):87–90; M. Nestle and M. F. Jacobson, Halting the obesity epidemic: A public health policy approach, *Public Health Reports* 115 (2000): 12–24.

gies may seem radical, but dramatic measures may be needed if we are to curb the obesity epidemic that is sweeping across the nation.[133] Dozens of bills and resolutions are pending in Congress.[134] Whether changes in public policy—such as a tax on snack foods—will influence diet habits or simply generate revenues remains to be seen.[135]

IN SUMMARY

Preventing weight gains and maintaining weight losses require vigilant attention to diet and physical activity. Taking care of oneself is a lifelong responsibility.

Underweight

Underweight ◆ is a far less prevalent problem than overweight, affecting no more than 5 percent of U.S. adults (review Figure 8-7 on p. 260). Whether the underweight person needs to gain weight is a question of health and, like weight loss, a highly individual matter. People who are healthy at their present weight may stay there; there are no compelling reasons to try to gain weight. Those who are thin because of malnourishment or illness, however, might benefit from a diet that supports weight gain. Medical advice can help make the distinction.

Thin people may find gaining weight difficult. Those who wish to gain weight for appearance's sake or to improve their athletic performance need to be aware that healthful weight gains can be achieved only by physical conditioning combined with high energy intakes. On a high-kcalorie diet alone, a person may gain weight, but it will be mostly fat. Even if the gain improves appearance, it can be detrimental to health and might impair athletic performance. Therefore, in weight gain, as in weight loss, physical activity and energy intake are essential components of a sound plan.

◆ Reminder: *Underweight* is a body weight so low as to have adverse health effects; it is generally defined as BMI <18.5.

Problems of Underweight

The causes of underweight may be as diverse as those of overweight—genetic tendencies, hunger, appetite, and satiety irregularities; psychological traits; and metabolic factors. Habits learned early in childhood, especially food aversions, may perpetuate themselves.

The demand for energy to support physical activity and growth often contributes to underweight. An active, growing boy may need more than 4000 kcalories a day to maintain his weight and may be too busy to take time to eat adequately. Underweight people find it hard to gain weight due, in part, to their expenditure of energy in adaptive thermogenesis. So much energy may be expended adapting to a higher food intake that at first as many as 750 to 800 extra kcalories a day may be needed to gain a pound a week. Like those who want to lose weight, people who want to gain must learn new habits and learn to like new foods. They are also similarly vulnerable to potentially harmful schemes and would be wise to review the consumer bill of rights on p. 290, using "weight gain" instead of "weight loss" where appropriate.

As described in Highlight 8, the underweight condition anorexia nervosa sometimes develops in people who employ self-denial to control their weight. They go to such extremes that they become severely undernourished, achieving final body weights of 70 pounds or even less. The distinguishing feature of a person with anorexia nervosa, as opposed to other underweight people, is that the starvation is intentional. (See Highlight 8 for a review of anorexia nervosa and other eating disorders.)

Weight-Gain Strategies

Weight-gain strategies center on eating energy-dense foods that provide many kcalories in a small volume and exercising to build muscle. By using the USDA Food

Guide recommendations for the higher kcalorie levels (see Table 2-3 on p. 41), a person can gain weight while meeting nutrient needs.

Energy-Dense Foods Energy-dense foods (the very ones eliminated from a successful weight-loss diet) hold the key to weight gain. Pick the highest-kcalorie items from each food group—that is, milk shakes instead of fat-free milk, salmon instead of snapper, avocados instead of cucumbers, a cup of grape juice instead of a small apple, and whole-wheat muffins instead of whole-wheat bread. Because fat provides more than twice as many kcalories per teaspoon as sugar does, fat adds kcalories without adding much bulk.

Although eating high-kcalorie, high-fat foods is not healthy for most people, it may be essential for an underweight individual who needs to gain weight. An underweight person who is physically active and eating a nutritionally adequate diet can afford a few extra kcalories from fat. For health's sake, it is wise to select foods with monounsaturated and polyunsaturated fats instead of those with saturated or *trans* fats: for example, sautéing vegetables in olive oil instead of butter or hydrogenated margarine.

Regular Meals Daily People who are underweight need to make meals a priority and take the time to plan, prepare, and eat each meal. They should eat at least three healthy meals every day and learn to eat more food within the first 20 minutes of a meal. Another suggestion is to eat meaty appetizers or the main course first and leave the soup or salad until later.

Large Portions Underweight people need to learn to eat more food at each meal. For example, they can add extra slices of ham and cheese on the sandwich for lunch, drink milk from a larger glass, and eat cereal from a larger bowl.

The person should expect to feel full. Most underweight individuals are accustomed to small quantities of food. When they begin eating significantly more, they feel uncomfortable. This is normal and passes over time.

Extra Snacks Since a substantially higher energy intake is needed each day, in addition to eating more food at each meal, it is necessary to eat more frequently. Between-meal snacks do not interfere with later meals; they can readily lead to weight gains.[136] For example, a student might make three sandwiches in the morning and eat them between classes in addition to the day's three regular meals. Snacking on dried fruit, nuts, and seeds is also an easy way to add kcalories.

Juice and Milk Beverages provide an easy way to increase energy intake. Consider that 6 cups of cranberry juice add almost 1000 kcalories to the day's intake. kCalories can be added to milk by mixing in powdered milk or packets of instant breakfast.

For people who are underweight due to illness, concentrated liquid formulas are often recommended because a weak person can swallow them easily. A physician or registered dietitian can recommend high-protein, high-kcalorie formulas to help an underweight person maintain or gain weight. Used in addition to regular meals, these supplements can help considerably.

Exercising to Build Muscles To gain weight, use strength training primarily, and increase energy intake to support that exercise. Eating extra food will then support a gain of both muscle and fat. An additional 500 to 1000 kcalories a day above normal energy needs is enough to support the exercise as well as the building of muscle.[137]

IN SUMMARY

Both the incidence of underweight and the health problems associated with it are less prevalent than overweight and its associated problems. To gain weight, a person must train physically and increase energy intake by selecting energy-dense foods, eating regular meals, taking larger portions, and consuming extra snacks and beverages. Table 9-5 (p. 299) includes a summary of weight-gain strategies.

Nutrition Portfolio

ThomsonNOW™
www.thomsonedu.com/thomsonnow

To enjoy good health and maintain a reasonable body weight, combine sensible eating habits and regular physical activity.

■ Calculate your BMI and consider whether you need to lose or gain weight for the sake of good health.

■ Reflect on your weight over the past year or so and explain any weight gains or loses.

■ Describe the potential risks and possible benefits of fad diets and over-the-counter weight-loss drugs or herbal supplements.

NUTRITION ON THE NET

ThomsonNOW™
For further study of topics covered in this chapter, log on to www.thomsonedu .com/thomsonnow. Go to Chapter 9, then to Nutrition on the Net.

• Search for "obesity" and "weight control" at the U.S. Government health information site: www.healthfinder.gov

• Review the Clinical Guidelines on the Identification, Evaluation, and Treatment of Overweight and Obesity in Adults: www.nhlbi.nih.gov/guidelines/obesity/ ob_home.htm

• Learn about the drugs used for weight loss from the Center for Drug Evaluation and Research: www.fda.gov/cder

• Learn about weight control and the WIN program from the Weight-control Information Network: www.win.niddk.nih.gov

• Visit weight-loss support groups, such as Take Off Pounds Sensibly (TOPS), Overeaters Anonymous (OA), and Weight Watchers: www.tops.org, www.oa.org, and www .weightwatchers.com

• See what the obesity professionals think at the North American Association for the Study of Obesity and the

• American Society for Bariatric Surgery: www.naaso.org and www.asbs.org

• Consider the nondietary approaches of HUGS International: www.hugs.com

• Learn about the 10,000 Step Program from Shape Up America!: www.shapeup.org/10000steps.html

• Find helpful information on achieving and maintaining a healthy weight from the Calorie Control Council: www.caloriecontrol.org

• Learn how to end size discrimination and improve the quality of life for fat people from the National Association to Advance Fat Acceptance: www.naafa.org

• Find good advice on starting a weight-loss program from the Partnership for Healthy Weight Management: www.consumer.gov/weightloss

• Consider ways to live a healthy life at any weight: www.bodypositive.com

NUTRITION CALCULATIONS

ThomsonNOW™ For additional practice log on to www.thomsonedu.com/thomsonnow. Go to Chapter 9, then to Nutrition Calculations.

These problems give you practice in doing simple energy-balance calculations (see p. 314 for answers). Once you have mastered these examples, you will be prepared to examine your own food choices. Be sure to show your calculations for each problem.

1. Critique a commercial weight-loss plan. Consumers spend billions of dollars a year on weight-loss programs such as Slim-Fast, Sweet Success, Weight Watchers, Nutri/System, Jenny Craig, Optifast, Medifast, and Formula One. One

such plan calls for a milk shake in the morning, at noon, and as an afternoon snack and "a sensible, balanced, low-fat dinner" in the evening. One shake mixed in 8 ounces of vitamin A- and D-fortified fat-free milk offers 190 kcalories; 32 grams of carbohydrate, 13 grams of protein, and 1 gram of fat; at least one-third of the Daily Value for all vitamins and minerals; plus 2 grams of fiber.

   a. Calculate the kcalories and grams of carbohydrate, protein, and fat that three shakes provide.

b. How do these values compare with the criteria listed in item 2 in Table H9-4 on p. 320?

c. Plan "a sensible, balanced, low-fat dinner" that will help make this weight-loss plan adequate and balanced. Now, how do the day's totals compare with the criteria in item 2 in Table H9-4 on p. 320?

d. Critique this plan using the other criteria described in Table H9-4 on p. 320 as a guide.

2. Evaluate a weight-gain attempt. People attempting to gain weight sometimes have a hard time because they choose low-kcalorie, high-bulk foods that make it hard to consume enough energy. Consider the following lunch: a chef's salad consisting of 2 cups iceberg lettuce, 1 whole tomato, 1 ounce swiss cheese, 1 ounce roasted ham (extra lean), 1 hard-boiled egg, ½ cup grated carrots, and ¼ cup Thousand Island salad dressing. If you weighed these foods, you'd find that they totaled 442 grams. This is a pretty filling meal.

a. The meal provides 459 kcalories. What is the energy density of this meal, expressed in kcalories per gram?

b. To gain weight, this person is advised to eat an additional 500 kcalories at this meal. Using foods with this same energy density, how much more chef's salad will this person have to eat?

c. Suppose a person simply can't do this. Try to reduce the bulk of this meal by replacing some of the lettuce with more energy-dense foods. Delete 1 cup lettuce from the salad and add another ounce roast ham and 1 ounce cheddar cheese. Show how these changes influence the weight and kcalories of this meal. (Use Appendix H.)

Item No./Food	Weight (g)	Energy (kcal)
Original totals:	442	459
Minus:		
#5083 Lettuce, 1 c	−	−
Plus:		
#12212 Roast ham, 1 oz	+	+
#1007 Cheddar cheese, 1 oz	+	+
Totals:		

d. How many kcalories did the changes add?

e. How much more *weight* of food did these changes add?

This exercise should reveal why people attempting to gain weight are advised to add high-fat items, within reason, to their daily meals.

STUDY QUESTIONS

These questions will help you review the chapter. You will find the answers in the discussions on the pages provided.

1. Describe how body fat develops, and suggest some reasons why it is difficult for an obese person to maintain weight loss. (pp. 282–283)

2. What factors contribute to obesity? (pp. 283–288)

3. List several aggressive ways to treat obesity, and explain why such methods are not recommended for every overweight person. (pp. 292–293)

4. Discuss reasonable dietary strategies for achieving and maintaining a healthy body weight. (pp. 294–299)

5. What are the benefits of increased physical activity in a weight-loss program? (pp. 299–302)

6. Describe the behavioral strategies for changing an individual's dietary habits. What role does personal attitude play? (pp. 303–305)

7. Describe strategies for successful weight gain. (pp. 307–308)

These multiple choice questions will help you prepare for an exam. Answers can be found on p. 314.

1. With weight loss, fat cells:
   a. decrease in size only.
   b. decrease in number only.
   c. decrease in both number and size.
   d. decrease in number, but increase in size.

2. Obesity is caused by:
   a. overeating.
   b. inactivity.
   c. defective genes.
   d. multiple factors.

3. The protein produced by the fat cells under the direction of the *ob* gene is called:
   a. leptin.
   b. serotonin.
   c. sibutramine.
   d. phentermine.

4. The biggest problem associated with the use of drugs in the treatment of obesity is:
   a. cost.
   b. chronic dosage.
   c. ineffectiveness.
   d. adverse side effects.

5. A realistic goal for weight loss is to reduce body weight:
   a. down to the weight a person was at age 25.
   b. down to the ideal weight in the weight-for-height tables.
   c. by 10 percent over six months.
   d. by 15 percent over three months.

6. A nutritionally sound weight-loss diet might restrict daily energy intake to create a:
   a. 1000-kcalorie-per-month deficit.
   b. 500-kcalorie-per-month deficit.
   c. 500-kcalorie-per-day deficit.
   d. 3500-kcalorie-per-day deficit.

7. Successful weight loss depends on:
   a. avoiding fats and limiting water.
   b. taking supplements and drinking water.
   c. increasing proteins and restricting carbohydrates.
   d. reducing energy intake and increasing physical activity.

8. Physical activity does *not* help a person to:
   a. lose weight.
   b. retain muscle.
   c. maintain weight loss.
   d. lose fat in trouble spots.

9. Which strategy would *not* help an overweight person to lose weight?
   a. Exercise.
   b. Eat slowly.
   c. Limit high-fat foods.
   d. Eat energy-dense foods regularly.

10. Which strategy would *not* help an underweight person to gain weight?
   a. Exercise.
   b. Drink plenty of water.
   c. Eat snacks between meals.
   d. Eat large portions of foods.

REFERENCES

1. State-specific prevalence of obesity among adults—United States, 2005, *Morbidity and Mortality Weekly Report* 55 (2006): 985-988; C. L. Ogden and coauthors, Prevalence of overweight and obesity in the United States, 1999-2004, *Journal of the American Medical Association* 295 (2006): 1549-1555.
2. Ogden and coauthors, 2006; National Center for Health Statistics, *Chartbook on Trends in the Health of Americans, 2005*, www.cdc.gov/nchs, site visited on January 18, 2006.
3. Ogden and coauthors, 2006.
4. T. E. Kottke, L. A. Wu, and R. S. Hoffman, Economic and psychological implications of the obesity epidemic, *Mayo Clinic Proceedings* 78 (2003): 92-94; M. Kohn and M. Booth, The worldwide epidemic of obesity in adolescents, *Adolescent Medicine* 14 (2003): 1-9; G. du Toit and M. T. van der Merwe, The epidemic of childhood obesity, *South African Medical Journal* 93 (2003): 49-50; C. J. Schrodt, The obesity epidemic and physician responsibility, *Journal of the Kentucky Medical Association* 101 (2003): 27-28.
5. E. D. Rosen, The molecular control of adipogenesis with special reference to lymphatic pathology, *Annals of the New York Academy of Sciences* 979 (2002): 143-158.
6. J. E. Schaffer, Lipotoxicity: When tissues overeat, *Current Opinion in Lipidology* 14 (2003): 281-287.
7. R. J. F. Loos and T. Rankinen, Gene-diet interactions on body weight changes, *Journal of the American Dietetic Association* 105 (2005): S29-S34; S. Tholin and coauthors, Genetic and environmental influences on eating behavior: The Swedish Young Male Twins Study, *American Journal of Clinical Nutrition* 81 (2005): 564-569.
8. T. Rankinen and C. Bouchard, Genetics of food intake and eating behavior phenotypes in humans, *Annual Review of Nutrition* 26 (2006): 413-434; H. N. Lyon and J. N. Hirschhorn, Genetics of common forms of obesity: A brief overview, *American Journal of Clinical Nutrition* 82 (2005): 215S-217S.
9. H. K. Tiwari and coauthors, Is GAD2 on chromosome 10p12 a potential candidate gene for morbid obesity? *Nutrition Reviews* 63 (2005): 315-319; L. Bouchard and coauthors, Neuromedin: A strong candidate gene linking eating behaviors and susceptibility to obesity, *American Journal of Clinical Nutrition* 80 (2004): 1478-1486; E. Suviolahti and coauthors, The SLC6A14 gene shows evidence of association with obesity, *Journal of Clinical Investigation* 112 (2003): 1762-1772; D. E. Cummings and M. W. Schwartz, Genetics and pathophysiology of human obesity, *Annual Reviews of Medicine* 54 (2003): 453-471.

10. C. Pico and coauthors, Gastric leptin: A putative role in the short-term regulation of food intake, *British Journal of Nutrition* 90 (2003): 735-741.
11. S. O'Rahilly and coauthors, Minireview: Human obesity—Lessons from monogenic disorders, *Endocrinology* 144 (2003): 3757-3764.
12. A. M. Prentice and coauthors, Leptin and undernutrition, *Nutrition Reviews* 60 (2002): S56-S67.
13. J. Harvey and M. L. Ashford, Leptin in the CNS: Much more than a satiety signal, *Neuropharmacology* 44 (2003): 845-854.
14. P. Fietta, Focus on leptin, a pleiotropic hormone, *Minerva Medica* 96 (2005): 65-75; S. Takeda, F. Elefteriou, and G. Karsenty, Common endocrine control of body weight, reproduction, and bone mass, *Annual Review of Nutrition* 23 (2003): 403-411.
15. S. Shalitin and M. Phillip, Role of obesity and leptin in the pubertal process and pubertal growth-A review, *International Journal of Obesity Related Metabolic Disorders* 27 (2003): 869-874.
16. V. Popovic and L. H. Duntas, Brain somatic cross-talk: Ghrelin, leptin, and ultimate challengers of obesity, *Nutritional Neuroscience* 8 (2005): 1-5; J. Williams and S. Mobarhan, A critical interaction: Leptin and ghrelin, *Nutrition Reviews* 61 (2003): 391-393.
17. M. Kojima and K. Kangawa, Ghrelin, an orexigenic signaling molecule from the gastrointestinal tract, *Current Opinion in Pharmacology* 2 (2002): 665-668.
18. D. E. Cummings, K. E. Foster-Schubert, and J. Overduin, Ghrelin and energy balance: Focus on current controversies, *Current Drug Targets* 6 (2005): 153-169; J. Eisenstein and A. Greenberg, Ghrelin: Update 2003, *Nutrition Reviews* 61 (2003): 101-104; O. Ukkola and S. Poykko, Ghrelin, growth and obesity, *Annals of Medicine* 34 (2002): 102-108.
19. H. S. Callahan and coauthors, Postprandial suppression of plasma ghrelin level is proportional to ingested caloric load but does not predict intermeal interval in humans, *Journal of Clinical Endocrinology and Metabolism* 89 (2003): 1319-1324; G. Schaller and coauthors, Plasma ghrelin concentrations are not regulated by glucose or insulin: A double-blind, placebo-controlled crossover clamp study, *Diabetes* 52 (2003): 16-20; G. Iniguez and coauthors, Fasting and post-glucose ghrelin levels in SGA infants: Relationships with size and weight gain at one year of age, *Journal of Clinical Endocrinology and Metabolism* 87 (2002): 5830-5833.
20. M. Tanaka and coauthors, Habitual binge/purge behavior influences circulating ghrelin levels in eating disorders, *Journal of*

Psychiatric Research 37 (2003): 17-22; J. H. Lindeman and coauthors, Ghrelin and the hyposomatotropism of obesity, *Obesity Research* 10 (2002): 1161-1166.
21. M. Tanaka and coauthors, Effect of nutritional rehabilitation on circulating ghrelin and growth hormone levels in patients with anorexia nervosa, *Regulatory Peptides* 122 (2004): 163-168; V. Tolle and coauthors, Balance in ghrelin and leptin plasma levels in anorexia nervosa patients and constitutionally thin women, *Journal of Clinical Endocrinology and Metabolism* 88 (2003): 109-116; M. F. Saad and coauthors, Insulin regulates plasma ghrelin concentration, *Journal of Clinical Endocrinology and Metabolism* 87 (2002): 3997-4000.
22. A. M. Haqq and coauthors, Serum ghrelin levels are inversely correlated with body mass index, age, and insulin concentrations in normal children and are markedly increased in Prader-Willi syndrome, *Journal of Clinical Endocrinology and Metabolism* 88 (2003): 174-178; A. DelParigi and coauthors, High circulating ghrelin: A potential cause for hyperphagia and obesity in Prader-Willi syndrome, *Journal of Clinical Endocrinology and Metabolism* 87 (2002): 5461-5464.
23. A. Geliebter, M. E. Gluck, and S. A. Hashim, Plasma ghrelin concentrations are lower in binge-eating disorder, *Journal of Nutrition* 135 (2005): 1326-1330; P. J. English and coauthors, Food fails to suppress ghrelin levels in obese humans, *Journal of Clinical Endocrinology and Metabolism* 87 (2002): 2984.
24. D. E. Cummings and coauthors, Plasma ghrelin levels after diet-induced weight loss or gastric bypass surgery, *New England Journal of Medicine* 346 (2002): 1623-1630.
25. Cummings, Foster-Schubert, and Overduin, 2005.
26. Cummings, Foster-Schubert, and Overduin, 2005.
27. Iniguez and coauthors, 2002.
28. J. Korner and R. L. Leibel, To eat or not to eat—How the gut talks to the brain, *New England Journal of Medicine* 349 (2003): 926-930.
29. R. L. Batterham and coauthors, Inhibition of food intake in obese subjects by peptide YY3-36, *New England Journal of Medicine* 349 (2003): 941-948.
30. J. Orr and B. Davy, Dietary influences on peripheral hormones regulating energy intake: Potential applications for weight management, *Journal of the American Dietetic Association* 105 (2005): 1115-1124.
31. F. Broglio and coauthors, Ghrelin: Endocrine and non-endocrine actions, *Journal of Pediatric Endocrinology and Metabolism* 15 (2002): 1219-1227.

32. J. C. Weikel and coauthors, Ghrelin promotes slow-wave sleep in humans, American Journal of Physiology. *Endocrinology and Metabolism* 284 (2003): E407-E415.

33. N. D. Kohatsu and coauthors, Sleep duration and body mass index in rural population, *Archives of Internal Medicine* 166 (2006): 1701-1705; R. D. Verona and coauthors, Overweight and obese patients in a primary care population report less sleep than patients with a normal body mass index, *Archives of Internal Medicine* 165 (2005): 25-34; K. Spiegel and coauthors, Sleep curtailment in healthy young men is associated with decreased leptin levels, elevated ghrelin levels, and increased hunger and appetite, *Annals of Internal Medicine* 141 (2004): 846-850; G. Hasler and coauthors, The association between short sleep duration and obesity in young adults: A 13-year prospective study, *Sleep* 27 (2004): 661-666.

34. P. Hamet and J. Tremblay, Genetics of sleep-wake cycles and its disorders, *Metabolism* 55 (2006): S7-S12.

35. A. S. Avram, M. M. Avram, and W. D. James, Subcutaneous fat in normal and diseased states: 2. Anatomy and physiology of white and brown adipose tissue, *Journal of the American Academy of Dermatology* 53 (2005): 671-673.

36. P. Trayhurn, The biology of obesity, *Proceedings of the Nutrition Society* 64 (2005): 31-38; J. S. Kim-Han and L. L. Dugan, Mitochondrial uncoupling proteins in the central nervous system, *Antioxidants and Redox Signaling* 7 (2005): 1173-1181; R. J. F. Roos and T. Rankinen, Gene-diet interactions on body weight changes, *Journal of the American Dietetic Association* 105 (2005): S29-S34.

37. P. Laurberg, S. Andersen, and J. Karmisholt, Cold adaptation and thyroid hormone metabolism, *Hormone and Metabolic Research* 37 (2005): 545-549.

38. Avram, Avram, and James, 2005.

39. D. Ricquier, Respiration uncoupling and metabolism in the control of energy expenditure, *Proceedings of the Nutrition Society* 64 (2005): 47-52; W. D. van Marken Lichtenbelt and H. A. Daanen, Cold-induced metabolism, *Current Opinion in Clinical Nutrition and Metabolic Care* 6 (2003): 469-475.

40. S. Y. S. Kimm and coauthors, Racial differences in the relation between uncoupling protein genes and resting energy expenditure, *American Journal of Clinical Nutrition* 75 (2002): 714-719.

41. Y. Ma and coauthors, Association between eating patterns and obesity in a free-living US adult population, *American Journal of Epidemiology* 158 (2003): 85-92.

42. J. Maurer and coauthors, The psychological and behavioral characteristics related to energy misreporting, *Nutrition Reviews* 64 (2006): 53-66.

43. J. C. Peters, The challenge of managing body weight in the modern world, *Asia Pacific Journal of Clinical Nutrition* 11 (2002): S714-S717.

44. B. Wansink and J. Kim, Bad popcorn in big buckets: Portion size can influence intake as much as taste, *Journal of Nutrition Education and Behavior* 37 (2005): 242-245.

45. B. J. Rolls, E. L. Morris, and L. S. Roe, Portion size of food affects energy intake in normal-weight and overweight men and women, *American Journal of Clinical Nutrition* 76 (2002): 1207-1213.

46. S. J. Nielsen and B. M. Popkin, Patterns and trends in food portion sizes, 1977-1998, *Journal of the American Medical Association* 289 (2003): 450-453; H. Smiciklas-Wright and coauthors, Foods commonly eaten in the United States, 1989-1991 and 1994-1996: Are portion sizes changing? *Journal of the American Dietetic Association* 103 (2003): 41-47.

47. L. R. Young and M. Nestle, Expanding portion sizes in the US marketplace: Implications for nutrition counseling, *Journal of the American Dietetic Association* 103 (2003): 231-234.

48. L. R. Young and M. Nestle, The contribution of expanding portion sizes to the US obesity epidemic, *American Journal of Public Health* 92 (2002): 246-249.

49. J. E. Tillotson, America's obesity: Conflicting public policies, industrial economic development, and unintended human consequences, *Annual Review of Nutrition* 24 (2004): 617-643; Y. Ma and coauthors, Association between eating patterns and obesity in a free-living US adult population, *American Journal of Epidemiology* 158 (2003): 85-92.

50. S. A. Bowman and B. T. Vinyard, Fast food consumption of U.S. adults: Impact on energy and nutrient intakes and overweight status, *Journal of the American College of Nutrition* 23 (2004): 163-168; S. Paeratakul and coauthors, Fast-food consumption among US adults and children: Dietary and nutrient intake profile, *Journal of the American Dietetic Association* 103 (2003): 1332-1338.

51. B. J. Rolls, L. S. Roe, and J. S. Meengs, Reductions in portion size and energy density of foods are additive and lead to sustained decreases in energy intake, *American Journal of Clinical Nutrition* 83 (2006): 11-17; T. V. E. Kral, L. S. Roe, and B. J. Rolls, Combined effects of energy density and portion size on energy intake in women, *American Journal of Clinical Nutrition* 79 (2004): 962-968.

52. B. J. Rolls, The supersizing of America: Portion size and the obesity epidemic, *Nutrition Today* 38 (2003): 42-53.

53. A. Drewnowski and N. Darmon, The economics of obesity: Dietary energy density and energy cost, *American Journal of Clinical Nutrition* 82 (2005): 265S-273S.

54. C. H. Powers and M. A. Hess, A message to the restaurant industry: It's time to "step up to the plate," *Journal of the American Dietetic Association* 103 (2003): 1136-1138.

55. K. M. Booth, M. M. Pinkston, and W. S. C. Poston, Obesity and the built environment, *Journal of the American Dietetic Association* 105 (2005): S110-S117.

56. M. Lahti-Koski and coauthors, Associations of body mass index and obesity with physical activity, food choices, alcohol intake, and smoking in the 1982-1997 FINRISK Studies, *American Journal of Clinical Nutrition* 75 (2002): 809-817.

57. F. B. Hu and coauthors, Television watching and other sedentary behaviors in relation to risk of obesity and type 2 diabetes mellitus in women, *Journal of the American Medical Association* 289 (2003): 1785-1791.

58. J. A. Levine and coauthors, Interindividual variation in posture allocation: Possible role in human obesity, *Science* 307 (2005): 584-586.

59. *U.S. News and World Report,* June 16, 2003, p. 36; www.niddk.nih.gov/healthnutrit/pubs/statobes.htm.

60. R. F. Kushner and D. J. Blatner, Risk assessment of the overweight and obese patient, *Journal of the American Dietetic Association* 105 (2005): S53-S62; National Institutes of Health Obesity Education Initiative, *The Practical Guide: Identification, Evaluation, and Treatment of Overweight and Obesity in Adults,* NIH publication no. 00-4084 (Washington, D.C.: U.S. Department of Health and Human Services, 2000).

61. National Institutes of Health Obesity Education Initiative, 2000.

62. N. S. Wellman and B. Friedberg, Causes and consequences of adult obesity: Health, social and economic impacts in the United States, *Asia Pacific Journal of Clinical Nutrition* 11 (2002): S705-S709.

63. P. G. Shekelle and coauthors, Efficacy and safety of ephedra and ephedrine for weight loss and athletic performance: A meta-analysis, *Journal of the American Medical Association* 289 (2003): 1537-1545.

64. J. T. Dwyer, D. B. Allison, and P. M. Coates, Dietary supplements in weight reduction, *Journal of the American Dietetic Association* 105 (2005): S80-S86; R. B. Saper, D. M. Eisenberg, and R. S. Phillips, Common dietary supplements for weight loss, *American Family Physician* 70 (2004): 1731-1738; United States General Accounting Office, *Dietary Supplements for Weight Loss,* July 31, 2002.

65. S. P. Dolan and coauthors, Analysis of dietary supplements for arsenic, cadmium, mercury, and lead using inductively coupled plasma mass spectrometry, *Journal of Agricultural and Food Chemistry* 51 (2003): 1307-1312; A. H. Feifer, N. E. Fleshner, and L. Klotz, Analytical accuracy and reliability of commonly used nutritional supplements in prostate disease, *Journal of Urology* 168 (2002): 150-154.

66. S. Z. Yanovski and J. A. Yanovski, Obesity, *New England Journal of Medicine* 346 (2002): 591-602.

67. K. M. McTigue and coauthors, Screening and interventions for obesity in adults: Summary of the evidence for the U.S. Preventive Services Task Force, *Annals of Internal Medicine* 139 (2003): 933-949.

68. S. Schurgin and R. D. Siegel, Pharmacotherapy of obesity: An update, *Nutrition in Clinical Care* 6 (2003): 27-37.

69. S. B. Moyers, Medications as adjunct therapy for weight loss: Approved and off-label agents in use, *Journal of the American Dietetic Association* 105 (2005): 948-959.

70. R. Steinbrook, Surgery for severe obesity, *New England Journal of Medicine* 350 (2004): 1075-1079.

71. Cummings, Foster-Schubert, and Overduin, 2005.

72. G. L. Blackburn, Solutions in weight control: Lessons from gastric surgery, *American Journal of Clinical Nutrition* 82 (2005): 248S-252S; H. Buchwald and coauthors, Bariatric surgery: A systematic review and meta-analysis, *Journal of the American Medical Association* 292 (2004): 1724-1737.

73. E. N. Hansen, A. Torquati, and N. N. Abumrad, Results of bariatric surgery, *Annual Review of Nutrition* 26 (2006): 481-511; L. Sjöström and coauthors, Lifestyle, diabetes, and cardiovascular risk factors 10 years after bariatric surgery, *New England Journal of Medicine* 351 (2004): 2683-2693; Buchwald and coauthors, 2004.

74. S. E. Barlow, Bariatric surgery in adolescents: For treatment failures or health care system failures? *Pediatrics* 114 (2004): 252-253; H. Buchwald, Surgery for severely obese adolescents: Further insight from the American Society for Bariatric Surgery, *Pediatrics* 114 (2004): 253-254; B. M. Rodgers, Bariatric surgery for adolescents: A view from the American Pediatric Surgical Association, *Pediatrics* 144 (2004): 255-256.

75. T. H. Inge and coauthors, Bariatric surgery for severely overweight adolescents: Concerns and recommendations, *Pediatrics* 114 (2004): 217-223.

76. M. Shah, V. Simha, and A. Garg, Long-term impact of bariatric surgery on body weight, co-morbidities, and nutritional status: A review, *Journal of Clinical Endocrinology and Metabolism,* September 5, 2006.

77. R. E. Brolin, Bariatric surgery and long-term control of morbid obesity, *Journal of the American Medical Association* 288 (2002): 2793-2796.

78. S. Klein and coauthors, Absence of an effect of liposuction on insulin action and risk factors for coronary heart disease, *New England Journal of Medicine* 350 (2004): 2549-2557.

79. C. A. Nonas and G. D. Foster, Setting achievable goals for weight loss, *Journal of the American Dietetic Association* 105 (2005): S118-S123.

80. G. D. Foster and coauthors, Obese patients' perceptions of treatment outcomes and the factors that influence them, *Archives of Internal Medicine* 161 (2001): 2133-2139.

81. National Institutes of Health Obesity Education Initiative, 2000, p. 2.

82. Position of the American Dietetic Association: Weight management, *Journal of the American Dietetic Association* 102 (2002): 1145-1155.

83. National Institutes of Health Obesity Education Initiative, 2000, pp. 26-27.

84. J. T. Dwyer, D. B. Allison, and P. M. Coates, Dietary supplements in weight reduction, *Journal of the American Dietetic Association* 105 (2005): S80-S86.

85. Nielsen and Popkin, 2003; Smiciklas-Wright and coauthors, 2003; Young and Nestle, 2002.

86. B. J. Rolls and coauthors, Increasing the portion size of a sandwich increases energy intake, *Journal of the American Dietetic Association* 104 (2004): 367-372.

87. B. Wansink and J. Kim, Bad popcorn in big buckets: Portion size can influence intake as much as taste, *Journal of Nutrition Education and Behavior* 37 (2005): 242-245.

88. M. P. Mattson, Energy intake, meal frequency, and health: A neurobiological perspective, *Annual Review of Nutrition* 25 (2005): 237-260; T. V. Kral, L. S. Roe, and B. J. Rolls, Does nutrition information about the energy density of meals affect food intake in normal-weight women? *Appetite* 39 (2002): 137-145.

89. J. A. Ello-Martin, J. H. Ledikwe, and B. J. Rolls, The influence of food portion size and energy density on energy intake: Implications for weight management, *American Journal of Clinical Nutrition* 82 (2005): 236S-241S.

90. B. J. Rolls, A. Drewnowski, and J. H. Ledikwe, Changing the energy density of the diet as a strategy for weight management, *Journal of the American Dietetic Association* 105 (2005): S98-S103.

91. J. H. Ledikwe and coauthors, Low-energy-density diets are associated with high diet quality in adults in the United States, *Journal of the American Dietetic Association* 106 (2006): 1172-1180.

92. B. M. Popkin and coauthors, A new proposed guidance system for beverage consumption in the United States, *American Journal of Clinical Nutrition* 83 (2006): 529-542.

93. S. A. Bowman and J. T. Spence, A comparison of low-carbohydrate vs. high-carbohydrate diets: Energy restriction, nutrient quality and correlation to body mass index, *Journal of the American College of Nutrition* 21 (2002): 268-274.

94. B. J. Rolls, J. A. Ello-Martin, and B. C. Tohill, What can intervention studies tell us about the relationship between fruit and vegetable consumption and weight management? *Nutrition Reviews* 62 (2004): 1-17.

95. A. Astrup and coauthors, Low-fat diets and energy balance: How does the evidence stand in 2002? *Proceedings of the Nutrition Society* 61 (2002): 299-309; S. D. Poppitt and coauthors, Long-term effects of ad libitum low-fat, high-carbohydrate diets on weight and serum lipids in overweight subjects with metabolic syndrome, *American Journal of Clinical Nutrition* 75 (2002): 11-20.

96. G. D. Foster and coauthors, A randomized trial of a low-carbohydrate diet for obesity, *New England Journal of Medicine* 348 (2003): 2082-2090.

97. D. K. Layman and coauthors, A reduced ratio of dietary carbohydrate to protein improves body composition and blood lipid profiles during weight loss in adult women, *Journal of Nutrition* 133 (2003): 411-417; D. M. Bravata and coauthors, Efficacy and safety of low-carbohydrate diets, *Journal of the American Medical Association* 289 (2003): 1837-1850; S. Pirozzo and coauthors, Advice on low-fat diets for obesity, *Cochrane Database of Systematic Review* (2002), available at www.update-software.com/abstracts/ab003640.htm.

98. Astrup and coauthors, 2002.

99. J. M. Jakicic and A. D. Otto, Treatment and prevention of obesity: What is the role of exercise? *Nutrition Reviews* 64 (2006): S57-S61.

100. J. Kruger and coauthors, Physical activity profiles of U.S. adults trying to lose weight: NHIS 1998, *Medicine and Science in Sports and Exercise* 37 (2005): 364-368.

101. Committee on Dietary Reference Intakes, *Dietary Reference Intakes for Energy, Carbohydrate, Fiber, Fat, Fatty Acids, Cholesterol, Protein, and Amino Acids,* (Washington, D.C.: National Academies Press, 2002/2005).

102. L. L. Frank and coauthors, Effects of exercise on metabolic risk variables in overweight postmenopausal women: A randomized clinical trial, *Obesity Research* 13 (2005): 615-625; J. F. Carroll and C. K. Kyser, Exercise training in obesity lowers blood pressure independent of weight change, *Medicine and Science in Sports and Exercise* 34 (2002): 596-601; B. Gutin and coauthors, Effects of exercise intensity on cardiovascular fitness, total body composition, and visceral adiposity of obese adolescents, *American Journal of Clinical Nutrition* 75 (2002): 818-826.

103. C. A. Holcomb, D. L. Heim, and T. M. Loughin, Physical activity minimizes the association of body fatness with abdominal obesity in white, premenopausal women: Results from the Third National Health and Nutrition Examination Survey, *Journal of the American Dietetic Association* 104 (2004): 1859-1862; Gutin and coauthors, 2002.

104. M. Pomerleau and coauthors, Effects of exercise intensity on food intake and appetite in women, *American Journal of Clinical Nutrition* 80 (2004): 1230-1236.

105. R. W. Jeffery and coauthors, Physical activity and weight loss: Does prescribing higher physical activity goals improve outcome? *American Journal of Clinical Nutrition* 78 (2003): 684-689; C. A. Slentz and coauthors, Effects of the amount of exercise on body weight, body composition, and measures of central obesity: STRRIDE—A randomized controlled study, *Archives of Internal Medicine* 164 (2004): 31-39.

106. D. L. Thompson, J. Rakow, and S. M. Perdue, Relationship between accumulated walking and body composition in middle-aged women, *Medicine and Science in Sports and Exercise* 36 (2004): 911-914; H. R. Wyatt and coauthors, A Colorado statewide survey of walking and its relation to excessive weight, *Medicine and Science in Sports and Exercise* 37 (2005): 724-730.

107. B. Wansink, Environmental factors that increase the food intake and consumption volume of unknowing consumers, *Annual Review of Nutrition* 24 (2004): 455-479.

108. N. Stroebele and J. M. DeCastro, Effect of ambience on food intake and food choice, *Nutrition* 20 (2004): 821-838.

109. B. Wansink, J. E. Painter, and Y. K. Lee, The office candy dish: Proximity's influence on estimated and actual consumption, *International Journal of Obesity* 30 (2006): 871-875.

110. P. Pliner and coauthors, Meal duration mediates the effect of "social facilitation" on eating in humans, *Appetite* 46 (2006): 189-198.

111. J. M. Poothullil, Recognition of oral sensory satisfaction and regulation of the volume of intake in humans, *Nutritional Neuroscience* 8 (2005): 245-250.

112. Wansink, Painter, and Lee, 2006.

113. B. E. Kahn and B. Wansink, The influence of assortment structure on perceived variety and consumption quantities, *Journal of Consumer Research* 30 (2004): 519-533.

114. M. M. Hetherington and coauthors, Understanding variety: Tasting different foods delays satiation, *Physiology and Behavior* 87 (2006): 263-271.

115. S. J. Nielsen and B. M. Popkin, Patterns and trends in food portion sizes, 1977-1998, *Journal of the American Medical Association* 289 (2003): 450-453; H. Smiciklas-Wright and coauthors, Foods commonly eaten in the United States, 1989-1991 and 1994-1996: Are portion sizes changing? *Journal of the American Dietetic Association* 103 (2003): 41-47; L. R. Young and M. Nestle, Expanding portion sizes in the US marketplace: Implications for nutrition counseling, *Journal of the American Dietetic Association* 103 (2003): 231-234;

116. B. J. Rolls and coauthors, Increasing the portion size of a packaged snack increases energy intake in men and women, *Appetite* 42 (2004): 63-69.

117. B. Wansink, J. E. Painter, and J. North, Bottomless bowls: Why visual cues of portion size may influence intake, *Obesity Research* 13 (2005): 93-100.

118. B. Wansink and M. M. Cheney, Super bowls: Serving bowl size and food consumption, *Journal of the American Medical Association* 293 (2005): 1727-1728.

120. B. Wansink, K. van Ittersum, and J. E. Painter, Ice cream illusions bowls, spoons, and self-served portion sizes, *American Journal of Preventive Medicine* 31 (2006): 240-243; B. Wansink and K. van Ittersum, Shape of glass and amount of alcohol poured: Comparative study of effect of practice and concentration, *British Medical Journal* 331 (2005): 1512-1514.

121. L. A. Berkel and coauthors, Behavioral interventions for obesity, *Journal of the American Dietetic Association* 105 (2005): S35-S43; G. D. Foster, A. P. Makris, and B. A. Bailer, Behavioral treatment of obesity, *American Journal of Clinical Nutrition* 82 (2005): 230S-235S.

122. S. M. Byrne, Psychological aspects of weight maintenance and relapse in obesity, *Journal of Psychosomatic Research* 53 (2002): 1029-1036.

123. D. F. Tate, E. H. Jackvony, and R. R. Wing, Effects of Internet behavioral counseling on weight loss in adults at risk for type 2 diabetes: A randomized trial, *Journal of the American Medical Association* 289 (2003): 1833-1836.

124. G. L. Blackburn, and B. A. Waltman, Expanding the limits of treatment—New strategic initiatives, *Journal of the American Dietetic Association* 105 (2005): S131-S135.

125. M. S. Leser, S. Z. Yanovski, and J. A. Yanovski, A low-fat intake and greater activity level are associated with lower weight regain 3 years after completing a very-low-calorie diet, *Journal of the American Dietetic Association* 102 (2002): 1252-1256.

126. R. L. Weinsier and coauthors, Free-living activity energy expenditure in women successful and unsuccessful at maintaining a normal body weight, *American Journal of Clinical Nutrition* 75 (2002): 499-504.

127. American College of Sports Medicine, 2001.
128. M. A. van Baak and coauthors, Leisure-time activity is an important determinant of long-term weight maintenance after weight loss in the Sibutramine Trial on Obesity Reduction and Maintenance (STORM trial), *American Journal of Clinical Nutrition* 78 (2003): 209-214.
129. R. R. Wing and coauthors, A self-regulation program for maintenance of weight loss, *New England Journal of Medicine* 355 (2006): 1563-1571.
130. R. R. Wing and S. Phelan, Long-term weight loss maintenance, *American Journal of Clinical Nutrition* 82 (2005): 222S-225S.
131. J. O. Hill, H. Thompson, and H. Wyatt, Weight maintenance: What's missing? *Journal of the American Dietetic Association* 105 (2005): S63-S66.

132. L. O. Gostin, Law as a tool to facilitate healthier lifestyles and prevent obesity, *Journal of the American Medical Association* 297 (2007): 87-90; M. M. Mello, D. M. Studdert, and T. A. Brennan, Obesity—The new frontier of public health law, *New England Journal of Medicine* 354 (2006): 2601-2610; R. E. Killingsworth, Health promoting community design: A new paradigm to promote healthy and active communities, *American Journal of Health Promotion* 17 (2003): 169-170.
133. S. L. Mercer and coauthors, Possible lessons from the tobacco experience for obesity control, *American Journal of Clinical Nutrition* 77 (2003): 1073S-1082S.
134. R. Smith, Passing an effective obesity bill, *Journal of the American Dietetic Association* 106 (2006): 1349-1350.

135. F. Kuchler, A. Tegene, and J. M. Harris, Taxing snack foods: What to expect for diet and tax revenues, *Current Issues in Economics of Food Markets,* Agriculture Information Bulletin No. 747-08, August 2004.
136. C. Marmonier and coauthors, Snacks consumed in a nonhungry state have poor satiating efficiency: Influence of snack composition on substrate utilization and hunger, *American Journal of Clinical Nutrition* 76 (2002): 518-528.
137. Position Paper: Nutrition and athletic performance—Position of the American Dietetic Association, Dietitians of Canada, and the American College of Sports Medicine, *Journal of the American Dietetic Association* 100 (2000): 1543-1556.

ANSWERS

Nutrition Calculations

1. a. Three milk shakes provide: 3 × 190 kcal = 570 kcal; 3 × 32 g carbohydrate = 96 g carbohydrate; 3 × 13 g protein = 39 g protein; and 3 × 1 g fat = 3 g fat.

   b. To meet this criteria, the plan needs *at least* an additional 430 kcalories (1000 kcal − 570 kcal = 430 kcal); an additional 7 to 17 grams of protein, depending on the person's RDA based on gender and age (56 g − 39 g = 17 g and 46 g − 39 g = 7 g); an additional 4 grams of carbohydrate (100 g − 96 g = 4 g); and some additional fat.

   c. Of course, there are many possible dinners that you could plan. One might be:

   Salad made with 1 c lettuce, 1 c chopped tomatoes and onions, ¼ c garbanzo beans, and 2 tbs low-fat dressing
   4 oz grilled chicken
   1 medium baked potato
   1 c summer squash and zucchini
   1 c melon cubes

   This meal brings the day's totals to 1215 kcalories, 90 g of protein, 192 g of carbohydrate, and 13 g of fat, which meets the goals for kcalories, protein, and carbohydrate. Because the milk shake has been fortified, all vitamin and mineral needs are covered as well. The only possible dietary shortcoming is that the day's percent kcalories from fat is low (only 10%), but because energy and nutrient recommendations have been met and the goal is weight loss, this may be acceptable.

   d. This weight-loss plan uses a liquid formula rather than foods, making clients dependent on a special device (the formula) rather than teaching them how to make good choices from the conventional food supply. It provides no information about dropout rates, the long-term success of clients, or weight maintenance after the program ends.

2. a. 459 kcal ÷ 442 g = 1.04 kcal/g

   b. More than another whole salad (1.04 kcal/g × 500 kcal = 520 g)

   c.

Item No./Food	Weight (g)	Energy (kcal)
Original totals:	442	459
Minus:		
#5083 Lettuce, 1 c	−55	−6
Plus:		
#12212 Roast ham, 1 oz	+28	+41
#1007 Cheddar cheese, 1 oz	+28	+113
Totals:	443 g	607 kcal

   d. 607 kcal − 459 kcal = 148 kcal added

   e. 443 g − 442 g = 1 g added

Study Questions (multiple choice)

1. a   2. d   3. a   4. d   5. c   6. c   7. d   8. d
9. d   10. b

The Latest and Greatest Weight-Loss Diet—Again

To paraphrase William Shakespeare, "a fad diet by any other name would still be a fad diet." And the names are legion: the Atkins Diet, the Calories Don't Count diet, the Protein Power diet, the Carbohydrate Addict's diet, the Lo-Carbo diet, the South Beach diet, the Zone diet.* Year after year, "new and improved" diets appear on bookstore shelves and circulate among friends. People of all sizes eagerly try the best diet on the market ever, hoping that this one will really work. Sometimes these diets seem to work for a while, but more often than not, their success is short-lived. Then another diet takes the spotlight. Here's how Dr. K. Brownell, an obesity researcher at Yale University, describes this phenomenon: "When I get calls about the latest diet fad, I imagine a trick birthday cake candle that keeps lighting up and we have to keep blowing it out."

Realizing that fad diets do not offer a safe and effective plan for weight loss, health professionals speak out, but they never get the candle blown out permanently. New fad diets can keep making outrageous claims because no one requires their advocates to prove what they say. Fad diet gurus do not have to conduct credible research on the benefits or dangers of their diets. They can simply make recommendations and then later, if questioned, search for bits and pieces of research that support the conclusions they have already reached. That's backwards. Diet and health recommendations should *follow* years of sound research that has been reviewed by panels of scientists *before* being offered to the public.

Because anyone can publish anything—in books or on the Internet—peddlers of fad diets can make unsubstantiated statements that fall far short of the truth but sound impressive to the uninformed. They often offer distorted bits of legitimate research. They may start with one or more actual facts but then leap from one erroneous conclusion to the next. Anyone who wants to believe these claims has to wonder how the thousands of scientists working on obesity research over the past century could possibly have missed such obvious connections. Table H9-1 (p. 316) presents some of the claims and truths of fad diets.

Fad diets come in almost as many shapes and sizes as the people who search them out. Some restrict fats or carbohydrates, some limit portion sizes, some focus on food combinations, and some claim that a person's genetic type or blood type determines the foods best suited to manage weight and prevent disease. Table H9-2 (p. 317) compares some of today's more popular diets. Regardless of their names, many popular diets espouse a carbohydrate-restricted or carbohydrate-modified diet. Some diets claim that all or some types of carbohydrates are bad. Some go so far as to equate carbohydrates with toxic poisons or addictive drugs. "Bad" carbohydrates—such as sugar, white flour, and potatoes—are considered evil because they are absorbed easily and raise blood glucose. The pancreas then responds by secreting insulin—and insulin is touted as the real villain responsible for our nation's epidemic of obesity. Whether restricting overall carbohydrate intake or replacing certain "bad" carbohydrates with "good" carbohydrates, these diets tend to overemphasize protein. This highlight examines some of the science and the science fiction behind a few carbohydrate-restricted or carbohydrate-modified, high-protein fad diets.

The Diet's Appeal

Perhaps the greatest appeal of fad diets such as the Atkins Diet is that it turns nutrient recommendations upside down. Foods such as meats and milk products that need to be selected carefully to limit saturated fat can be eaten with abandon on this diet. Grains, legumes, vegetables, and fruits that consumers are told to eat in abundance can now be ignored. For some people, this is a dream come true: steaks without the potatoes, ribs without the coleslaw, and meatballs without the pasta. Who can resist the promise of weight loss while eating freely from a list of favorite foods?

To lure dieters in, proponents of fad diets often blame current recommendations for our obesity troubles. They claim that the incidence of obesity is rising because we are eating less fat. Such a claim may impress the naive, but it sends skeptical people running for the facts. True, the incidence of obesity has risen dramatically over the past two decades.[1] True, our intake of fat has dropped from 35 to 33 percent of daily energy intake.[2] Such facts might seem to imply that lowering fat intake leads to obesity, but this is an erroneous conclusion. The *percentage* declined only because average energy intakes increased by almost 200 kcalories a

---

* The following sources offer comparisons and evaluations of various fad diets for your review: Battle of the diet books II, *Nutrition Action Healthletter,* July/August 2006, pp. 10–11; B. Liebman, Weighing the diet books, *Nutrition Action Healthletter,* January/February 2004, pp. 1–8; S. T. St. Jeor and coauthors, Dietary protein and weight reduction: A statement for healthcare professionals from the nutrition committee of the Council on Nutrition, Physical Activity, and Metabolism of the American Heart Association, *Circulation* 104 (2001): 1869–1874.

TABLE H9-1 The Claims and Truths of Fad Diets

The Claim:	You can lose weight "easily."
The Truth:	Most fad diet plans have complicated rules that require you to calculate protein requirements, count carbohydrate grams, combine certain foods, time meal intervals, purchase special products, plan daily menus, and measure serving sizes.
The Claim:	You can lose weight by eating a specific ratio of carbohydrates, protein, and fat.
The Truth:	Weight loss depends on spending more energy than you take in, not on the proportion of energy nutrients.
The Claim:	This "revolutionary diet" can "reset your genetic code."
The Truth:	You inherited your genes and cannot alter your genetic code.
The Claim:	High-protein diets are popular, selling more than 20 million books, because they work.
The Truth:	Weight-loss books are popular because people grasp for quick fixes and simple solutions to their weight problems. If book sales were an indication of weight-loss success, we would be a lean nation—but they're not, and neither are we.
The Claim:	People gain weight on low-fat diets.
The Truth:	People can gain weight on low-fat diets if they overindulge in carbohydrates and proteins while cutting fat; low-fat diets are not necessarily low-kcalorie diets. But people can also lose weight on low-fat diets if they cut kcalories as well as fat.
The Claim:	High-protein diets energize the brain.
The Truth:	The brain depends on glucose for its energy; the primary dietary source of glucose is carbohydrate, not protein.
The Claim:	Thousands of people have been successful with this plan.
The Truth:	Authors of fad diets have not published their research findings in scientific journals. Success stories are anecdotal and failures are not reported.
The Claim:	Carbohydrates raise blood glucose levels, triggering insulin production and fat storage.
The Truth:	Insulin promotes fat storage when energy intake exceeds energy needs. Furthermore, insulin is only one hormone involved in the complex processes of maintaining the body's energy balance and health.
The Claim:	Eat protein and lose weight.
The Truth:	For every complicated problem, there is a simple—and wrong—solution.

Low-carbohydrate meals overemphasize meat, fish, poultry, eggs, and cheeses, and shun breads, pastas, fruits, and vegetables.

Matthew Farruggio

day (from 1878 kcalories a day to 2056). Actual fat intake *increased* by 3 grams a day (from 73 grams to 76). Furthermore, fewer than half of us engage in regular physical activity.[3] Obesity experts blame our high energy intakes and low energy outputs for the increase in obesity. Weight loss, after all, depends on a negative energy balance. To their credit, some of these diet plans recommend exercise—and regular physical activity is an integral component of successful weight loss.[4]

Dieters are also lured into fad diets by sophisticated—yet often erroneous—explanations of the metabolic consequences of eating certain foods. Terms such as *eicosanoids* and *de novo lipogen-*

esis are scattered about, often intimidating readers into believing that the authors must be right given their brilliance in understanding the body. Several of the latest fad diets hold *insulin* responsible for the obesity problem and the *glycemic index* as the weight loss solution. Yet, among nutrition researchers, controversy continues to surround the questions of whether insulin promotes weight gain or a low-glycemic diet fosters weight loss.[5]

What does insulin do? Among its roles, insulin facilitates the transport of glucose into the cells, the storage of fatty acids as fat, and the synthesis of cholesterol. It is an anabolic hormone that builds and stores. True—but there's more to the story. Insulin is only one of many factors involved in the body's metabolism of nutrients and regulation of body weight. Furthermore, as Chapter 4's discussion of the glycemic index pointed out, blood glucose and insulin do not always respond to foods as might be expected. The glycemic effect of a food depends on how the food is ripened, processed, and cooked; the time of day the food is eaten; the other foods eaten with it; and the presence or absence of certain diseases such as type 2 diabetes in the person eating the food.[6] Thus the glycemic effect of a particular food varies—fad diet books mislead people by claiming that each food has a set glycemic effect. Many carbohydrates—fruits, vegetables, legumes, and whole grains—are rich in fibers that slow glucose absorption and moderate insulin response. Furthermore, there is no clear evidence that elevated blood insulin concentrations promote weight gain in healthy people or that foods with a low glycemic effect promote weight loss.[7] A review of the evidence thus far concludes that the ideal long-term study has not yet been conducted.[8]

Most importantly, insulin is critical to maintaining health, as any person with type 1 diabetes can attest. Insulin causes problems only when a person develops insulin resistance—that is, when the body's cells do not respond to the large quantities of insulin that the pancreas continues to pump out in an effort to get a response. Insulin resistance is a major health problem—but it is not caused by carbohydrate, or by protein, or by fat. It results from being overweight. When a person loses weight, insulin response improves.

TABLE H9-2 Popular Diets Compared

Diet	Major Premise Promoted	Strong Point(s)	Weak Point(s)
High Carbohydrate, Low-Fat			
Ornish Diet	• By strictly limiting fat (both animal and vegetable), you eat fewer kcalories without eating less food.	• High-fiber, low-fat foods in this plan can lower blood cholesterol and blood pressure.	• So little fat that essential fatty acids may be lacking. • Limits fish, nuts, and olive oil which may protect against heart disease.
Pritikin Program	• By eating low-fat, mainly plant-based foods, you can eat more food and still feel satisfied.	• No food group is completely eliminated in this high-fiber, low-fat diet program. • Some use of foods rich in omega-3 fatty acids are encouraged.	• For some people, very low-fat diets may be unsatisfying and therefore difficult to adhere to.
Low-Carbohydrate, High Protein			
Atkins Diet	• People are overweight or obese because they have metabolic imbalances caused by eating too many carbohydrates; by restricting carbohydrates, these imbalances can be corrected. • You can lose weight without lowering kcalorie intake.	• Quick, short-term weight loss is achieved.	• Restricts carbohydrates to a level that induces ketosis. • Ketosis can cause nausea, light-headedness, and fatigue. • Ketosis can worsen existing medical problems such as kidney disease. • A diet high in fat such as Atkins can increase the risk of heart disease and some cancers.
Low-Carbohydrate			
Zone Diet	• Eating the correct proportions of carbohydrates, fat, and protein leads to hormonal balance, weight loss, disease prevention, and increased vitality.	• Promotes weight loss because it is a low-kcalorie diet.	• The diet is rigid, restrictive, and complicated, making it difficult for most people to follow accurately. • The overblown health claims of the diet's proponents are based on misinterpreted science and remain unsubstantiated.
Carbohydrate-Modified			
South Beach Diet	• Eating "good carbohdrates" such as vegetables, whole-wheat pastas, and brown rice will maintain satiety and resist cravings for "bad carbohydrates" such as white rice and potatoes.	• Encourages consumption of vegetables, lean meats, and fish, and the use of unsaturated oils when cooking. • Restricts fatty meats and cheeses as well as sweets.	• Starchy carbohydrates and all fruits are completely excluded during the first two weeks.
The Ultimate Weight Solution Diet	• Foods that require great effort to prepare and eat are nutrient-dense; eating these kinds of foods (raw vegetables, vegetable soups, whole grains, beans, meats, poultry, and fish) will lead to weight loss. • Foods that take little effort to prepare and eat provide excess kcalories relative to nutrients; eating these kinds of foods (fast foods, puddings, high-kcalorie convenience foods, processed foods) leads to uncontrolled eating and weight gain.	• Encourages consumption of lean meats and fish; whole grains; vegetables; fruit; and low-fat milk, yogurt, and cheese. • Restricts fatty meats and cheeses as well as sweets. • Encourages exercise.	• Confusing as to exactly what to eat or how much.
Metabolic Type			
Eat Right 4 Your Type	• Your blood type determines which foods you should eat or not eat.	None	• Food groups or individual foods are excluded, depending on blood type. • No scientific data on the relationship between blood type and food choices.

Another distortion of the facts is the claim that high-protein foods expend more energy. As Chapter 8 mentioned, the thermic effect of food for protein is higher than for carbohydrate or fat, but the increase is still insignificant—perhaps the equivalent of two pounds per year, at most.

If low-carbohydrate, high-protein diets were as successful as some people claim, then consumers who tried them would lose weight, and their obesity problems would be solved. But this is not the case. Similarly, if high-protein diets were as worthless as others claim, then consumers would eventually stop pursuing them. Clearly, this is not happening either. These diets have enough going for them that they work for some people at least for a short time, but they fail to produce long-lasting results for most people. Studies report that people following high-protein, low-carbohydrate diets do lose weight.[9] In fact, they lose more than people following conventional high-carbohydrate, low-fat diets—but only for the first six months. Their later gains make up the difference, so total weight loss is no different after one year.[10] The following sections examine some of the apparent achievements and shortcomings of high-protein diets.[11]

The Diet's Achievements

With over half of our nation's adults overweight and many more concerned about their weight, the market for a weight-loss book, product, or program is huge (no pun intended). Americans spend an estimated $33 billion a year on weight-loss books and products. Even a plan that offers only minimal weight-loss success easily attracts a following. Carbohydrate-modified and high-protein, low-carbohydrate diet plans offer a little success to some people for a short time. Here's why.

Don't Count kCalories

Who wants to count kcalories? Even experienced dieters find counting kcalories burdensome, not to mention timeworn. They want a new, easy way to lose weight, and high-protein diet plans seem to offer this boon. But, though these diets often claim to disregard kcalories, their design typically ensures a low energy intake. Most of the sample menu plans provided by these diets, especially in the early stages, are designed to deliver an average of 1200 kcalories a day.

Even when counting kcalories is truly not necessary, the total for these diets tends to be low simply because food intake is so limited. Without its refried beans, tortilla wrapping, and chopped vegetables, a burrito is reduced to a pile of ground beef. Without the baked potato, there's no need for butter and sour cream. Weight loss occurs because of the low energy intake—not the proportion of energy nutrients.[12] Success, then, depends on the restricted intake, not on protein's magical powers or carbohydrate's evil forces. This is an important point. Any diet can produce weight loss, at least temporarily, if intake is restricted. The real value of a diet is determined by its ability to maintain weight loss and support good health over the long term. The goal is not simply weight loss, but health gains—and whether carbohydrate-modified or high-protein, low-carbohydrate diets can support optimal health over time remains unknown.

Satisfy Hunger

Protein may promote weight loss by providing satiety.[13] As Chapter 8 mentioned, of the three energy-yielding nutrients, protein is the most satiating. High-protein meals suppress hunger and delay the start of the next meal. Furthermore, people tend to eat less after a high-protein meal than after a low-protein one. In one study, when protein intake increased from 15 percent of total energy to 30 percent but carbohydrate was held constant at 50 percent of total energy, people decreased their energy intakes and lost body weight and body fat.[14] This research suggests that less emphasis should be placed on carbohydrate restriction.

In real-life situations, there is a strong association between a person's protein intake and BMI—the higher the intake, the higher the BMI.[15] This association remains apparent even after adjusting for energy intake and physical activity. All meals—whether designed for weight loss or not—should include enough protein to satisfy hunger, but not so much as to contribute to weight gain.

Follow a Plan

Most people need specific instructions and examples to make dietary changes. Popular diets offer dieters a plan. The user doesn't have to decide what foods to eat, how to prepare them, or how much to eat. Unfortunately, these instructions only serve short-term weight-loss needs. They do not provide for long-term changes in lifestyle that will support weight maintenance or health goals.

The success of any weight-loss diet depends on the person adopting the plan and sticking with it. People who prefer the high-protein, low-carbohydrate diet over the high-carbohydrate, low-fat diet may have more success at sticking with it. Again, weight loss occurs because of the duration of a low-kcalorie plan—not the proportion of energy nutrients.[16]

Limit Choices

Diets that omit hundreds of foods and several food groups limit a person's options and lack variety. Chapter 2 praised variety as a valuable way to ensure an adequate intake of nutrients, but variety also entices people to eat more food and gain more weight. Without variety, some people lose interest in eating, which further reduces energy intake. Even if the allowed foods are favorites, eating the same foods week after week can become monotonous.

The Diet's Shortcomings

Most of the foods that fad diets promote are healthy foods—lean meats, fat-free or low-fat milk and yogurt, vegetables, whole grains, beans, and fruit. The *Dietary Guidelines for Americans 2005* encourage consumers to eat the same foods. The *Dietary Guidelines* also advise consumers to eat less saturated fat, however, and some carbohydrate-restricted or carbohydrate-modified diets can be high in saturated fat. Like some of the carbohydrate-modified diets, the *Dietary Guidelines* also encourage people to eat a diet high in fiber-rich carbohydrate foods. Fad diet claims that people lose weight because they switch from eating "bad" carbohydrates to eating "good" ones, however, are misleading; in truth, people lose weight on these diets because they are eating fewer kcalories not because they are eating different kinds of kcalories. Still, people who have followed carbohydrate-restricted or carbohydrate-modified diet plans for several months have lost weight. Can these diets be harmful?

Too Much Fat

Some fad diets focus so intently on promoting protein and curbing carbohydrate that they fail to account for the fat that accompanies many high-protein foods. A breakfast of bacon and eggs, lunch of ham and cheese, and dinner of barbecued short ribs would provide 100 grams of protein—and 121 grams of fat! Yet this day's meals, even with a snack of peanuts, provide only 1600 kcalories. Without careful selection, protein-rich diets can be extraordinarily high in saturated fat and cholesterol—dietary factors that raise LDL cholesterol and the risks for heart disease.

Overall, studies report that people following high-protein, low-carbohydrate diets have little or no change in blood pressure or blood lipids—risk factors for heart disease.[17] Some researchers speculate that the weight loss that occurs on these diets offsets the adverse effects of a diet high in saturated fat and low in fruits and vegetables.[18] Others point out that different sources of protein have different effects on risk factors for heart disease.[19] For example, the effects of white meat from chicken or fish differ from those of red meat. Diets containing large amounts of red meat appear to increase the risk of heart disease. In contrast, replacing animal sources of protein with plant sources of protein may benefit health.

Too Much Protein

Moderation has been a recurring theme throughout this text, with recommendations to get enough, but not too much of anything, and cautions that too much can be as harmful as too little. Too much protein can contribute to weight gain just as too much carbohydrate or fat can. As mentioned earlier, protein intake is positively associated with BMI.[20] The DRI Committee did not establish an upper level for protein, but it does recognize that high-protein diets have been implicated in chronic diseases such as osteoporosis, kidney stones and kidney disease, some cancers, heart disease, and obesity.[21] Health recommendations typically advise a protein intake of 50 to 100 grams per day and within the range of 10 to 35 percent of energy intake.[22] This range allows for flexibility without risk of harm. By comparison, popular high-protein diets suggest a protein intake of 70 to 160 grams per day, representing 25 to 65 percent of energy intake.[23]

Guidelines from the DRI committee include higher protein intakes (10 to 35 percent of total energy) than recommended previously, but long-term studies of high-protein intakes are needed to ascertain the health consequences of such diets. One such study is currently under way: The DiOGenes (Diet, Obesity, and Genes) project is examining the interactions among a high dietary protein intake, the glycemic effect of foods, and genetic and behavioral factors in preventing weight gain and regain.[24] The study focuses on about 700 overweight or obese adults and their children in eight different countries across Europe and may involve the United States as well.

Too Little Everything Else

The quality of the diet suffers when carbohydrates are restricted.[25] Without fruits, vegetables, and whole grains, high-protein diets lack not only carbohydrate, but fiber, vitamins, minerals, and phytochemicals as well—all dietary factors protective against disease.[26] To help shore up some of these inadequacies, fad diets often recommend a dietary supplement. Conveniently, many of the companies selling fad diets also peddle these supplements. But as Highlights 10 and 11 explain, foods offer many more health benefits than any supplement can provide. Quite simply, if the diet is inadequate, it needs to be improved, not supplemented.

The Body's Perspective

When a person consumes a low-carbohydrate diet, a metabolism similar to that of fasting prevails. (See Chapter 7 for a review of fasting.) With little dietary carbohydrate coming in, the body uses its glycogen stores to provide glucose for the cells of the brain, nerves, and blood. Once the body depletes its glycogen reserves, it begins making glucose from the amino acids of protein (gluconeogenesis). A low-carbohydrate diet may provide abundant protein from food, but the body still uses some protein from body tissues.

Dieters can know glycogen depletion has occurred and gluconeogenesis has begun by monitoring their urine. Whenever glycogen or protein is broken down, water is released and urine production increases. Low-carbohydrate diets also induce ketosis, and ketones can be detected in the urine. Ketones form whenever glucose is lacking and fat breakdown is incomplete.

Many fad diets regard ketosis as the key to losing weight, but studies comparing weight-loss diets find no relation between ketosis and weight loss.[27] People in ketosis may experience a loss of

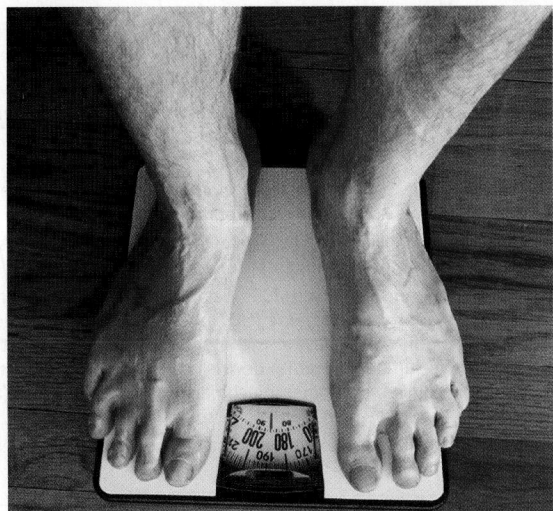

The wise consumer distinguishes between loss of fat and loss of weight.

TABLE H9-3 Adverse Side Effects of Low-Carbohydrate, Ketogenic Diets

- Nausea
- Fatigue (especially if physically active)
- Constipation
- Low blood pressure
- Elevated uric acid (which may exacerbate kidney disease and cause inflammation of the joints in those predisposed to gout)
- Stale, foul taste in the mouth (bad breath)
- In pregnant women, fetal harm and stillbirth

appetite and a dramatic weight loss within the first few days. They should know that much of this weight loss reflects the loss of glycogen and protein together with large quantities of body fluids and important minerals.[28] They need to appreciate the difference between loss of *fat* and loss of *weight*. Fat losses on ketogenic diets are no greater than on other diets providing the same number of kcalories. Once the dieter returns to well-balanced meals that provide adequate energy, carbohydrate, fat, protein, vitamins, and minerals, the body avidly retains these needed nutrients. The weight will return, quite often to a level higher than the starting point. Table H9-3 lists other consequences of a ketogenic diet.

Table H9-4 offers guidelines for identifying fad diets and other weight-loss scams; it includes the hallmarks of a reasonable weight-loss program as well. Diets that overemphasize protein and fall short on carbohydrate may not harm healthy people if used for only a little while, but they cannot support optimal health for long. Chapter 9 includes reasonable approaches to weight management and concludes that the ideal diet is one you can live with for the rest of your life. Keep that criterion in mind when you evaluate the next "latest and greatest weight-loss diet" that comes along.

TABLE H9-4 Guidelines for Identifying Fad Diets and Other Weight-Loss Scams

Fad Diets and Weight-Loss Scams

1. They promise dramatic, rapid weight loss.
2. They promote diets that are nutritionally unbalanced or extremely low in kcalories.

3. They use liquid formulas rather than foods.

4. They attempt to make clients dependent upon special foods or devices.

5. They fail to encourage permanent, realistic lifestyle changes.

6. They misrepresent salespeople as "counselors" supposedly qualified to give guidance in nutrition and/or general health.

7. They collect large sums of money at the start or require that clients sign contracts for expensive, long-term programs.

8. They fail to inform clients of the risks associated with weight loss in general or the specific program being promoted.
9. They promote unproven or spurious weight-loss aids such as human chorionic gonadotropin hormone (HCG), starch blockers, diuretics, sauna belts, body wraps, passive exercise, ear stapling, acupuncture, electric muscle-stimulating (EMS) devices, spirulina, amino acid supplements (e.g. arginine, ornithine), glucomannan, methylcellulose (a "bulking agent"), "unique" ingredients, and so forth.
10. They fail to provide for weight maintenance after the program ends.

Healthy Diet Guidelines

1. Weight loss should be gradual and not exceed 2 pounds per week.
2. Diets should provide:
   - A reasonable number of kcalories (not fewer than 1000 kcalories per day for women and 1200 kcalories per day for men)
   - Enough, but not too much, protein (between the RDA and twice the RDA)
   - Enough, but not too much, fat (between 20 and 35% of daily energy intake from fat)
   - Enough carbohydrates to spare protein and prevent ketosis (at least 100 grams per day) and 20 to 30 grams of fiber from food sources
   - A balanced assortment of vitamins and minerals from a variety of foods from each of the food groups
   - At least 1 liter (about 1 quart) of water daily or 1 milliliter per kcalorie daily—whichever is more.
3. Foods should accommodate a person's ethnic background, taste preferences, and financial means.
4. Programs should teach clients how to make good choices from the conventional food supply.
5. Programs should teach physical activity plans that involve spending at least 300 kcalories a day and behavior-modification strategies that help to correct poor eating habits.
6. Even if adequately trained, such "counselors" would still be objectionable because of the obvious conflict of interest that exists when providers profit directly from products they recommend and sell.
7. Programs should be reasonably priced and run on a pay-as-you-go basis.

8. They should provide information about dropout rates, the long-term success of their clients, and possible diet side effects.
9. They should focus on nutrient-rich foods and regular excercise.

10. They should provide a plan for weight maintenance after successful weight loss.

SOURCES: Adapted from American College of Sports Medicine, *ACSM's Guidelines for Exercise Testing and Prescription* (Baltimore: Williams & Wilkins, 1995), pp. 218–219; J. T. Dwyer, Treatment of obesity: Conventional programs and fad diets, in *Obesity*, ed. P. Björntorp and B.N. Brodoff (Philadelphia: J.B. Lippincott, 1992), p. 668; *National Council Against Health Fraud Newsletter*, March/April 1987, National Council Against Health Fraud, Inc.

NUTRITION ON THE NET

ThomsonNOW™

For furthur study of topics covered in this Highlight, log on to **www .thomsonedu.com/thomsonnow**. Go to Chapter 9, then to Highlights Nutrition on the Net.

- Search for the Great Nutrition Debate at the USDA's site: **www.usda.gov**

REFERENCES

1. C. L. Ogden and coauthors, Prevalence of overweight and obesity in the United States, 1999-2004, *Journal of the American Medical Association* 295 (2006): 1549-1555.
2. P. Chanmugam and coauthors, Did fat intake in the United States really decline between 1989-1991 and 1994-1996? *Journal of the American Dietetic Association* 103 (2003): 867-872.
3. P. M. Barnes and C. A. Schoenborn, *Physical Activity among Adults: United States, 2000,* 2003, available at www.cdc.gov/nchs/ about/major/nhis/released200306.htm#7.
4. J. M. Jakicic and A. D. Otto, Physical activity considerations for the treatment and prevention of obesity, *American Journal of Clinical Nutrition* 82 (2005): 226S-229S.
5. R. Clemens and P. Pressman, Clinical value of glycemic index unclear, *Food Technology* 58 (2004): 18; M. A. Pereira and coauthors, Effects of a low-glycemic load diet on resting energy expenditure and heart disease risk factors during weight loss, *Journal of the American Medical Association* 292 (2004): 2482-2490; A. Raben, Should obese patients be counselled to follow a low-glycaemic index diet? No, *Obesity Reviews* 3 (2002): 245-256; D. B. Pawlak, C. B. Ebbeling, and D. S. Ludwig, Should obese patients be counselled to follow a low-glycaemic index diet? Yes, *Obesity Reviews* 3 (2002): 235-243.
6. F. X. Pi-Sunyer, Glycemic index and disease, *American Journal of Clinical Nutrition* 76 (2002): 290S-298S.
7. Pi-Sunyer, 2002.
8. A. G. Pittas and S. B. Roberts, Dietary composition and weight loss: Can we individualize dietary prescriptions according to insulin sensitivity or secretion status? *Nutrition Reviews* 64 (2006): 435-448; Raben, 2002.
9. A. Astrup, T. M. Larsen, and A. Harper, Atkins and other low-carbohydrate diets: Hoax or an effective tool for weight loss? *The Lancet* 364 (2004): 897-899; E. C. Westman and coauthors, Effect of 6-month adherence to a very low carbohydrate diet program, *American Journal of Medicine* 113 (2002): 30-36.
10. L. Stern and coauthors, The effects of low-carbohydrate versus conventional weight loss diets in severely obese adults: One-year follow-up of a randomized trial, *Annals of Internal Medicine* 140 (2004): 778-785; G. D. Foster and coauthors, A randomized trial of a low-carbohydrate diet for obesity, *New England Journal of Medicine* 348 (2003): 2082-2090.
11. J. Eisenstein and coauthors, High-protein weight-loss diets: Are they safe and do they work? A review of the experimental and epidemiologic data, *Nutrition Reviews* 60 (2002): 189-200.
12. D. K. Layman and coauthors, A reduced ratio of dietary carbohydrate to protein improves body composition and blood lipid profiles during weight loss in adult women, *Journal of Nutrition* 133 (2003): 411-417; D. M. Bravata and coauthors, Efficacy and safety of low-carbohydrate diets, *Journal of the American Medical Association* 289 (2003): 1837-1850.
13. D. A. Schoeller and A. C. Buchholz, Energetics of obesity and weight control: Does diet composition matter? *Journal of the American Dietetic Association* 105 (2005): S24-S28; S. M. Nickols-Richardson and coauthors, Perceived hunger is lower and weight loss is greater in overweight premenopausal women consuming a low-carbohydrate/ high-protein vs high-carbohydrate/low-fat diet, *Journal of the American Dietetic Association* 105 (2005): 1433-1437.
14. D. S. Weigle and coauthors, A high-protein diet induces sustained reductions in appetite, ad libitum caloric intake, and body weight despite compensatory changes in diurnal plasma leptin and ghrelin concentrations, *American Journal of Clinical Nutrition* 82 (2005): 41-48.
15. A. Trichopoulou and coauthors, Lipid, protein and carbohydrate intake in relation to body mass index, *European Journal of Clinical Nutrition* 56 (2002): 37-43.
16. Bravata and coauthors, 2003.
17. Bravata and coauthors, 2003.
18. Foster and coauthors, 2003.
19. F. B. Hu, Protein, body weight, and cardiovascular health, *American Journal of Clinical Nutrition* 82 (2005): 242S-247S.
20. A. Trichopoulou and coauthors, Lipid, protein and carbohydrate intake in relation to body mass index, *European Journal of Clinical Nutrition* 56 (2002): 37-43.
21. Committee on Dietary Reference Intakes, *Dietary Reference Intakes for Energy, Carbohydrate, Fiber, Fat, Fatty Acids, Cholesterol, Protein, and Amino Acids* (Washington, D.C.: National Academies Press, 2002/2005).
22. Committee on Dietary Reference Intakes, 2002/2005; S. T. St. Jeor and coauthors, Dietary protein and weight reduction: A statement for healthcare professionals from the nutrition committee of the Council on Nutrition, Physical Activity, and Metabolism of the American Heart Association, *Circulation* 104 (2001): 1869-1874.
23. St. Jeor and coauthors, 2001.
24. W. H. M. Saris and A. Harper, DiOGenes: A multidisciplinary offensive focused on the obesity epidemic, *Obesity Reviews* 6 (2005): 175-176.
25. L. S. Greene-Finestone and coauthors, Adolescents' low-carbohydrate-density diets are related to poorer dietary intakes, *Journal of the American Dietetic Association* 105 (2005): 1783-1788; E. T. Kennedy and coauthors, Popular diets: Correlation to health, nutrition, and obesity, *Journal of the American Dietetic Association* 101 (2001): 411-420.
26. W. Cunningham and D. Hyson, The skinny on high-protein, low-carbohydrate diets, *Preventive Cardiology* 9 (2006): 166-171.
27. M. D. Coleman and S. M. Nickols-Richardson, Urinary ketones reflect serum ketone concentration but do not relate weight loss in overweight premenopausal women following a low-carbohydrate/high-protein diet, *Journal of the American Dietetic Association* 105 (2005): 608-611; Foster and coauthors, 2003.
28. St. Jeor and coauthors, 2001.

Thomson™ NOW! Throughout this chapter, the ThomsonNOW logo indicates an opportunity for online self-study, linking you to interactive tutorials and videos based on your level of understanding.

www.thomsonedu.com/thomsonnow

Figure 10-1: Animated! Coenzyme Action

Figure 10-13: Animated! Metabolic Pathways Involving B Vitamins

How To: Practice Problems

Nutrition Portfolio Journal

Nutrition Calculations: Practice Problems

Nutrition in Your Life

If you were playing a word game and your partner said "vitamins," how would you respond? If "pills" and "supplements" immediately come to mind, you may be missing the main message of the vitamin story—that hundreds of foods deliver over a dozen vitamins that participate in thousands of activities throughout your body. Quite simply, foods supply vitamins to support all that you are and all that you do—and supplements of any one of them, or even a combination of them, can't compete with foods in keeping you healthy.

The Water Soluble Vitamins: B Vitamins and Vitamin C

CHAPTER OUTLINE

The Vitamins—An Overview

The B Vitamins—As Individuals • Thiamin • Riboflavin • Niacin • Biotin • Pantothentic Acid • Vitamin B₆ • Folate • Vitamin B₁₂ • Non-B Vitamins

The B Vitamins—In Concert • B Vitamin Roles • B Vitamin Deficiencies • B Vitamin Toxicities • B Vitamin Food Sources

Vitamin C • Vitamin C Roles • Vitamin C Recommendations • Vitamin C Deficiency • Vitamin C Toxicity • Vitamin C Food Sources

HIGHLIGHT 10 Vitamin and Mineral Supplements

Earlier chapters focused on the energy-yielding nutrients, which play leading roles in the body. The vitamins and minerals are their supporting cast. This chapter begins with an overview of the vitamins and then examines each of the water-soluble vitamins and a nonvitamin relative named choline; the next chapter features the fat-soluble vitamins. Chapters 12 and 13 present the minerals.

The Vitamins—An Overview

Researchers first recognized that foods contain substances that are "vital to life" in the early 1900s. Since then, the world of vitamins has opened up dramatically. The vitamins ◆ are powerful substances, as their *absence* attests. Vitamin A deficiency can cause blindness; a lack of the B vitamin niacin can cause dementia; and a lack of vitamin D can retard bone growth. The consequences of deficiencies are so dire, and the effects of restoring the needed vitamins so dramatic, that people spend billions of dollars every year in the belief that vitamin pills will cure a host of ailments (see Highlight 10). Vitamins certainly support sound nutritional health, but they do not cure all ills. Furthermore, vitamin supplements do not offer the many benefits that come from vitamin-rich foods.

The *presence* of the vitamins also attests to their power. The B vitamin folate helps to prevent birth defects. Vitamin C seems to protect against certain types of cancer. Similarly, vitamin E seems to help protect against some facets of cardiovascular disease. As you will see, the vitamins' roles in supporting optimal health extend far beyond preventing deficiency diseases. In fact, some of the credit given to low-fat diets in preventing disease actually belongs to the vitamins found in vegetables, fruits, and whole grains (see Highlight 11 for more on vitamins in disease prevention).

The vitamins differ from carbohydrates, fats, and proteins in the following ways:

- *Structure.* Vitamins are individual units; they are not linked together (as are molecules of glucose or amino acids). Appendix C presents the chemical structure for each of the vitamins.

- *Function.* Vitamins do not yield usable energy when broken down; they assist the enzymes that release energy from carbohydrates, fats, and proteins.

- *Food contents.* The amounts of vitamins people ingest daily from foods and the amounts they require are measured in *micrograms* (μg) or *milligrams* (mg), rather than grams (g).◆

◆ Reminder: The *vitamins* are organic, essential nutrients required in tiny amounts to perform specific functions that promote growth, reproduction, or the maintenance of health and life.
- **vita** = life
- **amine** = containing nitrogen (the first vitamins discovered contained nitrogen)

◆ 1 g = 1000 mg
1 mg = 1000 μg
For perspective, a dollar bill weighs about 1 g.

To minimize vitamin losses, wrap cut fruits and vegetables or store them in airtight containers.

◆ **Water-soluble vitamins:**
- B vitamins:
  Thiamin
  Riboflavin
  Niacin
  Biotin
  Pantothenic acid
  Vitamin B_6
  Folate
  Vitamin B_{12}
- Vitamin C

Fat-soluble vitamins:
- Vitamin A
- Vitamin D
- Vitamin E
- Vitamin K

bioavailability: the rate at and the extent to which a nutrient is absorbed and used.

precursors: substances that precede others; with regard to vitamins, compounds that can be converted into active vitamins; also known as **provitamins.**

The vitamins are similar to the energy-yielding nutrients, though, in that they are vital to life, organic, and available from foods.

Bioavailability The amount of vitamins available from foods depends not only on the quantity provided by a food but also on the amount absorbed and used by the body—referred to as the vitamins' **bioavailability.** The quantity of vitamins in a food can be determined relatively easily. Researchers analyze foods to determine their vitamin contents and publish the results in tables of food composition such as Appendix H. Determining the bioavailability of a vitamin is a more complex task because it depends on many factors, including:

- Efficiency of digestion and time of transit through the GI tract
- Previous nutrient intake and nutrition status
- Other foods consumed at the same time (Chapters 10–13 describe factors that inhibit or enhance the absorption of individual vitamins and minerals.)
- Method of food preparation (raw, cooked, or processed)
- Source of the nutrient (synthetic, fortified, or naturally occurring)

Experts consider these factors when estimating recommended intakes.

Precursors Some of the vitamins are available from foods in inactive forms known as **precursors,** or provitamins. Once inside the body, the precursor is converted to an active form of the vitamin. Thus, in measuring a person's vitamin intake, it is important to count both the amount of the active vitamin and the potential amount available from its precursors. The discussions and summary tables throughout this chapter and the next indicate which vitamins have precursors.

Organic Nature Being organic, vitamins can be destroyed and left unable to perform their duties. Therefore, they must be handled with care during storage and in cooking. Prolonged heating may destroy much of the thiamin in food. Because riboflavin can be destroyed by the ultraviolet rays of the sun or by fluorescent light, foods stored in transparent glass containers are most likely to lose riboflavin. Oxygen destroys vitamin C, so losses occur when foods are cut, processed, and stored; these losses may be enough to reduce its action in the body.[1] Table 10-1 summarizes ways to minimize nutrient losses in the kitchen, and Chapter 19 provides more details.

Solubility As you may recall, carbohydrates and proteins are hydrophilic and lipids are hydrophobic. The vitamins divide along the same lines—the hydrophilic, water-soluble ones ◆ are the eight B vitamins and vitamin C; the hydrophobic, fat-soluble ones are vitamins A, D, E, and K. As each vitamin was discovered, it was given a name and sometimes a letter and number as well. Many of the water-soluble vitamins have multiple names, which has led to some confusion. The margin lists the standard names, and summary tables throughout this chapter provide the common alternative names.

Solubility is apparent in the food sources of the different vitamins, and it affects their absorption, transport, storage, and excretion by the body. The water-soluble vitamins are found in the watery compartments of foods; the fat-soluble vitamins

TABLE 10-1	Minimizing Nutrient Losses

- To slow the degradation of vitamins, refrigerate (most) fruits and vegetables.
- To minimize the oxidation of vitamins, store fruits and vegetables that have been cut in airtight wrappers, and store juices that have been opened in closed containers (and refrigerate them).
- To prevent losses during washing, rinse fruits and vegetables before cutting.
- To minimize losses during cooking, use a microwave oven or steam vegetables in a small amount of water. Add vegetables after water has come to a boil. Use the cooking water in mixed dishes such as casseroles and soups. Avoid high temperatures and long cooking times.

usually occur together in the fats and oils of foods. On being absorbed, the water-soluble vitamins move directly into the blood. Like fats, however, the fat-soluble vitamins must first enter the lymph, then the blood. Once in the blood, many of the water-soluble vitamins travel freely, whereas many of the fat-soluble vitamins require protein carriers for transport. Upon reaching the cells, water-soluble vitamins freely circulate in the water-filled compartments of the body, but fat-soluble vitamins are held in fatty tissues and the liver until needed. The kidneys, monitoring the blood that flows through them, detect and remove small excesses of water-soluble vitamins (large excesses, however, may overwhelm the system, creating adverse effects). Fat-soluble vitamins tend to remain in fat-storage sites in the body rather than being excreted, and so are more likely to reach toxic levels when consumed in excess.

Because the body stores fat-soluble vitamins, they can be eaten in large amounts once in a while and still meet the body's needs over time. Water-soluble vitamins are retained for varying periods in the body. Although a single day's omission from the diet does not bring on a deficiency, the water-soluble vitamins must still be eaten more regularly than the fat-soluble vitamins.

Toxicity Knowledge about some of the amazing roles of vitamins has prompted many people to assume that "more is better" and take vitamin supplements. But just as an inadequate intake can cause harm, so can an excessive intake. Even some of the water-soluble vitamins have adverse effects when taken in large doses.

That a vitamin can be both essential and harmful may seem surprising, but the same is true of most nutrients. The effects of every substance depend on its dose, and this is one reason consumers should not self-prescribe supplements for their ailments. See the "How to" below for a perspective on doses.

The Committee on Dietary Reference Intakes (DRI) addresses the possibility of adverse effects from high doses of nutrients by establishing Tolerable Upper Intake Levels. An Upper Level defines the highest amount of a nutrient that is likely not to cause harm for most healthy people when consumed daily. The risk of harm increases as intakes rise above the Upper Level. Of the nutrients discussed in this chapter, niacin, vitamin B$_6$, folate, choline, and vitamin C have Upper Levels, and these values are presented in their respective summary tables. Data are lacking to establish Upper Levels for the remaining B vitamins, but this does not mean that

---

HOW TO Understand Dose Levels and Effects

A substance may have a beneficial or harmful effect, but a critical thinker would not conclude that the substance itself was beneficial or harmful without first asking what dose was used. The accompanying figure shows three possible relationships between dose levels and effects. The third diagram represents the situation with nutrients—more is better up to a point, but beyond that point, still more can be harmful.

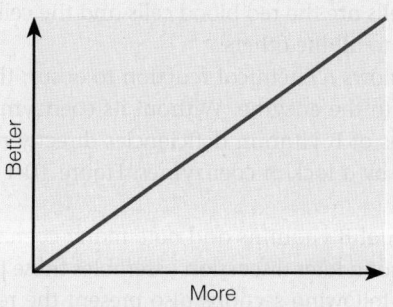

As you progress in the direction of more, the effect gets better and better, with no end in sight (real life is seldom, if ever, like this).

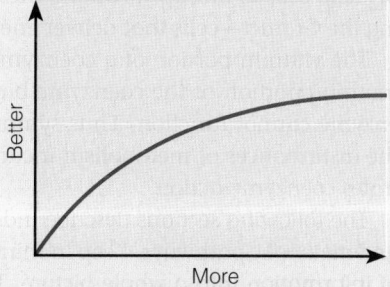

As you progress in the direction of more, the effect reaches a maximum and then a plateau, becoming no better with higher doses.

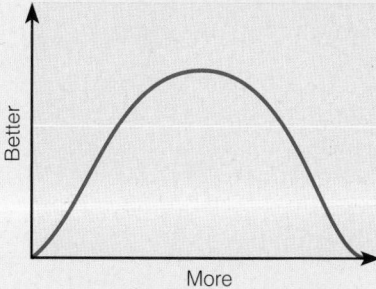

As you progress in the direction of more, the effect reaches an optimum at some intermediate dose and then declines, showing that more is better up to a point and then harmful. That too much can be as harmful as too little represents the situation with most nutrients.

excessively high intakes would be without risk. (The inside front cover pages present Upper Levels for the vitamins and minerals.)

IN SUMMARY

The vitamins are essential nutrients needed in tiny amounts in the diet both to prevent deficiency diseases and to support optimal health. The water-soluble vitamins are the B vitamins and vitamin C; the fat-soluble vitamins are vitamins A, D, E, and K. The accompanying table summarizes the differences between the water-soluble and fat-soluble vitamins.

	Water-Soluble Vitamins: B Vitamins and Vitamin C	Fat-Soluble Vitamins: Vitamins A, D, E, and K
Absorption	Directly into the blood	First into the lymph, then the blood
Transport	Travel freely	Many require protein carriers
Storage	Circulate freely in water-filled parts of the body	Stored in the cells associated with fat
Excretion	Kidneys detect and remove excess in urine	Less readily excreted; tend to remain in fat-storage sites
Toxicity	Possible to reach toxic levels when consumed from supplements	Likely to reach toxic levels when consumed from supplements
Requirements	Needed in frequent doses (perhaps 1 to 3 days)	Needed in periodic doses (perhaps weeks or even months)

NOTE: Exceptions occur, but these differences between the water-soluble and fat-soluble vitamins are valid generalizations.

The discussion of B vitamins that follows begins with a brief description of each of them, then offers a look at the ways they work together. Thus, a preview of the individual vitamins is followed by a survey of how they work together, in concert.

The B Vitamins—As Individuals

Despite supplement advertisements that claim otherwise, the vitamins do not provide the body with fuel for energy. It is true, though, that without B vitamins the body would lack energy. The energy-yielding nutrients—carbohydrate, fat, and protein—are used for fuel; the B vitamins help the body to use that fuel. Several of the B vitamins—thiamin, riboflavin, niacin, pantothenic acid, and biotin—form part of the coenzymes ◆ that assist certain enzymes in the release of energy from carbohydrate, fat, and protein. Other B vitamins play other indispensable roles in metabolism. Vitamin B_6 assists enzymes that metabolize amino acids; folate and vitamin B_{12} help cells to multiply. Among these cells are the red blood cells and the cells lining the GI tract—cells that deliver energy to all the others.

The vitamin portion of a coenzyme allows a chemical reaction to occur; the remaining portion of the coenzyme binds to the enzyme. Without its coenzyme, an enzyme cannot function. Thus symptoms of B vitamin deficiencies directly reflect the disturbances of metabolism incurred by a lack of coenzymes. Figure 10-1 illustrates coenzyme action.

The following sections describe individual B vitamins and note many coenzymes and metabolic pathways. Keep in mind that a later discussion assembles these pieces of information into a whole picture. The following sections also present the recommendations, deficiency and toxicity symptoms, and food sources for each vitamin. The recommendations for the B vitamins and vitamin C reflect the 1998 and 2000 DRI, respectively.[2] For thiamin, riboflavin, niacin, vitamin B_6, folate, vitamin B_{12}, and vitamin C, sufficient data were available to establish an RDA; for biotin, pantothenic acid, and choline, an Adequate Intake (AI) was set; only niacin, vitamin B_6, folate, choline, and vitamin C have Tolerable Upper Intake Levels. These values appear in the summary tables and figures that follow and on the pages of the inside front cover.

◆ Reminder: A *coenzyme* is a small organic molecule that associates closely with certain enzymes; many B vitamins form an integral part of coenzymes.

FIGURE 10-1   *Animated!* Coenzyme Action

Some vitamins form part of the coenzymes that enable enzymes either to synthesize compounds (as illustrated in this figure) or to dismantle compounds (as illustrated by the upper enzymes).

ThomsonNOW
To test your und
log on to www.t

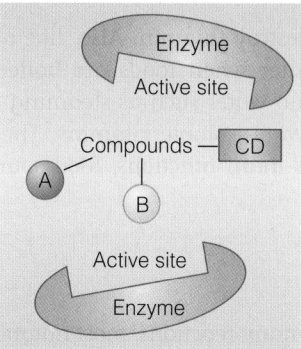
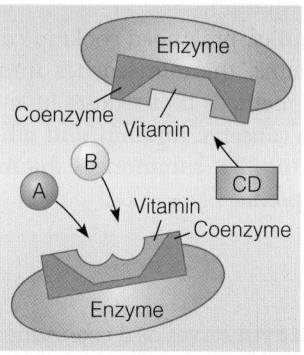
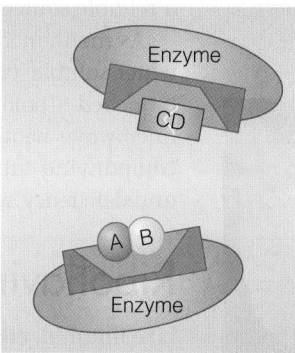
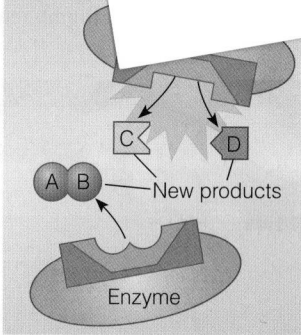

Without coenzymes, compounds A, B, and CD don't respond to their enzymes.

With the coenzymes in place, compounds are attracted to their sites on the enzymes . . .

. . . and the reactions proceed instantaneously. The coenzymes often donate or accept electrons, atoms, or groups of atoms.

The reactions are completed with either the formation of a new product, AB, or the breaking apart of a compound into two new products, C and D, and the release of energy.

Thiamin

Thiamin is the vitamin part of the coenzyme TPP (thiamin pyrophosphate), which assists in energy metabolism. The TPP coenzyme participates in the conversion of pyruvate to acetyl CoA (described in Chapter 7). The reaction removes one carbon from the 3-carbon pyruvate to make the 2-carbon acetyl CoA and carbon dioxide (CO_2). Later, TPP participates in a similar step in the TCA cycle where it helps convert a 5-carbon compound to a 4-carbon compound. Besides playing these pivotal roles in the energy metabolism of all cells, thiamin occupies a special site on the membranes of nerve cells. Consequently, processes in nerves and in their responding tissues, the muscles, depend heavily on thiamin.

Thiamin Recommendations Dietary recommendations are based primarily on thiamin's role in enzyme activity. Generally, thiamin needs will be met if a person eats enough food to meet energy needs—if that energy comes from nutritious foods. The average thiamin intake in the United States and Canada meets or exceeds recommendations.

Thiamin Deficiency and Toxicity People who fail to eat enough food to meet energy needs risk nutrient deficiencies, including thiamin deficiency. Inadequate thiamin intakes have been reported among the nation's malnourished and homeless people. Similarly, people who derive most of their energy from empty-kcalorie items risk thiamin deficiency. Alcohol ◆ is a good example. It contributes energy but provides few, if any, nutrients and often displaces food. In addition, alcohol impairs thiamin absorption and enhances thiamin excretion in the urine, doubling the risk of deficiency. An estimated four out of five alcoholics are thiamin deficient.

Prolonged thiamin deficiency can result in the disease **beriberi**, which was first observed in Indonesia when the custom of polishing rice became widespread.[3] Rice provided 80 percent of the energy intake of the people of that area, and the germ and bran of the rice grain was their principal source of thiamin. When the germ and bran were removed in the preparation of white rice, beriberi spread like wildfire. The symptoms of beriberi include damage to the nervous system as well as to the heart and other muscles. Figure 10-2 presents one of the symptoms of beriberi. No adverse effects have been associated with excesses of thiamin; no Upper Level has been determined.

◆ Severe thiamin deficiency in alcohol abusers is called the **Wernicke-Korsakoff** (VER-nee-key KORE-sah-kof) **syndrome**. Symptoms include disorientation, loss of short-term memory, jerky eye movements, and staggering gait.

thiamin (THIGH-ah-min): a B vitamin. The coenzyme form is **TPP (thiamin pyrophosphate)**.

beriberi: the thiamin-deficiency disease.
- **beri** = weakness
- **beriberi** = "I can't, I can't"

10-2 Thiamin-Deficiency ...om—The Edema of Beriberi

Beriberi may be characterized as "wet" (referring to edema) or "dry" (with muscle wasting, but no edema). Physical examination confirms that this person has wet beriberi. Notice how the impression of the physician's thumb remains on the leg.

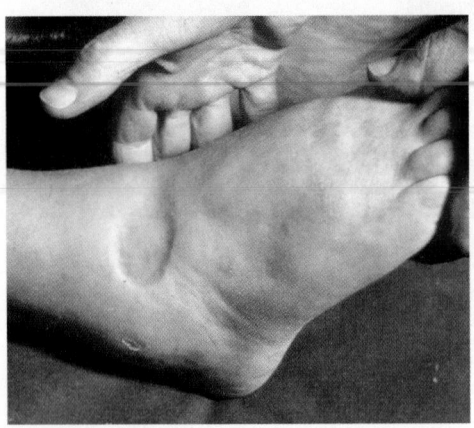

Thiamin Food Sources Before examining Figure 10-3, you may want to read the accompanying "How to," which describes the many features found in this and similar figures in this chapter and the next three chapters. When you look at Figure 10-3, notice that thiamin occurs in small quantities in many nutritious foods. The long red bar near the bottom of the graph shows that meats in the pork family are exceptionally rich in thiamin. Yellow bars confirm that enriched grains are a reliable source of thiamin.

As mentioned earlier, prolonged cooking can destroy thiamin. Also, like other water-soluble vitamins, thiamin leaches into water when foods are boiled or blanched. Cooking methods that require little or no water such as steaming and microwave heating conserve thiamin and other water-soluble vitamins. The accompanying table (p. 329) summarizes thiamin's main functions, food sources, and deficiency symptoms.

Riboflavin

Like thiamin, **riboflavin** serves as a coenzyme in many reactions, most notably in the release of energy from nutrients in all body cells. The coenzyme forms of riboflavin are FMN (flavin mononucleotide) and FAD (flavin adenine dinucleotide); both can accept and then donate two hydrogens (see Figure 10-4, p. 330). During energy metabolism, FAD picks up two hydrogens (with their electrons) from the TCA cycle and delivers them to the electron transport chain (described in Chapter 7).

FIGURE 10-3 Thiamin in Selected Foods

See the "How to" section on the next page for more information on using this figure.

Food	Serving size (kcalories)
Bread, whole wheat	1 oz slice (70 kcal)
Cornflakes, fortified	1 oz (110 kcal)
Spaghetti pasta	½ c cooked (99 kcal)
Tortilla, flour	1 10"-round (234 kcal)
Broccoli	½ c cooked (22 kcal)
Carrots	½ c shredded raw (24 kcal)
Potato	1 medium baked w/skin (133 kcal)
Tomato juice	¾ c (31 kcal)
Banana	1 medium raw (109 kcal)
Orange	1 medium raw (62 kcal)
Strawberries	½ c fresh (22 kcal)
Watermelon	1 slice (92 kcal)
Milk	1 c reduced-fat 2% (121 kcal)
Yogurt, plain	1 c low-fat (155 kcal)
Cheddar cheese	1½ oz (171 kcal)
Cottage cheese	½ c low-fat 2% (101 kcal)
Pinto beans	½ c cooked (117 kcal)
Peanut butter	2 tbs (188 kcal)
Sunflower seeds	1 oz dry (165 kcal)
Tofu (soybean curd)	½ c (76 kcal)
Ground beef, lean	3 oz broiled (244 kcal)
Chicken breast	3 oz roasted (140 kcal)
Tuna, canned in water	3 oz (99 kcal)
Egg	1 hard cooked (78 kcal)
Excellent, and sometimes unusual, sources:	
Pork chop, lean	3 oz broiled (169 kcal)
Soy milk	1 c (81 kcal)
Squash, acorn	½ c baked (69 kcal)

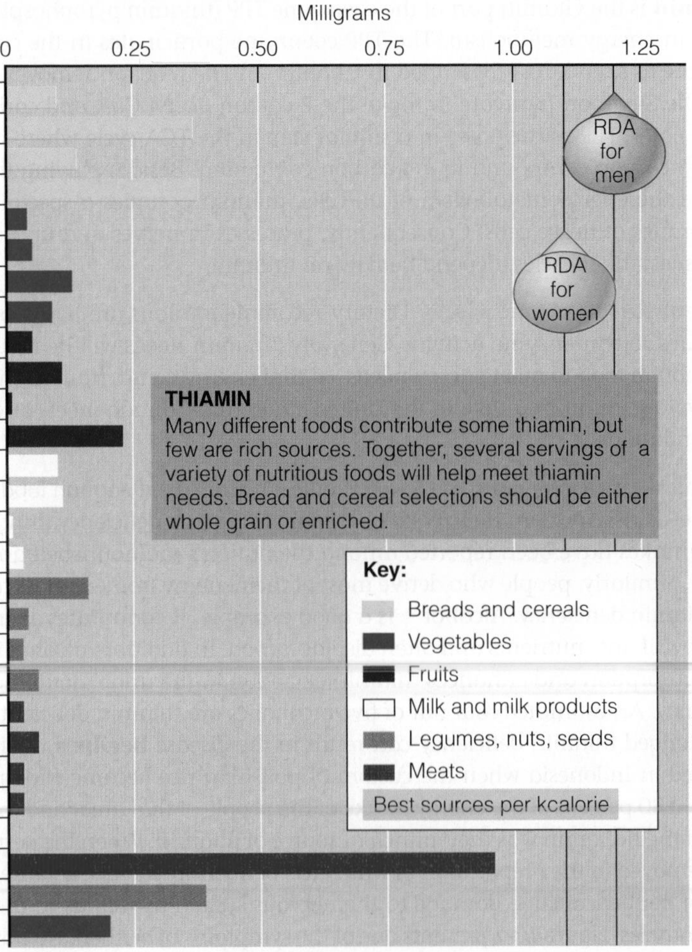

Milligrams: 0   0.25   0.50   0.75   1.00   1.25

RDA for men
RDA for women

THIAMIN
Many different foods contribute some thiamin, but few are rich sources. Together, several servings of a variety of nutritious foods will help meet thiamin needs. Bread and cereal selections should be either whole grain or enriched.

Key:
- Breads and cereals
- Vegetables
- Fruits
- Milk and milk products
- Legumes, nuts, seeds
- Meats
- Best sources per kcalorie

HOW TO Evaluate Foods for Their Nutrient Contributions

Figure 10-3 is the first of a series of figures in this and the next three chapters that present the vitamins and minerals in foods. Each figure presents the same 24 foods, which were selected to ensure a variety of choices representative of each of the food groups as suggested by the USDA Food Guide. For example, a bread, a cereal, and a pasta were chosen from the grain group. The suggestion to include a variety of vegetables was also considered: dark green, leafy vegetables (broccoli); deep orange and yellow vegetables (carrots); starchy vegetables (potatoes); legumes (pinto beans); and other vegetables (tomato juice). The selection of fruits followed suggestions to use whole fruits (bananas); citrus fruits (oranges); melons (watermelon); and berries (strawberries). Items were selected from the milk and meat groups in a similar way. In addition to the 24 foods that appear in all of the figures, three different

foods were selected for each of the nutrients to add variety and often reflect excellent, and sometimes unusual, sources.

Notice that the figures list the food, the serving size, and the food energy (kcalories) on the left. The amount of the nutrient per serving is presented in the graph on the right along with the RDA (or AI) for adults, so you can see how many servings would be needed to meet recommendations.

The colored bars show at a glance which food groups best provide a nutrient: yellow for breads and cereals; green for vegetables; purple for fruits; white for milk and milk products; brown for legumes; and red for meat, fish, and poultry. Because the USDA Food Guide mentions legumes with both the meat group and the vegetable group and because legumes are especially rich in many vitamins and minerals, they have been given their own color to highlight their nutrient contributions.

Notice how the bar graphs shift in the various figures. Careful study of all of the figures taken together will confirm that variety is the key to nutrient adequacy.

Another way to evaluate foods for their nutrient contributions is to consider their nutrient density (their thiamin *per 100 kcalories*, for example). Quite often, vegetables rank higher on a nutrient-per-kcalorie list than they do on a nutrient-per-serving list (see p. 38 to review how to evaluate foods based on nutrient density). The left column in the figure highlights about five foods that offer the best deal for your energy "dollar" (the kcalorie). Notice how many of them are vegetables.

Realistically, people cannot eat for single nutrients. Fortunately, most foods deliver more than one nutrient, allowing people to combine foods into nourishing meals.

IN SUMMARY   Thiamin

Other Names

Vitamin B₁

RDA

Men: 1.2 mg/day

Women: 1.1 mg/day

Chief Functions in the Body

Part of coenzyme TPP (thiamin pyrophosphate) used in energy metabolism

Significant Sources

Whole-grain, fortified, or enriched grain products; moderate amounts in all nutritious food; pork

Easily destroyed by heat

Deficiency Disease

Beriberi (wet, with edema; dry, with muscle wasting)

Deficiency Symptoms[a]

Enlarged heart, cardiac failure; muscular weakness; apathy, poor short-term memory, confusion, irritability; anorexia, weight loss

Toxicity Symptoms

None reported

[a]Severe thiamin deficiency is often related to heavy alcohol consumption with limited food consumption (Wernicke-Korsakoff syndrome).

© Polara Studios Inc.

Pork is the richest source of thiamin, but enriched or whole-grain products typically make the greatest contribution to a day's intake because of the quantities eaten. Legumes such as split peas are also valuable sources of thiamin.

Riboflavin Recommendations Like thiamin's RDA, riboflavin's RDA is based primarily on its role in enzyme activity. Most people in the United States and Canada meet or exceed riboflavin recommendations.

Riboflavin Deficiency and Toxicity Riboflavin deficiency ◆ most often accompanies other nutrient deficiencies. Lack of the vitamin causes inflammation of the membranes of the mouth, skin, eyes, and GI tract. Excesses of riboflavin appear to cause no harm; no Upper Level has been established.

Riboflavin Food Sources The greatest contributions of riboflavin come from milk and milk products (see Figure 10-5, p. 331). Whole-grain or enriched bread and cereal products are also valuable sources because of the quantities typically consumed.

◆ Riboflavin deficiency is called **ariboflavinosis** (ay-RYE-boh-FLAY-vin-oh-sis).
 • **a** = not
 • **osis** = condition

riboflavin (RYE-boh-flay-vin): a B vitamin. The coenzyme forms are **FMN (flavin mononucleotide)** and **FAD (flavin adenine dinucleotide)**.

FIGURE 10-4 Riboflavin Coenzyme, Accepting and Donating Hydrogens

This figure shows the chemical structure of the riboflavin portion of the coenzyme only; the remainder of the coenzyme structure is represented by dotted lines (see Appendix C for the complete chemical structures of FAD and FMN). The reactive sites that accept and donate hydrogens are highlighted in white.

FAD ⇌ FADH₂

During the TCA cycle, compounds release hydrogens, and the riboflavin coenzyme FAD picks up two of them. As it accepts two hydrogens, FAD becomes FADH₂.

FADH₂ carries the hydrogens to the electron transport chain. At the end of the electron transport chain, the hydrogens are accepted by oxygen, creating water, and FADH₂ becomes FAD again. For every FADH₂ that passes through the electron transport chain, 2 ATP are generated.

◆ Turn to p. 38 for a review of how to evaluate foods based on nutrient density (per kcalorie).

When riboflavin sources are ranked by nutrient density (per kcalorie), ◆ many dark green, leafy vegetables (such as broccoli, turnip greens, asparagus, and spinach) appear high on the list. Vegans and others who don't use milk must rely on ample servings of dark greens and enriched grains for riboflavin. Nutritional yeast is another good source.

Ultraviolet light and irradiation destroy riboflavin. For these reasons, milk is sold in cardboard or opaque plastic containers, and precautions are taken when vitamin D is added to milk by irradiation.* In contrast, riboflavin is stable to heat, so cooking does not destroy it. The following summary table lists riboflavin's chief functions, food sources, and deficiency symptoms.

* Vitamin D can be added to milk by feeding cows irradiated yeast or by irradiating the milk itself.

All of these foods are rich in riboflavin, but milk and milk products provide much of the riboflavin in the diets of most people.

© Polara Studios Inc.

IN SUMMARY Riboflavin

Other Names

Vitamin B₂

RDA

Men: 1.3 mg/day

Women: 1.1 mg/day

Chief Functions in the Body

Part of coenzymes FMN (flavin mononucleotide) and FAD (flavin adenine dinucleotide) used in energy metabolism

Significant Sources

Milk products (yogurt, cheese); whole-grain, fortified, or enriched grain products; liver

Easily destroyed by ultraviolet light and irradiation

Deficiency Disease

Ariboflavinosis (ay-RYE-boh-FLAY-vin-oh-sis)

Deficiency Symptoms

Sore throat; cracks and redness at corners of mouth;[a] painful, smooth, purplish red tongue;[b] inflammation characterized by skin lesions covered with greasy scales

Toxicity Symptoms

None reported

[a]Cracks at the corners of the mouth are called *angular stomatitis* or *cheilosis* (kye-LOH-sis or kee-LOH-sis).
[b]Smoothness of the tongue is caused by loss of its surface structures and is termed *glossitis* (gloss-EYE-tis).

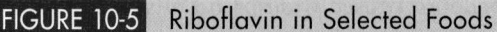

FIGURE 10-5 Riboflavin in Selected Foods

See the "How to" section on p. 329 for more information on using this figure.

Food	Serving size (kcalories)
Bread, whole wheat	1 oz slice (70 kcal)
Cornflakes, fortified	1 oz (110 kcal)
Spaghetti pasta	½ c cooked (99 kcal)
Tortilla, flour	1 10"-round (234 kcal)
Broccoli	½ c cooked (22 kcal)
Carrots	½ c shredded raw (24 kcal)
Potato	1 medium baked w/skin (133 kcal)
Tomato juice	¾ c (31 kcal)
Banana	1 medium raw (109 kcal)
Orange	1 medium raw (62 kcal)
Strawberries	½ c fresh (22 kcal)
Watermelon	1 slice (92 kcal)
Milk	1 c reduced-fat 2% (121 kcal)
Yogurt, plain	1 c low-fat (155 kcal)
Cheddar cheese	1½ oz (171 kcal)
Cottage cheese	½ c low-fat 2% (101 kcal)
Pinto beans	½ c cooked (117 kcal)
Peanut butter	2 tbs (188 kcal)
Sunflower seeds	1 oz dry (165 kcal)
Tofu (soybean curd)	½ c (76 kcal)
Ground beef, lean	3 oz broiled (244 kcal)
Chicken breast	3 oz roasted (140 kcal)
Tuna, canned in water	3 oz (99 kcal)
Egg	1 hard cooked (78 kcal)
Excellent, and sometimes unusual, sources:	
Liver	3 oz fried (184 kcal)
Clams, canned	3 oz (126 kcal)
Mushrooms	½ c cooked (21 kcal)

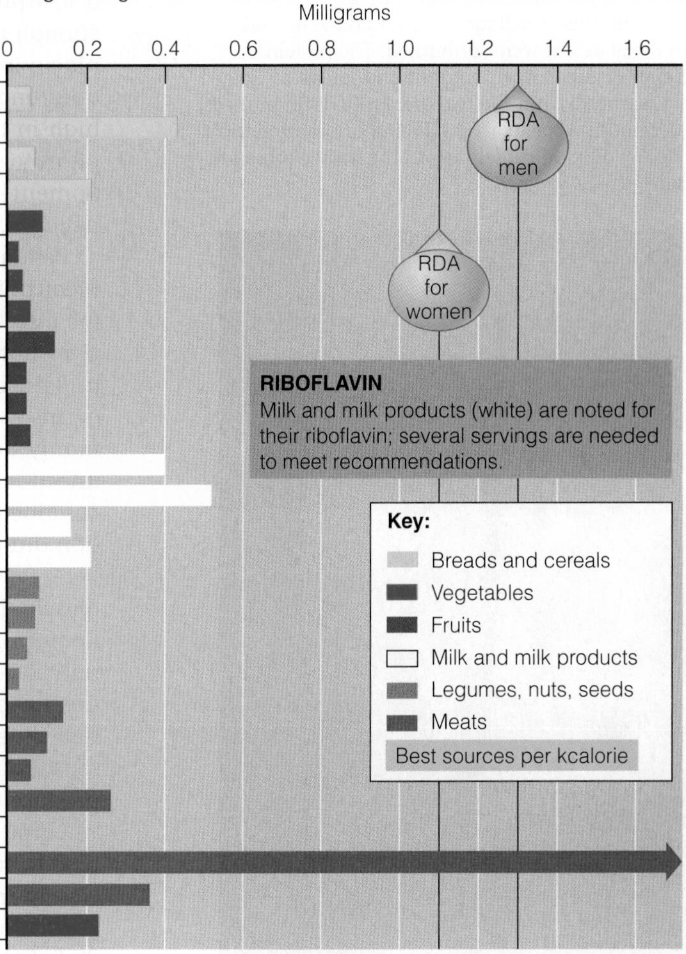

Milligrams: 0 0.2 0.4 0.6 0.8 1.0 1.2 1.4 1.6

RDA for men

RDA for women

RIBOFLAVIN
Milk and milk products (white) are noted for their riboflavin; several servings are needed to meet recommendations.

Key:
- Breads and cereals
- Vegetables
- Fruits
- Milk and milk products
- Legumes, nuts, seeds
- Meats
- Best sources per kcalorie

Niacin

The name **niacin** describes two chemical structures: nicotinic acid and nicotinamide (also known as niacinamide). The body can easily convert nicotinic acid to nicotinamide, which is the major form of niacin in the blood.

The two coenzyme forms of niacin, NAD (nicotinamide adenine dinucleotide) and NADP (the phosphate form), participate in numerous metabolic reactions. They are central in energy-transfer reactions, especially the metabolism of glucose, fat, and alcohol. NAD is similar to the riboflavin coenzymes in that it carries hydrogens (and their electrons) during metabolic reactions, including the pathway from the TCA cycle to the electron transport chain.

Niacin Recommendations Niacin is unique among the B vitamins in that the body can make it from the amino acid tryptophan. To make 1 milligram of niacin requires approximately 60 milligrams of dietary tryptophan. For this reason, recommended intakes are stated in **niacin equivalents (NE).** ◆ A food containing 1 milligram of niacin and 60 milligrams of tryptophan provides the equivalent of 2 milligrams of niacin, or 2 niacin equivalents. The RDA for niacin allows for this conversion and is stated in niacin equivalents; average niacin intakes in the United States and Canada exceed recommendations.

Niacin Deficiency The niacin-deficiency disease, **pellagra,** produces the symptoms of diarrhea, dermatitis, dementia, and eventually death (often called "the four Ds").

◆ 1 NE = 1 mg niacin or 60 mg tryptophan

niacin (NIGH-a-sin): a B vitamin. The coenzyme forms are **NAD (nicotinamide adenine dinucleotide)** and **NADP** (the phosphate form of NAD). Niacin can be eaten preformed or made in the body from its precursor, tryptophan, one of the amino acids.

niacin equivalents (NE): the amount of niacin present in food, including the niacin that can theoretically be made from its precursor, tryptophan, present in the food.

pellagra (pell-AY-gra): the niacin-deficiency disease.
- **pellis** = skin
- **agra** = rough

FIGURE 10-6 Niacin-Deficiency Symptom—The Dermatitis of Pellagra

In the dermatitis of pellagra, the skin darkens and flakes away as if it were sunburned. The protein-deficiency disease kwashiorkor also produces a "flaky paint" dermatitis, but the two are easily distinguished. The dermatitis of pellagra is bilateral and symmetrical and occurs only on those parts of the body exposed to the sun.

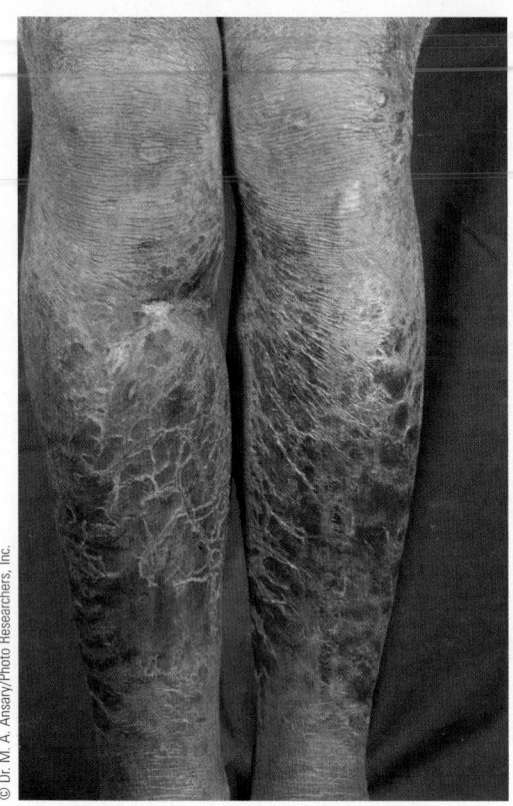

© Dr. M. A. Ansary/Photo Researchers, Inc.

◆ When a normal dose of a nutrient (levels commonly found in foods) provides a normal blood concentration, the nutrient is having a *physiological* effect. When a large dose (levels commonly available only from supplements) overwhelms some body system and acts like a drug, the nutrient is having a *pharmacological* effect.
• **physio** = natural
• **pharma** = drug

niacin flush: a temporary burning, tingling, and itching sensation that occurs when a person takes a large dose of nicotinic acid; often accompanied by a headache and reddened face, arms, and chest.

In the early 1900s, pellagra caused widespread misery and some 87,000 deaths in the U.S. South, where many people subsisted on a low-protein diet centered on corn. This diet supplied neither enough niacin nor enough tryptophan. At least 70 percent of the niacin in corn is bound to complex carbohydrates and small peptides, making it unavailable for absorption. Furthermore, corn is high in the amino acid leucine, which interferes with the tryptophan-to-niacin conversion, thus further contributing to the development of pellagra. Figure 10-6 illustrates the dermatitis of pellagra.

Pellagra was originally believed to be caused by an infection. Medical researchers spent many years and much effort searching for infectious microbes until they realized that the problem was not what was *present* in the food but what was *absent* from it. That a disease such as pellagra could be caused by diet—and not by germs—was a groundbreaking discovery. It contradicted commonly held medical opinions that diseases were caused only by infectious agents. By carefully following the scientific method (as described in Chapter 1), researchers advanced the science of nutrition dramatically.*

Niacin Toxicity Naturally occurring niacin from foods ◆ causes no harm, but large doses from supplements or drugs produce a variety of adverse effects, most notably **"niacin flush."** Niacin flush occurs when nicotinic acid is taken in doses only three to four times the RDA. It dilates the capillaries and causes a tingling sensation that can be painful. The nicotinamide form does not produce this effect—nor does it lower blood cholesterol.

Large doses of nicotinic acid have been used to help lower blood cholesterol and prevent heart disease. Such therapy must be closely monitored. People with the following conditions may be particularly susceptible to the toxic effects of niacin: liver disease, diabetes, peptic ulcers, gout, irregular heartbeats, inflammatory bowel disease, migraine headaches, and alcoholism.

Niacin Food Sources Tables of food composition typically list preformed niacin only, but as mentioned, niacin can also be made in the body from the amino acid tryptophan. Dietary tryptophan could meet about half the daily niacin need for most people, but the average diet easily supplies enough preformed niacin. The "How to" on p. 333 shows how to estimate the total amount of niacin available from both tryptophan and preformed niacin in the diet.

Figure 10-7 (p. 334) presents niacin in selected foods. Meat, poultry, legumes, and enriched and whole grains contribute about half the niacin people consume. Mushrooms, potatoes, and tomatoes are among the richest vegetable sources, and they can provide abundant niacin when eaten in generous amounts.

Niacin is less vulnerable to losses during food preparation and storage than other water-soluble vitamins. Being fairly heat-resistant, niacin can withstand reasonable cooking times, but like other water-soluble vitamins, it will leach into cooking water. The summary table includes food sources as well as niacin's various names, functions, and deficiency and toxicity symptoms.

---

* Dr. Joseph Goldberger, a physician for the U.S. government, headed the investigations that determined that pellagra was a dietary disorder, not an infectious disease. He died several years before Conrad Elevjhem discovered that a deficiency of niacin caused pellagra.

HOW TO Estimate Niacin Equivalents

To estimate niacin equivalents:

- Calculate total protein consumed (grams).
- Assuming that the RDA amount of protein will be used first to make body protein, subtract the RDA to obtain "leftover" protein available to make niacin (grams). (Actually, the RDA provides a generous protein allowance, so "leftover" protein may be even greater than this.)
- About 1 gram of every 100 grams of high-quality protein is tryptophan, so divide by 100 to obtain the tryptophan in this leftover protein (grams).
- Multiply by 1000 to express this amount of tryptophan in milligrams.
- Divide by 60 to get niacin equivalents (milligrams).
- Finally, add the amount of preformed niacin obtained in the diet (milligrams).

For example, suppose that a 19-year-old woman who weighs 130 pounds consumes 75 grams of protein in a day. To calculate her protein RDA, first convert pounds to kilograms if necessary, and then multiply by 0.8 g/kg:

$$130 \text{ lb} \div 2.2 \text{ lb/kg} = 59 \text{ kg}$$
$$59 \text{ kg} \times 0.8 \text{ g/kg} = 47 \text{ g}$$

Then determine her leftover protein by subtracting her RDA from her intake:

$$75 \text{ g protein intake} - 47 \text{ g protein RDA} = 28 \text{ g protein leftover}$$

Next calculate the amount of tryptophan in this leftover protein:

$$28 \text{ g protein} \div 100 = 0.28 \text{ g tryptophan}$$
$$0.28 \text{ g tryptophan} \times 1000 = 280 \text{ mg tryptophan}$$

Then convert milligrams of tryptophan to niacin equivalents:

$$280 \text{ mg tryptophan} \div 60 = 4.7 \text{ mg NE}$$

To determine the total amount of niacin available from the diet, add the amount available from tryptophan (4.7 mg NE) to the amount of preformed niacin obtained from the diet.

IN SUMMARY Niacin

Other Names

Nicotinic acid, nicotinamide, niacinamide, vitamin B₃; precursor is dietary tryptophan (an amino acid)

RDA

Men: 16 mg NE/day

Women: 14 mg NE/day

Upper Level

Adults: 35 mg/day

Chief Functions in the Body

Part of coenzymes NAD (nicotinamide adenine dinucleotide) and NADP (its phosphate form) used in energy metabolism

Significant Sources

Milk, eggs, meat, poultry, fish; whole-grain, fortified, and enriched grain products; nuts and all protein-containing foods

Deficiency Disease

Pellagra

Deficiency Symptoms

Diarrhea, abdominal pain, vomiting; inflamed, swollen, smooth, bright red tongue;[a] depression, apathy, fatigue, loss of memory, headache; bilateral symmetrical rash on areas exposed to sunlight

Toxicity Symptoms

Painful flush, hives, and rash ("niacin flush"); nausea and vomiting; liver damage, impaired glucose tolerance

[a]Smoothness of the tongue is caused by loss of its surface structures and is termed *glossitis* (gloss-EYE-tis).

Protein-rich foods such as meat, fish, poultry, and peanut butter contribute much of the niacin in people's diets. Enriched breads and cereals and a few vegetables are also rich in niacin.

Biotin

Biotin plays an important role in metabolism as a coenzyme that carries activated carbon dioxide. This role is critical in the TCA cycle: biotin delivers a carbon

biotin (BY-oh-tin): a B vitamin that functions as a coenzyme in metabolism.

FIGURE 10-7 Niacin in Selected Foods

See the "How to" section on p. 329 for more information on using this figure.

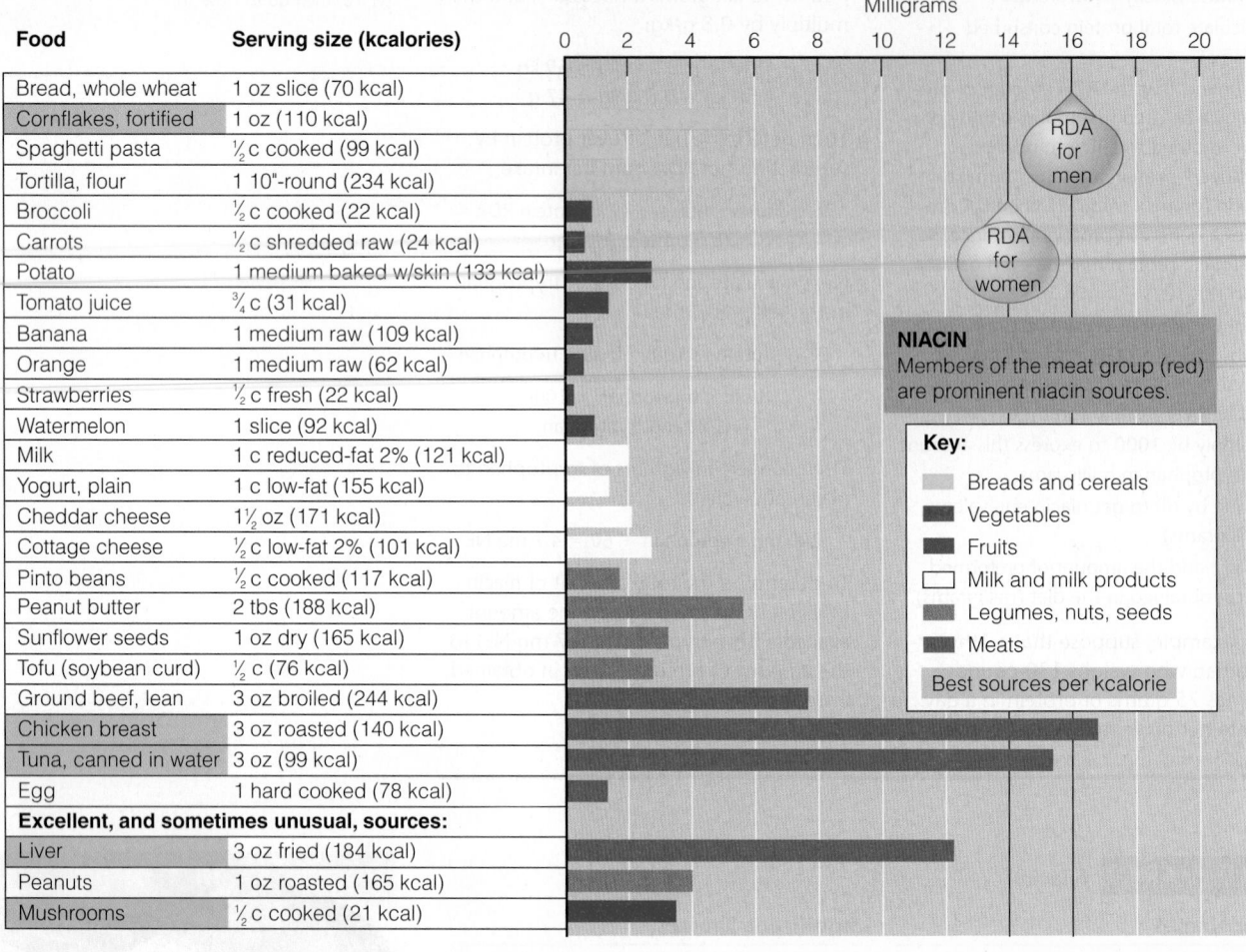

Food	Serving size (kcalories)
Bread, whole wheat	1 oz slice (70 kcal)
Cornflakes, fortified	1 oz (110 kcal)
Spaghetti pasta	½ c cooked (99 kcal)
Tortilla, flour	1 10"-round (234 kcal)
Broccoli	½ c cooked (22 kcal)
Carrots	½ c shredded raw (24 kcal)
Potato	1 medium baked w/skin (133 kcal)
Tomato juice	¾ c (31 kcal)
Banana	1 medium raw (109 kcal)
Orange	1 medium raw (62 kcal)
Strawberries	½ c fresh (22 kcal)
Watermelon	1 slice (92 kcal)
Milk	1 c reduced-fat 2% (121 kcal)
Yogurt, plain	1 c low-fat (155 kcal)
Cheddar cheese	1½ oz (171 kcal)
Cottage cheese	½ c low-fat 2% (101 kcal)
Pinto beans	½ c cooked (117 kcal)
Peanut butter	2 tbs (188 kcal)
Sunflower seeds	1 oz dry (165 kcal)
Tofu (soybean curd)	½ c (76 kcal)
Ground beef, lean	3 oz broiled (244 kcal)
Chicken breast	3 oz roasted (140 kcal)
Tuna, canned in water	3 oz (99 kcal)
Egg	1 hard cooked (78 kcal)
Excellent, and sometimes unusual, sources:	
Liver	3 oz fried (184 kcal)
Peanuts	1 oz roasted (165 kcal)
Mushrooms	½ c cooked (21 kcal)

NIACIN
Members of the meat group (red) are prominent niacin sources.

Key:
- Breads and cereals
- Vegetables
- Fruits
- Milk and milk products
- Legumes, nuts, seeds
- Meats

Best sources per kcalorie

◆ Reminder: *Gluconeogenesis* is the synthesis of glucose from noncarbohydrate sources such as amino acids or glycerol.

◆ The protein **avidin** (AV-eh-din) in egg whites binds biotin.
• **avid** = greedy

to 3-carbon pyruvate, thus replenishing oxaloacetate, the 4-carbon compound needed to combine with acetyl CoA to keep the TCA cycle turning. The biotin coenzyme also participates in gluconeogenesis, ◆ fatty acid synthesis, and the breakdown of certain fatty acids and amino acids. Recent research has uncovered roles for biotin in gene expression.[4]

Biotin Recommendations Biotin is needed in very small amounts. Instead of an RDA, an Adequate Intake (AI) has been determined.

Biotin Deficiency and Toxicity Biotin deficiencies rarely occur. Researchers can induce a biotin deficiency in animals or human beings by feeding them raw egg whites, which contain a protein ◆ that binds biotin and thus prevents its absorption. Biotin-deficiency symptoms include skin rash, hair loss, and neurological impairment. More than two dozen egg whites must be consumed daily for several months to produce these effects, however, and the eggs have to be raw; cooking denatures the binding protein. No adverse effects from high biotin intakes have been reported, but some research indicates that biotin supplementation damages DNA.[5] Biotin does not have an Upper Level.

Biotin Food Sources Biotin is widespread in foods (including egg yolks), so eating a variety of foods protects against deficiencies. Some biotin is also synthesized by GI tract bacteria, but this amount may not contribute much to the biotin absorbed. A review of biotin facts is provided in the summary table.

IN SUMMARY Biotin	
Adequate Intake (AI)	**Deficiency Symptoms**
Adults: 30 µg/day	Depression, lethargy, hallucinations, numb or tingling sensation in the arms and legs; red, scaly rash around the eyes, nose, and mouth; hair loss
Chief Functions in the Body	
Part of a coenzyme used in energy metabolism, fat synthesis, amino acid metabolism, and glycogen synthesis	**Toxicity Symptoms**
	None reported
Significant Sources	
Widespread in foods; liver, egg yolks, soybeans, fish, whole grains; also produced by GI bacteria	

Pantothenic Acid

Pantothenic acid is part of the chemical structure of coenzyme A—the same CoA that forms acetyl CoA, the "crossroads" compound in several metabolic pathways, including the TCA cycle. (Appendix C presents the chemical structures of these two molecules and shows that coenzyme A is made up in part of pantothenic acid.) As such, it is involved in more than 100 different steps in the synthesis of lipids, neurotransmitters, steroid hormones, and hemoglobin.

Pantothenic Acid Recommendations An Adequate Intake (AI) for pantothenic acid has been set. It reflects the amount needed to replace daily losses.

Pantothenic Acid Deficiency and Toxicity Pantothenic acid deficiency is rare. Its symptoms involve a general failure of all the body's systems and include fatigue, GI distress, and neurological disturbances. The "burning feet" syndrome that affected prisoners of war in Asia during World War II is thought to have been caused by pantothenic acid deficiency. No toxic effects have been reported, and no Upper Level has been established.

Pantothenic Acid Food Sources Pantothenic acid is widespread in foods, and typical diets seem to provide adequate intakes. Beef, poultry, whole grains, potatoes, tomatoes, and broccoli are particularly good sources. Losses of pantothenic acid during food production can be substantial because it is readily destroyed by the freezing, canning, and refining processes. The following summary table presents pantothenic acid facts.

IN SUMMARY Pantothenic Acid	
Adequate Intake (AI)	**Deficiency Symptoms**
Adults: 5 mg/day	Vomiting, nausea, stomach cramps; insomnia, fatigue, depression, irritability, restlessness, apathy; hypoglycemia, increased sensitivity to insulin; numbness, muscle cramps, inability to walk
Chief Functions in the Body	
Part of coenzyme A, used in energy metabolism	
Significant Sources	**Toxicity Symptoms**
Widespread in foods; chicken, beef, potatoes, oats, tomatoes, liver, egg yolk, broccoli, whole grains	None reported
Easily destroyed by food processing	

pantothenic (PAN-toe-THEN-ick) **acid:** a B vitamin. The principal active form is part of coenzyme A, called "CoA" throughout Chapter 7.
• **pantos** = everywhere

Vitamin B$_6$

Vitamin B$_6$ occurs in three forms—pyridoxal, pyridoxine, and pyridoxamine. All three can be converted to the coenzyme PLP (pyridoxal phosphate), which is active in amino acid metabolism. Because PLP can transfer amino groups (NH$_2$) from an amino acid to a keto acid, the body can make nonessential amino acids (review Figure 7-15, p. 226). The ability to add and remove amino groups makes PLP valuable in protein and urea metabolism as well. The conversions of the amino acid tryptophan to niacin or to the neurotransmitter serotonin ◆ also depend on PLP as does the synthesis of heme (the nonprotein portion of hemoglobin), nucleic acids (such as DNA and RNA), and lecithin.

A surge of research in the last decade has revealed that vitamin B$_6$ influences cognitive performance, immune function, and steroid hormone activity. Unlike other water-soluble vitamins, vitamin B$_6$ is stored extensively in muscle tissue.

Vitamin B$_6$ Recommendations Because the vitamin B$_6$ coenzymes play many roles in amino acid metabolism, previous RDA were expressed in terms of protein intakes; the current RDA for vitamin B$_6$, however, is not. Research does not support claims that large doses of vitamin B$_6$ enhance muscle strength or physical endurance. As Highlight 14 explains, vitamin supplements cannot compete with a nutritious diet and physical training.

Vitamin B$_6$ Deficiency Without adequate vitamin B$_6$, synthesis of key neurotransmitters diminishes, and abnormal compounds produced during tryptophan metabolism accumulate in the brain. Early symptoms of vitamin B$_6$ deficiency include depression and confusion; advanced symptoms include abnormal brain wave patterns and convulsions.

Alcohol contributes to the destruction and loss of vitamin B$_6$ from the body. As Highlight 7 described, when the body breaks down alcohol, it produces acetaldehyde. If allowed to accumulate, acetaldehyde dislodges the PLP coenzyme from its enzymes; once loose, PLP breaks down and is excreted. Low concentrations of PLP increase the risk of heart disease.[6]

Another drug that acts as a vitamin B$_6$ **antagonist** is INH, a medication that inhibits the growth of the tuberculosis bacterium.* This drug has saved countless lives, but as a vitamin B$_6$ antagonist, INH binds and inactivates the vitamin, inducing a deficiency. Whenever INH is used to treat tuberculosis, vitamin B$_6$ supplements must be given to protect against deficiency.

Vitamin B$_6$ Toxicity The first major report of vitamin B$_6$ toxicity appeared in the early 1980s. Until that time, everyone (including researchers and dietitians) believed that, like the other water-soluble vitamins, vitamin B$_6$ could not reach toxic concentrations in the body. The report described neurological damage in people who had been taking more than 2 *grams* of vitamin B$_6$ daily (20 times the current Upper Level of 100 *milligrams* per day) for two months or more.

Some people have taken vitamin B$_6$ supplements in an attempt to cure **carpal tunnel syndrome** and sleep disorders even though such treatment seems to be ineffective or at least inconclusive.[7] Self-prescribing is ill-advised because large doses of vitamin B$_6$ taken for months or years may cause irreversible nerve degeneration.

Vitamin B$_6$ Food Sources As you can see from the colors in Figure 10-8 (p. 337), meats, fish, and poultry (red bars), potatoes and a few other vegetables (green bars), and fruits (purple bars) offer vitamin B$_6$. As is true of most of the other vitamins, fruits and vegetables would rank considerably higher if foods were judged by nutrient density (vitamin B$_6$ per kcalorie). Several servings of vitamin B$_6$–rich foods are needed to meet recommended intakes.

Foods lose vitamin B$_6$ when heated. Information is limited, but vitamin B$_6$ bioavailability from plant-derived foods seems to be lower than from animal-

◆ Reminder: *Serotonin* is a neurotransmitter important in appetite control, sleep regulation, and sensory perception, among other roles; it is synthesized in the body from the amino acid tryptophan with the help of vitamin B$_6$.

vitamin B$_6$: a family of compounds—pyridoxal, pyridoxine, and pyridoxamine. The primary active coenzyme form is **PLP (pyridoxal phosphate).**

antagonist: a competing factor that counteracts the action of another factor. When a drug displaces a vitamin from its site of action, the drug renders the vitamin ineffective and thus acts as a vitamin antagonist.

carpal tunnel syndrome: a pinched nerve at the wrist, causing pain or numbness in the hand. It is often caused by repetitive motion of the wrist.

---

* INH stands for isonicotinic acid hydrazide.

FIGURE 10-8 Vitamin B$_6$ in Selected Foods

See the "How to" section on p. 329 for more information on using this figure.

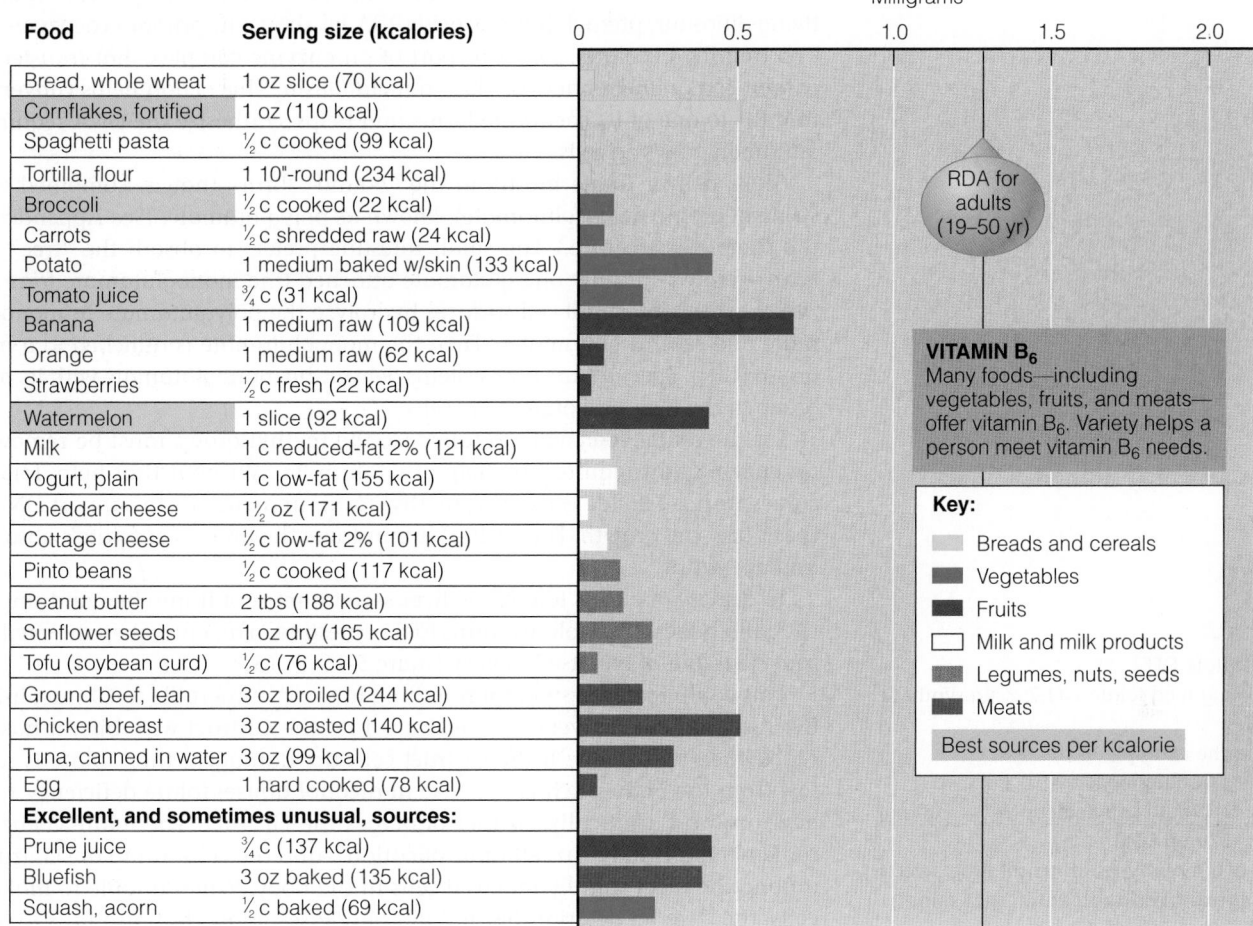

Food	Serving size (kcalories)
Bread, whole wheat	1 oz slice (70 kcal)
Cornflakes, fortified	1 oz (110 kcal)
Spaghetti pasta	½ c cooked (99 kcal)
Tortilla, flour	1 10"-round (234 kcal)
Broccoli	½ c cooked (22 kcal)
Carrots	½ c shredded raw (24 kcal)
Potato	1 medium baked w/skin (133 kcal)
Tomato juice	¾ c (31 kcal)
Banana	1 medium raw (109 kcal)
Orange	1 medium raw (62 kcal)
Strawberries	½ c fresh (22 kcal)
Watermelon	1 slice (92 kcal)
Milk	1 c reduced-fat 2% (121 kcal)
Yogurt, plain	1 c low-fat (155 kcal)
Cheddar cheese	1½ oz (171 kcal)
Cottage cheese	½ c low-fat 2% (101 kcal)
Pinto beans	½ c cooked (117 kcal)
Peanut butter	2 tbs (188 kcal)
Sunflower seeds	1 oz dry (165 kcal)
Tofu (soybean curd)	½ c (76 kcal)
Ground beef, lean	3 oz broiled (244 kcal)
Chicken breast	3 oz roasted (140 kcal)
Tuna, canned in water	3 oz (99 kcal)
Egg	1 hard cooked (78 kcal)
Excellent, and sometimes unusual, sources:	
Prune juice	¾ c (137 kcal)
Bluefish	3 oz baked (135 kcal)
Squash, acorn	½ c baked (69 kcal)

RDA for adults (19–50 yr)

VITAMIN B$_6$
Many foods—including vegetables, fruits, and meats—offer vitamin B$_6$. Variety helps a person meet vitamin B$_6$ needs.

Key:
- Breads and cereals
- Vegetables
- Fruits
- Milk and milk products
- Legumes, nuts, seeds
- Meats

Best sources per kcalorie

---

derived foods. Fiber does not appear to interfere with absorption of vitamin B$_6$. The summary table lists food sources of vitamin B$_6$ as well as its chief functions in the body and the common symptoms of deficiency and toxicity.

IN SUMMARY Vitamin B$_6$

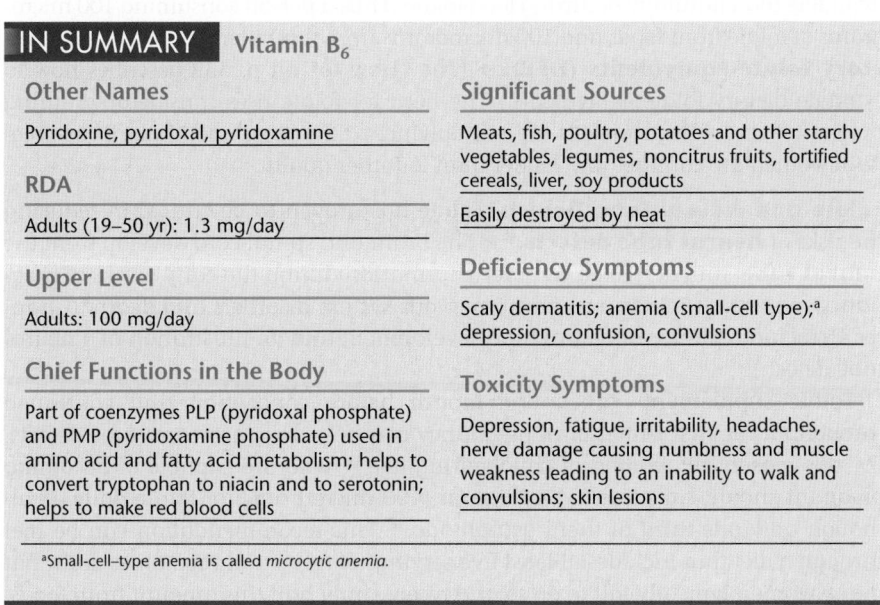

Other Names

Pyridoxine, pyridoxal, pyridoxamine

RDA

Adults (19–50 yr): 1.3 mg/day

Upper Level

Adults: 100 mg/day

Chief Functions in the Body

Part of coenzymes PLP (pyridoxal phosphate) and PMP (pyridoxamine phosphate) used in amino acid and fatty acid metabolism; helps to convert tryptophan to niacin and to serotonin; helps to make red blood cells

Significant Sources

Meats, fish, poultry, potatoes and other starchy vegetables, legumes, noncitrus fruits, fortified cereals, liver, soy products

Easily destroyed by heat

Deficiency Symptoms

Scaly dermatitis; anemia (small-cell type);[a] depression, confusion, convulsions

Toxicity Symptoms

Depression, fatigue, irritability, headaches, nerve damage causing numbness and muscle weakness leading to an inability to walk and convulsions; skin lesions

[a]Small-cell–type anemia is called *microcytic anemia*.

Most protein-rich foods such as meat, fish, and poultry provide ample vitamin B$_6$; some vegetables and fruits are good sources, too.

© Polara Studios Inc.

Folate

Folate, also known as folacin or folic acid, has a chemical name that would fit a flying dinosaur: pteroylglutamic acid (PGA for short). Its primary coenzyme form, THF (tetrahydrofolate), serves as part of an enzyme complex that transfers one-carbon compounds that arise during metabolism. This action helps convert vitamin B_{12} to one of its coenzyme forms and helps synthesize the DNA required for all rapidly growing cells.

Foods deliver folate mostly in the "bound" form—that is, combined with a string of amino acids (glutamate), known as polyglutamate. (See Appendix C for the chemical structure.) The small intestine prefers to absorb the "free" folate form—folate with only one glutamate attached (the monoglutamate form).[8] Enzymes on the intestinal cell surfaces hydrolyze the polyglutamate to monoglutamate and several glutamates. Then the monoglutamate is attached to a methyl group (CH_3). Special transport systems deliver the monoglutamate with its methyl group to the liver and other body cells.

For the folate coenzyme to function, the methyl group must be removed by an enzyme that requires the help of vitamin B_{12}. Without that help, folate becomes trapped inside cells in its methyl form, unavailable to support DNA synthesis and cell growth. Figure 10-9 summarizes the process of folate's absorption and activation.

To dispose of excess folate, the liver secretes most of it into bile and ships it to the gallbladder. Thus folate returns to the intestine in an enterohepatic circulation route like that of bile itself (review Figure 5-16, p. 151).

This complicated system for handling folate is vulnerable to GI tract injuries. Because folate is actively secreted back into the GI tract with bile, it has to be reabsorbed repeatedly. If the GI tract cells are damaged, then folate is rapidly lost from the body. Such is the case in alcohol abuse; folate deficiency rapidly develops and, ironically, further damages the GI tract. The folate coenzymes, remember, are active in cell multiplication—and the cells lining the GI tract are among the most rapidly renewed cells in the body. When unable to make new cells, the GI tract deteriorates and not only loses folate, but also fails to absorb other nutrients.

Folate Recommendations The bioavailability of folate ranges from 50 percent for foods to 100 percent for supplements taken on an empty stomach. These differences in bioavailability were considered when establishing the folate RDA. Naturally occurring folate from foods is given full credit. Synthetic folate from fortified foods and supplements is given extra credit because, on average, it is 1.7 times more available than naturally occurring food folate. Thus a person consuming 100 micrograms of folate from foods and 100 micrograms from a supplement receives 270 **dietary folate equivalents (DFE)**. ◆ (The "How to" on p. 339 describes how to estimate dietary folate equivalents.) The need for folate rises considerably during pregnancy and whenever cells are multiplying, so the recommendations for pregnant women are considerably higher than for other adults.

Folate and Neural Tube Defects Folate has proven to be critical in reducing the risks of **neural tube defects**.[9] ◆ The brain and spinal cord develop from the **neural tube,** and defects in its orderly formation during the early weeks of pregnancy may result in various central nervous system disorders and death. (Chapter 15 includes photos of neural tube development and an illustration of a neural tube defect.)

Folate supplements taken one month before conception and continued throughout the first trimester of pregnancy can help prevent neural tube defects. For this reason, all women of childbearing age ◆ who are capable of becoming pregnant should consume 0.4 milligram (400 micrograms) of folate daily, ◆ although only one-third of them actually do.[10] This recommendation can be met through a diet that includes at least five servings of fruits and vegetables daily, but many women typically fail to do so and receive only half this amount from foods.

◆ To calculate DFE:

DFE = µg food folate + (1.7 × µg synthetic folate)

Using the example in the text:

100 µg food
+ 170 µg supplement (1.7 × 100 µg)
270 µg DFE

◆ The two main types of neural tube defects are **spina bifida** (literally, "split spine") and **anencephaly** ("no brain").

◆ Women of childbearing age (15 to 45 yr) should:
  • Eat folate-rich foods
  • Eat folate-fortified foods
  • Take a multivitamin daily (most provide 400 µg folate)

◆ Reminder: A milligram (mg) is one-thousandth of a gram. A microgram (µg) is one-thousandth of a milligram (or one-millionth of a gram).
  • 0.4 mg = 400 µg

---

folate (FOLE-ate): a B vitamin; also known as folic acid, folacin, or pteroylglutamic (tare-o-EEL-glue-TAM-ick) acid (PGA). The coenzyme forms are **DHF (dihydrofolate)** and **THF (tetrahydrofolate).**

dietary folate equivalents (DFE): the amount of folate available to the body from naturally occurring sources, fortified foods, and supplements, accounting for differences in the bioavailability from each source.

neural tube defects: malformations of the brain, spinal cord, or both during embryonic development that often result in lifelong disability or death.

neural tube: the embryonic tissue that forms the brain and spinal cord.

FIGURE 10-9 Folate's Absorption and Activation

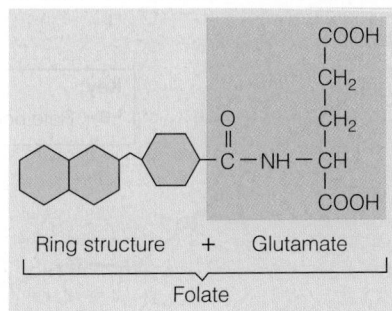

Ring structure + Glutamate

Folate

Spinach

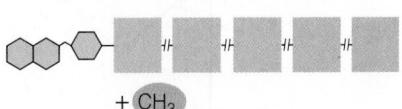

In foods, folate naturally occurs as polyglutamate. (Folate occurs as mono-glutamate in fortified foods and supplements.)

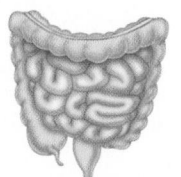
Intestine

$+ CH_3$

In the intestine, digestion breaks glutamates off . . . and adds a methyl group. Folate is absorbed and delivered to cells.

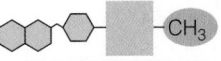
$-CH_3$

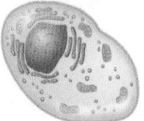
Cell

In the cells, folate is trapped in its inactive form.

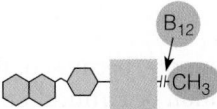
B_{12} CH_3

To activate folate, vitamin B_{12} removes and keeps the methyl group, which activates vitamin B_{12}.

$B_{12}-CH_3$

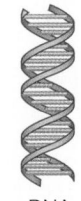
DNA

Both the folate coenzyme and the vitamin B_{12} coenzyme are now active and available for DNA synthesis.

HOW TO Estimate Dietary Folate Equivalents

Folate is expressed in terms of DFE (dietary folate equivalents) because synthetic folate from supplements and fortified foods is absorbed at almost twice (1.7 times) the rate of naturally occurring folate from other foods. Use the following equation to calculate:

DFE = µg food folate + (1.7 × µg synthetic folate)

Consider, for example, a pregnant woman who takes a supplement and eats a bowl of fortified cornflakes, 2 slices of fortified bread, and a cup of fortified pasta. From the supplement and fortified foods, she obtains synthetic folate:

Supplement	100 µg folate
Fortified cornflakes	100 µg folate
Fortified bread	40 µg folate
Fortified pasta	60 µg folate
	300 µg folate

To calculate the DFE, multiply the amount of synthetic folate by 1.7:

300 µg × 1.7 = 510 µg DFE

Now add the naturally occurring folate from the other foods in her diet—in this example, another 90 µg of folate.

510 µg DFE + 90 µg = 600 µg DFE

Notice that if we had not converted synthetic folate from supplements and fortified foods to DFE, then this woman's intake would appear to fall short of the 600 µg recommendation for pregnancy (300 µg + 90 µg = 390 µg). But as our example shows, her intake does meet the recommendation. At this time, supplement and fortified food labels list folate in µg only, not µg DFE, making such calculations necessary.

ThomsonNOW

To practice estimating folate equivalents, log on to **www.thomsonedu.com/thomsonnow**, go to Chapter 10, then go to How To.

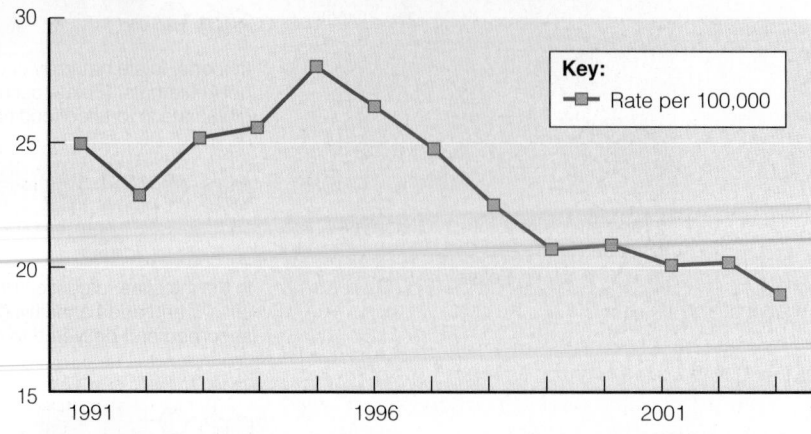

FIGURE 10-10   Decreasing Spina Bifida Rates since Folate Fortification

Neural tube defects have declined since folate fortification began in 1996.

Key:
Rate per 100,000

SOURCE: National Vital Statistics System, National Center for Health Statistics, Centers for Disease Control.

Furthermore, because of the enhanced bioavailability of synthetic folate, supplementation or fortification improves folate status significantly. Women who have given birth to infants with neural tube defects previously should consume 4 milligrams of folate daily before conception and throughout the first trimester of pregnancy.

Because half of the pregnancies each year are unplanned and because neural tube defects occur early in development before most women realize they are pregnant, the Food and Drug Administration (FDA) has mandated that grain products be fortified to deliver folate to the U.S. population.* Labels on fortified products may claim that "adequate intake of folate has been shown to reduce the risk of neural tube defects." Fortification has improved folate status in women of childbearing age and lowered the number of neural tube defects that occur each year, as Figure 10-10 shows.[11] Whether additional fortification will help save even more infants is a topic of current debate.[12]

Folate fortification raises safety concerns as well, especially because folate intakes from fortified foods are more than twice as high as originally predicted.[13] Because high intakes of folate complicate the diagnosis of a vitamin B_{12} deficiency, folate consumption should not exceed 1 milligram daily without close medical supervision.[14]

Some research suggests a relationship between abnormal folate metabolism and non-neural tube birth defects such as Down syndrome.[15] Folate's exact role, however, remains unclear, and supplementation does not appear to decrease the prevalence of Down syndrome.[16] Some women whose infants develop these defects are *not* deficient in folate, and others with severe folate deficiencies do *not* give birth to infants with birth defects.[17] Researchers continue to look for other factors that must also be involved.

Folate and Heart Disease The FDA's decision to fortify grain products with folate was strengthened by research indicating an important role for folate in defending against heart disease. As Chapter 6 mentioned, research indicates that high levels of the amino acid homocysteine and low levels of folate increase the risk of fatal heart disease.[18] One of folate's key roles in the body is to break down homocys-

---

* Bread products, flour, corn grits, cornmeal, farina, rice, macaroni, and noodles must be fortified with 140 micrograms of folate per 100 grams of grain. For perspective, 100 grams is roughly 3 slices of bread; 1 cup of flour; 1/2 cup of corn grits, cornmeal, farina, or rice; or 3/4 cup of macaroni or noodles.

teine. Without folate, homocysteine accumulates, which seems to enhance blood clot formation and arterial wall deterioration. Fortified foods and folate supplements raise blood folate and reduce blood homocysteine levels to an extent that may help to prevent heart disease.[19] Supplements do not seem to reduce the risk of death from cardiovascular causes.[20]

Folate and Cancer Folate may also play a role in preventing cancer.[21] Notably, folate may be most effective in protecting those most likely to develop cancers: men who smoke (against pancreatic cancer) and women who drink alcohol (against breast cancer).[22]

Folate Deficiency Folate deficiency impairs cell division and protein synthesis—processes critical to growing tissues. In a folate deficiency, the replacement of red blood cells and GI tract cells falters. Not surprisingly, then, two of the first symptoms of a folate deficiency are **anemia** and GI tract deterioration.

The anemia of folate deficiency is characterized by large, ◆ immature red blood cells. Without folate, DNA damage destroys many of the red blood cells as they attempt to divide and mature.[23] The result is fewer, but larger, red blood cells that cannot carry oxygen or travel through the capillaries as efficiently as normal red blood cells.

Folate deficiencies may develop from inadequate intake and have been reported in infants who were fed goat's milk, which is notoriously low in folate. Folate deficiency may also result from impaired absorption or an unusual metabolic need for the vitamin. Metabolic needs increase in situations where cell multiplication must speed up, such as pregnancies involving twins and triplets; cancer; skin-destroying diseases such as chicken pox and measles; and burns, blood loss, GI tract damage, and the like.

Of all the vitamins, folate appears to be most vulnerable to interactions with drugs, which can lead to a secondary deficiency. Some medications, notably anti-cancer drugs, have a chemical structure similar to folate's structure and can displace the vitamin from enzymes and interfere with normal metabolism. Like all cells, cancer cells need the real vitamin to multiply—without it, they die. Unfortunately, these drugs affect both cancerous cells and healthy cells, and they create a folate deficiency for all cells. (Highlight 17 discusses nutrient-drug interactions and includes a figure illustrating the similarities between the vitamin folate and the anticancer drug methotrexate.)

Aspirin and antacids also interfere with the body's handling of folate. Healthy adults who use these drugs to relieve an occasional headache or upset stomach need not be concerned, but people who rely heavily on aspirin or antacids should be aware of the nutrition consequences. Oral contraceptives may also impair folate status, as may smoking.[24]

Folate Toxicity Naturally occurring folate from foods alone appears to cause no harm. Excess folate from fortified foods or supplements, however, can reach levels that are high enough to obscure a vitamin B_{12} deficiency and delay diagnosis of neurological damage. For this reason, an Upper Level has been established for folate from fortified foods or supplements (see the inside front cover).

Folate Food Sources Figure 10-11 (p. 342) shows that folate is especially abundant in legumes, fruits, and vegetables. The vitamin's name suggests the word *foliage,* and indeed, leafy green vegetables are outstanding sources. With fortification, grain products also contribute folate. The small red and white bars in Figure 10-11 indicate that meats, milk, and milk products are poor folate sources. Heat and oxidation during cooking and storage can destroy as much as half of the folate in foods. The table on the next page provides a summary of folate information.

© Polara Studios Inc.

Leafy dark green vegetables (such as spinach and broccoli), legumes (such as black beans, kidney beans, and black-eyed peas), liver, and some fruits (notably citrus fruits and juices) are naturally rich in folate.

◆ Large-cell anemia is known as **macrocytic** or **megaloblastic anemia.**
- **macro** = large
- **cyte** = cell
- **mega** = large

anemia (ah-NEE-me-ah): literally, "too little blood." Anemia is any condition in which too few red blood cells are present, or the red blood cells are immature (and therefore large) or too small or contain too little hemoglobin to carry the normal amount of oxygen to the tissues. It is not a disease itself but can be a symptom of many different disease conditions, including many nutrient deficiencies, bleeding, excessive red blood cell destruction, and defective red blood cell formation.
- **an** = without
- **emia** = blood

FIGURE 10-11 Folate in Selected Foods

See the "How to" section on p. 329 for more information on using this figure.

Food	Serving size (kcalories)
Bread, whole wheat	1 oz slice (70 kcal)
Cornflakes, fortified	1 oz (110 kcal)
Spaghetti pasta	½ c cooked (99 kcal)
Tortilla, flour	1 10"-round (234 kcal)
Broccoli	½ c cooked (22 kcal)
Carrots	½ c shredded raw (24 kcal)
Potato	1 medium baked w/skin (133 kcal)
Tomato juice	½ c (31 kcal)
Banana	1 medium raw (109 kcal)
Orange	1 medium raw (62 kcal)
Strawberries	½ c fresh (22 kcal)
Watermelon	1 slice (92 kcal)
Milk	1 c reduced-fat 2% (121 kcal)
Yogurt, plain	1 c low-fat (155 kcal)
Cheddar cheese	1½ oz (171 kcal)
Cottage cheese	½ c low-fat 2% (101 kcal)
Pinto beans	½ c cooked (117 kcal)
Peanut butter	2 tbs (188 kcal)
Sunflower seeds	1 oz dry (165 kcal)
Tofu (soybean curd)	½ c (76 kcal)
Ground beef, lean	3 oz broiled (244 kcal)
Chicken breast	3 oz roasted (140 kcal)
Tuna, canned in water	3 oz (99 kcal)
Egg	1 hard cooked (78 kcal)
Excellent, and sometimes unusual, sources:	
Lentils	½ c cooked (115 kcal)
Asparagus	½ c cooked (22 kcal)
Orange juice	¾ c fresh (84 kcal)

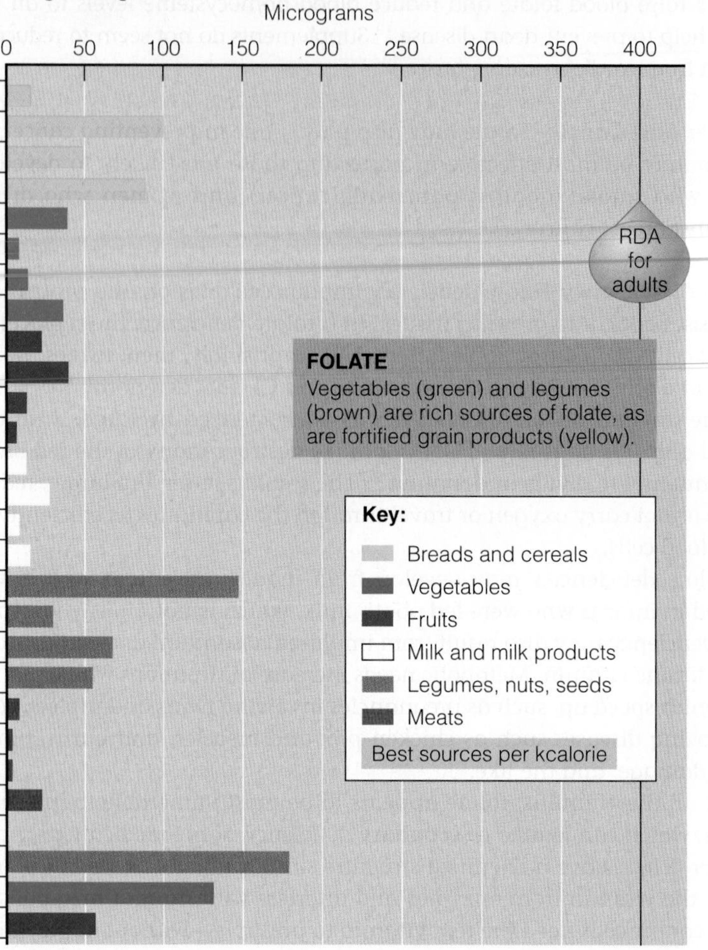

FOLATE
Vegetables (green) and legumes (brown) are rich sources of folate, as are fortified grain products (yellow).

Key:
- Breads and cereals
- Vegetables
- Fruits
- Milk and milk products
- Legumes, nuts, seeds
- Meats
- Best sources per kcalorie

RDA for adults

IN SUMMARY Folate

Other Names

Folic acid, folacin, pteroylglutamic acid (PGA)

RDA

Adults: 400 µg/day

Upper Level

Adults: 1000 µg/day

Chief Functions in the Body

Part of coenzymes THF (tetrahydrofolate) and DHF (dihydrofolate) used in DNA synthesis and therefore important in new cell formation

Significant Sources

Fortified grains, leafy green vegetables, legumes, seeds, liver

Easily destroyed by heat and oxygen

Deficiency Symptoms

Anemia (large-cell type);[a] smooth, red tongue;[b] mental confusion, weakness, fatigue, irritability, headache; shortness of breath; elevated homocysteine

Toxicity Symptoms

Masks vitamin B_{12}–deficiency symptoms

[a] Large-cell–type anemia is known as either *macrocytic* or *megaloblastic anemia*.
[b] Smoothness of the tongue is caused by loss of its surface structures and is termed *glossitis* (gloss-EYE-tis).

---

vitamin B_{12}: a B vitamin characterized by the presence of cobalt (see Figure 13-12, p. 462). The active forms of coenzyme B_{12} are **methylcobalamin** and **deoxyadenosylcobalamin**.

Vitamin B_{12}

Vitamin B_{12} and folate are closely related: each depends on the other for activation. Recall that vitamin B_{12} removes a methyl group to activate the folate coenzyme. When folate gives up its methyl group, the vitamin B_{12} coenzyme becomes activated (review Figure 10-9 on p. 339).

The regeneration of the amino acid methionine and the synthesis of DNA and RNA depend on both folate and vitamin B_{12}.* In addition, without any help from folate, vitamin B_{12} maintains the sheath that surrounds and protects nerve fibers and promotes their normal growth. Bone cell activity and metabolism also depend on vitamin B_{12}.

In the stomach, hydrochloric acid and the digestive enzyme pepsin release vitamin B_{12} from the proteins to which it is attached in foods. The stomach also secretes a molecule called **intrinsic factor.** As vitamin B_{12} passes to the small intestine, it binds with intrinsic factor. Bound together, intrinsic factor and vitamin B_{12} travel to the end of the small intestine, where receptors recognize the complex. (Importantly, the receptors do not recognize vitamin B_{12} alone without intrinsic factor.) There the intrinsic factor is degraded, and the vitamin is gradually absorbed into the bloodstream. Transport of vitamin B_{12} in the blood depends on specific binding proteins.

Like folate, vitamin B_{12} follows the enterohepatic circulation route. It is continually secreted into bile and delivered to the intestine, where it is reabsorbed. Because most vitamin B_{12} is reabsorbed, healthy people rarely develop a deficiency even when their intake is minimal.

Vitamin B_{12} Recommendations The RDA for adults is only 2.4 micrograms of vitamin B_{12} a day—just over two-millionths of a gram. The ink in the period at the end of this sentence may weigh about 2.4 micrograms. But tiny though this amount appears to the human eye, it contains billions of molecules of vitamin B_{12}, enough to provide coenzymes for all the enzymes that need its help.

Vitamin B_{12} Deficiency and Toxicity Most vitamin B_{12} deficiencies reflect inadequate absorption, not poor intake. Inadequate absorption typically occurs for one of two reasons: a lack of hydrochloric acid or a lack of intrinsic factor. Without hydrochloric acid, the vitamin is not released from the dietary proteins and so is not available for binding with the intrinsic factor. Without the intrinsic factor, the vitamin cannot be absorbed.

Many people, especially those over 50, develop **atrophic gastritis,** a common condition in older people that damages the cells of the stomach. Atrophic gastritis may also develop in response to iron deficiency or infection with *Helicobacter pylori,* the bacterium implicated in ulcer formation. Without healthy stomach cells, production of hydrochloric acid and intrinsic factor diminishes. Even with an adequate intake from foods, vitamin B_{12} status suffers. The vitamin B_{12} deficiency caused by atrophic gastritis and a lack of intrinsic factor is known as **pernicious anemia.**

Some people inherit a defective gene for the intrinsic factor. In such cases, or when the stomach has been injured and cannot produce enough of the intrinsic factor, vitamin B_{12} must be injected to bypass the need for intestinal absorption. Alternatively, the vitamin may be delivered by nasal spray; absorption is rapid, high, and well tolerated.

A prolonged inadequate intake, as can occur with a vegan diet, ◆ may also create a vitamin B_{12} deficiency.[25] People who stop eating animal-derived foods containing vitamin B_{12} may take several years to develop deficiency symptoms because the body recycles much of its vitamin B_{12}, reabsorbing it over and over again. Even when the body fails to absorb vitamin B_{12}, deficiency may take up to three years to develop because the body conserves its supply.

Because vitamin B_{12} is required to convert folate to its active form, one of the most obvious vitamin B_{12}–deficiency symptoms is the anemia of folate deficiency. This anemia is characterized by large, immature red blood cells, which indicate slow DNA synthesis and an inability to divide (see Figure 10-12, p. 344). When folate is

◆ Vitamin B_{12} is found primarily in foods derived from animals.

intrinsic factor: a glycoprotein (a protein with short polysaccharide chains attached) secreted by the stomach cells that binds with vitamin B_{12} in the small intestine to aid in the absorption of vitamin B_{12}.
• **intrinsic** = on the inside

atrophic (a-TRO-fik) **gastritis** (gas-TRY-tis): chronic inflammation of the stomach accompanied by a diminished size and functioning of the mucous membrane and glands.
• **atrophy** = wasting
• **gastro** = stomach
• **itis** = inflammation

pernicious (per-NISH-us) **anemia:** a blood disorder that reflects a vitamin B_{12} deficiency caused by lack of intrinsic factor and characterized by abnormally large and immature red blood cells. Other symptoms include muscle weakness and irreversible neurological damage.
• **pernicious** = destructive

---

* In the body, methionine serves as a methyl (CH_3) donor. In doing so, methionine can be converted to other amino acids. Some of these amino acids can regenerate methionine, but methionine is still considered an essential amino acid that is needed in the diet.

FIGURE 10-12   Normal and Anemic Blood Cells

The anemia of folate deficiency is indistinguishable from that of vitamin B_{12} deficiency. Appendix E describes the biochemical tests used to differentiate the two conditions.

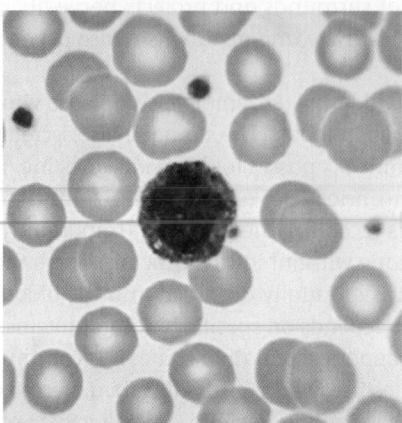

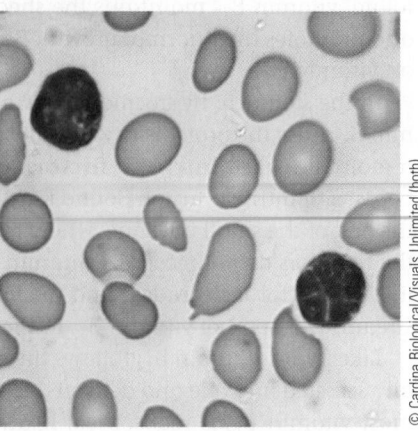

© Cardina Biological/Visuals Unlimited (both)

Normal blood cells. The size, shape, and color of these red blood cells show that they are normal.

Blood cells in pernicious anemia (megaloblastic). These megaloblastic blood cells are slightly larger than normal red blood cells, and their shapes are irregular.

trapped in its inactive (methyl folate) form due to vitamin B_{12} deficiency or is unavailable due to folate deficiency itself, DNA synthesis slows.

First to be affected in a vitamin B_{12} or folate deficiency are the rapidly growing blood cells. Either vitamin B_{12} or folate will clear up the anemia, but if folate is given when vitamin B_{12} is needed, the result is disastrous: devastating neurological symptoms. Remember that vitamin B_{12}, but not folate, maintains the sheath that surrounds and protects nerve fibers and promotes their normal growth. Folate "cures" the *blood* symptoms of a vitamin B_{12} deficiency, but cannot stop the *nerve* symptoms from progressing. By doing so, folate "masks" a vitamin B_{12} deficiency. Marginal vitamin B_{12} deficiency impairs performance on tests measuring intelligence, spatial ability, and short-term memory. Advanced neurological symptoms include a creeping paralysis that begins at the extremities and works inward and up the spine. Early detection and correction are necessary to prevent permanent nerve damage and paralysis. With sufficient folate in the diet, the neurological symptoms of vitamin B_{12} deficiency can develop without evidence of anemia. Such interactions between folate and vitamin B_{12} highlight some of the safety issues surrounding the use of supplements and the fortification of foods. No adverse effects have been reported for excess vitamin B_{12}, and no Upper Level has been set.

Vitamin B_{12} Food Sources   Vitamin B_{12} is unique among the vitamins in being found almost exclusively in foods derived from animals. Anyone who eats reasonable amounts of meat is guaranteed an adequate intake, and vegetarians who use milk products or eggs are also protected from deficiency. Vegans, who restrict all foods derived from animals, need a reliable source, such as vitamin B_{12}–fortified soy milk or vitamin B_{12} supplements. Yeast grown on a vitamin B_{12}–enriched medium and mixed with that medium provides some vitamin B_{12}, but yeast itself does not contain active vitamin B_{12}. Fermented soy products such as miso (a soybean paste) and sea algae such as spirulina also do *not* provide active vitamin B_{12}. Extensive research shows that the amounts listed on the labels of these plant products are inaccurate and misleading because the vitamin B_{12} is in an inactive, unavailable form.

As mentioned earlier, the water-soluble vitamins are particularly vulnerable to losses in cooking. For most of these nutrients, microwave heating minimizes losses as well as, or better than, traditional cooking methods. Such is not the case for vitamin B_{12}, however. Microwave heating inactivates vitamin B_{12}. To preserve this vitamin, use the oven or stovetop instead of a microwave to cook meats and milk products (major sources of vitamin B_{12}). The accompanying table provides a summary of information about vitamin B_{12}.

IN SUMMARY Vitamin B_{12}

Other Names

Cobalamin (and related forms)

RDA

Adults: 2.4 µg/day

Chief Functions in the Body

Part of coenzymes methylcobalamin and deoxyadenosylcobalamin used in new cell synthesis; helps to maintain nerve cells; reforms folate coenzyme; helps to break down some fatty acids and amino acids

Significant Sources

Foods of animal origin (meat, fish, poultry, shellfish, milk, cheese, eggs), fortified cereals

Easily destroyed by microwave cooking

Deficiency Disease

Pernicious anemia[a]

Deficiency Symptoms

Anemia (large-cell type);[b] fatigue, degeneration of peripheral nerves progressing to paralysis; sore tongue, loss of appetite, constipation

Toxicity Symptoms

None reported

[a]The name *pernicious anemia* refers to the vitamin B_{12} deficiency caused by atrophic gastritis and a lack of intrinsic factor, but not to that caused by inadequate dietary intake.
[b]Large-cell–type anemia is known as either *macrocytic* or *megaloblastic anemia*.

Non-B Vitamins

Nutrition scientists debate whether other dietary compounds might also be considered vitamins. In some cases, the compounds may be conditionally essential—that is, needed by the body from foods when synthesis becomes insufficient to support normal growth and metabolism. In other cases, the compounds may be vitamin impostors—not needed under any circumstances.

Choline Determining whether choline ◆ is an essential nutrient has been blurry for decades, in part because the body can make choline from the amino acid methionine. Furthermore, choline is commonly found in many foods as part of the lecithin molecule (review Figure 5-9 on p. 146). Consequently, choline deficiencies are rare. Without any dietary choline, however, synthesis alone appears to be insufficient to meet the body's needs, making choline a conditionally essential nutrient. For this reason, the 1998 DRI report established an Adequate Intake (AI) for choline. The body uses choline to make the neurotransmitter acetylcholine and the phospholipid lecithin. During fetal development, choline supports the structure and function of the brain and spinal chord.[26] The accompanying table summarizes key choline facts.

◆ Reminder: *Choline* is a nitrogen-containing compound found in foods and made in the body from the amino acid methionine. Choline is part of the phospholipid lecithin and the neurotransmitter acetylcholine.

IN SUMMARY Choline

Adequate Intake (AI)

Men: 550 mg/day

Women: 425 mg/day

Upper Level

Adults: 3500 mg/day

Chief Functions in the Body

Needed for the synthesis of the neurotransmitter acetylcholine and the phospholipid lecithin

Deficiency Symptoms

Liver damage

Toxicity Symptoms

Body odor, sweating, salivation, reduced growth rate, low blood pressure, liver damage

Significant Sources

Milk, liver, eggs, peanuts

Inositol and Carnitine **Inositol** is a part of cell membrane structures, and **carnitine** transports long-chain fatty acids from the cytosol to the mitochondria for oxidation. Like choline, these two substances can be made by the body, but unlike choline, no recommendations have been established. Researchers continue to explore the possibility that these substances may be essential. Even if they are essential, though, supplements are unnecessary because these compounds are widespread in foods.

Some vitamin companies include choline, inositol, and carnitine in their formulations to make their vitamin pills look more "complete" than others, but this strategy offers no real advantage. For a rational way to compare vitamin-mineral supplements, read Highlight 10.

Vitamin Impostors Other substances have been mistaken for essential nutrients for human beings because they are needed for growth by bacteria or other forms of life. Among them are PABA (para-aminobenzoic acid, a component of folate's ring structure), the bioflavonoids (vitamin P or hesperidin), pyrroloquinoline quinone (methoxatin), orotic acid, lipoic acid, and ubiquinone (coenzyme Q_{10}). Other names erroneously associated with vitamins are "vitamin O" (oxygenated salt water), "vitamin B_5" (another name for pantothenic acid), "vitamin B_{15}" (also called "pangamic acid," a hoax), and "vitamin B_{17}" (laetrile, an alleged "cancer cure" and not a vitamin or a cure by any stretch of the imagination—in fact, laetrile is a potentially dangerous substance).

IN SUMMARY

The B vitamins serve as coenzymes that facilitate the work of every cell. They are active in carbohydrate, fat, and protein metabolism and in the making of DNA and thus new cells. Historically famous B vitamin–deficiency diseases are beriberi (thiamin), pellagra (niacin), and pernicious anemia (vitamin B_{12}). Pellagra can be prevented by adequate protein because the amino acid tryptophan can be converted to niacin in the body. A high intake of folate can mask the blood symptoms of a vitamin B_{12} deficiency, but it will not prevent the associated nerve damage. Vitamin B_6 participates in amino acid metabolism and can be harmful in excess. Biotin and pantothenic acid serve important roles in energy metabolism and are common in a variety of foods. Many substances that people claim as B vitamins are not.

The B Vitamins—In Concert

This chapter has described some of the impressive ways that vitamins work individually, as if their many actions in the body could easily be disentangled. In fact, it is often difficult to tell which vitamin is truly responsible for a given effect because the nutrients are interdependent; the presence or absence of one affects another's absorption, metabolism, and excretion. You have already seen this interdependence with folate and vitamin B_{12}.

Riboflavin and vitamin B_6 provide another example. One of the riboflavin coenzymes, FMN, assists the enzyme that converts vitamin B_6 to its coenzyme form PLP. Consequently, a severe riboflavin deficiency can impair vitamin B_6 activity.[27] Thus a deficiency of one nutrient may alter the action of another. Furthermore, a deficiency of one nutrient may create a deficiency of another. For example, both riboflavin and vitamin B_6 (as well as iron) are required for the conversion of tryptophan to niacin. Consequently, an inadequate intake of either riboflavin or vitamin B_6 can diminish the body's niacin supply. These interdependent relationships are evident in many of the roles B vitamins play in the body.

inositol (in-OSS-ih-tall): a nonessential nutrient that can be made in the body from glucose. Inositol is a part of cell membrane structures.

carnitine (CAR-neh-teen): a nonessential, nonprotein amino acid made in the body from lysine that helps transport fatty acids across the mitochondrial membrane.

B Vitamin Roles

Figure 10-13 summarizes the metabolic pathways introduced in Chapter 7 and conveys an *impression* of the many ways B vitamins assist in those metabolic pathways. Metabolism is the body's work, and the B vitamin coenzymes are indispensable to every step. In scanning the pathways of metabolism depicted in the figure, note the many abbreviations for the coenzymes that keep the processes going.

Look at the now-familiar pathway of glucose breakdown. To break down glucose to pyruvate, the cells must have certain enzymes. For the enzymes to work, they must have the niacin coenzyme NAD. To make NAD, the cells must be supplied with niacin (or enough of the amino acid tryptophan to make niacin). They can make the rest of the coenzyme without dietary help.

FIGURE 10-13 *Animated!* **Metabolic Pathways Involving B Vitamins**

These metabolic pathways were introduced in Chapter 7 and are presented here to highlight the many coenzymes that facilitate the reactions. These coenzymes depend on the following vitamins:

- NAD and NADP: niacin
- TPP: thiamin
- CoA: pantothenic acid
- B$_{12}$: vitamin B$_{12}$
- FMN and FAD: riboflavin
- THF: folate
- PLP: vitamin B$_6$
- Biotin

Pathways leading toward acetyl CoA and the TCA cycle are catabolic, and those leading toward amino acids, glycogen, and fat are anabolic. For further details, see Appendix C.

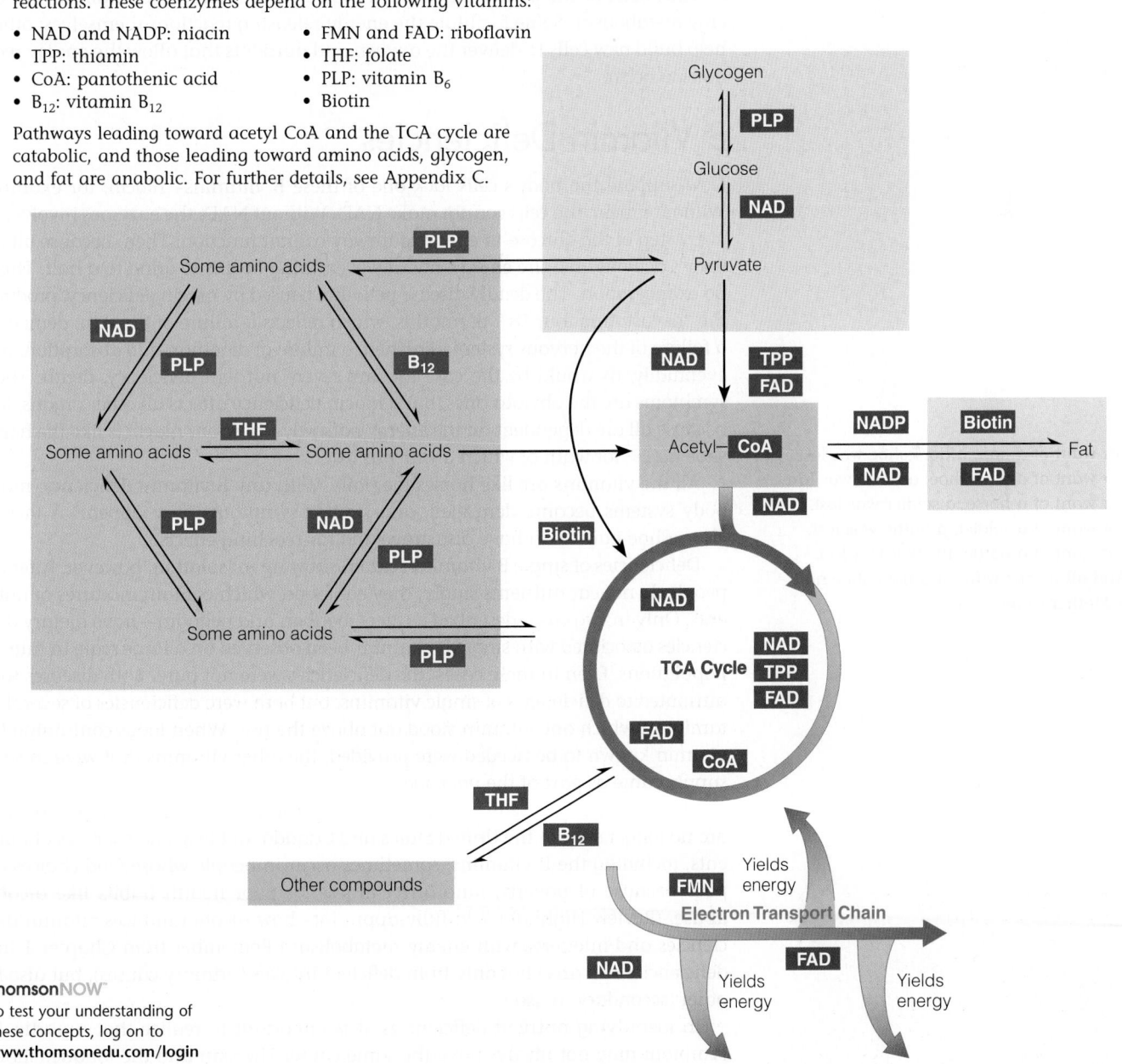

The next step is the breakdown of pyruvate to acetyl CoA. The enzymes involved in this step require both NAD and the thiamin and riboflavin coenzymes TPP and FAD, respectively. The cells can manufacture the enzymes they need from the vitamins, if the vitamins are in the diet.

Another coenzyme needed for this step is CoA. Predictably, the cells can make CoA except for an essential part that must be obtained in the diet—pantothenic acid. Another coenzyme requiring biotin serves the enzyme complex involved in converting pyruvate to oxaloacetate, the compound that combines with acetyl CoA to start the TCA cycle.

These and other coenzymes participate throughout all the metabolic pathways. When the diet provides riboflavin, the body synthesizes FAD—a needed coenzyme in the TCA cycle. Vitamin B_6 is an indispensable part of PLP—a coenzyme required for many amino acid conversions, for a crucial step in the making of the iron-containing portion of hemoglobin for red blood cells, and for many other reactions. Folate becomes THF—the coenzyme required for the synthesis of new genetic material and therefore new cells. The vitamin B_{12} coenzyme, in turn, regenerates THF to its active form; thus vitamin B_{12} is also necessary for the formation of new cells.

Thus each of the B vitamin coenzymes is involved, directly or indirectly, in energy metabolism. Some facilitate the energy-releasing reactions themselves; others help build new cells to deliver the oxygen and nutrients that allow the energy reactions to occur.

B Vitamin Deficiencies

Now suppose the body's cells lack one of these B vitamins—niacin, for example. Without niacin, the cells cannot make NAD. Without NAD, the enzymes involved in every step of the glucose-to-energy pathway cannot function. Then, because all the body's activities require energy, literally everything begins to grind to a halt. This is no exaggeration. The deadly disease pellagra, caused by niacin deficiency, produces the "devastating four Ds": dermatitis, which reflects a failure of the skin; dementia, a failure of the nervous system; diarrhea, a failure of digestion and absorption; and eventually, as would be the case for any severe nutrient deficiency, death. These symptoms are the obvious ones, but a niacin deficiency affects all other organs, too, because all are dependent on the energy pathways. In short, niacin is like the horseshoe nail ◆ for want of which a war was lost.

All the vitamins are like horseshoe nails. With any B vitamin deficiency, many body systems become deranged, and similar symptoms may appear. A lack of "horseshoe nails" can have disastrous and far-reaching effects.

Deficiencies of single B vitamins seldom show up in isolation, however. After all, people do not eat nutrients singly; they eat foods, which contain mixtures of nutrients. Only in two cases described earlier—beriberi and pellagra—have dietary deficiencies associated with single B vitamins been observed on a large scale in human populations. Even in these cases, the deficiencies were not pure. Both diseases were attributed to deficiencies of single vitamins, but both were deficiencies of several vitamins in which one vitamin stood out above the rest. When foods containing the vitamin known to be needed were provided, the other vitamins that were in short supply came as part of the package.

Major deficiency diseases of epidemic proportions such as pellagra and beriberi are no longer seen in the United States and Canada, but lesser deficiencies of nutrients, including the B vitamins, sometimes occur in people whose food choices are poor because of poverty, ignorance, illness, or poor health habits like alcohol abuse. (Review Highlight 7 to fully appreciate how alcohol induces vitamin deficiencies and interferes with energy metabolism.) Remember from Chapter 1 that deficiencies can arise not only from deficient intakes (primary causes), but also for other (secondary) reasons.

In identifying nutrient deficiencies, it is important to realize that a particular symptom may not always have the same cause. The skin and the tongue (shown in Figure 10-14) appear to be especially sensitive to B vitamin deficiencies, but iso-

◆ For want of a nail, a horseshoe was lost.
 For want of a horseshoe, a horse was lost.
 For want of a horse, a soldier was lost.
 For want of a soldier, a battle was lost.
 For want of a battle, the war was lost,
 And all for the want of a horseshoe nail!
 —Mother Goose

FIGURE 10-14 B Vitamin–Deficiency Symptoms—The Smooth Tongue of Glossitis and the Skin Lesions of Cheilosis

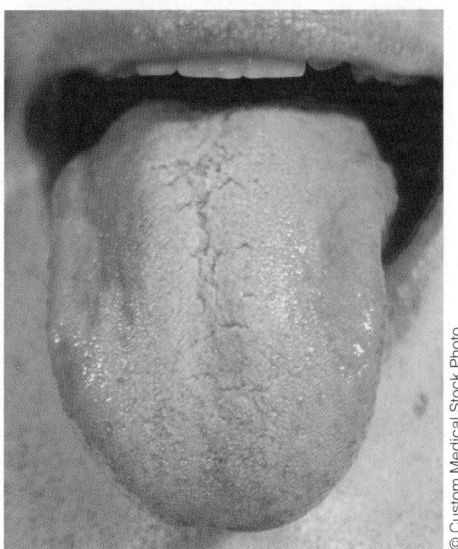

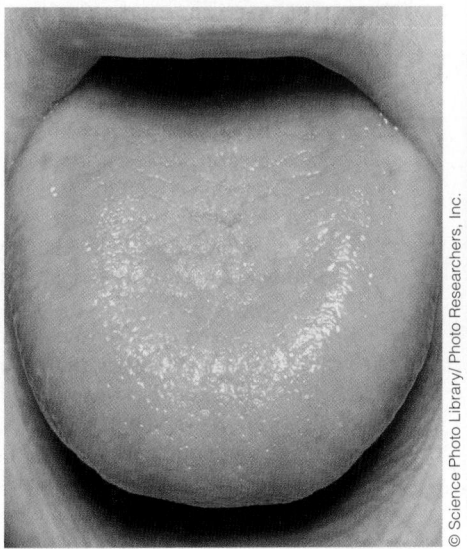

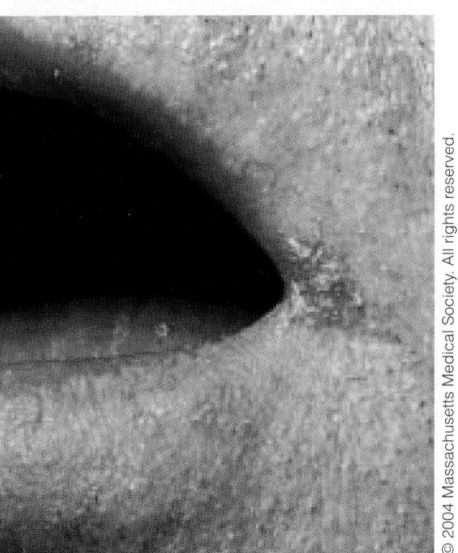

A healthy tongue has a rough and somewhat bumpy surface.

In a B vitamin deficiency, the tongue becomes smooth and swollen due to atrophy of the tissue (glossitis).

In a B vitamin deficiency, the corners of the mouth become irritated and inflamed (cheilosis).

lating these body parts in the summary tables earlier in this chapter gives them undue emphasis. Both the skin and the tongue ◆ are readily visible in a physical examination. The physician sees and reports the deficiency's outward symptoms, but the full impact of a vitamin deficiency occurs inside the cells of the body. If the skin develops a rash or lesions, other tissues beneath it may be degenerating, too. Similarly, the mouth and tongue are the visible part of the digestive system; if they are abnormal, most likely the rest of the GI tract is, too. The "How to" (p. 350) offers other insights into symptoms and their causes.

◆ Two symptoms commonly seen in B vitamin deficiencies are **glossitis** (gloss-EYE-tis), an inflammation of the tongue, and **cheilosis** (kye-LOH-sis or kee-LOH-sis), a condition of reddened lips with cracks at the corners of the mouth.
• **glossa** = tongue
• **cheilos** = lip

B Vitamin Toxicities

Toxicities of the B vitamins from foods alone are unknown, but they can occur when people overuse supplements. With supplements, the quantities can quickly overwhelm the cells. Consider that one small capsule can easily deliver 2 milligrams of vitamin B_6, but it would take more than 3000 bananas, 6600 cups of rice, or 3600 chicken breasts to supply an equivalent amount. When the cells become oversaturated with a vitamin, they must work to eliminate the excess. The cells dispatch water-soluble vitamins to the urine for excretion, but sometimes they cannot keep pace with the onslaught. Homeostasis becomes disturbed and symptoms of toxicity develop.

B Vitamin Food Sources

Significantly, deficiency diseases, such as beriberi and pellagra, were eliminated by supplying foods—not pills. Vitamin pill advertisements make much of the fact that vitamins are indispensable to life, but human beings obtained their nourishment from foods for centuries before vitamin pills existed. If the diet lacks a vitamin, the first solution is to adjust food intake to obtain that vitamin.

Manufacturers of so-called *natural* vitamins boast that their pills are purified from real foods rather than synthesized in a laboratory. Think back on the course of human evolution; it is not *natural* to take any kind of pill. In reality, the finest, most natural vitamin "supplements" available are whole grains, vegetables, fruits, meat, fish, poultry, eggs, legumes, nuts, and milk and milk products.

The cause of a symptom is not always apparent. The summary tables in this chapter show that deficiencies of riboflavin, niacin, biotin, and vitamin B_6 can all cause skin rashes. But so can a deficiency of protein, linoleic acid, or vitamin A. Because skin is on the outside and easy to see, it is a useful indicator of "things going wrong inside cells." But, by itself, a skin symptom says nothing about its possible cause.

The same is true of anemia. Anemia is often caused by iron deficiency, but it can also be caused by a folate or vitamin B_{12} deficiency; by digestive tract failure to absorb any of these nutrients; or by such nonnutritional causes as infections, parasites, cancer, or loss of blood. No single nutrient will always cure a given symptom.

A person who feels chronically tired may be tempted to self-diagnose iron-deficiency anemia and self-prescribe an iron supplement. But this will relieve tiredness only if the cause is indeed iron-deficiency anemia. If the cause is a folate deficiency, taking iron will only prolong the fatigue. A person who is better informed may decide to take a vitamin supplement with iron, covering the possibility of a vitamin deficiency. But the symptom may have a nonnutritional cause. If the cause of the tiredness is actually hidden blood loss due to cancer, the postponement of a diagnosis may be fatal. When fatigue is caused by a lack of sleep, of course, no nutrient or combination of nutrients can replace a good night's rest. A person who is chronically tired should see a physician rather than self-prescribe. If the condition is nutrition related, a registered dietitian should be consulted as well.

The bar graphs of selected foods in this chapter, taken together, sing the praises of a balanced diet. The grains deliver thiamin, riboflavin, niacin, and folate. The fruit and vegetable groups excel in folate. The meat group serves thiamin, niacin, vitamin B_6, and vitamin B_{12} well. The milk group stands out for riboflavin and vitamin B_{12}. A diet that offers a variety of foods from each group, prepared with reasonable care, serves up ample B vitamins.

IN SUMMARY

The B vitamin coenzymes work together in energy metabolism. Some facilitate the energy-releasing reactions themselves; others help build cells to deliver the oxygen and nutrients that permit the energy pathways to run. These vitamins depend on each other to function optimally; a deficiency of any of them creates multiple problems. Fortunately, a variety of foods from each of the food groups provides an adequate supply of all of the B vitamins.

Vitamin C

Two hundred and fifty years ago, any man who joined the crew of a seagoing ship knew he had at best a 50–50 chance of returning alive—not because he might be slain by pirates or die in a storm, but because he might contract the dread disease **scurvy.** As many as two-thirds of a ship's crew could die of scurvy during a long voyage. Only men on short voyages, especially around the Mediterranean Sea, were free of scurvy. No one knew the reason: that on long ocean voyages, the ship's cook used up the fresh fruits and vegetables early and then served only cereals and meats until the return to port.

The first nutrition experiment ever performed on human beings was devised in the mid-1700s to find a cure for scurvy. James Lind, a British physician, divided 12 sailors with scurvy into 6 pairs. Each pair received a different supplemental ration: cider, vinegar, sulfuric acid, seawater, oranges and lemons, or a strong laxative mixed with spices. Those receiving the citrus fruits quickly recovered, but sadly, it was 50 years before the British navy required all vessels to provide every sailor ◆ with lime juice daily.

◆ The tradition of providing British sailors with citrus juice daily to prevent scurvy gave them the nickname "limeys."

scurvy: the vitamin C–deficiency disease.

The antiscurvy "something" in limes and other foods was dubbed the **antiscorbutic factor.** Nearly 200 years later, the factor was isolated and found to be a six-carbon compound similar to glucose; it was named **ascorbic acid.** Shortly thereafter, it was synthesized, and today hundreds of millions of vitamin C pills are produced in pharmaceutical laboratories each year.

Vitamin C Roles

Vitamin C parts company with the B vitamins in its mode of action. In some settings, vitamin C serves as a cofactor ◆ helping a specific enzyme perform its job, but in others, it acts as an antioxidant participating in more general ways.

As an Antioxidant Vitamin C loses electrons easily, a characteristic that allows it to perform as an **antioxidant.** ◆ In the body, antioxidants defend against **free radicals.** Free radicals are discussed in Highlight 11, but for now, a simple definition will suffice. A free radical is a molecule with one or more unpaired electrons, which makes it unstable and highly reactive. By donating an electron or two, antioxidants neutralize free radicals and protect other substances from their damage. Figure 10-15 illustrates how vitamin C can give up electrons to stop free-radical damage and then accept them again to become reactivated. This recycling of vitamin C is key to limiting losses and maintaining a reserve of antioxidants in the body. Transporting and concentrating vitamin C in the cells enhances its role as an antioxidant.[28]

Vitamin C is like a bodyguard for water-soluble substances; it stands ready to sacrifice its own life to save theirs. In the cells and body fluids, vitamin C protects tissues from **oxidative stress** and thus may play an important role in preventing diseases. In the intestines, vitamin C enhances iron absorption by protecting iron from oxidation. (Chapter 13 provides more details about the relationship between vitamin C and iron.)

As a Cofactor in Collagen Formation Vitamin C helps to form the fibrous structural protein of connective tissues known as collagen. ◆ Collagen serves as the matrix on which bones and teeth are formed. When a person is wounded, collagen glues the separated tissues together, forming scars. Cells are held together largely by collagen; this is especially important in the artery walls, which must expand and contract with each beat of the heart, and in the thin capillary walls, which must withstand a pulse of blood every second or so without giving way.

Chapter 6 described how the body makes proteins by stringing together chains of amino acids. During the synthesis of collagen, each time a proline or lysine is added to the growing protein chain, an enzyme hydroxylates it (adds an OH group

◆ Reminder: A *cofactor* is a small, inorganic or organic substance that facilitates the action of an enzyme.

◆ Key antioxidant nutrients:
 • Vitamin C, vitamin E, beta-carotene
 • Selenium

◆ Reminder: *Collagen* is the structural protein from which connective tissues such as scars, tendons, ligaments, and the foundations of bones and teeth are made.

FIGURE 10-15   Active Forms of Vitamin C

The two hydrogens highlighted in yellow give vitamin C its acidity and its ability to act as an antioxidant.

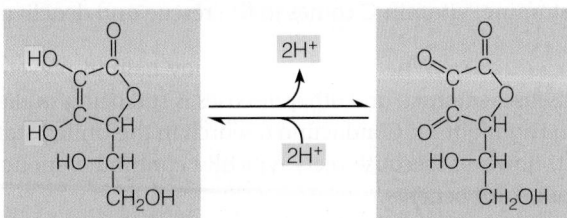

Ascorbic acid protects against oxidative damage by donating its two hydrogens with their electrons to free radicals (molecules with unpaired electrons). In doing so, ascorbic acid becomes dehydroascorbic acid.

Dehydroascorbic acid can readily accept hydrogens to become ascorbic acid. The reversibility of this reaction is key to vitamin C's role as an antioxidant.

antiscorbutic (AN-tee-skor-BUE-tik) **factor:** the original name for vitamin C.
• **anti** = against
• **scorbutic** = causing scurvy

ascorbic acid: one of the two active forms of vitamin C (see Figure 10-15). Many people refer to vitamin C by this name.
• **a** = without
• **scorbic** = having scurvy

antioxidant: a substance in foods that significantly decreases the adverse effects of free radicals on normal physiological functions in the human body.

free radicals: unstable molecules with one or more unpaired electrons.

oxidative stress: a condition in which the production of oxidants and free radicals exceeds the body's ability to handle them and prevent damage.

FIGURE 10-16   Vitamin C Intake (mg/day)

Recommendations for vitamin C are set generously above the minimum requirement and well below the toxicity level.

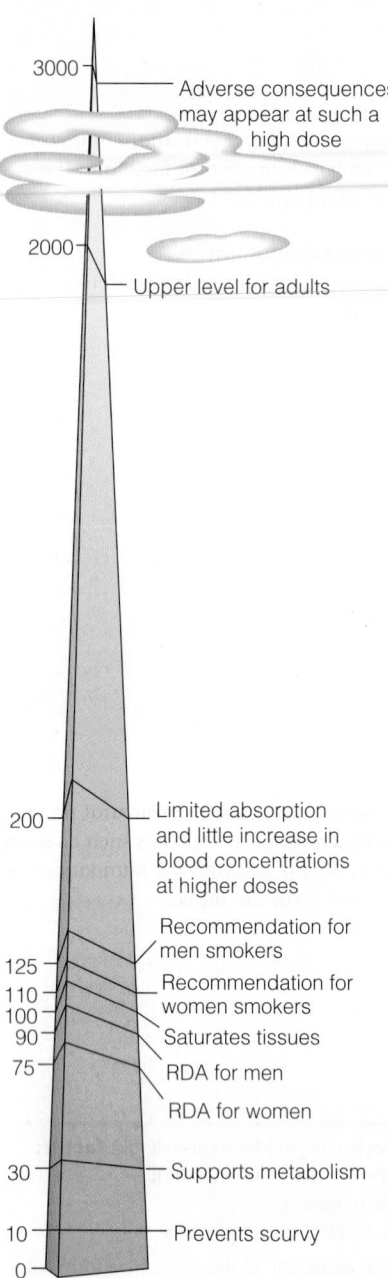

- 3000 — Adverse consequences may appear at such a high dose
- 2000 — Upper level for adults
- 200 — Limited absorption and little increase in blood concentrations at higher doses
- 125 — Recommendation for men smokers
- 110 — Recommendation for women smokers
- 100 — Saturates tissues
- 90 — RDA for men
- 75 — RDA for women
- 30 — Supports metabolism
- 10 — Prevents scurvy
- 0

histamine (HISS-tah-mean or HISS-tah-men): a substance produced by cells of the immune system as part of a local immune reaction to an antigen; participates in causing inflammation.

to it), making the amino acid hydroxyproline or hydroxylysine, respectively. These two special amino acids facilitate the binding together of collagen fibers to make strong, ropelike structures. The conversion of proline to hydroxyproline requires both vitamin C and iron. Iron works as a cofactor in the reaction, and vitamin C protects iron from oxidation, thereby allowing iron to perform its duty. Without vitamin C and iron, the hydroxylation step does not occur.

As a Cofactor in Other Reactions Vitamin C also serves as a cofactor in the synthesis of several other compounds. As in collagen formation, vitamin C helps in the hydroxylation of carnitine, a compound that transports long-chain fatty acids into the mitochondria of a cell for energy metabolism. It participates in the conversions of the amino acids tryptophan and tyrosine to the neurotransmitters serotonin and norepinephrine, respectively. Vitamin C also assists in the making of hormones, including thyroxin, which regulates the metabolic rate; when metabolism speeds up in times of extreme physical stress, the body's use of vitamin C increases.

In Stress The adrenal glands contain more vitamin C than any other organ in the body, and during stress, these glands release the vitamin, together with hormones, into the blood. The vitamin's exact role in the stress reaction remains unclear, but physical stresses raise vitamin C needs. Among the stresses known to increase vitamin C needs are infections; burns; extremely high or low temperatures; intakes of toxic heavy metals such as lead, mercury, and cadmium; the chronic use of certain medications, including aspirin, barbiturates, and oral contraceptives; and cigarette smoking. When immune system cells are called into action, they use a great deal of oxygen and produce free radicals. In this case, free radicals are helpful. They act as ammunition in an "oxidative burst" that demolishes the offending viruses and bacteria and destroys the damaged cells. Vitamin C steps in as an antioxidant to control this oxidative activity.

As a Cure for the Common Cold Newspaper headlines touting vitamin C as a cure for colds have appeared frequently over the years, but research supporting such claims has been conflicting and controversial. Some studies find no relationship between vitamin C and the occurrence of the common cold, whereas others report fewer colds, fewer days, and shorter duration of severe symptoms.[29] A review of the research on vitamin C in the treatment and prevention of the common cold reveals a modest benefit—a significant difference in duration of less than a day per cold in favor of those taking a daily dose of at least 1 gram of vitamin C.[30] The term *significant* means that *statistical* analysis suggests that the findings probably didn't arise by chance, but instead from the experimental treatment being tested. Is one day without a cold sufficient to warrant routine daily supplementation? Supplement users seem to think so.

Interestingly, those who received the placebo *but thought they were receiving vitamin C* had fewer colds than the group who received vitamin C *but thought they were receiving the placebo*. (Never underestimate the healing power of faith!)

Discoveries about how vitamin C works in the body provide possible links between the vitamin and the common cold. Anyone who has ever had a cold knows the discomfort of a runny or stuffed-up nose. Nasal congestion develops in response to elevated blood **histamine,** and people commonly take antihistamines for relief. Like an antihistamine, vitamin C comes to the rescue and deactivates histamine.

In Disease Prevention Whether vitamin C may help in preventing or treating cancer, heart disease, cataract, and other diseases is still being studied, and findings are presented in Highlight 11. Conducting research in the United States and Canada can be difficult, however, because diets typically contribute enough vitamin C to provide optimal health benefits.

Vitamin C Recommendations

How much vitamin C does a person need? As Figure 10-16 illustrates, recommendations are set generously above the minimum requirement to prevent scurvy and well below the toxicity level.[31]

The requirement—the amount needed to prevent the overt symptoms of scurvy—is only 10 milligrams daily. However, 10 milligrams a day does not saturate all the body tissues; higher intakes will increase the body's total vitamin C. At about 100 milligrams ◆ per day, 95 percent of the population probably reaches tissue saturation. At about 200 milligrams, absorption reaches a maximum, and there is little, if any, increase in blood concentrations at higher doses. Excess vitamin C is readily excreted.

As mentioned earlier, cigarette smoking increases the need for vitamin C. Cigarette smoke contains oxidants, which greedily deplete this potent antioxidant. Exposure to cigarette smoke, especially when accompanied by low intakes of vitamin C, depletes the body's pool in both active and passive smokers. People who chew tobacco also have low levels of vitamin C. Because people who smoke cigarettes regularly suffer significant oxidative stress, their requirement for vitamin C is increased an additional 35 milligrams; nonsmokers regularly exposed to cigarette smoke should also be sure to meet their RDA for vitamin C.

◆ For perspective, 1 c orange juice provides >100 mg vitamin C.

Vitamin C Deficiency

Two of the most notable signs of a vitamin C deficiency reflect its role in maintaining the integrity of blood vessels. The gums bleed easily around the teeth, and capillaries under the skin break spontaneously, producing pinpoint hemorrhages (see Figure 10-17).

When the vitamin C pool falls to about a fifth of its optimal size (this may take more than a month on a diet lacking vitamin C), scurvy symptoms begin to appear. Inadequate collagen synthesis causes further hemorrhaging. Muscles, including the heart muscle, degenerate. The skin becomes rough, brown, scaly, and dry. Wounds fail to heal because scar tissue will not form. Bone rebuilding falters; the ends of the long bones become softened, malformed, and painful, and fractures develop. The teeth become loose as the cartilage around them weakens. Anemia and infections are common. There are also characteristic psychological signs, including hysteria and depression. Sudden death is likely, caused by massive internal bleeding.

Once diagnosed, scurvy is readily resolved by vitamin C. Moderate doses in the neighborhood of 100 milligrams per day are sufficient, curing the scurvy within about five days. Such an intake is easily achieved by including vitamin C–rich foods in the diet.

Vitamin C Toxicity

The availability of vitamin C supplements and the publication of books recommending vitamin C to prevent colds and cancer have led thousands of people to

FIGURE 10-17 Vitamin C–Deficiency Symptoms—Scorbutic Gums and Pinpoint Hemorrhages

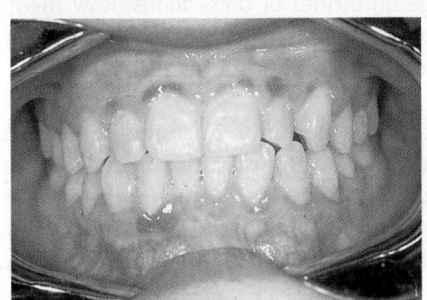

Scorbutic gums. Unlike other lesions of the mouth, scurvy presents a symmetrical appearance without infection.

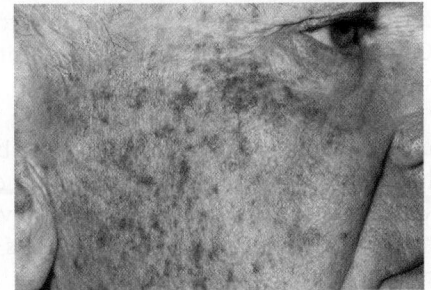

Pinpoint hemorrhages. Small red spots appear in the skin, indicating spontaneous bleeding internally.

When dietitians say "vitamin C," people think "citrus fruits" . . .

. . . but these foods are also rich in vitamin C.

♦ Reminder: *Gout* is a metabolic disease in which uric acid crystals precipitate in the joints.

take large doses of vitamin C. Not surprisingly, side effects of vitamin C supplementation such as nausea, abdominal cramps, and diarrhea are often reported.

Several instances of interference with medical regimens are also known. Large amounts of vitamin C excreted in the urine obscure the results of tests used to detect diabetes, giving a **false positive** result in some instances and a **false negative** in others. People taking anticlotting medications may unwittingly counteract the effect if they also take massive doses of vitamin C. Those with kidney disease, a tendency toward gout, ♦ or a genetic abnormality that alters vitamin C's breakdown to its excretion products are prone to forming kidney stones if they take large doses of vitamin C.* Vitamin C supplements may adversely affect people with iron overload. (Chapter 13 describes the damaging effects of too much iron.) Vitamin C enhances iron absorption and releases iron from body stores; free iron causes the kind of cellular damage typical of free radicals. These adverse consequences of vitamin C's effects on iron have not been seen in clinical studies, but they illustrate how vitamin C can act as a *prooxidant* when quantities exceed the body's needs.[32]

The estimated average intake from both diet and supplements is 187 milligrams of vitamin C a day. Few instances warrant consuming more than 200 milligrams a day. For adults who dose themselves with up to 2 grams a day (and relatively few do), the risks may not be great; those taking more should be aware of the distinct possibility of adverse effects.

Vitamin C Food Sources

Fruits and vegetables can easily provide a generous amount of vitamin C. A cup of orange juice at breakfast, a salad for lunch, and a stalk of broccoli and a potato for dinner alone provide more than 300 milligrams. Clearly, a person making such food choices needs no vitamin C pills.

Figure 10-18 shows the amounts of vitamin C in various common foods. The overwhelming abundance of purple and green bars reveals not only that the citrus fruits are justly famous for being rich in vitamin C, but that other fruits and vegetables are in the same league. A half cup of broccoli, bell pepper, or strawberries provides more than 50 milligrams of the vitamin (and an array of other nutrients). Because vitamin C is vulnerable to heat, raw fruits and vegetables usually have a higher nutrient density than their cooked counterparts. Similarly, because vitamin C is readily destroyed by oxygen, foods and juices should be stored properly and consumed within a week of opening.[33]

The potato is an important source of vitamin C, not because one potato by itself meets the daily need, but because potatoes are such a common staple that they make significant contributions. In fact, scurvy was unknown in Ireland until the potato blight of the mid-1840s when some two million people died of malnutrition and infection.

The lack of yellow, white, brown, and red bars in Figure 10-18 confirms that grains, milk (except breast milk), legumes, and meats are notoriously poor sources of vitamin C. Organ meats (liver, kidneys, and others) and raw meats contain some vitamin C, but most people don't eat large quantities of these foods. Raw meats and fish contribute enough vitamin C to be significant sources in parts of Alaska, Canada, and Japan, but elsewhere fruits and vegetables are necessary to supply sufficient vitamin C.

Because of vitamin C's antioxidant property, food manufacturers sometimes add a variation of vitamin C to some beverages and most cured meats, such as luncheon meats, to prevent oxidation and spoilage. This compound safely preserves these foods, but it does not have vitamin C activity in the body. Simply put, "ham and bacon cannot replace fruits and vegetables." See the accompanying table for a summary of vitamin C.

false positive: a test result indicating that a condition is present (positive) when in fact it is not (therefore false).

false negative: a test result indicating that a condition is not present (negative) when in fact it is present (therefore false).

* Vitamin C is inactivated and degraded by several routes, and sometimes oxalate, which can form kidney stones, is produced along the way. People may also develop oxalate crystals in their kidneys regardless of vitamin C status.

FIGURE 10-18   Vitamin C in Selected Foods

See the "How to" section on p. 329 for more information on using this figure.

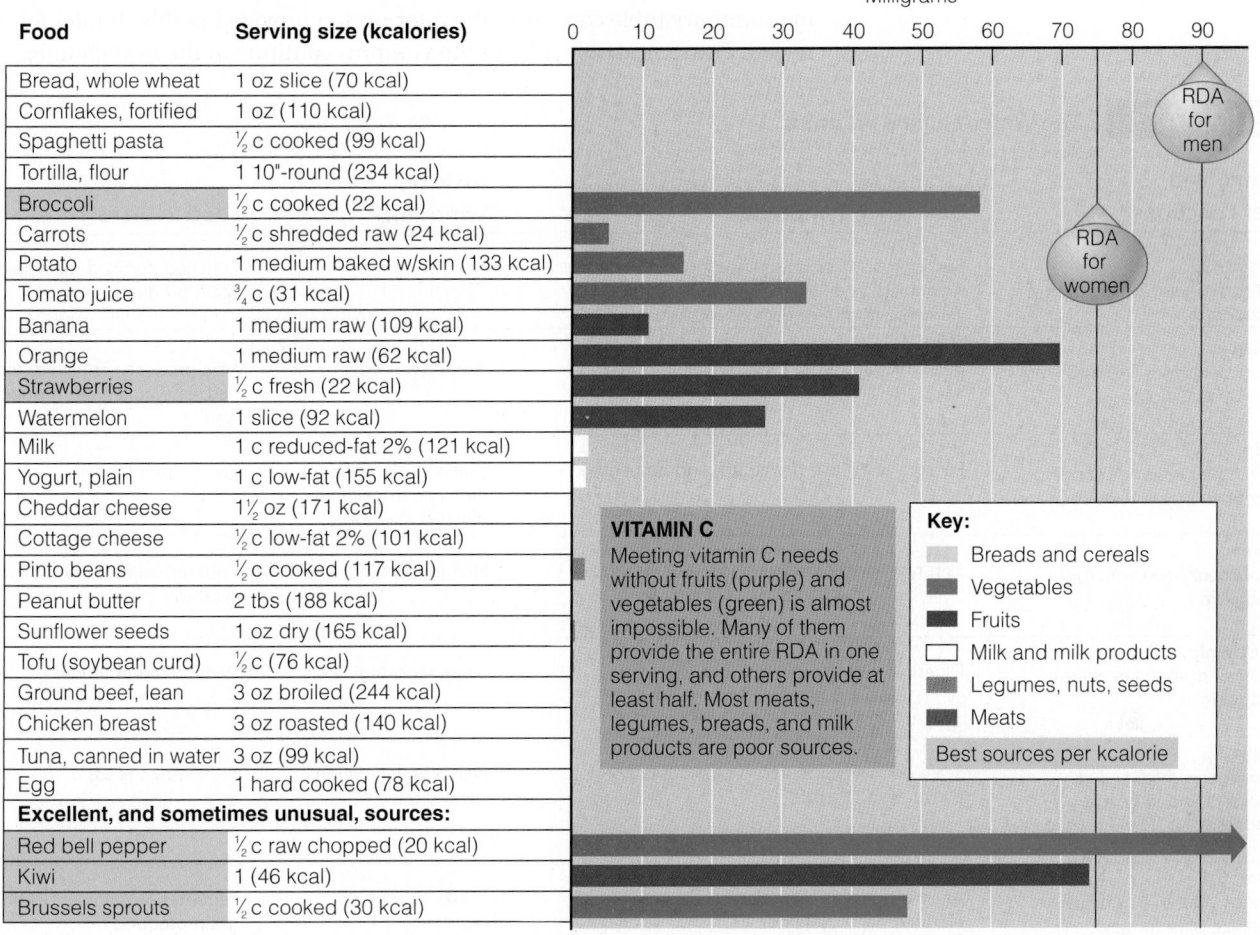

Food	Serving size (kcalories)
Bread, whole wheat	1 oz slice (70 kcal)
Cornflakes, fortified	1 oz (110 kcal)
Spaghetti pasta	½ c cooked (99 kcal)
Tortilla, flour	1 10"-round (234 kcal)
Broccoli	½ c cooked (22 kcal)
Carrots	½ c shredded raw (24 kcal)
Potato	1 medium baked w/skin (133 kcal)
Tomato juice	¾ c (31 kcal)
Banana	1 medium raw (109 kcal)
Orange	1 medium raw (62 kcal)
Strawberries	½ c fresh (22 kcal)
Watermelon	1 slice (92 kcal)
Milk	1 c reduced-fat 2% (121 kcal)
Yogurt, plain	1 c low-fat (155 kcal)
Cheddar cheese	1½ oz (171 kcal)
Cottage cheese	½ c low-fat 2% (101 kcal)
Pinto beans	½ c cooked (117 kcal)
Peanut butter	2 tbs (188 kcal)
Sunflower seeds	1 oz dry (165 kcal)
Tofu (soybean curd)	½ c (76 kcal)
Ground beef, lean	3 oz broiled (244 kcal)
Chicken breast	3 oz roasted (140 kcal)
Tuna, canned in water	3 oz (99 kcal)
Egg	1 hard cooked (78 kcal)
Excellent, and sometimes unusual, sources:	
Red bell pepper	½ c raw chopped (20 kcal)
Kiwi	1 (46 kcal)
Brussels sprouts	½ c cooked (30 kcal)

VITAMIN C
Meeting vitamin C needs without fruits (purple) and vegetables (green) is almost impossible. Many of them provide the entire RDA in one serving, and others provide at least half. Most meats, legumes, breads, and milk products are poor sources.

Key:
- Breads and cereals
- Vegetables
- Fruits
- Milk and milk products
- Legumes, nuts, seeds
- Meats
- Best sources per kcalorie

IN SUMMARY   Vitamin C

Other Names

Ascorbic acid

RDA

Men: 90 mg/day

Women: 75 mg/day

Smokers: +35 mg/day

Upper Level

Adults: 2000 mg/day

Chief Functions in the Body

Collagen synthesis (strengthens blood vessel walls, forms scar tissue, provides matrix for bone growth), antioxidant, thyroxin synthesis, amino acid metabolism, strengthens resistance to infection, helps in absorption of iron

Significant Sources

Citrus fruits, cabbage-type vegetables (such as brussels sprouts and cauliflower), dark green vegetables (such as bell peppers and broccoli), cantaloupe, strawberries, lettuce, tomatoes, potatoes, papayas, mangoes

Easily destroyed by heat and oxygen

Deficiency Disease

Scurvy

Deficiency Symptoms

Anemia (small-cell type),[a] atherosclerotic plaques, pinpoint hemorrhages; bone fragility, joint pain; poor wound healing, frequent infections; bleeding gums, loosened teeth; muscle degeneration and pain, hysteria, depression; rough skin, blotchy bruises

Toxicity Symptoms

Nausea, abdominal cramps, diarrhea; headache, fatigue, insomnia; hot flashes, rashes; interference with medical tests, aggravation of gout symptoms, urinary tract problems, kidney stones[b]

[a]Small-cell–type anemia is *microcytic anemia.*
[b]People with kidney disease, a tendency toward gout, or a genetic abnormality that alters the breakdown of vitamin C are prone to forming kidney stones. Vitamin C is inactivated and degraded by several routes, sometimes producing oxalate, which can form stones in the kidneys.

Vita means life. After this discourse on the vitamins, who could dispute that they deserve their name? Their regulation of metabolic processes makes them vital to the normal growth, development, and maintenance of the body. The accompanying summary table condenses the information provided in this chapter for a quick review. The remarkable roles of the vitamins continue in the next chapter.

IN SUMMARY — The Water-Soluble Vitamins

Vitamin and Chief Functions	Deficiency Symptoms	Toxicity Symptoms	Food Sources
Thiamin Part of coenzyme TPP in energy metabolism	Beriberi (edema or muscle wasting), anorexia and weight loss, neurological disturbances, muscular weakness, heart enlargement and failure	None reported	Enriched, fortified, or whole-grain products; pork
Riboflavin Part of coenzymes FAD and FMN in energy metabolism	Inflammation of the mouth, skin, and eyelids	None reported	Milk products; enriched, fortified, or whole-grain products; liver
Niacin Part of coenzymes NAD and NADP in energy metabolism	Pellagra (diarrhea, dermatitis, and dementia)	Niacin flush, liver damage, impaired glucose tolerance	Protein-rich foods
Biotin Part of coenzyme in energy metabolism	Skin rash, hair loss, neurological disturbances	None reported	Widespread in foods; GI bacteria synthesis
Pantothenic acid Part of coenzyme A in energy metabolism	Digestive and neurological disturbances	None reported	Widespread in foods
Vitamin B$_6$ Part of coenzymes used in amino acid and fatty acid metabolism	Scaly dermatitis, depression, confusion, convulsions, anemia	Nerve degeneration, skin lesions	Protein-rich foods
Folate Activates vitamin B$_{12}$; helps synthesize DNA for new cell growth	Anemia, glossitis, neurological disturbances, elevated homocysteine	Masks vitamin B$_{12}$ deficiency	Legumes, vegetables, fortified grain products
Vitamin B$_{12}$ Activates folate; helps synthesize DNA for new cell growth; protects nerve cells	Anemia; nerve damage and paralysis	None reported	Foods derived from animals
Vitamin C Synthesis of collagen, carnitine, hormones, neurotransmitters; antioxidant	Scurvy (bleeding gums, pinpoint hemorrhages, abnormal bone growth, and joint pain)	Diarrhea, GI distress	Fruits and vegetables

ThomsonNOW
www.thomsonedu.com/thomsonnow

Nutrition Portfolio

To obtain all the vitamins you need each day, be sure to select from a variety of foods.

■ Examine your daily choices of whole or enriched grains, dark green leafy vegetables, citrus fruits, and legumes and evaluate their contributions to your vitamin intakes.

■ If you are a woman of childbearing age, calculate the dietary folate equivalents you receive from folate-rich foods, fortified foods, and supplements and compare that to recommended intakes.

■ Compare your vitamin intakes from supplements with their upper levels.

NUTRITION ON THE NET

ThomsonNOW™
For further study of topics covered in this chapter, log on to **www.thomsonedu .com/thomsonnow**. Go to Chapter 10, then to Nutrition on the Net.

- Search for "vitamins" at the American Dietetic Association: **www.eatright.org**
- Visit the World Health Organization to learn about "vitamin deficiencies" around the world: **www.who.int**
- Learn more about neural tube defects from the Spina Bifida Association of America: **www.sbaa.org**

- Read about Dr. Joseph Goldberger and his groundbreaking discovery linking pellagra to diet by searching for his name at: **www.nih.gov** or **www.pbs.org**
- Learn how fruits and vegetables support a healthy diet rich in vitamins from the National Cancer Institute or the 5 A Day for Better Health program: **www.5aday.gov** or **5aday.org**

NUTRITION CALCULATIONS

ThomsonNOW™   For additional practice log on to **www.thomsonedu.com/thomsonnow**. Go to Chapter 10, then to Nutrition Calculations.

These problems give you practice in doing simple vitamin-related calculations (answers are provided on p. 359). Be sure to show your calculations for each problem.

1. Review the units in which vitamins are measured (a spot check).
   a. For each of these vitamins, note the unit of measure:

Thiamin	Folate
Riboflavin	Vitamin B_{12}
Niacin	Vitamin C
Vitamin B_6	

   b. Recall from the chapter's description of people's self-dosing with vitamin B_6 that people who suffer toxicity symptoms may be taking more than 2 grams a day, whereas the RDA is less than 2 *milli*grams. How much higher than 2 milligrams is 2 grams?
   c. Vitamin B_{12} is measured in micrograms. How many micrograms are in a gram? How many grams are in a teaspoon of a granular powder? How many micrograms does that represent? What is your RDA for vitamin B_{12}?

This exercise should convince you that the amount of vitamins a person needs is indeed quite small—yet still essential.

2. Be aware of how niacin intakes are affected by dietary protein availability.
   a. Refer to the "How to" on p. 333, and calculate how much niacin a woman receives from a diet that delivers 90 grams protein and 9 milligrams niacin. (Assume her RDA for protein is 46 grams/day.)
   b. Is this woman getting her RDA of niacin (14 milligrams NE)?

This exercise should demonstrate that protein helps meet niacin needs.

STUDY QUESTIONS

ThomsonNOW™
To assess your understanding of chapter topics, take the Student Practice Test and explore the modules recommended in your Personalized Study Plan. Log onto **www.thomsonedu.com/thomsonnow**.

These questions will help you review the chapter. You will find the answers in the discussions on the pages provided.

1. How do the vitamins differ from the energy nutrients? (pp. 323–324)
2. Describe some general differences between fat-soluble and water-soluble vitamins. (pp. 324–326)
3. Which B vitamins are involved in energy metabolism? Protein metabolism? Cell division? (p. 326)

4. For thiamin, riboflavin, niacin, biotin, pantothenic acid, vitamin B_6, folate, vitamin B_{12}, and vitamin C, state:
   - Its chief function in the body.
   - Its characteristic deficiency symptoms.
   - Its significant food sources. (See respective summary tables.)
5. What is the relationship of tryptophan to niacin? (p. 331)
6. Describe the relationship between folate and vitamin B_{12}. (pp. 338–345)
7. What risks are associated with high doses of niacin? Vitamin B_6? Vitamin C? (pp. 332, 336, 353–354)

These questions will help you prepare for an exam. Answers can be found on p. 359.

1. Vitamins:
   a. are inorganic compounds.
   b. yield energy when broken down.
   c. are soluble in either water or fat.
   d. perform best when linked in long chains.

2. The rate at and the extent to which a vitamin is absorbed and used in the body is known as its:
   a. bioavailability.
   b. intrinsic factor.
   c. physiological effect.
   d. pharmacological effect.

3. Many of the B vitamins serve as:
   a. coenzymes.
   b. antagonists.
   c. antioxidants.
   d. serotonin precursors.

4. With respect to thiamin, which of the following is the most nutrient dense?
   a. 1 slice whole-wheat bread (69 kcalories and 0.1 milligram thiamin)
   b. 1 cup yogurt (144 kcalories and 0.1 milligram thiamin)
   c. 1 cup snow peas (69 kcalories and 0.22 milligram thiamin)
   d. 1 chicken breast (141 kcalories and 0.06 milligram thiamin)

5. The body can make niacin from:
   a. tyrosine.
   b. serotonin.
   c. carnitine.
   d. tryptophan.

6. The vitamin that protects against neural tube defects is:
   a. niacin.
   b. folate.
   c. riboflavin.
   d. vitamin B_{12}.

7. A lack of intrinsic factor may lead to:
   a. beriberi.
   b. pellagra.
   c. pernicious anemia.
   d. atrophic gastritis.

8. Which of the following is a B vitamin?
   a. inositol
   b. carnitine
   c. vitamin B_{15}
   d. pantothenic acid

9. Vitamin C serves as a(n):
   a. coenzyme.
   b. antagonist.
   c. antioxidant.
   d. intrinsic factor.

10. The requirement for vitamin C is highest for:
    a. smokers.
    b. athletes.
    c. alcoholics.
    d. the elderly.

REFERENCES

1. C. S. Johnston and J. C. Hale, Oxidation of ascorbic acid in stored orange juice is associated with reduced plasma vitamin C concentrations and elevated lipid peroxides, *Journal of the American Dietetic Association* 105 (2005): 106-109.
2. Committee on Dietary Reference Intakes, *Dietary Reference Intakes for Vitamin C, Vitamin E, Selenium, and Carotenoids* (Washington, D.C.: National Academy Press, 2000); Committee on *Dietary Reference Intakes, Dietary Reference Intakes for Thiamin, Riboflavin, Niacin, Vitamin B6, Folate, Vitamin B12, Pantothenic Acid, Biotin, and Choline* (Washington, D.C.: National Academy Press, 1998).
3. K. J. Carpenter, *Beriberi, White Rice, and Vitamin B: A Disease, a Cause, and a Cure* (Berkeley: University of California Press, 2000).
4. J. Zempleni, Uptake, localization, and noncarboxylase roles of biotin, *Annual Review of Nutrition* 25 (2005): 175-196.
5. R. Rodriguez-Melendez, J. B. Griffin, and J. Zempleni, Biotin supplementation increases expression of the cytochrome P450 1B1 gene in Jurkat cells, increasing the occur-

rence of single-stranded DNA breaks, *Journal of Nutrition* 134 (2004): 2222-2228.
6. S. Friso and coauthors, Low plasma vitamin B-6 concentrations and modulation of coronary artery disease risk, *American Journal of Clinical Nutrition* 79 (2004): 992-998.
7. E. Aufiero and coauthors, Pyridoxine hydrochloride treatment of carpal tunnel syndrome: A review, *Nutrition Reviews* 62 (2004): 96-104; A. A. Gerritsen and coauthors, Conservative treatment options for carpal tunnel syndrome: A systematic review of randomized controlled trials, *Journal of Neurology* 249 (2002): 272-280; R. Luboshitzky and coauthors, The effect of pyridoxine administration on melatonin secretion in normal men, *Neuroendocrinology Letters* 23 (2002): 213-217.
8. A. Melse-Boonstra and coauthors, Bioavailability of heptaglutamyl relative to monoglutamyl folic acid in healthy adults, *American Journal of Clinical Nutrition* 79 (2004): 424-429.
9. L. B. Bailey and R. J. Berry, Folic acid supplementation and the occurrence of congenital heart defects, orofacial clefts, multiple births, and miscarriage, *American Journal of*

Clinical Nutrition 81 (2005): 1213S-1217S.
10. Use of dietary supplements containing folic acid among women of childbearing age-United States, 2005, *Morbidity and Mortality Weekly Report* 54 (2005): 955-957.
11. T. Tamura and M. F. Picciano, Folate and human reproduction, *American Journal of Clinical Nutrition* 83 (2006): 993-1016; Spina bifida and anencephaly before and after folic acid mandate—United States, 1995-1996 and 1999-2000, *Morbidity and Mortality Weekly Report* 53 (2004): 362-365.
12. R. L. Brent and G. P. Oakley, The folate debate, *Pediatrics* 117 (2006): 1418-1419; J. I. Rader and B. O. Schneeman, Prevalence of neural tube defects, folate status, and folate fortification of enriched cereal-grain products in the United States, *Pediatrics* 117 (2006): 1394-1399.
13. E. P. Quinlivan and J. F. Gregory III, Effect of food fortification on folic acid intake in the United States, *American Journal of Clinical Nutrition* 77 (2003): 221-225.
14. Committee on Dietary Reference Intakes, 1998.
15. T. K. Eskes, Abnormal folate metabolism in mothers with Down syndrome offspring:

Review of the literature, *European Journal of Obstetrics, Gynecology, and Reproductive Biology* 124 (2006): 130-133; J. L. Gueant and coauthors, Genetic determinants of folate and vitamin B12 metabolism: A common pathway in neural tube defect and Down syndrome? *Clinical Chemistry and Laboratory Medicine* 41 (2003): 1473-1477; N. Takamura and coauthors, Abnormal folic acid-homocysteine metabolism as maternal risk factors for Down syndrome in Japan, *European Journal of Nutrition* 43 (2004): 285-287.

16. H. S. Cuckle, Primary prevention of Down's syndrome, *International Journal of Medical Sciences* 2 (2005): 93-99; J. G. Ray and coauthors, Prevalence of trisomy 21 following folic acid food fortification, *American Journal of Medicinal Genetics, Part A* 120 (2003): 309-313.

17. P. J. Baggot and coauthors, A folate-dependent metabolite in amniotic fluid from pregnancies with normal or trisomy 21 chromosomes, *Fetal Diagnosis and Therapy* 21 (2006): 148-152; N. Takamura and coauthors, Abnormal folic acid-homocysteine metabolism as maternal risk factors for Down syndrome in Japan, *European Journal of Nutrition* 43 (2004): 285-287.

18. D. S. Wald, M. Law, and J. K. Morris, Homocysteine and cardiovascular disease: Evidence on causality from a meta-analysis, *British Medical Journal* 325 (2002): 1202.

19. Homocysteine Lowering Trialists' Collaboration, Dose-dependent effects of folic acid on blood concentrations of homocysteine: A meta-analysis of the randomized trials, *American Journal of Clinical Nutrition* 82 (2005): 806-812; C. M. Pfeiffer and coauthors, Biochemical indicators of B vitamin status in the US population after folic acid fortification: Results from the National Health and Nutrition Examination Survey 1999-2000, *American Journal of Clinical Nutrition* 82 (2005): 442-450; K. L. Tucker and coauthors, Breakfast cereal fortified with folic acid, vitamin B-6, and vitamin B-12 increases vitamin concentrations and reduces homocysteine concentrations: A randomized trial, *American Journal of Clinical Nutrition* 79 (2004): 805-811; F. V. van Oort and coauthors, Folic acid and reduction of plasma homocysteine concentrations in older adults: A dose-response study, *American Journal of Clinical Nutrition* 77 (2003): 1318-1323; B. J. Venn and coauthors, Dietary counseling to increase natural folate intake: A randomized placebo-controlled trial in free-living subjects to assess effects on serum folate and plasma total homocysteine, *American Journal of Clinical Nutrition* 76 (2002): 758-765.

20. E. Lonn and coauthors, Homocysteine lowering with folic acid and B vitamins in vascular disease, *New England Journal of Medicine* 354 (2006): 1567-1577.

21. Y. I. Kim, 5,10-methylenetetrahydrofolate reductase polymorphisms and pharmacogenetics: A new role of single nucleotide polymorphisms in the folate metabolic pathway in human health and disease, *Nutrition Reviews* 63 (2005): 398-407; H. J. Powers, Interaction among folate, riboflavin, genotype, and cancer, with reference to colorectal and cervical cancer, *Journal of Nutrition* 135 (2005): 2960S-2966S; D. C. McCabe and M. A. Caudill, DNA methylation, genomic silencing, and links to nutrition and cancer, *Nutrition Reviews* 63 (2005): 183-195; M. E. Martínez, S. M. Henning, and D. S. Alberts, Folate and colorectal neoplasia: Relation between plasma and dietary markers of folate and adenoma recurrence, *American Journal of Clinical Nutrition* 79 (2004): 691-697; G. C. Rampersaud, L. B. Bailey, and G. P. A. Kauwell, Relationship of folate to colorectal and cervical cancer: Review and recommendations for practitioners, *Journal of the American Dietetic Association* 102 (2002): 1273-1282.

22. A. Tjonneland and coauthors, Folate intake, alcohol and risk of breast cancer among postmenopausal women in Denmark, *European Journal of Clinical Nutrition* 60 (2006): 280-286; S. C. Larsson and coauthors, Folate intake and pancreatic cancer incidence: A prospective study of Swedish women and men, *Journal of the National Cancer Institute* 98 (2006): 407-413; L. Baglietto and coauthors, Does dietary folate intake modify effect of alcohol consumption on breast cancer risk? Prospective cohort study, *British Medical Journal* 331 (2005): 807-810.

23. M. J. Koury and P. Ponka, New insights into erythropoiesis: The roles of folate, vitamin B12, and iron, *Annual Review of Nutrition* 24 (2004): 105-131.

24. K. D. Stark and coauthors, Status of plasma folate after folic acid fortification of the food supply in pregnant African American women and the influences of diet, smoking, and alcohol consumption, *American Journal of Clinical Nutrition* 81 (2005): 669-671.

25. S. P. Stabler and R. H. Allen, Vitamin B12 deficiency as a worldwide problem, *Annual Review of Nutrition* 24 (2004): 299-326.

26. S. H. Zeisel, Choline: Critical role during fetal development and dietary requirements in adults, *Annual Review of Nutrition* 26 (2006): 229-250.

27. H. J. Powers, Riboflavin (vitamin B-2) and health, *American Journal of Clinical Nutrition* 77 (2003): 1352-1360.

28. J. X. Wilson, Regulation of vitamin C transport, *Annual Review of Nutrition* 25 (2005): 105-125.

29. B. Arroll, Non-antibiotic treatments for upper-respiratory tract infections (common cold), *Respiratory Medicine* 99 (2005): 1477-1484; S. Sasazuki and coauthors, Effect of vitamin C on common cold: Randomized controlled trial, *European Journal of Clinical Nutrition* 24 (2005): 9-17; H. Hemilä and coauthors, Vitamin C, vitamin E, and beta-carotene in relation to common cold incidence in male smokers, *Epidemiology* 13 (2002): 32-37; B. Takkouche and coauthors, Intake of vitamin C and zinc and risk of common cold: A cohort study, *Epidemiology* 13 (2002): 38-44; M. van Straten and P. Josling, Preventing the common cold with a vitamin C supplement: A double-blind, placebo-controlled survey, *Advances in Therapy* 19 (2002): 151-159.

30. E. S. Wintergerst, S. Maggini, and D. H. Hornig, Immune-enhancing role of vitamin C and zinc and effect on clinical conditions, *Annals of Nutrition and Metabolism* 50 (2006): 85-94; R. M. Douglas, E. B. Chalker, and B. Treacy, Vitamin C for preventing and treating the common cold (Cochrane Review), *Cochrane Database of Systematic Reviews* 2 (2000): CD000980.

31. Committee on Dietary Reference Intakes, 2000.

32. J. N. Hathcock and coauthors, Vitamins E and C are safe across a broad range of intakes, *American Journal of Clinical Nutrition* 81 (2005): 736-745.

33. C. S. Johnston and D. L. Bowling, Stability of ascorbic acid in commercially available orange juices, *Journal of the American Dietetic Association* 102 (2002): 525-529.

ANSWERS

Nutrition Calculations

1. a. Thiamin: mg   Folate: µg DFE

   Riboflavin: mg   Vitamin B$_{12}$: µg

   Niacin: mg NE   Vitamin C: mg

   Vitamin B$_6$: mg

   b. A thousand times higher (2 g × 1000 mg/g = 2000 mg; 2000 mg ÷ 2 mg = 1000)

   c. 1 g = 1000 mg; 1 mg = 1000 µg (1000 × 1000 = 1,000,000); 1 million µg = 1 g

   1 tsp = 5 g

   5 × 1,000,000 µg = 5,000,000 µg/tsp

   See inside front cover for your RDA based on age and gender.

2. a. She eats 90 g protein. Assume she uses 46 g as protein.

   This leaves 90 g − 46 g = 44 g protein "leftover."

   44 g protein ÷ 100 = 0.44 g tryptophan

   0.44 g tryptophan × 1000 = 440 mg tryptophan

   440 mg tryptophan ÷ 60 = 7.3 mg NE

   7.3 mg NE + 9 mg niacin = 16.3 mg NE

   b. Yes

Study Questions (multiple choice)

1. c   2. a   3. a   4. c   5. d   6. b   7. c   8. d

9. c   10. a

Vitamin and Mineral Supplements

David Young-Wolff/Getty Images

An estimated 29,000 supplements are currently on the market. One-third of the population in the United States takes a vitamin-mineral **supplement** daily, spending billions of dollars on them each year.[1] Many people take supplements as dietary insurance—in case they are not meeting their nutrient needs from foods alone. Others take supplements as health insurance—to protect against certain diseases.

One out of every five people takes multinutrient pills daily. Others take large doses of single nutrients, most commonly, vitamin C, vitamin E, beta-carotene, iron, and calcium. In many cases, taking supplements is a costly but harmless practice; sometimes, it is both costly and harmful to health.

For the most part, people self-prescribe supplements, taking them on the advice of friends, advertisements, websites, or books that may or may not be reliable. Sometimes, they take supplements on the recommendation of a physician. When such advice follows a valid nutrition assessment, supplementation may be warranted, but even then the preferred course of action is to improve food choices and eating habits.[2] Without an assessment, the advice to take supplements may be inappropriate. A registered dietitian can help with the decision.[3]

When people think of supplements, they often think of vitamins, but minerals are important, too, of course. People whose diets lack vitamins, for whatever reason, probably lack several minerals as well. This highlight asks several questions related to vitamin-mineral supplements. (The accompanying glossary defines supplements and related terms.) What are the arguments *for* taking supplements? What are the arguments *against* taking them? Finally, if people do take supplements, how can they choose the appropriate ones? (In addition to vitamins and minerals, supplements may also contain amino acids or herbs, which are discussed in Chapter 6 and Highlight 18, respectively.)

Arguments for Supplements

Vitamin-mineral supplements may be appropriate in some circumstances. In some cases, they can prevent or correct deficiencies; in others, they can reduce the risk of diseases.

Correct Overt Deficiencies

In the United States and Canada, adults rarely suffer nutrient deficiency diseases such as scurvy, pellagra, and beriberi, but they do still occur. To correct an overt deficiency disease, a physician may prescribe therapeutic doses two to ten times the RDA (or AI) of a nutrient. At such high doses, the supplement is acting as a drug.

Support Increased Nutrient Needs

As Chapters 15–17 explain, nutrient needs increase during certain stages of life, making it difficult to meet some of those needs without supplementation. For example, women who lose a lot of blood and therefore a lot of iron during menstruation each month may need an iron supplement. Women of childbearing age need folate supplements to reduce the risks of neural tube defects. Similarly, pregnant women and women who are breastfeeding their infants have exceptionally high nutrient needs and so usually need special supplements. Newborns routinely receive a single dose of vitamin K at birth to prevent abnormal bleeding. Infants may need other supplements as well, depending on whether they are breastfed or receiving formula, and on whether their water contains fluoride.

Improve Nutrition Status

In contrast to the classical deficiencies, which present a multitude of symptoms and are relatively easy to recognize, subclinical defi-

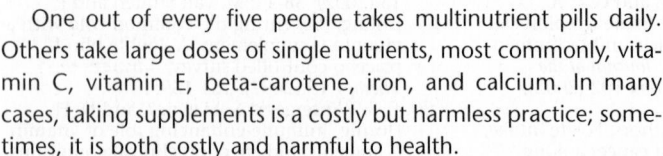

GLOSSARY

FDA (Food and Drug Administration): a part of the Department of Health and Human Services' Public Health Service that is responsible for ensuring the safety and wholesomeness of all dietary supplements and food processed and sold in interstate commerce except meat, poultry, and eggs (which are under the jurisdiction of the USDA); inspecting food plants and imported foods; and setting standards for food composition and product labeling.

high potency: 100% or more of the Daily Value for the nutrient in a single supplement and for at least two-thirds of the nutrients in a multinutrient supplement.

supplement: any pill, capsule, tablet, liquid, or powder that contains vitamins, minerals, herbs, or amino acids; intended to increase dietary intake of these substances.

ciencies are subtle and easy to overlook—and they are also more likely to occur. People who do not eat enough food to deliver the needed amounts of nutrients, such as habitual dieters and the elderly, risk developing subclinical deficiencies. Similarly, vegetarians who restrict their use of entire food groups without appropriate substitutions may fail to fully meet their nutrient needs. If there is no way for these people to eat enough nutritious foods to meet their needs, then vitamin-mineral supplements may be appropriate to help prevent nutrient deficiencies.

Improve the Body's Defenses

Health care professionals may provide special supplementation to people being treated for addictions to alcohol or other drugs and to people with prolonged illnesses, extensive injuries, or other severe stresses such as surgery.[4] Illnesses that interfere with appetite, eating, or nutrient absorption impair nutrition status. For example, the stomach condition atrophic gastritis often creates a vitamin B_{12} deficiency. In addition, nutrient needs are often heightened by diseases or medications. In all these cases, supplements are appropriate.

Reduce Disease Risks

Few people consume the optimal amounts of all the vitamins and minerals by diet alone. Inadequate intakes have been linked to chronic diseases such as heart disease, some cancers, and osteoporosis.[5] For this reason, some physicians recommend that all adults take vitamin-mineral supplements.[6] Such regular supplementation would provide an optimum intake to enhance metabolic harmony and prevent disease at relatively little cost.[7] Others recognize the lack of conclusive evidence and the potential harm of supplementation and advise against such a recommendation.[8] The most recent statement from the National Institutes of Health acknowledges that evidence is insufficient to recommend either for or against the use of supplements to prevent chronic diseases.[9]

Highlight 11 reviews the relationships between supplement use and disease prevention. It describes some of the accumulating evidence suggesting that intakes of certain nutrients at levels much higher than can be attained from foods alone may be beneficial in reducing disease risks. It also presents research confirming the associated risks. Clearly, consumers must be cautious in taking supplements to prevent disease.

Many people, especially postmenopausal women and those who are intolerant to lactose or allergic to milk, may not receive enough calcium to forestall the bone degeneration of old age, osteoporosis. For them, nonmilk calcium-rich foods are especially valuable, but calcium supplements may also be appropriate. (Highlight 12 provides more details.)

Who Needs Supplements?

In summary, the following list acknowledges that in these specific conditions, these people may need to take supplements:

- People with specific nutrient deficiencies need specific nutrient supplements.
- People whose energy intakes are particularly low (fewer than 1600 kcalories per day) need multivitamin and mineral supplements.

- Vegetarians who eat all-plant diets (vegans) and older adults with atrophic gastritis need vitamin B_{12}.
- People who have lactose intolerance or milk allergies or who otherwise do not consume enough milk products to forestall extensive bone loss need calcium.
- People in certain stages of the life cycle who have increased nutrient requirements need specific nutrient supplements. (For example, infants need iron and fluoride, women of childbearing age and pregnant women need folate and iron, and the elderly need vitamins B_{12} and D.)
- People who have inadequate milk intakes, limited sun exposure, or heavily pigmented skin need vitamin D.
- People who have diseases, infections, or injuries or who have undergone surgery that interferes with the intake, absorption, metabolism, or excretion of nutrients may need specific nutrient supplements.
- People taking medications that interfere with the body's use of specific nutrients may need specific nutrient supplements.

Except for people in these circumstances, most adults can normally get all the nutrients they need by eating a varied diet of nutrient-dense foods. Even athletes can meet their nutrient needs without the help of supplements, as Chapter 14 explains.

Arguments against Supplements

Foods rarely cause nutrient imbalances or toxicities, but supplements can. The higher the dose, the greater the risk of harm. People's tolerances for high doses of nutrients vary, just as their risks of deficiencies do. Amounts that some can tolerate may be harmful for others, and no one knows who falls where along the spectrum. It is difficult to determine just how much of a nutrient is enough—or too much. The Tolerable Upper Intake Levels of the DRI answer the question "How much is too much?" by defining the highest amount that appears safe for most healthy people. Table H10-1 (p. 362) presents these suggested Upper Levels and Daily Values for selected vitamins and minerals and the quantities typically found in supplements.

Toxicity

The extent and severity of supplement toxicity remain unclear. Only a few alert health care professionals can recognize toxicity, even when it is acute. When it is chronic, with the effects developing subtly and progressing slowly, it often goes unrecognized. In view of the potential hazards, some authorities believe supplements should bear warning labels, advising consumers that large doses may be toxic.

Toxic overdoses of vitamins and minerals in children are more readily recognized and, unfortunately, fairly common. Fruit-flavored, chewable vitamins shaped like cartoon characters entice young children to eat them like candy in amounts that can cause poisoning. High-potency iron supplements (30 milligrams of iron or more per tablet) are especially toxic and are the leading cause

TABLE H10-1 Vitamin and Mineral Intakes for Adults

Nutrient	Tolerable Upper Intake Levels[a]	Daily Values	Typical Multivitamin-Mineral Supplement	Average Single-Nutrient Supplement
Vitamins				
Vitamin A	3000 µg (10,000 IU)	5000 IU	5000 IU	8000 to 10,000 IU
Vitamin D	50 µg (2000 IU)	400 IU	400 IU	400 IU
Vitamin E	1000 mg (1500 to 2200 IU)[b]	30 IU	30 IU	100 to 1000 IU
Vitamin K	—[c]	80 µg	40 µg	—[e]
Thiamin	—[c]	1.5 mg	1.5 mg	50 mg
Riboflavin	—[c]	1.7 mg	1.7 mg	25 mg
Niacin (as niacinamide)	35 mg[b]	20 mg	20 mg	100 to 500 mg
Vitamin B6	100 mg	2 mg	2 mg	100 to 200 mg
Folate	1000 µg[b]	400 µg	400 µg	400 µg
Vitamin B12	—[c]	6 µg	6 µg	100 to 1000 µg
Pantothenic acid	—[c]	10 mg	10 mg	100 to 500 mg
Biotin	—[c]	300 µg	30 µg	300 to 600 µg
Vitamin C	2000 mg	60 mg	10 mg	500 to 2000 mg
Choline	3500 mg	—	10 mg	250 mg
Minerals				
Calcium	2500 mg	1000 mg	160 mg	250 to 600 mg
Phosphorus	4000 mg	1000 mg	110 mg	—[e]
Magnesium	350 mg[d]	400 mg	100 mg	250 mg
Iron	45 mg	18 mg	18 mg	18 to 30 mg
Zinc	40 mg	15 mg	15 mg	10 to 100 mg
Iodine	1100 µg	150 µg	150 µg	—[e]
Selenium	400 µg	70 µg	10 µg	50 to 200 µg
Fluoride	10 mg	—	—	—[e]
Copper	10 mg	2 mg	0.5 mg	—[e]
Manganese	11 mg	2 mg	5 mg	—[e]
Chromium	—[c]	120 µg	25 µg	200 to 400 µg
Molybdenum	2000 µg	75 µg	25 µg	—[e]

[a]Unless otherwise noted, Upper Levels represent total intakes from food, water, and supplements.
[b]Upper Levels represent intakes from supplements, fortified foods, or both.
[c]These nutrients have been evaluated by the DRI Committee for Tolerable Upper Intake Levels, but none were established because of insufficient data. No adverse effects have been reported with intakes of these nutrients at levels typical of supplements, but caution is still advised, given the potential for harm that accompanies excessive intakes.
[d]Upper Levels represent intakes from supplements only.
[e]Available as a single supplement by prescription.

of accidental ingestion fatalities among children. Even mild over-doses cause GI distress, nausea, and black diarrhea that reflects gastric bleeding. Severe overdoses result in bloody diarrhea, shock, liver damage, coma, and death.

Life-Threatening Misinformation

Another problem arises when people who are ill come to believe that high doses of vitamins or minerals can be therapeutic. Not only can high doses be toxic, but the person may take them in-stead of seeking medical help. Furthermore, there are no guaran-tees that the supplements will be effective. Marketing materials for supplements often make health statements that are required to be "truthful and not misleading," but they often fall far short of both. Highlight 18 revisits this topic and includes a discussion of herbal preparations and other alternative therapies.

Unknown Needs

Another argument against the use of supplements is that no one knows exactly how to formulate the "ideal" supplement. What nutrients should be included? Which, if any, of the phytochemi-cals should be included? How much of each? On whose needs should the choices be based? Surveys have repeatedly shown lit-tle relationship between the supplements people take and the nu-trients they actually need.

False Sense of Security

Another argument against supplement use is that it may lull people into a false sense of security. A person might eat irresponsibly, thinking, "My supplement will cover my needs." Or, experiencing a warning symptom of a disease, a person might postpone seeking a diagnosis, thinking, "I probably just need a supplement to make this go away." Such self-diagnosis is potentially dangerous.

Other Invalid Reasons

Other invalid reasons people might use for taking supplements include:

- The belief that the food supply or soil contains inadequate nutrients
- The belief that supplements can provide energy
- The belief that supplements can enhance athletic performance or build lean body tissues without physical work or faster than work alone (see Highlight 14)
- The belief that supplements will help a person cope with stress
- The belief that supplements can prevent, treat, or cure conditions ranging from the common cold to cancer

Ironically, people with health problems are more likely to take supplements than other people, yet today's health problems are more likely to be due to overnutrition and poor lifestyle choices than to nutrient deficiencies. The truth—that most people would benefit from improving their eating and exercise habits—is harder to swallow than a supplement pill.

Bioavailability and Antagonistic Actions

In general, the body absorbs nutrients best from foods in which the nutrients are diluted and dispersed among other substances that may facilitate their absorption. Taken in pure, concentrated form, nutrients are likely to interfere with one another's absorption or with the absorption of nutrients in foods eaten at the same time. Documentation of these effects is particularly extensive for minerals: zinc hinders copper and calcium absorption, iron hinders zinc absorption, calcium hinders magnesium and iron absorption, and magnesium hinders the absorption of calcium and iron. Similarly, binding agents in supplements limit mineral absorption.

Although minerals provide the most familiar and best-documented examples, interference among vitamins is now being seen as supplement use increases. The vitamin A precursor beta-carotene, long thought to be nontoxic, interferes with vitamin E metabolism when taken over the long term as a dietary supplement. Vitamin E, on the other hand, antagonizes vitamin K activity and so should not be used by people being treated for blood-clotting disorders. Consumers who want the benefits of optimal absorption of nutrients should eat ordinary foods, selected for nutrient density and variety.

Whenever the diet is inadequate, the person should first attempt to improve it so as to obtain the needed nutrients from foods. If that is truly impossible, then the person needs a multivitamin-mineral supplement that supplies between 50 and 150 percent of the Daily Value for each of the nutrients. These amounts reflect the ranges commonly found in foods and therefore are compatible with the body's normal handling of nutrients (its physiologic tolerance). The next section provides some pointers to assist in the selection of an appropriate supplement.

Selection of Supplements

Whenever a physician or registered dietitian recommends a supplement, follow the directions carefully. When selecting a supplement yourself, look for a single, balanced vitamin-mineral supplement. Supplements with a USP verification logo have been tested by the U.S. Pharmacopeia (USP) to assure that the supplement:

- Contains the declared ingredients and amounts listed on the label
- Does not contain harmful levels of contaminants
- Will disintegrate and release ingredients in the body
- Was made under safe and sanitary conditions

If you decide to take a vitamin-mineral supplement, ignore the eye-catching art and meaningless claims. Pay attention to the form the supplements are in, the list of ingredients, and the price. Here's where the truth lies, and from it you can make a rational decision based on facts. You have two basic questions to answer.

Form

The first question: What form do you want—chewable, liquid, or pills? If you'd rather drink your supplements than chew them, fine. (If you choose a chewable form, though, be aware that chewable vitamin C can dissolve tooth enamel.) If you choose pills, look for statements about the disintegration time. The USP suggests that supplements should completely disintegrate within 30 to 45 minutes.* Obviously, supplements that don't dissolve have little chance of entering the bloodstream, so look for a brand that claims to meet USP disintegration standards.

Contents

The second question: What vitamins and minerals do *you* need? Generally, an appropriate supplement provides vitamins and minerals in amounts that do not exceed recommended intakes. Avoid supplements that, in a daily dose, provide more than the Tolerable Upper Intake Level for *any* nutrient. Avoid preparations with more than 10 milligrams of iron per dose, except as prescribed by a physician. Iron is hard to get rid of once it's in the body, and an excess of iron can cause problems, just as a deficiency can (see Chapter 13).

Misleading Claims

Be aware that "organic" or "natural" supplements are no more effective than others and often cost more. The word *synthetic*

---

* The USP establishes standards for quality, strength, and purity of supplements.

may sound like "fake," but to synthesize just means to put together.

Avoid products that make **"high potency"** claims. More is not better (review the "How to" on p. 325). Remember that foods are also providing these nutrients. Nutrients can build up and cause unexpected problems. For example, a man who takes vitamins and begins to lose his hair may think his hair loss means he needs *more* vitamins, when in fact it may be the early sign of a vitamin A overdose. (Of course, it may be completely unrelated to nutrition as well.)

Be wise to fake vitamins and preparations that contain items not needed in human nutrition, such as carnitine and inositol. Such ingredients reveal a marketing strategy aimed at your pocket, not at your health. The manufacturer wants you to believe that its pills contain the latest "new" nutrient that other brands omit, but in reality, these substances are not known to be needed by human beings.

Realize that the claim that supplements "relieve stress" is another marketing ploy. If you give even passing thought to what people mean by "stress," you'll realize manufacturers could never design a supplement to meet everyone's needs. Is it stressful to take an exam? Well, yes. Is it stressful to survive a major car wreck with third-degree burns and multiple bone fractures? Definitely, yes. The body's responses to these stresses are different. The body does use vitamins and minerals in mounting a stress response, but a body fed a well-balanced diet can meet the needs of most minor stresses. For the major ones, medical intervention is needed. In any case, taking a vitamin supplement won't make life any less stressful.

Other marketing tricks to sidestep are "green" pills that contain dehydrated, crushed parsley, alfalfa, and other fruit and vegetable extracts. The nutrients and phytochemicals advertised can be obtained from a serving of vegetables more easily and for less money. Such pills may also provide enzymes, but enzymes are inactivated in the stomach during protein digestion.

Be aware that some geriatric "tonics" are low in vitamins and minerals and may be high in alcohol. The liquids designed for infants offer a more complete option.

Recognize the latest nutrition buzzwords. Manufacturers were marketing "antioxidant" supplements before the print had time to dry on the first scientific reports of antioxidant vitamins' action in preventing cancer and cardiovascular disease. Remember, too, that high doses can alter a nutrient's action in the body. An antioxidant in physiological quantities may be beneficial, but in pharmacological quantities, it may act as a prooxidant and produce harmful by-products. Highlight 11 explores antioxidants and supplement use in more detail.

Finally, be aware that advertising on the Internet is cheap and not closely regulated. Promotional e-mails can be sent to millions of people in an instant. Internet messages can easily cite references and provide links to other sites, implying an endorsement when in fact none has been given.[10] Be cautious when examining unsolicited information and search for a balanced perspective.

Cost

When shopping for supplements, remember that local or store brands may be just as good as nationally advertised brands. If they are less expensive, it may be because the price does not have to cover the cost of national advertising.

Regulation of Supplements

The Dietary Supplement Health and Education Act of 1994 was intended to enable consumers to make informed choices about nutrient supplements. The act subjects supplements to the same general labeling requirements that apply to foods. Specifically:

- Nutrition labeling for dietary supplements is required.
- Labels may make nutrient claims (as "high" or "low") according to specific criteria (for example, "an excellent source of vitamin C").
- Labels may claim that the lack of a nutrient can cause a deficiency disease, but if they do, they must also include the prevalence of that deficiency disease in the United States.
- Labels may make health claims that are supported by significant scientific agreement and are not brand specific (for example, "folate protects against neural tube defects").
- Labels may claim to diagnose, treat, cure, or relieve common complaints such as menstrual cramps or memory loss, but may *not* make claims about specific diseases (except as noted above).
- Labels may make structure-function claims about the role a nutrient plays in the body, how the nutrient performs its function, and how consuming the nutrient is associated with general well-being. These claims must be accompanied by an **FDA** disclaimer statement: "This statement has not been evaluated by the Food and Drug Administration. This product is not intended to diagnose, treat, cure or prevent any disease." Figure H10-1 provides an example of a supplement label that complies with the requirements.

The multibillion-dollar-a-year supplement industry spends much money and effort influencing these regulations. The net effect of the Dietary Supplement Health and Education Act was a deregulation of the supplement industry. Unlike food additives or

Structure-function claims do not need FDA authorization, but they must be accompanied by a disclaimer.

FIGURE H10-1 An Example of a Supplement Label

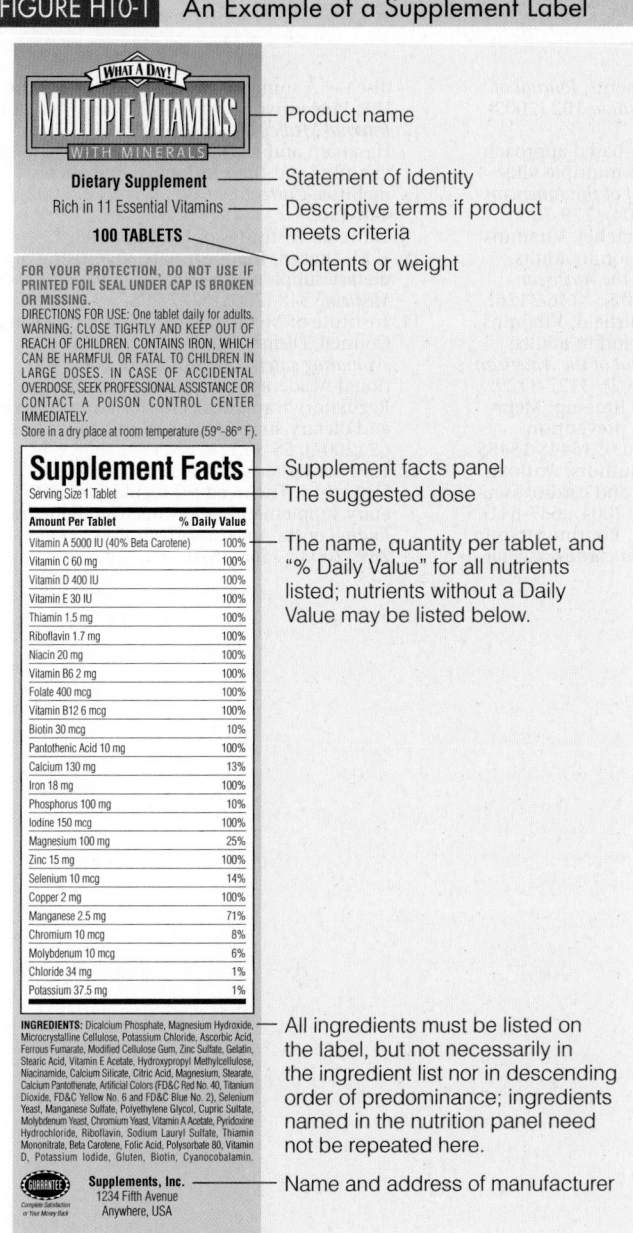

— Product name

— Statement of identity

— Descriptive terms if product meets criteria

— Contents or weight

— Supplement facts panel

— The suggested dose

— The name, quantity per tablet, and "% Daily Value" for all nutrients listed; nutrients without a Daily Value may be listed below.

— All ingredients must be listed on the label, but not necessarily in the ingredient list nor in descending order of predominance; ingredients named in the nutrition panel need not be repeated here.

— Name and address of manufacturer

drugs, supplements do not need to be proved safe and effective, nor do they need the FDA's approval before being marketed. Furthermore, there are no standards for potency or dosage and no requirements for providing warnings of potential side effects. Should a problem arise, the burden falls to the FDA to prove that the supplement poses a "significant or unreasonable risk of illness or injury."[11] Only then would it be removed from the market. When asked, most Americans express support for greater regulation of dietary supplements. Health professionals agree.[12]

If all the nutrients we need can come from food, why not just eat food? Foods have so much more to offer than supplements do. Nutrients in foods come in an infinite variety of combinations with a multitude of different carriers and absorption enhancers. They come with water, fiber, and an array of beneficial phytochemicals. Foods stimulate the GI tract to keep it healthy. They provide energy, and as long as you need energy each day, why not have nutritious foods deliver it? Foods offer pleasure, satiety, and opportunities for socializing while eating. In no way can nutrient supplements hold a candle to foods as a means of meeting human health needs. For further proof, read Highlight 11.

NUTRITION ON THE NET

ThomsonNOW
For furthur study of topics covered in this Highlight, log on to www .thomsonedu.com/thomsonnow. Go to Chapter 10, then to Highlights Nutrition on the Net.

- Gather information from the Office of Dietary Supplements or Health Canada: **dietary-supplements.info .nih.gov** or **www.hc-sc.gc.ca**

- Report adverse reactions associated with dietary supplements to the FDA's MedWatch program: **www.fda.gov/medwatch**

- Search for "supplements" at the American Dietetic Association: **www.eatright.org**

- Learn more about supplements from the FDA Center for Food Safety and Applied Nutrition: **www.cfsan.fda.gov/~dms/supplmnt.html**

- Obtain consumer information on dietary supplements from the U.S. Pharmacopeia: **www.usp.org**

- Review the Federal Trade Commission policies for dietary supplement advertising: **www.ftc.gov/bcp/ conline/pubs/buspubs/dietsupp.htm**

REFERENCES

1. National Institutes of Health, Multivitamin/mineral supplements and chronic disease prevention, *Annals of Internal Medicine* 145 (2006): 364-371; A. E. Millen, K. W. Dodd, and A. F. Subar, Use of vitamin, mineral, nonvitamin, and nonmineral supplements in the United States: The 1987, 1992, and 2000 National Health Interview Survey results, *Journal of the American Dietetic Association* 104 (2004): 942-950.

2. Position of the American Dietetic Association: Fortification and nutritional supplements, *Journal of the American Dietetic Association* 105 (2005): 1300-1311.

3. Practice Paper of the American Dietetic Association: Dietary supplements, *Journal of the American Dietetic Association* 105 (2005): 460-470; J. R. Hunt, Tailoring advice on dietary supplements: An opportunity for dietetics professionals, *Journal of the American Dietetic Association* 102 (2002): 1754-1755; C. Thomson and coauthors, Guidelines regarding the recommendation and sale of dietary supplements, *Journal of the American Dietetic Association* 102 (2002): 1158-1164.

4. D. E. Wildish, An evidence-based approach for dietitian prescription of multiple vitamins with minerals, *Journal of the American Dietetic Association* 104 (2004): 779-786.

5. K. M. Fairfield and R. H. Fletcher, Vitamins for chronic disease prevention in adults: Scientific review, *Journal of the American Medical Association* 287 (2002): 3116-3126.

6. R. H. Fletcher and K. M. Fairfield, Vitamins for chronic disease prevention in adults: Clinical applications, *Journal of the American Medical Association* 287 (2002): 3127-3129.

7. B. N. Ames, The metabolic tune-up: Metabolic harmony and disease prevention, *Journal of Nutrition* 133 (2003): 1544S-1548S.

8. P.M. Kris-Etherton and coauthors, Antioxidant vitamin supplements and cardiovascular disease, *Circulation* 110 (2004): 637-641; C. D. Morris and S. Carson, Routine vitamin supplementation to prevent cardiovascular disease: A summary of the evidence for the U.S. Preventive Services Task Force, *Annals of Internal Medicine* 139 (2003): 56-70; B. Hasanain and A. D. Mooradian, Antioxidant vitamins and their influence in diabetes mellitus, *Current Diabetes Reports* 2 (2002): 448-456.

9. National Institutes of Health, 2006.

10. J. M. Drazen, Inappropriate advertising of dietary supplements, *New England Journal of Medicine* 348 (2003): 777-778.

11. Institute of Medicine and National Research Council, *Dietary supplements: A framework for evaluating safety,* (Washington, D.C.: National Academy Press, 2004); C. L. Taylor, Regulatory frameworks for functional foods and dietary supplements, *Nutrition Reviews* 62 (2004): 55-59.

12. P. B. Fontanarosa, D. Rennie, and C. D. DeAngelis, The need for regulation of dietary supplements—Lessons from ephedra, *Journal of the American Medical Association* 289 (2003): 1568-1570.

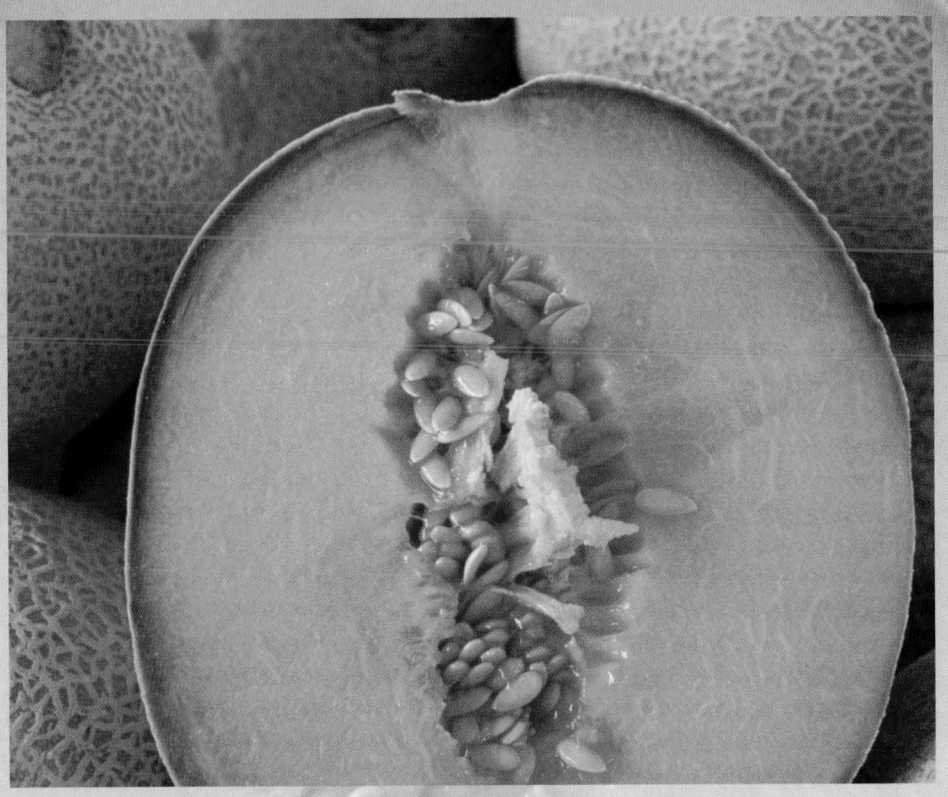

Nutrition in Your Life

Realizing that vitamin A from vegetables participates in vision, a mom encourages her children to "eat your carrots" because "they're good for your eyes." A dad takes his children outside to "enjoy the fresh air and sunshine" because they need the vitamin D that is made with the help of the sun. A physician recommends that a patient use vitamin E to slow the progression of heart disease. Another physician gives a newborn a dose of vitamin K to protect against life threatening blood loss. These common daily occurrences highlight some of the heroic work of the fat-soluble vitamins.

The Fat Soluble Vitamins: A, D, E, and K

CHAPTER OUTLINE

Vitamin A and Beta-Carotene • Roles in the Body • Vitamin A Deficiency • Vitamin A Toxicity • Vitamin A Recommendations • Vitamin A in Foods

Vitamin D • Roles in the Body • Vitamin D Deficiency • Vitamin D Toxicity • Vitamin D Recommendations and Sources

Vitamin E • Vitamin E as an Antioxidant • Vitamin E Deficiency • Vitamin E Toxicity • Vitamin E Recommendations • Vitamin E in Foods

Vitamin K • Roles in the Body • Vitamin K Deficiency • Vitamin K Toxicity • Vitamin K Recommendations and Sources

The Fat-Soluble Vitamins— In Summary

HIGHLIGHT 11 Anitoxidant Nutrients in Disease Prevention

The fat-soluble vitamins A, D, E, and K differ from the water-soluble vitamins in several significant ways (review the table on p. 326). Being insoluble in the watery GI juices, the fat-soluble vitamins require bile for their absorption. Upon absorption, fat-soluble vitamins travel through the lymphatic system within chylomicrons before entering the bloodstream, where many of them require protein carriers for transport. The fat-soluble vitamins participate in numerous activities throughout the body, but excesses are stored primarily in the liver and adipose tissue. The body maintains blood concentrations by retrieving these vitamins from storage as needed; thus people can eat less than their daily need for days, weeks, or even months or years without ill effects. They need only ensure that, over time, *average* daily intakes approximate recommendations. By the same token, because fat-soluble vitamins are not readily excreted, the risk of toxicity is greater than it is for the water-soluble vitamins.

Vitamin A and Beta-Carotene

Vitamin A was the first fat-soluble vitamin to be recognized. Almost a century later, vitamin A and its precursor, **beta-carotene,** ◆ continue to intrigue researchers with their diverse roles and profound effects on health.

Three different forms of vitamin A are active in the body: retinol, retinal, and retinoic acid. Collectively, these compounds are known as **retinoids.** Foods derived from animals provide compounds (retinyl esters) that are readily digested and absorbed as retinol in the intestine.[1] Foods derived from plants provide **carotenoids,** ◆ some of which have **vitamin A activity.*** The most studied of the carotenoids is beta-carotene, which can be split to form retinol in the intestine and liver. Beta-carotene's absorption and conversion are significantly less efficient than those of the retinoids.[2] Figure 11-1 (p. 370) illustrates the structural similarities and differences of these vitamin A compounds and the cleavage of beta-carotene.

The cells can convert retinol and retinal to the other active forms of vitamin A as needed. The conversion of retinol to retinal is reversible, but the further conversion of

---

◆ A compound that can be converted into an active vitamin is called a *precursor.*

◆ Carotenoids are among the best-known phytochemicals.

vitamin A: all naturally occurring compounds with the biological activity of retinol (RET-ih-nol), the alcohol form of vitamin A.

beta-carotene (BAY-tah KARE-oh-teen): one of the carotenoids; an orange pigment and vitamin A precursor found in plants.

retinoids (RET-ih-noyds): chemically related compounds with biological activity similar to that of retinol; metabolites of retinol.

carotenoids (kah-ROT-eh-noyds): pigments commonly found in plants and animals, some of which have vitamin A activity. The carotenoid with the greatest vitamin A activity is beta-carotene.

vitamin A activity: a term referring to both the active forms of vitamin A and the precursor forms in foods without distinguishing between them.

---

* Carotenoids with vitamin A activity include alpha-carotene, beta-carotene, and beta-cryptoxanthin; carotenoids with no vitamin A activity include lycopene, lutein, and zeaxanthin.

FIGURE 11-1 Forms of Vitamin A

In this diagram, corners represent carbon atoms, as in all previous diagrams in this book. A further simplification here is that methyl groups (CH_3) are understood to be at the ends of the lines extending from corners. (See Appendix C for complete structures.)

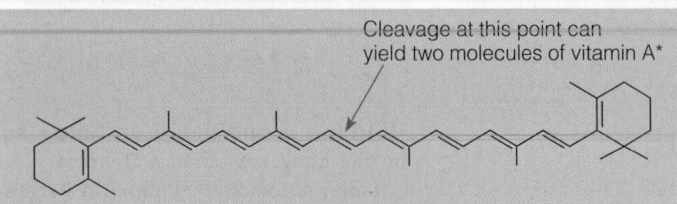

Retinol, the alcohol form

Retinal, the aldehyde form

Retinoic acid, the acid form

Cleavage at this point can yield two molecules of vitamin A*

*Sometimes cleavage occurs at other points as well, so that one molecule of beta-carotene may yield only one molecule of vitamin A. Furthermore, not all beta-carotene is converted to vitamin A, and absorption of beta-carotene is not as efficient as that of vitamin A. For these reasons, 12 µg of beta-carotene are equivalent to 1 µg of vitamin A. Conversion of other carotenoids to vitamin A is even less efficient.

Beta-carotene, a precursor

retinal to retinoic acid is irreversible (see Figure 11-2). This irreversibility is significant because each form of vitamin A performs a function that the others cannot.

Several proteins participate in the digestion and absorption of vitamin A.[3] After absorption via the lymph system, vitamin A eventually arrives at the liver, where it is stored. There, a special transport protein, **retinol-binding protein (RBP)**, picks up vitamin A from the liver and carries it in the blood. Cells that use vitamin A have special protein receptors for it, as if the vitamin were fragile and had to be passed carefully from hand to hand without being dropped. Each form of vitamin A has its own receptor protein (retinol has several) within the cells.

Roles in the Body

Vitamin A is a versatile vitamin, known to influence over 500 genes.[4] Its major roles include:

- Promoting vision
- Participating in protein synthesis and cell differentiation (and thereby maintaining the health of epithelial tissues and skin)
- Supporting reproduction and growth

As mentioned, each form of vitamin A performs specific tasks. Retinol supports reproduction and is the major transport and storage form of the vitamin. Retinal is active in vision and is also an intermediate in the conversion of retinol to retinoic acid (review Figure 11-2). Retinoic acid acts like a hormone, regulating cell differentiation, growth, and embryonic development.[5] Animals raised on retinoic acid

FIGURE 11-2 Conversion of Vitamin A Compounds

Notice that the conversion from retinol to retinal is reversible, whereas the pathway from retinal to retinoic acid is not.

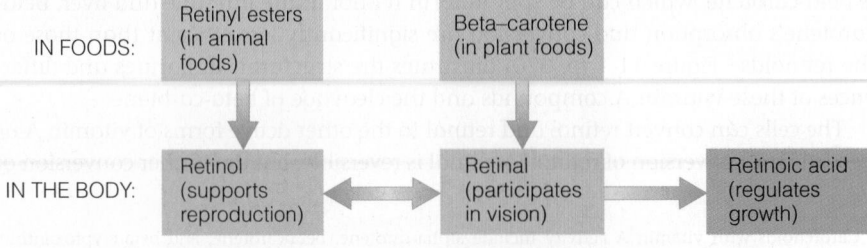

IN FOODS:

Retinyl esters (in animal foods)

Beta–carotene (in plant foods)

IN THE BODY:

Retinol (supports reproduction)

Retinal (participates in vision)

Retinoic acid (regulates growth)

retinol-binding protein (RBP): the specific protein responsible for transporting retinol.

as their sole source of vitamin A can grow normally, but they become blind because retinoic acid cannot be converted to retinal (review Figure 11-2).

Vitamin A in Vision Vitamin A plays two indispensable roles in the eye: it helps maintain a crystal-clear outer window, the **cornea**, and it participates in the conversion of light energy into nerve impulses at the **retina** (see Figure 11-3 for details). The cells of the retina contain **pigment** molecules called **rhodopsin;** each rhodopsin molecule is composed of a protein called **opsin** bonded to a molecule of retinal. ◆ When light passes through the cornea of the eye and strikes the cells of the retina, rhodopsin responds by changing shape and becoming bleached. As it does, the retinal shifts from a *cis* to a *trans* configuration, just as fatty acids do during hydrogenation (see pp. 143–145). The *trans*-retinal cannot remain bonded to opsin. When retinal is released, opsin changes shape, thereby disturbing the membrane of the cell and generating an electrical impulse that travels along the cell's length. At the other end of the cell, the impulse is transmitted to a nerve cell, which conveys the message to the brain. Much of the retinal is then converted back to its active *cis* form and combined with the opsin protein to regenerate the pigment rhodopsin. Some retinal, however, may be oxidized to retinoic acid, a biochemical dead end for the visual process. Visual activity leads to repeated small losses of retinal, necessitating its constant replenishment either directly from foods or indirectly from retinol stores.

Vitamin A in Protein Synthesis and Cell Differentiation Despite its important role in vision, only one-thousandth of the body's vitamin A is in the retina. Much more is in the cells lining the body's surfaces. There, the vitamin participates in protein synthesis and **cell differentiation**, a process by which each type of cell develops to perform a specific function. Its role in cell differentiation helps explain how vitamin A may prevent cancer.[6]

All body surfaces, both inside and out, are covered by layers of cells known as **epithelial cells.** The **epithelial tissue** on the outside of the body is, of course, the skin—and vitamin A helps to protect against skin damage from sunlight.[7] The epithelial tissues that line the inside of the body are the **mucous membranes:** the linings of the mouth, stomach, and intestines; the linings of the lungs and the passages leading to them; the linings of the urinary bladder and urethra; the linings of the uterus and vagina; and the linings of the eyelids and sinus passageways. Within the body, the mucous membranes of the GI tract alone line an area larger than a quarter of a football field, and vitamin A helps to maintain their integrity (see Figure 11-4, p. 372).

Vitamin A promotes differentiation of epithelial cells and goblet cells, one-celled glands that synthesize and secrete mucus. Mucus coats and protects the epithelial cells from invasive microorganisms and other harmful substances, such as gastric juices.

◆ More than 100 million cells reside in the retina, and each contains about 30 million molecules of vitamin A-containing visual pigments.

---

cornea (KOR-nee-uh): the transparent membrane covering the outside of the eye.

retina (RET-in-uh): the layer of light-sensitive nerve cells lining the back of the inside of the eye; consists of rods and cones.

pigment: a molecule capable of absorbing certain wavelengths of light so that it reflects only those that we perceive as a certain color.

rhodopsin (ro-DOP-sin): a light-sensitive pigment of the retina; contains the retinal form of vitamin A and the protein opsin.
• **rhod** = red (pigment)
• **opsin** = visual protein

opsin (OP-sin): the protein portion of the visual pigment molecule.

cell differentiation (DIF-er-EN-she-AY-shun): the process by which immature cells develop specific functions different from those of the original that are characteristic of their mature cell type.

epithelial (ep-i-THEE-lee-ul) **cells**: cells on the surface of the skin and mucous membranes.

epithelial tissue: the layer of the body that serves as a selective barrier between the body's interior and the environment. (Examples are the cornea of the eyes, the skin, the respiratory lining of the lungs, and the lining of the digestive tract.)

mucous (MYOO-kus) **membranes:** the membranes, composed of mucus-secreting cells, that line the surfaces of body tissues.

FIGURE 11-3 *Animated!* Vitamin A's Role in Vision

ThomsonNOW
To test your understanding of these concepts, log on to **www.thomsonedu.com/thomsonnow.**

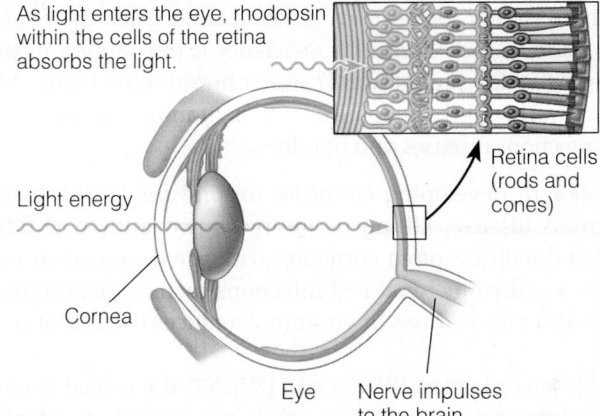

As light enters the eye, rhodopsin within the cells of the retina absorbs the light.

Retina cells (rods and cones)

Light energy

Cornea

Eye   Nerve impulses to the brain

The cells of the retina contain rhodopsin, a molecule composed of opsin (a protein) and *cis*-retinal (vitamin A).

cis-Retinal   *trans*-Retinal

As rhodopsin absorbs light, retinal changes from *cis* to *trans*, which triggers a nerve impulse that carries visual information to the brain.

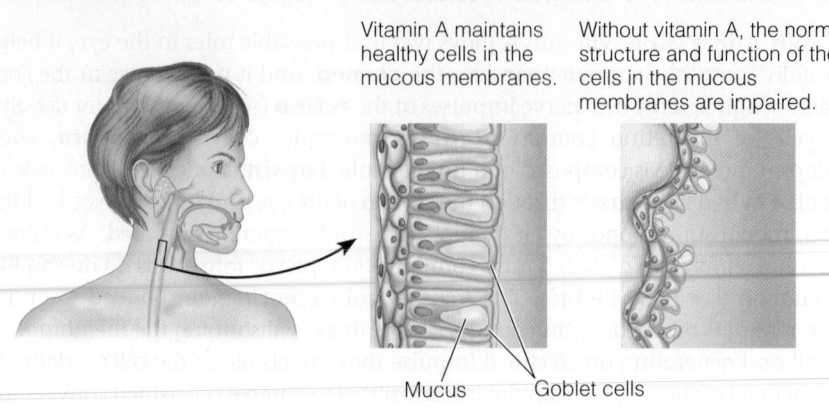

FIGURE 11-4 Mucous Membrane Integrity

Vitamin A maintains healthy cells in the mucous membranes.

Without vitamin A, the normal structure and function of the cells in the mucous membranes are impaired.

Mucus   Goblet cells

Vitamin A in Reproduction and Growth As mentioned, vitamin A also supports reproduction and growth. In men, retinol participates in sperm development, and in women, vitamin A supports normal fetal development during pregnancy. Children lacking vitamin A fail to grow. When given vitamin A supplements, these children gain weight and grow taller.

The growth of bones illustrates that growth is a complex phenomenon of **remodeling.** To convert a small bone into a large bone, the bone-remodeling cells must "undo" some parts of the bone as they go, ◆ and vitamin A participates in the dismantling. The cells that break down bone contain sacs of degradative enzymes. ◆ With the help of vitamin A, these enzymes eat away at selected sites in the bone, removing the parts that are not needed.

Beta-Carotene as an Antioxidant In the body, beta-carotene serves primarily as a vitamin A precursor.[8] Not all dietary beta-carotene is converted to active vitamin A, however. Some beta-carotene may act as an antioxidant ◆ capable of protecting the body against disease. (See Highlight 11 for details.)

Vitamin A Deficiency

Vitamin A status depends mostly on the adequacy of vitamin A stores, 90 percent of which are in the liver. Vitamin A status also depends on a person's protein status because retinol-binding proteins serve as the vitamin's transport carriers inside the body.

If a person were to stop eating vitamin A–containing foods, deficiency symptoms would not begin to appear until after stores were depleted—one to two years for a healthy adult but much sooner for a growing child. Then the consequences would be profound and severe. Vitamin A deficiency is uncommon in the United States, but it is one of the developing world's major nutrition problems. More than 100 million children worldwide have some degree of vitamin A deficiency and thus are vulnerable to infectious diseases and blindness.

Infectious Diseases In developing countries around the world, measles is a devastating infectious disease, killing as many as two million children each year. The severity of the illness often correlates with the degree of vitamin A deficiency; deaths are usually due to related infections such as pneumonia and severe diarrhea. Providing large doses of vitamin A reduces the risk of dying from these infections.

The World Health Organization (WHO) and UNICEF (the United Nations International Children's Emergency Fund) have made the control of vitamin A deficiency a major goal in their quest to improve child health and survival throughout

---

◆ The cells that destroy bone during growth are **osteoclasts;** those that build bone are **osteoblasts.**
- **osteo** = bone
- **clast** = break
- **blast** = build

◆ The sacs of degradative enzymes are **lyso-somes** (LYE-so-zomes).

◆ Key antioxidant nutrients:
- Vitamin C, vitamin E, beta-carotene
- Selenium

remodeling: the dismantling and reformation of a structure, in this case, bone.

FIGURE 11-5 Vitamin A–Deficiency Symptom—Night Blindness

These photographs illustrate the eyes' slow recovery in response to a flash of bright light at night. In animal research studies, the response rate is measured with electrodes.

In dim light, you can make out the details in this room. You are using your rods for vision.

A flash of bright light momentarily blinds you as the pigment in the rods is bleached.

You quickly recover and can see the details again in a few seconds.

With inadequate vitamin A, you do not recover but remain blinded for many seconds.

the developing world. They recommend routine vitamin A supplementation for all children with measles in areas where vitamin A deficiency is a problem or where the measles death rate is high. In the United States, the American Academy of Pediatrics recommends vitamin A supplementation for certain groups of measles-infected infants and children. Vitamin A supplementation also protects against the complications of other life-threatening infections, including malaria, lung diseases, and HIV (human immunodeficiency virus, the virus that causes AIDS).[9]

Night Blindness **Night blindness** is one of the first detectable signs of vitamin A deficiency and permits early diagnosis. In night blindness, the retina does not receive enough retinal to regenerate the visual pigments bleached by light. The person loses the ability to recover promptly from the temporary blinding that follows a flash of bright light at night or to see after the lights go out. In many parts of the world, after the sun goes down, vitamin A–deficient people become night-blind: children cannot find their shoes or toys, and women cannot fetch water or wash dishes. They often cling to others or sit still, afraid that they may trip and fall or lose their way if they try to walk alone. In many developing countries, night blindness due to vitamin A deficiency is so common that the people have special words to describe it. In Indonesia, the term is *buta ayam,* which means "chicken eyes" or "chicken blindness." (Chickens do not have the cells of the retina that respond to dim light and therefore cannot see at night.) Figure 11-5 shows the eyes' slow recovery in response to a flash of bright light in night blindness.

Blindness (Xerophthalmia) Beyond night blindness is total blindness—failure to see at all. Night blindness is caused by a lack of vitamin A at the back of the eye, the retina; total blindness is caused by a lack at the front of the eye, the cornea. Severe vitamin A deficiency is the major cause of childhood blindness in the world, causing more than half a million preschool children to lose their sight each year. Blindness due to vitamin A deficiency, known as **xerophthalmia,** develops in stages. At first, the cornea becomes dry and hard, a condition known as **xerosis.** Then, corneal xerosis can quickly progress to **keratomalacia,** the softening of the cornea that leads to irreversible blindness.

Keratinization Elsewhere in the body, vitamin A deficiency affects other surfaces. On the body's outer surface, the epithelial cells change shape and begin to secrete the protein **keratin**—the hard, inflexible protein of hair and nails. As Figure 11-6 shows, the skin becomes dry, rough, and scaly as lumps of keratin accumulate (**keratinization**). Without vitamin A, the goblet cells in the GI tract diminish in number and activity, limiting the secretion of mucus. With less mucus, normal digestion and absorption of nutrients falter, and this, in turn, worsens malnutrition by limiting the absorption of whatever nutrients the diet may deliver. Similar changes in the cells of

FIGURE 11-6 Vitamin A–Deficiency Symptom—The Rough Skin of Keratinization

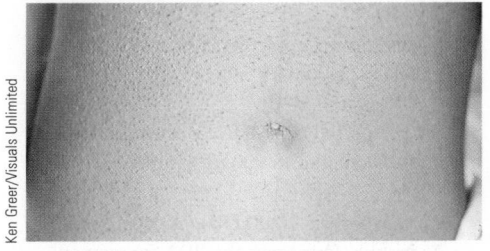

In vitamin A deficiency, the epithelial cells secrete the protein keratin in a process known as *keratinization.* (Keratinization doesn't occur in the GI tract, but mucus-producing cells dwindle and mucus production declines.) The extreme of this condition is *hyperkeratinization* or *hyperkeratosis.* When keratin accumulates around hair follicles, the condition is known as *follicular hyperkeratosis.*

night blindness: slow recovery of vision after flashes of bright light at night or an inability to see in dim light; an early symptom of vitamin A deficiency.

xerophthalmia (zer-off-THAL-mee-uh): progressive blindness caused by severe vitamin A deficiency.
• **xero** = dry
• **ophthalm** = eye

xerosis (zee-ROW-sis): abnormal drying of the skin and mucous membranes; a sign of vitamin A deficiency.

keratomalacia (KARE-ah-toe-ma-LAY-shuh): softening of the cornea that leads to irreversible blindness; seen in severe vitamin A deficiency.

keratin (KARE-uh-tin): a water-insoluble protein; the normal protein of hair and nails.

keratinization: accumulation of keratin in a tissue; a sign of vitamin A deficiency.

other epithelial tissues weaken defenses, making infections of the respiratory tract, the GI tract, the urinary tract, the vagina, and possibly the inner ear likely.

Vitamin A Toxicity

Just as a deficiency of vitamin A affects all body systems, so does a toxicity. Symptoms of toxicity begin to develop when all the binding proteins are swamped, and free vitamin A damages the cells. Such effects are unlikely when a person depends on a balanced diet for nutrients, but toxicity is a real possibility when concentrated amounts of **preformed vitamin A** in foods derived from animals, fortified foods, or supplements is consumed.[10] Children are most vulnerable to toxicity because they need less vitamin A and are more sensitive to overdoses. An Upper Level has been set for preformed vitamin A (see inside front cover).

Beta-carotene, which is found in a wide variety of fruits and vegetables, is not converted efficiently enough in the body to cause vitamin A toxicity; instead, it is stored in the fat just under the skin. Although overconsumption of beta-carotene from foods may turn the skin yellow, this is not harmful (see Figure 11-7).[11] In contrast, overconsumption of beta-carotene from supplements may be quite harmful. In excess, this antioxidant may act as a prooxidant, promoting cell division and destroying vitamin A. Furthermore, the adverse effects of beta-carotene supplements are most evident in people who drink alcohol and smoke cigarettes.

Bone Defects Excessive intake of vitamin A over the years may weaken the bones and contribute to fractures and osteoporosis.[12] Research findings suggest that most people should not take vitamin A supplements.[13] Even multivitamin supplements ◆ provide more vitamin A than most people need.

Birth Defects Excessive vitamin A poses a **teratogenic** risk. High intakes (10,000 IU ◆ of supplemental vitamin A daily) before the seventh week of pregnancy appear to be the most damaging. For this reason, vitamin A is not given as a supplement in the first trimester of pregnancy without specific evidence of deficiency, which is rare.

Not for Acne Adolescents need to know that massive doses of vitamin A have no beneficial effect on **acne.** The prescription medicine Accutane is made from vitamin A but is chemically different. Taken orally, Accutane is effective against the deep lesions of cystic acne. It is highly toxic, however, especially during growth, and has caused birth defects in infants when women have taken it during their pregnancies. For this reason, women taking Accutane must begin using two effective forms of contraception at least one month before taking the drug and continue using contraception at least one month after discontinuing its use. They should also refrain from taking any supplements containing vitamin A to avoid additive toxic effects.

Another vitamin A relative, Retin-A, fights acne, the wrinkles of aging, and other skin disorders. Applied topically, this ointment smooths and softens skin; it also lightens skin that has become darkly pigmented after inflammation. During treatment, the skin becomes red and tender and peels.

Vitamin A Recommendations

Because the body can derive vitamin A from various retinoids and carotenoids, its contents in foods and its recommendations are expressed as **retinol activity equivalents (RAE).** A microgram of retinol counts as 1 RAE, ◆ as does 12 micrograms of dietary beta-carotene. Most food and supplement labels report their vitamin A contents using international units (IU), ◆ an old measure of vitamin activity used before direct chemical analysis was possible.

Vitamin A in Foods

The richest sources of the retinoids are foods derived from animals—liver, fish liver oils, milk and milk products, butter, and eggs. Because vitamin A is fat soluble, it is

---

◆ Multivitamin supplements typically provide:
- 750 μg (2500 IU)
- 1500 μg (5000 IU)

For perspective, the RDA for vitamin A is 700 μg for women and 900 μg for men.

◆ For perspective, 10,000 IU ≈ 3000 μg vitamin A, roughly four times the RDA for women.

◆ 1 μg RAE = 1 μg retinol
= 2 μg beta-carotene (supplement)
= 12 μg beta-carotene (dietary)
= 24 μg of other vitamin A precursor carotenoids

◆ 1 IU retinol = 0.3 μg retinol or 0.3 μg RAE
1 IU beta-carotene (supplement) = 0.5 IU retinol or 0.15 μg RAE
1 IU beta-carotene (dietary) = 0.165 IU retinol or 0.05 μg RAE
1 IU other vitamin A precursor carotenoids = 0.025 μg RAE

preformed vitamin A: dietary vitamin A in its active form.

teratogenic (ter-AT-oh-jen-ik): causing abnormal fetal development and birth defects.
- **terato** = monster
- **genic** = to produce

acne: a chronic inflammation of the skin's follicles and oil-producing glands, which leads to an accumulation of oils inside the ducts that surround hairs; usually associated with the maturation of young adults.

retinol activity equivalents (RAE): a measure of vitamin A activity; the amount of retinol that the body will derive from a food containing preformed retinol or its precursor beta-carotene.

lost when milk is skimmed. To compensate, reduced-fat, low-fat, and fat-free milks are often fortified so as to supply 6 to 10 percent of the Daily Value per cup.* Margarine is usually fortified to provide the same amount of vitamin A as butter.

Plants contain no retinoids, but many vegetables and some fruits contain vitamin A precursors—the carotenoids, red and yellow pigments of plants. Only a few carotenoids have vitamin A activity; the carotenoid with the greatest vitamin A activity is beta-carotene. The bioavialability of carotenoids depends in part on fat accompanying the meal; more carotenoids are absorbed when salads have regular dressing than when reduced-fat dressing is used and essentially no carotenoid absorption occurs when fat-free dressing is used.[14]

The Colors of Vitamin A Foods The dark leafy greens (like spinach—not celery or cabbage) and the rich yellow or deep orange vegetables and fruits (such as winter squash, cantaloupe, carrots, and sweet potatoes—not corn or bananas) help people meet their vitamin A needs (see Figure 11-8). A diet including several servings of such carotene-rich sources helps to ensure a sufficient intake.

An attractive meal that includes foods of different colors most likely supplies vitamin A as well. Most foods with vitamin A activity are brightly colored—green, yellow, orange, and red. Any plant-derived food with significant vitamin A activity must have some color, since beta-carotene is a rich, deep yellow, almost orange

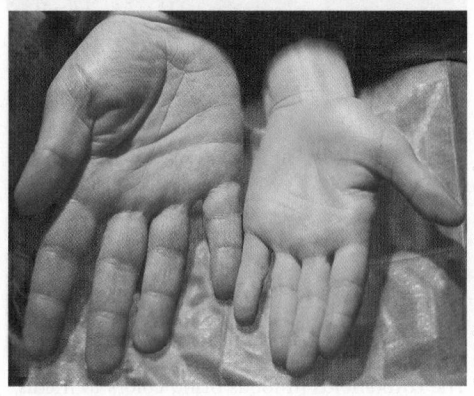

FIGURE 11-7 Symptom of Beta-Carotene Excess—Discoloration of the Skin

© 2002 Massachusetts Medical Society

The hand on the right shows the skin discoloration that occurs when blood levels of beta-carotene rise in response to a low-kcalorie diet that features carrots, pumpkins, and orange juice. (The hand on the left belongs to someone else and is shown here for comparison.)

* Vitamin A fortification of milk in the United States is required to a level found in whole milk (1200 IU per quart), but many manufacturers commonly fortify to a higher level (2000 IU per quart). Similarly, in Canada all milk that has had fat removed must be fortified with vitamin A.

FIGURE 11-8 Vitamin A in Selected Foods

See the "How to" section on p. 329 for more information on using this figure.

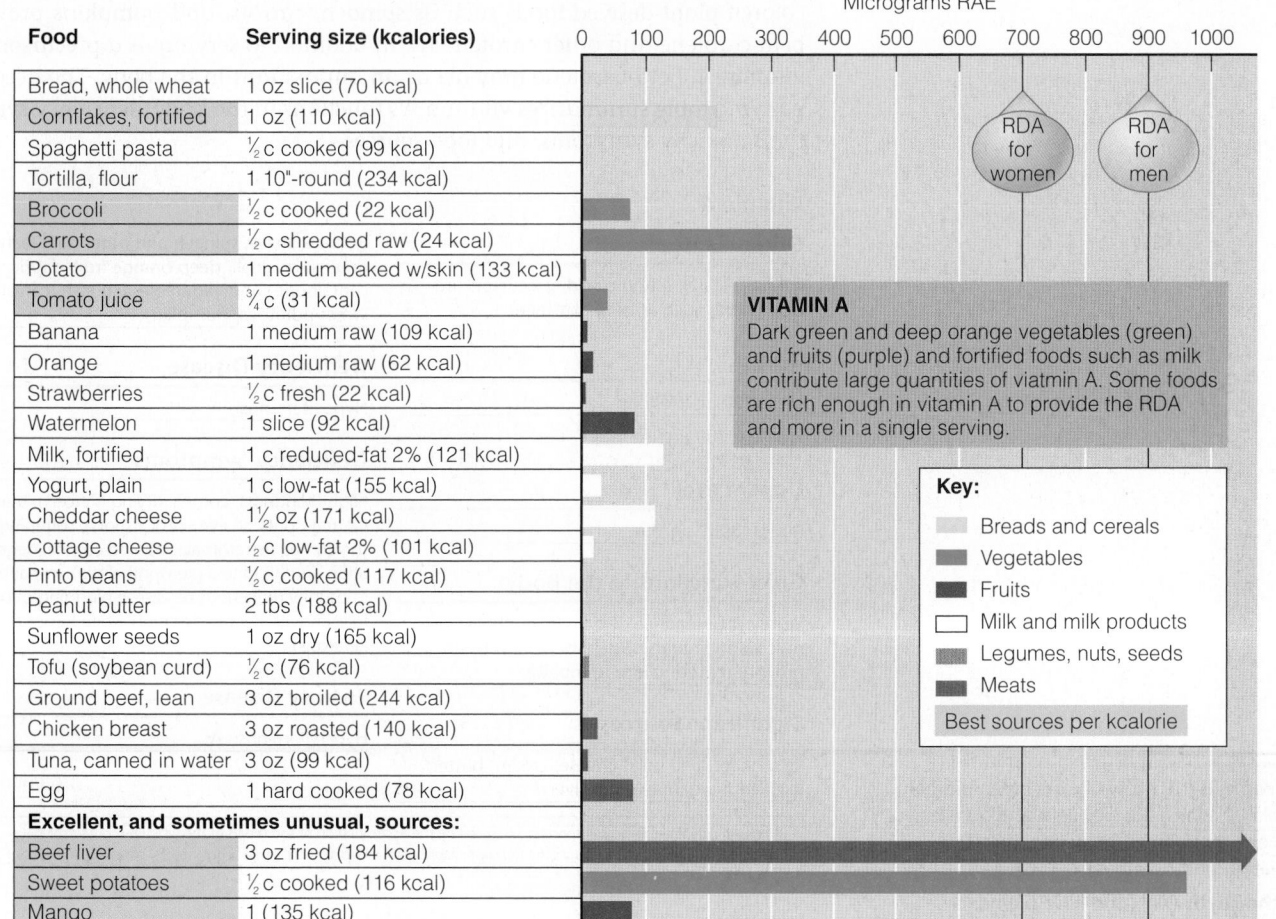

Micrograms RAE

Food	Serving size (kcalories)
Bread, whole wheat	1 oz slice (70 kcal)
Cornflakes, fortified	1 oz (110 kcal)
Spaghetti pasta	½ c cooked (99 kcal)
Tortilla, flour	1 10"-round (234 kcal)
Broccoli	½ c cooked (22 kcal)
Carrots	½ c shredded raw (24 kcal)
Potato	1 medium baked w/skin (133 kcal)
Tomato juice	¾ c (31 kcal)
Banana	1 medium raw (109 kcal)
Orange	1 medium raw (62 kcal)
Strawberries	½ c fresh (22 kcal)
Watermelon	1 slice (92 kcal)
Milk, fortified	1 c reduced-fat 2% (121 kcal)
Yogurt, plain	1 c low-fat (155 kcal)
Cheddar cheese	1½ oz (171 kcal)
Cottage cheese	½ c low-fat 2% (101 kcal)
Pinto beans	½ c cooked (117 kcal)
Peanut butter	2 tbs (188 kcal)
Sunflower seeds	1 oz dry (165 kcal)
Tofu (soybean curd)	½ c (76 kcal)
Ground beef, lean	3 oz broiled (244 kcal)
Chicken breast	3 oz roasted (140 kcal)
Tuna, canned in water	3 oz (99 kcal)
Egg	1 hard cooked (78 kcal)
Excellent, and sometimes unusual, sources:	
Beef liver	3 oz fried (184 kcal)
Sweet potatoes	½ c cooked (116 kcal)
Mango	1 (135 kcal)

RDA for women
RDA for men

VITAMIN A
Dark green and deep orange vegetables (green) and fruits (purple) and fortified foods such as milk contribute large quantities of viatmin A. Some foods are rich enough in vitamin A to provide the RDA and more in a single serving.

Key:
☐ Breads and cereals
☐ Vegetables
☐ Fruits
☐ Milk and milk products
☐ Legumes, nuts, seeds
☐ Meats
☐ Best sources per kcalorie

The carotenoids in foods bring colors to meals; the retinoids in our eyes allow us to see them.

compound. The beta-carotene in dark green, leafy vegetables is abundant but masked by large amounts of the green pigment **chlorophyll.**

Bright color is not always a sign of vitamin A activity, however. Beets and corn, for example, derive their colors from the red and yellow **xanthophylls,** which have no vitamin A activity. As for white plant foods such as potatoes, cauliflower, pasta, and rice, they also offer little or no vitamin A.

Vitamin A–Poor Fast Foods Fast foods often lack vitamin A. Anyone who dines frequently on hamburgers, French fries, and colas is wise to emphasize colorful vegetables and fruits at other meals.

Vitamin A–Rich Liver People sometimes wonder if eating liver too frequently can cause vitamin A toxicity. Liver is a rich source because vitamin A is stored in the livers of animals, just as in humans.* Arctic explorers who have eaten large quantities of polar bear liver have become ill with symptoms suggesting vitamin A toxicity, as have young children who regularly ate a chicken liver spread that provided three times their daily recommended intake. Liver offers many nutrients, and eating it periodically may improve a person's nutrition status. But caution is warranted not to eat too much too often, especially for pregnant women. With one ounce of beef liver providing more than three times the RDA for vitamin A, intakes can rise quickly.

IN SUMMARY

Vitamin A is found in the body in three forms: retinol, retinal, and retinoic acid. Together, they are essential to vision, healthy epithelial tissues, and growth. Vitamin A deficiency is a major health problem worldwide, leading to infections, blindness, and keratinization. Toxicity can also cause problems and is most often associated with supplement abuse. Animal-derived foods such as liver and whole or fortified milk provide retinoids, whereas brightly colored plant-derived foods such as spinach, carrots, and pumpkins provide beta-carotene and other carotenoids. In addition to serving as a precursor for vitamin A, beta-carotene may act as an antioxidant in the body. The accompanying table summarizes vitamin A's functions in the body, deficiency symptoms, toxicity symptoms, and food sources.

Vitamin A

Other Names

Retinol, retinal, retinoic acid; precursors are carotenoids such as beta-carotene

RDA

Men: 900 µg RAE/day

Women: 700 µg RAE/day

Upper Level

Adults: 3000 µg/day

Chief Functions in the Body

Vision; maintenance of cornea, epithelial cells, mucous membranes, skin; bone and tooth growth; reproduction; immunity

Significant Sources

Retinol: fortified milk, cheese, cream, butter, fortified margarine, eggs, liver

Beta-carotene: spinach and other dark leafy greens; broccoli, deep orange fruits (apricots, cantaloupe) and vegetables (squash, carrots, sweet potatoes, pumpkin)

Deficiency Disease

Hypovitaminosis A

Deficiency Symptoms

Night blindness, corneal drying (xerosis), triangular gray spots on eye (Bitot's spots), softening of the cornea (keratomalacia), and corneal degeneration and blindness (xerophthalmia); impaired immunity (infectious diseases); plugging of hair follicles with keratin, forming white lumps (hyperkeratosis)

Toxicity Disease

Hypervitaminosis A[a]

(continued)

[a] A related condition, *hypercarotenemia*, is caused by the accumulation of too much of the vitamin A precursor beta-carotene in the blood, which turns the skin noticeably yellow. Hypercarotenemia is not, strictly speaking, a toxicity symptom.

chlorophyll (KLO-row-fil): the green pigment of plants, which absorbs light and transfers the energy to other molecules, thereby initiating photosynthesis.

xanthophylls (ZAN-tho-fills): pigments found in plants; responsible for the color changes seen in autumn leaves.

* The liver is not the only organ that stores vitamin A. The kidneys, adrenals, and other organs do, too, but the liver stores the most and is the most commonly eaten organ meat.

Vitamin A (continued)	
Chronic Toxicity Symptoms	**Acute Toxicity Symptoms**
Increased activity of osteoclasts[b] causing reduced bone density; liver abnormalities; birth defects	Blurred vision, nausea, vomiting, vertigo; increase of pressure inside skull, mimicking brain tumor; headaches; muscle incoordination

[b]*Osteoclasts* are the cells that destroy bone during its growth. Those that build bone are *osteoblasts.*

Vitamin D

Vitamin D (calciferol) ◆ is different from all the other nutrients in that the body can synthesize it, with the help of sunlight, from a precursor that the body makes from cholesterol. Therefore, vitamin D is not an essential nutrient; given enough time in the sun, people need no vitamin D from foods.

Figure 11-9 diagrams the pathway for making and activating vitamin D. Ultraviolet rays from the sun hit the precursor in the skin and convert it to previtamin D_3. This compound works its way into the body and slowly, over the next 36 hours, is converted to its active form with the help of the body's heat. The biological activity of the active vitamin is 500- to 1000-fold greater than that of its precursor.

Regardless of whether the body manufactures vitamin D_3 or obtains it directly from foods, two hydroxylation reactions must occur before the vitamin becomes fully active.[15] First, the liver adds an OH group, and then the kidneys add another OH group to produce the active vitamin. A review of Figure 11-9 reveals how diseases affecting either the liver or the kidneys can interfere with the activation of vitamin D and produce symptoms of deficiency.

Roles in the Body

Though called a vitamin, vitamin D is actually a hormone—a compound manufactured by one part of the body that causes another part to respond. Like vitamin A, vitamin D has a binding protein that carries it to the target organs—most notably, the intestines, the kidneys, and the bones. All respond to vitamin D by making the minerals needed for bone growth and maintenance available.

Vitamin D in Bone Growth Vitamin D is a member of a large and cooperative bone-making and maintenance team ◆ composed of nutrients and other compounds, including vitamins A, C, and K; hormones (parathyroid hormone and calcitonin); the protein collagen; and the minerals calcium, phosphorus, magnesium, and fluoride. Vitamin D's special role in bone growth is to maintain blood concentrations of calcium and phosphorus. The bones grow denser and stronger as they absorb and deposit these minerals.

Vitamin D raises blood concentrations of these minerals in three ways. It enhances their absorption from the GI tract, their reabsorption by the kidneys, and their mobilization from the bones into the blood.[16] The vitamin may work alone, as it does in the GI tract, or in combination with parathyroid hormone, as it does in the bones and kidneys. Vitamin D is the director, but the star of the show is calcium. Details of calcium balance appear in Chapter 12.

Vitamin D in Other Roles Scientists have discovered many other vitamin D target tissues, including cells of the immune system, brain and nervous system, pancreas, skin, muscles and cartilage, and reproductive organs. Because vitamin D has numerous functions, it may be valuable in treating a number of disorders. Recent evidence suggests that vitamin D may protect against tuberculosis, gum inflammation, multiple sclerosis, and some cancers.[17]

◆ Vitamin D comes in many forms, the two most important being a plant version called **vitamin D_2** or **ergocalciferol** (ER-go-kal-SIF-er-ol) and an animal version called **vitamin D_3** or **cholecalciferol** (KO-lee-kal-SIF-er-ol).

◆ Key bone nutrients:
• Vitamin D, vitamin K, vitamin A
• Calcium, phosphorus, magnesium, fluoride

FIGURE 11-9 *Animated!* **Vitamin D Synthesis and Activation**

The precursor of vitamin D is made in the liver from cholesterol (see Figure 5-11 on p. 147 and Appendix C). The activation of vitamin D is a closely regulated process. The final product, active vitamin D, is also known as 1,25-dihydroxycholecalciferol (or calcitriol).

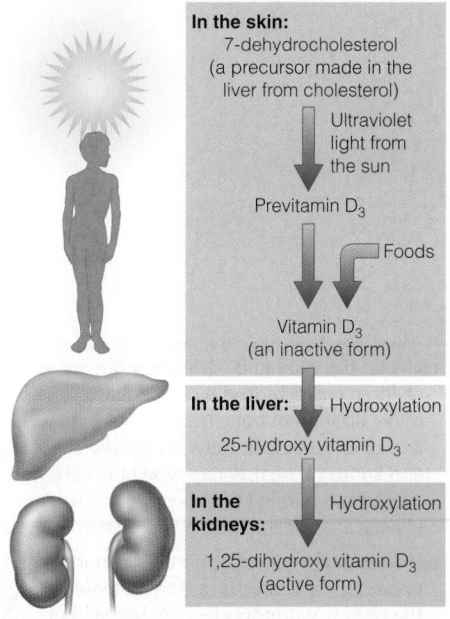

In the skin:
7-dehydrocholesterol (a precursor made in the liver from cholesterol)

Ultraviolet light from the sun

Previtamin D_3

Foods

Vitamin D_3 (an inactive form)

In the liver: Hydroxylation
25-hydroxy vitamin D_3

In the kidneys: Hydroxylation
1,25-dihydroxy vitamin D_3 (active form)

ThomsonNOW™
To test your understanding of these concepts, log on to **www.thomsonedu.com/thomsonnow.**

Vitamin D Deficiency

Factors that contribute to vitamin D deficiency include dark skin, breastfeeding without supplementation, lack of sunlight, and not using fortified milk. In vitamin D deficiency, production of the protein that binds calcium in the intestinal cells slows. Thus, even when calcium in the diet is adequate, it passes through the GI tract unabsorbed, leaving the bones undersupplied. Consequently, a vitamin D deficiency creates a calcium deficiency and increases the risks of several chronic diseases, most notably osteoporosis.[18] Vitamin D–deficient adolescents may not reach their peak bone mass.[19]

Rickets Worldwide, the vitamin D–deficiency disease **rickets** still afflicts many children.[20] In the United States, rickets is not common, but when it occurs, young, breast-fed, black children are the ones most likely to be affected.[21] In rickets, the bones fail to calcify normally, causing growth retardation and skeletal abnormalities. The bones become so weak that they bend when they have to support the body's weight (see Figure 11-10). A child with rickets who is old enough to walk characteristically develops bowed legs, often the most obvious sign of the disease. Another sign is the beaded ribs ◆ that result from the poorly formed attachments of bones to the cartilage.

Osteomalacia In adults, the poor mineralization of bone results in the painful bone disease **osteomalacia**.[22] The bones become increasingly soft, flexible, brittle, and deformed.

Osteoporosis Any failure to synthesize adequate vitamin D or obtain enough from foods sets the stage for a loss of calcium from the bones, which can result in fractures. Highlight 12 describes the many factors that lead to osteoporosis, a condition of reduced bone density.

The Elderly Vitamin D deficiency is especially likely in older adults for several reasons. For one, the skin, liver, and kidneys lose their capacity to make and activate vi-

◆ Because the poorly formed rib attachments resemble rosary beads, this symptom is commonly known as **rachitic** (ra-KIT-ik) **rosary** ("the rosary of rickets").

rickets: the vitamin D–deficiency disease in children characterized by inadequate mineralization of bone (manifested in bowed legs or knock-knees, outward-bowed chest, and knobs on ribs). A rare type of rickets, not caused by vitamin D deficiency, is known as *vitamin D–refractory rickets*.

osteomalacia (OS-tee-oh-ma-LAY-shuh): a bone disease characterized by softening of the bones. Symptoms include bending of the spine and bowing of the legs. The disease occurs most often in adult women.
• **osteo** = bone
• **malacia** = softening

FIGURE 11-10 Vitamin D–Deficiency Symptoms—Bowed Legs and Beaded Ribs of Rickets

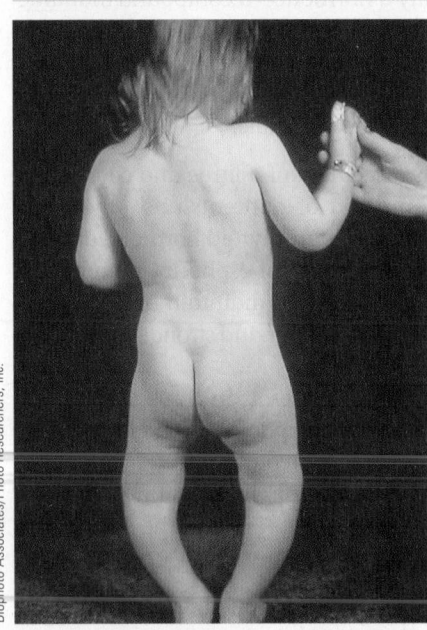

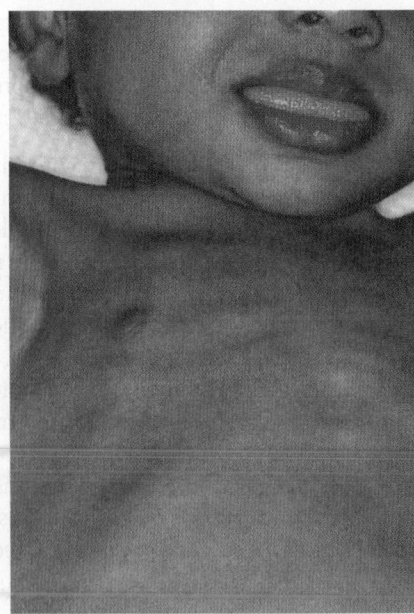

Bowed legs. In rickets, the poorly formed long bones of the legs bend outward as weight-bearing activities such as walking begin.

Beaded ribs. In rickets, a series of "beads" develop where the cartilages and bones attach.

tamin D with advancing age. For another, older adults typically drink little or no milk—the main dietary source of vitamin D. And finally, older adults typically spend much of the day indoors, and when they do venture outside, many of them cautiously wear protective clothing or apply sunscreen to all sun-exposed areas of their skin. Dark-skinned people living in northern regions are particularly vulnerable.[23] All of these factors increase the likelihood of vitamin D deficiency and its consequences: bone losses and fractures. Vitamin D supplementation helps to reduce the risks of falls and fractures in elderly persons.[24]

Vitamin D Toxicity

Vitamin D clearly illustrates how nutrients in optimal amounts support health, but both inadequacies and excesses cause trouble. Vitamin D is the most likely of the vitamins to have toxic effects when consumed in excessive amounts. The amounts of vitamin D made by the skin and found in foods are well within the safe limits set by the Upper Level, but supplements containing the vitamin in concentrated form should be kept out of the reach of children and used cautiously, if at all, by adults.

Excess vitamin D raises the concentration of blood calcium. ◆ Excess blood calcium tends to precipitate in the soft tissue, forming stones, especially in the kidneys where calcium is concentrated in the effort to excrete it. Calcification may also harden the blood vessels and is especially dangerous in the major arteries of the heart and lungs, where it can cause death.

◆ High blood calcium is known as **hypercalcemia** and may develop from a variety of disorders, including vitamin D toxicity. It does *not* develop from a high calcium intake.

Vitamin D Recommendations and Sources

Only a few foods contain vitamin D naturally. Fortunately, the body can make vitamin D with the help of a little sunshine. In setting dietary recommendations, however, the DRI Committee assumed that no vitamin D was available from skin synthesis. Current recommendations may be insufficient, however, given recent research showing numerous health benefits and safety of higher intakes.[25]

Vitamin D in Foods Most adults, especially in sunny regions, need not make special efforts to obtain vitamin D from food. People who are not outdoors much or who live in northern or predominantly cloudy or smoggy areas are advised to drink at least 2 cups of vitamin D–fortified milk a day. The fortification of milk with vitamin D is the best guarantee that people will meet their needs and underscores the importance of milk in a well-balanced diet.* Despite vitamin-D fortification, the average intake in the United States falls short of recommendations.[26]

Without adequate sunshine, fortification, or supplementation, a vegan diet cannot meet vitamin D needs. Vegetarians who do not include milk in their diets may use vitamin D–fortified soy milk and cereals. Importantly, feeding infants and young children nonfortified "health beverages" instead of milk or infant formula can create severe nutrient deficiencies, including rickets.

Vitamin D from the Sun Most of the world's population relies on natural exposure to sunlight to maintain adequate vitamin D nutrition. The sun imposes no risk of vitamin D toxicity; prolonged exposure to sunlight degrades the vitamin D precursor in the skin, preventing its conversion to the active vitamin. Even lifeguards on southern beaches are safe from vitamin D toxicity from the sun.

Prolonged exposure to sunlight does, however, prematurely wrinkle the skin and present the risk of skin cancer. Sunscreens help reduce these risks, but unfortunately, sunscreens with sun protection factors (SPF) of 8 and higher also prevent vitamin D synthesis. A strategy to avoid this dilemma is to apply sunscreen after enough time has elapsed to provide sufficient vitamin D synthesis. For

A cold glass of milk refreshes as it replenishes vitamin D and other bone-building nutrients.

---

* Vitamin D fortification of milk in the United States is 10 micrograms cholecalciferol (400 IU) per quart; in Canada, it is 9 to 12 micrograms (350 to 470 IU) per liter, with a current proposal to raise it slightly.

The sunshine vitamin—vitamin D.

FIGURE 11-11 | Vitamin D Synthesis and Latitude

Above 40° north latitude (and below 40° south latitude in the southern hemisphere), vitamin D synthesis essentially ceases for the four months of winter. Synthesis increases as spring approaches, peaks in summer, and declines again in the fall. People living in regions of extreme northern (or extreme southern) latitudes may miss as much as six months of vitamin D production.

most people, exposing hands, face, and arms on a clear summer day for 5 to 10 minutes two or three times a week should be sufficient to maintain vitamin D nutrition.[27]

The pigments of dark skin provide some protection from the sun's damage, but they also reduce vitamin D synthesis. Dark-skinned people require longer sunlight exposure than light-skinned people: heavily pigmented skin achieves the same amount of vitamin D synthesis in three hours as fair skin in 30 minutes. Latitude, season, and time of day ◆ also have dramatic effects on vitamin D synthesis (see Figure 11-11). Heavy clouds, smoke, or smog block the ultraviolet (UV) rays of the sun that promote vitamin D synthesis. Differences in skin pigmentation, latitude, and smog may account for the finding that African American people, especially those in northern, smoggy cities, are most likely to be vitamin D deficient and develop rickets.[28] To ensure an adequate vitamin D status, supplements may be needed.[29] The body's vitamin D stores from summer synthesis alone are insufficient to meet winter needs.[30]

◆ Factors that may limit sun exposure and, therefore, vitamin D synthesis:
- Geographic location
- Season of the year
- Time of day
- Air pollution
- Clothing
- Tall buildings
- Indoor living
- Sunscreens

Dietary Guidelines for Americans 2005

People with dark skin and those with insufficient exposure to sunlight should consume extra vitamin D from vitamin D-fortified foods and/or supplements.

Depending on the radiation used, the UV rays from tanning lamps and tanning beds may also stimulate vitamin D synthesis and increase bone density.[31] The potential hazards of skin damage, however, may outweigh any possible benefits.* The Food and Drug Administration (FDA) warns that if the lamps are not properly filtered, people using tanning booths risk burns, damage to the eyes and blood vessels, and skin cancer.

---

* The best wavelengths for vitamin D synthesis are UV-B rays between 290 and 310 nanometers. Some tanning parlors advertise "UV-A rays only, for a tan without the burn," but UV-A rays can damage the skin.

IN SUMMARY

Vitamin D can be synthesized in the body with the help of sunlight or obtained from fortified milk. It sends signals to three primary target sites: the GI tract to absorb more calcium and phosphorus, the bones to release more, and the kidneys to retain more. These actions maintain blood calcium concentrations and support bone formation. A deficiency causes rickets in childhood and osteomalacia in later life. The table below summarizes vitamin D facts.

Vitamin D

Other Names

Calciferol (kal-SIF-er-ol), 1,25-dihydroxy vitamin D (calcitriol); the animal version is vitamin D_3 or cholecalciferol; the plant version is vitamin D_2 or ergocalciferol; precursor is the body's own cholesterol

Adequate Intake (AI)

Adults: 5 µg/day (19–50 yr)

   10 µg/day (51–70 yr)

   15 µg/day (>70 yr)

Upper Level

Adults: 50 µg/day

Chief Functions in the Body

Mineralization of bones (raises blood calcium and phosphorus by increasing absorption from digestive tract, withdrawing calcium from bones, stimulating retention by kidneys)

Significant Sources

Synthesized in the body with the help of sunlight; fortified milk, margarine, butter, juices, cereals, and chocolate mixes; veal, beef, egg yolks, liver, fatty fish (herring, salmon, sardines) and their oils

Deficiency Symptoms

Rickets in Children

Inadequate calcification, resulting in misshapen bones (bowing of legs); enlargement of ends of long bones (knees, wrists); deformities of ribs (bowed, with beads or knobs);[a] delayed closing of fontanel, resulting in rapid enlargement of head (see figure below); lax muscles resulting in protrusion of abdomen; muscle spasms

Osteomalacia or Osteoporosis in Adults

Loss of calcium, resulting in soft, flexible, brittle, and deformed bones; progressive weakness; pain in pelvis, lower back, and legs

Toxicity Disease

Hypervitaminosis D

Toxicity Symptoms

Elevated blood calcium; calcification of soft tissues (blood vessels, kidneys, heart, lungs, tissues around joints)

Fontanel
A fontanel is an open space in the top of a baby's skull before the bones have grown together. In rickets, closing of the fontanel is delayed.

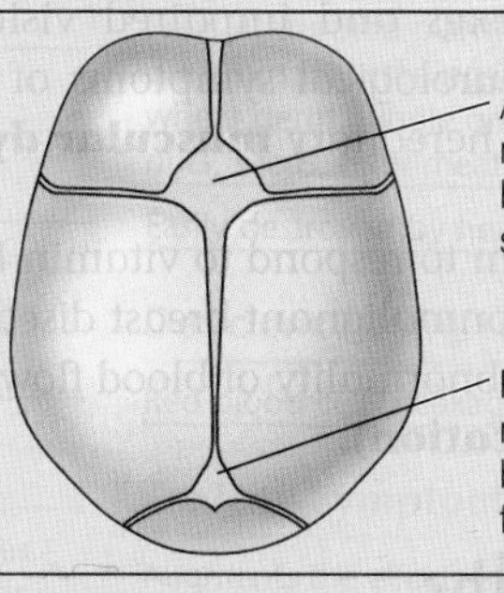

Anterior fontanel normally closes by the end of the second year.

Posterior fontanel normally closes by the end of the first year.

[a]Bowing of the ribs causes the symptoms known as *pigeon breast*. The beads that form on the ribs resemble rosary beads; thus this symptom is known as *rachitic* (ra-KIT-ik) *rosary* ("the rosary of rickets").

Vitamin E

Researchers discovered a component of vegetable oils necessary for reproduction in rats and named this antisterility factor **tocopherol,** which means "to bring forth offspring." When chemists isolated four different tocopherol compounds, they designated them by the first four letters of the Greek alphabet: alpha, beta, gamma, and delta. The tocopherols consist of a complex ring structure and a long saturated side chain. (Appendix C provides the chemical structures.) The positions of methyl

tocopherol (tuh-KOFF-er-ol): a general term for several chemically related compounds, one of which has vitamin E activity. (See Appendix C for chemical structures.)

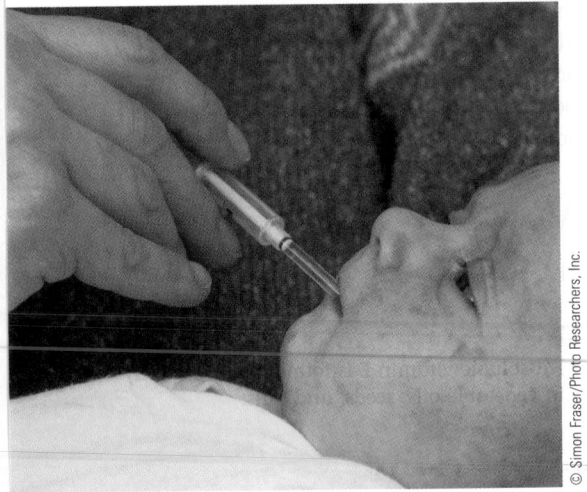

Soon after birth, newborn infants receive a dose of vitamin K to prevent hemorrhagic disease.

◆ Hemophilia is caused by a genetic defect and has no relation to vitamin K.

◆ Reminder: A *primary deficiency* develops in response to an inadequate dietary intake whereas a *secondary deficiency* occurs for other reasons.

when the integrity of that system is disturbed. (If blood did not clot, a single pinprick could drain the entire body of all its blood.)

Roles in the Body

More than a dozen different proteins and the mineral calcium are involved in making a blood clot. Vitamin K is essential for the activation of several of these proteins, among them prothrombin, made by the liver as a precursor of the protein thrombin (see Figure 11-12). When any of the blood-clotting factors is lacking, **hemorrhagic disease** results. If an artery or vein is cut or broken, bleeding goes unchecked. (Of course, this is not to say that hemorrhaging is always caused by vitamin K deficiency. Another cause is the hereditary disorder **hemophilia,** ◆ which is not curable with vitamin K.)

Vitamin K also participates in the synthesis of bone proteins. Without vitamin K, the bones produce an abnormal protein that cannot bind to the minerals that normally form bones, resulting in low bone density.[38] An adequate intake of vitamin K helps to make the bone protein correctly, decreases bone turnover, and protects against hip fractures.[39]

Vitamin K is historically known for its role in blood clotting, and more recently for its participation in bone building, but researchers continue to discover proteins needing vitamin K's assistance.[40] These proteins have been identified in the plaques of atherosclerosis, the kidneys, and the nervous system.

Vitamin K Deficiency

A primary deficiency ◆ of vitamin K is rare, but a secondary deficiency may occur in two circumstances. First, whenever fat absorption falters, as occurs when bile production fails, vitamin K absorption diminishes. Second, some drugs disrupt vitamin K's synthesis and action in the body: antibiotics kill the vitamin K–producing bacteria in the intestine, and anticoagulant drugs interfere with vitamin K metabolism and activity. When vitamin K deficiency does occur, it can be fatal.

Newborn infants present a unique case of vitamin K nutrition because they are born with a **sterile** intestinal tract, and the vitamin K–producing bacteria take weeks to establish themselves. At the same time, plasma prothrombin concentrations are low. (This reduces the likelihood of fatal blood clotting during the stress of

hemorrhagic (hem-oh-RAJ-ik) **disease:** a disease characterized by excessive bleeding.

hemophilia (HE-moh-FEEL-ee-ah): a hereditary disease in which the blood is unable to clot because it lacks the ability to synthesize certain clotting factors.

sterile: free of microorganisms, such as bacteria.

FIGURE 11-12	Blood-Clotting Process

When blood is exposed to air, foreign substances, or secretions from injured tissues, platelets (small, cell-like structures in the blood) release a phospholipid known as thromboplastin. Thromboplastin catalyzes the conversion of the inactive protein prothrombin to the active enzyme thrombin. Thrombin then catalyzes the conversion of the precursor protein fibrinogen to the active protein fibrin that forms the clot.

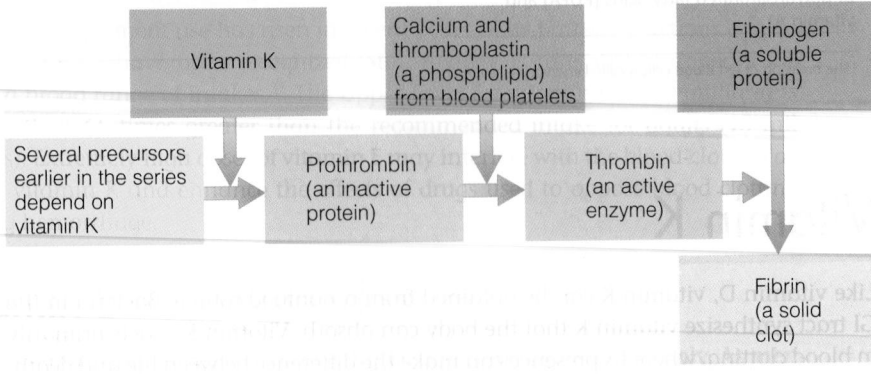

birth.) To prevent hemorrhagic disease in the newborn, a single dose of vitamin K
◆ (usually as the naturally occurring form, phylloquinone) is given at birth either
orally or by intramuscular injection. Concerns that vitamin K given at birth raises
the risks of childhood cancer are unproved and unlikely.

Vitamin K Toxicity

Toxicity is not common, and no adverse effects have been reported with high intakes
of vitamin K. Therefore, an Upper Level has not been established. High doses of vitamin K can reduce the effectiveness of anticoagulant drugs used to prevent blood
clotting.[41] People taking these drugs should eat vitamin K–rich foods in moderation
and keep their intakes consistent from day to day.

Vitamin K Recommendations and Sources

As mentioned earlier, vitamin K is made in the GI tract by the billions of bacteria
that normally reside there. Once synthesized, vitamin K is absorbed and stored in
the liver. This source provides only about half of a person's needs. Vitamin K–rich
foods such as green vegetables and vegetable oils can easily supply the rest.

◆ The natural form of vitamin K is **phylloquinone** (FILL-oh-KWIN-own); the synthetic form is **menadione** (men-uh-DYE-
own). See Appendix C for the chemistry of
these structures.

Notable food sources of vitamin K include
green vegetables such as collards, spinach, bib
lettuce, brussels sprouts, and cabbage and vegetable oils such as soybean oil and canola oil.

IN SUMMARY

Vitamin K helps with blood clotting, and its deficiency causes hemorrhagic disease (uncontrolled bleeding). Bacteria in the GI tract can make the vitamin;
people typically receive about half of their requirements from bacterial synthesis and half from foods such as green vegetables and vegetable oils. Because
people depend on bacterial synthesis for vitamin K, deficiency is most likely in
newborn infants and in people taking antibiotics. The accompanying table
provides a summary of vitamin K facts.

Vitamin K

Other Names	Significant Sources
Phylloquinone, menaquinone, menadione, naphthoquinone	Bacterial synthesis in the digestive tract;[a] liver; leafy green vegetables, cabbage-type vegetables; milk
Adequate Intakes (AI)	**Deficiency Symptoms**
Men: 120 µg/day	Hemorrhaging
Women: 90 µg/day	**Toxicity Symptoms**
Chief Functions in the Body	None known
Synthesis of blood-clotting proteins and bone proteins	

[a]Vitamin K needs cannot be met from bacterial synthesis alone; however, it is a potentially important source in the small
intestine, where absorption efficiency ranges from 40 to 70 percent.

The Fat-Soluble Vitamins—
In Summary

The four fat-soluble vitamins play many specific roles in the growth and maintenance of the body. Their presence affects the health and function of the eyes, skin,
GI tract, lungs, bones, teeth, nervous system, and blood; their deficiencies become
apparent in these same areas. Toxicities of the fat-soluble vitamins are possible,
especially when people use supplements, because the body stores excesses.

As with the water-soluble vitamins, the function of one fat-soluble vitamin often depends on the presence of another. Recall that vitamin E protects vitamin A from oxidation. In vitamin E deficiency, vitamin A absorption and storage are impaired. Three of the four fat-soluble vitamins—A, D, and K—play important roles in bone growth and remodeling. As mentioned, vitamin K helps synthesize a specific bone protein, and vitamin D regulates that synthesis. Vitamin A, in turn, may control which bone-building genes respond to vitamin D.

Fat-soluble vitamins also interact with minerals. Vitamin D and calcium cooperate in bone formation, and zinc is required for the synthesis of vitamin A's transport protein, retinol-binding protein. Zinc also assists the enzyme that regenerates retinal from retinol in the eye.

The roles of the fat-soluble vitamins differ from those of the water-soluble vitamins, and they appear in different foods—yet they are just as essential to life. The need for them underlines the importance of eating a wide variety of nourishing foods daily. The following table condenses the information on fat-soluble vitamins into a short summary.

IN SUMMARY   The Fat-Soluble Vitamins

Vitamin and Chief Functions	Deficiency Symptoms	Toxicity Symptoms	Significant Sources
Vitamin A Vision; maintenance of cornea, epithelial cells, mucous membranes, skin; bone and tooth growth; reproduction; immunity	Infectious diseases, night blindness, blindness (xerophthalmia), keratinization	Reduced bone mineral density, liver abnormalities, birth defects	Retinol: milk and milk products Beta-carotene: dark green leafy and deep yellow/orange vegetables
Vitamin D Mineralization of bones (raises blood calcium and phosphorus by increasing absorption from digestive tract, withdrawing calcium from bones, stimulating retention by kidneys)	Rickets, osteomalacia	Calcium imbalance (calcification of soft tisues and formation of stones)	Synthesized in the body with the help of sunshine; fortified milk
Vitamin E Antioxidant (stabilization of cell membranes, regulation of oxidation reactions, protection of polyunsaturated fatty acids [PUFA] and vitamin A)	Erythrocyte hemolysis, nerve damage	Hemorrhagic effects	Vegetable oils
Vitamin K Synthesis of blood-clotting proteins and bone proteins	Hemorrhage	None known	Synthesized in the body by GI bacteria; green leafy vegetables

Nutrition Portfolio

For the fat-soluble vitamins, select colorful fruits and vegetables, fortified milk or soy products, and vegetable oils; use supplements with caution, if at all.

■ Examine your weekly choices of vegetables and evaluate whether you meet the recommendations for dark green or orange and deep yellow vegetables.

■ Consider whether you drink enough vitamin D-fortified milk or go outside in the sunshine regularly.

■ Describe the vegetable oils you use when you cook and their vitamin contributions.

NUTRITION ON THE NET

ThomsonNOW™
For further study of topics covered in this chapter, log on to **www.thomsonedu.com/thomsonnow**. Go to Chapter 11, then to Nutrition on the Net.

- Search for "vitamins" at the American Dietetic Association: **www.eatright.org**
- Review the Dietary Reference Intakes for vitamins A, D, E, and K and the carotenoids by searching for "DRI": **www.nap.edu**

- Visit the World Health Organization to learn about "vitamin deficiencies" around the world: **www.who.int**
- Search for "vitamins" at the U.S. Government health information site: **www.healthfinder.gov**
- Learn how fruits and vegetables support a healthy diet rich in vitamins from the 5 A Day for Better Health program: **www.5aday.com** or **www.5aday.gov**

NUTRITION CALCULATIONS

ThomsonNOW™ For additional practice log on to **www.thomsonedu.com/thomsonnow**. Go to Chapter 11, then to Nutrition Calculations.

These exercises will help you learn the best food sources for the vitamins and prepare you to examine your own food choices. See p. 389 for answers.

1. Review the units in which vitamins are measured (a spot check). For each of these vitamins, note the unit of measure:

   Vitamin A   Vitamin D
   Vitamin E   Vitamin K

2. Analyze the vitamin contents of foods. Review the figures, photos, and food sources sections in Chapters 10 and 11 and list the food group(s) that contributed the

most of each vitamin. Which food groups offer the most thiamin? The most riboflavin? The most niacin? The most vitamin B_6? The most folate? The most vitamin B_{12}? The most vitamin C? The most vitamin A? The most vitamin D? The most vitamin E?

List the groups that provide "the most" and compare them with the USDA Food Guide in Chapter 2.

This exercise should convince you that each of the food groups provides some, but not all, of the vitamins needed daily. For a full array, a person needs to eat a variety of foods from each of the food groups regularly.

STUDY QUESTIONS

ThomsonNOW™
To assess your understanding of chapter topics, take the Student Practice Test and explore the modules recommended in your Personalized Study Plan. Log onto **www.thomsonedu.com/thomsonnow**.

These questions will help you review the chapter. You will find the answers in the discussions on the pages provided.

1. List the fat-soluble vitamins. What characteristics do they have in common? How do they differ from the water-soluble vitamins? (p. 369)

2. Summarize the roles of vitamin A and the symptoms of its deficiency. (pp. 370–374)

3. What are vitamin precursors? Name the precursors of vitamin A, and tell in what classes of foods they are located. Give examples of foods with high vitamin A activity. (pp. 369, 374–376)

4. How is vitamin D unique among the vitamins? What is its chief function? What are the richest sources of this vitamin? (pp. 377, 379–380)

5. Describe vitamin E's role as an antioxidant. What are the chief symptoms of vitamin E deficiency? (p. 382)

6. What is vitamin K's primary role in the body? What conditions may lead to vitamin K deficiency? (pp. 384–385)

These multiple choice questions will help you prepare for an exam. Answers can be found on p. 389.

1. Fat-soluble vitamins:
   a. are easily excreted.
   b. seldom reach toxic levels.
   c. require bile for absorption.
   d. are not stored in the body's tissues.

2. The form of vitamin A active in vision is:
   a. retinal.
   b. retinol.
   c. rhodopsin.
   d. retinoic acid.

Antioxidant Nutrients in Disease Prevention

Count on supplement manufacturers to exploit the day's hot topics in nutrition. The moment bits of research news surface, new supplements appear—and terms like "antioxidants" and "lycopene" become household words. Friendly faces in TV commercials try to persuade us that these supplements hold the magic in the fight against aging and disease. New supplements hit the market and cash registers ring. Vitamin C, for years the leading single nutrient supplement, gains new popularity, and sales of lutein, beta-carotene, and vitamin E supplements soar as well.

In the meantime, scientists and medical experts around the world continue their work to clarify and confirm the roles of antioxidants in preventing chronic diseases. This highlight summarizes some of the accumulating evidence. It also revisits the advantages of foods over supplements. But first it is important to introduce the troublemakers—the **free radicals.** (The accompanying glossary defines free radicals and related terms.)

Free Radicals and Disease

Chapter 7 described how the body's cells use oxygen in metabolic reactions. In the process, oxygen sometimes reacts with body compounds and produces highly unstable molecules known as free radicals. In addition to normal body processes, environmental factors such as ultraviolet radiation, air pollution, and tobacco smoke generate free radicals.

A free radical is a molecule with one or more unpaired electrons.* An electron without a partner is unstable and highly reactive. To regain its stability, the free radical quickly finds a stable but vulnerable compound from which to steal an electron.

With the loss of an electron, the formerly stable molecule becomes a free radical itself and steals an electron from another nearby molecule. Thus, an electron-snatching chain reaction is under way with free radicals producing more free radicals. Antioxidants neutralize free radicals by donating one of their own electrons, thus ending the chain reaction. When they lose electrons, antioxidants do not become free radicals because they are stable in either form. (Review Figure 10-15 on p. 351 to see how ascorbic acid can give up two hydrogens with their electrons and become dehydroascorbic acid.)

Once formed, free radicals attack. Occasionally, these free-radical attacks are helpful. For example, cells of the immune system use free radicals as ammunition in an "oxidative burst" that demolishes disease-causing viruses and bacteria. Most often, however, free-radical attacks cause widespread damage. They commonly damage the polyunsaturated fatty acids in lipoproteins and in cell membranes, disrupting the transport of substances into and out of cells. Free radicals also alter DNA, RNA, and proteins, creating excesses and deficiencies of specific proteins, impairing cell functions, and eliciting an inflammatory response. All of these actions contribute to cell damage, disease progression, and aging (see Figure H11-1).

---

* Many free radicals exist, but oxygen-derived free radicals are most common in the human body. Examples of oxygen-derived free radicals include superoxide radical (O_2^-), hydroxyl radical (OH·), and nitric oxide (NO·). (The dots in the symbols represent the unpaired electrons.) Technically, hydrogen peroxide (H_2O_2) and singlet oxygen are not free radicals because they contain paired electrons, but the unstable conformation of their electrons makes radical-producing reactions likely. Scientists sometimes use the term *reactive oxygen species (ROS)* to describe all of these compounds.

GLOSSARY

free radicals: unstable and highly reactive atoms or molecules that have one or more unpaired electrons in the outer orbital. (See Appendix B for a review of basic chemistry concepts.)

oxidants (OKS-ih-dants): compounds (such as oxygen itself) that oxidize other compounds. Compounds that prevent oxidation are called *antioxidants*, whereas those that promote it are called *prooxidants*.
• **anti** = against
• **pro** = for

prooxidants: substances that significantly induce oxidative stress.

Reminders: **Dietary antioxidants** are substances typically found in foods that significantly decrease the adverse effects of free radicals on normal functions in the body. **Nonnutrients** are compounds in foods that do not fit into the six classes of nutrients.

Phytochemicals are nonnutrient compounds found in plant-derived foods that have biological activity in the body.
Oxidative stress is a condition in which the production of oxidants and free radicals exceeds the body's ability to handle them and prevent damage.

FIGURE H11-1 Free Radical Damage

Free radicals are highly reactive. They might attack the polyunsaturated fatty acids in a cell membrane, which generates lipid radicals that damage cells and accelerate disease progression. Free radicals might also attack and damage DNA, RNA, and proteins, which interferes with the body's ability to maintain normal cell function, causing disease and premature aging.

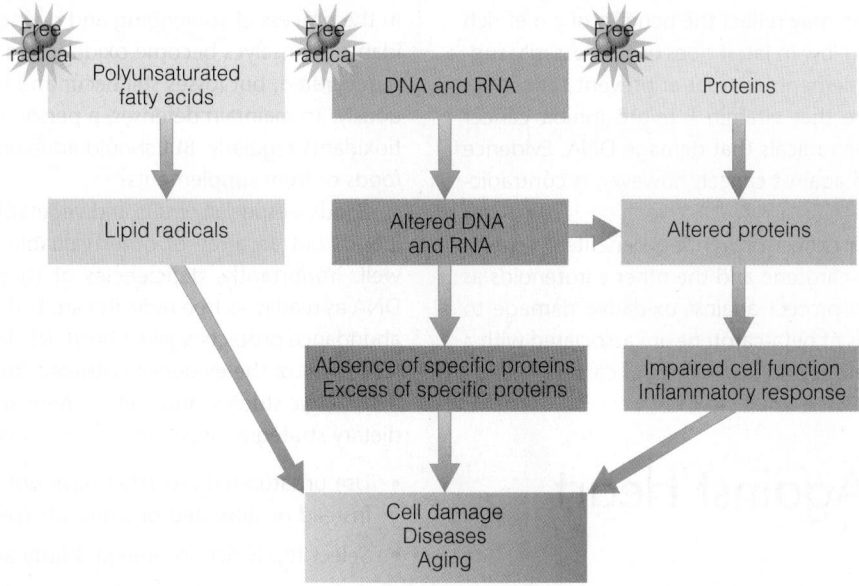

The body's natural defenses and repair systems try to control the destruction caused by free radicals, but these systems are not 100 percent effective. In fact, they become less effective with age, and the unrepaired damage accumulates. To some extent, **dietary antioxidants** defend the body against **oxidative stress,** but if antioxidants are unavailable or if free-radical production becomes excessive, health problems may develop.[1] Oxygen-derived free radicals may cause diseases, not only by indiscriminately destroying the valuable components of cells, but also by serving as signals for specific activities within the cells. Scientists have identified oxidative stress as a causative factor and antioxidants as a protective factor in cognitive performance and the aging process as well as in the development of diseases such as cancer, arthritis, cataracts, diabetes, and heart disease.[2]

Defending Against Free Radicals

The body maintains a couple lines of defense against free-radical damage. A system of enzymes disarms the most harmful **oxidants.*** The action of these enzymes depends on the minerals selenium, copper, manganese, and zinc. If the diet fails to provide adequate supplies of these minerals, this line of defense weakens. The body also uses the antioxidant vitamins—vitamin E, beta-

carotene, and vitamin C. Vitamin E defends the body's lipids (cell membranes and lipoproteins, for example) by efficiently stopping the free-radical chain reaction. Beta-carotene also acts as an antioxidant in lipid membranes. Vitamin C protects other tissues, such as the skin and fluid of the blood, against free-radical attacks.[3] Vitamin C seems especially adept at neutralizing free radicals from polluted air and cigarette smoke; it may also restore oxidized vitamin E to its active state.

Dietary antioxidants may also include **nonnutrients**—some of the **phytochemicals** (featured in Highlight 13). Together, nutrients and phytochemicals with antioxidant activity minimize damage in the following ways:

- Limiting free-radical formation
- Destroying free radicals or their precursors
- Stimulating antioxidant enzyme activity
- Repairing oxidative damage
- Stimulating repair enzyme activity

These actions play key roles in defending the body against cancer and heart disease.

Defending Against Cancer

Cancers arise when cellular DNA is damaged—sometimes by free-radical attacks. Antioxidants may reduce cancer risks by protecting DNA from this damage. Many researchers have reported low rates of cancer in people whose diets include abundant vegetables and fruits, rich in antioxidants.[4] Preliminary reports suggest an inverse relationship between DNA damage and vegetable

---

* These enzymes include glutathione peroxidase, thioredoxin reductase, superoxide dismutase, and catalase.

intake and a positive relationship with beef and pork intake. Laboratory studies with animals and with cells in tissue culture also seem to support such findings.

Foods rich in vitamin C seem to protect against certain types of cancers, especially those of the mouth, larynx, esophagus, and stomach. Such a correlation may reflect the benefits of a diet rich in fruits and vegetables and low in fat; it does not necessarily support taking vitamin C supplements to treat or prevent cancer.

Researchers hypothesize that vitamin E might inhibit cancer formation by attacking free radicals that damage DNA. Evidence that vitamin E helps guard against cancer, however, is contradictory and inconclusive.[5]

Several studies report a cancer-preventing benefit of vegetables and fruits rich in beta-carotene and the other carotenoids as well. Carotenoids seem to protect against oxidative damage to DNA.[6] High concentrations of beta-carotene are associated with a lower mortality from all causes and lower rates of cancer.[7]

Defending Against Heart Disease

High blood cholesterol carried in LDL is a major risk factor for cardiovascular disease, but how do LDL exert their damage? One scenario is that free radicals within the arterial walls oxidize LDL, changing their structure and function. The oxidized LDL then accelerate the formation of artery-clogging plaques.[8] These free radicals also oxidize the polyunsaturated fatty acids of the cell membranes, sparking additional changes in the arterial walls, which impede the flow of blood. Susceptibility to such oxidative damage within the arterial walls is heightened by a diet high in saturated fat or cigarette smoke. In contrast, diets that include plenty of fruits and vegetables, especially when combined with little saturated fat, strengthen antioxidant defenses against LDL oxidation. Antioxidant nutrients taken as supplements also seem to slow the early progression of atherosclerosis.[9]

Antioxidants, especially vitamin E, may protect against cardiovascular disease.[10] Epidemiological studies suggest that people who eat foods rich in vitamin E have relatively few atherosclerotic plaques and low rates of death from heart disease.[11] Similarly, large doses of vitamin E supplements may slow the progression of heart disease. Among its many protective roles, vitamin E defends against LDL oxidation, inflammation, arterial injuries, and blood clotting.[12] Less clear is whether vitamin E supplements benefit people who already have heart disease or multiple risk factors for it. Antioxidant supplements may not be beneficial and, in fact, may even be harmful for these people.[13]

Vitamin C supplements may reduce the risk of heart disease.[14] Some studies suggest that vitamin C protects against LDL oxidation, raises HDL, lowers total cholesterol, and improves blood pressure. Vitamin C may also minimize inflammation and the free-radical action within the arterial wall.[15]

Foods, Supplements, or Both?

In the process of scavenging and quenching free radicals, antioxidants themselves become oxidized. To some extent, they can be regenerated, but losses still occur and free radicals attack continuously. To maintain defenses, a person must replenish dietary antioxidants regularly. But should antioxidants be replenished from foods or from supplements?

Foods—especially fruits and vegetables—offer not only antioxidants, but an array of other valuable vitamins and minerals as well. Importantly, deficiencies of these nutrients can damage DNA as readily as free radicals can. Eating fruits and vegetables in abundance protects against both deficiencies and diseases. A major review of the evidence gathered from metabolic studies, epidemiologic studies, and dietary intervention trials identified three dietary strategies most effective in preventing heart disease:[16]

- Use unsaturated fats (that have not been hydrogenated) instead of saturated or *trans* fats (see Highlight 5).
- Select foods rich in omega-3 fatty acids (see Chapter 5).
- Consume a diet high in fruits, vegetables, nuts, and whole grains and low in refined grain products.

Such a diet combined with exercise, weight control, and not smoking serves as the best prescription for health. Notably, taking supplements is not among these disease-prevention recommendations.

Some research suggests a protective effect from as little as a daily glass of orange juice or carrot juice (rich sources of vitamin C and beta-carotene, respectively). Other intervention studies, however, have used levels of nutrients that far exceed current recommendations and can be achieved only by taking supplements. In making their recommendations for the antioxidant nutrients, members of the DRI Committee considered whether these studies support substantially higher intakes to help protect against chronic diseases. They did raise the recommendations for vitamins C and E, but they do not support taking vitamin pills over eating a healthy diet.

While awaiting additional research, should people anticipate the "go-ahead" and start taking antioxidant supplements now? Most scientists agree that the evidence is insufficient for such a recommendation.[17] Though fruits and vegetables containing many antioxidant nutrients and phytochemicals have been associated with a diminished risk of many cancers, supplements have not always proved beneficial. In fact, sometimes the benefits are more apparent when the vitamins come from foods rather than from supplements. In other words, the antioxidant actions of fruits and vegetables are greater than their nutrients alone can explain.[18] Without data to confirm the benefits of supplements, we cannot accept the potential risks.[19] And the risks are real.

Consider the findings from meta-analysis studies of the relationships between daily supplements of vitamin E, beta-carotene, or both and total mortality. Researchers concluded that supplements either had *no benefit* or *increased* mortality and should be avoided.[20]

Even if research clearly proves that a particular nutrient is the ultimate protective ingredient in foods, supplements would not be the answer because their contents are limited. Vitamin E supplements, for example, usually contain alpha-tocopherol, but foods provide an assortment of tocopherols among other nutrients, many of which provide valuable protection against free-radical damage. In addition to a full array of nutrients, foods provide phytochemicals that also fight against many diseases.[21] Supplements shortchange users. Furthermore, supplements should only be used as an adjunct to other measures such as smoking cessation, weight control, physical activity, and medication as needed.[22]

Clearly, much more research is needed to define optimal and dangerous levels of intake. This much we know: antioxidants behave differently under various conditions. At physiological levels typical of a healthy diet, they act as antioxidants, but at pharmacological doses typical of supplements, they may act as **prooxidants,** stimulating the production of free radicals and altering metabolism in a way that may promote disease. A high intake of vitamin C from supplements, for example, may *increase* the risk of heart disease in women with diabetes.[23] High doses (more than 400 IU per day) of vitamin E supplements may increase mortality.[24] Until the optimum intake of antioxidant nutrients can be determined, the risks of supplement use remain unclear. The best way to add antioxidants to the diet is to eat generous servings of fruits and vegetables daily.

It should be clear by now that we cannot know the identity and action of every chemical in every food. Even if we did, why create a supplement to replicate a food? Why not eat foods and

Many cancer-fighting products are available now at your local produce counter.

© Bryan Reinhart

enjoy the pleasure, nourishment, and health benefits they provide? The beneficial constituents in foods are widespread among plants. Among the fruits, pomegranates, berries, and citrus rank high in antioxidants; top antioxidant vegetables include kale, spinach, and brussels sprouts; millet and oats contain the most antioxidants among the grains; pinto beans and soybeans are the outstanding legumes; and walnuts outshine the other nuts.[25] But don't try to single out one particular food for its magic nutrient, antioxidant, or phytochemical. Instead, eat a wide variety of fruits, vegetables, grains, legumes, and nuts every day—and get *all* the magic compounds these foods have to offer.

REFERENCES

1. A. J. McEligot, S. Yang, and F. L. Meyskens, Redox regulation by intrinsic species and extrinsic nutrients in normal and cancer cells, *Annual Review of Nutrition* 25 (2005): 261-295; S. F. Clark, The biochemistry of antioxidants revisited, *Nutrition in Clinical Practice* 17 (2002): 5-17.
2. J. L. Evans and coauthors, Are oxidative stress-activated signaling pathways mediators of insulin resistance and beta-cell dysfunction? *Diabetes* 52 (2003): 1-8; F. Grodstein, J. Chen, and W. C. Willett, High-dose antioxidant supplements and cognitive function in community-dwelling elderly women, *American Journal of Clinical Nutrition* 77 (2003): 975-984; M. J. Engelhart and coauthors, Dietary intake of antioxidants and risk of Alzheimer disease, *Journal of the American Medical Association* 287 (2002): 3223-3229.
3. M. V. Catani and coauthors, Biological role of vitamin C in keratinocytes, *Nutrition Reviews* 63 (2005): 81-90.
4. D. P. Hayes, The protective role of fruits and vegetables against radiation-induced cancer, *Nutrition Reviews* 63 (2005): 303-311; A. Martin and coauthors, Roles of vitamins E and C on neurodegenerative diseases and

cognitive performance, *Nutrition Reviews* 60 (2002): 308-326; H. Chen and coauthors, Dietary patterns and adenocarcinoma of the esophagus and distal stomach, *American Journal of Clinical Nutrition* 75 (2002): 137-144.
5. D. Q. Pham and R. Plakogiannis, Vitamin E supplementation in cardiovascular disease and cancer prevention: Part 1, *Annals of Pharmacotherapy* 39 (2005): 1870-1878.
6. X. Zhao and coauthors, Modification of lymphocyte DNA damage by carotenoid supplementation in postmenopausal women, *American Journal of Clinical Nutrition* 83 (2006): 163-169.
7. B. Buijsse and coauthors, Plasma carotene and α-tocopherol in relation to 10-y all-cause and cause-specific mortality in European elderly: The Survey in Europe on Nutrition and the Elderly, a Concerted Action (SENECA), *American Journal of Clinical Nutrition* 82 (2005): 879-886.
8. G. A. A. Ferns and D. J. Lamb, What does the lipoprotein oxidation phenomenon mean? *Biochemical Society Transactions* 32 (2004): 160-163; W. Jessup, L. Kritharides, and R. Stocker, Lipid oxidation in atherogenesis: An overview, *Biochemical Society Transactions* 32 (2004): 134-138.

9. L. Liu and M. Meydani, Combined vitamin C and E supplementation retards early progression of arteriosclerosis in heart transplant patients, *Nutrition Reviews* 60 (2002): 368-371; H. Y. Huang and coauthors, Effects of vitamin C and vitamin E on in vivo lipid peroxidation: Results of a randomized controlled trial, *American Journal of Clinical Nutrition* 76 (2002): 549-555.
10. E. K. Kabagambe and coauthors, Some dietary and adipose tissue carotenoids are associated with the risk of nonfatal acute myocardial infarction in Costa Rica, *Journal of Nutrition* 135 (2005): 1763-1769; A. Iannuzzi and coauthors, Dietary and circulating antioxidant vitamins in relation to carotid plaques in middle-aged women, *American Journal of Clinical Nutrition* 76 (2002): 582-587.
11. A. Iannuzzi and coauthors, Dietary and circulating antioxidant vitamins in relation to carotid plaques in middle-aged women, *American Journal of Clinical Nutrition* 76 (2002): 582-587.
12. U. Singh, S. Devaraj, and I. Jialal, Vitamin E, oxidative stress, and inflammation, *Annual Review of Nutrition* 25 (2005): 151-174; S. Devaraj, A. Harris, and I. Jialal, Modulation of monocyte-macrophage function with

α-tocopherol: Implications for atherosclerosis, *Nutrition Reviews* 60 (2002): 8-14; L. J. van Tits and coauthors, α-Tocopherol supplementation decreases production of superoxide and cytokines by leukocytes ex vivo in both normolipidemic and hypertriglyceridemic individuals, *American Journal of Clinical Nutrition* 71 (2000): 458-464; M. Meydani, Vitamin E and prevention of heart disease in high-risk patients, *Nutrition Reviews* 58 (2000): 278-281.

13. The HOPE and HOPE-TOO Investigators, Effects of long-term vitamin E supplementation on cardiovascular events and cancer: A randomized controlled trial, *Journal of the American Medical Association* 293 (2005): 1338-1347; D. D. Waters and coauthors, Effects of hormone replacement therapy and antioxidant vitamin supplements on coronary atherosclerosis in postmenopausal women: A randomized controlled trial, *Journal of the American Medical Association* 288 (2002): 2432-2440.

14. P. Knekt and coauthors, Antioxidant vitamins and coronary heart disease risk: A pooled analysis of 9 cohorts, *American Journal of Clinical Nutrition* 80 (2004): 1508-1520.

15. S. G. Wannamethee and coauthors, Associations of vitamin C status, fruit and vegetable intakes, and markers of inflammation and hemostasis, *American Journal of Clinical Nutrition* 83 (2006): 567-574.

16. F. B. Hu and W. C. Willett, Optimal diets for prevention of coronary heart disease, *Journal of the American Medical Association* 288 (2002): 2569-2578.

17. H. Y. Huang and coauthors, The efficacy and safety of multivitamin and mineral supplement use to prevent cancer and chronic disease in adults: A systematic review for a National Institutes of Health state-of-the-science conference, *Annals of Internal Medicine* 145 (2006): 372-385; P. M. Kris-Etherton and coauthors, Antioxidant vitamin supplements and cardiovascular disease, *Circulation* 110 (2004): 637-641.

18. L. O. Dragsted and coauthors, The 6-a-day study: Effects of fruit and vegetables on markers of oxidative stress and antioxidative defense in healthy nonsmokers, *American Journal of Clinical Nutrition* 79 (2004): 1060-1072.

19. S. Hercberg, The history of β-carotene and cancers: From observational to intervention studies. What lessons can be drawn for future research on polyphenols? *American Journal of Clinical Nutrition* 81 (2005): 218S-222S.

20. E. R. Miller and coauthors, Meta-analysis: High-dosage vitamin E supplementation may increase all-cause mortality, *Annals of Internal Medicine* 142 (2005): 37-46; I. Lee and coauthors, Vitamin E in the primary prevention of cardiovascular disease and cancer—The Women's Health Study: A randomized controlled trial, *Journal of the American Medical Association* 294 (2005): 56-65; D. P. Vivekananthan and coauthors, Use of antioxidant vitamins for the prevention of cardiovascular disease: Meta-analysis of randomised trials, *Lancet* 361 (2003): 2017-2023.

21. P. M. Kris-Etherton and coauthors, Bioactive compounds in nutrition and health-research methodologies for establishing biological function: The antioxidant and anti-inflammatory effects of flavonoids on atherosclerosis, *Annual Review of Nutrition* 24 (2004): 511-538.

22. J. E. Manson, S. S. Bassuk, and M. J. Stampfer, Does vitamin E supplementation prevent cardiovascular events? *Journal of Womens Health* 12 (2003): 123-136.

23. D. H. Lee and coauthors, Does supplemental vitamin C increase cardiovascular disease risk in women with diabetes? *American Journal of Clinical Nutrition* 80 (2004): 1194-1200.

24. E. R. Miller and coauthors, Meta-analysis: High-dosage vitamin E supplementation may increase all-cause mortality, *Annals of Internal Medicine* 142 (2005): 37-46.

25. B. L. Halvorsen and coauthors, A systematic screening of total antioxidants in dietary plants, *Journal of Nutrition* 132 (2002): 461-471.

Paul Webster/Getty Images

Thomson™ NOW! Throughout this chapter, the ThomsonNOW logo indicates an opportunity for online self-study, linking you to interactive tutorials and videos based on your level of understanding.

www.thomsonedu.com/thomsonnow

Figure 12-2: Animated! A Nephron, One of the Kidney's Many Functioning Units

Figure 12-3: Animated! How the Body Regulates Blood Volume

Figure 12-12: Animated! Calcium Balance

How To: Practice Problems

Nutrition Portfolio Journal

Nutrition Calculations: Practice Problems

Nutrition in Your Life

What's your beverage of choice? If you said water, then congratulate yourself for recognizing its importance in maintaining your body's fluid balance. If you answered milk, then pat yourself on the back for taking good care of your bones. Faced with a lack of water, you would realize within days how vital it is to your very survival. The consequences of a lack of milk (or other calcium-rich foods) are also dramatic, but may not become apparent for decades. Water, calcium, and all the other major minerals support fluid balance and bone health. Before getting too comfortable reading this chapter, you might want to get yourself a glass of water or milk. Your body will thank you.

Water and the Major Minerals

CHAPTER OUTLINE

Water and the Body Fluids • Water Balance and Recommended Intakes • Blood Volume and Blood Pressure • Fluid and Electrolyte Balance • Fluid and Electrolyte Imbalance • Acid-Base Balance

The Minerals—An Overview

Sodium

Chloride

Potassium

Calcium • Calcium Roles in the Body • Calcium Recommendation and Sources • Calcium Deficiency

Phosphorus

Magnesium

Sulfate

HIGHLIGHT 12 Osteoporosis and Calcium

Water is an essential nutrient, more important to life than any of the others. The body needs more water each day than any other nutrient. Furthermore, you can survive only a few days without water, whereas a deficiency of the other nutrients may take weeks, months, or even years to develop.

This chapter begins with a look at water and the body's fluids. The body maintains an appropriate balance and distribution of fluids with the help of another class of nutrients—the minerals. In addition to introducing the minerals that help regulate body fluids, this chapter describes many of the other important functions minerals perform in the body. Chapter 19 revisits water as a beverage and addresses consumer concerns about its safety.

Water and the Body Fluids

Water constitutes about 60 percent of an adult's body weight and a higher percentage of a child's (see Figure 1–1, p. 6). Because water makes up about three-fourths of the weight of lean tissue and less than one-fourth of the weight of fat, a person's body composition influences how much of the body's weight is water. The proportion of water is generally smaller in females, obese people, and the elderly because of their smaller proportion of lean tissue.

In the body, water is the fluid in which all life processes occur. The water in the body fluids:

- Carries nutrients and waste products throughout the body

- Maintains the structure of large molecules such as proteins and glycogen

- Participates in metabolic reactions

- Serves as the solvent for minerals, vitamins, amino acids, glucose, and many other small molecules so that they can participate in metabolic activities

- Acts as a lubricant and cushion around joints and inside the eyes, the spinal cord, and, in pregnancy, the amniotic sac surrounding the fetus in the womb

- Aids in the regulation of normal body temperature (As Chapter 14 explains, evaporation of sweat from the skin removes excess heat from the body.)

- Maintains blood volume

© Michael Pole/CORBIS

Water is the most indispensable nutrient.

◆ Water balance: intake = output

◆ Fluids in the body:
  • Intracellular (inside cells)
  • Extracellular (outside cells)
    • Interstitial (between cells)
    • Intravascular (inside blood vessels)

◆ Reminder: The *hypothalamus* is a brain center that controls activities such as maintenance of water balance, regulation of body temperature, and control of appetite.

To support these and other vital functions, the body actively maintains an appropriate **water balance.** ◆

Water Balance and Recommended Intakes

Every cell contains fluid of the exact composition that is best for that cell **(intracellular fluid)** and is bathed externally in another such fluid **(interstitial fluid).** Interstitial fluid is the largest component of **extracellular fluid.** ◆ Figure 12-1 illustrates a cell and its associated fluids. These fluids continually lose and replace their components, yet the composition in each compartment remains remarkably constant under normal conditions. Because imbalances can be devastating, the body quickly responds by adjusting both water intake and excretion as needed. Consequently, the entire system of cells and fluids remains in a delicate, but controlled, state of homeostasis.

Water Intake **Thirst** and satiety influence water intake, apparently in response to changes sensed by the mouth, hypothalamus, ◆ and nerves. When water intake is inadequate, the blood becomes concentrated (having lost water but not the dissolved substances within it), the mouth becomes dry, and the hypothalamus initiates drinking behavior. When water intake is excessive, the stomach expands and stretch receptors send signals to stop drinking. Similar signals are sent from receptors in the heart as blood volume increases.

Thirst drives a person to seek water, but it lags behind the body's need. When too much water is lost from the body and not replaced, **dehydration** develops. A first sign of dehydration is thirst, the signal that the body has already lost some of its fluid. If a person is unable to obtain fluid or, as in many elderly people, fails to perceive the thirst message, the symptoms of dehydration may progress rapidly from thirst to weakness, exhaustion, and delirium—and end in death if not corrected (see Table 12-1). Dehydration may easily develop with either water deprivation or excessive water losses. (Chapter 14 revisits dehydration and the fluid needs of athletes.)

Water intoxication, on the other hand, is rare but can occur with excessive water ingestion and kidney disorders that reduce urine production. The symptoms may include confusion, convulsions, and even death in extreme cases. Excessive water ingestion (10 to 20 liters) within a few hours contributes to the dangerous condition known as hyponatremia, sometimes seen in endurance athletes. For this reason, guidelines suggest limiting fluid intake during times of heavy sweating to 1 to 1.5 liters per hour.[1] (Chapter 14 revisits hyponatremia.)

Water Sources The obvious dietary sources of water are water itself and other beverages, but nearly all foods also contain water. Most fruits and vegetables contain up to 90 percent water, and many meats and cheeses contain at least 50 percent. (See Table 12-2 for selected foods and Appendix H for many more.) Also, water is generated during metabolism. Recall from Chapter 7 that when the energy-yielding

water balance: the balance between water intake and output (losses).

intracellular fluid: fluid within the cells, usually high in potassium and phosphate. Intracellular fluid accounts for approximately two-thirds of the body's water.
  • **intra** = within

interstitial (IN-ter-STISH-al) **fluid:** fluid between the cells (intercellular), usually high in sodium and chloride. Interstitial fluid is a large component of extracellular fluid.
  • **inter** = in the midst, between

extracellular fluid: fluid outside the cells. Extracellular fluid includes two main components—the interstitial fluid and plasma. Extracellular fluid accounts for approximately one-third of the body's water.
  • **extra** = outside

thirst: a conscious desire to drink.

dehydration: the condition in which body water output exceeds water input. Symptoms include thirst, dry skin and mucous membranes, rapid heartbeat, low blood pressure, and weakness.

water intoxication: the rare condition in which body water contents are too high in all body fluid compartments.

TABLE 12-1	Signs of Dehydration

Body Weight Lost (%)	Symptoms
1–2	Thirst, fatigue, weakness, vague discomfort, loss of appetite
3–4	Impaired physical performance, dry mouth, reduction in urine, flushed skin, impatience, apathy
5–6	Difficulty concentrating, headache, irritability, sleepiness, impaired temperature regulation, increased respiratory rate
7–10	Dizziness, spastic muscles, loss of balance, delirium, exhaustion, collapse

NOTE: The onset and severity of symptoms at various percentages of body weight lost depend on the activity, fitness level, degree of acclimation, temperature, and humidity. If not corrected, dehydration can lead to death.

TABLE 12-2	Percentage of Water in Selected Foods
100%	Water
90–99%	Fat-free milk, strawberries, watermelon, lettuce, cabbage, celery, spinach, broccoli
80–89%	Fruit juice, yogurt, apples, grapes, oranges, carrots
70–79%	Shrimp, bananas, corn, potatoes, avocados, cottage cheese, ricotta cheese
60–69%	Pasta, legumes, salmon, ice cream, chicken breast
50–59%	Ground beef, hot dogs, feta cheese
40–49%	Pizza
30–39%	Cheddar cheese, bagels, bread
20–29%	Pepperoni sausage, cake, biscuits
10–19%	Butter, margarine, raisins
1–9%	Crackers, cereals, pretzels, taco shells, peanut butter, nuts
0%	Oils, sugars

nutrients break down, their carbons and hydrogens combine with oxygen to yield carbon dioxide (CO_2) and water (H_2O). As Table 12-3 shows, the water derived daily from these three sources averages about 2$\frac{1}{2}$ liters (roughly 2$\frac{1}{2}$ quarts or 10$\frac{1}{2}$ cups).

Water Losses The body must excrete a minimum of about 500 milliliters (about 2 cups) of water each day ♦ as urine—enough to carry away the waste products generated by a day's metabolic activities. Above this amount, excretion adjusts to balance intake. If a person drinks more water, the kidneys excrete more urine, and the urine becomes more dilute. In addition to urine, water is lost from the lungs as vapor and from the skin as sweat; some is also lost in feces.* The amount of fluid lost from each source varies, depending on the environment (such as heat or humidity) and physical conditions (such as exercise or fever). On average, daily losses total about 2$\frac{1}{2}$ liters. Table 12-3 shows how water excretion balances intake; maintaining this balance requires healthy kidneys and an adequate intake of fluids.

Water Recommendations Because water needs vary depending on diet, activity, environmental temperature, and humidity, a general water requirement is difficult to establish. Recommendations ♦ are sometimes expressed in proportion to the amount of energy expended under average environmental conditions.[2] The recommended water intake for a person who expends 2000 kcalories a day, for example, is 2 to 3 liters of water (about 8 to 12 cups). This recommendation is in line with the Adequate Intake (AI) for *total* water set by the DRI Committee. ♦ Total water includes not only drinking water, but water in other beverages and in foods as well.

TABLE 12-3	Water Balance		
Water Sources	**Amount (mL)**	**Water Losses**	**Amount (mL)**
Liquids	550 to 1500	Kidneys (urine)	500 to 1400
Foods	700 to 1000	Skin (sweat)	450 to 900
Metabolic water	200 to 300	Lungs (breath)	350
		GI tract (feces)	150
Total	1450 to 2800	Total	1450 to 2800

NOTE: For perspective, 100 mL is a little less than $\frac{1}{2}$ cup and 1000 mL is a little more than 1 quart (1 mL = 0.03 oz).

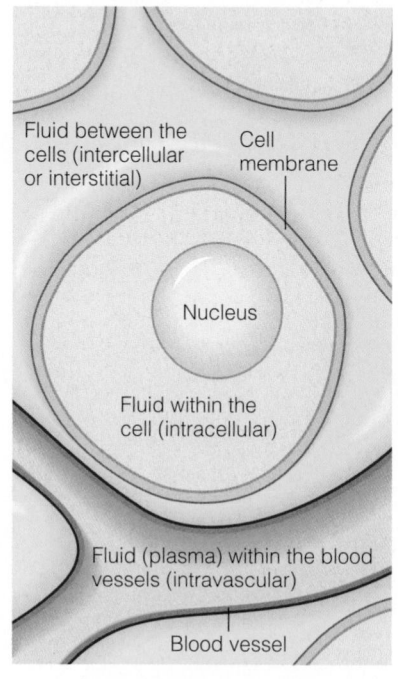

FIGURE 12-1 One Cell and Its Associated Fluids

Fluids are found within the cells (intracellular) or outside the cells (extracellular). Extracellular fluids include plasma (the fluid portion of blood in the intravascular spaces of blood vessels) and interstitial fluids (the tissue fluid that fills the intercellular spaces between the cells).

Fluid between the cells (intercellular or interstitial)

Cell membrane

Nucleus

Fluid within the cell (intracellular)

Fluid (plasma) within the blood vessels (intravascular)

Blood vessel

♦ The amount of water the body has to excrete each day to dispose of its wastes is the **obligatory** (ah-BLIG-ah-TORE-ee) **water excretion**—about 500 mL (about 2 c, or a pint).

♦ Water recommendation:
• 1.0 to 1.5 mL/kcal expended (adults)**
• 1.5 mL/kcal expended (infants and athletes)
Conversion factors:
• 1 mL = 0.03 fluid ounce
• 125 mL ≈ $\frac{1}{2}$ c
Easy estimation: $\frac{1}{2}$ c per 100 kcal expended

♦ AI for *total* water:
• Men: 3.7 L/day
• Women: 2.7 L/day
Conversion factors:
• 1 L ≈ 1 qt ≈ 32 oz ≈ 4 c

---

* Water lost from the lungs and skin accounts for almost one-half of the daily losses even when a person is not visibly perspiring; these losses are commonly referred to as *insensible water losses*.
** For those using kilojoules: 4.2 to 6.3 mL/kJ expended.

Because a wide range of water intakes will prevent dehydration and its harmful consequences, the AI is based on average intakes. People who are physically active or who live in hot environments may need more.[3]

Which beverages are best? Any beverage can readily meet the body's fluid needs, but those with few or no kcalories do so without contributing to weight gain. Given that obesity is a major health problem and that beverages currently represent over 20 percent of the total energy intake in the United States, most people would do well to select water as their preferred beverage. Other choices include tea, coffee, nonfat and low-fat milk and soymilk, artificially sweetened beverages, fruit and vegetable juices, sports drinks, and lastly, sweetened nutrient-poor beverages.[4]

Some research indicates that people who drink caffeinated beverages lose a little more fluid than when drinking water because caffeine acts as a diuretic. The DRI Committee considered such findings in their recommendations for water intake and concluded: "Caffeinated beverages contribute to the daily total water intake similar to that contributed by non-caffeinated beverages."[5] In other words, it doesn't seem to matter whether people rely on caffeine-containing beverages or other beverages to meet their fluid needs.

As Highlight 7 explained, alcohol acts as a diuretic, and it has many adverse effects on health and nutrition status. Alcohol should not be used to meet fluid needs.

Health Effects of Water In addition to meeting the body's fluid needs, drinking plenty of water may protect against urinary stones and constipation.[6] Even mild dehydration seems to interfere with daily tasks involving concentration, alertness, and short-term memory.[7]

The kind of water a person drinks may also make a difference to health. Water is usually either hard or soft. **Hard water** has high concentrations of calcium and magnesium; sodium or potassium is the principal mineral of **soft water.** (See the accompanying glossary for these and other common terms used to describe water.) In practical terms, soft water makes more bubbles with less soap; hard water leaves a ring on the tub, a crust of rocklike crystals in the teakettle, and a gray residue in the laundry.

Soft water may seem more desirable around the house, and some homeowners purchase water softeners that replace magnesium and calcium with sodium. In the body, however, soft water with sodium may aggravate hypertension and heart disease. In contrast, the minerals in hard water may benefit these conditions.

GLOSSARY OF WATER TERMS

artesian water: water drawn from a well that taps a confined aquifer in which the water is under pressure.

bottled water: drinking water sold in bottles.

carbonated water: water that contains carbon dioxide gas, either naturally occurring or added, that causes bubbles to form in it; also called *bubbling* or *sparkling water.* Seltzer, soda, and tonic waters are legally soft drinks and are not regulated as water.

distilled water: water that has been vaporized and recondensed, leaving it free of dissolved minerals.

filtered water: water treated by filtration, usually through *activated carbon filters* that reduce the lead in tap water, or by *reverse osmosis* units that force pressurized water across a membrane removing lead, arsenic, and some microorganisms from tap water.

hard water: water with a high calcium and magnesium content.

mineral water: water from a spring or well that typically contains 250 to 500 parts per million (ppm) of minerals. Minerals give water a distinctive flavor. Many mineral waters are high in sodium.

natural water: water obtained from a spring or well that is certified to be safe and sanitary. The mineral content may not be changed, but the water may be treated in other ways such as with ozone or by filtration.

public water: water from a municipal or county water system that has been treated and disinfected.

purified water: water that has been treated by distillation or other physical or chemical processes that remove dissolved solids. Because purified water contains no minerals or contaminants, it is useful for medical and research purposes.

soft water: water with a high sodium or potassium content.

spring water: water originating from an underground spring or well. It may be bubbly (carbonated), or "flat" or "still," meaning not carbonated. Brand names such as "Spring Pure" do not necessarily mean that the water comes from a spring.

well water: water drawn from ground water by tapping into an aquifer.

Soft water also more easily dissolves certain contaminant minerals, such as cadmium and lead, from old plumbing pipes. As Chapter 13 explains, these contaminant minerals harm the body by displacing the nutrient minerals from their normal sites of action. People who live in old buildings should run the cold water tap a minute to flush out harmful minerals whenever the water faucet has been off for more than six hours.

Many people select **bottled water,** believing it to be safer than tap water and therefore worth its substantial cost. Chapter 19 offers a discussion of bottled water safety and regulations.

IN SUMMARY

Water makes up about 60 percent of the adult body's weight. It assists with the transport of nutrients and waste products throughout the body, participates in chemical reactions, acts as a solvent, serves as a shock absorber, and regulates body temperature. To maintain water balance, intake from liquids, foods, and metabolism must equal losses from the kidneys, skin, lungs, and GI tract. The amount and type of water a person drinks may have positive or negative health effects.

Blood Volume and Blood Pressure

Fluids maintain the blood volume, which in turn influences blood pressure. The kidneys are central to the regulation of blood volume and blood pressure.[8] All day, every day, the kidneys reabsorb needed substances and water and excrete wastes with some water in the urine (see Figure 12-2 on p. 402). The kidneys meticulously adjust the volume and the concentration of the urine to accommodate changes in the body, including variations in the day's food and beverage intakes. Instructions on whether to retain or release substances or water come from ADH, renin, angiotensin, and aldosterone.

ADH and Water Retention Whenever blood volume or blood pressure falls too low, or whenever the extracellular fluid becomes too concentrated, the hypothalamus signals the pituitary gland to release antidiuretic hormone (ADH). ◆ ADH is a water-conserving hormone ◆ that stimulates the kidneys to reabsorb water. Consequently, the more water you need, the less your kidneys excrete. These events also trigger thirst. Drinking water and retaining fluids raise the blood volume and dilute the concentrated fluids, thus helping to restore homeostasis.

Renin and Sodium Retention Cells in the kidneys respond to low blood pressure by releasing an enzyme called **renin.** Through a complex series of events, renin causes the kidneys to reabsorb sodium. Sodium reabsorption, in turn, is always accompanied by water retention, which helps to restore blood volume and blood pressure.

Angiotensin and Blood Vessel Constriction In addition to its role in sodium retention, renin converts the blood protein angiotensinogen to its active form—**angiotensin.** Angiotensin is a powerful **vasoconstrictor** that narrows the diameters of blood vessels, thereby raising the blood pressure.

Aldosterone and Sodium Retention In addition to acting as a vasoconstrictor, angiotensin stimulates the release of the hormone **aldosterone** from the **adrenal glands.** Aldosterone signals the kidneys to retain more sodium, and therefore water, because when sodium moves, fluids follow. Again, the effect is that when more water is needed, less is excreted.

All of these actions are presented in Figure 12-3 (p. 403) and help to explain why high-sodium diets aggravate conditions such as hypertension or edema. Too much

◆ Reminder: *Antidiuretic hormone (ADH)* is a hormone produced by the pituitary gland in response to dehydration (or a high sodium concentration in the blood). It stimulates the kidneys to reabsorb more water and therefore to excrete less.

◆ Recall from Highlight 7 that alcohol depresses ADH activity, thus promoting fluid losses and dehydration. In addition to its antidiuretic effect, ADH elevates blood pressure and so is also called **vasopressin** (VAS-oh-PRES-in).
 • **vaso** = vessel
 • **press** = pressure

renin (REN-in): an enzyme from the kidneys that activates angiotensin.

angiotensin (AN-gee-oh-TEN-sin)**:** a hormone involved in blood pressure regulation. Its precursor protein is called *angiotensinogen*; it is activated by *renin,* an enzyme from the kidneys.

vasoconstrictor (VAS-oh-kon-STRIK-tor)**:** a substance that constricts or narrows the blood vessels.

aldosterone (al-DOS-ter-own): a hormone secreted by the adrenal glands that regulates blood pressure by increasing the reabsorption of sodium by the kidneys. Aldosterone also regulates chloride and potassium concentrations.

adrenal glands: glands adjacent to, and just above, each kidney.

FIGURE 12-2 *Animated!* A Nephron, One of the Kidney's Many Functioning Units

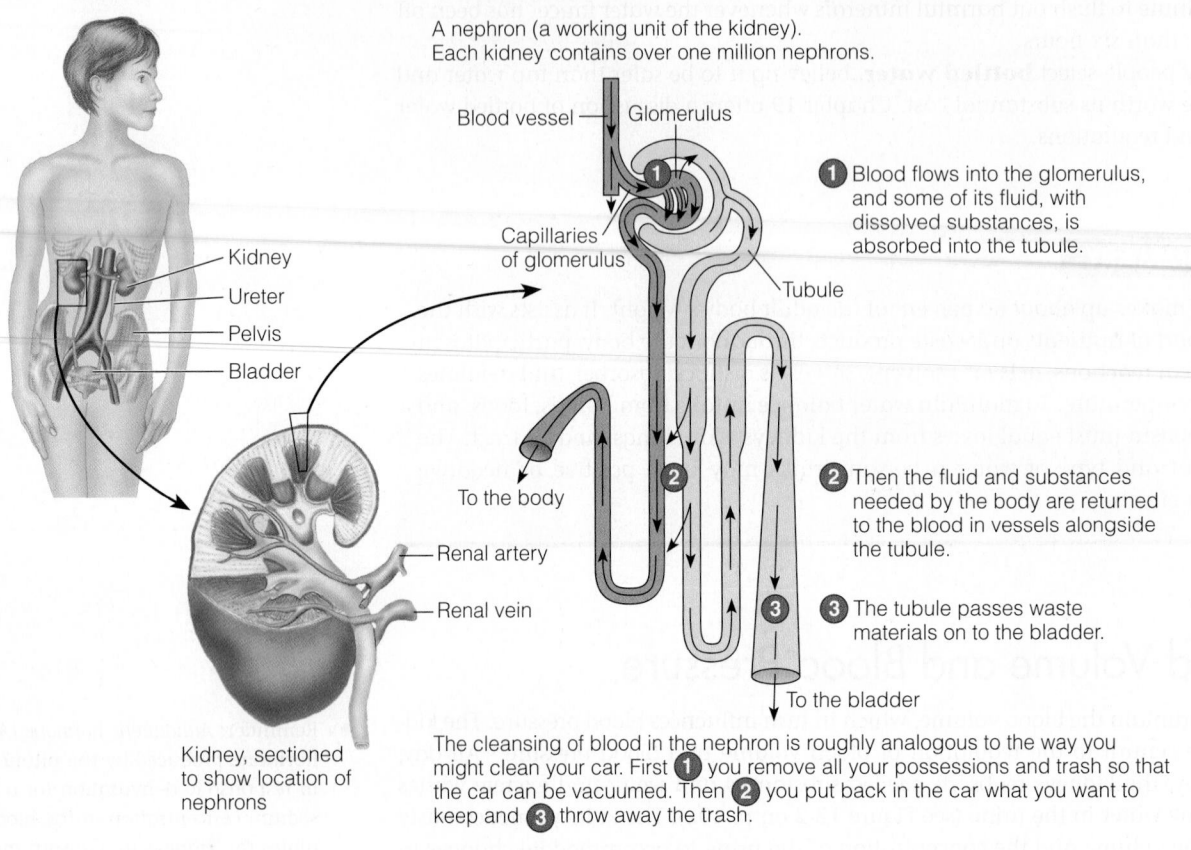

A nephron (a working unit of the kidney).
Each kidney contains over one million nephrons.

Blood vessel — Glomerulus

1. Blood flows into the glomerulus, and some of its fluid, with dissolved substances, is absorbed into the tubule.

Capillaries of glomerulus

Tubule

Kidney
Ureter
Pelvis
Bladder

To the body

Renal artery

Renal vein

2. Then the fluid and substances needed by the body are returned to the blood in vessels alongside the tubule.

3. The tubule passes waste materials on to the bladder.

To the bladder

Kidney, sectioned to show location of nephrons

The cleansing of blood in the nephron is roughly analogous to the way you might clean your car. First **1** you remove all your possessions and trash so that the car can be vacuumed. Then **2** you put back in the car what you want to keep and **3** throw away the trash.

sodium causes water retention and an accompanying rise in blood pressure or swelling in the interstitial spaces. Chapter 18 discusses hypertension in detail.

IN SUMMARY

In response to low blood volume, low blood pressure, or highly concentrated body fluids, these actions combine to effectively restore homeostasis:

- ADH retains water.
- Renin retains sodium.
- Angiotensin constricts blood vessels.
- Aldosterone retains sodium.

These actions can maintain water balance only if a person drinks enough water.

◆ The major minerals:
  - Sodium
  - Chloride
  - Potassium
  - Calcium
  - Phosphorus
  - Magnesium
  - Sulfur

Fluid and Electrolyte Balance

Maintaining a balance of about two-thirds of the body fluids inside the cells and one-third outside is vital to the life of the cells. If too much water were to enter the cells, they might rupture; if too much water were to leave, they would collapse. To control the movement of water, the cells direct the movement of the major minerals. ◆

| FIGURE 12-3 | *Animated!* How the Body Regulates Blood Volume |

ThomsonNOW
To test your understanding of these concepts, log on to www.thomsonedu.com/login

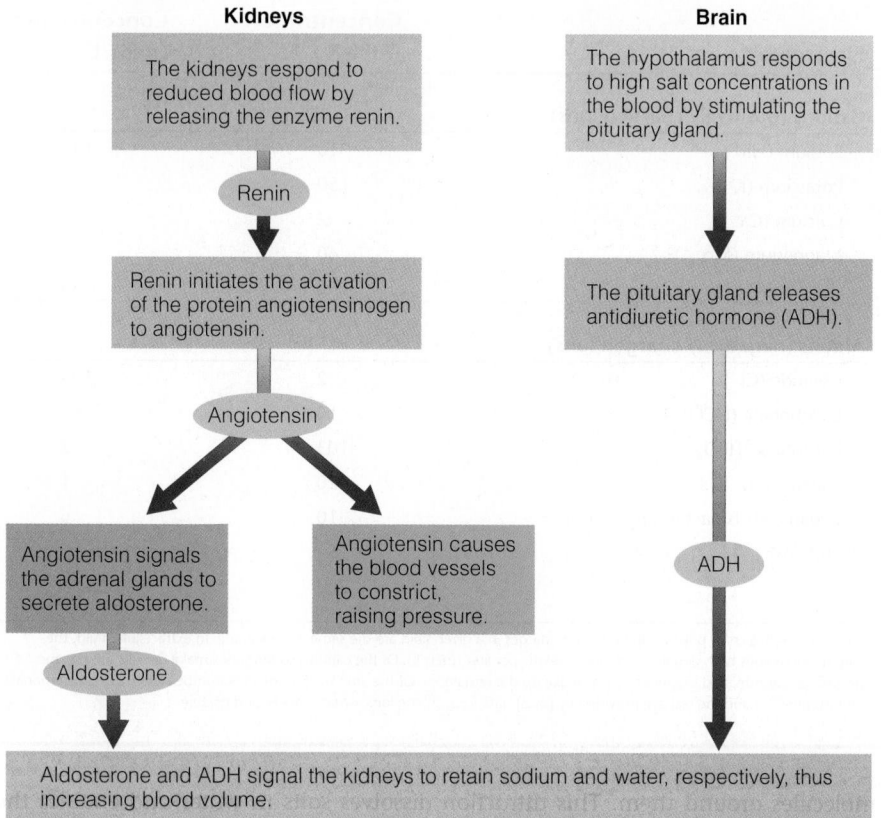

Kidneys

The kidneys respond to reduced blood flow by releasing the enzyme renin.

↓ Renin

Renin initiates the activation of the protein angiotensinogen to angiotensin.

↓ Angiotensin

Angiotensin signals the adrenal glands to secrete aldosterone.

↓ Aldosterone

Angiotensin causes the blood vessels to constrict, raising pressure.

Brain

The hypothalamus responds to high salt concentrations in the blood by stimulating the pituitary gland.

↓

The pituitary gland releases antidiuretic hormone (ADH).

↓ ADH

Aldosterone and ADH signal the kidneys to retain sodium and water, respectively, thus increasing blood volume.

◆ To remember the difference between cations and anions, think of the "t" in cations as a "plus" (+) sign and the "n" in anions as "negative."

◆ A neutral molecule, such as water, that has opposite charges spatially separated within the molecule is **polar.** See Appendix B for more details.

salt: a compound composed of a positive ion other than H^+ and a negative ion other than OH^-. An example is sodium chloride ($Na^+ Cl^-$).
- **Na** = sodium
- **Cl** = chloride

dissociates (dis-SO-see-aites): physically separates.

ions (EYE-uns): atoms or molecules that have gained or lost electrons and therefore have electrical charges. Examples include the positively charged sodium ion (Na^+) and the negatively charged chloride ion (Cl^-). For a closer look at ions, see Appendix B.

cations (CAT-eye-uns): positively charged ions.

anions (AN-eye-uns): negatively charged ions.

electrolytes: salts that dissolve in water and dissociate into charged particles called ions.

electrolyte solutions: solutions that can conduct electricity.

milliequivalents (mEq): the concentration of electrolytes in a volume of solution. Milliequivalents are a useful measure when considering ions because the number of charges reveals characteristics about the solution that are not evident when the concentration is expressed in terms of weight.

Dissociation of Salt in Water When a mineral **salt** such as sodium chloride (NaCl) dissolves in water, it separates **(dissociates)** into **ions**—positively and negatively charged particles (Na^+ and Cl^-). The positive ions are **cations;** the negative ones are **anions.** ◆ Unlike pure water, which conducts electricity poorly, ions dissolved in water carry electrical current. For this reason, salts that dissociate into ions are called **electrolytes,** and fluids that contain them are **electrolyte solutions.**

In all electrolyte solutions, anion and cation concentrations are balanced (the number of negative and positive charges are equal). If a fluid contains 1000 negative charges, it must contain 1000 positive charges, too. If an anion enters the fluid, a cation must accompany it or another anion must leave so that electrical neutrality will be maintained. Thus, whenever sodium (Na^+) ions leave a cell, potassium (K^+) ions enter, for example. In fact, it's a good bet that whenever Na^+ and K^+ ions are moving, they are going in opposite directions.

Table 12-4 (p. 404) shows that, indeed, the positive and negative charges inside and outside cells are perfectly balanced even though the numbers of each kind of ion differ over a wide range. Inside the cells, the positive charges total 202 and the negative charges balance these perfectly. Outside the cells, the amounts and proportions of the ions differ from those inside, but again the positive and negative charges balance. (Scientists count these charges in **milliequivalents, mEq.**)

Electrolytes Attract Water Electrolytes attract water. Each water molecule has a net charge of zero, ◆ but the oxygen side of the molecule has a slight negative charge, and the hydrogens have a slight positive charge. Figure 12-4 (p. 404) shows the result in an electrolyte solution: both positive and negative ions attract clusters of water

TABLE 12-4	Important Body Electrolytes		
Electrolytes		Intracellular (inside cells) Concentration (mEq/L)	Extracellular (outside cells) Concentration (mEq/L)
Cations (positively charged ions)			
Sodium (Na$^+$)		10	142
Potassium (K$^+$)		150	5
Calcium (Ca^{++})		2	5
Magnesium (Mg^{++})		40	3
		202	155
Anions (negatively charged ions)			
Chloride (Cl$^-$)		2	103
Bicarbonate (HCO$_3^-$)		10	27
Phosphate (HPO$_4^=$)		103	2
Sulfate (SO$_4^=$)		20	1
Organic acids (lactate, pyruvate)		10	6
Proteins		57	16
		202	155

NOTE: The numbers of positive and negative charges in a given fluid are the same. For example, in extracellular fluid, the cations and anions both equal 155 milliequivalents per liter (mEq/L). Of the cations, sodium ions make up 142 mEq/L; and potassium, calcium, and magnesium ions make up the remainder. Of the anions, chloride ions number 103 mEq/L; bicarbonate ions number 27; and the rest are provided by phosphate ions, sulfate ions, organic acids, and protein.

molecules around them. This attraction dissolves salts in water and enables the body to move fluids into appropriate compartments.

Water Follows Electrolytes As Figure 12-5 shows, some electrolytes reside primarily outside the cells (notably, sodium and chloride), whereas others reside predominantly inside the cells (notably, potassium, magnesium, phosphate, ◆ and sulfate). Cell membranes are *selectively permeable,* meaning that they allow the pas-

◆ The word ending *-ate* denotes a salt of the mineral. Thus, phosphate is the salt form of the mineral phosphorus, and sulfate is the salt form of sulfur.

FIGURE 12-4 Water Dissolves Salts and Follows Electrolytes

The structural arrangement of the two hydrogen atoms and one oxygen atom enables water to dissolve salts. Water's role as a solvent is one of its most valuable characteristics.

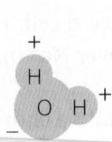

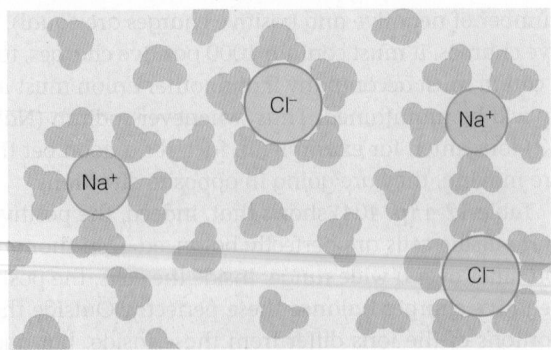

The negatively charged electrons that bond the hydrogens to the oxygen spend most of their time near the oxygen atom. As a result, the oxygen is slightly negative, and the hydrogens are slightly positive (see Appendix B).

In an electrolyte solution, water molecules are attracted to both anions and cations. Notice that the negative oxygen atoms of the water molecules are drawn to the sodium cation (Na$^+$), whereas the positive hydrogen atoms of the water molecules are drawn to the chloride ions (Cl$^-$).

FIGURE 12-5 A Cell and Its Electrolytes

All of these electrolytes are found both inside and outside the cells, but each can be found mostly on one side or the other of the cell membrane.

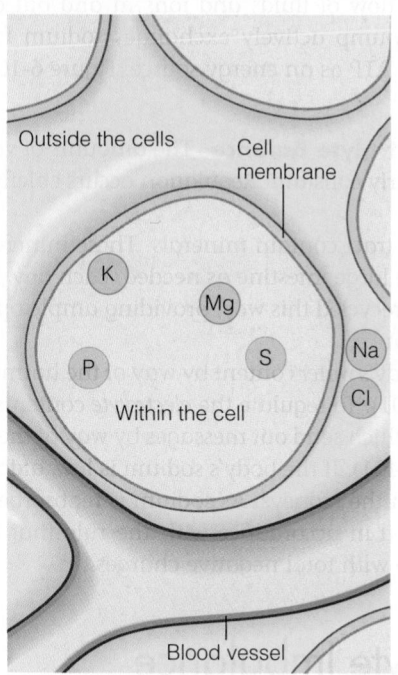

Outside the cells

Cell membrane

Within the cell

Blood vessel

Chemical symbols:
- K = potassium
- P = phosphorus
- Mg = magnesium
- S = sulfate
- Na = sodium
- Cl = chloride

Key:

Cations

Anions

When immersed in water, raisins become plump because water moves toward the higher concentration of sugar inside the raisins.

When sprinkled with salt, vegetables "sweat" because water moves toward the higher concentration of salt outside the eggplant.

sage of some molecules, but not others. Whenever electrolytes move across the membrane, water follows.

The movement of water across a membrane toward the more concentrated **solutes** is called **osmosis.** The amount of pressure needed to prevent the movement of water across a membrane is called the **osmotic pressure.** Figure 12-6 presents osmosis, and the photos of salted eggplant and rehydrated raisins provide familiar examples.

Proteins Regulate Flow of Fluids and Ions Chapter 6 described how proteins attract water and help to regulate fluid movement. In addition, transport proteins in

FIGURE 12-6 Osmosis

Water flows in the direction of the more highly concentrated solution.

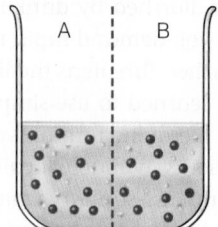
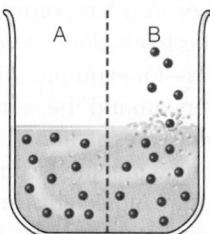
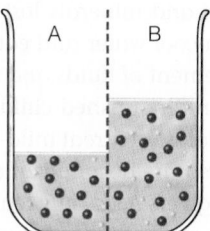

1 With equal numbers of solute particles on both sides of the semipermeable membrane, the concentrations are equal, and the tendency of water to move in either direction is about the same.

2 Now additional solute is added to side B. Solute cannot flow across the divider (in the case of a cell, its membrane).

3 Water can flow both ways across the divider, but has a greater tendency to move from side A to side B, where there is a greater concentration of solute. The volume of water becomes greater on side B, and the concentrations on side A and B become equal.

solutes (SOLL-yutes): the substances that are dissolved in a solution. The number of molecules in a given volume of fluid is the **solute concentration.**

osmosis: the movement of water across a membrane *toward* the side where the solutes are more concentrated.

osmotic pressure: the amount of pressure needed to prevent the movement of water across a membrane.

Physically active people must remember to replace their body fluids.

♦ Health care workers use **oral rehydration therapy (ORT)**—a simple solution of sugar, salt, and water, taken by mouth—to treat dehydration caused by diarrhea. A simple ORT recipe (cool before giving):
- $1/2$ L boiling water
- A small handful of sugar (4 tsp)
- 3 pinches of salt ($1/2$ tsp)

♦ Reminder: *pH* is the unit of measure expressing a substance's acidity or alkalinity.

the cell membranes regulate the passage of positive ions and other substances from one side of the membrane to the other. Negative ions follow positive ions, and water flows toward the more concentrated solution.

A protein that regulates the flow of fluids and ions in and out of cells is the sodium-potassium pump. The pump actively exchanges sodium for potassium across the cell membrane, using ATP as an energy source. Figure 6-10 on p. 192 illustrates this action.

Regulation of Fluid and Electrolyte Balance The amounts of various minerals in the body must remain nearly constant. Regulation occurs chiefly at two sites: the GI tract and the kidneys.

The digestive juices of the GI tract contain minerals. These minerals and those from foods are reabsorbed in the large intestine as needed. Each day, 8 liters of fluids and associated minerals are recycled this way, providing ample opportunity for the regulation of electrolyte balance.

The kidneys' control of the body's *water* content by way of the hormone ADH has already been described (see p. 401). To regulate the *electrolyte* contents, the kidneys depend on the adrenal glands, which send out messages by way of the hormone aldosterone (also explained on p. 401). If the body's sodium is low, aldosterone stimulates sodium reabsorption from the kidneys. As sodium is reabsorbed, potassium (another positive ion) is excreted in accordance with the rule that total positive charges must remain in balance with total negative charges.

Fluid and Electrolyte Imbalance

Normally, the body defends itself successfully against fluid and electrolyte imbalances. Certain situations and some medications, however, may overwhelm the body's ability to compensate. Severe, prolonged vomiting and diarrhea as well as heavy sweating, burns, and traumatic wounds may incur such great fluid and electrolyte losses as to precipitate a medical emergency.

Different Solutes Lost by Different Routes Different solutes are lost depending on why fluid is lost. If fluid is lost by vomiting or diarrhea, sodium is lost indiscriminately. If the adrenal glands oversecrete aldosterone, as may occur when they develop a tumor, the kidneys may excrete too much potassium. Also, the person with uncontrolled diabetes may lose glucose, a solute not normally excreted, and large amounts of fluid with it. Each situation results in dehydration, but drinking water alone cannot restore electrolyte balance. Medical intervention is required.

Replacing Lost Fluids and Electrolytes In many cases, people can replace the fluids and minerals lost in sweat or in a temporary bout of diarrhea by drinking plain cool water and eating regular foods. Some cases, however, demand rapid replacement of fluids and electrolytes—for example, when diarrhea threatens the life of a malnourished child. Caregivers around the world have learned to use simple formulas ♦ to treat mild-to-moderate cases of diarrhea. These lifesaving formulas do not require hospitalization and can be prepared from ingredients available locally. Caregivers need only learn to measure ingredients carefully and use sanitary water. Once rehydrated, a person can begin eating foods. (Chapter 14 presents a discussion of sport drinks.)

Acid-Base Balance

The body uses its ions not only to help maintain fluid and electrolyte balance, but also to regulate the acidity (pH) ♦ of its fluids. The pH scale introduced in Chapter 3 is repeated here, in Figure 12-7, with the normal and abnormal pH ranges of the blood added. As you can see, the body must maintain the pH within a narrow range to avoid life-threatening consequences. Slight deviations in either direction can de-

FIGURE 12-7 The pH Scale

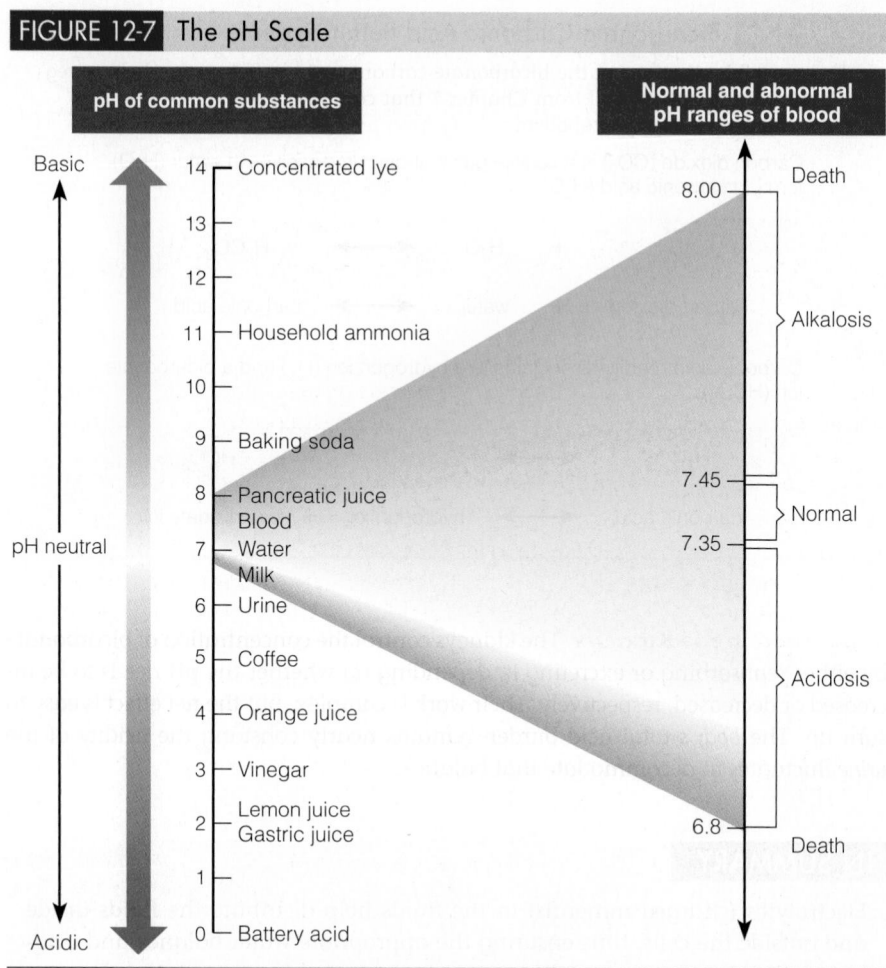

pH of common substances

Normal and abnormal pH ranges of blood

Basic
14 — Concentrated lye
13 —
12 —
11 — Household ammonia
10 —
9 — Baking soda
8 — Pancreatic juice
Blood
pH neutral 7 — Water
Milk
6 — Urine
5 — Coffee
4 — Orange juice
3 — Vinegar
2 — Lemon juice
Gastric juice
1 —
Acidic 0 — Battery acid

8.00 — Death
Alkalosis
7.45 —
Normal
7.35 —
Acidosis
6.8 — Death

NOTE: Each step is ten times as concentrated in base (⅒ as much acid, or H⁺) as the one below it.

nature proteins, causing metabolic mayhem. Enzymes couldn't catalyze reactions and hemoglobin couldn't carry oxygen—to name just two examples.

The acidity of the body's fluids is determined by the concentration of hydrogen ions (H^+). ◆ A high concentration of hydrogen ions is very acidic. Normal energy metabolism generates hydrogen ions, as well as many other acids, that must be neutralized. Three systems defend the body against fluctuations in pH—buffers in the blood, respiration in the lungs, and excretion in the kidneys.

Regulation by the Buffers Bicarbonate ◆ (a base) and **carbonic acid** (an acid) in the body fluids (as well as some proteins) protect the body against changes in acidity by acting as buffers—substances that can neutralize acids or bases. Figure 12-8 (p. 408) presents the chemical reactions of this buffer system, which is primarily under the control of the lungs and kidneys.

Carbon dioxide, which is formed all the time during energy metabolism, dissolves in water to form carbonic acid in the blood. Carbonic acid, in turn, dissociates to form hydrogen ions and bicarbonate ions. The appropriate balance between carbonic acid and bicarbonate is essential to maintaining optimal blood pH.

Regulation in the Lungs The lungs control the concentration of carbonic acid by raising or slowing the respiration rate, depending on whether the pH needs to be increased or decreased. If too much carbonic acid builds up, the respiration rate speeds up; this hyperventilation increases the amount of carbon dioxide exhaled, thereby lowering the carbonic acid concentration and restoring homeostasis. Conversely, if bicarbonate builds up, the respiration rate slows; carbon dioxide is retained and forms more carbonic acid. Again, homeostasis is restored.

◆ The lower the pH, the higher the H^+ ion concentration and the stronger the acid. A pH above 7 is alkaline, or base (a solution in which OH^- ions predominate).

◆ Reminder: *Bicarbonate* is an alkaline compound with the formula HCO_3. It is produced in all cell fluids from the dissociation of carbonic acid to help maintain the body's acid-base balance. (Bicarbonate is also secreted from the pancreas during digestion as part of the pancreatic juice.)

carbonic acid: a compound with the formula H_2CO_3 that results from the combination of carbon dioxide (CO_2) and water (H_2O); of particular importance in maintaining the body's acid-base balance.

FIGURE 12-8 Bicarbonate-Carbonic Acid Buffer System

The reversible reactions of the bicarbonate-carbonic acid buffer system help to regulate the body's pH. Recall from Chapter 7 that carbon dioxide and water are formed during energy metabolism.

Carbon dioxide (CO_2) is a volatile gas that quickly dissolves in water (H_2O), forming carbonic acid (H_2CO_3):

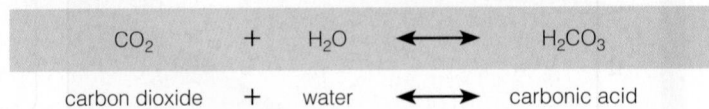

$$CO_2 \quad + \quad H_2O \quad \longleftrightarrow \quad H_2CO_3$$

carbon dioxide + water ⟷ carbonic acid

Carbonic acid readily dissociates to a hydrogen ion (H^+) and a bicarbonate ion (HCO_3^-):

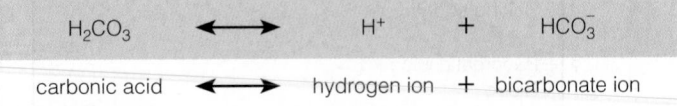

$$H_2CO_3 \quad \longleftrightarrow \quad H^+ \quad + \quad HCO_3^-$$

carbonic acid ⟷ hydrogen ion + bicarbonate ion

Regulation in the Kidneys The kidneys control the concentration of bicarbonate by either reabsorbing or excreting it, depending on whether the pH needs to be increased or decreased, respectively. Their work is complex, but the net effect is easy to sum up. The *body's* total acid burden remains nearly constant; the acidity of the *urine* fluctuates to accommodate that balance.

IN SUMMARY

Electrolytes (charged minerals) in the fluids help distribute the fluids inside and outside the cells, thus ensuring the appropriate water balance and acid-base balance to support all life processes. Excessive losses of fluids and electrolytes upset these balances, and the kidneys play a key role in restoring homeostasis.

The Minerals—An Overview

Figure 12-9 (p. 409) shows the amounts of the **major minerals** found in the body and, for comparison, some of the trace minerals. The distinction between the major and trace minerals does not mean that one group is more important than the other—all minerals are vital. The major minerals are so named because they are present, and needed, in larger amounts in the body. They are shown at the top of the figure and are discussed in this chapter. The trace minerals (shown at the bottom) are discussed in Chapter 13. A few generalizations pertain to all of the minerals and distinguish them from the vitamins. Especially notable is their chemical nature.

Inorganic Elements Unlike the organic vitamins, which are easily destroyed, minerals are inorganic elements ◆ that always retain their chemical identity. Once minerals enter the body proper, they remain there until excreted; they cannot be changed into anything else. Iron, for example, may temporarily combine with other charged elements in salts, but it is always iron. Neither can minerals be destroyed by heat, air, acid, or mixing. Consequently, little care is needed to preserve minerals during food preparation. In fact, the ash that remains when a food is burned contains all the minerals that were in the food originally. Minerals can be lost from food only when they leach into cooking water that is then poured down the drain.

◆ Reminder: An *inorganic* substance does not contain carbon.

major minerals: essential mineral nutrients found in the human body in amounts larger than 5 g; sometimes called **macrominerals.**

FIGURE 12-9   Minerals in a 60-kilogram (132-pound) Human Body

Not only are the major minerals present in the body in larger amounts than the trace minerals, but they are also needed by the body in larger amounts. Recommended intakes for the major minerals are stated in *hundreds of milligrams* or *grams,* whereas those for the trace minerals are listed in *tens of milligrams* or even *micrograms.*

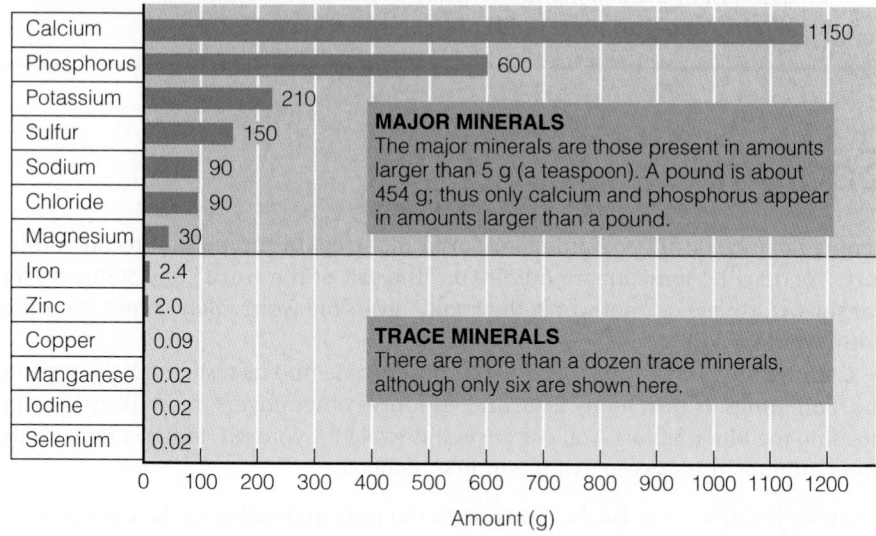

MAJOR MINERALS
The major minerals are those present in amounts larger than 5 g (a teaspoon). A pound is about 454 g; thus only calcium and phosphorus appear in amounts larger than a pound.

TRACE MINERALS
There are more than a dozen trace minerals, although only six are shown here.

Mineral	Amount (g)
Calcium	1150
Phosphorus	600
Potassium	210
Sulfur	150
Sodium	90
Chloride	90
Magnesium	30
Iron	2.4
Zinc	2.0
Copper	0.09
Manganese	0.02
Iodine	0.02
Selenium	0.02

The Body's Handling of Minerals   The minerals also differ from the vitamins in the amounts the body can absorb and in the extent to which they must be specially handled. Some minerals, such as potassium, are easily absorbed into the blood, transported freely, and readily excreted by the kidneys, much like the water-soluble vitamins. Other minerals, such as calcium, are more like fat-soluble vitamins in that they must have carriers to be absorbed and transported. And, like some of the fat-soluble vitamins, minerals taken in excess can be toxic.

Variable Bioavailability   The bioavailability ◆ of minerals varies. Some foods contain **binders** that combine chemically with minerals, preventing their absorption and carrying them out of the body with other wastes. Examples of binders include phytates, which are found primarily in legumes and grains, and oxalates, which are present in rhubarb and spinach, among other foods. These foods contain more minerals than the body actually receives for use.

Nutrient Interactions   Chapter 10 described how the presence or absence of one vitamin can affect another's absorption, metabolism, and excretion. The same is true of the minerals. The interactions between sodium and calcium, for example, cause both to be excreted when sodium intakes are high. Phosphorus binds with magnesium in the GI tract, so magnesium absorption is limited when phosphorus intakes are high. These are just two examples of the interactions involving minerals featured in this chapter. Discussions in both this chapter and the next point out additional problems that arise from such interactions. Notice how often they reflect an excess of one mineral creating an inadequacy of another and how supplements—not foods—are most often to blame.

Varied Roles   Although all the major minerals help to maintain the body's fluid balance as described earlier, sodium, chloride, and potassium are most noted for that role.◆ For this reason, these three minerals are discussed first here. Later sections describe the minerals most noted for their roles in bone growth and health—calcium, phosphorus, and magnesium.

◆ Reminder: *Bioavailability* refers to the rate at and the extent to which a nutrient is absorbed and used.

◆ Key fluid balance nutrients:
• Sodium, potassium, chloride

binders: chemical compounds in foods that combine with nutrients (especially minerals) to form complexes the body cannot absorb. Examples include **phytates** (FYE-tates) and **oxalates** (OCK-sa-lates).

IN SUMMARY

The major minerals are found in larger quantities in the body, whereas the trace minerals occur in smaller amounts. Minerals are inorganic elements that retain their chemical identities. They usually receive special handling and regulation in the body, and they may bind with other substances or interact with other minerals, thus limiting their absorption.

Sodium

People have held salt (sodium chloride) in high regard throughout recorded history. We describe someone we admire as "the salt of the earth" and someone we consider worthless as "not worth their salt." Even the word *salary* comes from the Latin word for salt.

Cultures vary in their use of salt, but most people find its taste innately appealing. Salt brings its own tangy taste and enhances other flavors, most likely by suppressing the bitter flavors. You can taste this effect for yourself: tonic water with its bitter quinine tastes sweeter with a little salt added.

Sodium Roles in the Body **Sodium** is the principal cation of the extracellular fluid and the primary regulator of its volume. Sodium also helps maintain acid-base balance and is essential to nerve impulse transmission and muscle contraction.*

Sodium is readily absorbed by the intestinal tract and travels freely in the blood until it reaches the kidneys, which filter all the sodium out of the blood. Then, with great precision, the kidneys return to the bloodstream the exact amount of sodium the body needs. Normally, the amount excreted is approximately equal to the amount ingested on a given day. When blood sodium rises, as when a person eats salted foods, thirst signals the person to drink until the appropriate sodium-to-water ratio is restored. Then the kidneys excrete both the excess water and the excess sodium together.

Sodium Recommendations Diets rarely lack sodium, and even when intakes are low, the body adapts by reducing sodium losses in urine and sweat, thus making deficiencies unlikely. Sodium recommendations ◆ are set low enough to protect against high blood pressure, but high enough to allow an adequate intake of other nutrients with a typical diet. Because high sodium intakes correlate with high blood pressure, the Upper Level for adults is set at 2300 milligrams per day, slightly lower than the Daily Value used on food labels (2400 milligrams). The average sodium intake for adults in the United States exceeds the Upper Level—and most adults will develop hypertension at some point in their lives.

Sodium and Hypertension For years, a high *sodium* intake was considered the primary factor responsible for high blood pressure. Then research pointed to *salt* (sodium chloride) as the dietary culprit. Salt has a greater effect on blood pressure than either sodium or chloride alone or in combination with other ions.

For some individuals, blood pressure increases in response to excesses in salt intake. People most likely to have a **salt sensitivity** include those whose parents had high blood pressure, those with chronic kidney disease or diabetes, African Americans, and people over 50 years of age.** Overweight people also appear to be particularly sensitive to the effect of salt on blood pressure. For them, a high salt intake correlates strongly with heart disease, and salt restriction helps to lower their blood pressure.

In fact, a salt-restricted diet lowers blood pressure in people without hypertension as well. Because reducing salt intake causes no harm and diminishes the risk

◆ AI for sodium:
- 1500 mg/day (19–50 yr)
- 1300 mg/day (51–70 yr)
- 1200 mg/day (>70 yr)

sodium: the principal cation in the extracellular fluids of the body; critical to the maintenance of fluid balance, nerve impulse transmissions, and muscle contractions.

salt sensitivity: a characteristic of individuals who respond to a high salt intake with an increase in blood pressure or to a low salt intake with a decrease in blood pressure.

* One of the ways the kidneys regulate acid-base balance is by excreting hydrogen ions (H^+) in exchange for sodium ions (Na^+).
** Compared with others, salt-sensitive individuals have elevated concentrations of renin in their blood.

Dietary Guidelines for Americans 2005

Consume less than 2300 mg (approximately 1 tsp of salt) of sodium per day.

◆ Salt (sodium chloride) is about 40% sodium.
1 g salt contributes 400 mg sodium
5 g salt = 1 tsp
1 tsp salt contributes 2000 mg sodium

of hypertension and heart disease, the 2005 *Dietary Guidelines* advise limiting daily *salt* intake to about 1 teaspoon ◆ (the equivalent of 2.3 grams or 2300 milligrams of *sodium*). Higher intakes seem to be well tolerated in most healthy people, however. The accompanying "How to" offers strategies for cutting salt (and therefore sodium) intake.

One diet plan, known as the DASH (Dietary Approaches to Stop Hypertension) diet, also lowers blood pressure. The DASH approach emphasizes fruits, vegetables, and low-fat milk products; includes whole grains, nuts, poultry, and fish; and calls for reduced intakes of red meat, butter, and other high-fat foods. The DASH diet in combination with a reduced sodium intake is even more effective in lowering blood pressure than either strategy alone. Chapter 18 offers a complete discussion of hypertension and the dietary recommendations for its prevention and treatment.

Sodium and Bone Loss (Osteoporosis) A high salt intake is also associated with increased calcium excretion, but its influence on bone loss is less clear.[9] In addition, potassium may prevent the increase in calcium excretion caused by a high-salt diet.[10] For these reasons, dietary advice to prevent bone loss parallel those suggested for hypertension—a DASH diet that is low in sodium and abundant in potassium-rich fruits and vegetables and calcium-rich low-fat milk products.[11]

Sodium in Foods In general, processed foods have the most sodium, whereas unprocessed foods such as fresh fruits, vegetables, milk, and meats have the least. In fact, as much as 75 percent of the sodium in people's diets comes from salt added to foods by manufacturers; about 15 percent comes from salt added during cooking and at the table; and only 10 percent comes from the natural content in foods.

HOW TO Cut Salt (and Sodium) Intake

Most people eat more salt (and therefore sodium) than they need. Some people can lower their blood pressure by avoiding highly salted foods and removing the saltshaker from the table. Foods eaten without salt may seem less tasty at first, but with repetition, people can learn to enjoy the natural flavors of many unsalted foods. Strategies to cut salt intake include:

- Select fresh, unprocessed foods.
- Cook with little or no added salt.
- Prepare foods with sodium-free spices such as basil, bay leaves, curry, garlic, ginger, mint, oregano, pepper, rosemary, and thyme; lemon juice; vinegar; or wine.
- Add little or no salt at the table; taste foods before adding salt.
- Read labels with an eye open for sodium. (See the glossary on p. 58 for terms used to describe the sodium contents of foods on labels.)

- Select low-salt or salt-free products when available.

Use these foods sparingly:

- Foods prepared in brine, such as pickles, olives, and sauerkraut
- Salty or smoked meats, such as bologna, corned or chipped beef, bacon, frankfurters, ham, lunch meats, salt pork, sausage, and smoked tongue
- Salty or smoked fish, such as anchovies, caviar, salted and dried cod, herring, sardines, and smoked salmon
- Snack items such as potato chips, pretzels, salted popcorn, salted nuts, and crackers
- Condiments such as bouillon cubes; seasoned salts; MSG; soy, teriyaki, Worcestershire, and barbeque sauces; prepared horseradish, catsup, and mustard
- Cheeses, especially processed types
- Canned and instant soups

Fresh herbs add flavor to a recipe without adding salt.

© BSIP Agency/Index Stack Imagery

Because processed foods may contain sodium without chloride, as in additives such as sodium bicarbonate or sodium saccharin, they do not always taste salty. Most people are surprised to learn that 1 ounce of cornflakes contains more sodium than 1 ounce of salted peanuts—and that $1/2$ cup of instant chocolate pudding contains still more. (The peanuts taste saltier because the salt is all on the surface, where the tongue's sensors immediately pick it up.)

Figure 12-10 shows that processed foods not only contain more sodium than their less processed counterparts but also have less potassium. Low potassium may be as significant as high sodium when it comes to blood pressure regulation, so processed foods have two strikes against them.

Dietary Guidelines for Americans 2005

Choose and prepare foods with little salt. At the same time, consume potassium-rich foods, such as fruits and vegetables.

Sodium Deficiency If blood sodium drops, as may occur with vomiting, diarrhea, or heavy sweating, both sodium and water must be replenished. Under normal conditions of sweating due to physical activity, salt losses can easily be replaced later in the day with ordinary foods. Salt tablets are not recommended because too much salt, especially if taken with too little water, can induce dehydration. During intense activities, such as ultra-endurance events, athletes can lose so much sodium and drink so much water that they develop hyponatremia—the dangerous condition of having too little sodium in the blood. Chapter 14 offers details about hyponatremia and guidelines for ultra-endurance athletes.

FIGURE 12-10 What Processing Does to the Sodium and Potassium Contents of Foods

People who eat foods high in salt often happen to be eating fewer potassium-containing foods at the same time. Notice how potassium is lost and sodium is gained as foods become more processed, causing the potassium-to-sodium ratio to fall dramatically. Even when potassium isn't lost, the addition of sodium still lowers the potassium-to-sodium ratio. Limiting sodium intake may help in two ways, then—by lowering blood pressure in salt-sensitive individuals and by indirectly raising potassium intakes in all individuals.

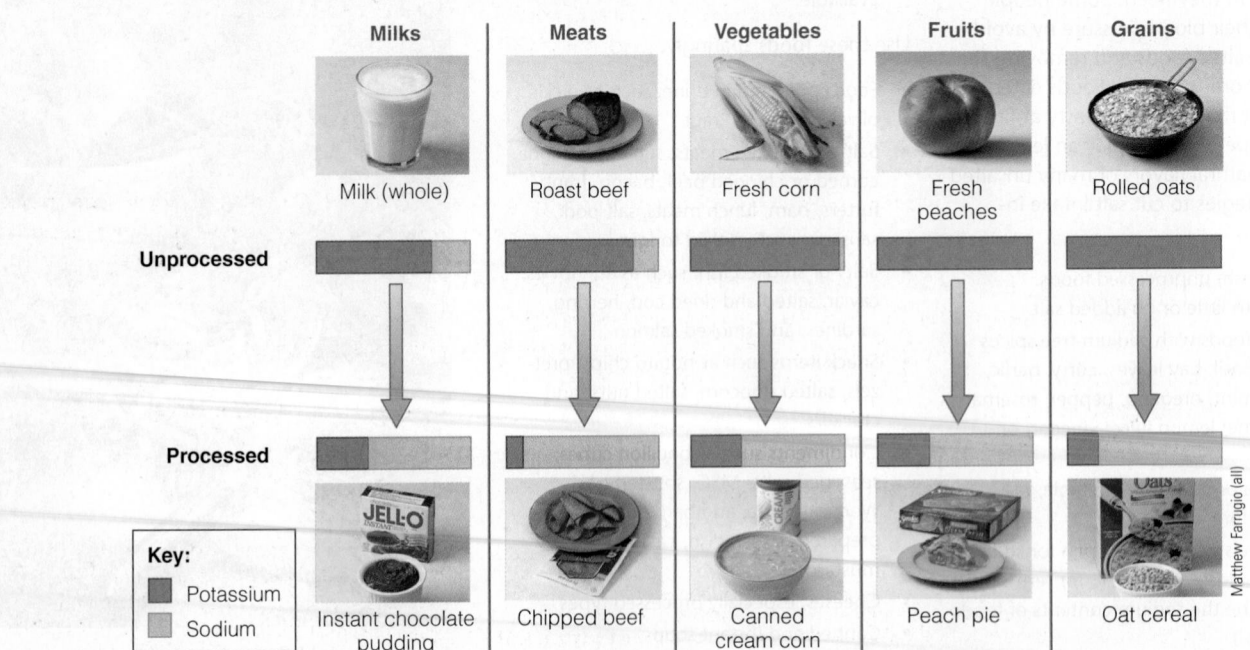

Key:
Potassium
Sodium

Sodium Toxicity and Excessive Intakes The immediate symptoms of acute sodium toxicity are edema and hypertension, but such toxicity poses no problem as long as water needs are met. Prolonged excessive sodium intake ◆ may contribute to hypertension in some people, as explained earlier.

◆ UL for sodium: 2300 mg/day

IN SUMMARY

Sodium is the main cation outside cells and one of the primary electrolytes responsible for maintaining fluid balance. Dietary deficiency is rare, and excesses may aggravate hypertension in some people. For this reason, health professionals advise a diet moderate in salt and sodium. The accompanying table summarizes information about sodium.

Sodium

Adequate Intake (AI)	Deficiency Symptoms
Adults: 1500 mg/day (19–50 yr) 1300 mg/day (51–70 yr) 1200 mg/day (>70 yr)	Muscle cramps, mental apathy, loss of appetite
Upper Level	**Toxicity Symptoms**
Adults: 2300 mg/day	Edema, acute hypertension
Chief Functions in the Body	**Significant Sources**
Maintains normal fluid and electrolyte balance; assists in nerve impulse transmission and muscle contraction	Table salt, soy sauce; moderate amounts in meats, milks, breads, and vegetables; large amounts in processed foods

Chloride

The element *chlorine* (Cl_2) is a poisonous gas. When chlorine reacts with sodium or hydrogen, however, it forms the negative chloride ion (Cl^-). *Chloride*, an essential nutrient, is required in the diet.

Chloride Roles in the Body **Chloride** is the major anion of the extracellular fluids (outside the cells), where it occurs mostly in association with sodium. Chloride moves passively across membranes through channels and so also associates with potassium inside cells. Like sodium and potassium, chloride maintains fluid and electrolyte balance.

In the stomach, the chloride ion is part of hydrochloric acid, which maintains the strong acidity of the gastric juice. One of the most serious consequences of vomiting is the loss of this acid ◆ from the stomach, which upsets the acid-base balance.* Such imbalances are commonly seen in bulimia nervosa, as described in Highlight 8.

◆ Reminder: The loss of acid can lead to *alkalosis*, an above-normal alkalinity in the blood and body fluids.

Chloride Recommendations and Intakes Chloride is abundant in foods (especially processed foods) as part of sodium chloride and other salts. Because the proportion of chloride in salt is greater than sodium, ◆ chloride recommendations are slightly higher than, but still equivalent to, those of sodium. In other words, $3/4$ teaspoon of salt will deliver some sodium, more chloride, and still meet the AI for both.

◆ Salt (sodium chloride) is about 60% chloride.
1 g salt contributes 600 mg chloride
5 g salt = 1 tsp
1 tsp salt contributes 3000 mg chloride

Chloride Deficiency and Toxicity Diets rarely lack chloride. Chloride losses may occur in conditions such as heavy sweating, chronic diarrhea, and vomiting. The only known cause of high blood chloride concentrations is dehydration due to

chloride (KLO-ride): the major anion in the extracellular fluids of the body. Chloride is the ionic form of chlorine, Cl^-. See Appendix B for a description of the chlorine-to-chloride conversion.

---

* Hydrochloric acid secretion into the stomach involves the addition of bicarbonate ions (base) to the plasma. These bicarbonate ions (HCO_3^-) are neutralized by hydrogen ions (H^+) from the gastric secretions that are reabsorbed into the plasma. When hydrochloric acid is lost during vomiting, these hydrogen ions are no longer available for reabsorption, and so, in effect, the concentrations of bicarbonate ions in the plasma are increased. In this way, excessive vomiting of acidic gastric juices leads to *metabolic alkalosis*.

water deficiency. In both cases, consuming ordinary foods and beverages can restore chloride balance.

IN SUMMARY

Chloride is the major anion outside cells, and it associates closely with sodium. In addition to its role in fluid balance, chloride is part of the stomach's hydrochloric acid. The accompanying table summarizes information on chloride.

Chloride

Adequate Intake (AI)	Deficiency Symptoms
Adults: 2300 mg/day (19–50 yr)	Do not occur under normal circumstances
2000 mg/day (51—70 yr)	
1800 mg/day (>70 yr)	**Toxicity Symptoms**
	Vomiting
Upper Level	
Adults: 3600 mg/day	**Significant Sources**
	Table salt, soy sauce; moderate amounts in
Chief Functions in the Body	meats, milks, eggs; large amounts in processed foods
Maintains normal fluid and electrolyte balance; part of hydrochloric acid found in the stomach, necessary for proper digestion	

Potassium

Like sodium, **potassium** is a positively charged ion. In contrast to sodium, potassium is the body's principal intracellular cation, *inside* the body cells.

Potassium Roles in the Body Potassium plays a major role in maintaining fluid and electrolyte balance and cell integrity. During nerve impulse transmission and muscle contraction, potassium and sodium briefly trade places across the cell membrane. The cell then quickly pumps them back into place. Controlling potassium distribution is a high priority for the body because it affects many aspects of homeostasis, including a steady heartbeat.

Potassium Recommendations and Intakes Potassium is abundant in all living cells, both plant and animal. Because cells remain intact unless foods are processed, the richest sources of potassium are *fresh* foods—as Figure 12-11 (p. 415) shows. In contrast, most processed foods such as canned vegetables, ready-to-eat cereals, and luncheon meats contain less potassium—and more sodium (recall Figure 12-10, p. 412). To meet the AI for potassium, most people need to increase their intake of fruits and vegetables to five to nine servings daily.

Potassium and Hypertension Diets low in potassium seem to play an important role in the development of high blood pressure. Low potassium intakes raise blood pressure, whereas high potassium intakes, especially when combined with low sodium intakes, appear to both prevent and correct hypertension.[12] ◆ Potassium-rich fruits and vegetables also appear to reduce the risk of stroke—more so than can be explained by the reduction in blood pressure alone.

Potassium Deficiency Potassium deficiency is characterized by an increase in blood pressure, salt sensitivity, kidney stones, and bone turnover. As deficiency progresses, symptoms include irregular heartbeats, muscle weakness, and glucose intolerance.

Potassium Toxicity Potassium toxicity does not result from overeating foods high in potassium; therefore an Upper Level was not set. It can result from overconsumption of potassium salts or supplements (including some "energy fitness shakes") and from certain diseases or treatments. Given more potassium than the body needs, the

◆ Reminder: The DASH diet, used to lower blood pressure, emphasizes potassium-rich foods such as fruits and vegetables.

potassium: the principal cation within the body's cells; critical to the maintenance of fluid balance, nerve impulse transmissions, and muscle contractions.

FIGURE 12-11 Potassium in Selected Foods

See the "How to" on p. 329 for more information on using this figure.

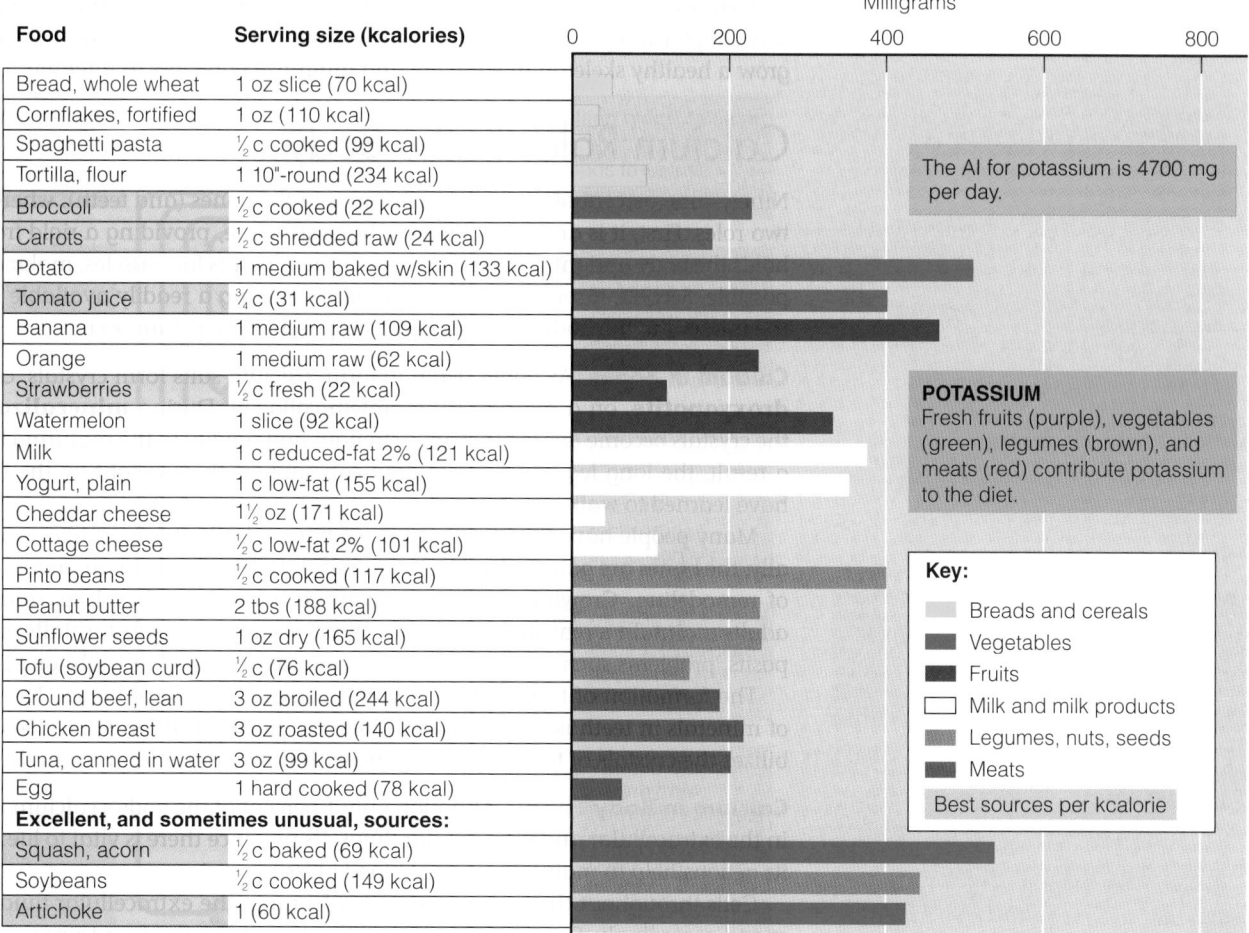

The AI for potassium is 4700 mg per day.

POTASSIUM
Fresh fruits (purple), vegetables (green), legumes (brown), and meats (red) contribute potassium to the diet.

Key:
- Breads and cereals
- Vegetables
- Fruits
- Milk and milk products
- Legumes, nuts, seeds
- Meats
- Best sources per kcalorie

Food	Serving size (kcalories)
Bread, whole wheat	1 oz slice (70 kcal)
Cornflakes, fortified	1 oz (110 kcal)
Spaghetti pasta	½ c cooked (99 kcal)
Tortilla, flour	1 10"-round (234 kcal)
Broccoli	½ c cooked (22 kcal)
Carrots	½ c shredded raw (24 kcal)
Potato	1 medium baked w/skin (133 kcal)
Tomato juice	¾ c (31 kcal)
Banana	1 medium raw (109 kcal)
Orange	1 medium raw (62 kcal)
Strawberries	½ c fresh (22 kcal)
Watermelon	1 slice (92 kcal)
Milk	1 c reduced-fat 2% (121 kcal)
Yogurt, plain	1 c low-fat (155 kcal)
Cheddar cheese	1½ oz (171 kcal)
Cottage cheese	½ c low-fat 2% (101 kcal)
Pinto beans	½ c cooked (117 kcal)
Peanut butter	2 tbs (188 kcal)
Sunflower seeds	1 oz dry (165 kcal)
Tofu (soybean curd)	½ c (76 kcal)
Ground beef, lean	3 oz broiled (244 kcal)
Chicken breast	3 oz roasted (140 kcal)
Tuna, canned in water	3 oz (99 kcal)
Egg	1 hard cooked (78 kcal)
Excellent, and sometimes unusual, sources:	
Squash, acorn	½ c baked (69 kcal)
Soybeans	½ c cooked (149 kcal)
Artichoke	1 (60 kcal)

kidneys accelerate their excretion. If the GI tract is bypassed, however, and potassium is injected directly into a vein, it can stop the heart.

IN SUMMARY

Potassium, like sodium and chloride, is an electrolyte that plays an important role in maintaining fluid balance. Potassium is the primary cation inside cells; fresh foods, notably fruits and vegetables, are its best sources. The table below summarizes facts about potassium.

Potassium

Adequate Intake (AI)

Adults: 4700 mg/day

Chief Functions in the Body

Maintains normal fluid and electrolyte balance; facilitates many reactions; supports cell integrity; assists in nerve impulse transmission and muscle contractions

Deficiency Symptoms[a]

Irregular heartbeat, muscular weakness, glucose intolerance

Toxicity Symptoms

Muscular weakness; vomiting; if given into a vein, can stop the heart

Significant Sources

All whole foods: meats, milks, fruits, vegetables, grains, legumes

[a]Deficiency accompanies dehydration.

Fresh foods, especially fruits and vegetables, provide potassium in abundance.

FIGURE 12-15 Bioavailability of Calcium from Selected Foods

≥50% absorbed	Cauliflower, watercress, brussels sprouts, rutabaga, kale, mustard greens, bok choy, broccoli, turnip greens
≈30% absorbed	Milk, calcium-fortified soy milk, calcium-set tofu, cheese, yogurt, calcium-fortified foods and beverages
≈20% absorbed	Almonds, sesame seeds, pinto beans, sweet potatoes
≤5% absorbed	Spinach, rhubarb, Swiss chard

ThomsonNOW

To practice estimating calcium intake, log on to www.thomsonedu.com/login, go to Chapter 12, then go to How To.

Milk and milk products are notorious for their calcium, but calcium-set tofu, bok choy, kale, calcium-fortified orange juice, and broccoli are also rich in calcium.

With the exception of foods such as spinach that contain calcium binders, however, the calcium content of foods is usually more important than bioavailability. Consequently, recognizing that people eat a variety of foods containing calcium, the DRI Committee did not consider calcium bioavailability when setting recommendations. Figure 12-15 ranks selected foods according to their calcium bioavailability.

Oysters are also a rich source of calcium, as are small fish eaten with their bones, such as canned sardines. Many Asians prepare a stock from bones that helps account for their adequate calcium intake without the use of milk. They soak the cracked bones from chicken, turkey, pork, or fish in vinegar and then slowly boil the bones until they become soft. The bones release calcium into the acidic broth, and most of the vinegar boils off. Cooks then use the stock, which contains more than 100 milligrams of calcium per tablespoon, in place of water to prepare soups, vegetables, and rice. Similarly, cooks in the Navajo tribe use an ash prepared from the branches and needles of the juniper tree in their recipes. One teaspoon of juniper ash provides about as much calcium as a cup of milk.

Some mineral waters provide as much as 500 milligrams of calcium per liter, offering a convenient way to meet both calcium and water needs.[24] Similarly, calcium-fortified orange juice and other fruit and vegetable juices allow a person to obtain both calcium and vitamins easily. Other examples of calcium-fortified foods include high-calcium milk (milk with extra calcium added) and calcium-fortified cereals. Fortified juices and foods help consumers increase calcium intakes, but depending on the calcium sources, the bioavailability may be significantly less than quantities listed on food labels.[25] The "How to" below describes a shortcut method for estimating your calcium intake. Highlight 12 discusses calcium supplements.

HOW TO Estimate Your Calcium Intake

Most dietitians have developed useful shortcuts to help them estimate nutrient intakes and "see" inadequacies in the diet. They can tell at a glance whether a day's meals fall short of calcium recommendations, for example.

To estimate calcium intakes, keep two bits of information in mind:

- A cup of milk provides about 300 milligrams of calcium.
- Adults need between 1000 and 1200 milligrams of calcium per day, which represents 3 to 4 cups of milk—or the equivalent:

$$1000 \text{ mg} \div 300 \text{ mg/c} = 3\frac{1}{3} \text{ c}$$
$$1200 \text{ mg} \div 300 \text{ mg/c} = 4 \text{ c}$$

If a person drinks 3 to 4 cups of milk a day, it's easy to see that calcium needs are being met. If not, it takes some detective work to identify the other sources and estimate total calcium intake.

To estimate a person's daily calcium intake, use this shortcut, which compares the calcium in calcium-rich foods to the calcium content of milk. The calcium in a cup of milk is assigned 1 point, and the goal is to attain 3 to 4 points per day. Foods are given points as follows:

- 1 c milk, yogurt, or fortified soy milk or 1½ oz cheese = 1 point

- 4 oz canned fish with bones (sardines) = 1 point
- 1 c ice cream, cottage cheese, or calcium-rich vegetable (see the text) = ½ point

Then, because other foods also contribute small amounts of calcium, together they are given a point.

- Well-balanced diet containing a variety of foods = 1 point

Now consider a day's meals with calcium in mind. Cereal with 1 cup of milk for breakfast (1 point for milk), a ham and cheese sub sandwich for lunch (1 point for cheese), and a cup of broccoli and lasagna for dinner (½ point for calcium-rich vegetable and 1 point for cheese in lasagna)—plus 1 point for all other foods eaten that day—adds up to 4½ points. This shortcut estimate indicates that calcium recommendations have been met, and a diet analysis of these few foods reveals a calcium intake of over 1000 milligrams. By knowing the best sources of each nutrient, you can learn to scan the day's meals and quickly see if you are meeting your daily goals.

A generalization that has been gaining strength throughout this book is supported by the information given here about calcium. A balanced diet that supplies a variety of foods is the best plan to ensure adequacy for all essential nutrients. All food groups should be included, and none should be overemphasized. In our culture, calcium intake is usually inadequate wherever milk is lacking in the diet—whether through ignorance, poverty, simple dislike, fad dieting, lactose intolerance, or allergy. By contrast, iron is usually lacking whenever milk is overemphasized, as Chapter 13 explains.

Calcium Deficiency

A low calcium intake during the growing years limits the bones' ability to reach their optimal mass and density. Most people achieve a peak bone mass by their late 20s, and dense bones best protect against age-related bone loss and fractures (see Figure 12-16). All adults lose bone as they grow older, beginning between the ages of 30 and 40. When bone losses reach the point of causing fractures under common, everyday stresses, the condition is known as **osteoporosis.** Osteoporosis affects more than 44 million people in the United States, mostly older women.

Unlike many diseases that make themselves known through symptoms such as pain, shortness of breath, skin lesions, tiredness, and the like, osteoporosis is silent. The body sends no signals saying bones are losing their calcium and, as a result, their integrity. Blood samples offer no clues because blood calcium remains normal regardless of bone content, and measures of bone density are not routinely taken. Highlight 12 suggests strategies to protect against bone loss, of which eating calcium-rich foods is only one.

FIGURE 12-16 **Phases of Bone Development throughout Life**

The active growth phase occurs from birth to approximately age 20. The next phase of peak bone mass development occurs between the ages of 12 and 30. The final phase, when bone resorption exceeds formation, begins between the ages of 30 and 40 and continues through the remainder of life.

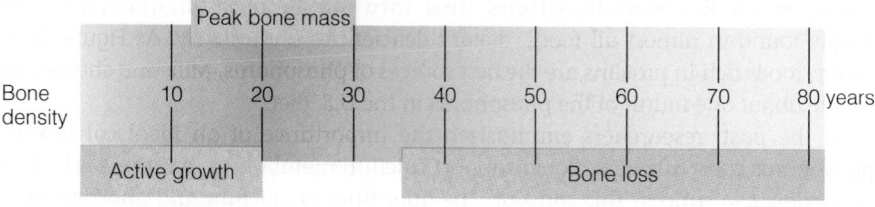

IN SUMMARY

Most of the body's calcium is in the bones where it provides a rigid structure and a reservoir of calcium for the blood. Blood calcium participates in muscle contraction, blood clotting, and nerve impulses, and it is closely regulated by a system of hormones and vitamin D. Calcium is found predominantly in milk and milk products, but some other foods including certain vegetables and tofu also provide calcium. Even when calcium intake is inadequate, blood calcium remains normal, but at the expense of bone loss, which can lead to osteoporosis. Calcium's roles, deficiency symptoms, and food sources are summarized on the next page.

(continued)

osteoporosis (OS-tee-oh-pore-OH-sis): a disease in which the bones become porous and fragile due to a loss of minerals; also called **adult bone loss.**
• **osteo** = bone
• **porosis** = porous

Calcium (continued)

Adequate Intake (AI)

Adults: 1000 mg/day (19–50 yr)
1200 mg/day (>51 yr)

Upper Level

Adults: 2500 mg/day

Chief Functions in the Body

Mineralization of bones and teeth; also involved in muscle contraction and relaxation, nerve functioning, blood clotting, blood pressure

Deficiency Symptoms

Stunted growth in children; bone loss (osteoporosis) in adults

Toxicity Symptoms

Constipation; increased risk of urinary stone formation and kidney dysfunction; interference with absorption of other minerals

Significant Sources

Milk and milk products, small fish (with bones), calcium-set tofu, greens (bok choy, broccoli, chard, kale), legumes

Phosphorus

Phosphorus is the second most abundant mineral in the body. About 85 percent of it is found combined with calcium in the hydroxyapatite crystals of bones and teeth.

Phosphorus Roles in the Body Phosphorus salts (phosphates) are found not only in bones and teeth, but in all body cells as part of a major buffer system (phosphoric acid and its salts). Phosphorus is also part of DNA and RNA and is therefore necessary for all growth.

Phosphorus assists in energy metabolism. Many enzymes and the B vitamins become active only when a phosphate group is attached. ATP itself, the energy currency of the cells, uses three phosphate groups to do its work.

Lipids containing phosphorus as part of their structures (phospholipids) help to transport other lipids in the blood. Phospholipids are also the major structural components of cell membranes, where they control the transport of nutrients into and out of the cells. Some proteins, such as the casein in milk, contain phosphorus as part of their structures (phosphoproteins).

Phosphorus Recommendations and Intakes Because phosphorus is commonly found in almost all foods, dietary deficiencies are unlikely. As Figure 12-17 shows, foods rich in proteins are the best sources of phosphorus. Milk and cheese contribute about one-fourth of the phosphorus in the U.S. diet.

In the past, researchers emphasized the importance of an ideal calcium-to-phosphorus ratio from the diet to support calcium metabolism, but there is little or no evidence to support this concept. The quantities of calcium and phosphorus in the diet are far more important than their ratio to each other. A high phosphorus intake has been blamed for bone loss when, in fact, a low calcium intake—not a phosphorus toxicity or an improper ratio—is responsible. Research shows that the displacement of milk in the diet by cola drinks, not the phosphoric acid content of the beverages, has adverse effects on bone. No adverse effects of high dietary phosphorus intakes have been reported; still, an Upper Level has been established (see inside front cover).

IN SUMMARY

Phosphorus accompanies calcium both in the crystals of bone and in many foods such as milk. Phosphorus is also important in energy metabolism, as part of phospholipids, and as part of the genetic materials DNA and RNA. The summary table on the next page lists functions of, and other information about, phosphorus.

(continued)

phosphorus: a major mineral found mostly in the body's bones and teeth.

FIGURE 12-17 Phosphorus in Selected Foods

See the "How to" on p. 329 for more information on using this figure.

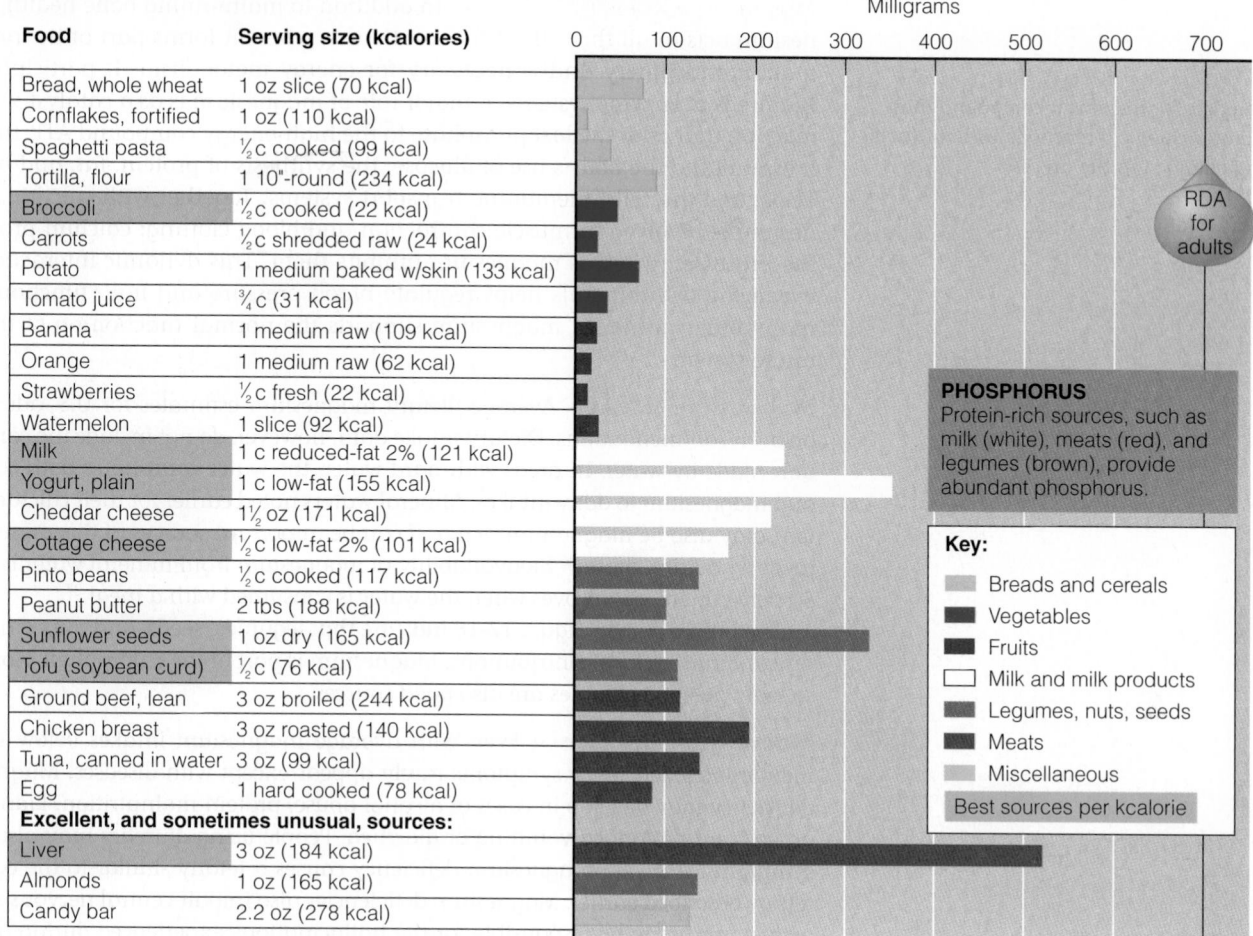

Food	Serving size (kcalories)
Bread, whole wheat	1 oz slice (70 kcal)
Cornflakes, fortified	1 oz (110 kcal)
Spaghetti pasta	½ c cooked (99 kcal)
Tortilla, flour	1 10"-round (234 kcal)
Broccoli	½ c cooked (22 kcal)
Carrots	½ c shredded raw (24 kcal)
Potato	1 medium baked w/skin (133 kcal)
Tomato juice	¾ c (31 kcal)
Banana	1 medium raw (109 kcal)
Orange	1 medium raw (62 kcal)
Strawberries	½ c fresh (22 kcal)
Watermelon	1 slice (92 kcal)
Milk	1 c reduced-fat 2% (121 kcal)
Yogurt, plain	1 c low-fat (155 kcal)
Cheddar cheese	1½ oz (171 kcal)
Cottage cheese	½ c low-fat 2% (101 kcal)
Pinto beans	½ c cooked (117 kcal)
Peanut butter	2 tbs (188 kcal)
Sunflower seeds	1 oz dry (165 kcal)
Tofu (soybean curd)	½ c (76 kcal)
Ground beef, lean	3 oz broiled (244 kcal)
Chicken breast	3 oz roasted (140 kcal)
Tuna, canned in water	3 oz (99 kcal)
Egg	1 hard cooked (78 kcal)
Excellent, and sometimes unusual, sources:	
Liver	3 oz (184 kcal)
Almonds	1 oz (165 kcal)
Candy bar	2.2 oz (278 kcal)

PHOSPHORUS
Protein-rich sources, such as milk (white), meats (red), and legumes (brown), provide abundant phosphorus.

Key:
- Breads and cereals
- Vegetables
- Fruits
- Milk and milk products
- Legumes, nuts, seeds
- Meats
- Miscellaneous
- Best sources per kcalorie

RDA for adults

Phosphorus

RDA

Adults: 700 mg/day

Upper Level

Adults (19–70 yr): 4000 mg/day

Chief Functions in the Body

Mineralization of bones and teeth; part of every cell; important in genetic material, part of phospholipids, used in energy transfer and in buffer systems that maintain acid-base balance

Deficiency Symptoms

Muscular weakness, bone pain[a]

Toxicity Symptoms

Calcification of nonskeletal tissues, particularly the kidneys

Significant Sources

All animal tissues (meat, fish, poultry, eggs, milk)

[a]Dietary deficiency rarely occurs, but some drugs can bind with phosphorus making it unavailable and resulting in bone loss that is characterized by weakness and pain.

Magnesium

Magnesium barely qualifies as a major mineral: only about 1 ounce of magnesium is present in the body of a 130-pound person. Over half of the body's magnesium is in the bones. Much of the rest is in the muscles and soft tissues, with only 1

magnesium: a cation within the body's cells, active in many enzyme systems.

percent in the extracellular fluid. As with calcium, bone magnesium may serve as a reservoir to ensure normal blood concentrations.

Magnesium Roles in the Body In addition to maintaining bone health, magnesium acts in all the cells of the soft tissues, where it forms part of the protein-making machinery and is necessary for energy metabolism. It participates in hundreds of enzyme systems. A major role of magnesium is as a catalyst ◆ in the reaction that adds the last phosphate to the high-energy compound ATP, making it essential to the body's use of glucose; the synthesis of protein, fat, and nucleic acids; and the cells' membrane transport systems. Together with calcium, magnesium is involved in muscle contraction and blood clotting: calcium promotes the processes, whereas magnesium inhibits them. This dynamic interaction between the two minerals helps regulate blood pressure and lung function. Like many other nutrients, magnesium supports the normal functioning of the immune system.

◆ Reminder: A *catalyst* is a compound that facilitates chemical reactions without itself being changed in the process.

Magnesium Intakes Average dietary magnesium estimates for U.S. adults fall below recommendations. Dietary intake data, however, do not include the contribution made by water. In areas with hard water, the water contributes both calcium and magnesium to daily intakes. Mineral waters noted earlier for their calcium content may also be magnesium-rich and can be important sources of this mineral for those who drink them.[26] Bioavailability of magnesium from mineral water is about 50 percent, but it improves when the water is consumed with a meal.[27]

The brown bars in Figure 12-18 indicate that legumes, seeds, and nuts make significant magnesium contributions. Magnesium is part of the chlorophyll molecule, so leafy green vegetables are also good sources.

Magnesium Deficiency Even with average magnesium intakes below recommendations, deficiency symptoms rarely appear except with diseases. Magnesium deficiency may develop in cases of alcohol abuse, protein malnutrition, kidney disorders, and prolonged vomiting or diarrhea. People using diuretics may also show symptoms. A severe magnesium deficiency causes a tetany similar to the calcium tetany described earlier. Magnesium deficiencies also impair central nervous system activity and may be responsible for the hallucinations experienced during alcohol withdrawal.

Magnesium and Hypertension Magnesium is critical to heart function and seems to protect against hypertension and heart disease.[28] Interestingly, people living in areas of the country with hard water, which contains high concentrations of calcium and magnesium, tend to have low rates of heart disease. With magnesium deficiency, the walls of the arteries and capillaries tend to constrict—a possible explanation for the hypertensive effect.

Magnesium Toxicity Magnesium toxicity is rare, but it can be fatal. The Upper Level for magnesium applies only to nonfood sources such as supplements or magnesium salts.

IN SUMMARY

Like calcium and phosphorus, magnesium supports bone mineralization. Magnesium is also involved in numerous enzyme systems and in heart function. It is found abundantly in legumes and leafy green vegetables and, in some areas, in water. The table below offers a summary.

Magnesium

RDA	Upper Level
Men (19–30 yr): 400 mg/day	Adults: 350 mg nonfood magnesium/day
Women (19–30 yr): 310 mg/day	

(continued)

FIGURE 12-18 Magnesium in Selected Foods

See the "How to" on p. 329 for more information on using this figure.

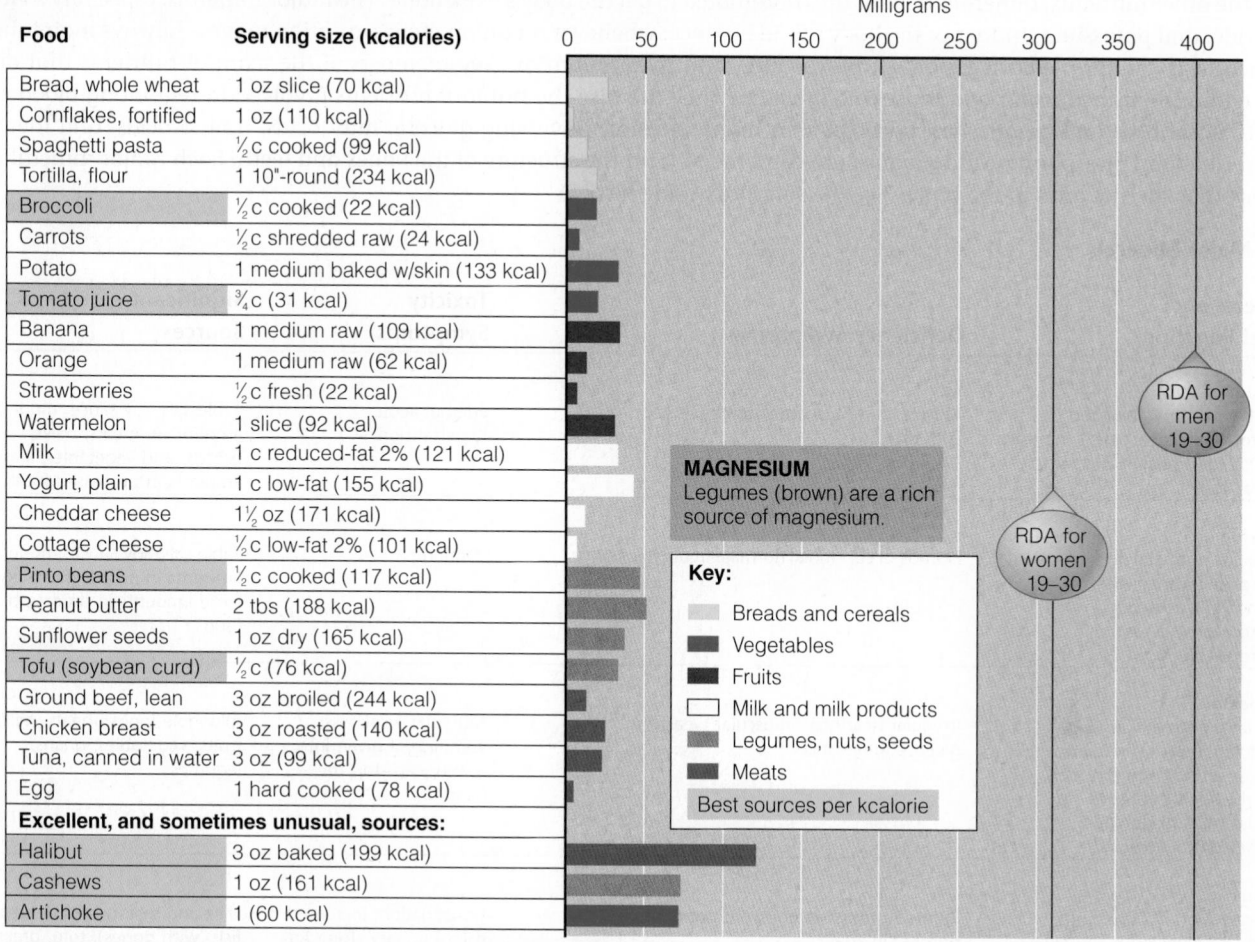

MAGNESIUM
Legumes (brown) are a rich source of magnesium.

Key:
- Breads and cereals
- Vegetables
- Fruits
- Milk and milk products
- Legumes, nuts, seeds
- Meats
- Best sources per kcalorie

Magnesium (continued)

Chief Functions in the Body

Bone mineralization, building of protein, enzyme action, normal muscle contraction, nerve impulse transmission, maintenance of teeth, and functioning of immune system

Deficiency Symptoms

Weakness; confusion; if extreme, convulsions, bizarre muscle movements (especially of eye and face muscles), hallucinations, and difficulty in swallowing; in children, growth failure[a]

Toxicity Symptoms

From nonfood sources only; diarrhea, alkalosis, dehydration

Significant Sources

Nuts, legumes, whole grains, dark green vegetables, seafood, chocolate, cocoa

[a]A still more severe deficiency causes tetany, an extreme, prolonged contraction of the muscles similar to that caused by low blood calcium.

Sulfate

Sulfate is the oxidized form of the mineral **sulfur,** as it exists in food and water. The body's need for sulfate is easily met by a variety of foods and beverages. In addition, the body receives sulfate from the amino acids methionine and cysteine found in dietary proteins. These sulfur-containing amino acids help determine the contour of protein molecules. The sulfur-containing side chains in cysteine molecules can link to each other, forming disulfide bridges, which stabilize the protein structure. (See the drawing of insulin with its disulfide bridges on p. 184.) Skin, hair, and nails contain some of the body's more rigid proteins, which have a high sulfur content.

Because the body's sulfate needs are easily met with normal protein intakes, there is no recommended intake for sulfate. Deficiencies do not occur when diets contain protein. Only when people lack protein to the point of severe deficiency will they lack the sulfur-containing amino acids.

sulfate: the oxidized form of sulfur.

sulfur: a mineral present in the body as part of some proteins.

IN SUMMARY

Like the other nutrients, minerals' actions are coordinated to get the body's work done. The major minerals, especially sodium, chloride, and potassium, influence the body's fluid balance; whenever an anion moves, a cation moves—always maintaining homeostasis. Sodium, chloride, potassium, calcium, and magnesium are key members of the team of nutrients that direct nerve impulse transmission and muscle contraction. They are also the primary nutrients involved in regulating blood pressure. Phosphorus and magnesium participate in many reactions involving glucose, fatty acids, amino acids, and the vitamins. Calcium, phosphorus, and magnesium combine to form the structure of the bones and teeth. Each major mineral also plays other specific roles in the body. (See the summary table below.)

The Major Minerals

Mineral and Chief Functions	Deficiency Symptoms	Toxicity Symptoms	Significant Sources
Sodium Maintains normal fluid and electrolyte balance; assists in nerve impulse transmission and muscle contraction	Muscle cramps, mental apathy, loss of appetite	Edema, acute hypertension	Table salt, soy sauce; moderate amounts in meats, milks, breads, and vegetables; large amounts in processed foods
Chloride Maintains normal fluid and electrolyte balance; part of hydrochloric acid found in the stomach, necessary for proper digestion	Do not occur under normal circumstances	Vomiting	Table salt, soy sauce; moderate amounts in meats, milks, eggs; large amounts in processed foods
Potassium Maintains normal fluid and electrolyte balance; facilitates many reactions; supports cell integrity; assists in nerve impulse transmission and muscle contractions	Irregular heartbeat, muscular weakness, glucose intolerance	Muscular weakness; vomiting; if given into a vein, can stop the heart	All whole foods; meats, milks, fruits, vegetables, grains, legumes
Calcium Mineralization of bones and teeth; also involved in muscle contraction and relaxation, nerve functioning, blood clotting, and blood pressure	Stunted growth in children; bone loss (osteoporosis) in adults	Constipation; increased risk of urinary stone formation and kidney dysfunction; interference with absorption of other minerals	Milk and milk products, small fish (with bones), tofu, greens (bok choy, broccoli, chard), legumes
Phosphorus Mineralization of bones and teeth; part of every cell; important in genetic material, part of phospholipids, used in energy transfer and in buffer systems that maintain acid-base balance	Muscular weakness, bone pain[a]	Calcification of nonskeletal tissues, particularly the kidneys	All animal tissues (meat, fish, poultry, eggs, milk)
Magnesium Bone mineralization, building of protein, enzyme action, normal muscle contraction, nerve impulse transmission, maintenance of teeth, and functioning of immune system	Weakness; confusion; if extreme, convulsions, bizarre muscle movements (especially of eye and face muscles), hallucinations, and difficulty in swallowing; in children, growth failure[b]	From nonfood sources only; diarrhea, alkalosis, dehydration	Nuts, legumes, whole grains, dark green vegetables, seafood, chocolate, cocoa
Sulfate As part of proteins, stabilizes their shape by forming disulfide bridges; part of the vitamins biotin and thiamin and the hormone insulin	None known; protein deficiency would occur first	Toxicity would occur only if sulfur-containing amino acids were eaten in excess; this (in animals) suppresses growth	All protein-containing foods (meats, fish, poultry, eggs, milk, legumes, nuts)

[a]Dietary deficiency rarely occurs, but some drugs can bind with phosphorus making it unavailable and resulting in bone loss that is characterized by weakness and pain.
[b]A still more severe deficiency causes tetany, an extreme, prolonged contraction of the muscles similar to that caused by low blood calcium.

With all of the tasks these minerals perform, they are of great importance to life. Consuming enough of each of them every day is easy, given a variety of foods from each of the food groups. Whole-grain breads supply magnesium; fruits, vegetables, and legumes provide magnesium and potassium, too; milks offer calcium and phosphorus; meats offer phosphorus and sulfate as well; all foods provide sodium and chloride, with excesses being more problematic than inadequacies. The message is quite simple and has been repeated throughout this text: for an adequate intake of all the nutrients, including the major minerals, choose different foods from each of the five food groups. And drink plenty of water.

Nutrition Portfolio

Thomson NOW
www.thomsonedu.com/thomsonnow

Many people may miss the mark when it comes to drinking enough water to keep their bodies well hydrated or obtaining enough calcium to promote strong bones; in contrast, sodium intakes often exceed those recommended for health.

- Describe your strategy for ensuring that you drink plenty of water—about 8 glasses—every day.

- Explain the importance of selecting and preparing foods with less salt.

- Determine whether you drink at least 3 glasses of milk—or get the equivalent in calcium—every day.

NUTRITION ON THE NET

Thomson NOW
For further study of topics covered in this chapter, log on to **www.thomsonedu .com/thomsonnow**. Go to Chapter 12, then to Nutrition on the Net.

- Search for "minerals" at the American Dietetic Association site: **www.eatright.org**

- Learn about sodium in foods and on food labels from the Food and Drug Administration: **www.fda.gov/fdac/ foodlabel/sodium.html**

- Find tips and recipes for including more milk in the diet: **www.whymilk.com**

- Learn about the benefits of calcium from the National Dairy Council: **www.nationaldairycouncil.org**

NUTRITION CALCULATIONS

Thomson NOW For additional practice log on to **www.thomsonedu.com/thomsonnow**. Go to Chapter 12, then to Nutrition Calculations.

These problems give you an appreciation for the minerals in foods. Be sure to show your calculations (see p. 430 for answers).

1. For each of these minerals, note the unit of measure:
   Calcium   Magnesium   Phosphorus
   Potassium   Sodium

2. Learn to appreciate calcium-dense foods. The foods in the accompanying table are ranked in order of their calcium contents per serving.
   a. Which foods offer the most calcium per kcalorie? To calculate calcium density, divide calcium (mg) by energy (kcal). Record your answer in the table (round your answers); the first one is done for you.

active, trabecular bone is sensitive to hormones that govern day-to-day deposits and withdrawals of calcium. It readily gives up minerals whenever blood calcium needs replenishing. Losses of trabecular bone start becoming significant for men and women in their 30s, although losses can occur whenever calcium withdrawals exceed deposits.

Cortical bone also gives up calcium, but slowly and at a steady pace. Cortical bone losses typically begin at about age 40 and continue slowly but surely thereafter.

Losses of trabecular and cortical bone reflect two types of osteoporosis, which cause two types of bone breaks. **Type I osteoporosis** involves losses of trabecular bone (see Figure H12-1). These losses sometimes exceed three times the expected rate, and bone breaks may occur suddenly. Trabecular bone becomes so fragile that even the body's own weight can overburden the spine—vertebrae may suddenly disintegrate and crush down, painfully pinching major nerves. Wrists may break as bone ends weaken, and teeth may loosen or fall out as the trabecular bone of the jaw recedes. Women are most often the victims of this type of osteoporosis, outnumbering men six to one.

In **type II osteoporosis,** the calcium of both cortical and trabecular bone is drawn out of storage, but slowly over the years. As old age approaches, the vertebrae may compress into wedge shapes, forming what is often called a "dowager's hump," the posture many older people assume as they "grow shorter." Figure H12-2 (p. 433) shows the effect of compressed spinal bone on a woman's height and posture. Because both the cortical shell and the trabecular interior weaken, breaks most often occur in the hip, as mentioned in the introductory paragraph. A woman is twice as likely as a man to suffer type II osteoporosis.

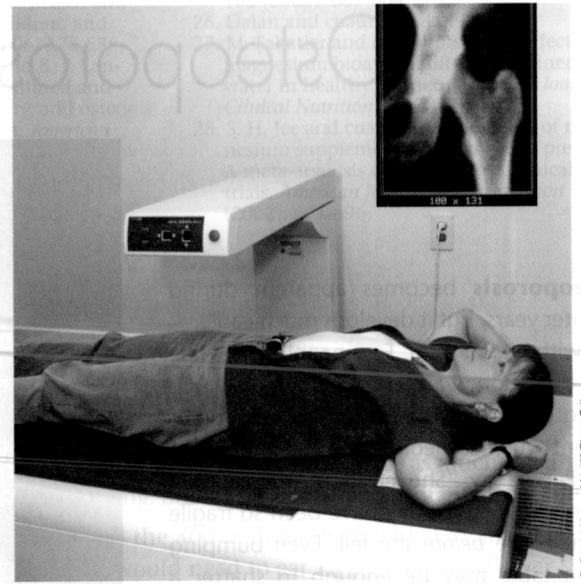

Using a DEXA (dual-energy X-ray absorpiometry) scan to measure bone mineral density identifies osteoporosis, determines risks for fractures, and tracks responses to treatment.

Table H12-1 summarizes the differences between the two types of osteoporosis. Physicians can diagnose osteoporosis and assess the risk of bone fractures by measuring **bone density** using dual-energy X-ray absorptiometry (DEXA scan) or ultrasound. They also consider risk factors that predict bone fractures, including age, personal and family history of fracture, BMI, and physical inactivity.[2] Table H12-2 summarizes the major risk factors and protective factors for osteo-

---

FIGURE H12-1 | Healthy and Osteoporotic Trabecular Bones

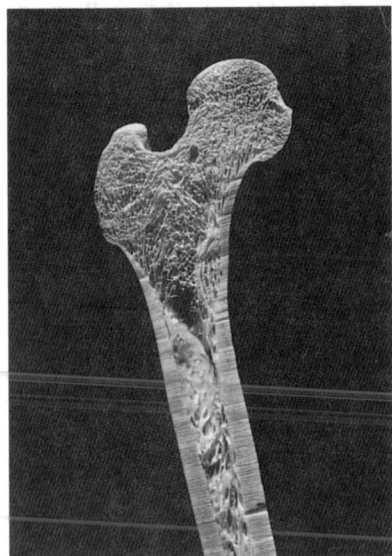

Trabecular bone is the lacy network of calcium-containing crystals that fills the interior. Cortical bone is the dense, ivorylike bone that forms the exterior shell.

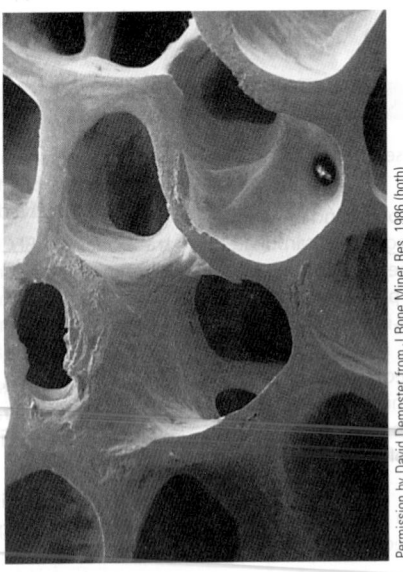

Electron micrograph of healthy trabecular bone.

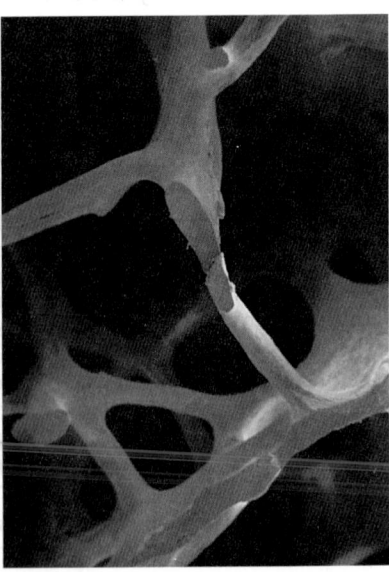

Electron micrograph of trabecular bone affected by osteoporosis.

FIGURE H12-2 Loss of Height in a Woman Caused by Osteoporosis

The woman on the left is about 50 years old. On the right, she is 80 years old. Her legs have not grown shorter. Instead, her back has lost length due to collapse of her spinal bones (vertebrae). Collapsed vertebrae cannot protect the spinal nerves from pressure that causes excruciating pain.

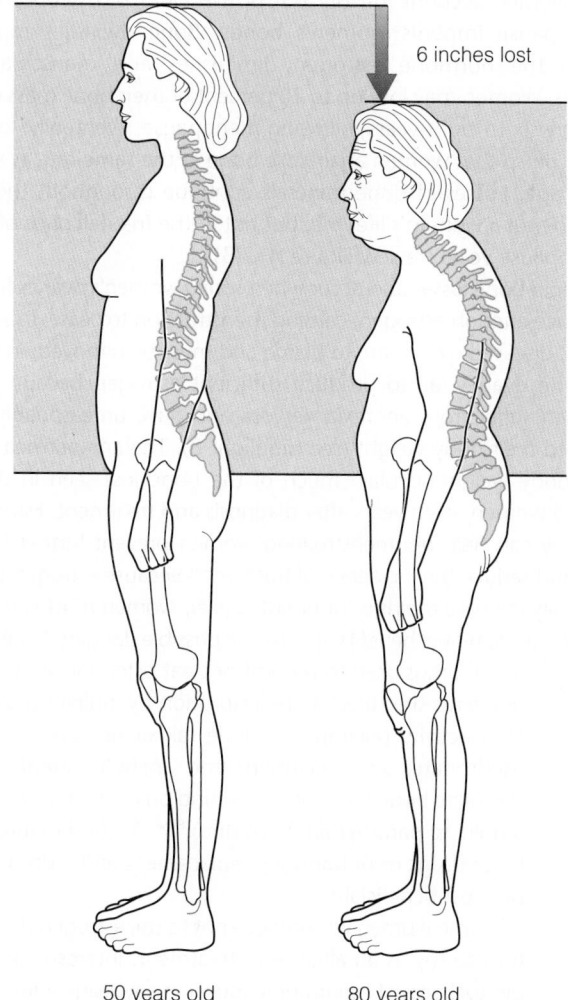

6 inches lost

50 years old   80 years old

porosis. The more risk factors that apply to a person, the greater the chances of bone loss. Notice that several risk factors that are influential in the development of osteoporosis—such as age, gender, and genetics—cannot be changed. Other risk factors—such as diet, physical activity, body weight, smoking, and alcohol use—are personal behaviors that can be changed. By eating a calcium-rich, well-balanced diet, being physically active, abstaining from smoking, and drinking alcohol in moderation (if at all), people can defend themselves against osteoporosis. These decisions are particularly important for those with other risk factors that cannot be changed.

Whether a person develops osteoporosis seems to depend on the interactions of several factors, including nutrition. The strongest predictor of bone density is age: osteoporosis is responsible for 90 percent of the hip fractures in women and 80 percent in men over the age of 65.

Age and Bone Calcium

Two major stages of life are critical in the development of osteoporosis. The first is the bone-acquiring stage of childhood and adolescence. The second is the bone-losing decades of late adulthood (especially in women after menopause). The bones gain strength and density all through the growing years and into young adulthood. As people age, the cells that build bone gradually become less active, but those that dismantle bone continue working. The result is that bone loss exceeds bone formation. Some bone loss is inevitable, but losses can be curtailed by maximizing bone mass.

TABLE H12-1 Types of Osteoporosis Compared

	Type I	Type II
Other name	Postmenopausal osteoporosis	Senile osteoporosis
Age of onset	50 to 70 years old	70 years and older
Bone loss	Trabecular bone	Both trabecular and cortical bone
Fracture sites	Wrist and spine	Hip
Gender incidence	6 women to 1 man	2 women to 1 man
Primary causes	Rapid loss of estrogen in women following menopause; loss of testosterone in men with advancing age	Reduced calcium absorption, increased bone mineral loss, increased propensity to fall

TABLE H12-2 Risk Factors and Protective Factors for Osteoporosis

Risk Factors	Protective Factors
• Older age	• Younger age
• Low BMI	• High BMI
• Caucasian, Asian, or Hispanic heritage	• African American heritage
• Cigarette smoking	• No smoking
• Alcohol consumption in excess	• Alcohol consumption in moderation
• Sedentary lifestyle	• Regular weight-bearing exercise
• Use of glucocorticoids or anticonvulsants	• Use of diuretics
• Female gender	• Male gender
• Maternal history of osteoporosis fracture or personal history of fracture	• Bone density assessment and treatment (if necessary)
• Estrogen deficiency in women (amenorrhea or menopause, especially early or surgically induced); testosterone deficiency in men	• Use of estrogen therapy
• Lifetime diet inadequate in calcium and vitamin D	• Lifetime diet rich in calcium and vitamin D

Maximizing Bone Mass

To maximize bone mass, the diet must deliver an adequate supply of calcium during the first three decades of life. Children and teens who get enough calcium and vitamin D have denser bones than those with inadequate intakes.[3] With little or no calcium from the diet, the body must depend on bone to supply calcium to the blood—bone mass diminishes, and bones lose their density and strength. When people reach the bone-losing years of middle age, those who formed dense bones during their youth have the advantage. They simply have more bone starting out and can lose more before suffering ill effects. Figure H12-3 demonstrates this effect.

Minimizing Bone Loss

Not only does dietary calcium build strong bones in youth, but it remains important in protecting against losses in the later years. Unfortunately, calcium intakes of older adults are typically low, and calcium absorption declines after menopause.[4] The kidneys do not activate vitamin D as well as they did earlier (recall that active vitamin D enhances calcium absorption). Also, sunlight is needed to form vitamin D, and many older people spend little or no time outdoors in the sunshine. For these reasons, and because intakes of vitamin D are typically low anyway, blood vitamin D declines.

Some of the hormones that regulate bone and calcium metabolism also change with age and accelerate bone mineral withdrawal.* Together, these age-related factors contribute to bone loss: inefficient bone remodeling, reduced calcium intakes, impaired calcium absorption, poor vitamin D status, and hormonal changes that favor bone mineral withdrawal.

Gender and Hormones

After age, gender is the next strongest predictor of osteoporosis. Men have greater bone density than women at maturity, and women have greater losses than men in later life. Consequently, men develop bone problems about 10 years later than women, and women account for four out of five cases of osteoporosis.[5] Menopause imperils women's bones. Bone dwindles rapidly when the hormone estrogen diminishes and menstruation ceases. Women may lose up to 20 percent of their bone mass during the six to eight years following menopause. Eventually, losses taper off so that women again lose bone at the same rate as men their age. Losses of bone minerals continue throughout the remainder of a woman's lifetime, but not at the free-fall pace of the menopause years (review Figure H12-3).

Rapid bone losses also occur when *young* women's ovaries fail to produce enough estrogen, causing menstruation to cease. In some cases, diseased ovaries are to blame and must be removed; in others, the ovaries fail to produce sufficient estrogen because the women suffer from anorexia nervosa and have unreasonably restricted their body weight (see Highlight 8). The amenorrhea and low body weights explain much of the bone loss seen in these young women, even years after diagnosis and treatment. Estrogen therapy can help nonmenstruating women prevent further bone loss and reduce the incidence of fractures.[6] Because estrogen therapy may increase the risks for breast cancer, women must carefully weigh any potential benefits against the possible dangers.[7] The two main classes of drugs used to prevent or treat osteoporosis are antiresorptive agents that block bone resorption by inhibiting osteoclast activity (examples include raloxifene, alendronate, risedronate, and calcitonin) and anabolic agents that stimulate bone formation by acting on osteoblasts (an example is parathyroid hormone).[8]** A combination of these drugs or of hormone replacement and a drug may be most beneficial.[9]

Some women who choose not to use estrogen therapy turn to soy as an alternative treatment. Interestingly, the phytochemicals commonly found in soybeans mimic the actions of estrogen in the body. When natural estrogen is lacking, as after menopause, these phytochemicals may step in to stimulate estrogen-sensitive tissues. By way of this action, soy and its phytochemicals may help to prevent the rapid bone losses of the menopause years.[10] Research is far from conclusive, but some evidence suggests that soy may indeed offer some protection.[11]

If estrogen deficiency is a major cause of osteoporosis in women, what is the cause of bone loss in men? The male sex hormone testosterone appears to play a role. Men with low levels of testosterone, as occurs after re-

---

FIGURE H12-3 Bone Losses over Time Compared

Peak bone mass is achieved by age 30. Women gradually lose bone mass until menopause, when losses accelerate dramatically and then gradually taper off.

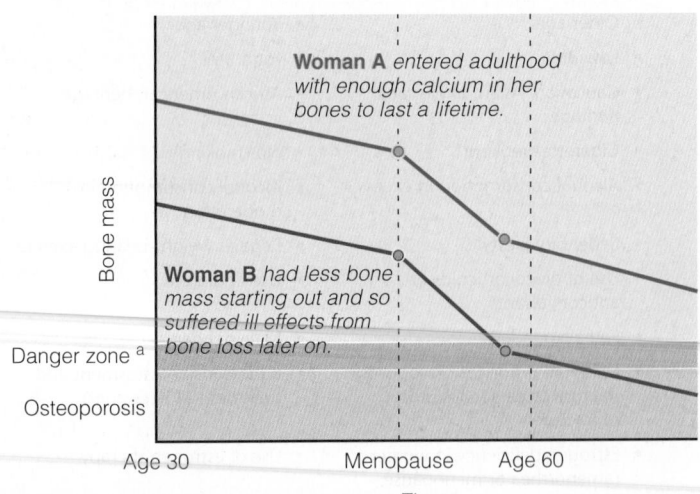

Woman A entered adulthood with enough calcium in her bones to last a lifetime.

Woman B had less bone mass starting out and so suffered ill effects from bone loss later on.

Bone mass · *Danger zone* [a] · *Osteoporosis*

Age 30 · *Menopause* · *Age 60* · *Time*

[a]People with a moderate degree of bone mass reduction are said to have *osteopenia* and are at increased risk of fractures.
SOURCE: Data from Committee on Dietary Reference Intakes, *Dietary Reference Intakes for Calcium, Phosphorus, Magnesium, Vitamin D, and Fluoride* (Washington, D.C.: National Academy Press, 1997), pp. 71–145.

---

*Among the hormones suggested as influential are parathyroid hormone, calcitonin, and estrogen.
**Raloxifene (rah-LOX-ih-feen) is a selective estrogen-receptor modulator (SERM), marketed as Evista; alendronate (a-LEN-droe-nate) is a bisphosphonate, marketed as Fosamax; risedronate (rih-SEH-droe-nate) is a bisphosphonate, marketed as Actonel; and calcitonin is a hormone, marketed as Calcimar and Miacalcin.

moval of diseased testes or when testes lose function with aging, suffer more fractures. Treatment for men with osteoporosis includes testosterone replacement therapy. Thus both male and female sex hormones participate in the development and treatment of osteoporosis.

Genetics and Ethnicity

Osteoporosis may, in part, be hereditary, and family history of osteoporosis or fracture is a risk factor. The exact role of genetics is unclear, but it most likely influences both the peak bone mass achieved during growth and the bone loss incurred during the later years. The extent to which a given genetic potential is realized, however, depends on many outside factors. Diet and physical activity, for example, can maximize peak bone density during growth, whereas alcohol and tobacco abuse can accelerate bone losses later in life.

Risks of osteoporosis appear to run along racial lines and reflect genetic differences in bone development. African Americans, for example, seem to use and conserve calcium more efficiently than Caucasians.[12] Consequently, even though their calcium intakes are typically lower, black people have denser bones than white people do. Greater bone density expresses itself in less bone loss, fewer fractures, and a lower rate of osteoporosis among blacks.[13] Fractures, for example, are about twice as likely in white women age 65 or older as in black women.

Other ethnic groups have a high risk of osteoporosis. Asians from China and Japan, Mexican Americans, Hispanic people from Central and South America, and Inuit people from St. Lawrence Island typically have lower bone density than Caucasians. One might expect that these groups would suffer more bone fractures, but this is not always the case. Again, genetic differences may explain why. Asians, for example, generally have small, compact hips, which makes them less susceptible to fractures.

Findings from around the world demonstrate that although a person's genes may lay the groundwork for bone health, environmental factors influence the genes' ultimate expression. Diet in general, and calcium in particular, are among those environmental factors. Others include physical activity, body weight, smoking, and alcohol. Importantly, all of these factors are within a person's control.

Physical Activity and Body Weight

Physical activity may be the single most important factor supporting bone growth during adolescence.[14] Muscle strength and bone strength go together. When muscles work, they pull on the bones, stimulating them to develop more trabeculae and grow denser. The hormones that promote new muscle growth also favor the building of bone. As a result, active bones are denser and stronger than sedentary bones.[15]

To keep bones healthy, a person should engage in weight training or weight-bearing endurance activities (such as tennis

and jogging or vigorous walking) regularly.[16] Regular physical activity combined with an adequate calcium intake helps to maximize bone density in adolescence.[17] Adults can also maximize and maintain bone density with a regular program of weight training. Even past menopause, when most women are losing bone, weight training improves bone density.[18]

Strength training helps to build strong bones.

Heavier body weights and weight gains place a similar stress on the bones and promote their density. In fact, weight losses reduce bone density and increase the risk of fractures—in part because energy restriction diminishes calcium absorption and compromises calcium balance.[19] As mentioned in Highlight 8, the combination of underweight, severely restricted energy intake, extreme daily exercise, and amenorrhea reliably predicts bone loss.

Smoking and Alcohol

Add bone damage to the list of ill consequences associated with smoking. The bones of smokers are less dense than those of nonsmokers—even after controlling for differences in age, body weight, and physical activity habits.[20] Fortunately, the damaging effects can be reversed with smoking cessation. Blood indicators of beneficial bone activity are apparent six weeks after a person stops smoking.[21] In time, bone density is similar for former smokers and nonsmokers.

People who abuse alcohol often suffer from osteoporosis and experience more bone breaks than others. Several factors appear to be involved. Alcohol enhances fluid excretion, leading to excessive calcium losses in the urine; upsets the hormonal balance required for healthy bones; slows bone formation, leading to lower bone density; stimulates bone breakdown; and increases the risk of falling.

Dietary Calcium

Bone strength later in life depends most on how well the bones were built during childhood and adolescence. Adequate calcium nutrition during the growing years is essential to achieving optimal peak bone mass. Simply put, growing children who do not get enough calcium do not have strong bones.[22] Neither do adults who did not get enough calcium during their childhood and adolescence.[23] To that end, the DRI Committee recommends 1300 milligrams of calcium per day for everyone 9 through 18 years of age. Unfortunately, few girls meet the recommendations for calcium during these bone-forming years. (Boys generally obtain intakes close to those recommended because they eat more food.) Consequently, most girls start their adult years with less-than-optimal bone density. As adults, women rarely meet their recommended intakes of 1000 to 1200 milligrams from food. Some authorities suggest 1500 milligrams of calcium for post-menopausal women who are not receiving estrogen, but they warn that intakes exceeding 2500 milligrams a day could cause health problems.

Other Nutrients

Much research has focused on calcium, but other nutrients support bone health, too.[24] Adequate protein protects bones and reduces the likelihood of hip fractures.[25] As mentioned earlier, vitamin D is needed to maintain calcium metabolism and optimal bone health.[26] Supplementation with vitamin D reduces bone loss and the risk of fractures.[27] Vitamin K decreases bone turnover and protects against hip fractures.[28] The minerals magnesium and potassium also help to maintain bone mineral density. Vitamin A is needed in the bone-remodeling process, but too much vitamin A may be associated with osteoporosis.[29] Omega-3 fatty acids may help preserve bone integrity.[30] Additional research points to the bone benefits not of a specific nutrient, but of a diet rich in fruits and vegetables.[31] In contrast, diets containing too much salt are associated with bone losses.[32] Clearly, a well-balanced diet that depends on all the food groups to supply a full array of nutrients is central to bone health.

A Perspective on Supplements

Bone health depends, in part, on calcium. People who do not consume milk products or other calcium-rich foods in amounts that provide even half the recommended calcium should consider consulting a registered dietitian who can assess the diet and suggest food choices to correct any inadequacies. For those who are unable to consume enough calcium-rich foods, taking calcium supplements may help to enhance bone density and protect against bone loss.[33]

Selecting a calcium supplement requires a little investigative work to sort through the many options. Before examining calcium supplements, recognize that multivitamin-mineral pills contain little or no calcium. The label may list a few milligrams of calcium, but remember that the recommended intake is a gram or more for adults.

Calcium supplements are typically sold as compounds of calcium carbonate (common in **antacids** and fortified chocolate candies), citrate, gluconate, lactate, malate, or phosphate. These supplements often include magnesium, vitamin D, or both. In addition, some calcium supplements are made from **bone meal**, **oyster shell**, or **dolomite** (limestone). Many calcium supplements, especially those derived from these natural products, contain lead—which impairs health in numerous ways, as Chapter 13 points out.[34] Fortunately, calcium interferes with the absorption and action of lead in the body.

The first question to ask is how much calcium the supplement provides. Most calcium supplements provide between 250 and 1000 milligrams of calcium. To be safe, total calcium intake from both foods and supplements should not exceed 2500 milligrams a day. Read the label to find out how much a dose supplies. Unless the label states otherwise, supplements of calcium carbonate are 40 percent calcium; those of calcium citrate are 21 percent; lactate, 13 percent; and gluconate, 9 percent. Select a low-dose supplement, and take it several times a day rather than taking a large-dose supplement all at once. Taking supplements in doses of 500 milligrams or less improves absorption. Small doses also help ease the GI distress (constipation, intestinal bloating, and excessive gas) that sometimes accompanies calcium supplement use.

The next question to ask is how well the body absorbs and uses the calcium from various supplements. Most healthy people absorb calcium equally well (and as well as from milk) from any of these supplements: calcium carbonate, citrate, or phosphate. More important than supplement solubility is tablet disintegration. When manufacturers compress large quantities of calcium into small pills, the stomach acid has difficulty penetrating the pill. To test a supplement's ability to dissolve, drop it into a 6-ounce cup of vinegar, and stir occasionally. A high-quality formulation will dissolve within half an hour.

Finally, people who choose supplements must take them regularly. Furthermore, consideration should be given to the best time to take the supplements. To circumvent adverse nutrient interactions, take calcium supplements between, not with, meals. (Importantly, do not take calcium supplements with iron supplements or iron-rich meals; calcium inhibits iron absorption.) To enhance calcium absorption, take supplements with meals. If such contradictory advice drives you crazy, reconsider the benefits of food sources of calcium. Most experts agree that foods are the best source of most nutrients.

Some Closing Thoughts

Unfortunately, many of the strongest risk factors for osteoporosis are beyond people's control: age, gender, and genetics. But several strategies are still effective for prevention.[35] First, ensure an optimal peak bone mass during childhood and adolescence by eating a balanced diet rich in calcium and engaging in regular physical activity. Then, maintain that bone mass by continuing those healthy diet and activity habits, abstaining from cigarette smoking, and using alcohol moderately, if at all. Finally, minimize bone loss by maintaining an adequate nutrition and exercise regimen, and, for women, consult a physician about calcium supplements or other drug therapies that may be effective both in preventing bone loss and in restoring lost bone. The reward is the best possible chance of preserving bone health throughout life.

NUTRITION ON THE NET

ThomsonNOW™
For furthur study of topics covered in this Highlight, log on to **www.thomsonedu.com/thomsonnow**. Go to Chapter 12, then to Highlights Nutrition on the Net.

- Search for "falls and fractures" at the National Institute on Aging: **www.nih.gov/nia**

- Visit the National Institutes of Health Osteoporosis and Related Bone Diseases' National Resource Center: **www.osteo.org**

- Obtain additional information from the National Osteoporosis Foundation: **www.nof.org**

REFERENCES

1. U.S. Department of Health and Human Services, *Bone Health and Osteoporosis: A report of the Surgeon General,* (Rockville, Md.: U.S. Department of Health and Human Services, Office of the Surgeon General, 2004).

2. L. G. Raisz, Screening for osteoporosis, *New England Journal of Medicine* 353 (2005): 164-171.

3. F. R. Greer, N. F. Krebs, and the Committee on Nutrition, Optimizing bone health and calcium intakes of infants, children, and adolescents, *Pediatrics* 117 (2006) 578-585.

4. B. E. C. Nordin and coauthors, Effect of age on calcium absorption in postmenopausal women, *American Journal of Clinical Nutrition* 80 (2004): 998-1002.

5. J. M. Campion and M. J. Maricic, Osteoporosis in men, *American Family Physician* 67 (2003): 1521-1526.

6. H. J. Kloosterboer and A. G. Ederveen, Pros and cons of existing treatment modalities in osteoporosis: A comparison between tibolone, SERMs and estrogen (+/- progestogen) treatments, *Journal of Steroid Biochemistry and Molecular Biology* 83 (2002): 157-165; R. A. Sayegh and P. G. Stubblefield, Bone metabolism and the perimenopause overview, risk factors, screening, and osteoporosis preventive measures, *Obstetrics and Gynecology Clinics of North America* 29 (2002): 495-510.

7. R. T. Chlebowski and coauthors, Influence of estrogen plus progestin on breast cancer and mammography in healthy postmenopausal women: The Women's Health Initiative Randomized Trial, *Journal of the American Medical Association* 289 (2003): 3243-3253; C. G. Solomon and R. G. Dluhy, Rethinking postmenopausal hormone therapy, *New England Journal of Medicine* 348 (2003): 579-580; Writing Group for the Women's Health Initiative Investigators, Risks and benefits of estrogen plus progestin in healthy postmenopausal women: Principal results from the Women's Health Initiative Randomized Controlled Trial, *Journal of the American Medical Association* 288 (2002): 321-333; O. Ylikorkala and M. Metsaheikkila, Hormone replacement therapy in women with a history of breast cancer, *Gynecological Endocrinology* 16 (2002): 469-478.

8. C. J. Rosen, Postmenopausal osteoporosis, *New England Journal of Medicine* 353 (2005): 595-603; J. F. Whitfield, How to grow bone to treat osteoporosis and mend fractures, *Current Rheumatology Reports* 5 (2003): 45-56.

9. R. P. Heaney and R. R. Recker, Combination and sequential therapy of osteoporosis, *New England Journal of Medicine* 353 (2005): 624-625; S. L. Greenspan, N. M. Resnick, and R. A. Parker, Combination therapy with hormone replacement and alendronate for prevention of bone loss in elderly women: A randomized controlled trial, *Journal of the American Medical Association* 289 (2003): 2525-2533.

10. C. Atkinson and coauthors, The effects of phytoestrogen isoflavones on bone density in women: A double-blind, randomized, placebo-controlled trial, *American Journal of Clinical Nutrition* 79 (2004): 326-333; R. Brynin, Soy and its isoflavones: A review of their effects on bone density, *Alternative Medicine Review* 7 (2002): 317-327.

11. B. H. Arjmandi and coauthors, Soy protein has a greater effect on bone in postmenopausal women not on hormone replacement therapy, as evidenced by reducing bone resorption and urinary calcium excretion, *Journal of Clinical Endocrinology and Metabolism* 88 (2003): 1048-1054; T. Uesugi, Y. Fukui, and Y. Yamori, Beneficial effects of soybean isoflavone supplementation on bone metabolism and serum lipids in postmenopausal Japanese women: A four-week study, *Journal of the American College of Nutrition* 21 (2002): 97-102.

12. K. Wigertz and coauthors, Racial differences in calcium retention in response to dietary salt in adolescent girls, *American Journal of Clinical Nutrition* 81 (2005): 845-850.

13. J. A. Cauley and coauthors, Longitudinal study of changes in hip bone mineral density in Caucasian and African-American women, *Journal of the American Geriatrics Society* 53 (2005): 183-189; J. A. Cauley and coauthors, Bone mineral density and the risk of incident nonspinal fractures in black and white women, *Journal of the American Medical Association* 293 (2005): 2102-2108.

14. A. J. Lanou, S. E. Berkow, and N. D. Barnard, Calcium, dairy products, and bone health in children and young adults: A reevaluation of the evidence, *Pediatrics* 115 (2005): 736-743.

15. F. R. Greer, Bone health: It's more than calcium intake, *Pediatrics* 115 (2005): 792-794.

16. American College of Sports Medicine Position Stand, Physical activity and bone health, *Medicine and Science in Sports and Exercise* 36 (2004): 1985-1996.

17. J. M. Welch and C. M. Weaver, Calcium and exercise affect the growing skeleton, *Nutrition Reviews* 63 (2005): 361-373; T. Lloyd and coauthors, Lifestyle factors and the development of bone mass and bone strength in young women, *Journal of Pediatrics* 144 (2004): 776-782; M. C. Wang and coauthors, Diet in midpuberty and sedentary activity in prepuberty predict peak bone mass, *American Journal of Clinical Nutrition* 77 (2003): 495-503; S. J. Stear and coauthors, Effect of a calcium and exercise intervention on the bone mineral status of 16-18-y-old adolescent girls, *American Journal of Clinical Nutrition* 77 (2003): 985-992.

18. E. C. Cussler and coauthors, Weight lifted in strength training predicts bone change in postmenopausal women, *Medicine and Science in Sports and Exercise* 35 (2003): 10-17.

19. M. Cifuentes and coauthors, Weight loss and calcium intake influence calcium absorption in overweight postmenopausal women, *American Journal of Clinical Nutrition* 80 (2004): 123-130; T. L. Radak, Caloric restriction and calcium's effect on bone metabolism and body composition in overweight and obese premenopausal women, *Nutrition Reviews* 62 (2004): 468-481.

20. P. Gerdhem and K. J. Obrant, Effects of cigarette-smoking on bone mass as assessed by dual-energy X-ray absorptiometry and ultrasound, *Osteoporosis International* 13 (2002): 932-936.

21. C. Oncken and coauthors, Effects of smoking cessation or reduction on hormone profiles and bone turnover in postmenopausal women, *Nicotine and Tobacco Research* 4 (2002): 451-458.

22. R. E. Black and coauthors, Children who avoid drinking cow milk have low dietary calcium intakes and poor bone health, *American Journal of Clinical Nutrition* 76 (2002): 675-680.

23. H. J. Kalkwarf, J. C. Khoury, and B. P. Lanphear, Milk intake during childhood and adolescence, adult bone density, and osteoporotic fractures in US women, *American Journal of Clinical Nutrition* 77 (2003): 257-265.

24. J. W. Nieves, Osteoporosis: The role of micronutrients, *American Journal of Clinical Nutrition* 81 (2005): 1232S-1239S.

25. J. Bell, Elderly women need dietary protein to maintain bone mass, *Nutrition Reviews* 60 (2002): 337-341; B. Dawson-Hughes and S. S. Harris, Calcium intake influences the association of protein intake with rates of bone loss in elderly men and women, *American Journal of Clinical Nutrition* 75 (2002): 773-779; J. H. E. Promislow and coauthors, Protein consumption and bone mineral density in the elderly: The Rancho Bernardo Study, *American Journal of Epidemiology* 155 (2002): 636-644.

26. L. Steingrimsdotir and coauthors, Relationship between serum parathyroid hormone levels, vitamin D sufficiency, and calcium intake, *Journal of the American Medical Association* 294 (2005): 2336-2341.

27. H. A. Bischoff-Ferrari and coauthors, Fracture prevention with vitamin D supplementation: A meta-analysis of randomized controlled trials, *Journal of the American Medical Association* 293 (2005): 2257-2264; D. Feskanich, W. C. Willett, and G. A. Colditz, Calcium, vitamin D, milk consumption, and hip fractures: A prospective study among postmenopausal women,

American Journal of Clinical Nutrition 77 (2003): 504-511.

28. H. J. Kalkwarf and coauthors, Vitamin K, bone turnover, and bone mass in girls, *American Journal of Clinical Nutrition* 80 (2004): 1075-1080; N. C. Binkley and coauthors, A high phylloquinone intake is required to achieve maximal osteocalcin γ-carboxylation, *American Journal of Clinical Nutrition* 76 (2002): 1055-1060.

29. K. Michaelsson and coauthors, Serum retinol levels and the risk of fractures, *New England Journal of Medicine* 348 (2003): 287-294; D. Feskanich and coauthors, Vitamin A intake and hip fractures among postmenopausal women, *Journal of the American Medical Association* 287 (2002): 47-54; S. Johnasson and coauthors, Subclinical hypervitaminosis A causes fragile bones in rats, *Bone* 31 (2002): 685-689.

30. L. A. Weiss, E. Barrett-Connor, and D. von Mühlen, Ratio of n -6 to n -3 fatty acids and bone mineral density in older adults: The Rancho Bernardo Study, *American Journal of Clinical Nutrition* 81 (2005): 934-938.

31. H. Vatanparast and coauthors, Positive effects of vegetable and fruit consumption and calcium intake on bone mineral accrual in boys during growth from childhood to adolescence: The University of Saskatchewan Pediatric Bone Mineral Accrual Study, *American Journal of Clinical Nutrition* 82 (2005): 700-706; C. P. McGartland and coauthors, Fruit and vegetable consumption and bone mineral density: The Northern Ireland Young Hearts Project, *American Journal of Clinical Nutrition* 80 (2004): 1019-1023; L. Doyle and K. D. Cashman, The DASH diet may have beneficial effects on bone health, *Nutrition Reviews* 62 (2004): 215-220; K. L. Tucker and coauthors, Bone mineral density and dietary patterns in older adults: The Framingham Osteoporosis Study, *American Journal of Clinical Nutrition* 76 (2002): 245-252.

32. M. Harrington and K. D. Cashman, High salt intake appears to increase bone resorption in postmenopausal women but high potassium intake ameliorates this adverse effect, *Nutrition Reviews* 61 (2003): 179-183; Tucker and coauthors, 2002.

33. V. Matkovic and coauthors, Calcium supplementation and bone mineral density in females from childhood to young adulthood: A randomized controlled trial, *American Journal of Clinical Nutrition* 81 (2005): 175-188; R. P. Dodiuk-Gad and coauthors, Sustained effect of short-term calcium supplementation on bone mass in adolescent girls with low calcium intake, *American Journal of Clinical Nutrition* 81 (2005): 168-174; L. D. McCabe and coauthors, Dairy intakes affect bone density in the elderly, *American Journal of Clinical Nutrition* 80 (2004): 1066-1074.

34. E. A. Ross, N. J. Szabo, and I. R. Tebbett, Lead content of calcium supplements, *Journal of the American Medical Association* 284 (2000): 1425-1429.

35. NIH Consensus Development Panel on Osteoporosis Prevention, Diagnosis, and Therapy, Osteoporosis prevention, diagnosis, and therapy, *Journal of the American Medical Association* 285 (2001): 785-795.

Nutrition in Your Life

Trace—barely a perceptible amount. But the trace minerals tackle big jobs. Your blood can't carry oxygen without iron, and insulin can't deliver glucose without chromium. Teeth become decayed without fluoride, and thyroid glands develop goiter without iodine. Together, the trace minerals—iron, zinc, iodine, selenium, copper, manganese, fluoride, chromium, and molybdenum—keep you healthy and strong. Where can you get these amazing minerals? A variety of foods, especially those from the meat and meat alternate group, sprinkled with a little iodized salt and complemented by a glass of fluoridated water will do the trick. It's remarkable what your body can do with only a few milligrams—or even micrograms—of the trace minerals.

The Trace Minerals

CHAPTER OUTLINE

**The Trace Minerals—
An Overview**

Iron • Iron Roles in the Body • Iron Absorption and Metabolism • Iron Deficiency • Iron Toxicity • Iron Recommendations and Sources • Iron Contamination and Supplementation

Zinc • Zinc Roles in the Body • Zinc Absorption and Metabolism • Zinc Deficiency • Zinc Toxicity • Zinc Recommendations and Sources • Zinc Supplementation

Iodine

Selenium

Copper

Manganese

Fluoride

Chromium

Molybdenum

Other Trace Minerals

Contaminant Minerals

Closing Thoughts on the Nutrients

HIGHLIGHT 13 Phytochemicals and Functional Foods

Figure 12-9 in the last chapter (p. 409) showed the tiny quantities of **trace minerals** in the human body. The trace minerals are so named because they are present, and needed, in relatively small amounts in the body. All together, they would produce only a bit of dust, hardly enough to fill a teaspoon. Yet they are no less important than the major minerals or any of the other nutrients. Each of the trace minerals performs a vital role. A deficiency of any of them may be fatal, and an excess of many is equally deadly. Remarkably, people's diets normally supply just enough of these minerals to maintain health.

The Trace Minerals—An Overview

The body requires the trace minerals in minuscule quantities. They participate in diverse tasks all over the body, each having special duties that only it can perform.

Food Sources The trace mineral contents of foods depend on soil and water composition and on how foods are processed. Furthermore, many factors in the diet and within the body affect the minerals' bioavailability. ◆ Still, outstanding food sources for each of the trace minerals, just like those for the other nutrients, include a wide variety of foods, especially unprocessed, whole foods.

Deficiencies Severe deficiencies of the better-known minerals are easy to recognize. Deficiencies of the others may be harder to diagnose, and for all minerals, mild deficiencies are easy to overlook. Because the minerals are active in all the body systems—the GI tract, cardiovascular system, blood, muscles, bones, and central nervous system—deficiencies can have wide-reaching effects and can affect people of all ages. The most common result of a deficiency in children is failure to grow and thrive.

Toxicities Some of the trace minerals are toxic at intakes not far above the estimated requirements. Thus it is important not to habitually exceed the Upper Level of recommended intakes. Many vitamin-mineral supplements contain trace minerals, making it easy for users to exceed their needs. Highlight 10 discusses supplement use and some of the regulations included in the Dietary Supplement Health

◆ Reminder: *Bioavailability* refers to the rate at and the extent to which a nutrient is absorbed and used.

trace minerals: essential mineral nutrients found in the human body in amounts smaller than 5 g; sometimes called **microminerals.**

and Education Act. As that discussion notes, the Food and Drug Administration (FDA) has no authority to limit the amounts of trace minerals in supplements; consumers have demanded the freedom to choose their own doses of nutrients.* Individuals who take supplements must therefore be aware of the possible dangers and select supplements that contain no more than 100 percent of the Daily Value. It would be easier and safer to meet nutrient needs by selecting a variety of foods than by combining an assortment of supplements (see Highlight 10).

Interactions Interactions among the trace minerals are common and often well coordinated to meet the body's needs. For example, several of the trace minerals support insulin's work, influencing its synthesis, storage, release, and action.

At other times, interactions lead to nutrient imbalances. An excess of one may cause a deficiency of another. (A slight manganese overload, for example, may aggravate an iron deficiency.) A deficiency of one may interfere with the work of another. (A selenium deficiency halts the activation of the iodine-containing thyroid hormones.) A deficiency of a trace mineral may even open the way for a contaminant mineral to cause a toxic reaction. (Iron deficiency, for example, makes the body vulnerable to lead poisoning.) These examples reinforce the need to balance intakes and to use supplements wisely, if at all. A good food source of one nutrient may be a poor food source of another, and factors that enhance the action of some trace minerals may interfere with others. (Meats are a good source of iron but a poor source of calcium; vitamin C enhances the absorption of iron but hinders that of copper.) Research on the trace minerals is active, suggesting that we have much more to learn about them.

> ### IN SUMMARY
>
> Although the body uses only tiny amounts of the trace minerals, they are vital to health. Because so little is required, the trace minerals can be toxic at levels not far above estimated requirements—a consideration for supplement users. Like the other nutrients, the trace minerals are best obtained by eating a variety of whole foods.

Iron

Iron is an essential nutrient, vital to many of the cells' activities, but it poses a problem for millions of people. Some people simply don't eat enough iron-containing foods to support their health optimally, whereas others absorb so much iron that it threatens their health. Iron exemplifies the principle that both too little and too much of a nutrient in the body can be harmful. In its wisdom, the body has several ways to achieve iron homeostasis, protecting against both deficiency and overload.[1]

Iron Roles in the Body

◆ Iron's two ionic states:
• Ferrous iron (reduced): Fe^{++}
• Ferric iron (oxidized): Fe^{+++}

Iron has the knack of switching back and forth between two ionic states. ◆ In the reduced state, iron has lost two electrons and therefore has a net positive charge of two; it is known as *ferrous iron*. In the oxidized state, iron has lost a third electron, has a net positive charge of three, and is known as *ferric iron*. Ferrous iron can be oxidized to ferric iron, and ferric iron can be reduced to ferrous iron. Thus iron can serve as a cofactor ◆ to enzymes involved in oxidation-reduction reactions—reactions so widespread in metabolism that they occur in all cells. Enzymes involved in making amino acids, collagen, hormones, and neurotransmitters all require iron. (For details about ions, oxidation, and reduction, see Appendix B.)

◆ Reminder: A *cofactor* is a substance that works with an enzyme to facilitate a chemical reaction.

---

* Canada regulates the amounts of trace minerals in supplements.

Iron forms a part of the electron carriers that participate in the electron transport chain (discussed in Chapter 7).* In this pathway, these carriers transfer hydrogens and electrons to oxygen, forming water, and in the process, make ATP for the cells' energy use.

Most of the body's iron is found in two proteins: hemoglobin ◆ in the red blood cells and **myoglobin** in the muscle cells. In both, iron helps accept, carry, and then release oxygen.

Iron Absorption and Metabolism

The body conserves iron. Because it is difficult to excrete iron once it is in the body, balance is maintained primarily through absorption. More iron is absorbed when stores are empty and less is absorbed when stores are full.[2]

Iron Absorption Special proteins help the body absorb iron from food (see Figure 13-1). One protein, called mucosal **ferritin,** receives iron from food and stores it in the mucosal cells ◆ of the small intestine. When the body needs iron, mucosal ferritin releases some iron to another protein, called mucosal **transferrin.** Mucosal transferrin transfers the iron to another protein, *blood transferrin,* which transports the iron to the rest of the body. If the body does not need iron, it is carried out when the intestinal cells are shed and excreted in the feces; intestinal cells are replaced about every three to five days. By holding iron temporarily, these cells control iron absorption by either delivering iron when the day's intake falls short or disposing of it when intakes exceed needs.

Heme and Nonheme Iron Iron absorption depends in part on its dietary source.[3] Iron occurs in two forms in foods: as **heme** iron, which is found only in foods derived from the flesh of animals, such as meats, poultry, and fish and as nonheme iron, which is found in both plant-derived and animal-derived foods (see Figure 13-2, p. 444). On average, heme iron represents about 10 percent of the iron a

---

* The iron-containing electron carriers of the electron transport chain are known as *cytochromes.* See Appendix C for details of this pathway.

◆ Reminder: *Hemoglobin* is the oxygen-carrying protein of the red blood cells that transports oxygen from the lungs to tissues throughout the body; hemoglobin accounts for 80% of the body's iron.

◆ A mucous membrane such as the one that lines the GI tract is sometimes called the **mucosa** (mu-KO-sa). The adjective of mucosa is **mucosal** (mu-KO-sal).

---

myoglobin: the oxygen-holding protein of the muscle cells.
• **myo** = muscle

ferritin (FAIR-ih-tin): the iron storage protein.

transferrin (trans-FAIR-in): the iron transport protein.

heme (HEEM): the iron-holding part of the hemoglobin and myoglobin proteins. About 40% of the iron in meat, fish, and poultry is bound into heme; the other 60% is **nonheme** iron.

| FIGURE 13-1 | Iron Absorption |

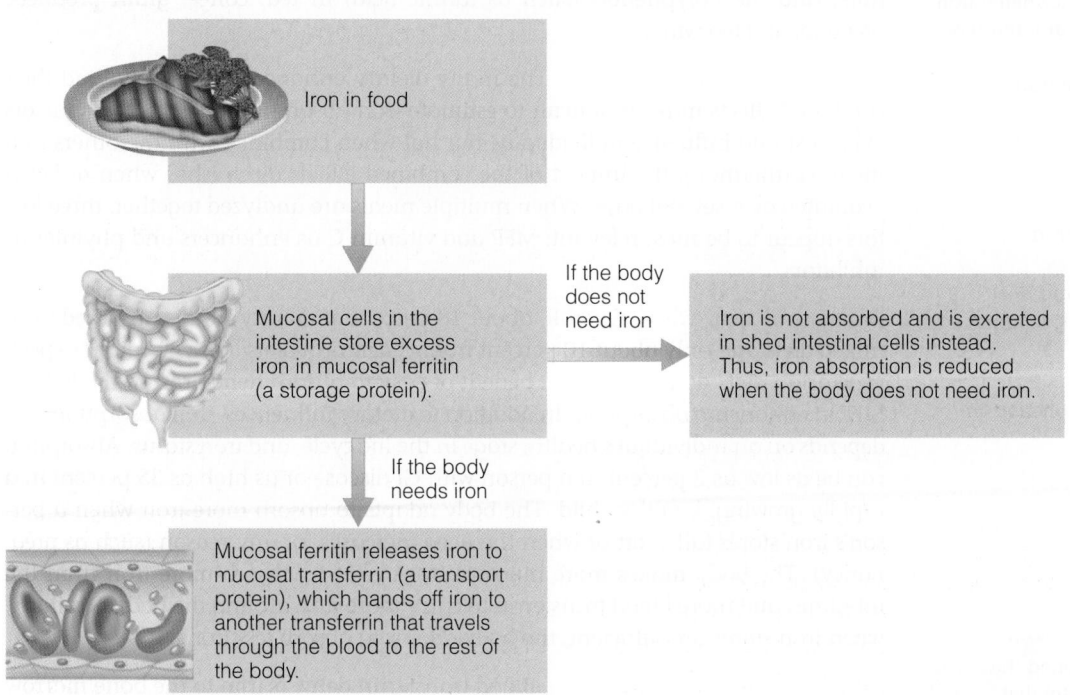

Iron in food

Mucosal cells in the intestine store excess iron in mucosal ferritin (a storage protein).

If the body does not need iron → Iron is not absorbed and is excreted in shed intestinal cells instead. Thus, iron absorption is reduced when the body does not need iron.

If the body needs iron

Mucosal ferritin releases iron to mucosal transferrin (a transport protein), which hands off iron to another transferrin that travels through the blood to the rest of the body.

FIGURE 13-2 Heme and Nonheme Iron in Foods

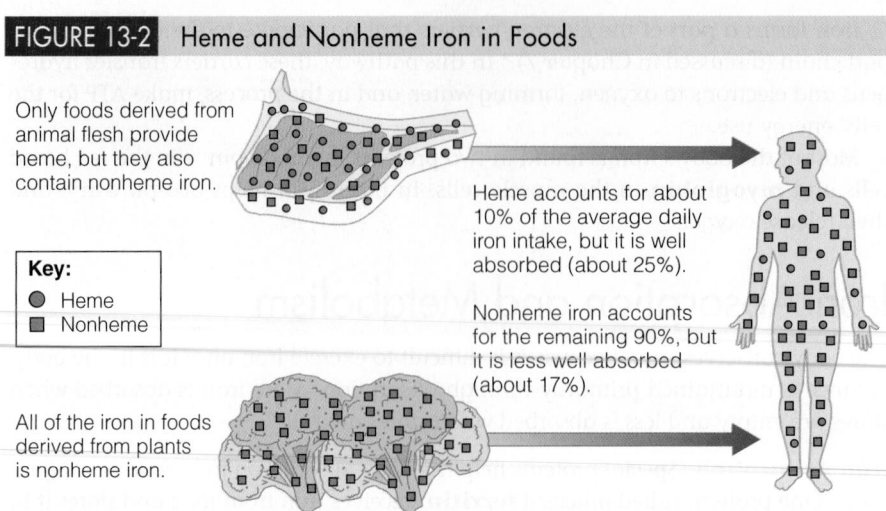

Only foods derived from animal flesh provide heme, but they also contain nonheme iron.

Key:
● Heme
■ Nonheme

All of the iron in foods derived from plants is nonheme iron.

Heme accounts for about 10% of the average daily iron intake, but it is well absorbed (about 25%).

Nonheme iron accounts for the remaining 90%, but it is less well absorbed (about 17%).

This chili dinner provides several factors that may enhance iron absorption: heme and nonheme iron and MFP from meat, nonheme iron from legumes, and vitamin C from tomatoes.

◆ Factors that *enhance* nonheme iron absorption:
- MFP factor
- Vitamin C (ascorbic acid)

◆ Factors that *inhibit* nonheme iron absorption:
- Phytates (legumes, grains, and rice)
- Vegetable proteins (soybeans, legumes, nuts)
- Calcium (milk)
- Tannic acid (and other polyphenols in tea and coffee)

MFP factor: a peptide released during the digestion of **m**eat, **f**ish, and **p**oultry that enhances nonheme iron absorption.

person consumes in a day. Even though heme iron accounts for only a small proportion of the intake, it is so well absorbed that it contributes significant iron. About 25 percent of heme iron and 17 percent of nonheme iron is absorbed, depending on dietary factors and the body's iron stores.[4] In iron deficiency, absorption increases. In iron overload, absorption declines.[5] Researchers disagree as to whether heme iron absorption responds to iron stores as sensitively as nonheme iron absorption does.

Absorption-Enhancing Factors Meat, fish, and poultry contain not only the well-absorbed heme iron, but also a peptide (called the **MFP factor)** that promotes the absorption of nonheme iron ◆ from other foods eaten at the same meal.[6] Vitamin C also enhances nonheme iron absorption from foods eaten in the same meal by capturing the iron and keeping it in the reduced ferrous form, ready for absorption. Some acids and sugars also enhance nonheme iron absorption.

Absorption-Inhibiting Factors Some dietary factors bind with nonheme iron, inhibiting absorption. ◆ These factors include the phytates in legumes, whole grains, and rice; the vegetable proteins in soybeans, other legumes, and nuts; the calcium in milk; and the polyphenols (such as tannic acid) in tea, coffee, grain products, oregano, and red wine.

Dietary Factors Combined The many dietary enhancers, inhibitors, and their combined effects make it difficult to estimate iron absorption. Most of these factors exert a strong influence individually, but not when combined with the others in a meal. Furthermore, the impact of the combined effects diminishes when a diet is evaluated over several days. When multiple meals are analyzed together, three factors appear to be most relevant: MFP and vitamin C as enhancers and phytates as inhibitors.

Individual Variation Overall, about 18 percent of dietary iron is absorbed from mixed diets and only about 10 percent from vegetarian diets.[7] As you might expect, vegetarian diets do not have the benefit of easy-to-absorb heme iron or the help of MFP in enhancing absorption. In addition to dietary influences, iron absorption also depends on an individual's health, stage in the life cycle, and iron status. Absorption can be as low as 2 percent in a person with GI disease or as high as 35 percent in a rapidly growing, healthy child. The body adapts to absorb more iron when a person's iron stores fall short or when the need increases for any reason (such as pregnancy). The body makes more mucosal transferrin to absorb more iron from the intestines and more blood transferrin to carry more iron around the body. Similarly, when iron stores are sufficient, the body adapts to absorb less iron.

Iron Transport and Storage Blood transferrin delivers iron to the bone marrow and other tissues. The bone marrow uses large quantities to make new red blood

© Benjamin F. Fink Jr./Brand X Pictures/Getty Images

cells, whereas other tissues use less. Surplus iron is stored in the protein ferritin, primarily in the liver, but also in the bone marrow and spleen. When dietary iron has been plentiful, ferritin is constantly and rapidly made and broken down, providing an ever-ready supply of iron. When iron concentrations become abnormally high, the liver converts some ferritin into another storage protein called **hemosiderin.** Hemosiderin releases iron more slowly than ferritin does. By storing excess iron, the body protects itself: free iron acts as a free radical, attacking cell lipids, DNA, and protein. (See Highlight 11 for more information on free radicals and the damage they can cause.)

Iron Recycling The average red blood cell lives about four months; then the spleen and liver cells remove it from the blood, take it apart, and prepare the degradation products for excretion or recycling. The iron is salvaged: the liver attaches it to blood transferrin, which transports it back to the bone marrow to be reused in making new red blood cells. Thus, although red blood cells live for only about four months, the iron recycles through each new generation of cells (see Figure 13-3). The body loses some iron daily via the GI tract and, if bleeding occurs, in blood. Only tiny amounts of iron are lost in urine, sweat, and shed skin.*

Iron Balance Maintaining iron balance depends on the careful regulation of iron absorption, transport, storage, recycling, and losses. The hormone **hepcidin** is central to the regulation of iron balance.[8] Produced by the liver, hepcidin helps to maintain blood iron within the normal range by inhibiting absorption from the intestines and transport out of storage as needed.

Iron Deficiency

Worldwide, **iron deficiency** is the most common nutrient deficiency, affecting more than 1.2 billion people.[9] In developing countries, almost half of preschool chil-

---

* Adults lose about 1.0 milligram of iron per day. Women lose additional iron in menses. Menstrual losses vary considerably, but over a month, they average about 0.5 milligram per day.

hemosiderin (heem-oh-SID-er-in): an iron-storage protein primarily made in times of iron overload.

hepcidin: a hormone produced by the liver that regulates iron balance.

iron deficiency: the state of having depleted iron stores.

FIGURE 13-3   *Animated!* **Iron Recycled in the Body**

Once iron enters the body, most of it is recycled. Some is lost with body tissues and must be replaced by eating iron-containing food.

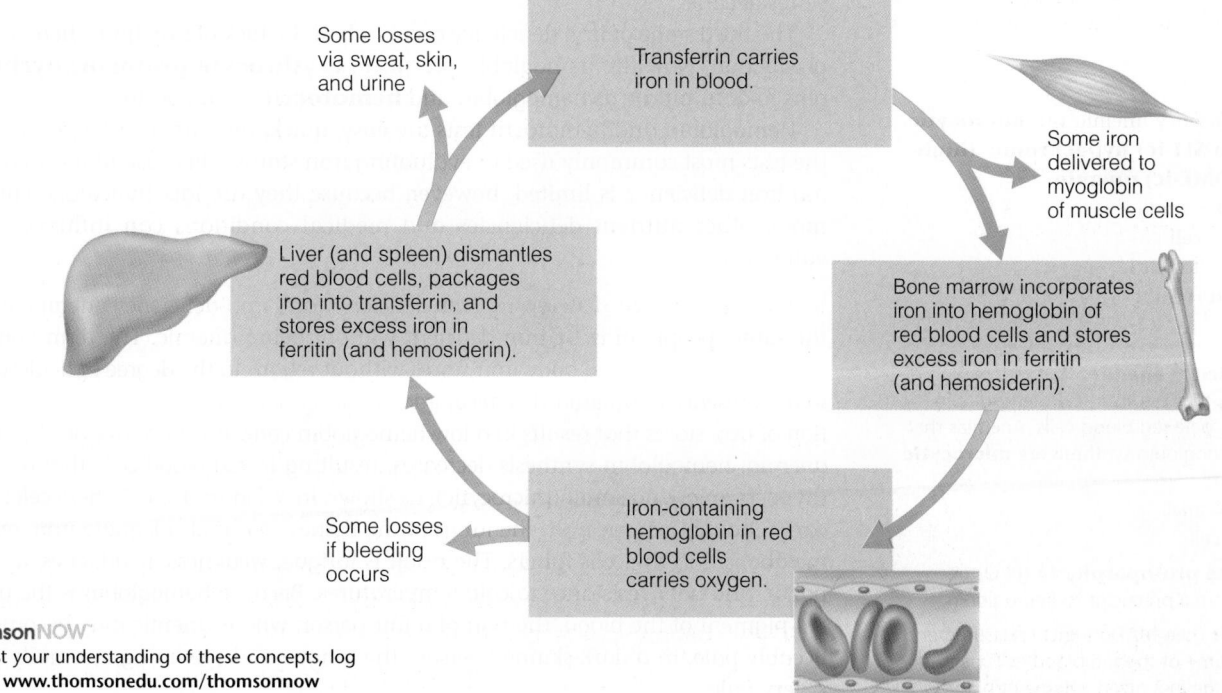

Some losses via sweat, skin, and urine

Transferrin carries iron in blood.

Some iron delivered to myoglobin of muscle cells

Liver (and spleen) dismantles red blood cells, packages iron into transferrin, and stores excess iron in ferritin (and hemosiderin).

Bone marrow incorporates iron into hemoglobin of red blood cells and stores excess iron in ferritin (and hemosiderin).

Some losses if bleeding occurs

Iron-containing hemoglobin in red blood cells carries oxygen.

ThomsonNOW
To test your understanding of these concepts, log on to **www.thomsonedu.com/thomsonnow**

dren and pregnant women suffer from **iron-deficiency anemia.**[10] In the United States, iron deficiency is less prevalent, but it still affects 10 percent of toddlers, adolescent girls, and women of childbearing age. Iron deficiency is also relatively common among overweight children and adolescents compared with those who are normal weight.[11] Preventing and correcting iron deficiency are high priorities.[12]

Vulnerable Stages of Life Some stages of life ◆ demand more iron but provide less, making deficiency likely. Women in their reproductive years are especially prone to iron deficiency because of repeated blood losses during menstruation. Pregnancy demands additional iron to support the added blood volume, growth of the fetus, and blood loss during childbirth. Infants and young children receive little iron from their high-milk diets, yet need extra iron to support their rapid growth. Iron deficiency among toddlers in the United States is common.[13] The rapid growth of adolescence, especially for males, and the menstrual losses of females also demand extra iron that a typical teen diet may not provide. An adequate iron intake is especially important during these stages of life.

Blood Losses Bleeding ◆ from any site incurs iron losses. In some cases, such as an active ulcer, the bleeding may not be obvious, but even small chronic blood losses significantly deplete iron reserves. In developing countries, blood loss is often brought on by malaria and parasitic infections of the GI tract. People who donate blood regularly also incur losses and may benefit from iron supplements. As mentioned, menstrual losses can be considerable as they tap women's iron stores regularly.

Assessment of Iron Deficiency Iron deficiency develops in stages. ◆ This section provides a brief overview of how to detect these stages, and Appendix E provides more details. In the first stage of iron deficiency, iron stores diminish. Measures of serum ferritin (in the blood) reflect iron stores and are most valuable in assessing iron status at this earliest stage.

The second stage of iron deficiency is characterized by a decrease in transport iron: serum iron falls, and the iron-carrying protein transferrin *increases* (an adaptation that enhances iron absorption). Together, measurements of serum iron and transferrin can determine the severity of the deficiency—the more transferrin and the less iron in the blood, the more advanced the deficiency is. Transferrin saturation—the percentage of transferrin that is saturated with iron—decreases as iron stores decline.

The third stage of iron deficiency occurs when the lack of iron limits hemoglobin production. Now the hemoglobin precursor, **erythrocyte protoporphyrin**, begins to accumulate as hemoglobin and **hematocrit** values decline.

Hemoglobin and hematocrit tests are easy, quick, and inexpensive, so they are the tests most commonly used in evaluating iron status. Their usefulness in detecting iron deficiency is limited, however, because they are late indicators. Furthermore, other nutrient deficiencies and medical conditions can influence their values.

Iron Deficiency and Anemia Iron deficiency and iron-deficiency anemia are not the same: people may be iron deficient without being anemic. The term *iron deficiency* refers to depleted body iron stores without regard to the degree of depletion or to the presence of anemia. The term *iron-deficiency anemia* refers to the severe depletion of iron stores that results in a low hemoglobin concentration. In iron-deficiency anemia, hemoglobin synthesis decreases, resulting in red blood cells that are pale (hypochromic) and small (microcytic), as shown in ◆ Figure 13-4.[14] These cells can't carry enough oxygen from the lungs to the tissues. Without adequate iron, energy metabolism in the cells falters. The result is fatigue, weakness, headaches, apathy, pallor, and poor resistance to cold temperatures. Because hemoglobin is the bright red pigment of the blood, the skin of a fair person who is anemic may become noticeably pale. In a dark-skinned person, the tongue and eye lining, normally pink, is very pale.

◆ High risk for iron deficiency:
• Women in their reproductive years
• Pregnant women
• Infants and young children
• Teenagers

◆ The iron content of blood is about 0.5 mg/100 mL blood. A person donating a pint of blood (approximately 500 mL) loses about 2.5 mg of iron.

◆ Stages of iron deficiency:
• Iron stores diminish
• Transport iron decreases
• Hemoglobin production declines

◆ Iron-deficiency anemia is a **microcytic (my-cro-SIT-ic) hypochromic (high-po-KROME-ic) anemia.**
• **micro** = small
• **cytic** = cell
• **hypo** = too little
• **chrom** = color

iron-deficiency anemia: severe depletion of iron stores that results in low hemoglobin and small, pale red blood cells. Anemias that impair hemoglobin synthesis are **microcytic** (small cell).
• **micro** = small
• **cytic** = cell

erythrocyte protoporphyrin (PRO-toe-PORE-fe-rin): a precursor to hemoglobin.

hematocrit (hee-MAT-oh-krit): measurement of the volume of the red blood cells packed by centrifuge in a given volume of blood.

| FIGURE 13-4 | Normal and Anemic Blood Cells |

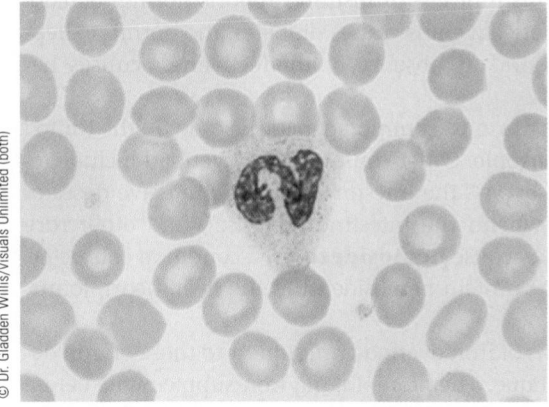 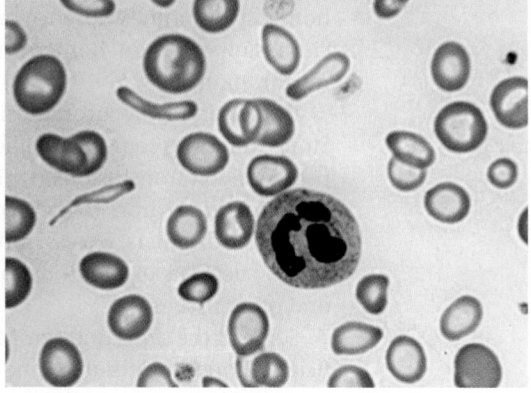

Both size and color are normal in these blood cells.

Blood cells in iron-deficiency anemia are small (microcytic) and pale (hypochromic) because they contain less hemoglobin.

The fatigue that accompanies iron-deficiency anemia differs from the tiredness a person experiences from a simple lack of sleep. People with anemia feel fatigue only when they exert themselves. Iron supplementation can relieve the fatigue and improve the body's response to physical activity.[15] (The iron needs of physically active people and the special iron deficiency known as sports anemia are discussed in Chapter 14.)

Iron Deficiency and Behavior Long before the red blood cells are affected and anemia is diagnosed, a developing iron deficiency affects behavior. Even at slightly lowered iron levels, energy metabolism is impaired and neurotransmitter synthesis is altered, reducing physical work capacity and mental productivity.[16] Without the physical energy and mental alertness to work, plan, think, play, sing, or learn, people simply do these things less. They have no obvious deficiency symptoms; they just appear unmotivated, apathetic, and less physically fit. Work productivity and voluntary activities decline.

Many of the symptoms associated with iron deficiency are easily mistaken for behavioral or motivational problems. A restless child who fails to pay attention in class might be thought contrary. An apathetic homemaker who has let housework pile up might be thought lazy. No responsible dietitian would ever claim that all behavioral problems are caused by nutrient deficiencies, but poor nutrition is always a possible contributor to problems like these. When investigating a behavioral problem, check the adequacy of the diet and seek a routine physical examination before undertaking more expensive, and possibly harmful, treatment options. (The effects of iron deficiency on children's behavior are discussed further in Chapter 16.)

Iron Deficiency and Pica A curious behavior seen in some iron-deficient people, especially in women and children of low-income groups, is **pica**—an appetite for ice, clay, paste, and other nonfood substances. These substances contain no iron and cannot remedy a deficiency; in fact, clay actually inhibits iron absorption, which may explain the iron deficiency that accompanies such behavior.

Iron Toxicity

In general, even a diet that includes fortified foods poses no special risk for iron toxicity.[17] The body normally absorbs less iron when its stores are full, but some individuals are poorly defended against excess iron. Once considered rare, **iron overload** has emerged as an important disorder of iron metabolism and regulation.

pica (PIE-ka): a craving for nonfood substances. Also known as **geophagia** (gee-oh-FAY-gee-uh) when referring to clay eating and **pagophagia** (pag-oh-FAY-gee-uh) when referring to ice craving.

iron overload: toxicity from excess iron.

© Dr. Gladden Willis/Visuals Unlimited (both)

Iron Overload The iron overload disorder known as **hemochromatosis** is usually caused by a genetic failure to prevent unneeded iron in the diet from being absorbed.[18] Recent research suggests that just as insulin supports normal glucose homeostasis and its absence or ineffectiveness causes diabetes, the hormone hepcidin supports iron homeostasis and its absence or ineffectiveness causes hemochromatosis.

Hereditary hemochromatosis is the most common genetic disorder in the United States, affecting some 1.5 million people. Other causes of iron overload include repeated blood transfusions (which bypass the intestinal defense), massive doses of supplementary iron (which overwhelm the intestinal defense), and other rare metabolic disorders. Excess iron may cause **hemosiderosis**, a condition characterized by deposits of the iron storage protein hemosiderin in the liver, heart, joints, and other tissues.

Some of the signs and symptoms of iron overload are similar to those of iron deficiency: apathy, lethargy, and fatigue. Therefore, taking iron supplements before assessing iron status is clearly unwise; hemoglobin tests alone would fail to make the distinction because excess iron accumulates in storage. Iron overload assessment tests measure transferrin saturation and serum ferritin.

Iron overload is characterized by tissue damage, especially in iron-storing organs such as the liver. Infections are likely because bacteria thrive on iron-rich blood. Symptoms are most severe in alcohol abusers because alcohol damages the intestine, further impairing its defenses against absorbing excess iron. Untreated hemochromatosis increases the risks of diabetes, liver cancer, heart disease, and arthritis.

Iron overload is more common in men than in women and is twice as prevalent among men as iron deficiency. The widespread fortification of foods with iron makes it difficult for people with hemochromatosis to follow a low-iron diet, and greater dangers lie in the indiscriminate use of iron and vitamin C supplements. Vitamin C not only enhances iron absorption, but also releases iron from ferritin, allowing free iron to wreak the damage typical of free radicals. Thus vitamin C acts as a *prooxidant* when taken in high doses. (See Highlight 11 for a discussion of free radicals and their effects on disease development.)

Iron and Heart Disease Some research suggests a link between heart disease and iron, especially when accompanied by alcohol consumption.[19] As mentioned, free radicals can attack ferritin, causing it to release iron from storage. Free iron, in turn, acts as an oxidant that can generate more free radicals. Whether iron's role in oxidative stress contributes to the development of diseases is unclear.[20]

Iron and Cancer There may be an association between iron and some cancers.[21] Explanations for how iron might be involved in causing cancer focus on its free-radical activity, which can damage DNA (see Highlight 11). One of the benefits of a high-fiber diet may be that the accompanying phytates bind iron, making it less available for such reactions.

Iron Poisoning Large doses of iron supplements cause GI distress, including constipation, nausea, vomiting, and diarrhea. These effects may not be as serious as other consequences of iron toxicity, but they are consistent enough to establish an Upper Level of 45 milligrams per day for adults.

Ingestion of iron-containing supplements remains a leading cause of accidental poisoning in small children. Symptoms of toxicity include nausea, vomiting, diarrhea, a rapid heartbeat, a weak pulse, dizziness, shock, and confusion. As few as five iron tablets containing as little as 200 milligrams of iron have caused the deaths of dozens of young children. The exact cause of these deaths is uncertain, but excessive free-radical damage is thought to play a role in heart failure and respiratory distress. Autopsy reports reveal iron deposits and cell death in the stomach, small intestine, liver, and blood vessels (which can cause internal bleeding). Keep iron-containing tablets out of the reach of children. If you suspect iron poisoning, call the nearest poison control center or a physician immediately.

hemochromatosis (HE-moh-KRO-ma-toe-sis): a genetically determined failure to prevent absorption of unneeded dietary iron that is characterized by iron overload and tissue damage.

hemosiderosis (HE-moh-sid-er-OH-sis): a condition characterized by the deposition of hemosiderin in the liver and other tissues.

Iron Recommendations and Sources

To obtain enough iron, people must first select iron-rich foods and then take advantage of factors that maximize iron absorption. This discussion begins by identifying iron-rich foods and then reviews the factors affecting absorption.

Recommended Iron Intakes The usual diet in the United States provides about 6 to 7 milligrams of iron for every 1000 kcalories. The recommended daily intake for men is 8 milligrams, and because most men eat more than 2000 kcalories a day, they can meet their iron needs with little effort. Women in their reproductive years, however, need 18 milligrams a day. The accompanying "How to" explains how to calculate the recommended intake.

Vegetarians need 1.8 times as much iron ◆ to make up for the low bioavailability typical of their diets.[22] To maximize iron absorption, vegetarians should incorporate iron-rich foods into a diet that is low in inhibitors (foods such as leavened breads and fermented soy products such as miso and tempeh) and high in enhancers (foods rich in vitamin C and the organic acids found in fruits and vegetables). Good vegetarian sources of iron include soy foods (such as soybeans and tofu), legumes (such as lentils and kidney beans), nuts (such as cashews and almonds), seeds (such as pumpkin seeds and sunflower seeds), cereals (such as cream of wheat and oatmeal), dried fruit (such as apricots and raisins), vegetables (such as mushrooms and potatoes), and blackstrap molasses.

Because women have higher iron needs and lower energy needs, they sometimes have trouble obtaining enough iron. On average, women receive only 12 to 13 milligrams of iron per day, which is not enough iron for women until after menopause. To meet their iron needs from foods, premenopausal women need to select iron-rich foods at every meal.

◆ To calculate the RDA for vegetarians, multiply by 1.8:
- 8 mg × 1.8 = 14 mg/day (vegetarian men)
- 18 mg × 1.8 = 32 mg/day (vegetarian women, 19 to 50 yr)

Dietary Guidelines for Americans 2005

Women of childbearing age who may become pregnant should eat foods high in heme-iron and/or consume iron-rich plant foods or iron-fortified foods with an enhancer of iron absorption, such as vitamin C-rich foods.

Iron in Foods Figure 13-5 (p. 450) shows the amounts of iron in selected foods. Meats, fish, and poultry contribute the most iron per serving; other protein-rich foods such as legumes and eggs are also good sources. Although an indispensable part of the diet, foods in the milk group are notoriously poor in iron. Grain products vary, with whole-grain, enriched, and fortified breads and cereals contributing significantly to iron intakes. Finally, dark greens (such as broccoli) and dried fruits (such as raisins) contribute some iron.

When the label on a grain product says "enriched," it means iron and several B vitamins have been added.

HOW TO | Estimate the Recommended Daily Intake for Iron

To calculate the recommended daily iron intake, the DRI Committee considers a number of factors. For example, for a woman of childbearing age (19 to 50):

- Losses from feces, urine, sweat, and shed skin: 1.0 milligram
- Losses through menstruation: 0.5 milligram (about 14 milligrams total averaged over 28 days)

These losses reflect an average daily need (total) of 1.5 milligrams of *absorbed* iron.

An estimated average requirement is determined based on the daily need and the assumption that an average of 18 percent of ingested iron is absorbed:

1.5 mg iron (needed)
÷ 0.18 (percent iron absorbed)
= 8 mg iron (estimated average requirement)

Then, a margin of safety is added to cover the needs of essentially all women of childbearing age, and the RDA is set at 18 milligrams.

FIGURE 13-5 Iron in Selected Foods

See the "How to" section on p. 329 for more information on using this figure.

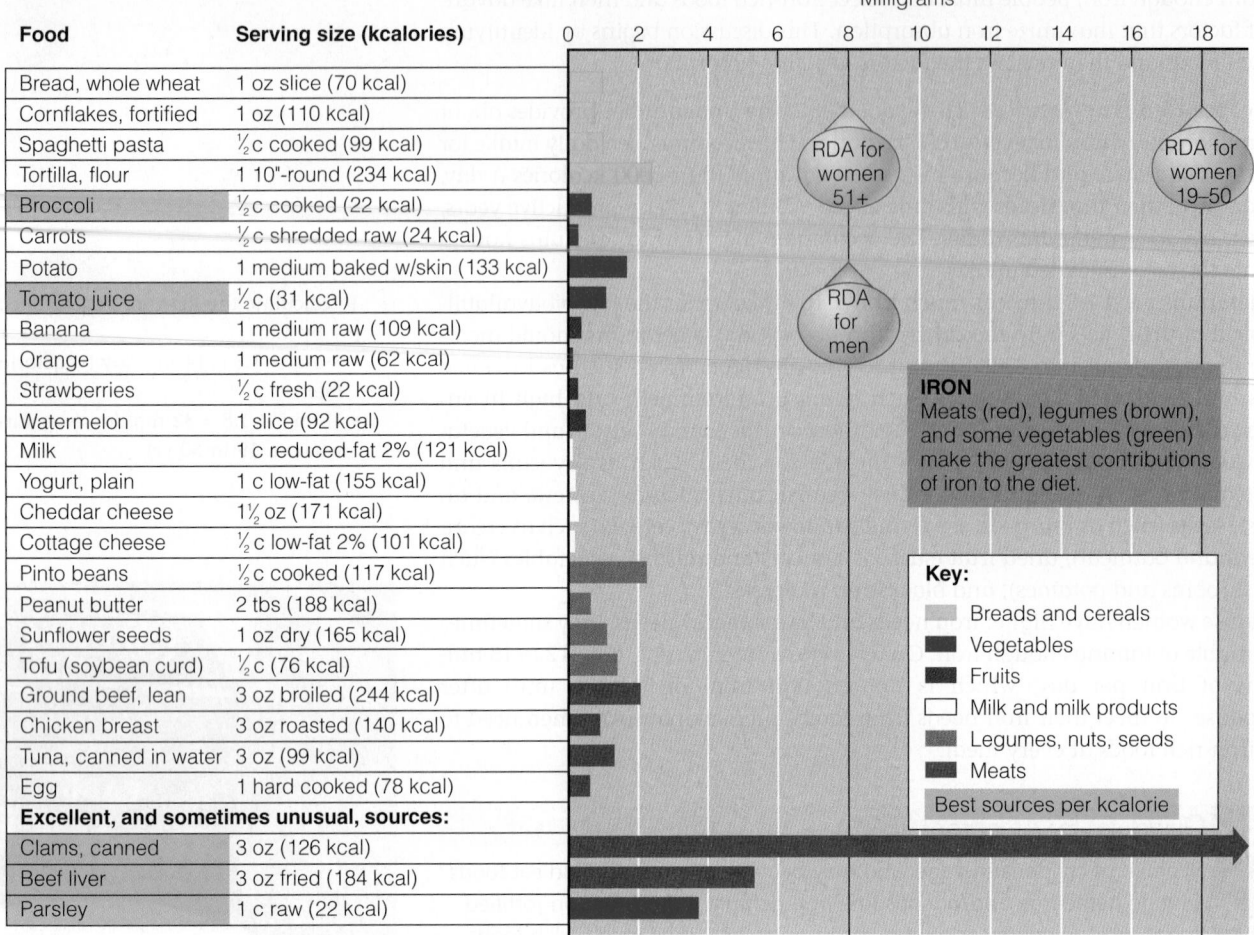

Iron-Enriched Foods Iron is one of the enrichment nutrients for grain products. One serving of enriched bread or cereal provides only a little iron, but because people eat many servings of these foods, the contribution can be significant. Iron added to foods is not absorbed as well as naturally occurring iron, but when eaten with absorption-enhancing foods, enrichment iron can make a difference. In cases of iron overload, enrichment may exacerbate the problem.[23]

Maximizing Iron Absorption In general, the bioavailability of iron is high in meats, fish, and poultry, intermediate in grains and legumes, and low in most vegetables, especially those containing oxalates such as spinach. As mentioned earlier, the amount of iron ultimately absorbed from a meal depends on the combined effects of several enhancing and inhibiting factors. For maximum absorption of nonheme iron, eat meat for MFP and fruits or vegetables for vitamin C. The iron of baked beans, for example, will be enhanced by the MFP in a piece of ham served with them. The iron of bread will be enhanced by the vitamin C in a slice of tomato on a sandwich.

Iron Contamination and Supplementation

contamination iron: iron found in foods as the result of contamination by inorganic iron salts from iron cookware, iron-containing soils, and the like.

In addition to the iron from foods, **contamination iron** from nonfood sources of inorganic iron salts can contribute to the day's intakes. People can also get iron from supplements.

Contamination Iron Foods cooked in iron cookware take up iron salts. The more acidic the food and the longer it is cooked in iron cookware, the higher the iron content. The iron content of eggs can triple in the time it takes to scramble them in an iron pan. Admittedly, the absorption of this iron may be poor (perhaps only 1 to 2 percent), but every little bit helps a person who is trying to increase iron intake.

Iron Supplements People who are iron deficient may need supplements as well as an iron-rich, absorption-enhancing diet. Many physicians routinely recommend iron supplements to pregnant women, infants, and young children. Iron from supplements is less well absorbed than that from food, so the doses must be high. The absorption of iron taken as ferrous sulfate or as an iron **chelate** is better than that from other iron supplements. Absorption also improves when supplements are taken between meals, at bedtime on an empty stomach, and with liquids (other than milk, tea, or coffee, which inhibit absorption). Taking iron supplements in a single dose instead of several doses per day is equally effective and may improve a person's willingness to take it regularly.

There is no benefit to taking iron supplements with orange juice because vitamin C does not enhance absorption from supplements as it does from foods. (Vitamin C enhances iron absorption by converting insoluble ferric iron in foods to the more soluble ferrous iron, and supplemental iron is already in the ferrous form.) Constipation is a common side effect of iron supplementation; drinking plenty of water may help to relieve this problem.

An old-fashioned iron skillet adds iron to foods.

IN SUMMARY

Most of the body's iron is in hemoglobin and myoglobin where it carries oxygen for use in energy metabolism; some iron is also required for enzymes involved in a variety of reactions. Special proteins assist with iron absorption, transport, and storage—all helping to maintain an appropriate balance, because both too little and too much iron can be damaging. Iron deficiency is most common among infants and young children, teenagers, women of childbearing age, and pregnant women. Symptoms include fatigue and anemia. Iron overload is most common in men. Heme iron, which is found only in meat, fish, and poultry, is better absorbed than nonheme iron, which occurs in most foods. Nonheme iron absorption is improved by eating iron-containing foods with foods containing the MFP factor and vitamin C; absorption is limited by phytates and oxalates. The summary table presents a few iron facts.

Iron

RDA

Men: 8 mg/day

Women: 18 mg/day (19–50 yr)

8 mg/day (51+)

Upper Level

Adults: 45 mg/day

Chief Functions in the Body

Part of the protein hemoglobin, which carries oxygen in the blood; part of the protein myoglobin in muscles, which makes oxygen available for muscle contraction; necessary for the utilization of energy as part of the cells' metabolic machinery

Significant Sources

Red meats, fish, poultry, shellfish, eggs, legumes, dried fruits

Deficiency Symptoms

Anemia: weakness, fatigue, headaches; impaired work performance and cognitive function; impaired immunity; pale skin, nailbeds, mucous membranes, and palm creases; concave nails; inability to regulate body temperature; pica

Toxicity Symptoms

GI distress
Iron overload: infections, fatigue, joint pain, skin pigmentation, organ damage

chelate (KEY-late): a substance that can grasp the positive ions of a mineral.
• **chele** = claw

Zinc

Zinc is a versatile trace element required as a cofactor ◆ by more than 100 enzymes. Virtually all cells contain zinc, but the highest concentrations are found in muscle and bone.[24]

Zinc Roles in the Body

Zinc supports the work of numerous proteins in the body, such as the **metalloenzymes,** ◆ which are involved in a variety of metabolic processes, including the regulation of gene expression.* In addition, zinc stabilizes cell membranes, helping to strengthen their defense against free-radical attacks. Zinc also assists in immune function and in growth and development. Zinc participates in the synthesis, storage, and release of the hormone insulin in the pancreas, although it does not appear to play a direct role in insulin's action. Zinc interacts with platelets in blood clotting, affects thyroid hormone function, and influences behavior and learning performance. It is needed to produce the active form of vitamin A (retinal) in visual pigments and the retinol-binding protein that transports vitamin A. It is essential to normal taste perception, wound healing, the making of sperm, and fetal development. A zinc deficiency impairs all these and other functions, underlining the vast importance of zinc in supporting the body's proteins.

Zinc Absorption and Metabolism

The body's handling of zinc resembles that of iron in some ways and differs in others. A key difference is the circular passage of zinc from the intestine to the body and back again.

Zinc Absorption The rate of zinc absorption varies from about 15 to 40 percent, depending on a person's zinc status—if more is needed, more is absorbed. Also, dietary factors influence zinc absorption. For example, phytates bind zinc, thus limiting its bioavailability.[25]

Upon absorption into an intestinal cell, zinc has two options. It may become involved in the metabolic functions of the cell itself. Alternatively, it may be retained within the cell by **metallothionein,** a special binding protein similar to the iron storage protein, mucosal ferritin.

Metallothionein in the intestinal cells helps to regulate zinc absorption by holding it in reserve until the body needs zinc. Then metallothionein releases zinc into the blood where it can be transported around the body. Metallothionein in the liver performs a similar role, binding zinc until other body tissues signal a need for it.

Zinc Recycling Some zinc eventually reaches the pancreas, where it is incorporated into many of the digestive enzymes that the pancreas releases into the intestine at mealtimes. The intestine thus receives two doses of zinc with each meal—one from foods and the other from the zinc-rich pancreatic secretions. The recycling of zinc in the body from the pancreas to the intestine and back to the pancreas is referred to as the **enteropancreatic circulation** of zinc. As this zinc circulates through the intestine, it may be excreted in shed intestinal cells or absorbed into the body on any of its times around (see Figure 13-6). The body loses zinc primarily in feces. Smaller losses occur in urine, shed skin, hair, sweat, menstrual fluids, and semen.

Zinc Transport Zinc's main transport vehicle in the blood is the protein albumin. Some zinc also binds to transferrin—the same transferrin that carries iron in the

---

◆ Reminder: A *cofactor* is a substance that works with an enzyme to facilitate a chemical reaction.

◆ Metalloenzymes that require zinc:
- Help make parts of the genetic materials DNA and RNA
- Manufacture heme for hemoglobin
- Participate in essential fatty acid metabolism
- Release vitamin A from liver stores
- Metabolize carbohydrates
- Synthesize proteins
- Metabolize alcohol in the liver
- Dispose of damaging free radicals

metalloenzymes (meh-TAL-oh-EN-zimes): enzymes that contain one or more minerals as part of their structures.

metallothionein (meh-TAL-oh-THIGH-oh-neen): a sulfur-rich protein that avidly binds with and transports metals such as zinc.
- **metallo** = containing a metal
- **thio** = containing sulfur
- **ein** = a protein

enteropancreatic (EN-ter-oh-PAN-kree-AT-ik) **circulation:** the circulatory route from the pancreas to the intestine and back to the pancreas.

---

* Among the metalloenzymes requiring zinc are carbonic anhydrase, deoxythymidine kinase, DNA and RNA polymerase, and alkaline phosphatase.

FIGURE 13-6	*Animated!* Enteropancreatic Circulation of Zinc

Some zinc from food is absorbed by the small intestine and sent to the pancreas to be incorporated into digestive enzymes that return to the small intestine. This cycle is called the enteropancreatic circulation of zinc.

ThomsonNOW™
To test your understanding of these concepts, log on to **www .thomsonedu.com/thomsonnow**

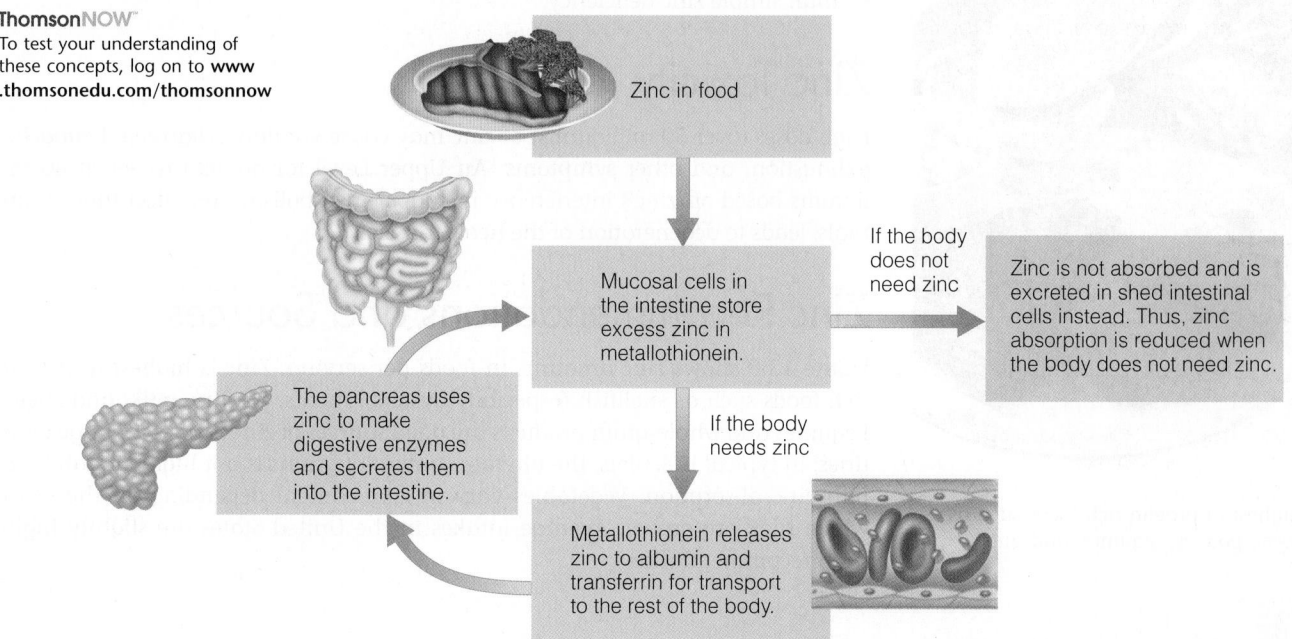

Zinc in food

Mucosal cells in the intestine store excess zinc in metallothionein.

If the body does not need zinc

Zinc is not absorbed and is excreted in shed intestinal cells instead. Thus, zinc absorption is reduced when the body does not need zinc.

The pancreas uses zinc to make digestive enzymes and secretes them into the intestine.

If the body needs zinc

Metallothionein releases zinc to albumin and transferrin for transport to the rest of the body.

blood. In healthy individuals, transferrin is usually less than 50 percent saturated with iron, but in iron overload, it is more saturated. Diets that deliver more than twice as much iron as zinc leave too few transferrin sites available for zinc. The result is poor zinc absorption. The converse is also true: large doses of zinc inhibit iron absorption.

Large doses of zinc create a similar problem with another essential mineral, copper. These nutrient interactions highlight one of the many reasons why people should use supplements conservatively, if at all: supplementation can easily create imbalances.

Zinc Deficiency

Severe zinc deficiencies are not widespread in developed countries, but they do occur in vulnerable groups—pregnant women, young children, the elderly, and the poor. Human zinc deficiency was first reported in the 1960s in children and adolescent boys in Egypt, Iran, and Turkey. Children have especially high zinc needs because they are growing rapidly and synthesizing many zinc-containing proteins, and the native diets among those populations were not meeting these needs. Middle Eastern diets are typically low in the richest zinc source, meats, and the staple foods are legumes, unleavened breads, and other whole-grain foods—all high in fiber and phytates, which inhibit zinc absorption.*

Figure 13-7 shows the severe growth retardation and mentions the immature sexual development characteristic of zinc deficiency. In addition, zinc deficiency hinders digestion and absorption, causing diarrhea, which worsens malnutrition not only for zinc, but for all nutrients. It also impairs the immune response, making infections likely—among them, GI tract infections, which worsen malnutrition, including zinc malnutrition (a classic downward spiral of events).[26] Chronic zinc deficiency damages the central nervous system and brain and may lead to poor motor development and cognitive performance. Because zinc deficiency directly impairs vitamin A metabolism, vitamin A–deficiency symptoms often appear. Zinc

FIGURE 13-7	Zinc-Deficiency Symptom—The Stunted Growth of Dwarfism

The growth retardation, known as dwarfism, is rightly ascribed to zinc deficiency because it is partially reversible when zinc is restored to the diet.

The Egyptian man on the right is an adult of average height. The Egyptian boy on the left is 17 years old but is only 4 feet tall, like a 7-year-old in the United States. His genitalia are like those of a 6-year-old.

© H. Sanstead, University of Texas at Galveston

---

* Unleavened bread contains no yeast, which normally breaks down phytates during fermentation.

Zinc is highest in protein-rich foods such as oysters, beef, poultry, legumes, and nuts.

deficiency also disturbs thyroid function and the metabolic rate. It alters taste, causes loss of appetite, and slows wound healing—in fact, its symptoms are so pervasive that generalized malnutrition and sickness are more likely to be the diagnosis than simple zinc deficiency.

Zinc Toxicity

High doses (over 50 milligrams) of zinc may cause vomiting, diarrhea, headaches, exhaustion, and other symptoms. An Upper Level for adults was set at 40 milligrams based on zinc's interference in copper metabolism—an effect that, in animals, leads to degeneration of the heart muscle.

Zinc Recommendations and Sources

Figure 13-8 shows zinc amounts in foods per serving. Zinc is highest in protein-rich foods such as shellfish (especially oysters), meats, poultry, milk, and cheese. Legumes and whole-grain products are good sources of zinc if eaten in large quantities; in typical U.S. diets, the phytate content of grains is not high enough to impair zinc absorption. Vegetables vary in zinc content depending on the soil in which they are grown. Average intakes in the United States are slightly higher than recommendations.

FIGURE 13-8 Zinc in Selected Foods

See the "How to" section on p. 329 for more information on using this figure.

Food	Serving size (kcalories)
Bread, whole wheat	1 oz slice (70 kcal)
Cornflakes, fortified	1 oz (110 kcal)
Spaghetti pasta	½ c cooked (99 kcal)
Tortilla, flour	1 10"-round (234 kcal)
Broccoli	½ c cooked (22 kcal)
Carrots	½ c shredded raw (24 kcal)
Potato	1 medium baked w/skin (133 kcal)
Tomato juice	¾ c (31 kcal)
Banana	1 medium raw (109 kcal)
Orange	1 medium raw (62 kcal)
Strawberries	½ c fresh (22 kcal)
Watermelon	1 slice (92 kcal)
Milk	1 c reduced-fat 2% (121 kcal)
Yogurt, plain	1 c low-fat (155 kcal)
Cheddar cheese	1½ oz (171 kcal)
Cottage cheese	½ c low-fat 2% (101 kcal)
Pinto beans	½ c cooked (117 kcal)
Peanut butter	2 tbs (188 kcal)
Sunflower seeds	1 oz dry (165 kcal)
Tofu (soybean curd)	½ c (76 kcal)
Ground beef, lean	3 oz broiled (244 kcal)
Chicken breast	3 oz roasted (140 kcal)
Tuna, canned in water	3 oz (99 kcal)
Egg	1 hard cooked (78 kcal)
Excellent, and sometimes unusual, sources:	
Oysters	3 oz cooked (139 kcal)
Sirloin steak, lean	3 oz broiled (172 kcal)
Crab	3 oz cooked (94 kcal)

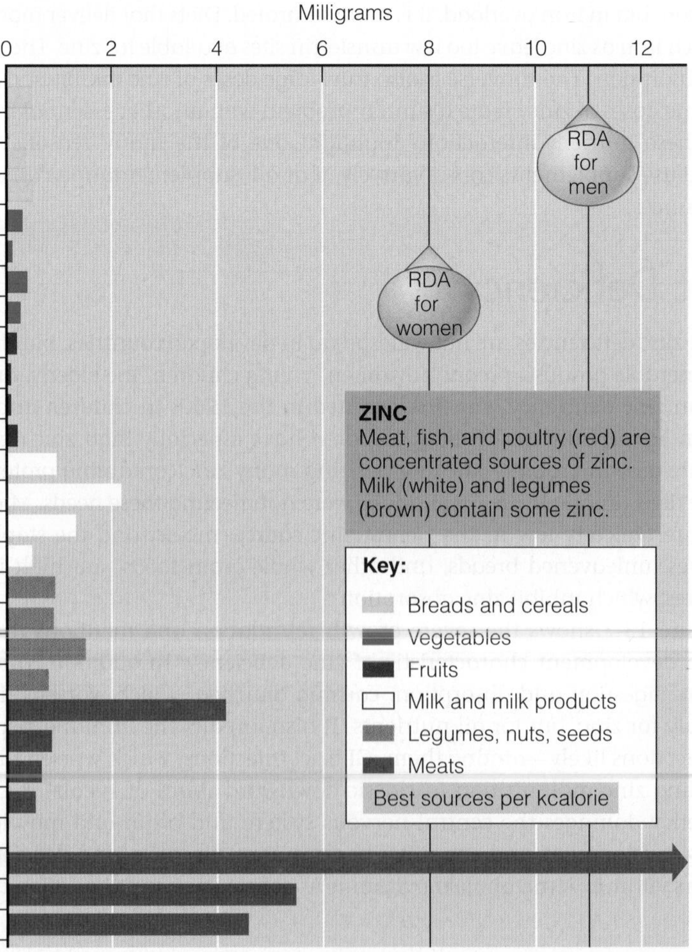

Milligrams: 0 2 4 6 8 10 12

RDA for men
RDA for women

ZINC
Meat, fish, and poultry (red) are concentrated sources of zinc. Milk (white) and legumes (brown) contain some zinc.

Key:
- Breads and cereals
- Vegetables
- Fruits
- Milk and milk products
- Legumes, nuts, seeds
- Meats
- Best sources per kcalorie

Zinc Supplementation

In developed countries, most people obtain enough zinc from the diet without resorting to supplements. In developing countries, zinc supplements play a major role in the treatment of childhood infectious diseases. Zinc supplements effectively reduce the incidence of disease and death associated with diarrhea.[27]

The use of zinc lozenges to treat the common cold has been controversial and inconclusive, with some studies finding them effective and others not.[28] The different study results may reflect the effectiveness of various zinc compounds. Some studies using zinc gluconate report shorter duration of cold symptoms, whereas most studies using other combinations of zinc report no effect. Common side effects of zinc lozenges include nausea and bad taste reactions.

IN SUMMARY

Zinc-requiring enzymes participate in a multitude of reactions affecting growth, vitamin A activity, and pancreatic digestive enzyme synthesis, among others. Both dietary zinc and zinc-rich pancreatic secretions (via enteropancreatic circulation) are available for absorption. Absorption is monitored by a special binding protein (metallothionein) in the intestine. Protein-rich foods derived from animals are the best sources of bioavailable zinc. Fiber and phytates in cereals bind zinc, limiting absorption. Growth retardation and sexual immaturity are hallmark symptoms of zinc deficiency. These facts and others are included in the following table.

Zinc

RDA

Men: 11 mg/day

Women: 8 mg/day

Upper Level

Adults: 40 mg/day

Chief Functions in the Body

Part of many enzymes; associated with the hormone insulin; involved in making genetic material and proteins, immune reactions, transport of vitamin A, taste perception, wound healing, the making of sperm, and the normal development of the fetus

Significant Sources

Protein-containing foods: red meats, shellfish, whole grains; some fortified cereals

Deficiency Symptoms[a]

Growth retardation, delayed sexual maturation, impaired immune function, hair loss, eye and skin lesions, loss of appetite

Toxicity Symptoms

Loss of appetite, impaired immunity, low HDL, copper and iron deficiencies

[a]A rare inherited disease of zinc malabsorption, acrodermatitis (AK-roh-der-ma-TIE-tis) enteropathica (EN-ter-oh-PATH-ick-ah), causes additional and more severe symptoms.

Iodine

Traces of the iodine ion (called iodide) ◆ are indispensable to life. In the GI tract, iodine from foods becomes iodide. This chapter uses the term iodine when referring to the nutrient in foods and iodide when referring to it in the body. Iodide occurs in the body in minuscule amounts, but its principal role in the body and its requirement are well established.

Iodide Roles in the Body Iodide is an integral part of the thyroid hormones ◆ that regulate body temperature, metabolic rate, reproduction, growth, blood cell production, nerve and muscle function, and more. By controlling the rate at which the cells use oxygen, these hormones influence the amount of energy released during basal metabolism.

◆ The ion form of iodine is called iodide.

◆ The thyroid gland releases tetraiodothyronine (T_4), commonly known as **thyroxine** (thigh-ROCKS-in), to its target tissues. Upon reaching the cells, T_4 is deiodinated to triiodothyronine (T_3), which is the active form of the hormone.

FIGURE 13-9 Iodine-Deficiency Symptom—The Enlarged Thyroid of Goiter

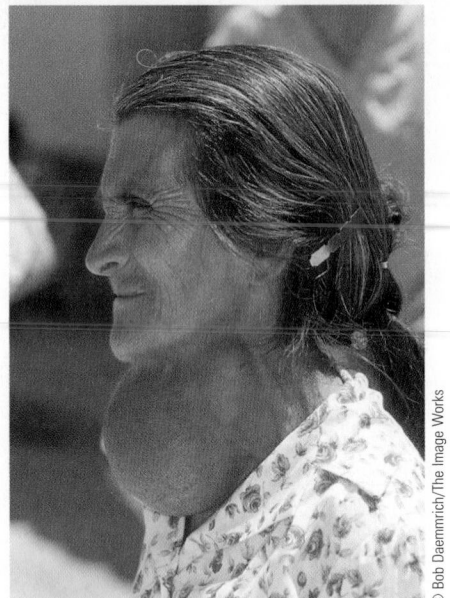

In iodine deficiency, the thyroid gland enlarges—a condition known as simple goiter.

◆ Thyroid-stimulating hormone is also called *thyrotropin.*

◆ Examples of goitrogen-containing foods:
  • Cabbage, spinach, radishes, rutabagas
  • Soybeans, peanuts
  • Peaches, strawberries

◆ The underactivity of the thyroid gland is known as *hypothyroidism* and may be caused by iodine deficiency or any number of other causes. Without treatment, an infant with *congenital hypothyroidism* will develop the physical and mental retardation of *cretinism.*

◆ Iodized salt contains about 60 μg iodine per gram salt.

◆ On average, ¹/₂ tsp iodized salt provides the RDA for iodine.

---

goiter (GOY-ter): an enlargement of the thyroid gland due to an iodine deficiency, malfunction of the gland, or overconsumption of a goitrogen. Goiter caused by iodine deficiency is **simple goiter**.

goitrogen (GOY-troh-jen): a substance that enlarges the thyroid gland and causes **toxic goiter.** Goitrogens occur naturally in such foods as cabbage, kale, brussels sprouts, cauliflower, broccoli, and kohlrabi.

cretinism (CREE-tin-ism): a congenital disease characterized by mental and physical retardation and commonly caused by maternal iodine deficiency during pregnancy.

Iodine Deficiency The hypothalamus regulates thyroid hormone production by controlling the release of the pituitary's thyroid-stimulating hormone (TSH). ◆ With iodine deficiency, thyroid hormone production declines, and the body responds by secreting more TSH in a futile attempt to accelerate iodide uptake by the thyroid gland. If a deficiency persists, the cells of the thyroid gland enlarge to trap as much iodide as possible. Sometimes the gland enlarges until it makes a visible lump in the neck, a simple **goiter** (shown in Figure 13-9).

Goiter afflicts about 200 million people the world over, many of them in South America, Asia, and Africa. In all but 4 percent of these cases, the cause is iodine deficiency. As for the 4 percent (8 million), most have goiter because they regularly eat excessive amounts of foods ◆ that contain an antithyroid substance (**goitrogen**) whose effect is not counteracted by dietary iodine. The goitrogens present in plants remind us that even natural components of foods can cause harm when eaten in excess.

Goiter may be the earliest and most obvious sign of iodine deficiency, but the most tragic and prevalent damage occurs in the brain. Children with even a mild iodine deficiency typically have goiters and perform poorly in school. With sustained treatment, however, mental performance in the classroom as well as thyroid function improves.[29]

A severe iodine deficiency during pregnancy causes the extreme and irreversible mental and physical retardation known as **cretinism.** ◆ Cretinism affects approximately 6 million people worldwide and can be averted by the early diagnosis and treatment of maternal iodine deficiency. A worldwide effort to provide iodized salt to people living in iodine-deficient areas has been dramatically successful. Because iron deficiency is common among people with iodine deficiency and because iron deficiency reduces the effectiveness of iodized salt, dual fortification with both iron and iodine may be most beneficial.[30]

Iodine Toxicity Excessive intakes of iodine can interfere with thyroid function and enlarge the glands, just as deficiency can.[31] During pregnancy, exposure to excessive iodine from foods, prenatal supplements, or medications is especially damaging to the developing infant. An infant exposed to toxic amounts of iodine during gestation may develop a goiter so severe as to block the airways and cause suffocation. The Upper Level is over 1100 micrograms per day for an adult—several times higher than average intakes.

Iodine Recommendations and Sources The ocean is the world's major source of iodine. In coastal areas, seafood, water, and even iodine-containing sea mist are dependable iodine sources. Further inland, the amount of iodine in foods is variable and generally reflects the amount present in the soil in which plants are grown or on which animals graze. Landmasses that were once under the ocean have soils rich in iodine; those in flood-prone areas where water leaches iodine from the soil are poor in iodine. In the United States and Canada, the iodization of salt ◆ has eliminated the widespread misery caused by iodine deficiency during the 1930s, but iodized salt is not available in many parts of the world. Some countries add iodine to bread, fish paste, or drinking water instead.

Although average consumption of iodine in the United States exceeds recommendations, it falls below toxic levels. Some of the excess iodine in the U.S. diet stems from fast foods, which use iodized salt liberally. Some iodine comes from bakery products and from milk. The baking industry uses iodates (iodine salts) as dough conditioners, and most dairies feed cows iodine-containing medications and use iodine to disinfect milking equipment. Now that these sources have been identified, food industries have reduced their use of these compounds, but the sudden emergence of this problem points to a need for continued surveillance of the food supply. Processed foods in the United States use regular salt, not iodized salt.

The recommended intake of iodine for adults is a minuscule amount. The need for iodine is easily met by consuming seafood, vegetables grown in iodine-rich soil, and iodized salt. ◆ In the United States, labels indicate whether salt is iodized; in Canada, all table salt is iodized.

IN SUMMARY

Iodide, the ion of the mineral iodine, is an essential component of the thyroid hormone. An iodine deficiency can lead to simple goiter (enlargement of the thyroid gland) and can impair fetal development, causing cretinism. Iodization of salt has largely eliminated iodine deficiency in the United States and Canada. The table provides a summary of iodine.

Iodine

RDA	Deficiency Disease
Adults: 150 µg/day	Simple goiter, cretinism

Upper Level	Deficiency Symptoms
1100 µg/day	Underactive thyroid gland, goiter, mental and physical retardation in infants (cretinism)

Chief Functions in the Body	Toxicity Symptoms
A component of two thyroid hormones that help to regulate growth, development, and metabolic rate	Underactive thyroid gland, elevated TSH, goiter

Significant Sources	
Iodized salt, seafood, bread, dairy products, plants grown in iodine-rich soil and animals fed those plants	

Only "iodized salt" has had iodine added.

Selenium

The essential mineral **selenium** shares some of the chemical characteristics of the mineral sulfur. This similarity allows selenium to substitute for sulfur in the amino acids methionine, cysteine, and cystine.[32]

Selenium Roles in the Body Selenium is one of the body's antioxidant nutrients,
◆ working primarily as a part of proteins—most notably, the enzyme glutathione peroxidase.[33] Glutathione peroxidase and vitamin E work in tandem. Glutathione peroxidase prevents free-radical formation, thus blocking the chain reaction before it begins; if free radicals do form and a chain reaction starts, vitamin E stops it. (Highlight 11 describes free-radical formation, chain reactions, and antioxidant action in detail.) Another enzyme that converts the thyroid hormone to its active form also contains selenium.

◆ Key antioxidant nutrients:
 • Vitamin C, vitamin E, beta-carotene
 • Selenium

Selenium Deficiency Selenium deficiency is associated with a heart disease ◆ that is prevalent in regions of China where the soil and foods lack selenium. Although the primary cause of this heart disease is probably a virus, selenium deficiency appears to predispose people to it, and adequate selenium seems to prevent it.

◆ The heart disease associated with selenium deficiency is named **Keshan** (KESH-an or ka-SHAWN) **disease** for one of the provinces of China where it was studied. Keshan disease is characterized by heart enlargement and insufficiency; fibrous tissue replaces the muscle tissue that normally composes the middle layer of the walls of the heart.

Selenium and Cancer Some research suggests that selenium may protect against some types of cancers.[34] Given the potential for harm and the lack of conclusive evidence, however, recommendations to take selenium supplements would be premature—and perhaps ineffective as well. Selenium from foods appears to be more effective in inhibiting cancer growth than selenium from supplements. Such a finding reinforces a theme that has been repeated throughout this text—foods offer many more health benefits than supplements.

Selenium Recommendations and Sources Selenium is found in the soil, and therefore in the crops grown for consumption.[35] People living in regions with selenium-poor soil may still get enough selenium, partly because they eat vegetables

selenium (se-LEEN-ee-um): a trace element.

and grains transported from other regions and partly because they eat meats and other animal products, which are reliable sources of selenium. Average intakes in the United States and Canada are above the RDA, which is based on the amount needed to maximize glutathione peroxidase activity.

Selenium Toxicity Because high doses of selenium are toxic, an Upper Level has been set. Selenium toxicity causes loss and brittleness of hair and nails, garlic breath odor, and nervous system abnormalities.

IN SUMMARY

Selenium is an antioxidant nutrient that works closely with the glutathione peroxidase enzyme and vitamin E. Selenium is found in association with protein in foods. Deficiencies are associated with a predisposition to a type of heart abnormality known as Keshan disease. See the table below for a summary of selenium.

Selenium

RDA	Deficiency Symptoms
Adults: 55 µg/day	Predisposition to heart disease characterized by cardiac tissue becoming fibrous (Keshan disease)
Upper Level	
Adults: 400 µg/day	**Toxicity Symptoms**
Chief Functions in the Body	Loss and brittleness of hair and nails; skin rash, fatigue, irritability, and nervous system disorders; garlic breath odor
Defends against oxidation; regulates thyroid hormone	
Significant Sources	
Seafood, meat, whole grains, fruits, and vegetables (depending on soil content)	

Copper

The body contains about 100 milligrams of copper. It is found in a variety of cells and tissues.

Copper Roles in the Body Copper serves as a constituent of several enzymes. The copper-containing enzymes have diverse metabolic roles with one common characteristic: all involve reactions that consume oxygen or oxygen radicals. For example, copper-containing enzymes catalyze the oxidation of ferrous iron to ferric iron.*[36] Copper's role in iron metabolism makes it a key factor in hemoglobin synthesis. Two copper- and zinc-containing enzymes participate in the body's natural defense against free radicals.** Still another copper enzyme helps to manufacture collagen and heal wounds.† Copper, like iron, is needed in many of the metabolic reactions related to the release of energy.‡

Copper Deficiency and Toxicity Typical U.S. diets provide adequate amounts of copper and deficiency is rare. In animals, copper deficiency raises blood cholesterol and damages blood vessels, raising questions about whether low dietary copper might contribute to cardiovascular disease in humans.

---

* The copper-containing enzyme *ceruloplasmin* participates in the oxidation of ferrous iron to ferric iron.
** Two copper-containing *superoxide dismutase* enzymes defend against free radicals.
† The copper-containing enzyme *lysyl oxidase* helps synthesize connective tissues.
‡ The copper-containing enzyme *cytochrome C oxidase* participates in the electron transport chain.

Some genetic disorders create a copper toxicity, but excessive intakes from foods are unlikely. Excessive intakes from supplements may cause liver damage, and therefore an Upper Level has been set.

Two rare genetic disorders affect copper status in opposite directions. In Menkes disease, the intestinal cells absorb copper, but cannot release it into circulation, causing a life-threatening deficiency. In Wilson's disease, copper accumulates in the liver and brain, creating a life-threatening toxicity. Wilson's disease can be controlled by reducing copper intake, using chelating agents such as penicillamine, and taking zinc supplements, which interfere with copper absorption. (The use of chelation in health care is mentioned in Highlight 18's discussion of alternative therapies.)

Copper Recommendations and Sources The richest food sources of copper are legumes, whole grains, nuts, shellfish, and seeds. Over half of the copper from foods is absorbed, and the major route of elimination appears to be bile. Water may also provide copper, depending on the type of plumbing pipe and the hardness of the water.

IN SUMMARY

Copper is a component of several enzymes, all of which are involved in some way with oxygen or oxidation. Some act as antioxidants; others are essential to iron metabolism. Legumes, whole grains, and shellfish are good sources of copper. See the table for a summary of copper facts.

Copper

RDA	Significant Sources
Adults: 900 µg/day	Seafood, nuts, whole grains, seeds, legumes

Upper Level	Deficiency Symptoms
Adults: 10,000 µg/day (10 mg/day)	Anemia, bone abnormalities

Chief Functions in the Body	Toxicity Symptoms
Necessary for the absorption and use of iron in the formation of hemoglobin; part of several enzymes	Liver damage

---

Manganese

The human body contains a tiny 20 milligrams of manganese. Most of it can be found in the bones and metabolically active organs such as the liver, kidneys, and pancreas.

Manganese Roles in the Body Manganese acts as a cofactor for many enzymes that facilitate the metabolism of carbohydrate, lipids, and amino acids. In addition, manganese-containing metalloenzymes assist in bone formation and the conversion of pyruvate to a TCA cycle compound.

Manganese Deficiency and Toxicity Manganese requirements are low, and many plant foods contain significant amounts of this trace mineral, so deficiencies are rare. As is true of other trace minerals, however, dietary factors such as phytates inhibit its absorption. In addition, high intakes of iron and calcium limit manganese absorption, so people who use supplements of those minerals regularly may impair their manganese status.

Toxicity is more likely to occur from an environment contaminated with manganese than from dietary intake.[37] Miners who inhale large quantities of manganese dust on the job over prolonged periods show symptoms of a brain disease, along with abnormalities in appearance and behavior. Still, an Upper Level has been established based on intakes from food, water, and supplements.

Manganese Recommendations and Sources Grain products make the greatest contribution of manganese to the diet. With insufficient information to establish an RDA, an AI was set based on average intakes.

IN SUMMARY

Manganese-dependent enzymes are involved in bone formation and various metabolic processes. Because manganese is widespread in plant foods, deficiencies are rare, although regular use of calcium and iron supplements may limit manganese absorption. A summary of manganese appears in the table below.

Manganese

AI	Significant Sources
Men: 2.3 mg/day	Nuts, whole grains, leafy vegetables, tea
Women: 1.8 mg/day	**Deficiency Symptoms**
Upper Level	Rare
Adults: 11 mg/day	**Toxicity Symptoms**
Chief Functions in the Body	Nervous system disorders
Cofactor for several enzymes; bone formation	

Fluoride

Fluoride is present in virtually all soils, water supplies, plants, and animals. Only a trace of fluoride occurs in the human body, but with this amount, the crystalline deposits in bones and teeth are larger and more perfectly formed.

Fluoride Roles in the Body As Chapter 12 explained, during the mineralization of bones ◆ and teeth, calcium and phosphorus form crystals called hydroxyapatite. Then fluoride replaces the hydroxyl (OH) portions of the hydroxyapatite crystal, forming **fluorapatite**, which makes the bones stronger and the teeth more resistant to decay.

Dental caries ranks as the nation's most widespread health problem: an estimated 95 percent of the population have decayed, missing, or filled teeth. By interfering with a person's ability to chew and eat a wide variety of foods, these dental problems can quickly lead to a multitude of nutrition problems. Where fluoride is lacking, dental decay is common.

Drinking water is usually the best source of fluoride, and more than 65 percent of the U.S. population served by public water systems receives optimal levels of fluoride (see Figure 13-10).[38] (Most bottled waters lack fluoride.) Fluoridation of drinking water (to raise the concentration to 1 part fluoride per 1 million ◆ parts water) offers the greatest protection against dental caries at virtually no risk of toxicity.[39] By fluoridating the drinking water, a community offers its residents, particularly the children, a safe, economical, practical, and effective way to defend against dental caries.

Fluoride Toxicity Too much fluoride can damage the teeth, causing **fluorosis**.[40] For this reason, an Upper Level has been established. In mild cases, the teeth develop small white specks; in severe cases, the enamel becomes pitted and permanently stained (as shown in Figure 13-11). Fluorosis occurs only during tooth development and cannot be reversed, making its prevention ◆ a high priority. To limit fluoride in-

---

◆ Key bone nutrients:
  • Vitamin D, vitamin K, vitamin A
  • Calcium, phosphorus, magnesium, fluoride

◆ For perspective, 1 part per million (1 ppm) is approximately 1 mg per liter.

◆ To prevent fluorosis:
  • Monitor the fluoride content of the local water supply.
  • Supervise toddlers when they brush their teeth—using only a little toothpaste (pea-size amount).
  • Use fluoride supplements only as prescribed by a physician.

fluorapatite (floor-APP-uh-tite): the stabilized form of bone and tooth crystal, in which fluoride has replaced the hydroxyl groups of hydroxyapatite.

fluorosis (floor-OH-sis): discoloration and pitting of tooth enamel caused by excess fluoride during tooth development.

gestion, take care not to swallow fluoride-containing dental products such as tooth-paste and mouthwash.

Fluoride Recommendations and Sources As mentioned earlier, much of the U.S. population has access to water with an optimal fluoride concentration, which typically delivers about 1 milligram per person per day.[41] Fish and most teas contain appreciable amounts of natural fluoride.

IN SUMMARY

Fluoride makes bones stronger and teeth more resistant to decay. Fluoridation of public water supplies can significantly reduce the incidence of dental caries, but excess fluoride during tooth development can cause fluorosis—discolored and pitted tooth enamel. The table below summarizes fluoride information.

Flouride

AI	Significant Sources
Men: 3.8 mg/day	Drinking water (if fluoride containing or fluori-dated), tea, seafood
Women: 3.1 mg/day	
Upper Level	**Deficiency Symptoms**
Adults: 10 mg/day	Susceptibility to tooth decay
Chief Functions in the Body	**Toxicity Symptoms**
Maintains health of bones and teeth; helps to make teeth resistant to decay	Fluorosis (pitting and discoloration of teeth)

Chromium

Chromium is an essential mineral that participates in carbohydrate and lipid metabolism. Like iron, chromium assumes different charges. In chromium, the Cr^{+++} ion is the most stable and most commonly found in foods.

Chromium Roles in the Body Chromium helps maintain glucose homeostasis by enhancing the activity of the hormone insulin. ◆ When chromium is lacking, a diabetes-like condition may develop with elevated blood glucose and impaired glucose tolerance, insulin response, and glucagon response. In spite of these relationships, research findings suggest that chromium supplements do not effectively improve glucose or insulin responses in diabetes.[42]

Chromium Recommendations and Sources Chromium is present in a variety of foods. The best sources are unrefined foods, particularly liver, brewer's yeast, and whole grains. The more refined foods people eat, the less chromium they ingest.

Chromium Supplements Supplement advertisements have succeeded in convincing consumers that they can lose fat and build muscle by taking chromium picolinate. Whether chromium supplements (either picolinate or plain) reduce body fat or improve muscle strength remains controversial. (Highlight 14 revisits chromium picolinate and other supplements athletes use in the hopes of improving their performance.)

IN SUMMARY

Chromium enhances insulin's action. A deficiency can result in a diabetes-like condition. Chromium is widely available in unrefined foods including brewer's yeast, whole grains, and liver. The following table provides a summary of chromium.

(continued)

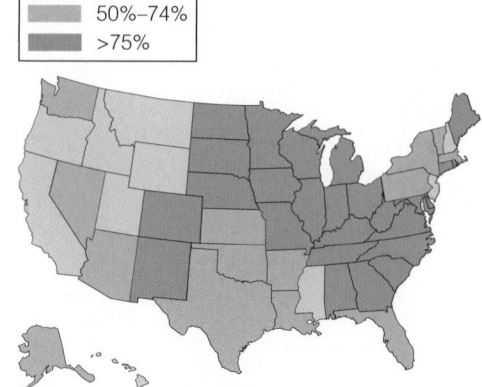

FIGURE 13-10 U.S. Population with Access to Fluoridated Water through Public Water Systems

Key:
- <49%
- 50%–74%
- >75%

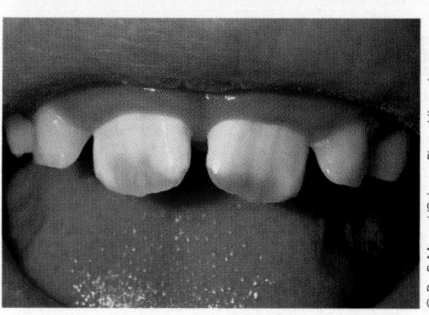

FIGURE 13-11 Fluoride-Toxicity Symptom—The Mottled Teeth of Fluorosis

© Dr. P. Marrazzi/Science Photo Library/Photo Researchers, Inc.

◆ Small organic compounds that enhance insulin's action are called **glucose tolerance factors (GTF).** Some glucose tolerance factors contain chromium.

Chromium (continued)		
AI		**Deficiency Symptoms**
Men: 35 µg/day		Diabetes-like condition
Women: 25 µg/day		
		Toxicity Symptoms
Chief Functions in the Body		None reported
Enhances insulin action and may improve glucose tolerance		
Significant Sources		
Meats (especially liver), whole grains, brewer's yeast		

Molybdenum

Molybdenum acts as a working part of several metalloenzymes. Dietary deficiencies of molybdenum are unknown because the amounts needed are minuscule—as little as 0.1 part per million parts of body tissue. Legumes, breads and other grain products, leafy green vegetables, milk, and liver are molybdenum-rich foods. Average daily intakes fall within the suggested range of intakes.

Molybdenum toxicity in people is rare. It has been reported in animal studies, and an Upper Level has been established. Characteristics of molybdenum toxicity include kidney damage and reproductive abnormalities. For a summary of molybdenum facts, see the accompanying table.

IN SUMMARY

Molybdenum		Significant Sources
RDA		Legumes, cereals, nuts
Adults: 45 µg/day		**Deficiency Symptoms**
Upper Level		Unknown
Adults: 2 mg/day		**Toxicity Symptoms**
Chief Functions in the Body		None reported; reproductive effects in animals
Cofactor for several enzymes		

Other Trace Minerals

Research to determine whether other trace minerals are essential is difficult because their quantities in the body are so small and also because human deficiencies are unknown. Guessing their functions in the body can be particularly problematic. Much of the available knowledge comes from research using animals.

Nickel may serve as a cofactor for certain enzymes. Silicon is involved in the formation of bones and collagen. Vanadium, too, is necessary for growth and bone development and for normal reproduction. Cobalt is a key mineral in the large vitamin B_{12} molecule (see Figure 13-12), but it is not an essential nutrient and no recommendation has been established. Boron may play a key role in brain activities; in animals, boron strengthens bones.[43]

In the future, we may discover that many other trace minerals play key nutritional roles. Even arsenic—famous as a poison used by murderers and known to be a carcinogen—may turn out to be essential for human beings in tiny quantities. It has already proved useful in the treatment of some types of leukemia.

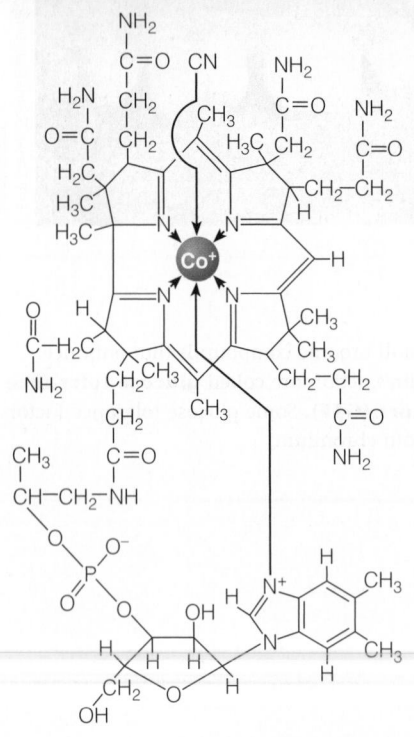

FIGURE 13-12   Cobalt with Vitamin B_{12}

The intricate vitamin B_{12} molecule contains one atom of the mineral cobalt. The alternative name for vitamin B_{12}, cobalamin, reflects the presence of cobalt in its structure.

molybdenum (mo-LIB-duh-num): a trace element.

Contaminant Minerals

Chapter 12 and this chapter have told of the many ways minerals serve the body—maintaining fluid and electrolyte balance, providing structural support to the bones, transporting oxygen, and assisting enzymes. In contrast to the minerals that the body requires, contaminant minerals impair the body's growth, work capacity, and general health. Contaminant minerals include the **heavy metals** lead, mercury, and cadmium that enter the food supply by way of soil, water, and air pollution. This section focuses on lead poisoning because it is a serious environmental threat to young children and because reducing blood lead levels in children is a goal of Healthy People 2010.[44] Much of the information on lead applies to the other contaminant minerals as well—they all disrupt body processes and impair nutrition status similarly.

Like other minerals, lead is indestructible; the body cannot change its chemistry. Chemically similar to nutrient minerals like iron, calcium, and zinc (cations with two positive charges), lead displaces them from some of the metabolic sites they normally occupy but is then unable to perform their roles. For example, lead competes with iron in heme, but it cannot carry oxygen. Similarly, lead competes with calcium in the brain, but it cannot signal messages from nerve cells. Excess lead in the blood also deranges the structure of red blood cell membranes, making them leaky and fragile. Lead interacts with white blood cells, too, impairing their ability to fight infection, and it binds to antibodies, thwarting their effort to resist disease.

In addition to its effects on the blood, lead impairs many body systems, most notably causing irreversible damage to the central nervous system.[45] It impairs such normal activities as growth by interfering with hormone activity.[46] It interferes with tooth development and may contribute to dental caries as well.[47] Even at low levels, blood lead concentrations correlate with poor IQ scores.[48] In short, lead's interactions in the body have profound adverse effects—the greater the exposure, the more damaging the effects. The American Academy of Pediatrics recommends testing children who have been identified as having a high risk for lead poisoning. Follow-up testing is critical to ensuring appropriate intervention.[49] Children with high blood lead levels are treated with chelating agents—medications that bind specifically to lead and carry it out in the urine.[50] Table 13-1 lists symptoms of lead toxicity.

Lead typifies the ways all heavy metals behave in the body: they interfere with nutrients that are trying to do their jobs. The "good guy" nutrients are shoved aside by the "bad guy" contaminants. Then, when the contaminants cannot perform the roles of the nutrients, health diminishes. To safeguard our health, we must defend ourselves against contamination by eating nutrient-rich foods and preserving a clean environment.

Closing Thoughts on the Nutrients

This chapter completes the introductory lessons on the nutrients. Each nutrient from the amino acids to zinc has been described rather thoroughly—its chemistry, roles in the body, sources in the diet, symptoms of deficiency and toxicity, and influences on health and disease. Such a detailed examination is informative, but it can also be misleading. It is important to step back from the detailed study of the individual nutrients to look at them as a whole. After all, people eat foods, not nutrients, and most foods deliver dozens of nutrients. Furthermore, nutrients work cooperatively with each other in the body; their actions are most often *interactions*. This chapter alone mentioned how iron depends on vitamin C to keep it in its active form and copper to incorporate it into hemoglobin, how zinc is needed to activate and transport vitamin

TABLE 13-1 Symptoms of Lead Toxicity

In Children
- Learning disabilities (reduced short-term memory; impaired concentration)
- Low IQ
- Behavior problems
- Slow growth
- Iron-deficiency anemia
- Dental caries
- Sleep disturbances (night waking, restlessness, head banging)
- Nervous system disorders; seizures
- Slow reaction time; poor coordination
- Impaired hearing

In Adults
- Hypertension
- Reproductive complications
- Kidney failure

heavy metals: mineral ions such as mercury and lead, so called because they are of relatively high atomic weight. Many heavy metals are poisonous.

A, and how both iodine and selenium are needed for the synthesis of thyroid hormone. The accompanying table condenses the information on the trace minerals for your review.

IN SUMMARY — The Trace Minerals

Mineral and Chief Functions	Deficiency Symptoms	Toxicity Symptoms[a]	Significant Sources
Iron Part of the protein hemoglobin, which carries oxygen in the blood; part of the protein myoglobin in muscles, which makes oxygen available for muscle contraction; necessary for energy metabolism	Anemia: weakness, fatigue, headaches; impaired work performance; impaired immunity; pale skin, nail beds, mucous membranes, and palm creases; concave nails; inability to regulate body temperature; pica	GI distress; iron overload: infections, fatigue, joint pain, skin pigmentation, organ damage	Red meats, fish, poultry, shellfish, eggs, legumes, dried fruits
Zinc Part of insulin and many enzymes; involved in making genetic material and proteins, immune reactions, transport of vitamin A, taste perception, wound healing, the making of sperm, and normal fetal development	Growth retardation, delayed sexual maturation, impaired immune function, hair loss, eye and skin lesions, loss of appetite.	Loss of appetite, impaired immunity, low HDL, copper and iron deficiencies	Protein-containing foods: red meats, fish, shellfish, poultry, whole grains; fortified cereals
Iodine A component of the thyroid hormones that help to regulate growth, development, and metabolic rate	Underactive thyroid gland, goiter, mental and physical retardation (cretinism)	Underactive thyroid gland, elevated TSH, goiter	Iodized salt; seafood; plants grown in iodine-rich soil and animals fed those plants
Selenium Part of an enzyme that defends against oxidation; regulates thyroid hormone	Associated with Keshan disease	Nail and hair brittleness and loss; fatigue, irritability, and nervous system disorders, skin rash, garlic breath odor	Seafoods, organ meats; other meats, whole grains, fruits, and vegetables (depending on soil content)
Copper Helps form hemoglobin; part of several enzymes	Anemia, bone abnormalities	Liver damage	Seafood, nuts, legumes, whole grains, seeds
Manganese Cofactor for several enzymes; bone formation	Rare	Nervous symptom disorders	Nuts, whole grains, leafy vegetables, tea
Fluoride Maintains health of bones and teeth; confers decay resistance on teeth	Susceptibility to tooth decay	Fluorosis (pitting and discoloration) of teeth,	Drinking water (if fluoridated), tea, seafood
Chromium Enhances insulin action, may improve glucose intolerance	Diabetes-like condition	None reported	Meats (liver), whole grains, brewer's yeast
Molybdenum Cofactor for several enzymes	Unknown	None reported	Legumes, cereals, nuts

[a] Acute toxicities of many minerals cause abdominal pain, nausea, vomiting, and diarrhea.

How much of each particular nutrient does the body need? Estimates fall somewhere between intakes that are inadequate and cause illness and intakes that are excessive and cause illness. A wide range of intakes that support health, to varying degrees, lies between deficiency and toxicity. In the past, nutrient needs were determined by how much was needed to prevent deficiency symptoms. If lack of a nutrient caused illness, it was defined as essential. Today, nutrient needs are based on how much is needed to support optimal health. The amount of vitamin C needed to prevent scurvy is much less than the amount correlated with reducing the risk of cancer, for example. Furthermore, nutrients are being examined within the context of the whole diet. Health benefits are not credited to vitamin C alone, but also to the vitamin C–rich fruits and vegetables that provide many other nutrients—and nonnutrients (phytochemicals)—important to health.

People can also improve their health with physical activity. Energy expenditure is unlike money expenditure: it is desirable to *spend* energy, not to save it (within reason, of course). The more energy people spend, the more food they can afford to eat—food that delivers both nutrients and pleasure. The next chapter presents details on nutrition and physical activity.

Nutrition Portfolio

ThomsonNOW™
www.thomsonedu.com/thomsonnow

Trace minerals from a variety of foods, especially those in the meat and meat alternate group, support many of your body's activities.

■ Examine the variety in your food intake, taking particular notice of how often you include meats, seafood, poultry, or legumes, weekly.

■ Describe the advantages of using iodized salt.

■ Determine whether your community provides fluoridated water.

NUTRITION ON THE NET

ThomsonNOW™
For further study of topics covered in this chapter, log on to www.thomsonedu.com/thomsonnow. Go to Chapter 13, then to Nutrition on the Net.

WEBSITES

• Search for "minerals" at the American Dietetic Association: **www.eatright.org**

• Search for the individual minerals by name at the U.S. Government health information site: **www.healthfinder.gov**

• Learn more about iron overload from the Iron Overload Diseases Association: **www.ironoverload.org**

• Learn more about iodine and thyroid disease from the American Thyroid Association: **www.thyroid.org**

• Learn more about lead in paint, dust, and soil from the Centers for Disease Control or Environmental Protection Agency: **www.cdc.gov/lead** or **www.epa.gov/lead**

NUTRITION CALCULATIONS

ThomsonNOW™ For additional practice log on to www.thomsonedu.com/thomsonnow. Go to Chapter 13, then to Nutrition Calculations.

Once you have mastered these examples, you will understand minerals a little better and be prepared to examine your own food choices. Be sure to show your calculations for each problem. (See p. 468 for answers.)

1. For each of these minerals, note the unit of measure for recommendations:

Iron	Manganese
Zinc	Fluoride
Iodine	Chromium
Selenium	Molybdenum
Copper	

2. Appreciate foods for their iron density. Following is a list of foods with the energy amount and the iron content per serving (p. 466).
   a. Rank these foods by iron per serving.
   b. Calculate the iron density (divide milligrams by kcalories) for these foods and rank them by their iron per kcalorie.

c. Name three foods that are higher on the second list than they were on the first list.

d. What do these foods have in common?

Food	Iron (mg)	Energy (kcal)	Iron Density (mg/kcal)
Milk, fat-free, 1 c	0.10	85	
Cheddar cheese, 1 oz	0.19	114	
Broccoli, cooked from fresh, chopped, 1 c	1.31	44	
Sweet potato, baked in skin, 1 ea	0.51	117	
Cantaloupe melon, ½	0.56	93	
Carrots, from fresh, ½ c	0.48	35	
Whole-wheat bread, 1 slice	0.87	64	
Green peas, cooked from frozen, ½ c	1.26	62	
Apple, medium	0.38	125	
Sirloin steak, lean, 4 oz	3.81	228	
Pork chop, lean, broiled, 1 ea	0.66	166	

STUDY QUESTIONS

ThomsonNOW™

To assess your understanding of chapter topics, take the Student Practice Test and explore the modules recommended in your Personalized Study Plan. Log onto **www.thomsonedu.com/thomsonnow**.

These questions will help you review the chapter. You will find the answers in the discussions on the pages provided.

1. Distinguish between heme and nonheme iron. Discuss the factors that enhance iron absorption. (pp. 443–444)

2. Distinguish between iron deficiency and iron-deficiency anemia. What are the symptoms of iron-deficiency anemia? (pp. 445–447)

3. What causes iron overload? What are its symptoms? (p. 448)

4. Describe the similarities and differences in the absorption and regulation of iron and zinc. (pp. 443–445, 452–453)

5. Discuss possible reasons for a low intake of zinc. What factors affect the bioavailability of zinc? (p. 454)

6. Describe the principal functions of iodide, selenium, copper, manganese, fluoride, chromium, and molybdenum in the body. (pp. 455–462)

7. What public health measure has been used in preventing simple goiter? What measure has been recommended for protection against tooth decay? (pp. 456–457, 460–461)

8. Discuss the importance of balanced and varied diets in obtaining the essential minerals and avoiding toxicities. (pp. 463–465)

9. Describe some of the ways trace minerals interact with each other and with other nutrients. (p. 463)

These multiple choice questions will help you prepare for an exam. Answers can be found on p. 468.

1. Iron absorption is impaired by:
   a. heme.
   b. phytates.
   c. vitamin C.
   d. MFP factor.

2. Which of these people is *least* likely to develop an iron deficiency?
   a. 3-year-old boy
   b. 52-year-old man
   c. 17-year-old girl
   d. 24-year-old woman

3. Which of the following would *not* describe the blood cells of a severe iron deficiency?
   a. anemic
   b. microcytic
   c. pernicious
   d. hypochromic

4. Which provides the most absorbable iron?
   a. 1 apple
   b. 1 c milk
   c. 3 oz steak
   d. ½ c spinach

5. The intestinal protein that helps to regulate zinc absorption is:
   a. albumin.
   b. ferritin.
   c. hemosiderin.
   d. metallothionein.

6. A classic sign of zinc deficiency is:
   a. anemia.
   b. goiter.
   c. mottled teeth.
   d. growth retardation.

7. Cretinism is caused by a deficiency of:
   a. iron.
   b. zinc.
   c. iodine.
   d. selenium.

8. The mineral best known for its role as an antioxidant is:
   a. copper.
   b. selenium.
   c. manganese.
   d. molybdenum.

9. Fluorosis occurs when fluoride:
   a. is excessive.
   b. is inadequate.
   c. binds with phosphorus.
   d. interacts with calcium.

10. Which mineral enhances insulin activity?
   a. zinc
   b. iodine
   c. chromium
   d. manganese

REFERENCES

1. M. W. Hentze, M. U. Muckenthaler, and N. C. Andrews, Molecular control of mammalian iron metabolism, *Cell* 117 (2004): 285-297.

2. R. E. Fleming and B. R. Bacon, Orchestration of iron homeostasis, *New England Journal of Medicine* 352 (2005): 1741-1744; Chung and Wessling-Resnick, Lessons learned from genetic and nutritional iron deficiencies, *Nutrition Reviews* 62 (2004): 212-220.

3. E. G. Theil, Iron, ferritin, and nutrition, *Annual Review of Nutrition* 24 (2004): 327-343.

4. Committee on Dietary Reference Intakes, *Dietary Reference Intakes for Vitamin A, Vitamin K, Arsenic, Boron, Chromium, Copper, Iodine, Iron, Manganese, Molybdenum, Nickel, Silicon, Vanadium, and Zinc* (Washington, D.C.: National Academy Press, 2001), p. 315.

5. S. Miret, R. J. Simpson, and A. T. McKie, Physiology and molecular biology of dietary iron absorption, *Annual Review of Nutrition* 23 (2003): 283-301.

6. R. F. Hurrell and coauthors, Meat protein fractions enhance nonheme iron absorption in humans, *Journal of Nutrition* 136 (2006): 2808-2812.

7. Committee on Dietary Reference Intakes, 2001, p. 351.

8. E. Nemeth and T. Ganz, Regulation of iron metabolism by hepcidin, *Annual Review of Nutrition* 26 (2006): 323-342.

9. J. L. Beard and J. R. Connor, Iron status and neural functioning, *Annual Review of Nutrition* 23 (2003): 41-58.

10. World Health Organization, http://www.who.int/nut/ida.htm.

11. K. G. Nead and coauthors, Overweight children and adolescents: A risk group for iron deficiency, *Pediatrics* 114 (2004): 104-108.

12. Iron deficiency—United States, 1999-2000, *Morbidity and Mortality Weekly Report* 51 (2002): 897-899.

13. K. C. White, Anemia is a poor predictor of iron deficiency among toddlers in the United States: For heme the bell tolls, *Pediatrics* 115 (2005): 315-320.

14. M. J. Koury and P. Ponka, New insights into erythropoiesis: The roles of folate, vitamin B12, and iron, *Annual Review of Nutrition* 24 (2004): 105-131.

15. T. Brownlie and coauthors, Marginal iron deficiency without anemia impairs aerobic adaptation among previously untrained women, *American Journal of Clinical Nutrition* 75 (2002): 734-742.

16. J. Beard, Iron deficiency alters brain development and functioning, *Journal of Nutrition* 133 (2003): 1468S-1472S; E. M. Ross, Evaluation and treatment of iron deficiency in adults, *Nutrition in Clinical Care* 5 (2002): 220-224.

17. P. C. Adams and coauthors, Hemochromatosis and iron-overload screening in a racially diverse population, *New England Journal of Medicine* 352 (2005): 1769-1778; A. L. M. Heath and S. J. Fairweather-Tait, Health implications of iron overload: The role of diet and genotype, *Nutrition Reviews* 61 (2003): 45-62.

18. A. Pietrangelo, Hereditary hemochromatosis, *Annual Review of Nutrition* 26 (2006): 251-270.

19. D. Lee, A. R. Folsom, and D. R. Jacobs, Iron, zinc, and alcohol consumption and mortality from cardiovascular diseases: The Iowa Women's Health Study, *American Journal of Clinical Nutrition* 81 (2005): 787-791; U. Ramakrishnan, E. Kuklina, and A. D. Stein, Iron stores and cardiovascular disease risk factors in women of reproductive age in the United States, *American Journal of Clinical Nutrition* 76 (2002): 1256-1260.

20. M. B. Reddy and L. Clark, Iron, oxidative stress, and disease risk, *Nutrition Reviews* 62 (2004): 120-124; J. L. Derstine and coauthors, Iron status in association with cardiovascular disease risk in 3 controlled feeding studies, *American Journal of Clinical Nutrition* 77 (2003): 56-62.

21. A. G. Mainous and coauthors, Iron, lipids, and risk of cancer in the Framingham Offspring Cohort, *American Journal of Epidemiology* 160 (2005): 1115-1122.

22. Committee on Dietary Reference Intakes, 2001, p. 351.

23. J. R. Backstrand, The history and future of food fortification in the United States: A public health perspective, *Nutrition Reviews* 60 (2002): 15-26.

24. H. Tapiero and K. D. Tew, Trace elements in human physiology and pathology: Zinc and metallothioneins, *Biomedicine and Pharmacotherapy* 57 (2003): 399-411.

25. C. L. Adams and coauthors, Zinc absorption from a low-phytic acid maize, *American Journal of Clinical Nutrition* 76 (2002): 556-559.

26. C. F. Walker and R. E. Black, Zinc and the risk for infectious disease, *Annual Review of Nutrition* 24 (2004): 255-275.

27. J. M. M. Gardner and coauthors, Zinc supplementation and psychosocial stimulation: Effects on the development of undernourished Jamaican children, *American Journal of Clinical Nutrition* 82 (2005): 399-405; T. A. Strand and coauthors, Effectiveness and efficacy of zinc for the treatment of acute diarrhea in young children, *Pediatrics* 109 (2002): 898-903; N. Bhandari and coauthors, Substantial reduction in severe diarrheal morbidity by daily zinc supplementation in young North Indian children, *Pediatrics* 109 (2002): e86.

28. G. A. Eby and W. W. Halcomb, Ineffectiveness of zinc gluconate nasal spray and zinc orotate lozenges in common-cold treatment: A double-blind placebo-controlled clinical trial, *Alternative Therapies in Health and Medicine* 12 (2006): 34-48; B. Arroll, Non-antibiotic treatments for upper-respiratory tract infections (common cold), *Respiratory Medicine* 99 (2005): 1477-1484; B. H. McElroy and S. P. Miller, Effectiveness of zinc gluconate glycine lozenges (Cold-Eeze) against the common cold in school-aged subjects: A retrospective chart review, *American Journal of Therapeutics* 9 (2002): 472-475.

29. M. B. Zimmermann and coauthors, Rapid relapse of thyroid dysfunction and goiter in school-age children after discontinuation of salt iodization, *American Journal of Clinical Nutrition* 79 (2004): 642-645.

30. M. B. Zimmerman, The influence of iron status on iodine utilization and thyroid function, *Annual Review of Nutrition* 26 (2006): 367-389.

31. W. Teng and coauthors, Effect of iodine intake on thyroid diseases in China, *New England Journal of Medicine* 354 (2006): 2783-2793.

32. D. M. Driscoll and P. R. Copeland, Mechanism and regulation of selenoprotein synthesis, *Annual Review of Nutrition* 23 (2003): 17-40.

33. R. F. Burk and K. E. Hill, Selenoprotein P: An extracellular protein with unique physical characteristics and a role in selenium homeostasis, *Annual Review of Nutrition* 25 (2005): 215-235.

34. A. J. Duffield-Lillico, I. Shureiqi, and S. M. Lippman, Can selenium prevent colorectal cancer? A signpost from epidemiology, *Journal of the National Cancer Institute* 96 (2004): 1645-1647.

35. J. W. Finley, Selenium accumulation in plant foods, *Nutrition Reviews* 63 (2005): 196-202.

36. N. E. Hellman and J. D. Gitlin, Ceruloplasmin metabolism and function, *Annual Review of Nutrition* 22 (2002): 439-458.

37. J. W. Finley, Does environmental exposure to manganese pose a health risk to healthy adults? *Nutrition Reviews* 62 (2004): 148-153.

38. Populations receiving optimally fluoridated public drinking water—United States, 2000, *Morbidity and Mortality Weekly Report* 51 (2002): 144-147.

39. Position of the American Dietetic Association: The impact of fluoride on health, *Journal of the American Dietetic Association* 105 (2005): 1620-1628.

40. Surveillance for dental caries, dental sealants, tooth retention, edentulism, and enamel fluorosis—United States, 1988-1994 and 1999-2002, *Morbidity and Mortality Weekly Report* 54 (2005): 1-44.

41. Populations receiving optimally fluoridated public drinking water—United States, 2000, 2002.

42. M. D. Althuis and coauthors, Glucose and insulin responses to dietary chromium supplements: A meta-analysis, *American Journal of Clinical Nutrition* 76 (2002): 148-155.

43. T. A. Devirian and S. L. Volpe, The physiological effects of dietary boron, *Critical Reviews in Food and Science Nutrition* 43 (2003): 219-231.

44. Committee on Environmental Health, Lead exposure in children: Prevention, detection, and management, *Pediatrics* 116 (2005): 1036-1046; Blood lead levels—United States, 1999-2002, *Morbidity and Mortality Weekly Report* 54 (2005): 513-527.

45. D. C. Bellinger, Lead, *Pediatrics* 113 (2004): 1016-1022.

46. S. G. Selevan and coauthors, Blood lead concentration and delayed puberty in girls, *New England Journal of Medicine* 348 (2003): 1527-1536.

47. R. J. Billings, R. J. Berkowitz, and G. Watson, Teeth, *Pediatrics* 113 (2004): 1120-1127.

48. R. L. Canfield and coauthors, Intellectual impairment in children with blood lead concentrations below 10 μg per deciliter, *New England Journal of Medicine* 348 (2003): 1517-1526.

49. A. R. Kemper and coauthors, Follow-up testing among children with elevated screening blood lead levels, *Journal of the American Medical Association* 293 (2005): 2232-2237.

50. K. Kalia and S. J. Flora, Strategies for safe and effective therapeutic measures for chronic arsenic and lead poisoning, *Journal of Occupational Health* 47 (2005): 1-21; S. P. Murphy and coauthors, Simple measures of dietary variety are associated with improved dietary quality, *Journal of the American Dietetic Association* 106 (2006): 425–429.

ANSWERS

Nutrition Calculations

1. Iron: mg   Selenium: μg   Fluoride: mg

   Zinc: mg   Copper: μg   Chromium: μg

   Iodine: μg   Manganese: mg   Molybdenum: μg

2. a. Ranked by iron per serving: sirloin steak > broccoli > green peas > bread > pork chop > cantaloupe > sweet potato > carrots > apple > cheese > milk

   b.

Food	Iron Density (mg/kcal)
Milk, fat-free, 1 c	0.10 mg ÷ 85 kcal = 0.0012 mg/kcal
Cheddar cheese, 1 oz	0.19 mg ÷ 114 kcal = 0.0017 mg/kcal
Broccoli, cooked from fresh, chopped, 1 c	1.31 mg ÷ 44 kcal = 0.0298 mg/kcal
Sweet potato, baked in skin, 1 ea	0.51 mg ÷ 117 kcal = 0.0044 mg/kcal
Cantaloupe melon, ½	0.56 mg ÷ 93 kcal = 0.0060 mg/kcal
Carrots, from fresh, ½ c	0.48 mg ÷ 35 kcal = 0.0137 mg/kcal
Whole-wheat bread, 1 slice	0.87 mg ÷ 64 kcal = 0.0136 mg/kcal
Green peas, cooked from frozen, ½ c	1.26 mg ÷ 62 kcal = 0.0203 mg/kcal
Apple, medium	0.38 mg ÷ 125 kcal = 0.0030 mg/kcal
Sirloin steak, lean, 4 oz	3.81 mg ÷ 228 kcal = 0.0167 mg/kcal
Pork chop, lean broiled, 1 ea	0.66 mg ÷ 166 kcal = 0.0040 mg/kcal

   Ranked by iron density (iron per kcalorie): broccoli > green peas > sirloin steak > carrots > bread > cantaloupe > sweet potato > pork chop > apple > cheese > milk

   c. Broccoli, green peas, and carrots are all higher on the per-kcalorie list.

   d. They are all vegetables.

Study Questions (multiple choice)

1. b   2. b   3. c   4. c   5. d   6. d   7. c   8. b   9. a   10. c

Phytochemicals and Functional Foods

© John E. Kelly/FoodPix/Getty Images

Chapter 13 completes the introductory discussions on the six classes of nutrients—carbohydrates, lipids, proteins, vitamins, minerals, and water. In addition to these nutrients, foods contain thousands of nonnutrient compounds, including the phytochemicals. Chapter 1 introduced the **phytochemicals** as compounds found in plant-derived foods (*phyto* means plant) that have biological activity in the body. Research on phytochemicals is unfolding daily, adding to our knowledge of their roles in human health, but there are still many questions and only tentative answers. Just a few of the tens of thousands of phytochemicals have been researched at all, and only a sampling are mentioned in this highlight—enough to illustrate their wide variety of food sources and roles in supporting health.

The concept that foods provide health benefits beyond those of the nutrients emerged from numerous epidemiological studies showing the protective effects of plant-based diets on cancer and heart disease. People have been using foods to maintain health and prevent disease for years, but now these foods have been given a name—they are called **functional foods.** (The accompanying glossary defines this and other terms.) As Chapter 1 explained, functional foods include all foods (whole, fortified, or modified foods) that have a potentially beneficial effect on health.[1] Much of this text touts the benefits of nature's functional foods—grains rich in dietary fibers, fish rich in omega-3 fatty acids, and fruits rich in phytochemicals, for example. This highlight begins with a look at some of these familiar functional foods, the phytochemicals they contain, and their roles in disease pre-

vention. Then the discussion turns to examine the most controversial of functional foods—novel foods to which phytochemicals have been added to promote health. How these foods fit into a healthy diet is still unclear.[2]

The Phytochemicals

In foods, phytochemicals impart tastes, aromas, colors, and other characteristics. They give hot peppers their burning sensation, garlic its pungent flavor, and tomatoes their dark red color. In the body, phytochemicals can have profound physiological effects, acting as antioxidants, mimicking hormones, and suppressing the development of diseases.[3] Table H13-1 (p. 470) presents the names, possible effects, and food sources of some of the better-known phytochemicals.

Defending Against Cancer

A variety of phytochemicals from a variety of foods appear to protect against DNA damage and defend the body against cancer. A few examples follow.

Soybeans and products made from them correlate with low rates of some cancers.[4] Soybeans—as well as other legumes, **flaxseeds,** whole grains, fruits, and vegetables—are a rich source of an array of phytochemicals, among them the **phytoestrogens.** Because the chemical structure of these phytochemicals is similar to the steroid hormone estrogen, they can weakly mimic or modulate the effects of estrogen in the body.[5] They also have antioxidant

GLOSSARY

flavonoids (FLAY-von-oyds): yellow pigments in foods; phytochemicals that may exert physiological effects on the body.

flaxseeds: the small brown seeds of the flax plant; valued as a source of linseed oil, fiber, and omega-3 fatty acids.

lignans: phytochemicals present in flaxseed, but not in flax oil, that are converted to phytosterols by intestinal bacteria and are under study as

possible anticancer agents.

lutein (LOO-teen): a plant pigment of yellow hue; a phytochemical believed to play roles in eye functioning and health.

lycopene (LYE-koh-peen): a pigment responsible for the red color of tomatoes and other red-hued vegetables; a phytochemical that may act as an antioxidant in the body.

phytoestrogens: plant-derived compounds that have structural and functional similarities to human estrogen. Phytoestrogens include the isoflavones genistein, daidzein, and glycitein.

phytosterols: plant-derived compounds that have structural similarities to cholesterol and lower blood cholesterol by competing with cholesterol for absorption. Phytosterols include sterol esters and stanol esters.

Reminders: **Phytochemicals** are nonnutrient compounds found in plant-derived foods that have biological activity in the body.

Functional foods are foods that contain physiologically active compounds that provide health benefits beyond basic nutrition.

TABLE H13-1 Phytochemicals—Their Food Sources and Actions

Name	Possible Effects	Food Sources
Alkylresorcinols[a]	May contribute to the protective effect of grains in reducing the risks of diabetes, heart disease, and some cancers.	Whole grain wheat and rye
Capsaicin	Modulates blood clotting, possibly reducing the risk of fatal clots in heart and artery disease.	Hot peppers
Carotenoids (include beta-carotene, lycopene, lutein, and hundreds of related compounds)[b]	Act as antioxidants, possibly reducing risks of cancer and other diseases.	Deeply pigmented fruits and vegetables (apricots, broccoli, cantaloupe, carrots, pumpkin, spinach, sweet potatoes, tomatoes)
Curcumin	May inhibit enzymes that activate carcinogens.	Tumeric, a yellow-colored spice
Flavonoids (include flavones, flavonols, isoflavones, catechins, and others)[a,c]	Act as antioxidants; scavenge carcinogens; bind to nitrates in the stomach, preventing conversion to nitrosamines; inhibit cell proliferation.	Berries, black tea, celery, citrus fruits, green tea, olives, onions, oregano, purple grapes, purple grape juice, soybeans and soy products, vegetables, whole wheat, wine
Indoles[d]	May trigger production of enzymes that block DNA damage from carcinogens; may inhibit estrogen action.	Broccoli and other cruciferous vegetables (brussels sprouts, cabbage, cauliflower), horseradish, mustard greens
Isothiocyanates (including sulforaphane)	Inhibit enzymes that activate carcinogens; trigger production of enzymes that detoxify carcinogens.	Broccoli and other cruciferous vegetables (brussels sprouts, cabbage, cauliflower), horseradish, mustard greens
Lignans[e]	Block estrogen activity in cells, possibly reducing the risk of cancer of the breast, colon, ovaries, and prostate.	Flaxseed and its oil, whole grains
Monoterpenes (include limonene)	May trigger enzyme production to detoxify carcinogens; inhibit cancer promotion and cell proliferation.	Citrus fruit peels and oils
Organosulfur compounds	May speed production of carcinogen-destroying enzymes; slow production of carcinogen-activating enzymes.	Chives, garlic, leeks, onions
Phenolic acids[a]	May trigger enzyme production to make carcinogens water soluble, facilitating excretion.	Coffee beans, fruits (apples, blueberries, cherries, grapes, oranges, pears, prunes), oats, potatoes, soybeans
Phytic acid	Binds to minerals, preventing free-radical formation, possibly reducing cancer risk.	Whole grains
Phytoestrogens (genistein and daidzein)	Estrogen inhibition may produce these actions: inhibit cell replication in GI tract; reduce risk of breast, colon, ovarian, prostate, and other estrogen-sensitive cancers; reduce cancer cell survival. Estrogen mimicking may reduce risk of osteoporosis.	Soybeans, soy flour, soy milk, tofu, textured vegetable protein, other legume products
Protease inhibitors	May suppress enzyme production in cancer cells, slowing tumor growth; inhibit hormone binding; inhibit malignant changes in cells.	Broccoli sprouts, potatoes, soybeans and other legumes, soy products
Resveratrol	Offsets artery-damaging effects of high-fat diets.	Red wine, peanuts
Saponins	May interfere with DNA replication, preventing cancer cells from multiplying; stimulate immune response.	Alfalfa sprouts, other sprouts, green vegetables, potatoes, tomatoes
Tannins[a]	May inhibit carcinogen activation and cancer promotion; act as antioxidants.	Black-eyed peas, grapes, lentils, red and white wine, tea

[a]A subset of the larger group *phenolic phytochemicals*.
[b]Other carotenoids include alpha-carotene, beta-cryptoxanthin, and zeaxanthin.
[c]Other flavonoids of interest include ellagic acid and ferulic acid; see also *phytoestrogens*.
[d]Indoles include dithiothiones, isothiocyantes, and others.
[e]Lignans act as phytosterols and phytoestrogens, but their food sources are limited.

activity that appears to slow the growth of breast and prostate cancers.[6] However, the use of phytoestrogen supplements is ill-advised as they may stimulate the growth of estrogen-dependent cancers (such as breast cancer).[7] Even the role of soy foods for breast cancer survivors is uncertain. Soy foods may be most effective when consumed in moderation throughout life. The American Cancer Society recommends: "Breast cancer survivors should consume only moderate amounts of soy foods as part of a healthy plant-based diet and should not intentionally ingest very high levels of soy products."[8]

Tomatoes seem to offer protection against cancers of the esophagus, lungs, prostate, and stomach. Among the phytochemicals responsible for this effect is **lycopene,** one of beta-carotene's many carotenoid relatives. Lycopene is the pigment that gives apricots, guava, papaya, pink grapefruits, and watermelon their red color—and it is especially abundant in tomatoes and cooked tomato products. Lycopene is a powerful antioxidant that seems to inhibit the growth of cancer cells.[9] Importantly, these benefits are seen when people eat *foods* containing lycopene.[10]

Soybeans and tomatoes are only two of the many fruits and vegetables credited with providing anticancer activity. Strong and convincing evidence shows that the risk of many cancers, and perhaps of cancer in general, decreases when diets include an abundance of fruits and vegetables.[11] To that end, current recommendations urge consumers to eat five to nine servings of fruits and vegetables a day.

Defending against Heart Disease

Diets based primarily on unprocessed foods appear to support heart health better than those founded on highly refined foods—perhaps because of the abundance of nutrients, fiber, or phytochemicals such as the **flavonoids**.[12] Flavonoids, a large group of phytochemicals known for their health-promoting qualities, are found in whole grains, legumes, soy, vegetables, fruits, herbs, spices, teas, chocolate, nuts, olive oil, and red wines.[13] Flavonoids are powerful antioxidants that may help to protect LDL cholesterol against oxidation and reduce blood platelet stickiness, making blood clots less likely.[14] An abundance of flavonoid-containing *foods* in the diet lowers the risks of chronic diseases.[15] Importantly, no claims can be made for flavonoids themselves as the protective factor, particularly when they are extracted from foods and sold as supplements.[16]

In addition to flavonoids, fruits and vegetables are rich in carotenoids. Studies suggest that a diet rich in carotenoids is also associated with a lower risk of heart disease.[17] Notable among the carotenoids that may defend against heart disease are **lutein** and lycopene.[18]

The **phytosterols** of soybeans and the **lignans** of flaxseed may also protect against heart disease.[19] These cholesterol-like molecules are naturally found in all plants and inhibit cholesterol absorption in the body. As a result, blood cholesterol levels decline.[20] These phytochemicals also seem to protect against heart disease by acting as antioxidants and lowering blood pressure.[21]

The Phytochemicals in Perspective

Because foods deliver thousands of phytochemicals in addition to dozens of nutrients, researchers must be careful in giving credit for particular health benefits to any one compound. Diets rich in whole grains, legumes, vegetables, fruits, and nuts seem to protect against heart disease and cancer, but identifying *the* specific foods or components of foods that are responsible is difficult.[22] Each food possesses a unique array of phytochemicals—citrus fruits provide monoterpenes; grapes, resveratrol; and flaxseed, lignans. (Review Table H13-1 for the possible effects and other food sources of these phytochemicals.) Broccoli may contain as many as 10,000 different phytochemicals—each with the potential to influence some action in the body. Beverages such as wine, spices such as oregano, and oils such as olive oil (especially virgin olive oil) contain many phytochemicals that may explain, in part, why people who live in the Mediterranean region have reduced risks of heart disease and cancer.[23] Phytochemicals might also explain why the DASH diet is so effective in lowering blood pressure and blood lipids.[24] Even identifying all of the phytochemicals and their effects doesn't answer all the questions because the actions of phytochemicals may be complementary or overlapping—which reinforces the principle of variety in diet planning. For an appreciation of the array of phytochemicals offered by a variety of fruits and vegetables, see Figure H13-1 (p. 472).

Functional Foods

Because foods naturally contain thousands of phytochemicals that are biologically active in the body, virtually all of them have some special value in supporting health. In other words, even simple, whole foods, in reality, are functional foods. Cranberries may help protect against urinary tract infections; garlic may lower blood cholesterol; and tomatoes may protect against some cancers, just to name a few examples.[25] But that hasn't stopped food manufacturers from trying to create functional foods as well. The creation of more functional foods has become the fastest-growing trend and the greatest influence transforming the American food supply.[26]

Many processed foods become functional foods when they are fortified with nutrients or enhanced with phytochemicals or herbs (calcium-fortified orange juice, for example). Less frequently, an entirely new food is created, as in the case of a meat substitute made of mycoprotein—a protein derived from a fungus.*[27] This functional food not only provides dietary fiber, polyunsaturated fats, and high-quality protein, but it lowers LDL cholesterol, raises HDL cholesterol, improves glucose response, and prolongs satiety after a meal. Such a novel functional food raises the question—is it a food or a drug?

Foods as Pharmacy

Not too long ago, most of us could agree on what was a food and what was a drug. Today, functional foods blur the distinctions.[28] They have characteristics similar to both foods and drugs, but do not fit neatly into either category. Consider margarine, for example.

Eating nonhydrogenated margarine sparingly instead of butter generously may lower blood cholesterol slightly over several months and clearly falls into the food category. Taking the drug Lipitor, on the other hand, lowers blood cholesterol significantly within weeks and clearly falls into the drug category. But margarine enhanced with a phytosterol that lowers blood cholesterol is in a gray area between the two. The margarine looks and tastes like a food, but it acts like a drug.

The use of functional foods as drugs creates a whole new set of diet-planning challenges. Not only must foods provide an adequate intake of all the nutrients to support good health, but they must

Nature offers a variety of functional foods that provide us with many health benefits.

---

* This mycoprotein product is marketed under the trade name Quorn (pronounced KWORN).

FIGURE H13-1 An Array of Phytochemicals in a Variety of Fruits and Vegetables

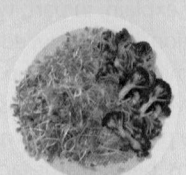

Broccoli and broccoli sprouts contain an abundance of the cancer-fighting phytochemical sulforaphane.

An apple a day—rich in flavonoids—may protect against lung cancer.

The phytoestrogens of soybeans seem to starve cancer cells and inhibit tumor growth; the phytosterols may lower blood cholesterol and protect

Garlic, with its abundant organosulfur compounds, may lower blood cholesterol and protect against stomach cancer.

The phytochemical resveratrol found in grapes (and nuts) protects against cancer by inhibiting cell growth and against heart disease by limiting clot formation and inflammation.

The ellagic acid of strawberries may inhibit certain types of cancer.

Tomatoes, with their abundant lycopene, may defend against cancer by protecting DNA from oxidative damage.

The monoterpenes of citrus fruits (and cherries) may inhibit cancer growth.

The flavonoids in black tea may protect against heart disease, whereas those in green tea may defend against cancer.

The flavonoids in cocoa and chocolate defend against oxidation and reduce the tendency of blood to clot.

Spinach and other colorful vegetables contain the carotenoids lutein and zeaxanthin, which help protect the eyes against macular degeneration.

Flaxseed, the richest source of lignans, may prevent the spread of cancer.

Blueberries, a rich source of flavonoids, improve memory in animals.

---

also deliver drug-like ingredients to protect against disease. Like drugs used to treat chronic diseases, functional foods may need to be eaten several times a day for several months or years to have a beneficial effect. Sporadic users may be disappointed in the results. Margarine enriched with 2 to 3 grams of phytosterols may reduce cholesterol by up to 15 percent, much more than regular margarine does, but not nearly as much as the more than 30 percent reduction seen with cholesterol-lowering drugs.[29] For this reason, functional foods may be more useful for prevention and mild cases of disease than for intervention and more severe cases.

Foods and drugs differ dramatically in cost as well. Functional foods such as fruits and vegetables incur no added costs, of course, but foods that have been manufactured with added phytochemicals can be expensive, costing up to six times as much as

their conventional counterparts. The price of functional foods typically falls between that of traditional foods and medicines.

Unanswered Questions

To achieve a desired health effect, which is the better choice: to eat a food designed to affect some body function or simply to adjust the diet? Does it make more sense to use a margarine enhanced with a phytosterol that lowers blood cholesterol or simply to limit the amount of butter eaten?* Is it smarter to eat eggs enriched with omega-3 fatty acids or to restrict egg consumption?

---

* Margarine products that lower blood cholesterol contain either sterol esters from vegetable oils, soybeans, and corn or stanol esters from wood pulp.

Might functional foods offer a sensible solution for improving our nation's health—if done correctly? Perhaps so, but the problem is that the food industry is moving too fast for either scientists or the Food and Drug Administration to keep up. Consumers were able to buy soup with St. John's wort that claimed to enhance mood and fruit juice with echinacea that was supposed to fight colds while scientists were still conducting their studies on these ingredients. Research to determine the safety and effectiveness of these substances is still in progress. Until this work is complete, consumers are on their own in finding the answers to the following questions:

- *Does it work?* Research is generally lacking and findings are often inconclusive.

- *How much does it contain?* Food labels are not required to list the quantities of added phytochemicals. Even if they were, consumers have no standard for comparison and cannot deduce whether the amounts listed are a little or a lot. Most importantly, until research is complete, food manufacturers do not know what amounts (if any) are most effective—or most toxic.

- *Is it safe?* Functional foods can act like drugs. They contain ingredients that can alter body functions and cause allergies, drug interactions, drowsiness, and other side effects. Yet, unlike drug labels, food labels do not provide instructions for the dosage, frequency, or duration of treatment.

- *Is it healthy?* Adding phytochemicals to a food does not magically make it a healthy choice. A candy bar may be fortified with phytochemicals, but it is still made mostly of sugar and fat.

Critics suggest that the designation "functional foods" may be nothing more than a marketing tool. After all, even the most experienced researchers cannot yet identify the perfect combination of nutrients and phytochemicals to support optimal health. Yet manufacturers are freely experimenting with various concoctions as if they possessed that knowledge. Is it okay for them to sprinkle phytochemicals on fried snack foods or caramel candies and label them "functional," thus implying health benefits?

Future Foods

Nature has elegantly designed foods to provide us with a complex array of dozens of nutrients and thousands of additional

Functional foods currently on the market promise to "enhance mood," "promote relaxation and good karma," "increase alertness," and "improve memory," among other claims.

compounds that may benefit health—most of which we have yet to identify or understand. Over the years, we have taken those foods, deconstructed them, and then reconstructed them in an effort to "improve" them. With new scientific understandings of how nutrients—and the myriad other compounds in foods—interact with genes, we may someday be able to design foods to meet the *exact* health needs of *each* individual.[30] Indeed, our knowledge of the human genome and of human nutrition may well merge to allow specific recommendations for individuals based on their predisposition to diet-related diseases.

If the present trend continues, someday physicians may be able to prescribe the perfect foods to enhance your health, and farmers will be able to grow them. As Highlight 19 explains, scientists have already developed gene technology to alter the composition of food crops. They can grow rice enriched with vitamin A and tomatoes containing a hepatitis vaccine, for example. It seems quite likely that foods can be created to meet every possible human need. But then, in a sense, that was largely true 100 years ago when we relied on the bounty of nature.

NUTRITION ON THE NET

ThomsonNOW
For furthur study of topics covered in this Highlight, log on to **www.thomsonedu.com/thomsonnow**. Go to Chapter 13, then to Highlights Nutrition on the Net.

- Search for "functional foods" at the International Food Information Council: **www.ific.org**

- Search for "functional foods" at the Center for Science in the Public Interest: **www.cspinet.org**

- Find out if warnings have been issued for any food ingredients at the FDA website: **www.fda.gov**

REFERENCES

1. Position of the American Dietetic Association: Functional foods, *Journal of the American Dietetic Association* 104 (2004): 814-826.
2. C. H. Halsted, Dietary supplements and functional foods: 2 sides of a coin? *American Journal of Clinical Nutrition* 77 (2003): 1001S-1007S.
3. C. Manach and coauthors, Polyphenols: Food sources and bioavailability, *American Journal of Clinical Nutrition* 79 (2004): 727-747; P. M. Kris-Etherton and coauthors, Bioactive compounds in foods: Their role in the prevention of cardiovascular disease and cancer, *American Journal of Medicine* 113 (2002): 71S-88S.
4. M. B. Schabath and coauthors, Dietary phytoestrogens and lung cancer risk, *Journal of the American Medical Association* 294 (2005): 1493-1504; W. H. Xu and coauthors, Soya food intake and risk of endometrial cancer among Chinese women in Shanghai: Population based case-control study, *British Medical Journal* 328 (2004): 1285-1288.
5. I. C. Munro and coauthors, Soy isoflavones: A safety review, *Nutrition Reviews* 61 (2003): 1-33.
6. T. A. Ryan-Borchers and coauthors, Soy isoflavones modulate immune function in healthy postmenopausal women, *American Journal of Clinical Nutrition* 83 (2006): 1118-1125; C. A. Lamartiniere and coauthors, Genistein chemoprevention: Timing and mechanisms of action in murine mammary and prostate, *Journal of Nutrition* 132 (2002): 552S-558S.
7. M. Messina, W. McCaskill-Stevens, J. W. Lampe, Addressing the soy and breast cancer relationship: Review, commentary, and workshop proceedings, *Journal of the National Cancer Institute* 98 (2006): 1275-1284.
8. G. Maskarinec, Soy foods for breast cancer survivors and women at high risk for breast cancer? *Journal of the American Dietetic Association* 105 (2005): 1524-1528.
9. A. Basu and V. Imrhan, Tomatoes versus lycopene in oxidative stress and carcinogenesis: Conclusions from clinical trials, *European Journal of Clinical Nutrition* (2006); D. Heber and Q. Y. Lu, Overview of mechanisms of action of lycopene, *Experimental Biology and Medicine* 227 (2002): 920-923; T. M. Vogt and coauthors, Serum lycopene, other serum carotenoids, and risk of prostate cancer in US blacks and whites, *American Journal of Epidemiology* 155 (2002): 1023-1032.
10. S. Ellinger, J. Ellinger, and P. Stehle, Tomatoes, tomato products and lycopene in the prevention and treatment of prostate cancer: Do we have the evidence from intervention studies? *Current Opinion in Clinical Nutrition and Metabolic Care* 9 (2006): 722-727; E. Giovannucci and coauthors, A prospective study of tomato products, lycopene, and prostate cancer risk, *Journal of the National Cancer Institute* 94 (2002): 391-398.
11. C. A. Gonzalez, Nutrition and cancer: The current epidemiological evidence, *British Journal of Nutrition* 96 (2006): S42-S45; H. Vainio and E. Weiderpass, Fruit and vegetables in cancer prevention, *Nutrition and Cancer* 54 (2006): 111-142.

12. J. A. Ross and C. M. Kasum, Dietary flavonoids: Bioavailability, metabolic effects, and safety, *Annual Review of Nutrition* 22 (2002): 19-34.
13. M. B. Engler and M. M. Engler, The emerging role of flavonoid-rich cocoa and chocolate in cardiovascular health and disease, *Nutrition Reviews* 64 (2006): 109-118; M. W. Ariefdjohan and D. A. Savaiano, Chocolate and cardiovascular health: Is it too good to be true? *Nutrition Reviews* 63 (2005): 427-430; F. M. Steinberg, M. M. Bearden, and C. L. Keen, Cocoa and chocolate flavonoids: Implications for cardiovascular health, *Journal of the American Dietetic Association* 103 (2003): 215-223; F. Visioli and C. Galli, Biological properties of olive oil phytochemicals, *Critical Reviews in Food Science and Nutrition* 42 (2002): 209-221; Y. J. Surh, Anti-tumor promoting potential of selected spice ingredients with antioxidative and anti-inflammatory activities: A short review, *Food and Chemical Toxicology* 40 (2002): 1091-1097; J. M. Geleijnse and coauthors, Inverse association of tea and flavonoid intakes with incident myocardial infarction: The Rotterdam Study, *American Journal of Clinical Nutrition* 75 (2002): 880-886.
15. M. Messina, C. Gardner, and S. Barnes, Gaining insight into the health effects of soy but a long way still to go: Commentary on the Fourth International Symposium on the Role of Soy in Preventing and Treating Chronic Disease, *Journal of Nutrition* 132 (2002): 547S-551S; P. Knekt and coauthors, Flavonoid intake and risk of chronic diseases, *American Journal of Clinical Nutrition* 76 (2002): 560-568.
16. Ross and Kasum, 2002.
17. S. K. Osganian and coauthors, Dietary carotenoids and risk of coronary artery disease in women, *American Journal of Clinical Nutrition* 77 (2003): 1390-1399; S. Liu and coauthors, Intake of vegetables rich in carotenoids and risk of coronary heart disease in men: The Physicians' Heart Study, *International Journal of Epidemiology* 30 (2001): 130-135.
18. T. H. Rissanen and coauthors, Serum lycopene concentrations and carotid atherosclerosis: The Kuopio Ischaemic Heart Disease Risk Factor Study, *American Journal of Clinical Nutrition* 77 (2003): 133-138; Heber and Lu, 2002.
19. L. T. Bloedon and P. O. Szapary, Flaxseed and cardiovascular risk, *Nutrition Reviews* 62 (2004): 18-27; X. Zhang and coauthors, Soy food consumption is associated with lower risk of coronary heart disease in Chinese women, *Journal of Nutrition* 133 (2003): 2874-2878; R. E. Ostlund, Jr., Phytosterols in human nutrition, *Annual Review of Nutrition* 22 (2002): 533-549.
20. V. W. Y. Lau, M. Journoud, and P. J. H. Jones, Plant sterols are efficacious in lowering plasma LDL and non-HDL cholesterol in hypercholesterolemic type 2 diabetic and nondiabetic persons, *American Journal of Clinical Nutrition* 81 (2005): 1351-1358; S. Zhan and S. C. Ho, Meta-analysis of the effects of soy protein containing isoflavones on the lipid profile, *American Journal of*

Clinical Nutrition 81 (2005): 397-408; E. A. Lucas and coauthors, Flaxseed improves lipid profile without altering biomarkers of bone metabolism in postmenopausal women, *Journal of Clinical Endocrinology and Metabolism* 87 (2002): 1527-1532; C. A. Vanstone and coauthors, Unesterified plant sterols and stanols lower LDL-cholesterol concentrations equivalently in hypercholesterolemic persons, *American Journal of Clinical Nutrition* 76 (2002): 1272-1278.
21. L. T. Bloedon and P. O. Szapary, Flaxseed and cardiovascular risk, *Nutrition Reviews* 62 (2004): 18-27; M. Rivas and coauthors, Soy milk lowers blood pressure in men and women with mild to moderate essential hypertension, *Journal of Nutrition* 132 (2002): 1900-1902.
23. M. I. Covas and coauthors, The effect of polyphenols in olive oil on heart disease risk factors: A randomized trial, *Annals of Internal Medicine* 145 (2006): 333-341; Y. Z. H-Y. Hashim and coauthors, Components of olive oil and chemoprevention of colorectal cancer, *Nutrition Reviews* 63 (2005): 374-386; F. Visioli, A. Poli, and C. Gall, Antioxidant and other biological activities of phenols from olives and olive oil, *Medicinal Research Reviews* 22 (2002): 65-75.
24. M. M. Most, Estimated phytochemical content of the Dietary Approaches to Stop Hypertension (DASH) Diet is higher than in the control study diet, *Journal of the American Dietetic Association* 104 (2004): 1725-1727.
25. A. B. Howell and B. Foxman, Cranberry juice and adhesion of antibiotic resistant uropathogens, *Journal of the American Medical Association* 287 (2002): 3082-3083; C. W. Hadley and coauthors, Tomatoes, lycopene, and prostate cancer: Progress and promise, *Experimental Biology and Medicine* 227 (2002): 869-880.
26. Position of the American Dietetic Association, 2004.
27. T. Peregrin, Mycoprotein: Is America ready for a meat substitute derived from a fungus? *Journal of the American Dietetic Association* 102 (2002): 628.
28. C. L. Taylor, Regulatory frameworks for functional foods and dietary supplements, *Nutrition Reviews* 62 (2004): 55-59.
29. C. S. Patch, L. C. Tapsell, and P. G. Williams, Plant sterol/stanol prescription is an effective treatment strategy for managing hypercholesterolemia in outpatient clinical practice, *Journal of the American Dietetic Association* 105 (2005): 46-52; D. A. J. M. Kerckhoffs and coauthors, Effects on the human serum lipoprotein profile of ß-glucan, soy protein and isoflavones, plant sterols and stanols, garlic and tocotrienols, *Journal of Nutrition* 132 (2002): 2494-2505; L. A. Simons, Additive effect of plant sterol-ester margarine and cerivastatin in lowering low-density lipoprotein cholesterol in primary hypercholesterolemia, *American Journal of Cardiology* 90 (2002): 737-740.
30. J. A. Milner, Functional foods and health: A US perspective, *British Journal of Nutrition* 88 (2002): S151-158.

Tony Generico/Getty Images

Figure 14-2: Animated! Delivery of Oxygen by the Heart and Lungs to the Muscles

Nutrition Portfolio Journal

Nutrition in Your Life

You choose to be physically active or inactive, and your choice can make a huge difference in how well you feel and how long you live. Today's world makes it easy to be inactive—too easy in fact—but the many health rewards of being physically active make it well worth the effort. You may even discover how much fun it is to be active, and with a little perseverance, you may become physically fit as well. As you become more active, you will find that the foods you eat can make a difference in how fast you run, how far you swim, or how much weight you lift. It's up to you. The choice is yours.

Fitness: Physical Activity, Nutrients, and Body Adaptations

CHAPTER OUTLINE

Fitness • Benefits of Fitness • Developing Fitness • Cardiorespiratory Endurance • Weight Training

Energy Systems, Fuels, and Nutrients to Support Activity • The Energy Systems of Physical Activity—ATP and CP • Glucose Use during Physical Activity • Fat Use during Physical Activity • Protein Use during Physical Activity—and between Times • Vitamins and Minerals to Support Activity • Fluids and Electrolytes to Support Activity • Poor Beverage Choices: Caffeine and Alcohol

Diets for Physically Active People • Choosing a Diet to Support Fitness • Meals before and after Competition

HIGHLIGHT 14 Supplements as Ergogenic Aids

Are you physically fit? If so, the following description applies to you. Your joints are flexible, your muscles are strong, and your body is lean with enough, but not too much, fat. You have the endurance to engage in daily physical activities with enough reserve energy to handle added challenges. Carrying heavy suitcases, opening a stuck window, or climbing four flights of stairs, which might strain an unfit person, is easy for you. What's more, you are prepared to meet mental and emotional challenges, too. All these characteristics of **fitness** describe the same wonderful condition of a healthy body.

Or perhaps you are leading a **sedentary** life. Today's world encourages inactivity, and people who go through life exerting minimal physical effort, become weak and unfit and may begin to feel unwell. In fact, a sedentary lifestyle fosters the development of several chronic diseases.

Regardless of your level of fitness, this chapter is written for "you," whoever you are and whatever your goals—whether you want to improve your health, lose weight, hone your athletic skills, ensure your position on a sports team, or simply adopt an active lifestyle. This chapter begins by discussing fitness and its benefits and then goes on to explain how the body uses energy nutrients to fuel physical activity. Finally, it describes diets to support fitness.

Fitness

Fitness depends on a certain minimum amount of **physical activity** or **exercise.** Both physical activity and exercise involve body movement, muscle contraction, and enhanced energy expenditure, but a distinction is made between the two terms. Exercise is often considered to be vigorous, structured, and planned physical activity. This chapter focuses on how the active body uses energy nutrients—whether that body is pedaling a bike across campus or pedaling a stationary bike in a gym. Thus, for our purposes, the terms *physical activity* and *exercise* are used interchangeably.

fitness: the characteristics that enable the body to perform physical activity; more broadly, the ability to meet routine physical demands with enough reserve energy to rise to a physical challenge; or the body's ability to withstand stress of all kinds.

sedentary: physically inactive (literally, "sitting down a lot").

physical activity: bodily movement produced by muscle contractions that substantially increase energy expenditure.

exercise: planned, structured, and repetitive body movements that promote or maintain physical fitness.

Physical activity, or its lack, exerts a significant and pervasive influence on everyone's nutrition and overall health.

◆ Each comparison influences the risks associated with chronic disease and death similarly:
- Vigorous exercise vs. minimal exercise
- Healthy weight vs. 20% overweight
- Nonsmoking vs. smoking (one pack a day)

Benefits of Fitness

Extensive evidence confirms that regular physical activity promotes health ◆ and reduces the risk of developing a number of diseases.[1] Still, despite an increasing awareness of the health benefits that physical activity confers, more than half of adults in the United States are not regularly active, and 25 percent are completely inactive.[2] Physical inactivity is linked to the major degenerative diseases—heart disease, cancer, stroke, diabetes, and hypertension—the primary killers of adults in developed countries.[3] Every year an estimated $77 billion is spent on health care costs attributed to physical inactivity in the United States.[4]

As a person becomes physically fit, the health of the entire body improves. In general, physically fit people enjoy:

- *Restful sleep.* Rest and sleep occur naturally after periods of physical activity. During rest, the body repairs injuries, disposes of wastes generated during activity, and builds new physical structures.

- *Nutritional health.* Physical activity expends energy and thus allows people to eat more food. If they choose wisely, active people will consume more nutrients and be less likely to develop nutrient deficiencies.

- *Optimal body composition.* A balanced program of physical activity limits body fat and increases or maintains lean tissue. Thus physically active people have relatively less body fat than sedentary people at the same body weight.[5]

- *Optimal bone density.* Weight-bearing physical activity builds bone strength and protects against osteoporosis.[6]

- *Resistance to colds and other infectious diseases.* Fitness enhances immunity.*[7]

- *Low risks of some types of cancers.* Lifelong physical activity may help to protect against colon cancer, breast cancer, and some other cancers.[8]

- *Strong circulation and lung function.* Physical activity that challenges the heart and lungs strengthens the circulatory system.

- *Low risk of cardiovascular disease.* Physical activity lowers blood pressure, slows resting pulse rate, and lowers blood cholesterol, thus reducing the risks of heart attacks and strokes.[9] Some research suggests that physical activity may reduce the risk of cardiovascular disease in another way as well—by reducing intra-abdominal fat stores.[10]

- *Low risk of type 2 diabetes.* Physical activity normalizes glucose tolerance.[11] Regular physical activity reduces the risk of developing type 2 diabetes and benefits those who already have the condition.

- *Reduced risk of gallbladder disease in women.* Regular physical activity reduces women's risk of gallbladder disease—perhaps by facilitating weight control and lowering blood lipid levels.[12]

- *Low incidence and severity of anxiety and depression.* Physical activity may improve mood and enhance the quality of life by reducing depression and anxiety.[13]

- *Strong self-image.* The sense of achievement that comes from meeting physical challenges promotes self-confidence.

- *Long life and high quality of life in the later years.* Active people have a lower mortality rate than sedentary people.[14] Even a two-mile walk daily can add years to a person's life. In addition to extending longevity, physical activity supports independence and mobility in later life by reducing the risk of falls and minimizing the risk of injury should a fall occur.[15]

---

* Moderate physical activity can stimulate immune function. Intense, vigorous, prolonged activity such as marathon running, however, may compromise immune function.

Dietary Guidelines for Americans 2005

Engage in regular physical activity and reduce sedentary activities to promote health, psychological well-being, and a healthy body weight.

What does a person have to do to reap the health rewards of physical activity? The *Dietary Guidelines for Americans 2005* specify that, for *health's* sake, people need to spend an accumulated minimum of 30 minutes in some sort of physical activity on most days of each week.[16] Eight minutes spent climbing up stairs, another 10 spent pulling weeds, and 12 more spent walking the dog all contribute to the day's total (see Figure 14-1). Both the *Dietary Guidelines 2005* and the DRI Committee, however, advise that 30 minutes of physical activity each day is not enough for adults to maintain a healthy body weight (BMI of 18.5 to 24.9) and recommend at least 60 minutes of moderately intense activity such as walking or jogging each day.[17] The hour or more of activity can be split into shorter sessions throughout the day—two 30-minute sessions, or four 15-minute sessions, for example.[18]

To develop and maintain *fitness,* the American College of Sports Medicine (ACSM) recommends the types and amounts of physical activities presented in Table 14-1 (p. 480).[19] Following these guidelines will help adults improve their cardiorespiratory endurance, body composition, ◆ strength, and flexibility. At this level of fitness, a person can reap even greater health benefits (further reduction of cardiovascular disease risk, for example).[20]

The bottom line is that any physical activity, even moderate activity, provides some health benefits, and these benefits follow a dose-response relationship.

◆ Reminder: *Body composition* refers to the proportions of muscle, bone, fat, and other tissue that make up a person's total body weight.

FIGURE 14-1 Physical Activity Pyramid

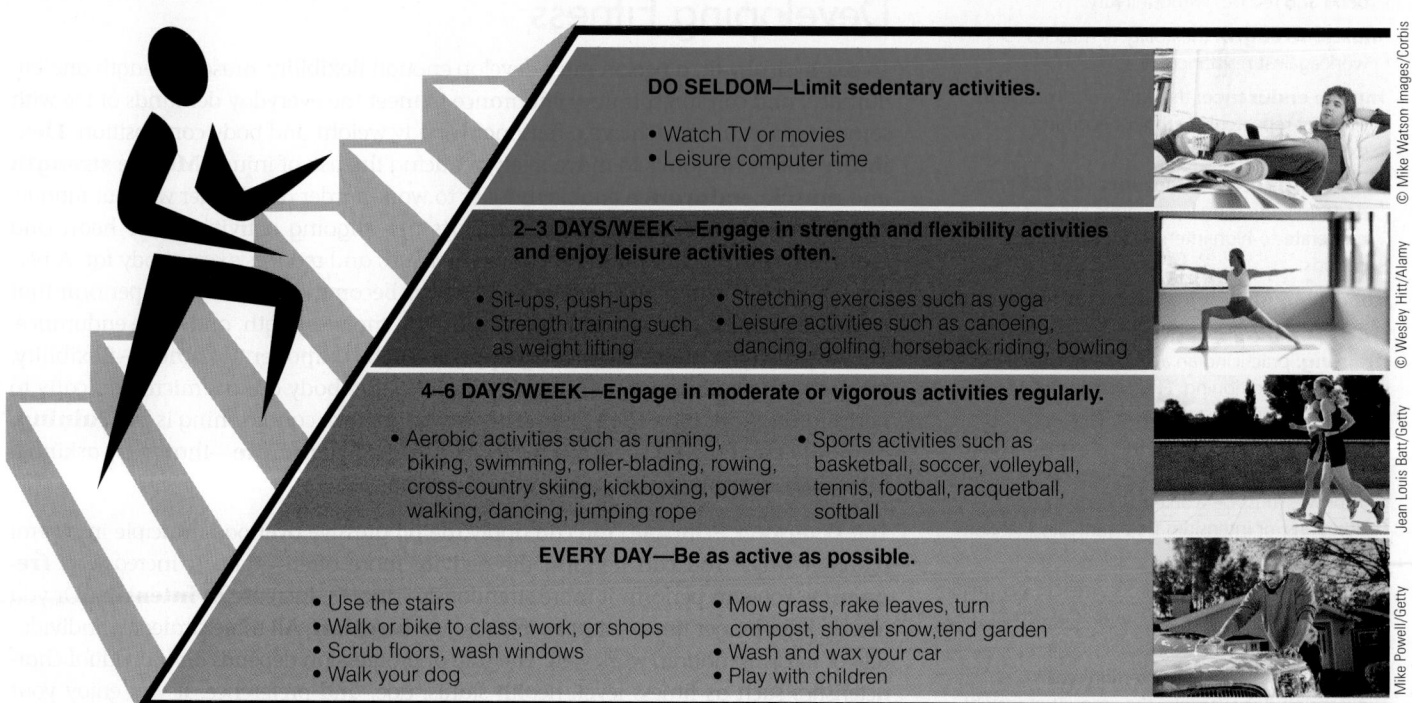

NOTE: Tips for increasing physical activity every day can be found at **MyPyramid.gov**.

TABLE 14-1 Guidelines for Physical Fitness	Cardiorespiratory	Strength	Flexibility
Type of Activity	Aerobic activity that uses large-muscle groups and can be maintained continuously	Resistance activity that is performed at a controlled speed and through a full range of motion	Stretching activity that uses the major muscle groups
Frequency	3 to 5 days per week	2 to 3 days per week	2 to 7 days per week
Intensity	55 to 90% of maximum heart rate	Enough to enhance muscle strength and improve body composition	Enough to develop and maintain a full range of motion
Duration	20 to 60 minutes	8 to 12 repetitions of 8 to 10 different exercises (minimum)	2 to 4 repetitions of 15 to 30 seconds per muscle group
Examples	Running, cycling, swimming, inline skating, rowing, power walking, cross-country skiing, kickboxing, jumping rope; sports activities such as basketball, soccer, raquetball, tennis, volleyball	Pull-ups, push-ups, weight lifting, pilates	Yoga

SOURCE: Adapted from American College of Sports Medicine, General principles of exercise prescription, in *ACSM's Guidelines for Exercise Testing and Prescription*, 7th ed. (Philadelphia, PA: Lippincott Williams & Wilkins, 2006), pp.133–173.

flexibility: the capacity of the joints to move through a full range of motion; the ability to bend and recover without injury.

muscle strength: the ability of muscles to work against resistance.

muscle endurance: the ability of a muscle to contract repeatedly without becoming exhausted.

cardiorespiratory endurance: the ability to perform large-muscle, dynamic exercise of moderate-to-high intensity for prolonged periods.

conditioning: the physical effect of training; improved flexibility, strength, and endurance.

training: practicing an activity regularly, which leads to conditioning. (Training is what you do; conditioning is what you get.)

progressive overload principle: the training principle that a body system, in order to improve, must be worked at frequencies, durations, or intensities that gradually increase physical demands.

frequency: the number of occurrences per unit of time (for example, the number of activity sessions per week).

intensity: the degree of exertion while exercising (for example, the amount of weight lifted or the speed of running).

duration: length of time (for example, the time spent in each activity session).

Therefore, some activity is better than none, and more activity is better still—up to a point. (Pursued in excess, intense physical activity, especially when combined with poor eating habits, can undermine health, as Highlight 8 explained.)

Developing Fitness

To be physically fit, a person must develop enough flexibility, muscle strength and endurance, and cardiorespiratory endurance to meet the everyday demands of life with some to spare and to achieve a reasonable body weight and body composition. **Flexibility** allows the joints to move freely, reducing the risk of injury. **Muscle strength** and **muscle endurance** enable muscles to work harder and longer without fatigue. **Cardiorespiratory endurance** supports the ongoing activity of the heart and lungs. Physical activity supports lean body tissues and reduces excess body fat. A person who practices a physical activity *adapts* by becoming better able to perform that activity after each session—with more flexibility, more strength, and more endurance.

The principles of **conditioning** apply to each component of fitness—flexibility, strength, and endurance. During conditioning, the body adapts microscopically to perform the work it is asked to do. The way to achieve conditioning is by **training**, primarily by applying the **progressive overload principle**—that is, by asking a little more of the body in each training session.

The Overload Principle You can apply the progressive overload principle in several different ways. You can perform the activity more often—that is, increase its **frequency.** You can perform it more strenuously—that is, increase its **intensity.** Or you can do it for longer times—that is, increase its **duration.** All three strategies, individually or in combination, work well. The rate of progression depends on individual characteristics such as fitness level, health status, age, and preference. If you enjoy your workout, do it more often. If you do not have much time, increase intensity. If you dislike hard work, take it easy, and do it for longer time periods. If you want continuous improvements, remember to overload progressively as you reach higher levels of fitness.

When increasing the frequency, intensity, or duration of a workout, however, exercise to a point that only *slightly* exceeds the comfortable capacity to work. It is better to progress slowly than to risk injury by overexertion.

The Body's Response to Physical Activity Fitness develops in response to demand and wanes when demand ceases. Muscles gain size and strength after being made to work repeatedly, a response called **hypertrophy.** Conversely, without activity, muscles diminish in size and lose strength, a response called **atrophy.**

Hypertrophy and atrophy are adaptive responses to the muscles' greater and lesser work demands, respectively. Thus cyclists often have strong, well-developed legs but less arm or chest strength; a tennis player may have one superbly strong arm, while the other is just average. A variety of physical activities produces the best overall fitness, and to this end, people need to work different muscle groups from day to day. This strategy provides a day or two of rest for different muscle groups, giving them time to replenish nutrients and to repair any minor damage incurred by the activity.

Other tips for building fitness and minimizing the risk of overuse injuries are:

* Be active all week, not just on the weekends.

* Use proper equipment and attire.

* Perform exercises using proper form.

* Include **warm-up** and **cool-down** activities in each session. Warming up helps to prepare muscles, ligaments, and tendons for the upcoming activity and mobilizes fuels to support strength and endurance activities. Cooling down reduces muscle cramping and allows the heart rate to slow gradually.

* Train hard enough to challenge your strength or endurance a few times each week rather than every time you work out. Between challenges, do moderate workouts and include at least one day of rest each week.

* Pay attention to body signals. Symptoms such as abnormal heartbeats, dizziness, lightheadedness, cold sweat, confusion, or pain or pressure in the middle of the chest, teeth, jaw, neck, or arm demand immediate medical attention.

* Work out wisely. Do not start with activities so demanding that pain stops you within a day or two. Learn to enjoy small steps toward improvement. Fitness builds slowly.

Cautions on Starting a Fitness Program Before beginning a fitness program, make sure it is safe for you to do so. Most apparently healthy people can begin a **moderate exercise** program such as walking or increasing daily activities without a medical examination, but people with any of the risk factors listed in the margin ◆ may need medical advice.[21]

Physical activity helps you look good, feel good, and have fun, and it brings many long-term health benefits as well.

◆ Major coronary risk factors:
* Family history of heart disease
* Cigarette smoking
* Hypertension
* Serum cholesterol >200 mg/dL or HDL <40 mg/dL, or taking lipid-lowering medication
* Diabetes
* Sedentary lifestyle
* Obesity (BMI ≥30)

hypertrophy (high-PER-tro-fee): growing larger; with regard to muscles, an increase in size (and strength) in response to use.

atrophy (AT-ro-fee): becoming smaller; with regard to muscles, a decrease in size (and strength) because of disuse, undernutrition, or wasting diseases.

warm-up: 5 to 10 minutes of light activity, such as easy jogging or cycling, prior to a workout to prepare the body for more vigorous activity.

cool-down: 5 to 10 minutes of light activity, such as walking or stretching, following a vigorous workout to gradually return the body's core to near-normal temperature.

moderate exercise: activity equivalent to the rate of exertion reached when walking at a speed of 4 miles per hour (15 minutes to walk one mile).

People's bodies are shaped by the activities they perform.

The key to regular physical activity is finding an activity that you enjoy.

◆ Recall from Chapter 7 that *aerobic* means requiring oxygen.

◆ Cardiorespiratory conditioning:
- Increases cardiac output and oxygen delivery
- Increases stroke volume
- Slows resting pulse
- Increases breathing efficiency
- Improves circulation
- Reduces blood pressure

VO₂max: the maximum rate of oxygen consumption by an individual at sea level.

cardiorespiratory conditioning: improvements in heart and lung function and increased blood volume, brought about by aerobic training.

cardiac output: the volume of blood discharged by the heart each minute; determined by multiplying the stroke volume by the heart rate. The stroke volume is the amount of oxygenated blood the heart ejects toward the tissues at each beat.

Cardiac output (volume/minute) = stroke volume (volume/beat) × heart rate (beats/minute)

Cardiorespiratory Endurance

The length of time a person can remain active with an elevated heart rate—that is, the ability of the heart, lungs, and blood to sustain a given demand—defines a person's cardiorespiratory endurance. Cardiorespiratory endurance training improves a person's ability to sustain vigorous activities such as running, brisk walking, or swimming. Such training enhances the capacity of the heart, lungs, and blood to deliver oxygen to, and remove waste from, the body's cells. Cardiorespiratory endurance training, therefore, is *aerobic*. ◆ As the cardiorespiratory system gradually adapts to the demands of aerobic activity, the body delivers oxygen more efficiently. In fact, the accepted measure of a person's cardiorespiratory fitness is maximal oxygen uptake **(VO₂max).** The benefits of cardiorespiratory training are not just physical, though, because all of the body's cells, including the brain cells, require oxygen to function. When the cells receive more oxygen more readily, both the body and the mind benefit.

Cardiorespiratory Conditioning **Cardiorespiratory conditioning** ◆ occurs as aerobic workouts improve heart and lung activities. **Cardiac output** increases, thus enhancing oxygen delivery.[22] The heart becomes stronger, and each beat pumps more blood. Because the heart pumps more blood with each beat, fewer beats are necessary, and the resting heart rate slows down. The average resting pulse rate for adults is around 70 beats per minute, but people who achieve cardiorespiratory conditioning may have resting pulse rates of 50 or even lower. The muscles that work the lungs become stronger, too, so breathing becomes more efficient. Circulation through the arteries and veins improves. Blood moves easily, and blood pressure falls.[23]

Cardiorespiratory endurance reflects the health of the heart and circulatory system, on which all other body systems depend. Figure 14-2 shows the major relationships among the heart, circulatory system, and lungs.

To improve your cardiorespiratory endurance, the activity you choose must be sustained for 20 minutes or longer and use most of the large-muscle groups of the body (legs, buttocks, and abdomen). You must also train at an intensity that elevates your heart rate.

A person's own perceived effort is usually a reliable indicator of the intensity of an activity. In general, when you're working out, do so at an intensity that raises your heart rate but still leaves you able to talk comfortably. If you are more competitive and want to work to your limit on some days, a treadmill test can reveal your maximum heart rate. You can work out safely at up to 90 percent of that rate. The ACSM guidelines for developing and maintaining cardiorespiratory fitness are given in Table 14-1 on p. 480.

Muscle Conditioning One of the benefits of cardiorespiratory training is that fit muscles use oxygen efficiently, reducing the heart's workload. An added bonus is that muscles that use oxygen efficiently can burn fat longer—a plus for body composition and weight control.

A Balanced Fitness Program The intensity and type of physical activities that are best for one person may not be good for another. The intensity to choose depends on your present fitness: work hard enough to breathe heavily, but not so hard as to incur an oxygen debt. A person who has been sedentary will initially perform at a dramatically different level of intensity than a fit person.

The type of physical activity that is best for you depends, too, on what you want to achieve and what you enjoy doing. Some people love walking, whereas others prefer to dance or ride a bike. If you want to be stronger and firmer, lift weights. And remember, muscle is more metabolically active than body fat, so the more muscle you have, the more energy you'll burn.

In a balanced fitness program, aerobic activity improves cardiorespiratory fitness, stretching enhances flexibility, and weight training develops muscle strength and endurance. Table 14-2 provides an example of a balanced fitness program.

FIGURE 14-2   *Animated!* Delivery of Oxygen by the Heart and Lungs to the Muscles

ThomsonNOW™
To test your understanding of these concepts, log on to **www.thomsonedu.com/thomsonnow.**

The cardiorespiratory system responds to the muscles' demand for oxygen by building up its capacity to deliver oxygen. Researchers can measure cardiorespiratory fitness by measuring the maximum amount of oxygen a person consumes per minute while working out, a measure called VO_2max.

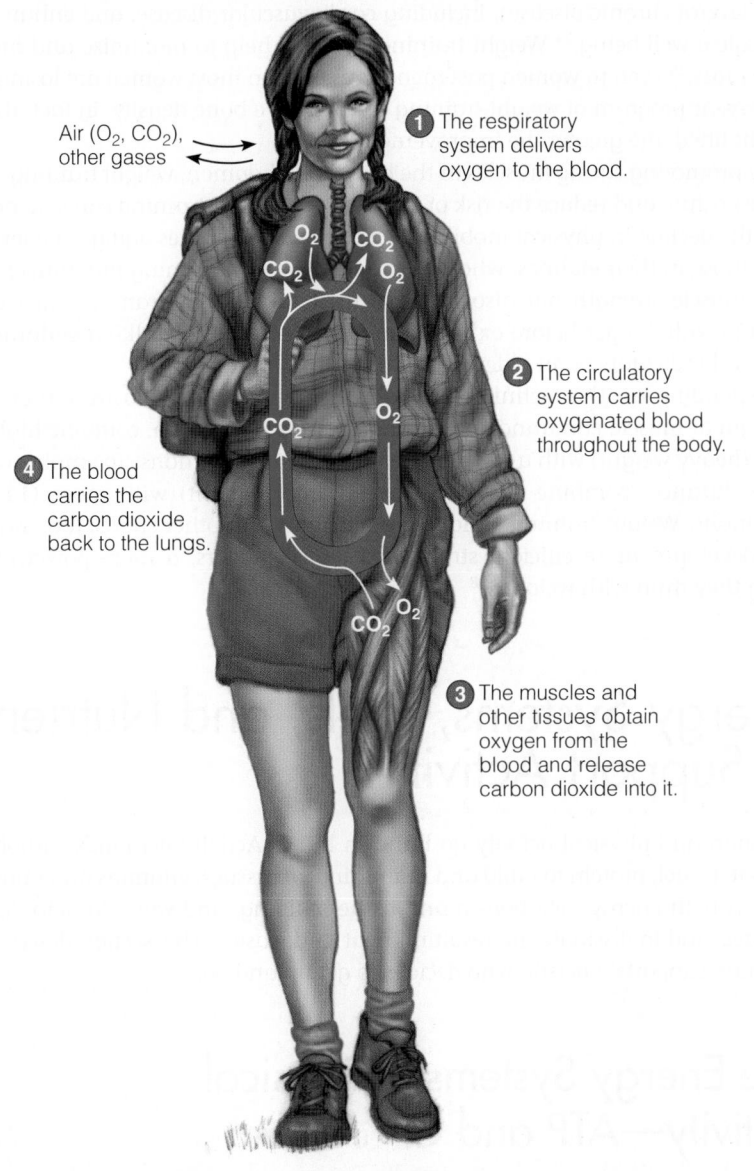

Air (O_2, CO_2), other gases

1 The respiratory system delivers oxygen to the blood.

2 The circulatory system carries oxygenated blood throughout the body.

4 The blood carries the carbon dioxide back to the lungs.

3 The muscles and other tissues obtain oxygen from the blood and release carbon dioxide into it.

 Dietary Guidelines for Americans 2005

Achieve physical fitness by including cardiovascular conditioning, stretching exercises for flexibility, and resistance exercises or calisthenics for muscle strength and endurance.

IN SUMMARY

Physical activity brings positive rewards: good health and long life. To develop fitness—whose components are flexibility, muscle strength and endurance, and cardiorespiratory endurance—a person must condition the body, through training, to adapt to the activity performed.

TABLE 14-2   A Sample Balanced Fitness Program

Monday, Tuesday, Wednesday, Thursday, Friday:

- 5 minutes of warm-up activity
- 45 minutes of aerobic activity
- 10 minutes of cool-down activity and stretching

Tuesday, Thursday, Saturday:

- 5 minutes of warm-up activity
- 30 minutes of weight training
- 10 minutes of cool-down activity and stretching

Saturday and/or Sunday:

- Sports, walking, hiking, biking, or swimming

Weight Training

Weight training has long been recognized as a means to build lean body mass and develop and maintain muscle strength and endurance. Additional benefits of weight training, however, have emerged only recently. Progressive weight training not only increases muscle strength and endurance, but it also prevents and manages several chronic diseases, including cardiovascular disease, and enhances psychological well-being.[24] Weight training can also help to maximize and maintain bone mass.[25] Even in women past menopause (when most women are losing bone), a one-year program of weight training can improve bone density; in fact, the more weight lifted, the greater the improvement.[26]

By promoting strong muscles in the back and abdomen, weight training can improve posture and reduce the risk of back injury. Weight training can also help prevent the decline in physical mobility that often accompanies aging.[27] Older adults, even those in their eighties, who participate in weight training programs not only gain muscle strength but also improve their muscle endurance, which enables them to walk longer before exhaustion. Leg strength and walking endurance are powerful indicators of an older adult's physical abilities.

Depending on the technique, weight training can emphasize either muscle strength or muscle endurance. To emphasize muscle strength, combine high resistance (heavy weight) with a low number (8 to 10) of repetitions. To emphasize muscle endurance, combine less resistance (lighter weight) with more (12 to 15) repetitions. Weight training enhances performance in other sports, too. Swimmers can develop a more efficient stroke and tennis players, a more powerful serve, when they train with weights.[28]

Energy Systems, Fuels, and Nutrients to Support Activity

Nutrition and physical activity go hand in hand. Activity demands carbohydrate and fat as fuel, protein to build and maintain lean tissues, vitamins and minerals to support both energy metabolism and tissue building, and water to help distribute the fuels and to dissipate the resulting heat and wastes. This section describes how nutrition supports a person who decides to get up and go.

The Energy Systems of Physical Activity—ATP and CP

Muscles contract fast. When called upon, they respond quickly without taking time to metabolize fat or carbohydrate for energy. In the first fractions of a second, muscles starting to move depend on their supplies of quick-energy compounds to power their movements. Exercise physiologists know these compounds by their abbreviations, ATP and CP.

ATP As Chapter 7 described, all of the energy-yielding nutrients—carbohydrate, fat, and protein—can enter metabolic pathways that make the high-energy compound ATP (adenosine triphosphate). ATP is present in small amounts in all body tissues all the time, and it can deliver energy instantly. In the muscles, ATP provides the chemical driving force for contraction. When an ATP molecule is split, its energy is released, and the muscle cells channel some of that energy into mechanical movement and most of it into heat.

CP Immediately after the onset of a demand, before muscle ATP pools dwindle, a muscle enzyme begins to break down another high-energy compound that is stored

weight training (also called **resistance training**): the use of free weights or weight machines to provide resistance for developing muscle strength and endurance. A person's own body weight may also be used to provide resistance as when a person does push-ups, pull-ups, or abdominal crunches.

in the muscle, **CP,** or **creatine phosphate.** CP is made from creatine, a compound commonly found in muscles, with a phosphate group attached, and it can split (anaerobically) ◆ to release phosphate and replenish ATP supplies. Supplies of CP in a muscle last for only about 10 seconds, producing enough quick energy without oxygen for a 100-meter dash.

When activity ceases and the muscles are resting, ATP feeds energy back to CP by giving up one of its phosphate groups to creatine. Thus CP is produced during rest by reversing the process that occurs during muscular activity. ◆ (Highlight 14 includes creatine supplements in its discussion of substances commonly used in the pursuit of fitness.)

The Energy-Yielding Nutrients To meet the more prolonged demands of sustained activity, the muscles generate ATP from the more abundant fuels: carbohydrate, fat, and protein. The breakdown of these nutrients generates ATP all day every day, and so maintains the supply. Muscles always use a mixture of fuels—never just one.

During rest, the body derives more than half of its ATP from fatty acids and most of the rest from glucose, along with a small percentage from amino acids. During physical activity, the body adjusts its mixture of fuels. How much of which fuel ◆ the muscles use during physical activity depends on an interplay among the fuels available from the diet, the intensity and duration of the activity, and the degree to which the body is conditioned to perform that activity. The next sections explain these relationships by examining each of the energy-yielding nutrients individually, but keep in mind that although one fuel may predominate at a given time, the other two will still be involved. Table 14-3 shows how fuel use changes according to the intensity and duration of the activity.

As you read about each of the energy-yielding nutrients, notice how its contribution to the fuel mixture shifts depending on whether the activity is anaerobic or aerobic. Anaerobic activities are associated with strength, agility, and split-second surges of power. The jump of the basketball player, the slam of the tennis serve, the heave of a bodybuilder lifting weights, and the blast of the fullback through the opposing line all involve anaerobic work. Such high-intensity, short-duration activities depend mostly on glucose as the chief energy fuel.

Endurance activities of low-to-moderate intensity and long duration depend more on fat to provide energy aerobically. The ability to continue swimming to the shore, to keep on hiking to the top of the mountain, or to continue pedaling all the way home reflects aerobic capacity. As mentioned earlier, aerobic capacity is also crucial to maintaining a healthy heart and circulatory system. The relationships among fuels and physical activity bear heavily on what foods best support your chosen activities.

Split-second surges of power as in the heave of a barbell or jump of a basketball player involve anaerobic work.

◆ Recall from Chapter 7 that *anaerobic* means not requiring oxygen.

◆ During rest: ATP + creatine →CP
During activity: CP →ATP + creatine

◆ Fuel mixture during activity depends on:
• Diet
• Intensity and duration of activity
• Training

Glucose Use during Physical Activity

Glucose, stored in the liver and muscles as glycogen, is vital to physical activity. During exertion, the liver breaks down its glycogen and releases the glucose into the bloodstream. The muscles use this glucose as well as their own private glycogen

CP, creatine phosphate (also called **phosphocreatine**): a high-energy compound in muscle cells that acts as a reservoir of energy that can maintain a steady supply of ATP. CP provides the energy for short bursts of activity.

TABLE 14-3	Fuels Used for Activities of Different Intensities and Durations			
Activity Intensity	**Activity Duration**	**Preferred Fuel Source**	**Oxygen Needed?**	**Activity Example**
Extreme[a]	8 to 10 sec	ATP-CP (immediate availability)	No (anaerobic)	100-yard dash, shot put
Very high	20 sec to 3 min	ATP from carbohydrate (lactate)	No (anaerobic)	¼-mile run at maximal speed
High	3 min to 20 min	ATP from carbohydrate	Yes (aerobic)	Cycling, swimming, or running
Moderate	More than 20 min	ATP from fat	Yes (aerobic)	Hiking

[a]All levels of activity intensity use the ATP-CP system initially; extremely intense short-term activities rely solely on the ATP-CP system.

Sustained muscular efforts as in a long-distance rowing event or a cross-country run involve aerobic work.

◆ To fill glycogen stores, eat plenty of carbohydrate-rich foods.

◆ Reminder: *Lactate* is the product of anaerobic glycolysis.

stores to fuel their work. Glycogen supplies can easily support everyday activities but are limited to less than 2000 kcalories of energy, enough for about 20 miles of running.[29] The more glycogen the muscles store, the longer the glycogen will last during physical activity, which in turn influences performance. When glycogen is depleted, the muscles become fatigued.

Diet Affects Glycogen Storage and Use How much carbohydrate a person eats influences how much glycogen is stored. ◆ A classic study compared fuel use during activity among three groups of runners on different diets.[30] For several days before testing, one group consumed a normal mixed diet, a second group consumed a high-carbohydrate diet, and the third group consumed a no-carbohydrate diet (fat and protein diet). As Figure 14-3 shows, the high-carbohydrate diet allowed the runners to keep going longer before exhaustion. This study and many others that followed have confirmed that high-carbohydrate diets enhance endurance by ensuring ample glycogen stores.

Intensity of Activity Affects Glycogen Use How long an exercising person's glycogen will last depends not only on diet, but also on the intensity of the activity. Moderate activities, such as jogging, during which breathing is steady and easy, use glycogen slowly. The lungs and circulatory system have no trouble keeping up with the muscles' need for oxygen. The individual breathes easily, and the heart beats steadily—the activity is aerobic. The muscles derive their energy from both glucose and fatty acids. By depending partly on fatty acids, moderate aerobic activity conserves glycogen.

Intense activities—the kind that make it difficult "to catch your breath," such as a quarter-mile race—use glycogen quickly. In such activities, the muscles break down glucose to pyruvate anaerobically, producing ATP quickly.

Lactate When the rate of glycolysis exceeds the capacity of the mitochondria to accept hydrogens with their electrons for the electron transport chain, the accumulating pyruvate molecules are converted to lactate. ◆ At low intensities, lactate is readily cleared from the blood, but at higher intensities, lactate accumulates. When the rate of lactate production exceeds the rate of clearance, intense activity can be maintained for only 1 to 3 minutes (as in a 400- to 800-meter race or a boxing

---

FIGURE 14-3 The Effect of Diet on Physical Endurance

A high-carbohydrate diet can increase an athlete's endurance. In this study, the fat and protein diet provided 94 percent of kcalories from fat and 6 percent from protein; the normal mixed diet provided 55 percent of kcalories from carbohydrate; and the high-carbohydrate diet provided 83 percent of kcalories from carbohydrate.

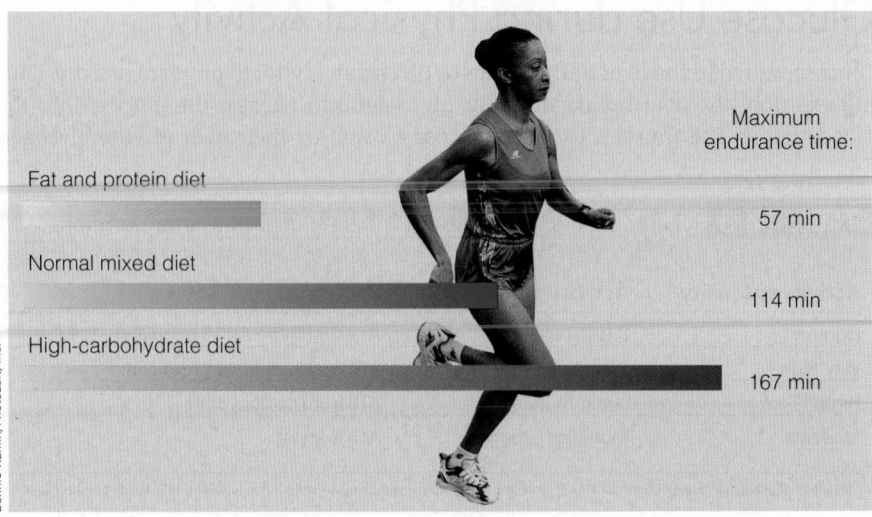

Maximum endurance time:

Fat and protein diet — 57 min

Normal mixed diet — 114 min

High-carbohydrate diet — 167 min

match). Lactate was long blamed for muscle fatigue, but recent research disputes this idea. Working muscles may produce lactate and experience fatigue, but the lactate does not cause the fatigue.[31]

When production of lactate exceeds the ability of the muscles to use it, they release it, and it travels in the blood to the liver. There, liver enzymes convert the lactate back into glucose. Glucose can then return to the muscles to fuel additional activity. (The recycling process that regenerates glucose from lactate is known as the *Cori cycle,* as shown in Figure 7-6 on p. 220.)

Duration of Activity Affects Glycogen Use Glycogen use depends not only on the intensity of an activity, but also on its duration. Within the first 20 minutes or so of moderate activity, a person uses mostly glycogen for fuel—about one-fifth of the available glycogen. As the muscles devour their own glycogen, they become ravenous for more glucose, and the liver responds by emptying out its glycogen stores.

After 20 minutes, a person who continues exercising moderately (mostly aerobically) begins to use less and less glycogen and more and more fat for fuel (review Table 14-3 on p. 485). Still, glycogen use continues, and if the activity lasts long enough and is intense enough, blood glucose declines and muscle and liver glycogen stores are depleted. Physical activity can continue for a short time thereafter only because the liver scrambles to produce, from lactate and certain amino acids, the minimum amount of glucose needed to briefly forestall total depletion.

Glucose Depletion After a couple of hours of strenuous activity, glucose stores are depleted. When depletion occurs, it brings nervous system function to a near halt, making continued exertion almost impossible. Marathon runners refer to this point of glucose exhaustion as "hitting the wall."

To avoid such debilitation, endurance athletes try to maintain their blood glucose for as long as they can. The following guidelines will help endurance atheletes maximize glucose supply:

- Eat a high-carbohydrate diet (approximately 8 grams of carbohydrate per kilogram of body weight or about 70 percent of energy intake) regularly.*

- Take glucose (usually in sports drinks) periodically during activities that last for 45 minutes or more.

- Eat carbohydrate-rich foods (approximately 60 grams of carbohydrate) ♦ immediately following activity.

- Train the muscles to store as much glycogen as possible.

The last section of this chapter, "Diets for Physically Active People," discusses how to design a high-carbohydrate diet for performance, and the "How to" on p. 488 describes **carbohydrate loading**—a technique used to maximize glycogen stores for long endurance competitions.

Glucose during Activity Muscles can obtain the glucose they need not only from glycogen stores, but also from foods and beverages consumed during activity. Consuming carbohydrate is especially useful during exhausting endurance activities (lasting more than 45 minutes) and during games such as soccer or hockey, which last for hours and demand repeated bursts of intense activity.[32] Endurance athletes often run short of glucose by the end of competitive events, and they are wise to take light carbohydrate snacks or drinks (about 200 kcalories) periodically during activity.[33] During the last stages of an endurance competition, when glycogen is running low, glucose consumed during the event can slowly make its way from the digestive tract to the muscles and augment the body's supply of glucose enough to forestall exhaustion.

Moderate- to high-intensity aerobic exercises that can be sustained for only a short time (less than 20 minutes) use some fat, but more glucose for fuel.

♦ For perspective, snack ideas providing 60 g carbohydrate:
- 16 oz sports drink and a small bagel
- 16 oz milk and 4 oatmeal cookies
- 8 oz pineapple juice and a granola bar

carbohydrate loading: a regimen of moderate exercise followed by the consumption of a high-carbohydrate diet that enables muscles to store glycogen beyond their normal capacities; also called **glycogen loading** or **glycogen super compensation.**

---

* Percentage of energy intake is meaningful only when total energy intake is known. Consider that at high energy intakes (say, 5000 kcalories/day), even a moderate carbohydrate diet (40 percent of energy intake) supplies 500 grams of carbohydrate—enough for a 137-pound (62 kilogram) athlete in heavy training. By comparison, at a moderate energy intake (2000 kcalories/day), a high carbohydrate intake (70 percent of energy intake) supplies 350 grams—plenty of carbohydrate for most people, but not enough for athletes in heavy training.

HOW TO Maximize Glycogen Stores: Carbohydrate Loading

Some athletes use a technique called carbohydrate loading to trick their muscles into storing extra glycogen before a competition. Carbohydrate loading can nearly double muscle glycogen concentrations. In general, the athlete tapers training during the week before the competition and then eats a high-carbohydrate diet during the three days just prior to the event.[a] Specifically, the athlete follows the plan in the accompanying table. In this carbohydrate loading plan, glycogen storage occurs slowly, and athletes must alter their training for several days before the event.

In contrast, a group of researchers have designed a quick method of carbohydrate loading that has produced promising results. The researchers found that athletes

Before the Event	Training Intensity	Training Duration	Dietary Carbohydrate
6 days	Moderate (70% VO₂max)	90 min	Normal (5 g/kg body weight)
4–5 days	Moderate (70% VO₂max)	40 min	Normal (5 g/kg body weight)
2–3 days	Moderate (70% VO₂max)	20 min	High-carbohydrate (10 g/kg body weight)
1 day	Rest	—	High-carbohydrate (10 g/kg body weight)

could attain above-normal concentrations of muscle glycogen by eating a high-carbohydrate diet (10 g/kg body weight) after a short (3 minutes) but very intense bout of exercise.[b] More studies are needed to confirm these findings and to determine whether an exercise session of less intensity and shorter duration would accomplish the same results.

Extra glycogen gained through carbohydrate loading can benefit an athlete who must keep going for 90 minutes or longer. Those who exercise for shorter times simply need a regular high-carbohydrate diet. In a hot climate, extra glycogen confers an additional advantage: as glycogen breaks down, it releases water, which helps to meet the athlete's fluid needs.

[a]E. Coleman, Carbohydrate and exercise, in *Sports Nutrition: A Practice Manual for Professionals*, 4th ed., ed. M. Dunford (Chicago: The American Dietetic Association, 2006), pp. 14–32.

[b]T. J. Fairchild and coauthors, Rapid carbohydrate loading after a short bout of near maximal-intensity exercise, *Medicine and Science in Sports and Exercise* 34 (2002): 980–986.

Abundant energy from the breakdown of fat can come only from aerobic metabolism.

© PhotoDisc/Getty Images

◆ In popular magazine articles and on the Internet, foods with a high glycemic index are sometimes called "high impact carbs," and foods with a low glycemic index are sometimes called "low impact carbs."

◆ Reminder: The *mitochondria* are the structures within a cell responsible for producing ATP (see Figure 7-1 on p. 214).

Glucose after Activity Eating high-carbohydrate foods *after* physical activity also enlarges glycogen stores. A high-carbohydrate meal eaten within 15 minutes after physical activity accelerates the rate of glycogen storage by 300 percent. After two hours, the rate of glycogen storage declines by almost half. Despite this slower rate of glycogen restoration, muscles continue to accumulate glycogen as long as athletes eat carbohydrate-rich foods within two hours following activity.[34] This is particularly important to athletes who train hard more than once a day.

Chapter 4 introduced the glycemic effect and discussed the possible health benefits of eating a *low*-glycemic diet. For athletes wishing to maximize muscle glycogen synthesis after strenuous training, however, eating foods with a *high* glycemic index may be more beneficial (see Figure 4-13 on p. 116).[35] Foods with a high glycemic index elicit greater rates of glycogen synthesis compared to foods with a low glycemic index.[36] ◆

Training Affects Glycogen Use Training, too, affects how much glycogen muscles will store. Muscle cells that repeatedly deplete their glycogen through hard work adapt to store greater amounts of glycogen to support that work.

Conditioned muscles also rely less on glycogen and more on fat for energy, so glycogen breakdown and glucose use occur more slowly in trained than in untrained individuals at a given work intensity.[37] A person attempting an activity for the first time uses much more glucose than an athlete who is trained to perform it. Oxygen delivery to the muscles by the heart and lungs plays a role, but equally importantly, trained muscles are better equipped to use the oxygen because their cells contain more mitochondria. ◆ Untrained muscles depend more heavily on anaerobic glucose breakdown, even when physical activity is just moderate.

Fat Use during Physical Activity

As Figure 14-3 (p. 486) shows, researchers have long recognized the importance of a high-carbohydrate diet for endurance performance. When endurance athletes "fat load" by consuming high-fat, low-carbohydrate diets for one to three days, their performance is impaired because their small glycogen stores are depleted quickly.[38] Endurance athletes who adhere to a high-fat, low-carbohydrate diet for more than a week, however, adapt by relying more on fat to fuel activity. Even with fat adaptation, however, performance benefits are not consistently evident.[39] In some cases, athletes on high-fat diets experience greater fatigue and perceive the activity to be more strenuous than athletes on high-carbohydrate diets.[40]

Diets high in saturated fat carry risks of heart disease, too. Physical activity offers some protection against cardiovascular disease, but athletes, like everyone else, can suffer heart attacks and strokes. Most nutrition experts agree that the potential for adverse health effects of prolonged high-fat diets continues to outweigh any possible benefit to performance.

Sports nutrition experts recommend that endurance athletes consume 20 to 30 percent of their energy from fat to meet nutrient and energy needs.[41] Athletes who restrict fat below 20 percent of total energy intake may fail to consume adequate energy and nutrients.

In contrast to *dietary* fat, *body* fat stores are extremely important during physical activity, as long as the activity is not too intense. Unlike glycogen stores, the body's fat stores can usually provide more than 70,000 kcalories and fuel hours of activity without running out.[42]

The fat used in physical activity is liberated as fatty acids from the internal fat stores and from the fat under the skin. Areas that have the most fat to spare donate the greatest amounts to the blood (although they may not be the areas that appear fattiest). Thus "spot reducing" doesn't work because muscles do not "own" the fat that surrounds them. Fat cells release fatty acids into the blood, not into the underlying muscles. Then the blood gives to each muscle the amount of fat that it needs. Proof of this is found in a tennis player's arms—the skinfold measures are the same in both arms, even though the muscles of one arm work much harder and may be larger than those of the other. A balanced fitness program that includes strength training, however, will tighten muscles underneath the fat, improving the overall appearance. Keep in mind that some body fat is essential to good health.

Duration of Activity Affects Fat Use Early in an activity, as the muscles draw on fatty acids, blood levels fall. If the activity continues for more than a few minutes, the hormone epinephrine signals the fat cells to begin breaking down their stored triglycerides and liberating fatty acids into the blood. After about 20 minutes of physical activity, the blood fatty acid concentration surpasses the normal resting concentration. Thereafter, sustained, moderate activity uses body fat stores as its major fuel.

Intensity of Activity Affects Fat Use The intensity of physical activity also affects fat use. As the intensity of activity increases, fat makes less and less of a contribution to the fuel mixture. Remember that fat can be broken down for energy only by aerobic metabolism. For fat to fuel activity, then, oxygen must be abundantly available. If a person is breathing easily during activity, the muscles are getting all the oxygen they need and are able to use more fat in the fuel mixture.

Training Affects Fat Use Training—repeated aerobic activity—produces the adaptations that permit the body to draw more heavily on fat for fuel. Training stimulates the muscle cells to manufacture more and larger mitochondria, the "power house" structures of the cells that produce ATP for energy. Another adaptation: the heart and lungs become stronger and better able to deliver oxygen to muscles at high activity intensities. Still another: hormones in the body of a trained person slow glucose release from the liver and speed up the use of fat instead. These adaptations reward not only trained athletes but all active people; a person who trains by way of aerobic activities such as distance running or cycling becomes well suited to the activity.

Low- to moderate-intensity aerobic exercises that can be sustained for a long time (more than 20 minutes) use some glucose, but more fat for fuel.

Protein Use during Physical Activity—and between Times

Table 14-3 on p. 485 summarizes the fuel uses discussed so far, but does not include the third energy-yielding nutrient, protein, because protein is not a major fuel for physical activity. Nevertheless, physically active people use protein just as other people do—to build muscle and other lean tissues and, to some extent, to fuel activity. The body does, however, handle protein differently during activity than during rest.

Protein Used in Muscle Building Synthesis of body proteins is suppressed during activity. In the hours of recovery following activity, though, protein synthesis accelerates beyond normal resting levels. As noted earlier, eating high-carbohydrate foods immediately after exercise accelerates muscle glycogen storage. Similarly, research shows that eating carbohydrate, together with protein, enhances muscle protein synthesis.[43] Remember that the body adapts and builds the molecules, cells, and tissues it needs for the next period of activity. Whenever the body remodels a part of itself, it also tears down old structures to make way for new ones. Repeated activity, with just a slight overload, triggers the protein-dismantling and protein-synthesizing equipment of each muscle cell to make needed changes—that is, to adapt.

The physical work of each muscle cell acts as a signal to its DNA and RNA to begin producing the kinds of proteins that will best support that work. Take jogging, for example. In the first difficult sessions, the body is not yet equipped to perform aerobic work easily, but with each session, the cells' genetic material gets the message that an overhaul is needed. In the hours that follow the session, the genes send molecular messages to the protein-building equipment that tell it what old structures to break down and what new structures to build. Within the limits of its genetic potential, the body responds. An athlete may add between $1/4$ ounce and 1 ounce (between 7 and 28 grams) of body protein to existing muscle mass each day during active muscle-building phases of training. Also, more mitochondria are created to facilitate efficient aerobic metabolism. Over a few weeks' time, remodeling occurs and jogging becomes easier.

Protein Used as Fuel Not only do athletes retain more protein in their muscles, but they also use more protein as fuel. Muscles speed up their use of amino acids for energy during physical activity, just as they speed up their use of fat and carbohydrate. Still, protein contributes only about 10 percent of the total fuel used, both during activity and during rest. The most active people of all, endurance athletes, use up large amounts of all energy fuels, including protein, during performance, but such athletes also eat more food and therefore usually consume enough protein.

Diet Affects Protein Use during Activity The factors that affect how much protein is used during activity seem to be the same three that influence the use of fat and carbohydrate—one factor is diet. People who consume diets adequate in energy and rich in *carbohydrate* ◆ use less protein than those who eat protein- and fat-rich diets. Recall that carbohydrates spare proteins from being broken down to make glucose when needed. Because physical activity requires glucose, a diet lacking in carbohydrate necessitates the conversion of amino acids to glucose. The same is true for diet high in fat because fatty acids can never provide glucose.

Intensity and Duration of Activity Affect Protein Use during Activity A second factor, the intensity and duration of activity, also modifies protein use. Endurance athletes who train for more than an hour a day, engaging in aerobic activity of moderate intensity and long duration, may deplete their glycogen stores by the end of their workouts and become somewhat more dependent on body protein for energy.

In contrast, anaerobic strength training does not use more protein for energy, but it does demand more protein to build muscle. Thus the protein needs of both endurance and strength athletes are higher than those of sedentary people, but certainly not as high as the protein intakes many athletes consume.

◆ To conserve protein, eat a diet adequate in energy and rich in carbohydrate.

Training Affects Protein Use A third factor that influences a person's use of protein during physical activity is the extent of training. Particularly in strength athletes such as bodybuilders, the higher the degree of training, the less protein a person uses during an activity.

Protein Recommendations for Active People As mentioned, all active people, and especially athletes in training, probably need more protein than sedentary people do. Endurance athletes, such as long-distance runners and cyclists, use more protein for fuel than strength or power athletes do, and they retain some, especially in the muscles used for their sport. Strength athletes, such as bodybuilders, and power athletes, such as football players, use less protein for fuel, but they still use some and retain much more. Therefore, *all* athletes in training should attend to protein needs, but they should first meet their energy needs with adequate carbohydrate intakes. Without adequate carbohydrate intake, athletes will burn off as fuel the very protein that they wish to retain in muscle.

How much protein, then, should an active person consume? Although the DRI Committee does not recommend greater than normal protein intakes for athletes, other authorities do.[44] These recommendations specify different protein intakes for athletes pursuing different activities (see Table 14-4).[45] A later section translates protein recommendations into a diet plan and shows that no one needs protein supplements, or even large servings of meat, to obtain the highest recommended protein intakes. (Chapter 6 concluded that most people receive more than enough protein without supplements and reviewed the potential dangers of using protein and amino acid supplements.)

For perfect functioning, every nutrient is needed.

IN SUMMARY

The mixture of fuels the muscles use during physical activity depends on diet, the intensity and duration of the activity, and training. During intense activity, the fuel mix is mostly glucose, whereas during less intense, moderate activity, fat makes a greater contribution. With endurance training, muscle cells adapt to store more glycogen and to rely less on glucose and more on fat for energy. Athletes in training may need more protein than sedentary people do, but they typically eat more food as well and therefore obtain enough protein.

Vitamins and Minerals to Support Activity

Many of the vitamins and minerals assist in releasing energy from fuels and in transporting oxygen. This knowledge has led many people to believe, mistakenly,

TABLE 14-4 Recommended Protein Intakes for Athletes

	Recommendations (g/kg/day)	Protein Intakes (g/day)	
		Males	Females
RDA for adults	0.8	56	44
Recommended intake for power (strength or speed) athletes	1.6–1.7	112–119	88–94
Recommended intake for endurance athletes	1.2–1.6	84–112	66–88
U.S. average intake		95	65

NOTE: Daily protein intakes are based on a 70-kilogram (154-pound) man and 55-kilogram (121-pound) woman.
SOURCES: Committee on Dietary Reference Intakes, *Dietary Reference Intakes for Energy, Carbohydrate, Fiber, Fat, Fatty Acids, Cholesterol, Protein and Amino Acids* (Washington, D.C.: National Academies Press, 2005), pp. 660–661; Position of the American Dietetic Association, Dietitians of Canada, and the American College of Sports Medicine: Nutrition and athletic performance, *Journal of the American Dietetic Association* 100 (2000): 1543–1556.

that vitamin and mineral *supplements* offer physically active people both health benefits and athletic advantages. (Review Highlight 10 for a discussion of vitamin and mineral supplements, and see Highlight 14, which explores supplements and other products people use in the hope of enhancing athletic performance.)

Supplements Nutrient supplements do not enhance the performance of well-nourished people. Deficiencies of vitamins and minerals, however, do impede performance. In general, active people who eat enough nutrient-dense foods to meet energy needs also meet their vitamin and mineral needs. After all, active people eat more food; it stands to reason that with the right choices, they'll get more nutrients.

Athletes who lose weight to meet low body-weight requirements, however, may eat so little food that they fail to obtain all the nutrients they need.[46] The practice of "making weight" is opposed by many health and fitness organizations, but for athletes who choose this course of action, a single daily multivitamin-mineral supplement that provides no more than the DRI recommendations for nutrients may be beneficial.

Some athletes believe that taking vitamin or mineral supplements directly before competition will enhance performance. These beliefs are contrary to scientific reality. Most vitamins and minerals function as small parts of larger working units. After entering the blood, they have to wait for the cells to combine them with their appropriate other parts so that they can do their work. This takes time—hours or days. Vitamins or minerals taken right before an event are useless for improving performance, even if the person is actually suffering deficiencies of them.

In general, then, most active people who eat well-balanced meals do not need vitamin or mineral supplements. Two nutrients, vitamin E and iron, do merit special mention here, however, each for a different reason. Vitamin E is discussed because so many athletes take vitamin E supplements. Iron is discussed because some athletes may be unaware that they need iron supplements.

Vitamin E Vitamin E and other antioxidant nutrients may be especially effective for athletes exercising in extreme environments, such as heat, cold, and high altitudes. During prolonged, high-intensity physical activity, the muscles' consumption of oxygen increases tenfold or more, enhancing the production of damaging free radicals in the body.[47] Vitamin E is a potent antioxidant that vigorously defends cell membranes against oxidative damage. Some athletes and active people take megadoses of vitamin E in hopes of preventing such oxidative damage to muscles. ◆ In some studies, supplementation with vitamin E does seem to protect against exercise-induced oxidative stress. Other studies show no effect on oxidative stress, however, and a few show enhanced stress after vitamin E supplementation.[48] There is little evidence that vitamin E supplements can improve performance.[49] Clearly, more research is needed, but in the meantime, active people can benefit by using vegetable oils and eating generous servings of antioxidant-rich fruits and vegetables regularly.

Iron Deficiency Physically active young women, especially those who engage in endurance activities such as distance running, are prone to iron deficiency.[50] Habitually low intakes of iron-rich foods, high iron losses through menstruation, and the high demands of muscles for the iron-containing electron carriers of the mitochondria and the muscle protein myoglobin can cause iron deficiency in physically active young women.

Adolescent female athletes who eat vegetarian diets may be particularly vulnerable to iron deficiency.[51] As Chapter 13 explained, the bioavailability of iron is often poor in vegetarian diets. To protect against iron deficiency, vegetarian athletes need to select good dietary sources of iron (fortified cereals, legumes, nuts, and seeds) and include vitamin C-rich foods with each meal. As long as vegetarian athletes, like all athletes, consume enough nutrient-dense foods, they can perform as well as anyone.

Iron-Deficiency Anemia Iron-deficiency anemia impairs physical performance because the hemoglobin in red blood cells is needed to deliver oxygen to the cells for energy metabolism.◆ Without adequate oxygen, an active person cannot perform

◆ The Tolerable Upper Intake Level (UL) for vitamin E is 1000 mg per day.

◆ Reminder: Iron is an essential component of hemoglobin, the protein that transports oxygen throughout the body.

aerobic activities and tires easily. Whether iron deficiency without clinical signs of anemia impairs physical performance is less clear.[52]

Sports Anemia Early in training, athletes may develop low blood hemoglobin for a while. This condition, sometimes called **"sports anemia,"** is not a true iron-deficiency condition. Strenuous aerobic activity promotes destruction of the more fragile, older red blood cells, and the resulting cleanup work reduces the blood's iron content temporarily. Strenuous activity also expands the blood's plasma volume, thereby reducing the red blood cell count per unit of blood. However, the red blood cells do not diminish in size or number as in anemia, so their oxygen-carrying capacity is not hindered. Most researchers view sports anemia as an *adaptive,* temporary response to endurance training. Iron-deficiency anemia requires iron supplementation, but sports anemia does not.

Iron Recommendations for Athletes The best strategy for maintaining adequate iron nutrition depends on the individual. Menstruating women may border on iron deficiency even without the iron losses incurred by physical activity. Active teens of both genders have high iron needs because they are growing. Especially for women and teens, then, prescribed supplements may be needed to correct iron deficiencies. Physicians use the results of blood tests to determine whether such supplementation is needed. (Review Chapter 13 for many more details about iron, and see Appendix E for a description of the tests used in assessing its status.)

To prevent dehydration and the fatigue that accompanies it, drink liquids before, during, and after physical activity.

IN SUMMARY

With the possible exception of iron, well-nourished active people and athletes do not need nutrient supplements. Female athletes need to pay special attention to their iron needs.

Fluids and Electrolytes to Support Activity

The need for water far surpasses the need for any other nutrient. The body relies on watery fluids as the medium for all of its life-supporting activities, and if it loses too much water, its well-being will be compromised.

Obviously, the body loses water via sweat. Breathing uses water, too, exhaled as vapor. During physical activity, water losses from both routes are significant, and dehydration becomes a threat. Dehydration's first symptom is fatigue: a water loss of greater than 2 percent of body weight can reduce a person's capacity to do muscular work.[53] With a water loss of about 7 percent, a person is likely to collapse.

Fluid Losses via Sweat Recall from Chapter 7 that working muscles produce heat as a by-product of energy metabolism. During intense activity, muscle heat production can be 15 to 20 times greater than at rest. The body cools itself by sweating. Each liter of sweat dissipates almost 600 kcalories of heat, preventing a rise in body temperature of almost 10 degrees ◆ on the Celsius scale. The body routes its blood supply through the capillaries just under the skin, and the skin secretes sweat to evaporate and cool the skin and the underlying blood. The blood then flows back to cool the deeper body chambers.

◆ Note: 10 degrees on the Celsius scale is about 18 degrees on the Fahrenheit scale.

Hyperthermia In hot, humid weather, sweat doesn't evaporate well because the surrounding air is already laden with water. In **hyperthermia**, body heat builds up and triggers maximum sweating, but without sweat evaporation, little cooling takes place. In such conditions, active people must take precautions to prevent **heat stroke.** To reduce the risk of heat stroke, drink enough fluid before and during the activity, rest in the shade when tired, and wear lightweight clothing that allows sweat to evaporate.[54] (Hence the danger of rubber or heavy suits that supposedly promote weight loss during physical activity—they promote profuse sweating, prevent sweat evaporation, and invite heat stroke.) If you ever experience any of the

sports anemia: a transient condition of low hemoglobin in the blood, associated with the early stages of sports training or other strenuous activity.

hyperthermia: an above-normal body temperature.

heat stroke: a dangerous accumulation of body heat with accompanying loss of body fluid.

Water is the best fluid for most physically active people, but some consumers prefer the flavors of sports drinks.

◆ Symptoms of dehydration and heat stroke:
- Headache
- Nausea
- Dizziness
- Clumsiness
- Stumbling
- Sudden cessation of sweating (hot, dry skin)
- Confusion or other mental changes

symptoms of heat stroke listed in the margin, ◆ stop your activity, sip fluids, seek shade, and ask for help. Heat stroke can be fatal, young people often die of it, and these symptoms demand attention.

Hypothermia In cold weather, **hypothermia,** or low body temperature, can be as serious as heat stroke is in hot weather. Inexperienced, slow runners participating in long races on cold or wet, chilly days are especially vulnerable to hypothermia. Slow runners who produce little heat can become too cold if clothing is inadequate. Early symptoms of hypothermia include shivering and euphoria. As body temperature continues to fall, shivering may stop, and weakness, disorientation, and apathy may occur. Each of these symptoms can impair a person's ability to act against a further drop in body temperature. Even in cold weather, however, the active body still sweats and still needs fluids. The fluids should be warm or at room temperature to help protect against hypothermia.

Fluid Replacement via Hydration Endurance athletes can easily lose 1.5 liters or more of fluid during *each hour* of activity. To prepare for fluid losses, a person must hydrate before activity. To replace fluid losses, the person must rehydrate during and after activity. (Table 14-5 presents one schedule of hydration for physical activity.) Even then, in hot weather, the GI tract may not be able to absorb enough water fast enough to keep up with sweat losses, and some degree of dehydration may be inevitable. Athletes who know their body's **hourly sweat rate** can strive to replace the total amount of fluid lost during activity to prevent dehydration.[55]

Athletes who are preparing for competition are often advised to drink extra fluids in the *days* immediately before the event, especially if they are still training. The extra water is not stored in the body, but drinking extra water ensures maximum hydration at the start of the event. Full hydration is imperative for every athlete both in training and in competition. The athlete who arrives at an event even slightly dehydrated begins with a disadvantage.

What is the best fluid for an exercising body? For noncompetitive, everyday active people, plain, cool water is recommended, especially in warm weather, for two reasons: (1) Water rapidly leaves the digestive tract to enter the tissues where it is needed, and (2) it cools the body from the inside out. For endurance athletes, carbohydrate-containing beverages may be appropriate. Fluid ingestion during the event has the dual purposes of replenishing water lost through sweating and providing a source of carbohydrate to supplement the body's limited glycogen stores. Carbohydrate depletion brings on fatigue in the athlete, but as already mentioned, fluid loss and the accompanying buildup of body heat can be life-threatening. Thus the first priority for endurance athletes should be to replace fluids. Many good-tasting drinks are marketed for active people; the "How to" on p. 495 compares them with water.

Electrolyte Losses and Replacement When a person sweats, small amounts of electrolytes—the electrically charged minerals sodium, potassium, chloride, and

TABLE 14-5	Hydration Schedule for Physical Activity
When to Drink	**Amount of Fluid**
2 hr before activity	2 to 3 c
15 min before activity	1 to 2 c
Every 15 min during activity	½ to 2 c (Drink enough to minimize loss of body weight, but don't overdrink.)
After activity	2 c for each pound of body weight lost[a]

[a] Drinking 2 cups of fluid every 20 to 30 minutes after exercise until the total amount required is consumed is more effective for rehydration than drinking the needed amount all at once. Rapid fluid replacement after exercise stimulates urine production and results in less body water retention.

SOURCE: R. Murray, Fluid, electrolytes, and exercise in *Sports Nutrition: A Practice Manual for Professionals.* 4th ed., ed. M. Dunford (Chicago: The American Dietetic Association, 2005), pp. 94–115; D.J. Casa, P.M. Clarkson, and W.O. Roberts, American College of Sports Medicine Roundtable on Hydration and Physical Activity: Consensus Statements, *Current Sports Medicine Reports* 4 (2005): 115–127.

hypothermia: a below-normal body temperature.

hourly sweat rate: the amount of weight lost plus fluid consumed during exercise per hour.

magnesium—are lost from the body along with water. Losses are greatest in beginners; training improves electrolyte retention.

To replenish lost electrolytes, a person ordinarily needs only to eat a regular diet that meets energy and nutrient needs. In events lasting more than one hour, sports drinks may be needed to replace fluids and electrolytes. Salt tablets can worsen dehydration and impair performance; they increase potassium losses, irritate the stomach, and cause vomiting.

Hyponatremia When athletes compete in endurance sports lasting longer than three hours, replenishing electrolytes is crucial. If athletes sweat profusely over a long period of time and do not replace lost sodium, a dangerous condition known as **hyponatremia** may result. Research shows that some athletes who sweat profusely may also lose more sodium in their sweat than others—and are prone to debilitating heat cramps.[56] These athletes lose twice as much sodium in sweat as athletes who don't cramp. Depending on individual variation, exercise intensity, and changes in ambient temperature and humidity, sweat rates for these athletes can exceed 2 liters per hour.[57]

Hyponatremia may also occur when endurance athletes drink such large amounts of water over the course of a long event that they overhydrate, diluting the body's fluids to such an extent that the sodium concentration becomes extremely low. During long competitions, when athletes lose sodium through heavy sweating and consume excessive amounts of liquids, especially water, hyponatremia becomes likely.

Some athletes may still be vulnerable to hyponatremia even when they drink sports drinks during an event.[58] Sports drinks do contain sodium, but as the "How to" points out, the sodium content of sports drinks is low and, in some cases, too low to replace sweat losses. Still, sports drinks do offer more sodium than plain water.

To prevent hyponatremia, athletes need to replace sodium during prolonged events. They should favor sports drinks over water and eat pretzels in the last half

hyponatremia (HIGH-poe-na-TREE-mee-ah): a decreased concentration of sodium in the blood.
• **hypo** = below
• **natrium** = sodium (Na)
• **emia** = blood

glucose polymers: compounds that supply glucose, not as single molecules, but linked in chains somewhat like starch. The objective is to attract less water from the body into the digestive tract (osmotic attraction depends on the number, not the size, of particles).

HOW TO Evaluate Sports Drinks

Hydration is critical to optimal performance. Water best meets the fluid needs of most people, yet manufacturers market many good-tasting sports drinks for active people. More than 20 "power beverages" compete for their share of the more than $1 billion market. What do sports drinks have to offer?

• *Fluid.* Sports drinks offer fluids to help offset the loss of fluids during physical activity, but plain water can do this, too. Alternatively, diluted fruit juices or flavored water can be used if preferred to plain water.

• *Glucose.* Sports drinks offer simple sugars or **glucose polymers** that help maintain hydration and blood glucose and enhance performance as effectively as, or maybe even better than, water. Such measures are especially beneficial for strenuous endurance activities lasting longer than 45 minutes, during intense activities, or during prolonged competitive games that demand repeated intermittent activity.[a] Sports drinks are also suitable for events lasting

less than 45 minutes although plain water is appropriate as well.[b]

Fluid transport to the tissues from beverages containing up to 8 percent glucose is rapid. Most sports drinks contain about 7 percent carbohydrate (about half the sugar of ordinary soft drinks, or about 5 teaspoons in each 12 ounces). Less than 6 percent may not enhance performance, and more than 8 percent may cause abdominal cramps, nausea, and diarrhea.

Although glucose does enhance endurance performance in strenuous competitive events, for the moderate exerciser, it can be counterproductive if weight loss is the goal. Glucose is sugar, and like candy, it provides only empty kcalories—no vitamins or minerals. Most sports drinks provide between 50 and 100 kcalories per cup.

• *Sodium and other electrolytes.* Sports drinks offer sodium and other electrolytes to help replace those lost during physical activity. Sodium in sports drinks also helps to increase the rate of fluid absorption from the

GI tract and maintain plasma volume during activity and recovery.

Most physically active people do not need to replace the minerals lost in sweat immediately; a meal eaten within hours of competition replaces these minerals soon enough. Most sports drinks are relatively low in sodium, however, so those who choose to use these beverages run little risk of excessive intake.

• *Good taste.* Manufacturers reason that if a drink tastes good, people will drink more, thereby ensuring adequate hydration. For athletes who prefer the flavors of sports drinks over water, it may be worth paying for good taste to replace lost fluids.

• *Psychological edge.* Sports drinks provide a psychological edge for some people who associate the drinks with athletes and sports. The need to belong is valid. If the drinks boost morale and are used with care, they may do no harm.

For athletes who exercise for 45 minutes or more, sports drinks provide an advantage over water. For most physically active people, though, water is the best fluid to replenish lost fluids. The most important thing to do is drink—even if you don't feel thirsty.

[a] D.J. Casa, P.M. Clarkson, and W.O. Roberts, American College of Sports Medicine Roundtable on Hydration and Physical Activity: Consensus Statements, *Current Sports Medicine Reports* 4 (2005): 115–127; E. Coleman, Fluid replacement for athletes, *Sports Medicine Digest* 25 (2003): 76–77; Inter-association Task Force on Exertional Heat Illness Consensus Statement, *NATA News*, June 2003.
[b] Position of the American Dietetic Association, Dietitians of Canada, and the American College of Sports Medicine: Nutrition and athletic performance, *Journal of the American Dietetic Association* 100 (2000): 1543–1556.

◆ Symptoms of hyponatremia:
- Severe headache
- Vomiting
- Bloating, puffiness from water retention (shoes tight, rings tight)
- Confusion
- Seizure

◆ Beer facts:
- *Beer is not carbohydrate-rich.* Beer is *kcalorie*-rich, but only $1/3$ of its kcalories are from carbohydrates. The other $2/3$ are from alcohol.
- *Beer is mineral-poor.* Beer contains a few minerals, but to replace the minerals lost in sweat, athletes need good sources such as fruit juices.
- *Beer is vitamin-poor.* Beer contains traces of some B vitamins, but it cannot compete with food sources.
- *Beer causes fluid losses.* Beer is a fluid, but alcohol is a diuretic and causes the body to lose valuable fluid.

of a long race.[59] Some athletes may need beverages with higher sodium concentrations than commercial sports drinks. In the days before the event, especially an event in the heat, athletes should not restrict salt in their diets. The symptoms of hyponatremia are similar to, but not the same as, those of dehydration (see the margin). ◆

Poor Beverage Choices: Caffeine and Alcohol

Athletes, like others, sometimes drink beverages that contain caffeine or alcohol. Each of these substances can influence physical performance.

Caffeine Caffeine is a stimulant, and athletes sometimes use it to enhance performance as Highlight 14 explains. Carbonated soft drinks, whether they contain caffeine or not, may not be a wise choice for athletes: bubbles make a person feel full quickly and so limit fluid intake.

Alcohol Some athletes mistakenly believe that they can replace fluids and load up on carbohydrates by drinking beer. ◆ A 12-ounce beer provides 13 grams of carbohydrate—one-third the amount of carbohydrate in a glass of orange juice the same size. In addition to carbohydrate, beer also contains alcohol, of course. Energy from alcohol breakdown generates heat, but it does not fuel muscle work because alcohol is metabolized in the liver.

It is difficult to overstate alcohol's detrimental effects on physical activity. Alcohol's diuretic effect impairs the body's fluid balance, making dehydration likely; after physical activity, a person needs to replace fluids, not lose them by drinking beer. Alcohol also impairs the body's ability to regulate its temperature, increasing the likelihood of hypothermia or heat stroke.

Alcohol also alters perceptions; slows reaction time; reduces strength, power, and endurance; and hinders accuracy, balance, eye-hand coordination, and coordination in general—all opposing optimal athletic performance. In addition, it deprives people of their judgment, thereby compromising their safety in sports. Many sports-related fatalities and injuries involve alcohol or other drugs.

Clearly, alcohol impairs performance, but physically active people do drink on occasion. A word of caution: do not drink alcohol before exercising, and drink plenty of water after exercising before drinking alcohol.

IN SUMMARY

Active people need to drink plenty of water; endurance athletes need to drink both water and carbohydrate-containing beverages, especially during training and competition. During events lasting longer than 3 hours, athletes need to pay special attention to replace sodium losses to prevent hyponatremia.

Diets for Physically Active People

No one diet best supports physical performance. Active people who choose foods within the framework of the diet-planning principles presented in Chapter 2 can design many excellent diets.

Choosing a Diet to Support Fitness

Above all, keep in mind that water is depleted more rapidly than any other nutrient. A diet to support fitness must provide water, energy, and all the other nutrients.

Water Even casual exercisers must attend conscientiously to their fluid needs. Physical activity blunts the thirst mechanism, especially in cold weather. During activity, thirst signals come too late, so don't wait to feel thirsty before drinking. To find out how much water is needed to replenish activity losses, weigh yourself before and after the activity—the difference is almost all water. One pound equals roughly 2 cups (500 milliliters) of fluid.

Nutrient Density A healthful diet is based on nutrient-dense foods—foods that supply adequate vitamins and minerals for the energy they provide. Active people need to eat both for nutrient adequacy and for energy. A diet that is high in carbohydrate (60 to 70 percent of total kcalories), moderate in fat (20 to 30 percent), and adequate in protein (10 to 20 percent) ensures full glycogen and other nutrient stores.

Carbohydrate On two occasions, the active person's regular high-carbohydrate, ◆ fiber-rich diet may require temporary adjustment. Both of these exceptions involve training for competition rather than for fitness in general. One special occasion is the pregame meal, when fiber-rich, bulky foods are best avoided. The pregame meal is discussed in a later section.

◆ Carbohydrate recommendation for athletes in heavy training: 8 to 10 g/kg body weight.

The other occasion is during intensive training, when energy needs may be so high as to outstrip the person's capacity to eat enough food to meet them. At that point, added sugar and fat may be needed. The athlete can add concentrated carbohydrate foods, such as dried fruits, sweet potatoes, and nectars, and even high-fat foods, such as avocados and nuts. Still, a nutrient-rich diet remains central for adequacy's sake. Though vital, energy alone is not enough to support performance.

Some athletes use commercial high-carbohydrate liquid supplements to obtain the carbohydrate and energy needed for heavy training and top performance. These supplements do not *replace* regular food; they are meant to be used in *addition* to it. Unlike the sports beverages discussed in the "How to" on p. 495, these high-carbohydrate supplements are too concentrated in carbohydrate to be used for fluid replacement.

Protein In addition to carbohydrate and some fat (and the energy they provide), physically active people need protein. Meats and milk products are rich protein sources, but recommending that active people emphasize these foods is narrow advice. As mentioned repeatedly, active people need diets rich in carbohydrate, and of course, meats have none to offer. Legumes, whole grains, and vegetables provide some protein with abundant carbohydrate. Table 14-4 (p. 491) shows recommended protein intakes for active people.

A Performance Diet Example A person who engages in vigorous physical activity on a daily basis could easily require more than 3000 kcalories per day. To meet this need, the person can choose a variety of nutrient-dense foods. Figure 14-4 (p. 498) shows one example of meals that provide just over 3000 kcalories. These meals supply about 125 grams of protein, equivalent to the highest recommended intake for an athlete weighing 160 pounds. Obviously, the higher a person's energy intake, the more protein that person will receive, assuming the foods chosen are nutrient dense. This relationship between energy and protein intakes breaks down only when people meet their energy needs with high-fat, high-sugar confections. The meals shown in Figure 14-4 provide almost 520 grams of carbohydrate, or over 60 percent of total kcalories. Athletes who train exhaustively for endurance events may want to aim for somewhat higher carbohydrate intakes. Beyond these specific concerns of total energy, protein, and carbohydrate, the diet most beneficial to athletic performance is remarkably similar to the diet recommended for most people.[60]

Meals before and after Competition

No single food improves speed, strength, or skill in competitive events, although some *kinds* of foods do support performance better than others as already explained. Still, a competitor may eat a particular food before or after an event for psychological reasons. One eats a steak the night before wrestling. Another eats some honey just five minutes after diving. As long as these practices remain harmless, they should be respected.

A variety of foods is the best source of nutrients for athletes.

FIGURE 14-4 An Example of an Athlete's Meal Selections

This sample menu provides about 3000 kcalories, with almost 520 grams of carbohydrate (63 percent of total kcalories) and about 125 grams of protein (15 percent of total kcalories). In addition to meeting the carbohydrate and protein needs of an athlete, these meals also meet or exceed recommendations for all vitamin and minerals.

© Polara Studios Inc. (all)

Breakfast
1 c shredded wheat with
  low-fat milk and banana
2 slices whole-wheat toast
  with jelly
1½ c orange juice

Lunch
2 turkey sandwiches
1½ c low-fat milk
Large bunch of grapes

Snack
3 c plain popcorn
A smoothie made from:
  1½ c apple juice
  1½ frozen banana

Dinner
Salad: 1 c spinach, carrots,
  and mushrooms with
  ½ c garbanzo beans,
  1 tbs sunflower seeds, and
  1 tbs ranch salad dressing
1 c spaghetti with meat sauce
1 c green beans
1 corn on the cob
2 slices Italian bread
4 tsp butter
1 piece angel food cake with
  fresh strawberries and
  whipping cream
1 c low-fat milk

Total kcal: about 3000
63% kcal from carbohydrate
22% kcal from fat
15% kcal from protein

All vitamin and mineral intakes exceed
the RDA for both men and women.

Pregame Meals Science indicates that the pregame meal or snack should include plenty of fluids and be light and easy to digest. It should provide between 300 and 800 kcalories, primarily from carbohydrate-rich foods that are familiar and well tolerated by the athlete. The meal should end three to four hours before competition to allow time for the stomach to empty before exertion.

Breads, potatoes, pasta, and fruit juices—that is, carbohydrate-rich foods low in fat and fiber—form the basis of the best pregame meal (see Figure 14-5 for some examples). Bulky, fiber-rich foods such as raw vegetables or high-bran cereals, al-

FIGURE 14-5 Examples of High-Carbohydrate Pregame Meals

Pregame meals should be eaten three to four hours before the event and provide 300 to 800 kcalories, primarily from carbohydrate-rich foods. Each of these sample meals provides at least 65% of total kcalories from carbohydrate.

Matthew Farruggio (all)

300-kcalorie meal
1 large apple
4 saltine crackers
1½ tbs reduced-fat
  peanut butter

500-kcalorie meal
1 large whole-wheat bagel
2 tbs jelly
1½ c low-fat milk

750-kcalorie meal
1 large baked potato
2 tsp margarine
1 c steamed broccoli
1 c mixed carrots and green
  peas
5 vanilla wafers
1½ c apple or pineapple juice

though usually desirable, are best avoided just before competition. Fiber in the digestive tract attracts water and can cause stomach discomfort during performance. Liquid meals ◆ are easy to digest, and many such meals are commercially available. Alternatively, athletes can mix fat-free milk or juice, frozen fruits, and flavorings in a blender.

Postgame Meals As mentioned earlier, eating high-carbohydrate foods *after* physical activity enhances glycogen storage. Because people are usually not hungry immediately following physical activity, carbohydrate-containing beverages such as sports drinks or fruit juices may be preferred. If an active person does feel hungry after an event, then foods high in carbohydrate and low in protein, fat, and fiber are the ones to choose—the same ones recommended prior to competition.

◆ High-carbohydrate, liquid pregame meal ideas:
  • Apple juice, frozen banana, and cinnamon
  • Papaya juice, frozen strawberries, and mint
  • Fat-free milk, frozen banana, and vanilla

IN SUMMARY

The person who wants to excel physically will apply accurate nutrition knowledge along with dedication to rigorous training. A diet that provides ample fluid and includes a variety of nutrient-dense foods in quantities to meet energy needs will enhance not only athletic performance, but overall health as well. Carbohydrate-rich foods that are light and easy-to-digest are recommended for both the pregame and the postgame meal. Training and genetics being equal, who will win a competition—the athlete who habitually consumes inadequate amounts of needed nutrients or the competitor who arrives at the event with a long history of full nutrient stores and well-met metabolic needs?

Some athletes learn that nutrition can support physical performance and turn to pills and powders instead of foods. In case you need further convincing that a healthful diet surpasses such potions, the following highlight addresses this issue.

Nutrition Portfolio

ThomsonNOW™
www.thomsonedu.com/thomsonnow

The foods and beverages you eat and drink provide fuel and other nutrients to support your physical activity.

■ Describe your daily physical activities and how they compare with recommendations to be physically active for at least 30 minutes, and preferably 60 minutes, a day on most or all days of the week.

■ Estimate your daily fluid intake, making note of whether you drink fluids, especially water, before, during, and after physical activity.

■ Evaluate the carbohydrate contents of your diet and consider whether it would meet the needs of a physically active person.

NUTRITION ON THE NET

• Visit the U.S. Government site: **www.fitness.gov**

• Search for "physical fitness" at the American College of Sports Medicine information site: **www.acsm.org**

• Review the Surgeon General's Report on Physical Activity: **www.cdc.gov/nccdphp/sgr/sgr.htm**

• Review resources offered on the Nutrition and Physical Activity site from the Centers for Disease Control and Prevention: **www.cdc.gov/nccdphp/dnpa**

- Learn about the President's Council on Physical Fitness and Sports: **www.presidentschallenge.com**
- Visit Shape Up America: **www.shapeup.org**
- Visit the American Council on Exercise (ACE): **www.acefitness.org**
- Visit the Canadian Council of Sports Medicine: **www.ccsm.info**

- Find fitness information at the Cooper Institute for Aerobics Research: **www.cooperinst.org**
- Find information on sports drinks and other nutrition and fitness topics at the Gatorade Sports Science Institute site: **www.gssiweb.com**

STUDY QUESTIONS

ThomsonNOW
To assess your understanding of chapter topics, take the Student Practice Test and explore the modules recommended in your Personalized Study Plan. Log onto www.thomsonedu.com/thomsonnow.

These questions will help you review the chapter. You will find the answers in the discussions on the pages provided.

1. Define fitness, and list its benefits. (pp. 477–478)
2. Explain the overload principle. (p. 480)
3. Define cardiorespiratory conditioning and list some of its benefits. (p. 482)
4. What types of activity are anaerobic? Which are aerobic? (pp. 485–487)
5. Describe the relationships among energy expenditure, type of activity, and oxygen use. (p. 485)
6. What factors influence the body's use of glucose during physical activity? How? (pp. 485–488)
7. What factors influence the body's use of fat during physical activity? How? (pp. 488–490)
8. What factors influence the body's use of protein during physical activity? How? (pp. 490–491)
9. Why are some athletes likely to develop iron-deficiency anemia? Compare iron-deficiency anemia and sports anemia, explaining the differences. (pp. 492–493)
10. Discuss the importance of hydration during training, and list recommendations to maintain fluid balance. (pp. 493–496)
11. Describe the components of a healthy diet for athletic performance. (pp. 496–499)

These multiple choice questions will help you prepare for an exam. Answers can be found on p. 502.

1. Physical inactivity is linked to all of the following diseases except:
   a. cancer.
   b. diabetes.
   c. emphysema.
   d. hypertension.
2. The progressive overload principle can be applied by performing:
   a. an activity less often.
   b. an activity with more intensity.

   c. an activity in a different setting.
   d. a different activity each day of the week.
3. The process that regenerates glucose from lactate is known as the:
   a. Cori cycle.
   b. ATP-CP cycle.
   c. adaptation cycle.
   d. cardiac output cycle.
4. "Hitting the wall" is a term runners sometimes use to describe:
   a. dehydration.
   b. competition.
   c. indigestion.
   d. glucose depletion.
5. The technique endurance athletes use to maximize glycogen stores is called:
   a. aerobic training.
   b. muscle conditioning.
   c. carbohydrate loading.
   d. progressive overloading.
6. Conditioned muscles rely less on ____ and more on ____ for energy.
   a. protein; fat
   b. fat; protein
   c. glycogen; fat
   d. fat; glycogen
7. Vitamin or mineral supplements taken just before an event are useless for improving performance because the:
   a. athlete sweats the nutrients out during the event.
   b. stomach can't digest supplements during physical activity.
   c. nutrients are diluted by all the fluids the athlete drinks.
   d. body needs hours or days for the nutrients to do their work.
8. Physically active young women, especially those who are endurance athletes, are prone to:
   a. energy excess.
   b. iron deficiency.
   c. protein overload.
   d. vitamin A toxicity.

9. The body's need for ____ far surpasses its need for any other nutrient.
   a. water
   b. protein
   c. vitamins
   d. carbohydrate

10. A recommended pregame meal includes plenty of fluids and provides between:
    a. 300 and 800 kcalories, mostly from fat-rich foods.
    b. 50 and 100 kcalories, mostly from fiber-rich foods.
    c. 1000 and 2000 kcalories, mostly from protein-rich foods.
    d. 300 and 800 kcalories, mostly from carbohydrate-rich foods.

REFERENCES

1. D. E. Warburton, C. W. Nicol, and S. S. Bredin, Health benefits of physical activity: The evidence, *Canadian Medical Association Journal* 174 (2006): 801-809; T. S. Altena and coauthors, Lipoprotein subfraction changes after continuous or intermittent exercise training, *Medicine and Science in Sports and Exercise* 38 (2006): 367-372; K. J. Stewart and coauthors, Exercise and risk factors associated with metabolic syndrome in older adults, *American Journal of Preventive Medicine* 28 (2005): 9-18; M.B. Conroy and coauthors, Past physical activity, current physical activity, and risk of coronary heart disease, *Medicine and Science in Sports and Exercise* 37 (2005): 1251-1256; R. G. Ketelhut, I. W. Franz, and J. Scholze, Regular exercise as an effective approach in antihypertensive therapy, *Medicine and Science in Sports and Exercise* 36 (2004): 4-8.

2. Centers for Disease Control and Prevention, Adult participation in recommended levels of physical activity—United States, 2001 and 2003, *Morbidity and Mortality Weekly Report* 54 (2005): 1208-1210; Centers for Disease Control and Prevention, Trends in leisure-time physical inactivity by age, sex, and race/ethnicity—United States, 1994-2004, *Morbidity and Mortality Weekly Report* 54 (2005): 991-994.

3. M. R. Carnethon, M. Gulati, and P. Greenland, Prevalence and cardiovascular disease correlates of low cardiorespiratory fitness in adolescents and adults, *Journal of the American Medical Association* 294 (2005): 2981-2988; M. B. Conroy and coauthors, Past physical activity, current physical activity, and risk of coronary heart disease, *Medicine and Science in Sports and Exercise* 37 (2005): 1251-1256; C. Richardson and coauthors, Physical activity and mortality across cardiovascular disease risk factors, *Medicine and Science in Sports and Exercise* 36 (2004): 1923-1929; K. R. Evenson and coauthors, The effect of cardiorespiratory fitness and obesity on cancer mortality in women and men, *Medicine and Science in Sports and Exercise* 35 (2003): 270-277; J. Dorn and coauthors, Lifetime physical activity and breast cancer risk in pre- and postmenopausal women, *Medicine and Science in Sports and Exercise* 35 (2003): 278-285; C. D. Lee and S. N. Blair, Cardiorespiratory fitness and stroke mortality in men, *Medicine and Science in Sports and Exercise* 34 (2002): 592-595.

4. M. Pratt, C. A. Macera, and G. Wang, Higher direct medical costs associated with physical inactivity, *The Physician and Sportsmedicine* 28 (2000): 63-70.

5. P. T. Williams and R. R. Pate, Cross-sectional relationships of exercise and age to adiposity in 60,617 male runners, *Medicine and Science in Sports and Exercise* 37 (2005): 1329-1337; U. G. Kyle and coauthors, Physical activity and fat-free and fat mass by bioelectrical impedance in 3853 adults, *Medicine and Science in Sports and Exercise* 33 (2001): 576-584.

6. American College of Sports Medicine, Position stand: Physical activity and bone health, *Medicine and Science in Sports and Exercise* 36 (2004): 1985-1996; T. Lloyd and coauthors, Lifestyle factors and the development of bone mass and bone strength in young women, *Journal of Pediatrics* 144 (2004): 776-782.

7. R. Jankord and B. Jemiolo, Influence of physical activity on serum IL-6 and IL-10 levels in healthy older men, *Medicine and Science in Sports and Exercise* 36 (2004): 960-964; D. C. Nieman, Current perspectives on exercise immunology, *Current Sports Medicine Reports* 2 (2003): 239-242; C. E. Matthews and coauthors, Moderate to vigorous physical activity and risk of upper-respiratory tract infection, *Medicine and Science in Sports and Exercise* 34 (2002): 1242-1248.

8. B. Tehard and coauthors, Effect of physical activity on women at increased risk of breast cancer: Results from the E3N cohort study, *Cancer Epidemiology, Biomarkers, and Prevention* 15 (2006): 57-64; L. Bernstein and coauthors, Lifetime recreational exercise activity and breast cancer risk among black women and white women, *Journal of the National Cancer Institute* 16 (2005): 1671-1679; M. L. Slattery, Physical activity and colorectal cancer, *Sports Medicine* 34 (2004): 239-252; C. M. Friedenreich, Physical activity and cancer: Lessons learned from nutritional epidemiology, *Nutrition Reviews* 59 (2001): 349-357.

9. M. B. Conroy and coauthors, Past physical activity, current physical activity, and risk of coronary heart disease, *Medicine and Science in Sports and Exercise* 37 (2005): 1251-1256; C. Richardson and coauthors, Physical activity and mortality across cardiovascular disease risk groups, *Medicine and Science in Sports and Exercise* 36 (2004): 1923-1929; J. E. Manson and coauthors, Walking compared with vigorous exercise for the prevention of cardiovascular events in women, *New England Journal of Medicine* 347 (2002): 716-725; C. D. Lee and S. N. Blair, Cardiorespiratory fitness and stroke mortality in men, *Medicine and Science in Sports and Exercise* 34 (2002): 592-595.

10. S. L. Wong and coauthors, Cardiorespiratory fitness is associated with lower abdominal fat independent of body mass index, *Medicine and Science in Sports and Exercise* 36 (2004): 286-291; A. Trichopoulou and coauthors, Physical activity and energy intake selectively predict the waist-to-hip ratio in men but not in women, *American Journal of Clinical Nutrition* 74 (2001): 574-578.

11. American Diabetes Association, Position statement; Physical activity/exercise and diabetes mellitus, *Diabetes Care* 26 (2003): S73-S77; R. M. van Dam and coauthors, Physical activity and glucose tolerance in elderly men: The Zutphen Elderly Study, *Medicine and Science in Sports and Exercise* 34 (2002): 1132-1136; K. J. Stewart, Exercise training and the cardiovascular consequences of type 2 diabetes and hypertension: Plausible mechanisms for improving cardiovascular health, *Journal of the American Medical Association* 288 (2002): 1622-1631.

12. K. L. Storti and coauthors, Physical activity and decreased risk of clinical gallstone disease among post-menopausal women, *Preventive Medicine* 41 (2005): 772-777.

13. D. I. Galper and coauthors, Inverse association between physical inactivity and mental health in men and women, *Medicine and Science in Sports and Exercise* 38 (2006): 173-178; J. B. Bartholomew, D. Morrison, and J. T. Ciccolo, Effects of acute exercise on mood and well-being in patients with major depressive disorder, *Medicine and Science in Sports and Exercise* 37 (2005): 2032-2037; W. J. Strawbridge and coauthors, Physical activity reduces the risk of subsequent depression for older adults, *American Journal of Epidemiology* 156 (2002): 328-334.

14. American College of Sports Medicine, Expert panel, Physical activity programs and behavior counseling in older populations, *Medicine and Science in Sports and Exercise* 36 (2004): 1997-2003; G. Huang and coauthors, Resting heart rate changes after endurance training in older adults: A meta-analysis, *Medicine and Science in Sports and Exercise* 37 (2005): 1381-1386; J. Meyers and coauthors, Exercise capacity and mortality among men referred for exercise testing, *New England Journal of Medicine* 346 (2002): 793-801.

15. W. W. N. Tsang and C. W. Y. Hui-Chan, Comparison of muscle torque, balance, and confidence in older Tai Chi and healthy adults, *Medicine and Science in Sports and Exercise* 37 (2005): 280-289; F. Li, and coauthors, Tai Chi: Improving functional balance and predicting subsequent falls in older persons, *Medicine and Science in Sports and Exercise* 36 (2004): 2046-2052.

16. U.S. Department of Agriculture and U.S. Department of Health and Human Services, *Nutrition and Your Health: Dietary Guidelines for Americans 2005*, 6th ed., Home and Garden Bulletin no. 232 (Washington D.C.: 2005), available online at www.healthierus.gov/dietaryguidelines.

17. U.S. Department of Agriculture and U.S. Department of Health and Human Services, 2005; Committee on Dietary Reference Intakes, *Dietary Reference Intakes for Energy, Carbohydrate, Fiber, Fat, Fatty Acids, Cholesterol, Protein, and Amino Acids* (Washington, D.C.: National Academies Press, 2005), pp. 880-935.

18. W. D. Schmidt, C. J. Biwer, and L. K. Kalscheuer, Effects of long versus short bout exercise on fitness and weight loss in overweight females, *Journal of the American College of Nutrition* 20 (2001): 494-501.

19. American College of Sports Medicine, Position stand: The recommended quantity and quality of exercise for developing and maintaining cardiorespiratory and muscular fitness, and flexibility in healthy adults, *Medicine and Science in Sports and Exercise* 30 (1998): 975-991.

20. D. E. Warburton, C. W. Nicol, and S. S. Bredin, Health benefits of physical activity: The evidence, *Canadian Medical Association Journal* 174 (2006): 801-809; C. Rosenbloom and M. Bahns, What can we learn about diet and physical activity from master athletes? *Nutrition Today* 40 (2005): 267-272; Manson and coauthors, 2002.

21. American College of Sports Medicine, *ACSM's Guidelines for Exercise Testing and Prescription*, 7th ed. (Philadelphia, Pa.: Lippincott, Williams, and Wilkins, 2006), pp. 19-35.

22. S. Sharma, Athlete's heart—Effect of age, sex, ethnicity and sporting discipline, *Experimental Physiology* 88 (2003): 665-669.

23. American College of Sports Medicine, Position stand: Exercise and Hypertension, *Medicine and Science in Sports and Exercise* 36 (2004): 533-553; R. G. Ketelhut, I. W. Franz, and J. Scholze, Regular exercise as an effective approach in antihypertensive therapy, *Medicine and Science in Sports and Exercise* 36 (2004): 4-8.

24. American College of Sports Medicine, Position stand: Progression models in resistance training for healthy adults, *Medicine and Science in Sports and Exercise* 34 (2002): 364-380.

25. American College of sports Medicine, Position Stand: Physical activity and bone health, *Medicine and Science in Sports and Exercise* 36 (2004): 1985-1996.

26. E. C. Cussler and coauthors, Weight lifted in strength training predicts bone change in postmenopausal women, *Medicine and Science in Sports and Exercise* 35 (2003): 10-17.

27. J. A. Katula and coauthors, Strength training in older adults: An empowering intervention, *Medicine and Science in Sports and Exercise* 38 (2006): 106-111; American College of Sports Medicine, Expert Panel, Physical activity programs and behavior counseling in older adult populations *Medicine and Science in Sports and Exercise* 36 (2004): 1997-2003; R. Seguin and M. E. Nelson, The benefits of strength training for older adults, *American Journal of Preventive Medicine* 25 (2003): 141-149.

28. W. J. Kraemer and coauthors, Physiological changes with periodized resistance training in women tennis players, *Medicine and Science in Sports and Exercise* 35 (2003): 157-168.

29. J. H. Wilmore and D. L. Costill, Physical energy: Fuel metabolism, *Nutrition Reviews* 59 (2001): S13-S16.

30. J. Bergstrom and coauthors, Diet, muscle glycogen and physical performance, *Acta Physiologica Scandanavica* 71 (1967): 140-150.

31. S. P. Cairns, Lactic acid and exercise performance: Culprit or friend? *Sports Medicine* 36 (2006): 279-291; T. Pedersen and coauthors, Intracellular acidosis enhances the excitability of working muscle, *Science* 305 (2004): 1144-1147; D. Allen and H. Westerblad, Enhanced: Lactic acid-the latest performance-enhancing drug, *Science* 305 (2004): 1112-1113; R. A. Robergs, F. Ghiasvand, and D. Parker, Biochemistry of exercise-induced metabolic acidosis, *American Journal of Physiology Regulatory, Integrative, and Comparative Physiology* 287 (2004): R502-R516.

32. J. J. Winnick and coauthors, Carbohydrate feedings during team sport exercise preserve physical and CNS function, *Medicine and Science in Sports and Exercise* 37 (2005): 306-315; A. C. Utter and coauthors, Carbohydrate supplementation and perceived exertion during prolonged running, *Medicine and Science in Sports and Exercise* 36 (2004): 1036-1041; R. S. Welsh and coauthors, Carbohydrates and physical/mental performance during intermittent exercise to fatigue, *Medicine and Science in Sports and Exercise* 34 (2002): 723-731.

33. Position of the American Dietetic Association, Dietitians of Canada, and the American College of Sports Medicine: Nutrition and athletic performance, *Journal of the American Dietetic Association* 100 (2000): 1543-1556.

34. Position of the American Dietetic Association, Dietitians of Canada, and the American College of Sports Medicine, 2000.

35. E. J. Coleman, Carbohydrate and exercise, in *Sports Nutrition: A Practice Manual for Professionals*, 4th ed., ed. M. Dunford (Chicago: The American Dietetic Association, 2006), pp. 14-32; P. M. Siu and S. H. S. Wong, Use of the glycemic index: Effects on feeding patterns and exercise performance, *Journal of Physiological Anthropology and Applied Human Science* 23 (2004): 1-6.

36. S. L. Wee and coauthors, Ingestion of a high-glycemic index meal increases muscle glycogen storage at rest but augments its utilization during subsequent exercise, *Journal of Applied Physiology* 99 (2005): 707-714; Siu and Wong, 2004.

37. J. Manetta and coauthors, Fuel oxidation during exercise in middle-aged men: Role of training and glucose disposal, *Medicine and Science in Sports and Exercise* 34 (2002): 423-429.

38. L. M. Burke and J. A. Hawley, Effects of short-term fat adaptation on metabolism and performance of prolonged exercise, *Medicine and Science in Sports and Exercise* 34 (2002): 1492-1498.

39. L. Havemann and coauthors, Fat adaptation followed by carbohydrate loading compromises high-intensity sprint performance, *Journal of Applied Physiology* 100 (2006): 194-202; Burke and Hawley, 2002; L. M. Burke and coauthors, Adaptations to short-term high-fat diet persist during exercise despite high carbohydrate availability, *Medicine and Science in Sports and Exercise* 34 (2002): 83-91.

40. J. W. Helge, Long-term fat diet adaptation, effects on performance, training capacity, and fat utilization, *Medicine and Science in Sports and Exercise* 34 (2002): 1499-1504; N. D. Stepto and coauthors, Effect of short-term fat adaptation on high-intensity training, *Medicine and Science in Sports and Exercise* 34 (2002): 449-455.

41. Position of the American Dietetic Association, Dietitians of Canada, and the American College of Sports Medicine, 2000.

42. Wilmore and Costill, 2001.

43. M. Suzuki, Glycemic carbohydrates consumed with amino acids or protein right after exercise enhance muscle formation, *Nutrition Reviews* 61 (2003): S88-S94.

44. Committee on Dietary Reference Intakes, 2005; Position of the American Dietetic Association, Dietitians of Canada, and the American College of Sports Medicine, 2000.

45. Position of the American Dietetic Association, Dietitians of Canada, and the American College of Sports Medicine, 2000.

46. Position of the American Dietetic Association, Dietitians of Canada, and the American College of Sports Medicine, 2000.

47. J. Finaud G. Lac, and E. Filaire, Oxidative stress: Relationship with exercise and training, *Sports Medicine* 36 (2006): 327-358; T. A. Watson and coauthors, Antioxidant restriction and oxidative stress in short-duration exhaustive exercise, *Medicine and Science in Sports and Exercise* 37 (2005): 63-71.

48. S. L. Williams and coauthors, Antioxidant requirements of endurance athletes: Implications for health, *Nutrition Reviews* 64 (2006): 93-108.

49. M. L. Urso and P. M. Clarkson, Oxidative stress, exercise, and antioxidant supplementation, *Toxicology* 189 (2003): 41-54; W. J. Evans, Vitamin E, vitamin C and exercise, *American Journal of Clinical Nutrition* 72 (2000): 647S-652S.

50. S. L. Akabas and K. R. Dolins, Micronutrient requirements of physically active women: What can we learn from iron? *American Journal of Clinical Nutrition* 81 (2005): 1246S-1251S.

51. S. I. Barr and C. A. Rideout, Nutritional considerations for vegetarian athletes, *Nutrition* 20 (2004): 696-703; Position of The American Dietetic Association, Dietitians of Canada, and the American College of Sports Medicine, 2000; Beard and Tobin, 2000.

52. T. Brownlie and coauthors, Marginal iron deficiency without anemia impairs aerobic adaptation among previously untrained women, *American Journal of Clinical Nutrition* 75 (2002): 734-742.

53. D. J. Casa, P. M. Clarkson, and W. O. Roberts, American College of Sports Medicine Roundtable on Hydration and Physical Activity: Consensus Statements, *Current Sports Medicine Reports* 4 (2005): 115-127; Committee on Dietary Reference Intakes, *Dietary Reference Intakes for Water, Potassium, Sodium, Chloride, and Sulfate* (Washington, D.C.: National Academies Press, 2005), pp. 108-110.

54. C. K. Seto, D. Way, and N. O'Connor, Environmental illness in athletes, *Clinics in Sports Medicine* 24 (2005): 695-718.

55. Casa, Clarkson, and Roberts, 2005.

56. Seto, Way, and O'Connor, 2005; J. R. Stofan and coauthors, Sweat and sodium losses in NCAA Division 1 football players with a history of whole-body muscle cramping, presented at the annual meeting of the American College of Sports Medicine, 2003, unpublished.

57. Committee on Dietary Reference Intakes, *Dietary Reference Intakes for Water, Potassium, Sodium, Chloride, and Sulfate* (Washington, D.C.: National Academies Press, 2005), pp.127-132.

58. M. Hsieh and coauthors, Hyponatremia in runners requiring on-site medical treatment at a single marathon, *Medicine and Science in Sports and Exercise* 34 (2002): 185-189.

59. E. R. Eichner, Exertional hyponatremia: Why so many women? *Sports Medicine Digest* 24 (2002): 54, 56.

60. Position of the American Dietetic Association, Dietitians of Canada, and the American College of Sports Medicine, 2000.

ANSWERS

Study Questions (multiple choice)

1. c   2. b   3. a   4. d   5. c   6. c   7. d   8. b   9. a   10. d

Supplements as Ergogenic Aids

© Ellen Stagg/Stone/Getty Images

Athletes gravitate to promises that they can enhance their performance by taking pills, powders, or potions. Unfortunately, they often hear such promises from their coaches and peers, who advise them to use nutrient supplements, take drugs, or follow procedures that claim to deliver results with little effort.[1] When such performance-enhancing aids are harmless, they are only a waste of money; when they impair performance or harm health, they waste athletic potential and cost lives. This highlight looks at some promises of magic to enhance physical performance.

Ergogenic Aids

Many substances or treatments claim to be *ergogenic,* meaning work enhancing. The glossary below defines several of the commonly used **ergogenic aids** discussed in this highlight. The glossary on p. 504 presents additional substances promoted as ergogenic aids. For the large majority of these substances, research findings do not support those claims.[2] Athletes who hear that a product is ergogenic should ask who is making the claim and who will profit from the sale.

Sometimes it is difficult to distinguish valid claims from bogus ones. Fitness magazines and Internet websites are particularly troublesome because many of them present both valid and invalid nutrition

information along with slick advertisements for nutrition products. Advertisements often feature colorful anatomical figures, graphs, and tables that appear scientific. Some ads even include references, citing or linking to such credible sources as the *American Journal of Clinical Nutrition* and the *Journal of the American Medical Association.* These ads create the illusion of endorsement and credibility to gain readers' trust. Keep in mind, however, that the ads are created not to teach, but to sell. A careful reading of the cited research might reveal that the ads have presented the research findings out of context.[3] In one such case, an ad cited a research article to support the invalid conclusion that its human growth hormone supplement "increases lean body mass and bone mineral." Researchers reporting in the cited article had reached another conclusion: "Its general use now or in the immediate future is not justified." Scientific facts had been exaggerated and twisted to promote sales. Highlight 1 described ways to recognize misinformation and quackery.

Dietary Supplements

A variety of supplements make claims based on misunderstood nutrition principles. The claims may sound good, but for the most part, they have little or no factual basis. Chapter 6 included a discussion on protein powders and amino acid supplements (pp. 202–203).

GLOSSARY

The glossary on p. 504 includes additional supplements commonly used to enhance performance.

anabolic steroids: drugs related to the male sex hormone, testosterone, that stimulate the development of lean body mass.
- **anabolic** = promoting growth
- **sterols** = compounds chemically related to cholesterol

caffeine: a natural stimulant found in many common foods and beverages, including coffee, tea, and chocolate; may enhance endurance by stimulating fatty acid release. High doses cause headaches, trembling, rapid heart rate, and other undesirable side effects.

chromium picolinate (CROW-mee-um pick-oh-LYN-ate): a trace mineral supplement; falsely promoted as building muscle, enhancing energy, and burning fat. **Picolinate** is a derivative of the amino acid tryptophan that seems to enhance chromium absorption.

creatine (KREE-ah-tin): a nitrogen-containing compound that combines with phosphate to form the high-energy compound creatine phosphate (or phosphocreatine) in muscles. Claims that creatine enhances energy use and muscle strength need further confirmation.

DHEA (dehydroepiandrosterone) and **androstenedione:** hormones made in the adrenal

glands that serve as precursors to the male hormone testosterone; falsely promoted as burning fat, building muscle, and slowing aging. Side effects include acne, aggressiveness, and liver enlargement.

ergogenic (ER-go-JEN-ick) **aids:** substances or techniques used in an attempt to enhance physical performance.
- **ergo** = work
- **genic** = gives rise to

hGH (human growth hormone): a hormone produced by the brain's pituitary gland that regulates normal growth and development; also called *somatotropin.* Some athletes misuse this hormone to increase their height and strength.

Reminders: **Carnitine** is a nonessential nonprotein amino acid made in the body from lysine that helps transport fatty acids across the mitochondrial membrane. Carnitine supposedly "burns" fat and spares glycogen during endurance events, but in reality it does neither.

Conjugated linoleic acid is a naturally occuring *trans* fatty acid with 18 carbons and 2 double bonds; sometimes taken as a supplement to improve body composition.

GLOSSARY OF SUBSTANCES PROMOTED AS ERGOGENIC AIDES

The glossary on p. 503 includes supplements mentioned in the text. Chapter 6 includes a discussion on protein and amino acid supplements (pp. 202–203).

arginine: a nonessential amino acid falsely promoted as enhancing the secretion of human growth hormone, the breakdown of fat, and the development of muscle.

boron: a nonessential mineral that is promoted to increase muscle mass.

coenzyme Q10: a lipid found in cells (mitochondria) shown to improve exercise performance in heart disease patients, but

not effective in improving the performance of healthy athletes.

gamma-oryzanol: a plant sterol that supposedly provides the same physical responses as anabolic steroids without the adverse side effects; also known as *ferulic acid, ferulate,* or *FRAC.*

ginseng: a plant whose extract supposedly boosts energy. Side effects of chronic use include nervousness, confusion, and depression.

HMB (beta-hydroxy-beta-methylbutyrate): a metabolite of the branched-chain amino acid leucine. Claims that HMB increases muscle mass and

strength are based on the results of two studies from the lab that developed HMB as a supplement.

pyruvate: a 3-carbon compound that plays a key role in energy metabolism. Supplements claim to burn fat and enhance performance.

ribose: a 5-carbon sugar falsely promoted as improving the regeneration of ATP and thereby the speed of recovery after high-power exercise.

royal jelly: the substance produced by worker bees and fed to the queen bee; falsely

promoted as increasing strength and enhancing performance.

sodium bicarbonate: baking soda; an alkaline salt believed to neutralize blood lactic acid and thereby to reduce pain and enhance possible workload. "Soda loading" may cause intestinal bloating and diarrhea.

spirulina: a kind of alga ("blue-green manna") that supposedly contains large amounts of protein and vitamin B_{12}, suppresses appetite, and improves athletic performance. It does none of these things and is potentially toxic.

Carnitine

Carnitine, a nonessential nutrient, is often promoted as a "fat burner." Some athletes use it, hoping carnitine will help them burn more fat, thereby sparing glycogen during endurance events.

In the body, carnitine facilitates the transfer of fatty acids across the mitochondrial membrane. Supplement manufacturers suggest that with more carnitine available, fat oxidation will be enhanced, but this does not seem to be the case. Carnitine supplementation neither raises muscle carnitine concentrations nor enhances exercise performance.[4] It does, however, produce diarrhea in about half of the people who use it. Milk and meat products are good sources of carnitine, and supplements are not needed.

Chromium Picolinate

Chapter 13 introduced chromium as an essential trace mineral involved in carbohydrate and lipid metabolism. Advertisements in bodybuilding magazines claim that **chromium picolinate,** which is more easily absorbed than chromium alone, builds muscle, enhances energy, and burns fat. Such claims derive from one or two initial studies reporting that men who weight trained while taking chromium picolinate supplements increased lean body mass and reduced body fat. Most subsequent studies, however, show no effects of chromium picolinate supplementation on strength, lean body mass, or body fat.[5] In fact, some research suggests that chromium picolinate supplements promote oxidative damage to lipids and DNA.[6] Other forms of chromium supplements, such as chromium chloride, do not seem to have this effect and are thus gaining popularity.

Complete Nutrition Supplements

Several drinks and candy bars appeal to athletes by claiming to provide "complete" nutrition. These products usually taste good and provide extra food energy, but they fall short of providing "complete" nutrition. They can be useful as a pregame meal or a between-meal snack, but they should not replace regular meals.

A nutritionally "complete" drink may help a nervous athlete who cannot tolerate solid food on the day of an event. A liquid meal two or three hours before competition can supply some of the fluid and carbohydrate needed in a pregame meal, but a shake of fat-free milk or juice (such as apple or papaya) and ice milk or frozen fruit (such as strawberries or bananas) can do the same thing less expensively.

Creatine

Interest in—and use of—**creatine** supplements to enhance performance during intense activity has grown dramatically in the last few years. Power athletes such as weight lifters use creatine supplements to enhance stores of the high-energy compound creatine phosphate (CP) in muscles. Theoretically, the more creatine phosphate in muscles, the higher the intensity at which an athlete can train. High-intensity training stimulates the muscles to adapt, which, in turn, improves performance.

The results of some studies suggest that creatine supplementation does enhance performance of short-term, repetitive, high-intensity activity such as weight lifting or sprinting.[7] Creatine may improve performance by increasing muscle strength and size, cell hydration, or glycogen loading capacity.[8] In contrast, creatine supplementation has not been shown to benefit endurance activity.[9]

The question of whether short-term use of creatine supplements is safe continues to be studied, but so far, the supplements are viewed to be safe for healthy adults.[10] In a study of 23 football players, long-term use (21 months) of creatine supplements revealed no adverse effects on kidney or liver function.[11] More research is needed, however, to confirm the safety of long-term creatine use. Creatine supplementation may pose risks to athletes with kidney disease or other conditions. One side effect of creatine supplementation that no one disputes is weight gain. For some athletes, weight gain, especially muscle gain, is beneficial, but for others, it is not.

Some medical and fitness experts voice concern that, like many performance enhancement supplements before it, creatine is being taken in huge doses (5 to 30 grams per day) before evidence of its value has been ascertained. Even people who eat red meat, which is a creatine-rich food, do not consume nearly the amount supplements provide. (Creatine content varies, but on average, pork, chicken, and beef provide 65 to 180 milligrams per ounce.) Despite the uncertainties, creatine supplements are not illegal in international competition. The American Academy of Pediatrics strongly discourages the use of creatine supplements, as well as the use of any performance-enhancing substance in adolescents less than 18 years old.[12]

Conjugated Linoleic Acid

Conjugated linoleic acid (CLA) derives from the essential fatty acid, linoleic acid. CLA is part of a group of naturally occurring polyunsaturated fatty acids found in beef, lamb, and dairy products. In animal studies, CLA has been shown to reduce body fat and increase lean body mass—findings that have sparked interest in CLA as a performance-enhancing aid.[13] Only a few studies on the effects of supplemental CLA on body composition in human beings have been conducted, however, and the results seem less promising.[14] When researchers studied the combined effects of supplemental CLA and resistance training on body composition in men and women, they found small increases in lean body mass and reductions in body fat—but no improvements in strength.[15] The researchers noted that although the effects were statistically significant, they were nevertheless small and should be weighed against the relatively high cost of supplemental CLA.

Caffeine

Some research supports the use of **caffeine** to enhance endurance and, to some extent, to enhance short-term, high-intensity exercise performance.[16] Caffeine may stimulate fatty acid release during endurance activity, but in contrast to what was previously thought, caffeine does not slow muscle glycogen use. Light activity before a workout also stimulates fat release, but in addition, the activity warms the muscles and connective tissues, making them flexible and resistant to injury. Caffeine does not offer these added benefits.

Caffeine is a stimulant that elicits a number of physiological and psychological effects in the body. Caffeine enhances alertness and reduces fatigue.[17] The possible benefits of caffeine use must be weighed against its adverse effects—stomach upset, nervousness, irritability, headaches, and diarrhea. Caffeine-containing beverages should be used in moderation, if at all, and *in addition* to other fluids, not as a substitute for them. College, national, and international athletic competitions prohibit the use of caffeine in amounts greater than the equivalent of 5 to 6 cups of coffee consumed in a two-hour period prior to competition. Urine tests that detect more caffeine than this disqualify athletes from competition. (The table at the start of Appendix H provides a list of common caffeine-containing items and the doses they deliver.)

Oxygenated Water

Oxygenated water—water infused with oxygen—claims to "improve athletic performance, increase endurance, and sharpen concentration" by delivering extra oxygen to the muscles. What's wrong with this claim? One thing wrong is the assumption that oxygen can enter the bloodstream by way of the GI tract—which it can't. Another thing wrong is the assumption that the body can use more oxygen than it receives from the lungs—which it can't. The only time athletes might benefit from oxygen (inhaled, *not* swallowed) might be when exercising at elevations higher than they are accustomed to. Any benefits of oxygenated water come from the water, not the oxygen.

Hormonal Supplements

The dietary supplements discussed this far may or may not help athletic performance, but in the doses commonly taken, they seem to cause little harm. The remaining discussion features supplements that are clearly damaging.

Anabolic Steroids

Among the most dangerous and illegal ergogenic practices is the taking of **anabolic steroids.** These drugs are derived from the male sex hormone testosterone, which promotes the development of male characteristics and lean body mass. The athletes who take steroids do so to stimulate muscle bulking.

To athletes struggling to excel, the promise of bigger, stronger muscles than training alone can produce is tempting. Athletes who lack superstar genetic material and who normally would not be able to break into the elite ranks can, with the help of steroids, suddenly compete with true champions. Especially in professional circles such as Major League Baseball and the National Football League, where monetary rewards for excellence are sky-high, steroid use is common despite its illegality and side effects.

The American Academy of Pediatrics and the American College of Sports Medicine condemn athletes' use of anabolic steroids, and the International Olympic Committee bans their use. These authorities cite the known toxic side effects and maintain that taking these drugs is a form of cheating. Other athletes are put in the difficult position of either conceding an unfair advantage to competitors who use steroids or taking them and accepting the risk of harmful side effects (see Table H14-1, p. 506). Young athletes should not be forced to make such a choice.

The price for the potential competitive edge that steroids confer is high—sometimes it is life itself. Steroids are not simple pills that build bigger muscles. They are complex chemicals to which the body reacts in many ways, particularly when bodybuilders and other athletes take large amounts.[18] The safest, most effective way to build muscle has always been through hard training and a sound diet, and—despite popular misconceptions—it still is.

Some manufacturers peddle specific herbs as legal substitutes for steroid drugs. They falsely claim that these herbs contain hormones, enhance the body's hormonal activity, or both. In some cases, an herb may contain plant sterols, such as gamma-oryzanol, but these compounds are poorly absorbed. Even if absorption occurs, the body cannot convert herbal compounds to anabolic steroids. None of these products has any proven anabolic steroid activity, none enhances muscle strength, and some contain natural toxins. In short, "natural" does not mean "harmless."

TABLE H14-1 Anabolic Steroids: Side Effects and Adverse Reactions

Mind

- Extreme aggression with hostility ("steroid rage"); mood swings; anxiety; dizziness; drowsiness; unpredictability; insomnia; psychotic depression; personality changes, suicidal thoughts

Face and Hair

- Swollen appearance; greasy skin; severe, scarring acne; mouth and tongue soreness; yellowing of whites of eyes (jaundice)
- In females, male-pattern hair loss and increased growth of face and body hair

Voice

- In females, irreversible deepening of voice

Chest

- In males, breathing difficulty, breast development
- In females, breast atrophy

Heart

- Heart disease; elevated or reduced heart rate; heart attack; stroke; hypertension; increased LDL; reduced HDL

Abdominal Organs

- Nausea; vomiting; bloody diarrhea; pain; edema; liver tumors (possibly cancerous); liver damage, disease, or rupture leading to fatal liver failure; kidney stones and damage; gallstones; frequent urination; possible rupture of aneurysm or hemorrhage

Blood

- Blood clots; high risk of blood poisoning; those who share needles risk contracting HIV (the AIDS virus) or other disease-causing organisms; septic shock (from injections)

Reproductive System

- In males, permanent shrinkage of testes; prostate enlargement with increased risk of cancer; sexual dysfunction; loss of fertility; excessive and painful erections
- In females, loss of menstruation and fertility; permanent enlargement of external genitalia; fetal damage, if pregnant

Muscles, Bones, and Connective Tissues

- Increased susceptibility to injury with delayed recovery times; cramps; tremors; seizurelike movements; injury at injection site
- In adolescents, failure to grow to normal height

Other

- Fatigue; increased risk of cancer

DHEA and Androstenedione

Some athletes use **DHEA** and **androstenedione** as alternatives to anabolic steroids. Androstenedione made headlines in the late 1990s when the media reported that baseball great Mark McGwire had been using it. DHEA (dehydroepiandrosterone) and androstenedione are hormones made in the adrenal glands that serve as precursors to the male hormone testosterone. Advertisements claim the hormones "burn fat," "build muscle," and "slow aging," but evidence to support such claims is lacking.

Short-term side effects of DHEA and androstenedione may include oily skin, acne, body hair growth, liver enlargement, testicular shrinkage, and aggressive behavior. Long-term effects, such as serious liver damage may take years to become evident. The potential for harm from DHEA and androstenedione supplements is great, and athletes, as well as others, should avoid them.

Recently, the Food and Drug Administration (FDA) sent letters to producers of dietary supplements warning that products containing androstenedione are considered to be adulterated, and therefore illegal to sell, and that criminal penalties could result from continued sales. The National Collegiate Athletic Association, the National Football League, and the International Olympic Committee have banned the use of androstenedione and DHEA in competition. The American Academy of Pediatrics and many other medical professional groups have spoken out against the use of these and other "hormone replacement" substances.

Human Growth Hormone

Some short or average-sized athletes sometimes use **hGH (human growth hormone)** to build lean tissue and increase their height if they are still in their growing years. Athletes in power sports such as weight lifting and judo are most likely to experiment with hGH, believing the injectable hormone will provide the benefits of anabolic steroids without the dangerous side effects.

Taken in large quantities, hGH causes the disease acromegaly, in which the body becomes huge and the organs and bones overenlarge. Other effects include diabetes, thyroid disorder, heart disease, menstrual irregularities, diminished sexual desire, and shortened life span. The U.S. Olympic Committee bans hGH use, but tests cannot definitively distinguish between naturally occurring hGH and hGH used as a drug.[19] The committee maintains that the use of hGH is a form of cheating that undermines the quest for physical excellence and that its use is coercive to other athletes.

The search for a single food, nutrient, drug, or technique that will safely and effectively enhance athletic performance will no doubt continue as long as people strive to achieve excellence in sports. When athletic performance does improve after use of an ergogenic aid, the improvement can often be attributed to the placebo effect, which is strongly at work in athletes. Even if a reliable source reports a performance boost from a newly tried product, give the effect time to fade away. Chances are excellent that it simply reflects the power of the mind over the body.

The overwhelming majority of performance-enhancing aids sold for athletes are frauds. Wishful thinking will not substitute for talent, hard training, adequate diet, and mental preparedness in competition. But don't discount the power of mind over body for a minute—it is formidable, and sports psychologists dedicate their work to harnessing it. You can use it by imagining yourself a winner and visualizing yourself excelling in your sport. You don't have to buy magic to obtain a winning edge; you already possess it—your physically fit mind and body.

NUTRITION ON THE NET

ThomsonNOW‍

For further study of topics covered in this Highlight, log on to **www**
.thomsonedu.com/thomsonnow. Go to Chapter 14, then to Highlights
Nutrition on the Net.

- Find information on sports drinks and other nutrition and
  fitness topics at the Gatorade Sports Science Institute site:
  www.gssiweb.com

REFERENCES

1. K. A. Erdman, T. S. Fung, and R. A. Reimer, Influence of performance level on dietary supplementation in elite Canadian athletes, *Medicine and Science in Sports and Exercise* 38 (2006): 349–356.
2. F. Brouns and coauthors, Functional foods and food supplements for athletes: From myths to benefit claims substantiation through the study of selected biomarkers, *British Journal of Nutrition* 88 (2002): S177–S186.
3. J. M. Drazen, Inappropriate advertising of dietary supplements, *New England Journal of Medicine* 348 (2003): 777–778.
4. E. M. Broad, R. J. Maughan, S. D. Galloway, Effects of four weeks L-carnitine L-tartrate ingestion on substrate utilization during prolonged exercise, *International Journal of Sport Nutrition and Exercise Metabolism* 15 (2005): 665–679; E. P. Brass, Carnitine and sports medicine: Use or abuse? *Annals of the New York Academy of Sciences* 1033 (2004): 67–78.
5. J. B. Vincent, The potential value and toxicity of chromium picolinate as a nutritional supplement, weight loss agent and muscle development agent, *Sports Medicine* 33 (2003): 213–230.
6. Vincent, 2003.
7. M. C. Peyrebrune and coauthors, Effect of creatine supplementation on training for competition in elite swimmers, *Medicine and Science in Sports and Exercise* 37 (2005): 2140–2147; R. L. Dempsey, M. F. Mazzone, and L. N. Meurer, Does oral creatine supplementation improve strength? A meta-analysis, *Journal of Family Practice* 51 (2002): 945–951; J. S. Volek and coauthors, Physiological responses to short-term exercise in the heat after creatine loading, *Medicine and Science in Sports and Medicine* 33 (2001): 1101–1108; D. Preen and coauthors, Effect

of creatine loading on long-term sprint exercise performance and metabolism, *Medicine and Science in Sports and Medicine* 33 (2001): 814–821.
8. P. D. Chilibeck and coauthors, Effect of creatine ingestion after exercise on muscle thickness in males and females, *Medicine and Science in Sports and Medicine* 36 (2004): 1781–1788; A. G. Nelson, Muscle glycogen supercompensation is enhanced by prior creatine supplementation, *Medicine and Science in Sports and Medicine* 33 (2001): 1096–1100; M. G. Bemben and coauthors, Creatine supplementation during resistance training in college football athletes, *Medicine and Science in Sports and Medicine* 33 (2001): 1667–1673; D. Willoughby and J. Rosene, Effects of oral creatine and resistance training on myosin heavy chain expression, *Medicine and Science in Sports and Medicine* 33 (2001): 1674–1681.
9. T. L. Schwenk and C. D. Costley, When food becomes a drug: Nonanabolic nutritional supplement use in athletes, *The American Journal of Sports Medicine* 30 (2003): 907–916.
10. M. Dunford and M. Smith, Dietary supplements and ergogenic aids, in *Sports Nutrition: A Practice Manual for Professionals,* 4th ed., ed. M. Dunford (Chicago: American Dietetic Association, 2006), pp. 116–141; E. Bizzarini and L. De Angelis, Is the use of oral creatine supplementation safe? *Journal of Sports Medicine and Physical Fitness* 44 (2004): 411–416.
11. R. B. Kreider and coauthors, Long-term creatine supplementation does not significantly affect clinical markers of health in athletes, *Molecular and Cellular Biochemistry* 244 (2003): 95–104.
12. American Academy of Pediatrics, Policy Statement, Committee on Sports Medicine

and Fitness, Use of performance-enhancing substances, *Pediatrics* 115 (2005): 1103–1106.
13. A. M. Bhattacharya and coauthors, The combination of dietary conjugated linoleic acid and treadmill exercise lowers gain in body fat mass and enhances lean body mass in high fat-fed male Balb/C mice, *Journal of Nutrition* 135 (2005): 1124–1130; M. A. Belury, Dietary conjugated linoleic acid in health: Physiological effects and mechanisms of action, *Annual Review of Nutrition* 22 (2002): 505–531.
14. A. H. M. Terpstra, Effect of conjugated linoleic acid on body composition and plasma lipids in humans: An overview of the literature, *American Journal of Clinical Nutrition* 79 (2004): 352–361.
15. C. Pinkoski and coauthors, The effects of conjugated linoleic acid supplementation during resistance training, *Medicine and Science in Sports and Exercise* 38 (2006): 339–348.
16. K. T. Schneiker and coauthors, Effects of caffeine on prolonged intermittent-sprint ability in team-sport athletes, *Medicine and Science in Sports and Exercise* 38 (2006): 578–585; G. R. Stuart and coauthors, Multiple effects of caffeine on simulated high-intensity team-sport performance, *Medicine and Science in Sports and Exercise* 37 (2005): 1998–2005; S. A. Paluska, Caffeine and exercise, *Current Sports Medicine Reports* 2 (2003): 213–219.
17. Stuart and coauthors, 2005; Paluska, 2003.
18. A. B. Parkinson and N. A. Evans, Anabolic androgenic steroids: A survey of 500 users, *Medicine and Science in Sports and Exercise* 38 (2006): 644–651.
19. L. di Luigi and L. Guidetti, IGF-1, IGFBP-2, and -3: Do they have a role in detecting rhGH abuse in trained men? *Medicine and Science in Sports and Medicine* 34 (2002): 1270–1278.

Nutrition in Your Life

Food choices have consequences. Sometimes they happen immediately, as when you get heartburn after eating a pepperoni and jalapeño pizza. Other times they sneak up on you, as when you gain weight after repeatedly overindulging in double hot fudge sundaes. Quite often, they are temporary and easily resolved, as when hunger pangs strike after you drink only a diet cola for lunch. During pregnancy, however, the consequences of a woman's food choices are dramatic. They affect not just her health, but also the growth and development of another human being—and not just for today, but for years to come. Making smart food choices is a huge responsibility, but fortunately, it's fairly simple.

Life Cycle Nutrition: Pregnancy and Lactation

CHAPTER OUTLINE

Nutrition prior to Pregnancy

Growth and Development during Pregnancy • Placental Development • Fetal Growth and Development • Critical Periods

Maternal Weight • Weight prior to Conception • Weight Gain during Pregnancy • Exercise during Pregnancy

Nutrition during Pregnancy • Energy and Nutrient Needs during Pregnancy • Vegetarian Diets during Pregnancy and Lactation • Common Nutrition-Related Concerns of Pregnancy

High-Risk Pregnancies • The Infant's Birthweight • Malnutrition and Pregnancy • Food Assistance Programs • Maternal Health • The Mother's Age • Practices Incompatible with Pregnancy

Nutrition during Lactation • Lactation: A Physiological Process • Breast-feeding: A Learned Behavior • Maternal Energy and Nutrient Needs during Lactation • Maternal Health • Practices Incompatible with Lactation

HIGHLIGHT 15 Fetal Alcohol Syndrome

All people—pregnant and lactating women, infants, children, adolescents, and adults—need the same nutrients, but the amounts they need vary depending on their stage of life. This chapter focuses on nutrition in preparation for, and support of, pregnancy and lactation. The next two chapters address the needs of infants, children, adolescents, and older adults.

Nutrition prior to Pregnancy

A section on nutrition prior to pregnancy must, by its nature, focus mainly on women. Both a man's and a woman's nutrition may affect **fertility** and possibly the genetic contributions they make to their children, but it is the woman's nutrition that has the most direct influence on the developing fetus. Her body provides the environment for the growth and development of a new human being. Prior to pregnancy, a woman has a unique opportunity to prepare herself physically, mentally, and emotionally for the many changes to come. In preparation for a healthy pregnancy, a woman can establish the following habits:[1]

- *Achieve and maintain a healthy body weight.* Both underweight and overweight are associated with infertility.[2] Overweight and obese men have low sperm counts and hormonal changes that reduce fertility.[3] Excess body fat in women disrupts menstrual regularity and ovarian hormone production.[4] Should a pregnancy occur, mothers, both underweight and overweight, and their newborns, face increased risks of complications.

- *Choose an adequate and balanced diet.* Malnutrition reduces fertility and impairs the early development of an infant should a woman become pregnant.

- *Be physically active.* A woman who wants to be physically active when she is pregnant needs to become physically active beforehand.

- *Receive regular medical care.* Regular health care visits can help ensure a healthy start to pregnancy.

- *Manage chronic conditions.* Diseases such as diabetes, HIV/AIDS, PKU, and sexually transmitted diseases can adversely affect a pregnancy and need close medical attention to help ensure a healthy outcome.

fertility: the capacity of a woman to produce a normal ovum periodically and of a man to produce normal sperm; the ability to reproduce.

Young adults can prepare for a healthy pregnancy by taking care of themselves today.

- *Avoid harmful influences.* Both maternal and paternal ingestion of harmful substances (such as cigarettes, alcohol, drugs, or environmental contaminants) can cause abnormalities, alter genes or their expression, and interfere with fertility.

Young adults who nourish and protect their bodies do so not only for their own sakes, but also for future generations.[5]

Dietary Guidelines for Americans 2005

- Women of childbearing age who may become pregnant should eat foods high in heme-iron and/or consume iron-rich plant foods or iron-fortified foods with an enhancer of iron absorption, such as vitamin C-rich foods.

- Women of childbearing age who may become pregnant should consume adequate synthetic folate daily from fortified foods or supplements in addition to naturally occurring folate from a variety of foods.

Growth and Development during Pregnancy

A whole new life begins at **conception.** Organ systems develop rapidly, and nutrition plays many supportive roles. This section describes placental development and fetal growth, paying close attention to times of intense developmental activity.

Placental Development

In the early days of pregnancy, a spongy structure known as the **placenta** develops in the **uterus.** Two associated structures also form (see Figure 15-1). One is the **amniotic sac,** a fluid-filled balloonlike structure that houses the developing fetus. The other is the **umbilical cord,** a ropelike structure containing fetal blood vessels that extends through the fetus's "belly button" (the umbilicus) to the placenta. These three structures play crucial roles during pregnancy and then are expelled from the uterus during childbirth.

The placenta develops as an interweaving of fetal and maternal blood vessels embedded in the uterine wall. The maternal blood transfers oxygen and nutrients to the fetus's blood and picks up fetal waste products. By exchanging oxygen, nutrients, and waste products, the placenta performs the respiratory, absorptive, and excretory functions that the fetus's lungs, digestive system, and kidneys will provide after birth.

The placenta is a versatile, metabolically active organ. Like all body tissues, the placenta uses energy and nutrients to support its work. Like a gland, it produces an array of hormones that maintain pregnancy and prepare the mother's breasts for lactation (making milk). A healthy placenta is essential for the developing fetus to attain its full potential.[6]

Fetal Growth and Development

Fetal development begins with the fertilization of an **ovum** by a **sperm.** Three stages follow: the zygote, the embryo, and the fetus (see Figure 15-2).

The Zygote The newly fertilized ovum, or **zygote,** begins as a single cell and divides to become many cells during the days after fertilization. Within two weeks, the zygote embeds itself in the uterine wall—a process known as **implantation.** Cell division continues as each set of cells divides into many other cells. As development proceeds, the zygote becomes an embryo.

conception: the union of the male sperm and the female ovum; fertilization.

placenta (plah-SEN-tuh): the organ that develops inside the uterus early in pregnancy, through which the fetus receives nutrients and oxygen and returns carbon dioxide and other waste products to be excreted.

uterus (YOU-ter-us): the muscular organ within which the infant develops before birth.

amniotic (am-nee-OTT-ic) **sac:** the "bag of waters" in the uterus, in which the fetus floats.

umbilical (um-BILL-ih-cul) **cord:** the ropelike structure through which the fetus's veins and arteries reach the placenta; the route of nourishment and oxygen to the fetus and the route of waste disposal from the fetus. The scar in the middle of the abdomen that marks the former attachment of the umbilical cord is the **umbilicus** (um-BILL-ih-cus), commonly known as the "belly button."

ovum (OH-vum): the female reproductive cell, capable of developing into a new organism upon fertilization; commonly referred to as an egg.

sperm: the male reproductive cell, capable of fertilizing an ovum.

zygote (ZY-goat): the product of the union of ovum and sperm; so-called for the first two weeks after fertilization.

implantation: the stage of development in which the zygote embeds itself in the wall of the uterus and begins to develop; occurs during the first two weeks after conception.

FIGURE 15-1 The Placenta and Associated Structures

To understand how placental villi absorb nutrients without maternal and fetal blood interacting directly, think of how the intestinal villi work. The GI side of the intestinal villi is bathed in a nutrient-rich fluid (chyme). The intestinal villi absorb the nutrient molecules and release them into the body via capillaries. Similarly, the maternal side of the placental villi is bathed in nutrient-rich maternal blood. The placental villi absorb the nutrient molecules and release them to the fetus via fetal capillaries.

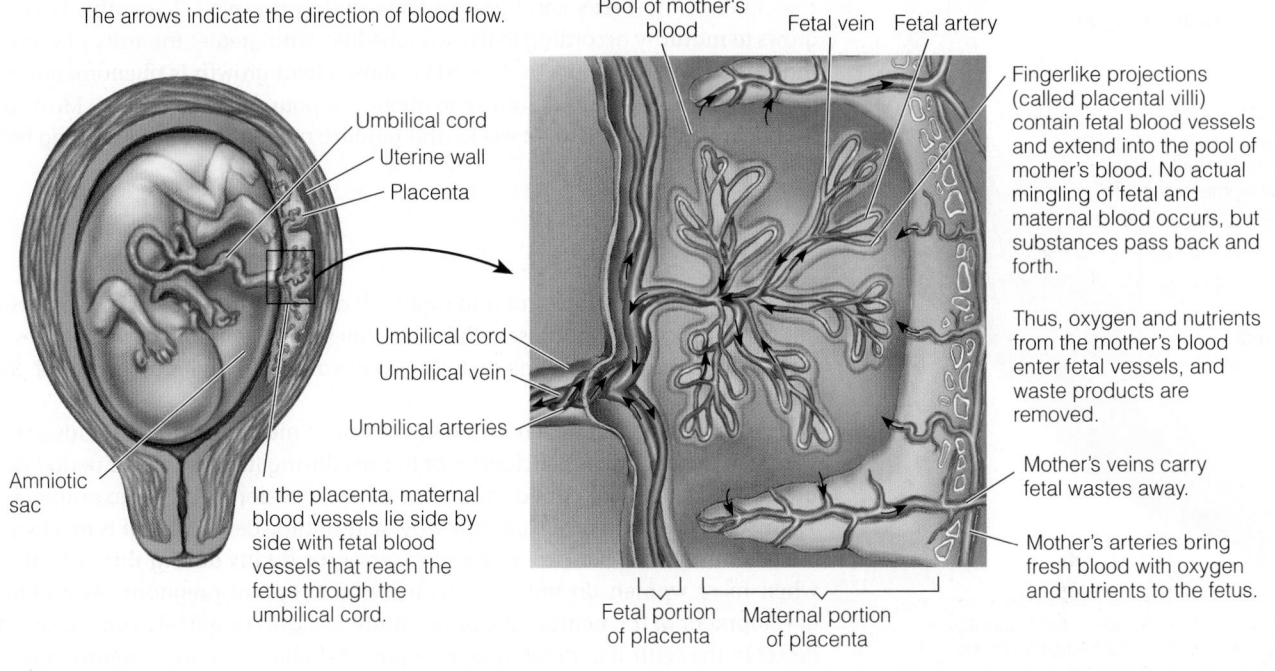

The arrows indicate the direction of blood flow.

Umbilical cord
Uterine wall
Placenta

Amniotic sac

In the placenta, maternal blood vessels lie side by side with fetal blood vessels that reach the fetus through the umbilical cord.

Umbilical cord
Umbilical vein
Umbilical arteries

Pool of mother's blood
Fetal vein   Fetal artery

Fingerlike projections (called placental villi) contain fetal blood vessels and extend into the pool of mother's blood. No actual mingling of fetal and maternal blood occurs, but substances pass back and forth.

Thus, oxygen and nutrients from the mother's blood enter fetal vessels, and waste products are removed.

Mother's veins carry fetal wastes away.

Mother's arteries bring fresh blood with oxygen and nutrients to the fetus.

Fetal portion of placenta   Maternal portion of placenta

FIGURE 15-2 Stages of Embryonic and Fetal Development

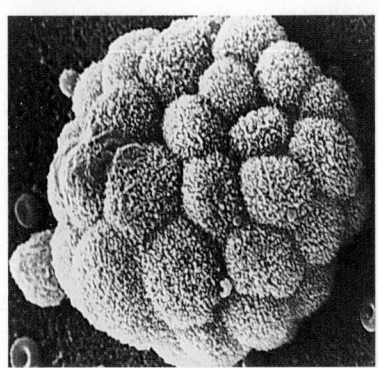

1 A newly fertilized ovum is about the size of a period at the end of this sentence. This **zygote** at less than one week after fertilization is not much bigger and is ready for implantation.

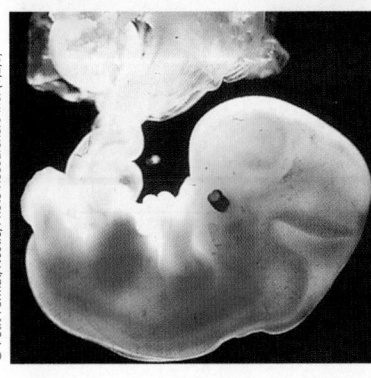

2 After implantation, the placenta develops and begins to provide nourishment to the developing embryo. An **embryo** 5 weeks after fertilization is about ¹/₂ inch long.

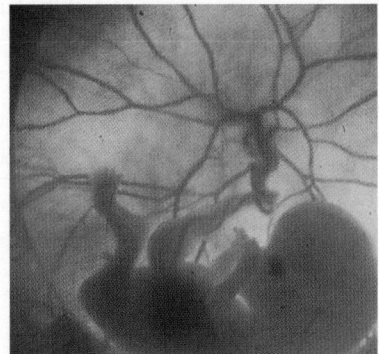

3 A **fetus** after 11 weeks of development is just over an inch long. Notice the umbilical cord and blood vessels connecting the fetus with the placenta.

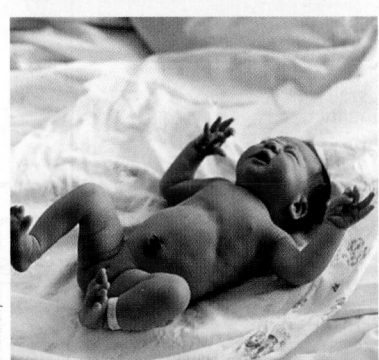

4 A **newborn infant** after nine months of development measures close to 20 inches in length. From 8 weeks to term, this infant grew 20 times longer and 50 times heavier.

© Petit Format/Nestle/Photo Researchers Inc. (1,2,3)

© Anthony M. Vannelli

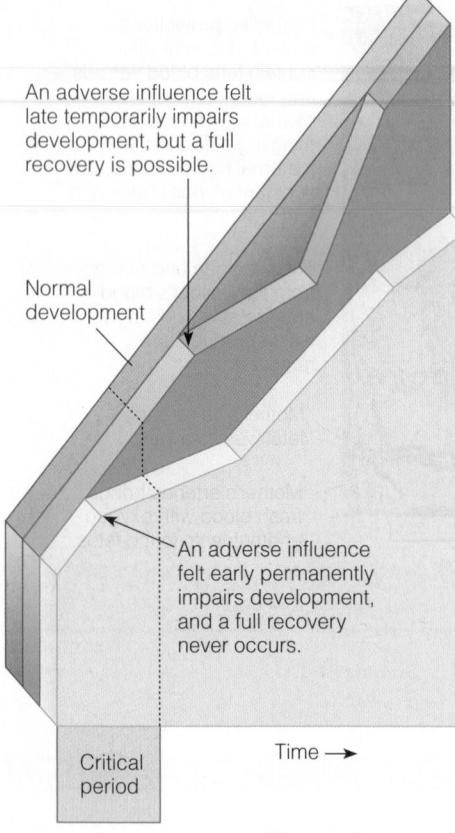

FIGURE 15-3 The Concept of Critical Periods in Fetal Development

Critical periods occur early in fetal development. An adverse influence felt early in pregnancy can have a much more severe and prolonged impact than one felt later on.

An adverse influence felt late temporarily impairs development, but a full recovery is possible.

Normal development

An adverse influence felt early permanently impairs development, and a full recovery never occurs.

Critical period

Time →

◆ Reminder: The *neural tube* is the structure that eventually becomes the brain and spinal cord.

embryo (EM-bree-oh): the developing infant from two to eight weeks after conception.

fetus (FEET-us): the developing infant from eight weeks after conception until term.

critical periods: finite periods during development in which certain events occur that will have irreversible effects on later developmental stages; usually a period of rapid cell division.

gestation (jes-TAY-shun): the period from conception to birth. For human beings, the average length of a healthy gestation is 40 weeks. Pregnancy is often divided into three-month periods, called **trimesters**.

The Embryo The **embryo** develops at an amazing rate. At first, the number of cells in the embryo doubles approximately every 24 hours; later the rate slows, and only one doubling occurs during the final 10 weeks of pregnancy. At 8 weeks, the 1¼-inch embryo has a complete central nervous system, a beating heart, a digestive system, well-defined fingers and toes, and the beginnings of facial features.

The Fetus The **fetus** continues to grow during the next 7 months. Each organ grows to maturity according to its own schedule, with greater intensity at some times than at others. As Figure 15-2 (p. 511) shows, fetal growth is phenomenal: weight increases from less than an ounce to about 7½ pounds (3500 grams). Most successful pregnancies last 38 to 42 weeks and produce a healthy infant weighing between 6½ and 9 pounds.

Critical Periods

Times of intense development and rapid cell division are called **critical periods**— critical in the sense that those cellular activities can occur only at those times. If cell division and number are limited during a critical period, full recovery is not possible (see Figure 15-3).

The development of each organ and tissue is most vulnerable to adverse influences (such as nutrient deficiencies or toxins) during its own critical period (see Figure 15-4). The critical period for neural tube ◆ development, for example, is from 17 to 30 days **gestation.** Consequently, neural tube development is most vulnerable to nutrient deficiencies, nutrient excesses, or toxins during this critical time— when most women do not even realize that they are pregnant. Any abnormal development of the neural tube or its failure to close completely can cause a major defect in the central nervous system. Figure 15-5 shows photos of neural tube development in the early weeks of gestation.

FIGURE 15-4 Critical Periods of Development

During embryonic development (from 2 to 8 weeks), many of the tissues are in their critical periods (purple area of the bars); events occur that will have irreversible effects on the development of those tissues. In the later stages of development (green area of the bars), the tissues continue to grow and change, but the events are less critical in that they are relatively minor or reversible.

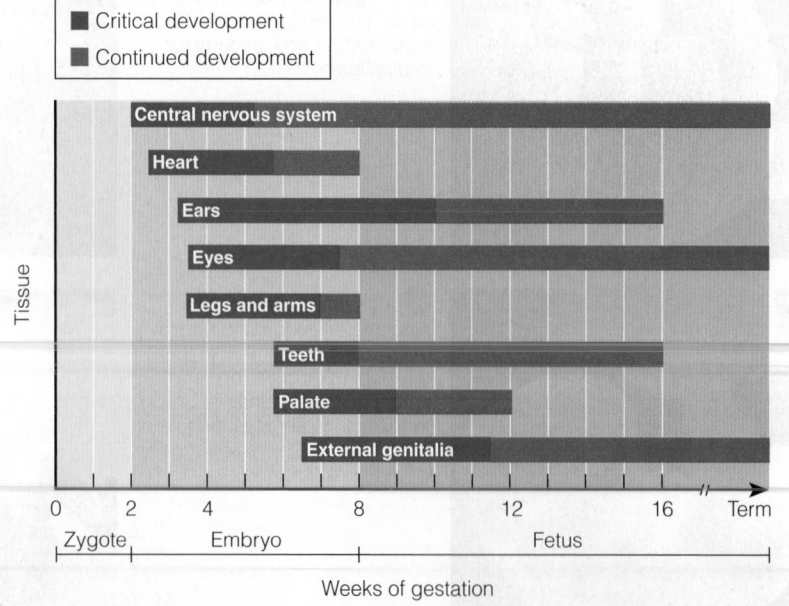

SOURCE: Adapted from *Before We Are Born: Essentials of Embryology and Birth Defects* by K. L. Moore. and T. V. N. Persaud: W. B. Saunders, 2003.

FIGURE 15-5 Neural Tube Development

The neural tube is the beginning structure of the brain and spinal cord. Any failure of the neural tube to close or to develop normally results in central nervous system disorders such as spina bifida and anencephaly. Successful development of the neural tube depends, in part, on the vitamin folate.

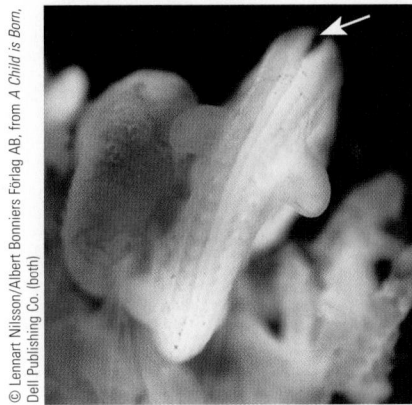
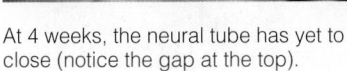

At 4 weeks, the neural tube has yet to close (notice the gap at the top).

At 6 weeks, the neural tube (outlined by the delicate red vertebral arteries) has successfully closed.

Neural Tube Defects In the United States, approximately 30 of every 100,000 newborns are born with a neural tube defect; ◆ some 1000 or so infants are affected each year.* Many other pregnancies with neural tube defects end in abortions or stillbirths.

The two most common types of neural tube defects are anencephaly and spina bifida. In **anencephaly,** the upper end of the neural tube fails to close. Consequently, the brain is either missing or fails to develop. Pregnancies affected by anencephaly often end in miscarriage; infants born with anencephaly die shortly after birth.

Spina bifida is characterized by incomplete closure of the spinal cord and its bony encasement (see Figure 15-6 on p. 514). The meninges membranes covering the spinal cord often protrude as a sac, which may rupture and lead to meningitis, a life-threatening infection. Spina bifida is accompanied by varying degrees of paralysis, depending on the extent of the spinal cord damage. Mild cases may not even be noticed, but severe cases lead to death. Common problems include clubfoot, dislocated hip, kidney disorders, curvature of the spine, muscle weakness, mental handicaps, and motor and sensory losses.

The cause of neural tube defects is unknown, but researchers are examining several gene-gene, gene-nutrient, and gene-environment interactions.[7] A pregnancy affected by a neural tube defect can occur in any woman, but these factors make it more likely:

- A previous pregnancy affected by a neural tube defect
- Maternal diabetes (type 1)
- Maternal use of antiseizure medications
- Maternal obesity
- Exposure to high temperatures early in pregnancy (prolonged fever or hot-tub use)
- Race/ethnicity (more common among whites and Hispanics than others)
- Low socioeconomic status

Folate supplementation reduces the risk.

◆ Reminder: A *neural tube defect* is a malformation of the brain, spinal cord, or both during embryonic development. The two main types of neural tube defects are **spina bifida** (literally, "split spine") and **anencephaly** ("no brain").

anencephaly (AN-en-SEF-a-lee): an uncommon and always fatal type of neural tube defect; characterized by the absence of a brain.
- **an** = not (without)
- **encephalus** = brain

spina (SPY-nah) **bifida** (BIFF-ih-dah): one of the most common types of neural tube defects; characterized by the incomplete closure of the spinal cord and its bony encasement.
- **spina** = spine
- **bifida** = split

* Worldwide, some 300,000 to 400,000 infants are born with neural tube defects each year.

FIGURE 15-6 Spina Bifida

Spina bifida, a common neural tube defect, occurs when the vertebrae of the spine fail to close around the spinal cord, leaving it unprotected. The B vitamin folate helps prevent spina bifida and other neural tube defects.

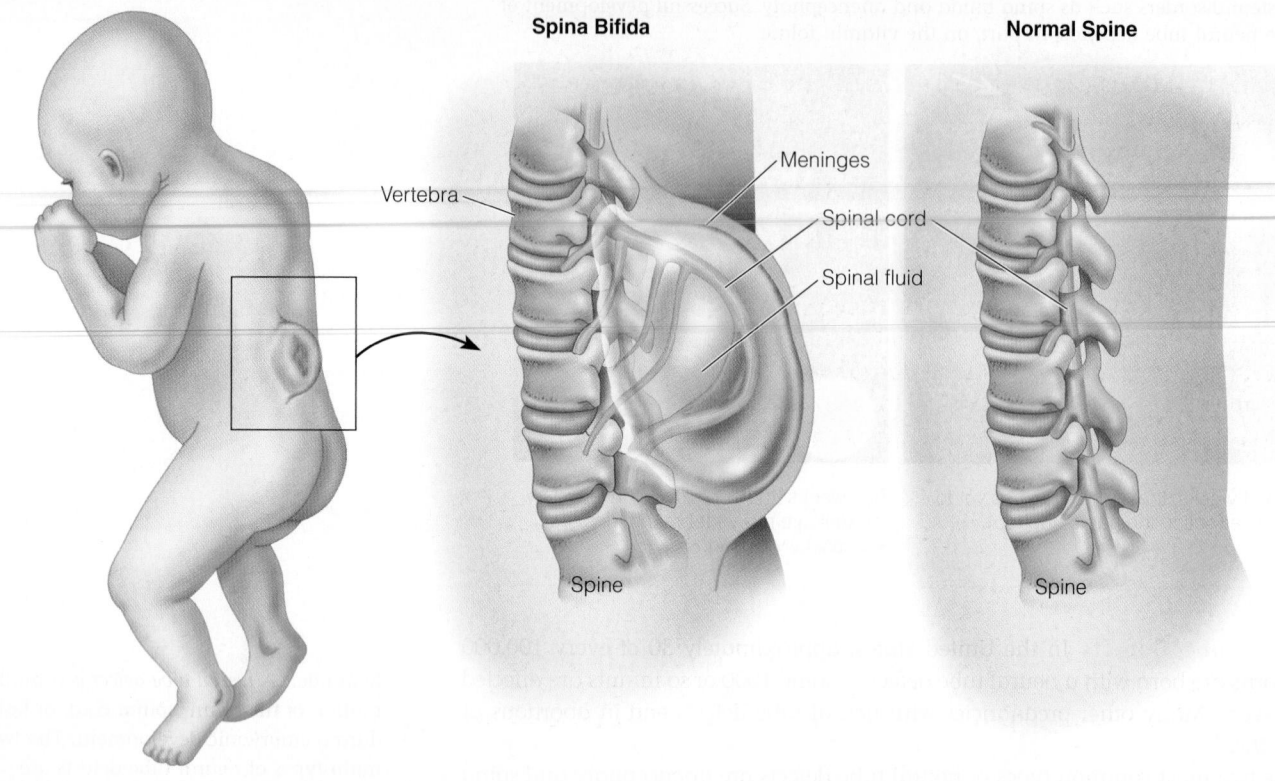

Spina Bifida

Vertebra

Meninges

Spinal cord

Spinal fluid

Spine

Normal Spine

Spine

SOURCE: From the *Journal of the American Medical Association*, June 20, 2001, Vol. 285, No. 23, p. 3050. Reprinted with permission of the American Medical Association.

◆ Folate RDA:
  • For women: 400 µg (0.4 mg)/day
  • During pregnancy: 600 µg (0.6 mg)/day

Folate Supplementation Chapter 10 described how folate supplements taken one month before conception and continued throughout the first trimester can help support a healthy pregnancy, prevent neural tube defects, and reduce the severity of those that do occur.[8] For this reason, all women of childbearing age ◆ who are capable of becoming pregnant should consume 400 micrograms (0.4 milligram) of folate daily. A woman who has previously had an infant with a neural tube defect may be advised by her physician to take folate supplements in doses ten times larger—4 milligrams daily. Because high doses of folate can mask the symptoms of the pernicious anemia of a vitamin B_{12} deficiency, quantities of 1 milligram or more require a prescription. Most over-the-counter multivitamin supplements contain 400 micrograms of folate; prenatal supplements usually contain at least 800 micrograms.

 **Dietary** Guidelines for Americans 2005

Women in their first trimester of pregnancy should consume adequate synthetic folate daily from fortified foods or supplements in addition to naturally occurring folate from a variety of foods.

Because half of the pregnancies each year are unplanned and because neural tube defects occur early in development before most women realize they are pregnant, grain products in the United States are fortified with folate to help ensure an adequate intake. Labels on fortified products may claim that an "adequate intake of folate has been shown to reduce the risk of neural tube defects." Fortification has improved folate status in women of childbearing age and lowered the number of neural tube defects that occur each year, as Figure 10-10 on p. 340 showed.[9]

Whether folate fortification should be increased further is still the subject of much debate.[10]

Chronic Diseases Much research suggests that adverse influences at critical times during fetal development set the stage for the infant to develop chronic diseases in adult life.[11] Poor maternal diet during critical periods may permanently alter body functions such as blood pressure, glucose tolerance, and immune functions that influence disease development.[12] For example, maternal diet may alter blood vessel growth and program lipid metabolism and lean body mass development in such a way that the infant will develop risk factors for cardiovascular disease as an adult.[13]

Malnutrition during the critical period of pancreatic cell growth provides an example of how type 2 diabetes may develop in adulthood.[14] The pancreatic cells responsible for producing insulin (the beta cells) normally increase more than 130-fold between 12 weeks gestation and 5 months after birth. Nutrition is a primary determinant of beta cell growth, and infants who have suffered prenatal malnutrition have significantly fewer beta cells than well-nourished infants. They are also more likely to be low-birthweight infants—and low birthweight and premature birth correlate with insulin resistance and type 2 diabetes later in life.[15] One hypothesis suggests that diabetes may develop from the interaction of inadequate nutrition early in life with abundant nutrition later in life: the small mass of beta cells developed in times of undernutrition during fetal development may be insufficient in times of overnutrition during adulthood when the body needs more insulin.[16]

Hypertension may develop from a similar scenario of inadequate growth during placental and gestational development followed by accelerated growth during early childhood: the small mass of kidney cells developed during malnutrition may be insufficient to handle the excessive demands of later life.[17] Low-birthweight infants who gain weight rapidly as young children are likely to develop hypertension and heart disease as adults.[18]

Fetal Programming Recent genetic research may help to explain the phenomenon of substances such as nutrients influencing the development of diseases later on in adulthood—a process known as **fetal programming.** In the case of pregnancy, the mother's nutrition can permanently change gene expression in the fetus.[19] Some research suggests that fetal programming may influence several succeeding generations.[20]

IN SUMMARY

Maternal nutrition before and during pregnancy affects both the mother's health and the infant's growth. As the infant develops through its three stages—the zygote, embryo, and fetus—its organs and tissues grow, each on its own schedule. Times of intense development are critical periods that depend on nutrients to proceed smoothly. Without folate, for example, the neural tube fails to develop completely during the first month of pregnancy, prompting recommendations that all women of childbearing age take folate daily.

Because critical periods occur throughout pregnancy, a woman should continuously take good care of her health. That care should include achieving and maintaining a healthy body weight prior to pregnancy and gaining sufficient weight during pregnancy to support a healthy infant.

Maternal Weight

Birthweight is the most reliable indicator of an infant's health. As a later section of this chapter explains, an underweight infant is more likely to have physical and mental defects, become ill, and die than a normal-weight infant. In general, higher birthweights present fewer risks for infants. Two characteristics of the mother's

fetal programming: the influence of substances during fetal growth on the development of diseases in later life.

◆ BMI was introduced in Chapter 8.
• Underweight = BMI <18.5
• Normal weight = BMI 18.5 to 24.9
• Overweight = BMI 25 to 29.9
• Obesity = BMI ≥30

◆ The term **macrosomia** (mak-roh-SO-me-ah) describes high-birthweight infants (roughly 9 lb, or 4000 g, or more); macrosomia results from prepregnancy obesity, excessive weight gain during pregnancy, or uncontrolled diabetes.
• **macro** = large
• **soma** = body

preterm (infant): an infant born prior to the 38th week of pregnancy; also called a **premature infant.** A **term** infant is born between the 38th and 42nd week of pregnancy.

post term (infant): an infant born after the 42nd week of pregnancy.

cesarean section: a surgically assisted birth involving removal of the fetus by an incision into the uterus, usually by way of the abdominal wall.

weight influence an infant's birthweight: her weight *prior* to conception and her weight gain *during* pregnancy.

Weight prior to Conception

A woman's weight ◆ prior to conception influences fetal growth. Even with the same weight gain during pregnancy, underweight women tend to have smaller babies than heavier women.

Underweight An underweight woman has a high risk of having a low-birthweight infant, especially if she is malnourished or unable to gain sufficient weight during pregnancy. In addition, the rates of **preterm** births and infant deaths are higher for underweight women. An underweight woman improves her chances of having a healthy infant by gaining sufficient weight prior to conception or by gaining extra pounds during pregnancy. To gain weight and ensure nutrient adequacy, an underweight woman can follow the dietary recommendations for pregnant women (described on pp. 520–523).

Overweight and Obesity An estimated one-third of all pregnant women in the United States are obese, which can create problems related to pregnancy and childbirth.[21] Obese women have an especially high risk of medical complications such as hypertension, gestational diabetes, and postpartum infections. Compared with other women, obese women are also more likely to have other complications of labor and delivery.[22]

Overweight women have the lowest rate of low-birthweight infants. In fact, infants of overweight women are more likely to be born **post term** and to weigh more than 9 pounds. ◆ Large newborns increase the likelihood of a difficult labor and delivery, birth trauma, and **cesarean section.** Consequently, these infants have a greater risk of poor health and death than infants of normal weight.

Of greater concern than infant birthweight is the poor development of infants born to obese mothers. Obesity may double the risk for neural tube defects. Folate's role has been examined, but a more likely explanation seems to be poor glycemic control.[23] In addition, both overweight and obese women have a greater risk of giving birth to infants with heart defects and other abnormalities.[24]

Weight-loss dieting during pregnancy is never advisable. Overweight women should try to achieve a healthy body weight before becoming pregnant, avoid excessive weight gain during pregnancy, and postpone weight loss until after childbirth. Weight loss is best achieved by eating moderate amounts of nutrient-dense foods and exercising to lose body fat.

Weight Gain during Pregnancy

All pregnant women must gain weight—fetal growth and maternal health depend on it. Maternal weight gain during pregnancy correlates closely with infant birthweight, which is a strong predictor of the health and subsequent development of the infant.

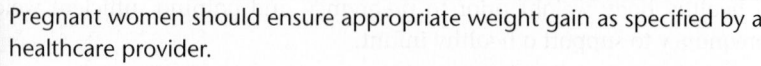
Dietary Guidelines for Americans 2005

Pregnant women should ensure appropriate weight gain as specified by a healthcare provider.

Recommended Weight Gains Table 15-1 presents recommended weight gains for various prepregnancy weights. The recommended gain for a woman who begins pregnancy at a healthy weight and is carrying a single fetus is 25 to 35 pounds. An underweight woman needs to gain between 28 and 40 pounds; and an overweight

TABLE 15-1	Recommended Weight Gains Based on Prepregnancy Weight
Prepregnancy Weight	**Recommended Weight Gain**
Underweight (BMI <18.5)	28 to 40 lb (12.5 to 18.0 kg)
Healthy weight (BMI 18.5 to 24.9)	25 to 35 lb (11.5 to 16.0 kg)
Overweight (BMI 25.0 to 29.9)	15 to 25 lb (7.0 to 11.5 kg)
Obese (BMI ≥30)	15 lb minimum (6.8 kg minimum)

NOTE: These classifications for BMI are slightly different from those developed in 1990 by the Committee on Nutritional Status during Pregnancy and Lactation for the publication *Nutrition during Pregnancy* (Washington, D.C.: National Academy Press). That committee acknowledged that because such classifications had not been validated by research on pregnancy outcome, "any cut off points will be arbitrary for women of reproductive age." For these reasons, it seems appropriate to use the values developed for adults in 1998 by the National Institutes of Health (see Chapter 8).

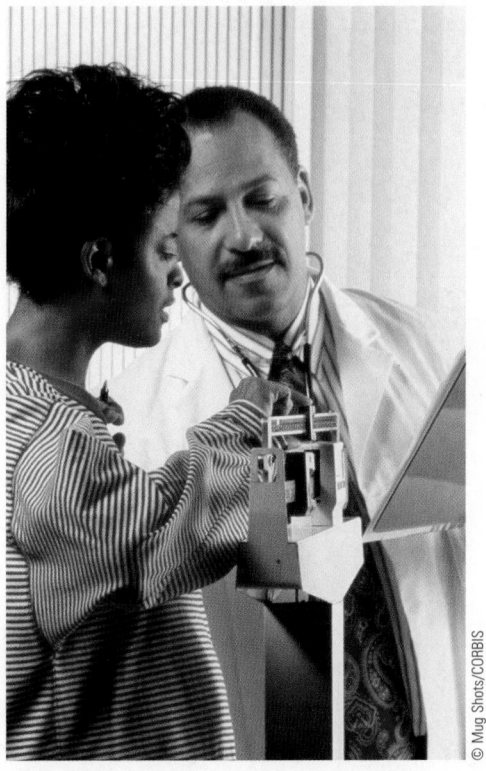

Fetal growth and maternal health depend on a sufficient weight gain during pregnancy.

woman, between 15 and 25 pounds. Some women should strive for gains at the upper end of the target range, notably, adolescents who are still growing themselves and black women whose infants tend to be smaller than white infants even with the same maternal weight gain. Short women (5 feet 2 inches and under) should strive for gains at the lower end of the target range. Women who are carrying twins should aim for a weight gain of 35 to 45 pounds.[25] If a woman gains more than is recommended early in pregnancy, she should not restrict her energy intake later in order to lose weight. A large weight gain over a short time, however, indicates excessive fluid retention and may be the first sign of the serious medical complication preeclampsia, which is discussed later.

Weight-Gain Patterns For the normal-weight woman, weight gain ideally follows a pattern of $3^{1}/_{2}$ pounds during the first trimester and 1 pound per week thereafter. Health care professionals monitor weight gain using a prenatal weight-gain grid (see Figure 15-7).

Components of Weight Gain Women often express concern about the weight gain that accompanies a healthy pregnancy. They may find comfort by remembering that most of the gain supports the growth and development of the placenta, uterus, blood, and breasts, the increase in blood supply and fluid volume, as well as

FIGURE 15-7	Recommended Prenatal Weight Gain Based on Prepregnancy Weight

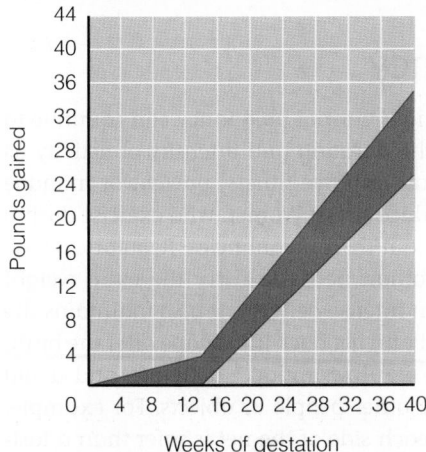

Normal-weight women should gain about $3^{1}/_{2}$ pounds in the first trimester and just under 1 pound/week thereafter, achieving a total gain of 25 to 35 pounds by term.

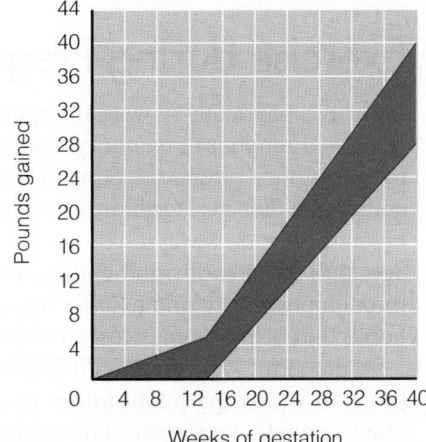

Underweight women should gain about 5 pounds in the first trimester and just over 1 pound/week thereafter, achieving a total gain of 28 to 40 pounds by term.

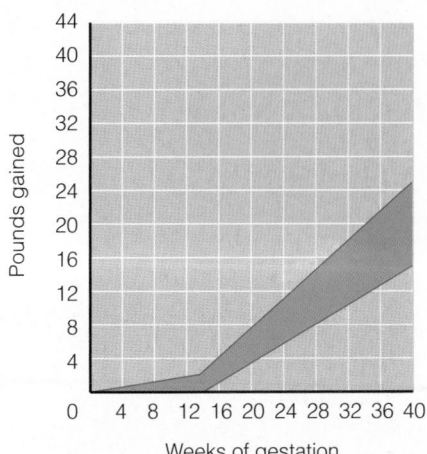

Overweight women should gain about 2 pounds in the first trimester and $^{2}/_{3}$ pound/week thereafter, achieving a total gain of 15 to 25 pounds.

FIGURE 15-8 Components of Weight Gain during Pregnancy

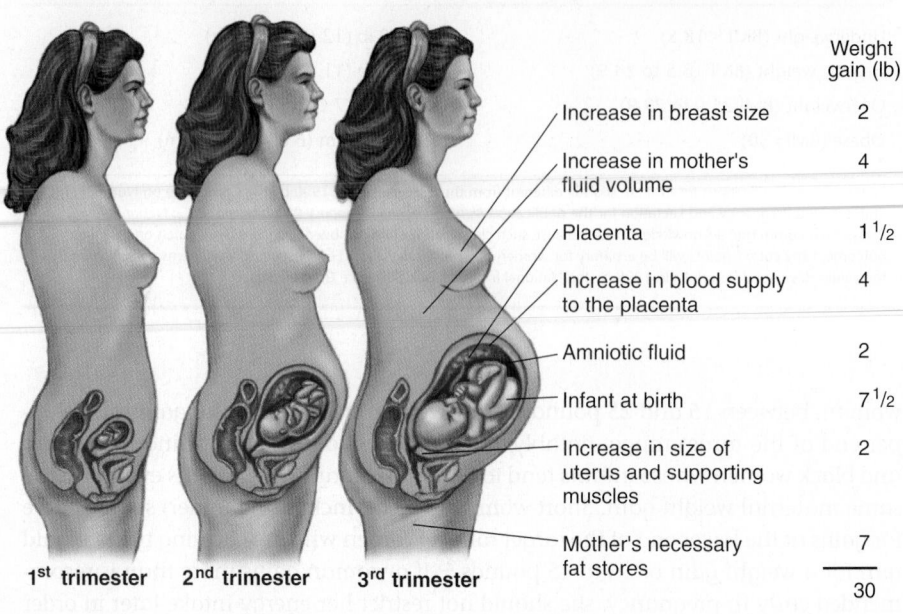

	Weight gain (lb)
Increase in breast size	2
Increase in mother's fluid volume	4
Placenta	1 1/2
Increase in blood supply to the placenta	4
Amniotic fluid	2
Infant at birth	7 1/2
Increase in size of uterus and supporting muscles	2
Mother's necessary fat stores	7
	30

1st trimester   2nd trimester   3rd trimester

an optimally healthy 7 1/2-pound infant. A small amount goes into maternal fat stores, and even that fat is there for a special purpose—to provide energy for labor and lactation. Figure 15-8 shows the components of a typical 30-pound weight gain.

Weight Loss after Pregnancy The pregnant woman loses some weight at delivery. In the following weeks, she loses more as her blood volume returns to normal and she sheds accumulated fluids. The typical woman does not, however, return to her prepregnancy weight. In general, the more weight a woman gains beyond the needs of pregnancy, the more she retains. Even with an average weight gain during pregnancy, most women tend to retain a couple of pounds with each pregnancy. When those couple of pounds become 7 or more and BMI increases by a unit or more, complications such as diabetes and hypertension in future pregnancies as well as chronic diseases in later life can increase—even for women who are not overweight.[26]

Exercise during Pregnancy

An active, physically fit woman experiencing a normal pregnancy can continue to exercise throughout pregnancy, adjusting the duration and intensity of activity as the pregnancy progresses. Staying active can improve fitness, prevent or manage gestational diabetes, facilitate labor, and reduce stress. Women who exercise during pregnancy report fewer discomforts throughout their pregnancies. Regular exercise develops the strength and endurance a woman needs to carry the extra weight through pregnancy and to labor through an intense delivery. It also maintains the habits that help a woman lose excess weight and get back into shape after the birth.

A pregnant woman should participate in "low-impact" activities and avoid sports in which she might fall or be hit by other people or objects. For example, playing singles tennis with one person on each side of the net is safer than a fast-moving game of racquetball in which the two competitors can collide. Swimming and water aerobics are particularly beneficial because they allow the body to remain cool and move freely with the water's support, thus reducing back pain. Figure 15-9 provides some guidelines for exercise during pregnancy.[27] Several of the guidelines are aimed at preventing excessively high internal body temperature and

FIGURE 15-9 Exercise Guidelines during Pregnancy

DO

Do begin to exercise gradually.

Do exercise regularly (most, if not all, days of the week).

Do warm up with 5 to 10 minutes of light activity.

Do 30 minutes or more of moderate physical activity; 20 to 60 minutes of more intense activity on 3 to 5 days a week will provide greater benefits.

Do cool down with 5 to 10 minutes of slow activity and gentle stretching.

Do drink water before, after, and during exercise.

Do eat enough to support the needs of pregnancy plus exercise.

Do rest adequately.

© Tracy Frankel/Image Bank/Getty Images

Pregnant women can enjoy the benefits of exercise.

DON'T

Don't exercise vigorously after long periods of inactivity.

Don't exercise in hot, humid weather.

Don't exercise when sick with fever.

Don't exercise while lying on your back after the first trimester of pregnancy or stand motionless for prolonged periods.

Don't exercise if you experience any pain, discomfort, or fatigue.

Don't participate in activities that may harm the abdomen or involve jerky, bouncy movements.

dehydration, both of which can harm fetal development. To this end, pregnant women should also stay out of saunas, steam rooms, and hot tubs or hot whirlpool baths.

 Dietary Guidelines for Americans 2005

Healthy pregnant women should incorporate 30 minutes or more of moderately intense physical activity on most, if not all, days of the week and avoid activities with a high risk of falling or abdominal trauma.

IN SUMMARY

A healthy pregnancy depends on a sufficient weight gain. Women who begin their pregnancies at a healthy weight need to gain about 30 pounds, which covers the growth and development of the placenta, uterus, blood, breasts, and infant. By remaining active throughout pregnancy, a woman can develop the strength she needs to carry the extra weight and maintain habits that will help her lose it after the birth.

Nutrition during Pregnancy

A woman's body changes dramatically during pregnancy. Her uterus and its supporting muscles increase in size and strength; her blood volume increases by half to carry the additional nutrients and other materials; her joints become more flexible in preparation for childbirth; her feet swell in response to high concentrations of the hormone estrogen, which promotes water retention and helps to ready the uterus for delivery; and her breasts enlarge in preparation for lactation. The hormones that mediate all these changes may influence her mood. She can best prepare to handle these changes given a nutritious diet, regular physical activity, plenty of rest, and caring companions. This section highlights the role of nutrition.

© Rick Gomez/CORBIS

A pregnant woman's food choices support both her health and her infant's growth and development.

Energy and Nutrient Needs during Pregnancy

From conception to birth, all parts of the infant—bones, muscles, organs, blood cells, skin, and other tissues—are made from nutrients in the foods the mother eats. For most women, nutrient needs during pregnancy and lactation ◆ are higher than at any other time (see Figure 15-10). To meet the high nutrient demands of pregnancy, a woman will need to make careful food choices, but her body will also help by maximizing absorption and minimizing losses.

Energy The enhanced work of pregnancy raises the basal metabolic rate dramatically and demands extra energy.[28] Energy needs of pregnant women are greater than those of nonpregnant women—an additional 340 kcalories per day during the second trimester and an extra 450 kcalories per day during the third. ◆ A woman can easily get these added kcalories with nutrient dense selections from the five food groups. See Table 2-3 (p. 41) for suggested dietary patterns for several kcalorie levels and Figure 15-11 (p. 522) for a sample menu for pregnant and lactating women.

For a 2000-kcalorie daily intake, these added kcalories represent about 15 to 20 percent more food energy than before pregnancy. The increase in nutrient needs is often greater than this, so nutrient-dense foods should be chosen to supply the extra kcalories: foods such as whole-grain breads and cereals, legumes, dark green vegetables, citrus fruits, low-fat milk and milk products, and lean meats, fish, poultry, and eggs. Ample carbohydrate (ideally, 175 grams or more per day and certainly no less than 135 grams) is necessary to fuel the fetal brain. Sufficient carbohydrate ensures that the protein needed for growth will not be broken down and used to make glucose.

Protein The protein RDA ◆ for pregnancy is an additional 25 grams per day higher than for nonpregnant women. Pregnant women can easily meet their protein needs by selecting meats, milk products, and protein-containing plant foods such as legumes, whole grains, nuts, and seeds. Because use of high-protein supplements during pregnancy may be harmful to the infant's development, it is discouraged.

Essential Fatty Acids The high nutrient requirements of pregnancy leave little room in the diet for excess fat, but the essential long-chain polyunsaturated fatty acids are particularly important to the growth and development of the fetus. The brain is largely made of lipid material, and it depends heavily on the long-chain omega-3 and omega-6 fatty acids for its growth, function, and structure.[29] (See Table 5-2 on p. 159 for a list of good food sources of the omega fatty acids.)

Nutrients for Blood Production and Cell Growth New cells are laid down at a tremendous pace as the fetus grows and develops. At the same time, the mother's red blood cell mass expands. All nutrients are important in these processes, but for folate, vitamin B_{12}, iron, and zinc, the needs are especially great due to their key roles in the synthesis of DNA and new cells.

The requirement for folate increases dramatically during pregnancy. ◆ It is best to obtain sufficient folate from a combination of supplements, fortified foods, and a diet that includes fruits, juices, green vegetables, and whole grains.[30] The "How to" feature in Chapter 10 on p. 339 described how folate from each of these sources contributes to a day's intake.

The pregnant woman also has a slightly greater need for the B vitamin that activates the folate enzyme—vitamin B_{12}. ◆ Generally, even modest amounts of meat, fish, eggs, or milk products together with body stores easily meet the need for vitamin B_{12}. Vegans who exclude all foods of animal origin, however, need daily supplements of vitamin B_{12} or vitamin B_{12}-fortified foods to prevent the neurological complications of a deficiency.

◆ The Dietary Reference Intakes (DRI) table on the inside front cover provides separate listings for women during pregnancy and lactation, reflecting their heightened nutrient needs. Chapters 10–13 presented details on the vitamins and minerals.

◆ Energy requirement during pregnancy:
• 2nd trimester: + 340 kcal/day
• 3rd trimester: + 450 kcal/day

◆ Protein RDA during pregnancy:
• + 25 g/day

◆ Folate RDA during pregnancy:
• 600 μg/day

◆ Vitamin B_{12} RDA during pregnancy:
• 2.6 μg/day

FIGURE 15-10 Comparison of Nutrient Recommendations for Nonpregnant, Pregnant, and Lactating Women

For actual values, turn to the table on the inside front cover.

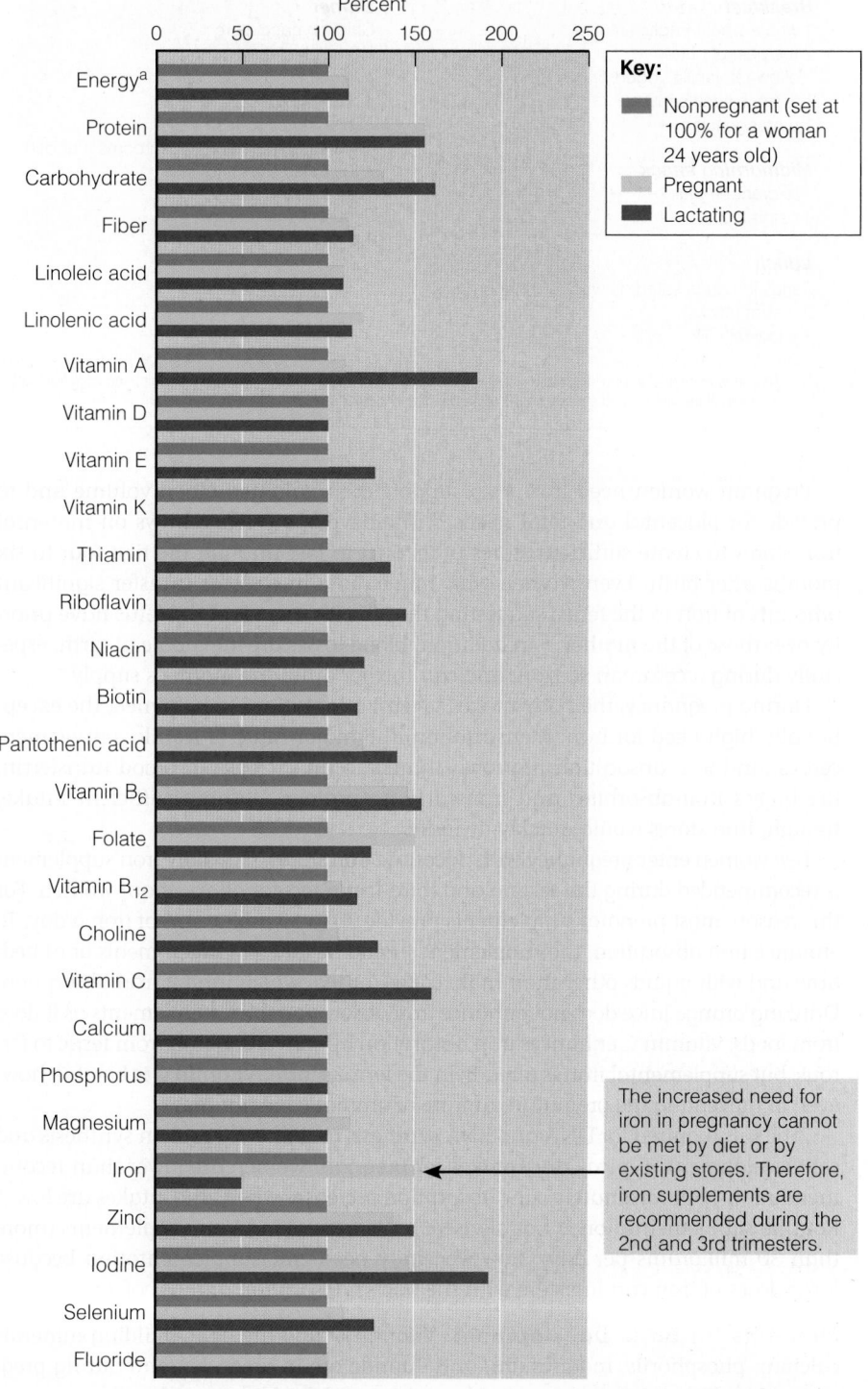

Key:
- Nonpregnant (set at 100% for a woman 24 years old)
- Pregnant
- Lactating

The increased need for iron in pregnancy cannot be met by diet or by existing stores. Therefore, iron supplements are recommended during the 2nd and 3rd trimesters.

[a]Energy allowance during pregnancy is for 2nd trimester; energy allowance during the 3rd trimester is slightly higher; no additional allowance is provided during the 1st trimester. Energy allowance during lactation is for the first 6 months; energy allowance during the second 6 months is slightly higher.

FIGURE 15-11 Daily Food Choices for Pregnant and Lactating Women

SAMPLE MENU

Breakfast
1 whole-wheat English muffin
2 tbs peanut butter
1 c low-fat vanilla yogurt
½ c fresh strawberries
1 c orange juice

Midmorning snack
½ c cranberry juice
1 oz pretzels

Lunch
Sandwich (tuna salad on whole-wheat bread)
½ carrot (sticks)
1 c low-fat milk

Dinner
Chicken cacciatore
  3 oz chicken
  ½ c stewed tomatoes
1 c rice
½ c summer squash
1½ c salad (spinach, mushrooms, carrots)
1 tbs salad dressing
1 slice Italian bread
2 tsp soft margarine
1 c low-fat milk

NOTE: This sample meal plan provides about 2500 kcalories (55% from carbohydrate, 20% from protein, and 25% from fat) and meets most of the vitamin and mineral needs of pregnant and lactating women.

◆ Iron RDA during pregnancy:
• 27 mg/day

Pregnant women need iron ◆ to support their enlarged blood volume and to provide for placental and fetal needs.[31] The developing fetus draws on maternal iron stores to create sufficient stores of its own to last through the first four to six months after birth. Even women with inadequate iron stores transfer significant amounts of iron to the fetus, suggesting that the iron needs of the fetus have priority over those of the mother.[32] In addition, blood losses are inevitable at birth, especially during a cesarean section, and can further drain the mother's supply.*

During pregnancy, the body makes several adaptations to help meet the exceptionally high need for iron. Menstruation, the major route of iron loss in women, ceases, and iron absorption improves thanks to an increase in blood transferrin, the body's iron-absorbing and iron-carrying protein. Without sufficient intake, though, iron stores would quickly dwindle.

Few women enter pregnancy with adequate iron stores, so a daily iron supplement is recommended during the second and third trimesters for all pregnant women. For this reason, most prenatal supplements provide 30 to 60 milligrams of iron a day. To enhance iron absorption, the supplement should be taken between meals or at bedtime and with liquids other than milk, coffee, or tea, which inhibit iron absorption. Drinking orange juice does not enhance iron absorption from supplements as it does from foods; vitamin C enhances iron absorption by converting iron from ferric to ferrous, but supplemental iron is already in the ferrous form. Vitamin C is helpful, however, in preventing the premature rupture of amniotic membranes.[33]

◆ Zinc RDA during pregnancy:
• 12 mg/day (≤18 yr)
• 11 mg/day (19–50 yr)

Zinc ◆ is required for DNA and RNA synthesis and thus for protein synthesis and cell development. Typical zinc intakes for pregnant women are lower than recommendations, but fortunately, zinc absorption increases when zinc intakes are low.[34] Routine supplementation is not advised.[35] Women taking iron supplements (more than 30 milligrams per day), however, may need zinc supplementation because large doses of iron can interfere with the body's absorption and use of zinc.

Nutrients for Bone Development Vitamin D and the bone-building minerals calcium, phosphorus, magnesium, and fluoride are in great demand during pregnancy. Insufficient intakes may produce abnormal fetal bones and teeth.

◆ The AI for vitamin D does not increase during pregnancy.

Vitamin D ◆ plays a vital role in calcium absorption and utilization. Consequently, severe maternal vitamin D deficiency interferes with normal calcium metabolism, resulting in rickets in the infant and osteomalacia in the mother.[36] Regular exposure to sunlight and consumption of vitamin D–fortified milk are usually sufficient to provide the recommended amount of vitamin D during preg-

* On average, almost twice as much blood is lost during a cesarean delivery as during the average vaginal delivery of a single fetus.

nancy, although some researchers question whether current recommendations are adequate.[37] Routine supplementation is not recommended because of the toxicity risk. Vegans who avoid milk, eggs, and fish may receive enough vitamin D from regular exposure to sunlight and from fortified soy milk.

Calcium absorption and retention increases dramatically in pregnancy, helping the mother to meet the calcium needs of pregnancy.[38] ◆ During the last trimester, as the fetal bones begin to calcify, over 300 milligrams a day are transferred to the fetus. Recommendations to ensure an adequate calcium intake during pregnancy help to conserve maternal bone while supplying fetal needs.[39]

Calcium intakes for pregnant women ◆ typically fall below recommendations. Because bones are still actively depositing minerals until about age 30, adequate calcium is especially important for young women. Pregnant women under age 25 who receive less than 600 milligrams of dietary calcium daily need to increase their intake of milk, cheese, yogurt, and other calcium-rich foods. Alternatively, and less preferably, they may need a daily supplement of 600 milligrams of calcium.

Other Nutrients The nutrients mentioned here are those most intensely involved in blood production, cell growth, and bone growth. Of course, other nutrients are also needed during pregnancy to support the growth and health of both fetus and mother. Even with adequate nutrition, repeated pregnancies, less than a year apart, deplete nutrient reserves. When this happens, fetal growth may be compromised, and maternal health may decline. The optimal interval between pregnancies is 18 to 23 months.

Nutrient Supplements Pregnant women who make wise food choices can meet most of their nutrient needs, with the possible exception of iron. Even so, physicians routinely recommend daily multivitamin-mineral supplements for pregnant women. Prenatal supplements typically contain greater amounts of folate, iron, and calcium than regular vitamin-mineral supplements. These supplements are particularly beneficial for women who do not eat adequately and for those in high-risk groups: women carrying multiple fetuses, cigarette smokers, and alcohol and drug abusers. The use of prenatal supplements may help reduce the risks of preterm delivery, low infant birthweights, and birth defects. Supplement use *prior* to conception also seems to reduce the risk of preterm births.[40] Figure 15-12 presents a label from a standard prenatal supplement.

◆ The AI for calcium does not increase during pregnancy.

◆ The USDA Food Guide suggests consuming 3 cups per day of fat-free or low-fat milk or the equivalent in milk products.

FIGURE 15-12 Example of a Prenatal Supplement

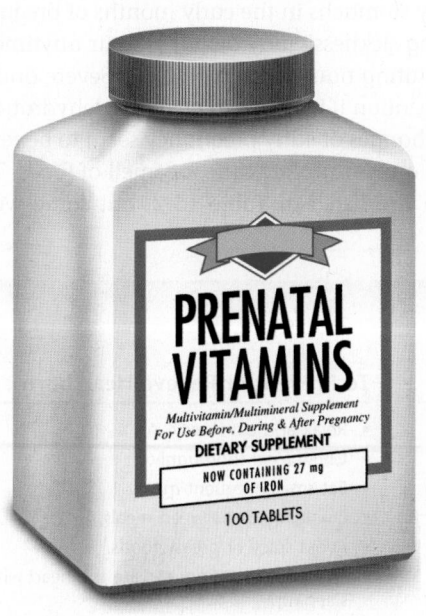

Supplement Facts
Serving Size 1 Tablet

Amount Per Tablet	% Daily Value for Pregnant/ Lactating Women
Vitamin A 4000 IU	50%
Vitamin C 100 mg	167%
Vitamin D 400 IU	100%
Vitamin E 11 IU	37%
Thiamin 1.84 mg	108%
Riboflavin 1.7 mg	85%
Niacin 18 mg	90%
Vitamin B6 2.6 mg	104%
Folate 800 mcg	100%
Vitamin B12 4 mcg	50%
Calcium 200 mg	15%
Iron 27 mg	150%
Zinc 25 mg	167%

INGREDIENTS: calcium carbonate, microcrystalline cellulose, dicalcium phosphate, ascorbic acid, ferrous fumarate, zinc oxide, acacia, sucrose ester, niacinamide, modified cellulose gum, di-alpha tocopheryl acetate, hydroxypropyl methylcellulose, hydroxypropyl cellulose, artificial colors (FD&C blue no. 1 lake, FD&C red no. 40 lake, FD&C yellow no. 6 lake, titanium dioxide), polyethylene glycol, starch, pyridoxine hydrochloride, vitamin A acetate, riboflavin, thiamin mononitrate, folic acid, beta carotene, cholecalciferol, maltodextrin, gluten, cyanocobalamin, sodium bisulfite.

Vegetarian Diets during Pregnancy and Lactation

In general, a vegetarian diet can support a healthy pregnancy and successful lactation if it provides adequate energy; includes milk and milk products; and contains a wide variety of legumes, cereals, fruits, and vegetables.[41] Many vegetarian women are well nourished, with nutrient intakes from diet alone exceeding the RDA for all vitamins and minerals except iron, which is low for most women. In contrast, vegan women who restrict themselves to an exclusively plant-based diet generally have low food energy intakes and are thin. For pregnant women, this can be a problem. Women with low prepregnancy weights and small weight gains during pregnancy jeopardize a healthy pregnancy.

Vegan diets may require supplementation with vitamin B_{12}, calcium, and vitamin D, or the addition of foods fortified with these nutrients. Infants of vegan parents may suffer spinal cord damage and develop severe psychomotor retardation due to a lack of vitamin B_{12} in the mother's diet during pregnancy. Breastfed infants of vegan mothers have been reported to develop vitamin B_{12} deficiency and severe movement disorders. Giving the infants vitamin B_{12} supplements corrects the blood and neurological symptoms of deficiency, as well as the structural abnormalities, but cognitive and language development delays may persist. A vegan mother needs a regular source of vitamin B_{12}-fortified foods or a supplement that provides 2.6 micrograms daily.

A pregnant woman who cannot meet her calcium needs through diet alone may need 600 milligrams of supplemental calcium daily, taken with meals. Pregnant women who do not receive sufficient dietary vitamin D or enough exposure to sunlight may need a supplement that provides 10 micrograms daily.

Common Nutrition-Related Concerns of Pregnancy

Nausea, constipation, heartburn, and food sensitivities are common nutrition-related concerns during pregnancy. A few simple strategies can help alleviate maternal discomforts (see Table 15-2).

Nausea Not all women have queasy stomachs in the early months of pregnancy, but many do. The nausea of "morning sickness" may actually occur anytime and ranges from mild queasiness to debilitating nausea and vomiting. Severe and continued vomiting may require hospitalization if it results in acidosis, dehydration, or excessive weight loss. The hormonal changes of early pregnancy seem to be responsible for a woman's sensitivities to the appearance, texture, or smell of foods. Traditional strategies for quelling nausea are listed in Table 15-2, but some women

| TABLE 15-2 | Strategies to Alleviate Maternal Discomforts |

To Alleviate the Nausea of Pregnancy	To Prevent or Alleviate Constipation	To Prevent or Relieve Heartburn
• On waking, arise slowly. • Eat dry toast or crackers. • Chew gum or suck hard candies. • Eat small, frequent meals. • Avoid foods with offensive odors. • When nauseated, drink carbonated beverages instead of citrus juice, water, milk, coffee, or tea.	• Eat foods high in fiber (fruits, vegetables, and whole-grain cereals). • Exercise regularly. • Drink at least eight glasses of liquids a day. • Respond promptly to the urge to defecate. • Use laxatives only as prescribed by a physician; do not use mineral oil, because it interferes with absorption of fat-soluble vitamins.	• Relax and eat slowly. • Chew food thoroughly. • Eat small, frequent meals. • Drink liquids between meals. • Avoid spicy or greasy foods. • Sit up while eating; elevate the head while sleeping. • Wait an hour after eating before lying down. • Wait two hours after eating before exercising.

benefit most from resting when nauseous and simply eating the foods they want when they feel like eating. They may also find comfort in a cleaner, quieter, and more temperate environment.

Constipation and Hemorrhoids As the hormones of pregnancy alter muscle tone and the growing fetus crowds intestinal organs, an expectant mother may experience constipation. She may also develop hemorrhoids (swollen veins of the rectum). Hemorrhoids can be painful, and straining during bowel movements may cause bleeding. She can gain relief by following the strategies listed in Table 15-2.

Heartburn Heartburn is another common complaint during pregnancy. The hormones of pregnancy relax the digestive muscles, and the growing fetus puts increasing pressure on the mother's stomach. This combination allows stomach acid to back up into the lower esophagus, creating a burning sensation near the heart. Tips to help relieve heartburn are included in Table 15-2.

Food Cravings and Aversions Some women develop cravings for, or aversions to, particular foods and beverages during pregnancy. **Food cravings** and **food aversions** are fairly common, but they do not seem to reflect real physiological needs. In other words, a woman who craves pickles does not necessarily need salt. Similarly, cravings for ice cream are common in pregnancy but do not signify a calcium deficiency. Cravings and aversions that arise during pregnancy are most likely due to hormone-induced changes in sensitivity to taste and smell.

Nonfood Cravings Some pregnant women develop cravings for nonfood items ◆ such as freezer frost, laundry starch, clay, soil, or ice—a practice known as pica. Pica is a cultural phenomenon that reflects a society's folklore; it is especially common among African American women.[42] Pica is often associated with iron-deficiency anemia, but whether iron deficiency leads to pica or pica leads to iron deficiency is unclear. Eating clay or soil may interfere with iron absorption and displace iron-rich foods from the diet.

◆ Reminder: *Pica* is the general term for eating nonfood items. The specific craving for nonfood items that come from the earth, such as clay or dirt, is known as *geophagia*.

IN SUMMARY

Energy and nutrient needs are high during pregnancy. A balanced diet that includes an extra serving from each of the five food groups can usually meet these needs, with the possible exception of iron and folate (supplements are recommended). The nausea, constipation, and heartburn that sometimes accompany pregnancy can usually be alleviated with a few simple strategies. Food cravings do not typically reflect physiological needs.

◆ Nutrition advice in prenatal care:
• Eat well-balanced meals.
• Gain enough weight to support fetal growth.
• Take prenatal supplements as prescribed.
• Stop drinking alcohol.

High-Risk Pregnancies

Some pregnancies jeopardize the life and health of the mother and infant. Table 15-3 (p. 526) identifies several characteristics of a **high-risk pregnancy.** A woman with none of these risk factors is said to have a **low-risk pregnancy.** The more factors that apply, the higher the risk. All pregnant women, especially those in high-risk categories, need prenatal care, including dietary ◆ advice.

The Infant's Birthweight

A high-risk pregnancy is likely to produce an infant with **low birthweight.** Low-birthweight infants, defined as infants who weigh $5^1/_2$ pounds or less, are classified according to their gestational age. Preterm infants are born before they are fully developed; they are often underweight and have trouble breathing because their lungs are immature. Preterm infants may be small, but if their size and

food cravings: strong desires to eat particular foods.

food aversions: strong desires to avoid particular foods.

high-risk pregnancy: a pregnancy characterized by indicators that make it likely the birth will be surrounded by problems such as premature delivery, difficult birth, retarded growth, birth defects, and early infant death.

low-risk pregnancy: a pregnancy characterized by indicators that make a normal outcome likely.

low birthweight (LBW): a birthweight of 5 $^1/_2$ lb (2500 g) or less; indicates probable poor health in the newborn and poor nutrition status in the mother during pregnancy, before pregnancy, or both. Normal birthweight for a full-term baby is $6^1/_2$ to $8^3/_4$ lb (about 3000 to 4000 g).

Low-birthweight babies need special care and nourishment.

© Terry Vine/Getty Images

TABLE 15-3	High-Risk Pregnancy Factors
Factor	**Condition That Raises Risk**
Maternal weight	
• Prior to pregnancy	Prepregnancy BMI either <18.5 or >25
• During pregnancy	Insufficient or excessive pregnancy weight gain
Maternal nutrition	Nutrient deficiencies or toxicities; eating disorders
Socioeconomic status	Poverty, lack of family support, low level of education, limited food available
Lifestyle habits	Smoking, alcohol or other drug use
Age	Teens, especially 15 years or younger; women 35 years or older
Previous pregnancies	
• Number	Many previous pregnancies (3 or more to mothers under age 20; 4 or more to mothers age 20 or older)
• Interval	Short or long intervals between pregnancies (<18 months or >59 months)
• Outcomes	Previous history of problems
• Multiple births	Twins or triplets
• Birthweight	Low- or high-birthweight infants
Maternal health	
• High blood pressure	Development of pregnancy-related hypertension
• Diabetes	Development of gestational diabetes
• Chronic diseases	Diabetes; heart, respiratory, and kidney disease; certain genetic disorders; special diets and medications

◆ The weight of some preterm infants is **appropriate for gestational age (AGA)**; others are **small for gestational age (SGA)**, often reflecting malnutrition.

weight are appropriate for their age, ◆ they can catch up in growth given adequate nutrition support. In contrast, small-for-gestational-age infants have suffered growth failure in the uterus and do not catch up as well. For the most part, survival improves with increased gestational age and birthweight.

Low-birthweight infants are more likely to experience complications during delivery than normal-weight babies. They also have a statistically greater chance of having physical and mental birth defects, contracting diseases, and dying early in life. Of infants who die before their first birthdays, about two-thirds were low-birthweight newborns. Very-low-birthweight infants ($3^1/_2$ pounds or less) struggle not only for their immediate physical health and survival, but for their future cognitive development and abilities as well.

A strong relationship is evident between socioeconomic disadvantage and low birthweight. Low socioeconomic status impairs fetal development by causing stress and by limiting access to medical care and to nutritious foods. Low socioeconomic status often accompanies teen pregnancies, smoking, and alcohol and drug abuse—all predictors of low birthweight.

Malnutrition and Pregnancy

Good nutrition clearly supports a pregnancy. In contrast, malnutrition interferes with the ability to conceive, the likelihood of implantation, and the subsequent development of a fetus should conception and implantation occur.[43]

Malnutrition and Fertility The nutrition habits and lifestyle choices people make can influence the course of a pregnancy they are not even planning at the time. Severe malnutrition and food deprivation can reduce fertility because women may develop amenorrhea, ◆ and men may be unable to produce viable sperm. Furthermore, both men and women lose sexual interest during times of starvation. Starvation arises predictably during famines, wars, and droughts, but it can also occur amidst peace and plenty. Many young women who diet excessively are starving and suffering from malnutrition (see Highlight 8).

◆ Reminder: *Amenorrhea* is the temporary or permanent absence of menstrual periods. Amenorrhea is normal before puberty, after menopause, during pregnancy, and during lactation; otherwise it is abnormal.

Malnutrition and Early Pregnancy If a malnourished woman does become pregnant, she faces the challenge of supporting both the growth of a baby and her own health with inadequate nutrient stores. Malnutrition prior to and around conception prevents the placenta from developing fully. A poorly developed placenta cannot deliver optimum nourishment to the fetus, and the infant will be born small and possibly with physical and cognitive abnormalities. If this small infant is a female, she may develop poorly and have an elevated risk of developing a chronic condition that could impair her ability to give birth to a healthy infant. Thus a woman's malnutrition can adversely affect not only her children but her *grandchildren*.

Malnutrition and Fetal Development Without adequate nutrition during pregnancy, fetal growth and infant health are compromised. In general, consequences of malnutrition during pregnancy include fetal growth retardation, congenital malformations (birth defects), spontaneous abortion and stillbirth, preterm birth, and low infant birthweight. Preterm birth and low infant birthweight, in turn, predict the risk of stillbirth in a *subsequent* pregnancy.[44] Malnutrition, coupled with low birthweight, is a factor in more than half of all deaths of children under four years of age worldwide.

Food Assistance Programs

Women in high-risk pregnancies can find assistance from the WIC program—a high-quality, cost-effective health care and nutrition services program for women, infants, and children in the United States. Formally known as the Special Supplemental Nutrition Program for Women, Infants, and Children, WIC provides nutrition education and nutritious foods to infants, children up to age five, and pregnant and breastfeeding women who qualify financially and have a high risk of medical or nutritional problems. ◆ The program is both remedial and preventive: services include health care referrals, nutrition education, and food packages or vouchers for specific foods. These foods supply nutrients known to be lacking in the diets of the target population—most notably, protein, calcium, iron, vitamin A, and vitamin C. WIC-sponsored foods include tuna fish, carrots, eggs, milk, iron-fortified cereal, vitamin C-rich juice, cheese, legumes, peanut butter, and infant formula.

◆ WIC participants:
- $^1/_3$ of all pregnant women
- $^1/_2$ of all infants
- $^1/_4$ of all children ages 1–4 yr

More than 7 million people—most of them young children—receive WIC benefits each month. Prenatal WIC participation can effectively reduce infant mortality, low birthweight, and maternal and newborn medical costs. In 2003, Congress appropriated over $4.5 billion for WIC. For every dollar spent on WIC, an estimated three dollars in medical costs are saved in the first two months after birth.

Maternal Health

Medical disorders can threaten the life and health of both mother and fetus. If diagnosed and treated early, many diseases can be managed to ensure a healthy outcome—another strong argument for early prenatal care. Furthermore, the changes in pregnancy can reveal disease risks, making screening important and early intervention possible.[45]

Preexisting Diabetes Whether diabetes presents risks depends on how well it is controlled before and during pregnancy. Without proper management of maternal diabetes, women face high infertility rates, and those who do conceive may experience episodes of severe hypoglycemia or hyperglycemia, spontaneous abortions, and pregnancy-related hypertension. Infants may be large, suffer physical and mental abnormalities, and experience other complications such as severe hypoglycemia or respiratory distress, both of which can be fatal. Ideally, a woman with diabetes will receive the prenatal care needed to achieve glucose control before conception and continued glucose control throughout pregnancy.

Gestational Diabetes For every 14 women entering pregnancy without diabetes, one will develop a condition known as **gestational diabetes** during pregnancy. Gestational diabetes usually develops during the second half of pregnancy, with subsequent return to normal after childbirth. Some women with gestational diabetes, however, develop diabetes (usually type 2) after pregnancy, especially if they are overweight. For this reason, health care professionals strongly advise against excessive weight gain during pregnancy.

The most common consequences of gestational diabetes are complications during labor and delivery and a high infant birthweight.[46] Birth defects associated with gestational diabetes include heart damage, limb deformities, and neural tube defects. To ensure that the problems of gestational diabetes are dealt with promptly, physicians screen for the risk factors ◆ listed in the margin and test high-risk women for glucose intolerance immediately and average-risk women between 24 and 28 weeks gestation.[47] Dietary recommendations should meet the needs of pregnancy and maternal blood glucose goals.[48] To maintain normal blood glucose levels, carbohydrates should be restricted to 35 to 40 percent of energy intake. To limit excessive weight gain, obese women should limit energy intake to about 25 kcalories per kilogram body weight. Diet and moderate exercise may control gestational diabetes, but if blood glucose fails to normalize, insulin or other drugs may be required. Importantly, treatment reduces birth complications, infant deaths, and maybe even postpartum depression.[49]

Preexisting Hypertension Hypertension complicates pregnancy and affects its outcome in different ways, depending on when the hypertension first develops and on how severe it becomes. In addition to the threats hypertension always carries (such as heart attack and stroke), high blood pressure increases the risks of a low-birthweight infant or the separation of the placenta from the wall of the uterus before the birth, resulting in stillbirth. Ideally, before a woman with hypertension becomes pregnant, her blood pressure is under control.

Transient Hypertension of Pregnancy Some women develop hypertension during the second half of pregnancy.* Most often, the rise in blood pressure is mild and does not affect the pregnancy adversely. Blood pressure usually returns to normal during the first few weeks after childbirth. This **transient hypertension of pregnancy** differs from the life-threatening hypertensive diseases ◆ of pregnancy —preeclampsia and eclampsia.

Preeclampsia and Eclampsia Hypertension may signal the onset of **preeclampsia,** a condition characterized not only by high blood pressure but also by protein in the urine and fluid retention (edema). The edema ◆ of preeclampsia is a whole-body edema, distinct from the localized fluid retention women normally experience late in pregnancy.

The cause of preeclampsia remains unclear, but it usually occurs with first pregnancies ◆ and most often after 20 weeks gestation.[50] Symptoms typically regress within two days of delivery. Both men and women who were born of pregnancies complicated by preeclampsia are more likely to have a child born of a pregnancy complicated by preeclampsia, suggesting a genetic predisposition. Black women have a much greater risk of preeclampsia than white women.

Preeclampsia affects almost all of the mother's organs—the circulatory system, liver, kidneys, and brain. Blood flow through the vessels that supply oxygen and nutrients to the placenta diminishes. For this reason, preeclampsia often retards fetal growth. In some cases, the placenta separates from the uterus, resulting in preterm birth or stillbirth.

Preeclampsia can progress rapidly to **eclampsia**—a condition characterized by convulsive seizures and coma. Maternal death during pregnancy and childbirth is

---

◆ Risk factors for gestational diabetes:
- Age 25 or older
- BMI >25 or excessive weight gain
- Complications in previous pregnancies, including gestational diabetes or high-birthweight infant
- Prediabetes or symptoms of diabetes
- Family history of diabetes
- Hispanic, black, Native American, South or East Asian, Pacific Islander, or indigenous Australian

◆ The hypertensive diseases of pregnancy are sometimes called **toxemia.**

◆ The normal edema of pregnancy responds to gravity; fluid pools in the ankles. The edema of preeclampsia is a generalized edema. The differences between these two types of edema help with the diagnosis of preeclampsia.

◆ Warning signs of preeclampsia:
- Hypertension
- Protein in the urine
- Upper abdominal pain
- Severe and constant headaches
- Swelling, especially of the face
- Dizziness
- Blurred vision
- Sudden weight gain (1 lb/day)
- Fetal growth retardation

gestational diabetes: abnormal glucose tolerance during pregnancy.

transient hypertension of pregnancy: high blood pressure that develops in the second half of pregnancy and resolves after childbirth, usually without affecting the outcome of the pregnancy.

preeclampsia (PRE-ee-KLAMP-see-ah): a condition characterized by hypertension, fluid retention, and protein in the urine; formerly known as *pregnancy-induced hypertension.**

eclampsia (eh-KLAMP-see-ah): a severe stage of preeclampsia characterized by convulsions.

* The Working Group on High Blood Pressure in Pregnancy, convened by the National High Blood Pressure Education Program of the National Heart, Lung, and Blood Institute, suggested abandoning the term *pregnancy-induced hypertension* because it failed to differentiate between the mild, transient hypertension of pregnancy and the life-threatening hypertension of preeclampsia.

---

* Blood pressure of 140/90 millimeters mercury or greater during the second half of pregnancy in a woman who has not previously exhibited hypertension indicates high blood pressure. So does a rise in systolic blood pressure of 30 millimeters or in diastolic blood pressure of 15 millimeters on at least two occasions more than six hours apart. By this rule, an apparently "normal" blood pressure of 120/85 is high for a woman whose normal value is 90/70.

extremely rare in developed countries, but when it does occur, eclampsia is a common cause. The rate of death for black women with eclampsia is more than four times the rate for white women.

Preeclampsia demands prompt medical attention. Treatment focuses on controlling blood pressure and preventing convulsions. If preeclampsia develops early and is severe, induced labor or cesarean section may be necessary, regardless of gestational age. The infant will be preterm, with all of the associated problems, including poor lung development and special care needs. Several dietary factors have been studied, but none have proved conclusive in preventing preeclampsia. Limited research suggests that exercise may protect against preeclampsia by stimulating placenta growth and vascularity and reducing oxidative stress.[51]

The Mother's Age

Maternal age also influences the course of a pregnancy. Compared with women of the physically ideal childbearing age of 20 to 25, both younger and older women face more complications of pregnancy.

Pregnancy in Adolescents Many adolescents become sexually active before age 19, and approximately 900,000 adolescent girls face pregnancies each year in the United States; slightly more than half of them give birth.[52] Nourishing a growing fetus adds to a teenage girl's nutrition burden, especially if her growth is still incomplete. Simply being young increases the risks of pregnancy complications independently of important socioeconomic factors.

Common complications among adolescent mothers include iron-deficiency anemia (which may reflect poor diet and inadequate prenatal care) and prolonged labor (which reflects the mother's physical immaturity). On a positive note, maternal death is lowest for mothers under age 20.

Pregnant teenagers have higher rates of stillbirths, preterm births, and low-birthweight infants than do adult women. Many of these infants suffer physical problems, require intensive care, and die within the first year. The care of infants born to teenagers costs our society an estimated $1 billion annually. Because teenagers have few financial resources, they cannot pay these costs. Furthermore, their low economic status contributes significantly to the complications surrounding their pregnancies. At a time when prenatal care is most important, it is less accessible. And the pattern of teenage pregnancies continues from generation to generation, with almost 40 percent of the daughters born to teenage mothers becoming teenage mothers themselves. Clearly, teenage pregnancy is a major public health problem.

To support the needs of both mother and fetus, young teenagers (13 to 16 years old) are encouraged to strive for the highest weight gains recommended for pregnancy. For a teen who enters pregnancy at a healthy body weight, a weight gain of approximately 35 pounds is recommended; this amount minimizes the risk of delivering a low-birthweight infant. Gaining less weight may limit fetal growth. Pregnant and lactating teenagers can use the USDA Food Guide presented in Table 2-3 and Figure 2-1 (pp. 41–43), making sure to select a high enough kcalorie level to support adequate weight gain.

Without the appropriate economic, social, and physical support, a young mother will not be able to care for herself during her pregnancy and for her child after the birth. To improve her chances for a successful pregnancy and a healthy infant, she must seek prenatal care. WIC helps pregnant teenagers obtain adequate food for themselves and their infants. (WIC is introduced on p. 527.)

Pregnancy in Older Women In the last several decades, many women have delayed childbearing while they pursue education and careers. As a result, the number of first births to women 35 and older has increased dramatically. Most of these women, even those over age 50, have healthy pregnancies.[53]

The few complications associated with later childbearing often reflect chronic conditions such as hypertension and diabetes, which can complicate an otherwise healthy pregnancy. These complications may result in a cesarean section, which is twice as common in women over 35 as among younger women. For all these reasons, maternal death rates are higher in women over 35 than in younger women.

The babies of older mothers face problems of their own including higher rates of preterm births and low birthweight.[54] Their rates of birth defects are also high. Because 1 out of 50 pregnancies in older women produces an infant with genetic abnormalities, obstetricians routinely screen women older than 35. For a 40-year-old mother, the risk of having a child with **Down syndrome,** for example, is about 1 in 100 compared with 1 in 300 for a 35-year-old and 1 in 10,000 for a 20-year-old. In addition, fetal death is twice as high for women 35 years and older than for younger women. Why this is so remains a bit of a mystery. One possibility is that the uterine blood vessels of older women may not fully adapt to the increased demands of pregnancy.

Practices Incompatible with Pregnancy

Besides malnutrition, a variety of lifestyle factors can have adverse effects on pregnancy, and some may be teratogenic. ◆ People who are planning to have children can make the choice to practice healthy behaviors.

Alcohol One out of ten pregnant women drinks alcohol at some time during her pregnancy; 1 out of 50 drinks frequently.[55] Alcohol consumption during pregnancy can cause irreversible mental and physical retardation of the fetus—fetal alcohol syndrome (FAS). Of the leading causes of mental retardation, FAS is the only one that is totally *preventable*. To that end, the surgeon general urges all pregnant women to refrain from drinking alcohol. Fetal alcohol syndrome is the topic of Highlight 15, which includes mention of how alcohol consumption by men may also affect fertility and fetal development.

Medicinal Drugs Drugs other than alcohol can also cause complications during pregnancy, problems in labor, and serious birth defects. For these reasons, pregnant women should not take any medicines without consulting their physicians, who must weigh the benefits against the risks.

Herbal Supplements Similarly, pregnant women should seek a physician's advice before using herbal supplements. Women sometimes seek herbal preparations during their pregnancies to quell nausea, induce labor, aid digestion, promote water loss, support restful sleep, and fight depression. As Highlight 18 explains, some herbs may be safe, but many others are definitely harmful.

Illicit Drugs The recommendation to avoid drugs during pregnancy also includes illicit drugs, of course. Unfortunately, use of illicit drugs, such as cocaine and marijuana, is common among some pregnant women.

Drugs of abuse, such as cocaine, easily cross the placenta and impair fetal growth and development. Furthermore, they are responsible for preterm births, low-birthweight infants, perinatal deaths, ◆ and sudden infant deaths. If these newborns survive, central nervous system damage is evident: their cries, sleep, and behaviors early in life are abnormal, and their cognitive development later in life is impaired.[56] They may be hypersensitive or underaroused; those who test positive for drugs suffer the greatest effects of toxicity and withdrawal.

Smoking and Chewing Tobacco Unfortunately, an estimated one out of nine pregnant women in the United States smokes, with higher rates for older teens.[57] Smoking cigarettes and chewing tobacco at any time exert harmful effects, and pregnancy dramatically magnifies the hazards of these practices. Smoking restricts the blood supply to the growing fetus and thus limits oxygen and nutrient delivery and waste removal. A mother who smokes is more likely to have a complicated birth and a low-birthweight infant. Indeed, of all preventable causes of low birthweight in the United States, smoking is at the top of the list. Although, most infants born to cigarette smokers are low birthweight, some are not, suggesting that the effect of smoking on birthweight also depends, in part, on genes involved in the metabolism of smoking toxins.[58]

◆ Reminder: The word *teratogenic* describes a factor that causes abnormal fetal development and birth defects.

◆ The word *perinatal* refers to the time between the 28th week of gestation and 1 month after birth.

Down syndrome: a genetic abnormality that causes mental retardation, short stature, and flattened facial features.

In addition to contributing to low birthweight, smoking interferes with lung growth and increases the risks of respiratory infections and childhood asthma.[59] It can also cause death in an otherwise healthy fetus or newborn. A positive relationship exists between **sudden infant death syndrome (SIDS)** and both cigarette smoking during pregnancy and postnatal exposure to passive smoke.[60] Smoking during pregnancy may even harm the intellectual and behavioral development of the child later in life. The margin ◆ lists other complications of smoking during pregnancy.

Infants of mothers who chew tobacco also have low birthweights and high rates of fetal deaths. Any woman who smokes cigarettes or chews tobacco and is considering pregnancy or who is already pregnant should try to quit.

Environmental Contaminants Proving that environmental contaminants cause reproductive damage is difficult, but evidence in wildlife is established and seems likely for human beings.[61] Infants and young children of pregnant women exposed to environmental contaminants such as lead show signs of delayed mental and psychomotor development. During pregnancy, lead readily moves across the placenta, inflicting severe damage on the developing fetal nervous system.[62] In addition, infants exposed to even low levels of lead during gestation weigh less at birth and consequently struggle to survive. For these reasons, it is particularly important that pregnant women receive foods and beverages grown and prepared in environments free of contamination. A diet high in calcium will help to defend against lead contamination, and breastfeeding may help to counterbalance developmental damage incurred from contamination during pregnancy.[63]

Mercury is among the contaminants of concern. As Chapter 5 mentioned, fatty fish are a good source of omega-3 fatty acids, but some fish contain large amounts of the pollutant mercury, which can harm the developing brain and nervous system.[64] Because the benefits of moderate fish consumption outweigh the risks, pregnant (and lactating) women should do the following:[65]

- Avoid shark, swordfish, king mackerel, and tilefish (also called golden snapper or golden bass).
- Limit average weekly consumption to 12 ounces (cooked or canned) of seafood *or* to 6 ounces (cooked or canned) of white (albacore) tuna.

Supplements of fish oil are not recommended because they may contain concentrated toxins and because their effects on pregnancy remain unknown.

Foodborne Illness As Chapter 19 explains, foodborne illnesses arise when people eat foods that contain infectious microbes or microbes that produce toxins. At best, the vomiting and diarrhea associated with these illnesses can leave a pregnant woman exhausted and dehydrated; at worse, foodborne illnesses can cause meningitis, pneumonia, or even fetal death. Pregnant women are about 20 times more likely than other healthy adults to get the foodborne illness **listeriosis**. The margin ◆ presents tips to prevent listeriosis, and Chapter 19 includes precautions to minimize the risks of other common foodborne illness.

Dietary Guidelines for Americans 2005

- Pregnant women should not eat or drink unpasteurized milk, milk products, or juices; raw or undercooked eggs, meat, or poultry; or raw sprouts.
- Pregnant women should only eat certain deli meats and frankfurters that have been reheated to steaming hot.

Vitamin-Mineral Megadoses The pregnant woman who is trying to eat well may mistakenly assume that more is better when it comes to vitamin-mineral supplements. This is simply not true; many vitamins and minerals are toxic when taken

◆ Complications associated with smoking during pregnancy:
- Fetal growth retardation
- Low birthweight
- Complications at birth (prolonged final stage of labor)
- Mislocation of the placenta
- Premature separation of the placenta
- Vaginal bleeding
- Spontaneous abortion
- Fetal death
- Sudden infant death syndrome (SIDS)
- Middle ear diseases
- Cardiac and respiratory diseases

◆ Listeriosis can be prevented in the following ways:
- Use only pasteurized juices and dairy products; avoid Mexican soft cheeses, feta cheese, brie, Camembert, and blue-veined cheeses such as Roquefort.
- Thoroughly cook meat, poultry, eggs, and seafood.
- Thoroughly reheat hot dogs, luncheon meats, and deli meats, including cured meats such as salami.
- Wash all fruits and vegetables.
- Avoid refrigerated pâté, meat spreads, smoked seafood such as salmon or trout, and any fish labeled "nova," "lox," or "kippered," unless prepared in a cooked dish.

sudden infant death syndrome (SIDS): the unexpected and unexplained death of an apparently well infant; the most common cause of death of infants between the second week and the end of the first year of life; also called *crib death.*

listeriosis: an infection caused by eating food contaminated with the bacterium *Listeria monocytogenes,* which can be killed by pasteurization and cooking but can survive at refrigerated temperatures; certain ready-to-eat foods, such as hot dogs and deli meats, may become contaminated after cooking or processing, but before packaging.

Breastfeeding: A Learned Behavior

Lactation is an automatic physiological process that virtually all mothers are capable of doing. Breastfeeding, on the other hand, is a learned behavior that not all mothers decide to do. Of women who do breastfeed, those who receive early and repeated information and support breastfeed their infants longer than others. Health care professionals ◆ play an important role in providing encouragement and accurate information on breastfeeding.[71] Women who have been successful breastfeeding can offer advice and dispel misperceptions about lifestyle issues. Table 15-5 lists ten steps maternity facilities and health care professionals can take to promote successful breastfeeding among new mothers.[72]

The mother's partner also plays an important role in encouraging breastfeeding.[73] When partners support the decision, mothers are more likely to start and continue breastfeeding. Clearly, educating those closest to the mother could change attitudes and promote breastfeeding.

Most healthy women who want to breastfeed can do so with a little preparation. Physical obstacles to breastfeeding are rare, although most nursing mothers quit before the recommended six months because of perceived difficulties.[74] Obese mothers seem to have a particularly difficult time, perhaps because of reduced prolactin levels.[75] Successful breastfeeding requires adequate nutrition and rest. This, plus the support of all who care, will help to enhance the well-being of mother and infant.

◆ Some hospitals employ *certified lactation consultants* who specialize in helping new mothers establish a healthy breastfeeding relationship with their newborn. These consultants are often registered nurses with specialized training in breast and infant anatomy and physiology.

Maternal Energy and Nutrient Needs during Lactation

Ideally, the mother who chooses to breastfeed her infant will continue to eat nutrient-dense foods throughout lactation. An adequate diet is needed to support the stamina, patience, and self-confidence that nursing an infant demands.

Energy Intake and Exercise A nursing mother produces about 25 ounces of milk per day, with considerable variation from woman to woman and in the same woman from time to time, depending primarily on the infant's demand for milk. To produce an adequate supply of milk, a woman needs extra energy—almost 500

TABLE 15-5	Ten Steps to Successful Breastfeeding

To promote breastfeeding, every maternity facility should:

- Develop a written breastfeeding policy that is routinely communicated to all health care staff
- Train all health care staff in the skills necessary to implement the breastfeeding policy
- Inform all pregnant women about the benefits and management of breastfeeding
- Help mothers initiate breastfeeding within ½ hour of birth
- Show mothers how to breastfeed and how to maintain lactation, even if they need to be separated from their infants
- Give newborn infants no food or drink other than breast milk, unless medically indicated
- Practice rooming-in, allowing mothers and infants to remain together 24 hours a day
- Encourage breastfeeding on demand
- Give no artificial nipples or pacifiers to breastfeeding infants[a]
- Foster the establishment of breastfeeding support groups and refer mothers to them at discharge from the facility

[a]Compared with nonusers, infants who use pacifiers breastfeed less frequently and stop breastfeeding at a younger age. C. G. Victora and coauthors, Pacifier use and short breastfeeding duration: Cause, consequence, or coincidence? *Pediatrics* 99 (1997): 445–453.
SOURCE: United Nations Children's Fund and World Health Organization, *Protecting, Promoting and Supporting Breastfeeding: The Special Role of Maternity Services.*

A jog through the park provides an opportunity for physical activity and fresh air.

© Randy M. Ury/Corbis

kcalories a day above her regular need during the first six months of lactation. To meet this energy need, ◆ she can eat an extra 330 kcalories of food each day and let the fat reserves she accumulated during pregnancy provide the rest. Most women need at least 1800 kcalories a day to receive all the nutrients required for successful lactation. Severe energy restriction may hinder milk production.

After the birth of the infant, many women actively try to lose the extra weight and body fat they accumulated during pregnancy.[76] Opinions differ as to whether breastfeeding helps with postpartum weight loss. Lactating women may lose body *fat* more slowly than nonlactating women, but the rate of *weight* loss is about the same.[77] In general, most women lose one to two pounds a month during the first four to six months of lactation; some may lose more, and others may maintain or even gain weight. Neither the quality nor the quantity of breast milk is adversely affected by moderate weight loss, and infants grow normally.

◆ Energy requirement during lactation:
• 1st 6 mo: +330 kcal/day
• 2nd 6 mo: +400 kcal/day

Dietary Guidelines for Americans 2005

Moderate weight reduction is safe for breastfeeding women and does not compromise weight gain of the nursing infant.

Women often exercise to lose weight and improve fitness, and this is compatible with breastfeeding and infant growth. Because intense physical activity can raise the lactate concentration of breast milk and influence the milk's taste, some infants may prefer milk produced prior to exercise. In these cases, mothers can either breastfeed before exercise or express their milk before exercise for use afterward.

Dietary Guidelines for Americans 2005

Neither acute nor regular exercise adversely affects the mother's ability to successfully breastfeed.

Energy Nutrients Recommendations for protein and fatty acids intakes remain about the same during lactation as during pregnancy, but they increase for carbohydrates and fibers. Nursing mothers need additional carbohydrate to replace the glucose used to make the lactose in breast milk. The fiber recommendation is 1 gram higher simply because it is based on kcalorie intake, which increases during lactation.

Vitamins and Minerals A question often raised is whether a mother's milk may lack a nutrient if she fails to get enough in her diet. The answer differs from one nutrient to the next, but in general, nutritional inadequacies reduce the *quantity,* not the *quality,* of breast milk. Women can produce milk with adequate protein, carbohydrate, fat, and most minerals, even when their own supplies are limited. For these nutrients and for the vitamin folate as well, milk quality is maintained at the expense of maternal stores. This is most evident in the case of calcium: dietary calcium has no effect on the calcium concentration of breast milk, but maternal bones lose some density during lactation if calcium intakes are inadequate.[78] Bone density increases again when lactation ends; breastfeeding has no long-term harmful effects on bones.[79] The nutrients in breast milk that are most likely to decline in response to prolonged inadequate intakes are the vitamins—especially vitamins B_6, B_{12}, A, and D. Review Figure 15-10 (p. 521) to compare a lactating woman's nutrient needs with those of pregnant and nonpregnant women.

Water Despite misconceptions, a mother who drinks more fluid does not produce more breast milk. To protect herself from dehydration, however, a lactating woman

Nutritious foods support successful lactation.

◆ AI for *total* water (including drinking water, other beverages, and foods) during lactation: 3.8 L/day

needs to drink plenty of fluids. ◆ A sensible guideline is to drink a glass of milk, juice, or water at each meal and each time the infant nurses.

Nutrient Supplements Most lactating women can obtain all the nutrients they need from a well-balanced diet without taking vitamin-mineral supplements. Nevertheless, some may need iron supplements, not to enhance the iron in their breast milk, but to refill their depleted iron stores. The mother's iron stores dwindle during pregnancy as she supplies the developing fetus with enough iron to last through the first four to six months of the infant's life. In addition, childbirth may have incurred blood losses. Thus woman may need iron supplements during lactation even though, until menstruation resumes, her iron requirement is about half that of other nonpregnant women her age.

Food Assistance Programs In general, women most likely to participate in the food assistance program WIC—those who are poor and have little education—are less likely to breastfeed. Furthermore, WIC provides infant formula at no cost. Because WIC recognizes the many benefits of breastfeeding, efforts are made to overcome this dilemma. In addition to nutrition education, breastfeeding mothers receive the following WIC incentives:

- Higher priority in certification into WIC
- Longer eligibility to participate in WIC
- More foods and larger quantities
- Breast pumps and other support materials

Together, these efforts help to provide nutrition support and encourage WIC mothers to breastfeed.

Particular Foods Foods with strong or spicy flavors (such as garlic) may alter the flavor of breast milk. A sudden change in the taste of the milk may annoy some infants. Familiar flavors may enhance enjoyment.

Infants who develop symptoms of food allergy may be more comfortable if the mother's diet excludes the most common offenders—cow's milk, eggs, fish, peanuts, and tree nuts. Generally, infants with a strong family history of food allergies benefit from breastfeeding.

A nursing mother can usually eat whatever nutritious foods she chooses. If she suspects a particular food is causing the infant discomfort, her physician may recommend a dietary challenge: eliminate the food from the diet to see if the infant's reactions subside; then return the food to the diet, and again monitor the infant's reactions. If a food must be eliminated for an extended time, appropriate substitutions must be made to ensure nutrient adequacy.

Maternal Health

If a woman has an ordinary cold, she can continue nursing without worry. If susceptible, the infant will catch it from her anyway. (Thanks to the immunological protection of breast milk, the baby may be less susceptible than a formula-fed baby would be.) With appropriate treatment, a woman who has an infectious disease such as tuberculosis or hepatitis can breastfeed; transmission is rare.[80] Women with HIV (human immunodeficiency virus) infections, however, should consider other options.

HIV Infection and AIDS Mothers with HIV infections can transmit the virus (which causes AIDS) to their infants through breast milk, especially during the early months of breastfeeding.[81] Where safe alternatives are available, HIV-positive women should *not* breastfeed their infants. In developing countries, where the feeding of inappropriate or contaminated formulas causes 1.5 million infant deaths each year, the decision is less obvious. To prevent the mother-to-child transmission of HIV, WHO and UNICEF urge mothers in developing countries *not* to breastfeed. However, they stress the importance of finding suitable feeding alternatives to prevent the malnutrition, disease, and death that commonly occur when women in these countries do not breastfeed.

Diabetes Women with diabetes (type 1) may need careful monitoring and counseling to ensure successful lactation. These women need to adjust their energy intakes and insulin doses to meet the heightened needs of lactation. Maintaining good glucose control helps to initiate lactation and support milk production.

Postpartum Amenorrhea Women who breastfeed experience prolonged **postpartum amenorrhea.** Absent menstrual periods, however, do not protect a woman from pregnancy. To prevent pregnancy, a couple must use some form of contraception. Breastfeeding women who use oral contraceptives should use progestin-only agents for at least the first six months.[82] Estrogen-containing oral contraceptives reduce the volume and the protein content of breast milk.

Breast Health Some women fear that breastfeeding will cause their breasts to sag. The breasts do swell and become heavy and large immediately after the birth, but even when they produce enough milk to nourish a thriving infant, they eventually shrink back to their prepregnant size. Given proper support, diet, and exercise, breasts often return to their former shape and size when lactation ends. Breasts change their shape as the body ages, but breastfeeding does not accelerate this process.

Whether the physical and hormonal events of pregnancy and lactation protect women from later breast cancer is an area of active research.[83] Some research suggests no association between breastfeeding and breast cancer, whereas other research suggests a protective effect. Protection against breast cancer is most apparent for premenopausal women who were young when they breastfed and who breastfed for a long time.

Practices Incompatible with Lactation

Some substances impair milk production or enter breast milk and interfere with infant development. This section discusses practices that a breastfeeding mother should avoid.

Alcohol Alcohol easily enters breast milk, and its concentration peaks within an hour of ingestion. Infants drink less breast milk when their mothers have consumed even small amounts of alcohol (equivalent to a can of beer). Three possible reasons, acting separately or together, may explain why. For one, the alcohol may have altered the flavor of the breast milk and thereby the infants' acceptance of it. For another, because infants metabolize alcohol inefficiently, even low doses may be potent enough to suppress their feeding and cause sleepiness. Third, the alcohol may have interfered with lactation by inhibiting the hormone oxytocin.

In the past, alcohol has been recommended to mothers to facilitate lactation despite a lack of scientific evidence that it does so. The research summarized here suggests that alcohol actually hinders breastfeeding. An occasional alcoholic beverage may be within safe limits, but breastfeeding should be avoided for at least two hours afterwards.

Medicinal Drugs Most medicines are compatible with breastfeeding, but some are contraindicated, either because they suppress lactation or because they are secreted into breast milk and can harm the infant.[84] As a precaution, a nursing mother should consult with her physician prior to taking any drug, including herbal supplements.

Illicit Drugs Illicit drugs, of course, are harmful to the physical and emotional health of both the mother and the nursing infant. Breast milk can deliver such high doses of illicit drugs as to cause irritability, tremors, hallucinations, and even death in infants. Women whose infants have overdosed on illicit drugs contained in breast milk have been convicted of murder.

postpartum amenorrhea: the normal temporary absence of menstrual periods immediately following childbirth.

Smoking Because cigarette smoking reduces milk volume, smokers may produce too little milk to meet their infants' energy needs. The milk they do produce contains nicotine, which alters its smell and flavor. Consequently, infants of breastfeeding mothers who smoke gain less weight than infants of those who do not smoke. Furthermore, infant exposure to passive smoke negates the protective effect breastfeeding offers against SIDS and increases the risks dramatically.

Environmental Contaminants Chapter 19 discusses environmental contaminants in the food supply. Some of these environmental contaminants, such as DDT, PCBs, and dioxin, can find their way into breast milk. Inuit mothers living in Arctic Québec who eat seal and beluga whale blubber have high concentrations of DDT and PCBs in their breast milk, but the impact on infant development is unclear. Preliminary studies indicate that the children of these Inuit mothers are developing normally. Researchers speculate that the abundant omega-3 fatty acids of the Inuit diet may protect against damage to the central nervous system. Breast milk tainted with dioxins interferes with tooth development during early infancy, producing soft, mottled teeth that are vulnerable to dental caries. To limit mercury intake, lactating women should heed the fish restrictions mentioned earlier for pregnant women (see p. 531).

Caffeine Caffeine enters breast milk and may make an infant irritable and wakeful. As during pregnancy, caffeine consumption should be moderate—the equivalent of one to two cups of coffee a day. Larger doses of caffeine may interfere with the bioavailability of iron from breast milk and impair the infant's iron status.

IN SUMMARY

The lactating woman needs extra fluid and enough energy and nutrients to produce about 25 ounces of milk a day. Breastfeeding is contraindicated for those with HIV/AIDS. Alcohol, other drugs, smoking, and contaminants may reduce milk production or enter breast milk and impair infant development.

This chapter has focused on the nutrition needs of the mother during pregnancy and lactation. The next chapter explores the dietary needs of infants, children, and adolescents.

ThomsonNOW™
www.thomsonedu.com/thomsonnow

Nutrition Portfolio

The choices a woman makes in preparation for, and in support of, pregnancy and lactation can influence both her health and her infant's development—today and for decades to come.

■ For women of childbearing age, determine whether you consume at least 400 micrograms of dietary folate equivalents daily.

■ For women who are pregnant, evaluate whether you are meeting your nutrition needs and gaining the amount of weight recommended.

■ For women who are about to give birth, carefully consider all the advantages of breastfeeding your infant and obtain the needed advice to support you.

NUTRITION ON THE NET

ThomsonNOW™
For further study of topics covered in this chapter, log on to www.thomsonedu
.com/thomsonnow. Go to Chapter 15, then to Nutrition on the Net.

- Visit the pregnancy and child health center of the Mayo Clinic: **www.mayohealth.org**
- Learn more about having a healthy baby and about birth defects from the March of Dimes and the National Center on Birth Defects and Developmental Disabilities: **www.modimes.org** and **www.cdc.gov/ncbddd**
- Learn more about neural tube defects from the Spina Bifida Association of America: **www.sbaa.org**
- Search for "birth defects," "pregnancy," "adolescent pregnancy," "maternal and infant health," and "breastfeeding" at the U.S. Government health information site: **www.healthfinder.gov**

- Search for "pregnancy" at the American Dietetic Association site: **www.eatright.org**
- Learn more about the WIC program: **www.fns.usda.gov/fns**
- Visit the American College of Obstetricians and Gynecologists: **www.acog.org**
- Learn more about gestational diabetes from the American Diabetes Association: **www.diabetes.org**
- Learn more about breastfeeding from LaLeche League International: **www.lalecheleague.org**
- Obtain prenatal nutrition guidelines from Health Canada: **www.hc-sc.gc.ca**

STUDY QUESTIONS

ThomsonNOW™
To assess your understanding of chapter topics, take the Student Practice Test and explore the modules recommended in your Personalized Study Plan. Log onto www.thomsonedu.com/thomsonnow.

These questions will help you review the chapter. You will find the answers in the discussions on the pages provided.

1. Describe the placenta and its function. (p. 510)
2. Describe the normal events of fetal development. How does malnutrition impair fetal development? (pp. 510–512, 527)
3. Define the term *critical period*. How do adverse influences during critical periods affect later health? (pp. 512–515)
4. Explain why women of childbearing age need folate in their diets. How much is recommended, and how can women ensure that these needs are met? (pp. 513–515)
5. What is the recommended pattern of weight gain during pregnancy for a woman at a healthy weight? For an underweight woman? For an overweight woman? (pp. 516–518)
6. What does a pregnant woman need to know about exercise? (pp. 518–519)
7. Which nutrients are needed in the greatest amounts during pregnancy? Why are they so important? Describe wise food choices for the pregnant woman. (pp. 519–523)
8. Define low-risk and high-risk pregnancies. What is the significance of infant birthweight in terms of the child's future health? (pp. 525–526)
9. Describe some of the special problems of the pregnant adolescent. Which nutrients are needed in increased amounts? (p. 529)
10. What practices should be avoided during pregnancy? Why? (pp. 530–532)
11. How do nutrient needs during lactation differ from nutrient needs during pregnancy? (pp. 521, 534–536)

These multiple choice questions will help you prepare for an exam. Answers can be found on p. 542.

1. The spongy structure that delivers nutrients to the fetus and returns waste products to the mother is called the:
   a. embryo.
   b. uterus.
   c. placenta.
   d. amniotic sac.
2. Which of these strategies is *not* a healthy option for an overweight woman?
   a. Limit weight gain during pregnancy.
   b. Postpone weight loss until after pregnancy.
   c. Follow a weight-loss diet during pregnancy.
   d. Try to achieve a healthy weight before becoming pregnant.
3. A reasonable weight gain during pregnancy for a normal-weight woman is about:
   a. 10 pounds.
   b. 20 pounds.
   c. 30 pounds.
   d. 40 pounds.
4. Energy needs during pregnancy increase by about:
   a. 100 kcalories/day.
   b. 300 kcalories/day.
   c. 500 kcalories/day.
   d. 700 kcalories/day.

5. To help prevent neural tube defects, grain products are now fortified with:
   a. iron.
   b. folate.
   c. protein.
   d. vitamin C.

6. Pregnant women should *not* take supplements of:
   a. iron.
   b. folate.
   c. vitamin A.
   d. vitamin C.

7. The combination of high blood pressure, protein in the urine, and edema signals:
   a. jaundice.
   b. preeclampsia.
   c. gestational diabetes.
   d. gestational hypertension.

8. To facilitate lactation, a mother needs:
   a. about 5000 kcalories a day.
   b. adequate nutrition and rest.
   c. vitamin and mineral supplements.
   d. a glass of wine or beer before each feeding.

9. A breastfeeding woman should drink plenty of water to:
   a. produce more milk.
   b. suppress lactation.
   c. prevent dehydration.
   d. dilute nutrient concentration.

10. A woman may need iron supplements during lactation:
   a. to enhance the iron in her breast milk.
   b. to provide iron for the infant's growth.
   c. to replace the iron in her body's stores.
   d. to support the increase in her blood volume.

REFERENCES

1. Recommendations to improve preconception health and health care—United States, *Morbidity and Mortality Weekly Report* 55 (2006): 1-23.
2. M. J. Davies, Evidence for effects of weight on reproduction in women, *Reproductive Biomedicine Online* 12 (2006): 552-561.
3. M. Sallmen and coauthors, Reduced fertility among overweight and obese men, *Epidemiology* 17 (2006): 520-523; H. I. Kort and coauthors, Impact of body mass index values on sperm quantity and quality, *Journal of Andrology* 27 (2006): 450-452.
4. R. Pasquali and A. Gambineri, Metabolic effects of obesity on reproduction, *Reproductive Biomedicine Online* 12 (2006): 542-551.
5. R. M. Sharpe and S. Franks, Environment, lifestyle and infertility—An inter-generational issue, *Nature Cell Biology* 4 (2002): s33-s40.
6. J. C. Cross and L. Mickelson, Nutritional influences on implantation and placental development, *Nutrition Reviews* 64 (2006): S12-S18.
7. R. Padmanabhan, Etiology, pathogenesis and prevention of neural tube defects, *Congenital Anomalies* 46 (2006): 55-67.
8. K. A. Bol, J. S. Collins, and R. S. Kirby, Survival of infants with neural tube defects in the presence of folic acid fortification, *Pediatrics* 117 (2006): 803-813; T. Tamura and M. F. Picciano, Folate and human reproduction, *American Journal of Clinical Nutrition* 83 (2006): 993-1016; L. B. Bailey and R. J. Berry, Folic acid supplementation and the occurrence of congenital heart defects, orofacial clefts, multiple births, and miscarriage, *American Journal of Clinical Nutrition* 81 (2005): 1213S-1217S.
9. Spina bifida and anencephaly before and after folic acid mandate—United States, 1995-1996 and 1999-2000, *Morbidity and Mortality Weekly Report* 53 (2004): 362-365; J. Erickson, Folic acid and prevention of spina bifida and anencephaly, *Morbidity and Mortality Weekly Report* 51 (2002): 1-3.
10. R. L. Brent and G. P. Oakley, The folate debate, *Pediatrics* 117 (2006): 1418-1419; J. I. Rader and B. O. Schneeman, Prevalence of neural tube defects, folate status, and folate fortification of enriched cereal-grain products in the United States, *Pediatrics* 117 (2006): 1394-1399.
11. M. Hanson and coauthors, Report on the 2nd World Congress on Fetal Origins of Adult Disease, Brighton, U.K., June 7-10, 2003, *Pediatric Research* 55 (2004): 894-897; G. Wu and coauthors, Maternal nutrition and fetal development, *Journal of Nutrition* 134 (2004): 2169-2172; C. N. Hales and S. E. Ozanne, For debate: Fetal and early postnatal growth restriction lead to diabetes, the metabolic syndrome and renal failure, *Diabetologia* 46 (2003): 1013-1019.
12. S. E. Moore and coauthors, Birth weight predicts response to vaccination in adults born in an urban slum in Lahore, Pakistan, *American Journal of Clinical Nutrition* 80 (2004): 453-459; B. E. Birgisdottir and coauthors, Size at birth and glucose intolerance in a relatively genetically homogeneous, high-birth weight population, *American Journal of Clinical Nutrition* 76 (2002): 399-403.
13. R. C. Painter and coauthors, Early onset of coronary artery disease after prenatal exposure to the Dutch famine, *American Journal of Clinical Nutrition* 84 (2006): 322-327; O. A. Kensara and coauthors, Fetal programming of body composition: Relation between birth weight and body composition measured with dual-energy X-ray absorptiometry and anthropometric methods in older Englishmen, *American Journal of Clinical Nutrition* 82 (2005): 980-987; P. Szitányi, J. Janda, and R. Poledne, Intrauterine undernutrition and programming as a new risk of cardiovascular disease in later life, *Physiological Research* 52 (2003): 389-395; A. Singhal and coauthors, Programming of lean body mass: A link between birth weight, obesity, and cardiovascular disease? *American Journal of Clinical Nutrition* 77 (2003): 726-730.
14. G. Wolf, Adult type 2 diabetes induced by intrauterine growth retardation, *Nutrition Reviews* 61 (2003): 176-179.
15. P. L. Hofman and coauthors, Premature birth and later insulin resistance, *New England Journal of Medicine* 351 (2004): 2179-2186; M. A. Sperling, Prematurity—A window of opportunity? *New England Journal of Medicine* 351 (2004): 2229-2231.
16. Hofman and coauthors, 2004; Sperling, 2004.
17. L. Adair and D. Dahly, Developmental determinants of blood pressure in adults, *Annual Review of Nutrition* 25 (2005): 407-434; K. M. Moritz, M. Dodic, and E. M. Wintour, Kidney development and the fetal programming of adult disease, *Bioessays* 25 (2003): 212-220; M. Symonds and coauthors, Maternal nutrient restriction during placental growth, programming of fetal adiposity and juvenile blood pressure control, *Archives of Physiology and Biochemistry* 111 (2003): 45-52.
18. Adair and Dahly, 2005; C. M. Law and coauthors, Fetal, infant, and childhood growth and adult blood pressure: A longitudinal study from birth to 22 years of age, *Circulation* 105 (2002): 1088-1092.
19. R. A. Waterland and R. L. Jirtle, Transposable elements: Targets for early nutritional effects on epigenetic gene regulation, *Molecular and Cellular Biology* 23 (2003): 5293-5300.
20. A. J. Drake and B. R. Walker, The intergenerational effects of fetal programming: Non-genomic mechanisms for the inheritance of low birth weight and cardiovascular risk, *Journal of Endocrinology* 180 (2004): 1-16.
21. D. B. Sarwer and coauthors, Pregnancy and obesity: A review and agenda for future research, *Journal of Women's Health* 15 (2006): 720-733; T. Henriksen, Nutrition and pregnancy outcome, *Nutrition Reviews* 64 (2006): S19-S23; J. C. King, Maternal obesity, metabolism, and pregnancy outcomes, *Annual Review of Nutrition* 26 (2006): 271-291.
22. T. K. Young and B. Woodmansee, Factors that are associated with cesarean delivery in a large private practice: The importance of pregnancy body mass index and weight gain, *American Journal of Obstetrics and Gynecology* 187 (2002): 312-318.
23. J. C. King, Maternal obesity, metabolism, and pregnancy outcomes, *Annual Review of Nutrition* 26 (2006): 271-291.
24. M. L. Watkins and coauthors, Maternal obesity and risk for birth defects, *Pediatrics* 111 (2003): 1152-1158.
25. M. E. Roselló-Soberón, L. Fuentes-Chaparro, and E. Casanueva, Twin pregnancies: Eating for three? Maternal nutrition update, *Nutrition Reviews* 63 (2005): 295-302.
26. D. A. Krummel, Postpartum weight control: A vicious cycle, *Journal of the American Dietetic Association* 107 (2007): 37-40; E. Villamor and S. Cnattingius, Interpregnancy weight change and risk of adverse pregnancy outcomes: A population-based study, *Lancet* 368 (2006): 1164-1170.

27. R. Artal and M. O'Toole, Guidelines of the American College of Obstetricians and Gynecologists for exercise during pregnancy and the postpartum period, *British Journal of Sports Medicine* 37 (2003): 6-12; Committee of Obstetric Practice, Exercise during pregnancy and the postpartum period, *Obstetrics and Gynecology* 99 (2002): 171-173.

28. M. Lof and coauthors, Changes in basal metabolic rate during pregnancy in relation to changes in body weight and composition, cardiac output, insulin-like growth factor I, and thyroid hormones and in relation to fetal growth, *American Journal of Clinical Nutrition* 81 (2005): 678-685; N. F. Butte and coauthors, Energy requirements during pregnancy based on total energy expenditure and energy deposition, *American Journal of Clinical Nutrition* 79 (2004): 1078-1087.

29. R. Uauy and A. D. Dangour, Nutrition in brain development and aging: Role of essential fatty acids, *Nutrition Reviews* 64 (2006): S24-S33.

30. Committee on Dietary Reference Intakes, *Dietary Reference Intakes for Thiamin, Riboflavin, Niacin, Vitamin B6, Folate, Vitamin B12, Pantothenic Acid, Biotin, and Choline* (Washington, D.C.: National Academy Press, 1998), pp. 196-305.

31. T. O. Scholl, Iron status during pregnancy: Setting the stage for mother and infant, *American Journal of Clinical Nutrition* 81 (2005): 1218S-1222S.

32. K. O. O'Brien and coauthors, Maternal iron status influences iron transfer to the fetus during the third trimester of pregnancy, *American Journal of Clinical Nutrition* 77 (2003): 924-930.

33. E. Casanueva and coauthors, Vitamin C supplementation to prevent premature rupture of the chorioamniotic membranes: A randomized trial, *American Journal of Clinical Nutrition* 81 (2005): 859-863.

34. C. M. Donangelo and coauthors, Zinc absorption and kinetics during pregnancy and lactation in Brazilian women, *American Journal of Clinical Nutrition* 82 (2005): 118-124.

35. D. Shah and H. P. S. Sachdev, Zinc deficiency in pregnancy and fetal outcome, *Nutrition Reviews* 64 (2006): 15-30.

36. N. Pawley and N. J. Bishop, Prenatal and infant predictors of bone health: The influence of vitamin D, *American Journal of Clinical Nutrition* 80 (2004): 1748S-1751S.

37. B. W. Hollis and C. L. Wagner, Assessment of dietary vitamin D requirements during pregnancy and lactation, *American Journal of Clinical Nutrition* 79 (2004): 717-726.

38. C. L. V. Zapata and coauthors, Calcium homeostasis during pregnancy and lactation in Brazilian women with low calcium intakes: A longitudinal study, *American Journal of Clinical Nutrition* 80 (2004): 417-422.

39. K. O. O'Brien and coauthors, Bone calcium turnover during pregnancy and lactation in women with low calcium diets is associated with calcium intake and circulating insulin-like growth factor 1 concentrations, *American Journal of Clinical Nutrition* 83 (2006): 317-323.

40. A. Vahratian and coauthors, Multivitamin use and the risk of preterm birth, *American Journal of Epidemiology* 160 (2004): 886-892.

41. Position of the American Dietetic Association and Dietitians of Canada: Vegetarian diets, *Journal of the American Dietetic Association* 103 (2003): 748-765.

42. R. W. Corbett, C. Ryan, and S. P. Weinrich, Pica in pregnancy: Does it affect pregnancy outcomes? *American Journal of Maternal Child Nursing* 28 (2003): 183-189.

43. L. H. Allen, Multiple micronutrients in pregnancy and lactation: An overview, *American Journal of Clinical Nutrition* 81 (2005): 1206S-1212S.

44. P. J. Surkan and coauthors, Previous preterm and small-for-gestational-age births and the subsequent risk of stillbirth, *New England Journal of Medicine* 350 (2004): 777-785.

45. R. J. Kaaja and I. A. Greer, Manifestations of chronic disease during pregnancy, *Journal of the American Medical Association* 294 (2005): 2751-2757.

46. W. van Wootten and R. E. Turner, Macrosomia in neonates of mothers with gestational diabetes is associated with body mass index and previous gestational diabetes, *Journal of the American Dietetic Association* 102 (2002): 241-243.

47. American Diabetes Association, Diagnosis and classification of diabetes mellitus, *Diabetes Care* 29 (2006): S43-S48; Report of the Expert Committee on the Diagnosis and Classification of Diabetes Mellitus, *Diabetes Care* 26 (2003): S5-S20.

48. Position statement from the American Diabetes Association: Gestational diabetes mellitus, *Diabetes Care* 26 (2003): S103-S105.

49. C. A. Crowther and coauthors, Effect of treatment of gestational diabetes mellitus on pregnancy outcomes, *New England Journal of Medicine* 352 (2005): 2477-2486; O. Langer and coauthors, Overweight and obese in gestational diabetes: The impact on pregnancy outcomes, *American Journal of Obstetrics and Gynecology* 192 (2005): 1768-1776.

50. C. G. Solomon and E. W. Seely, Preeclampsia—Searching for the cause, *New England Journal of Medicine* 350 (2004): 641-642.

51. C. B. Rudra and coauthors, Perceived exertion during prepregnancy physical activity and preeclampsia risk, *Medicine and Science in Sports and Exercise* 37 (2005): 1836-1841; T. L. Weissgerber, L. A. Wolfe, and G. A. L. Davies, The role of regular physical activity in preeclampsia prevention, *Medicine and Science in Sports and Exercise* 36 (2004): 2024-2031.

52. J. D. Klein and the Committee on Adolescence, Adolescent pregnancy: Current trends and issues, *Pediatrics* 116 (2005): 281-286.

53. R. J. Paulson and coauthors, Pregnancy in the sixth decade of life—Obstetric outcomes in women of advanced reproductive age, *Journal of the American Medical Association* 288 (2002): 2320-2323.

54. S. C. Tough and coauthors, Delayed childbearing and its impact on population rate changes in lower birth weight, multiple birth, and preterm delivery, *Pediatrics* 109 (2002): 399-403.

55. Alcohol consumption among women who are pregnant or who might become pregnant—United States, 2002, *Morbidity and Mortality Weekly Report* 53 (2004): 1178-1181.

56. L. T. Singer and coauthors, Cognitive and motor outcomes of cocaine-exposed infants, *Journal of the American Medical Association* 287 (2002): 1952-1960.

57. Smoking during pregnancy—United States, 1990-2002, *Morbidity and Mortality Weekly Report* 53 (2004): 911-915.

58. X. Wang and coauthors, Maternal cigarette smoking, metabolic gene polymorphism, and infant birth weight, *Journal of the American Medical Association* 287 (2002): 195-202.

59. J. R. DiFranza, C. A. Aligne, and M. Weitzman, Prenatal and postnatal environmental tobacco smoke exposure and children's health, *Pediatrics* 113 (2004): 1007-1015.

60. DiFranza, Aligne, and Weitzman, 2004.

61. R. L. Brent, S. Tanski, and M. Weitzman, A pediatric perspective on the unique vulnerability and resilience of the embryo and the child to environmental toxicants: The importance of rigorous research concerning age and agent, *Pediatrics* 113 (2004): 935-944; R. M. Sharpe and D. S. Irvine, How strong is the evidence of a link between environmental chemicals and adverse effects on human reproductive health? *British Medical Journal* 328 (2004): 447-451.

62. A. Gomaa and coauthors, Maternal bone lead as an independent risk factor for fetal neurotoxicity: A prospective study, *Pediatrics* 110 (2002): 110-118.

63. N. Ribas-Fitó and coauthors, Breastfeeding, exposure to organochlorine compounds, and neurodevelopment in infants, *Pediatrics* 111 (2003): e580-e585.

64. S. E. Schober and coauthors, Blood mercury levels in US children and women of childbearing age, 1999-2000, *Journal of the American Medical Association* 289 (2003): 1667-1674.

65. D. Mozaffarian and E. B. Rimm, Fish intake, contaminants, and human health: Evaluating the risks and the benefits, *Journal of the American Medical Association* 296 (2006): 1885-1899; Institute of Medicine report brief, *Seafood Choices: Balancing Benefits and Risks*, October 2006.

66. B. H. Bech and coauthors, Coffee and fetal death: A cohort study with prospective data, *American Journal of Epidemiology* 162 (2005): 983-990.

67. Position of the American Dietetic Association: Use of nutritive and nonnutritive sweeteners, *Journal of the American Dietetic Association* 104 (2004): 255-275.

68. Position of the American Dietetic Association: Nutrition and lifestyle for a healthy pregnancy outcome, *Journal of the American Dietetic Association* 102 (2002): 1479-1490.

69. R. Li and coauthors, Breastfeeding rates in the United States by characteristics of the child, mother, or family: The 2002 National Immunization Survey, *Pediatrics* 115 (2005): e31; R. Li and coauthors, Prevalence of breastfeeding in the United States: The 2001 National Immunization Survey, *Pediatrics* 111 (2003): 1198-1201; A. S. Ryan, Z. Wenjun, and A. Acosta, Breastfeeding continues to increase into the new millennium, *Pediatrics* 110 (2002): 1103-1109.

70. American Academy of Pediatrics, Breastfeeding and the use of human milk, *Pediatrics* 115 (2005): 496-506; Position of the American Dietetic Association: Promoting and supporting breastfeeding, *Journal of the American Dietetic Association* 105 (2005): 810-818.

71. K. A. Bonuck and coauthors, Randomized, controlled trial of a prenatal and postnatal lactation consultant intervention on duration and intensity of breastfeeding up to 12 months, *Pediatrics* 116 (2005): 1413-1426; J. Labarere and coauthors, Efficacy of breastfeeding support provided by trained clinicians during an early, routine, preventive visit: A prospective, randomized, open trial of 226 Mother-infant pairs, *Pediatrics* 115 (2005): e139; E. M. Taveras and coauthors, Mothers' and clinicians' perspectives on breastfeeding counseling during routine preventive visits, *Pediatrics* 113 (2004): e405.

72. S. Merten, J. Dratva, and U. Ackermann-Liebrich, Do baby-friendly hospitals influence breastfeeding duration on a national level? *Pediatrics* 116 (2005): e702; A. Merewood and coauthors, Breastfeeding rates in US baby-friendly hospitals: Results of a national survey, *Pediatrics* 116 (2005): 628-634.

73. A. Pisacane and coauthors, A controlled trial of the father's role in breastfeeding promotion, *Pediatrics* 116 (2005): e494; C. L. Dennis, Breastfeeding initiation and duration: A 1990-2000 literature review, Journal of Obstetric, *Gynecologic and Neonatal Nursing* 31 (2002): 12-32.

74. Dennis, 2002.

75. C. A. Lovelady, Is maternal obesity a cause of poor lactation performance? *Nutrition Reviews* 63 (2005): 352-355.

76. D. A. Krummel and coauthors, Stages of

change for weight management in postpartum women, *Journal of the American Dietetic Association* 104 (2004): 1102-1108.

77. K. S. Wosje and H. J. Kalkwarf, Lactation, weaning, and calcium supplementation: Effects on body composition in postpartum women, *American Journal of Clinical Nutrition* 80 (2004): 423-429.

78. K. O. O'Brien and coauthors, Bone calcium turnover during pregnancy and lactation in women with low calcium diets is associated with calcium intake and circulating insulin-like growth factor 1 concentrations, *American Journal of Clinical Nutrition* 83 (2006): 317-323.

79. F. F. Bezerra and coauthors, Bone mass is recovered from lactation to postweaning in adolescent mothers with low calcium in-

takes, *American Journal of Clinical Nutrition* 80 (2004): 1322-1326; L. M. Paton and coauthors, Pregnancy and lactation have no long-term deleterious effect on measures of bone mineral in healthy women: A twin study, *American Journal of Clinical Nutrition* 77 (2003): 707-714.

80. J. S. Wang, Q. R. Zhu, and X. H. Wang, Breastfeeding does not pose any additional risk of immunoprophylaxis failure on infants of HBV carrier mothers, *International Journal of Clinical Practice* 57 (2003): 100-102; J. B. Hill and coauthors, Risk of hepatitis B transmission in breast-fed infants of chronic hepatitis B carriers, *Obstetrics and Gynecology* 99 (2002): 1049-1052; M. L. Newell and L. Pembrey, Mother-to-child transmission of hepatitis C virus infection,

Drugs of Today 38 (2002): 321-337.

81. J. S. Read and the Committee on Pediatric AIDS, human milk, breastfeeding, and transmission of human immunodeficiency virus type 1 in the United States, *Pediatrics* 112 (2003): 1196-1205.

82. R. Lesnewski and L. Prine, Initiating hormonal contraception, *American Family Physician* 74 (2006): 105-112.

83. S. Cnattingius and coauthors, Pregnancy characteristics and maternal risk of breast cancer, *Journal of the American Medical Association* 294 (2005): 2474-2480.

84. S. Ito and A. Lee, Drug excretion into breast milk—Overview, *Advanced Drug Delivery Reviews* 55 (2003): 617-627.

ANSWERS

1. c   2. c   3. c   4. b   5. b   6. c   7. b   8. b   9. c   10. c

Fetal Alcohol Syndrome

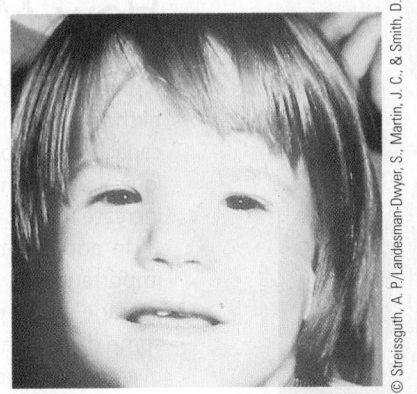

© Streissguth, A. P./Landesman-Dwyer, S. Martin, J. C., & Smith, D. W.

As Chapter 15 mentioned, drinking alcohol during pregnancy endangers the fetus. Alcohol crosses the placenta freely and deprives the developing fetus of both nutrients and oxygen. The damaging effects of alcohol on the developing fetus cover a range of abnormalities referred to as **fetal alcohol spectrum disorder** (see the glossary on p. 544).[1] Those at the most severe end of the spectrum are described as having **fetal alcohol syndrome (FAS)**, a cluster of physical, mental, and neurobehavioral symptoms that includes:

- Prenatal and postnatal growth retardation

- Impairment of the brain and central nervous system, with consequent mental retardation, poor motor skills and coordination, and hyperactivity

- Abnormalities of the face and skull (see Figure H15-1)

- Increased frequency of major birth defects: cleft palate, heart defects, and defects in ears, eyes, genitals, and urinary system

Tragically, the damage evident at birth persists: children with FAS never fully recover.[2]

Each year, as many as 6000 infants are born with FAS because their mothers drank too much alcohol during pregnancy.[3] In addition, some 4 million infants are born with **prenatal alcohol exposure**. The cluster of mental problems associated with prenatal alcohol exposure is known as **alcohol-related neurodevelopmental disorder (ARND)**, and the physical malformations are referred to as **alcohol-related birth defects (ARBD)**. Some children with ARBD and ARND have no outward signs; others may be short or have only minor facial abnormalities. They often go undiagnosed even when they develop learning difficulties in the early school years. Mood disorders and problem behaviors, such as aggression, are common.[4]

The surgeon general states that pregnant women should abstain from alcohol. Abstinence from alcohol is the best policy for pregnant women both because alcohol consumption during pregnancy has such severe consequences and because FAS can only be pre-vented—it cannot be treated. Further, because the most severe damage occurs around the time of conception—*before a woman may even realize that she is pregnant*—the warning to abstain includes women who may become pregnant.

Drinking during Pregnancy

As mentioned in Chapter 15, 1 out of 10 pregnant women drinks alcohol at some time during her pregnancy; 1 out of 50 uses alcohol frequently and admits to binge drinking.[5] When a woman drinks during pregnancy, she causes damage in two ways: directly, by intoxication, and indirectly, by malnutrition. Prior to the

---

FIGURE H15-1 Typical Facial Characteristics of FAS

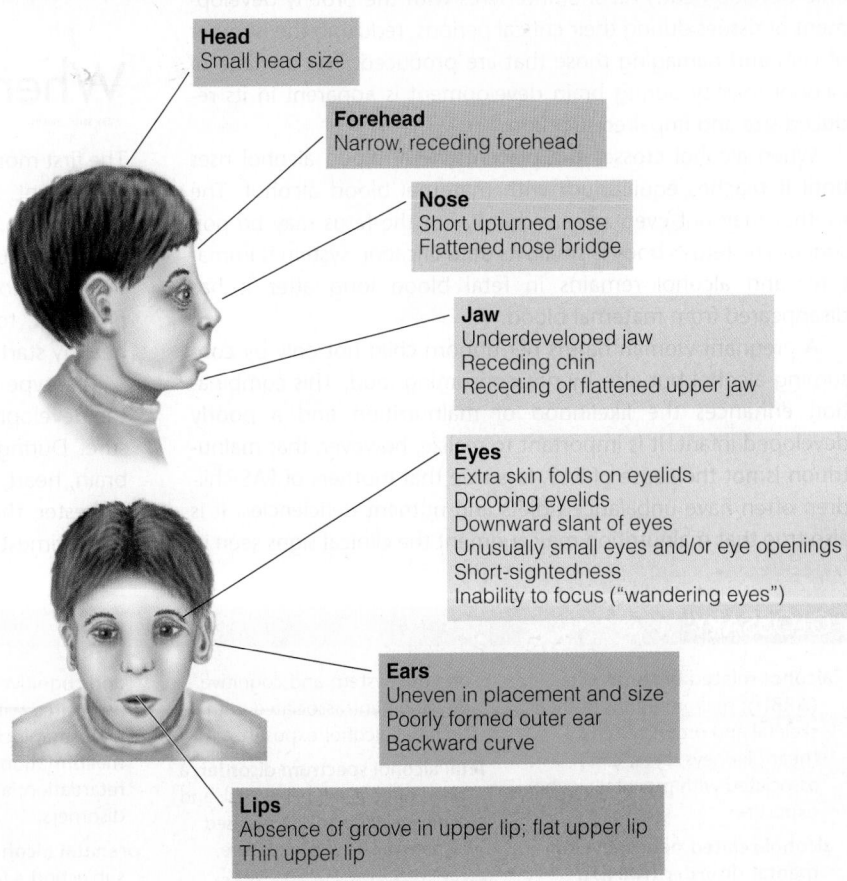

Head
Small head size

Forehead
Narrow, receding forehead

Nose
Short upturned nose
Flattened nose bridge

Jaw
Underdeveloped jaw
Receding chin
Receding or flattened upper jaw

Eyes
Extra skin folds on eyelids
Drooping eyelids
Downward slant of eyes
Unusually small eyes and/or eye openings
Short-sightedness
Inability to focus ("wandering eyes")

Ears
Uneven in placement and size
Poorly formed outer ear
Backward curve

Lips
Absence of groove in upper lip; flat upper lip
Thin upper lip

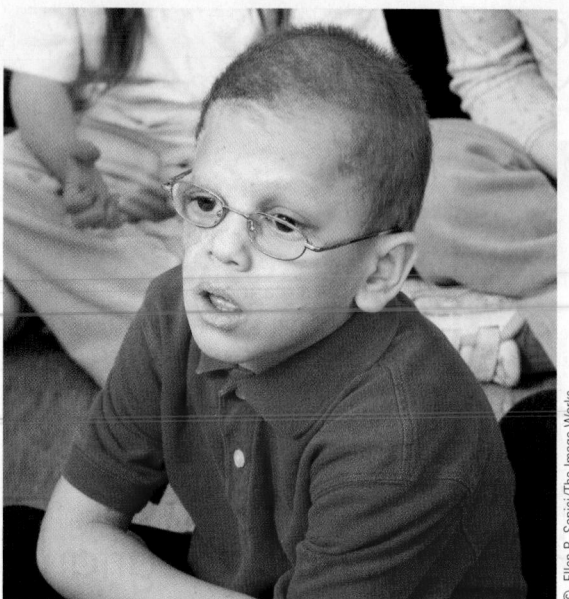

Characteristic facial features may diminish with time, but children with FAS typically continue to be short and underweight for their age.

complete formation of the placenta (approximately 12 weeks), alcohol diffuses directly into the tissues of the developing embryo, causing incredible damage. (Review Figure 15-4 on p. 512 and note that the critical periods for most tissues occur during embryonic development.) Alcohol interferes with the orderly development of tissues during their critical periods, reducing the number of cells and damaging those that are produced. The damage of alcohol toxicity during brain development is apparent in its reduced size and impaired function.[6]

When alcohol crosses the placenta, fetal blood alcohol rises until it reaches equilibrium with maternal blood alcohol. The mother may not even appear drunk, but the fetus may be poisoned. The fetus's body is small, its detoxification system is immature, and alcohol remains in fetal blood long after it has disappeared from maternal blood.

A pregnant woman harms her unborn child not only by consuming alcohol but also by not consuming food. This combination enhances the likelihood of malnutrition and a poorly developed infant. It is important to realize, however, that malnutrition is not the cause of FAS. It is true that mothers of FAS children often have unbalanced diets and nutrient deficiencies. It is also true that malnutrition may augment the clinical signs seen in these children, but it is the *alcohol* that causes the damage. An adequate diet alone will not prevent FAS if alcohol abuse continues.

How Much Is Too Much?

A pregnant woman need not have an alcohol-abuse problem to give birth to a baby with FAS. She need only drink in excess of her liver's capacity to detoxify alcohol. Even one drink a day threatens neurological development and behaviors.[7] Four drinks a day dramatically increase the risk of having an infant with physical malformations.

In addition to total alcohol intake, drinking patterns play an important role. Most FAS studies report their findings in terms of average intake per day, but people usually drink more heavily on some days than on others. For example, a woman who drinks an *average* of 1 ounce of alcohol (2 drinks) a day may not drink at all during the week, but then have 10 drinks on Saturday night, exposing the fetus to extremely toxic quantities of alcohol. Whether various drinking patterns incur damage depends on the frequency of consumption, the quantity consumed, and the stage of fetal development at the time of each drinking episode.

An occasional drink may be innocuous, but researchers are unable to say how much alcohol is safe to consume during pregnancy. For this reason, health care professionals urge women to stop drinking alcohol as soon as they realize they are pregnant or better, as soon as they *plan* to become pregnant. Why take any risk? Only the woman who abstains is sure of protecting her infant from FAS.

When Is the Damage Done?

The first month or two of pregnancy is a critical period of fetal development. Because pregnancy usually cannot be confirmed before five to six weeks, a woman may not even realize she is pregnant during that critical time. Therefore, it is advisable for women who are trying to conceive, or who suspect they might be pregnant, to abstain or curtail their alcohol intakes to ensure a healthy start.

The type of abnormality observed in an FAS infant depends on the developmental events occurring at the times of alcohol exposure. During the first trimester, developing organs such as the brain, heart, and kidneys may be malformed. During the second trimester, the risk of spontaneous abortion increases. During the third trimester, body and brain growth may be retarded.

GLOSSARY

alcohol-related birth defects (ARBD): malformations in the skeletal and organ systems (heart, kidneys, eyes, ears) associated with prenatal alcohol exposure.

alcohol-related neurodevelopmental disorder (ARND): abnormalities in the central nervous system and cognitive development associated with prenatal alcohol exposure.

fetal alcohol spectrum disorder: a range of physical, behavioral, and cognitive abnormalities caused by prenatal alcohol exposure.

fetal alcohol syndrome (FAS): a cluster of physical, behavioral, and cognitive abnormalities associated with prenatal alcohol exposure, including facial malformations, growth retardation, and central nervous disorders.

prenatal alcohol exposure: subjecting a fetus to a pattern of excessive alcohol intake characterized by substantial regular use or heavy episodic drinking.

NOTE: See Highlight 7 for other alcohol-related terms and information.

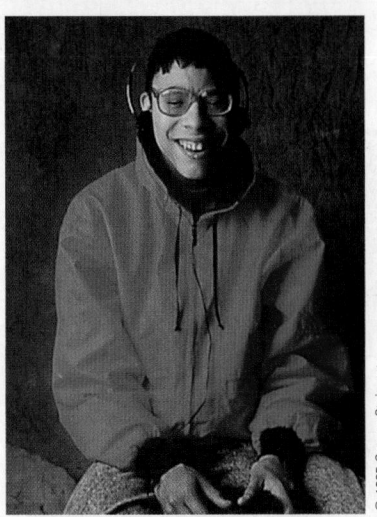

Children born with FAS must live with the long-term consequences of prenatal brain damage.

© 1995 George Steinmetz

Male alcohol ingestion may also affect fertility and fetal development.[8] Animal studies have found smaller litter sizes, lower birthweights, reduced survival rates, and impaired learning ability in the offspring of males consuming alcohol prior to conception. An association between paternal alcohol intake one month prior to conception and low infant birthweight is also apparent in human beings. (Paternal alcohol intake was defined as an average of 2 or more drinks daily or at least 5 drinks on one occasion.) This relationship was independent of either parent's smoking and of the mother's use of alcohol, caffeine, or other drugs.

In view of the damage caused by FAS, prevention efforts focus on educating women not to drink during pregnancy.[9] Everyone should know of the potential dangers. Women who drink alcohol and who are sexually active may benefit from counseling and ef-

Matthew Farruggio

All containers of beer, wine, and liquor warn women not to drink alcoholic beverages during pregnancy because of the risk of birth defects.

fective contraception to prevent pregnancy.[10] Almost half of all pregnancies are unintended, with many conceived during a binge-drinking episode.[11]

Public service announcements and alcohol beverage warning labels help to raise awareness. Everyone should hear the message loud and clear: Don't drink alcohol prior to conception or during pregnancy.

NUTRITION ON THE NET

ThomsonNOW

For furthur study of topics covered in this Highlight, log on to **www.thomsonedu.com/thomsonnow**. Go to Chapter 15, then to Highlights Nutrition on the Net.

- Visit the National Organization on Fetal Alcohol Syndrome: **www.nofas.org**

- Search for "fetal alcohol syndrome" at the U.S. Government health information site: **www.healthfinder.gov**

- Request information on fetal alcohol syndrome from the National Clearinghouse for Alcohol and Drug Information: **ncadi.samsha.gov**

- Request information on drinking during pregnancy from the National Institute on Alcohol Abuse and Alcoholism: **www.niaaa.nih.gov**

- Gather facts on fetal alcohol syndrome from the March of Dimes: **www.modimes.org**

REFERENCES

1. H. E. Hoyme and coauthors, A practical clinical approach to diagnosis of fetal alcohol spectrum disorders: Clarification of the 1996 Institute of Medicine Criteria, *Pediatrics* 115 (2005): 39–47.
2. N. L. Day and coauthors, Prenatal alcohol exposure predicts continued deficits in offspring size at 14 years of age, *Alcoholism: Clinical and Experimental Research* 26 (2002): 1584–1591; M. D. Cornelius and coauthors, Alcohol, tobacco and marijuana use among pregnant teenagers: 6-year follow-up of offspring growth effects, *Neurotoxicology and Teratology* 24 (2002): 703–710.
3. Guidelines for identifying and referring persons with fetal alcohol syndrome, *Morbidity and Mortality Weekly Report* 54 (2005): 1–10.
4. M. J. O'Connor and coauthors, Psychiatric illness in a clinical sample of children with prenatal alcohol exposure, *American Journal of Drug and Alcohol Abuse* 28 (2002): 743–754.
5. Alcohol consumption among women who are pregnant or who might become pregnant—United States, 2002, *Morbidity and Mortality Weekly Report* 53 (2004): 1178–1181.
6. J. W. Olney and coauthors, The enigma of fetal alcohol neurotoxicity, *Annals of Medicine* 34 (2002): 109–119.
7. S. W. Jacobson and coauthors, Validity of maternal report of prenatal alcohol, cocaine, and smoking in relation to neurobehavioral outcome, *Pediatrics* 109 (2002): 815–825.
8. H. Klonoff-Cohen, P. Lam-Kruglick, and C. Gonzalez, Effects of maternal and paternal alcohol consumption on the success rates of in vitro fertilization and gamete intrafallopian transfer, *Fertility and Sterility* 79 (2003): 330–339.
9. J. R. Hankin, Fetal alcohol syndrome prevention research, *Alcohol Research and Health* 26 (2002): 58–65.
10. The Project CHOICES Intervention Research Group, Reducing the risk of alcohol-exposed pregnancies: A study of a motivational intervention in community settings, *Pediatrics* 111 (2003): 1131–1135.
11. T. S. Naimi and coauthors, Binge drinking in the preconception period and the risk of unintended pregnancy: Implications for women and their children, *Pediatrics* 111 (2003): 1136–1141.

Nutrition in Your Life

Much of this book has focused on you—your food choices and how they might affect your health. This chapter shifts the focus from you the recipient to you the caregiver. One day (if not already), children will depend on you to feed them well and teach them wisely. The responsibility of nourishing children can seem overwhelming at times, but the job is fairly simple. Offer children a variety of nutritious foods to support their growth, and teach them how to make healthy food and activity choices. Presenting foods in a relaxed and supportive environment nourishes both physical and emotional well-being.

Life Cycle Nutrition: Infancy, Childhood, and Adolescence

CHAPTER OUTLINE

Nutrition during Infancy • Energy and Nutrient Needs • Breast Milk • Infant Formula • Special Needs of Preterm Infants • Introducing Cow's Milk • Introducing Solid Foods • Mealtimes with Toddlers

Nutrition during Childhood • Energy and Nutrient Needs • Hunger and Malnutrition in Children • The Malnutrition-Lead Connection • Hyperactivity and "Hyper" Behavior • Food Allergy and Intolerance • Childhood Obesity • Mealtimes at Home • Nutrition at School

Nutrition during Adolescence • Growth and Development • Energy and Nutrient Needs • Food Choices and Health Habits • Problems Adolescents Face

HIGHLIGHT 16 Childhood Obesity and the Early Development of Chronic Diseases

The first year of life is a time of phenomenal growth and development. After the first year, a child continues to grow and change, but more slowly. Still, the cumulative effects over the next decade are remarkable. Then, as the child enters the teen years, the pace toward adulthood accelerates dramatically. This chapter examines the special nutrient needs of infants, children, and adolescents.

Nutrition during Infancy

Initially, the infant drinks only breast milk or formula but later begins to eat some foods, as appropriate. Common sense in the selection of infant foods along with a nurturing, relaxed environment support an infant's health and well-being.

Energy and Nutrient Needs

An infant grows fast during the first year, as Figure 16-1 shows. Growth directly reflects nutrient intake and is an important parameter in assessing the nutrition status of infants and children. Health care professionals measure the heights and weights of infants and children at intervals and compare the measurements with standard growth curves for gender and age and with previous measures of each child (see the "How to," p. 548).

Energy Intake and Activity A healthy infant's birthweight doubles by about five months of age and triples by one year, typically reaching 20 to 25 pounds. The infant's length changes more slowly than weight, increasing about 10 inches from birth to one year. By the end of the first year, infant growth slows considerably; during the second year, an infant typically gains less than 10 pounds and grows about 5 inches in height.

Not only do infants grow rapidly, but their energy requirement is remarkably high—about twice that of an adult, based on body weight. A newborn baby requires about 450 kcalories per day, whereas most adults require about 2000 kcalories per day. In terms of body weight, the difference is remarkable. Infants require about 100 kcalories per kilogram of body weight per day, whereas most adults need fewer than 40 (see Table 16-1, p. 548). If an infant's energy needs were applied to an adult, a 170-pound adult would require over 7000 kcalories a day. After six months, the infant's energy needs decline as the growth rate slows, but some of the energy saved by slower growth is spent in increased activity.

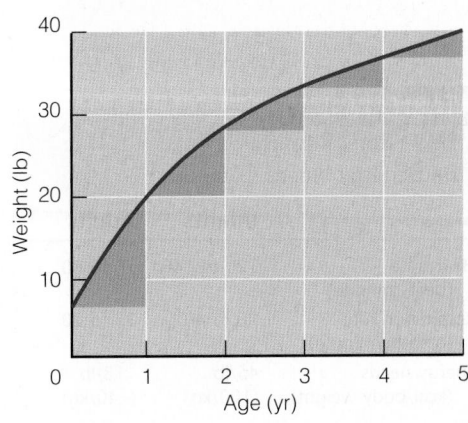

FIGURE 16-1 Weight Gain of Infants in Their First Five Years of Life

In the first year, an infant's birthweight may triple, but over the following several years, the rate of weight gain gradually diminishes.

HOW TO Plot Measures on a Growth Chart

You can assess the growth of infants and children by plotting their measurements on a percentile graph. Percentile graphs divide the measures of a population into 100 equal divisions so that half of the population falls at or above the 50th percentile and half falls below. Using percentiles allows for comparisons among people of the same age and gender.

To plot measures on a growth chart, follow these steps:

- Select the appropriate chart based on age and gender. For this example, use the accompanying chart, which gives percentiles for weight for girls from birth to 36 months. (Appendix E provides other growth charts for both boys and girls of various ages.)
- Locate the infant's age along the horizontal axis at the bottom of the chart (in this example, 6 months).
- Locate the infant's weight in pounds or kilograms along the vertical axis of the chart (in this example, 17 pounds or 7.7 kilograms).
- Mark the chart where the age and weight lines intersect (shown here with a red dot), and follow the curved line to find the percentile.

This six-month-old infant is at the 75th percentile. Her pediatrician will weigh her again over the next few months and expect the growth curve to follow the same percentile throughout the first year. In general, dramatic changes or measures much above the 80th percentile or much below the 10th percentile may be cause for concern.

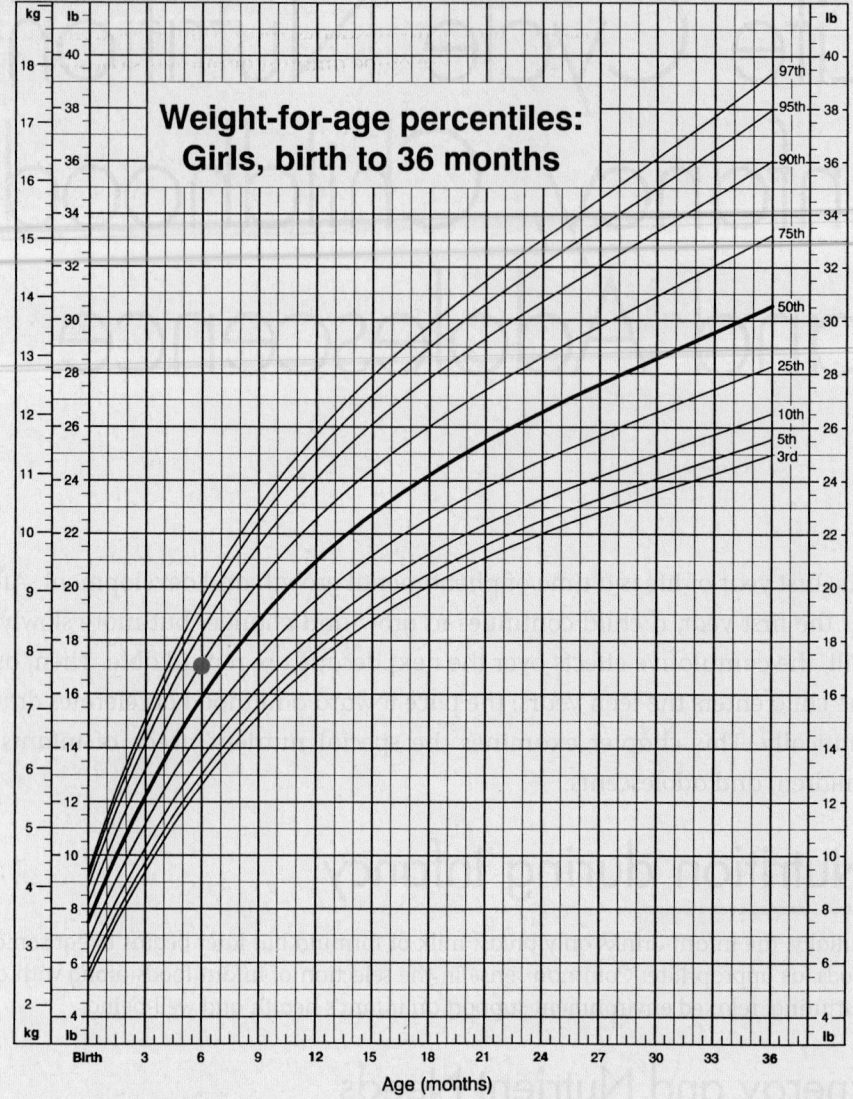

Weight-for-age percentiles: Girls, birth to 36 months

SOURCE: Developed by the National Center for Health Statistics in collaboration with the National Center for Chronic Disease Prevention and Health Promotion (2000).

ThomsonNOW™

To practice plotting measures on a growth chart, log on to **www.thomsonedu.com/thomsonnow**, go to Chapter 16, then go to How To.

TABLE 16-1 Infant and Adult Heart Rate, Respiration Rate, and Energy Needs Compared

	Infants	Adults
Heart rate (beats/minute)	120 to 140	70 to 80
Respiration rate (breaths/minute)	20 to 40	15 to 20
Energy needs (kcal/body weight)	45/lb (100/kg)	<18/lb (<40/kg)

Energy Nutrients Recommendations for the energy nutrients—carbohydrate, fat, and protein—during the first six months of life are based on the average intakes of healthy, full-term infants fed breast milk.[1] During the second six months of life, recommendations reflect typical intakes from solid foods as well as breast milk.

As discussed in Chapter 4, carbohydrates provide energy to all the cells of the body, especially those in the brain, which depend primarily on glucose to fuel activities. Relative to the size of the body, an infant's brain is larger and uses relatively more glucose—about 60 percent of the day's total energy intake.[2]

Fat provides most of the energy in breast milk and standard infant formula. Its high energy density supports the rapid growth of early infancy.

No single nutrient is more essential to growth than protein. All of the body's cells and most of its fluids contain protein; it is the basic building material of the body's tissues. Chapter 6 detailed the problems inadequate protein can cause. Excess dietary protein can cause problems, too, especially in a small infant. Too much protein stresses the liver and kidneys, which have to metabolize and excrete the excess nitrogen. Signs of protein overload include acidosis, dehydration, diarrhea, elevated blood ammonia, elevated blood urea, and fever. Such problems are not common, but they have been observed in infants fed inappropriate foods, such as fat-free milk or concentrated formula.

Vitamins and Minerals As with the energy nutrients, the recommendations for the vitamins and minerals are based on the average amount of nutrients consumed by thriving infants breastfed by well-nourished mothers. An infant's needs for most of these nutrients, in proportion to body weight, are more than double those of an adult. Figure 16-2 illustrates this by comparing a five-month-old infant's needs per unit of body weight with those of an adult man. Some of the differences are extraordinary.

Water One of the most essential nutrients for infants, as for everyone, is water. The younger the infant, the greater the percentage of body weight is water. During early infancy, breast milk or infant formula normally provides enough water to replace fluid losses in a healthy infant. Even in hot, dry climates, neither breastfed nor bottle-fed infants need supplemental water.[3] Because much of the fluid in an infant's body is located *outside* the cells—between the cells and in the blood vessels—rapid fluid losses and the resulting dehydration can be life-threatening. Conditions that cause rapid fluid loss, such as diarrhea or vomiting, require treatment with an electrolyte solution designed for infants.

After six months, energy saved by slower growth is spent in increased activity.

FIGURE 16-2 Recommended Intakes of an Infant and an Adult Compared on the Basis of Body Weight

Because infants are small, they need smaller total amounts of the nutrients than adults do, but when comparisons are based on body weight, infants need more than twice as much of many nutrients. Infants use large amounts of energy and nutrients, in proportion to their body size, to keep all their metabolic processes going.

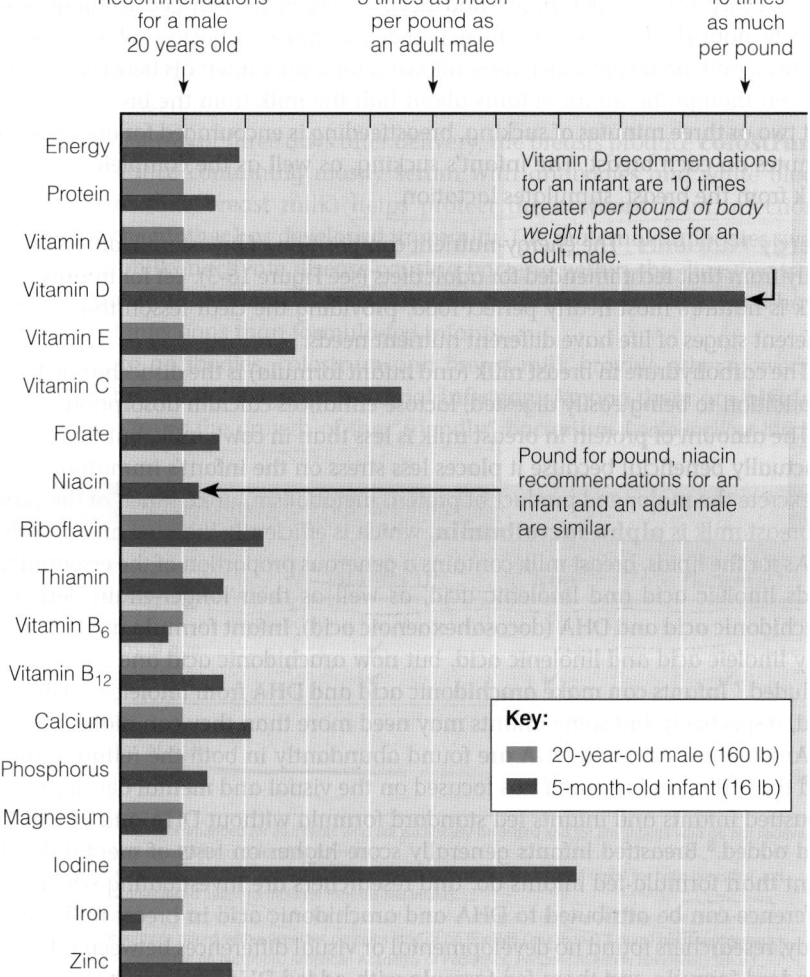

in the infant's digestive tract, so that other, harmful bacteria cannot become established. An iron-binding protein in breast milk, **lactoferrin**, keeps bacteria from getting the iron they need to grow, helps absorb iron into the infant's bloodstream, and kills some bacteria directly.[15] The protein **lactadherin** in breast milk binds to, and inhibits replication of, the virus that causes most infant diarrhea.[16] Breastfeeding also protects against other common illnesses of infancy such as middle ear infection and respiratory illness.[17] In addition, a growth factor that is present in breast milk stimulates the development and maintenance of the infant's digestive tract and its protective factors. Several breast milk enzymes such as lipase also help protect the infant against infection. Clearly, breast milk is a very special substance.

Allergy and Disease Protection In addition to protection against infection, breast milk may offer protection against the development of allergies. Compared with formula-fed infants, breastfed infants have a lower incidence of allergic reactions, such as asthma, recurrent wheezing, and skin rash.[18] This protection is especially noticeable among infants with a family history of allergies.[19] Similarly, breast milk may offer protection against the development of cardiovascular disease. Compared with formula-fed infants, breastfed infants have lower blood pressure and lower blood cholesterol as adults.[20]

Other Potential Benefits Breastfeeding may also help protect against excessive weight gain later. A review of more than 60 published studies investigating the relationship between infant feeding and obesity suggests that initial breastfeeding protects against obesity in later life.[21] A well-controlled survey of more than 15,000 adolescents and their mothers indicated that those who were mostly breastfed for the first six months of life were less likely to become overweight than those who were fed formula.[22] A study of much younger children (three to five years of age), however, found no clear evidence that breastfeeding influences body weight.[23] These researchers noted that other factors, especially the mother's weight, strongly predict overweight in children.

Many studies suggest a beneficial effect of breastfeeding on intelligence, but when subjected to strict standards of methodology (for example, large sample size and appropriate intelligence testing), the evidence is less convincing.[24] Nevertheless, the possibility that breastfeeding may positively affect later intelligence is intriguing. It may be that some specific component of breast milk, such as DHA, stimulates brain development or that certain factors associated with the feeding process itself promote intellect. Most likely, a combination of factors are involved. More large, well-controlled studies are needed to confirm the effects, if any, of breastfeeding on later intelligence.

Breast Milk Banks Similar to blood banks that collect blood from individuals to give to others in need, **breast milk banks** receive milk from lactating women who have an abundant supply to give to infants whose own mothers' milk is unavailable or insufficient. The women who donate breast milk are carefully screened to exclude those who smoke cigarettes, use illegal drugs, take medications (including high doses of dietary supplements), drink more than two alcoholic beverages a day, or have communicable diseases. The breast milk from several donors is pooled to ensure an even distribution of all components, pasteurized to destroy bacteria, checked for contamination, and frozen before being shipped overnight to hospitals, where it is dispensed by physician prescription. In the absence of mother's own breast milk, donor milk may be the life saving solution for fragile infants, most notably those with very low birthweight or unusual medical conditions.[25]

Infant Formula

A woman who breastfeeds for a year can **wean** her infant to cow's milk, bypassing the need for infant formula. However, a woman who decides to feed her infant for-

---

lactoferrin (lack-toh-FERR-in): a protein in breast milk that binds iron and keeps it from supporting the growth of the infant's intestinal bacteria.

lactadherin (lack-tad-HAIR-in): a protein in breast milk that attacks diarrhea-causing viruses.

breast milk bank: a service that collects, screens, processes, and distributes donated human milk.

wean: to gradually replace breast milk with infant formula or other foods appropriate to an infant's diet.

mula from birth, to wean to formula after less than a year of breastfeeding, or to substitute formula for breastfeeding on occasion must select an appropriate infant formula and learn to prepare it.

Infant Formula Composition Formula manufacturers attempt to copy the nutrient composition of breast milk as closely as possible. Figure 16-4 illustrates the energy-nutrient balance of both. The AAP recommends that all formula-fed infants receive iron-fortified infant formulas. The increasing use of iron-fortified formulas during the past few decades is a major reason for the decline in iron-deficiency anemia among U.S. infants.

Risks of Formula Feeding Infant formulas contain no protective antibodies for infants, but in general, vaccinations, purified water, and clean environments in developed countries help protect infants from infections. Formulas can be prepared safely by following the rules of proper food handling and by using water that is free of contamination. Of particular concern is lead-contaminated water, a major source of lead poisoning in infants. Because the first water drawn from the tap each day is highest in lead, a person living in a house with old, lead-soldered plumbing should let the water run a few minutes before drinking or using it to prepare formula or food.

In developing countries and in poor areas of the United States, formula may be unavailable, prepared with contaminated water, or overdiluted in an attempt to save money. Contaminated formulas often cause infections, leading to diarrhea, dehydration, and malabsorption. Without sterilization and refrigeration, formula is an ideal breeding ground for bacteria. Whenever such risks are present, breastfeeding can be a life-saving option: breast milk is sterile, and its antibodies enhance an infant's resistance to infections.

Infant Formula Standards National and international standards have been set for the nutrient contents of infant formulas. In the United States, the standard developed by the AAP reflects "human milk taken from well-nourished mothers during the first or second month of lactation, when the infant's growth rate is high." The Food and Drug Administration (FDA) mandates the safety and nutritional quality of infant formulas. Formulas meeting these standards have similar nutrient compositions. Small differences among formulas are sometimes confusing, but they are usually unimportant.

Special Formulas Standard cow's milk-based formulas are inappropriate for some infants. Special formulas have been designed to meet the dietary needs of infants with specific conditions such as prematurity or inherited diseases. Infants allergic to milk protein can drink special **hypoallergenic formulas** or formulas based on soy protein.[26] Soy formulas also use cornstarch and sucrose instead of lactose and so are recommended for infants with lactose intolerance as well. They are also useful as an alternative to milk-based formulas for vegan families. Despite these limited uses, soy formulas account for one-fourth of the infant formulas sold today. While soy formulas support the normal growth and development of infants, for infants who don't need them, they offer no advantage over milk formulas.

Inappropriate Formulas Caregivers must use only products designed for infants; soy *beverages,* for example, are nutritionally incomplete and inappropriate for infants. Goat's milk is also inappropriate for infants in part because of its low folate content. An infant receiving goat's milk is likely to develop "goat's milk anemia," an anemia characteristic of folate deficiency.

Nursing Bottle Tooth Decay An infant cannot be allowed to sleep with a bottle because of the potential damage to developing teeth. Salivary flow, which normally cleanses the mouth, diminishes as the infant falls asleep. Prolonged sucking on a bottle of formula, milk, or juice bathes the upper teeth in a carbohydrate-rich fluid that nourishes decay-producing bacteria. (The tongue covers and protects most of the lower teeth, but they, too, may be affected.) The result is extensive and rapid tooth decay (see Figure 16-5, p. 554). To prevent **nursing bottle tooth decay,** no infant should be put to bed with a bottle of nourishing fluid.

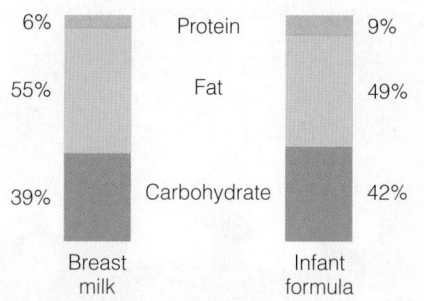

FIGURE 16-4 Percentages of Energy-Yielding Nutrients in Breast Milk and in Infant Formula

The average proportions of energy-yielding nutrients in human breast milk and formula differ slightly. In contrast, cow's milk provides too much protein (20%) and too little carbohydrate (30%).

	Breast milk		Infant formula
Protein	6%		9%
Fat	55%		49%
Carbohydrate	39%		42%

© Jon Feingersh/Corbis

The infant thrives on infant formula offered with affection.

hypoallergenic formulas: clinically tested infant formulas that support infant growth and development but do not provoke reactions in 90% of infants or children with confirmed cow's milk allergy.

nursing bottle tooth decay: extensive tooth decay due to prolonged tooth contact with formula, milk, fruit juice, or other carbohydrate-rich liquid offered to an infant in a bottle.

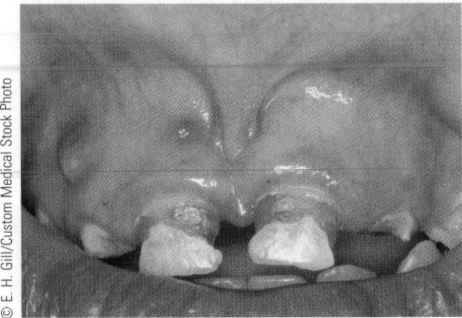

FIGURE 16-5 Nursing Bottle Tooth Decay

This child was frequently put to bed sucking on a bottle filled with apple juice, so the teeth were bathed in carbohydrate for long periods of time—a perfect medium for bacterial growth. The upper teeth show signs of decay.

Special Needs of Preterm Infants

An estimated one out of eight pregnancies in the United States results in a preterm birth.[27] The terms *preterm* and *premature* imply incomplete fetal development, or immaturity, of many body systems. As might be expected, preterm birth is a leading cause of infant deaths. Preterm infants face physical independence from their mothers before some of their organs and body tissues are ready. The rate of weight gain in the fetus is greater during the last trimester of gestation than at any other time. Therefore, a preterm infant is most often a low-birthweight infant as well. A premature birth deprives the infant of the nutritional support of the placenta during a time of maximal growth.

The last trimester of gestation is also a time of building nutrient stores. Being born with limited nutrient stores intensifies the already precarious situation for the infant. The physical and metabolic immaturity of preterm infants further compromises their nutrition status. Nutrient absorption, especially of fat and calcium, from an immature GI tract is limited. Consequently, preterm, low-birthweight infants are candidates for nutrient imbalances. Deficiencies of the fat-soluble vitamins, calcium, iron, and zinc are common.

Preterm breast milk is well suited to meet a preterm infant's needs. During early lactation, preterm milk contains higher concentrations of protein and is lower in volume than term milk. The low milk volume is advantageous because preterm infants consume small quantities of milk per feeding, and the higher protein concentration allows for better growth. In many instances, supplements of nutrients specifically designed for preterm infants are added to the mother's expressed breast milk and fed to the infant from a bottle. When fortified with a preterm supplement, preterm breast milk supports growth at a rate that approximates the growth rate that would have occurred within the uterus.

Introducing Cow's Milk

The age at which whole cow's milk should be introduced to the infant's diet has long been a source of controversy. The AAP advises that whole cow's milk is not appropriate during the first year.[28] Children one to two years of age should not be given reduced-fat, low-fat, or fat-free milk routinely; they need the fat of whole milk. Between the ages of two and five years, a gradual transition from whole milk to the lower-fat milks can take place, but care should be taken to avoid excessive restriction of dietary fat.

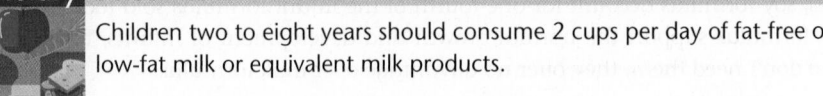

Dietary Guidelines for Americans 2005

Children two to eight years should consume 2 cups per day of fat-free or low-fat milk or equivalent milk products.

In some infants, particularly those younger than six months of age, whole cow's milk may cause intestinal bleeding, which can lead to iron deficiency. Cow's milk is also a poor source of iron. Consequently, it both causes iron loss and fails to replace iron. Furthermore, the bioavailability of iron from infant cereal and other foods is reduced when cow's milk replaces breast milk or iron-fortified formula during the first year. Compared with breast milk or iron-fortified formula, cow's milk is higher in calcium and lower in vitamin C, characteristics that reduce iron absorption. Furthermore, the higher protein concentration of cow's milk can stress the infant's kidneys. In short, cow's milk is a poor choice during the first year of life; infants need breast milk or iron-fortified infant formula.

Introducing Solid Foods

The high nutrient needs of infancy are met first by breast milk or formula only and then by the limited addition of selected foods over time. Infants gradually develop the ability to chew, swallow, and digest the wide variety of foods available to adults. The caregiver's selection of appropriate foods at the appropriate stages of development is prerequisite to the infant's optimal growth and health.

When to Begin In addition to breast milk or formula, an infant can begin eating solid foods between four and six months.[29] The AAP supports exclusive breastfeeding for six months but recognizes that infants are often developmentally ready to accept complementary foods between four and six months of age.[30] The main purpose of introducing solid foods is to provide needed nutrients that are no longer supplied adequately by breast milk or formula alone. The foods chosen must be those ◆ that the infant is developmentally capable of handling both physically and metabolically. The exact timing depends on the individual infant's needs and developmental readiness (see Table 16-3), which vary from infant to infant because of differences in growth rates, activities, and environmental conditions. ◆ In short, the addition of foods to an infant's diet should be governed by three considerations: the infant's nutrient needs, the infant's physical readiness to handle different forms of foods, and the need to detect and control allergic reactions.

Food Allergies To prevent allergy and to facilitate its prompt identification should it occur, experts recommend introducing single-ingredient foods, one at a time, in small portions, and waiting four to five days before introducing the next new food.[31] For example, rice cereal is usually the first cereal introduced because it

◆ The German word **beikost** (BYE-cost) describes any nonmilk foods given to an infant.

◆ Digestive secretions gradually increase throughout the first year of life, making the digestion of solid foods more efficient.

TABLE 16-3 Infant Development and Recommended Foods

Because each stage of development builds on the previous stage, the foods from an earlier stage continue to be included in all later stages.

Age (mo)	Feeding Skill	Appropriate Foods Added to the Diet
0–4	Turns head toward any object that brushes cheek. Initially swallows using back of tongue; gradually begins to swallow using front of tongue as well. Strong reflex (extrusion) to push food out during first 2 to 3 months.	Feed breast milk or infant formula.
4–6	Extrusion reflex diminishes, and the ability to swallow nonliquid foods develops. Indicates desire for food by opening mouth and leaning forward. Indicates satiety or disinterest by turning away and leaning back. Sits erect with support at 6 months. Begins chewing action. Brings hand to mouth. Grasps objects with palm of hand.	Begin iron-fortified cereal mixed with breast milk, formula, or water. Begin pureed vegetables and fruits.
6–8	Able to self-feed finger foods. Develops pincer (finger to thumb) grasp. Begins to drink from cup.	Begin textured vegetables and fruits. Begin unsweetened, diluted fruit juices from cup.
8–10	Begins to hold own bottle. Reaches for and grabs food and spoon. Sits unsupported.	Begin breads and cereals from table. Begin yogurt. Begin pieces of soft, cooked vegetables and fruit from table. Gradually begin finely cut meats, fish, casseroles, cheese, eggs, and mashed legumes.
10–12	Begins to master spoon, but still spills some.	Add variety. Gradually increase portion sizes.[a]

[a]Portion sizes for infants and young children are smaller than those for an adult. For example, a grain serving might be ½ slice of bread instead of 1 slice, or ¼ cup rice instead of ½ cup.

SOURCE: Adapted in part from Committee on Nutrition, American Academy of Pediatrics, *Pediatric Nutrition Handbook*, 5th ed., ed. R. E. Kleinman (Elk Grove Village, Ill.: American Academy of Pediatrics, 2004), pp. 103–115.

Foods such as iron-fortified cereals and formulas, mashed legumes, and strained meats provide iron.

is the least allergenic. When it is clear that rice cereal is not causing an allergy, another grain, perhaps barley or oats, is introduced. Wheat cereal is offered last because it is the most common offender. If a cereal causes an allergic reaction such as a skin rash, digestive upset, or respiratory discomfort, it should be discontinued before introducing the next food. A later section in this chapter offers more information about food allergies.

Choice of Infant Foods Infant foods should be selected to provide variety, balance, and moderation. Commercial baby foods offer a wide variety of palatable, nutritious foods in a safe and convenient form. Homemade infant foods can be as nutritious as commercially prepared ones, as long as the cook minimizes nutrient losses during preparation. Ingredients for homemade foods should be fresh, whole foods without added salt, sugar, or seasonings. Pureed food can be frozen in ice cube trays, providing convenient-sized blocks of food that can be thawed, warmed, and fed to the infant. To guard against foodborne illnesses, hands and equipment must be kept clean.

Because recommendations to restrict fat do not apply to children under age two, labels on foods for children under two (such as infant meats and cereals) cannot carry information about fat. Fat information is omitted from infant food labels to prevent parents from restricting fat in infants' diets. Fearing that their infant will become overweight, parents may unintentionally malnourish the infant by limiting fat. In fact, infants and young children, because of their rapid growth, need more fat than older children and adults.

Foods to Provide Iron Rapid growth demands iron. At about four to six months, the infant begins to need more iron than body stores plus breast milk or iron-fortified formula can provide. In addition to breast milk or iron-fortified formula, infants can receive iron from iron-fortified cereals and, once they readily accept solid foods, from meat or meat alternates such as legumes. Iron-fortified cereals contribute a significant amount of iron to an infant's diet, but the iron's bioavailability is poor.[32] Caregivers can enhance iron absorption from iron-fortified cereals by serving vitamin C–rich foods with meals.

Foods to Provide Vitamin C The best sources of vitamin C are fruits and vegetables (see pp. 354–355 in Chapter 10). It has been suggested that infants who are introduced to fruits before vegetables may develop a preference for sweets and find the vegetables less palatable, but there is no evidence to support offering these foods in a particular order.[33]

Fruit juice is a good source of vitamin C, but drinking too much juice can lead to diarrhea in infants and young children.[34] AAP recommendations limit juice consumption for infants and young children (one to six years of age) to between 4 and 6 ounces per day.[35] Beyond these limits, fruit juices contribute excessive kcalories and displace other nutrient-rich foods. Fruit juices should be diluted and served in a cup, not a bottle, once the infant is six months of age or older.

Foods to Omit Concentrated sweets, including baby food "desserts," have no place in an infant's diet. They convey no nutrients to support growth, and the extra food energy can promote obesity. Products containing sugar alcohols such as sorbitol should also be limited, as they may cause diarrhea. Canned vegetables are also inappropriate for infants, as they often contain too much sodium. Honey and corn syrup should never be fed to infants because of the risk of **botulism.*** Infants and young children are vulnerable to foodborne illnesses, and the *Dietary Guidelines 2005* address this risk.

---

botulism (BOT-chew-lism): an often fatal foodborne illness caused by the ingestion of foods containing a toxin produced by bacteria that grow without oxygen. (See Chapter 19 for details.)

---

* In infants, but not in older individuals, ingestion of *Clostridium botulinum* spores can cause illness when the spores germinate in the intestine and produce a toxin, which is absorbed. Symptoms include poor feeding, constipation, loss of tension in the arteries and muscles, weakness, and respiratory compromise. Infant botulism has been implicated in 5 percent of cases of sudden infant death syndrome (SIDS).

Dietary Guidelines for Americans 2005

Infants and young children should not eat or drink unpasteurized milk, milk products, or juices; raw or undercooked eggs, meat, poultry, fish, or shellfish; or raw sprouts.

Ideally, a one-year-old eats many of the same foods as the rest of the family.

Infants and even young children cannot safely chew and swallow any of the foods listed in the margin; ◆ they can easily choke on these foods, a risk not worth taking. Nonfood items may present even greater choking hazards to infants and young children.[36] Parents and caregivers must pay careful attention to eliminate choking hazards in children's environments.

Vegetarian Diets during Infancy   The newborn infant is a lactovegetarian. As long as the infant has access to sufficient quantities of either infant formula or breast milk (plus a vitamin D supplement) from a mother who eats an adequate diet, the infant will thrive during the early months. "Health-food beverages," such as rice milk, are inappropriate choices because they lack the protein, vitamins, and minerals infants and toddlers need; in fact, their use can lead to severe nutritional deficiencies.

Infants beyond about six months of age present a greater challenge in terms of meeting nutrient needs by way of vegetarian and, especially, vegan diets. Continued breastfeeding or formula feeding is recommended, but supplementary feedings are necessary to ensure adequate energy and iron intakes. Infants and young children in vegetarian families should be given iron-fortified infant cereals well into the second year. Mashed or pureed legumes, tofu, and cooked eggs can be added to their diets in place of meat.

The risks of malnutrition in infants increase with weaning and reliance on table foods. Infants who receive a well-balanced vegetarian diet that includes milk products and a variety of other foods can easily meet their nutritional requirements for growth. This is not always true for vegan infants; the growth of vegan infants slows significantly around the time of transition from breast milk to solid foods. Protein-energy malnutrition and deficiencies of vitamin D, vitamin B_{12}, iron, and calcium have been reported in infants fed vegan diets. Vegan diets that are high in fiber, other complex carbohydrates, and water will fill infants' stomachs before meeting their energy needs. This problem can be partially alleviated by providing more energy-dense foods, such as nut butters, legumes, dried fruit spreads, and mashed avocado. Using soy formulas (or milk) fortified with calcium, vitamin B_{12}, and vitamin D and including vitamin C–containing foods at meals to enhance iron absorption will help prevent other nutrient deficiencies in vegan diets. Parents or caregivers who choose to feed their infants vegan diets should consult with their pediatrician and a registered dietitian frequently to ensure a nutritionally adequate diet that will support growth.

Foods at One Year   At one year of age, whole cow's milk can become a primary source of most of the nutrients an infant needs; 2 to 3 cups a day meets those needs sufficiently. Ingesting more milk than this can displace iron-rich foods, which can lead to **milk anemia.** If powdered milk is used, it should contain fat.

Other foods—meats, iron-fortified cereals, enriched or whole-grain breads, fruits, and vegetables—should be supplied in variety and in amounts sufficient to round out total energy needs. Ideally, a one-year-old will sit at the table, eat many of the same foods everyone else eats, and drink liquids from a cup, not a bottle. Figure 16-6 shows a meal plan that meets a one-year-old's requirements.

Mealtimes with Toddlers

The nurturing of a young child involves more than nutrition. Those who care for young children are responsible not only for providing nutritious milk, foods, and water, but also a safe, loving, secure environment in which the children may grow

---

◆ To prevent choking, do not give infants or young children:

- Raw carrots
- Cherries
- Gum
- Hard or gel-type candies
- Hot dog slices
- Marshmallows

- Nuts
- Peanut butter
- Popcorn
- Raw celery
- Whole beans
- Whole grapes

Keep these nonfood items out of their reach:

- Coins
- Small balls

- Balloons
- Pen tops

FIGURE 16-6   Sample Meal Plan for a One-Year-Old

✳ SAMPLE MENU ✳

Breakfast	½ c iron-fortified, unsweetened breakfast cereal
	¼ c whole milk (with cereal)
	½ c orange juice
Morning snack	½ c yogurt
	½ c fruit[a]
Lunch	½ sandwich: 1 slice bread with 2 tbs tuna salad or egg salad
	½ c vegetables[b] (steamed carrots)
	½ c whole milk
Afternoon snack	½ slice whole-wheat toast
	1 tbs apple butter
	½ c whole milk
Dinner	1 oz chopped meat or ¼ c well-cooked mashed legumes
	¼ c potato, rice, or pasta
	½ c vegetables[b] (chopped broccoli)
	½ c whole milk

[a]Include citrus fruits, melons, and berries.
[b]Include dark green, leafy and deep yellow vegetables.

---

milk anemia: iron-deficiency anemia that develops when an excessive milk intake displaces iron-rich foods from the diet.

Toddlers need vitamin A– and vitamin D– fortified whole milk.

and develop. In light of toddlers' developmental and nutrient needs and their often contrary and willful behavior, a few feeding guidelines may be helpful:

- Discourage unacceptable behavior, such as standing at the table or throwing food, by removing the young child from the table to wait until later to eat. Be consistent and firm, not punitive. The child will soon learn to sit and eat.
- Let toddlers explore and enjoy food, even if this means eating with fingers for a while. Learning to use a spoon will come in time.
- Don't force food on children. Rejecting new foods is normal and acceptance is more likely as children become familiar with new foods through repeated opportunities to taste them.
- Provide nutritious foods, and let children choose which ones, and how much, they will eat. Gradually, they will acquire a taste for different foods.
- Limit sweets. Infants and young children have little room for empty-kcalorie foods in their daily energy allowance. Do not use sweets as a reward for eating meals.
- Don't turn the dining table into a battleground. Make mealtimes enjoyable. Teach healthy food choices and eating habits in a pleasant environment.

IN SUMMARY

The primary food for infants during the first 12 months is either breast milk or iron-fortified formula. In addition to nutrients, breast milk also offers immunological protection. At about four to six months, infants should gradually begin eating solid foods. By one year, they are drinking from a cup and eating many of the same foods as the rest of the family.

Nutrition during Childhood

Each year from age one to adolescence, a child typically grows taller by 2 to 3 inches and heavier by 5 to 6 pounds. Growth charts provide valuable clues to a child's health. Weight gains out of proportion to height gains may reflect overeating and inactivity, whereas measures significantly below the standard suggest malnutrition.

Increases in height and weight are only two of the many changes growing children experience (see Figure 16-7). At age one, children can stand alone and are beginning to toddle; by two, they can walk and are learning to run; and by three, they can jump and climb with confidence. Bones and muscles increase in mass and density to make these accomplishments possible. Thereafter, lengthening of the long bones and increases in musculature proceed unevenly and more slowly until adolescence.

Energy and Nutrient Needs

Children's appetites begin to diminish around one year, consistent with the slowing growth. Thereafter, children spontaneously vary their food intakes to coincide with their growth patterns; they demand more food during periods of rapid growth than during slow growth. Sometimes they seem insatiable, and other times they seem to live on air and water.

Children's energy intakes also vary widely from meal to meal. Even so, their total daily intakes remain remarkably constant.[37] If children eat less at one meal, they typically eat more at the next, and vice versa. Overweight children are exceptions: they do not always adjust their energy intakes appropriately and may eat in response to external cues, disregarding hunger and satiety signals.

Energy Intake and Activity Individual children's energy needs vary widely, depending on their growth and physical activity. A one-year-old child needs about 800 kcalo-

FIGURE 16-7 Body Shape of One-Year-Old and Two-Year-Old Compared

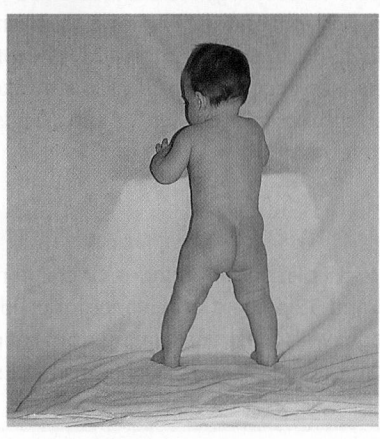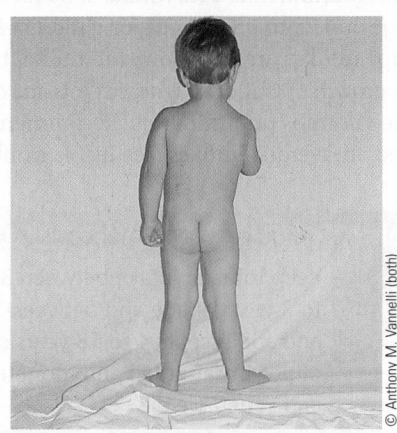

The body shape of a one-year-old (left) changes dramatically by age two (right). The two-year-old has lost much of the baby fat; the muscles (especially in the back, buttocks, and legs) have firmed and strengthened; and the leg bones have lengthened.

ries a day; an active six-year-old needs twice as many kcalories a day. By age ten, an active child needs about 2000 kcalories a day. Total energy needs increase slightly with age, but energy needs per kilogram of body weight actually decline gradually.

Physically active children of any age need more energy because they expend more, and inactive children can become obese even when they eat less food than the average. Unfortunately, our nation's children are becoming less and less active, with young girls showing a marked reduction in their physical activity. Schools would serve our children well by offering activities to promote physical fitness.[38] Children who learn to enjoy physical play and exercise, both at home and at school, are best prepared to maintain active lifestyles as adults.

Dietary Guidelines for Americans 2005

Children should engage in at least 60 minutes of physical activity on most, preferably all, days of the week.

Some children, notably those adhering to a vegan diet, may have difficulty meeting their energy needs. Grains, vegetables, and fruits provide plenty of fiber, adding bulk, but may provide too few kcalories to support growth. Soy products, other legumes, and nut or seed butters offer more concentrated sources of energy to support optimal growth and development.[39]

Carbohydrate and Fiber Carbohydrate recommendations are based on glucose use by the brain. After one year of age, brain glucose use remains fairly constant and is within the adult range. Carbohydrate recommendations for children from the age of one year on are therefore the same as for adults (see inside front cover).[40]

Fiber recommendations ◆ derive from adult intakes shown to reduce the risk of coronary heart disease and are based on energy intakes. Consequently, fiber recommendations for younger children with low energy intakes are less than those for older ones with high energy intakes.[41]

Dietary Guidelines for Americans 2005

Children and adolescents should consume whole-grain products often, and at least half of the grains should be whole grains.

◆ Fiber recommendations for children:

Age (yr)	AI (g/day)
1–3	19
4–8	25
9–13	
Boys	31
Girls	26
14–18	
Boys	38
Girls	26

Fat and Fatty Acids No RDA for total fat has been established, but the DRI Committee recommends a fat intake of 30 to 40 percent of energy for children 1 to 3 years of age and 25 to 35 percent for children 4 to 18 years of age.[42] As long as children's energy intakes are adequate, fat intakes below 30 percent of total energy do not impair growth.[43] Children who eat low-fat diets, however, tend to have low intakes of some vitamins and minerals. Recommended intakes of the essential fatty acids are based on average intakes (see inside front cover).

Dietary Guidelines for Americans 2005

Keep total fat intake between 30 to 35 percent of kcalories for children 2 to 3 years of age and between 25 and 35 percent of kcalories for children and adolescents 4 to 18 years of age, with most fats coming from sources of polyunsaturated and monounsaturated fatty acids, such as fish, nuts, and vegetable oils.

Protein Like energy needs, total protein needs increase slightly with age, but when the child's body weight is considered, the protein requirement actually declines slightly (see inside front cover). Protein recommendations must consider the requirements for maintaining nitrogen balance, the quality of protein consumed, and the added needs of growth.

Vitamins and Minerals The vitamin and mineral needs of children increase with age (see inside front cover). A balanced diet of nutritious foods can meet children's needs for these nutrients, with the notable exception of iron. Iron-deficiency anemia is a major problem worldwide, as well as being prevalent among U.S. and Canadian children, especially toddlers one to two years of age.[44] During the second year of life, toddlers progress from a diet of iron-rich infant foods such as breast milk, iron-fortified formula, and iron-fortified infant cereal to a diet of adult foods and iron-poor cow's milk. In addition, their appetites often fluctuate—some become finicky about the foods they eat, and others prefer milk and juice to solid foods.[45] All of these situations can interfere with children eating iron-rich foods at a critical time for brain growth and development.

To prevent iron deficiency, children's foods must deliver 7 to 10 milligrams of iron per day. To achieve this goal, snacks and meals should include iron-rich foods, and milk intake should be reasonable so that it will not displace lean meats, fish, poultry, eggs, legumes, and whole-grain or enriched products. (Chapter 13 described iron-rich foods and ways to maximize iron absorption.)

Supplements With the exception of specific recommendations for fluoride, iron, and vitamin D during infancy and childhood, the AAP and other professional groups agree that well-nourished children do not need vitamin and mineral supplements. Despite this, many children and adolescents take supplements.[46] Ironically, children with poor nutrient intakes typically do not receive supplements, and those who do take supplements typically receive extra nutrients they do not need.[47] Furthermore, researchers are still studying the safety of supplement use by children.[48] The Federal Trade Commission has warned parents about giving supplements advertised to prevent or cure childhood illnesses such as colds, ear infections, or asthma. Dietary supplements on the market today include many herbal products that have not been tested for safety and effectiveness in children.

Planning Children's Meals To provide all the needed nutrients, children's meals should include a variety of foods from each food group—in amounts suited to their appetites and needs. Figure 16-8 presents MyPyramid ◆ designed for children 6 to 11 years of age and includes the recommended amounts of food for an 1800-kcalorie intake. Table 16-4 (p. 562) lists amounts of food for several kcalorie levels below 1800 kcalories, which are appropriate for most younger children and sedentary older children. Review Table 2-3 on page 41 for recommended daily amounts of foods from each group for higher kcalorie levels, which are appropriate for active older children.

◆ www.MyPyramid.gov/kids

FIGURE 16-8   Food Guide Pyramid for Young Children

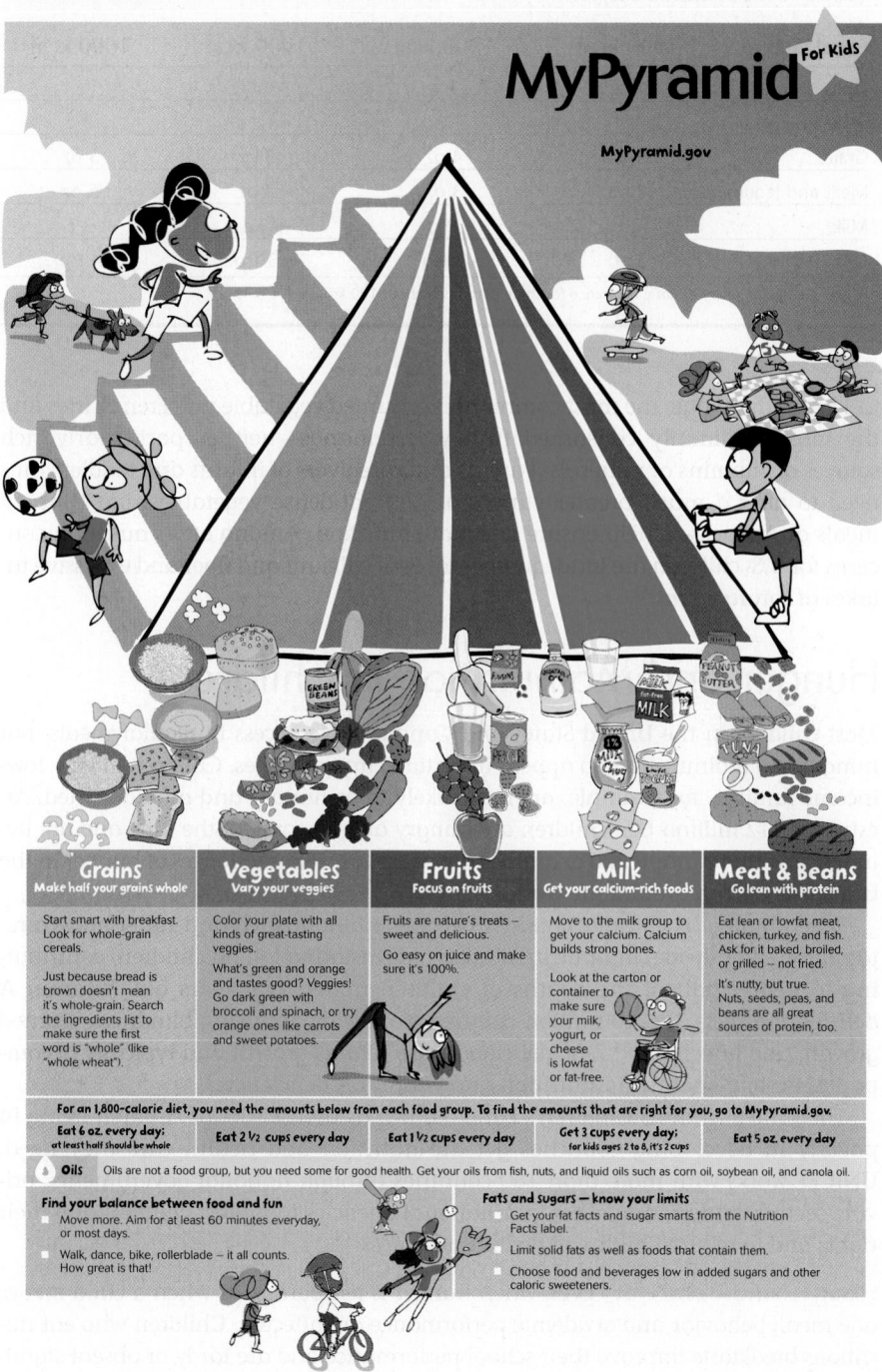

Estimated daily kcalorie needs for active and sedentary children of various ages are shown in Table 16-5 (p. 562).

Children whose diets follow the pattern presented in Figure 16-8 meet their nutrient needs fully, but few children eat according to these recommendations. Based on an analysis of the most recent national food intake data, the USDA found that most (81 percent) children between two and nine years of age have diets that need substantial improvement.[49] A comprehensive survey, called the Feeding Infants and Toddlers Study (FITS), assessed the food and nutrient intakes of more than 3000 infants and toddlers.[50] The survey found that fruit and vegetable intakes of infants and toddlers are limited, and in fact, about 25 percent of infants and toddlers older than 9 months did not eat a single serving of fruits or vegetables in a day.[51] By 15

TABLE 16-4 Recommended Daily Amounts from Each Food Group (1000 to 1600 kCalories)				
Food Group	1000 kcal	1200 kcal	1400 kcal	1600 kcal
Fruits	1 c	1 c	1½ c	1½ c
Vegetables	1 c	1½ c	1½ c	2 c
Grains	3 oz	4 oz	5 oz	5 oz
Meat and legumes	2 oz	3 oz	4 oz	5 oz
Milk	2 c	2 c	2 c	3 c
Oils	3 tsp	3 tsp	3 tsp	4 tsp

NOTE: The discretionary kcalorie allowance for these patterns is about 100 kcalories.

TABLE 16-5 Estimated Daily kCalorie Needs for Children		
Children	Sedentary[a]	Active[b]
2 to 3 yr	1000	1400
Females		
4 to 8 yr	1200	1800
9 to 13 yr	1600	2200
Males		
4 to 8 yr	1400	2000
9 to 13 yr	1800	2600

[a] *Sedentary* describes a lifestyle that includes only the activities typical of day-to-day life.
[b] *Active* describes a lifestyle that includes at least 60 minutes per day of moderate physical activity (equivalent to walking more than 3 miles per day at 3 to 4 miles per hour) in addition to the activities of day-to-day life.

to 18 months of age, the most commonly consumed vegetable was French fries and the most commonly consumed fruit was bananas—neither particularly rich sources of vitamins or minerals. Parents and caregivers of infants and toddlers thus need to offer a much greater variety of nutrient-dense vegetables and fruits at meals and snacks to help ensure adequate nutrition. Among other nutrition concerns for U.S. children are inadequate intakes of calcium and fiber and excessive intakes of saturated fat.[52]

Hunger and Malnutrition in Children

Most children in the United States and Canada have access to regular meals, but hunger and malnutrition do appear in certain circumstances. Children in very low-income families, for example, are more likely to be hungry and malnourished. An estimated 12 million U.S. children are hungry at least some of the time and are living in poverty.[53] Chapter 20 examines the causes and consequences of hunger in the United States and around the world.

When hunger is chronic, children become malnourished and suffer growth retardation. Worldwide, malnutrition takes a devastating toll on children, contributing to nearly half of the deaths of children under four years old. Vitamin A deficiency afflicts 3 to 10 million children worldwide, inducing blindness, stunted growth, and infections.[54] Zinc deficiency also retards growth and typically accompanies protein-energy malnutrition and vitamin A deficiency.

The United Nations Children's Fund, known as UNICEF, helps children living in poverty in developing countries get the nutrition and health care they need. UNICEF works with more than 160 countries through national governments, private-sector partners, and other international agencies to protect children and their rights and to reduce childhood death and illness.

Hunger and Behavior Even when hunger is temporary, as when a child misses one meal, behavior and academic performance are affected. Children who eat nutritious breakfasts improve their school performance and are tardy or absent significantly less often than their peers who do not. A nutritious breakfast is a central feature of a diet that meets the needs of children and supports their healthy growth and development.[55] Children who skip breakfast typically do not make up the deficits at later meals—they simply have lower intakes of energy, vitamins, and minerals than those who eat breakfast. Without breakfast, children perform poorly in tasks requiring concentration, their attention spans are shorter, and they even score lower on intelligence tests than their well-fed peers. Malnourished children are particularly vulnerable. Common sense dictates that it is unreasonable to expect anyone to learn and perform without fuel. For the child who hasn't had breakfast, the morning's lessons may be lost altogether. Even if a child has eaten breakfast, discomfort from hunger may become distracting by late morning. Teachers aware of the late-morning slump in their classrooms wisely request that midmorning snacks be provided; snacks improve classroom performance all the way to lunchtime.

Iron Deficiency and Behavior Iron deficiency has well-known and widespread effects on children's behavior and intellectual performance.[56] In addition to carrying oxygen in the blood, iron transports oxygen within cells, which use it for energy metabolism. Iron is also used to make neurotransmitters—most notably, those that regulate the ability to pay attention, which is crucial to learning. Consequently, iron deficiency not only causes an energy crisis, but also directly impairs attention span and learning ability.

Iron deficiency is often diagnosed by a quick, easy, inexpensive hemoglobin or hematocrit test that detects a deficit of iron in the *blood*. A child's *brain,* however, is sensitive to low iron concentrations long before the blood effects appear. Iron deficiency lowers the "motivation to persist in intellectually challenging tasks" and impairs overall intellectual performance. Anemic children perform poorly on tests and are disruptive in the classroom; iron supplementation improves learning and memory. When combined with other nutrient deficiencies, iron-deficiency anemia has synergistic effects that are especially detrimental to learning. Furthermore, children who had iron-deficiency anemia *as infants* continue to perform poorly as they grow older, even if their iron status improves.[57] The long-term damaging effects on mental development make prevention and treatment of iron deficiency during infancy and early childhood a high priority.

Healthy, well-nourished children are alert in the classroom and energetic at play.

Other Nutrient Deficiencies and Behavior A child with any of several nutrient deficiencies may be irritable, aggressive, and disagreeable, or sad and withdrawn. Such a child may be labeled "hyperactive," "depressed," or "unlikable," when in fact these traits may be due to simple, even marginal, malnutrition. Parents and medical practitioners often overlook the possibility that malnutrition may account for abnormalities of appearance and behavior. Any departure from normal healthy appearance and behavior is a sign of possible poor nutrition (see Table 16-6). In any such case, inspection of the child's diet by a registered dietitian or other qualified health care professional is in order. Any suspicion of dietary inadequacies, no matter what other causes may be implicated, should prompt steps to correct those inadequacies immediately.

TABLE 16-6	Physical Signs of Malnutrition in Children		
	Well-Nourished	**Malnourished**	**Possible Nutrient Deficiencies**
Hair	Shiny, firm in the scalp	Dull, brittle, dry, loose; falls out	PEM
Eyes	Bright, clear pink membranes; adjust easily to light	Pale membranes; spots; redness; adjust slowly to darkness	Vitamin A, the B vitamins, zinc, and iron
Teeth and gums	No pain or caries, gums firm, teeth bright	Missing, discolored, decayed teeth; gums bleed easily and are swollen and spongy	Minerals and vitamin C
Face	Clear complexion without dryness or scaliness	Off-color, scaly, flaky, cracked skin	PEM, vitamin A, and iron
Glands	No lumps	Swollen at front of neck, cheeks	PEM and iodine
Tongue	Red, bumpy, rough	Sore, smooth, purplish, swollen	B vitamins
Skin	Smooth, firm, good color	Dry, rough, spotty; "sandpaper" feel or sores; lack of fat under skin	PEM, essential fatty acids, vitamin A, B vitamins, and vitamin C
Nails	Firm, pink	Spoon-shaped, brittle, ridged	Iron
Internal systems	Regular heart rhythm, heart rate, and blood pressure; no impairment of digestive function, reflexes, or mental status	Abnormal heart rate, heart rhythm, or blood pressure; enlarged liver, spleen; abnormal digestion; burning, tingling of hands, feet; loss of balance, coordination; mental confusion, irritability, fatigue	PEM and minerals
Muscles and bones	Muscle tone; posture, long bone development appropriate for age	"Wasted" appearance of muscles; swollen bumps on skull or ends of bones; small bumps on ribs; bowed legs or knock-knees	PEM, minerals, and vitamin D

Old, lead-based paint threatens the health of an exploring child.

The Malnutrition-Lead Connection

Children who are malnourished are vulnerable to lead poisoning. They absorb more lead if their stomachs are empty; if they have low intakes of calcium, zinc, vitamin C, or vitamin D; and, of greatest concern because it is so common, if they have iron deficiencies. Iron deficiency weakens the body's defenses against lead absorption, and lead poisoning can cause iron deficiency. Common to both iron deficiency and lead poisoning are a low socioeconomic background and a lack of immunizations against infectious diseases. Another common factor is pica—a craving for nonfood items. Many children with lead poisoning eat dirt or chips of old paint, two common sources of lead.

The anemia brought on by lead poisoning may be mistaken for a simple iron deficiency and therefore may be incorrectly treated. Like iron deficiency, mild lead toxicity has nonspecific symptoms, including diarrhea, irritability, and fatigue. Adding iron to the diet does not reverse the symptoms; exposure to lead must stop and treatment for lead poisoning must begin. With further exposure, the symptoms become more pronounced, and children develop learning disabilities and behavioral problems. Still more severe lead toxicity can cause irreversible nerve damage, paralysis, mental retardation, and death.

More than 300,000 children in the United States—most of them under age six—have blood lead concentrations high enough to cause mental, behavioral, and other health problems.[58] Lead toxicity in young children comes from their own behaviors and activities—putting their hands in their mouths, playing in dirt and dust, and chewing on nonfood items.[59] Unfortunately, the body readily absorbs lead during times of rapid growth and hoards it possessively thereafter. Lead is not easily excreted and accumulates mainly in the bones, but also in the brain, teeth, and kidneys. Tragically, a child's neuromuscular system is also maturing during these first few years of life. No wonder children with elevated lead levels experience impairment of balance, motor development, and the relaying of nerve messages to and from the brain. Deficits in intellectual development are only partially reversed when lead levels decline.[60]

Federal laws mandating reductions in leaded gasolines, lead-based solder, and other products over the past four decades have helped to reduce the amounts of lead in food and in the environment in the United States. As a consequence, the prevalence of lead toxicity in children has declined dramatically for most of the United States, but lead exposure is still a threat in certain communities.[61] The accompanying "How to" presents strategies for defending children against lead toxicity.

Hyperactivity and "Hyper" Behavior

All children are naturally active, and many of them become overly active on occasion—for example, in anticipation of a birthday party. Such behavior is markedly different from true **hyperactivity.**

Hyperactivity Hyperactive children have trouble sleeping, cannot sit still for more than a few minutes at a time, act impulsively, and have difficulty paying attention. These behaviors interfere with social development and academic progress. The cause of hyperactivity remains unknown, but it affects about 5 to 10 percent of young school-age children.[62] To resolve the problems surrounding hyperactivity, physicians often recommend specific behavioral strategies, special educational programs, and psychological counseling. In many cases, they prescribe medication.[63]

Parents of hyperactive children sometimes seek help from alternative therapies, including special diets. They mistakenly believe a solution may lie in manipulating the diet—most commonly, by excluding sugar or food additives. Adding carrots or eliminating candy is such a simple solution that many parents eagerly give such dietary advice a try. However, these dietary changes will not solve the problem, and studies have consistently found no convincing evidence that sugar causes hyperactivity or worsens behavior.

hyperactivity: inattentive and impulsive behavior that is more frequent and severe than is typical of others a similar age; professionally called **attention-deficit/hyperactivity disorder (ADHD).**

HOW TO Protect against Lead Toxicity

Researchers simultaneously made three major discoveries about lead toxicity: lead poisoning has *subtle* effects, the effects are *permanent,* and they occur at *low levels of exposure.* The amount of lead recognized to cause harm is only 10 micrograms per 100 milliliters of blood. Some research shows that blood lead concentrations *below* this amount may adversely affect children's scores on intelligence tests.[a] Consequently, consumers should take ultraconservative measures to protect themselves, and especially their infants and young children, from lead poisoning. The American Academy of Pediatrics and the Centers for Disease Control recommend screening in communities with a substantial number of houses built before 1950 and in those with a substantial number of children with elevated lead levels. In addition to screening children most likely to be exposed, pediatricians should alert all parents to the possible dangers of lead exposure and explain prevention strategies.

Preventive strategies include:

- In contaminated environments, keep small children from putting dirty or old painted objects in their mouths, and make sure children wash their hands before eating. Similarly, keep small children from eating any nonfood items. Lead poisoning has been reported in young children who have eaten crayons or pool cue chalk.
- Wet-mop floors and damp-sponge walls regularly. Children's blood lead levels decline when the homes they live in are cleaned regularly.
- Be aware that other countries do not have the same regulations protecting consumers against lead. Children have been poisoned by eating crayons made in China and drinking fruit juice canned in Mexico.
- Do not use lead-contaminated water to make infant formula.
- Once you have opened canned food, store it in a lead-free container to prevent lead migration into the food.
- Do not store acidic foods or beverages (such as vinegar or orange juice) in ceramic dishware or alcoholic beverages in pewter or crystal decanters.
- Many manufacturers are now making lead-safe products. Old, handmade, or imported ceramic cups and bowls may contain lead and should not be used to heat coffee or tea or acidic foods such as tomato soup.
- U.S. wineries have stopped using lead in their foil seals, but older bottles may still be around, and other countries may still use lead. To be safe, wipe the foil-sealed rim of a wine bottle with a clean wet cloth before removing the cork.
- Feed children nutritious meals regularly.
- Before using your newspaper to wrap food, mulch garden plants, or add to your compost, confirm with the publisher that the paper uses no lead in its ink.

The Environmental Protection Agency (EPA) also publishes a booklet, *Lead and Your Drinking Water,* in which the following cautions appear:

- Have the water in your home tested by a competent laboratory.
- Use only cold water for drinking, cooking, and making formula (cold water absorbs less lead).
- When water has been standing in pipes for more than two hours, flush the cold-water pipes by running water through them for 30 seconds before using it for drinking, cooking, or mixing formulas.
- If lead contamination of your water supply seems probable, obtain additional information and advice from the EPA and your local public health agency.

By taking these steps, parents can protect themselves and their children from this preventable danger.[b]

[a] R. L. Canfield and coauthors, Intellectual impairment in children with blood lead concentrations below 10 µg per deciliter, *New England Journal of Medicine* 348 (2003): 1517–1526.

[b] Call the National Lead Information Center hotline at (800) 424-LEAD (424-5323) for general information.

Misbehaving Even a child who is not truly hyperactive can be difficult to manage at times. Michael may act unruly out of a desire for attention, Jessica may be cranky because of a lack of sleep, Christopher may react violently after watching too much television, and Sheila may be unable to sit still in class due to a lack of exercise. All of these children may benefit from more consistent care—regular hours of sleep, regular mealtimes, and regular outdoor activity.

Food Allergy and Intolerance

Food allergy is frequently blamed for physical and behavioral abnormalities in children, but just 6 percent of children are diagnosed with true food allergies.[64] Food allergies diminish with age, until in adulthood they affect only about 1 or 2 percent of the population.[65]

A true food allergy occurs when fractions of a food protein or other large molecule are absorbed into the blood and elicit an immunologic response. (Recall that proteins are normally dismantled in the digestive tract to amino acids that are absorbed without such a reaction.) The body's immune system reacts to these large food molecules as it does to other antigens—by producing antibodies, histamines, or other defensive agents.

Detecting Food Allergy Allergies may have one or two components. They always involve antibodies, but they may or may not involve symptoms. ◆ This means

◆ A person who produces antibodies *without* having any symptoms has an **asymptomatic allergy;** a person who produces antibodies *and* has symptoms has a **symptomatic allergy.**

food allergy: an adverse reaction to food that involves an immune response; also called **food-hypersensitivity reaction.**

These normally wholesome foods may cause life-threatening symptoms in people with allergies.

© Polara Studios, Inc.

♦ Symptoms of impending anaphylactic shock:
  • Tingling sensation in mouth
  • Swelling of the tongue and throat
  • Irritated, reddened eyes
  • Difficulty breathing, asthma
  • Hives, swelling, rashes
  • Vomiting, abdominal cramps, diarrhea
  • Drop in blood pressure
  • Loss of consciousness
  • Death

♦ Reminder: *Epinephrine* is a hormone of the adrenal gland that modulates the stress response; formerly called **adrenaline.** When administered by injection, epinephrine counteracts anaphylactic shock by opening the airways and maintaining heartbeat and blood pressure.

anaphylactic (ana- fill-LAC-tic) **shock:** a life-threatening, whole-body allergic reaction to an offending substance.

adverse reactions: unusual responses to food (including intolerances and allergies).

food intolerances: adverse reactions to foods that do not involve the immune system.

that allergies can be diagnosed only by testing for antibodies. Even symptoms exactly like those of an allergy may not be caused by an allergy. However, once a food allergy has been diagnosed, the required treatment is strict elimination of the offending food. Children with allergies, like all children, need all their nutrients, so it is important to include other foods that offer the same nutrients as the omitted foods.[66]

Allergic reactions to food may be immediate or delayed. In either case, the antigen interacts immediately with the immune system, but the timing of symptoms varies from minutes to 24 hours after consumption of the antigen. Identifying the food that causes an immediate allergic reaction is fairly easy because the symptoms appear shortly after the food is eaten. Identifying the food that causes a delayed reaction is more difficult because the symptoms may not appear until much later. By this time, many other foods may have been eaten, complicating the picture.

Anaphylactic Shock   The life-threatening food allergy reaction of **anaphylactic shock** is most often caused by peanuts, tree nuts, milk, eggs, wheat, soybeans, fish, or shellfish. Among these foods, eggs, milk, soy, and peanuts most often cause problems in children. Children are more likely to outgrow allergies to eggs, milk, and soy than allergies to peanuts. Peanuts cause more life-threatening reactions than do all other food allergies combined. Research is currently under way to help people with peanut allergies tolerate small doses, thus saving lives and minimizing reactions.[67] One possible solution depends on finding a natural, hypoallergenic peanut among the 14,000 varieties of peanuts. Families of children with a life-threatening food allergy and school personnel who supervise them must guard them against any exposure to the allergen. The child must learn to identify which foods pose a problem and then learn and use refusal skills for all foods that may contain the allergen.

Parents of children with allergies can pack safe foods for lunches and snacks and ask school officials to strictly enforce a "no swapping" policy in the lunchroom. The child must be able to recognize the symptoms of impending anaphylactic shock, ♦ such as a tingling of the tongue, throat, or skin, or difficulty breathing. Any person with food allergies severe enough to cause anaphylactic shock should wear a medical alert bracelet or necklace. Finally, the responsible child and the school staff should be prepared with injections of epinephrine, ♦ which prevents anaphylaxis after exposure to the allergen. Many preventable deaths occur each year when people with food allergies accidentally ingest the allergen but have no epinephrine available.

Food Labeling   As of 2006, food labels must list the presence of common allergens in plain language, using the names of the eight most common allergy-causing foods.[68] For example, a food containing "textured vegetable protein" must say "soy" on its label. Similarly, "casein" must be identified as "milk," and so forth. Food producers must also prevent cross-contamination during production and clearly label foods in which it is likely to occur.[69] For example, equipment used for making peanut butter must be scrupulously clean before being used to pulverize cashew nuts for cashew butter to protect unsuspecting cashew butter consumers from peanut allergens.

Technology may soon offer new solutions. New drugs are being developed that may interfere with the immune response that causes allergic reactions.[70] Also, through genetic engineering, scientists may one day create allergen-free peanuts, soybeans, and other foods to make them safer.

Food Intolerances   Not all **adverse reactions** to foods are food allergies, although even physicians may describe them as such. Signs of adverse reactions to foods include stomachaches, headaches, rapid pulse rate, nausea, wheezing, hives, bronchial irritation, coughs, and other such discomforts. Among the causes may be reactions to chemicals in foods, such as the flavor enhancer monosodium glutamate (MSG), the natural laxative in prunes, or the mineral sulfur; digestive diseases, such as obstructions or injuries; enzyme deficiencies, such as lactose intolerance; and even psychological aversions. These reactions involve symptoms but no antibody production. Therefore, they are **food intolerances,** not allergies.

Pesticides on produce may also cause adverse reactions. Pesticides that were applied in the fields may linger on the foods. Health risks from pesticide exposure may be low for healthy adults, but children are vulnerable. Therefore, government agencies have set a **tolerance level** for each pesticide by first identifying foods that children commonly eat in large amounts and then considering the effects of pesticide exposure during each developmental stage. Chapter 19 revisits the issues surrounding the use of pesticides on food crops.

Hunger, lead poisoning, hyperactivity, and allergic reactions can all adversely affect a child's nutrition status and health. Fortunately, each of these problems has solutions. They may not be easy solutions, but at least we have a reasonably good understanding of the problems and ways to correct them. Such is not the case with the most pervasive health problem for children in the United States—obesity.

Childhood Obesity

The number of overweight children has increased dramatically over the past three decades (see Figure 16-9). Like their parents, children in the United States are becoming fatter. An estimated 17 percent of U.S. children and adolescents 2 to 19 years of age are overweight.[71] Based on data from the BMI-for-age growth charts, children and adolescents are categorized as *at risk of overweight* above the 85th percentile and as *overweight* at the 95th percentile and above. Prevalence data reflect only children and adolescents in the overweight category. If those at risk of overweight were also included, the estimated 17 percent would likely double. Figure 16-10 (p. 568) presents the BMI for children and adolescents, indicating cutoff points for overweight and at risk of overweight.

The use of the term *overweight* instead of *obese* when referring to children with a BMI above the age- and gender-specific 95th percentiles is controversial. Some experts think it is best not to label children as obese, whereas others think it important to recognize the full extent of the problem. The Institute of Medicine's Committee on Prevention of Obesity in Children and Youth acknowledges the use of the term *overweight* to describe obese children but asserts that *obese* conveys the seriousness, urgency, medical nature, and need for immediate action more effectively than the term *overweight* does.[72]

The problem of obesity in children is especially troubling because overweight children have the potential of becoming obese adults with all the social, economic, and medical ramifications that often accompany obesity. They have additional problems, too, arising from differences in their growth, physical health, and psychological development. In trying to explain the rise in childhood obesity, researchers point to both genetic and environmental factors.

Genetic and Environmental Factors   Parental obesity predicts an early increase in a young child's BMI, and it more than doubles the chances that a young child will become an obese adult. Children with neither parent obese have a less than 10 percent chance of becoming obese in adulthood, whereas overweight teens with at least one obese parent have a greater than 80 percent chance of being obese adults. Also, as children grow older, their body weight becomes an important factor in determining their obesity as adults.[73] The link between parental and child obesity reflects both genetic and environmental factors (as described in Chapter 9).

Diet and physical inactivity must also play a role in explaining why children are heavier today than they were 30 or so years ago. As the prevalence of childhood obesity throughout the United States has more than doubled for young children and adolescents, and tripled for children 6 to 11 years of age, the society our children live in has changed considerably.[74] In many families today, both parents work outside the home and work longer hours; more emphasis is placed on convenience foods and foods eaten away from home; meal choices at school are more diverse and often less nutritious; sedentary activities such as watching television and playing video or computer games occupy much of children's free time; and opportunities for

FIGURE 16-9   Trends in Childhood Obesity

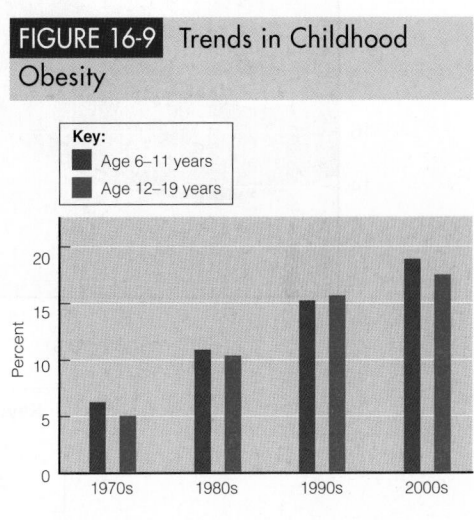

Key:
- ■ Age 6–11 years
- ■ Age 12–19 years

tolerance level: the maximum amount of residue permitted in a food when a pesticide is used according to the label directions.

FIGURE 16-10 Body Mass Index-for-Age Percentiles: Boys and Girls, Age 2 to 20

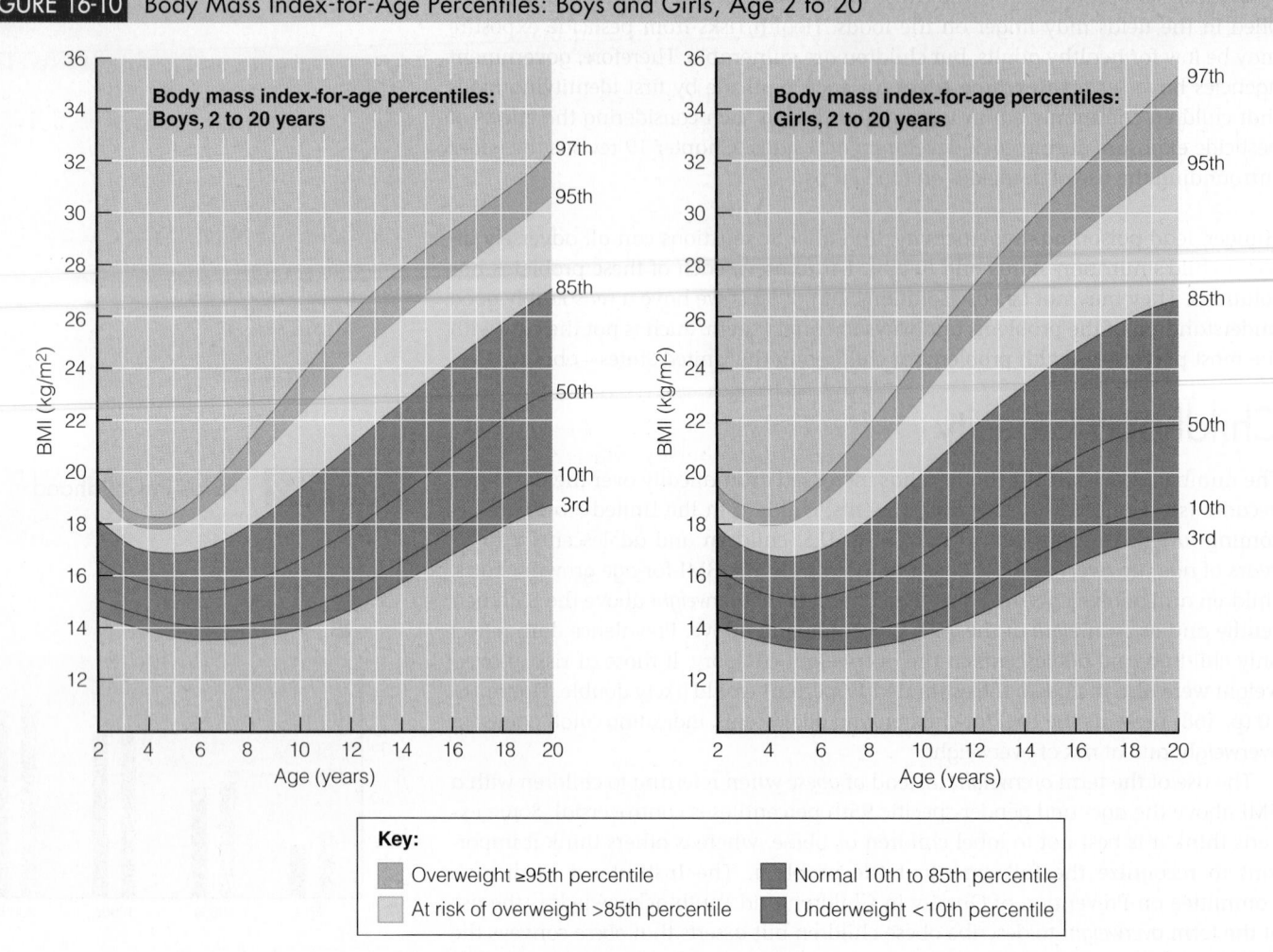

Key:
Overweight ≥95th percentile
At risk of overweight >85th percentile
Normal 10th to 85th percentile
Underweight <10th percentile

physical activity and outdoor play both during and after school have declined.[75] All of these factors—and many others—influence children's eating and activity patterns.

Children learn food behaviors from their families, and research confirms the significant roles parents play in teaching their children about healthy food choices, providing nutrient-dense foods, and serving as role models.[76] When parents eat fruits and vegetables frequently, their children do, too.[77] The more fruits and vegetables children eat, the more vitamins, minerals, and fibers, and the less saturated fat in their diets.

Research shows that one in four toddlers (19 to 24 months of age) exceeds estimated energy requirements as a result of eating such foods as candy, pizza, chicken nuggets, soda, sweet tea, and salty snacks like cheese puffs and chips.[78] Thus, when researchers ask, "Are today's children eating more kcalories than those of 30 years ago?" the answer is, "Yes." Some researchers report an increase of 100 to 200 kcalories a day for all age groups, enough to account for significant weight gains.[79]

Coincidentally or not, as the prevalence of obesity among both children and adults has surged over the past three decades, so has the consumption of added sugars and, especially, high-fructose corn syrup—the easily consumed, energy-dense liquid sugar added to soft drinks. Each 12-ounce can of soft drink provides the equivalent of about 10 teaspoons of sugar and 150 kcalories. More than half of children in school consume at least one soft drink each day at school; adolescent males consume the most—four or more cans daily.[80] According to one estimate, the risk of obesity increases by 60 percent with each sugared soft drink consumed daily.[81]

No doubt, the tremendous increase in soft drink consumption plays a role, but much of the obesity epidemic can be explained by lack of physical activity. Children have become more sedentary, and sedentary children are more often overweight.[82] Television watching ◆ may contribute most to physical inactivity. A child who spends more than an hour or two each day in front of a television, computer monitor, or other media can become overweight and develop unhealthy blood lipids even while eating fewer kcalories than a more active child.[83]

Children who have television sets in their bedrooms spend more time watching TV and are more likely to be overweight than children who do not have televisions in their rooms.[84] Children who watch a great deal of television are most likely to be overweight and least likely to eat family meals or fruits and vegetables.[85] They often snack on the nutrient-poor, energy-dense foods that are advertised.[86] The average child sees an estimated 30,000 TV commercials a year—many peddling foods high in sugar, saturated fat, and salt such as sugar-coated breakfast cereals, candy bars, chips, fast foods, and carbonated beverages. More than half of all food advertisements are aimed specifically at children and market their products as fun and exciting.[87] Not surprisingly, the more time children spend watching television, the more they request these advertised foods and beverages—and they get their requests about half of the time.[88] The most popular foods and beverages are marketed to children and adolescents on the Internet as well, using "advergaming" (advertised product as part of a game), cartoon characters or "spokes-characters," and designated children's areas.[89]

The physically inactive time spent watching television is second only to time spent sleeping. Children also spend more time playing video games. These activities use no more energy than resting, displace participation in more vigorous activities, and foster snacking on high-fat foods.[90] Simply reducing the amount of time spent watching television (and playing video games) can improve a child's BMI. The American Academy of Pediatrics (AAP) now recommends limiting television and video time to two hours per day as a strategy to help prevent childhood obesity.[91]

Growth Overweight children develop a characteristic set of physical traits. They typically begin puberty earlier and so grow taller than their peers at first, but then they stop growing at a shorter height. They develop greater bone and muscle mass in response to the demand of having to carry more weight—both fat and lean weight. Consequently, they appear "stocky" even when they lose their excess fat.

Physical Health Like overweight adults, overweight children display a blood lipid profile indicating that atherosclerosis is beginning to develop—high levels of total cholesterol, triglycerides, and LDL cholesterol. Overweight children also tend to have high blood pressure; in fact, obesity is a leading cause of pediatric hypertension.[92] Their risks for developing type 2 diabetes and respiratory diseases (such as asthma) are also exceptionally high.[93] These relationships between childhood obesity and chronic diseases are discussed fully in Highlight 16.

Psychological Development In addition to the physical consequences, childhood obesity brings a host of emotional and social problems.[94] Because people frequently judge others on appearance more than on character, overweight children are often victims of prejudice. Many suffer discrimination by adults and rejection by their peers. They may have poor self-images, a sense of failure, and a passive approach to life. Television shows, which are a major influence in children's lives, often portray the fat person as the bumbling misfit. Overweight children may come to accept this negative stereotype in themselves and in others, which can lead to additional emotional and social problems. Researchers investigating children's reactions to various body types find that both normal-weight and underweight children respond unfavorably to overweight bodies.

Prevention and Treatment of Obesity Medical science has worked wonders in preventing or curing many of even the most serious childhood diseases, but obesity remains a challenge.[95] Once excess fat has been stored, it is challenging to lose. In light of all this, parents are encouraged to make major efforts to prevent childhood

◆ TV fosters obesity because it:
- Requires no energy beyond basal metabolism
- Replaces vigorous activities
- Encourages snacking
- Promotes a sedentary lifestyle

Playing video games influences children's activity patterns similarly.

© Corbis

Television watching influences children's eating habits and activity patterns.

obesity or to begin treatment early—before adolescence.[96] Treatment must consider the many aspects of the problem and possible solutions. The most successful approach integrates diet, physical activity, psychological support, and behavioral changes.[97]

Diet The initial goal for overweight children is to reduce the rate of weight gain; that is, to maintain weight while the child grows taller. Continued growth will then accomplish the desired change in weight for height. Weight loss is usually not recommended because diet restriction can interfere with growth and development. Intervention for some older, overweight children with accompanying medical conditions may warrant weight loss, but this treatment requires an individualized approach based on the degree of overweight and severity of the medical conditions.[98] Whether the goal is to treat or prevent obesity, the following strategies may be helpful:

- Serve family meals that reflect kcalorie control both in the foods offered and in the ways foods are prepared.
- Involve children in shopping for food and preparing meals.
- Encourage children to eat only when they are hungry, to eat slowly, to pause and enjoy their table companions, and to stop eating when they are full.
- Teach them how to select nutrient-dense foods (low-fat and non-fat milk and milk products for children 3 years of age and older, fruits and vegetables, whole grains, legumes, fish, and lean meat) that will meet their nutrient needs within their energy allowances. Also, teach them to serve themselves appropriate portions at meals; the amount of food offered influences the amount of food eaten.[99]
- Limit foods high in saturated and *trans* fats (see Table H5-1 in Highlight 5) and high-sugar foods, including sugar-sweetened soft drinks.
- Never force children to clean their plates.
- Plan for snack times and provide a variety of nutritious snacks (see Table 16-8 later in this chapter).
- Discourage eating while watching TV.

Dietary Guidelines for Americans 2005

Help overweight children reduce the rate of body weight gain while allowing growth and development. Consult a healthcare provider before placing a child on a weight-reduction diet.

Physical Activity The many benefits of physical activity are well known but often are not enough to motivate overweight people, especially children. Yet regular vigorous activity can improve a child's weight, body composition, and physical fitness.[100] Ideally, parents will limit sedentary activities and encourage daily physical activity to promote strong skeletal, muscular, and cardiovascular development and instill in their children the desire to be physically active throughout life. Most importantly, parents need to set a good example. Physical activity is a natural and lifelong behavior of healthy living. It can be as simple as riding a bike, playing tag, jumping rope, or doing chores. It need not be an organized sport; it just needs to be some activity on a regular basis. The AAP supports the efforts of schools to include more physical activity in the curriculum and encourages parents to support their children's participation.[101]

Psychological Support Weight-loss programs that involve parents and other caregivers in treatment report greater success than those without parental involvement. Because obesity in parents and their children tends to be positively correlated, both benefit when parents participate in a weight-loss program. Parental attitudes about food greatly influence children's eating behavior, so it is important that the influence be positive. Otherwise, eating problems may become exacerbated.

Behavioral Changes In contrast to traditional weight-loss programs that focus on *what* to eat, behavioral programs focus on *how* to eat. These techniques involve changing learned habits that lead a child to eat excessively.

Obesity is prevalent in our society. Because treatment of obesity is frequently unsuccessful, it is most important to prevent its onset. Above all, be sensible in teaching children how to maintain appropriate body weight. Children can easily get the impression that their worth is tied to their body weight. Parents and the media are most influential in shaping self-concept, weight concerns, and dieting practices.[102] Some parents fail to realize that society's ideal of slimness can be perilously close to starvation and that a child encouraged to "diet" cannot obtain the energy and nutrients required for normal growth and development. Even healthy children without diagnosable eating disorders have been observed to limit their growth through "dieting." Weight gain in truly overweight children can be managed without compromising growth, but it should be overseen by a health care professional.

Eating is more fun for children when friends are there.

Mealtimes at Home

Traditionally, parents served as **gatekeepers,** determining what foods and activities were available in their children's lives. Then the children made their own selections. Gatekeepers who wanted to promote nutritious choices and healthful habits provided access to nutrient-dense, delicious foods and opportunities for active play at home.

In today's consumer-oriented society, children have greater influence over family decisions concerning food—the fast-food restaurant the family chooses when eating out, the type of food the family eats at home, and the specific brands the family purchases at the grocery store. Parental guidance in food choices is still necessary, but teaching children consumer skills to help them make informed choices is equally important.

Honoring Children's Preferences Researchers attempting to explain children's food preferences encounter contradictions. Children say they like colorful foods, yet they most often reject green and yellow vegetables in favor of brown peanut butter and white potatoes, apple wedges, and bread. They seem to like raw vegetables better than cooked ones, so it is wise to offer vegetables that are raw or slightly undercooked, served separately, and easy to eat. Foods should be warm, not hot, because a child's mouth is much more sensitive than an adult's. The flavor should be mild because a child has more taste buds, and smooth foods such as mashed potatoes or split-pea soup should contain no lumps (a child wonders, with some disgust, what the lumps might be). Children prefer foods that are familiar, so offer various foods regularly.

Make mealtimes fun for children. Young children like to eat at little tables and to be served small portions of food. They like sandwiches cut in different geometric shapes and common foods called silly names. They also like to eat with other children, and they tend to eat more when in the company of their friends. Children are also more likely to give up their prejudices against foods when they see their peers eating them.

Learning through Participation Allowing children to help plan and prepare the family's meals provides enjoyable learning experiences and encourages children to eat the foods they have prepared. Vegetables are pretty, especially when fresh, and provide opportunities for children to learn about color, seeds, growing vegetables, and shapes and textures—all of which are fascinating to young children. Measuring, stirring, washing, and arranging foods are skills that even a young child can practice with enjoyment and pride (see Table 16-7).

Avoiding Power Struggles Problems over food often arise during the second or third year, when children begin asserting their independence. Many of these problems stem from the conflict between children's developmental stages and capabilities and parents who, in attempting to do what they think is best for their children,

TABLE 16-7	Food Skills of Preschool Children[a]

Age 1 to 2 years, when large muscles develop:

- Uses short-shanked spoon
- Helps feed self
- Lifts and drinks from cup
- Helps scrub, tear, break, or dip foods

Age 3 years, when medium hand muscles develop:

- Spears food with fork
- Feeds self independently
- Helps wrap, pour, mix, shake, or spread foods
- Helps crack nuts with supervision

Age 4 years, when small finger muscles develop:

- Uses all utensils and napkin
- Helps roll, juice, mash, or peel foods
- Cracks egg shells

Age 5 years, when fine coordination of fingers and hands develops:

- Helps measure, grind, grate, and cut (soft foods with dull knife)
- Uses hand mixer with supervision

[a]These ages are approximate. Healthy, normal children develop at their own pace.

gatekeepers: with respect to nutrition, key people who control other people's access to foods and thereby exert profound impacts on their nutrition. Examples are the spouse who buys and cooks the food, the parent who feeds the children, and the caregiver in a day-care center.

Children enjoy eating the foods they help to prepare.

try to control every aspect of eating. Such conflicts can disrupt children's abilities to regulate their own food intakes or to determine their own likes and dislikes. For example, many people share the misconception that children must be persuaded or coerced to try new foods. In fact, the opposite is true. When children are forced to try new foods, even by way of rewards, they are less likely to try those foods again than are children who are left to decide for themselves. Similarly, when children are restricted from eating their favorite foods, they are more likely to want those foods.[103] Wise parents provide healthful foods and allow their child to determine *how much* and even *whether* to eat.

When introducing new foods, offer them one at a time and only in small amounts such as one bite at first. The more often a food is presented to a young child, the more likely the child will accept that food. Offer the new food at the beginning of the meal, when the child is hungry, and allow the child to make the decision to accept or reject it. Never make an issue of food acceptance.

Choking Prevention Parents must always be alert to the dangers of choking. A choking child is silent, so an adult should be present whenever a child is eating. Make sure the child sits when eating; choking is more likely when a child is running or falling. (See p. 557 for a list of foods and nonfood items most likely to cause choking.)

Playing First Children may be more relaxed and attentive at mealtime if outdoor play or other fun activities are scheduled before, rather than immediately after, mealtime. Otherwise children "hurry up and eat" so that they can go play.

Snacking Parents may find that when their children snack, they aren't hungry at mealtimes. Instead of teaching children *not* to snack, parents are wise to teach them *how* to snack. Provide snacks that are as nutritious as the foods served at mealtime. Snacks can even be mealtime foods served individually over time, instead of all at once on one plate. When providing snacks to children, think of the five food groups and offer such snacks as pieces of cheese, tangerine slices, and egg salad on whole-wheat crackers (see Table 16-8). Snacks that are easy to prepare should be readily available to children, especially if they arrive home from school before their parents.

To ensure that children have healthy appetites and plenty of room for nutritious foods when they are hungry, parents and teachers must limit access to candy, soft drinks, and other concentrated sweets. Limiting access includes limiting the amount of pocket money children have to buy such foods themselves.[104] If these foods are permitted in large quantities, the only possible outcomes are nutrient deficiencies, obesity, or both. The preference for sweets is innate; most children do not naturally select nutritious foods on the basis of taste. When children are allowed to create meals freely from a variety of foods, they typically select foods that provide a lot of sugar. When their parents are watching, or even when they only think their parents are watching, children improve their selections.

Sweets need not be banned altogether. Children who are exceptionally active can enjoy high-kcalorie foods such as ice cream or pudding from the milk group or pancakes from the bread group. Sedentary children need to become more active so they can also enjoy some of these foods without unhealthy weight gain.

Preventing Dental Caries Children frequently snack on sticky, sugary foods that stay on the teeth and provide an ideal environment for the growth of bacteria that cause dental caries. Teach children to brush and floss after meals, to brush or rinse after eating snacks, to avoid sticky foods, and to select crisp or fibrous foods frequently.

Serving as Role Models In an effort to practice these many tips, parents may overlook perhaps the single most important influence on their children's food habits—themselves.[105] Parents who don't eat carrots shouldn't be surprised when their children refuse to eat carrots. Likewise, parents who comment negatively on the smell of brussels sprouts may not be able to persuade children to try them. Children learn much through imitation. It is not surprising that children prefer the foods other family members enjoy and dislike foods that are never offered to them.[106] Parents, older

TABLE 16-8	Healthful Snack Ideas—Think Food Groups, Alone and in Combination

Selecting two or more foods from different food groups adds variety and nutrient balance to snacks. The combinations are endless, so be creative. Whenever possible, choose whole grains, low fat or reduced fat milk products, and lean meats.

Grains

Grain products are filling snacks, especially when combined with other foods:

- Cereal with fruit and milk
- Crackers and cheese
- Whole-grain toast with peanut butter
- Popcorn with grated cheese
- Oatmeal raisin cookies with milk

Vegetables

Cut-up, fresh, raw vegetables make great snacks alone or in combination with foods from other food groups:

- Celery with peanut butter
- Broccoli, cauliflower, and carrot sticks with a flavored cottage cheese dip

Fruits

Fruits are delicious snacks and can be eaten alone—fresh, dried, or juiced—or combined with other foods:

- Apples and cheese
- Bananas and peanut butter
- Peaches with yogurt
- Raisins mixed with sunflower seeds or nuts

Meats and Legumes

Meats and legumes add protein to snacks:

- Refried beans with nachos and cheese
- Tuna on crackers
- Luncheon meat on whole-grain bread

Milk and Milk Products

Milk can be used as a beverage with any snack, and many other milk products, such as yogurt and cheese, can be eaten alone or with other foods as listed above.

---

siblings, and other caregivers set an irresistible example by sitting with younger children, eating the same foods, and having pleasant conversations during mealtimes.

While serving and enjoying food, caregivers can promote both physical and emotional growth at every stage of a child's life. They can help their children develop both a positive self-concept and a positive attitude toward food. With good beginnings, children will grow without the conflicts and confusions about food that can lead to nutrition and health problems.

Nutrition at School

While parents are doing what they can to establish good eating habits in their children at home, others are preparing and serving foods to their children at day-care centers and schools. In addition, children begin to learn about food and nutrition in the classroom. Meeting the nutrition and education needs of children is critical to supporting their healthy growth and development.[107] ◆

Meals at School The U.S. government assists schools financially so that every student can receive nutritious meals at school. Both the School Breakfast Program and

◆ The American Dietetic Association has set nutrition standards for child-care programs. Among them, meal plans should include the following:
- Be nutritionally adequate and consistent with the *Dietary Guidelines for Americans*
- Involve parents in planning
- Follow recommended meal patterns that balance energy and nutrients with children's ages, appetites, activity levels, and special needs while respecting cultural and ethnic differences
- Minimize added fat, sugar, and sodium
- Emphasize fresh fruit, fresh and frozen vegetables, and whole grains
- Provide furniture and eating utensils that are age appropriate and developmentally suitable to encourage children to accept and enjoy mealtime

School lunches provide children with nourishment at little or no charge.

◆ The school breakfast must contain at a minimum:
- One serving of fluid milk
- One serving of fruit or vegetable or full-strength juice
- Two servings of bread or bread alternates; or two servings of meat or meat alternates; or one of each

the National School Lunch Program provide meals at a reasonable cost to children from families with the financial means to pay. Meals are available free or at reduced cost to children from low-income families. In addition, schools can obtain food commodities. Nationally, the U.S. Department of Agriculture (USDA) administers the programs; on the state level, state departments of education operate them.* The programs usually cost local school districts little, but the educational rewards are great. Several studies have reported that children who participate in school food programs perform better in the classroom.[108]

More than 28 million children receive lunches through the National School Lunch Program—half of them free or at a reduced price.[109] School lunches offer a variety of food choices and help children meet at least one-third of their recommended intakes for energy, protein, vitamin A, vitamin C, iron, and calcium. Table 16-9 shows school lunch patterns for children of different ages and specifies the numbers of servings of milk, protein-rich foods (meat, poultry, fish, cheese, eggs, legumes, or peanut butter), vegetables, fruits, and breads or other grain foods. In an effort to help reduce disease risk, all government-funded meals served at schools must follow the *Dietary Guidelines for Americans.*

Parents often rely on school lunches to meet a significant part of their children's nutrient needs on school days. Indeed, students who regularly eat school lunches have higher intakes of many nutrients and fiber than students who do not.[110]

The School Breakfast Program ◆ is available in more than 80 percent of the nation's schools that offer school lunch, and close to 9 million children participate in it.[111] Nevertheless, for many children who need it, the School Breakfast Program is either unavailable, or the children do not participate in it.[112] The majority of children who eat school breakfasts are from low-income families. As research results continue to emphasize the positive impact breakfast has on school performance and health, vigorous campaigns to expand school breakfast programs are under way.

TABLE 16-9	School Lunch Patterns for Different Ages[a]				
				Grade School through High School (Grade)	
Food Group	Preschool (Age)				
	1 to 2	3 to 4	K to 3	4 to 6	7 to 12
Meat or meat alternate 1 serving:					
Lean meat, poultry, or fish	1 oz	1½ oz	1½ oz	2 oz	3 oz
Cheese	1 oz	1½ oz	1½ oz	2 oz	3 oz
Large egg(s)	½	¾	¾	1	1½
Cooked dry beans or peas	¼ c	⅜ c	⅜ c	½ c	¾ c
Peanut butter	2 tbs	3 tbs	3 tbs	4 tbs	6 tbs
Yogurt	½ c	¾ c	¾ c	1 c	1½ c
Peanuts, soynuts, tree nuts, or seeds[b]	½ oz	¾ oz	¾ oz	1 oz	1½ oz
Vegetable and/or fruit 2 or more servings, both to total	½ c	½ c	½ c	¾ c	¾ c
Bread or bread alternate[c] Servings	5/week	8/week	8/week	8/week	10/week
Milk 1 serving of fluid milk	¾ c	¾ c	1 c	1 c	1 c

[a]The quantities listed represent per-lunch minimums for each age and grade except those for the oldest group, which are recommendations. Schools unable to serve the recommended quantities for grades 7 to 12 must provide at least the amount shown for grades 4 to 6.
[b]These meat alternates may be used to meet no more than half of the meat or meat alternate requirement; therefore, they must be used in a meal with another meat or meat alternate.
[c]Schools must serve daily at least ½ serving of bread or bread alternate to the youngest age group and at least 1 serving to older children.
SOURCE: U.S. Department of Agriculture, National School Lunch Program Regulations, revised January 1, 1998.

*School lunches in Canada are administered locally and therefore vary from area to area.

Another federal program, the Child and Adult Care Food Program (CACFP), operates similarly and provides funds to organized child-care programs. All eligible children, centers, and family day-care homes may participate. Sponsors are reimbursed for most meal costs and may also receive USDA commodity foods.

Competing Influences at School Serving healthful lunches is only half the battle; students need to eat them, too. Short lunch periods and long waiting lines prevent some students from eating a school lunch and leave others with too little time to complete their meals.[113] Nutrition efforts at schools are also undermined when students can buy what the USDA labels "competitive foods"—meals from fast-food restaurants or a la carte foods such as pizza or snack foods and carbonated beverages from snack bars, school stores, and vending machines.[114] In one study, students who selected competitive foods in addition to, or instead of, school meals consumed more energy and fat and less calcium and vitamin A than those who selected only the school lunch.[115]

Increasingly, school-based nutrition issues are being addressed by legislation. Some states restrict the sale of competitive foods and have higher rates of participation in school meal programs than the national average. Federal legislation mandates that all school districts that participate in the USDA's National School Lunch Program develop and put in place a local wellness policy.[116] Nutrition professionals advocate further legislative measures that would prohibit sales of food and beverages from vending machines or school stores in middle and high schools until 30 minutes after the end of the last meal unless they are part of the school foodservice and meet *Dietary Guidelines* standards.[117] Reducing the prices of nutritious foods also greatly increases the likelihood that students will purchase them.[118]

> ## IN SUMMARY
>
> Children's appetites and nutrient needs reflect their stage of growth. Those who are chronically hungry and malnourished suffer growth retardation; when hunger is temporary and nutrient deficiencies are mild, the problems are usually more subtle—such as poor academic performance. Iron deficiency is widespread and has many physical and behavioral consequences. "Hyper" behavior is not caused by poor nutrition; misbehavior may be due to lack of sleep, too little physical activity, or too much television, among other things. Childhood obesity has become a major health problem. Adults at home and at school need to provide children with nutrient-dense foods and teach them how to make healthful diet and activity choices.

Nutrition during Adolescence

Teenagers make many more choices for themselves than they did as children. They are not fed, they eat; they are not sent out to play, they choose to go. At the same time, social pressures thrust choices at them, such as whether to drink alcoholic beverages and whether to develop their bodies to meet extreme ideals of slimness or athletic prowess. Their interest in nutrition—both valid information and misinformation—derives from personal, immediate experiences. They are concerned with how diet can improve their lives now—they engage in fad dieting in order to fit into a new bathing suit, avoid greasy foods in an effort to clear acne, or eat a pile of spaghetti to prepare for a big sporting event. In presenting information on the nutrition and health of adolescents, this section includes many topics of interest to teens.

Growth and Development

With the onset of **adolescence,** the steady growth of childhood speeds up abruptly and dramatically, and the growth patterns of female and male become distinct.

adolescence: the period from the beginning of puberty until maturity.

Nutritious snacks contribute valuable nutrients to an active teen's diet.

Hormones direct the intensity of the adolescent growth spurt, profoundly affecting every organ of the body, including the brain. After two to three years of intense growth and a few more at a slower pace, physically mature adults emerge.

In general, the adolescent growth spurt begins at age 10 or 11 for females and at 12 or 13 for males. It lasts about two and a half years. Before **puberty,** male and female body compositions differ only slightly, but during the adolescent spurt, differences between the genders become apparent in the skeletal system, lean body mass, and fat stores. In females, fat assumes a larger percentage of the total body weight, and in males, the lean body mass—principally muscle and bone—increases much more than in females (review Figure 8-8, p. 261). On average, males grow 8 inches taller, and females, 6 inches taller. Males gain approximately 45 pounds, and females, about 35 pounds.

Energy and Nutrient Needs

Energy and nutrient needs are greater during adolescence than at any other time of life, except pregnancy and lactation. In general, nutrient needs rise throughout childhood, peak in adolescence, and then level off or even diminish as the teen becomes an adult.

Energy Intake and Activity The energy needs of adolescents vary greatly, depending on their current rate of growth, gender, body composition, and physical activity.[119] Boys' energy needs may be especially high; they typically grow faster than girls and, as mentioned, develop a greater proportion of lean body mass. An exceptionally active boy of 15 may need 3500 kcalories or more a day just to maintain his weight. Girls start growing earlier than boys and attain shorter heights and lower weights, so their energy needs peak sooner and decline earlier than those of their male peers. A sedentary girl of 15 whose growth is nearly at a standstill may need fewer than 1800 kcalories a day if she is to avoid excessive weight gain. Thus adolescent girls need to pay special attention to being physically active and selecting foods of high nutrient density so as to meet their nutrient needs without exceeding their energy needs.

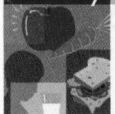 **Dietary** Guidelines for Americans 2005

Adolescents should engage in at least 60 minutes of physical activity on most, preferably all, days of the week.

The insidious problem of obesity becomes ever more apparent in adolescence and often continues into adulthood. The problem is most evident in females of African American descent and in Hispanic children of both genders. Without intervention, overweight adolescents face numerous physical and socioeconomic consequences for years to come. The consequences of obesity are so dramatic and our society's attitude toward obese people is so negative that even teens of normal or below-normal weight may perceive a need to lose weight. When taken to extremes, restrictive diets bring dramatic physical consequences of their own, as Highlight 8 explained.

Vitamins The RDA (or AI) for most vitamins increases during the adolescent years (see the table on the inside front cover). Several of the vitamin recommendations for adolescents are similar to those for adults, including the recommendation for vitamin D. During puberty, both the activation of vitamin D and the absorption of calcium are enhanced, thus supporting the intense skeletal growth of the adolescent years without additional vitamin D.

Iron The need for iron increases during adolescence for both females and males, but for different reasons. Iron needs increase for females as they start to menstruate

puberty: the period in life in which a person becomes physically capable of reproduction.

and for males as their lean body mass develops. Hence, the RDA increases at age 14 for both males and females. For females, the RDA remains high into late adulthood. For males, the RDA returns to preadolescent values in early adulthood.

In addition, iron needs increase when the adolescent growth spurt begins, whether that occurs before or after age 14. Therefore, boys in a growth spurt need an additional 2.9 milligrams of iron per day above the RDA for their age; girls need an additional 1.1 milligrams per day.[120]

Furthermore, iron recommendations for girls before age 14 do not reflect the iron losses of menstruation. The average age of menarche (first menstruation) in the United States is 12.5 years, however.[121] Therefore, for girls under the age of 14 who have started to menstruate, an additional 2.5 milligrams of iron per day is recommended.[122] Thus the RDA for iron depends not only on age and gender but also on whether the individual is in a growth spurt or has begun to menstruate, as listed in the margin. ◆

Iron intakes often fail to keep pace with increasing needs, especially for females, who typically consume less iron-rich foods such as meat and fewer total kcalories than males. Not surprisingly, iron deficiency is most prevalent among adolescent girls. Iron-deficient children and teens score lower on standardized tests than those who are not iron deficient.

Calcium Adolescence is a crucial time for bone development, and the requirement for calcium reaches its peak during these years.[123] Unfortunately, low calcium intakes among adolescents have reached crisis proportions: 90 percent of females and 70 percent of males ages 12 to 19 years have calcium intakes below recommendations.[124] Low calcium intakes during times of active growth, especially if paired with physical inactivity, can compromise the development of peak bone mass, which is considered the best protection against adolescent fractures and adult osteoporosis. Increasing milk products in the diet to meet calcium recommendations greatly increases bone density.[125] Once again, however, teenage girls are most vulnerable, for their milk—and therefore their calcium—intakes begin to decline at the time when their calcium needs are greatest.[126] Furthermore, women have much greater bone losses than men in later life. In addition to dietary calcium, bones grow stronger with physical activity. However, because few high schools require students to attend physical education classes, most adolescents must make a point to be physically active during leisure time.

◆ Iron RDA for males:
- 9–13 yr: 8 mg/day
- 9–13 yr in growth spurt: 10.9 mg/day
- 14–18 yr: 11 mg/day
- 14–18 yr in growth spurt: 13.9 mg/day

Iron RDA for females:
- 9–13 yr: 8 mg/day
- 9–13 yr in menarche: 10.5 mg/day
- 9–13 yr in menarche and growth spurt: 11.6 mg/day
- 14–18 yr: 15 mg/day
- 14–18 yr in growth spurt: 16.1 mg/day

Dietary Guidelines for Americans 2005

Children 9 years of age and older should consume 3 cups per day of fat-free or low-fat milk or equivalent milk products.

Food Choices and Health Habits

Teenagers like the freedom to come and go as they choose. They eat what they want if it is convenient and if they have the time.[127] With a multitude of afterschool, social, and job activities, they almost inevitably fall into irregular eating habits. At any given time on any given day, a teenager may be skipping a meal, eating a snack, preparing a meal, or consuming food prepared by a parent or restaurant. Adolescents who frequently eat meals with their families, however, eat more fruits, vegetables, grains, and calcium-rich foods, and drink fewer soft drinks, than those who seldom eat with their families.[128] Furthermore, the more often teenagers eat dinner with their families, the less likely they are to smoke, drink, or use drugs.[129] Many adolescents also begin to skip breakfast on a regular basis, missing out on important nutrients that are not made up at later meals during the day. Compared with those who skip breakfast, teenagers who do eat breakfast have higher intakes of vitamins A, C, and riboflavin, as well as calcium, iron, and zinc.[130] Teenagers who eat breakfast are therefore more likely to meet their nutrient intake recommendations.

Because their lunches rarely include fruits, vegetables, or milk, many teens fail to get all the vitamins and minerals they need each day.

◆ For perspective, caffeine-containing soft drinks typically deliver between 30 and 55 mg of caffeine per 12-ounce can. A pharmacologically active dose of caffeine is defined as 200 mg. Appendix H starts with a table listing the caffeine contents of selected foods, beverages, and drugs.

Ideally, in light of adolescents' busy schedules and desire for freedom, the adult continues to play the role of gatekeeper, controlling the type and availability of food in the teenager's environment. Teenagers should find plenty of nutritious, easy-to-grab foods in the refrigerator (meats for sandwiches; low-fat cheeses; fresh, raw vegetables and fruits; fruit juices; and milk) and more in the cabinets, (whole-grain breads, peanut butter, nuts, popcorn, and cereal). In many households today, the adults work outside the home, and teenagers perform some of the gatekeepers' roles, such as shopping for groceries or choosing fast or prepared foods.

Snacks Snacks typically provide at least a fourth of the average teenager's daily food energy intake. Most often, favorite snacks are too high in saturated fat and sodium and too low in fiber to support the future health of the arteries.[131] Table 16-8, p. 573 shows how to combine foods from different food groups to create healthy snacks.

Beverages Most frequently, adolescents drink soft drinks instead of fruit juice or milk with lunch, supper, and snacks. About the only time they select fruit juices is at breakfast. When teens drink milk, they are more likely to consume it with a meal (especially breakfast) than as a snack. Soft drinks, when chosen as the primary beverage, may affect bone density because they displace milk from the diet.[132] Because of their greater food intakes, boys are more likely than girls to drink enough milk to meet their calcium needs.

Over the past three decades, teens (especially girls) have been drinking more soft drinks and less milk.[133] Adolescents who drink soft drinks regularly have a higher energy intake and a lower calcium intake than those who do not; they are also more likely to be overweight.[134]

Soft drinks containing caffeine present a different problem if caffeine ◆ intake becomes excessive. Caffeine seems to be relatively harmless when used in moderate doses (the equivalent of fewer than three 12-ounce cola beverages a day). In greater amounts, however, it can cause the symptoms associated with anxiety, such as sweating, tenseness, and inability to concentrate.

Eating Away from Home Adolescents eat about one-third of their meals away from home, and their nutritional welfare is enhanced or hindered by the choices they make. A lunch consisting of a hamburger, a chocolate shake, and French fries supplies substantial quantities of many nutrients at a kcalorie cost of about 800, an energy intake some adolescents can afford. When they eat this sort of lunch, teens can adjust their breakfast and dinner choices to include fruits and vegetables for vitamin A, vitamin C, folate, and fiber and lean meats and legumes for iron and zinc. (See Appendix H for the nutrient contents of fast foods.) Fortunately, many fast food restaurants are offering more nutritious choices than the standard hamburger meal.

Peer Influence Many of the food and health choices adolescents make reflect the opinions and actions of their peers. When others perceive milk as "babyish," a teen may choose soft drinks instead; when others skip lunch and hang out in the parking lot, a teen may join in for the camaraderie, regardless of hunger. Adults need to remember that adolescents have the right to make their own decisions—even if they are contrary to the adults' views. Gatekeepers can set up the environment so that nutritious foods are available and can stand by with reliable nutrition information and advice, but the rest is up to the adolescents. Ultimately, they make the choices. (Highlight 8 examines the influence of social pressures on the development of eating disorders.)

Problems Adolescents Face

Physical maturity and growing independence present adolescents with new choices. The consequences of those choices will influence their nutritional health both today and throughout life. Some teenagers begin using drugs, alcohol, and tobacco; others wisely refrain. Information about the use of these substances is presented here because most people are first exposed to them during adolescence, but it actually applies to people of all ages.

Marijuana   Almost half of the high school students in the United States report having at least tried marijuana.[135] Marijuana is unique among drugs in that it seems to enhance the enjoyment of eating, especially of sweets, a phenomenon commonly known as "the munchies." Prolonged use of marijuana, however, does not seem to bring about a weight gain.

Cocaine, Crack, and Methamphetamine   Cocaine, crack, and methamphetamine stimulate the nervous system and elicit the stress response—constricted blood vessels, raised blood pressure, dilated pupils, and increased body temperature. These drugs also drive away feelings of fatigue. They occasionally cause immediate death—usually by heart attack, stroke, or seizure in an already damaged body system. During prolonged episodes of drug use, abusers suffer dehydration and electrolyte imbalances. Decreases in appetite, weight loss, and malnutrition are common. Notably, the craving for these drugs replaces hunger; rats given unlimited cocaine will choose it over food until they starve to death. Thus, unlike marijuana use, cocaine, crack, and methamphetamine use has major nutritional consequences.

Ecstasy   The club drug ecstasy has become alarmingly popular in recent years. Ecstasy signals the nerve cells to dump all their stored serotonin ◆ at once and then prevents its reabsorption. The rush of serotonin flooding the gap between the nerve cells (the *synapse*) alters a person's mood, but it may also damage nerve cells and impair memory. Because serotonin helps to regulate body temperature, overheating is a common and potentially dangerous side effect of this drug. People who use ecstasy regularly tend to lose weight.

◆ Reminder: *Serotonin* is a neurotransmitter important in the regulation of appetite, sleep, and body temperature.

Drug Abuse, in General   The nutrition problems associated with other drugs vary in degree, but drug abusers in general face multiple nutrition problems. ◆ During withdrawal from drugs, an important part of treatment is to identify and correct nutrient deficiencies.

Alcohol Abuse   Sooner or later all teenagers face the decision of whether to drink alcohol. The law forbids the sale of alcohol to people under 21, but most adolescents who want it can get it. By the end of high school, 77 percent of students have tried alcohol, and about half have been drunk at least once.[136] Highlight 7 describes how alcohol affects nutrition status. To sum it up, alcohol provides energy but no nutrients, and it can displace nutritious foods from the diet. Alcohol alters nutrient absorption and metabolism, so imbalances develop. People who cannot keep their alcohol use moderate must abstain to maintain their health. Highlight 7 lists resources for people with alcohol-related problems.

◆ Nutrition problems of drug abusers:
- They buy drugs with money that could be spent on food.
- They lose interest in food during "highs."
- They use drugs that suppress appetite.
- Their lifestyle fails to promote good eating habits.
- If they use intravenous (IV) drugs, they may contract AIDS, hepatitis, or other infectious diseases, which increase their nutrient needs. Hepatitis also causes taste changes and loss of appetite.
- Medicines used to treat drug abuse may alter nutrition status.

Smoking   Slightly less than 30 percent of U.S. high school students report smoking a cigarette in the previous month.[137] This is the lowest rate of smoking among high school students since 1991. Cigarette smoking is a pervasive health problem causing thousands of people to suffer from cancer and diseases of the cardiovascular, digestive, and respiratory systems. These effects are beyond the scope of nutrition, but smoking cigarettes does influence hunger, body weight, and nutrient status.

Smoking a cigarette eases feelings of hunger. When smokers receive a hunger signal, they can quiet it with cigarettes instead of food. Such behavior ignores body signals and postpones energy and nutrient intake. Indeed, smokers tend to weigh less than nonsmokers and to gain weight when they stop smoking. People contemplating giving up cigarettes should know that the average weight gain is about 10 pounds in the first year. Smokers wanting to quit should prepare for the possibility of weight gain and adjust their diet and activity habits so as to maintain weight during and after quitting. Smoking cessation programs need to include strategies for weight management.

Nutrient intakes of smokers and nonsmokers differ. Smokers tend to have lower intakes of dietary fiber, vitamin A, beta-carotene, folate, and vitamin C. The association between smoking and low intakes of fruits and vegetables rich in these nutrients may be noteworthy, considering their protective effect against lung cancer (see Highlight 11).

◆ The vitamin C requirement for people who regularly smoke cigarettes is an additional 35 mg/day.

Compared with nonsmokers, smokers require more vitamin C ◆ to maintain steady body pools. Oxidants in cigarette smoke accelerate vitamin C metabolism and deplete smokers' body stores of this antioxidant. This depletion is even evident to some degree in nonsmokers who are exposed to passive smoke.[138]

Beta-carotene enhances the immune response and protects against some cancer activity. Specifically, the risk of lung cancer is greatest for smokers who have the lowest intakes. Of course, such evidence should not be misinterpreted. It does not mean that as long as people eat their carrots, they can safely use tobacco. Nor does it mean that beta-carotene *supplements* are beneficial; smokers taking beta-carotene supplements actually had a higher incidence of lung cancer and risk of death than those taking a placebo. (See Highlight 11 for more details.) Smokers are ten times more likely to get lung cancer than nonsmokers. Both smokers and non-smokers, however, can reduce their cancer risks by eating fruits and vegetables rich in antioxidants. (See Highlight 11 for details on antioxidant nutrients and disease prevention.)

Smokeless Tobacco Like cigarettes, smokeless tobacco use is linked to many health problems, from minor mouth sores to tumors in the nasal cavities, cheeks, gums, and throat. The risk of mouth and throat cancers is even greater than for smoking to-bacco. Other drawbacks to tobacco chewing and snuff dipping include bad breath, stained teeth, and blunted senses of smell and taste. Tobacco chewing also damages the gums, tooth surfaces, and jawbones, making teeth loss later in life likely.

The nutrition and lifestyle choices people make as children and adolescents have long-term, as well as immediate, effects on their health. Highlight 16 describes how sound choices and good habits during childhood and adolescence can help prevent chronic diseases later in life.

ThomsonNOW™
www.thomsonedu.com/thomsonnow

Nutrition Portfolio

Encouraging children to eat nutritious foods today helps them learn how to make healthy food choices tomorrow.

▪ If there are children in your life, think about the food they eat and consider whether they receive enough food for healthy growth, but not so much as to lead to obesity.

▪ Describe the advantages of physical activity to children's health and well-being.

▪ Plan a day's menu for a child 4 to 8 years of age, making sure to include foods that provide enough calcium and iron.

NUTRITION ON THE NET

ThomsonNOW™
For further study of topics covered in this chapter, log on to **www.thomsonedu .com/thomsonnow**. Go to Chapter 16, then to Nutrition on the Net.

• Learn more about breast milk banks from the Human Milk Banking Association of North America: **www.hmbana.com**

• Search for "infants," "baby bottle tooth decay," "premature birth," "hyperactivity," "food allergies," and "adolescent health," at the U.S. Government health information site: **www.healthfinder.gov**

• Learn how to care for infants, children, and adolescents from the American Academy of Pediatrics and the Canadian Paediatric Society: **www.aap.org** and **www.cps.ca**

• Download the current growth charts and learn about their most recent revision: **www.cdc.gov/growthcharts**

• Get information on the Food Guide Pyramid for young children from the USDA: **www.MyPyramid.gov/kids**

• Get tips for feeding children from the American Dietetic Association: **www.eatright.org**

- Get tips for keeping children healthy from the Nemours Foundation: **www.kidshealth.org**
- Visit the National Center for Education in Maternal & Child Health and the National Institute of Child Health and Human Development: **www.ncemch.org** and **www.nichd.nih.gov**
- Learn about the Child Nutrition Programs: **www.fns.usda.gov/fns**
- Learn how UNICEF works to protect children: **www.unicef.org**
- Learn how to reduce lead exposure in your home from the U.S. Department of Housing and Urban Development Office of Lead Hazard Control: **www.hud.gov/lead**
- Learn more about food allergies from the American Academy of Allergy, Asthma, and Immunology; the Food Allergy Network; and the International Food Information Council: **www.aaaai.org, www.foodallergy.org,** and **www.ific.org**
- Learn more about hyperactivity from Children and Adults with Attention Deficit/Hyperactivity Disorders: **www.chadd.org**

- Visit the Milk Matters section of the National Institute of Child Health and Human Development (NICHD): **www.nichd.nih.gov**
- Learn more about caffeine from the International Food Information Council: **www.ific.org**
- To learn about healthy foods and to find recipes and ideas for physical activities, visit: **www.kidnetic.com**
- Get weight-loss tips for children and adolescents: **www.shapedown.com**
- Learn about nondietary approaches to weight loss from HUGS International: **www.hugs.com**
- Read the message for parents and teens on the risks of tobacco use from the American Academy of Pediatrics: **www.aap.org**
- Get help quitting smoking at QuitNet: **www.quitnet.com**
- Visit the Tobacco Information and Prevention Source (TIPS) of the Centers for Disease Control and Prevention: **www.cdc.gov/tobacco/sgr/sgr_2000**

STUDY QUESTIONS

ThomsonNOW™

To assess your understanding of chapter topics, take the Student Practice Test and explore the modules recommended in your Personalized Study Plan. Log onto **www.thomsonedu.com/thomsonnow**.

These questions will help you review the chapter. You will find the answers in the discussions on the pages provided.

1. Describe some of the nutrient and immunological attributes of breast milk. (pp. 550–552)

2. What are the appropriate uses of formula feeding? What criteria would you use in selecting an infant formula? (pp. 552–553)

3. Why are solid foods not recommended for an infant during the first few months of life? When is an infant ready to start eating solid food? (pp. 555–557)

4. Identify foods that are inappropriate for infants and explain why they are inappropriate. (pp. 554, 556–557)

5. What nutrition problems are most common in children? What strategies can help prevent these problems? (pp. 562–564)

6. Describe the relationships between nutrition and behavior. How does television influence nutrition? (pp. 564–565, 569)

7. Describe a true food allergy. Which foods most often cause allergic reactions? How do food allergies influence nutrition status? (pp. 565–567)

8. Describe the problems associated with childhood obesity and the strategies for prevention and treatment. (pp. 567–571)

9. List strategies for introducing nutritious foods to children. (pp. 571–573)

10. What impact do school meal programs have on the nutrition status of children? (pp. 573–575)

11. Describe the changes in nutrient needs from childhood to adolescence. Why is an adolescent girl more likely to develop an iron deficiency than is a boy? (pp. 575–577)

12. How do adolescents' eating habits influence their nutrient intakes? (pp. 577–578)

13. How does the use of illicit drugs influence nutrition status? (p. 579)

14. How do the nutrient intakes of smokers differ from those of nonsmokers? What impacts can those differences exert on health? (pp. 579–580)

These multiple choice questions will help you prepare for an exam. Answers can be found on p. 585.

1. A reasonable weight for a healthy five-month-old infant who weighed 8 pounds at birth might be:
   a. 12 pounds.
   b. 16 pounds.
   c. 20 pounds.
   d. 24 pounds.

2. Dehydration can develop quickly in infants because:
   a. much of their body water is extracellular.
   b. they lose a lot of water through urination and tears.
   c. only a small percentage of their body weight is water.
   d. they drink lots of breast milk or formula, but little water.

3. An infant should begin eating solid foods between:
   a. 2 and 4 weeks.
   b. 1 and 3 months.
   c. 4 and 6 months.
   d. 8 and 10 months.

4. Among U.S. and Canadian children, the most prevalent nutrient deficiency is of:
   a. iron.
   b. folate.
   c. protein.
   d. vitamin D.

5. A true food allergy always:
   a. elicits an immune response.
   b. causes an immediate reaction.
   c. creates an aversion to the offending food.
   d. involves symptoms such as headaches or hives.

6. Which of the following strategies is *not* effective?
   a. Play first, eat later.
   b. Provide small portions.
   c. Encourage children to help prepare meals.
   d. Use dessert as a reward for eating vegetables.

7. To help teenagers consume a balanced diet, parents can:
   a. monitor the teens' food intake.
   b. give up—parents can't influence teenagers.
   c. keep the pantry and refrigerator well stocked.
   d. forbid snacking and insist on regular, well-balanced meals.

8. During adolescence, energy and nutrient needs:
   a. reach a peak.
   b. fall dramatically.
   c. rise, but do not peak until adulthood.
   d. fluctuate so much that generalizations can't be made.

9. The nutrients most likely to fall short in the adolescent diet are:
   a. sodium and fat.
   b. folate and zinc.
   c. iron and calcium.
   d. protein and vitamin A.

10. To balance the day's intake, an adolescent who eats a hamburger, fries, and cola at lunch might benefit most from a dinner of:
    a. fried chicken, rice, and banana.
    b. ribeye steak, baked potato, and salad.
    c. pork chop, mashed potatoes, and apple juice.
    d. spaghetti with meat sauce, broccoli, and milk.

REFERENCES

1. Committee on Dietary Reference Intakes, *Dietary Reference Intakes for Energy, Carbohydrate, Fiber, Fat, Fatty Acids, Cholesterol, Protein, and Amino Acids* (Washington, D.C.: National Academies Press, 2005).
2. Committee on Dietary Reference Intakes, 2005, pp. 280-281.
3. Committee on Nutrition, American Academy of Pediatrics, *Pediatric Nutrition Handbook*, 5th ed., ed. R. E. Kleinman (Elk Grove Village, Ill.: American Academy of Pediatrics, 2004), pp. 103-115.
4. Position of the American Dietetic Association: Promoting and supporting breastfeeding, *Journal of the American Dietetic Association* 105 (2005): 810-818.
5. American Academy of Pediatrics, Policy statement: Breastfeeding and the use of human milk, *Pediatrics* 115 (2005): 496-506; M. Boland, Exclusive breastfeeding should continue to six months, *Paediatrics and Child Health* 10 (2005): 148-149; Position of the American Dietetic Association, 2005.
6. American Academy of Pediatrics, 2005.
7. J. D. Carver, Advances in nutritional modifications of infant formulas, *American Journal of Clinical Nutrition* 77 (2003): 1550S-1554S.
8. W. C. Heird and A. Lapillonne, The role of essential fatty acids in development, *Annual Review of Nutrition* 25 (2005): 549-571; J. C. McCann and B. N. Ames, Is docosahexaenoic acid, an n-3 long-chain polyunsaturated fatty acid, required for development of normal brain function? An overview of evidence from cognitive and behavioral tests in humans and animals, *American Journal of Clinical Nutrition* 82 (2005): 281-

295; N. Auestad and coauthors, Visual, cognitive, and language assessments at 39 months: A follow-up study of children fed formulas containing long-chain polyunsaturated fatty acids to 1 year of age, *Pediatrics* 112 (2003): e177-183.
9. C. L. Cheatham, J. Columbo, and S. E. Carlson, n-3 Fatty acids and cognitive and visual acuity development: Methodologic and conceptual considerations, *American Journal of Clinical Nutrition* 83 (2006): 1458S-1466S; W. W. Koo, Efficacy and safety of docosahexaenoic acid and arachidonic acid addition to infant formulas: Can one buy better vision and intelligence? *Journal of the American College of Nutrition* 22 (2003): 101-107; E. E. Birch and coauthors, A randomized controlled trial of long-chain polyunsaturated fatty acid supplementation of formula in term infants after weaning at 6 wk of age, *American Journal of Clinical Nutrition* 75 (2002): 570-580.
10. Auestad and coauthors, 2003.
11. E. E. Birch and coauthors, Visual maturation of term infants fed long-chain polyunsaturated fatty acid-supplemented or control formula for 12 mo, *American Journal of Clinical Nutrition* 81 (2005): 871-879; E. E. Birch and coauthors, A randomized controlled trial of long-chain polyunsaturated fatty acid supplementation of formula in term infants after weaning at 6 wk of age, *American Journal of Clinical Nutrition* 75 (2002): 570-580.
12. L. M. Gartner, F. R. Greer, and the Section on Breastfeeding and Committee on Nutrition, Prevention of rickets and vitamin D

deficiency: New guidelines for vitamin D intake, *Pediatrics* 111 (2003): 908-910.
13. Gartner, Greer, and the Section on Breastfeeding and Committee on Nutrition, 2003.
14. American Academy of Pediatrics, 2005; Position of the American Dietetic Association, 2005.
15. B. Lönnerdal, Nutritional and physiologic significance of human milk proteins, *American Journal of Clinical Nutrition* 77 (2003): 1537S-1543S.
16. D. S. Newburg, G. M. Ruiz-Palacios, and A. L. Morrow, Human milk glycans protect infants against enteric pathogens, *Annual Review of Nutrition* 25 (2005): 37-58.
17. C. J. Chantry, C. R. Howard, and P. Auinger, Full breastfeeding duration and associated decrease in respiratory tract infection in US children, *Pediatrics* 117 (2006): 425-432; American Academy of Pediatrics, 2005; Position of the American Dietetic Association, 2005.
18. R. S. Zeiger and N. J. Friedman, The relationship of breastfeeding to the development of atopic disorders, *Nestle Nutrition Workshop Series: Pediatric Program* 57 (2006): 93-108.
19. M. Gdalevich, D. Mimouni, and M. Mimouni, Breastfeeding and the risk of bronchial asthma in childhood: A systematic review with meta-analysis of prospective studies, *Journal of Pediatrics* 139 (2001): 261-266.
20. A. Singhal, Early nutrition and long-term cardiovascular health, *Nutrition Reviews* 64 (2006): S44-S49; R. M. Martin, D. Gunnell, and G. D. Smith, Breastfeeding in infancy

and blood pressure in later life: Systematic review and meta-analysis, *American Journal of Epidemiology* 161 (2005): 15-26; C. G. Owen and coauthors, Infant feeding and blood cholesterol: A study in adolescents and systematic review, *Pediatrics* 110 (2002): 597-608.

21. C. G. Owen and coauthors, Effect of infant feeding on the risk of obesity across the life course: A quantitative review of published evidence, *Pediatrics* 115 (2005): 1367-1377.

22. M. W. Gillman and coauthors, Risk of overweight among adolescents who were breastfed as infants, *Journal of the American Medical Association* 285 (2001): 2461-2467.

23. M. L. Hediger and coauthors, Association between infant breastfeeding and overweight in young children, *Journal of the American Medical Association* 285 (2001): 2453-2460.

24. M. C. Daniels and L. S. Adair, Breastfeeding influences cognitive development in Filipino children, *Journal of Nutrition* 135 (2005): 2589-2595; E. L. Mortensen and coauthors, The association between duration of breastfeeding and adult intelligence, *Journal of the American Medical Association* 287 (2002): 2365-2371; A. Jain, J. Concato, and J. M. Leventhal, How good is the evidence linking breastfeeding and intelligence? *Pediatrics* 109 (2002): 1044-1053.

25. M. R. Tully, L. Lockhart-Borman, and K. Updegrove, Stories of success: The use of donor milk is increasing in North America, *Journal of Human Lactation* 20 (2004): 75-77.

26. L. Seppo and coauthors, A follow-up study of nutrient intake, nutritional status, and growth in infants with cow milk allergy fed either a soy formula or an extensively hydrolyzed whey formula, *American Journal of Clinical Nutrition* 82 (2005): 140-145; Committee on Nutrition, American Academy of Pediatrics, *Pediatric Nutrition Handbook,* 5th ed., ed. R. Kleinman (Elk grove Village, Ill.: American Academy of Pediatrics, 2004), pp. 87-97.

27. D. Hoyert and coauthors, Annual summary of vital statistics: 2004, *Pediatrics* 117 (2006): 168-183.

28. Committee on Nutrition, American Academy of Pediatrics, 2004, p. 111.

29. American Academy of Pediatrics, Breastfeeding and the use of human milk, *Pediatrics* 115 (2005): 496-506.

30. Committee on Nutrition, American Academy of Pediatrics, 2004, pp. 105-108.

31. A. Fiocchi, A. Assa'ad, and S. Bahna, Food allergy and the introduction of solid foods to infants: A consensus document, *Annals of Allergy, Asthma and Immunology* 97 (2006): 10-21.

32. L. Hallberg and coauthors, The role of meat to improve the critical iron balance during weaning, *Pediatrics* 111 (2003): 864-870.

33. Committee on Nutrition, American Academy of Pediatrics, 2004, pp. 105-108.

34. Committee on Nutrition, American Academy of Pediatrics, 2004, pp. 103-115.

35. Committee on Nutrition, American Academy of Pediatrics, 2004, pp. 103-115.

36. Centers for Disease Control and Prevention, Nonfatal choking-related episodes among children—United States, 2001, *Morbidity and Mortality Weekly Report* 51 (2002): 945-948.

37. M. K. Fox and coauthors, Relationship between portion size and energy intake among infants and toddlers: Evidence of self-regulation, *Journal of the American Dietetic Association* 106 (2006): S77-S83.

38. American Academy of Pediatrics, Council on Sports Medicine and Fitness and Council on School Health, Active healthy living: Prevention of childhood obesity through increased physical activity, *Pediatrics* 117 (2006): 1834-1842.

39. V. Messina and A. R. Mangels, Considerations in planning vegan diets: Children, *Journal of the American Dietetic Association* 101 (2001): 661-669.

40. Committee on Dietary Reference Intakes, 2005, Chapter 6.

41. Committee on Dietary Reference Intakes, 2005, Chapter 7.

42. Committee on Dietary Reference Intakes, 2005, Chapter 11.

43. Committee on Dietary Reference Intakes, 2005, Chapter 8.

44. K. C. White, Anemia is a poor predictor of iron deficiency among toddlers in the United States: For heme the bell tolls, *Pediatrics* 115 (2005): 315-320; Centers for Disease Control and Prevention, Iron deficiency—United States, 1999-2000, *Morbidity and Mortality Weekly Report* 51 (2002): 897-899.

45. S. L. Johnson, Children's food acceptance patterns: The interface of ontogeny and nutrition needs, *Nutrition Reviews* 60 (2002): S91-S94.

46. R. E. Kleinman, Current approaches to standards of care for children: How does the pediatric community currently approach this issue? *Nutrition Today* 37 (2002): 177-178.

47. R. Briefel and coauthors, Feeding Infants and Toddlers Study: Do vitamin and mineral supplements contribute to nutrient adequacy or excess among US infants and toddlers? *Journal of the American Dietetic Association* 106 (2006): S52-S65.

48. D. J. Raiten, M. F. Picciano, and P. Coates, Dietary supplement use in children: Who, what, why, and where do we go from here: Executive summary, *Nutrition Today* 37 (2002): 167-169.

49. M. Lino, and coauthors, U.S. Department of Agriculture, Center for Nutrition Policy and Promotion, The quality of young children's diets, *Family Economics and Nutrition Review* 14 (2002): 52-59.

50. P. Ziegler and coauthors, Feeding infants and toddlers study (FITS): Development of the FITS Survey in comparison to other dietary survey methods, *Journal of the American Dietetic Association* 106 (2006): S12-S27.

51. J. Stang, Improving the eating patterns of infants and toddlers, *Journal of the American Dietetic Association* 106 (2006): S7-S9; M. K. Fox and coauthors, Feeding infants and toddlers study: What foods are infants and toddlers eating? *Journal of the American Dietetic Association* 104 (2004): S22-S30.

52. Position of the American Dietetic Association: Dietary guidance for healthy children ages 2 to 11 years, *Journal of the American Dietetic Association* 104 (2004): 660-677.

53. M. Nord, M. Andrews, and S. Carlson, Household food security in the United States, 2005, November 2006 available at www.ers.usda.gov/publications/err29.

54. Committee on Dietary Reference Intakes, *Dietary Reference Intakes for Vitamin A, Vitamin K, Arsenic, Boron, Chromium, Copper, Iodine, Iron, Manganese, Molybdenum, Nickel, Silicon, Vanadium, and Zinc* (Washington, D.C.: National Academy Press, 2001), pp. 82-161.

55. G. C. Rampersaud and coauthors, Breakfast habits, nutritional status, body weight, and academic performance in children and adolescents, *Journal of the American Dietetic Association* 105 (2005): 743-760; S. G. Affenito and coauthors, Breakfast consumption by African-American and white adolescent girls correlates positively with calcium and fiber intake and negatively with body mass index, *Journal of the American Dietetic Association* 105 (2005): 938-945; Position of the American Dietetic Association, 2004.

56. J. L. Beard and J. R. Connor, Iron status and neural functioning, *Annual Review of Nutrition* 23 (2003): 41-58; Committee on Dietary Reference Intakes, 2001, pp. 290-393.

57. B. Lozhoff and coauthors, Long-lasting neural and behavioral effects of iron deficiency in infancy, *Nutrition Reviews* 64 (2006): S34-S43; Beard and Connor, 2003.

58. Centers for Disease Control and Prevention, Blood lead levels—United States, 1999-2002, *Morbidity and Mortality Weekly Report* 54 (2005): 513-616.

59. Committee on Environmental Health, American Academy of Pediatrics, Policy statement: Lead exposure in children: Prevention, detection, and management, *Pediatrics* 116 (2005): 1036-1046.

60. Committee on Environmental Health, American Academy of Pediatrics, 2005; X. Liu and coauthors, Do children with falling blood lead levels have improved cognition? *Pediatrics* 110 (2002): 787-791.

61. Centers for Disease Control and Prevention, 2005.

62. E. Romano and coauthors, Development and prediction of hyperactive symptoms from 2 to 7 years in a population-based sample, *Pediatrics* 117 (2006): 2101-2109; L. T. Blanchard, M. J. Gurka, and J. A. Blackman, Emotional, developmental, and behavioral health of American children and their families: A report from the 2003 National Survey of Children's Health, *Pediatrics* 117 (2006): e1202-1212.

63. M. L. Wolraich and coauthors, Attention-deficit/hyperactivity disorder among adolescents: A review of the diagnosis, treatment, and clinical implications, *Pediatrics* 115 (2006): 1734-1746; S. Parmet, C. Lynm, and R. M. Glass, Attention-deficit/hyperactivity disorder, *Journal of the American Medical Association* 288 (2002): 1804; Subcommittee on Attention-Deficit/Hyperactivity Disorder, American Academy of Pediatrics, Clinical practice guideline: Treatment of the school-aged child with attention-deficit/hyperactivity disorder, *Pediatrics* 108 (2001): 1033-1044.

64. U. S. Department of Health and Human Services, National Institutes of Health, National Institute of Allergy and Infectious Diseases, *Food Allergy: An Overview*, NIH publication no. 04-5518 (July 2004), available at www.niaid.nih.gov; R. Formanek, Food allergies: When food becomes the enemy, *FDA Consumer*, July/August 2001, pp. 10-16.

65. Formanek, 2001.

66. L. Christie and coauthors, Food allergies in children affect nutrient intake and growth, *Journal of the American Dietetic Association* 102 (2002): 1648-1651.

67. H. Metzger, Two approaches to peanut allergy, *New England Journal of Medicine* 348 (2003): 1046-1048.

68. Food Allergen Labeling and Consumer Protection Act of 2004, available at http://thomas.loc.gov/cgi-bin/query/F?c108:6:./temp/~c108Dz8zuL:e48634.

69. Formanek, 2001.

70. B. Merz, Studying peanut anaphylaxis, *New England Journal of Medicine* 348 (2003): 975-976; Metzger, 2003; X. M. Li and coauthors, Persistent protective effect of heat-killed *Escherichia coli* producing "engineered," recombinant peanut proteins in a murine model of peanut allergy, *Journal of Allergy and Clinical Immunology* 112 (2003): 159-167.

71. C. L. Ogden and coauthors, Prevalence of overweight and obesity in the United States, 1999-2004, *Journal of the American Medical Association* 295 (2006): 1549-1555.

72. J. P. Koplan, C. T. Liverman, and V. I. Kraak, eds., *Preventing Childhood Obesity: Health in the Balance* (Washington, D.C.: National Academies Press, 2005), pp. 79-123.

73. A. Must, Does overweight in childhood have an impact on adult health? *Nutrition Reviews* 61 (2003): 139-142; S. S. Guo and coauthors, Predicting overweight and obe-

sity in adulthood from body mass index values in childhood and adolescence, *American Journal of Clinical Nutrition* 76 (2002): 653-658; A. D. Salbe and coauthors, Assessing risk factors for obesity between childhood and adolescence: I. Birth weight, childhood adiposity, parental obesity, insulin, and leptin, *Pediatrics* 110 (2002): 299-306.

74. Koplan Liverman, and Kraak, 2005.

75. American Academy of Pediatrics, Council on Sports Medicine and Fitness and Council on School Health, Active healthy living: Prevention of childhood obesity through increased physical activity, *Pediatrics* 117 (2006): 1834-1842; Koplan, Liverman, and Kraak, 2005.

76. D. Benton, Role of parents in the determination of the food preferences of children and the development of obesity, *International Journal of Obesity Related Metabolic Disorders* 28 (2004): 858-869.

77. J. O. Fisher and coauthors, Parental influences on young girls' fruit and vegetable, micronutrient, and fat intakes, *Journal of the American Dietetic Association* 102 (2002): 58-64.

78. S. A. Lederman and coauthors, Summary of the presentations at the Conference on Preventing Childhood Obesity, December 8, 2003, *Pediatrics* 114 (2004): 1146-1173.

79. S. Kranz, A. M. Siega-Riz, and A. H. Herring, Changes in diet quality of American preschoolers between 1977 and 1998, *American Journal of Public Health* 94 (2004): 1525-1530; S. J. Nielsen, A. M. Siega-Riz, and B. M. Popkin, Trends in energy intake in U.S. between 1977 and 1996: Similar shifts seen across age groups, *Obesity Research* 10 (2002): 370-378.

80. Committee on School Health, American Academy of Pediatrics, Soft drinks in schools, *Pediatrics* 113 (2004): 152-154.

81. D. S. Ludwig, K. E. Peterson, and L. S. Gortmaker, Relation between consumption of sugar-sweetened drinks and childhood obesity: A prospective, observational analysis, *Lancet* 357 (2001): 505-508.

82. American Academy of Pediatrics, Council on Sports Medicine and Fitness and Council on School Health, Active healthy living: Prevention of childhood obesity through increased physical activity, *Pediatrics* 117 (2006): 1834-1842.

83. M. H. Proctor and coauthors, Television viewing and change in body fat from preschool to early adolescence: The Framingham Children's Study, *International Journal of Obesity and Related Metabolic Disorders* 27 (2003): 827-833.

84. B. A. Dennison, T. A. Erb, and P. L. Jenkins, Television viewing and television in bedroom associated with overweight risk among low-income preschool children, *Pediatrics* 109 (2002): 1028-1035.

85. S. Gable, Y. Chang, and J. L. Krull, Television watching and frequency of family meals are predictive of overweight onset and persistance in a national sample of school-aged children, *Journal of the American Dietetic Association* 107 (2006): 53-61; K. A. Coon and coauthors, Relationships between use of television during meals and children's food consumption patterns, *Pediatrics* 107 (2001): e71.

86. J. L. Wiecha and coauthors, When children eat what they watch: Impact of television viewing on dietary intake in youth, *Archives of Pediatrics & Adolescent Medicine* 160 (2006): 436-442; S. C. Folta and coauthors, Food advertising targeted at school-age children: A content analysis, *Journal of Nutrition Education and Behavior* 38 (2006): 244-248.

87. S. M. Connor, Food-related advertising on preschool television: Building brand recognition in young viewers, *Pediatrics* 118 (2006): 1478-1485; Folta and coauthors, 2006.

88. L. J. Chamberlain, Y. Wang, and T. N. Robinson, Does children's screen time predict requests for advertised products? Cross-sectional and prospective analyses, *Archives of Pediatrics & Adolescent Medicine* 160 (2006): 363-368; Y. Aktas-Arnas, the effects of television food advertisement on children's food purchasing requests, *Pediatrics International* 48 (2006): 138-145; M. O'Dougherty, M. Story, and J. Stang, Observations of parent-child co-shoppers in supermarkets: Children's involvement in food selections, parental yielding, and refusal strategies, *Journal of Nutrition Education and Behavior* 38 (2006): 183-188.

89. K. Weber, M. Story, and L. Harnack, Internet food marketing strategies aimed at children and adolescents: A content analysis of food and beverage brand web sites, *Journal of the American Dietetic Association* 106 (2006): 1463-1466.

90. J. Utter and coauthors, Couch potatoes or french fries: Are sedentary behaviors associated with body mass index, physical activity, and dietary behaviors among adolescents? *Journal of the American Dietetic Association* 103 (2003): 1298-1305.

91. American Academy of Pediatrics, Committee on Nutrition, Prevention of pediatric overweight and obesity, *Pediatrics* 112 (2003): 424-430.

92. R. Jago and coauthors, Prevalence of abnormal lipid and blood pressure values among an ethnically diverse population of eighth-grade adolescents and screening implications, *Pediatrics* 117 (2006): 2065-2073.

93. M. L. Cruz and coauthors, Pediatric obesity and insulin resistance: Chronic disease risk and implications for treatment and prevention beyond body weight modification, *Annual Review of Nutrition* 25 (2005): 435-468; A. Must and S. E. Anderson, Effects of obesity on morbidity in children and adolescents, *Nutrition in Clinical Care* 6 (2003): 4-12.

94. J. B. Schwimmer, T. M. Burwinkle, and J. W. Varni, Health-related quality of life of severely obese children and adolescents, *Journal of the American Medical Association* 289 (2003): 1813-1819.

95. S. Caprio and M. Genel, Confronting the epidemic of childhood obesity, *Pediatrics* 115 (2005): 494-495.

96. Position of the American Dietetic Association: Individual-, family-, school-, and community-based interventions for pediatric overweight, *Journal of the American Dietetic Association* 106 (2006): 925-945; S. Kirk, B. J. Scott, and S. R. Daniels, Pediatric obesity epidemic: Treatment options, *Journal of the American Dietetic Association* 105 (2005): S44-S51.

97. Kirk, Scott, and Daniels, 2005.

98. Kirk, Scott, and Daniels, 2005.

99. K. L. McConahy and coauthors, Portion size of common foods predicts energy intake among preschool-aged children, *Journal of the American Dietetic Association* 104 (2004): 975-979; B. J. Rolls, D. Engell, and L. L. Birch, Serving portion size influences 5-year-old but not 3-year-old children's food intakes, *Journal of the American Dietetic Association* 100 (2000): 232-234.

100. American Academy of Pediatrics, Council on Sports Medicine and Fitness and Council on School Health, Active healthy living: Prevention of childhood obesity through increased physical activity, *Pediatrics* 117 (2006): 1834-1842.

101. American Academy of Pediatrics, 2006.

102. Position of the American Dietetic Association: Individual-, family-, school-, and community-based interventions for pediatric overweight, *Journal of the American Dietetic Association* 106 (2006): 925-945;

American Academy of Pediatrics, Committee on Nutrition, Prevention of pediatric overweight and obesity, *Pediatrics* 112 (2003): 424-430; D. Spruijt-Metz and coauthors, Relation between mothers' child-feeding practices and children's adiposity, *American Journal of Clinical Nutrition* 75 (2002): 581-586; A. E. Field and coauthors, Peer, parent, and media influences on the development of weight concerns and frequent dieting among preadolescent and adolescent girls and boys, *Pediatrics* 107 (2001): 54-60.

103. D. Benton, Role of parents in the determination of the food preferences of children and the development of obesity, *International Journal of Obesity and Related Metabolic Disorders* 28 (2004): 858-869.

104. B. P. Roberts, A. S. Blinkhorn, and J. T. Duxbury, The power of children over adults when obtaining sweet snacks, *International Journal of Paediatric Dentistry* 13 (2003): 76-84.

105. J. Wardle, S. Carnell, and L. Cooke, Parental control over feeding and children's fruit and vegetable intake: How are they related? *Journal of the American Dietetic Association* 105 (2005): 227-232; A. T. Galloway and coauthors, Parental pressure, dietary patterns, and weight status among girls who are "picky eaters," *Journal of the American Dietetic Association* 105 (2005): 541-548; L. J. Cooke and coauthors, Demographic, familial and trait predictors of fruit and vegetable consumption by pre-school children, *Public Health Nutrition* 2 (2004): 251-252.

106. J. D. Skinner and coauthors, Children's food preferences: A longitudinal analysis, *Journal of the American Dietetic Association* 102 (2002): 1638-1647.

107. Position of the American Dietetic Association: Benchmarks for nutrition programs in child care settings, *Journal of the American Dietetic Association* 105 (2005): 979-986; Position of the American Dietetic Association, Society of Nutrition Education, and American School Food Service Association-Nutrition services: An essential component of comprehensive school health programs, *Journal of the American Dietetic Association* 103 (2003): 505-514.

108. Position of the American Dietetic Association, Society of Nutrition Education, and American School Food Service Association, 2003.

109. Position of the American Dietetic Association: Local support for nutrition integrity in schools, *Journal of the American Dietetic Association* 106 (2006): 122-133.

110. Position of the American Dietetic Association: Dietary guidance for healthy children ages 2 to 11 years, *Journal of the American Dietetic Association* 104 (2004): 660-677; 2004; K. W. Cullen and I. Zakeri, Fruits, vegetables, milk, and sweetened beverages consumption and access to a la carte/snack bar meals at school, *American Journal of Public Health* 94 (2004): 463-467; P. M. Gleason and C. W. Suitor, Eating at school: How the National School Lunch Program affects children's diets, *American Journal of Agricultural Economics* 85 (2003): 1047-1051.

111. Position of the American Dietetic Association, 2006.

112. Position of the American Dietetic Association, 2006.

113. Position of the American Dietetic Association, 2006.

114. Position of the American Dietetic Association, 2006; C. Probart and coauthors, Competitive foods available in Pennsylvania public high schools, *Journal of the American Dietetic Association* 105 (2005): 1243-1249; Cullen and Zakeri, 2004; Committee on School Health, American Academy of Pediatrics, Soft drinks in schools, *Pediatrics* 113 (2004): 152-154.

115. S. B. Templeton and coauthors, Competitive foods increase the intake of energy and decrease the intake of certain nutrients by adolescents consuming school lunch, *Journal of the American dietetic Association* 105 (2005): 215-220.

116. Position of the American Dietetic Association, 2006.

117. Position of the American Dietetic Association, Society for Nutrition Education, and American School Food Service Association, Nutrition Services: An essential component of comprehensive school health programs, *Journal of the American Dietetic Association* 103 (2003): 505-514.

118. S. A. French, Pricing effects on food choices, *Journal of Nutrition* 133 (2003): 841S-843S.

119. Committee on Dietary Reference Intakes, 2005, Chapter 5.

120. Committee on Dietary Reference Intakes, 2001, pp. 290-393.

121. W. C. Chumlea and coauthors, Age at menarche and racial comparisons in US girls, *Pediatrics* 111 (2003): 110-113.

122. Committee on Dietary Reference Intakes, 2001, pp. 290-393.

123. F. R. Greer, N. F. Krebs, and the Committee on Nutrition, American Academy of Pediatrics, Optimizing bone health and calcium intakes of infants, children, and adolescents, *Pediatrics* 117 (2006): 578-585.

124. Greer, Krebs, and the Committee on Nutrition, 2006.

125. H. J. Kalkwarf, J. C. Khoury, and B. P. Lanphear, Milk intake during childhood and adolescence, adult bone density, and osteoporotic fractures in US women, *American Journal of Clinical Nutrition* 77 (2003): 257-265.

126. S. A. Bowman, Beverage choices of young females: Changes and impact on nutrient intakes, *Journal of the American Dietetic Association* 102 (2002): 1234-1239.

127. M. Story, D. Neumark-Sztainer, and S. French, Individual and environmental influences on adolescent eating behaviors, *Journal of the American Dietetic Association* 102 (2002): S40-S51.

128. D. Neumark-Sztainer and coauthors, Family meal patterns: Associations with sociodemographic characteristics and improved dietary intake among adolescents, *Journal of the American Dietetic Association* 103 (2003): 317-322.

129. National Center on Addiction and Substance Abuse (CASA) at Columbia University, *The Importance of Family Dinners*, September, 2003.

130. Rampersaud and coauthors, 2005.

131. American Heart Association, S. S. Gidding and coauthors, Dietary recommendations for children and adolescents: A guide for practitioners, *Pediatrics* 117 (2006): 544-559.

132. Greer, Krebs, and the Committee on Nutrition, 2006; H. Vatanparast and coauthors, Positive effects of vegetable and fruit consumption and calcium intake on bone mineral accrual in boys during growth from childhoodto adolescence: The University of Saskatchewan Pediatric Bone Mineral Accrual Study, *American Journal of Clinical Nutrition* 82 (2005): 700-706; G. Mrdjenovic and D. A. Levitsky, Nutritional and energetic consequences of sweetened drink consumption in 6- to 13-year-old children, *Journal of Pediatrics* 142 (2003): 604-610.

133. S. A. French, B. H. Lin, and J. F. Guthrie, National trends in soft drink consumption among children and adolescents age 6 to 17 years: Prevalence, amounts, and sources, 1997/1978 to 1994/1998, *Journal of the American Dietetic Association* 103 (2003): 1326-1331; Bowman, 2002.

134. J. James and coauthors, Preventing childhood obesity by reducing consumption of carbonated drinks: Cluster randomised controlled trial, *British Medical Journal* 328 (2004): 1237.

135. American Academy of Pediatrics, J. W. King and Committee on substance abuse, tobacco, alcohol, and other drugs: The role of the pediatrician in prevention, identification, and management of substance abuse, *Pediatrics* 115 (2005): 816-821.

136. American Academy of Pediatrics, King and Committee on Substance Abuse, 2005.

137. Centers for Disease Control and Prevention, Youth tobacco surveillance—United States, 2001-2002, *Morbidity and Mortality Weekly Report* 55 (2006): entire supplement.

138. A. M. Preston and coauthors, Influence of environmental tobacco smoke on vitamin C status in children, *American Journal of Clinical Nutrition* 77 (2003): 167-172.

ANSWERS

Study Questions (multiple choice)

1. b   2. a   3. c   4. a   5. a   6. d   7. c   8. a   9. c   10. d

Childhood Obesity and the Early Development of Chronic Diseases

When people think about the health problems of children and adolescents, they typically think of ear infections, colds, and acne—not heart disease, diabetes, or hypertension. Today, however, unprecedented numbers of U.S. children are being diagnosed with obesity and the serious "adult diseases," such as type 2 diabetes, that accompany overweight.[1] When type 2 diabetes develops before the age of 20, the incidence of diabetic kidney disease and death in middle age increases dramatically, largely because of the long duration of the disease.[2] For children born in the United States in the year 2000, the risk of developing type 2 diabetes sometime in their lives is estimated to be 30 percent for boys and 40 percent for girls.[3] U.S. children are not alone—rapidly rising rates of obesity threaten the health of an alarming number of children around the globe.[4] Without immediate intervention, millions of children are destined to develop type 2 diabetes and hypertension in childhood followed by **cardiovascular disease (CVD)** in early adulthood.

This highlight focuses on efforts to prevent childhood obesity and the development of heart disease and type 2 diabetes, but the benefits extend to other obesity-related diseases as well. The years of childhood (ages 2 to 18) are emphasized here, because the earlier in life health-promoting habits become established, the better they will stick. Chapter 18 fills in the rest of the story of nutrition's role in reducing chronic disease risk.

Invariably, questions arise as to what extent genetics is involved in disease development. For heart disease and type 2 diabetes, genetics does not appear to play a *determining* role; that is, a person is not simply destined at birth to develop these diseases. Instead, genetics appears to play a *permissive* role—the potential is inherited and will develop if given a push by poor health choices such as excessive weight gain, poor diet, sedentary lifestyle, and cigarette smoking.

Many experts agree that preventing or treating obesity in childhood will reduce the rate of chronic diseases in adulthood. Without intervention, most overweight children become overweight adolescents who become overweight adults, and being overweight exacerbates every chronic disease that adults face.[5]

Early Development of Type 2 Diabetes

In recent years, type 2 diabetes, a chronic disease closely linked with obesity, has been on the rise among children and adolescents

as the prevalence of obesity in U.S. youth has increased.[6] Obesity is the most important risk factor for type 2 diabetes—most of the children diagnosed with it are obese.[7] Most are diagnosed during puberty, but as children become more obese and less active, the trend is shifting to younger children. Type 2 diabetes is most likely to occur in those who are obese and sedentary and have a family history of diabetes.

In type 2 diabetes, the cells become insulin-resistant—that is, the cells become less sensitive to insulin, reducing the amount of glucose entering the cells from the blood. The combination of obesity and insulin resistance produces a cluster of symptoms, including high blood cholesterol and high blood pressure, which, in turn, promotes the development of atherosclerosis and the early development of CVD.[8] Other common problems evident by early adulthood include kidney disease, blindness, and miscarriages. The complications of diabetes, especially when encountered at a young age, can shorten life expectancy.

Prevention and treatment of type 2 diabetes depend on weight management, which can be particularly difficult in a youngster's world of food advertising, video games, and pocket money for candy bars. The activity and dietary suggestions to help defend against heart disease later in this highlight apply to type 2 diabetes as well.

Early Development of Heart Disease

Most people consider heart disease to be an adult disease because its incidence rises with advancing age, and symptoms rarely appear before age 30. The disease process actually begins much earlier.

Atherosclerosis

Most cardiovascular disease involves **atherosclerosis** (see the glossary, p. 587 for this and related terms). Atherosclerosis develops when regions of an artery's walls become progressively thickened with **plaque**—an accumulation of fatty deposits, smooth muscle cells, and fibrous connective tissue. If it progresses, atherosclerosis may eventually block the flow of blood to the heart and cause a heart attack or cut off blood flow to the brain and cause a stroke. Infants are born with healthy, smooth, clear arteries, but within the first decade of life, **fatty streaks** may begin to appear

GLOSSARY

atherosclerosis (ATH-er-oh-scler-OH-sis): a type of artery disease characterized by plaques (accumulations of lipid-containing material) on the inner walls of the arteries (see Chapter 18).
• **athero** = porridge or soft

• **scleros** = hard
• **osis** = condition

cardiovascular disease (CVD): a general term for all diseases of the heart and blood vessels. Atherosclerosis is the main cause of CVD. When the arteries that carry blood to the heart muscle

become blocked, the heart suffers damage known as **coronary heart disease (CHD).**
• **cardio** = heart
• **vascular** = blood vessels

fatty streaks: accumulations of cholesterol and other lipids along the walls of the arteries.

plaque (PLACK): an accumulation of fatty deposits, smooth muscle cells, and fibrous connective tissue that develops in the artery walls in atherosclerosis. Plaque associated with atherosclerosis is known as **atheromatous** (ATH-er-OH-ma-tus) **plaque.**

(see Figure H16-1). During adolescence, these fatty streaks may begin to accumulate fibrous connective tissue. By early adulthood, the fibrous plaques may begin to calcify and become raised lesions, especially in boys and young men. As the lesions grow more numerous and enlarge, the heart disease rate begins to rise, most dramatically at about age 45 in men and 55 in women. From this point on, arterial damage and blockage progress rapidly, and heart attacks and strokes threaten life. In short, the consequences of atherosclerosis, which become apparent only in adulthood, have their beginnings in the first decades of life.[9]

Atherosclerosis is not inevitable; people can grow old with relatively clear arteries. Early lesions may either progress or regress, depending on several factors, many of which reflect lifestyle behaviors. Smoking, for example, is strongly associated with the prevalence of fatty streaks and raised lesions, even in young adults.

Blood Cholesterol

As blood cholesterol rises, atherosclerosis worsens. Cholesterol values at birth are similar in all populations; differences emerge in early childhood. Standard values for cholesterol in children and adolescents (ages 2 to 18 years) are listed in Table H16-1 (p. 588).

In general, blood cholesterol tends to rise as dietary saturated fat intakes increase. Blood cholesterol also correlates with childhood obesity, especially abdominal obesity.[10] LDL cholesterol rises with obesity, and HDL declines. These relationships are apparent throughout childhood, and their magnitude increases with age.

Children who are both overweight and have high blood cholesterol are likely to have parents who develop heart disease early.[11] For this reason, selective screening is recommended for children and adolescents whose parents (or grandparents) have heart disease; those whose parents have elevated blood cholesterol; and those whose family history is unavailable, especially if other risk factors are evident.[12] Because blood cholesterol in children is a good predictor of adult values, some experts recommend universal screening for all children, and particularly for those who are overweight, smoke, are sedentary, or consume diets high in saturated fat.

Early—but not advanced—atherosclerotic lesions are reversible, making screening and education a high priority. Both those with family histories of heart disease and those with multiple risk factors need intervention. Children with the highest risks of developing heart disease are sedentary and obese, with high blood pressure and high blood cholesterol.[13] In contrast, children with the lowest risks of heart disease are physically active and of normal weight, with low blood pressure and favorable lipid profiles. Routine pediatric care should identify these known risk factors and provide intervention when needed.

Blood Pressure

Pediatricians routinely monitor blood pressure in children and adolescents. High blood pressure may signal an underlying disease or the early onset of hypertension. Hypertension accelerates the development of atheroscerlosis.[14]

FIGURE H16-1 The Formation of Plaques in Atherosclerosis

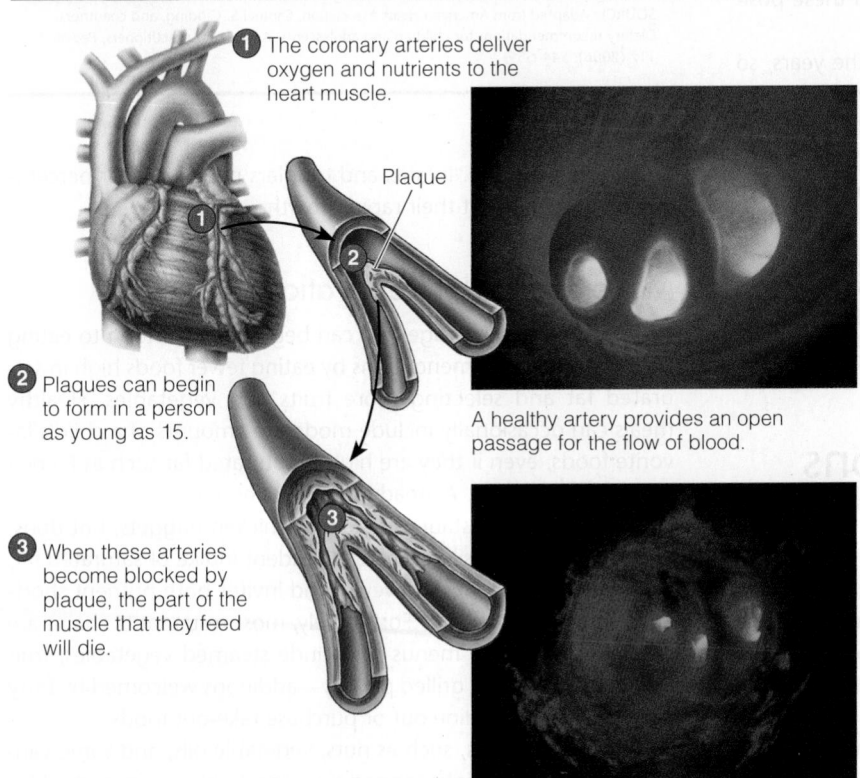

1. The coronary arteries deliver oxygen and nutrients to the heart muscle.

Plaque

2. Plaques can begin to form in a person as young as 15.

A healthy artery provides an open passage for the flow of blood.

3. When these arteries become blocked by plaque, the part of the muscle that they feed will die.

© Courtesy of Zeneca Pharmaceutical Division, Cheshire, England (both)

Plaques form along the artery's inner wall, reducing blood flow. Clots can form, aggravating the problem.

TABLE H16-1 Cholesterol Values for Children and Adolescents

Disease Risk	Total Cholesterol (mg/dL)	LDL Cholesterol (mg/dL)
Acceptable	<170	<100
Borderline	170–199	100–129
High	≥200	≥130

NOTE: Adult values appear in Table 18-4 on p. 630.

TABLE H16-2 American Heart Association Dietary Guidelines and Strategies for Children[a]

- Balance dietary kcalories with physical activity to maintain normal growth.
- Every day, engage in 60 minutes of moderate to vigorous play or physical activity.
- Eat vegetables and fruits daily. Use fresh, frozen, and canned vegetables and fruits and serve at every meal; limit those with added fats, salt, and sugar.
- Limit juice intake (4 to 6 ounces per day for children 1 to 6 years of age, 8 to 12 ounces for children 7 to 18 years of age).
- Use vegetable oils (canola, soybean, olive, safflower, or other unsaturated oils) and soft margarines low in saturated fat and *trans* fatty acids instead of butter or most other animal fats in the diet.
- Choose whole-grain breads and cereals rather than refined products; read labels and make sure that "whole grain" is the first ingredient.
- Reduce the intake of sugar-sweetened beverages and foods.
- Consume low-fat and nonfat milk and milk products daily.
- Include 2 servings of fish per week, especially fatty fish such as broiled or baked salmon.
- Choose legumes and tofu in place of meat for some meals.
- Choose only lean cuts of meat and reduced-fat meat products; remove the skin from poultry.
- Use less salt, including salt from processed foods. Breads, breakfast cereals, and soups may be high in salt and/or sugar so read food labels and choose high-fiber, low-salt, low-sugar alternatives.
- Limit the intake of high-kcalorie add-ons such as gravy, Alfredo sauce, cream sauce, cheese sauce, and hollandaise sauce.
- Serve age-appropriate portion sizes on appropriately sized plates and bowls.

[a] These guidelines are for children 3 years of age and older.
SOURCE: Adapted from American Heart Association, Samuel S. Gidding, and coauthors, Dietary recommendations for children and adolescents: A guide for practitioners, *Pediatrics* 117 (2006): 544–559.

Like atherosclerosis and high blood cholesterol, hypertension may develop in the first decades of life, especially among obese children, and worsen with time.[15] Children can control their hypertension by participating in regular aerobic activity and by losing weight or maintaining their weight as they grow taller. Evidence is needed to clarify whether restricting sodium in children's and adolescent's diets lowers blood pressure.

Physical Activity

Research has also confirmed an association between blood lipids and physical activity in children, similar to that seen in adults. Physically active children have a better lipid profile and lower blood pressure than physically inactive children, and these positive findings often persist into adulthood.

Just as blood cholesterol and obesity track over the years, so does a youngster's level of physical activity. Those who are inactive now are likely to still be inactive years later. Similarly, those who are physically active now tend to remain so. Compared with inactive teens, those who are physically active weigh less, smoke less, eat a diet lower in saturated fats, and have better blood lipid profiles. Both obesity and blood cholesterol correlate with the inactive pastime of watching television. The message is clear: physical activity offers numerous health benefits, and children who are active today are most likely to be active for years to come.

Dietary Recommendations for Children

Regardless of family history, experts agree that all children over age two should eat a variety of foods and maintain desirable weight (see Table H16-2). Children (4 to 18 years of age) should receive at least 25 percent and no more than 35 percent of total energy from fat, less than 10 percent from saturated fat, and less than 300 milligrams of cholesterol per day.[16] Recommendations limiting fat and cholesterol are not intended for infants or children

under two years old. Infants and toddlers need a higher percentage of fat to support their rapid growth.

Moderation, Not Deprivation

Healthy children over age two can begin the transition to eating according to recommendations by eating fewer foods high in saturated fat and selecting more fruits and vegetables. Healthy meals can occasionally include moderate amounts of a child's favorite foods, even if they are high in saturated fat such as French fries and ice cream. A steady diet of offerings from some "children's menus" in restaurants such as chicken nuggets, hot dogs, and French fries, easily exceeds a prudent intake of saturated fat, *trans* fat, and kcalories, however, and invites both nutrient shortages and weight gains.[17] Fortunately, most restaurants chains are changing children's menus to include steamed vegetables, fruit cups, and broiled or grilled poultry—additions welcomed by busy parents who often dine out or purchase take-out foods.

Other fatty foods, such as nuts, vegetable oils, and some varieties of fish such as light canned tuna or salmon, are important for their essential fatty acids. Low-fat milk and milk products also deserve special attention in a child's diet for the needed calcium and other nutrients they supply.[18]

Parents and caregivers play a key role in helping children establish healthy eating habits. Balanced meals need to provide lean meat, poultry, fish, and legumes; fruits and vegetables; whole grains; and low-fat milk products. Such meals can provide enough energy and nutrients to support growth and maintain blood cholesterol within a healthy range.

Pediatricians warn parents to avoid extremes. Although intentions may be good, excessive food restriction may create nutrient deficiencies and impair growth. Furthermore, parental control over eating may instigate battles and foster attitudes about foods that can lead to inappropriate eating behaviors.

Diet First, Drugs Later

Experts agree that children with high blood cholesterol should first be treated with diet. If blood cholesterol remains high in children ten years and older after 6 to 12 months of dietary intervention, then drugs may be necessary to lower blood cholesterol. Drugs can effectively lower blood cholesterol without interfering with adolescent growth or development.[19]

Smoking

Even though the focus of this text is nutrition, another risk factor for heart disease that starts in childhood and carries over into adulthood must also be addressed—cigarette smoking. Each day 3000 children light up for the first time—typically in grade school. Among high school students, almost two out of three have tried smoking, and one in five smokes regularly.[20] Approximately 80 percent of all adult smokers began smoking before the age of 18.

Of those teenagers who continue smoking, half will eventually die of smoking-related causes. Efforts to teach children about the dangers of smoking need to be aggressive. Children are not likely to consider the long-term health consequences of tobacco use. They are more likely to be struck by the immediate health

Cigarette smoking is the number one preventable cause of deaths.

consequences, such as shortness of breath when playing sports, or social consequences, such as having bad breath. Whatever the context, the message to all children and teens should be clear: don't start smoking. If you've already started, quit.

In conclusion, *adult* heart disease is a major *pediatric* problem. Without intervention, some 60 million children are destined to suffer its consequences within the next 30 years. Optimal prevention efforts focus on children, especially on those who are overweight.[21]

Just as young children receive vaccinations against infectious diseases, they need screening for, and education about, chronic diseases. Many health education programs have been implemented in schools around the country. These programs are most effective when they include education in the classroom, heart-healthy meals in the lunchroom, fitness activities on the playground, and parental involvement at home.

NUTRITION ON THE NET

ThomsonNOW™
For furthur study of topics covered in this Highlight, log on to **www .thomsonedu.com/thomsonnow**. Go to Chapter 16, then to Highlights Nutrition on the Net.

- Get weight-loss tips for children and adolescents: **www.shapedown.com**

- Learn about nondietary approaches to weight loss from HUGS International: **www.hugs.com**
- Visit the Nemours Foundation: **www.kidshealth.org**
- Find information on diabetes in children at the American Diabetes Association and Juvenile Diabetes Research Foundation: **www.diabetes.org** and **www.jdrf.org**

psychological stressors (such as exams, divorce, moving, and the death of a loved one) elicit the body's **stress response.** The body responds to such stressors with an elaborate series of physiological steps, as the nervous and hormonal systems bring about defensive readiness in every body part. These effects favor physical action—the classic fight-or-flight response. Prolonged or severe stress can drain the body of its reserves and leave it weakened, aged, and vulnerable to illness, especially if physical action is not taken. As people age, they lose their ability to adapt to both external and internal disturbances. When disease strikes, the reduced ability to adapt makes the aging individual more vulnerable to death than a younger person.

Because the stress response is mediated by hormones, it differs between men and women.[15] The fight-or-flight response may be more typical of men than of women. Women's reactions to stress more typically follow a pattern of "tend-and-befriend."[16] Women *tend* by nurturing and protecting themselves and their children. These actions promote safety and reduce stress. Women *befriend* by creating and maintaining a social group that can help in the process.

Highlight 11 described the oxidative stresses and cellular damage that occur when free radicals exceed the body's ability to defend itself. Increased free-radical activity and decreased antioxidant protection are common features of aging—and antioxidants seem to help slow the aging process.[17] Such findings seem to suggest that the fountain of youth may actually be a cornucopia of fruits and vegetables rich in antioxidants. (Return to Highlight 11 for more details on the antioxidant action of fruits and vegetables in defending against oxidative stress.)

Physiological Changes

As aging progresses, inevitable changes in each of the body's organs contribute to the body's declining function. These physiological changes influence nutrition status, just as growth and development do in the earlier stages of the life cycle.

Body Weight Two-thirds of older adults in the United States are now considered overweight or obese. Chapter 8 presented the many health problems that accompany obesity and the BMI guidelines for a healthy body weight (18.5 to 24.9). These guidelines apply to all adults, regardless of age, but they may be too restrictive for older adults. The importance of body weight in defending against chronic diseases differs for older adults. Being moderately *overweight* may not be harmful. For adults over 65, health risks do not become apparent until BMI reaches at least 27—and the relationship tends to diminish with age until it disappears by age 75. Older adults who are *obese*, however, face serious medical complications and can significantly improve their quality of life with weight loss.[18]

For some older adults, a low body weight may be more detrimental than a high one. Low body weight often reflects malnutrition and the trauma associated with a fall. Many older adults experience unintentional weight loss, in large part because of an inadequate food intake. Without adequate nutrient reserves, an underweight person may be unprepared to fight against diseases. For underweight people, even a slight weight loss (5 percent) increases the likelihood of disease and premature death, making every meal a life-saving event.

Body Composition In general, older people tend to lose bone and muscle and gain body fat. Many of these changes occur because some hormones that regulate appetite and metabolism become less active with age, whereas others become more active.[19]*

Loss of muscle, known as **sarcopenia,** can be significant in the later years, and its consequences can be quite dramatic (see Figure 17-2).[20] As muscles di-

stress response: the body's response to stress, mediated by both nerves and hormones.

sarcopenia (SAR-koh-PEE-nee-ah): loss of skeletal muscle mass, strength, and quality.
- **sarco** = flesh
- **penia** = loss or lack

* Causes of diminished appetite in older adults include increased cholecystokinin, leptin, and cytokines and decreased ghrelin and testosterone. Additional examples of hormones that change with age include growth hormone and androgens, which decline with advancing age, thus contributing to the decrease in lean body mass, and prolactin, which increases with age, helping to maintain body fat. Insulin sensitivity also diminishes as people grow older, most likely because of increases in body fat and decreases in physical activity.

FIGURE 17-2 Sarcopenia

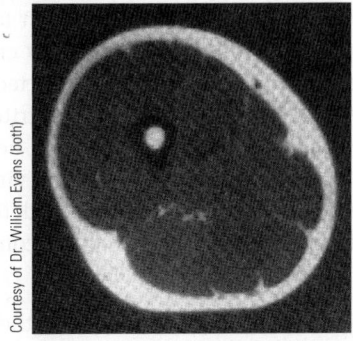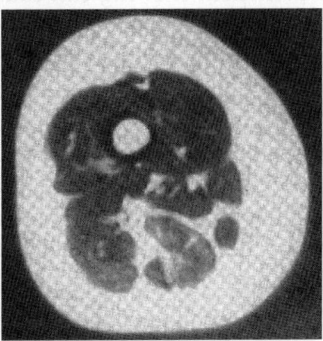

Courtesy of Dr. William Evans (both)

These cross sections of two women's thighs may appear to be about the same size from the outside, but the 20-year-old woman's thigh (left) is dense with muscle tissue. The 64-year-old woman's thigh (right) has lost muscle and gained fat, changes that may be largely preventable with strength-building physical activities.

minish and weaken, people lose the ability to move and maintain balance—making falls likely. The limitations that accompany the loss of muscle mass and strength play a key role in the diminishing health that often accompanies aging.[21] Optimal nutrition and regular physical activity can help maintain muscle mass and strength and minimize the changes in body composition associated with aging.[22]

Risk factors for sarcopenia include weight loss, little physical activity, and cigarette smoking.[23] Obesity and the inflammation that accompanies it may also contribute to sarcopenia.[24]

Immune System Changes in the immune system also bring declining function with age. In addition, the immune system is compromised by nutrient deficiencies. Thus the combination of age and malnutrition makes older people vulnerable to infectious diseases. Adding insult to injury, antibiotics often are not effective against infections in people with compromised immune systems. Consequently, infectious diseases are a major cause of death in older adults. Older adults may improve their immune system responses by exercising regularly.

GI Tract In the GI tract, the intestinal wall loses strength and elasticity with age, and GI hormone secretions change. All of these actions slow motility. Constipation is much more common in the elderly than in the young. Changes in GI hormone secretions also diminish appetite, leading to decreased energy intake and weight loss.[25]

Atrophic gastritis, a condition that affects almost one-third of those over 60, is characterized ♦ by an inflamed stomach, bacterial overgrowth, and a lack of hydrochloric acid and intrinsic factor. All of these can impair the digestion and absorption of nutrients, most notably, vitamin B_{12}, but also biotin, folate, calcium, iron, and zinc.

Difficulty in swallowing, medically known as **dysphagia,** occurs in all age groups, but especially in the elderly. Being unable to swallow a mouthful of food can be scary, painful, and dangerous. Even swallowing liquids can be a problem for some people. Consequently, the person may eat less food and drink fewer beverages, resulting in weight loss, malnutrition, and dehydration. Dietary intervention for dysphagia is highly individualized based on the person's abilities and tolerances. The diet typically provides moist, soft-textured, tender-cooked, or pureed foods and thickened liquids.

Tooth Loss Regular dental care over a lifetime protects against tooth loss and gum disease, which are common in old age. These conditions make chewing difficult or

♦ Consequences of atrophic gastritis:
• Inflamed stomach
• Increased bacterial growth
• Reduced hydrochloric acid
• Reduced intrinsic factor
• Increased risk of nutrient deficiencies, notably of vitamin B_{12}

dysphagia (dis-FAY-jah): difficulty in swallowing.

◆ The medical term for lack of teeth is **edentulous** (ee-DENT-you-lus).
 • **e** = without
 • **dens** = teeth

◆ Conditions requiring dental care:
 Dry mouth
 Eating difficulty
 No dental care within two years
 Tooth or mouth pain
 Altered food selections
 Lesions, sores, or lumps in mouth

painful. Dentures, even when they fit properly, are less effective than natural teeth, and inefficient chewing can cause choking. People with tooth loss, ◆ gum disease, and ill-fitting dentures tend to limit their food selections to soft foods. If foods such as corn on the cob, apples, and hard rolls are replaced by creamed corn, applesauce, and rice, then nutrition status may not be greatly affected. However, when food groups are eliminated and variety is limited, poor nutrition follows. People without teeth typically eat fewer fruits and vegetables and have less variety in their diets.[26] Consequently, they have low intakes of fiber and vitamins, which exacerbates their dental and overall health problems.[27] To determine whether a visit to the dentist is needed, an older adult can check the conditions listed in the margin. ◆

Sensory Losses and Other Physical Problems Sensory losses and other physical problems can also interfere with an older person's ability to obtain adequate nourishment. Failing eyesight, for example, can make driving to the grocery store impossible and shopping for food a frustrating experience. It may become so difficult to read food labels and count money that the person doesn't buy needed foods. Carrying bags of groceries may be an unmanageable task. Similarly, a person with limited mobility may find cooking and cleaning up too hard to do. Not too surprisingly, the prevalence of undernutrition is high among those who are homebound.

Sensory losses can also interfere with a person's ability or willingness to eat. Taste and smell sensitivities tend to diminish with age and may make eating less enjoyable. If a person eats less, then weight loss and nutrient deficiencies may follow. Loss of vision and hearing may contribute to social isolation, and eating alone may lead to poor intake.

Other Changes

In addition to the physiological changes that accompany aging, adults change in many other ways that influence their nutrition status.[28] Psychological, economic, and social factors play big roles in a person's ability and willingness to eat.

Psychological Changes Although not an inevitable component of aging, depression is common among older adults.[29] Depressed people, even those without disabilities, lose their ability to perform simple physical tasks. They frequently lose their appetite and the motivation to cook or even to eat. An overwhelming sense of grief and sadness at the death of a spouse, friend, or family member may leave a person, especially an elderly person, feeling powerless to overcome depression. When a person is suffering the heartache and loneliness of bereavement, cooking meals may not seem worthwhile. The support and companionship of family and friends, especially at mealtimes, can help overcome depression and enhance appetite.

Economic Changes Overall, older adults today have higher incomes than their cohorts of previous generations. Still, 10 percent of the people over age 65 live in poverty. Factors such as living arrangements and income make significant differences in the food choices, eating habits, and nutrition status of older adults, especially those over age 80. People of low socioeconomic means are likely to have inadequate food and nutrient intakes. Only about one-third of the needy elderly receive assistance from federal programs.

Social Changes Malnutrition among older adults is most common in hospitals and nursing homes.[30] In the community, malnutrition is most likely to occur among those living alone, especially men; those with the least education; those living in federally funded housing (an indicator of low income); and those who have recently experienced a change in lifestyle. Adults who live alone do not necessarily make poor food choices, but they often consume too little food. Loneliness is directly related to nutritional inadequacies, especially of energy intake.

Shared meals can brighten the day and enhance the appetite.

IN SUMMARY

Many changes that accompany aging can impair nutrition status. Among physiological changes, hormone activity alters body composition, immune system changes raise the risk of infections, atrophic gastritis interferes with digestion and absorption, and tooth loss limits food choices. Psychological changes such as depression, economic changes such as loss of income, and social changes such as loneliness contribute to poor food intake.

Energy and Nutrient Needs of Older Adults

Knowledge about the nutrient needs and nutrition status of older adults has grown considerably in recent years. The Dietary Reference Intakes (DRI) cluster people over 50 into two age categories—one group of 51 to 70 years and one of 71 and older. Increasingly, research is showing that the nutrition needs of people 50 to 70 years old differ from those of people over 70.

Setting standards for older people is difficult because individual differences become more pronounced as people grow older.[31] People start out with different genetic predispositions and ways of handling nutrients, and the effects of these differences become magnified with years of unique dietary habits. For example, one person may tend to omit fruits and vegetables from his diet, and by the time he is old, he may have a set of nutrition problems associated with a lack of fiber and antioxidants. Another person may have omitted milk and milk products all her life—her nutrition problems may be related to a lack of calcium. Also, as people age, they suffer different chronic diseases and take various medicines—both of which will affect nutrient needs. For all of these reasons, researchers have difficulty even defining "healthy aging," a prerequisite to developing recommendations to meet the "needs of practically all healthy persons." The following discussion gives special attention to the nutrients of greatest concern.

Growing old can be enjoyable for people who take care of their health and live each day fully.

Water

Despite real fluid needs, many older people do not seem to feel thirsty or notice mouth dryness. Many nursing home employees say it is hard to persuade their elderly clients to drink enough water and fruit juices. Older adults may find it difficult and bothersome to get a drink or to get to a bathroom. Those who have lost bladder control may be afraid to drink too much water.

Dehydration is a risk for older adults.[32] Total body water decreases as people age, so even mild stresses such as fever or hot weather can precipitate rapid dehydration in older adults. Dehydrated older adults seem to be more susceptible to urinary tract infections, pneumonia, **pressure ulcers,** and confusion and disorientation. To prevent dehydration, older adults need to drink *at least* six glasses of water a day.◆

◆ Beverage recommendation for adults 51+ yr:
• Men: 13 c/day
• Women: 9 c/day

Energy and Energy Nutrients

On average, energy needs decline an estimated 5 percent per decade. One reason is that people usually reduce their physical activity as they age, although they need not do so. Another reason is that basal metabolic rate declines 1 to 2 percent per decade in part because lean body mass and thyroid hormones diminish.[33]

The lower energy expenditure of older adults means that they need to eat less food to maintain their weights. Accordingly, the estimated energy requirements ◆ for adults decrease steadily after age 19, as the "How to" on p. 602 explains.

◆ When using the tables in Appendix F to estimate energy requirements:
• Men: Subtract 10 kcal/day for each year of age above 19
• Women: Subtract 7 kcal/day for each year of age above 19

pressure ulcers: damage to the skin and underlying tissues as a result of compression and poor circulation; commonly seen in people who are bedridden or chairbound.

The "How to" on p. 257 described how to estimate the energy requirements for adults using an equation that accounts for age, physical activity, weight, and height. Alternatively, energy requirements for older adults can be "guesstimated" by using the values listed in the tables in Appendix F for adults 30 years of age and subtracting 7 kcalories for women and 10 kcalories for men per day for each year over 30.

For example, Table F-4 lists 2556 kcalories per day for a woman who is 5 feet 5 inches tall, weighs 150 pounds, and has a low activity level. To estimate the energy requirements of a similar 50-year-old woman, subtract 7 kcalories per day for each year over 30:

$$50 - 30 = 20 \text{ yr}$$
$$20 \text{ yr} \times 7 \text{ kcal/day} = 140 \text{ kcal/day}$$
$$2556 \text{ kcal/day (at age 30)} - 140 \text{ kcal/day}$$
$$= 2416 \text{ kcal/day (at age 50)}$$

Similarly, using Table F-5 to estimate the energy requirements of a sedentary 65-year-old man who is 5 feet 11 inches tall and weighs 250 pounds, subtract 10 kcalories per day for each year over 30:

$$65 - 30 = 35 \text{ yr}$$
$$35 \text{ yr} \times 10 \text{ kcal/day} = 350 \text{ kcal/day}$$
$$3088 \text{ kcal/day (at age 30)} - 350 \text{ kcal/day}$$
$$= 2738 \text{ kcal/day (at age 65)}$$

(Adults between the ages of 19 and 30 can also use the values listed in the tables in Appendix F by adding 7 kcalories for women and 10 kcalories for men per day for each year below 30.)

On limited energy allowances, people must select mostly nutrient-dense foods. There is little leeway for added sugars, solid fats, or alcohol. The USDA Food Guide (pp. 41–47) offers a dietary framework for adults of all ages.

Protein Because energy needs decrease, protein must be obtained from low-kcalorie sources of high-quality protein, such as lean meats, poultry, fish, and eggs; fat-free and low-fat milk products; and legumes. Protein is especially important for the elderly to support a healthy immune system, prevent muscle wasting, and optimize bone mass.

Underweight or malnourished older adults need protein- and energy-dense snacks such as hard-boiled eggs, tuna fish and crackers, peanut butter on wheat toast, and hearty soups. Drinking liquid nutritional formulas between meals can also boost energy and nutrient intakes.[34] Importantly, the diet should provide enjoyment as well as nutrients.[35]

Carbohydrate and Fiber As always, abundant carbohydrate is needed to protect protein from being used as an energy source. Sources of complex carbohydrates such as legumes, vegetables, whole grains, and fruits are also rich in fiber and essential vitamins and minerals. Average fiber intakes among older adults are lower than current recommendations (14 grams per 1000 kcalories).[36] Eating high-fiber foods and drinking water can alleviate constipation—a condition common among older adults, especially nursing home residents. Physical inactivity and medications also contribute to the high incidence of constipation.

Fat As is true for people of all ages, fat intake needs to be moderate in the diets of most older adults—enough to enhance flavors and provide valuable nutrients, but not so much as to raise the risks of cancer, atherosclerosis, and other degenerative diseases. This recommendation should not be taken too far; limiting fat too severely may lead to nutrient deficiencies and weight loss—two problems that carry greater health risks in the elderly than overweight.

Vitamins and Minerals

Most people can achieve adequate vitamin and mineral intakes simply by including foods from all food groups in their diets, but older adults often omit fruits and vegetables. Similarly, few older adults consume the recommended amounts of milk or milk products.

◆ Reminder: *Atrophic gastritis* is a chronic inflammation of the stomach characterized by inadequate hydrochloric acid and intrinsic factor—two key players in vitamin B_{12} absorption.

Vitamin B_{12} An estimated 10 to 30 percent of adults over 50 have atrophic gastritis. ◆ As Chapter 10 explained, people with atrophic gastritis are particularly vulnerable to vitamin B_{12} deficiency. The bacterial overgrowth that accompanies this condition uses up the vitamin, and without hydrochloric acid and intrinsic factor, digestion and absorption of vitamin B_{12} are inefficient. Given the poor cognition, anemia, and devastating neurological effects associated with a vitamin B_{12} deficiency, an adequate intake is imperative.[37] The RDA for older adults is the same as for younger adults, but with the added suggestion to obtain most of a day's intake from vitamin B_{12}–fortified foods and supplements.[38] The bioavailability of vitamin B_{12} from these sources is better than from foods.

Taking time to nourish your body well is a gift you give yourself.

Dietary	Guidelines for Americans 2005
	People over age 50 should consume vitamin B_{12} from fortified foods or supplements.

Vitamin D Vitamin D deficiency is a problem among older adults. Only vitamin D–fortified milk provides significant vitamin D, and many older adults drink little or no milk. Further compromising the vitamin D status of many older people, especially those in nursing homes, is their limited exposure to sunlight. Finally, aging reduces the skin's capacity to make vitamin D and the kidneys' ability to convert it to its active form. Not only are older adults not getting enough vitamin D, but they may actually need more to improve both muscle and bone strength.[39] To prevent bone loss and to maintain vitamin D status, especially in those who engage in minimal outdoor activity, adults 51 to 70 years old need 10 micrograms daily, and those over 70 need 15 micrograms.[40]

Dietary	Guidelines for Americans 2005
	Older adults should consume extra vitamin D from vitamin D-fortified foods and/or supplements.

Calcium Both Chapter 12 and Highlight 12 emphasized the importance of abundant dietary calcium throughout life, especially for women after menopause, to protect against osteoporosis. The DRI Committee recommends 1200 milligrams of calcium daily, but the calcium intakes of older people in the United States are well below recommendations.[41] Some older adults avoid milk and milk products because they dislike these foods or associate them with stomach discomfort. Simple solutions include using calcium-fortified juices, adding powdered milk to recipes, and taking supplements. Chapter 12 offered many other strategies for including nonmilk sources of calcium for those who do not drink milk.

Iron The iron needs of men remain unchanged throughout adulthood. For women, iron needs decrease substantially when blood loss through menstruation ceases. Consequently, iron-deficiency anemia is less common in older adults than in younger people. In fact, elevated iron stores are more likely than deficiency in older people, especially those who take iron supplements, eat red meat regularly, and include vitamin C–rich fruits in their daily diet.[42]

Nevertheless, iron deficiency may develop in older adults, especially when their food energy intakes are low. Aside from diet, two other factors may lead to iron deficiency in older people: chronic blood loss from diseases and medicines and poor iron absorption due to reduced stomach acid secretion and antacid use. Iron deficiency impairs immunity and leaves older adults vulnerable to infectious diseases.[43] Anyone concerned with older people's nutrition should keep these possibilities in mind.

Nutrient Supplements

People judge for themselves how to manage their nutrition, and more than half of older adults turn to dietary supplements.[44] When recommended by a physician or registered dietitian, vitamin D and calcium supplements for osteoporosis or vitamin B_{12} for pernicious anemia may be beneficial. Many health care professionals recommend a daily multivitamin-mineral supplement that provides 100 percent or less of the Daily Value for the listed nutrients.[45] They reason that such a supplement is more likely to be beneficial than to cause harm.

People with small energy allowances would do well to become more active so they can afford to eat more food. Food is the best source of nutrients for everybody. Supplements are just that—supplements to foods, not substitutes for them. For anyone who is motivated to obtain the best possible health, it is never too late to learn to eat well, drink water, exercise regularly, and adopt other lifestyle habits such as quitting smoking and moderating alcohol use.

IN SUMMARY

The table below summarizes the nutrient concerns of aging. Although some nutrients need special attention in the diet, supplements are not routinely recommended. The ever-growing number of older people creates an urgent need to learn more about how their nutrient requirements differ from those of others and how such knowledge can enhance their health.

Nutrient	Effect of Aging	Comments
Water	Lack of thirst and decreased total body water make dehydration likely.	Mild dehydration is a common cause of confusion. Difficulty obtaining water or getting to the bathroom may compound the problem.
Energy	Need decreases as muscle mass decreases (sarcopenia).	Physical activity moderates the decline.
Fiber	Likelihood of constipation increases with low intakes and changes in the GI tract.	Inadequate water intakes and lack of physical activity, along with some medications, compound the problem.
Protein	Needs may stay the same or increase slightly.	Low-fat, high-fiber legumes and grains meet both protein and other nutrient needs.
Vitamin B_{12}	Atrophic gastritis is common.	Deficiency causes neurological damage; supplements may be needed.
Vitamin D	Increased likelihood of inadequate intake; skin synthesis declines.	Daily sunlight exposure in moderation or supplements may be beneficial.
Calcium	Intakes may be low; osteoporosis is common.	Stomach discomfort commonly limits milk intake; calcium substitutes or supplements may be needed.
Iron	In women, status improves after menopause; deficiencies are linked to chronic blood losses and low stomach acid output.	Adequate stomach acid is required for absorption; antacid or other medicine use may aggravate iron deficiency; vitamin C and meat increase absorption.

Nutrition-Related Concerns of Older Adults

Nutrition may play a greater role than has been realized in preventing many changes once thought to be inevitable consequences of growing older. The following discussions of vision, arthritis, and the aging brain show that nutrition may provide at least some protection against some of the conditions associated with aging.

Vision

One key aspect of healthy aging is maintaining good vision.[46] Age-related eye diseases that impair vision, such as cataract and macular degeneration, correlate with poor survival that cannot be explained by other risk factors.[47] Following a healthy diet as described by the *Dietary Guidelines for Americans* is one way to protect against these age-related vision problems.[48]

Cataracts **Cataracts** are age-related thickenings in the lenses of the eyes that impair vision. If not surgically removed, they ultimately lead to blindness. Cataracts

cataracts (KAT-ah-rakts): thickenings of the eye lenses that impair vision and can lead to blindness.

occur even in well-nourished individuals as a result of ultraviolet light exposure, oxidative stress, injury, viral infections, toxic substances, and genetic disorders. Many cataracts, however, are vaguely called senile cataracts—meaning "caused by aging." In the United States, more than half of all adults 65 and older have a cataract.

Oxidative stress appears to play a significant role in the development of cataracts, and the antioxidant nutrients may help minimize the damage. Studies have reported an inverse relationship between cataracts and dietary intakes of vitamin C, vitamin E, and carotenoids; taking supplements or eating fruits and vegetables rich in these antioxidant nutrients seems to slow the progression or reduce the risk of developing cataracts.[49]

One other diet-related factor may play a role in the development of cataracts—obesity.[50] Obesity appears to be associated with cataracts, but its role has not been identified. Risk factors that typically accompany overweight, such as inactivity, diabetes, or hypertension, do not explain the association.

Macular Degeneration The leading cause of visual loss among older people is age-related **macular degeneration,** a deterioration of the macular region of the retina.[51] As with cataracts, risk factors for age-related macular degeneration include oxidative stress from sunlight, and preventive factors may include supplements of antioxidant vitamins plus zinc and the carotenoids lutein and zeaxanthin.[52] Total dietary fat may also be a risk factor for macular degeneration, but the omega-3 fatty acids of fish may be protective.

Arthritis

More than 40 million people in the United States have some form of **arthritis.** As the population ages, it is expected that the prevalence will increase to 60 million by 2020.

Osteoarthritis The most common type of arthritis that disables older people is **osteoarthritis,** a painful deterioration of the cartilage in the joints. During movement, the ends of bones are normally protected from wear by cartilage and by small sacs of fluid that act as a lubricant. With age, the cartilage sometimes disintegrates, and the joints become malformed and painful to move.

One known connection between osteoarthritis ◆ and nutrition is overweight. Weight loss may relieve some of the pain for overweight persons with osteoarthritis, partly because the joints affected are often weight-bearing joints that are stressed and irritated by having to carry excess pounds. Interestingly, though, weight loss often relieves much of the pain of arthritis in the hands as well, even though they are not weight-bearing joints. Jogging and other weight-bearing exercises do not worsen arthritis. In fact, both aerobic activity and strength training offer improvements in physical performance and pain relief, especially when accompanied by even modest weight loss.[53]

Rheumatoid Arthritis Another type of arthritis known as **rheumatoid arthritis** has possible links to diet through the immune system.[54] In rheumatoid arthritis, the immune system mistakenly attacks the bone coverings as if they were made of foreign tissue. In some individuals, certain foods, notably vegetables and olive oil, may moderate the inflammatory response and provide some relief.[55]

The omega-3 fatty acids commonly found in fish oil reduce joint tenderness and improve mobility in some people with rheumatoid arthritis.[56] The same diet recommended for heart health—one low in saturated fat from meats and milk products and high in omega-3 fats from fish—helps prevent or reduce the inflammation in the joints that makes arthritis so painful.

Another possible link between nutrition and rheumatoid arthritis involves the oxidative damage to the membranes within joints that causes inflammation and swelling. The antioxidant vitamins C and E and the carotenoids defend against oxidation, and increased intakes of these nutrients may help prevent or relieve the pain of rheumatoid arthritis.[57]

◆ Risk factors for osteoarthritis:
- Age
- Smoking
- High BMI at age 40
- Lack of hormone therapy (in women)

---

macular (MACK-you-lar) **degeneration:** deterioration of the macular area of the eye that can lead to loss of central vision and eventual blindness. The **macula** is a small, oval, yellowish region in the center of the retina that provides the sharp, straight-ahead vision so critical to reading and driving.

arthritis: inflammation of a joint, usually accompanied by pain, swelling, and structural changes.

osteoarthritis: a painful, degenerative disease of the joints that occurs when the cartilage in a joint deteriorates; joint structure is damaged, with loss of function; also called **degenerative arthritis.**

rheumatoid (ROO-ma-toyd) **arthritis:** a disease of the immune system involving painful inflammation of the joints and related structures.

Gout Another form of arthritis, which most commonly affects men, is **gout,** a condition characterized by deposits of uric acid crystals in the joints. Uric acid derives from the breakdown of **purines,** primarily from those made by the body but also from those found in foods.[58] Foods such as meat and seafood that are rich in purines increase uric acid levels and the risk of gout, whereas milk products seem to lower uric acid levels and the risk of gout.[59]

Treatment Treatment for arthritis—dietary or otherwise—may help relieve discomfort and improve mobility, but it does not cure the condition. Traditional medical intervention for arthritis includes medication and surgery. Alternative therapies to treat arthritis abound, but none have proved safe and effective in scientific studies. Popular supplements—glucosamine, chondroitin, or a combination—may relieve pain and improve mobility as well as over-the-counter pain relievers, but mixed reports from studies emphasize the need for additional research.[60] Drugs and supplements used to relieve arthritis can impose nutrition risks; many affect appetite and alter the body's use of nutrients, as Highlight 17 explains.

The Aging Brain

The brain, like all of the body's organs, responds to both genetic and environmental factors that can enhance or diminish its amazing capacities. One of the challenges researchers face when studying the human brain is to distinguish among normal age-related physiological changes, changes caused by diseases, and changes that result from cumulative, environmental factors such as diet.

The brain normally changes in some characteristic ways as it ages. For one thing, its blood supply decreases. For another, the number of **neurons,** the brain cells that specialize in transmitting information, diminishes as people age. When the number of nerve cells in one part of the cerebral cortex diminishes, hearing and speech are affected. Losses of neurons in other parts of the cortex can impair memory and cognitive function. When the number of neurons in the hindbrain diminishes, balance and posture are affected. Losses of neurons in other parts of the brain affect still other functions. Some of the cognitive loss and forgetfulness generally attributed to aging may be due in part to environmental, and therefore controllable, factors—including nutrient deficiencies.

Nutrient Deficiencies and Brain Function Nutrients influence the development and activities of the brain. The ability of neurons to synthesize specific neurotransmitters depends in part on the availability of precursor nutrients that are obtained from the diet.[61] The neurotransmitter serotonin, for example, derives from the amino acid tryptophan. To function properly, the enzymes involved in neurotransmitter synthesis require vitamins and minerals. Thus nutrient deficiencies may contribute to the loss of memory and cognition that some older adults experience. Such losses may be preventable or at least diminished or delayed through diet and exercise.[62] Table 17-2 summarizes some of the better-known connections between brain function and nutrients.

In some instances, the degree of cognitive loss is extensive. Such **senile dementia** may be attributable to a specific disorder such as a brain tumor or Alzheimer's disease. Table 17-3 lists common signs of dementia.

Alzheimer's Disease Much attention has focused on the *abnormal* deterioration of the brain called **Alzheimer's disease,** which affects 10 percent of U.S. adults by age 65 and 30 percent of those over 85. Diagnosis of Alzheimer's disease depends on its characteristic symptoms: the victim gradually loses memory and reasoning, the ability to communicate, physical capabilities, and eventually life itself.[63] Nerve cells in the brain die, and communication between the cells breaks down.

Researchers are closing in on the exact cause of Alzheimer's disease.* Clearly, genetic factors are involved.[64] Free radicals and oxidative stress also seem to be in-

TABLE 17-2 Summary of Nutrient-Brain Relationships	
Brain Function	**Depends on an Adequate Intake of:**
Short-term memory	Vitamin B_{12}, vitamin C, vitamin E
Performance in problem-solving tests	Riboflavin, folate, vitamin B_{12}, vitamin C
Mental health	Thiamin, niacin, zinc, folate
Cognition	Folate, vitamin B_6, vitamin B_{12}, iron, vitamin E
Vision	Essential fatty acids, vitamin A
Neurotransmitter synthesis	Tyrosine, tryptophan, choline

gout (GOWT): a common form of arthritis characterized by deposits of uric acid crystals in the joints.

purines: compounds of nitrogen-containing bases such as adenine, guanine, and caffeine. Purines that originate from the body are *endogenous* and those that derive from foods are *exogenous.*

neurons: nerve cells; the structural and functional units of the nervous system. Neurons initiate and conduct nerve impulse transmissions.

senile dementia: the loss of brain function beyond the normal loss of physical adeptness and memory that occurs with aging.

Alzheimer's disease: a degenerative disease of the brain involving memory loss and major structural changes in neuron networks; also known as *senile dementia of the Alzheimer's type (SDAT), primary degenerative dementia of senile onset,* or *chronic brain syndrome.*

---

*A report on the genetic and other aspects of Alzheimer's is available from Alzheimer's Disease Education and Referral Center, P.O. Box 8250, Silver Springs, MD 20907-8250.

volved.[65] Nerve cells in the brains of people with Alzheimer's disease show evidence of free-radical attack—damage to DNA, cell membranes, and proteins. They also show evidence of the minerals that trigger free-radical attacks—iron, copper, zinc, and aluminum. Some research suggests that the antioxidant nutrients can limit free-radical damage and delay or prevent Alzheimer's disease.[66]

In Alzheimer's disease, the brain develops **senile plaques** and **neurofibrillary tangles.** Senile plaques are clumps of a protein fragment called beta-amyloid, whereas neurofibrillary tangles are snarls of the fibers that extend from the nerve cells. Both seem to occur in response to oxidative stress.[67] Researchers question whether these characteristics are the cause or the result of Alzheimer's disease.[68] In fact, scientists are unsure whether these plaques and tangles are causing the damage, serving as markers, or even protecting by sequestering the proteins that begin the dementia process.[69]

Late in the course of the disease there is a decline in the activity of the enzyme that assists in the production of the neurotransmitter acetylcholine from choline and acetyl CoA. Acetylcholine is essential to memory, but supplements of choline (or of lecithin, which contains choline) have no effect on memory or on the progression of the disease. Drugs that inhibit the breakdown of acetylcholine, on the other hand, have proved beneficial.

Research suggests that cardiovascular disease risk factors such as high blood pressure, diabetes, and elevated levels of homocysteine may be related to the development of Alzheimer's disease.[70] Diets designed to support a healthy heart, including omega-3 fatty acids and light-to-moderate alcohol intake, may benefit a healthy brain as well.[71]

Treatment for Alzheimer's disease involves providing care to clients and support to their families. Drugs are used to improve or at least to slow the loss of short-term memory and cognition, but they do not cure the disease. Other drugs may be used to control depression, anxiety, and behavior problems.

Maintaining appropriate body weight may be the most important nutrition concern for the person with Alzheimer's disease. Depression and forgetfulness can lead to changes in eating behaviors and poor food intake. Furthermore, changes in the body's weight-regulation system may contribute to weight loss. Perhaps the best that a caregiver can do nutritionally for a person with Alzheimer's disease is to supervise food planning and mealtimes. Providing well-liked and well-balanced meals and snacks in a cheerful atmosphere encourages food consumption. To minimize confusion, offer a few ready-to-eat foods, in bite-size pieces, with seasonings and sauces. To avoid mealtime disruptions, control distractions such as music, television, children, and the telephone.

TABLE 17-3	Common Signs of Dementia

- Agitated behavior
- Becoming lost in familiar surroundings or circumstances
- Confusion
- Delusions
- Loss of interest in daily activities
- Loss of memory
- Loss of problem-solving skills
- Unclear thinking

Both foods and mental challenges nourish the brain.

IN SUMMARY

Senile dementia and other losses of brain function afflict millions of older adults, and others face loss of vision due to cataracts or macular degeneration or cope with the pain of arthritis. As the number of people over age 65 continues to grow, the need for solutions to these problems becomes urgent. Some problems may be inevitable, but others are preventable and good nutrition may play a key role.

Food Choices and Eating Habits of Older Adults

Older people are an incredibly diverse group, and for the most part, they are independent, socially sophisticated, mentally lucid, fully participating members of society who report themselves to be happy and healthy. In fact, the quality of life

senile plaques: clumps of the protein fragment beta-amyloid on the nerve cells, commonly found in the brains of people with Alzheimer's dementia.

neurofibrillary tangles: snarls of the threadlike strands that extend from the nerve cells, commonly found in the brains of people with Alzheimer's dementia.

doctor? *New England Journal of Medicine* 345 (2001): 1819-1824.

46. T. Ostbye and coauthors, Ten dimensions of health and their relationships with overall self-reported health and survival in a predominately religiously active elderly population: The Cache County memory study, *Journal of the American Geriatrics Society* 54 (2006): 199-209.

47. M. D. Knudtson, B. E. Klein, and R. Klein, Age-related disease, visual impairment, and survival: The Beaver Dam Eye Study, *Archives of Ophthalmology* 124 (2006): 243-249.

48. S. M. Moeller and coauthors, Overall adherence to the Dietary Guidelines for Americans is associated with reduced prevalence of early age-related nuclear lens opacities in women, *Journal of Nutrition* 134 (2004): 1812-1819.

49. W. G. Christen and coauthors, Fruit and vegetable intake and the risk of cataract in women, *American Journal of Clinical Nutrition* 81 (2005): 1417-1422; C. Chitchumroonchokchai and coauthors, Xanthophylls and α-tocopherol decrease UVB-induced lipid peroxidation and stress signaling in human lens epithelial cells, *Journal of Nutrition* 134 (2004): 3225-3232; A. Taylor and coauthors, Long-term intake of vitamins and carotenoids and odds of early age-related cortical and posterior subcapsular lens opacities, *American Journal of Clinical Nutrition* 75 (2002): 540-549; THE REACT Group, The Roche European American Cataract Trial (REACT): A randomized clinical trial to investigate the efficacy of an oral antioxidant micronutrient mixture to slow progression of age-related cataract, *Ophthalmic Epidemiology* 9 (2002): 49-80.

50. J. M. Weintraub and coauthors, A prospective study of the relationship between body mass index and cataract extraction among US women and men, *International Journal of Obesity and Related Metabolic Disorders* 26 (2002): 1588-1595.

51. The Eye Diseases Prevalence Research Group, Age-related macular degeneration is the leading cause of blindness. . . , *Archives of Ophthalmology* 122 (2004): 564-572; J. L. Gottlieb, Age-related macular degeneration, *Journal of the American Medical Association* 288 (2002): 2233-2236.

52. P. R. Trumbo and K. C. Ellwood, Lutein and zeaxanthin intakes and risk of age-related macular degeneration and cataracts: An evaluation using the Food and Drug Administration's evidence-based review system for health claims, *American Journal of Clinical Nutrition* 84 (2006): 971-974; R. van Leeuwen and coauthors, Dietary intake of antioxidants and risk of age-related macular degeneration, *Journal of the American Medical Association* 294 (2005): 3101-3107; D. Hartmann and coauthors, Plasma kinetics of zeaxanthin and 3′-dehydro-lutein after multiple oral doses of synthetic zeaxanthin, *American Journal of Clinical Nutrition* 79 (2004): 410-417; N. I. Krinsky, J. T. Landrum, and R. A. Bone, Biologic mechanisms of the protective role of lutein and zeaxanthin in the eye, *Annual Review of Nutrition* 23 (2003): 171-201.

53. L. Devos-Comby, T. Cronan, and S. C. Roesch, Do exercise and self-management interventions benefit patients with osteoarthritis of the knee? A metaanalytic review, *Journal of Rheumatology* 33 (2006): 744-756; S. P. Messier and coauthors, Exercise and dietary weight loss in overweight and obese older adults with knee osteoarthritis:

The Arthritis, Diet, and Activity Promotion Trial, *Arthritis Rheumatism* 50 (2004): 1501-1510.

54. D. J. Pattison, D. P. Symmons, and A. Young, Does diet have a role in the aetiology of rheumatoid arthritis? *Proceedings of the Nutrition Society* 63 (2004): 137-143.

55. L. Skoldstam, L. Hagfors, and G. Johansson, An experimental study of a Mediterranean diet intervention for patients with rheumatoid arthritis, *Annals of the Rheumatic Diseases* 62 (2003): 208-214.

56. O. Adam, Dietary fatty acids and immune reactions in synovial tissue, *European Journal of Medical Research* 8 (2003): 381-387; L. Cleland, M. James, and S. Proudman, The role of fish oils in the treatment of rheumatoid arthritis, *Drugs* 63 (2003): 845-853.

57. D. J. Pattison and coauthors, Dietary ß-cryptoxanthin and inflammatory polyarthritis: Results from a population-based prospective study, *American Journal of Clinical Nutrition* 82 (2005): 451-455; J. R. Cerhan and coauthors, Antioxidant micronutrients and risk of rheumatoid arthritis in a cohort of older women, *American Journal of Epidemiology* 157 (2003): 345-354.

58. N. Schlesinger, Dietary factors and hyperuricaemia, *Current Pharmaceutical Design* 11 (2005): 4133-4138.

59. H. K. Choi, S. Liu, and G. Curhan, Intake of purine-rich foods, protein, and dairy products and relationship to serum levels of uric acid: The Third National Health and Nutrition Examination Survey, *Arthritis and Rheumatism* 52 (2005): 283-289; H. K. Choi and coauthors, Purine-rich foods, dairy and protein intake, and the risk of gout in men, *New England Journal of Medicine* 350 (2004): 1093-1103.

60. D. O. Clegg and coauthors, Glucosamine, chondroitin sulfate, and the two in combination for painful knee osteoarthritis, *New England Journal of Medicine* 354 (2006): 795-808; F. Richy and coauthors, Structural and symptomatic efficacy of glucosamine and chondroitin in knee osteoarthritis: A comprehensive meta-analysis, *Archives of Internal Medicine* 163 (2003): 1514-1522.

61. R. J. Wurtman and coauthors, Effects of normal meals rich in carbohydrates or proteins on plasma tryptophan and tyrosine ratios, *American Journal of Clinical Nutrition* 77 (2003): 128-132.

62. R. D. Abbott and coauthors, Walking and dementia in physically capable elderly men, *Journal of the American Medical Association* 292 (2004): 1447-1453; J. Weuve and coauthors, Physical activity, including walking, and cognitive function in older women, *Journal of the American Medical Association* 292 (2004): 1454-1461.

63. J. L. Cummings and G. Cole, Alzheimer disease, *Journal of the American Medical Association* 287 (2002): 2335-2338.

64. T. D. Bird, Genetic factors in Alzheimer's disease, *New England Journal of Medicine* 352 (2005): 862-864.

65. P. I. Moreira and coauthors, Oxidative stress: The old enemy in Alzheimer's disease pathophysiology, *Current Alzheimer Research* 2 (2005): 403-408.

66. M. C. Morris and coauthors, Relation of the tocopherol forms to incident Alzheimer disease and to cognitive change, *American Journal of Clinical Nutrition* 81 (2005): 508-514; P. P. Zandi and coauthors, Reduced risk of Alzheimer disease in users of antioxidant

vitamin supplements: The Cache County Study, *Archives of Neurology* 61 (2004): 82-88; M. J. Engelhart and coauthors, Dietary intake of antioxidants and risk of Alzheimer disease, *Journal of the American Medical Association* 287 (2002): 3223-3229; M. C. Morris, Dietary intake of antioxidant nutrients and the risk of incident Alzheimer disease in a biracial community study, *Journal of the American Medical Association* 287 (2002): 3230-3237.

67. R. J. Castellani and coauthors, Antioxidant protection and neurodegenerative disease: The role of amyloid-beta and tau, *American Journal of Alzheimer's Disease and Other Dementias* 21 (2006): 126-130; P. Zafrilla and coauthors, Oxidative stress in Alzheimer patients in different stages of the disease, *Current Medicinal Chemistry* 13 (2006): 1075-1083.

68. R. A. Armstrong, Plaques and tangles and the pathogenesis of Alzheimer's disease, *Folia Neuropathologica* 44 (2006): 1-11; G. L. Wenk, Neuropathologic changes in Alzheimer's disease: Potential targets for treatment, *Journal of Clinical Psychiatry* 67 (2006): 3-7.

69. A. Nunomura and coauthors, Neuropathology in Alzheimer's disease: Awaking from a hundred-year-old dream, *Science of Aging Knowledge Environment* (2006): pe10; R. E. Tanzi, Tangles and neurodegenerative disease—A surprising twist, *New England Journal of Medicine* 353 (2005): 1853-1855.

70. G. Ravaglia and coauthors, Homocysteine and folate as risk factors for dementia and Alzheimer disease, *American Journal of Clinical Nutrition* 82 (2005): 636-643; K. L. Tucker and coauthors, High homocysteine and low B vitamins predict cognitive decline in aging men: The Veterans Affairs Normative Aging Study, *American Journal of Clinical Nutrition* 82 (2005): 627-635; P. Quadri and coauthors, Homocysteine, folate, and vitamin B-12 in mild cognitive impairment, Alzheimer disease, and vascular dementia, *American Journal of Clinical Nutrition* 80 (2004): 114-122; S. Seshadri and coauthors, Plasma homocysteine as a risk factor for dementia and Alzheimer's disease, *New England Journal of Medicine* 346 (2002): 476-483.

71. R. Uauy and A. D. Dangour, Nutrition in brain development and aging: Role of essential fatty acids, *Nutrition Reviews* 64 (2006): S24-S33; T. den Heijer and coauthors, Alcohol intake in relation to brain magnetic resonance imaging findings in older persons without dementia, *American Journal of Clinical Nutrition* 80 (2004): 992-997; F. Calon and coauthors, Docosahexaenoic acid protects from dendritic pathology in an Alzheimer's disease mouse model, *Neuron* 43 (2004): 633-645.

72. V. A. Freedman, L. G. Martin, and R. F. Schoeni, Recent trends in disability and functioning among older adults in the United States: A systematic review, *Journal of the American Medical Association* 288 (2002): 3137-3146.

73. E. A. Gollub and D. O. Weddle, Improvements in nutritional intake and quality of life among frail homebound older adults receiving home-delivered breakfast and lunch, *Journal of the American Dietetic Association* 104 (2004): 1227-1235.

ANSWERS

Study Questions (multiple choice)

1. c   2. d   3. c   4. d   5. b   6. b   7. c   8. d   9. c   10. b

Nutrient-Drug Interactions

© David Woods/CORBIS

People over the age of 65 take about one-third of all the over-the-counter and prescription drugs sold in the United States. They receive an average of 13 prescriptions a year and may take as many as 6 drugs at a time. They take a variety of non-vitamin-mineral supplements, such as glucosamine, as well.[1] Most often, they take these drugs and supplements for heart disease, but also to treat arthritis, respiratory problems, and gastrointestinal disorders. They often go to different doctors for each condition and receive different prescriptions from each. To avoid harmful drug interactions, they need to inform all of their physicians and pharmacists of all the medicines being taken.[2] These medicines enable people of all ages to enjoy better health, but they also bring side effects and risks.

This highlight focuses on some of the nutrition-related consequences of medical drugs, both prescription drugs and nonprescription (over-the-counter) drugs. Highlight 7 described the relationships between nutrition and the drug alcohol, and Highlight 18 presents information on herbal supplements and other alternative therapies.

The Actions of Drugs

Most people think of drugs either as medicines that help them recover from illnesses or as illegal substances that lead to bodily harm and addiction. Actually, both uses of the term *drug* are correct because any substance that modifies one or more of the body's functions is, technically, a drug. Even medical drugs have both desirable and undesirable consequences within the body.

Consider aspirin. One action of aspirin is to limit the production of certain prostaglandins. Some prostaglandins help to produce fevers, some sensitize pain receptors, some cause contractions of the uterus, some stimulate digestive tract motility, some control nerve impulses, some regulate blood pressure, some promote blood clotting, and some cause inflammation. By interfering with prostaglandin actions, aspirin reduces fever and inflammation, relieves pain, and slows blood clotting, among other things.

A person cannot use aspirin to produce one of its effects without producing all of its other effects. Someone who is prone to strokes and heart attacks might take aspirin to prevent blood clotting, but it will also dull that person's sense of pain. Another person who takes aspirin only for pain will also experience slow blood clotting. The anticlotting effect might be dangerous if it causes abnormal bleeding. A single two-tablet dose of aspirin doubles the bleeding time of wounds, an effect that lasts from four to seven hours. For this reason, physicians instruct clients to refrain from taking aspirin before surgery.

The Interactions between Drugs and Nutrients

Hundreds of drugs and nutrients interact, and these interactions can lead to nutrient imbalances or interfere with drug effectiveness.[3] Adverse nutrient-drug interactions are most likely if drugs are taken over long periods, if several drugs are taken, or if nutrition status is poor or deteriorating. Understandably, then, elderly people with chronic diseases are most vulnerable.

Nutrients and medications may interact in many ways:

- Drugs can alter food intake and the absorption, metabolism, and excretion of nutrients.

- Foods and nutrients can alter the absorption, metabolism, and excretion of drugs.

The following paragraphs describe these interactions, and Table H17-1 (p. 616) summarizes this information and provides specific examples.

Altered Food Intake

Some medications can make eating difficult or unpleasant. Some induce nausea or vomiting, which diminishes the desire to eat. Some cause inflammation or lesions in the mouth, stomach, or intestinal lining, resulting in pain or discomfort when food is eaten. Taste perceptions may change, leading to food aversions that may persist even after treatment has been discontinued. All of these complications limit food intake and can lead to weight loss and malnutrition if not resolved.

Some medications, such as megestrol acetate, stimulate food intake and encourage weight gain. These medications may be prescribed in patients with debilitating diseases such as cancer or AIDS. Unintentional weight gain may result from the use of some antipsychotics, antidepressants, and corticosteroids (for example, prednisone). People using these drugs do not feel satiated and sometimes gain 40 to 60 pounds in just a few months.

TABLE H17-1 Examples of Nutrient-Drug Interactions

Drugs May Alter Food Intake by:

- Altering the appetite (Amphetamines suppress appetite; corticosteroids increase appetite.)
- Interfering with taste or smell (Amphetamines change taste perceptions.)
- Inducing nausea or vomiting (Digitalis may do both.)
- Interfering with oral function (Some antidepressants may cause dry mouth.)
- Causing sores or inflammation in the mouth (Methotrexate may cause painful mouth ulcers.)

Drugs May Alter Nutrient Absorption by:

- Changing the acidity of the digestive tract (Antacids may interfere with iron and folate absorption.)
- Damaging mucosal cells (Cancer chemotherapy may damage mucosal cells.)
- Binding to nutrients (Bile acid binders bind to fat-soluble vitamins.)

Foods and Nutrients May Alter Drug Absorption by:

- Stimulating secretion of gastric acid (The antifungal agent ketoconazole is absorbed better with meals due to increased acid secretion.)
- Altering rate of gastric emptying (Intestinal absorption of drugs may be delayed when they are taken with food.)
- Binding to drugs (Calcium binds to tetracycline, reducing drug and calcium absorption.)
- Competing for absorption sites in the intestines (Dietary amino acids interfere with levodopa absorption.)

Drugs and Nutrients May Interact and Alter Metabolism by:

- Acting as structural analogs (as do warfarin and vitamin K)
- Using similar enzyme systems (Phenobarbital induces liver enzymes that increase metabolism of folate, vitamin D, and vitamin K.)
- Competing for transport on plasma proteins (Fatty acids and drugs may compete for the same sites on the plasma protein albumin.)
- Increasing side effects of the drug (Caffeine in beverages can increase adverse effects of stimulants.)
- Increasing drug action to excessive levels (Grapefruit components may block metabolism of drugs and enhance drugs' actions and side effects.)

Drugs May Alter Nutrient Excretion by:

- Altering reabsorption in the kidneys (Some diuretics increase the excretion of sodium and potassium.)
- Causing diarrhea or vomiting (Diarrhea and vomiting may cause electrolyte losses.)

Foods May Alter Medication Excretion by:

- Inducing activities of liver enzymes that metabolize drugs to allow their excretion (Components of charcoal-broiled meats increase metabolism of warfarin, theophylline, and acetominophen.)

Medications prescribed for obesity intentionally suppress the appetite and promote weight loss. Examples include sibutramine, amphetamines, and amphetamine-like compounds such as phentermine. When amphetamines are prescribed for other purposes, such as narcolepsy or attention-deficit/hyperactivity disorder, appetite suppression and weight loss may be unwanted side effects.

Altered Nutrient Absorption

Nutrient malabsorption is most likely to occur with medications that damage the intestinal mucosa. Antineoplastic and antiretroviral drugs are especially detrimental; nonsteroidal anti-inflammatory drugs (NSAIDS) and some antibiotics can have similar, though milder, effects.

Some medications bind nutrients in the GI tract, preventing their absorption. For example, bile acid binders, used to reduce cholesterol levels, also bind to the fat-soluble vitamins A, D, E, and K. Some antibiotics, notably tetracycline and ciprofloxacin, bind to the calcium in foods and supplements, which reduces the absorption of both the drug and the calcium. Other minerals, such as iron, magnesium, and zinc, may also bind to antibiotics. For this reason, pharmacists advise consumers to use dairy products and all mineral supplements at least two hours apart from these medications.

Medications, such as antacids, that reduce stomach acidity may interfere with the absorption of vitamin B_{12}, folate, and iron. Other drugs impede absorption by interfering with the intestinal metabolism or transport of nutrients into mucosal cells. For example, the antibiotics trimethoprim and pyrimethamine compete with folate for absorption into intestinal cells.

Altered Drug Absorption

Most drugs are absorbed in the upper small intestine. Major influences on drug absorption include the stomach emptying rate, level of acidity, and direct interactions with dietary components. The drug's formulation also influences its absorption, and pharmacists often provide instructions advising whether food should be eaten or avoided when using a medication.

Drugs reach the small intestine more quickly when the stomach is empty. Therefore, taking a medication with meals may delay its absorption, although the total amount absorbed may not be affected. For example, aspirin works faster when taken on an empty stomach, but taking it with food is often encouraged to minimize stomach irritation.

Both nutrients and nonnutrients may bind to drugs and inhibit their absorption. For example, high-fiber diets may decrease the absorption of some tricyclic antidepressants. Phytates in foods can bind to digoxin, a drug prescribed for heart disease. As mentioned earlier, calcium and other minerals may bind to some antibiotics, reducing absorption of both the minerals and the drug.

Altered Metabolism

Drugs and nutrients interact metabolically because they use many of the same enzyme systems in the small intestine and the liver. Drugs may enhance or inhibit the activities of enzymes that are needed for nutrient metabolism, and conversely, dietary components may enhance or inhibit the activities of enzymes that break down drugs prior to excretion. These alterations may affect the availability of nutrients, the actions of medications in the body, or various other physiological processes.

To appreciate how nutrient-drug interactions can affect metabolism, consider medicines that resemble vitamins in structure.

The drug methotrexate, used to treat cancer and inflammatory conditions, resembles folate in structure (see Figure H17-1) and competes with the enzyme that converts folate to its active form.* The adverse effects of using methotrexate therefore include symptoms of folate deficiency. These adverse effects can be reduced by prescribing a pre-activated form of folate (called leucovorin) along with methotrexate.

FIGURE H17-1 Folate and Methotrexate

Methotrexate (a drug used in the treatment of cancer and rheumatoid arthritis) is structurally similar to the B vitamin folate. When this medication is used, it competes for the enzyme that normally activates folate, creating a secondary deficiency of folate. Notice the similarities in their chemical structures.

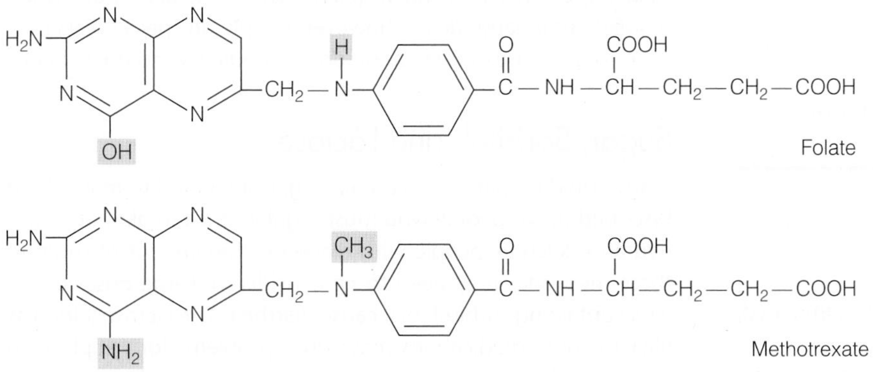

Folate

Methotrexate

TABLE H17-2 Grapefruit Juice–Drug Interactions—Selected Examples

Drug Category	Drugs Affected by Grapefruit Juice	Drugs Unaffected by Grapefruit Juice
Cardiovascular drugs	Felodipine Nicardipine Nifedipine Verapamil	Amlodipine Diltiazem Propafenone Quinidine
Cholesterol-lowering drugs	Atorvastatin Lovastatin Simvastatin	Pravastatin
Central nervous system drugs	Buspirone Carbamazepine Diazepam Triazolam	Clomipramine Haloperidol
Anti-infective drugs	Saquinavir	Clarithromycin Itraconazole
Estrogens	Ethinylestradiol	17-ß-estradiol
Anticoagulants		Acenocoumarol Warfarin
Immunosuppressants	Cyclosporine Tacrolimus	Prednisone
Antiasthmatic drugs		Theophylline

SOURCE: D. G. Bailey, M. O. Arnold, and J. D. Spence, Inhibitors in the diet: Grapefruit juice–drug interactions, in R. H. Levy and coeditors, *Metabolic Drug Interactions* (Philadelphia, Pa.: Lippincott Williams & Wilkins, 2000), pp. 661–669.

Some foods affect the activities of enzymes that metabolize drugs or counteract the drugs' effects in other ways. For example, compounds in grapefruit juice interfere with enzymes that metabolize a number of drugs, resulting in increased blood concentrations of the drugs, and consequently, stronger physiological effects.[4] Table H17-2 gives examples of drugs that interact with grapefruit juice, as well as some that are not affected.

A number of dietary factors affect the activity of the anticoagulant drug warfarin. The most important interaction is with vitamin K, which is structurally similar to warfarin. Warfarin acts by blocking the enzyme that activates vitamin K, thereby preventing the synthesis of blood-clotting factors. The amount of warfarin prescribed is dependent, in part, on how much vitamin K is in the diet. If vitamin K consumption from foods or supplements were to increase dramatically, it could weaken the effect of the drug. Individuals using warfarin are advised to consume similar amounts of vitamin K daily to keep warfarin activity stable. The dietary sources highest in vitamin K are green leafy vegetables.

Some combinations of foods and drugs can cause toxicity or exacerbate a drug's side effects. The combination of tyramine, a compound in some foods, and monoamine oxidase (MAO) inhibitors, medications that treat depression, can be fatal. MAO inhibitors block an enzyme that normally inactivates tyramine and the hormones epinephrine and norepinephrine. When people who take MAO inhibitors consume excessive tyramine, the tyramine causes a sudden release of accumulated norepinephrine. This surge in norepinephrine results in severe headaches, rapid heartbeat, and a dangerous increase in blood pressure. For this reason, people taking MAO inhibitors are advised to restrict their intakes of foods rich in tyramine (see Table H17-3, p. 618).

Altered Nutrient Excretion

Some medications may interfere with the reabsorption of minerals by the kidneys, increasing urinary losses. For example, some diuretics accelerate the excretion of calcium, potassium, and magnesium. Others may cause mineral retention instead. Risk of mineral depletion is highest if multiple

---

*Other folate antagonists include aminopterin, sulfasalazine, pyrimethamine, trimethoprim, triamterene, carbamazepine, phenytoin, phenobarbital, and primidone.

TABLE H17-3 Foods Restricted in a Tyramine-Controlled Diet

Beverages:	Red wines including chianti, sherry[a]
Cheeses:	Aged cheeses, American, camembert, cheddar, gouda, gruyère, mozzarella, parmesan, provolone, romano, roquefort, stilton[b]
Meats:	Liver; dried, salted, smoked, or pickled fish; sausage, pepperoni; dried meats
Vegetables:	Fava beans; Italian broad beans; sauerkraut; fermented pickles and olives
Other:	Brewer's yeast;[c] all aged and fermented products; soy sauce in large amounts; cheese-filled breads, crackers, and desserts; salad dressings containing cheese

NOTE: The tyramine contents of foods vary from product to product depending on the methods used to prepare, process, and store the food. In some cases, as little as 1 ounce of cheese can cause a severe hypertensive reaction in people taking monoamine oxidase (MAO) inhibitors. In general, the following foods contain small enough amounts of tyramine that they can be consumed in small quantities: ripe avocado, banana, yogurt, sour cream, acidophilus milk, buttermilk, raspberries, and peanuts.

[a] Most wine and domestic beer can be consumed in small quantities.
[b] Unfermented cheeses, such as ricotta, cottage cheese, and cream cheese, are allowed.
[c] Products made with baker's yeast are allowed.

drugs with the same effect are used, if kidney function is impaired, or if medications are used for a long time.

A number of drugs can increase excretion of vitamin B_6. An example is isoniazid (INH), an antituberculosis drug that is similar in structure to vitamin B_6. This drug induces excretion of vitamin B_6 and therefore has the potential to create a vitamin B_6 deficiency. Because the drug must be taken for at least six months to treat infection, vitamin B_6 supplements are routinely given to prevent deficiency.

Altered Drug Excretion

Nutrients may influence the reabsorption of drugs by the kidneys. For example, the amount of the medication lithium that is reabsorbed by the kidneys correlates with the amount of sodium reabsorbed. Consequently, dehydration or sodium depletion, which increase sodium reabsorption, may result in lithium retention. Similarly, a person with a high sodium intake will excrete more sodium in the urine and therefore more lithium. Individuals using lithium are advised to maintain a consistent sodium intake from day to day in order to maintain a stable blood level of lithium.

Urine acidity can also affect medication excretion. The medication quinidine, used to treat arrhythmias, is excreted more readily in acidic urine. Foods or drugs that cause urine to become more alkaline (for example, sodium bicarbonate) may reduce quinidine excretion and raise blood levels.

The Inactive Ingredients in Drugs

Besides the active ingredients, medicines may contain other substances such as sugar, sorbitol, lactose, and sodium. For most people who use medicines on occasion and in small amounts, such ingredients pose no problem. When medicines are taken regularly or in large doses, however, people on special diets may need to be aware of these additional ingredients and their effects.

Sugar, Sorbitol, and Lactose

Many liquid preparations contain sugar or sorbitol to make them taste better. For people who must regulate their intakes of carbohydrates, such as people with diabetes, the amount of sugar in these medicines may need to be considered. Large doses of liquids containing sorbitol may cause diarrhea. The lactose added as filler to some medications may cause problems for people who are lactose intolerant.

Sodium

Antibiotics and antacids often contain sodium. People who take Alka Seltzer, for example, may not realize that a single two-tablet dose may exceed their recommended sodium intake for a whole day. In addition, antacids neutralize stomach acid, and many nutrients depend on acid for their digestion. Taking any antacid regularly will reduce the absorption of many nutrients.

Nutrient interactions and risks are not unique to prescription drugs. People who buy over-the-counter drugs also need to protect themselves. The increasing availability of over-the-counter drugs allows people to treat themselves for many ailments from arthritis to yeast infections. Consumers need to ask their physicians about potential interactions and check with their pharmacists for instructions on taking drugs with foods. If problems arise, they should seek professional care without delay.

REFERENCES

1. R. S. Wold and coauthors, Increasing trends in elderly persons' use of nonvitamin, nonmineral dietary supplements and concurrent use of medications, *Journal of the American Dietetic Association* 105 (2005): 54-63.
2. K. E. Anderson and D. J. Greenblatt, Assessing and managing drug-nutrient interactions, *Journal of the American Pharmaceutical Association* 42 (2002): S28-S29.
3. L. E. Schmidt and K. Dalhoff, Food-drug interactions, *Drugs* 62 (2002): 1481-1502; L. Chan, Drug-nutrient interaction in clinical nutrition, *Current Opinion in Clinical Nutrition and Metabolic Care* 5 (2002): 327-332; J. M. Sorensen, Herb-drug, food-drug, nutrient-drug, and drug-drug interactions: Mechanisms involved and their medical implications, *Journal of Alternative and Complementary Medicine* 8 (2002): 293-308.
4. M. F. Paine and coauthors, A furanocoumarin-free grapefruit juice establishes furanocoumarins as the mediators of the grapefruit juice-felodipine interaction, *American Journal of Clinical Nutrition* 83 (2006): 1097-1105.

Frank Rothe/Getty Images

Nutrition in Your Life

No doubt, you're familiar with the recommendations. Eat more veggies. Eat more fiber. Eat more fish. Put down the saltshaker. Limit the fat. Be active. Don't smoke. And don't drink too much alcohol. What's the deal? If you follow this advice, will it really make a difference in how well or how long you live? In a word, yes. You can bet your life on it. If you could grow old in good health without having a heart attack or stroke, or getting diabetes, hypertension, or cancer, wouldn't you be willing to do just about anything—including improving your diet and activity habits? Of course, you would. And you can start today.

Diet and Health

CHAPTER OUTLINE

Nutrition and Infectious Diseases
• The Immune System • Nutrition and
Immunity • HIV and AIDS

Nutrition and Chronic Diseases

Cardiovascular Disease • How
Atherosclerosis Develops • Risk Factors
for Coronary Heart Disease • Recommendations for Reducing Coronary Heart
Disease Risk

Hypertension • How Hypertension
Develops • Risk Factors for Hypertension
• Treatment of Hypertension

Diabetes Mellitus • How Diabetes
Develops • Complications of Diabetes •
Recommendations for Diabetes

Cancer • How Cancer Develops •
Recommendations for Reducing
Cancer Risk

**Recommendations for Chronic
Diseases**

HIGHLIGHT 18 Complementary
and Alternative Medicine

Infectious diseases such as smallpox once claimed the lives of many children and limited the average life expectancy of adults. Thanks to medical science's ability to identify disease-causing microorganisms and develop preventive strategies, most people now live well into their later years, and the average life expectancy far exceeds that of our ancestors. In developed nations, purification of water and safe handling of foods help prevent the spread of infection. Antibiotics and immunizations provide additional protection for individuals.

Despite these advances, some infectious diseases still endanger many lives today. Growing threats around the globe include **bioterrorism,** the emergence of new diseases such as SARS (sudden acute respiratory syndrome), West Nile virus infections, and disease strains such as tuberculosis and some food-borne infections that have become resistant to antibiotics.[1] Although government security and public health measures such as emergency preparedness, safe food and water supplies, and medical care do much to contain infectious diseases, people are exposed to millions of microbes each day. Nutrition cannot directly prevent or cure infectious diseases, but good nutrition can strengthen, and malnutrition can weaken, the body's defenses against them.

This chapter begins with a description of the immune system and the relationships between nutrition and infectious diseases, but the bulk of the chapter focuses on the chronic diseases that pose the greatest threat to the lives of most people in developed countries. These chronic diseases develop over a lifetime as a result of metabolic abnormalities induced by such factors as genetics, age, gender, and lifestyle. As you have learned, diet is among the many lifestyle factors ◆ that influence the development of chronic diseases.[2]

◆ Other lifestyle factors that contribute to the development of chronic diseases:
• Physical inactivity
• Overweight
• Tobacco use
• Alcohol and drug abuse

Nutrition and Infectious Diseases

It is difficult to know exactly where infectious diseases fall among the leading causes of death. Compared with chronic diseases, infectious diseases pose a much greater challenge for public health officials who track disease prevalence. One physician might classify an ear infection as an infectious disease, whereas another calls it a

infectious diseases: diseases caused by bacteria, viruses, parasites, or other microorganisms that can be transmitted from one person to another through air, water, or food; by contact; or through vector organisms such as mosquitoes.

bioterrorism: the intentional spreading of disease-causing microorganisms or toxins.

disease of the ear. Trends change quickly as well. A disease, such as AIDS, that did not even exist until the early 1980s may suddenly appear and become one of the leading causes of death. A preventive strategy, such as food irradiation, may just as quickly eliminate hundreds of thousands of cases of foodborne infections each year. Public health strategies help the entire country defend against the spread of infection, and each individual's immune system provides a personal line of defense. A strong immune system depends on adequate nutrition. Poor nutrition weakens the immune system, which increases susceptibility to infections.

The Immune System

The **immune system** defends the body so diligently and silently that people do not even notice the thousands of enemy attacks mounted against them every day (the accompanying glossary defines immune system terms). If the immune system fails, though, the body suddenly becomes vulnerable to every wayward disease-causing agent that comes its way. Infectious disease invariably follows.

The body's first lines of defense against foreign substances—the skin, mucous membranes, and GI tract—normally deter invaders. If an invader penetrates these barriers and gains entry into the body, then the organs ◆ and cells of the immune system race into action. Foreign substances that elicit such a response are called **antigens.** Examples include bacteria, viruses, toxins, and food proteins that cause allergies.

Of the 100 trillion cells that make up the human body, one in every hundred is a white blood cell. Two types of white blood cells, ◆ the phagocytes and lymphocytes, defend the body against infectious diseases.

Phagocytes **Phagocytes,** the scavengers of the immune system, are the first to arrive at the scene if an invader, such as a microorganism, gains entry. Upon recognizing the foreign invader, the phagocyte engulfs and digests it, if possible, in a process called **phagocytosis.** ◆ Phagocytes also secrete special proteins called **cytokines** that activate the metabolic and immune responses to infection.

Lymphocytes: B-cells There are two distinct types of **lymphocytes**: B-cells and T-cells. **B-cells** respond to infection by rapidly dividing and producing large proteins known as **antibodies.** Antibodies travel in the bloodstream to the site of the infection. There they stick to the surfaces of the foreign particles and kill or otherwise inactivate them, making the foreign particles easy for the phagocytes to ingest.

The antibodies are members of a class of proteins known as **immunoglobulins**—literally, large globular proteins that produce immunity. Antibodies react selectively to a specific foreign organism, and the B-cells retain a memory of how to make them. Consequently, the immune system can respond with greater speed the next time it encounters the same foreign organism. B-cells play a major role in resistance to infection.

Lymphocytes: T-cells The **T-cells** travel directly to the invasion site to battle the invaders. T-cells recognize the antigens displayed on the surfaces of phagocyte cells and multiply in response. Then they release powerful chemicals to destroy all the

---

◆ Organs of the immune system:
- Spleen
- Lymph nodes
- Thymus

◆ Cells of the immune system:
- Phagocytes:
  - Neutrophils
  - Macrophages
- Lymphocytes:
  - B-cells
  - T-cells

◆ Two types of immune system cells ingest and destroy foreign antigens by phagocytosis: **neutrophils** and **macrophages.**

GLOSSARY OF IMMUNE SYSTEM TERMS

B-cells: lymphocytes that produce antibodies. *B* stands for *bone marrow* where the B-cells develop and mature.

cytokines (SIGH-toe-kines): special proteins that direct immune and inflammatory responses.

immune system: the body's natural defense against foreign materials that have penetrated the skin or mucous membranes.

immunoglobulins (IM-you-noh-GLOB-you-linz): proteins capable of acting as antibodies.

lymphocytes (LIM-foh-sites): white blood cells that participate in acquired immunity; B-cells and T-cells.

phagocytes (FAG-oh-sites): white blood cells (neutrophils and macrophages) that have the ability to ingest and destroy foreign substances.

- phagein = to eat

phagocytosis (FAG-oh-sigh-TOH-sis): the process by which phagocytes engulf and destroy foreign materials.

T-cells: lymphocytes that attack antigens. *T* stands for the thymus gland, where the T-cells mature.

Reminders: **Antibodies** are large proteins of the blood and body fluids, produced by the immune system in response to the invasion of the body by foreign molecules (usually proteins called *antigens*). Antibodies combine with and inactivate the foreign invaders, thus protecting the body.

Antigens are substances that elicit the formation of antibodies or an inflammation reaction from the immune system.

foreign particles that have this antigen on their surfaces. As the T-cells begin to win the battle against infection, they release signals to slow down the immune response.

Unlike the phagocytes, which are capable of inactivating many different types of invaders, T-cells are highly specific. Each T-cell can attack only one type of antigen. This specificity is remarkable, for nature creates millions of antigens. After destroying a particular antigen, some T-cells retain the necessary information to serve as memory cells so that the immune system can rapidly produce the same type of T-cells again if the identical infection recurs.

T-cells actively defend the body against fungi, viruses, parasites, and a few types of bacteria; they can also destroy cancer cells. In organ transplant patients, T-cells participate in the rejection of newly transplanted tissues, which is why physicians prescribe immunosuppressive drugs following such surgery.

Nutrition and Immunity

Of all the body's systems, the immune system responds most sensitively to subtle changes in nutrition status. Malnutrition compromises immunity.[3] Impaired immunity opens the way for infectious diseases, which typically raise nutrient needs and lower food intake. Consequently, nutrition status suffers further.[4] Thus disease and malnutrition create a **synergistic** downward spiral that must be broken for recovery to occur (see Figure 18-1).

Impaired immunity is a hallmark of protein-energy malnutrition (PEM). Table 18-1 presents the effects of PEM on the body's defenses. As Chapter 6 explained, without sufficient protein to make antibodies, the immune system loses its ability to fight infections. Deficiencies of vitamins and minerals also diminish the immune response, as may excesses.[5] Likewise, interactions between nutrients may enhance or impair immunity. Quite simply, optimal immunity depends on optimal nutrition—enough, but not too much, of each of the nutrients. ◆ People with weakened immune systems, such as the elderly, may benefit from a nutritious diet and supplements of selected nutrients.

HIV and AIDS

Perhaps the most infamous infectious disease today is **AIDS (acquired immune deficiency syndrome).** AIDS develops from infection by **HIV (human immunodeficiency virus),** which is transmitted by direct contact with contaminated body fluids, including semen, vaginal secretions, and blood (but not saliva), or by passage of the infection from a mother to her infant during pregnancy, birth, or breastfeeding. HIV attacks the immune system and disables the body's defenses against other diseases. Then these diseases, which would produce only mild, if any, illness in people with healthy immune systems, destroy health and life.

Table 18-2 (p. 624) shows the impact of AIDS worldwide and in the United States. For many years, the devastating effects of HIV infection seemed unstoppable. However, in the mid-to-late 1990s, the death rate in the United States from AIDS began

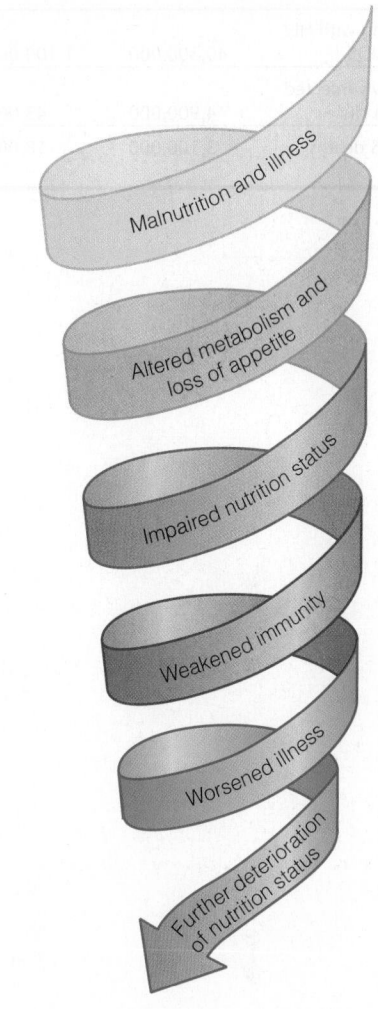

FIGURE 18-1 Nutrition and Immunity

Regardless of where a person enters the spiral, malnutrition, illness, and weakened immunity interact to compromise recovery and worsen malnutrition.

Malnutrition and illness

Altered metabolism and loss of appetite

Impaired nutrition status

Weakened immunity

Worsened illness

Further deterioration of nutrition status

◆ Nutrients known to affect immunity:
- Protein
- Folate
- Fatty acids
- Vitamin C
- Vitamin A
- Iron
- Vitamin E
- Zinc
- Vitamin B$_6$
- Selenium

synergistic (SIN-er-JIS-tick): multiple factors operating together in such a way that their combined effects are greater than the sum of their individual effects.

AIDS (acquired immune deficiency syndrome): the late stage of HIV infection, in which severe complications develop.

HIV (human immunodeficiency virus): the virus that causes AIDS. The infection progresses to become an immune system disorder that leaves its victims defenseless against numerous infections.

TABLE 18-1 Effects of Protein-Energy Malnutrition (PEM) on the Body's Defense Systems

Body's Defense System	Effects of PEM
Skin	Thinned, with less connective tissue to serve as a barrier to protect underlying tissues; delayed skin sensitivity reaction to antigens
Digestive tract and other body linings	Antibody secretions and immune cell number reduced
Lymph tissues[a]	Immune system organs reduced in size; cells of immune defense depleted
General response	Invader kill time prolonged; circulating immune cells reduced; antibody response impaired

[a]Lymph tissues include the thymus gland, lymph nodes, and spleen.

TABLE 18-2	HIV and AIDS Epidemic at a Glance, 2005	
	World	United States
Living with HIV or AIDS	40,300,000	1,100,000
Newly infected with HIV	4,900,000	43,000
AIDS deaths	3,100,000	18,000

to decline, and the progression from HIV to AIDS slowed dramatically.[6] Even though remarkable progress has been made in understanding and treating HIV infection, the disease still has no cure. Without a cure, the best course is prevention. Unlike the chronic diseases featured in the remainder of this chapter, AIDS prevention does not in any way depend on good nutrition. Although good nutrition cannot prevent or cure AIDS, an adequate diet may improve responses to drugs, shorten hospital stays, promote independence, and improve the quality of life. In addition, because common food bacteria can easily overwhelm a compromised immune system, attention to food safety is critical. (Chapter 19 provides food safety strategies.)

IN SUMMARY

Public health measures such as purification of water and safe handling of food help prevent the spread of infection in developed nations, and immunizations and antibiotics protect individuals. Nevertheless, some infectious diseases still endanger people today. Nutrition cannot prevent or cure infectious diseases, but adequate intakes of all the nutrients can help support the immune system as the body defends against disease-causing agents. If the immune system is impaired because of malnutrition or diseases such as AIDS, a person becomes vulnerable to infectious disease.

Nutrition and Chronic Diseases

Figure 18-2 shows the ten leading causes of death in the United States.[7] Four of these causes, including the top three, have some relationship with diet. Taken together, these four conditions account for 60 percent of the nation's more than 2 million deaths each year. Worldwide, statistics are similar, with developing nations sharing many of the same chronic diseases as developed nations.[8]

This chapter explains how the major chronic diseases develop and summarizes their major links with nutrition. Earlier chapters that described the connections between individual nutrients and diseases may have left the mistaken impression of "one disease–one nutrient" relationships. Indeed, valid links do exist between saturated fat and heart disease, calcium and osteoporosis, and antioxidant nutrients and cancer, but focusing only on these links oversimplifies the story. In reality, each

---

FIGURE 18-2 The Ten Leading Causes of Death in the United States[a]

Many deaths have multiple causes, but diet influences the development of several chronic diseases—notably, heart disease, some types of cancer, stroke, and diabetes.

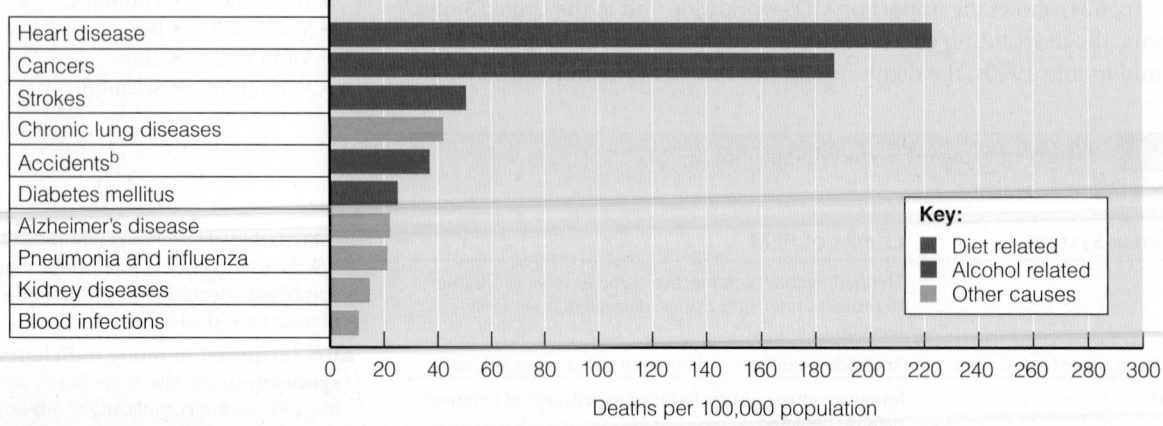

Deaths per 100,000 population

Key:
- Diet related
- Alcohol related
- Other causes

[a]Rates are age adjusted to allow relative comparisons of mortality among groups and over time.
[b]Motor vehicle and other accidents are the leading cause of death among people aged 15–24, followed by homicide, suicide, cancer, and heart disease. Alcohol contributes to about half of all accident fatalities.
SOURCE: Data from National Center for Health Statistics, 2006.

nutrient may have connections with several diseases because its role in the body is not specific to a disease, but to a body function. Furthermore, each of the chronic diseases develops in response to multiple risk factors, including many nondietary factors such as genetics, physical inactivity, and smoking. This chapter presents an integrated and balanced approach to disease prevention, paying careful attention to all of the factors involved. Figure 18-3 illustrates some of the relationships between risk factors and chronic diseases.

Notice how many of the diseases listed in Figure 18-3 have a genetic component. A family history of a certain disease is a powerful indicator of a person's tendency to contract that disease. Still, lifestyle factors are often pivotal in determining whether that tendency will be expressed. Genetics and lifestyle often work synergistically; for instance, cigarette smoking is especially likely to bring on heart disease in people who are genetically predisposed to develop it. Not smoking would benefit everyone's health, of course, regardless of genetic predisposition, but some recommendations to prevent chronic diseases best meet an individual's needs when family history is considered. For example, women with a family history of breast cancer might reduce their risks if they abstain from alcohol, whereas those with a family history of heart disease might benefit from one or two glasses of wine a week.

Vegetables rich in fiber, phytochemicals, and the antioxidant nutrients (beta-carotene, vitamin C, and vitamin E) help to protect against chronic diseases.

IN SUMMARY

Heart disease, cancers, and strokes are the three leading causes of death in the United States, and diabetes also ranks among the top ten. All four of these chronic diseases have significant links with nutrition, although other lifestyle risk factors and genetics are also important.

FIGURE 18-3 Risk Factors and Chronic Diseases

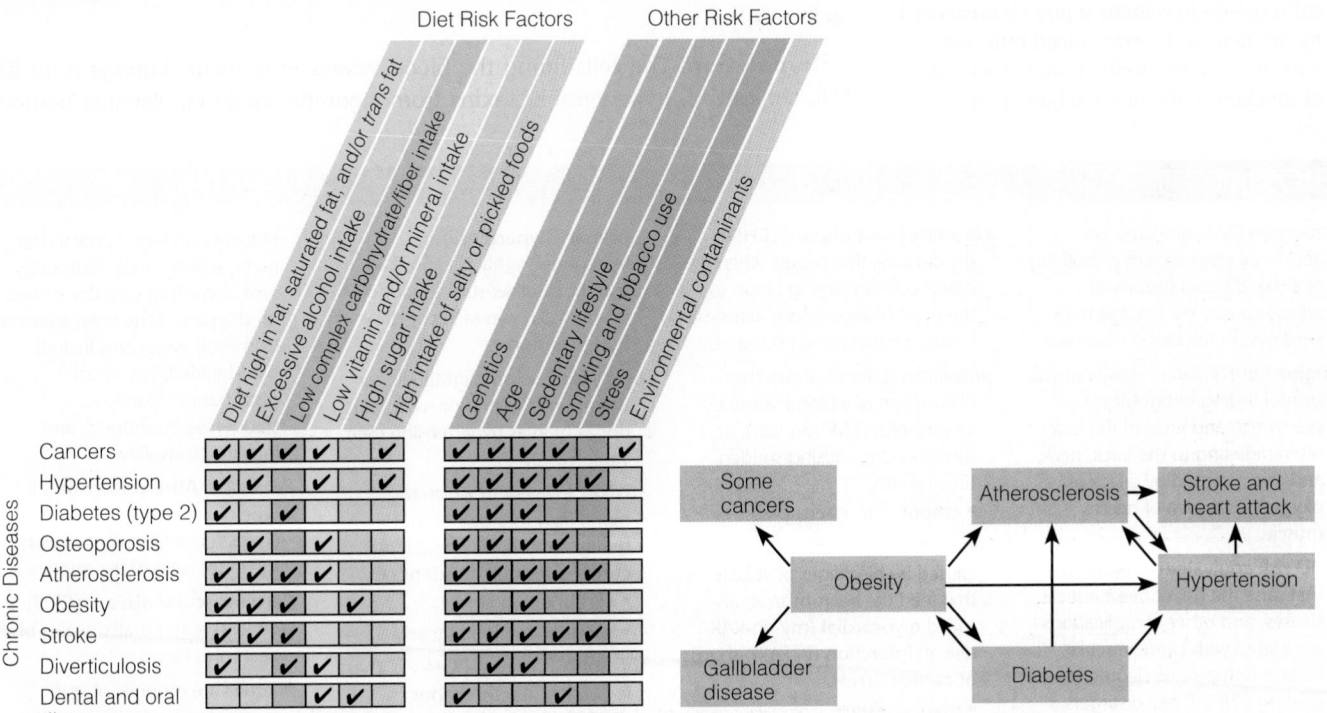

This chart shows that the same risk factor can affect many chronic diseases. Notice, for example, how many diseases have been linked to a sedentary lifestyle. The chart also shows that a particular disease, such as atherosclerosis, may have several risk factors.

This flow chart shows that many of these conditions are themselves risk factors for other chronic diseases. For example, a person with diabetes is likely to develop atherosclerosis and hypertension. These two conditions, in turn, worsen each other and may cause a stroke or heart attack. Notice how all of these chronic diseases are linked to obesity.

Cardiovascular Disease

The major causes of death around the world today are diseases of the heart and blood vessels, collectively known as **cardiovascular disease (CVD)**. (The accompanying glossary defines this and other heart disease terms.) In the United States, cardiovascular disease claims the lives of nearly 1 million people each year.[9]

Coronary heart disease (CHD) is the most common form of cardiovascular disease and is usually caused by **atherosclerosis** in the **coronary arteries** that supply blood to the heart muscle. Atherosclerosis is the accumulation of lipids and other materials in the arteries.

How Atherosclerosis Develops

As Highlight 16 pointed out, no one is free of the fatty streaks that may one day become the **plaques** ◆ of atherosclerosis. For most adults, the question is not whether you have plaques, but how advanced they are and what you can do to slow or reverse their progression.

Atherosclerosis or "hardening of the arteries" usually begins with the accumulation of soft fatty streaks along the inner arterial walls, especially at branch points (see Figure H16-1 on p. 587). These fatty streaks gradually enlarge and harden as they fill with cholesterol, other lipids, and calcium, and they become encased in fibrous connective tissue, forming plaques. Plaques stiffen the arteries and narrow the passages through them. Most people have well-developed plaques by the age of 30. As Chapter 5 pointed out, a diet high in saturated fat is a major contributor to the development of plaques and the progression of atherosclerosis.[10] But atherosclerosis is much more than the simple accumulation of lipids within the artery wall—it is a complex inflammatory response to tissue damage. Indeed, extensive evidence confirms that inflammation ◆ is centrally involved in all stages of atherosclerosis.[11]

Inflammation The cells lining the blood vessels may incur damage from high LDL cholesterol, hypertension, toxins from cigarette smoking, elevated homocys-

◆ Plaque associated with atherosclerosis is known as **atheromatous** (ATH-er-OH-ma-tus) **plaque.**

◆ Reminder: *Inflammation* is an immunological response to cellular injury characterized by an increase in white blood cells, redness, heat, pain, swelling, and often loss of function of the affected body part.

GLOSSARY OF HEART DISEASE TERMS

aneurysm (AN-you-rizm): an abnormal enlargement or bulging of a blood vessel (usually an artery) caused by damage to or weakness in the blood vessel wall.

angina (an-JYE-nah or AN-ji-nah): a painful feeling of tightness or pressure in and around the heart, often radiating to the back, neck, and arms; caused by a lack of oxygen to an area of heart muscle.

CHD risk equivalents: disorders that raise the risk of heart attacks, strokes, and other complications associated with cardiovascular disease to the same degree as existing CHD. These disorders include symptomatic carotid artery disease, peripheral arterial disease, abdominal aortic aneurysm, and diabetes mellitus.

coronary arteries: blood vessels that supply blood to the heart.

coronary heart disease (CHD): the damage that occurs when the blood vessels carrying blood to the heart (the **coronary arteries**) become narrow and occluded.

embolism (EM-boh-lizm): the obstruction of a blood vessel by an **embolus** (EM-boh-luss), or traveling clot, causing sudden tissue death.
• **embol** = to insert, plug

heart attack: sudden tissue death caused by blockages of vessels that feed the heart muscle; also called **myocardial** (my-oh-KAR-dee-al) **infarction** (in-FARK-shun) or **cardiac arrest.**
• **myo** = muscle
• **cardial** = heart
• **infarct** = tissue death

hypertension: higher-than-normal blood pressure. Hypertension that develops without an identifiable cause is known as **essential** or

primary hypertension; hypertension that is caused by a specific disorder such as kidney disease is known as **secondary hypertension.**

prehypertension: slightly higher-than-normal blood pressure, but not as high as hypertension (See Table 18-4).

stroke: an event in which the blood flow to a part of the brain is cut off; also called **cerebrovascular accident (CVA).**
• **cerebro** = brain
• **vascular** = blood vessels

thrombosis (throm-BOH-sis): the formation of a **thrombus** (THROM-bus), or a blood clot, that may obstruct a blood vessel, causing gradual tissue death.
• **thrombo** = clot

transient ischemic (is-KEY-mik) **attack (TIA):** a temporary

reduction in blood flow to the brain, which causes temporary symptoms that vary depending on the part of the brain affected. Common symptoms include light-headedness, visual disturbances, paralysis, staggering, numbness, and inability to swallow.

Reminders: **Atherosclerosis** is a type of artery disease characterized by plaques along the inner walls of the arteries.

Cardiovascular disease (CVD) is a general term for all diseases of the heart and blood vessels.

Plaques are mounds of lipid material, mixed with smooth muscle cells and calcium, that develop in the artery walls in atherosclerosis.

teine, or some viral and bacterial infections.[12] Such damage increases the permeability of the blood vessel walls and elicits an inflammatory response. The immune system sends in macrophages, ◆ and the smooth muscle cells of the artery wall try to repair the damage. Particles of LDL cholesterol become trapped in the blood vessel walls. Free radicals produced during inflammatory responses oxidize the LDL cholesterol, and the macrophages engulf it. The macrophages swell with large quantities of oxidized LDL cholesterol and eventually become the cells of plaque. Arterial damage and the inflammatory response also favor the formation of blood clots and allow minerals to harden plaque and form the fibrous connective tissue that encapsulates it.

The inflammatory response of atherosclerosis weakens the walls of the arteries and may cause an **aneurysm**—the abnormal bulging of a blood vessel wall. Aneurysms can rupture and lead to massive bleeding and death, particularly when a large blood vessel such as the aorta is affected. The central role of the inflammatory response in atherosclerosis has led researchers to look for signs or markers of inflammation in the blood vessel walls. One of the most promising of these markers is a protein known as **C-reactive protein (CRP)**. High levels of CRP have proved to more accurately predict future heart attack than high LDL cholesterol, which has a strong relationship with atherosclerosis, as a later section explains.[13]

Plaques Once plaques have formed, a sudden spasm or surge in blood pressure in an artery can tear away part of the fibrous coat covering a plaque, causing it to rupture. Some types of plaque are more unstable than others and are therefore more vulnerable to rupture.[14] Such plaques have a thin fibrous cap, a large lipid core, and an abundance of macrophages—characteristics that undermine plaque stability.[15] Researchers now know that the *composition* of a plaque rather than the *size* of a plaque (and how much arterial blockage it causes) is a key predictor of plaque rupture and subsequent clot formation.[16] When plaque ruptures, the body responds to the damage as it would to other tissue injuries.

Blood Clots **Platelets** are tiny disc-shaped bodies that cover an injured or damaged area, and along with other factors, they form a clot. Abnormal blood clotting can trigger life-threatening events. For example, a blood clot may gradually grow large enough to restrict or close off a blood vessel **(thrombosis).** ◆ A clot may also break free from an artery wall and travel through the circulatory system until it lodges in a small artery and suddenly shuts off flow to the tissues **(embolism)**.

The action of platelets is under the control of certain eicosanoids, known as prostaglandins and thromboxanes, which are made from the 20-carbon omega-6 and omega-3 fatty acids (introduced in Chapter 5). Each eicosanoid plays a specific role in helping to regulate ◆ many of the body's activities. Sometimes their actions oppose each other.[17] For example, one eicosanoid prevents clot formation, and another promotes it. Similarly, one dilates the blood vessels, and another constricts them. When omega-3 fatty acids are abundant in the diet, ◆ they make more of the kinds of eicosanoids that favor heart health.[18]

Blood Pressure and Atherosclerosis The heart must create enough pressure to push blood through the circulatory system. When arteries are narrowed by plaques, clots, or both, blood flow is restricted, and the heart must then generate more pressure to deliver blood to the tissues. This higher blood pressure further damages the artery walls, and plaques and clots are especially likely to form at damage points. Thus the development of atherosclerosis is a self-accelerating process. (A later section describes additional consequences of high blood pressure.)

The Result: Heart Attacks and Strokes When atherosclerosis in the coronary arteries becomes severe enough to restrict blood flow and deprive the heart muscle of oxygen, CHD develops. The person with CHD often experiences pain and pressure in the area around the heart **(angina).** If blood flow to the heart is cut off and that area of the heart muscle dies, a **heart attack** results. Restricted blood flow to the brain causes a **transient ischemic attack (TIA)** or **stroke.** Coronary heart

◆ **Macrophages** are large, phagocytic cells of the immune system.
• **macro** = large
• **phagein** = to eat

◆ A **coronary thrombosis** blocks blood flow through an artery that feeds the heart muscle. A **cerebral thrombosis** blocks blood flow through an artery that feeds the brain.

◆ Eicosanoids help to regulate:
• Blood pressure
• Blood clot formation
• Blood vessel contractions
• Immune response
• Nerve impulse transmissions

◆ Major sources of omega-3 fatty acids:
• Vegetable oils (canola, soybean, flaxseed)
• Walnuts, flaxseeds
• Fatty fish (mackerel, salmon, sardines)

C-reactive protein (CRP): a protein released during the acute phase of infection or inflammation that enhances immunity by promoting phagocytosis and activating platelets. Its presence may be used to assess a person's risk of an impending heart attack or stroke.

platelets: tiny, disc-shaped bodies in the blood, important in blood clot formation.

disease and strokes are the first and third leading causes of death, respectively, for adults in the United States.

Risk Factors for Coronary Heart Disease

Although atherosclerosis can develop in any blood vessel, the coronary arteries are most often affected, leading to CHD. Table 18-3 lists the major risk factors ◆ for CHD. The criteria for defining blood lipids, blood pressure, and obesity in relation to CHD risk are shown in Table 18-4; Table H16-1 on p. 587 presents cholesterol standards for children and adolescents.

◆ Some risk factors, such as diet and physical activity, are *modifiable*, meaning that they can be changed; others, such as genetics, age, and gender, cannot be changed.

By middle age, most adults have at least one risk factor for CHD, and many have more than one.[19] Public health officials in both the United States and Canada recommend screening to identify risk factors in individuals and offer preventive advice for the population. Regular screening and early detection have proven successful: since 1960, both blood cholesterol levels and deaths from cardiovascular disease among U.S. adults have shown a continuous and substantial downward trend.[20] These trends also reflect behavior changes in individuals. As adults grow older, many of them stop smoking, limit alcohol consumption, and become mindful that their food choices can improve their cardiovascular health.

Age, Gender, and Family History A review of Table 18-3 shows that three of the major risk factors for CHD cannot be modified by diet or otherwise: age, gender, and family history. As men and women grow older, the risk of CHD rises. The increasing risk of CHD with advancing age reflects the steady progression of atherosclerosis.[21] On average, older people have more atherosclerosis than younger people do.

In men, aging becomes a significant risk factor at age 45 or older. CHD occurs about 10 to 15 years later in women than in men. Women younger than 45 tend to have lower LDL cholesterol than men of the same age, but women's blood cholesterol typically begins to rise between ages 45 and 55. Thus aging becomes a significant risk factor for women who are 55 or older. The gender difference has been attributed to a protective effect of estrogen in women, but CHD rates do not suddenly accelerate at menopause as naturally-occurring estrogen levels taper off.[22] Rather, as in men, heart disease rates increase linearly with age. And, as in men, all of the major risk factors raise the risk of CHD in women. Ultimately, CHD kills as many women as men—and kills more women in the United States than any other disease.

Nonetheless, at every age, men have a greater risk of CHD than women do. The reasons for this gender difference are not completely understood, but they can be partly explained by the earlier onset of risk factors such as elevated LDL cholesterol and blood pressure in men. Levels of the amino acid homocysteine, which may damage artery walls and increase oxidative stress, rise with age and are generally

---

TABLE 18-3 Risk Factors for CHD

Major Risk Factors for CHD (not modifiable)

- Increasing age
- Male gender
- Family history of premature heart disease

Major Risk Factors for CHD (modifiable)

- High blood LDL cholesterol
- Low blood HDL cholesterol
- High blood pressure (hypertension)
- Diabetes
- Obesity (especially abdominal obesity)
- Physical inactivity
- Cigarette smoking
- An "atherogenic" diet (high in saturated fats and low in vegetables, fruits, and whole grains)

NOTE: Risk factors highlighted in color have relationships with diet.
SOURCE: Expert Panel on Detection, Evaluation, and Treatment of High Blood Cholesterol in Adults (Adult Treatment Panel III), *Third Report of the National Cholesterol Education Program (NCEP)*, NIH publication no. 02-5215 (Bethesda, MD.: National Heart, Lung, and Blood Institute, 2002), pp. II-15–II-20.

TABLE 18-4 Standards for CHD Risk Factors

Risk Factors	Desirable	Borderline	High Risk
Total blood cholesterol (mg/dL)	<200	200–239	≥240
LDL cholesterol (mg/dL)	<100[a]	130–159	160–189[b]
HDL cholesterol (mg/dL)	≥60	59–40	<40
Triglycerides, fasting (mg/dL)	<150	150–199	200–499[c]
Body mass index (BMI)[d]	18.5–24.9	25–29.9	≥30
Blood pressure (systolic and/or diastolic pressure)	<120/<80	120–139/80–89[e]	≥140/≥90[f]

[a]100–129 mg/dL LDL indicates a near or above optimal level.
[b]≥190 mg/dL LDL indicates a very high risk.
[c]≥500 md/dL triglycerides indicates a very high risk.
[d]Body mass index (BMI) was defined in Chapter 8; BMI standards are found on the inside back cover.
[e]These values indicate prehypertension.
[f]These values indicate stage one hypertension; ≥160/≥100 indicates stage two hypertension. Physicians use these classifications to determine medical treatment.

higher in men. Researchers have not determined whether the damage is caused by homocysteine itself or by a factor associated with it.[23]

A history of early CHD in immediate family members is an independent risk factor even when other risk factors are considered. The more family members affected and the earlier the age of onset, the greater the risk.[24]

High LDL and Low HDL Cholesterol In population studies, the relationship between total blood cholesterol and atherosclerosis is strong—and most of the total cholesterol is made up of LDL cholesterol. The higher the LDL cholesterol, the greater the risk of CHD.

The LDL are clearly the most atherogenic lipoproteins. As Chapter 5 explained, HDL also carry cholesterol, but raised HDL represents cholesterol returning from the cells to the liver and thus indicate a *reduced* risk of atherosclerosis and heart attack. High LDL and low HDL correlate *directly* with heart disease, ♦ whereas low LDL and high HDL correlate *inversely* with risk.

Any LDL cholesterol that remains in the blood after the body's cells take up the amount they need becomes vulnerable to oxidation. High blood levels of LDL cholesterol, especially oxidized LDL, promote the development of fibrous plaques. When the plaques weaken and become unstable, they can rupture, causing a heart attack. Evidence shows that elevated LDL contribute to plaque instability.[25] In the early stages of atherosclerosis, the goal of treatment is to slow the development of plaque. In the later stages, the goal of treatment is to stabilize plaques.

High Blood Pressure (Hypertension) Chronic high blood pressure **(hypertension)** frequently accompanies atherosclerosis, diabetes, and obesity. The higher blood pressure is above normal, the greater the risk of heart disease. However, even values only slightly higher than desirable—classified as **prehypertension** in Table 18-4—increases the risk of heart attack or stroke.[26] This relationship between hypertension and heart disease risk holds true for men and women, young and old. High blood pressure injures the artery walls and accelerates plaque formation, thus initiating or worsening the progression of atherosclerosis. Then the plaques and reduced blood flow raise blood pressure further, and hypertension and atherosclerosis become mutually aggravating conditions.

Diabetes Diabetes—a major independent risk factor for all forms of cardiovascular disease—substantially increases the risk of death from CHD.[27] In diabetes, blood vessels often become blocked and circulation diminishes. Atherosclerosis progresses rapidly. For many people with diabetes, the risk of CHD is similar to that of people with established CHD.[28] In fact, physicians describe diabetes and other disorders that have risks similar to CHD as **CHD risk equivalents**. Treatment to lower LDL cholesterol in diabetes follows the same recommendations as in CHD.

Obesity and Physical Inactivity Obesity, especially abdominal obesity, and physical inactivity significantly modify several of the risk factors for CHD, contributing to high LDL cholesterol, low HDL cholesterol, hypertension, and diabetes.[29] Conversely, weight loss and physical activity protect against CHD by lowering LDL, raising HDL, improving insulin sensitivity, and lowering blood pressure. Regular physical activity also increases energy expenditure and builds lean body mass, thereby improving body composition and physical fitness.

Cigarette Smoking Cigarette smoking is a powerful risk factor for CHD and other forms of cardiovascular disease. The risk increases the more a person smokes and is the same for men and women. Smoking damages the heart directly by increasing blood pressure and the heart's workload. It deprives the heart of oxygen and damages platelets, making blood clot formation likely. Toxins in cigarette smoke damage blood vessels, setting the stage for atherosclerosis. When people quit smoking, their risk of CHD declines within a few months.[30]

Atherogenic Diet Diet influences the risk of CHD. An "atherogenic diet"—high in saturated fats, *trans* fat, and cholesterol and low in fruits and vegetables—elevates

♦ Cholesterol is carried in several lipoproteins, chief among them LDL and HDL (see Chapter 5 for details). Remember them this way:
- LDL = **L**ow-density lipoproteins
  = **L**ess healthy
- HDL = **H**igh-density lipoproteins
  = **H**ealthy

Regular aerobic exercise can help to defend against heart disease by strengthening the heart muscle, promoting weight loss, and improving blood lipid and blood glucose levels.

LDL cholesterol. Conversely, diets rich in fruits, vegetables, and whole grains seem to lower the risk of CHD even more than might be expected based on risk factors such as LDL cholesterol alone. The specific nutrients responsible for this benefit remain to be defined, but some of the likely contenders include the antioxidant nutrients and omega-3 fatty acids. Dietary strategies to reduce the risk of CHD are discussed in a later section.

Other Risk Factors The major risk factors for CHD listed in Table 18-3 and discussed in the previous sections have solid associations with the development of CHD. Nevertheless, other factors also seem to influence a person's risk of CHD. These factors, known as **emerging risk factors,** may be helpful in assessing an individual's risk of CHD. For example, some people with CHD, especially those with diabetes and those who are overweight, have elevated triglycerides. Whether elevated blood triglycerides represent an independent risk factor for CHD remains debatable. In the latest report by the National Cholesterol Education Program Expert Panel, elevated blood triglycerides are considered a marker for other risk factors (high LDL, low HDL, overweight, and diabetes, for example), but they are not designated as a major risk factor.

Metabolic Syndrome As Table 18-3 shows, most of the modifiable risk factors for CHD are directly related to diet. Several of these diet-related risk factors—low HDL, high blood pressure, insulin resistance, ◆ and abdominal obesity—along with high blood triglycerides comprise a cluster of health risks known as the **metabolic syndrome.** Metabolic syndrome predicts an increased risk of coronary heart disease, but no more so than when each risk factor is considered individually.[31] Overeating and physical inactivity play a major role in the development of the metabolic syndrome. Based on the criteria listed in the margin, ◆ about 47 million people in the United States have the metabolic syndrome.[32] A new definition of the metabolic syndrome has recently been proposed to include greater emphasis on central obesity.[33] Regardless of slight differences in defining metabolic syndrome, experts agree that the prevalence of metabolic syndrome among U.S. adults is high, and that treatment to reduce these risk factors for heart disease and diabetes should begin early and focus on changes in lifestyle.

Recommendations for Reducing Coronary Heart Disease Risk

Recommendations to reduce cardiovascular disease risk include both screening and intervention. The accompanying "How to" provides a tool to assess a person's ten-year heart disease risk. Notice that total cholesterol and HDL cholesterol are included in the assessment, but LDL cholesterol is not. LDL cholesterol is routinely estimated from measures of total cholesterol and HDL cholesterol and thus would not add information to this assessment.[34] Once a person's risks have been identified, treatment focuses on lowering LDL cholesterol. Lowering LDL significantly reduces the incidence of CHD.[35] Treatment plans may include major lifestyle changes in diet, physical activity, and smoking cessation; medications; or both. The LDL cholesterol goals and treatment plans are specific to individuals, so they are best prescribed by a qualified health care provider.

Cholesterol Screening To determine an individual's risk of CHD, health care professionals review the person's health history and measure several blood lipids including total cholesterol, LDL cholesterol, HDL cholesterol, and triglycerides. Ideally, at least two measurements are taken at least one week apart and then compared to standards (shown earlier in Table 18-4 on p. 628). Single measurements may fail to identify those at risk or may misclassify them because blood cholesterol and other lipid concentrations vary significantly from day to day.

◆ Reminder: *Insulin resistance* is the condition in which a normal amount of insulin produces a subnormal effect, resulting in an elevated fasting glucose; a metabolic consequence of obesity that precedes type 2 diabetes.

◆ The metabolic syndrome includes any three of the following:
- Abdominal obesity: waist circumference >40 in (for men) or >35 in (for women)
- Triglycerides: ≥150 mg/dL
- HDL: <40 mg/dL (in men) or <50 mg/dL (in women)
- Blood pressure: ≥130/85 mm Hg
- Fasting glucose: ≥100 mg/dL

emerging risk factors: recently identified factors that enhance the ability to predict disease risk in an individual.

metabolic syndrome: a combination of risk factors—insulin resistance, hypertension, abnormal blood lipids, and abdominal obesity—that greatly increase a person's risk of developing coronary heart disease; also called **Syndrome X, insulin resistance syndrome,** or **dysmetabolic syndrome.**

HOW TO | Assess Your Risk of Heart Disease

Do you know your heart disease risk score? This assessment estimates your ten-year risk for CHD using charts from the Framingham Heart Study.* Be aware that a high score does not mean that you *will* develop heart disease, but it should warn you of the possibility and prompt you to consult a physician about your health. You will need to know your blood cholesterol (ideally, the average of at least two recent measurements) and blood pressure (ideally, the average of several recent measurements). With this information in hand, find yourself in the five tables below and add the points for each risk factor.

Age (years):

	Men	Women
20–34	−9	−7
35–39	−4	−3
40–44	0	0
45–49	3	3
50–54	6	6
55–59	8	8
60–64	10	10
65–69	11	12
70–74	12	14
75–79	13	16

HDL (mg/dL):

	Men	Women
≥60	−1	−1
50–59	0	0
40–49	1	1
<40	2	2

Systolic Blood Pressure (mm Hg):

	Untreated		Treated	
	Men	Women	Men	Women
<120	0	0	0	0
120–129	0	1	1	3
130–139	1	2	2	4
140–159	1	3	2	5
≥160	2	4	3	6

Total Cholesterol (mg/dL):

	Age 20–39		Age 40–49		Age 50–59		Age 60–69		Age 70–79	
	Men	Women	Men	Women	Men	Women	Men	Women	Men	Women
<160	0	0	0	0	0	0	0	0	0	0
160–199	4	4	3	3	2	2	1	1	0	1
200–239	7	8	5	6	3	4	1	2	0	1
240–279	9	11	6	8	4	5	2	3	1	2
≥280	11	13	8	10	5	7	3	4	1	2

Smoking (any cigarette smoking in the past month):

	Men	Women	Men	Women	Men	Women	Men	Women	Men	Women
Smoker	8	9	5	7	3	4	1	2	1	1
Nonsmoker	0	0	0	0	0	0	0	0	0	0

Scoring Your Heart Disease Risk

Add up your total points: _____ . Now find your total in the first column for your gender in the table at the right and then look to the next column for your approximate risk of developing heart disease within the next ten years. Depending on your risk category, the following strategies can help reduce your risk:

- *>20% = High risk (CHD risk equivalent).*
  Try to lower LDL using all lifestyle changes and, most likely, lipid-lowering medications as well.

- *10–20% = Moderate risk*
  Try to lower LDL using all lifestyle changes and, possibly, lipid-lowering medications.

- *<10% = Low risk*
  Maintain or initiate lifestyle choices that help prevent elevation of LDL to prevent future heart disease.

Men		Women	
Total	Risk	Total	Risk
<0	<1%	<9	<1%
0–4	1%	9–12	1%
5–6	2%	13–14	2%
7	3%	15	3%
8	4%	16	4%
9	5%	17	5%
10	6%	18	6%
11	8%	19	8%
12	10%	20	11%
13	12%	21	14%
14	16%	22	17%
15	20%	23	22%
16	25%	24	27%
≥17	≥30%	≥25	≥30%

*An electronic version of this assessment is available on the ATP III page of the National Heart, Lung, and Blood Institute's website (**www.nhlbi.nih.gov/guidelines/cholesterol**). Another risk inventory is available from the American Heart Association (**www.americanheart.org**).

SOURCE: Adapted from Expert Panel on Detection, Evaluation, and Treatment of High Blood Cholesterol in Adults (Adult Treatment Panel III), *Third Report of the National Cholesterol Education Program (NCEP)*, NIH publication no. 02-5216 (Bethesda, MD.: National Heart, Lung, and Blood Institute, 2002), section III.

ThomsonNOW
To assess your risk of heart disease, log on to **www.thomsonedu.com/thomsonnow**, go to Chapter 18, then go to How To.

Lifestyle Changes Recommendations to reduce the risk of CHD focus on lifestyle changes. To that end, people are encouraged to increase physical activity, lose weight (if necessary), implement dietary changes, and reduce exposure to tobacco smoke either by quitting smoking or by avoiding secondhand smoke. Treatment plans for people with existing CHD or conditions that place them at high risk for heart attacks and strokes (CHD risk equivalents) also focus on lifestyle changes first,

TABLE 18-5	Strategies to Reduce Risk of CHD

Dietary Strategies

- **Energy:** Balance energy intake and physical activity to prevent weight gain and to achieve or maintain a healthy body weight.
- **Saturated fat, *trans* fat, and cholesterol:** Choose lean meats, vegetables, and low-fat milk products; minimize intake of hydrogenated fats. Limit saturated fats to less than 7% of total kcalories, *trans* fat to less than 1% of total kcalories, and cholesterol to less than 300 milligrams a day (see Table H5-1).
- **Soluble fibers:** Choose a diet rich in vegetables, fruits, whole grains, and other foods high in soluble fibers.
- **Potassium and sodium:** Choose a diet high in potassium-rich fruits and vegetables, low-fat milk products, nuts and whole grains (see Table 18-7). Choose and prepare foods with little or no salt (limit sodium intake to 2300 milligrams per day).
- **Added sugars:** Minimize intake of beverages and foods with added sugars.
- **Fish and omega-3 fatty acids:** Consume fatty fish rich in omega-3 fatty acids (salmon, tuna, sardines) at least twice a week.
- **Plant sterols and stanols:** Consume food products that contain added plant sterols or stanols.
- **Soy:** Consume soy foods to replace animal and dairy products that contain saturated fat and cholesterol.
- **Alcohol:** If alcohol is consumed, limit it to one drink daily for women and two drinks daily for men.

Lifestyle Choices

- **Physical activity:** Participate in at least 30 minutes of moderate-intensity endurance activity on most days of the week. The eventual goal should be an expenditure of at least 2000 kcalories weekly.
- **Smoking cessation:** Minimize exposure to any form of tobacco or tobacco smoke.

SOURCE: AHA Scientific Statement: Diet and lifestyle recommendations revision 2006, *Circulation* 114 (2006) 82–96; F.M. Sacks and coauthors for the American Heart Association Nutrition Committee, Soy protein, isoflavones, and cardiovascular health, *Circulation* 113 (2006): 1034–1044; Expert Panel on Detection, Evaluation, and Treatment of High Blood Cholesterol in Adults (Adult Treatment Panel III) *Third Report of the National Cholesterol Education Program (NCEP)*, NIH publication no. 02-5215 (Bethesda, Md.: National Heart, Lung, and Blood Institute, 2002), p. V1–V28.

To guard against hypertension, have your blood pressure checked regularly.

but their target LDL is lower. Altering one's lifestyle is challenging, and instruction and counseling are critical for success. Health professionals can explain the reasons for change, set obtainable goals, and offer practical suggestions. If lifestyle changes fail to lower LDL or blood pressure to acceptable levels, then medications are prescribed. Table 18-5 summarizes strategies to reduce the risk of heart disease.[36] The "How to" box on p. 633 offers suggestions for implementing a heart-healthy diet.

IN SUMMARY

Atherosclerosis is characterized by a buildup of plaque in an artery wall. Rupture of plaque or abnormal blood clotting can cause heart attacks and strokes. Dietary recommendations to lower the risks of cardiovascular disease are summarized in Table 18-5. Quitting smoking and engaging in regular physical activity also improve heart health.

Hypertension

Anyone concerned about atherosclerosis and the risk it presents must also be concerned about hypertension. Together, the two are a life-threatening combination. The higher the blood pressure is above normal, the greater the risk. (Low blood pressure, on the other hand, is generally a sign of long life expectancy and low heart disease risk.) Hypertension affects at least 65 million people in the United States, about a third of the adult population.[37] It contributes to over a million heart attacks and half a million strokes each year. In fact, hypertension is the most consistent and powerful predictor of stroke.[38] People cannot feel the physical effects of high blood pressure, but it can impair life's quality and end life prematurely.

How Hypertension Develops

The underlying causes of most cases of hypertension are not fully understood, but much is known about the physiological factors that affect blood pressure. As shown

HOW TO   Implement a Heart-Healthy Diet

Following a heart-healthy diet can require major changes in dietary choices. People may find it easier to adopt a new diet if only a few changes are made at a time. It also helps to focus on positive choices (what to eat) first, rather than negative ones (what not to eat).

Breads, Cereals, and Pasta

- Choose whole-grain breads and cereals. Make sure the first ingredient on bread and cereal labels is "whole wheat" rather than "enriched wheat flour."
- Bakery products often contain *trans*-fatty acids. Choose foods whose labels *do not* list any *trans* fat in the Nutrition Facts panel or "hydrogenated oil" in the ingredients list. Crackers, chips, cookies, and doughnuts often include *trans* fats.
- Avoid products that contain tropical oils (coconut, palm, and palm kernel oil), which are high in saturated fat.

Fruits and Vegetables

- Consume fruits and vegetables frequently. Keeping the refrigerator stocked with a variety of colorful fruits and vegetables (baby carrots, grapes, blueberries, melon) makes it easier to choose healthy foods when the urge to nibble arises.
- Incorporate at least one or two servings of fruits and vegetables into each meal. People who rarely eat fruits or vegetables may start by adding at least one of their favorites to each meal.
- Choose canned products carefully. Canned vegetables (especially tomato-based products) may be high in sodium. Fruits that are canned in juice are higher in nutrient density than those canned in syrup.
- Restrict high-sodium foods such as pickles, olives, sauerkraut, and kimchee.
- Avoid French fries from fast-food restaurants, which are often loaded with *trans* fats.

Lunch and Dinner Entrées

- Limit meat, fish, and poultry servings to a maximum intake of 5 ounces per day.
- Select lean cuts of beef, such as sirloin tip, round steak, and arm roast, and lean cuts of pork, such as center-cut ham, loin chops, and tenderloin. Trim visible fat before cooking.
- Select extra-lean ground meat and drain well after cooking. Use lean ground turkey, without skin added, in place of ground beef.
- Limit cholesterol-rich organ meats (liver, brain, sweetbreads).
- Limit egg yolks to no more than two per week because the yolks are high in cholesterol (about 215 milligrams per yolk). Replace whole eggs in recipes with egg whites or commercial egg substitutes or similar reduced-cholesterol products.
- Include more vegetarian entrées or legume dishes to boost soluble fiber and soy protein intakes. Pasta and stir-fry recipes can help to reduce meat intake and increase vegetables in the diet.

- Restrict these high-sodium foods:
  - Cured or smoked meats such as beef jerky, bologna, corned or chipped beef, frankfurters, ham, luncheon meats, salt pork, and sausage
  - Salty or smoked fish, such as anchovies, caviar, salted or dried cod, herring, sardines, and smoked salmon
  - Packaged, canned, or frozen soups, sauces, and entrées

Milk Products

- Milk products can be good sources of protein, calcium, vitamin D, and potassium. To obtain two to three servings daily, include a portion of fat-free or low-fat milk, yogurt, or cottage cheese in each meal.
- Use yogurt or fat-free sour cream to make dips or salad dressings. Substitute evaporated fat-free milk for heavy cream.
- Restrict foods high in saturated fat or sodium, such as cheese, processed cheeses, ice cream, and many other milk-based desserts.

Fats and Oils

- Add nuts (not salted) and avocados to meals to increase monounsaturated fat intakes and make meals more appetizing.
- Include vegetable oils in salad dressings and recipes, such as canola, corn, olive, peanut, safflower, sesame, soybean, and sunflower oils.
- Use margarines with added plant sterols or stanols regularly to lower LDL cholesterol levels.
- Select soft margarines in tubs or liquid form; they have few, if any, *trans* fats. Avoid stick margarines and solid vegetable shortenings.
- Avoid products that contain tropical oils (coconut, palm, and palm kernel oil), which are high in saturated fat.

Spices and Seasonings

- Use salt only at the end of cooking, and you will need to add much less. Use salt substitutes at the table.
- Spices and herbs improve the flavor of foods without adding sodium. Try using more garlic, ginger, basil, curry or chili powder, cumin, pepper, lemon, mint, oregano, rosemary, and thyme.
- Check the sodium content on labels. Flavorings and sauces that are usually high in sodium include bouillon cubes, soy sauce, steak and barbecue sauces, relishes, mustard, and catsup.

Snacks and Desserts

- Select low-sodium and low–saturated fat choices such as unsalted pretzels and nuts, plain popcorn, and unsalted chips and crackers.
- Choose canned or dried fruits and some raw vegetables to boost fruit and vegetable intake.
- Enjoy angel food cake, which is made without egg yolks and added fat.
- Select low-fat frozen desserts such as sherbet, sorbet, fruit bars, and some low-fat ice creams

---

in Figure 18-4 (p. 634), blood pressure arises from the contractions in heart muscle that pump blood away from the heart (cardiac output) ◆ and the resistance blood encounters in the arterioles **(peripheral resistance)**. When either cardiac output or peripheral resistance increases, blood pressure rises. ◆ Cardiac output is raised when heart rate or blood volume increases; peripheral resistance is affected mostly

◆ Reminder: *Cardiac output* is the volume of blood discharged by the heart each minute.

◆ The equation describing this relationship is blood pressure = cardiac output × peripheral resistance.

peripheral resistance: the resistance to pumped blood in the small arterial branches (arterioles) that carry blood to tissues.

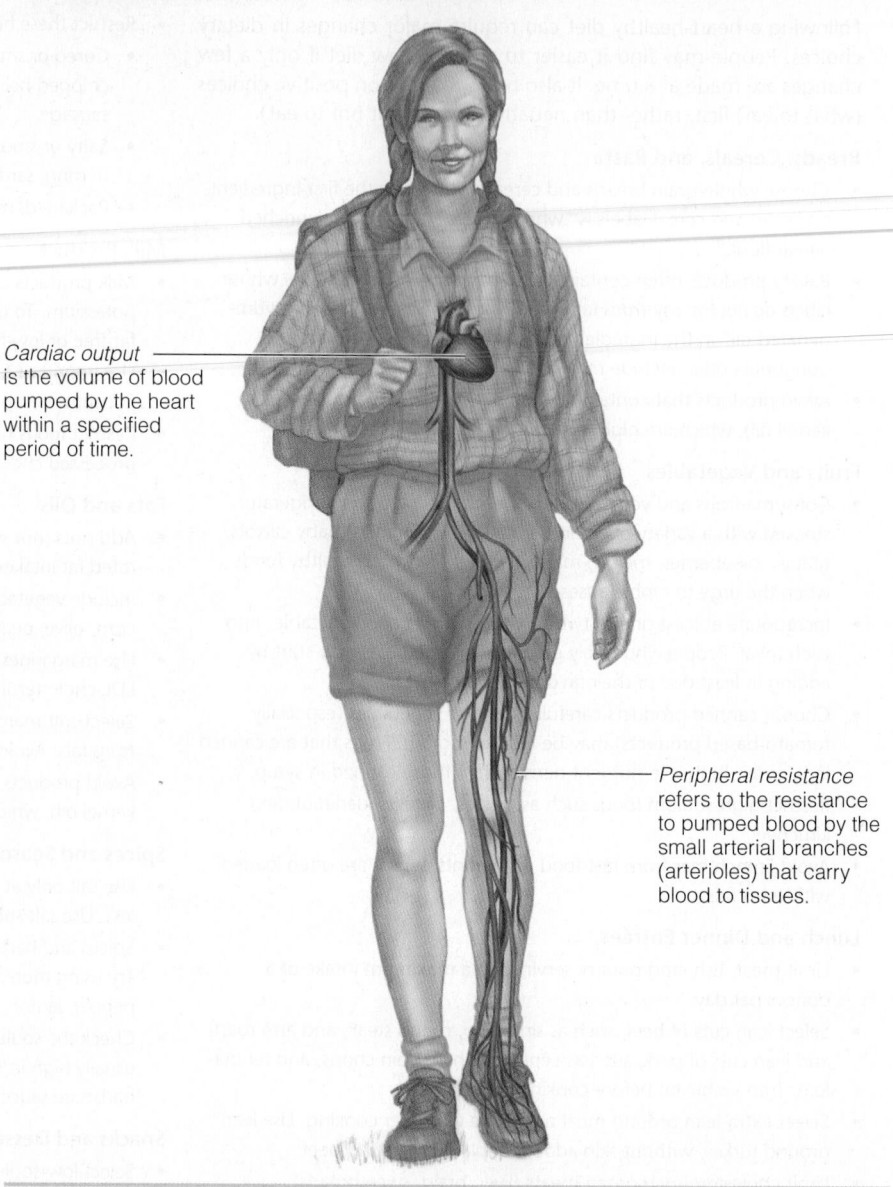

FIGURE 18-4   Determinants of Blood Pressure

Cardiac output is the volume of blood pumped by the heart within a specified period of time.

Peripheral resistance refers to the resistance to pumped blood by the small arterial branches (arterioles) that carry blood to tissues.

by the diameters of the arterioles. Blood pressure is therefore influenced by the nervous system, which regulates heart muscle contractions and the arteriole's diameters, and hormonal signals, which may cause fluid retention or blood vessel constriction. The kidneys also play a role in regulating blood pressure by controlling the secretion of the hormones involved in vasoconstriction and retention of sodium and water.[39]

Risk Factors for Hypertension

Several major risk factors predicting the development of hypertension have been identified, including:

- *Aging.* Hypertension risk increases with age. Individuals who have normal blood pressure at age 55 still have a 90 percent risk of developing high blood pressure during their lifetimes.[40]

- *Genetics.* Hypertension risk is similar among family members. It is also more prevalent and severe in certain ethnic groups: for African Americans in the United States, the prevalence of high blood pressure is among the highest in the world.[41] Compared with whites, African Americans develop high blood pressure earlier in life and their average blood pressure is much higher.

- *Obesity.* Most people with hypertension—an estimated 60 percent—are obese.[42] Obesity raises blood pressure in part by altering kidney function, promoting insulin resistance which damages blood vessels, and increasing blood volume and cardiac output without an appropriate reduction in peripheral resistance.[43]

- *Salt Sensitivity.* Among those with hypertension, approximately 30 to 50 percent have blood pressure that is sensitive to salt and can benefit by reducing salt in their diets.[44]

- *Alcohol.* Alcohol consumption, especially if consumed regularly in amounts greater than two drinks per day, is strongly associated with hypertension. Alcohol may interfere with drug therapy and is associated with strokes independently of hypertension.

Treatment of Hypertension

The single most effective step people can take against hypertension is to find out whether they have it. At checkup time, a health care professional can provide an accurate resting blood pressure reading. ◆ Under normal conditions, blood pressure fluctuates continuously in response to a variety of factors including stress and such actions as talking or shifting position. Some people react emotionally to the procedure, which raises the blood pressure reading. For these reasons, if the resting blood pressure is above normal, ◆ the reading should be repeated before confirming the diagnosis of hypertension. Thereafter, the blood pressure should be checked regularly. Both lifestyle modifications and drug therapies are used to treat hypertension. Table 18-6 describes the lifestyle changes that reduce blood pressure and the expected reduction in systolic blood pressure for each change.

Weight Control Efforts to reduce high blood pressure focus on weight control. Weight loss alone is one of the most effective nondrug treatments for hypertension. Those who are using drugs to control their blood pressure can often reduce or discontinue the drugs if they lose weight. Even a modest weight loss of 10 pounds can lower blood pressure significantly.

◆ Blood pressure is measured in millimeters of mercury (mm Hg). Blood pressure is measured both when the heart muscle contracts (*systolic* blood pressure) and when it relaxes (*diastolic* blood pressure).

◆ The optimal resting blood pressure for adults is <120 over <80 mm Hg. For adults 40 to 70 years of age, each increase of 20 mm Hg in systolic, or 10 mm Hg in diastolic, blood pressure doubles the risk of cardiovascular disease.

TABLE 18-6	Lifestyle Modifications to Reduce Blood Pressure	
Modification	**Recommendation**	**Expected Reduction in Systolic Blood Pressure**
Weight reduction	Maintain healthy body weight (BMI below 25).	5–20 mm Hg/10 kg lost
DASH eating plan	Adopt a diet rich in fruits, vegetables, and low-fat milk products with reduced saturated fat intake.	8–14 mm Hg
Sodium restriction	Reduce dietary sodium intake to less than 2400 milligrams sodium (less than 6 grams salt) per day.*	2–8 mm Hg
Physical activity	Perform aerobic physical activity for at least 30 minutes per day, most days of the week.	4–9 mm Hg
Moderate alcohol consumption	Men: Limit to 2 drinks per day. Women and lighter-weight men: Limit to 1 drink per day.	2–4 mm Hg

*According to the *Dietary Guidelines* and DRI recommendations, sodium intake should be limited to 2300 milligrams daily.
SOURCE: Adapted from *Reference Card from the Seventh Report of the Joint National Committee on Prevention, Detection, Evaluation, and Treatment of High Blood Pressure (JNC 7)*, NIH publication no. 03-5231 (Bethesda, Md.: National Institutes of Health, National Heart, Lung, and Blood Institute, and National High Blood Pressure Education Program, May 2003).

Physical Activity The higher the blood pressure and the less active a person is to begin with, the greater the effect physical activity has in reducing blood pressure. Physical activity helps with weight control, of course, but moderate aerobic activity, such as 30 to 60 minutes of brisk walking most days, also helps to lower blood pressure directly. Those who engage in regular aerobic activity may not need medication for mild hypertension.

The DASH Diet The results of the Dietary Approaches to Stop Hypertension (DASH) trial show that a diet rich in fruits, vegetables, nuts, and low-fat milk products and low in total fat and saturated fat can significantly lower blood pressure. The DASH eating plan provides more fiber, potassium, magnesium, and calcium than the typical American diet, which helps to reduce blood pressure. The diet also limits red meat, sweets, and sugar-containing beverages. Table 18-7 shows that the DASH eating plan is similar to the USDA Food Guide (introduced in Chapter 2). Both eating plans meet the goals specified in the *Dietary Guidelines for Americans 2005*.[45]

When the DASH diet is combined with a limited intake of sodium, the effects on blood pressure are greater still.[46] In addition to lowering blood pressure, the DASH diet lowers total cholesterol and LDL cholesterol.[47] ◆ Thus the heart-healthy dietary guidelines embrace these strategies in an overall diet to prevent and treat CHD.

For many years, controversy surrounded recommendations to restrict sodium or salt, but strong evidence supports the important role this strategy plays in preventing and reducing hypertension. Lowering sodium intake reduces blood pressure regardless of gender or race, presence or absence of preexisting hypertension, or whether people follow the DASH diet or a typical American diet. Furthermore, the lower the sodium intake, the greater the drop in blood pressure. (See the box in Chapter 12 on p. 411 for suggestions about limiting sodium intake.)

◆ Like other low-fat diets, the DASH diet also lowers HDL—a seemingly undesirable outcome. Whether a lowered HDL raises the risk of CHD is unknown, although some studies suggest that people with both low LDL and low HDL do not have an increased risk of CHD.

Dietary Guidelines for Americans 2005

Individuals with hypertension, blacks, and middle-aged and older adults should aim to consume no more than 1500 mg of sodium per day and to meet the potassium recommendation (4700 mg/day) with food.

Drug Therapy When diet and physical activity fail to reduce blood pressure, diuretics and antihypertensive agents may be prescribed. Diuretics lower blood pressure by increasing fluid loss. Some diuretics can lead to a potassium deficiency. People taking these diuretics need to include rich sources of potassium or supplements daily and watch for signs of potassium imbalances such as weakness (particularly of the legs), unexplained numbness or tingling sensation, cramps, irregular heartbeats, and excessive thirst and urination. Blood potassium should be monitored regularly.

TABLE 18-7	The DASH Eating Plan and the USDA Food Guide Compared	

Food Group	DASH	USDA Food Guide
Grains	6–8 oz	6 oz
Vegetables	2–2^1/$_2$ c	2^1/$_2$ c
Fruits	2–2^1/$_2$ c	2 c
Milk (fat-free/low-fat)	2–3 c	3 c
Lean meats, poultry, fish	6 oz or less	5^1/$_2$ oz
Nuts, seeds, legumes	4–5 oz per week	—[a]

NOTE: These diet plans are based on 2000 kcalories per day. Both DASH and the USDA Food Guide recommend that fats and sugars be used sparingly and with discretion.
[a] The USDA Food Guide combines nuts, seeds, and legumes with meat, poultry, and fish.

© Stefan Hallberg/Index Stock Imagery/Jupiter Images

The richest sources of potassium are *fresh* foods of all kinds.

Although some diuretics can lead to a potassium deficiency, others spare potassium. A combination of these two types of diuretics may be prescribed to prevent potassium deficiency.

IN SUMMARY

The most effective dietary strategy for preventing hypertension is weight control. Also beneficial are diets rich in fruits, vegetables, nuts, and low-fat milk products and low in fat, saturated fat, and sodium.

Diabetes Mellitus

The incidence of diabetes among children and adults has risen dramatically in the last decade (see Figure 18-5). It now affects more than 20 million people in the United States.[48] More than 6 million of those affected do not know they have the disease—a danger because damage to the body occurs before symptoms develop.

Diabetes mellitus ranks sixth among the leading causes of death (review Figure 18-2 on p. 624). In addition, diabetes underlies, or contributes to, several other major diseases, including heart disease, stroke, blindness, and kidney failure. Heart disease is the leading cause of diabetes-related deaths. In fact, people with diabetes are twice as likely to develop these cardiovascular problems as those without diabetes.

How Diabetes Develops

Diabetes mellitus describes a group of metabolic disorders characterized by high blood glucose concentrations and disordered insulin metabolism. People with diabetes may have insufficient insulin, ineffective insulin, or a combination of the two. The result is **hyperglycemia**, a marked elevation in blood glucose that can ultimately cause damage to blood vessels, nerves, and tissues. As many as 41 million U. S. adults between the ages of 40 and 74 have **prediabetes**—their blood glucose is elevated but not to such an extent as to be classified as diabetes. ◆ People with prediabetes have a high risk of developing diabetes.

The accompanying glossary defines diabetes, and Table 18-8 (p. 638) shows the distinguishing features of its two main forms, type 1 diabetes and type 2 diabetes. As described in the next section, the development of type 1 and type 2 diabetes differs, but some of the complications are similar.

To appreciate the problems presented by an absolute or relative lack of insulin, consider insulin's normal action. After a meal, insulin signals the body's cells to receive the energy nutrients from the blood—amino acids, glucose, and fatty acids. Insulin helps to maintain blood glucose within normal limits and stimulates protein synthesis, glycogen synthesis in liver and muscle, and fat synthesis. Without insulin, glucose regulation falters, and metabolism of the energy-yielding nutrients changes.

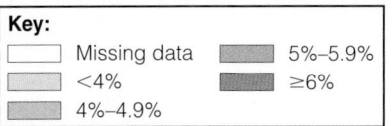

FIGURE 18-5 Prevalence of Diabetes among Adults in the United States

Key:
☐ Missing data   ☐ 5%–5.9%
☐ <4%   ☐ ≥6%
☐ 4%–4.9%

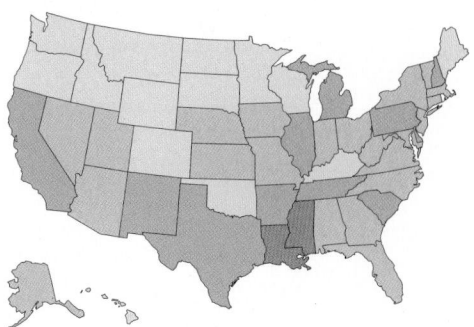

1994: 14 states had a prevalence of diabetes of less than 4% and only two states had a prevalence of 6% or greater.

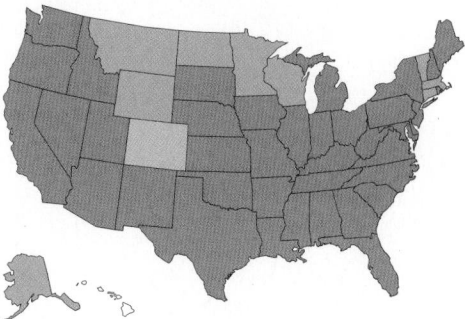

2004: No state had a prevalence of diabetes of less than 4%, and 39 states had a prevalence of 6% or greater.

SOURCE: Centers for Disease Control and Prevention, www.cdc.gov/nccdphp/aag/aag_ddt.htm.

◆ Fasting blood glucose
  • Normal: < 100 mg/dL
  • Prediabetes: 100–125 mg/dL
  • Diabetes: ≥125 mg/dL

hyperglycemia: elevated blood glucose concentrations.

GLOSSARY OF DIABETES TERMS

diabetes (DYE-uh-BEET-eez) **mellitus** (MELL-ih-tus or mell-EYE-tus): a group of metabolic diseases characterized by hyperglycemia resulting from defects in insulin secretion, insulin action, or both.

• **mellitus** = honey-sweet (sugar in urine)

prediabetes: condition in which blood glucose levels are higher than normal but not high enough to be diagnosed as diabetes; considered a major risk factor for future diabetes and cardiovascular diseases; formerly called **impaired glucose tolerance.**

type 1 diabetes: the type of diabetes that accounts for 5 to 10% of diabetes cases and usually results from autoimmune destruction of pancreatic beta cells. In this type of diabetes, the pancreas produces little or no insulin.

type 2 diabetes: the type of diabetes that accounts for 90 to 95% of diabetes cases and usually results from insulin resistance coupled with insufficient insulin secretion. Obesity is present in 80 to 90% of cases.

TABLE 18-8	Features of Type 1 and Type 2 Diabetes	
	Type 1	**Type 2**
Prevelence in diabetic population	5–10% of cases	90–95% of cases
Age of onset	<30 years	>40 years[a]
Associated conditions	Autoimmune diseases, viral infections, inherited factors	Obesity, aging, inherited factors
Major defect	Destruction of pancreatic beta cells; insulin deficiency	Insulin resistance; insulin deficiency (relative to needs)
Insulin secretion	Little or none	Varies; may be normal, increased, or decreased
Requirement for insulin therapy	Always	Sometimes
Older names	Juvenile-onset diabetes Insulin-dependent diabetes mellitus (IDDM)	Adult-onset diabetes Noninsulin-dependent diabetes mellitus (NIDDM)

[a] Incidence of type 2 diabetes is increasing in children and adolescence; in more than 90 percent of these cases, it is associated with overweight or obesity and a family history of type 2 diabetes.

Type 1 Diabetes In **type 1 diabetes**, the less common type of diabetes (about 5 to 10 percent of all diagnosed cases), the pancreas loses its ability to synthesize the hormone insulin. Type 1 diabetes is an **autoimmune disorder.**[49] In most cases, the individual inherits a defect in which immune cells mistakenly attack and destroy the insulin-producing beta cells of the pancreas. The rate of beta cell destruction in type 1 diabetes varies. In some people (mainly infants and children), destruction is rapid; in others (mainly adults), it is slow. Type 1 diabetes commonly occurs in childhood and adolescence, but it can occur at any age, even late in life.[50]

Without insulin, the body's energy metabolism changes, with such severe consequences as to threaten survival. The cells must have insulin to take up the needed fuels from the blood. People with type 1 diabetes must inject insulin or use external pumps; insulin cannot be taken orally because it is a protein, and the enzymes of the GI tract would digest it.

Type 2 Diabetes **Type 2 diabetes** is the most prevalent form of diabetes, accounting for 90 to 95 percent of cases, and is often asymptomatic.[51] The primary defect in type 2 diabetes is insulin resistance, a reduced sensitivity to insulin in muscle, adipose, and liver cells. To compensate, the pancreas secretes larger amounts of insulin, and plasma insulin concentrations can rise to abnormally high levels (hyperinsulinemia). Over time, the pancreas becomes less able to compensate for the cells' reduced sensitivity to insulin, and hyperglycemia worsens. The high demand for insulin can eventually exhaust the beta cells of the pancreas and lead to impaired insulin secretion and reduced plasma insulin concentrations. Type 2 diabetes is therefore associated both with insulin resistance and with relative insulin deficiency; that is, the amount of insulin is insufficient to compensate for its diminished effect in cells.

Although the actual causes of type 2 diabetes are unknown, the risk is substantially increased by obesity (especially abdominal obesity), aging, and physical inactivity. Most people with type 2 diabetes are obese, and obesity itself can directly cause some degree of insulin resistance.[52] As discussed in Highlight 16, obesity has led to a dramatic rise in the incidence of type 2 diabetes among children and adolescents during the past two decades.[53] Inherited factors also strongly influence risk, and type 2 diabetes is more common in certain ethnic populations, including Native Americans, Hispanic Americans, Mexican Americans, African Americans, Asian Americans, and Pacific Islanders.

autoimmune disorder: a condition in which the body develops antibodies to its own proteins and then proceeds to destroy cells containing these proteins. In type 1 diabetes, the body develops antibodies to its insulin and destroys the pancreatic cells that produce the insulin, creating an insulin deficiency.

Complications of Diabetes

In both types of diabetes, glucose fails to gain entry into the cells and consequently accumulates in the blood. These two problems lead to both acute and chronic complications. Figure 18-6 summarizes the metabolic changes and acute complications that can arise in uncontrolled diabetes. Notice that when some glucose enters the cells, as in type 2 diabetes, many of the symptoms of type 1 do not occur.

Over the long term, the person with diabetes suffers not only from the acute complications shown in Figure 18-6, but also from its chronic effects. Chronically elevated blood glucose alters glucose metabolism in virtually every cell of the body. Some cells begin to convert excess glucose to sugar alcohols, for example, causing toxicity and cell distention—distended cells in the lenses of the eyes, for example, cause blurry vision. Some cells produce glycoproteins by attaching excess glucose to an amino acid in a protein; the altered proteins cannot function normally, which leads to a host of other problems. The structures of the blood vessels and nerves become damaged, leading to loss of circulation and nerve function. Infections occur due to poor circulation coupled with glucose-rich blood and

---

FIGURE 18-6 Metabolic Consequences of Untreated Diabetes

The metabolic consequences of type 1 diabetes differ from those of type 2. In type 1, no insulin is available to allow any glucose to enter the cells. When glucose cannot enter the cells, a cascade of metabolic changes quickly follows. In type 2 diabetes, some glucose enters the cells. Because the cells are not "starved" for glucose, the body does not shift into the metabolism of fasting (losing weight and producing ketones).

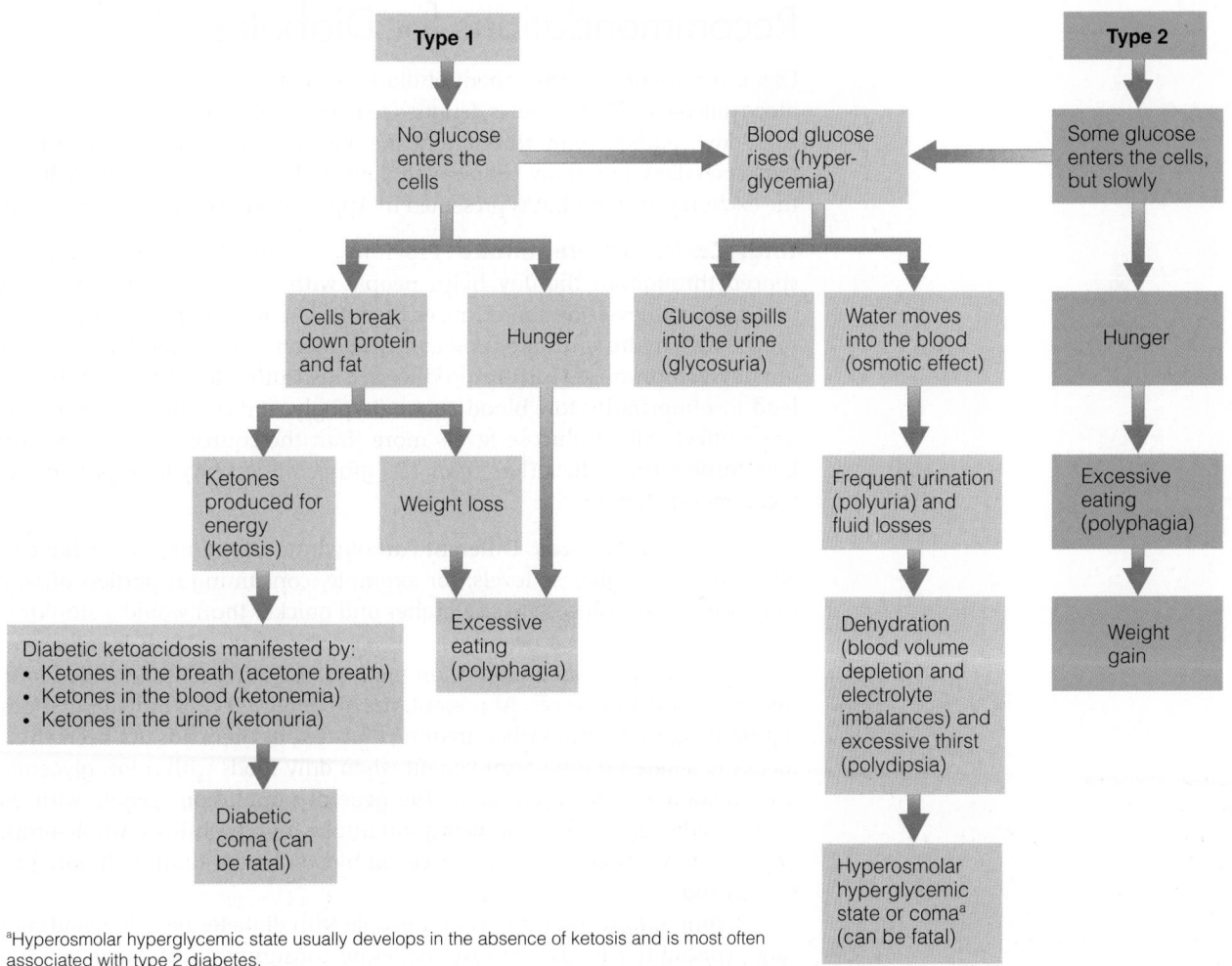

[a]Hyperosmolar hyperglycemic state usually develops in the absence of ketosis and is most often associated with type 2 diabetes.

urine. People with diabetes must pay special attention to hygiene and keep alert for early signs of infection. Early, aggressive treatment to control blood glucose significantly reduces the risk of long-term diabetes-related complications.

Diseases of the Large Blood Vessels As mentioned, atherosclerosis tends to develop early, progress rapidly, and be more severe in people with diabetes. The interrelationships among insulin resistance, obesity, hypertension, and atherosclerosis help explain why about 75 percent of people with diabetes die as a consequence of cardiovascular diseases, especially heart attacks. Research shows that intensive diabetes treatment, which keeps blood glucose levels tightly controlled, can reduce the risk of cardiovascular disease among those with type 1 diabetes.[54]

Diseases of the Small Blood Vessels For people with diabetes, disorders of the small blood vessels (capillaries) ◆ may also develop and lead to loss of kidney function and retinal degeneration with accompanying loss of vision. About 85 percent of people with diabetes have impaired kidney function, loss of vision, or both. Consequently, diabetes is a leading cause of both kidney failure and blindness.

Diseases of the Nerves Nerve tissues may also deteriorate with diabetes, expressed at first as a painful prickling sensation, often in the arms and legs. Later, the person loses sensation in the hands and feet. Injuries to these areas may go unnoticed, and infections can progress rapidly. With loss of both circulation and nerve function, undetected injury and infection may lead to death of tissue (gangrene), ◆ necessitating amputation of the limbs (most often the legs or feet). People with diabetes are advised to take conscientious care of their feet and visit a podiatrist regularly.

Recommendations for Diabetes

Diet is an important component of diabetes treatment. To maintain near-normal blood glucose levels, the diet is designed to deliver the same amount of carbohydrate each day, spaced evenly throughout the day. Several approaches can be used to plan such diets, but many people with diabetes learn to count carbohydrates using the exchange system that is presented in Appendix G (Appendix I for Canadians).

Total Carbohydrate Intake Providing a consistent carbohydrate intake spaced throughout the day helps people with diabetes maintain appropriate blood glucose levels and maximizes the effectiveness of drug therapy. Eating too much carbohydrate at one time can raise blood glucose too high, stressing the already-compromised insulin-producing cells. Eating too little carbohydrate can lead to abnormally low blood sugar (hypoglycemia). The *amount* of carbohydrate affects blood glucose levels more than the source of the carbohydrate.[55] Low carbohydrate diets (less than 130 grams of carbohydrate per day) are not recommended. [56]

Carbohydrate Sources Different carbohydrate-containing foods have varying effects on blood glucose levels; for example, consuming a portion of white rice may cause blood glucose to rise higher and quicker than would a similar portion of barley. As Chapter 4 described, this *glycemic effect* of foods is influenced by a food's fiber content, the preparation method, the other foods included in a meal, and individual tolerances. At present, the glycemic effect of individual foods is not a primary consideration when treating diabetes, as there has not been enough evidence to suggest a long-term benefit when only foods with a low glycemic effect are consumed.[57] However, as for the general population, people with diabetes should derive at least half of their grain intake from high-fiber, whole-grain products that have more moderate effects on blood glucose than do highly processed starchy foods.

   A common misconception is that people with diabetes need to avoid sugar and sugar-containing foods. Because moderate consumption of sugar has not been

◆ Disorders of the small blood vessels are called **microangiopathies**.
• **micro** = small
• **angeion** = vessel
• **pathos** = disease

◆ The death of tissue, usually due to deficient blood supply, is **gangrene** (GANG-green).

shown to adversely affect glycemic control, however, sugar recommendations for people with diabetes are similar to those for the general population, which suggests choosing foods and beverages with little added sugars. Sugars and sugary foods must be counted as part of the daily carbohydrate allowance, however.

Dietary Fat As mentioned earlier, people with diabetes have a high risk of developing cardiovascular diseases, and their guidelines for dietary fat are similar to those for others with high risks. Saturated fat intake should be limited to less than 7 percent of kcalories and cholesterol intake to less than 200 milligrams daily.[58] Dietary strategies for cardiovascular disease were discussed earlier in this chapter.

Protein Protein intakes in the United States generally range from 15 to 20 percent of total kcalories. Protein intakes in this range need not be modified for individuals with diabetes and normal kidney function.[59] Higher protein intakes are discouraged because they may be detrimental to kidney function.

Alcohol Use in Diabetes Adults with diabetes can drink alcohol in moderation. Guidelines are similar to those for the general population, which advise a daily limit of one drink for women and two drinks for men.[60] ◆

Recommendations for Type 1 Diabetes Normally, the body secretes a constant baseline amount of insulin at all times and secretes more as blood glucose rises following meals. People with type 1 diabetes, however, produce little or no insulin. They must learn to adjust the amount and schedule of their insulin doses to accommodate meals, physical activity, and health status. To maintain blood glucose within a fairly normal range requires a lifelong commitment to a carefully coordinated program of diet, physical activity, and insulin.

Nutrition therapy for type 1 diabetes focuses on maintaining optimal nutrition status, controlling blood glucose, achieving a desirable blood lipid profile, controlling blood pressure, and preventing and treating the complications of diabetes. In addition to meeting basic nutrient requirements, the diet must provide a fairly consistent carbohydrate intake from day to day and at each meal and snack to help minimize fluctuations in blood glucose. Further alterations in diet may be necessary for the person with chronic complications such as cardiovascular or kidney disease.

Participation in all levels of physical activity is possible for people with type 1 diabetes who have good blood glucose control and no complications, but they should check with their physician first. One potential problem is hypoglycemia, which can occur during, immediately after, or many hours after physical activity.[61] To avoid hypoglycemia, the person must monitor blood glucose before and after activity to identify when changes in insulin or food intake are needed. Carbohydrate-rich foods should be readily available during and after activity.

Recommendations for Type 2 Diabetes In overweight people with type 2 diabetes, even moderate weight loss (10 to 20 pounds) can help improve insulin resistance, blood lipids, and blood pressure. Together with diet, a regular routine of moderate physical activity not only supports weight loss, but also improves blood glucose control, blood lipid profiles, and blood pressure. Thus the benefits of regular, long-term physical activity for the treatment and prevention of type 2 diabetes are substantial.[62]

◆ Reminder: One drink is equivalent to 12 ounces of beer, 5 ounces of wine, 10 ounces of wine cooler, or 1¹/₂ ounces of 80 proof distilled spirits such as gin, rum, vodka, and whiskey.

For a person with type 1 diabetes, good health depends on coordinating the timing of meals, activities, and insulin.

IN SUMMARY

Diabetes is characterized by high blood glucose and either insufficient insulin, ineffective insulin, or a combination of the two. People with type 1 diabetes coordinate diet, insulin injections, and physical activity to help control their blood glucose. Those with type 2 benefit most from a diet and physical activity program that controls glucose fluctuations and promotes weight loss.

Cancer

Cancer, the growth of **malignant** tissue, ranks just below cardiovascular disease as a cause of death in the United States. (See the accompanying glossary of cancer terms.) As with cardiovascular disease, the prognosis for cancer today is far brighter than in the past. Identification of risk factors, new detection techniques, and innovative therapies offer hope and encouragement.

Cancer is not a single disorder. There are many **cancers,** that is, many different kinds of malignant growths. They have different characteristics, occur in different locations in the body, take different courses, and require different treatments.

How Cancer Develops

The development of cancer, called **carcinogenesis**, often proceeds slowly and continues for several decades. A cancer arises from mutations in the genes that control cell division in a single cell. These mutations may promote cellular growth, interfere with growth restraint, or prevent cellular death.[63] The affected cell thereby loses its built-in capacity for halting cell division, and it produces daughter cells with the same genetic defects. As the abnormal mass of cells, called a **tumor,** ◆ grows, a network of blood vessels develop to supply the tumor with the nutrients it needs to support its growth. The tumor can disrupt the functioning of the normal tissue around it, and some tumor cells may **metastasize,** or spread to another region in the body. Figure 18-7 illustrates cancer development. In leukemia (cancer affecting the white blood cells) the cells do not form a tumor, but rather accumulate in blood and other tissues.

The reasons cancers develop are numerous and varied. Vulnerability to cancer is sometimes inherited, as when a person is born with a genetic defect that alters DNA structure, function, or repair. Certain metabolic processes may initiate carcinogenesis, as when phagocytes (immune cells) produce oxidants that cause DNA damage or when chronic inflammation enhances the rate of cell division, which increases the risk of a damaging mutation. More often, cancers are caused by interactions between a person's genes and the environment. Exposure to cancer-causing substances, or **carcinogens,** may either induce genetic mutations that lead to cancer or promote proliferation of cancerous cells.

Environmental Factors Among environmental factors, exposure to radiation and sun, water and air pollution, and smoking are known to cause cancer. Lack of

◆ An abnormal mass of cells that is non-cancerous is called a *benign* tumor.

GLOSSARY OF CANCER TERMS

antipromoters: factors that oppose the development of cancer.

cancers: malignant growths or tumors that result from abnormal and uncontrolled cell division.

carcinogenesis (CAR-sin-oh-JEN-eh-sis): the process of cancer development.

carcinogens (CAR-sin-oh-jenz or car-SIN-oh-jenz): substances that can cause cancer (the adjective is *carcinogenic*).
• carcin = cancer
• gen = gives rise to

initiators: factors that cause mutations that give rise to cancer, such as radiation and carcinogens.

malignant (ma-LIG-nant): describes a cancerous cell or tumor, which can injure healthy tissue and spread cancer to other regions of the body.

metastasize (me-TAS-tah-size): the spread of cancer from one part of the body to another.

promoters: factors that favor the development of cancers once they have begun.

tumor: an abnormal tissue mass with no physiological function; also called a *neoplasm* (NEE-oh-plazm).

Cancers are classified by the tissues or cells from which they develop:
• **adenomas** (ADD-eh-NOH-mahz): cancers that arise from glandular tissues.
• **carcinomas** (KAR-see-NOH-mahz): cancers that arise from epithelial tissues.
• **gliomas** (gly-OH-mahz): cancers that arise from glial cells of the central nervous system.

• **leukemias** (loo-KEE-mee-ahz): cancers that arise from white blood cell precursors.
• **lymphomas** (lim-FOH-mahz): cancers that arise from lymph tissue.
• **melanomas** (MEL-ah-NOH-mahz): cancers that arise from pigmented skin cells.
• **sarcomas** (sar-KOH-mahz): cancers that arise from connective tissues, such as muscle or bone.

FIGURE 18-7 Cancer Development

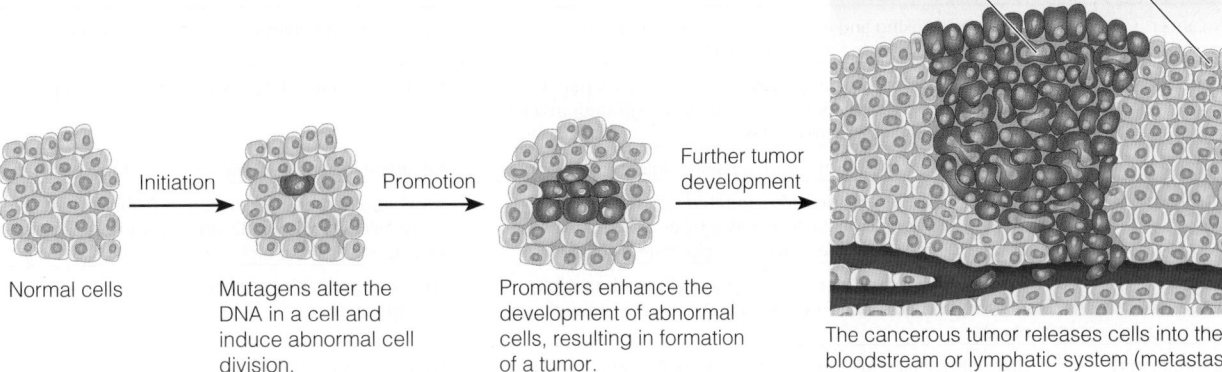

Normal cells

Initiation

Mutagens alter the DNA in a cell and induce abnormal cell division.

Promotion

Promoters enhance the development of abnormal cells, resulting in formation of a tumor.

Further tumor development

Malignant cells   Normal cells

The cancerous tumor releases cells into the bloodstream or lymphatic system (metastasis).

physical activity may also play a role in the development of some types of cancer.[64] Men and women whose lifestyles include regular, vigorous physical activity have the lowest risk of colon cancer.[65] Physical activity may also protect against breast cancer by reducing body weight and by other mechanisms not related to body weight.[66]

Obesity itself is clearly a risk factor for certain types of cancer (such as colon, breast in postmenopausal women, endometrial, kidney, and esophageal) and possibly for other types (such as ovarian and prostate) as well.[67] Because different cancers have various causes, the way obesity influences cancer development depends on the site as well as other factors, such as hormonal interactions. In the case of breast cancer in postmenopausal women, for example, the hormone estrogen is implicated. Obese postmenopausal women have much higher levels of estrogen than lean women do because fat tissue produces estrogen. Researchers believe that the extended exposure to estrogen in obese women is linked to an increased risk of breast cancer after menopause.[68] The relationships between excessive body weight and certain cancers provide yet another reason to adopt a lifestyle that embraces physical activity and sound nutrition.

As Table 18-9 (p. 644) shows, dietary constituents are also associated with an increased risk of certain cancers. Some dietary factors may initiate cancer development (**initiators**), others may promote cancer development once it has started (**promoters**), and still others may protect against the development of cancer (**antipromoters**).

Dietary Factors—Cancer Initiators We do not know to what extent diet contributes to cancer development, although some experts estimate that diet may be linked to as many as a third of all cases. Consequently, many people think that certain foods are carcinogenic, especially those that contain additives or pesticides. As Chapter 19 explains, our food supply is one of the safest in the world. Additives that have been approved for use in foods are not carcinogens. Some pesticides are carcinogenic at high doses, but not at the concentrations allowed on fruits and vegetables. The benefits of eating fruits and vegetables are far greater than any potential risk.

Cancers of the head and neck correlate strongly with the combination of alcohol and tobacco use and with low intakes of green and yellow fruits and vegetables. Alcohol intake alone is associated with cancers of the mouth, throat, and breast, and alcoholism often damages the liver and precedes the development of liver cancer.[69] These findings illustrate clearly why any potential benefit of moderate alcohol consumption on cardiovascular disease must be weighed against the potential dangers.

© Kent Meireis/The Image Works

People with cancer take comfort from the support of others and from the knowledge that medical science is waging an unrelenting battle in their defense.

TABLE 18-9	Factors Associated with Cancer at Specific Sites	

Cancer Sites	Associated with:	Probable Protective Effect from:
Bladder cancer	Cigarette smoking and alcohol; weak association with coffee and chlorinated drinking water	Fruits and vegetables (especially fruits); adequate fluid intake
Breast cancer	High intakes of food energy, alcohol intake; low vitamin A intake; obesity, sedentary lifestyle, probably high saturated fat intake; possibly high sucrose intake	Monounsaturated fats; vegetables and fruits; physical activity
Cervical cancer	Folate deficiency; viral infection; possibly, cigarette smoking	Adequate folate intake; possibly, fruits and vegetables
Colorectal cancer	High intakes of fat (particularly saturated fat), red meat, alcohol, and supplemental iron; low intakes of fiber, folate, vitamin D, and vegetables; inactivity; cigarette smoking	Vegetables, especially cruciferous (cabbage-type) vegetables; fruits; calcium, vitamin D, and dairy intake; possibly, whole wheat; wheat bran; high levels of physical activity
Kidney cancer	Possibly, high intakes of red meat (especially fried, sautéed, charred, burned, or cooked well-done); cigarette smoking; obesity	Fruit and vegetables, especially orange-colored and dark green ones
Mouth, throat, and esophagus cancers	Heavy use of alcohol, tobacco, and especially combined use; heavy use of preserved foods (such as pickles); low intakes of vitamins and minerals; obesity (esophageal)	Fruits and vegetables
Liver cancer	Infection with hepatitis virus; high intakes of alcohol; iron overload; toxins of a mold (aflatoxin) or other toxicity	Vegetables, especially yellow and green ones
Lung cancer	Smoking; low vitamin A; supplements of beta-carotene (in smokers); air pollution	Fruits and vegetables
Ovarian cancer	Possibly, high lactose intake from milk products; inversely correlated with oral contraceptive use	Vegetables, especially green leafy ones
Pancreatic cancer	Possibly, high intakes of red meat; physical inactivity; correlated with cigarette smoking and air pollution	Fruits and vegetables, especially green and yellow ones
Prostate cancer	High intakes of fats, especially saturated fats from red meats and possibly milk products	Possibly, cooked tomatoes, soybeans, soy products, and flaxseed; adequate selenium intake
Stomach cancer	High intakes of smoke- or salt-preserved foods (such as dried, salted fish); cigarette smoking; possibly, refined flour or starch; infection with ulcer-causing bacteria	Fresh fruits and vegetables, especially tomatoes

SOURCES: American Cancer Society, *The Complete Guide to Nutrition and Physical Activity,* available at: www.cancer.org/docroot/PED/content/PED_3_2X_Diet_and_Activity_Factors _that_Affect_Risks.asp?sitearea=PED; M. Pavia and coauthors, Association between fruit and vegetable consumption and oral cancer: A meta-analysis of observational studies, *American Journal of Clinical Nutrition* 83 (2006): 1126–1134; A. Flood and coauthors, Calcium from diet and supplements is associated with reduced risk of colorectal cancer in a prospective cohort of women, *Cancer Epidemiology, Biomarkers and Prevention* 14 (2005): 126–132; L. Bernstein and coauthors, Lifetime recreational exercise activity and breast cancer risk among black women and white women, *Journal of the National Cancer Institute* 97 (2005): 1671–1679; M. D. Holmes and

W. C. Willett, Does diet affect breast cancer risk? *Breast Cancer Research* 6 (2004): 170–178; I. Romieu and coauthors, Carbohydrates and the risk of breast cancer among Mexican women, *Cancer Epidemiology, Biomarkers and Prevention* 13 (2004): 1283–1289; C. E. Spiegelman and coauthors, Premenopausal fat intake and risk of breast cancer, *Journal of the National Cancer Institute* 95 (2003): 1079-1085; National Cancer Policy Board, Institute of Medicine, S. J. Curry, T. Byers, and M. Hewitt, eds., *Fulfilling the Potential of Cancer Prevention and Early Detection* (Washington, D.C.: National Academies Press, 2003), pp. 66–86; S. E. McCann and coauthors, Risk of human ovarian cancer is related to dietary intake of selected nutrients, phytochemicals and food groups, *Journal of Nutrition* 133 (2003): 1937–1942.

◆ To minimize carcinogen formation during cooking:
- When grilling, line the grill with foil, or wrap the food in foil.
- Take care not to burn foods.
- Marinate meats beforehand.

Grilling meat, ◆ fish, or other foods over a direct flame causes fat and added oils to splash on the fire and then vaporize, creating carcinogens that rise and stick to the food.* Eating grilled food introduces these carcinogens to the digestive system, where they may damage the stomach and intestinal lining. Once these compounds are absorbed into the blood, however, they are detoxified by the liver.

Evidence from population studies spanning the globe for over 20 years supports the theory that diets high in meat, especially red meat, are related to a moderately elevated risk of developing colon cancer.[70] In particular, meats cooked to the crispy well-done stage may be responsible.[71] Remember, however, that even strong correlation is not causation—certain foods may be implicated, but they have not been proven to actually cause cancer. Nevertheless, replacing most servings of red meat with poultry, fish, or legumes and choosing only occasional servings of grilled, fried, highly browned, or smoked foods is in the best interest of health.

Another reason to moderate consumption of fried foods such as French fries and potato chips is the presence of a substance called acrylamide, which is a potential

---

* The carcinogens of greatest concern are heterocyclicamines and benzopyrene.

carcinogen. Acrylamide is produced when certain starches such as potatoes are fried or baked at high temperatures. Chapter 19 offers a discussion of acrylamide in foods.

Dietary Factors—Cancer Promoters Unlike carcinogens, which initiate cancers, some dietary components promote cancers. That is, once the initiating step has taken place, these components may accelerate tumor development.

Studies of animals suggest that high-fat diets may promote cancer, but in studies of human beings, evidence is mixed.[72] One attribute of dietary fat is energy density—gram for gram, fat provides more kcalories than either carbohydrate or protein. Diets high in *kcalories* do seem to promote cancer, especially in laboratory settings.

The type of fat in the diet may influence cancer promotion or prevention. Some evidence implicates saturated and *trans*-fatty acids in cancer promotion and suggests that omega-3 fatty acids from fish may protect against some cancers.[73] Thus the same dietary fat advice applies to cancer protection as to heart health: reduce saturated and *trans*-fatty acids and increase omega-3 fatty acids.

Dietary Factors—Antipromoters Some foods may contain antipromoters—dietary compounds that defend against cancer. Research on dietary patterns of populations has identified such foods and led to recommendations aimed at reducing cancer risks.

Cruciferous vegetables, such as cauliflower, broccoli, and brussels sprouts, contain nutrients and phytochemicals that may inhibit cancer development.

Recommendations for Reducing Cancer Risk

Almost without exception, epidemiological studies find a link between eating plenty of fruits and vegetables and a low incidence of cancers. Fruits and vegetables contain both nutrients and phytochemicals with antioxidant activity, and these substances may prevent or reduce the oxidative reactions in cells that cause DNA damage. Phytochemicals may also help to inhibit carcinogen production in the body, enhance immune functions that protect against cancer development, and promote enzyme reactions that inactivate carcinogens.[74] For example, the **cruciferous vegetables**—cabbage, cauliflower, broccoli, and brussels sprouts—contain a variety of phytochemicals that have proven beneficial in defending against colon cancer.

In addition, fruits and vegetables, as well as legumes and whole-grains, are rich in fiber. As Chapter 4 explained, fiber may protect against cancer by binding, diluting, and rapidly removing potential carcinogens from the GI tract. High-fiber and whole-grain foods also help a person to maintain a healthy body weight—another preventive measure against cancer. Physical activity also helps to maintain a healthy body weight and reduce the risks of some cancers. Table 18-10 (p. 646) summarizes dietary and lifestyle recommendations for reducing cancer risk.

IN SUMMARY

Some dietary factors, such as alcohol and heavily smoked foods, may initiate cancer development; others, such as saturated fat or *trans*-fatty acids, may promote cancer once it has gotten started; and still others, such as fiber, antioxidant nutrients, and phytochemicals, may serve as antipromoters that protect against the development of cancer. By eating many fruits, vegetables, legumes, and whole grains and reducing saturated and *trans* fat intake, people obtain the best possible nutrition at the lowest possible risk. Minimizing weight gain through regular physical activity and a healthy diet is also beneficial.

cruciferous vegetables: vegetables of the cabbage family, including cauliflower, broccoli, and brussels sprouts.

TABLE 18-10	Recommendations for Reducing Cancer Risk

Healthy body weight: Choose foods that help maintain a healthy weight throughout life.
- Choose foods low in energy, fat, and sugar.
- Eat small portions of high-kcalorie, high-fat, or high-sugar foods.
- Balance energy intake with physical activity.
- Lose weight if currently overweight or obese.

Variety: Eat a variety of healthful foods, with an emphasis on plant sources.

Vegetables and fruits: Eat 5 or more servings of a variety of vegetables and fruits each day.
- Include vegetables and fruits at every meal and for snacks.
- Limit fried vegetables.
- If you drink juices, choose 100% fruit or vegetable juices.

Whole grains: Choose whole grains (such as oats and whole wheat bread) instead of refined grains (such as sweetened cereals and pastries) and sugars (such as soft drinks and candies).

Meats: Limit consumption of red meats, especially those high in fat and processed.
- Choose fish, poultry, and legumes as alternatives to beef, pork, and lamb.
- Select lean cuts and small portions.
- Bake, broil, or poach instead of frying or charbroiling.

Alcohol: If you drink alcoholic beverages, limit consumption to no more than 2 drinks a day for men and 1 drink a day for women.

Physical activity: Adopt a healthy active lifestyle.
- Engage in at least moderate activity for 30 minutes or more on 5 or more days of the week (45 minutes or more of moderate to vigorous activity on 5 or more days per week may further reduce the risk of breast and colon cancers).

SOURCE: L. H. Kushi and coauthors, American Cancer Society guidelines on nutrition and physical activity for cancer prevention: Reducing the risk of cancer with healthy food choices and physical activity, *CA: A Cancer Journal for Clinicians* 56 (2006): 254–281, available at http://caonline.amcancersoc.org/cgi/content/full/56/5/254.

Recommendations for Chronic Diseases

This chapter's discussion of chronic diseases began with the major cardiovascular diseases, described diabetes, and then went on to cancer—three different conditions with distinct sets of causes. Yet dietary excesses, particularly excess food energy and fat intakes, increase the likelihood of all three diseases.[75] Similarly, all are responsive to diet, and in most cases, the beneficial foods are similar.

Not all diet recommendations apply equally to all of the diseases or to all people with a particular disease, but fortunately for the consumer, dietary recommendations ◆ do not contradict one another. In fact, they support each other. Most people can gain some disease-prevention benefits by making dietary changes. To that end, the recommendations of the American Heart Association (Table 18-5), the DASH diet (Table 18-7), and the recommendations for reducing cancer risk (Table 18-10) describe the kinds of foods people should include or limit. Table 18-11 compares the *Dietary Guidelines for Americans 2005* with these recommendations for chronic diseases.

Several recommendations are aimed at weight control. Obesity is common in the United States, and it is linked with most of the chronic diseases that threaten life (review Figure 18-3 on p. 625). The problems of overweight people multiply when medical conditions develop. For example, overweight people readily develop diabetes, which is often accompanied by high blood pressure and high blood cholesterol. Such a combination of problems may require only one treatment: adopting a healthful diet and regular exercise program.

◆ A summary of the *Diet, Nutrition, and Prevention of Chronic Diseases* report from the World Health Organization (WHO) is presented in Appendix I.

Dietary Guidelines	Heart disease	Hypertension	Diabetes	Cancer
Maintain a healthy body weight.	✔	✔	✔	✔
Engage in regular physical activity.	✔	✔	✔	✔
Keep total fat 20–35%.	✔			
Limit saturated and *trans* fats.	✔			
Select fiber-rich fruits, vegetables, and whole grains.	✔	✔	✔	✔
Use little sugar.	✔		✔	
Use little salt.	✔	✔		
Drink alcohol in moderation.	✔	✔	✔	✔

TABLE 18-11 Dietary Guidelines and Recommendations for Chronic Diseases Compared

Dietary Guidelines for Americans 2005

To reduce the risk of chronic disease in adulthood, engage in at least 30 minutes of moderately intense physical activity, above usual activity, at work or at home on most days of the week. For most people, greater health benefits can be obtained by engaging in physical activity of more vigorous intensity or longer duration.

Recommendations for the Population The recommendations to prevent chronic diseases address the general population ◆ in the hope that all people at all levels of risk may benefit. Such a strategy is similar to national efforts to vaccinate to prevent measles, fluoridate water to prevent dental caries, and fortify grains with folate to prevent neural tube defects.

Recommendations for Individuals People's hereditary susceptibility to diseases and their responsiveness to dietary measures vary. Unlike nutrient-deficiency diseases, which develop when nutrients are lacking and disappear when the nutrients are provided, chronic diseases are neither caused nor prevented by diet alone. Many people have followed dietary advice and developed heart disease or cancer anyway; others have ignored all advice and lived long and healthy lives. For many people, though, diet does influence the time of onset and course of some chronic diseases, and many health care professionals urge dietary measures as part of a disease-prevention strategy.

To determine whether dietary recommendations are important to you personally, look at your family history to see which diseases are common to your relatives. In addition, examine your personal history, taking note of your blood pressure, blood lipid profile, and lifestyle habits such as smoking and physical activity.

Recommendations for Each Individual Even when recommendations are made "for individuals," they apply to large groups of people—those with hypertension or those with diabetes, for example. But that's expected to change in the next decade or so as research on the human genome ◆ provides the knowledge needed to create *specific* recommendations for *each* individual (as Highlight 6 explains).[76]

IN SUMMARY

Clearly, optimal nutrition plays a key role in keeping people healthy and reducing the risk of chronic diseases. To have the greatest impact possible, dietary recommendations are aimed at the entire population, not just at the individuals who might benefit most. Recommendations focus on weight control and urge people to limit saturated and *trans* fat, increase fiber-rich carbohydrates, and balance food intake with physical activity. A person can do no better than to incorporate those suggestions into his or her daily life.

◆ Recommendations that urge all people to make dietary changes believed to forestall or prevent diseases are taking a *preventive* or *population approach*. Alternatively, recommendations that urge dietary changes only for people who are known to need them are taking a *medical* or *individual approach*.

◆ Reminder: The full complement of genetic material (DNA) in the chromosomes of a cell is called *genome*. In human beings, the genome consists of 46 chromosomes. The study of genomes is called *genomics*.

© Bruce Ayres/Stone/Getty Images

Physical activity and a moderate weight loss of even 10 to 20 pounds can help improve blood glucose, blood lipids, and blood pressure.

ThomsonNOW™
www.thomsonedu.com/thomsonnow

Nutrition Portfolio

Identifying your risk factors is the first step in taking action to defend yourself against heart attack, stroke, hypertension, diabetes, and cancer.

▪ Review your personal and family history of heart disease, hypertension, diabetes, and cancer.

▪ Consider whether you are sedentary or overweight and how you might become more physically active and achieve a healthy body weight. If you smoke cigarettes, develop a reasonable plan for quitting.

▪ Learn whether you have high blood cholesterol or high blood pressure.

NUTRITION ON THE NET

ThomsonNOW™
For further study of topics covered in this chapter, log on to **www.thomsonedu .com/thomsonnow**. Go to Chapter 18, then to Nutrition on the Net.

- Find AIDS information at the Office of AIDS Research: **www.oar.nih.gov**

- Learn about HIV infections: **www.hivpositive.com**

- Review resources offered by the National Center for Chronic Disease Prevention and Health Promotion: **www.cdc.gov/nccdphp**

- Find information on health at the NIH Consumer Health Information site: **health.nih.gov**

- Visit the National Health Information Center site: **www.health.gov**

- Find information about health statistics at the National Center for Health Statistics site: **www.cdc.gov/nchs**

- Examine your family's health history at the U.S. Surgeon General's site: **familyhistory.hhs.gov**

- Search for "chronic diseases," "disease prevention," "men's health," "women's health," "heart disease," "stroke," "high blood pressure," "cancer," and "diabetes" at the U.S. Government site: **www.healthfinder.gov**

- Learn about women's health from the National Women's Health Information Center site: **www.4women.gov**

- Review the Surgeon General's Reports on Physical Activity and Health and Reducing Tobacco Use: **www .surgeongeneral.gov/library**

- Assess your heart disease risk at the American Heart Association site: **www.americanheart.org**

- Visit the National Stroke Association: **www.stroke.org**

- Find information on the DASH diet: **dashdiet.org**

- Visit the National Heart, Lung, and Blood Institute site and click on "clinical practice guidelines" for cholesterol and hypertension guidelines: **www.nhlbi.nih.gov/ index.htm**

STUDY QUESTIONS

ThomsonNOW™
To assess your understanding of chapter topics, take the Student Practice Test and explore the modules recommended in your Personalized Study Plan. Log onto **www.thomsonedu.com/thomsonnow**.

These questions will help you review the chapter. You will find the answers in the discussions on the pages provided.

1. How do the major diseases of today as a group differ from those of several decades ago as a group? Why is nutrition considered so important in connection with today's major diseases? (pp. 621, 624–625)

2. Identify the major diet-related risk factors for atherosclerosis, hypertension, diabetes, and cancer. (p. 625)

3. Describe some ways in which people can alter their diets to lower their blood cholesterol levels. (pp. 630–632)

4. Describe some steps that people with hypertension can take to lower their blood pressure. (pp. 635–636)

5. Name the two major types of diabetes and describe some differences between them. How do dietary recommendations for diabetes compare with the healthy diet recommended for all people? (pp. 637–641)

6. Differentiate between cancer initiators, promoters, and antipromoters. Which nutrients or foods fit into each of these categories? (pp. 643–645)

7. Describe the characteristics of a diet that might offer the best protection against the onset of cancer. (p. 646)

These multiple choice questions will help you prepare for an exam. Answers can be found on p. 651.

1. The immune cells of the body do *not* include:
   a. B-cells.
   b. T-cells.
   c. antigens.
   d. phagocytes.

2. Which of the following produce antibodies?
   a. phagocytes
   b. T-cells
   c. antigens
   d. B-cells

3. The leading cause of death in the United States is:
   a. AIDS.
   b. cancer.
   c. diabetes.
   d. heart disease.

4. Plaques in the arteries contribute to the development of:
   a. cancer.
   b. diabetes.
   c. atherosclerosis.
   d. infectious diseases.

5. Which blood lipid correlates directly with heart disease?
   a. HDL
   b. LDL
   c. VLDL
   d. triglycerides

6. Moderate amounts of alcohol may protect against heart disease by:
   a. promoting LDL oxidation.
   b. preventing clot formation.
   c. raising LDL and lowering HDL.
   d. accelerating plaque formation.

7. What is the most effective strategy for most people to lower their blood pressure?
   a. lose weight
   b. restrict salt
   c. monitor glucose
   d. supplement protein

8. Complications of diabetes may include all of the following *except*:
   a. blurry vision.
   b. nerve damge.
   c. impaired circulation.
   d. osteoporosis.

9. The most important dietary strategy in diabetes is to:
   a. provide for a consistent carbohydrate intake.
   b. restrict fat to 30 percent of daily kcalories.
   c. limit carbohydrate intake to 300 milligrams a day.
   d. take multiple vitamin and mineral supplements daily.

10. Which of the following help(s) to protect against cancer?
    a. alcohol
    b. pickled foods
    c. phytochemicals
    d. omega-6 fatty acids

REFERENCES

1. R. L. Monaghan and J. F. Barrett, Antibacterial drug discovery—then, now and the genomics future, *Biochemical Pharmacology* 30 (2006): 901-909; C. Dye and coauthors, Evolution of tuberculosis control and prospects for reducing tuberculosis incidence, prevalence, and deaths globally, *Journal of the American Medical Association* 293 (2005): 2767-2775; F. M. MacKenzie and coauthors, Report of the Consensus Conference on Antibiotic Resistance; Prevention and Control (ARPAC), *Clinical Microbiology and Infection* 11 (2005): 938-954; I. N. Okeke and coauthors, Antimicrobial resistance in developing countries, Part I: Recent trends and current status, *Lancet Infectious Diseases* 5 (2005): 481-493; I. N. Okeke and coauthors, Antimicrobial resistance in developing countries, Part II: Strategies for containment, *Lancet Infectious Diseases* 5 (2005):568-580; A. S. Fauci, Emerging infectious diseases: A clear and present danger to humanity, *Journal of the American Medical Association* 292 (2004): 1887-1888.
2. Committee on Dietary Reference Intakes, *Dietary Reference Intakes for Energy, Carbohydrate, Fiber, Fat, Fatty Acids, Cholesterol, Protein, and Amino Acids* (Washington, D.C.: National Academies Press, 2005), Chapter 11; B. E. Millen and coauthors, Unique dietary patterns and chronic disease risk profiles of adult men: The Framingham Nutrition Studies, *Journal of the American Dietetic Association* 105 (2005): 1723-1734; J. M. Genkinger and coauthors, Fruit, vegetables, and antioxidant intake and all-cause, cancer, and cardiovascular disease mortality in a community-dwelling population in Washington County, Maryland, *American Journal of Epidemiology* 160 (2004): 1223-1233; K. T. B. Knoops and coauthors, Mediterranean diet, lifestyle factors, and 10-year mortality in elderly European men and women, *Journal of the American Medical Association* 292 (2004): 1433-1439; F. B. Hu and W. C. Willett, Optimal diets for prevention of coronary heart disease, *Journal of the American Medical Association* 288 (2002): 2569-2578; Position of the American Dietetic Association: The role of dietetics professionals in health promotion and disease prevention, *Journal of the American Dietetic Association* 102 (2002): 1680-1687.
3. G. T. Keusch, The history of nutrition: Malnutrition, infection and immunity, *Journal of Nutrition* 133 (2003): 336S-340S; C. J. Field, I. R. Johnson, and P. D. Schley, Nutrients and their role in host resistance to infection, *Journal of Leukocyte Biology* 71 (2002): 16-32.
4. P. Bhaskaram, Micronutrient malnutrition, infection, and immunity: An overview, *Nutrition Reviews* 60 (2002): S40-S45.
5. Bhaskaram, 2002; Position of the American Dietetic Association and Dietitians of Canada: Nutrition intervention in the care of persons with human immunodeficiency virus infection, *Journal of the American Dietetic Association* 104 (2004): 1425-1441.
6. Centers for Disease Control and Prevention, Twenty-five years of HIV/AIDS—United States, 1981-2006, *Morbidity and Mortality Weekly Report* 55 (2006): 586-603.
7. K. D. Kochanek and coauthors, Deaths: Final data for 2002, *National Vital Statistics Reports*, October 12, 2004.
8. D. Yach and coauthors, the global burden of chronic diseases—Overcoming impediments to prevention and control, *Journal of the American Medical Association* 291 (2004): 2616-2622; *Executive Summary: Joint WHO/FAO Expert Report on Diet, Nutrition, and the Prevention of Chronic Disease*, www.who.int/hpr/nutrition/expertconsultationge.htm.
9. American Heart Association, *Heart Disease and Strokes Statistics—2006 Update*, www.americanheart.org/statistics/cvd.html, site visited August 18, 2006.
10. R. De Caterina and coauthors, Nutritional mechanisms that influence cardiovascular disease, *American Journal of Clinical Nutrition* 83 (2006): 421S-426S; T. Seo and coauthors, Saturated fat-rich diet enhances selective uptake of LDL cholesteryl esters in the arterial wall, *Journal of Clinical Investigation* 115 (2005): 2214-2222; Hu and Willett, 2002.
11. P. Libby, Inflammation and cardiovascular disease mechanisms, *American Journal of Clinical Nutrition* 83 (2006): 456S-460S; M. S. Elkind, Inflammation, atherosclerosis, and stroke, *Neurologist* 12 (2006): 140-148.
12. Libby, 2006; F. Pellegatta and coauthors, Different short- and long-term effects of

resveratrol on nuclear factor-kB phosphory-lation and nuclear appearance in human endothelial cells, *American Journal of Clinical Nutrition* 77 (2003): 1220-1228.

13. N. R. Cook, J. E. Buring, and P. M. Ridker, The effect of including C-reactive protein in cardiovascular risk prediction models for women, *Annals of Internal Medicine* 145 (2006): 21-29; L. M. Biasucci, CDC/AHA Workshop on Markers of Inflammation and Cardiovascular Disease: Application to Clini-cal and Public Health Practice: Clinical use of inflammatory markers in patients with cardiovascular diseases: A background paper, *Circulation* 110 (2004): e560-567; P. M. Ridker, High-sensitivity C-reactive protein, inflam-mation, and cardiovascular risk: From con-cept to clinical practice to clinical benefit, *American Heart Journal* 148 (2004): S19-S26.

14. Z. S. Galis, Vulnerable plaque: The devil is in the details, *Circulation* 110 (2004): 244-246; R. Corti and coauthors, Evolving con-cepts in the triad of atherosclerosis, inflammation and thrombosis, *Journal of Thrombosis and Thrombolysis* 17 (2004): 35-44; D. D. Heistad, Unstable coronary-artery plaques, *New England Journal of Medicine* 349 (2003): 2285-2287.

15. Heistad, 2003.

16. Corti and coauthors, 2004.

17. P. C. Calder, n-3 polyunsaturated fatty acids, inflammation, and inflammatory diseases, *American Journal of Clinical Nutrition* 83 (2006): 1505S-1519S.

18. J. L. Breslow, n-3 Fatty acids and cardiovas-cular disease, *American Journal of Clinical Nutrition* 83 (2006): 1477S-1482S; C. Wang and coauthors, n-3 Fatty acids from fish or fish-oil supplements, but not α-linolenic acid, benefit cardiovascular disease out-comes in primary-and secondary-prevention studies: A systematic review, *American Jour-nal of Clinical Nutrition* 84 (2006): 5-17; M. Laidlaw and B. J. Holub, Effects of supple-mentation with fish oil-derived n-3 fatty acids and γ-linolenic acid on circulating plasma lipids and fatty acid profiles in women, *American Journal of Clinical Nutrition* 77 (2003): 37-42; P. J. H. Jones, Effect of n-3 polyunsaturated fatty acids on risk reduc-tion of sudden death, *Nutrition Reviews* 60 (2002): 407-413.

19. E. S. Ford, W. H. Giles, and W. H. Dietz, Prevalence of the metabolic syndrome among US adults: Findings from the Third National Health and Nutrition Examination Survey, *Journal of the American Medical Association* 287 (2002): 356-359.

20. Y. Gerber and coauthors, Secular trends in deaths from cardiovascular diseases: A 25-year community study, *Circulation* 113 (2006): 2285-2292; M. D. Carroll and coau-thors, Trends in serum lipids and lipopro-teins of adults, 1960-2002, *Journal of the American Medical Association* 294 (2005): 1773-1781.

21. Expert Panel on Detection, Evaluation, and Treatment of High Blood Cholesterol in Adults (Adult Treatment Panel III), *Third Report of the National Cholesterol Education Program (NCEP)*, NIH publication no. 02-5215 (Bethesda, Md.: National Heart, Lung, and Blood Institute, 2002), p. II-18.

22. Expert Panel on Detection, Evaluation, and Treatment of High Blood Cholesterol in Adults (Adult Treatment Panel III), 2002, p. VIII-2.

23. A. M. Gori and coauthors, A proinflamma-tory state is associated with hyperhomocys-teinemia in the elderly, *American Journal of Clinical Nutrition* 82 (2005): 335-341; H. O'Grady and coauthors, Homocysteine and occlusive arterial disease, *British Journal of Surgery* 89 (2002): 838-844.

24. Expert Panel on Detection, Evaluation, and Treatment of High Blood Cholesterol in Adults (Adult Treatment Panel III), 2002, p. II-19.

25. R. De Caterina and coauthors, Nutritional mechanisms that influence cardiovascular disease, *American Journal of Clinical Nutrition* 83 (2006): 421S-426S; Expert Panel on Detection, Evaluation, and Treatment of High Blood Cholesterol in Adults (Adult Treatment Panel III), 2002, p. II-2-II-3.

26. Joint National Committee, *Prevention, Detection, Evaluation, and Treatment of High Blood Pressure, Seventh Report*, NIH publica-tion no. 03-5233 (Bethesda, Md.: National Heart, Lung, and Blood Institute, 2003), pp. 1-3.

27. De Caterina and coauthors, 2006; J. A. Beckman, M. A. Creager, and P. Libby, Diabetes and atherosclerosis: Epidemiology, pathophysiology, and management, *Journal of the American Medical Association* 287 (2002): 2570-2581.

28. Expert Panel on Detection, Evaluation, and Treatment of High Blood Cholesterol in Adults (Adult Treatment Panel III), 2002, pp. II-16, 11-50-11-53.

29. T. Weinbrenner and coauthors, Circulating oxidized LDL is associated with increased waist circumference independent of body mass index in men and women, *American Journal of Clinical Nutrition* 83 (2006): 30-35; T. S. Altena and coauthors, Lipoprotein subfraction changes after continuous or intermittent exercise training, *Medicine and Science in Sports and Exercise* 38 (2006): 367-372; C. E. Finley and coauthors, Cardiores-piratory fitness, macronutrient intake, and the metabolic syndrome: The Aerobics Center Longitudinal Study, *Journal of the American Dietetic Association* 106 (2006): 673-679; R. Edelman, Obesity, type 2 dia-betes, and cardiovascular disease, *Nutrition Today* May/June (2005): 119-121.

30. Expert Panel on Detection, Evaluation, and Treatment of High Blood Cholesterol in Adults (Adult Treatment Panel III), 2002, p. II-16.

31. P. Kohli and P. Greenland, Role of the meta-bolic syndrome in risk assessment for coro-nary heart disease, *Journal of the American Medical Association* 295 (2006): 819-821; C. M. Alexander and coauthors, NCEP-defined metabolic syndrome, diabetes, and preva-lence of coronary heart disease among NHANES III participants age 50 years and older, *Diabetes* 52 (2003): 1210-1214.

32. Ford, Giles, and Dietz, 2002.

33. E. S. Ford, Prevalence of the metabolic syndrome defined by the International Diabetes Federation among adults in the U.S., *Diabetes Care* 28 (2005): 2745-2749; Expert Panel on Detection, Evaluation, and Treatment of High blood Cholesterol in Adults (Adult Treatment Panel III), 2002, pp. II-26-II-28.

34. Expert Panel on Detection, Evaluation, and Treatment of High Blood Cholesterol in Adults (Adult Treatment Panel III), 2002, p. III-6.

35. Expert Panel on Detection, Evaluation, and Treatment of High Blood Cholesterol in Adults (Adult Treatment Panel III), 2002, p. II-1-II-4.

36. AHA Scientific Statement: Diet and lifestyle recommendations revision 2006, *Circulation* 114 (2006): 82–96; Expert Panel on Detec-tion, Evaluation, and Treatment of High Blood Cholesterol in Adults (Adult Treat-ment Panel III), 2002, pp. V-1–V-28.

37. N. D. Wong and coauthors, Prevalence, treatment, and control of combined hyper-tension and hypercholesterolemia in the United States, *American Journal of Cardiology* 98 (2006): 204-208; L. E. Fields and coau-thors, The burden of adult hypertension in the United States 1999-2000: A rising tide, *Hypertension* 44 (2004): 398-404.

38. J. A. Staessen, T. Kuznetsova, and K. Stolarz, Hypertension prevalence and stroke mortal-ity across populations, *Journal of the American Medical Association* 289 (2003): 2420-2422.

39. K. M. O'Shaughnessy and F. E. Karet, Salt handling and hypertension, *Annual Review of Nutrition* 26 (2006): 343-365.

40. R. S. Vasan and coauthors, Residual lifetime risk for developing hypertension in middle-aged women and men: The Framingham Heart study, *Journal of the American Medical Association* (287): 1003-1010.

41. American Heart Association, *Heart Disease and Stroke Statistics—2006 Update*, 2006.

42. T. A. Kotchen and J. M. Kotchen, Nutrition, diet, and hypertension, in M. E. Shils and coeditiors, *Modern Nutrition in Health and Disease*, 10th ed. (Philadelphia: Lippincott Williams & Wilkins, 2006), pp. 1095-1107.

43. De Caterina and coauthors, 2006; K. Rah-mouni and coauthors, Obesity-associated hypertension: New insights into mecha-nisms, *Hypertension* 45 (2005): 9-14.

44. Kotchen and Kotchen, 2006.

45. U.S. Department of Agriculture and U. S. Department of Health and Human Services, *Dietary Guidelines for Americans 2005* (Wash-ington, D.C.: Government Printing Office, January 2005).

46. F. M. Sacks and coauthors, Effects on blood pressure of reduced sodium and the Dietary Approaches to Stop Hypertension (DASH) diet: DASH-Sodium Collaborative Research Group, *New England Journal of Medicine* 344 (2001): 3-10.

47. E. Obarzanek and coauthors, Effects on blood lipids of a blood pressure-lowering diet: The Dietary Approaches to Stop Hyper-tension (DASH) Trial, *American Journal of Clinical Nutrition* 74 (2001): 80-89.

48. Centers for Disease Control, www.cdc.gov/nccdphp/publications/aag/ddt .htm. Site visited August 28, 2006

49. D. E. Lefebvre and coauthors, Dietary pro-teins as environmental modifiers of type 1 diabetes mellitus, *Annual Review of Nutrition* 26 (2006): 175-202; American Diabetes Association, Position Statement, Diagnosis and classification of diabetes mellitus, *Diabetes Care* 29 (2006): S43-S48.

50. American Diabetes Association, 2006.

51. American Diabetes Association, 2006.

52. American Diabetes Association, 2006.

53. T. S. Hannon, R. Goutham, and S. A. Arslan-ian, Childhood obesity and type 2 diabetes, *Pediatrics* 116 (2005): 473-480.

54. The Diabetes Control and Complications Trial/Epidemiology of Diabetes Interven-tions and Complications (DCCT/EDIC) Study Research Group, Intensive diabetes treatment and cardiovascular disease in patients with type 1 diabetes, *New England Journal of Medicine* 353 (2005): 2643-2653.

55. American Diabetes Association, Nutrition recommendations and interventions for diabetes, *Diabetes Care* 29 (2006): 2140-2157.

56. American Diabetes Association, Nutrition recommendations and interventions for diabetes, *Diabetes Care* 29 (2006): 2140-2157.

57. American Diabetes Association, Nutrition recommendations and interventions for diabetes, *Diabetes Care* 29 (2006): 2140-2157.

58. American Diabetes Association, Nutrition recommendations and interventions for diabetes, *Diabetes Care* 29 (2006): 2140-2157.

59. American Diabetes Association, Nutrition recommendations and interventions for diabetes, *Diabetes Care* 29 (2006): 2140-2157.

60. American Diabetes Association, Nutrition recommendations and interventions for diabetes, *Diabetes Care* 29 (2006): 2140-2157.

61. American Diabetes Association, Position statement: Physical activity/exercise and diabetes mellitus, *Diabetes Care* 26 (2003): S73-S77.

62. American Diabetes Association, 2003.

63. E. T. Liu, Oncohenes and suppressor genes: Genetic control of cancer, in L. Goldman and D. Ausiello, eds., *Cecil Textbook of Medicine* (Philadelphia: Saunders, 2004), pp. 1108-1116.

64. M. D. Holmes and coauthors, Physical activity and survival after breast cancer diagnosis, *Journal of the American Medical Association* 293 (2005): 2479-2486; F. B. Hu and coauthors, Adiposity as compared with physical activity in predicting mortality among women, *New England Journal of Medicine* 351 (2004): 2694-2703; M. L. Slattery, Physical activity and colorectal cancer, *Sports Medicine* 34 (2004): 239-252; Y. Mao and coauthors, Physical inactivity, energy intake, obesity and the risk of rectal cancer in Canada, *International Journal of Cancer* 105 (2003): 831-837; A. S. Furberg and I. Thune, Metabolic abnormalities (hypertension, hyperglycemia and overweight) lifestyle (high energy intake and physical inactivity) and endometrial cancer risk in a Norwegian cohort, *International Journal of Cancer* 104 (2003): 669-676; E. Giovannucci, Diet, body weight, and colorectal cancer: A summary of the epidemiologic evidence, *Journal of Women's Health* 12 (2003): 173-182.

65. M. L. Slattery, Physical activity and colorectal cancer, *Sports Medicine* 34 (2004): 239-252; National Cancer Policy Board, Institute of Medicine, S. J. Curry, T. Byers, and M. Hewitt, eds., *Fulfilling the Potential of Cancer Prevention and Early Detection* (Washington, D.C.: National Academies Press, 2003), pp. 58-61.

66. National Cancer Policy Board, 2003, pp. 59-60; J. B. Barnett, The relationship between obesity and breast cancer risk and mortality, *Nutrition Reviews* 61 (2003): 73-76.

67. E. Calle and coauthors, Overweight, obesity, and mortality from cancer in a prospectively studied cohort of U.S. adults, *New England Journal of Medicine* 348 (2003): 1625-1638; National Cancer Policy Board, 2003, pp. 61-66.

68. Barnett, 2003.

69. P. Boffetta and M. Hashibe, Alcohol and cancer, *Lancet Oncology* 7 (2006): 149-156.

70. M. J. Gunter and coauthors, Meat intake, cooking-related mutagens and risk of colorectal adenoma in a sigmoidoscopy-based case-control study, *Carcinogenesis* 26 (2005): 637-642; T. Norat and E. Riboli, Meat consumption and colorectal cancer: A review of epidemiologic evidence, *Nutrition Reviews* 59 (2001): 37-47.

71. Gunter and coauthors, 2005; M. G. Knize and J. S. Felton, Formation and human risk of carcinogenic heterocyclic amines formed from natural precursors in meat, *Nutrition Reviews* 63 (2005): 158-165.

72. R. L. Prentice and coauthors, Low-fat dietary pattern and risk of invasive breast cancer: The Women's Health Initiative Randomized Controlled Dietary Modification Trial, *Journal of the American Medical Association* 295 (2006): 629-642; S. A. A. Beresford and coauthors, Low-fat dietary pattern and risk of colorectal cancer: The Women's Health Initiative Randomized Controlled Dietary Modification Trial, *Journal of the American Medical Association* 295 (2006): 634-654; R. T. Chlebowski and coauthors, Dietary fat reduction in postmenopausal women with primary breast cancer: Phase III Women's Intervention Nutrition Study (WINS), *Journal of Clinical Oncology* 23 (2005): 10; L. K. Dennis and coauthors, Problems with the assessment of dietary fat in prostate cancer studies, *American Journal of Epidemiology* 160 (2004): 436-444; E. Cho and coauthors, Premenopausal fat intake and risk of breast cancer, *Journal of the National Cancer Institute* 95 (2003): 1079-1085; S. A. Bingham and coauthors, Are imprecise methods obscuring a relation between fat and breast cancer? *Lancet* 362 (2003): 212-214.

73. National Cancer Policy Board, 2003, p. 77; P. D. Terry, T. E. Rohan, and A. Wolk, Intakes of fish and marine fatty acids and the risks of cancers of the breast and prostate and of other hormone-related cancers: A review of the epidemiologic evidence, *American Journal of Clinical Nutrition* 77 (2003): 532-543.

74. R. H. Liu, Potential synergy of phytochemicals in cancer prevention: Mechanism of action, *Journal of Nutrition* 134 (2004): 3479S-3485S.

75. R. J. Deckelbaum and coauthors, AHA Conference Proceedings—Summary of a scientific conference on preventive nutrition: Pediatrics to geriatrics, *Circulation* 100 (1999): 450-456.

76. F. S. Collins and V. A. McKusick, Implications of the Human Genome Project for medical science, *Journal of the American Medical Association* 285 (2001): 540-544.

ANSWERS

Study Questions (multiple choice)

1. c   2. d   3. d   4. c   5. b   6. b   7. a   8. d   9. a   10. c

Complementary and Alternative Medicine

If you suffered from migraine headaches or severe joint pain, where would you turn for relief? Would you visit a physician? Or are you more likely to go to an herbalist or an acupuncturist? Most physicians diagnose and treat medical conditions in ways that are accepted by the established medical community; herbalists and acupuncturists, among others, offer alternatives to standard medical practice. Instead of taking two aspirin, for example, you might be advised to chew two fresh leaves of the herb feverfew or to swallow a tincture of white willow bark. Or you might receive a massage and several acupuncture needles.

Complementary and alternative medicine (CAM) has become increasingly popular in recent decades (see the glossary below for this and related terms).[1] People use these therapies for a variety of reasons. Some want to take more responsibility for both maintaining their own health and finding cures for their own diseases, especially when traditional medical therapies prove ineffective. Others have become distrustful of, and feel overwhelmed by, the high-tech diagnostic tests and costly treatments that **conventional medicine** offers. This highlight explores alternative therapies in search of their possible benefits and with an awareness of their potential harms.

Defining Complementary and Alternative Medicine

By definition, complementary and alternative medicine is not conventional medicine. It includes a variety of approaches, philosophies, and treatments, some of which are defined in the glossary of alternative therapies on the next page. When these therapies are used instead of conventional medicine, they are called *alternative;* when used together with conventional medicine, they are called *complementary.*

A growing number of health care professionals are learning about alternative therapies; half of U.S. medical schools now offer elective courses in alternative medicine, and even more include discussions of these therapies in their required courses. By incorporating some of the beneficial alternative therapies into their practices, an approach called **integrative medicine**, health care professionals take advantage of the best of both kinds of medicine.[2] To best serve their clients, these health care professionals provide balanced advice, guard against bias, and maintain trusting relationships.[3]

For some alternative therapies, preliminary and limited scientific evidence suggests some effectiveness; but for most, well-designed scientific studies have yet to determine safety and effectiveness. If proved safe and effective, an alternative therapy may be adopted by conventional medicine. Cancer radiation therapy, for example, was once considered an unconventional therapy, but it proved its clinical value and became part of accepted medical practice. In some cases, a therapy that is accepted by conventional medicine for a specific ailment is used for a different purpose in an alternative therapy. For example, chelation therapy, the preferred medical treatment for lead poisoning, is a common alternative therapy for cardiovascular disease.

Sound Research, Loud Controversy

Much information on alternative therapies comes from folklore, tradition, and testimonial accounts. Relatively few clinical trials

GLOSSARY

complementary and alternative medicine (CAM): diverse medical and health care systems, practices, and products that are not currently considered part of conventional medicine; also called *adjunctive, unconventional,* or *unorthodox therapies.*

complementary medicine: an approach that uses alternative therapies as an adjunct to, and not simply a replacement for, conventional medicine.

conventional medicine: diagnosis and treatment of diseases as practiced by medical doctors (M.D.) and doctors of osteopathy (D.O.) and allied health professionals such as physical therapists and registered nurses; also called *allopathy; Western, mainstream, orthodox,* or *regular medicine;* and *biomedicine.*

integrative medicine: an approach that incorporates alternative therapies into the practice of conventional medicine (similar to complementary medicine, but a closer relationship is implied).

GLOSSARY OF ALTERNATIVE THERAPIES

acupuncture (AK-you-PUNK-cher): a technique that involves piercing the skin with long thin needles at specific anatomical points to relieve pain or illness. Acupuncture sometimes uses heat, pressure, friction, suction, or electromagnetic energy to stimulate the points.

aroma therapy: a technique that uses oil extracts from plants and flowers (usually applied by massage or baths) to enhance physical, psychological, and spiritual health.

ayurveda (AH-your-VAY-dah): a traditional Hindu system of improving health by using herbs, diet, meditation, massage, and yoga to stimulate the body, mind, and spirit to prevent and treat disease.

bioelectromagnetic medical applications: the use of electrical energy, magnetic energy, or both to stimulate bone repair, wound healing, and tissue regeneration.

biofeedback: the use of special devices to convey information about heart rate, blood pressure, skin temperature, muscle relaxation, and the like to enable a person to learn how to consciously control these medically important functions.

biofield therapeutics: a manual healing method that directs a healing force from an outside source (commonly God or another supernatural being) through the practitioner and into the client's body; commonly known as "laying on of hands."

cartilage therapy: the use of cleaned and powdered connective tissue, such as collagen, to improve health.

chelation (kee-LAY-shun) **therapy:** the use of ethylene diamine tetraacetic acid (EDTA) to bind with metallic ions, thus healing the body by removing toxic metals.

chiropractic (KYE-roh-PRAK-tik): a manual healing method of manipulating the spine to restore health.

faith healing: healing by invoking divine intervention without the use of medical, surgical, or other traditional therapy.

herbal (ERB-al) **medicine:** the use of plants to treat disease or improve health; also known as *botanical medicine* or *phytotherapy*.

homeopathy (hoh-me-OP-ah-thee): a practice based on the theory that "like cures like," that is, that substances that cause symptoms in healthy people can cure those symptoms when given in very dilute amounts.
- **homeo** = like
- **pathos** = suffering

hydrotherapy: the use of water (in whirlpools, as douches, or packed as ice, for example) to promote relaxation and healing.

hypnotherapy: a technique that uses hypnosis and the power of suggestion to improve health behaviors, relieve pain, and heal.

imagery: a technique that guides clients to achieve a desired physical, emotional, or spiritual state by visualizing themselves in that state.

iridology: the study of changes in the iris of the eye and their relationships to disease.

macrobiotic diets: extremely restrictive diets limited to a few grains and vegetables; based on metaphysical beliefs and not nutrition. A macrobiotic diet might consist of brown rice, miso soup, and sea vegetables, for example.

massage therapy: a healing method in which the therapist manually kneads muscles to reduce tension, increase blood circulation, improve joint mobility, and promote healing of injuries.

meditation: a self-directed technique of relaxing the body and calming the mind.

naturopathic (nay-chur-oh-PATH-ick) **medicine:** a system that taps the natural healing forces within the body by integrating several practices, including traditional medicine, herbal medicine, clinical nutrition, homeopathy, acupuncture, East Asian medicine, hydrotherapy, and manipulative therapy.

orthomolecular medicine: the use of large doses of vitamins to treat chronic disease.

ozone therapy: the use of ozone gas to enhance the body's immune system.

qi gong (chée GUNG): a Chinese system that combines movement, meditation, and breathing techniques to enhance the flow of qi (vital energy) in the body.

---

have been conducted. Consequently, scientific evidence proving the safety and effectiveness of many alternative therapies is lacking. Some say that alternative therapies simply do not work; others suggest that these therapies have not been given a fair trial. In an effort to "explore complementary and alternative healing practices through vigorous science," the National Center for Complementary and Alternative Medicine supports clinical trials of these therapies. Articles reporting the results of these clinical trials are available online in a subset of PubMed created specifically for scientifically based, peer-reviewed journals on complementary and alternative therapies.

Sound research would answer two important questions. First, does the treatment offer better results than either doing nothing or giving a placebo? Second, do the benefits clearly outweigh the risks? Each of these points is worthy of elaboration.

Placebo Effect

Stories abound that credit alternative therapies with miraculous cures. Without scientific research to determine effectiveness, however, one is left to wonder whether it is the therapies or the placebo effect that produces the cure. Recall from Chapter 1 that giving a placebo often brings about a healing effect in people who believe they are receiving the treatment. Traditional medicine tends to neglect this powerful remedy, whereas many alternative therapies embrace it.

Risks versus Benefits

Ideally, a therapy provides benefits with little or no risk. Figure H18-1 (p. 654) presents several examples of herbal remedies that appear to be generally safe and possibly effective in treating various conditions.[4] Such findings, if replicated, hold promise that these alternative therapies may one day be integrated into conventional medicine.

Some alternative therapies are innocuous, providing little or no benefit for little or no risk. Sipping a cup of warm tea with a pleasant aroma, for example, won't cure heart disease, but it may improve one's mood and help relieve tension. Given no physical hazard and little financial risk, such therapies are acceptable.

In contrast, other products and procedures are downright dangerous, posing great risks while providing no benefits. One example is the folk practice of geophagia (eating earth or clay), which can cause GI impaction and impair iron absorption. Another is the taking of laetrile to treat cancer, which can cause cyanide poisoning. Clearly, such therapies are too harmful to be used.

FIGURE H18-1 Examples of Herbal Remedies

Ginger may relieve nausea and vomiting due to motion sickness or pregnancy.

Ginkgo may slow the loss of cognitive function associated with age.

St. John's wort may be effective in treating mild depression.

American ginseng may improve glucose control in people with type 2 diabetes.

Saw palmetto may improve the symptoms associated with an enlarged prostate.

The gel of an aloe vera plant soothes a minor burn.

Perhaps most controversial are alternative therapies that may provide benefits, but also carry significant, unknown, or debatable risks. Smoking marijuana is an example of such an alternative therapy.[5] The compounds in marijuana seem to provide relief from symptoms such as nausea, vomiting, and pain that commonly accompany cancer, AIDS, and other diseases, but marijuana use also pose risks that some people, including many physicians, consider acceptable whereas others, mainly politicians, deem intolerable. Physicians have focused on individuals and recognize that marijuana stimulates the appetite in their nauseated clients; politicians and others have focused on society and realize that marijuana is one of many drugs that can be abused. Figure H18-2 (p. 655) summarizes the relationships between risks and benefits.

Nutrition-Related Alternative Therapies

Most alternative therapies fall outside the field of nutrition, but nutrition itself can be an alternative therapy. Furthermore, many alternative therapies prescribe specific dietary regimens even though most practitioners are not registered dietitians (see Highlight 1). Nutrition-related alternative therapies include the use of foods, vitamin and mineral supplements, and herbs to prevent and treat illnesses.

FIGURE H18-2 Risk-Benefit Relationships

No (or little) **RISK** Much →

BENEFIT Much → No (or little)

Ideal situation Benefits with little or no risk. (Accept)	**Cautionary situation** Possible benefits with great or unknown risks. (Consider carefully)
Neutral situation Little or no benefit with little or no risk. (Accept or reject as preferred)	**Dangerous situation** No benefits with great risks. (Reject)

Foods

The many dietary recommendations presented throughout this text are based on scientific evidence and do *not* fall into the alternative therapies category; strategies that are still experimental, however, do. For example, alternative therapists may recommend macrobiotic diets to help prevent chronic diseases, whereas most registered dietitians would advise people to eat a balanced diet that includes four to five cups of fresh vegetables and fruits daily. Similarly, enough scientific evidence is available to recommend including soy foods in the diet to protect against heart disease—but not to determine whether the phytoestrogens of soy are safe or beneficial in managing the symptoms of menopause.

Highlight 13 explored the potential health benefits of soy and many other functional foods and concluded that no one food is magical. As part of a balanced diet, these foods can support good health and protect against disease. Importantly, the benefits derive from a variety of *foods*. More research is needed to determine the safety and effectiveness of taking supplements of the phytochemicals found in these foods.

Vitamin and Mineral Supplements

Like foods, vitamin and mineral supplements may fall into either the conventional or the alternative realm of medicine. For example, conventional advice recommends consuming 400 micrograms of folate to prevent neural tube defects, but not the taking of 1000 milligrams of vitamin C to prevent the common cold. Highlight 10 examined the appropriate use of supplements and potential dangers of excessive intakes.

As research on nutrition and chronic diseases has revealed many of the roles played by the vitamins and minerals in supporting health, conventional medicine has warmed up to the possibility that vitamin and mineral supplements might be an appropriate preventive therapy.[6] Some vitamin and mineral supplements appear to be in transition from alternative medicine to conventional medicine; that is, they have begun to prove their safety and effectiveness. Table H18-1 (p. 656) includes several nutrition-related therapies among those recognized to slow the progression of cancer and treat related symptoms. Herbal remedies, however, still remain clearly in the realm of complementary and alternative medicine.

Herbal Remedies

From earliest times, people have used myriad herbs and other plants to cure aches and ills with varying degrees of success (review Figure H18-1). Upon scientific study, dozens of these folk remedies reveal their secrets. For example, myrrh, a plant resin used as a painkiller in ancient times, does indeed have an analgesic effect. The herb valerian, which has long been used as a tranquilizer, contains oils that have a sedative effect. Senna leaves, brewed as a laxative tea, produce compounds that act as a potent cathartic drug. Green tea, brewed from the dried leaves of *Camellia sinensis,* contains phytochemicals that induce cancer cells to self-destruct.

Naturally occurring salicylates provide the same protective effects as low doses of aspirin. Salicylates are found in spices such as curry, paprika, and thyme; fruits; vegetables; teas; and candies flavored with wintergreen (methylsalicylate).

Beneficial compounds from wild species contribute to about half of our modern medicines. By analyzing these compounds, pharmaceutical labs can synthesize pure forms of the drugs. Unlike herbs and wild species, which vary from batch to batch, synthesized medicines deliver exact dosages. By synthesizing drugs, we are also able to conserve endangered species. Consider that it took all of the bark from one 40-foot-tall, 100-year-old Pacific yew tree to produce one 300-milligram dose of the anticancer drug paclitaxel (Taxol), until scientists learned how to synthesize it. Many yet undiscovered cures may be forever lost as wild species are destroyed, long before their secrets are revealed to medicine.

Digoxin, the most commonly prescribed heart medication, derives from the leaves of the foxglove plant (*Digitalis purpurea*).

TABLE H18-1 Advice and Precautions on Alternative Therapies for Cancer and Related Conditions

Therapy	Precautions
Accept/Consider Recommending—Evidence supports effectiveness and safety.	
Vitamin E (for prostate cancer)	Not appropriate for people with a low platelet count; those taking anticoagulant medications; or those undergoing radiation, chemotherapy, or surgery
Acupuncture (for nausea and vomiting)	Not appropriate for people with a low platelet count or those taking anticoagulant medications
Massage (for anxiety, nausea, and lymph drainage)	Not appropriate directly over tumors, stents, or prosthetic devices and in areas damaged by surgery or radiation; or in people with bleeding abnormalities
Accept—Evidence supports safety, but inconclusive on effectiveness.	
Low-fat diet (for breast and prostate cancer)	Not appropriate for people with poor nutrition status
Macrobiotic diet[a]	Not appropriate for people with poor nutrition status or those who have breast or endometrial cancer
Vitamin E (for some cancers)	Not appropriate for people with a low platelet count; those taking anticoagulant medications; or those undergoing radiation, chemotherapy, or surgery
Soy (for prostate cancer)	Not appropriate for people with a low platelet count or those taking anticoagulant medications or undergoing surgery
Mind-body therapies	Not appropriate for people who do not have reasonable expectations
Acupuncture (for chronic pain)	Not appropriate for people with a low platelet count or those taking anticoagulant medications
Massage (for pain)	Not appropriate directly over tumors, stents, or prosthetic devices and in areas damaged by surgery or radiation; or in people with bleeding abnormalities
Discourage—Evidence indicates either ineffectiveness or serious risk.	
Vitamin A supplements (both retinols and carotenoid precursors)	May increase the incidence of cancer in high-risk populations
Vitamin C supplements	May have anticoagulant effects
Soy (for breast or endometrial cancer)	May stimulate tumor growth and inhibit platelet aggregation

NOTE: Alternative therapies may be appropriate as an adjunct to, not a replacement of, conventional treatment; physicians need to monitor progress and revise recommendations as needed.
[a]When carefully planned, macrobiotic diets can provide adequate nutrition, little fat, and abundant phytoestrogens from soy. Restrictive macrobiotic diets, however, can cause malnutrition.

SOURCE: Adapted from W. A. Weiger and coauthors, Advising patients who seek complementary and alternative medical therapies for cancer, Annals of Internal Medicine 137 (2002): 889–903.

Herbal Precautions

Plants are "natural," but that does not mean all plants are beneficial or even safe. Nothing could be more natural—and deadly—than the poisonous herb hemlock. Several herbal remedies have toxic effects. The popular Chinese herbal potion jin bu huan, which is used as a pain and insomnia remedy, has been linked with several cases of acute hepatitis. Germanium, a nonessential mineral commonly found in many herbal products, has been associated with chronic kidney failure. Paraguay tea produces symptoms of agitation, confusion, flushed skin, and fever. Kombucha tea, commonly used in the hopes of preventing cancer, relieving arthritis, curing insomnia, and stimulating hair regrowth, can cause severe metabolic acidosis. Table H18-2 lists selected herbs, their common uses, and risks.[7]

Although some people use herbs to treat or prevent disease, herbs are not regulated as drugs; they are considered dietary supplements. The Food and Drug Administration (FDA) does not evaluate dietary supplements for safety or effectiveness, nor does it monitor their contents. Under the Dietary Supplement Health and Education Act, rather than the herb manufacturers having to prove the safety of their products, the FDA has the burden of proving that a product is not safe. Consequently, consumers may lack information about or find discrepancies regarding:

- *True identification of herbs.* Most mint teas are safe, for instance, but some varieties contain the highly toxic pennyroyal oil. Mistakenly used to soothe a colicky baby, mint tea laden with pennyroyal has been blamed for the liver and neurological injuries of at least two infants, one of whom died.

- *Purity of herbal preparations.* A young child diagnosed with lead poisoning had taken an herbal vitamin that contained large quantities of lead and mercury for four years. Twelve cases of lead poisoning among adults using ayurvedic remedies were reported to the Centers for Disease Control and Prevention in recent years.[8] Potentially toxic quantities of lead have been detected in 11 different dietary supplements.[9]

- *Appropriate uses and contraindications of herbs.* Herbal remedies alone may be appropriate for minor ailments—a cup of chamomile tea to ease gastric discomfort or the gel of an aloe vera plant to soothe a sunburn, for example—but not for major health problems such as cancer or AIDS.

- *Effectiveness of herbs.* Herbal remedies may claim to work wonders without having to prove effectiveness. Research studies often report conflicting findings, with some suggesting a benefit and others indicating no effectiveness.[10]

- *Variability of herbs.* Not all species are created equal. The various species of coneflower provide an example. *Echinacea*

TABLE H18-2 Selected Herbs, Their Common Use, and Risks

Common Name	Scientific Source Name	Claims and Uses	Risks[a]
Aloe (gel)	Aloe vera	Promote wound healing	Generally considered safe
Black cohosh	Actaea racemos (formerly Cimicifuga racemosa)	Ease menopause symptoms	May cause clotting in blood vessels of the eye, change the curvature of the cornea
Chamomile (flowers)	Matricaria chamomilla	Relieve indigestion	Generally considered safe
Chaparral (leaves and twigs)	Larrea tridentata	Slow aging, "cleanse" blood, heal wounds, cure cancer, treat acne	Acute, toxic hepatitis; liver damage
Comfrey (leafy plant)	Symphytum officinale, S. asperum, S. x uplandicum	Soothe nerves	Liver damage
Echinacea (roots)	Enchinacea angustifolia, E. pallida, E. purpurea	Alleviate symptoms of colds, flus, and infections; promote wound healing; boost immunity	Generally considered safe; may cause headache, dizziness, nausea
Ephedra (stems)	Ephedra sinica	Promote weight loss	Rapid heart rate, tremors, seizures, insomnia, headaches, hypertension
Feverfew (leaves)	Tanacetum parthenium	Prevent migraine headaches	Generally considered safe; may cause mouth irritation, swelling, ulcers, and GI distress
Garlic (bulbs)	Allium sativum	Lower blood lipids and blood pressure	Generally considered safe; may cause garlic breath, body odor, gas, and GI distress; inhibits blood clotting
Ginger	Zingiber officinale	Prevent motion sickness, nausea	Generally considered safe
Ginkgo (tree leaves)	Ginkgo biloba	Improve memory, relieve vertigo	Generally considered safe; may cause headache, GI distress, dizziness; may inhibit blood clotting
Ginseng (roots)	Panax ginseng (Asian), P. quinquefolius (American)	Boost immunity, increase endurance	Generally considered safe; may cause insomnia and high blood pressure
Goldenseal (roots)	Hydrastis canadensis	Relieve indigestion, treat urinary infections	Generally considered safe; not safe for people with hypertension or heart disease
Kava	Piper methysticum	Relieves anxiety, promotes relaxation	Liver failure
Saw palmetto (ripe fruits)	Serenoa repens	Relieve symptoms of enlarged prostate; diuretic; enhance sexual vigor	Generally considered safe; may cause nausea, vomiting, diarrhea
St. John's wort (leaves and tops)	Hypericum perforatum	Relieve depression and anxiety	Generally considered safe; may cause fatigue and GI distress
Valerian (roots)	Valeriana officinalis	Calm nerves, improve sleep	Long term use associated with liver damage
Yohimbe (tree bark)	Pausinystalia yohimbe	Enhance "male performance"	Kidney failure, seizures

[a]Allergies are always a possible risk; see Table H18-3 for drug interactions. Pregnant women should not use herbal supplements.

purpurea, for example, may help in the early treatment of colds, but Echinacea augustifolia may not.[11] Similarly, not all parts of a plant provide the same compounds. Leaves, roots, and oils contain different compounds and extracts, and the temperatures used during manufacturing may affect their potency. Consumers are not always aware of such differences, and manufacturers do not always make such distinctions when preparing and labeling supplements.

- *Accuracy of labels.* Supplements may contain none of an herb or mixed species, and labels are often inaccurate. More often than not, supplements do not contain the species or the quantities of active ingredients stated on their labels.[12] In at least two cases, supplements did not even contain herbs, but prescription medicines instead.[13] Such discrepancies in the contents of supplements interfere with scientific research and make it difficult to interpret the findings. Consumers may want to shop for supplements bearing a logo from either U.S.

Pharmacopeia or Consumer Lab indicating that the contents have been analyzed and found to contain the ingredients and quantities listed on the label.

- *Safe dosages of herbs.* Herbs may contain active ingredients—compounds that affect the body. Each of these active ingredients has a different potency, time of onset, duration of activity, and consequent effects, making the plant itself too unpredictable to be useful. Foxglove leaves, for example, contain dozens of compounds that have an effect on the heart; digoxin, a drug derived from foxglove, offers a standard dosage that allows for a more predictable cardiac response. Even when herbs are manufactured into capsules or liquids, their concentrations of active ingredients differ dramatically from batch to batch and from the quantities stated on the labels.[14]

- *Interactions of herbs with medicines and other herbs.* Like drugs, herbs may interfere with, or potentiate, the effects of other herbs and drugs (see Table H18-3). A person taking both cardiac medication and the herb foxglove may be headed for disaster from the combined effect on the heart. Similarly, taking St. John's wort with medicines used to treat heart disease, depression, seizures, and certain cancers might diminish or exaggerate the intended effects.[15] Because *Ginkgo biloba* impairs blood clotting, it can cause bleeding problems for people taking aspirin or other blood-thinning medicines regularly.

- *Adverse reactions and toxicity levels of herbs.* Herbs may produce undesirable reactions. The herb ephedra, commonly known as ma huang and used to promote weight loss, acts as a strong central nervous system stimulant, causing rapid heart rate, headaches, insomnia, tremors, seizures, and even death. The herbal root kava, commonly used to treat anxiety and insomnia, can cause liver abnormalities and may have such a sedating effect as to impair driving. Chinese herbal treatments containing *Aristolochia fangchi* are notorious for causing kidney damage and cancers. Table H18-2 (p. 657) includes risks associated with commonly used herbs.

To ensure the safety and standardization of herbal remedies, Congress needs to establish regulations.[16]

Because herbal medicines are sold as dietary supplements, their labels cannot claim to cure a disease, but they can make various other claims. Not surprisingly, when a label claims that an herbal product may strengthen immunity, improve memory, support eyesight, or maintain heart health, consumers believe that taking the product will provide those benefits. Beware. Manufacturers need not prove effectiveness; they only need to state on the product label that this claim "Has not been evaluated by the FDA." Consumers who decide to use herbs need to become informed of the possible risks.

Internet Precautions

As Highlight 1 pointed out, just because something appears on the Internet, "it ain't necessarily so." Keep in mind that the thousands of websites touting the benefits of herbal medicines and other dietary supplements are marketing their products. Most product advertisements claim to prevent or treat specific diseases, but few include the FDA disclaimer statement.[17] Many of the websites promote products by quoting researchers or physicians. Such quotations lend an air of authority to advertisements, but be aware that these sources may not even exist—and if they do, their comments may have been taken out of context. When asked, they may not agree at all with the claims attributed to them by the manufacturer.

Other deceits and dangers lurk in cyberspace as well. Potentially toxic substances, illegal and unavailable in many countries, are now easy to obtain via the Internet. Electronic access to products such as absinthe and oil of wormwood could be deadly. When the FDA discovers websites selling unapproved drugs, such as laetrile, it can order the business to shut down. But consumers need to remain vigilant because other similar businesses pop up quickly.

The Consumer's Perspective

Some health care professionals may dismiss alternative therapies as ineffective and perhaps even dangerous, but many consumers

TABLE H18-3	Herb and Drug Interactions	
Herb	**Drug**	**Interaction**
American ginseng	Estrogens, corticosteroids	Enhances hormonal response
American ginseng	Breast cancer therapeutic agent	Synergistically inhibits cancer cell growth
American ginseng, karela	Blood glucose regulators	Affect blood glucose levels
Echinacea (possible immunostimulant)	Cyclosporine and corticosteroids (immunosuppressants)	May reduce drug effectiveness
Evening primrose oil, borage	Anticonvulsants	Lower seizure threshold
Feverfew	Aspirin, ibuprofen, and other nonsteroidal anti-inflammatory drugs	Negates the effect of the herb in treating migraine headaches
Feverfew, garlic, ginkgo, ginger, and Asian ginseng	Warfarin, coumarin (anticlotting drugs, "blood thinners")	Prolong bleeding time; increase likelihood of hemorrhage
Garlic	Protease inhibitor (HIV drug)	May reduce drug effectiveness
Kava, valerian	Anesthetics	May enhance drug action
Kelp (iodine source)	Synthroid or other thyroid hormone replacers	Interferes with drug action
Kyushin, licorice, plantain, uzara root, hawthorn, Asian ginseng	Digoxin (cardiac antiarrhythmic drug derived from the herb foxglove)	Interfere with drug action and monitoring
St. John's wort, saw palmetto, black tea	Iron	Tannins in herbs inhibit iron absorption
St. John's wort	Protease inhibitors (HIV drugs), warfarin (anticlotting drug), digoxin (cardiac antiarrhytmic drug), oral contraceptives, tamoxifen (breast cancer drug)	May enhance or reduce drug effectiveness
Valerian	Barbiturates	Causes excessive sedation

think otherwise. In a survey of more than 2000 people, two-thirds had used at least one alternative therapy for a variety of medical complaints ranging from anxiety and headaches to cancer and tumors.[18] Interestingly, those who seek alternative therapies seem to do so not so much because they are dissatisfied with conventional medicine as because they find these alternatives more in line with their beliefs about health and life.

Most often, people use alternative therapies in addition to, rather than in place of, conventional therapies. Few consult an alternative therapist without also seeing a physician. In fact, most people seek alternative therapies for nonserious medical conditions or for health promotion. They simply want to feel better and access is easy. Sometimes their symptoms are chronic and subjective, such as pain and fatigue, and difficult to treat. In these cases, the chances of finding relief are often as good with a placebo, standard medical intervention, or even nonintervention.

Consumers spend billions of dollars on alternative health services and related products such as herbs, crystals, and aromas. As Highlight 1 pointed out, selecting a reliable practitioner depends on finding out about training, qualifications, and licenses. (To review how a person can identify health fraud and quackery, turn to pp. 33–34. For a list of credible sources of nutrition information, see p. 33.)

In addition, consumers should inform their physicians about the use of any alternative therapies so that a comprehensive treatment plan can be developed and potential problems can be averted. As mentioned, herb-drug interactions can create problems, and one in six clients who takes prescription drugs also uses herbal products.[19] When considering herbal products, remember to include supplements, teas, and garden plants.[20] Sometimes herbal products may need to be discontinued, especially before surgery when interactions with anesthesia or normal blood clotting can be life-threatening.[21]

Alternative therapies come in a variety of shapes and sizes. Both their benefits and their risks may be small, none, or great. Wise consumers and health care professionals accept the beneficial, or even neutral, practices with an open mind and reject those practices known to cause harm. Making healthful choices requires understanding all the choices.

NUTRITION ON THE NET

ThomsonNOW™
For furthur study of topics covered in this Highlight, log on to **www.thomsonedu.com/thomsonnow**. Go to Chapter 18, then to Highlights Nutrition on the Net.

- Search for "alternative medicine," "herbs," "holistic health," "homeopathy," and "preventive medicine" at the U.S. Government health information site: **www.healthfinder.gov**

- Learn about complementary and alternative medicine from the National Institutes of Health's National Center for Complementary and Alternative Medicine: **ww.nccam.nih.gov**

- Search CAM on PubMed for a literature search of the complementary and alternative subset of PubMed: **www.nlm.nih.gov/nccam/camonpubmed.html**

- Find out more about herbs from the American Botanical Council: **www.herbalgram.org**

- Report adverse effects associated with herbal remedies to the FDA MedWatch: **www.fda.gov/medwatch**

- Obtain information on herbal medications from HerbMed or from the Integrative Medicine Service at Memorial Sloan-Kettering Cancer Center: **www.herbmed.org** or **www.mskcc.org/aboutherbs**

- Get dietary supplement information from the National Institutes of Health's Office of Dietary Supplements: **dietary-supplements.info.nih.gov**

- Review the backgrounds and practices of many popular practitioners of alternative treatments: **www.quackwatch.com**

REFERENCES

1. P. M. Barnes and E. Powell-Griner, Complementary and alternative medicine use among adults: United States, 2002, *Advance Data from Vital and Health Statistics* 343 (2004): 1–19; G. M. Kuo and coauthors, Factors associated with herbal use among urban multiethnic primary care patients; A cross-sectional survey, *BMC Complementary and Alternative Medicine* 4 (2004): 18–32.

2. R. Touger-Decker and C. A. Thomson, Complementary and alternative medicine: Competencies for dietetics professionals, *Journal of the American Dietetic Association* 103 (2003): 1465–1469; M. A. Frenkel and J. M. Borkan, An approach for integrating complementary-alternative medicine into primary care, *Family Practice* 20 (2003): 324–332.

3. Committee on Children with Disabilities, American Academy of Pediatrics, Counseling families who choose complementary and alternative medicine for their child with chronic illness or disability, *Pediatrics* 107 (2001): 598–601.

4. R. S. DiPaola and R. A. Morton, Proven and unproven therapy for benign prostatic hyperplasia, *New England Journal of Medicine* 354 (2006): 632–634; M. D. Kostka-Rokosz and coauthors, Selected herbal therapies, *Nutrition Today* 40 (2005): 17–28; S. Lawvere and M. C. Mahoney, St. John's wort, *American Family Physician* 72 (2005): 2249–2254; G. Y. Yeh and coauthors, Systematic review of herbs and dietary supplements for glycemic control in diabetes, *Diabetes Care* 26 (2003): 1277–1294.

5. L. O. Gostin, Medical marijuana, American federalism, and the Supreme Court, *Journal of the American Medical Association* 294 (2005): 842–844.

6. C. D. Morris and S. Carson, Summary of evidence: Routine vitamin supplementation to prevent cardiovascular disease, *Annals of Internal Medicine* 139 (2003): 56–70; C. Ritenbaugh, K. Streit, and M. Helfand, Summary of evidence from randomized controlled trials: Routine vitamin supplementation to prevent cancer, available from the Agency for Healthcare Research and Quality, www.preventiveservices.ahrq.gov.

7. E. Ernst, The risk-benefit profile of commonly used herbal therapies: Ginkgo, St. John's wort, ginseng, echinacea, saw palmetto, and kava, *Annals of Internal Medicine*

136 (2002): 42–53; Hepatic toxicity possibly associated with kava-containing products—United States, Germany, and Switzerland, 1999–2002, *Morbidity and Mortality Weekly Report* 51 (2002): 1065–1067; S. Foster and V. E. Tyler, *Tyler's Honest Herbal: A Sensible Guide to the Use of Herbs and Related Remedies* (New York: Haworth Press, 1999).

8. Centers for Disease Control and Prevention, Lead poisoning associated with ayurvedi medications—Five states, 2000–2003, *Morbidity and Mortality Weekly Report* 53 (2004): 582–584.

9. S. P. Dolan and coauthors, Analysis of dietary supplements for arsenic, cadmium, mercury, and lead using inductively coupled plasma mass spectrometry, *Journal of Agricultural and Food Chemistry* 51 (2003): 1307–1312.

10. Hypericum Depression Trial Study Group, Effect of *Hypericum perforatum* (St John's wort) in major depressive disorder: A randomized controlled trial, *Journal of the American Medical Association* 287 (2002): 1807–1814; P. R. Solomon and coauthors, Ginkgo for memory enhancement: A randomized controlled trial, *Journal of the American Medical Association* 288 (2002): 835–840.

11. K. Linde and coauthors, Echinacea for preventing and treating the common cold, *Cochrane Database of Systematic Reviews* 25 (2006): CD000530.

12. C. M. Gilroy and coauthors, Echinacea and truth in labeling, *Archives of Internal Medicine* 163 (2003): 699–704; A. H. Feifer, N. E. Fleshner, and L. Klotz, Analytical accuracy and reliability of commonly used nutritional supplements in prostate disease, *Journal of Urology* 168 (2002): 150–154.

13. Dietary-supplement recall, *Consumer Reports on Health,* April 2002, p. 3.

14. M. R. Karkey and co-authors, Variability in commercial ginseng products: An analysis of 25 preparations, *American Journal of Clinical Nutrition* 73 (2001): 1101–1106.

15. J. S. Markowitz and coauthors, Effect of St. John's wort on drug metabolism by induction of cytochrome P450 3A4 enzyme, *Journal of the American Medical Association* 290 (2003): 1500–1504.

16. C. D. DeAngelis and P. B. Fontanarosa, Drugs alias dietary supplements, *Journal of the American Medical Association* 290 (2003): 1519–1520; D. M. Marcus and A. P. Grollman, Botanical medicines—The need for new regulations, *New England Journal of Medicine* 347 (2002): 2073–2076.

17. C. A. Morris and J. Avron, Internet marketing of herbal products, *Journal of the American Medical Association* 290 (2003): 1505–1509.

18. R. C. Kessler and coauthors, Long-term trends in the use of complementary and alternative medical therapies in the United States, *Annals of Internal Medicine* 135 (2001): 262–268.

19. D. W. Kaufman and coauthors, Recent patterns of medication use in the ambulatory adult population of the United States: The Slone Survey, *Journal of the American Medical Association* 287 (2002): 337–344.

20. M. A. Kuhn, Herbal remedies: Drug-herb interactions, *Critical Care Nurse* 22 (2002): 22–28.

21. M. K. Ang-Lee, J. Moss, and C. S. Yuan, Herbal medicines and perioperative care, *Journal of the American Medical Association* 286 (2001): 208–216.

Nutrition in Your Life

Do you know what causes food poisoning and how to protect yourself against it? Were you alarmed to learn that French fries contain acrylamide or that fish contain mercury? Are you concerned about the pesticides that might linger on fruits and vegetables—or the hormones and antibiotics that remain in beef and chicken? Do you wonder whether foods contain enough nutrients—or too many additives? Making informed choices and practicing a few food safety tips will allow you to enjoy a variety of foods while limiting your risks of experiencing food-related illnesses.

Consumer Concerns about Foods and Water

CHAPTER OUTLINE

Foodborne Illnesses • Foodborne Infections and Food Intoxications • Food Safety in the Marketplace • Food Safety in the Kitchen • Food Safety While Traveling • Advances in Food Safety

Nutritional Adequacy of Foods and Diets • Obtaining Nutrient Information • Minimizing Nutrient Losses

Environmental Contaminants • Harmfulness of Environmental Contaminants • Guidelines for Consumers

Natural Toxicants in Foods

Pesticides • Hazards and Regulations of Pesticides • Monitoring Pesticides • Consumer Concerns

Food Additives • Regulations Governing Additives • Intentional Food Additives • Indirect Food Additives

Consumer Concerns about Water Sources of Drinking Water • Water Systems and Regulations

HIGHLIGHT 19 Food Biotechnology

Take a moment to consider the task of supplying food to 300 million people in the United States (and millions more in all corners of the world). To feed this nation, farmers grow and harvest crops; dairy producers supply milk products; ranchers raise livestock; shippers deliver foods to manufacturers by land, sea, and air; manufacturers prepare, process, preserve, and package products for refrigerated food cases and grocery-store shelves; and grocers store the food and supply it to consumers. After much time, much labor, and extensive transport, an abundant supply of a large variety of safe foods finally reaches consumers at reasonable market prices.

The **FDA** and other government and international agencies monitor this huge system using a network of people and sophisticated equipment. (The glossary on p. 666 identifies the various food regulatory agencies by their abbreviations.) These agencies focus on the potential **hazard** of foods, which differs from the **toxicity** of a substance—a distinction worth understanding. Anything can be toxic. Toxicity simply means that a substance *can* cause harm *if* enough is consumed. We consume many substances that are toxic, without **risk,** because the amounts are so small. The term *hazard,* on the other hand, is more relevant to our daily lives because it refers to the harm that is *likely* under real-life conditions. Consumers rely on these monitoring agencies to set **safety** standards and can learn to protect themselves from food hazards by taking a few preventive measures.

After the events of September 11, 2001, the threat of deliberate contamination of the U.S. food supply became a pressing issue.[1] To tighten security around the nation's food supply, the FDA now requires all people who manufacture, produce, process, pack, transport, distribute, store, or import food to maintain records identifying the immediate previous source and subsequent recipient. The Agricultural and Food Biosecurity agency of the **USDA** works to protect agriculture and other aspects of the food supply. Other agencies are also taking action, but details of the war against domestic bioterrorism are beyond the scope of this discussion.

hazard: a source of danger; used to refer to circumstances in which harm is possible under normal conditions of use.

toxicity: the ability of a substance to harm living organisms. All substances are toxic if high enough concentrations are used.

risk: a measure of the probability and severity of harm.

safety: the condition of being free from harm or danger.

With the benefits of a safe and abundant food supply comes the responsibility to select, prepare, and store foods safely.

◆ Get medical help for these symptoms:
  • Bloody diarrhea
  • Diarrhea lasting more than 3 days
  • Difficulty breathing
  • Difficulty swallowing
  • Double vision
  • Fever lasting more than 24 hours
  • Headache, muscle stiffness, and fever
  • Numbness, muscle weakness, and tingling sensations in the skin
  • Rapid heart rate, fainting, and dizziness

◆ Among foodborne infections, *Salmonella* is the major cause of illness and *Listeria* is the major cause of death.

---

foodborne illness: illness transmitted to human beings through food and water, caused by either an infectious agent (foodborne infection) or a poisonous substance (food intoxication); commonly known as **food poisoning.**

pathogen (PATH-oh-jen): a microorganism capable of producing disease.

This chapter focuses on actions of individuals to promote food safety. It addresses the following food safety concerns:

- Foodborne illnesses
- Nutritional adequacy of foods
- Environmental contaminants
- Naturally occurring toxicants
- Pesticides
- Food additives
- Water safety

The chapter begins with the FDA's highest priority—the serious and prevalent threat of foodborne illnesses. The highlight that follows looks at genetically engineered foods.

Foodborne Illnesses

The FDA lists **foodborne illness** as the leading food safety concern because episodes of food poisoning far outnumber episodes of any other kind of food contamination. The **CDC** estimates that 76 million people experience foodborne illness each year in the United States.[2] For some 5000 people each year, the symptoms ◆ can be so severe as to cause death. Most vulnerable are pregnant women; very young, very old, sick, or malnourished people; and those with a weakened immune system (as in AIDS). By taking the proper precautions, people can minimize their chances of contracting foodborne illnesses.

Foodborne Infections and Food Intoxications

Foodborne illness can be caused by either an infection or an intoxication. Table 19-1 summarizes the most common or severe foodborne illnesses, along with their food sources, general symptoms, and prevention methods.

Foodborne Infections Foodborne infections are caused by eating foods contaminated by infectious microbes. The most common foodborne **pathogen** is *Salmonella,* ◆ which enters the GI tract in contaminated foods such as undercooked poultry and unpasteurized milk. Symptoms generally include abdominal cramps, fever, vomiting, and diarrhea.

GLOSSARY OF AGENCIES THAT MONITOR THE FOOD SUPPLY

CDC (Centers for Disease Control): a branch of the Department of Health and Human Services that is responsible for, among other things, monitoring foodborne diseases.
www.cdc.gov

EPA (Environmental Protection Agency): a federal agency that is responsible for, among other things, regulating pesticides and establishing water quality standards.
www.epa.gov

FAO (Food and Agriculture Organization): an international agency (part of the United Nations) that has adopted standards to regulate pesticide use among other responsibilities.
www.fao.org

USDA (U.S. Department of Agriculture): the federal agency responsible for enforcing standards for the wholesomeness and quality of meat, poultry, and eggs produced in the United States; conducting nutrition research;

and educating the public about nutrition.
www.usda.gov

WHO (World Health Organization): an international agency concerned with promoting health and eradicating disease.
www.who.ch

Reminder: **FDA (Food and Drug Administration)** is a part of the Department of Health and Human Services' Public Health Service that is responsible for

ensuring the safety and wholesomeness of all dietary supplements and foods processed and sold in interstate commerce except meat, poultry, and eggs (which are under the jurisdiction of the USDA); inspecting food plants and imported foods; and setting standards for food composition and product labeling.
www.fda.gov

TABLE 19-1 Foodborne Illnesses

Disease and Organism That Causes It	Most Frequent Food Sources	Onset and General Symptoms	Prevention Methods[a]
Foodborne Infections			
Campylobacteriosis (KAM-pee-loh-BAK-ter-ee-OH-sis) *Campylobacter* bacterium	Raw and undercooked poultry, unpasturized milk, contaminated water	Onset: 2 to 5 days. Diarrhea, vomiting, abdominal cramps, fever; sometimes bloody stools; lasts 2 to 10 days.	Cook foods thoroughly; use pasteurized milk; use sanitary food-handling methods.
Cryptosporidiosis (KRIP-toe-spo-rid-ee-OH-sis) *Crytosporidium parvum* parasite	Commonly contaminated swimming or drinking water, even from treated sources. Highly chlorine-resistant. Contaminated raw produce and unpasteurized juices and ciders	Onset: 2 to 10 days. Diarrhea, stomach cramps, upset stomach, slight fever; symptoms may come and go for weeks or months.	Wash all raw vegetables and fruits before peeling. Use pasteurized milk and juice. Do not swallow drops of water while using pools, hot tubs, ponds, lakes, rivers, or streams for recreation.
Cyclosporiasis (sigh-clo-spore-EYE-uh-sis) *Cyclospora cayetanensis* parasite	Contaminated water; contaminated fresh produce	Onset: 1 to 14 days. Watery diarrhea, loss of appetite, weight loss, stomach cramps, nausea, vomiting, fatigue; symptoms may come and go for weeks or months.	Use treated, boiled, or bottled water; cook foods thoroughly; peel fruits.
E. coli infection *Escherichia coli*[b] bacterium	Undercooked ground beef, unpasteurized milk and juices, raw fruits and vegetables, contaminated water, and person-to-person contact	Onset: 1 to 8 days. Severe bloody diarrhea, abdominal cramps, vomiting; lasts 5 to 10 days.	Cook ground beef thoroughly; use pasteurized milk; use sanitary food-handling methods; use treated, boiled, or bottled water.
Gastroenteritis[c] *Norwalk virus*	Person-to-person contact; raw foods, salads, sandwiches	Onset: 1 to 2 days. Vomiting; lasts 1 to 2 days.	Use sanitary food-handling methods.
Giardiasis (JYE-are-DYE-ah-sis) *Giardia intestinalis* parasite	Contaminated water; uncooked foods	Onset: 7 to 14 days. Diarrhea (but occasionally constipation), abdominal pain, gas.	Use sanitary food-handling methods; avoid raw fruits and vegetables where parasites are endemic; dispose of sewage properly.
Hepatitis (HEP-ah-TIE-tis) Hepatitis A virus	Undercooked or raw shellfish	Onset: 15 to 50 days (28 days average). Diarrhea, dark urine, fever, headache, nausea, abdominal pain, jaundice (yellowed skin and eyes from buildup of wastes); lasts 2 to 12 weeks.	Cook foods thoroughly.
Listeriosis (lis-TER-ee-OH-sis) *Listeria monocytogenes* bacterium	Unpasteurized milk; fresh soft cheeses; luncheon meats, hot dogs	Onset: 1 to 21 days. Fever, muscle aches; nausea, vomiting, blood poisoning, complications in pregnancy, and meningitis (stiff neck, severe headache, and fever).	Use sanitary food-handling methods; cook foods thoroughly; use pasteurized milk.
Perfringens (per-FRINGE-enz) **food poisoning** *Clostridium perfringens* bacterium	Meats and meat products stored at between 120° and 130°F	Onset: 8 to 16 hr. Abdominal pain, diarrhea, nausea; lasts 1 to 2 days.	Use sanitary food-handling methods; cook foods thoroughly; refrigerate foods promptly and properly.
Salmonellosis (sal-moh-neh-LOH-sis) *Salmonella* bacteria (>2300 types)	Raw or undercooked eggs, meats, poultry, raw milk and other dairy products, shrimp, frog legs, yeast, coconut, pasta, and chocolate	Onset: 1 to 3 days. Fever, vomiting, abdominal cramps, diarrhea; lasts 4 to 7 days; can be fatal.	Use sanitary food-handling methods; use pasteurized milk; cook foods thoroughly; refrigerate foods promptly and properly.
Shigellosis (shi-gel-LOH-sis) *Shigella* bacteria (>30 types)	Person-to-person contact, raw foods, salads, sandwiches, and contaminated water	Onset: 1 to 2 days. Bloody diarrhea, cramps, fever; lasts 4 to 7 days.	Use sanitary food-handling methods; cook foods thoroughly; proper refrigeration.
Vibrio (VIB-ree-oh) **bacteria** *Vibrio vulnificus*[d] bacterium	Raw or undercooked seafood and contaminated water.	Onset: 1 to 7 days. Diarrhea, abdominal cramps, nausea, vomiting; lasts 2 to 5 days; can be fatal.	Use sanitary food-handling methods; cook foods thoroughly.
Yersiniosis (yer-SIN-ee-OH-sis) *Yersinia enterocolitica* bacterium	Raw and undercooked pork, unpasteurized milk	Onset: 1 to 2 days. Diarrhea, vomiting, fever, abdominal pain; lasts 1 to 3 weeks.	Cook foods throughly; use pasteurized milk; use treated, boiled, or bottled water.
Food Intoxications			
Botulism (BOT-chew-lizm) Botulinum toxin [produced by *Clostridium botulinum* bacterium, which grows without oxygen, in low-acid foods, and at temperatures between 40° and 120°F; the **botulinum** (BOT-chew-line-um) **toxin** responsible for botulism is called **botulin** (BOT-chew-lin)]	Anaerobic environment of low acidity (canned corn, peppers, green beans, soups, beets, asparagus, mushrooms, ripe olives, spinach, tuna, chicken, chicken liver, liver pâte, luncheon meats, ham, sausage, stuffed eggplant, lobster, and smoked and salted fish)	Onset: 4 to 36 hr. Nervous system symptoms, including double vision, inability to swallow, speech difficulty, and progressive paralysis of the respiratory system; often fatal; leaves prolonged symptoms in survivors.	Use proper canning methods for low-acid foods; refrigerate homemade garlic and herb oils; avoid commercially prepared foods with leaky seals or with bent, bulging, or broken cans.
Staphylococcal (STAF-il-oh-KOK-al) **food poisoning** Staphylococcal toxin (produced by *Staphylococcus aureus* bacterium)	Toxin produced in improperly refrigerated meats; egg, tuna, potato, and macaroni salads; cream-filled pastries	Onset: 1 to 6 hr. Diarrhea, nausea, vomiting, abdominal cramps, fever; lasts 1 to 2 days.	Use sanitary food-handling methods; cook food thoroughly; refrigerate foods promptly and properly; use proper home-canning methods.

NOTE: Travelers' diarrhea is most commonly caused by *E. coli*, *Campylobacter jejuni*, *Shigella*, and *Salmonella*.
[a]The "How to" on pp. 672–673 provides more details on the proper handling, cooking, and refrigeration of foods.
[b]The most serious strain is *E. coli* STEC O157.

[c]Gastroenteritis refers to an inflammation of the stomach and intestines but is the most common name used for illnesses caused by Norwalk viruses.
[d]Most cases of *Vibrio vulnificus* occur in persons with underlying illness, particularly those with liver disorders, diabetes, cancer, and AIDS, and those who require long-term steroid use. The fatality rate is 50 percent for this population.

To prevent food intoxication from homemade flavored oils, wash and dry the herbs before adding them to the oil and keep the oil refrigerated.

Food Intoxications Food intoxications are caused by eating foods containing natural toxins or, more likely, microbes that produce toxins. The most common food toxin is produced by *Staphylococcus aureus;* it affects more than one million people each year. Less common, but more infamous, is *Clostridium botulinum,* an organism that produces a deadly toxin in anaerobic conditions such as improperly canned (especially home-canned) foods and homemade garlic or herb-flavored oils stored at room temperature. Because the toxin paralyzes muscles, a person with botulism has difficulty seeing, speaking, swallowing, and breathing.[3] Because death can occur within 24 hours of onset, botulism demands immediate medical attention. Even then, survivors may suffer the effects for months or years.

Food Safety in the Marketplace

Transmission of foodborne illness has changed as our food supply and lifestyles have changed.[4] In the past, foodborne illness was caused by one person's error in a small setting, such as improperly refrigerated egg salad at a family picnic, and affected only a few victims. Today, we eat more foods that have been prepared and packaged by others. Consequently, when a food manufacturer or restaurant chef makes an error, foodborne illness can become epidemic. An estimated 80 percent of reported foodborne illnesses are caused by errors in a commercial setting, such as the improper **pasteurization** of milk at a large dairy.

In the mid-1990s, when a fast-food restaurant served undercooked burgers tainted with an infectious strain of *Escherichia coli,* hundreds of patrons became ill, and at least three people died. In the early 2000s, a national food company had to recall more than 4 million pounds of poultry products after *Listeria* poisoning killed 7 people and made more than 50 others sick. In the 2006 *E. coli* outbreak due to contaminated fresh spinach, nearly 200 people became sick, and 2 elderly women and a 2-year-old boy died before consumers got the FDA message to not eat fresh spinach. These incidents and others have focused the national spotlight on two important safety issues: disease-causing organisms are commonly found in raw foods, and thorough cooking kills most of these foodborne pathogens. This heightened awareness sparked a much needed overhaul of national food safety programs.

Industry Controls To make our food supply safe for consumers, the USDA, the FDA, and the food-processing industries have developed and implemented programs to control foodborne illness.* The **Hazard Analysis Critical Control Points (HACCP)** system requires food manufacturers to identify points of contamination and implement controls to prevent foodborne disease. For example, after tracing two large outbreaks of salmonellosis to imported cantaloupe, producers began using chlorinated water to wash the melons and to make ice for packing and shipping. Safety procedures such as this prevent hundreds of thousands of foodborne illnesses each year and are responsible for the decline in infections over the past decade.[5]

This example raises another issue regarding the safety of imported foods. FDA inspectors cannot keep pace with the increasing numbers of imported foods; they inspect fewer than 2 percent of the almost 3 million shipments of fruits, vegetables, and seafood coming into more than 300 ports in the United States each year. The FDA is working with other countries to adopt the safe food-handling practices used in the United States.

Consumer Awareness Canned and packaged foods sold in grocery stores are easily controlled, but rare accidents do happen. Batch numbering makes it possible to recall contaminated foods through public announcements via newspapers, television, and radio. In the grocery store, consumers can buy items before the "sell by" date and inspect the safety seals and wrappers of packages. A broken seal, bulging can lid, or mangled package fails to protect the consumer against microbes, insects, spoilage, or even vandalism.

pasteurization: heat processing of food that inactivates some, but not all, microorganisms in the food; not a sterilization process. Bacteria that cause spoilage are still present.

Hazard Analysis Critical Control Points (HACCP): a systematic plan to identify and correct potential microbial hazards in the manufacturing, distribution, and commercial use of food products; commonly referred to as "HASS-ip."

---

* In addition to HACCP, these programs include the Emerging Infections Program (EIP), the Foodborne Diseases Active Surveillance Network (FoodNet), and the Food Safety Inspection Service (FSIS).

FIGURE 19-1	Food Safety from Farms to Consumers

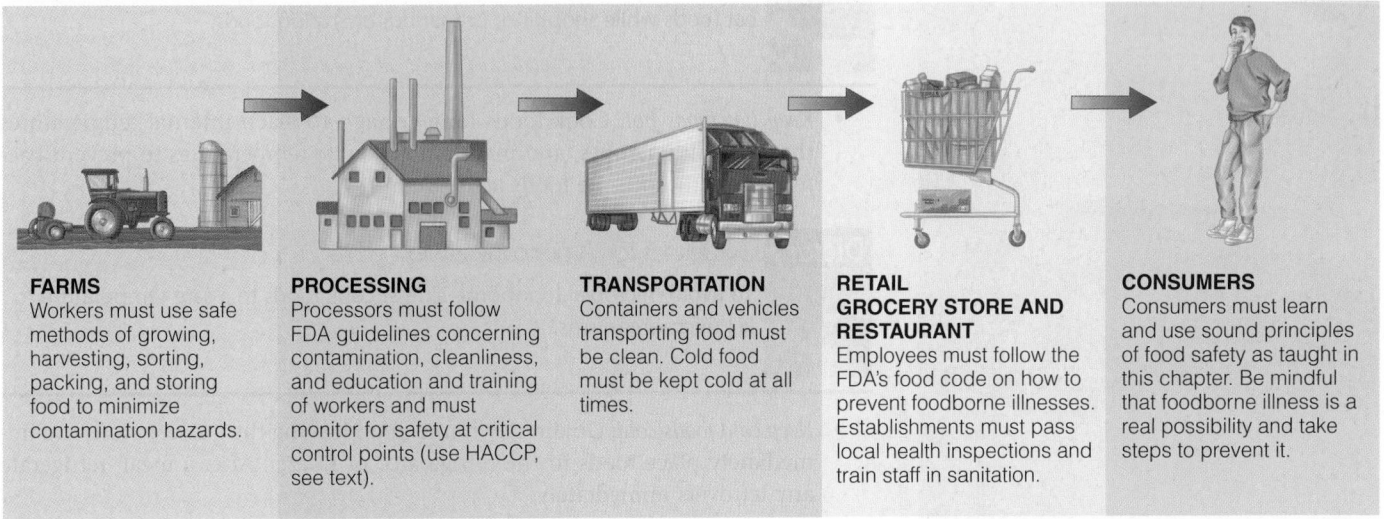

FARMS
Workers must use safe methods of growing, harvesting, sorting, packing, and storing food to minimize contamination hazards.

PROCESSING
Processors must follow FDA guidelines concerning contamination, cleanliness, and education and training of workers and must monitor for safety at critical control points (use HACCP, see text).

TRANSPORTATION
Containers and vehicles transporting food must be clean. Cold food must be kept cold at all times.

RETAIL GROCERY STORE AND RESTAURANT
Employees must follow the FDA's food code on how to prevent foodborne illnesses. Establishments must pass local health inspections and train staff in sanitation.

CONSUMERS
Consumers must learn and use sound principles of food safety as taught in this chapter. Be mindful that foodborne illness is a real possibility and take steps to prevent it.

State and local health regulations provide guidelines on the cleanliness of facilities and the safe preparation of foods for restaurants, cafeterias, and fast-food establishments. Even so, consumers can also take these actions to help prevent foodborne illnesses when dining out:

- Wash hands with hot, soapy water before meals.
- Expect clean tabletops, dinnerware, utensils, and food preparation areas.
- Expect cooked foods to be served piping hot and salads to be fresh and cold.
- Refrigerate doggy bags within two hours.

Improper handling of foods can occur anywhere along the line from commercial manufacturers to large supermarkets to small restaurants to private homes. Maintaining a safe food supply requires everyone's efforts (see Figure 19-1).

Food Safety in the Kitchen

Whether microbes multiply and cause illness depends, in part, on a few key food-handling behaviors in the kitchen—whether the kitchen is in your home, a school cafeteria, a gourmet restaurant, or a canning manufacturer.[6] Figure 19-2 summarizes the four simple things that can help most to prevent foodborne illness:

- *Keep a clean, safe kitchen.* Wash countertops, cutting boards, hands, sponges, and utensils in hot, soapy water before and after each step of food preparation.

Dietary Guidelines for Americans 2005

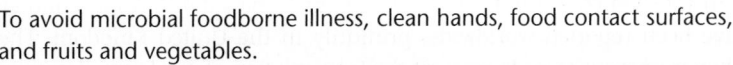

To avoid microbial foodborne illness, clean hands, food contact surfaces, and fruits and vegetables.

- *Avoid cross-contamination.* Keep raw eggs, meat, poultry, and seafood separate from other foods. Wash all utensils and surfaces (such as cutting boards or platters) that have been in contact with these foods with hot, soapy water before using them again. Bacteria inevitably left on the surfaces from the raw meat can recontaminate the cooked meat or other foods—a problem known as **cross-contamination.** Washing raw eggs, meat, and poultry is not recommended because the extra handling increases the risk of cross-contamination.

FIGURE 19-2	Fight Bac!

Four ways to keep food safe. The Fight Bac! website is at www.fightbac.org.

cross-contamination: the contamination of food by bacteria that occurs when the food comes into contact with surfaces previously touched by raw meat, poultry, or seafood.

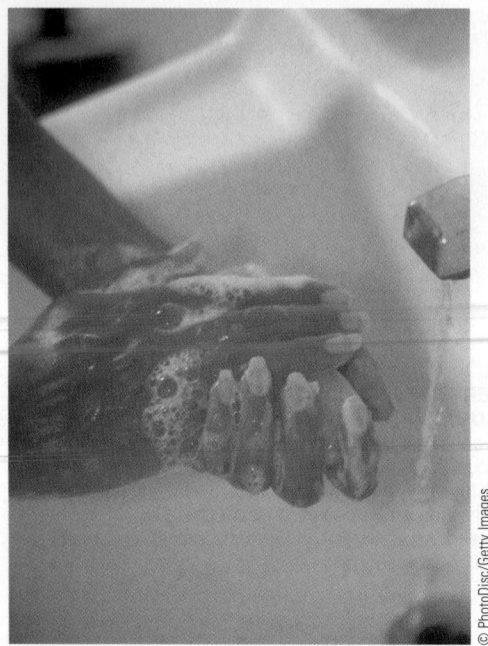

Wash your hands with warm water and soap for at least 20 seconds before preparing or eating food to reduce the chance of microbial contamination.

© PhotoDisc/Getty Images

Dietary Guidelines for Americans 2005

To avoid microbial foodborne illness, separate raw, cooked, and ready-to-eat foods while shopping, preparing, or storing foods.

• *Keep hot foods hot.* Cook foods long enough to reach internal temperatures that will kill microbes, and maintain adequate temperatures to prevent bacterial growth until the foods are served.

Dietary Guidelines for Americans 2005

To avoid microbial foodborne illness, cook foods to a safe temperature to kill microorganisms.

• *Keep cold foods cold.* Go directly home upon leaving the grocery store and immediately place foods in the refrigerator or freezer. After a meal, refrigerate any leftovers immediately.

Dietary Guidelines for Americans 2005

To avoid microbial foodborne illness, chill (refrigerate) perishable food promptly and defrost foods properly.

Unfortunately, consumers commonly fail to follow these simple food-handling recommendations.[7] See the "How to" on p. 670–671 for additional food safety tips.

Safe Handling of Meats and Poultry Figure 19-3 presents label instructions for the safe handling of meat and poultry and two types of USDA seals. Meats and poultry contain bacteria and provide a moist, nutrient-rich environment that favors microbial growth. Ground meat is especially susceptible because it receives more handling than other kinds of meat and has more surface exposed to bacterial contamination. Consumers cannot detect the harmful bacteria in or on meat. For safety's sake, cook meat thoroughly, using a thermometer to test the internal temperature (see Figure 19-4).

Dietary Guidelines for Americans 2005

To avoid microbial foodborne illness, meat and poultry should *not* be washed or rinsed.

Mad Cow Disease Reports on mad cow disease from dozens of countries, including Canada and the United States, have sparked consumer concerns.[8] Mad cow disease is a slowly progressive, fatal condition that affects the central nervous system of cattle.* A similar disease develops in people who have eaten contaminated beef from infected cows (milk products appear to be safe).** Approximately 150 cases have been reported worldwide, primarily in the United Kingdom. The USDA has taken numerous steps to prevent the transmission of mad cow disease in cattle, and if these measures are followed, then risks from U.S. cattle are low.[9] Because the infectious agents occur in the intestines, central nervous system, and other organs, but not in muscle meat, concerned consumers may want to select whole cuts of meat instead of ground beef or sausage. A few recent reports of hunters developing fatal neurological disorders have raised concerns about a similar disease in wild game. Hunters and consumers who regularly eat elk, deer, or antelope should check the advisories of their state department of agriculture.

---

*Mad cow disease is technically known as bovine spongiform encephalopathy (BSE).
** The human form of BSE is called the variant Creutzfeldt-Jakob Disease (vCJD).

FIGURE 19-3 Meat and Poultry Safety, Grading, and Inspection Seals

Inspection is mandatory; grading is voluntary. Neither guarantees that the product will not cause foodborne illnesses, but consumers can help to prevent food-borne illnesses by following the safe handling instructions.

The voluntary "Graded by USDA" seal indicates that the product has been graded for tenderness, juiciness, and flavor. Beef is graded Prime (abundant marbling of the meat muscle), Choice (less marbling), and Select (lean). Similarly, poultry is graded A, B, and C.

The mandatory "Inspected and Passed by the USDA" seal ensures that meat and poultry products are safe, wholesome, and correctly labeled. Inspection does not guarantee that the meat is free of potentially harmful bacteria.

Safe Handling Instructions

THIS PRODUCT WAS PREPARED FROM INSPECTED AND PASSED MEAT AND/OR POULTRY. SOME FOOD PRODUCTS MAY CONTAIN BACTERIA THAT CAN CAUSE ILLNESS IF THE PRODUCT IS MISHANDLED OR COOKED IMPROPERLY. FOR YOUR PROTECTION, FOLLOW THESE SAFE HANDLING INSTRUCTIONS.

KEEP REFRIGERATED OR FROZEN. THAW IN REFRIGERATOR OR MICROWAVE.

KEEP RAW MEAT AND POULTRY SEPARATE FROM OTHER FOODS. WASH WORKING SURFACES (INCLUDING CUTTING BOARDS), UTENSILS, AND HANDS AFTER TOUCHING RAW MEAT OR POULTRY.

COOK THOROUGHLY.

KEEP HOT FOODS HOT. REFRIGERATE LEFTOVERS IMMEDIATELY OR DISCARD.

The USDA requires that safe handling instructions appear on all packages of meat and poultry.

© Eric O'connell/Getty Images

Cook hamburgers to 160°F; color alone cannot determine doneness. Some burgers will turn brown before reaching 160°F, whereas others may retain some pink color, even when cooked to 175°F.

Avian Influenza Avian influenza (bird flu) is a very contagious and life-threatening viral infection that naturally occurs among birds, including chickens, ducks, and turkeys. The risk of bird flu in human beings is relatively low, and most cases have resulted from direct contact with infected birds or their contaminated environment. Because the virus can change easily, scientists are concerned that it could infect people and spread rapidly from person to person, creating a pandemic. Importantly, bird flu is not transmitted by eating poultry.

FIGURE 19-4 Recommended Safe Temperatures (Fahrenheit)

Bacteria multiply rapidly at temperatures between 40° and 140°F. Cook foods to the temperatures shown on this thermometer and hold them at 140°F or higher.

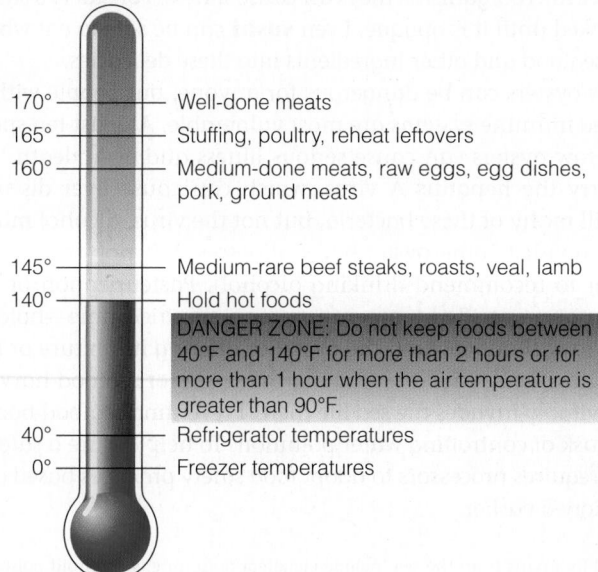

170° — Well-done meats

165° — Stuffing, poultry, reheat leftovers

160° — Medium-done meats, raw eggs, egg dishes, pork, ground meats

145° — Medium-rare beef steaks, roasts, veal, lamb

140° — Hold hot foods

DANGER ZONE: Do not keep foods between 40°F and 140°F for more than 2 hours or for more than 1 hour when the air temperature is greater than 90°F.

40° — Refrigerator temperatures

0° — Freezer temperatures

HOW TO Prevent Foodborne Illness

Most foodborne illnesses can be prevented by following four simple rules: keep a clean kitchen, avoid cross-contamination, keep hot foods hot, and keep cold foods cold.

Keep a Clean Kitchen

- Wash fruits and vegetables in a clean sink with a scrub brush and warm water; store washed and unwashed produce separately.
- Use hot, soapy water to wash hands, utensils, dishes, nonporous cutting boards, and countertops before handling food and between tasks when working with different foods. Use a bleach solution on cutting boards (one capful per gallon of water).
- Cover cuts with clean bandages before food preparation; dirty bandages carry harmful microorganisms.
- Mix foods with utensils, not hands; keep hands and utensils away from mouth, nose, and hair.
- Anyone may be a carrier of bacteria and should avoid coughing or sneezing over food. A person with a skin infection or infectious disease should not prepare food.
- Wash or replace sponges and towels regularly.
- Clean up food spills and crumb-filled crevices.

Avoid Cross-Contamination

- Wash all surfaces that have been in contact with raw meats, poultry, eggs, fish, and shellfish before reusing.
- Serve cooked foods on a clean plate. Separate raw foods from those that have been cooked.
- Don't use marinade that was in contact with raw meat for basting or sauces.

Keep Hot Foods Hot

- When cooking meats or poultry, use a thermometer to test the internal temperature. Insert the thermometer between the thigh and the body of a turkey or into the thickest part of other meats, making sure the tip of the thermometer is not in contact with bone or the pan. Cook to the temperature indicated for that particular meat (see Figure 19-4 on p. 669); cook hamburgers to at least medium well-done. If you have safety questions, call the USDA Meat and Poultry Hotline: (800) 535-4555.
- Cook stuffing separately, or stuff poultry just prior to cooking.
- Do not cook large cuts of meat or turkey in a microwave oven; it leaves some parts undercooked while overcooking others.
- Cook eggs before eating them (soft-boiled for at least 3½ minutes; scrambled until set, not runny; fried for at least 3 minutes on one side and 1 minute on the other).
- Cook seafood thoroughly. If you have safety questions about seafood call the FDA hotline: (800) FDA-4010.
- When serving foods, maintain temperatures at 140°F or higher.
- Heat leftovers thoroughly to at least 165°F.

Keep Cold Foods Cold

- When running errands, stop at the grocery store last. When you get home, refrigerate the perishable groceries (such as meats and dairy products) immediately. Do not leave perishables in the car any longer than it takes for ice cream to melt.
- Put packages of raw meat, fish, or poultry on a plate before refrigerating to prevent juices from dripping on food stored below.
- Buy only foods that are solidly frozen in store freezers.
- Keep cold foods at 40°F or less; keep frozen foods at 0°F or less (keep a thermometer in the refrigerator).
- Marinate meats in the refrigerator, not on the counter.

Eating raw seafood is a risky proposition.

© David Chasey/PhotoDisc Red/Getty Images

sushi: vinegar-flavored rice and seafood, typically wrapped in seaweed and stuffed with colorful vegetables. Some sushi is stuffed with raw fish; other varieties contain cooked seafood.

Safe Handling of Seafood Most seafood available in the United States and Canada is safe, but eating it undercooked or raw can cause severe illnesses—hepatitis, worms, parasites, viral intestinal disorders, and other diseases.* Rumor has it that freezing fish will make it safe to eat raw, but this is only partly true. Commercial freezing kills mature parasitic worms, but only cooking can kill all worm eggs and other microorganisms that can cause illness. For safety's sake, all seafood should be cooked until it is opaque. Even **sushi** can be safe to eat when chefs combine cooked seafood and other ingredients into these delicacies.

Eating raw oysters can be dangerous for anyone, but people with liver disease and weakened immune systems are most vulnerable. At least ten species of bacteria found in raw oysters can cause serious illness and even death.** Raw oysters may also carry the hepatitis A virus, which can cause liver disease. Some hot sauces can kill many of these bacteria, but not the virus; alcohol may also protect some people against some oyster-borne illnesses, but not enough to guarantee protection (or to recommend drinking alcohol). Pasteurization of raw oysters—holding them at a specified temperature for a specified time—holds promise for killing bacteria without cooking the oyster or altering its texture or flavor.

As population density increases along the shores of seafood-harvesting waters, pollution inevitably invades the sea life there. Preventing seafood-borne illness is in large part a task of controlling water pollution. To help ensure a safe seafood market, the FDA requires processors to adopt food safety practices based on the HACCP system mentioned earlier.

---

* Diseases caused by toxins from the sea include ciguatera poisoning, scombroid poisoning, and paralytic and neurotoxic shellfish poisoning.
** Raw oysters can carry the bacterium *Vibrio vulnificus;* see Table 19-1 for details.

HOW TO Prevent Foodborne Illness, *continued*

- Refrigerate leftovers promptly; use shallow containers to cool foods faster; use leftovers within 3 to 4 days.
- Thaw meats or poultry in the refrigerator, not at room temperature. If you must hasten thawing, use cool water (changed every 30 minutes) or a microwave oven.
- Freeze meat, fish, or poultry immediately if not planning to use within a few days.

In General

- Do not reuse disposable containers; use nondisposable containers or recycle instead.
- Do not taste food that is suspect. "If in doubt, throw it out."
- Throw out foods with danger-signaling odors. Be aware, though, that most food-poisoning bacteria are odorless, colorless, and tasteless.
- Do not buy or use items that have broken seals or mangled packaging; such containers cannot protect against microbes, insects, spoilage, or even vandalism. Check safety seals, buttons, and expiration dates.
- Follow label instructions for storing and preparing packaged and frozen foods; throw out foods that have been thawed or refrozen.

- Discard foods that are discolored, moldy, or decayed or that have been contaminated by insects or rodents.

For Specific Food Items

- *Canned goods.* Carefully discard food from cans that leak or bulge so that other people and animals will not accidentally ingest it; before canning, seek professional advice from the USDA Extension Service (check your phone book under U.S. government listings, or ask directory assistance).
- *Milk and cheeses.* Use only pasteurized milk and milk products. Aged cheeses, such as cheddar and Swiss, do well for an hour or two without refrigeration, but they should be refrigerated or stored in an ice chest for longer periods.
- *Eggs.* Use clean eggs with intact shells. Do not eat eggs, even pasteurized eggs, raw; raw eggs are commonly found in Caesar salad dressing, eggnog, cookie dough, hollandaise sauce, and key lime pie. Cook eggs until whites are firmly set and yolks begin to thicken.
- *Honey.* Honey may contain dormant bacterial spores, which can awaken in the human body to produce botulism. In adults, this poses little hazard, but infants under

one year of age should never be fed honey. Honey can accumulate enough toxin to kill an infant; it has been implicated in several cases of sudden infant death. (Honey can also be contaminated with environmental pollutants picked up by the bees.)
- *Mayonnaise.* Commercial mayonnaise may actually help a food to resist spoilage because of the acid content. Still, keep it cold after opening.
- *Mixed salads.* Mixed salads of chopped ingredients spoil easily because they have extensive surface area for bacteria to invade, and they have been in contact with cutting boards, hands, and kitchen utensils that easily transmit bacteria to food (regardless of their mayonnaise content). Chill them well before, during, and after serving.
- *Picnic foods.* Choose foods that last without refrigeration such as fresh fruits and vegetables, breads and crackers, and canned spreads and cheeses that can be opened and used immediately. Pack foods cold, layer ice between foods, and keep foods out of water.
- *Seafood.* Buy only fresh seafood that has been properly refrigerated or iced. Cooked seafood should be stored separately from raw seafood to avoid cross-contamination.

Chemical pollution and microbial contamination lurk not only in the water, but also in the boats and warehouses where seafood is cleaned, prepared, and refrigerated. Because seafood is one of the most perishable foods, time and temperature are critical to its freshness, flavor, and safety. To keep seafood as fresh as possible, people in the industry must "keep it cold, keep it clean, and keep it moving." Wise consumers eat it cooked.

Other Precautions and Procedures Fresh food generally smells fresh. Not all types of food poisoning are detectable by odor, but some bacterial wastes produce "off" odors. If an abnormal odor exists, the food is spoiled. Throw it out or, if it was recently purchased, return it to the grocery store. Do not taste it. Table 19-2 lists safe refrigerator storage times for selected foods.

Local health departments and the USDA Extension Service can provide additional information about food safety. If precautions fail and a mild foodborne illness develops, drink clear liquids to replace fluids lost through vomiting and diarrhea. If serious foodborne illness is suspected, first call a physician. Then wrap the remainder of the suspected food and label the container so that the food cannot be mistakenly eaten, place it in the refrigerator, and hold it for possible inspection by health authorities.

Dietary Guidelines for Americans 2005

To avoid microbial foodborne illness, avoid raw (unpasteurized) milk or any products made from unpasteurized milk, raw or partially cooked eggs or foods containing raw eggs, raw or undercooked meat and poultry, unpasteurized juices, and raw sprouts.

TABLE 19-2	Safe Refrigerator Storage Times (≤40°F)
1 to 2 Days	Raw ground meats, breakfast or other raw sausages, raw fish or poultry; gravies
3 to 5 Days	Raw steaks, roasts, or chops; cooked meats, poultry, vegetables, and mixed dishes; lunch meats (packages opened); mayonnaise salads (chicken, egg, pasta, tuna)
1 Week	Hard-cooked eggs, bacon or hot dogs (opened packages); smoked sausages or seafood
2 to 4 Weeks	Raw eggs (in shells); lunch meats, bacon, or hot dogs (packages unopened); dry sausages (pepperoni, hard salami); most aged and processed cheeses (Swiss, brick)
2 Months	Mayonnaise (opened jar); most dry cheese (parmesan, romano)

Food Safety While Traveling

People who travel to other countries have a 50–50 chance of contracting a food-borne illness, commonly described as **travelers' diarrhea**.[10] Like many other foodborne illnesses, travelers' diarrhea is a sometimes serious, always annoying bacterial infection of the digestive tract. The risk is high because, for one thing, some countries' cleanliness standards for food and water are lower than those in the United States and Canada. For another, every region's microbes are different, and although people are immune to the microbes in their own neighborhoods, they have had no chance to develop immunity to the pathogens in places they are visiting for the first time. The "How to" on the next page offers tips for food safety while traveling.

Advances in Food Safety

Advances in technology have dramatically improved the quality and safety of foods available on the market. From pasteurization in the early 1900s ◆ to irradiation in the early 2000s, these advances offer numerous benefits, but they also raise consumer concerns.[11]

◆ During the last century, pasteurization of milk helped to control typhoid fever, tuberculosis, scarlet fever, diphtheria, and other infectious diseases.

Irradiation The use of low-dose **irradiation** protects consumers from foodborne illnesses by:[12]

- Controlling mold in grains
- Sterilizing spices and teas for storage at room temperature
- Controlling insects and extending shelf life in fresh fruits and vegetables (inhibits the growth of sprouts on potatoes and onions and delays ripening in some fruits such as strawberries and mangoes)
- Destroying harmful bacteria in fresh and frozen beef, poultry, lamb, and pork

Some foods are not candidates for the treatment. For example, when irradiated, high-fat meats develop off-odors, egg whites turn milky, grapefruits become mushy, and milk products change flavor. (Incidentally, the milk in those boxes kept at room temperature on grocery-store shelves is not irradiated; it is sterilized with an **ultra-high temperature treatment**.)

The use of food irradiation has been extensively evaluated over the past 50 years; approved for use in more than 40 countries; and supported by numerous health agencies, including the **FAO, WHO,** and the American Medical Association. Irradiation does not make foods radioactive, nor does it noticeably change the taste, texture, or appearance of approved foods. ◆ Vitamin loss is minimal and comparable to amounts lost in other food-processing methods such as canning. Because irradiation kills bacteria without the use of heat, it is sometimes called "cold pasteurization."

◆ Foods approved for irradiation:
- Eggs
- Raw beef, lamb, poultry, pork
- Spices, tea
- Wheat
- Vegetables (potatoes, tomatoes, onions)
- Fresh fruit (strawberries, citrus, papaya)

Consumer Concerns about Irradiation Many consumers associate the term *radiation* with cancer, birth defects, and mutations, and consequently have strong negative emotions about using irradiation on foods. Some may mistakenly fear that irradiated food has been contaminated by radioactive particles, such as occurs in the aftermath of a nuclear accident. Some balk at the idea of irradiating, and thus sterilizing, contaminated foods and prefer instead the elimination of unsanitary slaughtering and food preparation conditions. Food producers, on the other hand, are eager to use irradiation, but they hesitate to do so until consumers are ready to accept it and willing to pay for it. Once consumers understand the benefits of irradiation, about half are willing to use irradiated foods, but only a fourth are willing to pay more.[13]

travelers' diarrhea: nausea, vomiting, and diarrhea caused by consuming food or water contaminated by any of several organisms, most commonly, *E. coli, Shigella, Campylobacter jejuni,* and *Salmonella*.

irradiation: sterilizing a food by exposure to energy waves, similar to ultraviolet light and microwaves.

ultrahigh temperature (UHT) treatment: sterilizing a food by brief exposure to temperatures above those normally used.

Regulation of Irradiation The FDA has established regulations governing the specific uses of irradiation and allowed doses. Each food that has been treated with

Achieve Food Safety While Traveling

Foodborne illnesses contracted while travel-ing are colloquially known as travelers' diarrhea. A bout of this ailment can ruin the most enthusiastic tourist's trip. To avoid foodborne illness, follow the food safety tips outlined on pp. 670–671. In addition, while traveling:

- Wash your hands often with soap and hot water, especially before handling food or eating. Use antiseptic gel or hand wipes.
- Eat only well-cooked and hot or canned foods. Eat raw fruits or vegetables only if you have washed them in purified water and peeled them yourself. Skip salads and raw fish and shellfish.

- Be aware that water, and ice made from it, may be unsafe. Use safe, bottled water for drinking, making ice cubes, and brushing teeth. Alternatively, take along disinfecting tablets or a device to boil water. Do not use ice unless it was made from purified or bottled water.
- Drink no beverages made with tap water. Drink only treated, boiled, canned, or bot-tled beverages, and drink them without ice, even if they are not chilled to your liking.
- Refuse dairy products unless they have been properly pasteurized and refrigerated.
- Do not buy food and drinks from street vendors.

- Before you leave on the trip, ask your physician to recommend an antimotility agent and an antibiotic to take with you in case your efforts to avoid illness fail.

To sum up these recommendations, "Boil it, cook it, peel it, or forget it." Chances are excellent that if you follow these rules, you will remain well.

---

irradiation must say so on its label. ◆ Labels can be misleading, however. Products that use irradiated foods as ingredients are not required to say so on the label. Fur-thermore, consumers may interpret the *absence* of the irradiation symbol to mean that the food was produced without any kind of treatment. This is not true; it is just that the FDA does not require label statements for other treatments used for the same purpose, such as postharvest fumigation with pesticides. If all treatment meth-ods were declared, consumers could make fully informed choices.

Other Pasteurizing Systems Other technologies using high-intensity pulsed light or electron beams have also been approved by the FDA. Like irradiation, these technologies kill microorganisms and extend the shelf life of foods without dimin-ishing their nutrient content.

◆ This international symbol, called the radura, indentifies retail foods that have been irradiated. The words "Treated by irra-diation" or "Treated with irradiation" must accompany the symbol. The irradiation label is not required on commercially pre-pared foods that contain irradiated ingredi-ents, such as spices.

IN SUMMARY

Millions of people suffer mild to life-threatening symptoms caused by food-borne illnesses (review Table 19-1). As the "How to" on pp. 670–671 describes, most of these illnesses can be prevented by storing and cooking foods at their proper temperatures and by preparing them in sanitary conditions. Irradia-tion of certain foods protects consumers from foodborne illnesses, but it also raises some concerns.

Nutritional Adequacy of Foods and Diets

In years past, when most foods were whole and farm fresh, the task of meeting nu-trient needs primarily involved balancing servings from the various food groups. To-day, however, foods have changed. Many "new" foods are available to appeal to consumers' demands for convenience and flavor, but not necessarily to deliver a bal-anced assortment of needed nutrients.

Obtaining Nutrient Information

To help consumers find their way among these foods and combine them into health-ful diets, the FDA has developed extensive nutrition labeling regulations, as Chap-ter 2 described. In addition, the USDA's *Dietary Guidelines* help consumers "eat to stay healthy," and the MyPyramid food guide helps them to put those recommendations into practice (see Chapter 2).

Minimizing Nutrient Losses

In addition to selecting nutritious foods and preparing them safely, consumers can improve their nutritional health by learning to store and cook foods in ways that minimize nutrient losses. Water-soluble vitamins are the most vulnerable of the nutrients, but both vitamins and minerals can be lost when they dissolve in water that is then discarded.

Fruits and vegetables contain enzymes that both synthesize and degrade vitamins. After a fruit or vegetable has been picked, vitamin synthesis stops, but degradation continues. To slow the degradation of vitamins, most fruits and vegetables should be kept refrigerated until used. (Degradative enzymes are most active at warmer temperatures.)

Some vitamins are easily destroyed by oxygen. To minimize the destruction of vitamins, store fruits and vegetables that have been cut and juice that has been opened in airtight containers and refrigerate them.

Water-soluble vitamins readily dissolve in water. To prevent losses during washing, wash fruits and vegetables before cutting. To minimize losses during cooking, steam or microwave vegetables. Alternatively, use the cooking water when preparing meals such as casseroles and soups.

Finally, keep in mind that most vitamin losses are not catastrophic and that a law of diminishing returns operates. Do not fret over small losses or waste time that may be valuable in improving your health in other ways. Be assured that if you start with plenty of fruits and vegetables and are reasonably careful in their storage and preparation, you will receive a sufficient supply of all the nutrients they provide.

IN SUMMARY

In the marketplace, food labels, the *Dietary Guidelines,* and the MyPyramid food guide all help consumers learn about nutrition and how to plan healthy diets. At home, consumers can minimize nutrient losses from fruits and vegetables by refrigerating them, washing them before cutting them, storing them in airtight containers, and cooking them for short times in minimal water.

Environmental Contaminants

Concern about environmental contamination of foods is growing as the world becomes more populated and more industrialized. Industrial processes pollute the air, water, and soil. Plants absorb the **contaminants,** and people consume the plants (grains, vegetables, legumes, and fruits) or the meat and milk products from livestock that have eaten the plants. Similarly, polluted water contaminates the fish and other seafood that people eat. Environmental contaminants present in air, water, and foods find their way into our bodies and have the potential to cause numerous health problems.[14]

Harmfulness of Environmental Contaminants

The potential harmfulness of a contaminant depends in part on its **persistence—** the extent to which it lingers in the environment or in the body. Some contaminants in the environment are short-lived because microorganisms or agents such as sunlight or oxygen can break them down. Some contaminants in the body may linger

contaminants: substances that make a food impure and unsuitable for ingestion.

persistence: stubborn or enduring continuance; with respect to food contaminants, the quality of persisting, rather than breaking down, in the bodies of animals and human beings.

for only a short time because the body rapidly excretes them or metabolizes them to harmless compounds. These contaminants present little cause for concern. Some contaminants, however, resist breakdown and can accumulate. Each level of the **food chain**, then, has a greater concentration than the one below (**bioaccumulation**). Figure 19-5 shows how bioaccumulation leads to high concentrations of toxins in people at the top of the food chain.

Contaminants enter the environment in various ways. Accidental spills are rare but can have devastating effects. More commonly, small amounts are released over long periods. The following paragraphs describe how three contaminants found their way into the food supply in the past. The first example involves a heavy metal; ◆ the others involve **organic halogens.**

Methylmercury A classic example of acute contamination occurred in 1953 when a number of people in Minamata, Japan, became ill with a disease no one had seen before. By 1960, 121 cases had been reported, including 23 in infants. Mortality was high; 46 died, and the survivors suffered blindness, deafness, lack of coordination, and intellectual deterioration. The cause was ultimately revealed to be methylmercury contamination of fish from the bay where these people lived. The infants who contracted the disease had not eaten any fish, but their mothers had, and even though the mothers exhibited no symptoms during their pregnancies, the poison affected their unborn babies. Manufacturing plants in the region were discharging mercury-containing waste into the waters of the bay, the mercury was

◆ Reminder: A *heavy metal* is any of a number of mineral ions such as mercury and lead, so called because they are of relatively high atomic weight. Many heavy metals are poisonous.

food chain: the sequence in which living things depend on other living things for food.

bioaccumulation: the accumulation of contaminants in the flesh of animals high on the food chain.

organic halogens: an organic compound containing one or more atoms of a halogen—fluorine, chlorine, iodine, or bromine.

FIGURE 19-5 Bioaccumulation of Toxins in the Food Chain

This example features fish as the food for human consumption, but bioaccumulation of toxins occurs on land as well when cows, pigs, and chickens eat or drink contaminated foods or water.

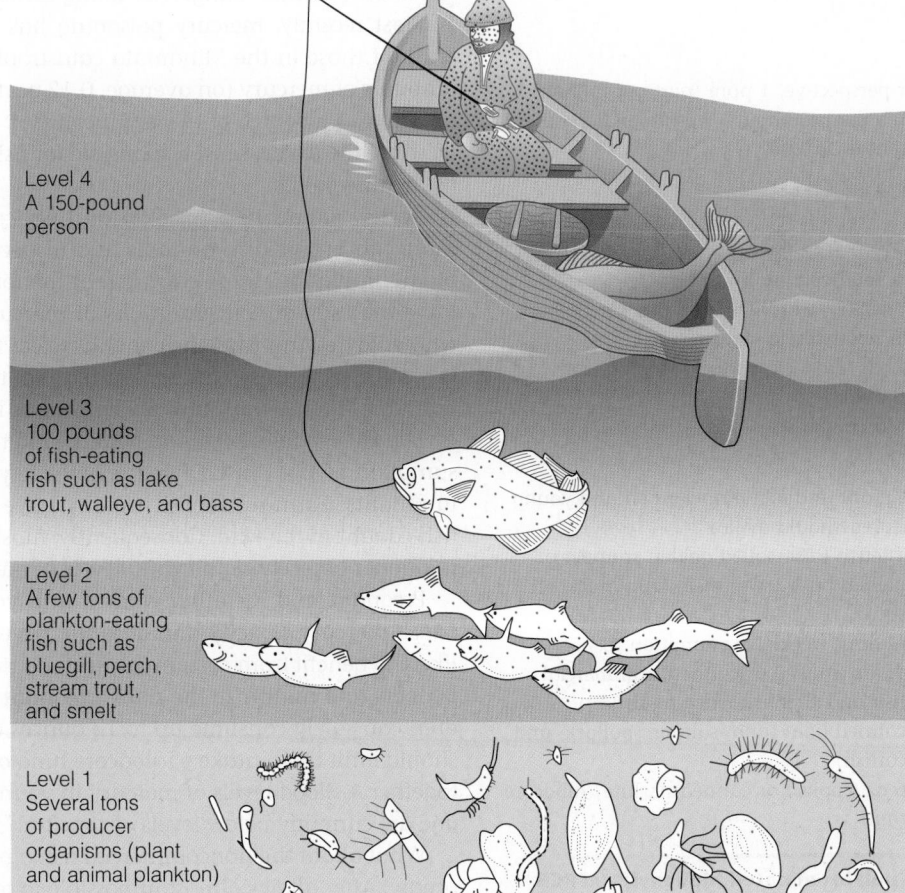

Key:
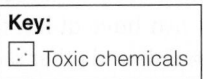 Toxic chemicals

4 If none of the chemicals are lost along the way, people ultimately receive all of the toxic chemicals that were present in the original plants and plankton.

3 Contaminants become further concentrated in larger fish that eat the small fish from the lower part of the food chain.

2 Contaminants become more concentrated in small fish that eat the plants and plankton.

1 Plants and plankton at the bottom of the food chain become contaminated with toxic chemicals, such as methylmercury (shown as red dots).

Level 4
A 150-pound person

Level 3
100 pounds of fish-eating fish such as lake trout, walleye, and bass

Level 2
A few tons of plankton-eating fish such as bluegill, perch, stream trout, and smelt

Level 1
Several tons of producer organisms (plant and animal plankton)

Because albacore ("white") tuna has more mercury than canned light tuna, consumers should limit their intake to no more than 6 ounces of albacore tuna per week.

turning into methylmercury, and the fish in the bay were accumulating this poison in their bodies. Some of the affected families had been eating fish from the bay every day.

PBB and PCB   In 1973, half a ton of **PBB (polybrominated biphenyl)**, a toxic organic compound, was accidentally mixed into some livestock feed that was distributed throughout the state of Michigan. The chemical found its way into millions of animals and then into the people who ate the meat. The seriousness of the accident came to light when dairy farmers reported that their cows were going dry, aborting their calves, and developing abnormal growths on their hooves. Although more than 30,000 cattle, sheep, and swine and more than a million chickens were destroyed, an estimated 97 percent of Michigan's residents had been exposed to PBB. Some of the exposed farm residents suffered nervous system aberrations and liver disorders.

A similar accident occurred in 1979 when **PCB (polychlorinated biphenyls)** contaminated rice oil in Taiwan. Women who had eaten the tainted rice oil gave birth to children with developmental problems. Decades later, young men who were exposed to PCB during gestation have reduced fertility. The interactive effects of PCB and mercury are especially damaging to brain functions such as balance and coordination.[15]

Guidelines for Consumers

How much of a threat do environmental contaminants pose to the food supply? For the most part, the hazards appear to be small. The FDA regulates the presence of contaminants in foods and requires foods with unsafe amounts to be removed from the market. Similarly, health agencies may issue advisories informing consumers about the potential dangers of eating contaminated foods.

Most recently, mercury poisoning has aroused concerns—even at levels one-tenth of those in the Minamata catastrophe. Virtually all fish have at least trace amounts of mercury (on average, 0.12 parts per million). ◆ Fish and other seafood are the main source of dietary mercury.[16] Mercury, PCB, chlordane, dioxins, and DDT are the toxins most responsible for fish contamination, but mercury leads the list by threefold.[17]

Review Figure 19-5 (p. 675) and notice how toxins such as mercury become more concentrated in animals and in people high in the food chain. Because of bioaccumulation, large gamefish at the top of the aquatic food chain ◆ generally have the highest concentrations of mercury (ten times the average). Consumers who enjoy eating these fish should select the smaller, younger ones (within legal limits). Also because of bioaccumulation, the concentrations in fish may be a million times higher than the concentrations in the water itself.

The **EPA** regulates commercial fishing to help ensure that fish destined for consumption in the United States meet safety standards for mercury and other contaminants. Farm-raised fish usually have lower concentrations of mercury than fish caught in the wild. Consequently, most consumers in the United States are not in danger of receiving harmful levels of mercury from fish.

Pregnant and lactating women and young children are most vulnerable because mercury toxicity damages the developing brain.[18] However, they are also likely to benefit from consuming seafood rich in omega-3 fatty acids. To receive the benefits and minimize the risks, pregnant and lactating women and young children can safely consume up to 12 ounces of seafood per week.[19] In addition, they should limit their intake of albacore tuna and avoid eating large predatory fish altogether.◆ Blood levels of mercury in young children and women of child-bearing age are currently below levels of concern.[20]

What about the noncommercial fish a person catches from a local lake, river, or ocean? After all, it's almost impossible to tell whether water is contaminated without sophisticated equipment. Each state monitors its waters and issues advisories to inform the public if chemical contaminants have been found in the local fish. To

◆ For perspective, 1 ppm (part per million) is equivalent to about 1 minute in 2 years or 1 cent in $10,000.

◆ Fish relatively high in mercury:
• Tilefish, swordfish, king mackerel, shark
Fish relatively low in mercury:
• Cod, haddock, pollock, salmon, sole, tilapia
• Most shellfish

◆ Pregnant and lactating women and young children should avoid:
• Tilefish (also called golden snapper or golden bass), swordfish, king mackerel, shark
And limit weekly consumption to:
• 12 oz (cooked or canned) commercial fish and shellfish (such as shrimp, canned light tuna, salmon, pollock, and catfish)
• 6 oz (cooked or canned) "white" albacore tuna

PBB (polybrominated biphenyl) and **PCB (polychlorinated biphenyl):** toxic organic compounds used in pesticides, paints, and flame retardants.

find out whether a fish advisory has been posted in your region, call the local or state environmental health department.

All things considered, fish continue to support a healthy diet, providing valuable protein, omega-3 fatty acids, and minerals. For most adults, the benefits of protecting against heart disease outweigh the risks of consuming seafood regularly. Ideally, consumers would select fish ◆ with high omega-3 fatty acids and low mercury.[21] In addition, they should select a variety of seafood to reduce the risk of exposure to contaminants from a single source.

◆ Fish relatively high in omega-3 fatty acids and low in mercury:
• Salmon, herring, sardines, shad, lake trout, mackerel, whitefish, flounder/sole, pollock

IN SUMMARY

Environmental contamination of foods is a concern, but so far, the hazards appear relatively small. In all cases, two principles apply. First, remain alert to the possibility of contamination of foods, and keep an ear open for public health announcements and advice. Second, eat a variety of foods. Varying food choices is an effective defensive strategy against the accumulation of toxins in the body. Each food eaten dilutes contaminants that may be present in other components of the diet.

Natural Toxicants in Foods

Consumers concerned about food contamination may think that they can eliminate all poisons from their diets by eating only "natural" foods. On the contrary, nature has provided plants with an abundant array of toxicants. A few examples will show how even "natural" foods may contain potentially harmful substances. They also show that although the *potential* for harm exists, *actual* harm rarely occurs.

Poisonous mushrooms are a familiar example of plants that can be harmful when eaten. Few people know, though, that other commonly eaten foods contain substances that can cause illnesses. Cabbage, turnips, mustard greens, kale, brussels sprouts, cauliflower, broccoli, kohlrabi, and radishes contain small quantities of goitrogens—compounds that can enlarge the thyroid gland. Eating exceptionally large amounts of goitrogen-containing vegetables can aggravate a preexisting thyroid problem, but it usually does not initiate one.

Lima beans and fruit seeds such as apricot pits contain cyanogens—inactive compounds that produce the deadly poison cyanide upon activation by a specific plant enzyme. For this reason, many countries restrict commercially grown lima beans to those varieties with the lowest cyanogen contents. As for fruit seeds, they are seldom deliberately eaten. An occasional swallowed seed or two presents no danger, but a couple of dozen seeds can be fatal to a small child. Perhaps the most infamous cyanogen in seeds is laetrile—a compound erroneously represented as a cancer cure. True, laetrile kills cancer, but only at doses that kill the person, too. The combination of cyanide poisoning and lack of medical attention is life-threatening.

The humble potato contains many natural poisons including **solanine,** a powerful narcotic-like substance. The small amounts of solanine normally found in potatoes are harmless, but solanine is toxic and presents a hazard when consumed in large quantities. Physical symptoms of solanine poisoning include headache, vomiting, abdominal pain, diarrhea, and fever; neurological symptoms include apathy, restlessness, drowsiness, confusion, stupor, hallucinations, and visual disturbances. Solanine production increases when potatoes are improperly stored in the light and in either very cold or fairly warm places. Cooking does not destroy solanine, but because most of a potato's solanine is in the green layer that develops just beneath the skin, it can be peeled off, making the potato safe to eat.

solanine (SOH-lah-neen): a poisonous narcotic-like substance present in potato peels and sprouts.

IN SUMMARY

Natural toxicants include the goitrogens in cabbage, cyanogens in lima beans, and solanine in potatoes. These examples of naturally occurring toxicants illustrate two familiar principles. First, any substance can be toxic when consumed in excess. Second, poisons are poisons, whether made by people or by nature. Remember: it is not the source of a chemical that makes it hazardous, but its chemical structure and the quantity consumed.

Pesticides

The use of **pesticides** in agriculture is controversial. They help to ensure the survival of crops, but they leave **residues** in the environment and on some of the foods we eat.

Hazards and Regulation of Pesticides

Ideally, a pesticide destroys the pest and quickly degenerates to nontoxic products without accumulating in the food chain. Then, by the time consumers eat the food, no harmful residues remain. Unfortunately, no such perfect pesticide exists. As new pesticides are developed, government agencies assess their risks and benefits and vigilantly monitor their use.

Hazards of Pesticides Pesticides applied in the field may linger on the foods. Health risks from pesticide exposure are probably small for healthy adults, but children, the elderly, and people with weakened immune systems may be vulnerable to some types of pesticide poisoning. To protect infants and children, government agencies set a **tolerance level** for each pesticide by first identifying foods that children commonly eat in large amounts and then considering the effects of pesticide exposure during each developmental stage.[22]

Regulation of Pesticides Consumers depend on the EPA and the FDA to keep pesticide use within safe limits. These agencies evaluate the risks and benefits of a pesticide's use by asking such questions as: How dangerous is it? How much residue is left on the crop? How much harm does the pesticide do to the environment? How necessary is it? What are the alternatives to its use?

If the pesticide is approved, the EPA establishes a tolerance level for its presence in foods, well below the level at which it could cause any conceivable harm. Tolerance regulations also state the specific crops to which each pesticide can be applied. If a pesticide is misused, growers risk fines, lawsuits, and destruction of their crops.

Once tolerances are set, the FDA enforces them by monitoring foods and livestock feeds for the presence of pesticides. Over the past several decades of testing, the FDA has seldom found residues above tolerance levels, so it appears that pesticides are generally used according to regulations. Minimal pesticide use means lower costs for growers. In addition to costs, many farmers are also concerned about the environment, the quality of their farmland, and a safe food supply. Where violations are found, they are usually due to unusual weather conditions, use of unapproved pesticides, or misuse—for example, application of a particular pesticide to a crop for which it has not been approved.

Pesticides from Other Countries Because other countries may not have the same pesticide regulations as the United States and Canada, imported foods may contain both pesticides that have been banned and permitted pesticides at concentrations higher than are allowed in domestic foods. A loophole in federal regulations allows U.S. companies to manufacture and sell, to other countries, pesticides that are banned in this country. The banned pesticides then return to the United States on imported foods—a circuitous route that concerned consumers have called the

As many as 400 varieties of fruits and vegetables are imported from other countries.

pesticides: chemicals used to control insects, weeds, fungi, and other pests on plants, vegetables, fruits, and animals. Used broadly, the term includes herbicides (to kill weeds), insecticides (to kill insects), and fungicides (to kill fungi).

residues: whatever remains. In the case of pesticides, those amounts that remain on or in foods when people buy and use them.

tolerance level: the maximum amount of a residue permitted in a food when a pesticide is used according to label directions.

"circle of poison." Federal inspectors sample imported foods and refuse entry if they are found to contain illegal pesticide residues. The United States, Mexico, and Canada work together to establish a pesticide policy for all of North America.

Monitoring Pesticides

The FDA collects and analyzes samples of both domestic and imported foods. If the agency finds samples in violation of regulations, it can seize the products or order them destroyed. The FDA may also invoke a **certification** requirement that forces manufacturers, at their own expense, to have their foods periodically inspected and certified safe by an independent testing agency. Individual states also scan for pesticides (as well as for industrial chemicals) and provide information to the FDA.

Food in the Fields In addition to its ongoing surveillance, the FDA conducts selective surveys to determine the presence of particular pesticides in specific crops. For example, one year the agency searched for aldicarb in potatoes, captan in cherries, and diaminozide (the chemical name for Alar) in apples, among others. The actions taken that year required several certifications. Thus one shipper in Australia had to certify apples; one in Canada, peppers; one in Costa Rica, chayotes. All grapes from Mexico had to be certified and so did all mangoes from anywhere. This shows, incidentally, how many foods come from abroad—not only those already named, but hundreds more—and that the FDA monitors them as carefully as it does the domestic food supply.

Food on the Plate In addition to monitoring foods in the field for pesticides, the FDA also monitors people's actual intakes. The agency conducts the Total Diet Study (sometimes called the "Market Basket Survey") to estimate the dietary intakes of pesticide residues by eight age and gender groups from infants to senior citizens. Four times a year, FDA surveyors buy more than 200 foods from U.S. grocery stores, each time in several cities. They prepare the foods table ready and then analyze them not only for pesticides, but also for essential minerals, industrial chemicals, heavy metals, and radioactive materials. In all, the survey reports on over 10,000 samples a year, and recently more than half the samples have been imported foods. Most heavily sampled are fresh vegetables, fruits, and dairy products.

The Total Diet Study provides a direct estimate of the amounts of pesticide residues that remain in foods as they are usually eaten—after they have been washed, peeled, and cooked. The FDA finds the intake of almost all pesticides to be less than 1 percent of the amount considered acceptable. The amount considered acceptable is "the daily intake of a chemical which, if ingested over a lifetime, appears to be without appreciable risk." ◆ All in all, these findings confirm the safety of the U.S. food supply.

Consumer Concerns

Despite these reassuring reports, consumers still worry that food monitoring may not be adequate. For one thing, manufacturers develop new pesticides all the time. For another, as described earlier, other countries use pesticides that are illegal for use here. For still another, although the regulations may protect U.S. foods adequately, they may not necessarily protect the environment or the people who work in the fields. Concerns over poisoning of soil, waterways, wildlife, and workers may well be valid.

The FDA does not sample *all* food shipments or test for *all* pesticides in each sample. The FDA is a *monitoring* agency, and as such, it cannot, nor can it be expected to, guarantee 100 percent safety in the food supply. Instead, it sets standards so that substances do not become a hazard, checks enough samples to adequately assess average food safety, and acts promptly when problems or suspicions arise.

Minimizing Risks Whether consumers ingest pesticide residues depends on a number of factors. How much of a given food does the consumer eat? What pesticide was

Washing fresh fruits and vegetables removes most, if not all, of the pesticide residues that might have been present.

◆ *Without appreciable risk* means "practical certainty that injury will not result even after a lifetime of exposure."

certification: the process in which a private laboratory inspects shipments of a product for selected chemicals and then, if the product is free of violative levels of those chemicals, issues a guarantee to that effect.

People can grow organic crops when their gardens or farms are relatively small.

◆ Organic foods that have met USDA standards may use this seal on their labels.

organic: in agriculture, crops grown and processed according to USDA regulations defining the use of fertilizers, herbicides, insecticides, fungicides, preservatives, and other chemical ingredients.

used on it? How much was used? How long ago was the food last sprayed? Did environmental conditions promote pest growth or pesticide breakdown? How well was the produce washed? Was it peeled or cooked? With so many factors, consumers cannot know for sure whether pesticide residues remain on foods, but they can minimize their risks by following the guidelines offered in the "How to" feature below. The food supply is protected well enough that consumers who take these precautions can feel secure that the foods they eat are safe.

Alternatives to Pesticides The use of pesticides has helped to generate higher crop yields that feed the world and protect against diseases transmitted by insects. Still, many consumers are leery. To feed a nation while using fewer pesticides requires creative farming methods. Highlight 19 describes how scientists can genetically alter plants to enhance their production of natural pesticides, and Highlight 20 presents alternative, or sustainable, agriculture methods. These methods include such practices as rotating crops, releasing organisms into fields to destroy pests, and planting nonfood crops nearby to kill pests or attract them away from the food crops. For example, releasing sterile male fruit flies into orchards helps to curb the population growth of these pests; some flowers, such as marigolds, release natural insecticides and are often planted near crops such as tomatoes. Such alternative farming methods are more labor-intensive and may produce smaller yields than conventional methods, at least initially. Over time, though, by eliminating expensive pesticides, fertilizers, and fuels, these alternatives may actually cut costs more than they cut yields.

Organically Grown Crops Alternative methods are especially useful for farmers who want to produce and market **organic** crops that are grown and processed according to USDA regulations defining the use of synthetic fertilizers, herbicides, insecticides, fungicides, preservatives, and other chemical ingredients. ◆ Similarly, meat, poultry, eggs, and dairy products may be called organic if the livestock has been raised according to USDA regulations defining the grazing conditions and the use of organic feed, hormones, and antibiotics. In addition, producers may *not* claim products are organic if they have been irradiated, genetically engineered, or grown with fertilizer made from sewer sludge. Figure 19-6 shows examples of food labels for products using organic ingredients.

Most organic foods are marked as such, but consumers can also learn how fruits and vegetables were grown by reading the product code on produce stickers. Codes for conventionally grown produce are four digits. Regular bananas, for example, have the code 4011. Codes for organic produce are five digits and begin with 9.

HOW TO Prepare Foods to Minimize Pesticide Residues

To remove or reduce any pesticide residues from foods:

- Trim the fat from meat, and remove the skin from poultry and fish; discard fats and oils in broths and pan drippings. (Pesticide residues concentrate in the animal's fat.)
- Select fruits and vegetables that do not have holes.
- Wash fresh produce in warm running water. Use a scrub brush, and rinse thoroughly.
- Use a knife to peel an orange or grapefruit; do not bite into the peel.
- Discard the outer leaves of leafy vegetables such as cabbage and lettuce.

- Peel waxed fruits and vegetables; waxes don't wash off and can seal in pesticide residues.
- Peel vegetables such as carrots and fruits such as apples when appropriate. (Peeling removes pesticides that remain in or on the peel, but also removes fibers, vitamins, and minerals.)
- Eat a variety of foods to minimize exposure to any one pesticide.
- Consider buying certified organic foods.

Information is available from the EPA's National Pesticide Hotline (800 858-PEST).

FIGURE 19-6 Food Labels for Organic Products

United States Department of Agriculture

Foods made with 100 percent organic ingredients may claim "100% organic" and use the seal.

Foods made with at least 95 percent organic ingredients may claim "organic" and use the seal.

Foods made with at least 70 percent organic ingredients may list up to three of those ingredients on the front panel.

Foods made with less than 70 percent organic ingredients may list them on the side panel, but cannot make any claims on the front.

(Thus the product code for organic bananas is 94011.) Codes for genetically modified produce are also five digits and begin with 8. (Genetically modified bananas are given the product code 84011.)

Implied in the marketing of *organic foods* is that organic products are safer or healthier for consumers than those grown using other methods, which may not be the case. Using unprocessed animal manure as an organic fertilizer, for example, may transmit bacteria, such as *E. coli,* to human beings. Both organic and conventional methods may have advantages and disadvantages, and consumers must remain informed.

Pesticide residues in organic foods are substantially lower than in conventionally grown foods.[23] As mentioned earlier, infants and children may be particularly vulnerable to the effects of pesticides. To determine whether organic foods might reduce their exposure to pesticides, children were given a five-day diet composed entirely of organic foods.[24] Before, during, and after the organic diet period, researchers tested the children's urine for chemicals known to arise from the ingestion of common pesticides. The results were dramatic and immediate: the concentrations of chemicals fell and remained low during the organic diet and increased again when the conventional diet resumed.

Are organic foods nutritionally superior to conventional foods? Any nutrient differences reported have been within the range that normally occurs in crops. Limited research suggests foods produced organically have increased amounts of some phytochemicals.[25]

© Polara Studios Inc.

Many consumers are willing to pay a little more for organic produce.

IN SUMMARY

Pesticides can safely improve crop yields when used according to regulations, but they can also be hazardous when used inappropriately. The FDA tests both domestic and imported foods for pesticide residues in the fields and in market basket surveys of foods prepared table ready. Consumers can minimize their ingestion of pesticide residues on foods by following the suggestions in the "How to" on p. 680. Alternative farming methods may allow farmers to grow crops with few or no pesticides.

Without additives, bread would quickly get moldy, and salad dressing would go rancid.

Food Additives

Additives confer many benefits on foods. Some reduce the risk of foodborne illness (for example, nitrites used in curing meat prevent poisoning from the botulinum toxin). Others enhance nutrient quality (as in vitamin D–fortified milk). Most additives are **preservatives** that help prevent spoilage during the time it takes to deliver foods long distances to grocery stores and then to kitchens. Some additives simply make foods look and taste good.

Intentional additives are put into foods on purpose, whereas indirect additives may get in unintentionally before or during processing. This discussion begins with the regulations that govern additives, then presents intentional additives class by class, and finally goes on to say a word about the indirect additives.

Regulations Governing Additives

The FDA's concern with additives hinges primarily on their safety. To receive permission to use a new additive in food products, a manufacturer must satisfy the FDA that the additive is:

- Effective (it does what it is supposed to do)
- Detectable and measurable in the final food product
- Safe (when fed in large doses to animals under strictly controlled conditions, it causes no cancer, birth defects, or other injury)

On approving an additive's use, the FDA writes a regulation stating in what amounts and in what foods the additive may be used. No additive receives permanent approval, and all must undergo periodic review.

The GRAS List   Many familiar substances are exempted from complying with the FDA's approval procedure because they are **generally recognized as safe (GRAS),** based either on their extensive, long-term use in foods or on current scientific evidence. Several hundred substances are on the GRAS list, including such items as salt, sugar, caffeine, and many spices. Whenever substantial scientific evidence or public outcry has questioned the safety of any substance on the GRAS list, it has been reevaluated. If a legitimate question has been raised about a substance, it has been removed or reclassified. Meanwhile, the entire GRAS list is subjected to ongoing review.

The Delaney Clause   One risk that the U.S. law on additives refuses to tolerate at any level is the risk of cancer. To remain on the GRAS list, an additive must not have been found to be a carcinogen in any test on animals or human beings. The **Delaney Clause** (the part of the law that states this criterion) is uncompromising in addressing carcinogens in foods and drugs; in fact, it has been under fire for many years for being too strict and inflexible.

The Delaney Clause is best understood as a product of a different historical era. It was adopted decades ago at a time when scientists knew less about the relationships between carcinogens and cancer development. At that time, most substances were detectable in foods only in relatively large amounts, such as parts per thousand. Today, scientific understanding of cancer has progressed, and technology has advanced so that carcinogens in foods can be detected even when they are present only in parts per billion or even per trillion. ◆ Earlier, "zero risk" may have seemed attainable, but today we know it is not: all substances, no matter how pure, can be shown to be contaminated at some level with one carcinogen or another. For these reasons, the FDA prefers to deem additives (and pesticides and other contaminants) safe if lifetime use presents no more than a one-in-a-million risk of cancer to human beings. Thus, instead of the "zero-risk" policy of the Delaney Clause, the FDA uses a "negligible-risk" standard, sometimes referred to as a *de minimis rule.* ◆

◆ For perspective, one part per trillion is equivalent to about one grain of sugar in an Olympic-size swimming pool; or 1 second in 32,000 years; or one hair on 10 million heads, assuming none are bald.

◆ The *de minimis* rule defines risk as a cancer rate of less than one cancer per million people exposed to a contaminant over a 70-year lifetime.

additives: substances not normally consumed as foods but added to food either intentionally or by accident.

preservatives: antimicrobial agents, antioxidants, and other additives that retard spoilage or maintain desired qualities, such as softness in baked goods.

generally recognized as safe (GRAS): food additives that have long been in use and are believed safe. First established by the FDA in 1958, the GRAS list is subject to revision as new facts become known.

Delaney Clause: a clause in the Food Additive Amendment to the Food, Drug, and Cosmetic Act that states that no substance that is known to cause cancer in animals or human beings at any dose level shall be added to foods.

Margin of Safety Whatever risk level is permitted, actual risks must be determined by experiments. To determine risks posed by an additive, researchers feed test animals the additive at several concentrations throughout their lives. The additive is then permitted in foods in amounts 100 times *below* the lowest level that is found to cause any harmful effect, that is, at a 1/100 **margin of safety.** In many foods, *naturally* occurring substances occur with narrower margins of safety. Even nutrients pose risks at dose levels above those recommended and normally consumed: for young adults, the recommendation for vitamin D is only 1/10 of the Upper Level. People consume common table salt daily in amounts only three to five times less than those that pose a hazard.

Risks versus Benefits Of course, additives would not be added to foods if they only presented risks. Additives are in foods because they offer benefits that outweigh the risks they present, or make the risks worth taking. In the case of color additives that only enhance the appearance of foods but do not improve their health value or safety, no amount of risk may be deemed worth taking. In contrast, the FDA finds that it is worth taking the small risks associated with the use of nitrites on meat products, for example, because nitrites inhibit the formation of the deadly botulinum toxin. The choice involves a compromise between the risks of using additives and the risks of doing without them.

It is the manufacturers' responsibility to use only the amounts of additives that are necessary to achieve the needed effect, and no more. The FDA also requires that additives *not* be used:

- To disguise faulty or inferior products
- To deceive the consumer
- When they significantly destroy nutrients
- When their effects can be achieved by economical, sound manufacturing processes

Intentional Food Additives

Intentional food additives are added to foods to give them some desirable characteristic: resistance to spoilage, color, flavor, texture, stability, or nutritional value. Table 19-3 presents an overview of additives, and the next sections describe additives people most often ask about.

Antimicrobial Agents Foods can go bad in two ways. One way is relatively harmless: by losing their flavor and attractiveness. (Additives to prevent this kind

margin of safety: when speaking of food additives, a zone between the concentration normally used and that at which a hazard exists. For common table salt, for example, the margin of safety is 1/5 (five times the amount normally used would be hazardous).

intentional food additives: additives intentionally added to foods, such as nutrients, colors, and preservatives.

TABLE 19-3 Intentional Food Additives

Food Additive	Purpose	Common Examples
Antimicrobial agents	Prevent microorganisms from growing	Salt, sugar, nitrites and nitrates (such as sodium nitrate)
Antioxidants	Delay or prevent rancidity of fats and other damage to foods caused by oxygen	Vitamin C (erythorbic acid, sodium ascorbate), vitamin E (tocopherol), sulfites, BHA and BHT
Colors	Enhance appearance	Artificial: indigotine, erythrosine, tartrazine Natural: annatto (yellow), caramel (yellowish brown), carotenoids (yellowish orange), dehydrated beets (reddish brown), grape skins (red, green)
Flavors	Enhance taste	Salt, sugar, spices, artificial sweeteners, MSG
Emulsifiers and gums	Thicken, stabilize, or otherwise improve the consistency	Emulsifiers: lecithin, alginates, mono- and diglycerides Gums: agar, alginates, carrageenan, guar, locust bean, psyllium, pectin, xanthan gum, gum arabic, cellulose derivatives
Nutrients (vitamins and minerals)	Improve the nutritive value	Thiamin, niacin, riboflavin, folate, iron (in grain products); iodine (in salt); vitamins A and D (in milk); vitamin C and calcium (in fruit drinks); vitamin B_{12} (in vegetarian foods)

Both salt and sugar act as preservatives by withdrawing water from food; microbes cannot grow without water.

of spoilage include antioxidants, discussed later.) The other way is by becoming contaminated with microbes that cause foodborne illnesses, a hazard that justifies the use of antimicrobial agents.

The most widely used antimicrobial agents are ordinary salt and sugar. Salt has been used throughout history to preserve meat and fish; sugar serves the same purpose in canned and frozen fruits and in jams and jellies. Both exert their protective effect primarily by capturing water and making it unavailable to microbes.

Other antimicrobial agents, the **nitrites,** are added to foods for three main purposes: to preserve color, especially the pink color of hot dogs and other cured meats; to enhance flavor by inhibiting rancidity, especially in cured meats and poultry; and to protect against bacterial growth. In amounts smaller than those needed to confer color, nitrites prevent the growth of the bacteria that produce the deadly botulinum toxin.

Nitrites clearly serve a useful purpose, but their use has been controversial. In the human body, nitrites can be converted to **nitrosamines.** At nitrite levels higher than those used in food products, nitrosamine formation causes cancer in animals. The food industry uses the minimal amount of nitrites necessary to achieve results, and nitrosamine formation has not been shown to cause cancer in human beings.

Detectable amounts of nitrosamine-related compounds are found in malt beverages (beer) and cured meats (primarily bacon). Yet even the quantities found in beer and bacon hardly make a difference in a person's overall exposure to nitrosamine-related compounds. An average cigarette smoker inhales 100 times the nitrosamines that the average bacon eater ingests. A beer drinker ingests twice as much as the bacon eater, but even so, nitrosamine exposure from new car interiors and cosmetics is higher than this.

Antioxidants Another way food can go bad is by exposure to oxygen (oxidation). Often, these changes involve no hazard to health, but they damage the food's appearance, flavor, and nutritional quality. Oxidation is easy to detect when sliced apples or potatoes turn brown or when oil goes rancid. Antioxidants prevent these reactions. Among the antioxidants approved for use in foods are vitamin C (ascorbate) and vitamin E (tocopherol).

Another group of antioxidants, the **sulfites,** ◆ cost less than the vitamins. Sulfites prevent oxidation in many processed foods, alcoholic beverages (especially wine), and drugs. Because some people experience adverse reactions, the FDA prohibits sulfite use on foods intended to be consumed raw, with the exception of grapes, and requires foods and drugs that contain sulfite additives to declare it on their labels. For most people, sulfites pose no hazard in the amounts used in products, but there is one more consideration—sulfites destroy the B vitamin thiamin. For this reason, the FDA prohibits their use in foods that are important sources of the vitamin, such as enriched grain products.

Two other antioxidants in wide use are **BHA** and **BHT,** which prevent rancidity in baked goods and snack foods.* Several tests have shown that animals fed large amounts of BHT develop *less* cancer when exposed to carcinogens and live *longer* than controls. Apparently, BHT protects against cancer through its antioxidant effect, which is similar to that of the antioxidant nutrients. The amount of BHT ingested daily from the U.S. diet, however, contributes little to the body's antioxidant defense system. A caution: at intakes higher than those that protect against cancer, BHT has *produced* cancer. Vitamins E and C remain the most important dietary antioxidants to strengthen defenses against cancer. (See Highlight 11 for a full discussion.)

Colors Only a few artificial colors remain on the FDA's list of additives approved for use in foods—a highly select group that has survived considerable testing. Colors derived from the natural pigments of plants must also meet standards of purity and safety. Examples of natural pigments commonly used by the food industry are the

◆ Sulfites appear on food labels as:
• Sulfur dioxide
• Sodium sulfite
• Sodium bisulfite
• Potassium bisulfite
• Sodium metabisulfite
• Potassium metabisulfite

nitrites (NYE-trites): salts added to food to prevent botulism. One example is sodium nitrite, which is used to preserve meats.

nitrosamines (nye-TROHS-uh-meens): derivatives of nitrites that may be formed in the stomach when nitrites combine with amines. Nitrosamines are carcinogenic in animals.

sulfites: salts containing sulfur that are added to foods to prevent spoilage.

BHA and **BHT:** preservatives commonly used to slow the development of off-flavors, odors, and color changes caused by oxidation.

---

* BHA is butylated hydroxyanisole; BHT is butylated hydroxytoluene.

caramel that tints cola beverages and baked goods and the carotenoids that color margarine, cheeses, and pastas. Carotenoids are also added to the feed for farm-raised salmon, which deepens the pink flesh color.

Artificial Flavors and Flavor Enhancers Natural flavors, artificial flavors, and flavor enhancers are the largest single group of food additives. Many foods taste wonderful because manufacturers have added the natural flavors of spices, herbs, essential oils, fruits, and fruit juices. Some spices, notably those used in Mediterranean cooking, provide antioxidant protection as well as flavors. Often, natural flavors are used in combination with artificial flavors. The sugar alternatives discussed in Highlight 4 are among the most widely used artificial flavor additives.

One of the best-known flavor enhancers is **monosodium glutamate**, or **MSG**—a sodium salt of the amino acid glutamic acid. MSG is used widely in a number of foods, especially Asian foods, canned vegetables, soups, and processed meats. Besides enhancing the well-known sweet, salty, bitter, and sour tastes, MSG itself may possess a pleasant flavor. Adverse reactions to MSG—known as the **MSG symptom complex**—may occur in people with asthma and in sensitive individuals who consume large amounts of MSG, especially on an empty stomach. Otherwise, MSG is considered safe for adults. It is not allowed in foods designed for infants, however. Food labels require ingredient lists to itemize all additives, including MSG.

Texture and Stability Some additives help to maintain a desirable consistency in foods. Emulsifiers keep mayonnaise stable, control crystallization in syrups, keep spices dispersed in salad dressings, and allow powdered coffee creamer to dissolve easily. Gums are added to thicken foods and help form gels. Yeast may be added to provide leavening, and bicarbonates and acids may be used to control acidity.

Nutrient Additives As mentioned earlier, manufacturers sometimes add nutrients to fortify or maintain the nutritional quality of foods. Included among nutrient additives are the five nutrients added to grains (thiamin, riboflavin, niacin, folate, and iron), the iodine added to salt, the vitamins A and D added to milk, and the nutrients added to fortified breakfast cereals. A nutrient-poor food with nutrients added may appear to be nutrient-rich, but it is rich only in those nutrients chosen for addition. Appropriate uses of nutrient additives are to:

- Correct dietary deficiencies known to result in diseases
- Restore nutrients to levels found in the food before storage, handling, and processing
- Balance the vitamin, mineral, and protein contents of a food in proportion to the energy content
- Correct nutritional inferiority in a food that replaces a more nutritious traditional food

As mentioned earlier, nutrients are sometimes also added for other purposes. For example, vitamins C and E are used for their antioxidant properties, and beta-carotene and other carotenoids are sometimes used for color.

Indirect Food Additives

Indirect or **incidental additives** find their way into foods during harvesting, production, processing, storage, or packaging. Incidental additives may include tiny bits of plastic, glass, paper, tin, and other substances from packages as well as chemicals from processing, such as the solvent used to decaffeinate coffee. The following paragraphs discuss six different types of indirect additives that sometimes make headline news.

Acrylamide Raw potatoes don't have it, but French fries do—acrylamide, a compound that forms when carbohydrate-rich foods ◆ are cooked at high temperatures.[26] Apparently, acrylamide has been in foods ever since we started baking,

Color additives not only make foods attractive, but they identify flavors as well. Everyone agrees that yellow jellybeans should taste lemony and black ones should taste like licorice.

◆ Common foods containing acrylamide:
- French fries
- Potato chips
- Breakfast cereals
- Cookies

monosodium glutamate (MSG): a sodium salt of the amino acid glutamic acid commonly used as a flavor enhancer. The FDA classifies MSG as a "generally recognized as safe" ingredient.

MSG symptom complex: an acute, temporary intolerance reaction that may occur after the ingestion of the additive MSG (monosodium glutamate). Symptoms include burning sensations, chest and facial flushing and pain, and throbbing headaches.

indirect or **incidental additives:** substances that can get into food as a result of contact during growing, processing, packaging, storing, cooking, or some other stage before the foods are consumed; sometimes called **accidental additives.**

frying, and roasting, but only recently has its presence been analyzed.[27] At high doses, acrylamide causes cancer and nerve damage in animals. As such, scientists classify it as both a carcinogen and a genotoxicant, ◆ but quantities commonly found in foods appear to be well below the amounts that cause such damage. The FDA is currently investigating how acrylamide is formed in foods, how its formation can be limited, and whether its presence is harmful.[28]

◆ A *carcinogen* is a substance that causes cancer, and a *genotoxicant* is a substance that mutates or damages genetic material.

Microwave Packaging Some microwave products are sold in "active packaging" that helps to cook the food; for example, pizzas are often heated on a metalized film laminated to paperboard. This film absorbs the microwave energy in the oven and reaches temperatures as high as 500°F. At such temperatures, packaging components migrate into the food. For this reason, manufacturers must perform specific tests to determine whether materials are migrating into foods. If they are, their safety must be confirmed by strict procedures similar to those governing intentional additives.

Most microwave products are sold in "passive packaging" that is transparent to microwaves and simply holds the food as it cooks. These containers don't get much hotter than the foods, but materials still migrate at high temperatures. Consumers should not reuse these containers in the microwave oven. Instead they should use only glass or ceramic containers ◆ designed for microwave ovens and avoid using disposable styrofoam or plastic containers such as those used for carryout or margarine. Plastic wrap has not been approved for use in microwave ovens, but if used, it should not touch the food.

◆ Quick test for using glass or ceramic containers in a microwave oven: Microwave the empty container for 1 min.
  • If it's warm, it's unsafe for the microwave.
  • If it's lukewarm, it's safe for short-term reheating in the microwave.
  • If it's cool, it's safe for long-term cooking in the microwave.

Dioxins Coffee filters, milk cartons, paper plates, and frozen food packages, if made from bleached paper, can contaminate foods with minute quantities of **dioxins**—compounds formed during chlorine treatment of wood pulp during paper manufacture. Dioxin contamination of foods from such products appears only in trace quantities—in the parts-per-trillion range (recall, for perspective, that one part per trillion is equal to 1 second in 32,000 years). Such levels appear to present no health risks to people, but scientists recognize that dioxins are extremely toxic and are likely to cause cancer in humans.[29] Accordingly, the paper industry has reduced its use of chlorine to cut dioxin exposure; in the meantime, the FDA has concluded that drinking milk from bleached-paper cartons presents no health hazard. Contrary to e-mail warnings, plastics do not yield dioxins when broken down and dioxins are not released from plastic wrap when microwaved.[30] Human exposure to dioxins comes primarily from foods such as beef, milk products, pork, fish, and shellfish.[31]

Decaffeinated Coffee Many consumers have tried to eliminate caffeine from their diets by selecting decaffeinated coffee. To remove caffeine from coffee beans, manufacturers often use methylene chloride in a process that leaves traces of the chemical in the final product. The FDA estimates that the average cup of coffee decaffeinated this way contains about 0.1 part per million of methylene chloride, which seems to pose no significant threat. A person drinking decaffeinated coffee containing 100 times as much methylene chloride every day for a lifetime has a one-in-a-million chance of developing cancer from it. People are exposed to much more methylene chloride from other sources such as hair sprays and paint stripping solutions. Still, some consumers prefer either to return to caffeine or to select coffee decaffeinated in another way, perhaps by steam. Unfortunately, manufacturers are not required to state on their labels the type of decaffeination process used in their products. Many labels provide consumer-information telephone numbers for those who have such questions.

dioxins (dye-OCK-sins): a class of chemical pollutants created as by-products of chemical manufacturing, incineration, chlorine bleaching of paper pulp, and other industrial processes. Dioxins persist in the environment and accumulate in the food chain.

bovine growth hormone (BGH): a hormone produced naturally in the pituitary gland of a cow that promotes growth and milk production; now produced for agricultural use by bacteria.
  • **bovine** = of cattle

Hormones Hormones are a unique type of incidental additive in that their use is intentional, but their presence in the final food product is not. The FDA has approved about a dozen hormones for use in food-producing animals, and the USDA has established limits for residues allowed in meat products.

Some ranchers in the United States treat cattle with **bovine growth hormone (BGH).** Hormone-treated animals produce leaner meats, and dairy cows produce more milk. All cows make BGH naturally. Scientists can also genetically alter bacteria to produce BGH, which allows laboratories to harvest huge quantities of the hormone and sell it to farmers as a drug. Genetic engineering practices such as this have aroused some consumer concerns (see Highlight 19).

Indeed, traces of BGH do remain in the meat and milk of both hormone-treated and untreated cows. BGH residues have not been tested for safety in human beings because residues of the natural hormone have always been present in milk and meat, and the amount found in treated cows is within the range that can occur naturally. Furthermore, BGH, being a peptide hormone, is denatured by the heat used in processing milk and cooking meat, and it is also digested by enzymes in the GI tract. If any BGH were to enter the bloodstream, it would have no effect because the chemical structures of animal growth hormones differ from those in human beings. Therefore, BGH does not stimulate receptors for *human* growth hormone. According to the National Institutes of Health, "As currently used in the United States, meat and milk from treated cows are as safe as those from untreated cows." Whether hormones that have passed through the animals into feces and then contaminated the soil and water interfere with plants or animals in the environment remains controversial.[32]

Antibiotics Like hormones, antibiotics are also intentionally given to livestock, and residues may remain in the meats and milks. Consequently, people consuming these foods receive tiny doses of antibiotics regularly, and those with sensitivity to antibiotics may suffer allergic reactions.[33] To minimize drug residues in foods, the FDA requires a specified time between the time of medication and the time of slaughter to allow for drug metabolism and excretion.

Of greater concern to the public's health is the development of antibiotic resistance, which occurs when antibiotics are overused. Physicians and veterinarians use an estimated 5 million pounds of antibiotics to treat infections in people and animals, but farmers add five times as much to livestock feed to enhance growth. Not surprisingly, meat from these animals contains resistant bacteria. Such indiscriminate use of antibiotics can be catastrophic to the treatment of disease in human beings. Antibiotics are less effective in treating people who are infected with resistant bacteria. The FDA continues to monitor the use of antibiotics in the food industry with the goal of ensuring that antibiotics remain effective in treating human disease.

IN SUMMARY

On the whole, the benefits of food additives seem to justify the risks associated with their use. The FDA regulates the use of the following intentional additives: antimicrobial agents (such as nitrites) to prevent microbial spoilage; antioxidants (such as vitamins C and E, sulfites, and BHA and BHT) to prevent oxidative changes; colors (such as tartrazine) and flavor enhancers (such as MSG) to appeal to senses; and nutrients (such as iodine in salt) to enrich or fortify foods. Incidental additives sometimes get into foods during processing, but rarely present a hazard, although some processes such as treating livestock with hormones and antibiotics raise consumer concerns.

Consumer Concerns about Water

Foods are not alone in transmitting diseases; water is guilty, too.[34] In fact, *Cryptosporidium* and *Cyclospora*, commonly found in fresh fruits and vegetables, and *Vibrio vulnificus,* found in raw oysters, are commonly transmitted through contaminated water. In addition to microorganisms, water may contain many of the same impurities that foods do: environmental contaminants, pesticides, and additives such as chlorine used to kill pathogenic microorganisms and fluoride used to protect against dental caries. A glass of "water" is more than just H_2O. This discussion examines

◆ Water that is suitable for drinking is called **potable** (POT-ah-bul). Only 1% of all the earth's water is potable.

the sources of drinking water, ◆ harmful contaminants, and ways to ensure water safety.

Sources of Drinking Water

Drinking water comes from two sources—surface water and groundwater. Each source supplies water for about half of the population.

Most major cities obtain their drinking water from surface water—the water in lakes, rivers, and reservoirs. Surface water is readily contaminated because it is directly exposed to acid rain, runoff from highways and urban areas, pesticide runoff from agricultural areas, and industrial wastes that are dumped directly into it. Surface water contamination is reversible, however, because fresh rain constantly replaces the water. It is also cleansed to some degree by aeration, sunlight, and plants and microorganisms that live in it.

Groundwater is the water in underground aquifers—rock formations that are saturated with and yield usable water. People who live in rural areas rely mostly on groundwater pumped up from private wells. Groundwater is contaminated more slowly than surface water, but also more permanently. Contaminants deposited on the ground migrate slowly through the soil before reaching groundwater. Once there, the contaminants break down less rapidly than in surface water due to the lack of aeration, sunlight, and aerobic microorganisms. The slow replacement of groundwater also helps contaminants remain for a long time. Groundwater is especially susceptible to contamination from hazardous waste sites, dumps and landfills, underground tanks storing gasoline and other chemicals, and improperly discarded household chemicals and solvents.

Water Systems and Regulations

Public water systems treat water to remove contaminants that have been detected above acceptable levels. During treatment, a disinfectant (usually, chlorine) is added to kill bacteria. The addition of chlorine to public water is an important public health measure that appears to offer great benefits and small risks. On the one hand, chlorinated water has eliminated such water-borne diseases as typhoid fever, which once ravaged communities, killing thousands of people. On the other hand, it has been associated with a slight increase in bladder and rectal cancers and with contamination of the environment with the toxic by-product dioxin. The EPA is responsible for ensuring that public water systems meet minimum standards for protecting the public health.*

Even safe water may have characteristics that some consumers find unpleasant. Most of these problems reflect the mineral content of the water. For example, manganese and copper give water a metallic taste, and sulfur produces a "rotten egg" odor. Iron leaves a rusty brown stain on plumbing fixtures and laundry. Calcium and magnesium (commonly found in "hard water") build up in coffeemakers and hot water heaters. Similarly, soap is not easily rinsed away in hard water, leaving bathtubs and laundry looking dingy. For these and other reasons, some consumers have adopted alternatives to the public water system.

Home Water Treatments To ease concerns about the quality of drinking water, some people purchase home water-treatment systems. Because the EPA does not certify or endorse these water-treatment systems, consumers must shop carefully. Manufacturers offer a variety of units for removing contaminants from drinking water. None of them removes all contaminants, and each has its own advantages and disadvantages. Choosing the right treatment unit depends on the kinds of contaminants in the water. For example, activated carbon filters are particularly effective in removing chlorine, heavy metals such as mercury, and organic contaminants from

Clean rivers represent irreplaceable water resources.

© PhotoDisc/Getty Images

---
* The EPA's safe drinking water hotline: (800) 426-4791.

sediment; reverse osmosis, which forces pressurized water across a membrane, flushes out sodium, arsenic, and some microorganisms such as *Giardia;* and distillation systems, which boil water and condense the steam to water, remove contaminants such as lead and kill microorganisms in the process. Therefore, before purchasing a home water-treatment unit, a consumer must first determine the quality of the water. In some cases, a state or county health department will test water samples or can refer the consumer to a certified laboratory.

Bottled Water Despite the higher cost, many people turn to bottled water as an alternative to tap water. The average consumer drinks more than 20 gallons of bottled water a year. Bottled water is classified as a food, so it is regulated nationwide by the FDA and locally by state health and environmental agencies. The FDA has established quality and safety standards for bottled drinking waters compatible with those set by the EPA for public water systems. In addition, all bottled waters must be processed, packaged, and labeled in accordance with FDA regulations. Its quality varies among brands because of variations in the source water used and company practices.

Labels on bottled water must identify the water's source. Approximately 75 percent of bottled waters derive from protected groundwater (from springs or wells) that has been disinfected with ozone rather than chlorine. Ozone kills microorganisms, then disintegrates spontaneously into water and oxygen, leaving behind no toxic by-products. Other bottled waters derive from municipal tap water that has been treated by carbon filtration to remove chlorine and inorganic compounds. Bottled waters may also be treated by reverse osmosis or ion exchange to remove inorganic compounds. Alternatively, the water may be distilled or deionized to remove dissolved solids. Most bottled waters do not contain fluoride; consequently, they do not provide the tooth protection of fluoridated water from community public water systems.

Despite government regulations, some contamination has been detected in some bottled waters. Although the amounts of most contaminants found in bottled waters are probably insignificant, consumers should be aware that bottled water is not always purer than the water from their taps. As a safeguard, the FDA recommends that bottled water be handled like other foods and be refrigerated after opening.

Protection of drinking water is the subject of an ongoing battle between environmentalists and industry. It may soon become a source of conflict between the world's nations as the population continues to grow and the renewable water supply remains constant. Estimates are that within the next 50 years, half of the world's people will not have enough clean water to meet their needs. To avert this potential calamity, we must take active steps to conserve water, clean polluted water, desalinate seawater, and curb population growth. The "How to" on the next page describes how to disinfect bacterially contaminated water.

IN SUMMARY

Like foods, water may contain infectious microorganisms, environmental contaminants, pesticide residues, and additives. The EPA monitors the safety of the public water system, but many consumers choose home water-treatment systems or bottled water instead of tap water.

As this chapter said at the start, supplying food safely to hundreds of millions of people is an incredible challenge—one that is met, for the most part, with incredible efficiency. The following chapter describes a contrasting situation—that of the food supply not reaching the people.

HOW TO Disinfect Water

In an extreme emergency, when safe water is unavailable, the EPA advises disinfecting water for drinking, cooking, and brushing teeth. Well water is safest, but lake or stream water may be used. Clear water is most easily treated; filter cloudy or discolored water through several layers of clean cloth or a coffee filter before disinfecting.

The preferred method of disinfecting water is to boil it vigorously for at least one minute to kill *all* disease-causing organisms. If boiling is not possible, *most* disease-causing microorganisms can be killed using chlorine or iodine disinfecting tablets available from drugstores and sporting good stores. Follow label directions.

Alternatively, use chlorine-containing laundry bleach and follow the directions on the bottle. If there are no directions, mix 5 drops of regular (not concentrated, scented, or color-safe) bleach with each quart of clear water. If water is cloudy or colored, double the amount. Let water stand for at least 30 minutes before using it. Properly treated water smells slightly of chlorine; if no chlorine odor is present, repeat the dosage. To remove the odor, pour water back and forth between clean containers to aerate it. Iodine tincture, a common first aid antiseptic for wounds, kills *some* disease-causing organisms, but it is less effective than chlorine. Add 5 drops of 2 percent iodine tincture to each quart of water (add 10 drops if water is cloudy). Let water stand for at least 30 minutes before using it.

ThomsonNOW™
www.thomsonedu.com/thomsonnow

Nutrition Portfolio

Practicing food safety allows you to eat a variety of foods, with little risk of food-related illnesses.

■ Review your food-handling practices and describe how effectively you wash your hands, utensils, and kitchen surfaces when preparing foods.

■ Describe the steps you take to separate raw and cooked foods while storing and preparing them.

■ Describe how you can ensure that you cook foods to a safe temperature and refrigerate perishable foods promptly.

NUTRITION ON THE NET

ThomsonNOW™
For further study of topics covered in this chapter, log on to **www.thomsonedu** **.com/thomsonnow**. Go to Chapter 19, then to Nutrition on the Net.

• Get food safety tips from the Government Food Safety Information site or from the Fight BAC! Campaign of the Partnership for Food Safety Education: **www.foodsafety.gov** or **www.fightbac.org**

• Learn more about foodborne illnesses from the National Center for Infectious Diseases at the Centers for Disease Control and Prevention: **www.cdc.gov/ncidod**

• Learn about the various types of food thermometers and how and when to use them from the USDA Thermy Campaign: **www.fsis.usda.gov/thermy**

• Find commonsense health tips for travelers at the Centers for Disease Control and Prevention site: **www.cdc.gov/travel**

• Learn more about food irradiation from the International Food Information Council: **www.ific.org**

• Report adverse reactions to the FDA's MedWatch program at (800) 332-1088 or: **www.fda.gov/medwatch**

• Get fish advisories from the Environmental Protection Agency: **www.epa.gov/ost/fish**

• Review tips from the Environmental Protection Agency on methods of food buying and preparation that will help minimize pesticide exposure: **www.epa.gov/pesticides/food**

• Visit the Canadian Food Inspection Agency (CFIA): **www.inspection.gc.ca**

• Learn more about food safety in the marketplace from the Food Safety and Inspection Service: **www.usda.gov/fsis**

Because albacore ("white") tuna has more mercury than canned light tuna, consumers should limit their intake to no more than 6 ounces of albacore tuna per week.

turning into methylmercury, and the fish in the bay were accumulating this poison in their bodies. Some of the affected families had been eating fish from the bay every day.

PBB and PCB   In 1973, half a ton of **PBB (polybrominated biphenyl),** a toxic organic compound, was accidentally mixed into some livestock feed that was distributed throughout the state of Michigan. The chemical found its way into millions of animals and then into the people who ate the meat. The seriousness of the accident came to light when dairy farmers reported that their cows were going dry, aborting their calves, and developing abnormal growths on their hooves. Although more than 30,000 cattle, sheep, and swine and more than a million chickens were destroyed, an estimated 97 percent of Michigan's residents had been exposed to PBB. Some of the exposed farm residents suffered nervous system aberrations and liver disorders.

A similar accident occurred in 1979 when **PCB (polychlorinated biphenyls)** contaminated rice oil in Taiwan. Women who had eaten the tainted rice oil gave birth to children with developmental problems. Decades later, young men who were exposed to PCB during gestation have reduced fertility. The interactive effects of PCB and mercury are especially damaging to brain functions such as balance and coordination.[15]

Guidelines for Consumers

How much of a threat do environmental contaminants pose to the food supply? For the most part, the hazards appear to be small. The FDA regulates the presence of contaminants in foods and requires foods with unsafe amounts to be removed from the market. Similarly, health agencies may issue advisories informing consumers about the potential dangers of eating contaminated foods.

◆ For perspective, 1 ppm (part per million) is equivalent to about 1 minute in 2 years or 1 cent in $10,000.

Most recently, mercury poisoning has aroused concerns—even at levels one-tenth of those in the Minamata catastrophe. Virtually all fish have at least trace amounts of mercury (on average, 0.12 parts per million). ◆ Fish and other seafood are the main source of dietary mercury.[16] Mercury, PCB, chlordane, dioxins, and DDT are the toxins most responsible for fish contamination, but mercury leads the list by threefold.[17]

Review Figure 19-5 (p. 675) and notice how toxins such as mercury become more concentrated in animals and in people high in the food chain. Because of bioaccumulation, large gamefish at the top of the aquatic food chain ◆ generally have the highest concentrations of mercury (ten times the average). Consumers who enjoy eating these fish should select the smaller, younger ones (within legal limits). Also because of bioaccumulation, the concentrations in fish may be a million times higher than the concentrations in the water itself.

◆ Fish relatively high in mercury:
• Tilefish, swordfish, king mackerel, shark
Fish relatively low in mercury:
• Cod, haddock, pollock, salmon, sole, tilapia
• Most shellfish

The **EPA** regulates commercial fishing to help ensure that fish destined for consumption in the United States meet safety standards for mercury and other contaminants. Farm-raised fish usually have lower concentrations of mercury than fish caught in the wild. Consequently, most consumers in the United States are not in danger of receiving harmful levels of mercury from fish.

◆ Pregnant and lactating women and young children should avoid:
• Tilefish (also called golden snapper or golden bass), swordfish, king mackerel, shark
And limit weekly consumption to:
• 12 oz (cooked or canned) commercial fish and shellfish (such as shrimp, canned light tuna, salmon, pollock, and catfish)
• 6 oz (cooked or canned) "white" albacore tuna

Pregnant and lactating women and young children are most vulnerable because mercury toxicity damages the developing brain.[18] However, they are also likely to benefit from consuming seafood rich in omega-3 fatty acids. To receive the benefits and minimize the risks, pregnant and lactating women and young children can safely consume up to 12 ounces of seafood per week.[19] In addition, they should limit their intake of albacore tuna and avoid eating large predatory fish altogether.◆ Blood levels of mercury in young children and women of child-bearing age are currently below levels of concern.[20]

What about the noncommercial fish a person catches from a local lake, river, or ocean? After all, it's almost impossible to tell whether water is contaminated without sophisticated equipment. Each state monitors its waters and issues advisories to inform the public if chemical contaminants have been found in the local fish. To

PBB (polybrominated biphenyl) and **PCB (polychlorinated biphenyl):** toxic organic compounds used in pesticides, paints, and flame retardants.

for only a short time because the body rapidly excretes them or metabolizes them to harmless compounds. These contaminants present little cause for concern. Some contaminants, however, resist breakdown and can accumulate. Each level of the **food chain**, then, has a greater concentration than the one below (**bioaccumulation**). Figure 19-5 shows how bioaccumulation leads to high concentrations of toxins in people at the top of the food chain.

Contaminants enter the environment in various ways. Accidental spills are rare but can have devastating effects. More commonly, small amounts are released over long periods. The following paragraphs describe how three contaminants found their way into the food supply in the past. The first example involves a heavy metal; ◆ the others involve **organic halogens.**

Methylmercury A classic example of acute contamination occurred in 1953 when a number of people in Minamata, Japan, became ill with a disease no one had seen before. By 1960, 121 cases had been reported, including 23 in infants. Mortality was high; 46 died, and the survivors suffered blindness, deafness, lack of coordination, and intellectual deterioration. The cause was ultimately revealed to be methylmercury contamination of fish from the bay where these people lived. The infants who contracted the disease had not eaten any fish, but their mothers had, and even though the mothers exhibited no symptoms during their pregnancies, the poison affected their unborn babies. Manufacturing plants in the region were discharging mercury-containing waste into the waters of the bay, the mercury was

◆ Reminder: A *heavy metal* is any of a number of mineral ions such as mercury and lead, so called because they are of relatively high atomic weight. Many heavy metals are poisonous.

food chain: the sequence in which living things depend on other living things for food.

bioaccumulation: the accumulation of contaminants in the flesh of animals high on the food chain.

organic halogens: an organic compound containing one or more atoms of a halogen—fluorine, chlorine, iodine, or bromine.

FIGURE 19-5 Bioaccumulation of Toxins in the Food Chain

This example features fish as the food for human consumption, but bioaccumulation of toxins occurs on land as well when cows, pigs, and chickens eat or drink contaminated foods or water.

Key:
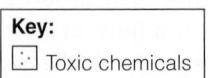 Toxic chemicals

❹ If none of the chemicals are lost along the way, people ultimately receive all of the toxic chemicals that were present in the original plants and plankton.

❸ Contaminants become further concentrated in larger fish that eat the small fish from the lower part of the food chain.

❷ Contaminants become more concentrated in small fish that eat the plants and plankton.

❶ Plants and plankton at the bottom of the food chain become contaminated with toxic chemicals, such as methylmercury (shown as red dots).

Level 4
A 150-pound person

Level 3
100 pounds of fish-eating fish such as lake trout, walleye, and bass

Level 2
A few tons of plankton-eating fish such as bluegill, perch, stream trout, and smelt

Level 1
Several tons of producer organisms (plant and animal plankton)

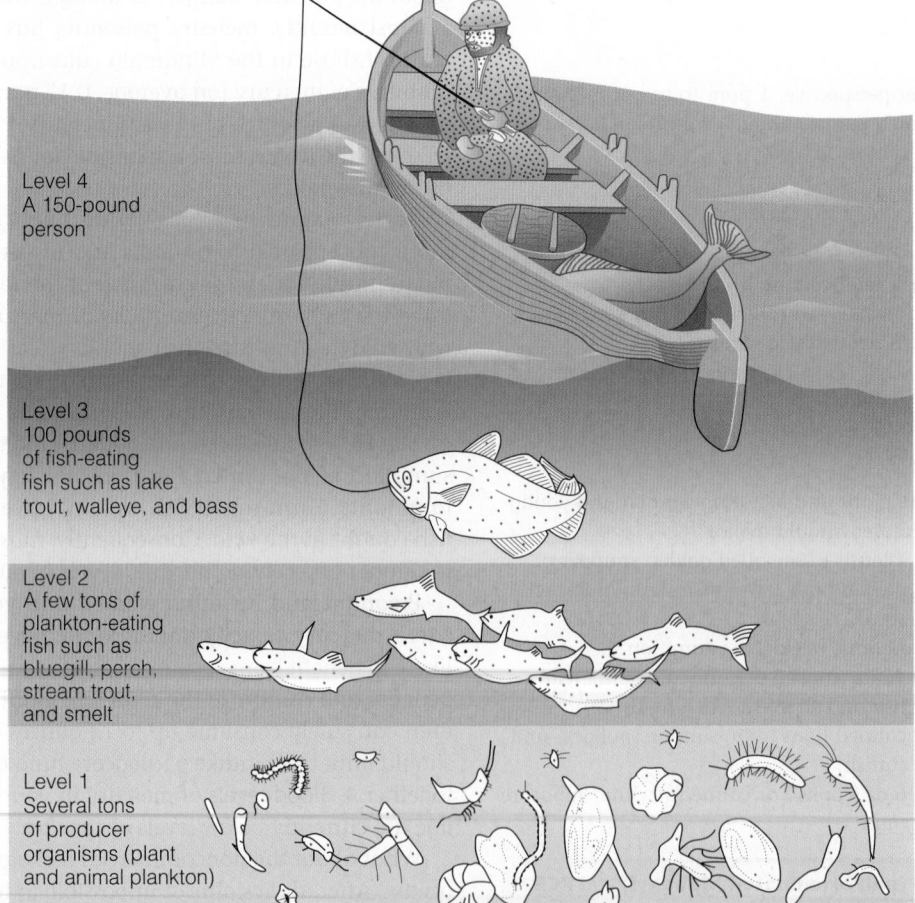

- Learn more about organic foods and national organic food standards from the National Organic Program: **www.ams.usda.gov/nop**

- Find information on foodborne illnesses and safe food handling from the American Dietetic Association: **www.homefoodsafety.org**

- Learn more about safe drinking water from the Environmental Protection Agency: **www.epa.gov/safewater**

- Enjoy the humor and music of food toxicologist Carl Winter at: **foodsafe.ucdavis.edu/music.html**

STUDY QUESTIONS

ThomsonNOW
To assess your understanding of chapter topics, take the Student Practice Test and explore the modules recommended in your Personalized Study Plan. Log onto **www.thomsonedu.com/thomsonnow**.

These questions will help you review the chapter. You will find the answers in the discussions on the pages provided.

1. To what extent does food poisoning present a real hazard to consumers eating U.S. foods? How often does it occur? (p. 664)

2. Distinguish between the two types of foodborne illnesses and provide an example of each. Describe measures that help prevent foodborne illnesses. (pp. 664–666, 670–671)

3. What special precautions apply to meats? To seafood? (pp. 668–671)

4. What is meant by a "persistent" contaminant of foods? Describe how contaminants get into foods and build up in the food chain. (pp. 674–676)

5. What dangers do natural toxicants present? (p. 677)

6. How do pesticides become a hazard to the food supply, and how are they monitored? In what ways can people reduce the concentrations of pesticides in and on foods that they prepare? (pp. 678–681)

7. What is the difference between a GRAS substance and a regulated food additive? Give examples of each. Name and describe the different classes of additives. (pp. 682–685)

These multiple choice questions will help you prepare for an exam. Answers can be found on p. 692.

1. Eating a contaminated food such as undercooked poultry or unpasteurized milk might cause a:
   a. food allergy.
   b. food infection.
   c. food intoxication.
   d. botulinum reaction.

2. The temperature danger zone for foods ranges from:
   a. −20°F to 120°F.
   b. 0°F to 100°F.
   c. 20°F to 120°F.
   d. 40°F to 140°F.

3. Examples of foods that frequently cause foodborne illness are:
   a. canned foods.
   b. steaming-hot foods.
   c. fresh fruits and vegetables.
   d. raw milk, seafood, meat, and eggs.

4. Irradiation can help improve our food supply by:
   a. cooking foods quickly.
   b. killing microorganisms.
   c. minimizing the use of preservatives.
   d. improving the nutrient content of foods.

5. Solanine is an example of a(n):
   a. heavy metal.
   b. artificial color.
   c. natural toxicant.
   d. animal hormone.

6. The standard that deems additives safe if lifetime use presents no more than a one-in-a-million risk of cancer is known as the:
   a. Delaney Clause.
   b. zero-risk policy.
   c. GRAS list of standards.
   d. negligible-risk policy.

7. Common antimicrobial additives include:
   a. salt and nitrites.
   b. carrageenan and MSG.
   c. dioxins and sulfites.
   d. vitamin C and vitamin E.

8. Common antioxidants include:
   a. BHA and BHT.
   b. tartrazine and MSG.
   c. sugar and vitamin E.
   d. nitrosamines and salt.

9. Incidental additives that may enter foods during processing include:
   a. dioxins and BGH.
   b. dioxins and folate.
   c. beta-carotene and agar.
   d. nitrites and irradiation.

10. Chlorine is added to water to:
   a. protect against dental caries.
   b. destroy harmful minerals such as lead and mercury.
   c. kill pathogenic microorganisms.
   d. remove the sulfur that produces a "rotten egg" odor.

REFERENCES

1. B. Bruemmer, Food biosecurity, *Journal of the American Dietetic Association* 103 (2003): 687-691; T. Peregrin, Bioterrorism and food safety: What nutrition professionals need to know to educate the American public, *Journal of the American Dietetic Association* 102 (2002): 14, 16; Food and Drug Administration, Food security guidance: Availability, *Federal Register* 67 (2002): 1224-1225; J. Sobel, A. S. Khan, and D. L. Swerdlow, Threat of a biological terrorist attack on the US food supply: The CDC perspective, *Lancet* 359 (2002): 874-880.
2. Centers for Disease Control and Prevention, *FoodNet Surveillance Report for 2004,* June 2006.
3. E. A. Coleman and M. E. Yergler, Botulism, *American Journal of Nursing* 102 (2002): 44-47.
4. Position of the American Dietetic Association: Food and water safety, *Journal of the American Dietetic Association* 103 (2003): 1203-1218.
5. Centers for Disease Control and Prevention, June 2006.
6. B. J. McCabe-Sellers and S. E. Beattie, Food safety: Emerging trends in foodborne illness surveillance and prevention, *Journal of the American Dietetic Association* 104 (2004): 1709-1717.
7. J. B. Anderson and coauthors, A camera's view of consumer food-handling behaviors, *Journal of the American Dietetic Association* 104 (2004): 186-191.
8. U.S. Food and Drug Administration, Consumer asked questions about BSE in products regulated by FDA's Center for Food Safety and Applied Nutrtition (CFSAN), www.cfsan.fda.gov/~comm/bsefaq.html, site updated September 14, 2005 and visited December 6, 2006; U.S. Department of Agriculture, Bovine spongiform encephalopathy (BSE) Q & A's, www.aphis.usda.gov/lpa/issues/bse/bse_q&a.html, site updated January 21, 2004 and visited December 6, 2006.
9. C. A. Donnelly, Bovine spongiform encephalopathy in the United States—An epidemiologist's view, *New England Journal of Medicine* 350 (2004): 539-542; T. Hampton, What now, mad cow? Experts put risk to US public in perspective, *Journal of the American Medical Association* 291 (2004): 543-549.
10. E. T. Ryan, M. E. Wilson, and K. C. Kain, Illness after international travel, *New England Journal of Medicine* 347 (2002): 505-516.
11. M. T. Osterholm and A. P. Norgan, The role of irradiation in food safety, *New England Journal of Medicine* 350 (2004): 1898-1901; D. W. Thayer, Irradiation of food—Helping to ensure food safety, *New England Journal of Medicine* 350 (2004): 1811-1812.
12. Position of the American Dietetic Association: Food irradiation, *Journal of the American Dietetic Association* 100 (2000): 246-253.
13. P. Frenzen and coauthors, Consumer acceptance of irradiated meat and poultry products, www.cdc.gov/foodnet/pub/publications.
14. R. W. Miller, How environmental hazards in childhood have been discovered: Carciogens, teratogens, neurotoxicants, and others, *Pediatrics* 113 (2004): 945-951; R. Sreedharan and D. I. Mehta, Gastrointestinal tract, *Pediatrics* 113 (2004): 1044-1050; Department of Health and Human Services, *Third National Report on Human Exposure to Environmental Chemicals,* July 2005.
15. C. S. Roegge and S. L. Schantz, Motor function following developmental exposure to PCBS and/or MEHG, *Neurotoxicology and Teratology* 28 (2006): 260-277.
16. Centers for Disease Control and Prevention, *Third National Report on Human Exposure to Environmental Chemicals,* July 2005.
17. EPA Fact Sheet, Update: National listing of fish and wildlife advisories, May 2002, available online at www.epa.gov/ost/fish.
18. P. W. Davidson, G. J. Myers, and B. Weiss, Mercury exposure and child development outcomes, *Pediatrics* 113 (2004): 1023-1029.
19. Institute of Medicine, *Seafood Choices: Balancing Benefits and Risks,* October 2006.
20. R. L. Jones and coauthors, Blood mercury levels in young children and childbearing-aged women—United States, 1999-2002, *Morbidity and Mortality Weekly Report* 53 (2004): 1018-1020.
21. C. W. Levenson and D. M. Axelrad, Too much of a good thing? Update on fish consumption and mercury exposure, *Nutrition Reviews* 64 (2006): 139-145.
22. B. Weiss, S. Amler, and R. W. Amler, Pesticides, *Pediatrics* 113 (2004): 1030-1036.
23. B. P. Baker and coauthors, Pesticide residues in conventional, integrated pest management (IPM)-grown and organic foods: Insights from three US data sets, *Food Additives and Contaminants* 19 (2002): 427-446.
24. C. Lu and coauthors, Organic diets significantly lower children's dietary exposure to organophosphorus pesticides, *Environmental Health Perspectives* 114 (2006): 260-263.
25. L. Grinder-Pedersen and coauthors, Effect of diets based on foods from conventional versus organic production on intake and excretion of flavonoids and markers of antioxidative defense in humans, *Journal of Agricultural and Food Chemistry* 51 (2003): 5671-5676.
26. M. DiNovi, The 2006 exposure assessment for acrylamide, July 2006, www.cfsan.fda.gov/~dms/acryexpo.html.
27. R. H. Stadler and G. Scholz, Acrylamide: An update on current knowledge in analysis, levels in food, mechanisms of formation, and potential strategies of control, *Nutrition Reviews* 62 (2004): 449-467.
28. FDA action plan for acrylamide in food, March 2004, www.cfsan.fda.gov/~dms/acrypla3.html.
29. National Academy of Sciences, EPA Assessment of dioxin understates uncertainty about health risks and may overstate human cancer risk, 2006, available at http://national-academies.org.
30. D. Schardt, Microwave myths: Fact vs. fiction, *Nutrition Action Heathletter,* April 2005, pp. 10-12.
31. National Academy of Sciences, *Health Risks from Dioxin and Related Compounds: Evaluation of the EPA Reassessment,* July 2006.
32. J. Raloff, Hormones: Here's the beef, *Science News* 161 (2002): 10-12.
33. D. H. Hammer and C. J. Gill, From the farm to the kitchen table: The negative impact of antimicrobial use in animals on humans, *Nutrition Reviews* 60 (2002): 261-264.
34. B. G. Blackburn and coauthors, Surveillance for waterborne-disease outbreaks associated with drinking water—United States, 2001-2002, *Morbidity and Mortality Weekly Report* 53 (2002): 23-45.

ANSWERS

Study Questions (multiple choice)

1. b   2. d   3. d   4. b   5. c   6. d   7. a   8. a   9. a   10. c

Food Biotechnology

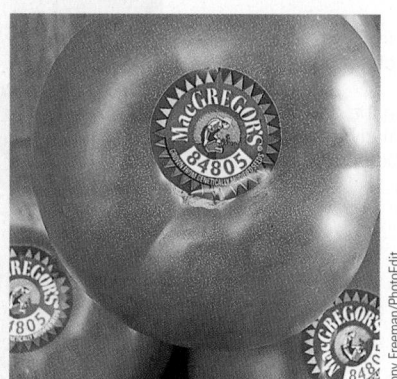

Advances in food **biotechnology** promise just about everything from the frivolous (a tear-free onion) to the profound (a hunger-free world). Already biotechnology has produced leaner meats, longer shelf lives, better nutrient composition, and greater crop yields grown with fewer pesticides. Overall, biotechnology offers numerous opportunities to overcome food shortages, improve the environment, and eliminate disease.[1] But it also raises concerns about possible risks to the environment and human health. Critics assert that biotechnology will exacerbate world hunger, destroy the environment, and endanger health. This highlight presents some of the many issues surrounding genetically engineered foods, and the accompanying glossary defines the terms used.

hoping for the best. With genetic engineering, scientists can improve crops (or livestock) by introducing a copy of the specific gene needed to produce the desired trait. Figure H19-1 (p. 694) illustrates the difference. Once introduced, the selected gene acts like any other gene—it provides instructions for making a protein. The protein then determines a characteristic in the genetically modified plant or animal. In short, the process is now faster and more refined. Farmers no longer need to wait patiently for breeding to yield improved crops and animals, nor must they even respect natural lines of reproduction among species. Laboratory scientists can now copy genes from any organism and insert them into almost any other organism—plant, animal, or microbe. Their work is changing not only the way farmers plant, fertilize, and harvest their crops, but also the ways the food industry processes food and consumers receive nutrients, phytochemicals, and drugs.

The Promises of Genetic Engineering

For centuries, farmers have been selectively breeding plants and animals to shape the characteristics of their crops and livestock. They have created prettier flowers, hardier vegetables, and leaner animals. Consider the success of selectively breeding corn. Early farmers in Mexico began with a wild, native plant called teosinte (tay-oh-SEEN-tay) that bears only five or six kernels on each small spike. Many years of patient selective breeding have produced large ears filled with hundreds of plump kernels aligned in perfect formation, row after row.

Such genetic improvements, together with the use of irrigation, fertilizers, and pesticides, were responsible for more than half of the increases in U.S. crop yields in the 20th century. Farmers still use selective breeding, but now, in the 21st century, advances in **genetic engineering** have brought rapid and dramatic changes to agriculture and food production.

Although selective breeding works, it is slow and imprecise because it involves mixing thousands of genes from two plants and

This wild predecessor of corn, with its sparse five or six kernels, bears little resemblance to today's large, full, sweet ears.

FIGURE H19-1 Selective Breeding and Genetic Engineering Compared

Traditional Selective Breeding

Traditional selective breeding combines many genes from two varieties of the same species to produce one with the desired characteristics.

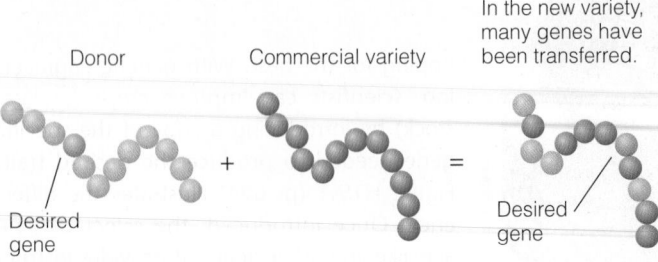

Donor   Commercial variety

In the new variety, many genes have been transferred.

Desired gene + = Desired gene

Genetic Engineering

Through genetic engineering, a single gene (or several) are transferred from the same or different species to produce one with the desired characteristics.

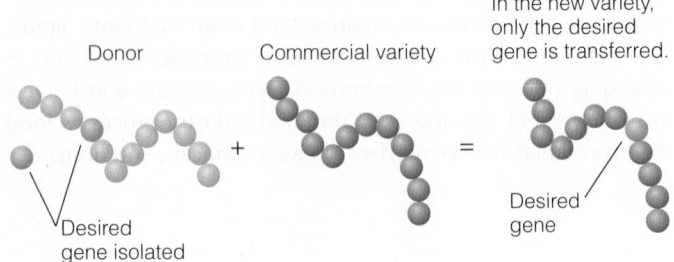

Donor   Commercial variety

In the new variety, only the desired gene is transferred.

Desired gene isolated + = Desired gene

SOURCE: © 1995 Monsanto Company

Genetically modified cauliflower is orange, reflecting a change in a single gene that increases its production of beta-carotene 100-fold.

Extended Shelf Life

Among the first products of genetic engineering to hit the market were tomatoes that stay firm and ripe longer than regular tomatoes that are typically harvested green and ripened in the stores. These genetically modified tomatoes promise less waste and higher profits. Normally, tomatoes produce a protein that softens them after they have been picked. Scientists can now introduce into a tomato plant a gene that is a mirror image of the one that codes for the "softening" enzyme. This gene fastens itself to the RNA of the native gene and blocks synthesis of the softening protein. Without this protein, the genetically altered tomato softens more slowly than a regular tomato, allowing growers to harvest it at its most flavorful and nutritious vine-ripe stage.

Improved Nutrient Composition

Genetic engineering can also improve the nutrient composition of foods.[2] Instead of manufacturers adding nutrients to foods during processing, plants can be genetically altered to do their own fortification work—a strategy called *biofortification*.[3] Biofortification of staple crops with key vitamins and minerals can effectively combat the nutrient deficiency diseases that claim so many lives worldwide.[4] Soybeans may be implanted with a gene that upgrades soy protein to a quality approaching that of milk. Corn may be modified to contain lysine and tryptophan, its two limiting amino acids. Soybean and canola plants can be genetically modified to alter the composition of their oils, making them richer in the heart-healthy monounsaturated fatty acids. "Golden rice," which has received genes from a daffodil and a bacterium that enable it to make beta-carotene, offers some promise in helping to correct vitamin A deficiency worldwide. (Chapter 11 described how vitamin A deficiency contributes to the deaths of 2 million children and the blindness of a half million each year.) Of course, increasing nutrients in crops may have unintended consequences as well. For example, when broccoli is manipulated to increase its selenium content, production of the cancer-fighting phytochemical sulforaphane declines.[5]

As you might predict, enhancing the chemical composition of plants is not limited to the essential nutrients. Genetically modified crops can also produce more of the phytochemicals that help maintain health and reduce the risks of chronic diseases (see Highlight 13).[6] They can also be coaxed to produce less phytate, which allows more zinc to be absorbed.[7] The possibilities seem endless.

Efficient Food Processing

Genetic engineering also helps to process foods more efficiently, which saves money. For example, the protein **rennin,** which is used to coagulate milk in the production of cheese, has traditionally been harvested from the stomachs of calves, a costly process. Now scientists can insert a copy of the rennin gene into bacteria and then use bacterial cultures to mass-produce rennin—saving time, money, space, and animals.

Genetic engineering can also help to bypass costly food-processing steps. At present, people who are lactose intolerant can buy milk that has been treated with the lactase enzyme. Wouldn't it be more convenient, and less expensive, if scientists could induce cows to make lactose-free milk directly? They're working on it. They have already successfully inserted into mice the genetic material needed to make lactase in their mammary glands, thereby producing low-lactose milk. Decaffeinated coffee beans are another real possibility.

Efficient Drug Delivery

Genetic research today has progressed well beyond tweaking a gene here and there to produce a desired trait. Scientists can now clone animals. By cloning animals, scientists have the ability to produce both needed food and pharmaceutical products. Using animals and other organisms in the development of pharmaceuticals is whimsically called "biopharming." For example, a cow cloned with the genetic equipment to make a vaccine in its milk could provide both nourishment and immunization to a whole village of people now left unprotected because they lack food and medical help. Similarly, researchers have figured out how to induce bananas and potatoes to make hepatitis vaccines and tobacco leaves to make AIDS drugs. They can also harvest vaccines by genetically altering hydroponically grown tomato plants to secrete a protein through their root systems into the water. Using foods to deliver drugs is only a small part of the promise and potential biotechnology offers the field of medicine.[8]

Genetically Assisted Agriculture

Genetic engineering has helped farmers to increase yields, extend growing seasons, and grow crops that resist herbicides. About half of the soybean crops in the United States have been genetically engineered to withstand a potent herbicide. As a result, farmers can spray whole fields with this herbicide and kill the weeds without harming the soybeans.

Similarly, farmers can grow crops that produce their own pesticides—substances known as **plant-pesticides.** Corn, broccoli, and potatoes have received a gene from a bacterium that produces a protein that is toxic to leaf-chewing caterpillars (but not to humans). Yellow squash has been given two viral genes that confer resistance to the most common viral diseases. Potatoes can now produce a beetle-killing toxin in their leaves. These crops and many others like them are currently being grown or tested in fields around the United States. Growing crops that make their own pesticides allows farmers to save time, increase yields, and use fewer, or less harmful, pesticides.[9]

Other Possibilities

Many other biotechnology possibilities are envisioned for the near future. Shrimp may be empowered to fight diseases with genetic ammunition borrowed from sea urchins. Plants may be given special molecules to help them grow in polluted soil. With these and other advances, farmers may reliably produce bumper crops of food every year on far fewer acres of land, with less loss of water and topsoil, and far less use of toxic pesticides and herbicides. Supporters of biotechnology predict that these efforts will enhance food production and help meet the challenge of feeding an ever-increasing world population. They contend that genetically modified crops have the potential to eliminate hunger and starvation. Others suggest that the problems of world hunger are more complex than biotechnology alone can resolve and that the potential risks of genetic engineering may outweigh the potential benefits.[10]

The projects mentioned in this highlight are already in progress. Close on their heels are many more ingenious ideas. What if salt tolerance could be transplanted from a coastal marsh plant into crop plants? Could crops then be irrigated with seawater, thus conserving dwindling freshwater supplies? Would the world food supply increase if rice farmers could grow plants that were immune to disease? What if consumers could dictate which traits scientists insert into food plants? Would they choose to add phytochemicals to fight cancer or reduce the risk of heart disease? These and other possibilities seem unlimited, and though they may sound incredible, many such products have already been developed and are awaiting approval from the FDA, EPA, and USDA.

The Potential Problems and Concerns

Although many scientists hail biotechnology with confidence, others have reservations. Some consumers also have concerns about what they call "Frankenfoods." Those who oppose biotechnology fear for the safety of a world where genetic tampering produces effects that are not yet fully understood. They suspect that the food industry may be driven by potential profits, without ethical considerations or laws to harness its effects. They point out that even the scientists who developed the techniques cannot predict the ultimate outcomes of their discoveries. These consumers don't want to eat a scientific experiment or interfere with natural systems. Genetic decisions, they say, are best left to the powers of nature.

If science and the marketplace are allowed to drive biotechnology without restraint, critics fear that these problems may result:

Some consumers believe that food biotechnology will cause more harm than good.

- *Disruption of natural ecosystems.* New, genetically unusual organisms that have no natural place in the food chain or evolutionary biological systems could escape into the environment and reproduce.

- *Introduction of diseases.* Newly created viruses may mutate to cause deadly diseases that may attack plants, animals, or human beings. Genetically modified bacteria may develop resistance to antibiotics, making the drugs useless in fighting infections.

- *Introduction of allergens and toxins.* Genetically modified crops may contain new substances that have consequences, such as causing allergies.[11]

- *Creation of biological weapons.* Fatal bacterial and viral diseases may be developed for use as weapons.

- *Ethical dilemmas.* Critics pose the question, "How many human genes does an organism have to contain before it is considered human? For instance, how many human genes would a green pepper have to contain before one would have qualms about eating it?"[12]

Proponents of biotechnology respond that evidence to date does not justify these concerns.[13] Opponents counter that the lack of evidence showing harm does not provide evidence showing safety. These opposing views illustrate the tension between the forward thrust of science and the hesitation of consumers. Both positions highlight the need for more research on the safety and effectiveness of genetically modified food. Table H19-1 summarizes the issues.

From another perspective, some argue that the concerns expressed by those protesting genetically engineered foods reflect prejudices acquired in an elitist world of fertile land and abundant food. Those living in poverty-stricken areas of the world do not have the luxury of determining how to grow crops and process foods. They cannot afford the delays created when protesters destroy test crops and disrupt scientific meetings. They need solutions now. People are starving, and genetic engineering holds great promise for providing them with food.

At a minimum, critics of biotechnology have made a strong case for rigorous safety testing and labeling of new products. They contend, for example, that when a new gene has been introduced into a food, tests should ensure that other, unwanted genes have not accompanied it. If a disease-producing microorganism has donated genetic material, scientists must prove that no dangerous characteristic from the microorganism has also entered the food. If the inserted genetic material comes from a source to which some people develop allergies, such as nuts, then the new product should be labeled to alert them. Furthermore, if the newly altered genetic material creates proteins that have never before been encountered by the human body, their effects should be studied to ensure that people can eat them safely.

FDA Regulations

The FDA has taken the position that foods produced through biotechnology and cloning are not substantially different from others and require no special testing, regulations, or labeling. After all, most foods available today have already been genetically altered by years of selective breeding. The new vegetable broccoflower, a product of sophisticated cross-breeding of broccoli with cauliflower, met no testing or approval barriers on its way to the dinner plate. When the vegetable became available on the market, scientists studied its nutrient contents (see Appendix H), but they did not question its safety.

In most cases, the new genetically modified food differs from the old conventional one only by a gene or two.[14] The rennin produced by bacteria is structurally and functionally the same as the rennin produced by calves, for example. For that reason, the FDA considers it and other genetically engineered foods "generally recognized as safe (GRAS)."[15]

A product such as the tomato described earlier need not be tested because its new genes *prevent* synthesis of a protein and add nothing but a tiny fragment of genetic material. Nor does this tomato require special labeling because it is not significantly different from the many other varieties of tomatoes on the market. On the other hand, any substances introduced into a food (such as a hormone or protein) by way of bioengineering must meet the same safety standards applied to all additives. A tomato plant with a gene that, for example, produces a pesticide cannot be marketed until tests prove it safe for consumption. The FDA assures consumers that all bioengineered foods on the market today are as safe as their traditional counterparts.

Foods produced through biotechnology that are substantially different from others must be labeled to identify that difference. For example, if the nutrient composition of the new product differs from its traditional counterpart, as in the soybean and canola oils mentioned earlier, then labeling is required. Similarly, if an allergy-causing protein has been introduced to a nonallergenic food, then labeling must warn consumers.

Most consumers want all genetically altered products clearly labeled. Consumer advocacy groups claim that by not requiring such labeling, the FDA forces millions of consumers to be guinea pigs, unwittingly testing genetically modified foods. Additionally, they say, people who have religious objections to consuming foods to which genes of prohibited organisms have been added have no way of identifying those foods. For example, someone keeping a kosher kitchen may unknowingly use a food containing genes from a pig. Currently, labeling is voluntary. Manufacturers may state that a product has been "genetically engineered." Those who do would be wise to explain its purpose and benefit. When consumers recognize a personal health benefit, most tend to accept genetically engineered foods.[16]

Speaking in defense of the FDA's position are the FDA itself, recognized as the nation's leading expert and advocate for food safety, and the American Dietetic Association, which represents current scientific thinking in nutrition.[17] Many other scientific organizations agree, contending that biotechnology can deliver an improved food supply if we give it a fair chance to do so.

Will our impressive new technologies provide foods to meet the needs of the future? Some would say yes. Biotechnology holds a world of promise, and with proper safeguards and controls, it may yield products that meet the needs of consumers almost perfectly.

TABLE H19-1 Food Biotechnology: Point, Counterpoint

Arguments in Opposition to Genetic Engineering	Arguments in Support of Genetic Engineering
1. **Ethical and moral issues.** It's immoral to "play God" by mixing genes from organisms unable to do so naturally. Religious and vegetarian groups object to genes from prohibited species occurring in their allowable foods.	1. **Ethical and moral issues.** Scientists throughout history have been persecuted and even put to death by fearful people who accuse them of playing God. Yet, today many of the world's citizens enjoy a long and healthy life of comfort and convenience due to once-feared scientific advances put to practical use.
2. **Imperfect technology.** The technology is young and imperfect—genes rarely function in just one way, their placement is imprecise ("shotgun"), and all of their potential effects are impossible to predict. Toxins are as likely to be produced as the desired trait. Over 95 percent of DNA is called "junk" because scientists have not yet determined its function.	2. **Advanced technology.** Recombinant DNA technology is precise and reliable. Many of the most exciting recent advances in medicine, agriculture, and technology were made possible by the application of this technology.
3. **Environmental concerns.** Environmental side effects are unknown. The power of a genetically modified organism to change the world's environments is unknown until such changes actually occur—then the "genie is out of the bottle." Once out, insects, birds, and the wind distribute genetically altered seed and pollen to points unknown.	3. **Environmental protection.** Genetic engineering may be the only hope of saving rain forest and other habitats from destruction. Through genetic engineering, farmers can make use of previously unproductive lands such as salt-rich soils and arid areas.
4. **"Genetic pollution."** Other kinds of pollution can often be cleaned up with money, time, and effort. Once genes are spliced into living things, those genes forever bear the imprint of human tampering.	4. **Genetic improvements.** Genetic side effects are more likely to benefit the environment than to harm it.
5. **Crop vulnerability.** Pests and disease can quickly adapt to overtake genetically identical plants or animals around the world. Diversity is key to defense.	5. **Improved crop resistance.** Pests and diseases can be specifically fought on a case-by-case basis. Biotechnology is the key to defense.
6. **Loss of gene pool.** Loss of genetic diversity threatens to deplete valuable gene banks from which scientists can develop new agricultural crops.	6. **Gene pool preserved.** Thanks to advances in genetics, laboratories around the world are able to stockpile the genetic material of millions of species that, without such advances, would have been lost forever.
7. **Profit motive.** Genetic engineering will profit industry more than the world's poor and hungry.	7. **Everyone profits.** Industries benefit from genetic engineering, and a thriving food industry benefits the nation and its people, as witnessed by countries lacking such industries. Genetic engineering promises to provide adequate nutritious food for millions who lack such food today. Developed nations gain cheaper, more attractive, more delicious foods with greater variety and availability year round.
8. **Unproven safety for people.** Human safety testing of genetically altered products is generally lacking. The population is an unwitting experimental group in a nationwide laboratory study for the benefit of industry.	8. **Safe for people.** Human safety testing of genetically altered products is unneeded because the products are essentially the same as the original foodstuffs.
9. **Increased allergens.** Allergens can unwittingly be transferred into foods.	9. **Control of allergens.** A few allergens can be transferred into foods, but these are known. Also, foods likely to contain them are clearly labeled to warn consumers.
10. **Decreased nutrients.** A fresh-looking tomato or other produce held for several weeks may have lost substantial nutrients.	10. **Increased nutrients.** Genetic modifications can easily enhance the nutrients in foods.
11. **No product tracking.** Without labeling, the food industry cannot track problems to the source.	11. **Excellent product tracking.** The identity and location of genetically altered foodstuffs are known, and they can be tracked should problems arise.
12. **Overuse of herbicides.** Farmers, knowing that their crops resist herbicide effects, will use them liberally.	12. **Conservative use of herbicides.** Farmers will not waste expensive herbicides in second or third applications when the prescribed amount gets the job done the first time.
13. **Increased consumption of pesticides.** When a pesticide is produced by the flesh of produce, consumers cannot wash it off the skin of the produce with running water as they can with ordinary sprays.	13. **Reduced pesticides on foods.** Pesticides produced by produce in tiny amounts known to be safe for consumption are more predictable than applications by agricultural workers who make mistakes. Because other genetic manipulations will eliminate the need for postharvest spraying, fewer pesticides will reach the dinner table.
14. **Lack of oversight.** Government oversight is run by industry people for the benefit of industry—no one is watching out for the consumer.	14. **Sufficient regulation and rapid response.** Government agencies are efficient in identifying and correcting problems as they occur in the industry.

NUTRITION ON THE NET

- Search for "biotechnology" on the USDA site:
  www.usda.gov

- Get a "pro" biotechnology perspective from the Council
  for Biotechnology Information: **www.whybiotech.com**

- For another "for" view, search for "biotechnology" at the
  International Food Information Council: **www.ific.org**

- Get a "con" biotechnology perspective from the Genetic
  Engineering section of Greenpeace, USA:
  www.greenpeaceusa.org

- Another "against" view is available from the Union of
  Concerned Scientists: **www.ucsusa.org**

REFERENCES

1. P. W. Phillips, Biotechnology in the global agri-food system, *Trends in Biotechnology* 20 (2002): 376–381.

2. L. Yan and P. S. Kerr, Genetically engineered crops: Their potential use for improvement of human nutrition, *Nutrition Reviews* 60 (2002): 135–141.

3. R. M. Welch, Biotechnology, biofortification, and global health, *Food and Nutrition Bulletin* 26 (2005): 419–421; H. E. Bouis, Plant breeding: A new tool for fighting micronutrient malnutrition, *Journal of Nutrition* 132 (2002): 491S–494S.

4. G. H. Lyons and coauthors, Exploiting micronutrient interaction to optimize biofortification programs: The case for inclusion of selenium and iodine in the *HarvestPlus* Program, *Nutrition Reviews* 62 (2004): 247–252.

5. J. W. Finley, Selenium accumulation in plant foods, *Nutrition Reviews* 63 (2005): 196–202.

6. M. A. Grusak, Phytochemicals in plants: Genomics-assisted plant improvement for nutritional and health benefits, *Current Opinion in Biotechnology* 13 (2002): 508–511.

7. K. M. Hambridge and coauthors, Zinc absorption from low-phytate hybrids of maize and their wild-type isohybrids, *American Journal of Clinical Nutrition* 79 (2004): 1053–1059.

8. P. B. Fontanarosa and C. D. DeAngelis, Medical applications of biotechnology, *Journal of the American Medical Association* 293 (2005): 866–867.

9. J. Huang, C. Pray, and S. Rozelle, Enhancing the crops to feed the poor, *Nature* 418 (2002): 678–684.

10. A. Bakshi, Potential adverse health effects of genetically modified crops, *Journal of Toxicology and Environmental Health. Part B, Critical Reviews* 6 (2003): 211–215.

11. H. V. Davies, GM organisms and the EU regulatory environment: Allergenicity as a risk component, *Proceedings of the Nutrition Society* 64 (2005): 481–486; R. Mazza and coauthors, Assessing the transfer of genetically modified DNA from feed to animal tissues, *Transgenic Research* 14 (2005): 775–784.

12. R. Epstein, Redesigning the world: Ethical questions about genetic engineering, an essay available at online.sfsu.edu/~rone/GE%20Essays/Redesigning.htm.

13. J. A. Thomas, Safety of foods derived from genetically modified plants, *Texas Medicine* 99 (2003): 66–69.

14. K. T. Atherton, Safety assessment of genetically modified crops, *Toxicology* 181 (2002): 421–426.

15. D. L. Pelletier, Science, law, and politics in the Food and Drug Administration's genetically engineered foods policy: FDA's 1992 policy statement, *Nutrition Reviews* 63 (2005): 171–181.

16. J. L. Brown and Y. Ping, Consumer perception of risk associated with eating genetically engineered soybeans is less in the presence of a perceived consumer benefit, *Journal of the American Dietetic Association* 103 (2003): 208–214.

17. Position of the American Dietetic Association: Agricultural and food biotechnology, *Journal of the American Dietetic Association* 106 (2006): 285–293.

Nutrition in Your Life

Imagine living with hunger from the moment you wake up until the time you thankfully fall asleep—and all through your dreams as well. Meal after meal, day after day, you have little or no food to eat. You know you need food, but you have no money. Would you beg on the street corner or go "dumpster diving" at the nearest fast-food restaurant? And then where would you find your next meal? How will you ever get enough to eat as long as you live in poverty? Resolving the hunger problem—whether in your community or on the other side of the world—depends on alleviating poverty and using resources wisely.

Hunger and the Global Environment

CHAPTER OUTLINE

Hunger in the United States •
Defining Hunger in the United States •
Relieving Hunger in the United States

World Hunger • Food Shortages •
Malnutrition • Diminishing Food Supply

Poverty and Overpopulation

**Environmental Degradation and
Hunger** • Environmental Limitations in
Food Production • Other Limitations in
Food Production

Solutions • Sustainable Development
Worldwide • Activism and Simpler
Lifestyles at Home

HIGHLIGHT 20 Progress toward Sustainable Food Production

Worldwide, one person in every eight experiences persistent **hunger**—not the healthy appetite triggered by anticipation of a hearty meal, but the painful sensation caused by a lack of food. In this chapter, hunger takes on the greater meaning—hunger that develops from prolonged, recurrent, and involuntary lack of food and results in discomfort, illness, weakness, or pain that exceeds the usual uneasy sensation. Such hunger deprives a person of the physical and mental energy needed to enjoy a full life and often leads to severe malnutrition and death. Tens of thousands of people die of starvation each day—one child every five seconds.[1]

The enormity of the world hunger problem is reflected not only by huge numbers, but also by major challenges. As people populate and pollute the earth, resources become depleted, making food less available. Hunger and poverty, population growth, and environmental degradation are linked together; thus they tend to worsen each other. Because their causes overlap, so do their solutions: any initiative a person takes to help solve one problem will help solve many others. Eliminating hunger requires a balance among the distribution of food, the numbers of people, and the care of the environment.

Resolving the hunger problem may seem at first beyond the influence of the ordinary person. Can one person's choice to limit family size or to recycle a bottle or to volunteer at a food recovery program make a difference? ◆ In truth, such choices produce several benefits. For one, a person's action may influence many other people over time. For another, a repeated action becomes a habit, with compounded benefits. For still another, making choices with an awareness of the consequences gives a person a sense of personal control, hope, and effectiveness. The daily actions of many concerned people can help solve the problems of hunger in their own neighborhoods or on the other side of the world.

◆ "Never doubt that a small group of thoughtful, committed people can change the world. Indeed, it is the only thing that ever has."—Margaret Mead

hunger: consequence of food insecurity that, because of prolonged, involuntary lack of food, results in discomfort, illness, weakness, or pain that goes beyond the usual uneasy sensation.

Hunger in the United States

Ideally, all people at all times would have access to enough food to support an active, healthy life. In other words, they would experience **food security.** ◆ Unfortunately, more than 35 million people in the United States, including 12 million children, ◆ live in poverty and cannot afford to buy enough food to maintain good health.[2] Said another way, one out of nine households experiences hunger or the threat of hunger. Given the agricultural bounty and enormous wealth in this country, do these numbers surprise you? The limited or uncertain availability of nutritionally adequate and safe foods is known as **food insecurity** ◆ and is a major social problem in our nation today. Inadequate diets lead to poor health in adults and impaired physical, psychological, and cognitive development in children.

The accompanying "How to" presents the questions used in national surveys to identify food insecurity in the United States, and Figure 20-1 shows the most recent findings. Responses to these questions provide crude, but necessary, data to estimate the degree of hunger in this country.[3]

Defining Hunger in the United States

At its most extreme, people experience hunger because they have absolutely no food. More often, they have too little food **(food insufficiency)** and try to stretch their limited resources by eating small meals or skipping meals—often for days at a time. Sometimes hungry people obtain enough food to satisfy their hunger, perhaps by seeking food assistance or finding food through socially unacceptable ways—begging from strangers, stealing from markets, or scavenging through garbage cans, for example. Sometimes obtaining food raises concerns for food safety—for example, when rot, slime, mold, or insects have damaged foods or when people eat others' leftovers or meat from roadkill.[4]

Hunger has many causes, but in developed countries, the primary cause is **food poverty.** People are hungry not because there is no food nearby to purchase, but because they lack money. An estimated one out of eight people in the United States lives in poverty. Even those above the poverty line may not have food security. Physical and mental illnesses and disabilities, unemployment, low-paying jobs, unexpected or ongoing medical expenses, and high living expenses threaten their financial stability. When money is tight, people are forced to choose between food and life's other necessities—utilities, housing, and medical care. Food costs are more variable and flexible; people can purchase fewer groceries to lower the monthly food bill, but they usually can't pay only a portion of the bills for electricity, rent, or medication. Other problems further contribute to food poverty, such as abuse of alcohol and other drugs; lack of awareness of available food assistance programs; and the reluctance of people, particularly the elderly, to accept what they perceive as "welfare" or "charity." Lack of resources remains the major cause of food poverty in developed countries, and solving this problem would do a lot to relieve hunger.

In the United States, poverty and hunger reach across various segments of society, touching single parents living in households with their children; Hispanics and African Americans; and those living in the inner cities more than others. People living in poverty are simply unable to buy sufficient amounts of nourishing foods, even if they are wise shoppers. For many of the children in these families, school lunch (and breakfast, where available) may be the only nourishment for the day. Otherwise they go hungry, waiting for an adult to find money for food. Not surprisingly, these children are more likely to have health problems than those who eat regularly.[5] They also tend to perform poorly in school and in social situations.[6]

Ironically, hunger and obesity exist side by side in the United States—sometimes within the same person. That hunger reflects an inadequate food intake and obesity implies an excessive intake seems paradoxical, but research studies have confirmed the relationship.[7] The highest rates of obesity occur among those living in the greatest poverty—the same people who live with food insecurity.[8] Unfortu-

---

◆ *Food security* categories:
- *High food security:* no indications of food-access problems or limitations
- *Marginal food security:* one or two indications of food-access problems but with little or no change in food intake

◆ An estimated one out of six children lives in poverty.

◆ *Food insecurity* categories:
- *Low food security:* reduced quantity of diet with little or no indication of reduced food intake; formerly known as *food insecurity without hunger*
- *Very low food security:* multiple indications of disrupted eating patterns and reduced food intake; formerly known as *food insecurity with hunger*

FIGURE 20-1 Prevalence of Food Insecurity and Hunger in U.S. Households, 2005

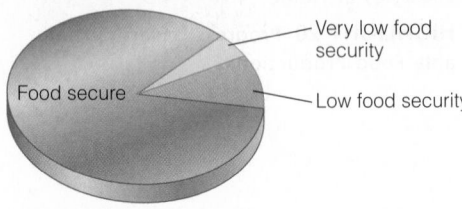

Very low food security

Food secure

Low food security

SOURCE: Economic Research Service, U.S. Department of Agriculture, www.ers.usda.gov/publications/, posted November 2006 and visited on December 7, 2006.

---

food security: access to enough food to sustain a healthy and active life.

food insecurity: limited or uncertain access to foods of sufficient quality or quantity to sustain a healthy and active life.

food insufficiency: an inadequate amount of food due to a lack of resources.

food poverty: hunger resulting from inadequate access to available food for various reasons, including inadequate resources, political obstacles, social disruptions, poor weather conditions, and lack of transportation.

HOW TO | Identify Food Insecurity in a U.S. Household

To determine the extent of food insecurity in a household, surveys ask questions about behaviors and conditions known to characterize households having difficulty meeting basic food needs during the past 12 months. Most often, adults tend to protect their children from hunger. In the most severe cases, children also suffer from hunger and eat less.

1. Did you worry whether food would run out before you got money to buy more?
2. Did you find that the food you bought just didn't last and you didn't have money to buy more?
3. Were you unable to afford to eat balanced meals?
4. Did you or other adults in your household ever cut the size of your meals or skip meals because there wasn't enough food?
5. Did this happen in 3 or more months during the previous year?
6. Did you ever eat less than you felt you should because there wasn't enough money for food?
7. Were you ever hungry but didn't eat because you couldn't afford enough food?

8. Did you ever lose weight because you didn't have enough money to buy food?
9. Did you or other adults in your household ever not eat for a whole day because you were running out of money to buy food?
10. Did this happen in 3 or more months during the previous year?
11. Did you rely on only a few kinds of low-cost food to feed your children because you were running out of money to buy food?
12. Were you unable to feed your children a balanced meal because you couldn't afford it?
13. Were your children not eating enough because you just couldn't afford enough food?
14. Did you ever cut the size of your children's meals because there wasn't enough money for food?
15. Were your children ever hungry but you just couldn't afford enough food?
16. Did your children ever skip a meal because there wasn't enough money for food?
17. Did this happen in 3 or more months during the previous year?

18. Did your children ever not eat for a whole day because there wasn't enough money for food?

The more positive responses, the greater the food insecurity. Households with children answer all of the questions and are categorized as follows:

≤ 2 positive responses = food secure
3–7 positive responses = low food security
≥ 8 positive responses = very low food security

Households without children answer the first 10 questions and are categorized as follows:

≤ 2 positive responses = food secure
3–5 positive responses = low food security
≥ 6 positive responses = very low food security

Figure 20-1 (on p. 702) shows the results of the 2005 surveys.

SOURCE: United States Department of Agriculture, *Household Food Security in the United States, 2005,* available at www.ers.usda.gov/publications/err29.

nately, many healthful food choices cost more than the energy-dense foods that foster weight gain but offer few, if any, nutrients.[9] Foods such as doughnuts, pizzas, and hamburgers provide the most energy and satiety for the least cost. Furthermore, people who are unsure about their next meal are likely to overeat when food or money are available. Interestingly, food insecure people who do not participate in food assistance programs have a greater risk of obesity than those who do participate—illustrating that providing food actually helps to prevent obesity.[10]

Relieving Hunger in the United States

The American Dietetic Association (ADA) calls for aggressive action to bring an end to domestic food insecurity and hunger and to achieve food and nutrition security for everybody living in the United States.[11] Many federal and local programs aim to prevent or relieve malnutrition and hunger in the United States.

Federal Food Assistance Programs Adequate nutrition and food security are essential in supporting good health and achieving the public health goals of the United States. To that end, an extensive network of federal assistance programs provides life-giving food to millions of U.S. citizens daily. One out of every six Americans receives food assistance of some kind, at a total cost of more than $40 billion per year. Even so, the programs are not fully successful in preventing hunger, but they do seem to improve the nutrient intakes of those who participate. Programs described in earlier chapters include the WIC program for low-income pregnant women, breastfeeding mothers, and their young children (Chapter 15); the school lunch, breakfast, and child-care food programs for children (Chapter 16); and the food assistance programs for older adults such as congregate meals and Meals on Wheels (Chapter 17).

The Food Stamp Program, administered by the U.S. Department of Agriculture (USDA), is the largest of the federal food assistance programs, both in amount of

Feeding the hungry—in the United States.

money spent and in number of people served. It provides assistance to almost 24 million people at a cost of more than $25 billion per year; more than half of the recipients are children.[12] The USDA issues debit cards through state agencies to households—people who buy and prepare food together. The amount a household receives depends on its size, resources, and income. The average monthly benefit is about $86 per person.[13] Recipients may use the cards to purchase food and food-bearing plants and seeds, but not to buy tobacco, cleaning items, alcohol, or other nonfood items. The accompanying "How to" offers shopping tips for those on a limited budget.

The Food Stamp Program improves nutrient intakes significantly, but hunger continues to plague the United States. Of the estimated 2 million homeless people in the United States who are eligible for food assistance, only 15 percent of single adults and 50 percent of families receive food stamps. For some, reading, understanding, and completing the application can be difficult. For others, having to show identification and proof of homelessness can be frustrating. For many, accepting hunger is simply easier than meeting these challenges.

National Food Recovery Programs Efforts to resolve the problem of hunger in the United States do not depend solely on federal assistance programs. National **food recovery** ◆ programs have made a dramatic difference. The largest program, Second Harvest, coordinates the efforts of more than 40,000 **food pantries, emergency shelters,** and **soup kitchens** that feed more than 25 million people a year.

Each year, an estimated one-fifth of our food supply is wasted in fields, commercial kitchens, grocery stores, and restaurants—that's enough food to feed 49 million people. Food recovery programs collect and distribute good food that would otherwise go to waste. Volunteers might pick corn left in an already harvested field, a grocer might deliver ripe bananas to a local **food bank,** and a caterer might take leftover chicken salad to a community shelter, for example. All of these efforts help to feed the hungry in the United States.

Community Efforts Food recovery programs depend on volunteers. Concerned citizens work through local agencies and churches to feed the hungry. Community-based food pantries provide groceries, and soup kitchens serve prepared meals. Meals often deliver adequate nourishment, but most homeless people receive fewer than one and a half meals a day, so many are still inadequately nourished. A combination of various strategies helps to build food security in a community.[14]

◆ Four common methods of food recovery are:
- *Field gleaning:* collecting crops from fields that either have already been harvested or are not profitable to harvest
- *Perishable food rescue or salvage:* collecting perishable produce from wholesalers and markets
- *Prepared food rescue:* collecting prepared foods from commercial kitchens
- *Nonperishable food collection:* collecting processed foods from wholesalers and markets

food recovery: collecting wholesome food for distribution to low-income people who are hungry.

food pantries: programs that provide groceries to be prepared and eaten at home.

emergency shelters: facilities that are used to provide temporary housing.

soup kitchens: programs that provide prepared meals to be eaten on site.

food bank: a facility that collects and distributes food donations to authorized organizations feeding the hungry.

HOW TO Plan Healthy, Thrifty Meals

Chapter 2 introduced the USDA MyPyramid Food Guide and principles for planning a healthy diet. Meeting that goal on a limited budget adds to the challenge. To save money and spend wisely, plan and shop for healthy meals with the following tips in mind:

Planning
- Make a grocery list before going to the store to avoid expensive "impulse" items.
- Do not shop when hungry.
- Use leftovers.
- Center meals on rice, noodles, and other grains.
- Use small quantities of meat, poultry, fish, or eggs.
- Use legumes instead of meat, poultry, fish, or eggs several times a week.
- Use cooked cereals such as oatmeal instead of ready-to-eat breakfast cereals.

- Cook large quantities when time and money allow.
- Check for sales and clip coupons for products you need; plan meals to take advantage of sale items.

Shopping
- Buy day-old bread and other products from the bakery outlet.
- Select whole foods instead of convenience foods (potatoes instead of instant mashed potatoes, for example).
- Try store brands.
- Buy fresh produce that is in season; buy canned or frozen items at other times.
- Buy only the amount of fresh foods that you will eat before it spoils. Buy large bags of frozen items or dry goods; when cooking, take out the amount needed and store the remainder.

- Buy fat-free dry milk; mix and refrigerate quantities needed for a day or two. Buy fresh milk by the gallon or half-gallon.
- Buy less expensive cuts of meat. Chuck and bottom round roast are usually inexpensive; cover during cooking and cook long enough to make meat tender. Buy whole chickens instead of pieces.
- Compare the unit price (cost per ounce, for example) of similar foods so that you can select the least expensive brand or size.
- Buy nonfood items such as toilet paper and laundry detergent at discount stores instead of grocery stores.

For daily menus and recipes for healthy, thrifty meals, visit the USDA Center for Nutrition Policy and Promotion: www.usda.gov/cnpp

IN SUMMARY

Food insecurity and hunger are widespread in the United States among those living in poverty. Ironically, hunger and poverty are common among obese people. Government assistance programs help to relieve poverty and hunger, but food recovery programs and other community efforts are equally important.

World Hunger

As distressing as hunger is in the United States, its prevalence is greater and its consequences more severe in developing countries. Although the hunger in these countries has diverse causes, once again, the primary cause is poverty, and the poverty is more extreme than in the United States. Most people cannot grasp the severity of poverty in the developing world. One-sixth of the world's 6.55 billion people have no land and no possessions *at all.* They are the "poorest poor." They survive on less than $1 a day each, they lack clean drinking water, and they cannot read or write. The average U.S. housecat receives twice as much protein every day as one of these people, and the cost of keeping that cat is greater than such a person's annual income.

The "poorest poor" are usually female. Many societies around the world undervalue females, providing girls with poorer diets and fewer opportunities than boys. Malnourished girls become malnourished mothers who give birth to low-birthweight infants—and the cycle of hunger, malnutrition, and poverty continues.

Not only does poverty cause hunger, but tragically, hunger worsens poverty by robbing a person of the good health and the physical and mental energy needed to be active and productive. Hungry people simply cannot work hard enough to get themselves out of poverty. Malnourished people with a low BMI earn less money performing manual labor; an increase in BMI of 1 percent correlates with an increase in wages of 2 percent. Economists calculate that cutting world hunger and malnutrition in half by 2015 would generate a value of more than $120 billion in longer, healthier, and more productive lives.[15]

© Tim Graham/Getty Images

Feeding the hungry—in Calcutta, India.

Food Shortages

World hunger brings to mind victims of **famine,** a severe food shortage in an area that causes widespread starvation and death. In recent years, the natural causes of famine—drought, flood, and pests—have become less important than the political causes created by people. Figure 20-2 shows the hunger hotspots in the world.

Political Turbulence A sudden increase in food prices, a drop in workers' incomes, or a change in government policy can quickly leave millions hungry. An estimated 30 million people died during the Chinese famine of 1959 through 1961, the worst famine of the 20th century. The main cause was government policies associated with the Great Leap Forward, a government initiative that was intended to transform China's economy. However, the poorly planned communal farm system and the widespread waste of resources devastated the Chinese agricultural system.

Armed Conflicts In the past decade, armed conflict and political unrest were the dominant cause of famine worldwide. In times of war, farmers become warriors, their agricultural fields become battlegrounds, the citizens go hungry, and the warring factions often block famine relief. The world continues to struggle to find a middle ground between respecting the sovereignty of nations and insisting that all nations allow humanitarian assistance to reach the people. When supplementary food programs reach the people in war-torn countries, the children benefit.[16]

famine: widespread and extreme scarcity of food in an area that causes starvation and death in a large portion of the population.

FIGURE 20-2 Hunger Hotspots

Hunger is prevalent in the developing world, with some countries reporting hunger and malnutrition in over one-third of their population.

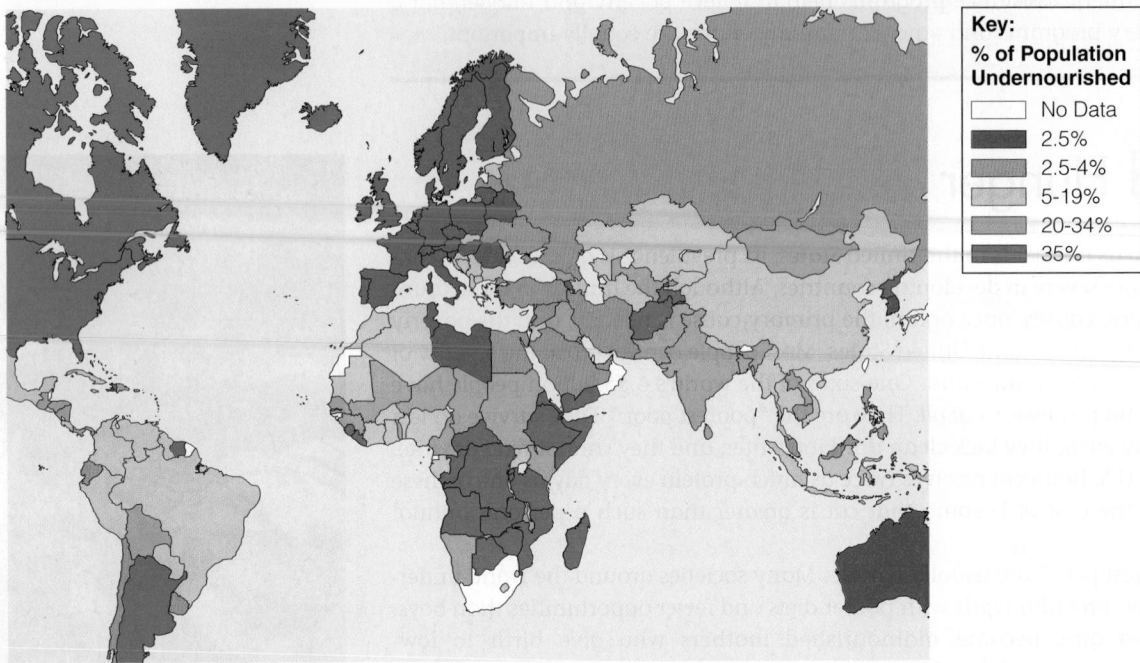

Key:
% of Population Undernourished

- No Data
- 2.5%
- 2.5-4%
- 5-19%
- 20-34%
- 35%

SOURCE: Food and Agriculture Organization of the United Nations, *The State of Food Insecurity in the World 2003* available from www.wfp.org/country_brief/hunger_map/map/hungermap_popup/map_popup.html

© Chris Hondros/Getty Images

International efforts help to relieve hunger and poverty in Afghanistan and around the world.

◆ To help prevent blindness and reduce measles mortality, health care workers distribute vitamin A supplements to millions of children worldwide.

Natural Disasters Natural disasters and other poor weather conditions create food shortages. In 2004, the drought and desert locust infestation in North and West Africa and the earthquake tsunami in Indonesia dramatically reduced food supplies.[17] During such natural disasters, food aid from countries around the world has provided a safety net for countries in need. But food aid now does more than just offset poor harvests and destroyed crops; it also delivers food relief to countries, such as Ethiopia, that are chronically short of food because of ongoing drought and poverty.

Malnutrition

Although we usually associate world hunger with famine, the numbers affected by famine are relatively small compared with those suffering from persistent hunger and malnutrition. More than 850 million people, mostly women and children, are hungry and malnourished, with another 2 billion perilously close.[18] The nutrients most likely to be lacking are iron, iodine, and vitamin A.[19] The prevalence and consequences of these deficiencies stagger the mind.[20] More than 30 percent of the world's population have iron-deficiency anemia, a leading cause of maternal deaths, premature births, low birthweights, infections, and premature deaths. Iodine deficiency affects one out of seven, resulting in stillbirths and irreversible mental retardation (cretinism) in 37 million newborns every year. Almost 80 million young children (under age five) suffer from symptoms of vitamin A deficiency—blindness, growth retardation, and poor resistance to common childhood infections such as measles. ◆ The deficiency symptoms of these nutrients and those of the other vitamins and minerals were presented in Chapters 10 through 13; Chapter 6 described protein-energy malnutrition; and Chapters 15 through 17 examined the effects of malnutrition during various stages of the life cycle. The consequences of nutrient deficiencies are felt not only by individuals, but by entire nations. When people suffer from mental retardation, growth failure, blindness, infections, and other consequences of malnutrition, the economy of their country declines as productivity decreases and health care costs increase. The dramatic signs of malnutrition are most evident at each end of the life span in a nation's high infant mortality rate and low life expectancy.

In addition to specific nutrient deficiencies, one child in six worldwide is born underweight, and one in four children are underweight by the age of five. ◆ These underweight children are malnourished and readily develop the diseases of poverty: parasitic and infectious diseases that cause diarrhea (dysentery and cholera), acute respiratory illnesses (pneumonia and whooping cough), measles, and malaria. The synergistic combination of infectious disease and malnutrition dramatically increases the likelihood of early death.[21] Compared with adequately nourished children, the risk of death is 2.5 times greater for children with mild malnutrition, 4.6 times greater for children with moderate malnutrition, and 8.4 times greater for children with severe malnutrition. Each year, 5.6 million children die as a result of hunger and malnutrition. Most of them do not starve to death—they die from the diarrhea and dehydration that accompany infections. Health care workers around the world save millions of lives ◆ each year by effectively reversing dehydration and correcting the diarrhea with **oral rehydration therapy (ORT)**.

◆ More than half of the world's underweight children live in just three countries:
• Bangladesh
• India
• Pakistan

◆ To prevent death from diarrheal disease, provide:
• Adequate sanitation
• Safe water
• Oral rehydration therapy

Diminishing Food Supply

Most disturbingly, such misery and starvation exist side by side with ample food supplies. Technological advances in farming have increased crop yields. And prices of many foods have fallen in response. But the demand for food is great. At the present rate of growth, the world's population may soon outstrip the rate of food production. Environmental degradation and dwindling water supplies may limit further growth in the world's food production in many agricultural areas. No part of the world is safely insulated against future food shortages. Developed countries may be the last to feel the effects, but they will ultimately go as the world goes.

IN SUMMARY

Natural causes such as drought, flood, and pests and political causes such as armed conflicts and government policies all contribute to the extreme hunger and poverty seen in the developing countries. To meet future demands for food, technology must improve food production, and nations must control overpopulation.

Poverty and Overpopulation

The world's population is rising at an alarming rate, as Figure 20-3 (p. 708) shows. Skyrocketing numbers threaten the earth's capacity ◆ to provide safe water and adequate food for its inhabitants.

The sheer magnitude of the world's annual population increase of more than 70 million people is difficult to comprehend. Every half-second, the population increases by another person. Every 40 days, the world adds the equivalent of another New York City. During the six months of the terrible 1992 famine in Somalia, an estimated 300,000 people starved to death. Yet it took the world only *29 hours* to replace their numbers!

As the world's population continues to grow, much of the increase is occurring in developing countries where hunger and malnutrition are already widespread. More people sharing the little food available can only worsen the problem. Stabilizing the population may be the only way the world's food production will be able

◆ The maximum number of people the earth can support over time is its **human carrying capacity.**

oral rehydration therapy (ORT): the administration of a simple solution of sugar, salt, and water, taken by mouth, to treat dehydration caused by diarrhea. A simple ORT recipe:
• 1 c boiling water
• 2 tsp sugar
• A pinch of salt

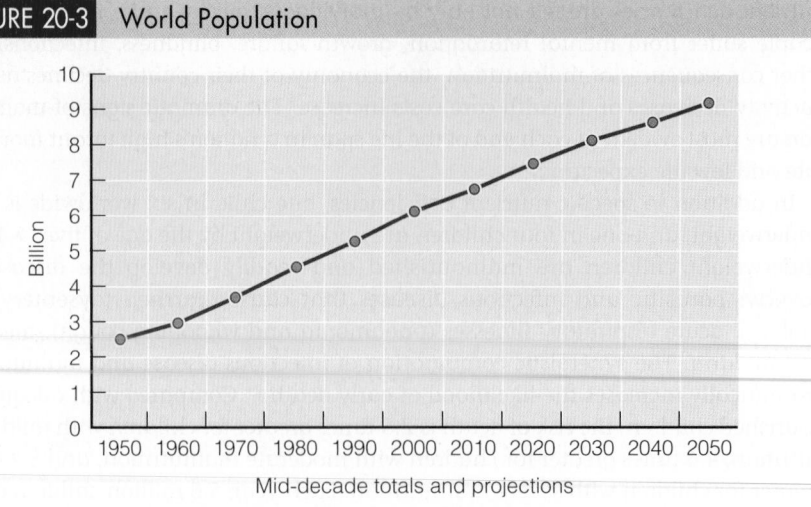

FIGURE 20-3 | World Population

Mid-decade totals and projections

to keep up with demands. Without population stabilization, the world can neither support the lives of people already born nor halt environmental deterioration around the globe. And before the population problem can be resolved, it may be necessary to remedy the poverty problem. In countries around the world, economic growth has been accompanied by slowed population growth.

Population growth is a central factor contributing to poverty and hunger. The reverse is also true: poverty and hunger contribute to population growth.

Population Growth Leads to Hunger and Poverty The first of these cause-and-effect relationships is easy to understand. As a population grows larger, more mouths must be fed, and the worse poverty and hunger become.

Population growth also contributes to hunger indirectly by preempting good agricultural land for growing cities and industry and forcing people onto marginal land, where they cannot produce sufficient food for themselves. The world's poorest people live in the world's most damaged and inhospitable environments.

Hunger and Poverty Lead to Population Growth How does poverty lead to overpopulation? Poverty and its consequences—inadequate food and shelter—leave women vulnerable to physical abuse, forced marriages, and prostitution. Furthermore, they lack access to reproductive health care and family planning counseling. Also, in some regions of the world, families depend on children to farm the land, haul water, and care for adults in their old age. Children are an economic asset for these families. Poverty claims many young children, who are among the most likely to die from malnutrition and disease. If a family faces ongoing poverty, the parents may choose to have many children to ensure that some will survive to adulthood. People are willing to risk having fewer children only if they are sure that their children will live and that the family can develop other economic assets (skills, businesses, land).

Breaking the Cycle Relieving poverty and hunger, then, may be a necessary first step in curbing population growth. When people attain better access to health care, education, and family planning, the death rate falls. At first, births outnumber deaths, but as the standard of living continues to improve, families become willing to risk having fewer children. Then the birth rate falls. Thus improvements in living standards help stabilize the population.

The link between improved economic status and slowed population growth has been demonstrated in several countries. Central to achieving this success is sustainable development that includes not only economic growth, but a sharing of resources among all groups. Where this has happened, population growth has slowed the most: in parts of Sri Lanka, Taiwan, Malaysia, and Costa Rica, for example. Where economic growth has occurred but only the rich have grown richer, population growth has remained high. Examples include Brazil, the Philippines, and Thailand, where large families continue to be a major economic asset for the poor.

Families in developing countries depend on their children to help provide for daily needs.

© Jeremy Horner/Corbis

As a society gains economic footing, education also becomes a higher priority. A society that educates its children, both males and females, experiences a drop in birth rates. Education, particularly for girls and women, brings improvements in family life, including improved nutrition, better sanitation, effective birth control, and elevated status. With improved conditions, more infants live to adulthood, making smaller families feasible.

IN SUMMARY

More people means more mouths to feed, which worsens the problems of poverty and hunger. Poverty and hunger, in turn, encourage parents to have more children. Breaking this cycle requires improving the economic status of the people and providing them with health care, education, and family planning.

Environmental Degradation and Hunger

Hunger, poverty, and overpopulation interact with another force: environmental degradation. The environment suffers as more and more people must share fewer and fewer resources. In developing countries, people living in poverty sell everything they own to obtain money for food, even the seeds that would have provided next year's crops. They cut trees for firewood or timber to sell, and then they lose the soil to erosion. Without these resources, they become poorer still. Thus poverty contributes to environmental ruin, and the ruin leads to hunger. Environmental degradation threatens the world's ability to produce enough food to feed its many people—and the vicious cycle of poverty, population growth, and environmental degradation continues.

Environmental Limitations in Food Production

Environmental problems that are slowing food production include:

- *Soil erosion, compaction, and salinization* due to overtillage and overirrigation result in extensive loss of productive croplands.
- *Deforestation and desertification* due to overgrazing lead to soil erosion.
- *Air pollution* produced from the burning of **fossil fuels** damages crops and depletes the ozone.
- *Ozone depletion* allows harmful radiation from the sun to damage crops, especially radiation-sensitive crops such as soybeans.
- *Climate changes* are caused by destruction of forests and concentration of heat-trapping carbon dioxide produced by fossil fuels. A rise in global temperature may reduce soil moisture, impair pollination of major food crops such as rice and corn, slow growth, weaken disease resistance, and disrupt many other factors affecting crop yields.[22]
- *Water pollution* from agricultural sediments, salts, fertilizers, pesticides, and manure limits agricultural yields, drinking water, and fishery production.
- *Water scarcity* due to overuse of surface and ground water for irrigation may limit human population growth even before food scarcity does. In many areas, the supplies of fresh water are already inadequate to fully support the survival of crops, livestock, and people.[23]
- *Extensive overgrazing* is causing rangelands to deteriorate. In nearly all developing countries, the food needs of livestock now exceed the capacity of their rangelands.

Without water, croplands become deserts.

© Holt Studios International Ltd/Alamy

fossil fuels: coal, oil, and natural gas.

- *Overfishing and water pollution* are destroying fisheries and diminishing the supply of seafood.

All in all, environmental problems are reducing the world's ability to feed its people and keep them healthy.[24]

Other Limitations in Food Production

With crop fields, rangelands, and fish yields diminishing, can advances in agriculture compensate for the losses caused by environmental degradation? Historically, agriculture has yields by making greater investments in irrigation, fertilizer, and genetic strains. Today, however, the contributions these measures can make are reaching their limits, in part because they have also created environmental problems. Irrigation can no longer compensate by improving crop yields because almost all the land that can benefit from irrigation is already receiving it. In fact, rising concentrations of salt in the soil—a by-product of irrigation—are *lowering* yields on nearly a quarter of the world's irrigated cropland. Nor can fertilizer use significantly enhance agricultural production. Much of the fertilizing that can be done is being done—and with great effect; fertilizer use supports some 40 percent of the world's total crop yields. Adding more fertilizer, however, brings no further rise in yield and adds to the pollution of nearby waterways. As for the development of high-yielding strains of crops, recent advances have been dramatic, but even they may be inadequate to change the overall trends. Furthermore, the raw materials necessary for developing new crops have become less available as genetic variation for many plant species is lost. Of the 5000 food plants grown throughout the world a few centuries ago, only 150 are cultivated in commercial agriculture today. Most of the world's population relies on only five cereals, three legumes, and three root crops to meet their energy needs. Even among these, valuable strains are vanishing.

◆ World agriculture produces enough food to provide each person with 2720 kcal/day.

The world still produces enough food to feed all of its people, ◆ and the problem of hunger today remains a problem of unequal distribution of land to grow crops or income to purchase foods. If present trends continue, however, the time is fast approaching when there will be an absolute deficit of food. This conclusion seems inescapable. The world's increasing population threatens the world's capacity to produce adequate food. Until the nations of the world resolve the population problem, they can neither support the lives of people already born nor remedy global trends toward environmental deterioration. And to resolve the population problem, a necessary first step is to remedy the poverty problems, for reasons already discussed. Of the 70 million people being added to the population each year, 95 percent are born in the most poverty-stricken areas of the world.

IN SUMMARY

Increasing environmental degradation reduces our ability to produce enough food to feed the world's people. The rapid increase in the world's population exacerbates the situation.

Solutions

Slowly but surely, improvements are evident in developing nations. Most nations have seen a rise in their gross domestic product, a key measure of economic well-being. Adult literacy rates and the proportion of children being sent to school have risen. The proportion of undernourished people has declined. Optimism abounds, though problems remain.

The keys to solving the world's hunger, poverty, and environmental problems are in the hands of both the poor and the rich nations but require different efforts

Each person's choice to get involved and be heard can help lead to needed change.

© Elsa Peterson-Stock Boston

from them. The poor nations need to provide contraceptive technology and family planning information to their citizens, develop better programs to assist the poor, and slow and reverse the destruction of environmental resources. The rich nations need to stem their wasteful and polluting uses of resources and energy, which are contributing to global environmental degradation. They also must become willing to ease the debt burden that many poor nations face.

Sustainable Development Worldwide

Many nations now recognize that improving all nations' economies is a prerequisite to meeting the world's other urgent needs: hunger relief, population stabilization, environmental preservation, and **sustainable** resources. More than 100 nations have agreed to a set of principles of sustainable development—development that would equitably meet both the economic and the environmental needs of present and future generations. They recognize that relieving poverty will help relieve environmental degradation and hunger.

To rephrase a well-known adage: If you give a man a fish, he will eat for a day. If you teach him to fish and enable him to buy and maintain his own gear and bait, he will eat for a lifetime and help to feed others. Unlike food giveaways and money doles, which are only stop-gap measures, social programs that permanently improve the lives of the poor can permanently solve the hunger problem.

The fight against hunger depends on the helping hands of caring volunteers.

Activism and Simpler Lifestyles at Home

Every segment of our society can join in the fight against hunger, poverty, and environmental degradation. The federal government, the states, local communities, big business and small companies, educators, and all individuals, including dietitians and foodservice managers, have many opportunities to resolve these problems.

Government Action Government policies can change to promote sustainability. For example, the government can use tax dollars and other resources to develop energy conservation services and crop protection.

Business Involvement Businesses can take the initiative to help; some already have. Several large corporations are major supporters of antihunger programs. Many grocery stores and restaurants participate in food recovery programs by giving their leftover foods to community distribution centers.

Education Educators, including nutrition educators, can teach others about the underlying social and political causes of poverty, the root cause of hunger. At the college level, they can teach the relationships between hunger and population, hunger and environmental degradation, hunger and the status of women, and hunger and global economics. They can advocate legislation to address these problems. They can teach the poor to develop and run nutrition programs in their own communities and to fight on their own behalf for antipoverty, antihunger legislation.

Foodservice Efforts Dietitians and foodservice managers have a special role to play, and their efforts can make an impressive difference. Their professional organization, the ADA, urges members to conserve resources and minimize waste in both their professional and their personal lives.[25] In addition, the ADA urges its members to educate themselves and others on hunger, its consequences, and programs to fight it; to conduct research on the effectiveness and benefits of programs; and to serve as advocates on the local, state, and national levels to help end hunger in the United States.[26] Globally, the ADA supports programs that combat malnutrition, provide food security, promote self-sufficiency, respect local cultures, protect the environment, and sustain the economy.[27]

Individual Choices Individuals can assist the global community in solving its poverty and hunger problems by joining and working for hunger-relief organizations (see Table 20-1 on p. 712). They can also support organizations that lobby for the needed changes in economic policies toward developing countries.

sustainable: able to continue indefinitely; using resources at such a rate that the earth can keep on replacing them and producing pollutants at a rate with which the environment and human cleanup efforts can keep pace, so that no net accumulation of pollution occurs.

TABLE 20-1	Hunger-Relief Organizations

Action without Borders
79 Fifth Ave., 17th Floor
New York, NY 10118
(212) 843-3973
www.idealist.org

Bread for the World
50 F St. NW, Suite 500
Washington, DC 20001
(800) 82-BREAD or (800) 822-7323
(202) 639-9400; fax (202) 639-9401
www.bread.org

Center on Hunger and Poverty
Brandeis University
Mailstop 077
Waltham, MA 02454
(781) 736-8885
www.centeronhunger.org

Community Food Security Coalition
P.O. Box 909
Venice, CA 90294
(310) 822-5410
www.foodsecurity.org

Congressional Hunger Center
229½ Pennsylvania Ave.
Washington, DC 20003
(202) 547-7022
www.hungercenter.org

HungerWeb
Tufts Nutrition
nutrition.tufts.edu/academic/
hungerweb/overview

Oxfam America
26 West St.
Boston, MA 02111-1206
(800) 77-OXFAM or
(800) 776-9326
www.oxfamamerica.org

Pan American Health Organization
525 23rd St. NW
Washington, DC 20037
(202) 974-3000
www.paho.org

Second Harvest
35 E. Wacker Dr., #2000
Chicago, IL 60601
(800) 771-2303
www.secondharvest.org

Society of St. Andrew
3383 Sweet Hollow Rd.
Big Island, VA 24526
(800) 333-4597
www.endhunger.org

Food and Agriculture
Organization (FAO) of the
United Nations
2175 K St. NW, Suite 300
Washington, DC 20437
(202) 653-2400
www.fao.org

United Nations Children's Fund
(UNICEF)
3 United Nations Plaza
New York, NY 10017-4414
(212) 326-7035
www.unicef.org

World Food Program
Via Vittorio Emanuele Orlando, 83
Rome, Italy 00148
www.wfp.org

World Health Organization (WHO)
525 23rd St. NW
Washington, DC 20037
(202) 974-3000
www.who.org

World Hunger Year (WHY)
505 Eighth Ave., 21st Floor
New York, NY 10018-6582
(800) GleanIt
www.worldhungeryear.org

◆ A popular adage urges us to "Think globally, act locally."

Most importantly, all individuals can try to make lifestyle choices ◆ that consider the environmental consequences. Many small decisions each day have major consequences for the environment. The accompanying "How to" describes how consumers can conserve resources and minimize waste when making food-related choices.

HOW TO	Make Environmentally Friendly Food-Related Choices

Food production taxes environmental resources and causes pollution. Consumers can make environmentally friendly choices at every step from food shopping to cooking and use of kitchen appliances to serving, cleanup, and waste disposal.

Food Shopping
Transportation:
• Whenever possible, walk or ride a bicycle; use car pools and mass transit.
• Shop only once a week, share trips, or take turns shopping for each other.
• When buying a car, choose an energy-efficient one.

Food choices:
• Choose foods low on the food chain; that is, eat more plants and fewer animals that eat plants (this suggestion complements the *Dietary Guidelines* for eating for good health).
• Eat small portions of meat; select range-fed beef, buffalo, poultry, and fish.
• Select local foods; they require less transportation, packaging, and refrigeration.

Food packages:
• Whenever possible, select foods with no packages; next best are minimal, reusable, or recyclable ones.
• Buy juices and sodas in large glass or recyclable plastic bottles (not small individual cans or cartons); grains in bulk (not separate little packages); and eggs in pressed fiber cartons (not foam, unless it is recycled locally).
• Carry reusable string or cloth shopping bags; alternatively, ask for plastic bags if they are recyclable.

Gardening
• Grow some of your own food, even if it is only herbs planted in pots on your kitchen windowsill.
• Compost all vegetable scraps, fruit peelings, and leftover plant foods.

Cooking Food
• Cook foods quickly in a stir-fry, pressure cooker, or microwave oven.
• When using the oven, bake a lot of food at one time and keep the door closed tightly.
• Use nondisposable utensils, dishes, and pans.
• Use pumps instead of spray products.

Kitchen Appliances
• Use fewer small electrical appliances; open cans, mix batters, sharpen knives, and chop vegetables by hand.
• When buying a large appliance, choose an energy-efficient one.
• Consider solar power to meet home electrical needs.
• Set the water heater at 130°F (54°C), no hotter; put it on a timer; wrap it and the hot-water pipes in insulation; install water-saving faucets.

Food Serving, Dish Washing, and Waste Disposal
• Use "real" plates, cups, and glasses instead of disposable ones.
• Use cloth towels and napkins, reusable storage containers with lids, reusable pans, and dishcloths instead of paper towels, plastic wrap, plastic storage bags, aluminum foil, and sponges.
• Run the dishwasher only when it is full.
• Recycle all glass, plastic, and aluminum.

These suggested lifestyle changes can easily be extended from food to other areas.

The personal rewards of the behaviors presented in the previous "How to" are many, from saving money to the satisfaction of knowing that you are treading lightly on the earth. But do they really help? They do, if enough people join in. Because we number more than 6 billion, individual actions can add up to exert an immense impact.

"Be part of the solution, not part of the problem," another adage says. In other words, don't waste time or energy moaning and groaning about how bad things are: do something to improve them. This adage is as applicable to today's global environmental problems as it is to an unwashed dish in the kitchen sink. They are our problems: human beings created them, and human beings must solve them.

IN SUMMARY

The global environment, which supports all life, is deteriorating, largely because of our irresponsible use of resources and energy. Governments, businesses, and all individuals have many opportunities to make environmentally conscious choices, which may help solve the hunger problem, improve the quality of life, and generate jobs. Personal choices, made by many people, can have a great impact.

NASA

"We do not inherit the earth from our ancestors, we borrow it from our children." Ascribed to Chief Seattle, a 19th century Native American leader.

ThomsonNOW™
www.thomsonedu.com/thomsonnow

Nutrition Portfolio

Your choice to get involved in the fight against hunger—whether in your community or across the globe—can make a big difference in the health and survival of others.

■ Find out about the hunger-relief programs in your area.

■ Write to your legislators and voice your opinions on issues such as food assistance programs, environmental degradation, and international debt relief.

■ Consider which environmentally friendly behaviors you are willing to adopt when making food-related choices.

NUTRITION ON THE NET

ThomsonNOW™
For further study of topics covered in this chapter, log on to **www.thomsonedu .com/thomsonnow**. Go to Chapter 20, then to Nutrition on the Net.

• Explore the problems of hunger, malnutrition, and food insecurity at the Feeding Minds, Fighting Hunger site: **www.feedingminds.org**

• Learn about constructive, community-based solutions to the problems of poverty and hunger within and between the public and private sectors from the National Hunger Clearinghouse: **www.worldhungeryear.org/nhc**

• Visit the USDA Food Stamp Program: **www.fns.usda.gov/fsp**

• Download recipes, sample menus, and numerous tips for planning, shopping for, and cooking healthy meals on a

tight budget from the USDA cookbook entitled "Recipes and Tips for Healthy, Thrifty Meals": **www.usda.gov/cnpp**

• Review the Best Practices Manual for Food Recovery and Gleaning at the USDA Food and Nutrition Service site: **www.fns.usda.gov/fdd/gleaning/gleanintro.htm**

• Find information on feeding the hungry from the Emergency Food and Shelter Program: **www.efsp.unitedway.org**

• Donate free food at The Hunger Site: **www.thehungersite .com**

• See Table 20-1 (on p. 712) for additional websites.

STUDY QUESTIONS

ThomsonNOW™
To assess your understanding of chapter topics, take the Student Practice Test and explore the modules recommended in your Personalized Study Plan. Log onto www.thomsonedu.com/thomsonnow.

These questions will help you review the chapter. You will find the answers in the discussions on the pages provided.

1. Identify some reasons why hunger is present in a country as wealthy as the United States. (pp. 702–703)

2. Identify some reasons why hunger is present in the developing countries of the world. (pp. 705–706)

3. Explain why relieving environmental problems will also help to alleviate hunger and poverty. (pp. 709–710)

4. Discuss the different paths by which rich and poor countries can attack the problems of world hunger and the environment. (p. 711)

5. Describe some strategies that consumers can use to minimize negative environmental impacts when shopping for food, preparing meals, and disposing of garbage. (p. 712)

These multiple choice questions will help you prepare for an exam. Answers can be found on p. 715.

1. Food insecurity refers to the:
   a. uncertainty of foods' safety.
   b. fear of eating too much food.
   c. limited availability of foods.
   d. reliability of food production.

2. The most common cause of hunger in the United States is:
   a. poverty.
   b. alcohol abuse.
   c. mental illness.
   d. lack of education.

3. Food stamp debit cards cannot be used to purchase:
   a. tomato plants.
   b. birthday cakes.
   c. cola beverages.
   d. laundry detergent.

4. Which action is not typical of a food recovery program?
   a. gathering potatoes from a harvested field
   b. collecting overripe tomatoes from a wholesaler
   c. offering food stamp debit cards to low-income people
   d. delivering restaurant leftovers to a community shelter

5. The primary cause of the worst famine in the 20th century was:
   a. armed conflicts.
   b. natural disasters.
   c. food contaminations.
   d. government policies.

6. The most likely cause of death in malnourished children is:
   a. growth failure.
   b. diarrheal disease.
   c. simple starvation.
   d. vitamin A deficiency.

7. Which of the following is most critical in providing food to all the world's people?
   a. decreasing air pollution
   b. increasing water supplies
   c. decreasing population growth
   d. increasing agricultural land

8. Which of these items is the most environmentally benign choice?
   a. sponges
   b. plastic bags
   c. aluminum foil
   d. cotton towels

9. Which of these methods uses the most fuel?
   a. baking
   b. stir-frying
   c. microwaving
   d. pressure cooking

10. Which of these purchases is the best choice, for environmental reasons?
    a. fresh fish from a local merchant
    b. frozen fish from a developing country
    c. canned fish from a nationally known food manufacturer
    d. packaged fish from the freezer section of a local supermarket

REFERENCES

1. Food and Agriculture Organization of the United Nations, *State of Food Insecurity in the World 2005*.
2. United States Department of Agriculture, *Household Food Security in the United States, 2005*, ERS Research Briefs, available from www.ers.usda.gov/publications.
3. J. S. Hampl and R. Hill, Dietetic approaches to US hunger and food insecurity, *Journal of the American Dietetic Association* 102 (2002): 919–923.
4. K. M. Kempson and coauthors, Food management practices used by people with limited resources to maintain food sufficiency as reported by nutrition educators, *Journal of the American Dietetic Association* 102 (2002): 1795–1799.
5. J. T. Cook and coauthors, Food insecurity is associated with adverse health outcomes among human infants and toddlers, *Journal of Nutrition* 134 (2004): 1432–1438.
6. D. F. Jyoti, E. A. Frongillo, and S. J. Jones, Food insecurity affects school children's academic performance, weight gain, and social skills, *Journal of Nutrition* 135 (2005): 2831–2839.
7. L. M. Scheier, What is the hunger-obesity paradox? *Journal of the American Dietetic Association* 105 (2005): 883–886.
8. P. E. Wilde and J. N. Peterman, Individual weight change is associated with household food security status, *Journal of Nutrition* 136 (2006): 1395–1400; A. Drewnowski and S. E. Specter, Poverty and obesity; The role of energy density and energy costs, *American Journal of Clinical Nutrition* 79 (2004): 6–16; E. J. Adams, L. Grummer-Strawn, and G. Chavez, Food insecurity is associated with increased risk of obesity in California women, *Journal of Nutrition* 133 (2003): 1070–1074.

9. Drewnowski and Specter, 2004.
10. S. J. Jones and E. A. Frongillo, The modifying effects of Food Stamp program participation on the relation between food insecurity and weight change in women, *Journal of Nutrition* 136 (2006): 1091–1094; S. J. Jones and coauthors, Lower risk of overweight in school-aged food insecure girls who participate in food assistance, *Archives of Pediatrics and Adolescent Medicine* 157 (2003): 780–784.
11. Position of the American Dietetic Association: Food insecurity and hunger in the United States, *Journal of the American Dietetic Association* 106 (2006): 446–458.
12. USDA Food and Nutrition Service, www.fns.usda.gov/fsp, site visited August 30, 2006.
13. USDA Food and Nutrition Service, www.fns.usda.gov/fsp, site visited August 30, 2006.
14. C. McCullum and coauthors, Evidence-based strategies to build community food security, *Journal of the American Dietetic Association* 105 (2005): 278–283.
15. Food and Agriculture Organization, *The State of Food Insecurity in the World 2004*, www.fao.org, site visited December 7, 2006.
16. J. Nielsen and coauthors, Malnourished children and supplementary feeding during the war emergency in Guinea-Bissau in 1998–1999, *American Journal of Clinical Nutrition* 80 (2004): 1036–1042.
17. Food and Agriculture Organization of the United Nations, *State of Food Insecurity in the World 2005*.
18. P. A. Sanchez and M. S. Swaminathan, Cutting world hunger in half, *Science* 307 (2005): 357–359; Food and Agriculture Organization of the United Nations, *State of Food Insecurity in the World 2005*.

19. U. Kapil and A. Bhavna, Adverse effects of poor micronutrient status during childhood and aolescence, *Nutrition Reviews* 60 (2002): S84–S90.
20. I. Darnton-Hill and coauthors, Micronutrient deficiencies and gender: Social and economic costs, *American Journal of Clinical Nutrition* 81 (2005): 1198S–1205S.
21. L. E. Caulfield and coauthors, Undernutrition as an underlying cause of child deaths associated with diarrhea, pneumonia, malaria, and measles, *American Journal of Clinical Nutrition* 80 (2004): 193–198; M. Peña and J. Bacallao, Malnutrition and poverty, *Annual Review of Nutrition* 22 (2002): 241–253.
22. S. Peng and coauthors, Rice yields decline with higher night temperature from global warming, *Proceedings of the National Academy of Sciences* 101 (2004): 9971–9975.
23. W. Jury and H. Vaux, The role of science in solving the world's emerging water problems, *The National Academy of Sciences,* 2004.
24. B. M. Kuehn, Desertification called global health threat, *Journal of the American Medical Association* 295 (2006): 2463–2465.
25. Position of the American Dietetic Association: Dietetic professionals can implement practices to conserve natural resources and protect the environment, *Journal of the American Dietetic Association* 101 (2001): 1221–1227.
26. Position of the American Dietetic Association, 2006.
27. Position of the American Dietetic Association: Addressing world hunger, malnutrition, and food insecurity, *Journal of the American Dietetic Association* 103 (2003): 1046–1057.

ANSWERS

Study Questions (multiple choice)

1. c   2. a   3. d   4. c   5. d   6. b   7. c   8. d   9. a   10. a

Progress toward Sustainable Food Production

© Paul Stover/Stone/Getty Images

While some individuals are making their own personal lifestyles more environmentally benign, as suggested in Chapter 20, others are seeking ways to improve whole sectors of human enterprise, among them, agriculture. To date, large agricultural enterprises have been among the world's biggest resource users and polluters. Is it possible for agriculture to become sustainable? What can consumers do to ease the environmental burden of food production? These questions are addressed in this highlight; the accompanying glossary presents terms important to these concepts.

Resource Waste and Pollution

The current environmental and social costs of agriculture and the food industry take many forms. Among them are resource waste and pollution (including energy overuse). Producing food costs the earth dearly. To grow food, we clear land—prairie, wetland, and forest—losing native ecosystems and wildlife. Then we plant crops or graze animals on the land. On the sea, we harvest fish with little thought of the dwindling supplies or the environmental damage incurred.

Planting Crops

The soil loses nutrients as each crop is taken from it, so fertilizer is applied. Some fertilizer runs off, polluting the waterways and stimulating algae growth. By the time rivers empty into the seas, the water is unsuitable for most forms of life.[1] Some plowed soil runs off, which clouds the waterways and interferes with the growth of aquatic plants and animals.

To protect crops against weeds and pests, we apply herbicides and pesticides. These chemicals also pollute the water and, wherever the wind carries them, the air. Most herbicides and pesticides injure more than weeds and pests; they also injure native plants, native insects, and animals that eat those plants and insects. Ironically, widespread use of pesticides and herbicides causes pests and weeds to evolve, becoming even more resistant. Consequently, farmers must use still more pesticides and herbicides. These chemicals pose hazards for farm workers who handle them, and the residues can create health problems for consumers as well (see Chapter 19).

Finally, we irrigate, a practice that causes salts to accumulate on the soil surface. The water evaporates, but the salts do not. As the surface soil becomes increasingly salty, plant growth suffers. Irrigation can also deplete the water supply over time because it pulls water from surface waters or from underground; then, the water evaporates or runs off. This process, carried to the extreme, can dry up rivers and lakes and lower the water table of a whole region. A vicious cycle develops. The drier the region becomes, the more the farmers must irrigate, and the more they irrigate, the drier the region becomes.

Raising Livestock

Raising livestock also takes a toll. Like plant crops, herds of livestock occupy land that once maintained itself in a natural state. The land suffers the losses of native plants and animals, soil erosion, water depletion, and desert formation. Alternatively, animals raised in large concentrated areas such as cattle feedlots or giant hog "farms" create environmental problems when huge masses of animal wastes are produced in the overcrowded, factory-style farms. These wastes leach into local soils and water supplies, polluting them. To prevent contamination of drinking water, the Environmental Protection Agency suggests several strategies for managing livestock, poultry, and horse waste. In addition to manure, cows produce large quantities of methane—a potent gas that may contribute to global warming. In addition to the waste problems, animals must be fed; grain is grown for them on other land. That land may require fertilizers, herbicides, pesticides, and irrigation, too. In the United States, more cropland is used to produce grains for livestock than to produce grains for people. Figure H20-1 compares the grain required to produce various foods.

FIGURE H20-1 Pounds of Grain Needed to Produce One Pound of Bread and One Pound of Animal Weight Gain

To gain one pound, animals raised for food have to eat many more pounds of grain than it takes to make a pound of bread.

SOURCE: Idea and data from T.R. Reid, Feeding the planet, *National Geographic*, October 1998, pp. 58–74

Fishing

Fishing also incurs environmental costs. Fishing easily becomes overfishing and depletes stocks of the very fish that people need to eat. Some fishing methods (such as nets and filament line) kill nonfood species and deplete large populations of aquatic animals, such as dolphins. Also, fishing is energy-intensive, requiring fuel for boats, refrigeration, processing, packing, and transport. Water pollution incurs health risks when people eat contaminated fish. Bioaccumulation of toxins in fish is a serious problem in some areas; in others it rules out fish consumption altogether.

Energy Overuse

The entire food industry, whether based on growing crops, raising livestock, or fishing, requires energy, which entails burning fossil fuels. Massive fossil fuel use threatens our planet by causing air and water pollution, global warming, ozone depletion, and other environmental and political problems.

In the United States, the food industry consumes about 20 percent of all the energy the nation uses. Most of this energy is used to run farm machinery and to produce fertilizers and pesticides. Energy is also used to prepare, package, transport, refrigerate, store, cook, and wash our foods.

The Cumulative Effects

Many national and international agencies are concerned about the environmental ramifications of agriculture. The prestigious National Academy of Sciences has reported that agriculture is the largest single source of **nonpoint water pollution** in the nation. Pollution from "point sources," such as sewage plants or factories, is relatively easy to control, but runoff from fields and pastures enters waterways from so many broad regions that it is nearly impossible to control.

Agriculture is destroying its own foundation. Agricultural activities have ruined millions of acres of fertile land that will be impossible to reclaim.

Agriculture is also weakening its own underpinnings by failing to conserve species diversity. By the year 2050, some 40,000 more plant species may become extinct. The United Nations' Food and Agriculture Organization attributes many of the losses, which are already occurring daily, to modern farming practices, as well as to population growth. The increasing uniformity of global eating habits also contributes. Wheat, rice, and maize provide more than half of the food energy around the world; only another two dozen crops provide the remainder. As people everywhere eat the same limited array of foods, local regions' native, genetically diverse plants no longer seem worth preserving. Yet, in the future, as the climate warms and the earth changes, those may be the very plants that people will need for food sources. A wild species of corn that grows in a dry climate, for example, might contain the genetic information necessary to help make domestic corn resistant to drought. (Highlight 19 offered several examples of how biotechnology is being used to improve food crops.)

The culprits that attend the growing of crops—land clearing; irrigation; fertilizer, pesticide, and herbicide overuse; and loss of genetic diversity—have taken a tremendous toll on the earth. In short, our ways of producing foods are, for the most part, not sustainable.

Sustainable Agriculture

For each of the problems described above, agricultural solutions are being devised, and indeed, some are being put into practice. Fully utilizing **sustainable agriculture** techniques across the country will require some new learning. Sustainable agriculture is not one system but a set of practices that can be adapted to meet the particular needs of a local area. The crop yields from farms that employ these practices often compare favorably with those from farms using less sustainable methods.[2] Table H20-1 (p. 718) contrasts low-input, sustainable agriculture methods with high-input, unsustainable methods. Many sustainable techniques are not really new, incidentally; they would be familiar to our great grandparents. Farmers today are rediscovering the benefits of old techniques as they adapt and experiment with them in the search for sustainable methods.

Consumer Choices

Table H20-2 (p. 718) lists several ways to save energy in the production of food. The last item in the table suggests that consumers should eat low on the food chain. For the most part, that

TABLE H20-1 Agricultural Methods Compared

Unsustainable Methods	Sustainable Methods
• Grow the same crop repeatedly on the same patch of land. This takes more and more nutrients out of the soil, making fertilizer use necessary; favors soil erosion; and invites weeds and pests to become established, making pesticide use necessary.	• Rotate crops. This increases nitrogen in the soil so there is less need to use fertilizers. If used with appropriate plowing methods, rotation reduces soil erosion. Rotation also reduces problems caused by weeds and pests.
• Use fertilizers generously. Excess fertilizer pollutes ground and surface water and costs both farmers' household money and consumers' tax money.	• Reduce the use of fertilizers, and use livestock manure more effectively. Store manure during the nongrowing season and apply it during the growing season. • Alternate nutrient-devouring crops with nutrient-restoring crops, such as legumes. • Compost on a large scale, including all plant residues not harvested. Plow the compost into the soil to improve its water-holding capacity.
• Feed livestock in feedlots where their manure produces a major water pollution probem. Piled in heaps, it also releases methane, a global-warming gas.	• Feed livestock or buffalo on the open range where their manure will fertilize the ground on which plants grow and will release no methane. Alternatively, at least collect feedlot animals' manure and use it for fertilizer or, at the very least, treat it before release.
• Spray herbicides and pesticides over large areas to wipe out weeds and pests.	• Apply ingenuity in weed and pest control. Use precision techniques if affordable or rotary hoes twice instead of herbicides once. Spot treat weeds by hand. • Rotate crops to foil pests that lay their eggs in the soil where last year's crop was grown. • Use resistant crops. • Use biological controls such as predators that destroy the pests.
• Plow the same way everywhere, allowing unsustainable water runoff and erosion.	• Plow in ways tailored to different areas. Conserve both soil and water by using cover crops, crop rotation, no-till planting, and contour plowing.
• Inject animals with antibiotics to prevent disease in livestock.	• Maintain animals' health so that they can resist disease.
• Irrigate on a large scale. Irrigation depletes water supplies and concentrates salts in the soil.	• Irrigate only during dry spells and apply only spot irrigation.

TABLE H20-2 Sustainable Energy-Saving Agricultural Techniques

• Use machinery scaled to the job at hand, and operate it at efficient speeds.
• Combine operations. Harrow, plant, and fertilize in the same operation.
• Use diesel fuel. Use solar and wind energy on farms. Use methane from manure. Be open-minded to alternative energy sources.
• Save on technological and chemical inputs, and spend some of the savings paying people to do manual jobs. Increasing labor has been considered inefficient—reverse this thinking. Creating more jobs is preferable to using more machinery and fuel.
• Partially return to the techniques of using animal manure and crop rotation. This will save energy because chemical fertilizers require much energy to produce.
• Choose crops that require few resources (fertilizer, pesticides, irrigation).
• Educate people to cook food efficiently and to eat low on the food chain.

means eating more foods derived from plants and fewer foods derived from animals. It also means eating more foods grown locally and fewer foods produced elsewhere.

Plant versus Animal

Some foods require more energy for their production than others. The least energy is needed for grains: it takes about one-third kcalorie of fuel to produce each kcalorie of grain. Fruits and vegetables are intermediate, and most animal-derived foods require from 10 to 90 kcalories of fuel per kcalorie of edible food. In general, meat-based diets require much more energy, as well as more land and water, than do plant-based diets.[3] An exception is livestock raised on the open range; these animals require about as much energy as most plant foods.[4] We raise so much more grain-fed, than range-fed, livestock, however, that the average energy requirement for meat production is high. Figure H20-2 shows how much less fuel vegetarian diets require than meat-based diets and shows that vegan diets require the least fuel of all.

To support our meat intake, we maintain several billion livestock, about four times our own weight in animals. Livestock consume ten times as much grain each day as we do. We could use much of that grain to make grain products for ourselves and for others around the world. Making this shift could free up enough grain to feed 400 million people while using less fuel, water, and land.

Part of the solution to the livestock problem may be to cease feeding grain to animals and return to grazing them on the open range, which can be a sustainable practice. Ranchers have to manage the grazing carefully to hold the cattle's numbers to what the land can support without environmental degradation. To accomplish this, the economic benefits of traditional livestock and feed-growing operations would have to end. If producers were to pay the true costs of the environmental damage incurred by irrigation water, fertilizers, pesticides, and fuels, the prices of

FIGURE H20-2 | Amounts of Fuel Required to Feed People Eating at Different Points on the Food Chain

Three people who eat differently are compared here. Each has the same energy intake: 3300 kcalories a day. The fossil fuel amounts necessary to produce these different diets are calculated based on U.S. conditions.

The meat eater consumes a typical U.S. diet of meat, other animal products, and plant foods:

The lacto-ovo-vegetarian eats a diet that excludes meats, but includes milk products and eggs:

The vegan eats a diet of plant foods only:

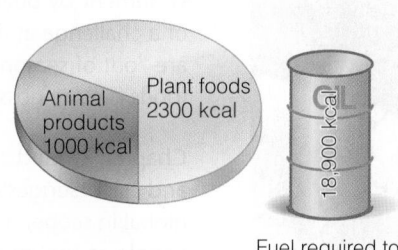
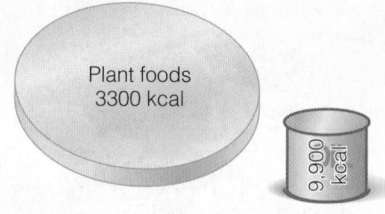

Fuel required to produce this food

Fuel required to produce this food

Fuel required to produce this food

SOURCE: Adapted from D. Pimentel, *Food, Energy and the Future of Society* (Boulder, Colo.: Associated University Press, 1980), Figure 5, p. 27.

meats might double or triple. According to classic economic theory, people would then buy less meat (reducing demand), and producers would respond by producing less meat (reducing supply). Meat production would then fall to a sustainable level.

The United Nations describes a nation's impact on the environment as its "ecological footprint"—a measure of the resources used to support a nation's consumption of food, materials, and energy. This measure takes into account the two most challenging aspects of sustainability—per capita resource consumption and population growth. As Figure H20-3 shows, the people of North America are the world's greatest consumers on a per capita basis. Some have estimated that it would take four more planet Earths to accommodate every person in the world using resources at the level currently used in the United States.[5]

Some consumers are taking action to do their part to solve some of these problems. Some are choosing smaller portions of meat or selecting range-fed beef or buffalo only. Livestock on the range eat grass, which people cannot eat. "Rangeburger" buffalo also offers nutrient advantages over grain-fed beef because it is lower in fat and because the fat has more polyunsaturated fatty acids, including the omega-3 type.

Some consumers are opting for vegetarian, and even vegan, diets—at least occasionally. Vegetarian diets have less of an environmental impact than meat-based diets.[6] Shifting to a fish diet does not appear to be a practical alternative at present, although fish farming shows promise of providing nutritious food at a price both people and the environment can afford.

Local versus Global

Plant-centered diets have an environmental advantage over meat-based diets, but some would

argue that they don't go far enough. The most ecologically responsible diets are also based on locally grown products. On average, an item of food is transported 1500 miles before it is eaten. That "our foods now travel more than we do" has several costly ramifications. Buying *globally* is:

- *Energetically costly.* Foods must be refrigerated and transported thousands of miles to provide a full array of all produce all year round.
- *Socially unjust.* Farmers in impoverished countries, where the people are malnourished, are paid meager wages to grow food for wealthy nations.

FIGURE H20-3 | Ecological Footprints

The width of a bar represents the region's population, and the height represents per capita consumption (in terms of area of productive land or sea required to produce the natural resources consumed). Thus the footprint of the bar represents the region's total consumption. For example, Asia's population is more than ten times greater than North America's, but because its consumption is only one-sixth as large, their footprints are similar in size.

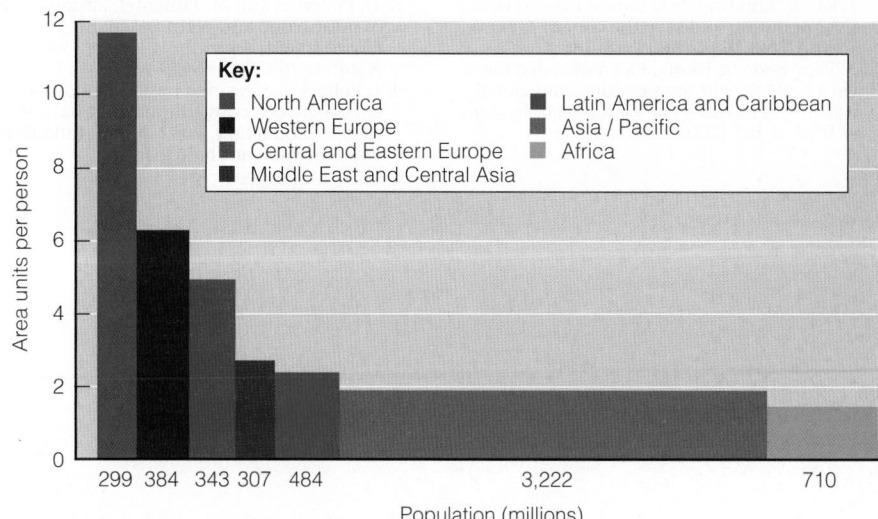

Key:
- North America
- Western Europe
- Central and Eastern Europe
- Middle East and Central Asia
- Latin America and Caribbean
- Asia / Pacific
- Africa

Locally grown foods offer benefits to both the local economy and the global environment.

© Paul Barton/CORBIS

- *Economically unwise.* It supports **agribusinesses** that buy land and labor cheaply in foreign countries instead of supporting local farmers raising crops in our communities.
- *Biologically risky.* Highly perishable foods are shipped from countries with unsafe drinking water and sanitation practices.

For all these reasons, consumers can best improve the global environment by buying locally. Adopting a local diet presents a bit of a challenge at first, especially when local fruits and vegetables are "out of season." But a nutritionally balanced diet of delicious foods is quite possible with a little creative planning.

Chapter 20 and this highlight have presented many problems and have suggested that, although many of the problems are global in scope, the solutions depend on the actions of individual people at the local level. On learning of this, concerned people may take a perfectionist attitude, believing that they "should" be doing more than they realistically can, and so feel defeated. Yet, striving for perfection, even while falling short, is a way to achieve progress and is well worth celebrating. A positive attitude can bring about improvement, and sometimes improvement is enough. Celebrate the changes that are possible today by making them a permanent part of your life; do the same with changes that become possible tomorrow and every day thereafter. The results may surprise you.

NUTRITION ON THE NET

ThomsonNOW™
For furthur study of topics covered in this Highlight, log on to **www.thomsonedu.com/thomsonnow**. Go to Chapter 20, then to Highlights Nutrition on the Net.

- Visit the USDA Alternative Farming Systems Information Center: **www.nal.usda.gov/afsic**

- Visit the Sustainable Agriculture Research and Education Program at UC Davis and the Leopold Center for Sustainable Agriculture at IA State: **www.sarep.ucdavis.edu** and **www.leopold.iastate.edu**

REFERENCES

1. J. Raloff, Limiting dead zones: How to curb river pollution and save the Gulf of Mexico, *Science News* 165 (2004): 378–380.
2. S. Peng and coauthors, Rice yields decline with higher night temperature from global warming, *Proceedings of the National Academy of Sciences* 101 (2004): 9971–9975.
3. D. Pimentel and M. Pimentel, Sustainability of meat-based and plant-based diets and the environment, *American Journal of Clinical Nutrition* 78 (2003): 660S–663S.
4. J. Robinson, Grass fed basics: Key differences between conventional and pasture animal production, 2002-2003, available at www.eatwild.com/basics.html.
5. E. O. Wilson, The bottleneck, *Scientific American*, February 2002, pp. 82–91.
6. L. Reijnders and S. Soret, Quantification of the environmental impact of different dietary protein choices, *American Journal of Clinical Nutrition* 78 (2003): 664S–668S; C. Leitzmann, Nutrition ecology: The contribution of vegetarian diets, *American Journal of Clinical Nutrition* 78 (2003): 657S–659S.

Appendixes

Appendix A
Cells, Hormones, and Nerves

Appendix B
Basic Chemistry Concepts

Appendix C
Biochemical Structures and Pathways

Appendix D
Measures of Protein Quality

Appendix E
Nutrition Assessment

Appendix F
Physical Activity and Energy Requirements

Appendix G
United States: Exchange Lists

Appendix H
Table of Food Composition

Appendix I
WHO: Nutrition Recommendations
Canada: Guidelines and Meal Planning

Appendix J
Healthy People 2010

Taylor S. Kennedy/Getty Images

CONTENTS

The Cell

The Hormones

The Nervous System

Putting It Together

GLOSSARY OF CELL STRUCTURES

cell: the basic structural unit of all living things.

cell membrane: the thin layer of tissue that surrounds the cell and encloses its contents; made primarily of lipid and protein.

chromosomes: a set of structures within the nucleus of every cell that contains the cell's genetic material, DNA, associated with other materials (primarily proteins).

cytoplasm (SIGH-toh-plazm): the cell contents, except for the nucleus.
- **cyto** = cell
- **plasm** = a form

cytosol: the fluid of cytoplasm; contains water, ions, nutrients, and enzymes.

endoplasmic reticulum (en-doh-PLAZ-mic reh-TIC-you-lum): a complex network of intracellular membranes. The **rough endoplasmic reticulum** is dotted with ribosomes, where protein synthesis takes place. The **smooth endoplasmic reticulum** bears no ribosomes.
- **endo** = inside
- **plasm** = the cytoplasm

Golgi (GOAL-gee) **apparatus:** a set of membranes within the cell where secretory materials are packaged for export.

lysosomes (LYE-so-zomes): cellular organelles; membrane-enclosed sacs of degradative enzymes.
- **lysis** = dissolution

mitochondria (my-toh-KON-dree-uh); singular **mitochondrion:** the cellular organelles responsible for producing ATP aerobically; made of membranes (lipid and protein) with enzymes mounted on them.
- **mitos** = thread (referring to their slender shape)
- **chondros** = cartilage (referring to their external appearance)

nucleus: a major membrane-enclosed body within every cell, which contains the cell's genetic material, DNA, embedded in chromosomes.
- **nucleus** = a kernel

organelles: subcellular structures such as ribosomes, mitochondria, and lysosomes.
- **organelle** = little organ

Cells, Hormones, and Nerves

This appendix is offered as an optional chapter for readers who want to enhance their understanding of how the body coordinates its activities. It presents a brief summary of the structure and function of the body's basic working unit (the cell) and of the body's two major regulatory systems (the hormonal system and the nervous system).

The Cell

The body's organs are made up of millions of cells and of materials produced by them. Each **cell** is specialized to perform its organ's functions, but all cells have common structures (see the accompanying glossary and Figure A-1). Every cell is contained within a **cell membrane.** The cell membrane assists in moving materials into and out of the cell, and some of its special proteins act as "pumps" (described in Chapter 6). Some features of cell membranes, such as microvilli (Chapter 3), permit cells to interact with other cells and with their environments in highly specific ways.

Inside the membrane lies the **cytoplasm,** which is filled with **cytosol,** or cell "fluid." The cytoplasm contains much more than just fluid, though. It is a highly organized system of fibers, tubes, membranes, particles, and subcellular **organelles** as complex as a city. These parts intercommunicate, manufacture and exchange materials, package and prepare materials for export, and maintain and repair themselves.

Within each cell is another membrane-enclosed body, the **nucleus.** Inside the nucleus are the **chromosomes,** which contain the genetic material, DNA. The DNA encodes all the instructions for carrying out the cell's activities. The role of DNA in coding for cell proteins is summarized in Figure 6-7 on p. 188. Chapter 6 also describes the variety of proteins produced by cells and the ways they perform the body's work.

Among the organelles within a cell are ribosomes, mitochondria, and lysosomes. Figure 6-7 briefly refers to the **ribosomes;** they assemble amino acids into proteins, following directions conveyed to them by RNA.

The **mitochondria** are made of intricately folded membranes that bear thousands of highly organized sets of enzymes on their inner and outer surfaces. Mitochondria are crucial to energy metabolism (described in Chapter 7) and muscles conditioned to work aerobically are packed with them. Their presence is implied whenever the TCA cycle and electron transport chain are mentioned because the mitochondria house the needed enzymes.[*]

The **lysosomes** are membranes that enclose degradative enzymes. When a cell needs to self-destruct or to digest materials in its surroundings, its lysosomes free their enzymes. Lysosomes are active when tissue repair or remodeling is taking place—for example, in cleaning up infections, healing wounds, shaping embryonic organs, and remodeling bones.

Besides these and other cellular organelles, the cell's cytoplasm contains a highly organized system of membranes, the **endoplasmic reticulum.** The ribosomes may either float free in the cytoplasm or be mounted on these membranes. A membranous surface dotted with ribosomes looks speckled under the microscope and is called "rough" endoplasmic reticulum; such a surface without ribosomes is called "smooth." Some intracellular membranes are organized into tubules that collect cellular materials, merge with the cell membrane, and discharge their contents to the outside of

---

[*]For the reactions of glycolysis, the TCA cycle, and the electron transport chain, see Chapter 7 and Appendix C. The reactions of glycolysis take place in the cytoplasm; the conversion of pyruvate to acetyl CoA takes place in the mitochondria, as do the TCA cycle and electron transport chain reactions. The mitochondria then release carbon dioxide, water, and ATP as their end products.

FIGURE A-1   The Structure of a Typical Cell

The cell shown might be one in a gland (such as the pancreas) that produces secretory products (enzymes) for export (to the intestine). The rough endoplasmic reticulum with its ribosomes produces the enzymes; the smooth reticulum conducts them to the Golgi region; the Golgi membranes merge with the cell membrane, where the enzymes can be released into the extracellular fluid.

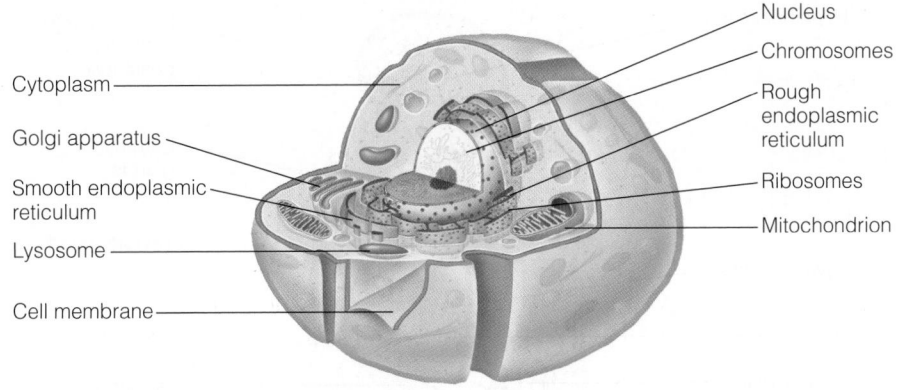

♦ The study of hormones and their effects is **endocrinology.**

♦ The **pituitary gland** in the brain has two parts—the **anterior** (front) and the **posterior** (hind).

> **ribosomes** (RYE-boh-zomes): protein-making organelles in cells; composed of RNA and protein.
> • **ribo** = containing the sugar ribose (in RNA)
> • **some** = body

the cell; these membrane systems are named the **Golgi apparatus,** after the scientist who first described them. The rough and smooth endoplasmic reticula and the Golgi apparatus are continuous with one another, so secretions produced deep in the interior of the cell can be efficiently transported to the outside and released. These and other cell structures enable cells to perform the multitudes of functions for which they are specialized.

The actions of cells are coordinated by both hormones and nerves, as the next sections show. Among the types of cellular organelles are receptors for the hormones delivering instructions that originate elsewhere in the body. Some hormones penetrate the cell and its nucleus and attach to receptors on chromosomes, where they activate certain genes to initiate, stop, speed up, or slow down synthesis of certain proteins as needed. Other hormones attach to receptors on the cell surface and transmit their messages from there. The hormones ♦ are described in the next section; the nerves, in the one following.

The Hormones

A chemical compound—a **hormone**—originates in a gland and travels in the bloodstream. The hormone flows everywhere in the body, but only its target organs respond to it, because only they possess the receptors to receive it.

The hormones, the glands they originate in, and their target organs and effects are described in this section. Many of the hormones you might be interested in are included, but only a few are discussed in detail. Figure A-2 (p. A-4) identifies the glands that produce the hormones, and the accompanying glossary defines the hormones discussed in this section.

Hormones of the Pituitary Gland and Hypothalamus

The anterior pituitary gland ♦ produces the following hormones, each of which acts on one or more target organs and elicits a characteristic response:

• **Adrenocorticotropin (ACTH)** acts on the adrenal cortex, promoting the production and release of its hormones.

• **Thyroid-stimulating hormone (TSH)** acts on the thyroid gland, promoting the production and release of thyroid hormones.

• **Growth hormone (GH)** or **somatotropin** acts on all tissues, promoting growth, fat breakdown, and the formation of antibodies.

GLOSSARY OF HORMONES

adrenocorticotropin (ad-REE-noh-KORE-tee-koh-TROP-in) or **ACTH:** a hormone, so named because it stimulates *(trope)* the adrenal cortex. The adrenal gland, like the pituitary, has two parts, in this case an outer portion *(cortex)* and an inner core *(medulla)*. The realease of ACTH is mediated by **corticotropin-releasing hormone (CRH).**

aldosterone: a hormone from the adrenal gland involved in blood pressure regulation.
• **aldo** = aldehyde

angiotensin: a hormone involved in blood pressure regulation that is activated by **renin** (REN-in), an enzyme from the kidneys.
• **angio** = blood vessels
• **tensin** = pressure
• **ren** = kidneys

antidiuretic hormone (ADH): the hormone that prevents water loss in urine (also called **vasopressin**).
• **anti** = against
• **di** = through
• **ure** = urine
• **vaso** = blood vessels
• **pressin** = pressure

calcitonin (KAL-see-TOH-nin): a hormone secreted by the thyroid gland that regulates (tones) calcium metabolism.

erythropoietin (eh-RITH-ro-POY-eh-tin): a hormone that stimulates red blood cell production.
• **erythro** = red (blood cell)
• **poiesis** = creating (like poetry)

estrogens: hormones responsible for the menstrual cycle and other female characteristics.
• **oestrus** = the egg-making cycle
• **gen** = gives rise to

FIGURE A-2 The Endocrine System

These organs and glands release hormones that regulate body processes. An *endocrine gland* secretes its product directly into *(endo)* the blood; for example, the pancreas cells that produce insulin. An *exocrine gland* secretes its product(s) out *(exo)* to an epithelial surface either directly or through a duct; the sweat glands of the skin and the enzyme-producing glands of the pancreas are both examples. The pancreas is therefore both an endocrine and an exocrine gland.

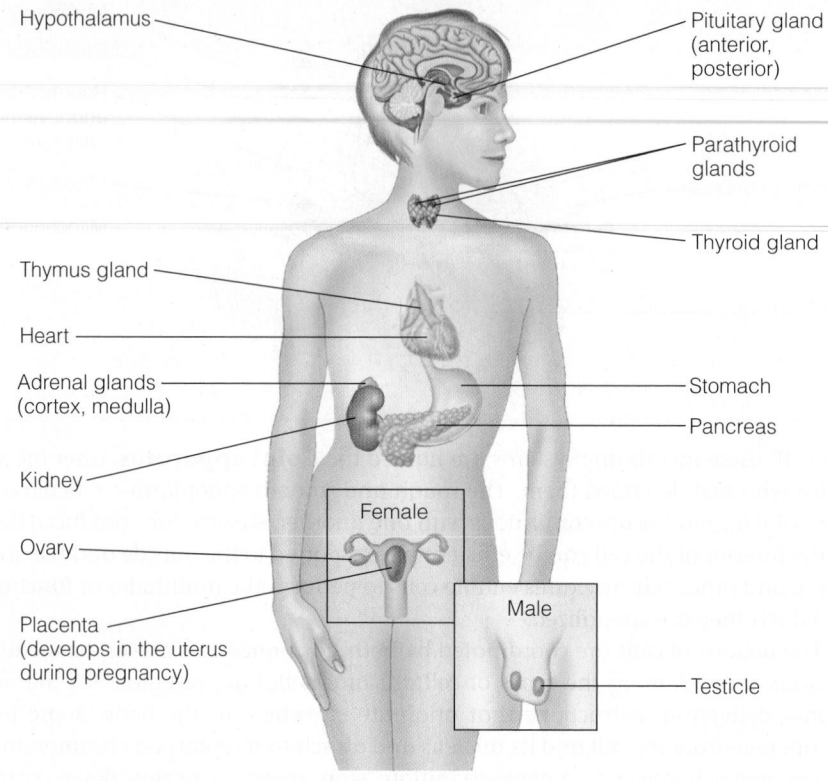

Hypothalamus
Pituitary gland (anterior, posterior)
Parathyroid glands
Thyroid gland
Thymus gland
Heart
Adrenal glands (cortex, medulla)
Stomach
Pancreas
Kidney
Female
Ovary
Male
Placenta (develops in the uterus during pregnancy)
Testicle

◆ Hormones that are turned off by their own effects are said to be regulated by **negative feedback.**

follicle-stimulating hormone (FSH): a hormone that stimulates maturation of the ovarian follicles in females and the production of sperm in males. (The ovarian follicles are part of the female reproductive system where the eggs are produced.) The release of FSH is mediated by **follicle-stimulating hormone releasing hormone (FSH–RH).**

glucocorticoids: hormones from the adrenal cortex that affect the body's management of glucose.
• **gluco** = glucose
• **corticoid** = from the cortex

growth hormone (GH): a hormone secreted by the pituitary that regulates the cell division and protein synthesis needed for normal growth (also called **somatotropin**). The release of GH is mediated by **GH-releasing hormone (GHRH)** and **GH-inhibiting hormone (GHIH).**

hormone: a chemical messenger. Hormones are secreted by a variety of endocrine glands in response to altered conditions in the body. Each hormone travels to one or more specific target tissues or organs, where it elicits a specific response to maintain homeostasis.

luteinizing (LOO-tee-in-EYE-zing) **hormone (LH):** a hormone that stimulates ovulation and the development of the corpus luteum (the small tissue that develops from a ruptured ovarian follicle and secretes hormones); so called because the follicle turns yellow as it matures. In men, LH stimulates testosterone secretion. The release of LH is mediated by **luteinizing hormone–releasing hormone (LH–RH).**
• **lutein** = a yellow pigment

- **Follicle-stimulating hormone (FSH)** acts on the ovaries in the female, promoting their maturation, and on the testicles in the male, promoting sperm formation.

- **Luteinizing hormone (LH)** also acts on the ovaries, stimulating their maturation, the production and release of progesterone and estrogens, and ovulation; and on the testicles, promoting the production and release of testosterone.

- **Prolactin,** secreted in the female during pregnancy and lactation, acts on the mammary glands to stimulate their growth and the production of milk.

Each of these hormones has one or more signals that turn it on and another (or others) that turns it off. ◆ Among the controlling signals are several hormones from the hypothalamus:

- **Corticotropin-releasing hormone (CRH),** which promotes release of ACTH, is turned on by stress and turned off by ACTH when enough has been released.

- **TSH-releasing hormone (TRH),** which promotes release of TSH, is turned on by large meals or low body temperature.

- **GH-releasing hormone (GHRH),** which stimulates the release of growth hormone, is turned on by insulin.

- **GH-inhibiting hormone (GHIH** or **somatostatin),** which inhibits the release of GH and interferes with the release of TSH, is turned on by hypoglycemia and/or physical activity and is rapidly destroyed by body tissues so that it does not accumulate.

- **FSH/LH–releasing hormone (FSH/LH–RH)** is turned on in the female by nerve messages or low estrogen and in the male by low testosterone.
- **Prolactin-inhibiting hormone (PIH)** is turned on by high prolactin levels and off by estrogen, testosterone, and suckling (by way of nerve messages).

Let's examine some of these controls. PIH, for example, responds to high prolactin levels (remember, prolactin promotes milk production). High prolactin levels ensure that milk is made and—by calling forth PIH—ensure that prolactin levels don't get too high. But when the infant is suckling—and creating a demand for milk—PIH is not allowed to work (suckling turns off PIH). The consequence: prolactin remains high, and milk production continues. Demand from the infant thus directly adjusts the supply of milk. The need is met through the interaction of the nerves and hormones.

As another example, consider CRH. Stress, perceived in the brain and relayed to the hypothalamus, switches on CRH. On arriving at the pituitary, CRH switches on ACTH. Then ACTH acts on its target organ, the adrenal cortex, which responds by producing and releasing stress hormones. The stress hormones trigger a cascade of events involving every body cell and many other hormones.

The numerous steps required to set the stress response in motion make it possible for the body to fine-tune the response; control can be exerted at each step. These two examples illustrate what the body can do in response to two different stimuli—producing milk in response to an infant's need and gearing up for action in an emergency.

The posterior pituitary gland produces two hormones, each of which acts on one or more target cells and elicits a characteristic response:

- **Antidiuretic hormone (ADH)**, or **vasopressin**, acts on the arteries, promoting their contraction, and on the kidneys, preventing water excretion. ADH is turned on whenever the blood volume is low, the blood pressure is low, or the salt concentration of the blood is high (see Chapter 12). It is turned off by the return of these conditions to normal.
- **Oxytocin** acts during late pregnancy on the uterus, inducing contractions, and during lactation on the mammary glands, causing milk ejection. Oxytocin is produced in response to reduced progesterone levels, suckling, or the stretching of the cervix.

Hormones That Regulate Energy Metabolism

Hormones produced by a number of different glands have effects on energy metabolism:

- Insulin from the pancreas beta cells is turned on by many stimuli, including raised blood glucose. It acts on cells to increase glucose and amino acid uptake into them and to promote the secretion of GHRH.
- Glucagon from the pancreas alpha cells responds to low blood glucose and acts on the liver to promote the breakdown of glycogen to glucose, the conversion of amino acids to glucose, and the release of glucose into the blood.
- Thyroxine from the thyroid gland responds to TSH and acts on many cells to increase their metabolic rate, growth, and heat production.
- Norepinephrine and epinephrine ◆ from the adrenal medulla respond to stimulation by sympathetic nerves and produce reactions in many cells that facilitate the body's readiness for fight or flight: increased heart activity, blood vessel constriction, breakdown of glycogen and glucose, raised blood glucose levels, and fat breakdown. Norepinephrine and epinephrine also influence the secretion of the many hormones from the hypothalamus that exert control on the body's other systems.
- Growth hormone (GH) from the anterior pituitary (already mentioned).
- **Glucocorticoids** from the adrenal cortex become active during times of stress and carbohydrate metabolism.

◆ Norepinephrine and epinephrine were formerly called **noradrenalin** and **adrenalin**, respectively.

oxytocin (OCK-see-TOH-sin): a hormone that stimulates the mammary glands to eject milk during lactation and the uterus to contract during childbirth.
- **oxy** = quick
- **tocin** = childbirth

progesterone: the hormone of gestation (pregnancy).
- **pro** = promoting
- **gest** = gestation (pregnancy)
- **sterone** = a steroid hormone

prolactin (proh-LAK-tin): a hormone so named because it promotes (pro) the production of milk (lacto). The release of prolactin is mediated by **prolactin-inhibiting hormone (PIH)**.

relaxin: the hormone of late pregnancy.

somatostatin (GHIH): a hormone that inhibits the release of growth hormone; the opposite of **somatotropin (GH)**.
- **somato** = body
- **stat** = keep the same
- **tropin** = make more

testosterone: a steroid hormone from the testicles, or testes. The steroids, as explained in Chapter 5, are chemically related to, and some are derived from, the lipid cholesterol.
- **sterone** = a steroid hormone

thyroid-stimulating hormone (TSH): a hormone secreted by the pituitary that stimulates the thyroid gland to secrete its hormones—thyroxine and triiodothyronine. The release of TSH is mediated by **TSH-releasing hormone (TRH)**.

Every body part is affected by these hormones. Each different hormone has unique effects; and hormones that oppose each other are produced in carefully regulated amounts, so each can respond to the exact degree that is appropriate to the condition.

Hormones That Adjust Other Body Balances

Hormones are involved in moving calcium into and out of the body's storage deposits in the bones:

- **Calcitonin** from the thyroid gland acts on the bones, which respond by storing calcium from the bloodstream whenever blood calcium rises above the normal range. It also acts on the kidneys to increase excretion of both calcium and phosphorus in the urine. Calcitonin plays a major role in infants and young children, but is less active in adults.

- Parathyroid hormone (parathormone or PTH) from the parathyroid gland responds to the opposite condition—lowered blood calcium—and acts on three targets: the bones, which release stored calcium into the blood; the kidneys, which slow the excretion of calcium; and the intestine, which increases calcium absorption.

- Vitamin D from the skin and activated in the kidneys acts with parathyroid hormone and is essential for the absorption of calcium in the intestine.

Figure 12-12 on p. 417 diagrams the ways vitamin D and the hormones calcitonin and parathyroid hormone regulate calcium homeostasis.

Another hormone has effects on blood-making activity:

- **Erythropoietin** from the kidneys is responsive to oxygen depletion of the blood and to anemia. It acts on the bone marrow to stimulate the making of red blood cells.

Another hormone is special for pregnancy:

- **Relaxin** from the ovaries is secreted in response to the raised progesterone and estrogen levels of late pregnancy. This hormone acts on the cervix and pelvic ligaments to allow them to stretch so that they can accommodate the birth process without strain.

Other agents help regulate blood pressure:

- **Renin** (an enzyme), from the kidneys, in cooperation with **angiotensin** in the blood responds to a reduced blood supply experienced by the kidneys and acts in several ways to increase blood pressure. Renin and angiotensin also stimulate the adrenal cortex to secrete the hormone aldosterone.

- **Aldosterone,** a hormone from the adrenal cortex, targets the kidneys, which respond by reabsorbing sodium. The effect is to retain more water in the bloodstream—thus, again, raising the blood pressure. Figure 12-3 (on p. 403) in Chapter 12 provides more details.

The Gastrointestinal Hormones

Several hormones are produced in the stomach and intestines in response to the presence of food or the components of food:

- Gastrin from the stomach and duodenum stimulates the production and release of gastric acid and other digestive juices and the movement of the GI contents through the system.

- Cholecystokinin from the duodenum signals the gallbladder and pancreas to release their contents into the intestine to aid in digestion.

- Secretin from the duodenum calls forth acid-neutralizing bicarbonate from the pancreas into the intestine and slows the action of the stomach and its secretion of acid and digestive juices.

- Gastric-inhibitory peptide from the duodenum and jejunum inhibits the secretion of gastric acid and slows the process of digestion.

These hormones are defined and presented in more detail in Chapter 3.

The Sex Hormones

There are three major sex hormones:

- **Testosterone** from the testicles is released in response to LH (described earlier) and acts on all the tissues that are involved in male sexuality, promoting their development and maintenance.

- **Estrogens** from the ovaries are released in response to both FSH and LH and act similarly in females.

- **Progesterone** from the ovaries' corpus luteum and from the placenta acts on the uterus and mammary glands, preparing them for pregnancy and lactation.

This brief description of the hormones and their functions should suffice to provide an awareness of the enormous impact these compounds have on body processes. The other overall regulating agency is the nervous system.

The Nervous System

The nervous system has a central control system that can evaluate information about conditions within and outside the body, and a vast system of wiring that receives information and sends instructions. The control unit is the brain and spinal cord, called the **central nervous system;** and the vast complex of wiring between the center and the parts is the **peripheral nervous system.** The smooth functioning that results from the system's adjustments to changing conditions is homeostasis.

The nervous system has two general functions: it controls voluntary muscles in response to sensory stimuli from them, and it controls involuntary, internal muscles and glands in response to nerve-borne and chemical signals about their status. In fact, the nervous system is best understood as two systems that use the same or similar pathways to receive and transmit their messages. The **somatic nervous system** controls the voluntary muscles; the **autonomic nervous system** controls the internal organs.

When scientists were first studying the autonomic nervous system, they noticed that when something hurt one organ of the body, some of the other organs reacted as if in sympathy for the afflicted one. They therefore named the nerve network they were studying the sympathetic nervous system. The term is still used today to refer to that branch of the autonomic nervous system that responds to pain and stress. The other branch is called the parasympathetic nervous system. (Think of the sympathetic branch as the responder when homeostasis needs restoring and the parasympathetic branch as the commander of function during normal times.) Both systems transmit their messages through the brain and spinal cord. Nerves of the two branches travel side by side along the same pathways to transmit their messages, but they oppose each other's actions (see Figure A-3 on p. A-8).

An example will show how the sympathetic and parasympathetic nervous systems work to maintain homeostasis. When you go outside in cold weather, your skin's temperature receptors send "cold" messages to the spinal cord and brain. Your conscious mind may intervene at this point to tell you to zip your jacket, but let's say you have no jacket. Your sympathetic nervous system reacts to the external stressor, the cold. It signals your skin-surface capillaries to shut down so that your blood will circulate deeper in your tissues, where it will conserve heat. Your sympathetic nervous system also signals involuntary contractions of the small muscles just under the skin surface. The product of these muscle contractions is heat, and the visible result is goose bumps. If these measures do not raise your body temperature enough, then the sympathetic nerves signal your large muscle groups

GLOSSARY OF NERVOUS SYSTEM

autonomic nervous system: the division of the nervous system that controls the body's automatic responses. Its two branches are the **sympathetic** branch, which helps the body respond to stressors from the outside environment, and the **parasympathetic** branch, which regulates normal body activities between stressful times.

- autonomos = self-governing

central nervous system: the central part of the nervous system; the brain and spinal cord.

peripheral (puh-RIFF-er-ul) **nervous system:** the peripheral (outermost) part of the nervous system; the vast complex of wiring that extends from the central nervous system to the body's outermost areas. It contains both somatic and autonomic components.

somatic (so-MAT-ick) **nervous system:** the division of the nervous system that controls the voluntary muscles, as distinguished from the autonomic nervous system, which controls involuntary functions.

- soma = body

Appendix A

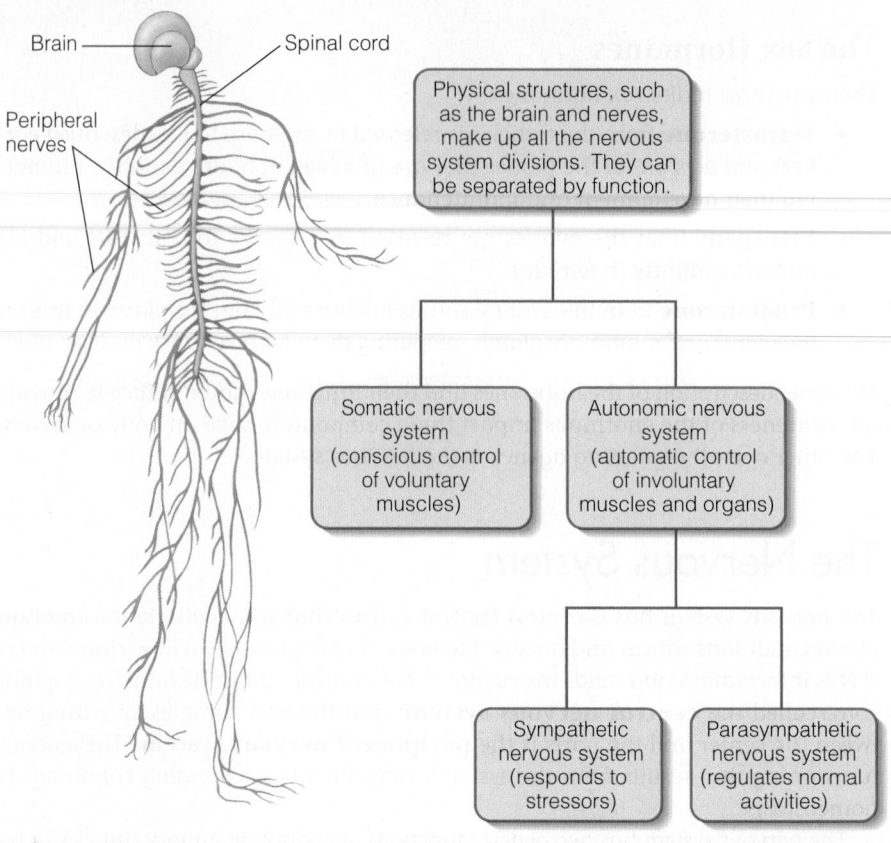

FIGURE A-3 The Organization of the Nervous System

FIGURE A-3 The Organization of the Nervous System

The brain and spinal cord evaluate information about conditions within and outside the body, and the peripheral nerves receive information and send instructions.

Brain — Spinal cord

Peripheral nerves

Physical structures, such as the brain and nerves, make up all the nervous system divisions. They can be separated by function.

Somatic nervous system (conscious control of voluntary muscles)

Autonomic nervous system (automatic control of involuntary muscles and organs)

Sympathetic nervous system (responds to stressors)

Parasympathetic nervous system (regulates normal activities)

to shiver; the contractions of these large muscles produce still more heat. All of this activity helps to maintain your homeostasis (with respect to temperature) under conditions of external extremes (cold) that would throw it off balance. The cold was a stressor; the body's response was resistance.

Now let's say you come in and sit by a fire and drink hot cocoa. You are warm and no longer need all that sympathetic activity. At this point, your parasympathetic nerves take over; they signal your skin-surface capillaries to dilate again, your goose bumps to subside, and your muscles to relax. Your body is back to normal. This is recovery.

Putting It Together

The hormonal and nervous systems coordinate body functions by transmitting and receiving messages. The point-to-point messages of the nervous system travel through a central switchboard (the spinal cord and brain), whereas the messages of the hormonal system are broadcast over the airways (the bloodstream), and any organ with the appropriate receptors can pick them up. Nerve impulses travel faster than hormonal messages do—although both are remarkably swift. Whereas your brain's command to wiggle your toes reaches the toes within a fraction of a second and stops as quickly, a gland's message to alter a body condition may take several seconds or minutes to get started and may fade away equally slowly.

Together, the two systems possess every characteristic a superb communication network needs: varied speeds of transmission, along with private communication lines or public broadcasting systems, depending on the needs of the moment. The hormonal system, together with the nervous system, integrates the whole body's functioning so that all parts act smoothly together.

Basic Chemistry Concepts

This appendix is intended to provide the background in basic chemistry you need to understand the nutrition concepts presented in this book. Chemistry is the branch of natural science that is concerned with the description and classification of **matter,** the changes that matter undergoes, and the **energy** associated with these changes. The accompanying glossary defines matter, energy, and other related terms.

Matter: The Properties of Atoms

Every substance has physical and chemical properties that distinguish it from all other substances and thus give it a unique identity. The physical properties include such characteristics as color, taste, texture, and odor, as well as the temperatures at which a substance changes its state (from a solid to a liquid or from a liquid to a gas) and the weight of a unit volume (its density). The chemical properties of a substance have to do with how it reacts with other substances or responds to a change in its environment so that new substances with different sets of properties are produced.

A physical change does not change a substance's chemical composition. The three physical states—ice, water, and steam—all consist of two hydrogen atoms and one oxygen atom bound together. In contrast, a chemical change occurs when an electric current passes through water. The water disappears, and two different substances are formed: hydrogen gas, which is flammable, and oxygen gas, which supports life.

Substances: Elements and Compounds

The smallest part of a substance that can exist separately without losing its physical and chemical properties is a **molecule.** If a molecule is composed of **atoms** that are alike, the substance is an **element** (for example, O_2). If a molecule is composed of two or more different kinds of atoms, the substance is a **compound** (for example, H_2O).

Just over 100 elements are known, and these are listed in Table B-1. A familiar example is hydrogen, whose molecules are composed only of hydrogen atoms linked together in pairs (H_2). On the other hand, over a million compounds are known. An example is the sugar glucose. Each of its molecules is composed of 6 carbon, 6 oxygen, and 12 hydrogen atoms linked together in a specific arrangement (as described in Chapter 4).

The Nature of Atoms

Atoms themselves are made of smaller particles. Within the atomic nucleus are protons (positively charged particles), and surrounding the nucleus are electrons (negatively charged particles). The number of protons (+) in the nucleus of an atom de-

CONTENTS

Matter: The Property of Atoms

Chemical Bonding

Formation of Ions

Water, Acids, and Bases

Chemical Reactions

Formation of Free Radicals

GLOSSARY

atoms: the smallest components of an element that have all of the properties of the element.

compound: a substance composed of two or more different atoms—for example, water (H_2O).

element: a substance composed of atoms that are alike—for example, iron (Fe).

energy: the capacity to do work.

matter: anything that takes up space and has mass.

molecule: two or more atoms of the same or different elements joined by chemical bonds. Examples are molecules of the element oxygen, composed of two oxygen atoms (O_2), and molecules of the compound water, composed of two hydrogen atoms and one oxygen atom (H_2O).

termines the number of electrons ($-$) around it. The positive charge on a proton is equal to the negative charge on an electron, so the charges cancel each other out and leave the atom neutral to its surroundings.

The nucleus may also include neutrons, subatomic particles that have no charge. Protons and neutrons are of equal mass, and together they give an atom its weight. Electrons bond atoms together to make molecules, and they are involved in chemical reactions.

Each type of atom has a characteristic number of protons in its nucleus. The hydrogen atom is the simplest of all. It possesses a single proton, with a single electron associated with it:

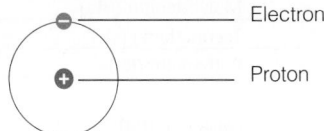

Hydrogen atom (H), atomic number 1.

Just as hydrogen always has one proton, helium always has two, lithium three, and so on. The atomic number of each element is the number of protons in the nucleus of that atom, and this never changes in a chemical reaction; it gives the atom its identity. The atomic numbers for the known elements are listed in Table B-1.

TABLE B-1 Chemical Symbols for the Elements

Key:
- Elements found in energy-yielding nutrients, vitamins, and water
- Major minerals
- Trace minerals

Number of Protons (Atomic Number)	Element	Number of Electrons in Outer Shell	Number of Protons (Atomic Number)	Element	Number of Electrons in Outer Shell
1	Hydrogen (H)	1			
2	Helium (He)	2	57	Lanthanum (La)	2
3	Lithium (Li)	1	58	Cerium (Ce)	2
4	Beryllium (Be)	2	58	Cerium (Ce)	2
5	Boron (B)	3	58	Cerium (Ce)	2
6	Carbon (C)	4	60	Neodymium (Nd)	2
7	Nitrogen (N)	5	61	Promethium (Pm)	2
8	Oxygen (O)	6	62	Samarium (Sm)	2
9	Fluorine (F)	7	63	Europium (Eu)	2
10	Neon (Ne)	8	64	Gadolinium (Gd)	2
11	Sodium (Na)	1	65	Terbium (Tb)	2
12	Magnesium (Mg)	2	66	Dysprosium (Dy)	2
13	Aluminum (Al)	3	67	Holmium (Ho)	2
14	Silicon (Si)	4	68	Erbium (Er)	2
15	Phosphorus (P)	5	69	Thulium (Tm)	2
16	Sulfur (S)	6	70	Ytterbium (Yb)	2
17	Chlorine (Cl)	7	71	Lutetium (Lu)	2
18	Argon (Ar)	8	72	Hafnium (Hf)	2
19	Potassium (K)	1	73	Tantalum (Ta)	2
20	Calcium (Ca)	2	74	Tungsten (W)	2
21	Scandium (Sc)	2	75	Rhenium (Re)	2
22	Titanium (Ti)	2	76	Osmium (Os)	2
23	Vanadium (V)	2	77	Iridium (Ir)	2
24	Chromium (Cr)	1	78	Platinum (Pt)	1
25	Manganese (Mn)	2	79	Gold (Au)	1
26	Iron (Fe)	2	80	Mercury (Hg)	2
27	Cobalt (Co)	2	81	Thallium (Tl)	3
28	Nickel (Ni)	2	82	Lead (Pb)	4
29	Copper (Cu)	1	83	Bismuth (Bi)	5
30	Zinc (Zn)	2	84	Polonium (Po)	6
31	Gallium (Ga)	3	85	Astatine (At)	7
32	Germanium (Ge)	4	86	Radon (Rn)	8
33	Arsenic (As)	5	87	Francium (Fr)	1
34	Selenium (Se)	6	88	Radium (Ra)	2
35	Bromine (Br)	7	89	Actinium (Ac)	2
36	Krypton (Kr)	8	90	Thorium (Th)	2
37	Rubidium (Rb)	1	91	Protactinium (Pa)	2
38	Strontium (Sr)	2	92	Uranium (U)	2
39	Yttrium (Y)	2	93	Neptunium (Np)	2
40	Zirconium (Zr)	2	94	Plutonium (Pu)	2
41	Niobium (Nb)	1	95	Americium (Am)	2
42	Molybdenum (Mo)	1	96	Curium (Cm)	2
43	Technetium (Tc)	1	97	Berkelium (Bk)	2
44	Ruthenium (Ru)	1	98	Californium (Cf)	2
45	Rhodium (Rh)	1	99	Einsteinium (Es)	2
46	Palladium (Pd)	—	100	Fermium (Fm)	2
47	Silver (Ag)	1	101	Mendelevium (Md)	2
48	Cadmium (Cd)	2	102	Nobelium (No)	2
49	Indium (In)	3	103	Lawrencium (Lr)	2
50	Tin (Sn)	4	104	Rutherfordium (Rf)	2
51	Antimony (Sb)	5	105	Dubnium (Db)	2
52	Tellurium (Te)	6	106	Seaborgium (Sg)	2
53	Iodine (I)	7	107	Bohrium (Bh)	2
54	Xenon (Xe)	8	108	Hassium (Hs)	2
55	Cesium (Cs)	1	109	Meitnerium (Mt)	2
56	Barium (Ba)	2	110	Darmstadtium (Ds)	2

Besides hydrogen, the atoms most common in living things are carbon (C), nitrogen (N), and oxygen (O), whose atomic numbers are 6, 7, and 8, respectively. Their structures are more complicated than that of hydrogen, but each of them possesses the same number of electrons as there are protons in the nucleus. These electrons are found in orbits, or shells (shown below).

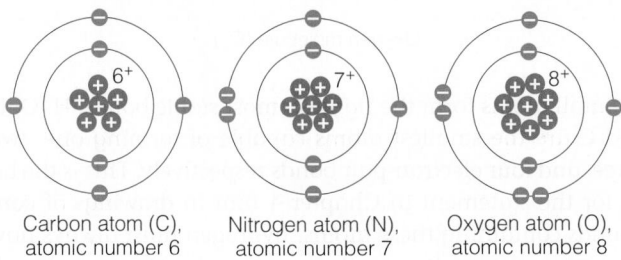

Carbon atom (C), atomic number 6

Nitrogen atom (N), atomic number 7

Oxygen atom (O), atomic number 8

In these and all diagrams of atoms that follow, only the protons and electrons are shown. The neutrons, which contribute only to atomic weight, not to charge, are omitted.

The most important structural feature of an atom for determining its chemical behavior is the number of electrons in its outermost shell. The first, or innermost, shell is full when it is occupied by two electrons; so an atom with two or more electrons has a filled first shell. When the first shell is full, electrons begin to fill the second shell.

The second shell is completely full when it has eight electrons. A substance that has a full outer shell tends not to enter into chemical reactions. Atomic number 10, neon, is a chemically inert substance because its outer shell is complete. Fluorine, atomic number 9, has a great tendency to draw an electron from other substances to complete its outer shell, and thus it is highly reactive. Carbon has a half-full outer shell, which helps explain its great versatility; it can combine with other elements in a variety of ways to form a large number of compounds.

Atoms seek to reach a state of maximum stability or of lowest energy in the same way that a ball will roll down a hill until it reaches the lowest place. An atom achieves a state of maximum stability:

- By gaining or losing electrons to either fill or empty its outer shell.
- By sharing its electrons with other atoms and thereby completing its outer shell.

The number of electrons determines how the atom will chemically react with other atoms. The atomic number, not the weight, is what gives an atom its chemical nature.

Chemical Bonding

Atoms often complete their outer shells by sharing electrons with other atoms. In order to complete its outer shell, a carbon atom requires four electrons. A hydrogen atom requires one. Thus, when a carbon atom shares electrons with four hydrogen atoms, each completes its outer shell (as shown in the next column). Electron sharing binds the atoms together and satisfies the conditions of maximum stability for the molecule. The outer shell of each atom is complete, since hydrogen effectively has the required two electrons in its first (outer)

shell, and carbon has eight electrons in its second (outer) shell; and the molecule is electrically neutral, with a total of ten protons and ten electrons.

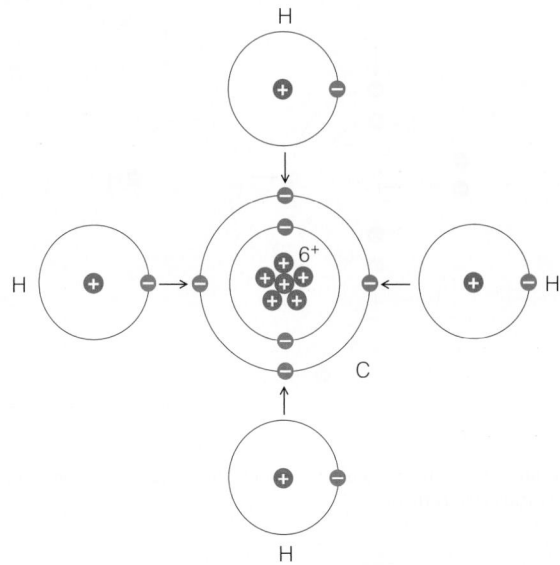

When a carbon atom shares electrons with four hydrogen atoms, a methane molecule is made.

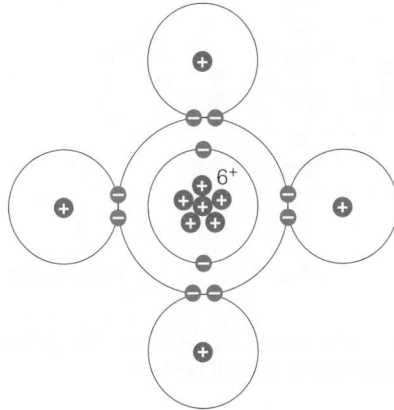

The chemical formula for methane is CH_4. Note that by sharing electrons, every atom achieves a filled outer shell.

Bonds that involve the sharing of electrons, like the bonds between carbon and the four hydrogens, are the most stable kind of association that atoms can form with one another. These bonds are called covalent bonds, and the resulting combination of atoms are called molecules. A single pair of shared electrons forms a single bond. A simplified way to represent a single bond is with a single line. Thus the structure of methane (CH_4) could be represented like this:

$$H-\underset{\underset{H}{|}}{\overset{\overset{H}{|}}{C}}-H$$

Methane (CH_4)

Similarly, one nitrogen atom and three hydrogen atoms can share electrons to form one molecule of ammonia (NH_3):

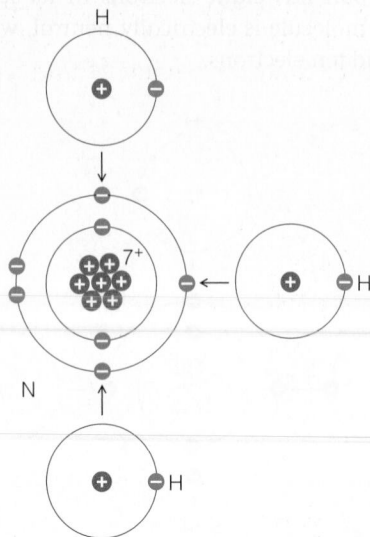

When a nitrogen atom shares electrons with three hydrogen atoms, an ammonia molecule is made.

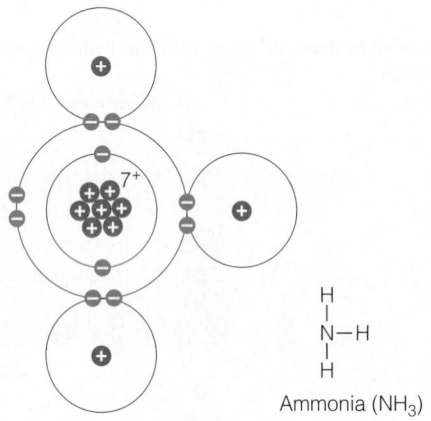

H
|
N—H
|
H

Ammonia (NH₃)

The chemical formula for ammonia is NH$_3$. Count the electrons in each atom's outer shell to confirm that it is filled.

One oxygen atom may be bonded to two hydrogen atoms to form one molecule of water (H$_2$O):

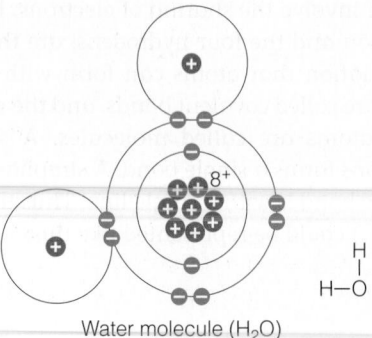

H
|
H—O

Water molecule (H$_2$O)

When two oxygen atoms form a molecule of oxygen, they must share two pairs of electrons. This double bond may be represented as two single lines:

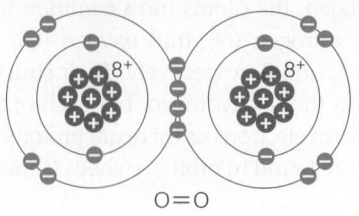

O=O

Oxygen molecule (O$_2$)

Small atoms form the tightest, most stable bonds. H, O, N, and C are the smallest atoms capable of forming one, two, three, and four electron-pair bonds respectively. This is the basis for the statement in Chapter 4 that in drawings of compounds containing these atoms, hydrogen must always have one, oxygen two, nitrogen three, and carbon four bonds radiating to other atoms:

$$H- \quad -O- \quad -\overset{|}{N}- \quad -\overset{|}{\underset{|}{C}}-$$

The stability of the associations between these small atoms and the versatility with which they can combine make them very common in living things. Interestingly, all cells, whether they come from animals, plants, or bacteria, contain the same elements in very nearly the same proportions. The elements commonly found in living things are shown in Table B-2.

TABLE B-2	Elemental Composition of the Human Body	
Element	Chemical Symbol	By Weight (%)
Oxygen	O	65
Carbon	C	18
Hydrogen	H	10
Nitrogen	N	3
Calcium	Ca	1.5
Phosphorus	P	1.0
Potassium	K	0.4
Sulfur	S	0.3
Sodium	Na	0.2
Chloride	Cl	0.1
Magnesium	Mg	0.1
Total		99.6[a]

[a]The remaining 0.40 percent by weight is contributed by the trace elements: chromium (Cr), copper (Cu), zinc (Zn), selenium (Se), molybdenum (Mo), fluorine (F), iodine (I), manganese (Mn), and iron (Fe). Cells may also contain variable traces of some of the following: boron (B), cobalt (Co), lithium (Li), strontium (Sr), aluminum (Al), silicon (Si), lead (Pb), vanadium (V), arsenic (As), bromine (Br), and others.

Formation of Ions

An atom such as sodium (Na, atomic number 11) cannot easily fill its outer shell by sharing. Sodium possesses a filled first shell of two electrons and a filled second shell of eight; there is only one electron in its outermost shell:

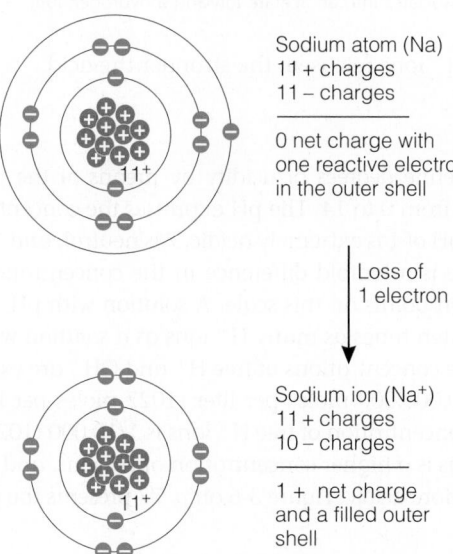

Sodium atom (Na)
11 + charges
11 – charges

0 net charge with one reactive electron in the outer shell

Loss of 1 electron

Sodium ion (Na⁺)
11 + charges
10 – charges

1 + net charge and a filled outer shell

If sodium loses this electron, it satisfies one condition for stability: a filled outer shell (now its second shell counts as the outer shell). However, it is not electrically neutral. It has 11 protons (positive) and only 10 electrons (negative). It therefore has a net positive charge. An atom or molecule that has lost or gained one or more electrons and so is electrically charged is called an ion.

An atom such as chlorine (Cl, atomic number 17), with seven electrons in its outermost shell, can share electrons to fill its outer shell, or it can gain one electron to complete its outer shell and thus give it a negative charge:

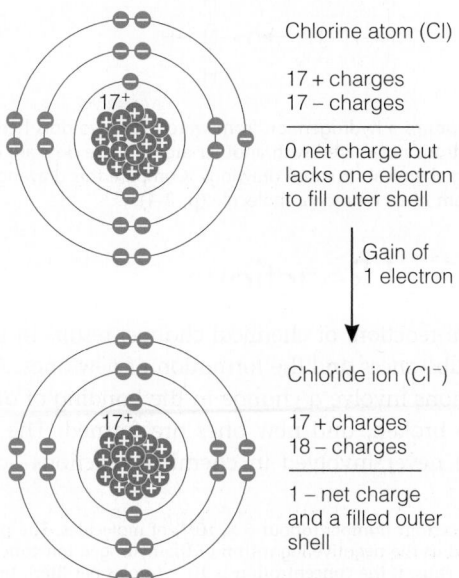

Chlorine atom (Cl)

17 + charges
17 – charges

0 net charge but lacks one electron to fill outer shell

Gain of 1 electron

Chloride ion (Cl⁻)

17 + charges
18 – charges

1 – net charge and a filled outer shell

A positively charged ion such as sodium ion (Na⁺) is called a cation; a negatively charged ion such as a chloride ion (Cl⁻) is called an anion. Cations and anions attract one another to form salts:

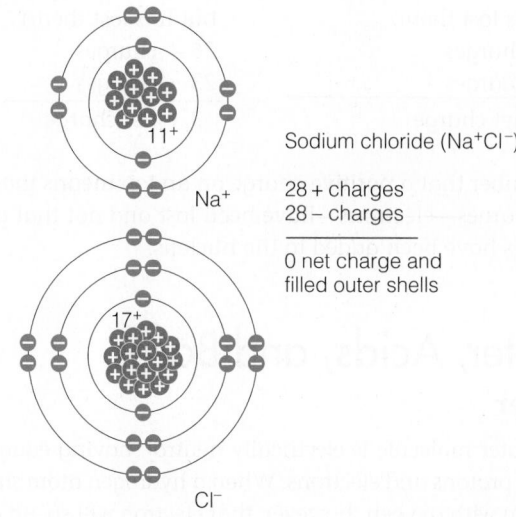

Sodium chloride (Na⁺Cl⁻)

28 + charges
28 – charges

0 net charge and filled outer shells

With all its electrons, sodium is a shiny, highly reactive metal; chlorine is the poisonous greenish yellow gas that was used in World War I. But after sodium and chlorine have transferred electrons, they form the stable white salt familiar to you as table salt, or sodium chloride (Na⁺Cl⁻). The dramatic difference illustrates how profoundly the electron arrangement can influence the nature of a substance. The wide distribution of salt in nature attests to the stability of the union between the ions. Each meets the other's needs (a good marriage).

When dry, salt exists as crystals; its ions are stacked very regularly into a lattice, with positive and negative ions alternating in a three-dimensional checkerboard structure. In water, however, the salt quickly dissolves, and its ions separate from one another, forming an electrolyte solution in which they move about freely. Covalently bonded molecules rarely dissociate like this in a water solution. The most common exception is when they behave like acids and release H⁺ ions, as discussed in the next section.

An ion can also be a group of atoms bound together in such a way that the group has a net charge and enters into reactions as a single unit. Many such groups are active in the fluids of the body. The bicarbonate ion is composed of five atoms—one H, one C, and three Os—and has a net charge of -1 (HCO_3^-). Another important ion of this type is a phosphate ion with one H, one P, and four O, and a net charge of -2 (HPO_4^{-2}).

Whereas many elements have only one configuration in the outer shell and thus only one way to bond with other elements, some elements have the possibility of varied configurations. Iron is such an element. Under some conditions iron loses two electrons, and under other circumstances it loses three. If iron loses two electrons, it then has a net charge of +2, and we call it ferrous iron (Fe^{++}). If it donates three electrons to another atom, it becomes the +3 ion, or ferric iron (Fe^{+++}).

Ferrous iron (Fe^{++})
(had 2 outer-shell electrons
but has lost them)
26 + charges
24 − charges
————————
2 + net charge

Ferric iron (Fe^{+++})
(had 3 outer-shell electrons
but has lost them)
26 + charges
23 − charges
————————
3 + net charge

Remember that a positive charge on an ion means that negative charges—electrons—have been lost and not that positive charges have been added to the nucleus.

Water, Acids, and Bases

Water

The water molecule is electrically neutral, having equal numbers of protons and electrons. When a hydrogen atom shares its electron with oxygen, however, that electron will spend most of its time closer to the positively charged oxygen nucleus. This leaves the positive proton (nucleus of the hydrogen atom) exposed on the outer part of the water molecule. We know, too, that the two hydrogens both bond toward the same side of the oxygen. These two facts explain why water molecules are polar: they have regions of more positive and more negative charge.

Polar molecules like water are drawn to one another by the attractive forces between the positive polar areas of one and the negative poles of another. These attractive forces, sometimes known as polar bonds or hydrogen bonds, occur among many molecules and also within the different parts of single large molecules. Although very weak in comparison with covalent bonds, polar bonds may occur in such abundance that they become exceedingly important in determining the structure of such large molecules as proteins and DNA.

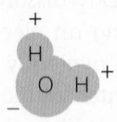

This diagram of the polar water molecule shows displacement of electrons toward the O nucleus; thus the negative region is near the O and the positive regions are near the H atoms.

Water molecules have a slight tendency to ionize, separating into positive (H^+) and negative (OH^-) ions. In pure water, a small but constant number of these ions is present, and the number of positive ions exactly equals the number of negative ions.

Acid

An acid is a substance that releases H^+ ions (protons) in a water solution. Hydrochloric acid (HCl^-) is such a substance because it dissociates in a water solution into H^+ and Cl^- ions.

Acetic acid is also an acid because it dissociates in water to acetate ions and free H^+:

$$H-\underset{\underset{H}{|}}{\overset{\overset{H}{|}}{C}}-\overset{\overset{O}{\parallel}}{C}-O-H \longrightarrow H-\underset{\underset{H}{|}}{\overset{\overset{H}{|}}{C}}-\overset{\overset{O}{\parallel}}{C}-O^- + H^+$$

Acetic acid dissociates into an acetate ion and a hydrogen ion.

The more H^+ ions released, the stronger the acid.

pH

Chemists define degrees of acidity by means of the pH scale, which runs from 0 to 14. The pH expresses the concentration of H^+ ions: a pH of 1 is extremely acidic, 7 is neutral, and 13 is very basic. There is a tenfold difference in the concentration of H^+ ions between points on this scale. A solution with pH 3, for example, has ten times as many H^+ ions as a solution with pH 4. At pH 7, the concentrations of free H^+ and OH^- are exactly the same—1/10,000,000 moles per liter (1027 moles per liter).* At pH 4, the concentration of free H^+ ions is 1/10,000 (1024) moles per liter. This is a higher concentration of H^+ ions, and the solution is therefore acidic. Figure 3-6 on p. 77 presents the pH scale.

Bases

A base is a substance that can combine with H^+ ions, thus reducing the acidity of a solution. The compound ammonia is such a substance. The ammonia molecule has two electrons that are not shared with any other atom; a hydrogen ion (H^+) is just a naked proton with no shell of electrons at all. The proton readily combines with the ammonia molecule to form an ammonium ion; thus a free proton is withdrawn from the solution and no longer contributes to its acidity. Many compounds containing nitrogen are important bases in living systems. Acids and bases neutralize each other to produce substances that are neither acid nor base.

$$:\underset{\underset{H}{|}}{\overset{\overset{H}{|}}{N}}-H + H^+ \longrightarrow H-\underset{\underset{H}{|}}{\overset{\overset{H}{|}}{N^+}}-H$$

Ammonia captures a hydrogen ion from water. The two dots here represent the two electrons not shared with another atom. These dots are ordinarily not shown in chemical structure drawings. Compare this drawing with the earlier diagram of an ammonia molecule (p. B-4).

Chemical Reactions

A chemical reaction, or chemical change, results in the breakdown of substances and the formation of new ones. Almost all such reactions involve a change in the bonding of atoms. Old bonds are broken, and new ones are formed. The nuclei of atoms are never involved in chemical reactions—only their

---

*A mole is a certain number (about 6×10^{23}) of molecules. The pH of a solution is defined as the negative logarithm of the hydrogen ion concentration of the solution. Thus, if the concentration is 10^{-2} (moles per liter), the pH is 2; if 10^{-8}, the pH is 8; and so on.

Diagrams:

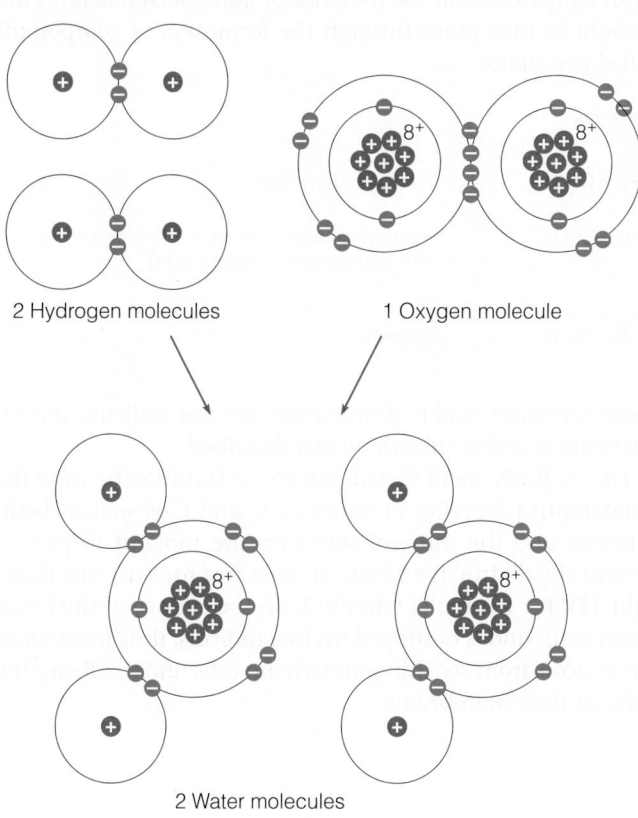

2 Hydrogen molecules   1 Oxygen molecule

2 Water molecules

Structures:

$$H-H$$
$$+$$
$$H-H$$
$$+$$
$$O=O$$

$$H-O-H$$
$$+$$
$$H-O-H$$

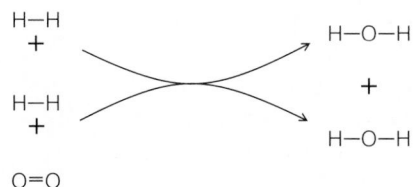

Formulas:

$$2H_2 + O_2 \longrightarrow 2H_2O$$

Hydrogen and oxygen react to form water.

outer-shell electrons take part. At the end of a chemical reaction, the number of atoms of each type is always the same as at the beginning. For example, two hydrogen molecules ($2H_2$) can react with one oxygen molecule (O_2) to form two water molecules ($2H_2O$). In this reaction two substances (hydrogen and oxygen) disappear, and a new one (water) is formed, but at the end of the reaction there are still four H atoms and two O atoms, just as there were at the beginning. Because the atoms are now linked in a different way, their characteristics or properties have changed.

In many instances chemical reactions involve not the relinking of molecules but the exchanging of electrons or protons among them. In such reactions the molecule that gains one or more electrons (or loses one or more hydrogen ions) is said to be reduced; the molecule that loses electrons (or gains

protons) is oxidized. A hydrogen ion is equivalent to a proton. Oxidation and reduction reactions take place simultaneously because an electron or proton that is lost by one molecule is accepted by another. The addition of an atom of oxygen is also oxidation because oxygen (with six electrons in the outer shell) accepts two electrons in becoming bonded. Oxidation, then, is loss of electrons, gain of protons, or addition of oxygen (with six electrons); reduction is the opposite—gain of electrons, loss of protons, or loss of oxygen. The addition of hydrogen atoms to oxygen to form water can thus be described as the reduction of oxygen *or* the oxidation of hydrogen.

If a reaction results in a net increase in the energy of a compound, it is called an endergonic, or "uphill," reaction (energy, *erg*, is added into, *endo*, the compound). An example is the chief result of photosynthesis, the making of sugar in a plant from carbon dioxide and water using the energy of sunlight. Conversely, the oxidation of sugar to carbon dioxide and water is an exergonic, or "downhill," reaction because the end products have less energy than the starting products. Oftentimes, but not always, reduction reactions are endergonic, resulting in an increase in the energy of the products. Oxidation reactions often, but not always, are exergonic.

Chemical reactions tend to occur spontaneously if the end products are in a lower energy state and therefore are more stable than the reacting compounds. These reactions often give off energy in the form of heat as they occur. The generation of heat by wood burning in a fireplace and the maintenance of human body warmth both depend on energy-yielding chemical reactions. These downhill reactions occur easily, although they may require some activation energy to get them started, just as a ball requires a push to start rolling.

Uphill reactions, in which the products contain more energy than the reacting compounds started with, do not occur until an energy source is provided. An example of such an energy source is the sunlight used in photosynthesis, where carbon dioxide and water (low-energy compounds) are combined to form the sugar glucose (a higher-energy compound). Another example is the use of the energy in glucose to combine two low-energy compounds in the body into the high-energy

Energy change as reaction occurs

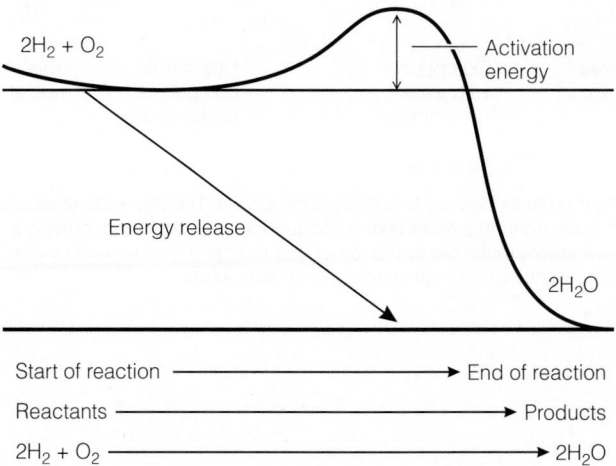

$2H_2 + O_2$

Activation energy

Energy release

$2H_2O$

Start of reaction ⟶ End of reaction

Reactants ⟶ Products

$2H_2 + O_2$ ⟶ $2H_2O$

compound ATP (see Chapter 7). The energy in ATP may be used to power many other energy-requiring, uphill reactions. Clearly, any of many different molecules can be used as a temporary storage place for energy.

Neither downhill nor uphill reactions occur until something sets them off (activation) or until a path is provided for them to follow. The body uses enzymes as a means of providing paths and controlling chemical reactions (see Chapter 6). By controlling the availability and the action of its enzymes, the cells can "decide" which chemical reactions to prevent and which to promote.

Formation of Free Radicals

Normally, when a chemical reaction takes place, bonds break and re-form with some redistribution of atoms and rearrangement of bonds to form new, stable compounds. Normally, bonds don't split in such a way as to leave a molecule with an odd, unpaired electron. When they do, free radicals are formed. Free radicals are highly unstable and quickly react with other compounds, forming more free radicals in a chain reaction. A cascade may ensue in which many highly reactive radicals are generated, resulting finally in the disruption of a living structure such as a cell membrane.

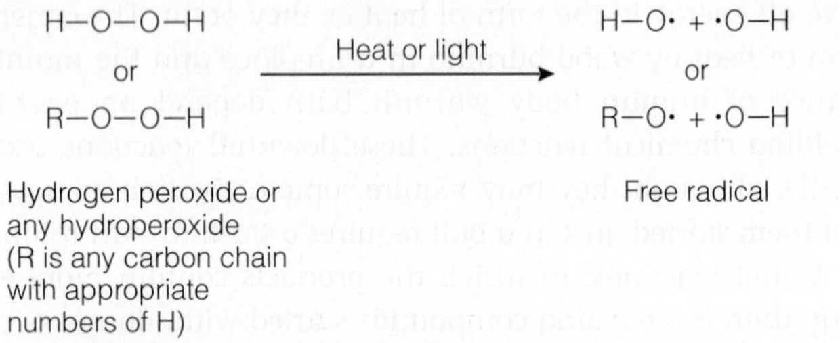

H—O—O—H
or
R—O—O—H

→ Heat or light →

H—O• + •O—H
or
R—O• + •O—H

Hydrogen peroxide or any hydroperoxide (R is any carbon chain with appropriate numbers of H)

Free radical

Free radicals are formed. The dots represent single electrons that are available for sharing (the atom needs another electron to fill its outer shell).

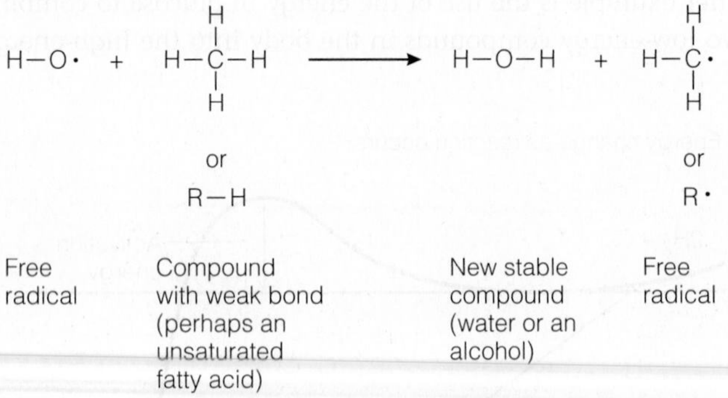

H—O• + H—C—H → H—O—H + H—C•
or R—H → R•

Free radical | Compound with weak bond (perhaps an unsaturated fatty acid) | New stable compound (water or an alcohol) | Free radical

Free radicals destroy biological compounds. The free radical attacks a weak bond in a biological compound, disrupting it and forming a new stable molecule and another free radical. This free radical can attack another biological compound, and so on.

Oxidation of some compounds can be induced by air at room temperature in the presence of light. Such reactions are thought to take place through the formation of compounds called peroxides:

Peroxides:

H—O—O—H   Hydrogen peroxide

R—O—O—H   Hydroperoxides (R is any carbon chain with appropriate numbers of H)

R—O—O—R   Peroxide

Some peroxides readily disintegrate into free radicals, initiating chain reactions like those just described.

Free radicals are of special interest in nutrition because the antioxidant properties of vitamins C and E as well as beta-carotene and the mineral selenium are thought to protect against the destructive effects of these free radicals (see Highlight 11). For example, vitamin E on the surface of the lungs reacts with, and is destroyed by, free radicals, thus preventing the radicals from reaching underlying cells and oxidizing the lipids in their membranes.

Biochemical Structures and Pathways

The diagrams of nutrients presented here are meant to enhance your understanding of the most important organic molecules in the human diet. Following the diagrams of nutrients are sections on the major metabolic pathways mentioned in Chapter 7—glycolysis, fatty acid oxidation, amino acid degradation, the TCA cycle, and the electron transport chain—and a description of how alcohol interferes with these pathways. Discussions of the urea cycle and the formation of ketone bodies complete the appendix.

CONTENTS

Carbohydrates
Lipids
Protein: Amino Acids
Vitamins and Coenzymes
Glycolysis
Fatty Acid Oxidation
Amino Acid Degradation
The TCA Cycle
The Electron Transport Chain
Alcohol's Interference with Energy Metabolism
The Urea Cycle
Formation of Ketone Bodies

C Appendix

Carbohydrates

Monosaccharides

Glucose (alpha form). The ring would be at right angles to the plane of the paper. The bonds directed upward are above the plane; those directed downward are below the plane. This molecule is considered an alpha form because the OH on carbon 1 points downward.

Glucose (beta form). The OH on carbon 1 points upward.
Fructose, galactose: see Chapter 4.

Glucose (alpha form) shorthand notation. This notation, in which the carbons in the ring and single hydrogens have been eliminated, will be used throughout this appendix.

Disaccharides

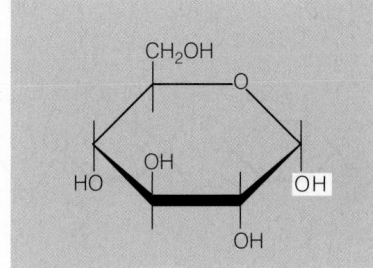

Maltose.

Glucose   Glucose

Galactose   Glucose

Lactose (alpha form).

Glucose   Fructose

Sucrose.

Polysaccharides

As described in Chapter 4, starch, glycogen, and cellulose are all long chains of glucose molecules covalently linked together.

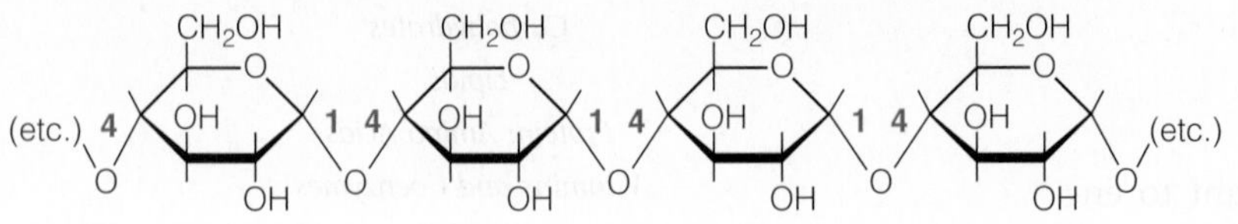

Amylose (unbranched starch)

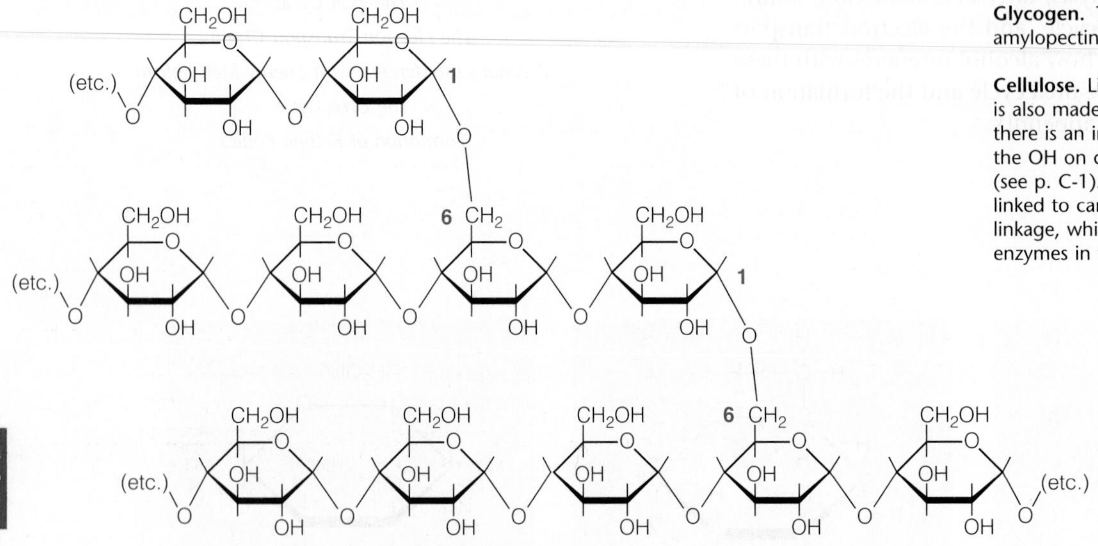

Starch. Two kinds of covalent linkages occur between glucose molecules in starch, giving rise to two kinds of chains. Amylose is composed of straight chains, with carbon 1 of one glucose linked to carbon 4 of the next (α-1,4 linkage). Amylopectin is made up of straight chains like amylose but has occasional branches arising where the carbon 6 of a glucose is also linked to the carbon 1 of another glucose (α-1,6 linkage).

Glycogen. The structure of glycogen is like amylopectin but with many more branches.

Cellulose. Like starch and glycogen, cellulose is also made of chains of glucose units, but there is an important difference: in cellulose, the OH on carbon 1 is in the beta position (see p. C-1). When carbon 1 of one glucose is linked to carbon 4 of the next, it forms a β-1,4 linkage, which cannot be broken by digestive enzymes in the human GI tract.

Amylopectin (branched starch)

Fibers, such as hemicelluloses, consist of long chains of various monosaccharides.

Monosaccharides common in the backbone chain of hemicelluloses:

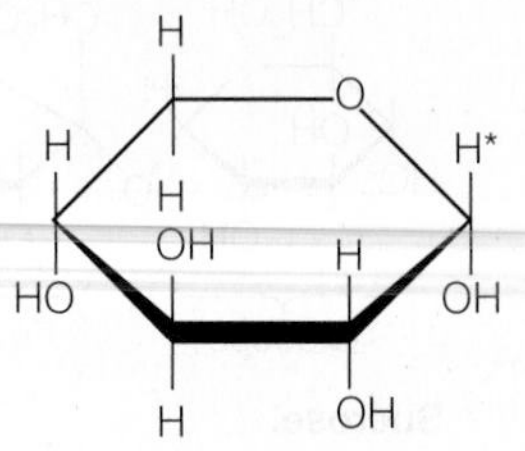

Xylose 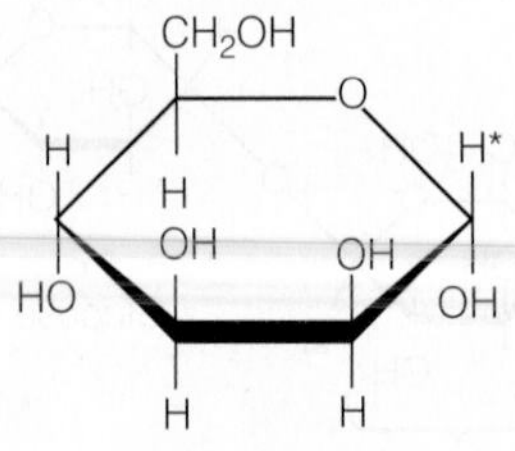   Mannose 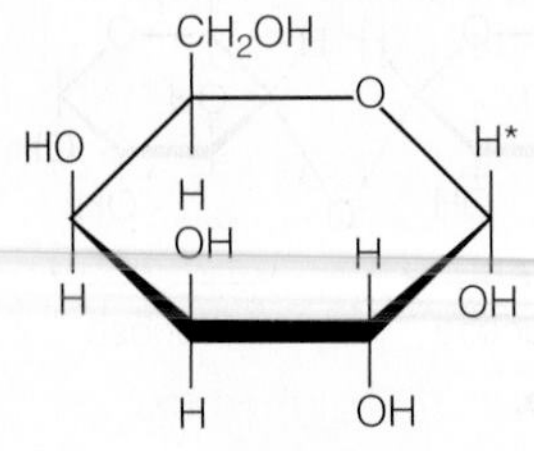   Galactose

---

*These structures are shown in the alpha form with the H on the carbon pointing upward and the OH pointing downward, but they may also appear in the beta form with the H pointing downward and the OH upward.

Monosaccharides common in the side chains of hemicelluloses:

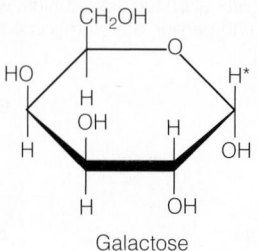

Arabinose   Glucuronic acid   Galactose

Hemicelluloses. The most common hemicelluloses are composed of a backbone chain of xylose, mannose, and galactose, with branching side chains of arabinose, glucuronic acid, and galactose.

Lipids

TABLE C-1	Saturated Fatty Acids Found in Natural Fats		
Saturated Fatty Acids	Chemical Formulas	Number of Carbons	Major Food Sources
Butyric	C_3H_7COOH	4	Butterfat
Caproic	$C_5H_{11}COOH$	6	Butterfat
Caprylic	$C_7H_{15}COOH$	8	Coconut oil
Capric	$C_9H_{19}COOH$	10	Palm oil
Lauric	$C_{11}H_{23}COOH$	12	Coconut oil, palm oil
Myristic[a]	$C_{13}H_{27}COOH$	14	Coconut oil, palm oil
Palmitic[a]	$C_{15}H_{31}COOH$	16	Palm oil
Stearic[a]	$C_{17}H_{35}COOH$	18	Most animal fats
Arachidic	$C_{19}H_{39}COOH$	20	Peanut oil
Behenic	$C_{21}H_{43}COOH$	22	Seeds
Lignoceric	$C_{23}H_{47}COOH$	24	Peanut oil

[a]Most common saturated fatty acids.

TABLE C-2	Unsaturated Fatty Acids Found in Natural Fats					
Unsaturated Fatty Acids	Chemical Formulas	Number of Carbons	Number of Double Bonds	Standard Notation[a]	Omega Notation[b]	Major Food Sources
Palmitoleic	$C_{15}H_{29}COOH$	16	1	16:1;9	16:1ω7	Seafood, beef
Oleic	$C_{17}H_{33}COOH$	18	1	18:1;9	18:1ω9	Olive oil, canola oil
Linoleic	$C_{17}H_{31}COOH$	18	2	18:2;9,12	18:2ω6	Sunflower oil, safflower oil
Linolenic	$C_{17}H_{29}COOH$	18	3	18:3;9,12,15	18:3ω3	Soybean oil, canola oil
Arachidonic	$C_{19}H_{31}COOH$	20	4	20:4;5,8,11,14	20:4ω6	Eggs, most animal fats
Eicosapentaenoic	$C_{19}H_{29}COOH$	20	5	20:5;5,8,11,14,17	20:5ω3	Seafood
Docosahexaenoic	$C_{21}H_{31}COOH$	22	6	22:6;4,7,10,13,16,19	22:6ω3	Seafood

NOTE: A fatty acid has two ends; designated the methyl (CH_3) end and the carboxyl, or acid (COOH), end.
[a]Standard chemistry notation begins counting carbons at the acid end. The number of carbons the fatty acid contains comes first, followed by a colon and another number that indicates the number of double bonds; next comes a semicolon followed by a number or numbers indicating the positions of the double bonds. Thus the notation for linoleic acid, an 18-carbon fatty acid with two double bonds between carbons 9 and 10 and between carbons 12 and 13, is 18:2;9,12.
[b]Because fatty acid chains are lengthened by adding carbons at the acid end of the chain, chemists use the omega system of notation to ease the task of identifying them. The omega system begins counting carbons at the methyl end. The number of carbons the fatty acid contains comes first, followed by a colon and the number of double bonds; next come the omega symbol (ω) and a number indicating the position of the double bond nearest the methyl end. Thus linoleic acid with its first double bond at the sixth carbon from the methyl end would be noted 18:2ω6 in the omega system.

Protein: Amino Acids

The common amino acids may be classified into the seven groups listed on the next page. Amino acids marked with an asterisk (*) are essential.

1. Amino acids with aliphatic side chains, which consist of hydrogen and carbon atoms (hydrocarbons):

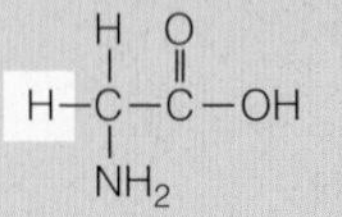

Glycine (Gly)

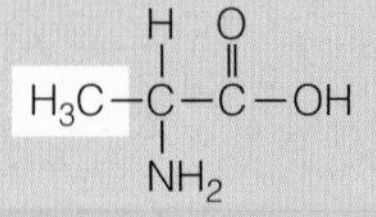

Alanine (Ala)

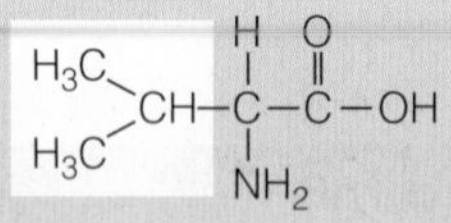

Valine* (Val)

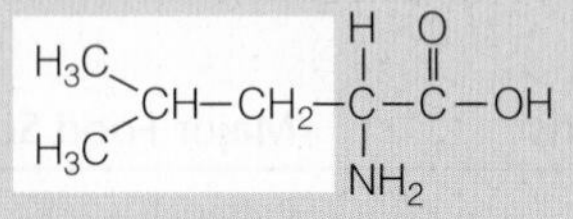

Leucine* (Leu)

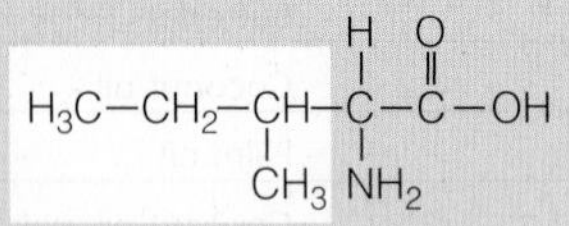

Isoleucine* (Ile)

2. Amino acids with hydroxyl (OH) side chains:

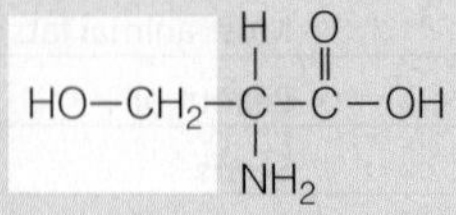

Serine (Ser)

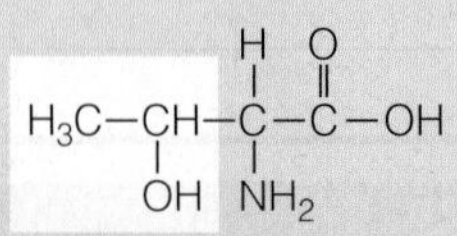

Threonine* (Thr)

3. Amino acids with side chains containing acidic groups or their amides, which contain the group NH_2:

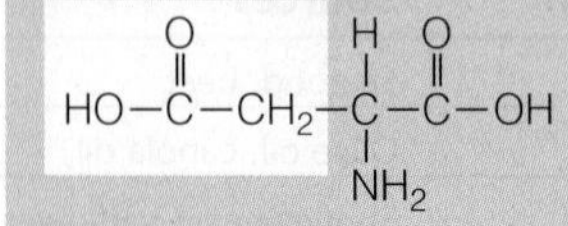

Aspartic acid (Asp)

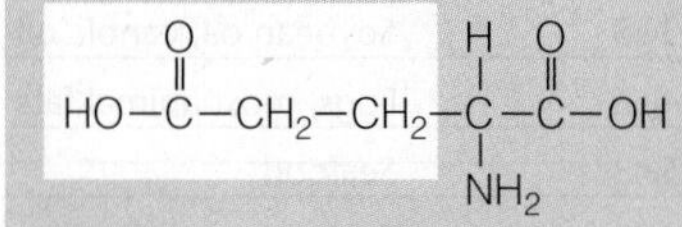

Glutamic acid (Glu)

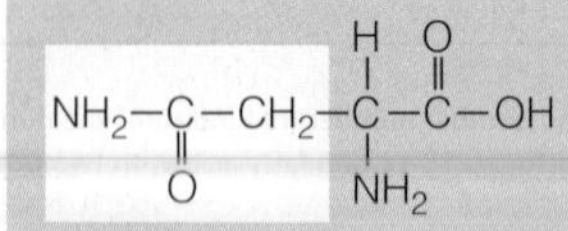

Asparagine (Asn)

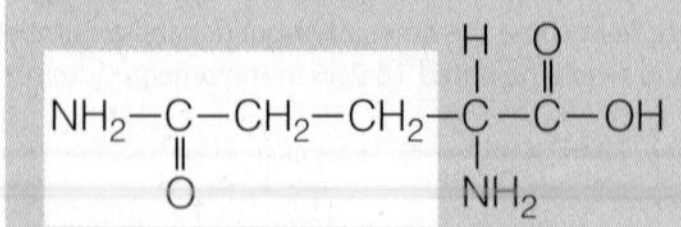

Glutamine (Gln)

4. Amino acids with basic side chains:

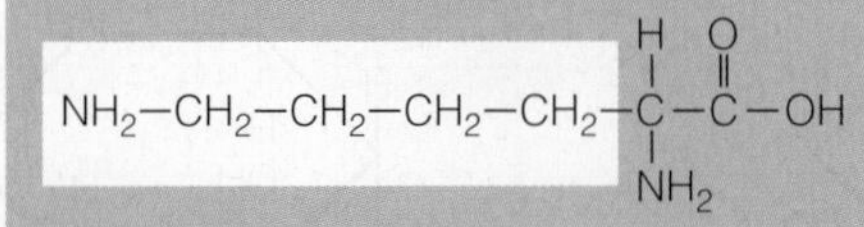

Lysine* (Lys)

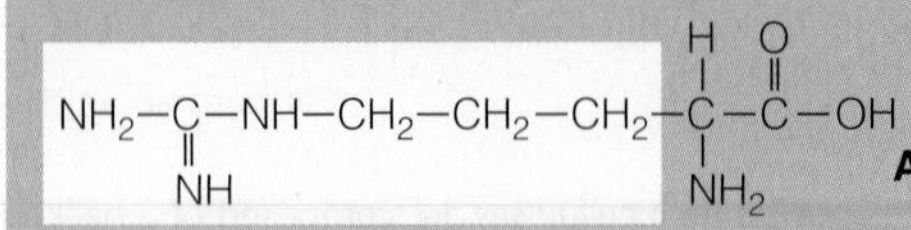

Arginine (Arg)

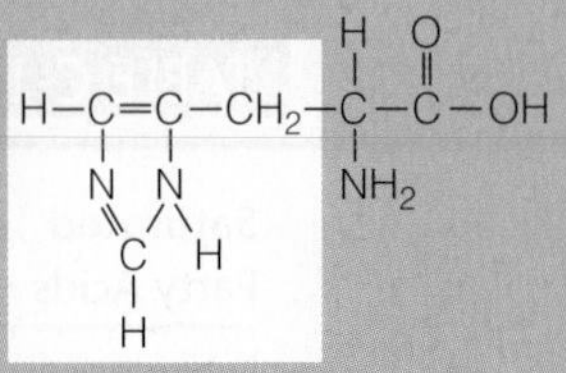

Histidine* (His)

5. Amino acids with aromatic side chains, which are characterized by the presence of at least one ring structure:

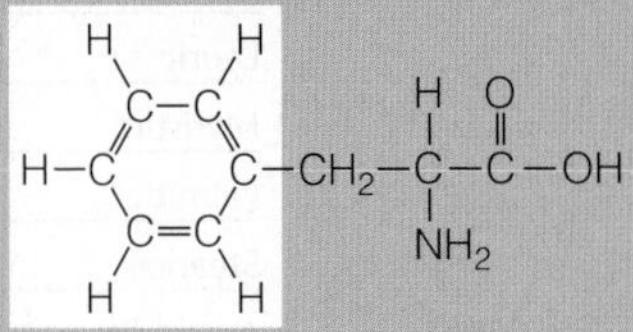

Phenylalanine* (Phe)

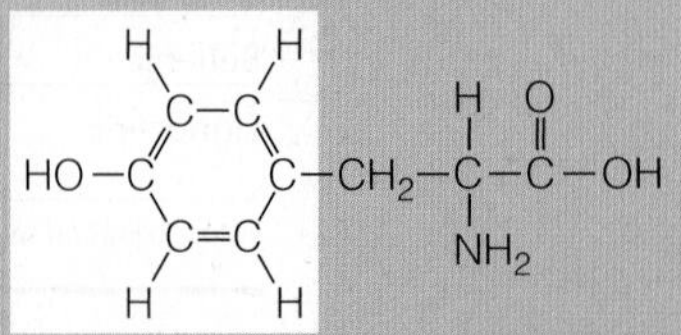

Tyrosine (Tyr)

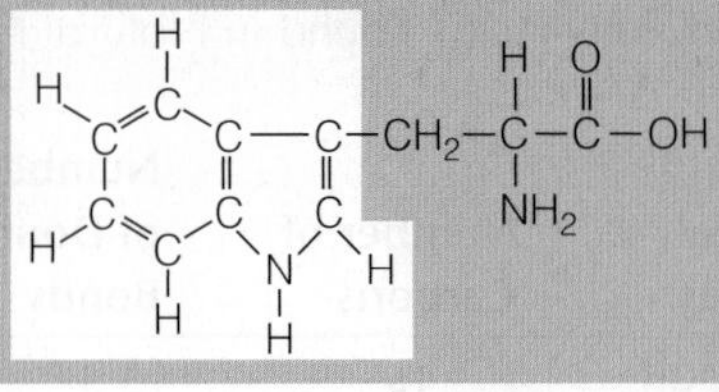

Tryptophan* (Trp)

6. Amino acids with side chains containing sulfur atoms:

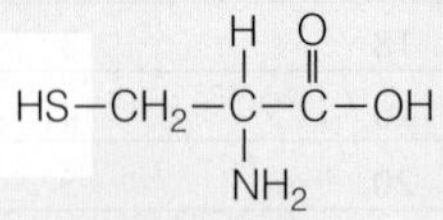

Cysteine (Cys)

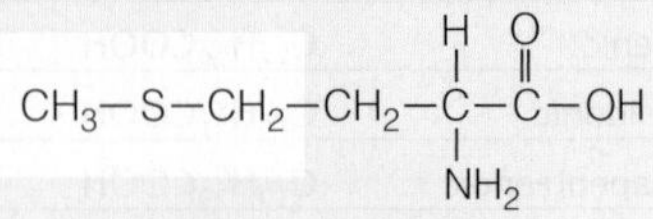

Methionine* (Met)

7. Imino acid:

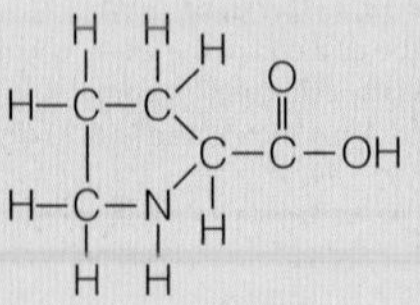

Proline (Pro)

Proline has the same chemical structure as the other amino acids, but its amino group has given up a hydrogen to form a ring.

Vitamins and Coenzymes

Vitamin A: retinol. This molecule is the alcohol form of vitamin A.

Vitamin A: retinal. This molecule is the aldehyde form of vitamin A.

Vitamin A: retinoic acid. This molecule is the acid form of vitamin A.

Vitamin A precursor: beta-carotene. This molecule is the carotenoid with the most vitamin A activity.

Thiamin. This molecule is part of the coenzyme thiamin pyrophosphate (TPP).

Thiamin pyrophosphate (TPP). TPP is a coenzyme that includes the thiamin molecule as part of its structure.

Riboflavin. This molecule is a part of two coenzymes—flavin mononucleotide (FMN) and flavin adenine dinucleotide (FAD).

Flavin mononucleotide (FMN). FMN is a coenzyme that includes the riboflavin molecule as part of its structure.

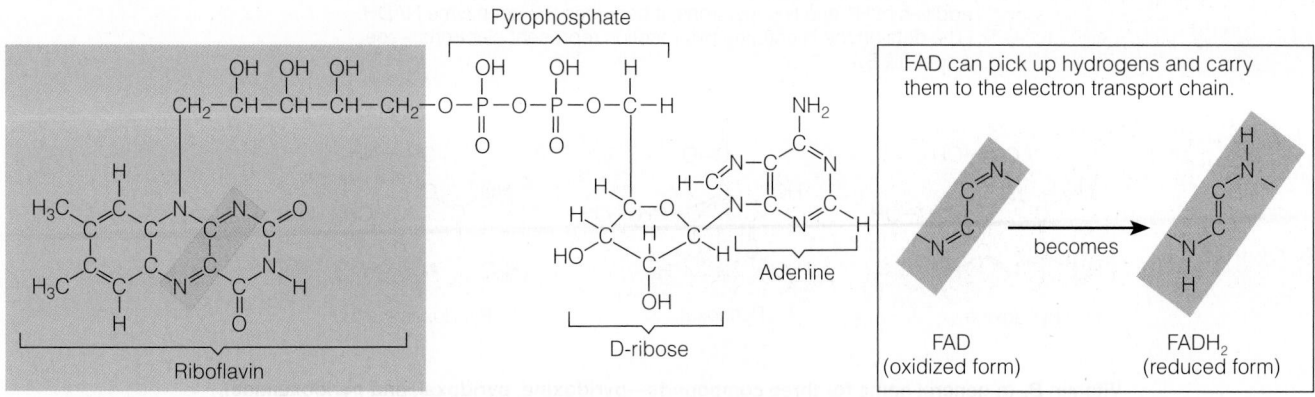

Flavin adenine dinucleotide (FAD). FAD is a coenzyme that includes the riboflavin molecule as part of its structure.

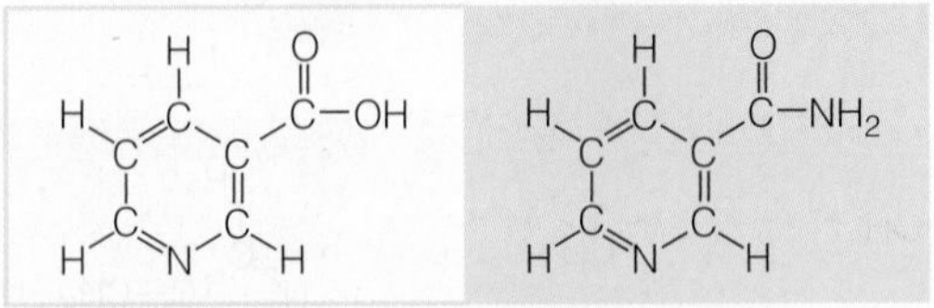

Nicotinic acid   Nicotinamide

Niacin (nicotinic acid and nicotinamide). These molecules are a part of two coenzymes—nicotinamide adenine dinucleotide (NAD^+) and nicotinamide adenine dinucleotide phosphate ($NADP^+$).

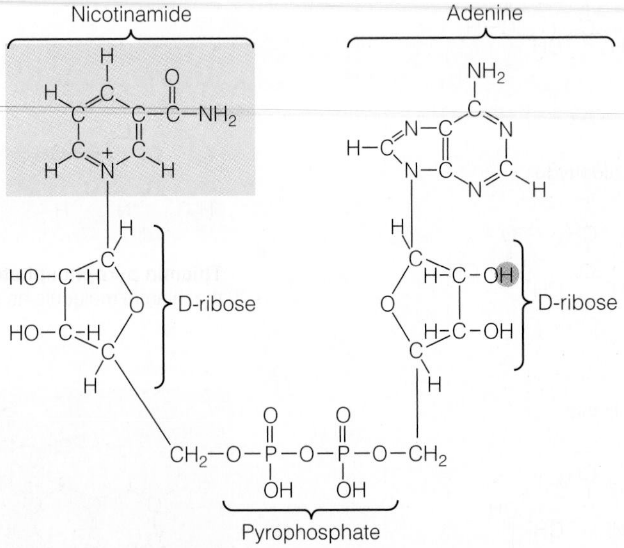

Nicotinamide   Adenine

D-ribose

D-ribose

Pyrophosphate

Nicotinamide adenine dinucleotide (NAD^+) and nicotinamide adenine dinucleotide phosphate ($NADP^+$). NADP has the same structure as NAD but with a phosphate group attached to the O instead of the ⒣.

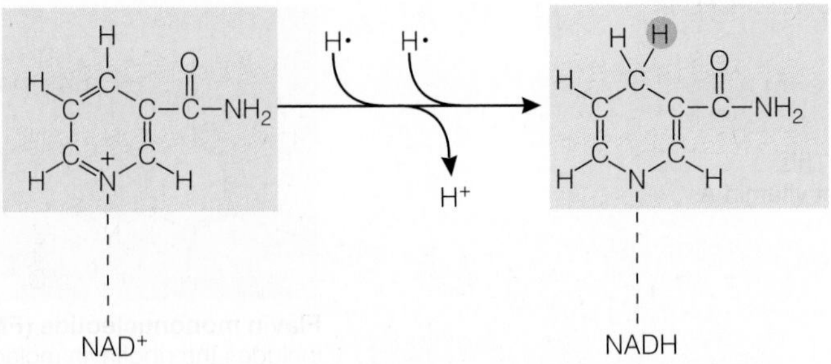

NAD$^+$ NADH

Reduced NAD^+ (NADH). When NAD^+ is reduced by the addition of H^+ and two electrons, it becomes the coenzyme NADH. (The dots on the H entering this reaction represent electrons—see Appendix B.)

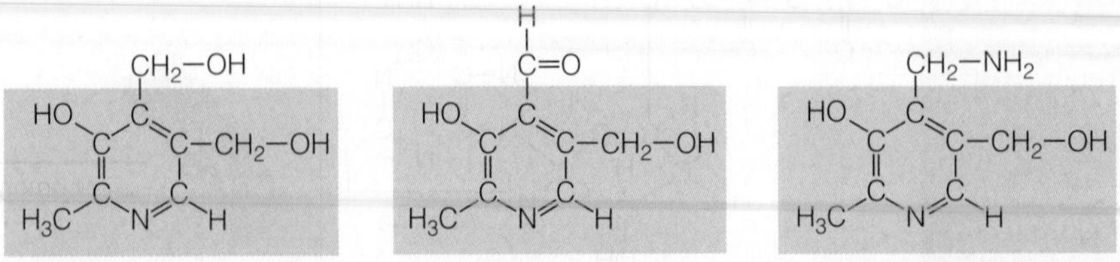

Pyridoxine   Pyridoxal   Pyridoxamine

Vitamin B$_6$ (a general name for three compounds—pyridoxine, pyridoxal, and pyridoxamine). These molecules are a part of two coenzymes—pyridoxal phosphate and pyridoxamine phosphate.

Pyridoxal phosphate (PLP) and pyridoxamine phosphate. These coenzymes include vitamin B_6 as part of their structures.

Vitamin B_{12} (cyanocobalamin). The arrows in this diagram indicate that the spare electron pairs on the nitrogens attract them to the cobalt.

Folate (folacin or folic acid). This molecule consists of a double ring combined with a single ring and at least one glutamate (a nonessential amino acid marked in the box). Folate's biologically active form is tetrahydrofolate.

Tetrahydrofolate. This active coenzyme form of folate has four added hydrogens. An intermediate form, dihydrofolate, has two added hydrogens.

Pantothenic acid. This molecule is part of coenzyme A (CoA).

Coenzyme A (CoA). Coenzyme A is a coenzyme that includes pantothenic acid as part of its structure.

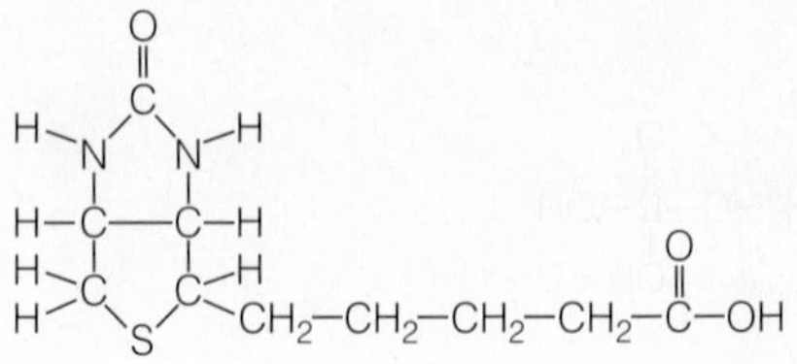

Biotin.

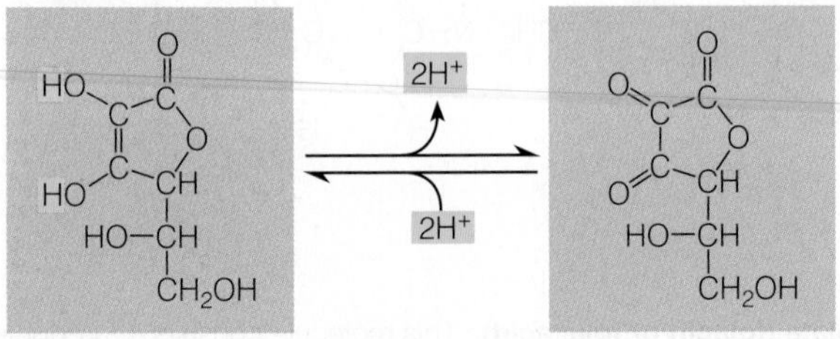

Ascorbic acid
(reduced form)

Dehydroascorbic acid
(oxidized form)

Vitamin C. Two hydrogen atoms with their electrons are lost when ascorbic acid is oxidized and gained when it is reduced again.

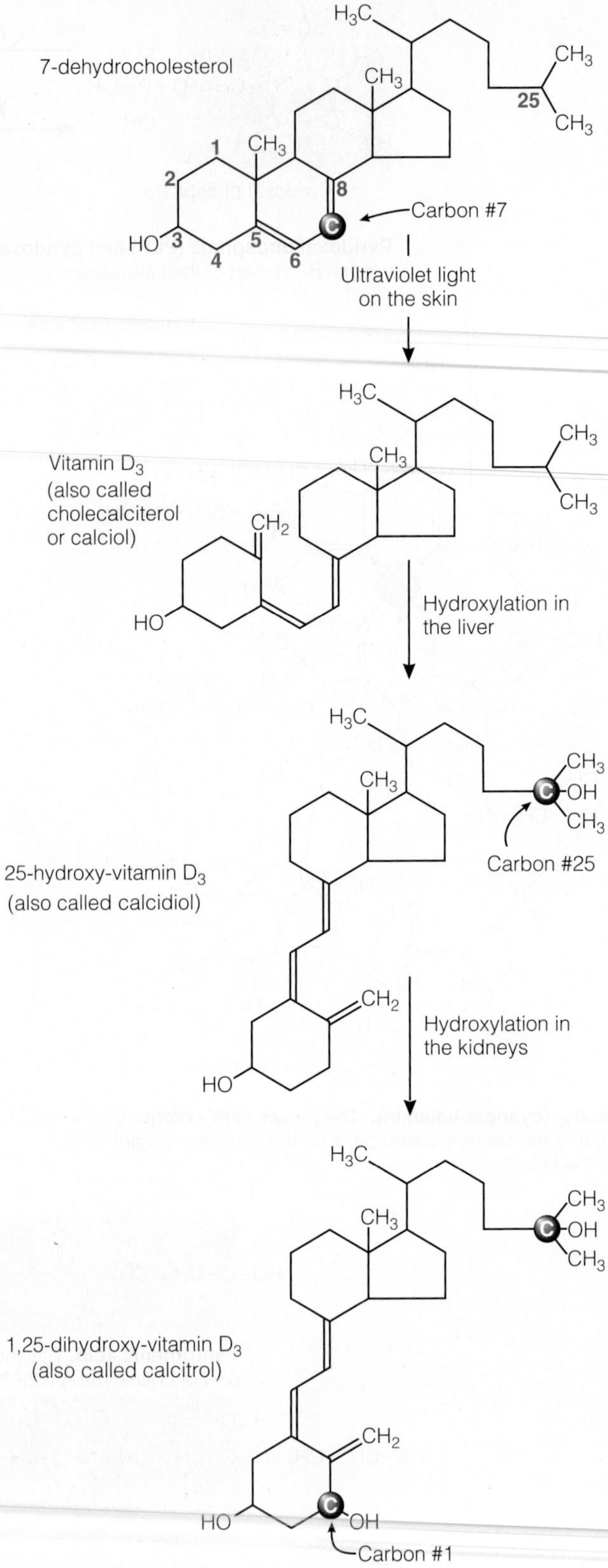

7-dehydrocholesterol

Carbon #7

Ultraviolet light
on the skin

Vitamin D$_3$
(also called
cholecalciterol
or calciol)

Hydroxylation in
the liver

25-hydroxy-vitamin D$_3$
(also called calcidiol)

Carbon #25

Hydroxylation in
the kidneys

1,25-dihydroxy-vitamin D$_3$
(also called calcitrol)

Carbon #1

Vitamin D. The synthesis of active vitamin D begins with 7-dehydrocholesterol. (The carbon atoms at which changes occur are numbered.)

Vitamin E (alpha-tocopherol). The number and position of the methyl groups (CH_3) bonded to the ring structure differentiate among the tocopherols.

Tocotrienols contain double bonds here.

Vitamin K. Naturally occurring compounds with vitamin K activity include phylloquinones (from plants) and menaquinones (from bacteria).

Menadione. This synthetic compound has the same activity as natural vitamin K.

Adenosine triphosphate (ATP), the energy carrier. The cleavage point marks the bond that is broken when ATP splits to become ADP + P.

Adenosine diphosphate (ADP).

Glycolysis

Figure C-1 depicts the events of glycolysis. The following text describes key steps as numbered on the figure.

FIGURE C-1 Glycolysis

Notice that galactose and fructose enter at different places but continue on the same pathway.

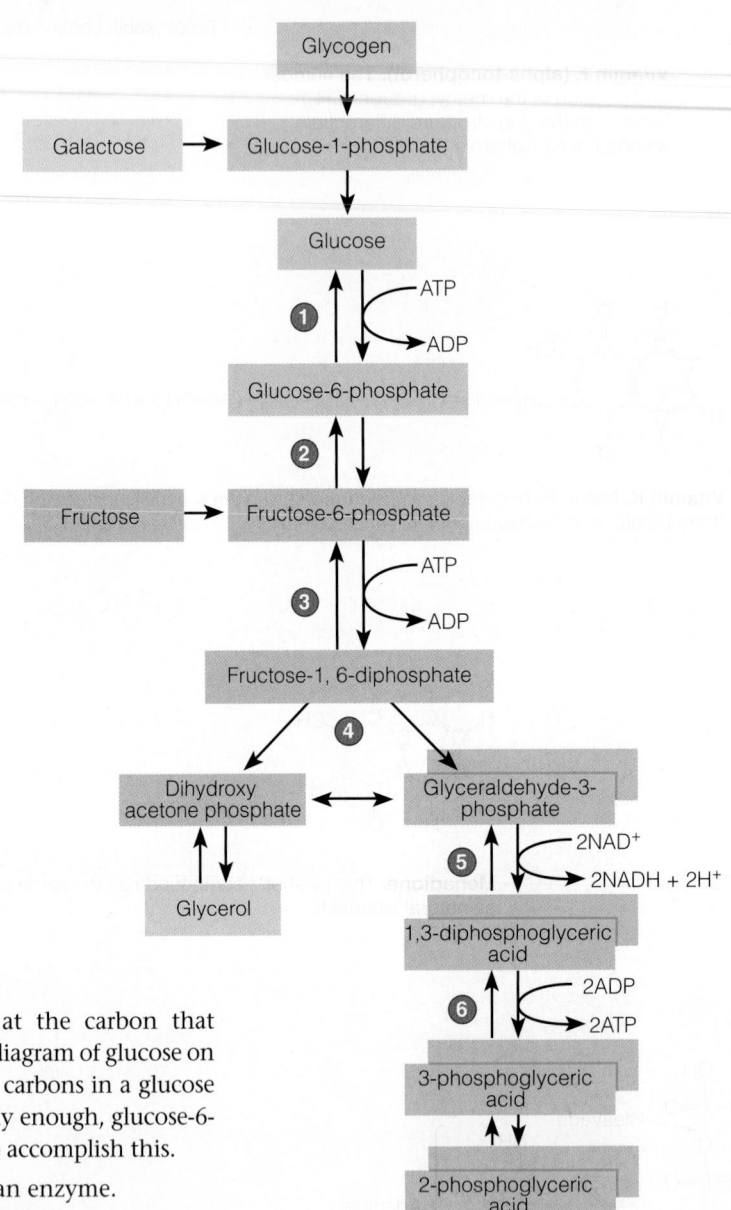

1. A phosphate is attached to glucose at the carbon that chemists call number 6 (review the first diagram of glucose on p. C-1 to see how chemists number the carbons in a glucose molecule). The product is called, logically enough, glucose-6-phosphate. One ATP molecule is used to accomplish this.

2. Glucose-6-phosphate is rearranged by an enzyme.

3. A phosphate is added in another reaction that uses another molecule of ATP. The product this time is fructose-1,6-diphosphate. At this point the six-carbon sugar has a phosphate group on its first and sixth carbons and is ready to break apart.

4. When fructose-1,6-diphosphate breaks in half, the two three-carbon compounds are not identical. Each has a phosphate group attached, but only glyceraldehyde-3-phosphate converts directly to pyruvate. The other compound, however, converts easily to glyceraldehyde-3-phosphate.

5. In the next step, enough energy is released to convert NAD^+ to $NADH + H^+$.

6. In two of the following steps ATP is regenerated.

Remember that in effect two molecules of glyceraldehyde-3-phosphate are produced from glucose; therefore, four ATP molecules are generated from each glucose molecule. Two ATP were needed to get the sequence started, so the net gain at this point is two ATP and two molecules of $NADH + H^+$. As you will see later, each $NADH + H^+$ moves to the electron transport chain to unload its hydrogens onto oxygen, producing more ATP.

Fatty Acid Oxidation

Figure C-2 presents fatty acid oxidation. The sequence is as follows.

1. The fatty acid is activated by combining with coenzyme A (CoA). In this reaction, ATP loses two phosphorus atoms (PP, or pyrophosphate) and becomes AMP (adenosine monophosphate)—the equivalent of a loss of two ATP.

2. In the next reaction, two H with their electrons are removed and transferred to FAD, forming $FADH_2$.

3. In a later reaction, two H are removed and go to NAD^+ (forming $NADH + H^+$).

4. The fatty acid is cleaved at the "beta" carbon, the second carbon from the carboxyl (COOH) end. This break results in a fatty acid that is two carbons shorter than the previous one and a two-carbon molecule of acetyl CoA. At the same time, another CoA is attached to the fatty acid, thus activating it for its turn through the series of reactions.

5. The sequence is repeated with each cycle producing an acetyl CoA and a shorter fatty acid until only a 2-carbon fatty acid remains—acetyl CoA.

In the example shown in Figure C-2, palmitic acid (a 16-carbon fatty acid) will go through this series of reactions seven times, using the equivalent of two ATP for the initial activation and generating seven $FADH_2$, seven $NADH + H^+$, and eight acetyl CoA. As you will see later, each of the seven $FADH_2$ will enter the electron transport chain to unload its hydrogens onto oxygen, yielding two ATP (for a total of 14). Similarly, each $NADH + H^+$ will enter the electron transport chain to unload its hydrogens onto oxygen, yielding three ATP (for a total of 21). Thus the oxidation of a 16-carbon fatty acid uses 2 ATP and generates 35 ATP. When the eight acetyl CoA enter the TCA cycle, even more ATP will be generated, as a later section describes.

Amino Acid Degradation

The first step in amino acid degradation is the removal of the nitrogen-containing amino group through either deamination (Figure 7-14 on p. 226) or transamination (Figure 7-15 on p. 226) reactions. Then the remaining carbon skeletons may enter the metabolic pathways at different places, as shown in Figure C-3.

The TCA Cycle

The tricarboxylic acid, or TCA, cycle is the set of reactions that break down acetyl CoA to carbon dioxide and hydrogens. To link glycolysis to the TCA cycle, pyruvate enters the mitochondrion, loses a carbon group, and bonds with a molecule of CoA to become acetyl CoA. The TCA cycle uses any substance that can be converted to acetyl CoA directly or indirectly through pyruvate.

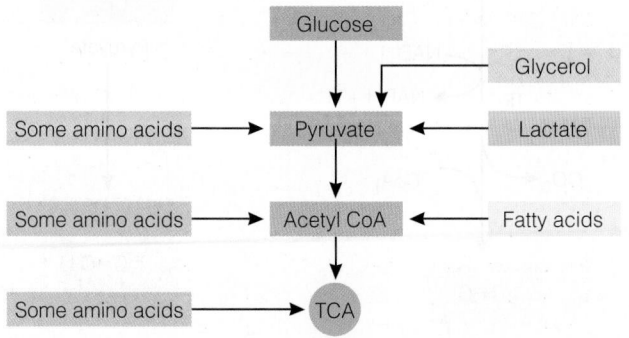

The step from pyruvate to acetyl CoA is complex. We have included only those substances that will help you understand

---

FIGURE C-2 Fatty Acid Oxidation

Palmitic acid (16C)

CoA + ATP → (1) → AMP + PP

Activated palmitic acid

FAD → (2) → $FADH_2$

H_2O

NAD^+ → (3) → $NADH + H^+$

CoA → (4)

Activated myristic acid (14C) + Acetyl CoA (2C)

(5)

FIGURE C-3 | Amino Acid Degradation

After losing their amino groups, carbon skeletons can be converted to one of seven molecules that can enter the TCA cycle (presented in Figure C-4).

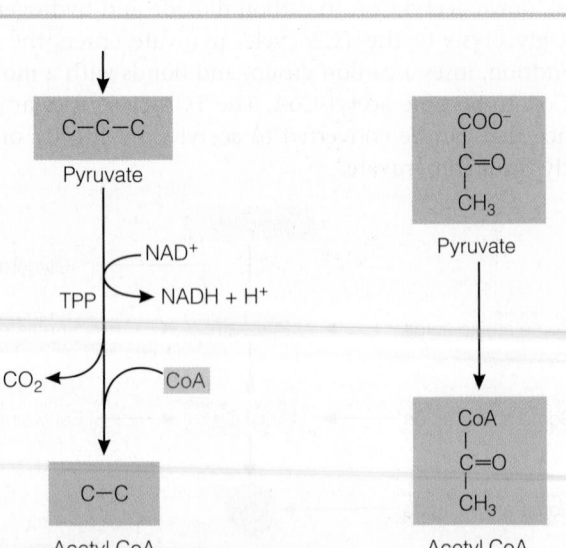

The step from pyruvate to acetyl CoA. (TPP and NAD are coenzymes containing the B vitamins thiamin and niacin, respectively.)

the transfer of energy from the nutrients. Pyruvate loses a carbon to carbon dioxide and is attached to a molecule of CoA. In the process, NAD^+ picks up two hydrogens with their associated electrons, becoming $NADH + H^+$.

Let's follow the steps of the TCA cycle (see the corresponding numbers in Figure C-4).

1. The two-carbon acetyl CoA combines with a four-carbon compound, oxaloacetate. The CoA comes off, and the product is a six-carbon compound, citrate.

2. The atoms of citrate are rearranged to form isocitrate.

3. Now two H (with their two electrons) are removed from the isocitrate. One H becomes attached to the NAD^+ with the two electrons; the other H is released as H^+. Thus NAD^+ becomes $NADH + H^+$. (Remember this $NADH + H^+$, but let's follow the carbons first.) A carbon is combined with two oxygens, forming carbon dioxide (which diffuses away into the blood and is exhaled). What is left is the five-carbon compound alpha-ketoglutarate.

FIGURE C-4   The TCA Cycle

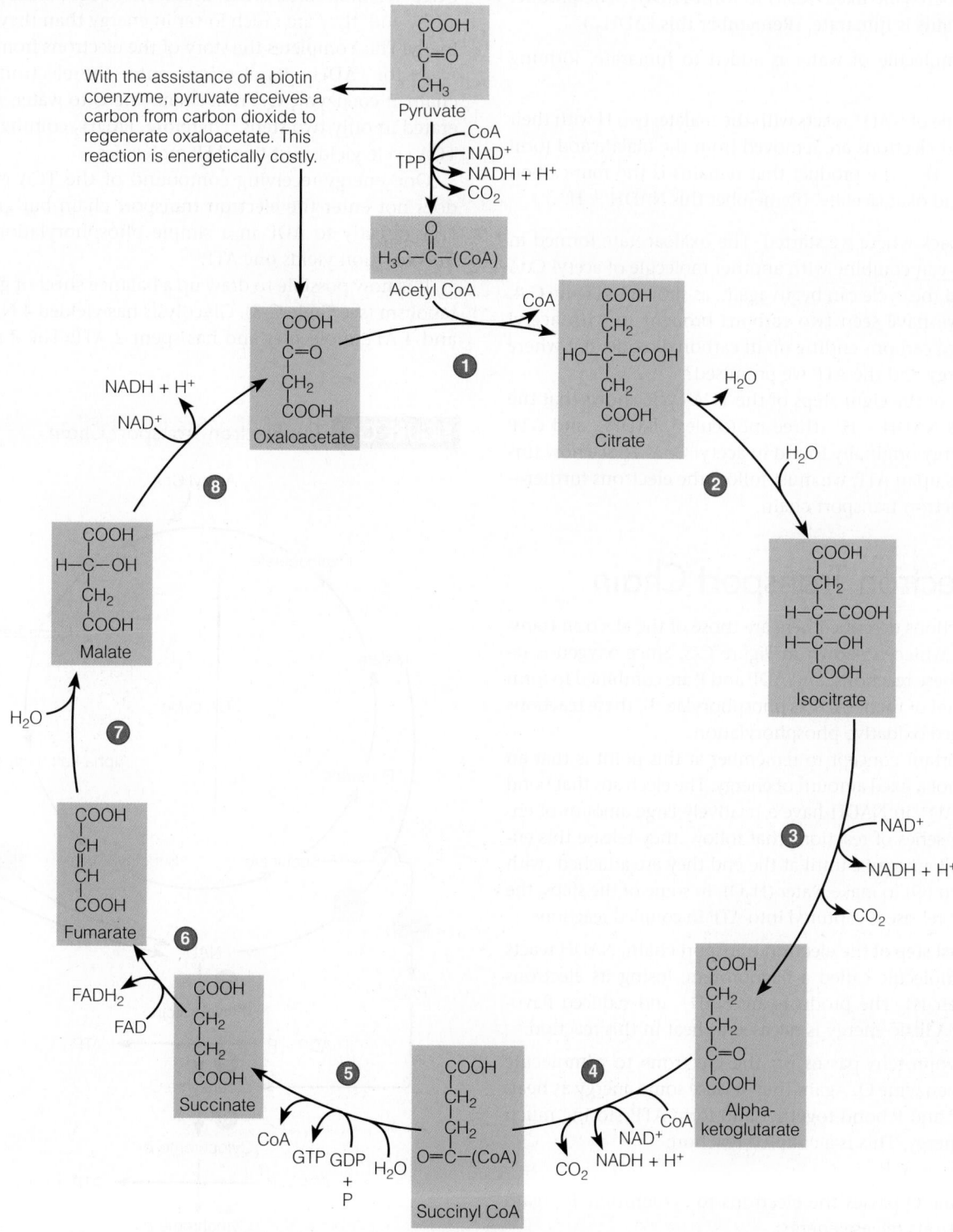

With the assistance of a biotin coenzyme, pyruvate receives a carbon from carbon dioxide to regenerate oxaloacetate. This reaction is energetically costly.

4. Now two compounds interact with alpha-ketoglutarate —a molecule of CoA and a molecule of NAD^+. In this complex reaction, a carbon and two oxygens are removed (forming carbon dioxide); two hydrogens are removed and go to NAD^+ (forming $NADH + H^+$); and the remaining four-carbon compound is attached to the CoA, forming succinyl

CoA. (Remember this $NADH + H^+$ also. You will see later what happens to it.)

5. Now two molecules react with succinyl CoA—a molecule called GDP and one of phosphate (P). The CoA comes off, the GDP and P combine to form the high-energy compound GTP (similar to ATP), and succinate remains. (Remember this GTP.)

6. In the next reaction, two H with their electrons are removed from succinate and are transferred to a molecule of FAD (a coenzyme like NAD⁺) to form FADH₂. The product that remains is fumarate. (Remember this FADH₂.)

7. Next a molecule of water is added to fumarate, forming malate.

8. A molecule of NAD⁺ reacts with the malate; two H with their associated electrons are removed from the malate and form NADH + H⁺. The product that remains is the four-carbon compound oxaloacetate. (Remember this NADH + H⁺.)

We are back where we started. The oxaloacetate formed in this process can combine with another molecule of acetyl CoA (step 1), and the cycle can begin again, as shown in Figure C-4.

So far, we have seen two carbons brought in with acetyl CoA and two carbons ending up in carbon dioxide. But where are the energy and the ATP we promised?

A review of the eight steps of the TCA cycle shows that the compounds NADH + H⁺ (three molecules), FADH₂, and GTP capture energy originally found in acetyl CoA. To see how this energy ends up in ATP, we must follow the electrons further—into the electron transport chain.

The Electron Transport Chain

The six reactions described here are those of the electron transport chain, which is shown in Figure C-5. Since oxygen is required for these reactions, and ADP and P are combined to form ATP in several of them (ADP is phosphorylated), these reactions are also called oxidative phosphorylation.

An important concept to remember at this point is that an electron is not a fixed amount of energy. The electrons that bond the H to NAD⁺ in NADH have a relatively large amount of energy. In the series of reactions that follow, they release this energy in small amounts, until at the end they are attached (with H) to oxygen (O) to make water (H₂O). In some of the steps, the energy they release is captured into ATP in coupled reactions.

1. In the first step of the electron transport chain, NADH reacts with a molecule called a flavoprotein, losing its electrons (and their H). The products are NAD⁺ and reduced flavoprotein. A little energy is released as heat in this reaction.

2. The flavoprotein passes on the electrons to a molecule called coenzyme Q. Again they release some energy as heat, but ADP and P bond together and form ATP, storing much of the energy. This is a coupled reaction: ADP + P → ATP.

3. Coenzyme Q passes the electrons to cytochrome *b*. Again the electrons release energy.

4. Cytochrome *b* passes the electrons to cytochrome *c* in a coupled reaction in which ATP is formed: ADP + P → ATP.

5. Cytochrome *c* passes the electrons to cytochrome *a*.

6. Cytochrome *a* passes them (with their H) to an atom of oxygen (O), forming water (H₂O). This is a coupled reaction in which ATP is formed: ADP + P → ATP.

As Figure C-5 shows, each time NADH is oxidized (loses its electrons) by this means, the energy it releases is captured into three ATP molecules. When the electrons are passed on to water at the end, they are much lower in energy than they were originally. This completes the story of the electrons from NADH.

As for FADH₂, its electrons enter the electron transport chain at coenzyme Q. From coenzyme Q to water, ATP is generated in only two steps. Therefore, FADH₂ coming out of the TCA cycle yields just two ATP molecules.

One energy-receiving compound of the TCA cycle (GTP) does not enter the electron transport chain but gives its energy directly to ADP in a simple phosphorylation reaction. This reaction yields one ATP.

It is now possible to draw up a balance sheet of glucose metabolism (see Table C-3). Glycolysis has yielded 4 NADH + H⁺ and 4 ATP molecules and has spent 2 ATP. The 2 acetyl CoA

FIGURE C-5 The Electron Transport Chain

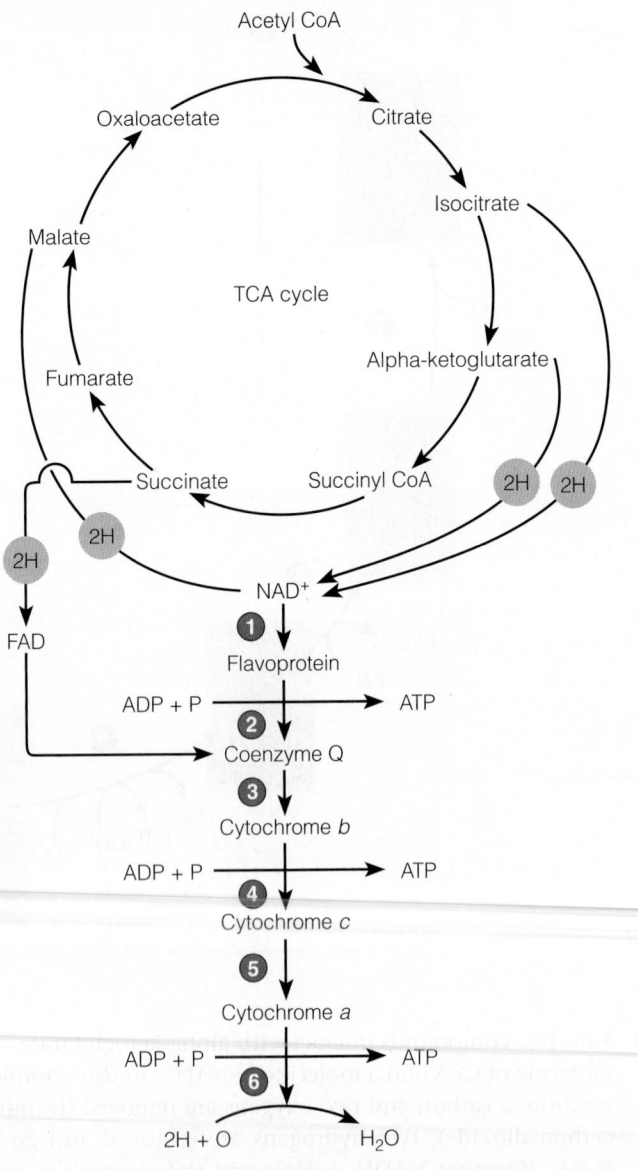

going through the TCA cycle have yielded 6 NADH + H$^+$, 2 FADH$_2$, and 2 GTP molecules. After the NADH + H$^+$ and FADH$_2$ have gone through the electron transport chain, there are 28 ATP. Added to these are the 4 ATP from glycolysis and the 2 ATP from GTP, making the total 34 ATP generated from one molecule of glucose. After the expense of 2 ATP is subtracted, there is a net gain of 32 ATP.*

A similar balance sheet from the complete breakdown of one 16-carbon fatty acid would show a net gain of 129 ATP. As mentioned earlier, 35 ATP were generated from the seven FADH$_2$ and seven NADH + H$^+$ produced during fatty acid oxidation. The eight acetyl CoA produced will each generate 12 ATP as they go through the TCA cycle and the electron transport chain, for a total of 96 more ATP. After subtracting the 2 ATP needed to activate the fatty acid initially, the net yield from one 16-carbon fatty acid: 35 + 96 − 2 = 129 ATP.

These calculations help explain why fat yields more energy (measured as kcalories) per gram than carbohydrate or protein. The more hydrogen atoms a fuel contains, the more ATP will be generated during oxidation. The 16-carbon fatty acid molecule, with its 32 hydrogen atoms, generates 129 ATP, whereas glucose, with its 12 hydrogen atoms, yields only 32 ATP.

The TCA cycle and the electron transport chain are the body's major means of capturing the energy from nutrients in ATP molecules. Other means, such as anaerobic glycolysis, contribute energy quickly, but the aerobic processes are the most efficient. Biologists and chemists understand much more about these processes than has been presented here.

Alcohol's Interference with Energy Metabolism

Highlight 7 provides an overview of how alcohol interferes with energy metabolism. With an understanding of the TCA cycle, a few more details may be appreciated. During alcohol metabolism, the enzyme alcohol dehydrogenase oxidizes alcohol to acetaldehyde while it simultaneously reduces a molecule of NAD$^+$ to NADH + H$^+$. The related enzyme acetaldehyde dehydrogenase reduces another NAD$^+$ to NADH + H$^+$ while it oxidizes acetaldehyde to acetyl CoA, the compound that enters the TCA cycle to generate energy. Thus, whenever alcohol is being metabolized in the body, NAD$^+$ diminishes, and NADH + H$^+$ accumulates. Chemists say that the body's "redox state" is altered, because NAD$^+$ can oxidize, and NADH + H$^+$ can reduce, many other body compounds. During alcohol metabolism, NAD$^+$ becomes unavailable for the multitude of reactions for which it is required.

TABLE C-3	Balance Sheet for Glucose Metabolism	
		ATP
Glycolysis:	4 ATP − 2 ATP	2
1 glucose to 2 pyruvate	2 NADH + H$^+$	3-5[a]
2 pyruvate to 2 acetyl CoA	2 NADH + H$^+$	5
TCA cycle and electron transport chain:		
2 isocitrate	2 NADH + H$^+$	5
2 alpha-ketoglutarate	2 NADH + H$^+$	5
2 succinyl CoA	2 GTP	2
2 succinate	2 FADH$_2$	3
2 malate	2 NADH + H$^+$	5
Total ATP collected from one molecule glucose:		30–32

[a]Each NADH + H$^+$ from glycolysis can yield 1.5 or 2.5 ATP. See the accompanying text.

As the previous sections just explained, for glucose to be completely metabolized, the TCA cycle must be operating, and NAD$^+$ must be present. If these conditions are not met (and when alcohol is present, they may not be), the pathway will be blocked, and traffic will back up—or an alternate route will be taken. Think about this as you follow the pathway shown in Figure C-6.

In each step of alcohol metabolism in which NAD$^+$ is converted to NADH + H$^+$, hydrogen ions accumulate, resulting in a dangerous shift of the acid-base balance toward acid (Chapter 12 explains acid-base balance). The accumulation of NADH + H$^+$ slows TCA cycle activity, so pyruvate and acetyl CoA build up. This condition favors the conversion of pyruvate to lactate, which serves as a temporary storage place for hydrogens from NADH + H$^+$. The conversion of pyruvate to lactate restores some NAD$^+$, but a lactate buildup has serious consequences of its own. It adds to the body's acid burden and interferes with the excretion of uric acid, causing goutlike symptoms. Molecules of acetyl CoA become building blocks for fatty acids or ketone bodies. The making of ketone bodies consumes acetyl CoA and generates NAD$^+$; but some ketone bodies are acids, so they push the acid-base balance further toward acid.

Thus alcohol cascades through the metabolic pathways, wreaking havoc along the way. These consequences have physical effects, which Highlight 7 describes.

The Urea Cycle

Chapter 7 sums up the process by which waste nitrogen is eliminated from the body by stating that ammonia molecules combine with carbon dioxide to produce urea. This is true, but it is not the whole story. Urea is produced in a multistep process within the cells of the liver.

---

*The total may sometimes be 30 ATP. The NADH + H$^+$ generated in the cytoplasm during glycolysis pass their electrons on to shuttle molecules, which move them into the mitochondria. One shuttle, malate, contributes its electrons to the electron transport chain before the first site of ATP synthesis, yielding 5 ATP. Another, glycerol phosphate, adds its electrons into the chain beyond that first site, yielding 3 ATP. Thus sometimes 5, and sometimes 3, ATP result from the NADH + H$^+$ that arise from glycolysis. The amount depends on the cell.

FIGURE C-6 Ethanol Enters the Metabolic Path

This is a simplified version of the glucose-to-energy pathway showing the entry of ethanol. The coenzyme NAD (which is the active form of the B vitamin niacin) is the only one shown here; however, many others are involved.

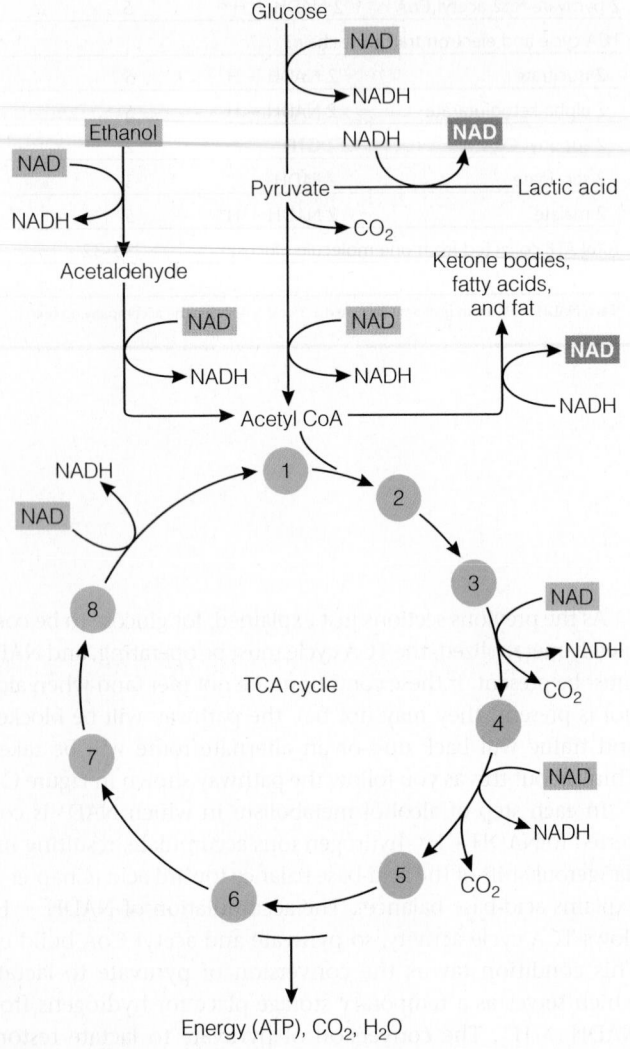

FIGURE C-7 The Urea Cycle

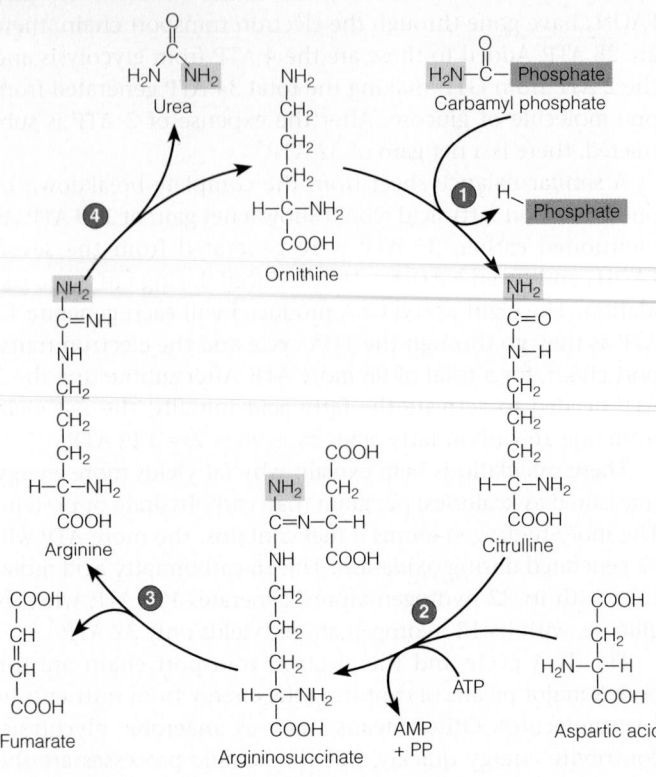

Figure C-7 shows the cycle of four reactions that follow.

1. Carbamyl phosphate combines with the amino acid ornithine, losing its phosphate group. The compound formed is citrulline.

2. Citrulline combines with the amino acid aspartic acid, to form argininosuccinate. The reaction requires energy from ATP. (ATP was shown earlier losing one phosphorus atom in a phosphate group, P, to become ADP. In this reaction, it loses two phosphorus atoms joined together, PP, and becomes adenosine monophosphate, AMP.)

3. Argininosuccinate is split, forming another acid, fumarate, and the amino acid arginine.

4. Arginine loses its terminal carbon with two attached amino groups and picks up an oxygen from water. The end product is urea, which the kidneys excrete in the urine. The compound that remains is ornithine, identical to the ornithine with which this series of reactions began, and ready to react with another molecule of carbamyl phosphate and turn the cycle again.

Ammonia, freed from an amino acid or other compound during metabolism anywhere in the body, arrives at the liver by way of the bloodstream and is taken into a liver cell. There, it is first combined with carbon dioxide and a phosphate group from ATP to form carbamyl phosphate:

$$CO_2 + NH_3 \xrightarrow[\text{2 ADP + P}]{\text{2 ATP}} H_2N-\overset{\displaystyle O}{\overset{\|}{C}}-O-\overset{\displaystyle O}{\underset{O^-}{\overset{\|}{P}}}-O^-$$

Carbon   Ammonia   Carbamyl phosphate
dioxide

Formation of Ketone Bodies

Normally, fatty acid oxidation proceeds all the way to carbon dioxide and water. However, in ketosis (discussed in Chapter 7), an intermediate is formed from the condensation of two molecules of acetyl CoA: acetoacetyl CoA. Figure C-8 shows the formation of ketone bodies from that intermediate.

FIGURE C-8   The Formation of Ketone Bodies

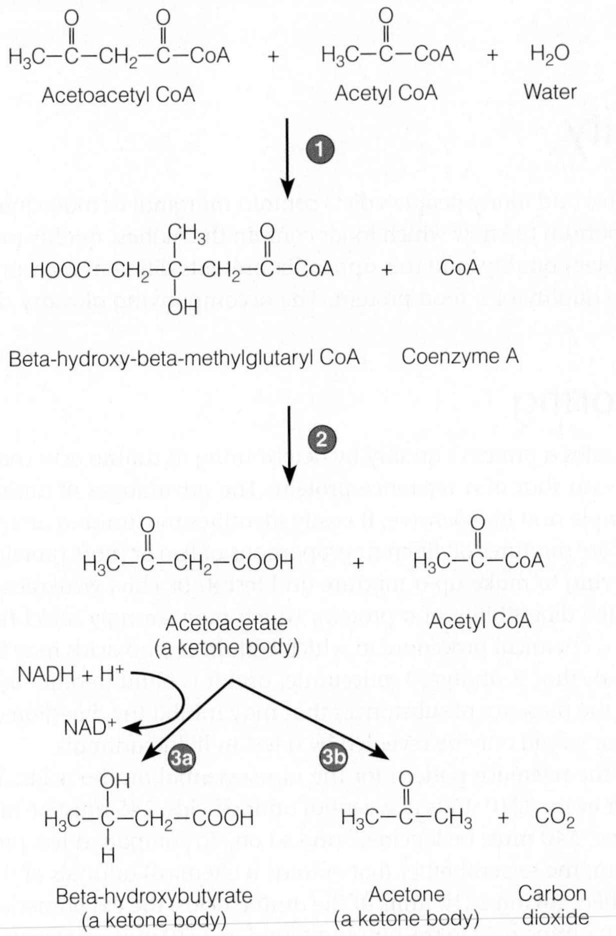

1. Acetoacetyl CoA condenses with acetyl CoA to form a six-carbon intermediate, beta-hydroxy-betamethylglutaryl CoA.

2. This intermediate is cleaved to acetyl CoA and acetoacetate.

3. Acetoactate can be metabolized either to beta-hydroxybutyrate acid (step 3a) or to acetone (3b).

Acetoacetate, beta-hydroxybutyrate, and acetone are the ketone bodies of ketosis. Two are real ketones (they have a C=O group between two carbons); the other is an alcohol that has been produced during ketone formation—hence the term *ketone bodies*, rather than ketones, to describe the three of them. There are many other ketones in nature; these three are characteristic of ketosis in the body.

CONTENTS

Amino Acid Scoring
PDCAAS
Biological Value
Net Protein Utilizatin
Protein Efficiency Ratio

GLOSSARY

amino acid scoring: a measure of protein quality assessed by comparing a protein's amino acid pattern with that of a reference protein; sometimes called **chemical scoring.**

biological value (BV): a measure of protein quality assessed by measuring the amount of protein nitrogen that is retained from a given amount of protein nitrogen absorbed.

net protein utilization (NPU): a measure of protein quality assessed by measuring the amount of protein nitrogen that is retained from a given amount of protein nitrogen eaten.

PDCAAS (protein digestibility–corrected amino acid score): a measure of protein quality assessed by comparing the amino acid score of a food protein with the amino acid requirements of preschool-age children and then correcting for the true digestibility of the protein; recommended by the FAO/WHO and used to establish protein quality of foods for Daily Value percentages on food labels.

protein efficiency ratio (PER): a measure of protein quality assessed by determining how well a given protein supports weight gain in growing rats; used to establish the protein quality for infant formulas and baby foods.

Appendix **D**

Measures of Protein Quality

In a world where food is scarce and many people's diets contain marginal or inadequate amounts of protein, it is important to know which foods contain the highest-quality protein. Chapter 6 describes protein quality, and this appendix presents different measures researchers use to assess the quality of a food protein. The accompanying glossary defines related terms.

Amino Acid Scoring

Amino acid scoring evaluates a protein's quality by determining its amino acid composition and comparing it with that of a reference protein. The advantages of amino acid scoring are that it is simple and inexpensive, it easily identifies the limiting amino acid, and it can be used to score mixtures of different proportions of two or more proteins mathematically without having to make up a mixture and test it. Its chief weaknesses are that it fails to estimate the digestibility of a protein, which may strongly affect the protein's quality; it relies on a chemical procedure in which certain amino acids may be destroyed, making the pattern that is analyzed inaccurate; and it is blind to other features of the protein (such as the presence of substances that may inhibit the digestion or utilization of the protein) that would only be revealed by a test in living animals.

Table D-1 (p. D-1) shows the reference pattern for the nine essential amino acids. To interpret the table, read, "For every 3210 units of essential amino acids, 145 must be histidine, 340 must be isoleucine, 540 must be leucine," and so on. To compare a test protein with the reference protein, the experimenter first obtains a chemical analysis of the test protein's amino acids. Then, taking 3210 units of the amino acids, the experimenter compares the amount of each amino acid to the amount found in 3210 units of essential amino acids in egg protein. For example, suppose the test protein contained (per 3210 units) 360 units of isoleucine; 500 units of leucine; 350 of lysine; and for each of the other amino acids, more units than egg protein contains. The two amino acids that are low are leucine (500 as compared with 540 in egg) and lysine (350 versus 440 in egg). The ratio, amino acid in the test protein divided by amino acid in egg, is 500/540 (or about 0.93) for leucine and 350/440 (or about 0.80) for lysine. Lysine is the limiting amino acid (the one that falls shortest compared with egg). If the protein's limiting amino acid is 80 percent of the amount found in the reference protein, it receives a score of 80.

PDCAAS

The **protein digestibility–corrected amino acid score**, or **PDCASS**, compares the amino acid composition of a protein with human amino acid requirements and corrects for digestibility. First the protein's amino acid composition is determined, and then it is compared against the amino acid requirements of preschool-age children. This comparison reveals the most limiting amino acid—the one that falls shortest compared with the reference. If a food protein's limiting amino acid is 70 percent of the amount found in the reference protein, it receives a score of 70. The amino acid score is multiplied by the food's protein digestibility percentage to determine the PDCAAS. The box on p. D-2 provides an example of how to calculate the PDCAAS, and Table D-2 (p. D-1) lists the PDCAAS values of selected foods.

Biological Value

The **biological value (BV)** of a protein measures its efficiency in supporting the body's needs. In a test of biological value, two nitrogen balance studies are done. In the first, no protein is fed, and nitrogen (N) excretions in the urine and feces are measured. It is assumed that under these conditions, N lost in the urine is the amount the body always necessarily loses by filtration into the urine each day, regardless of what protein is fed (endogenous N). The N lost in the feces (called metabolic N) is the amount the body invariably loses into the intestine each day, whether or not food protein is fed. (To help you remember the terms: endogenous N is "urinary N on a zero-protein diet"; metabolic N is "fecal N on a zero-protein diet.")

In the second study, an amount of protein slightly below the requirement is fed. Intake and losses are measured; then the BV is derived using this formula:

$$BV = \frac{N \text{ retained}}{N \text{ absorbed}} \times 100$$

The denominator of this equation expresses the amount of nitrogen *absorbed:* food N minus fecal N (excluding the metabolic N the body would lose in the feces anyway, even without food). The numerator expresses the amount of N *retained* from the N absorbed: absorbed N (as in the denominator) minus the N excreted in the urine (excluding the endogenous N the body would lose in the urine anyway, even without food). The more nitrogen retained, the higher the protein quality. (Recall that when an essential amino acid is missing, protein synthesis stops, and the remaining amino acids are deaminated and the nitrogen excreted.)

Egg protein has a BV of 100, indicating that 100 percent of the nitrogen absorbed is retained. Supplied in adequate quantity, a protein with a BV of 70 or greater can support human growth as long as energy intake is adequate. Table D-3 presents the BV for selected foods.

This method has the advantages of being based on experiments with human beings (it can be done with animals, too, of course) and of measuring actual nitrogen retention. But it is also cumbersome, expensive, and often impractical, and it is based on several assumptions that may not be valid. For example, the physiology, normal environment, or typical food intake of the subjects used for testing may not be similar to those for whom the test protein may ultimately be used. For another example, the retention of protein in the body does not necessarily mean that it is being well utilized. Considerable exchange of protein among tissues (protein turnover) occurs, but is hidden from view when only N intake and output are measured. The test of biological value wouldn't detect if one tissue were shorted.

Net Protein Utilization

Like BV, **net protein utilization (NPU)** measures how efficiently a protein is used by the body and involves two balance studies. The difference is that NPU measures retention of food nitrogen rather than food nitrogen absorbed (as in BV). The formula for NPU is:

$$NPU = \frac{N \text{ retained}}{N \text{ intake}} \times 100$$

The numerator is the same as for BV, but the denominator represents food N intake only—not N absorbed.

This method offers advantages similar to those of BV determinations and is used more frequently, with animals as the test subjects. A drawback is that if a low NPU is obtained, the test results offer no help in distinguishing between two possible causes: a poor amino acid composition of the test protein or poor digestibility. There is also a limit to the extent to which animal test results can be assumed to be applicable to human beings.

TABLE D-1	A Reference Pattern for Amino Acid Scoring of Proteins	
Essential Amino Acids	**Reference Protein—Whole Egg (mg amino acid/g nitrogen)**
Histidine	145
Isoleucine	340
Leucine	540
Lysine	440
Methionine + cystine[a]	355
Phenylalanine + tyrosine[b]	580
Threonine	294
Tryptophan	106
Valine	410
Total	3210

[a] Methionine is essential and is also used to make cystine. Thus the methionine requirement is lower if cystine is supplied.
[b] Phenylalanine is essential and is also used to make tyrosine if not enough of the latter is available. Thus the phenylalanine requirement is lower if tyrosine is also supplied.

TABLE D-2	PDCAAS Values of Selected Foods
Casein (milk protein)	1.00
Egg white	1.00
Soybean (isolate)	.99
Beef	.92
Pea flour	.69
Kidney beans (canned)	.68
Chickpeas (canned)	.66
Pinto beans (canned)	.66
Rolled oats	.57
Lentils (canned)	.52
Peanut meal	.52
Whole wheat	.40

NOTE: 1.0 is the maximum PDCAAS a food protein can receive.

TABLE D-3	Biological Values (BV) of Selected Foods
Egg	100
Milk	93
Beef	75
Fish	75
Corn	72

NOTE: 100 is the maximum BV a food protein can

Appendix D

HOW TO Measure Protein Quality Using PDCAAS

To calculate the PDCAAS (protein digestibility–corrected amino acid score), researchers first determine the amino acid profile of the test protein (in this example, pinto beans). The second column of the table below presents the essential amino acid profile for pinto beans. The third column presents the amino acid reference pattern.

To determine how well the food protein meets human needs, researchers calculate the ratio by dividing the second column by the third column (for example, 30 ÷ 18 = 1.67). The amino acid with the lowest ratio is the most limiting amino acid—in this case, methionine. Its ratio is the amino acid score for the protein—in this case, 0.84.

The amino acid score alone, however,

does not account for digestibility. Protein digestibility, as determined by rat studies, yields a value of 79 percent for pinto beans. Together, the amino acid score and the digestibility value determine the PDCAAS:

PDCAAS =
protein digestibility × amino acid score
PDCAAS for pinto beans =
0.79 × 0.84 = 0.66

Thus the PDCAAS for pinto beans is 0.66. Table D-2 lists the PDCAAS values of selected foods.

The PDCAAS is used to determine the % Daily Value on food labels. To calculate the % Daily Value for protein for canned pinto beans, multiply the number of grams of

protein in a standard serving (in the case of pinto beans, 7 grams per ½ cup) by the PDCAAS:

$$7 \text{ g} \times 0.66 = 4.62$$

This value is then divided by the recommended standard for protein (for children over age four and adults, 50 grams):

$$4.62 \div 50 = 0.09 \text{ (or 9\%)}$$

The food label for this can of pinto beans would declare that one serving provides 7 grams protein, and if the label included a % Daily Value for protein (which is optional), the value would be 9 percent.

Essential Amino Acids	Amino Acid Profile of Pinto Beans (mg/g protein)	Amino Acid Reference Pattern (mg/g protein)	Amino Acid Score
Histidine	30.0	18	1.67
Isoleucine	42.5	25	1.70
Leucine	80.4	55	1.46
Lysine	69.0	51	1.35
Methionine (+ cystine)	21.1	25	0.84
Phenylalanine (+ tyrosine)	90.5	47	1.93
Threonine	43.7	27	1.62
Tryptophan	8.8	7	1.26
Valine	50.1	32	1.57

TABLE D-4 Protein Efficiency Ratio (PER) Values of Selected Proteins

Casein (milk)	2.8
Soy	2.4
Glutein (wheat)	0.4

Protein Efficiency Ratio

The **protein efficiency ratio (PER)** measures the weight gain of a growing animal and compares it to the animal's protein intake. Until recently, the PER was generally accepted in the United States and Canada as the official method for assessing protein quality, and it is still used to evaluate proteins for infants.

Young rats are fed a measured amount of protein and weighed periodically as they grow. The PER is expressed as:

$$PER = \frac{\text{weight gain (g)}}{\text{protein intake (g)}}$$

This method has the virtues of economy and simplicity, but it also has many drawbacks. The experiments are time-consuming; the amino acid needs of rats are not the same as those of human beings; and the amino acid needs for growth are not the same as for the maintenance of adult animals (growing animals need more lysine, for example). Table D-4 presents PER values for selected foods.

Nutrition Assessment

Nutrition assessment evaluates a person's health from a nutrition perspective. Many factors influence or reflect nutrition status. Consequently, the assessor, usually a registered dietitian assisted by other qualified health care professionals, gathers information from many sources, including:

- Historical information.
- Anthropometric measurements.
- Physical examinations.
- Biochemical analyses (laboratory tests).

Each of these methods involves collecting data in a variety of ways and interpreting each finding in relation to the others to create a total picture.

The accurate gathering of this information and its careful interpretation are the basis for a meaningful evaluation. The more information gathered about a person, the more accurate the assessment will be. Gathering information is a time-consuming process, however, and time is often a rare commodity in the health care setting. Nutrition care is only one part of total care. It may not be practical or essential to collect detailed information on each person.

A strategic compromise is to screen clients by collecting preliminary data. Data such as height-weight and hematocrit are easy to obtain and can alert health care workers to potential problems. **Nutrition screening** identifies clients who will require additional nutrition assessment. This appendix provides a sample of the procedures, standards, and charts commonly used in nutrition assessment.

CONTENTS

Historical Information
Anthropometric Measurements
Physical Examinations
Biochemical Analyses
Cautions about Nutrition Assessment

Historical Information

Clues about present nutrition status become evident with a careful review of a person's historical data (see Table E-1). Even when the data are subjective, they reveal important facts about a person. A thorough history identifies risk factors associated with poor nutrition status (see Table E-2) and provides a sense of the whole person. As you can see, many aspects of a person's life influence nutrition status and provide clues to possible problems.

An adept history taker uses the interview both to gather facts and to establish a rapport with the client. This section briefly reviews the major areas of nutrition concern in a person's history: health, socioeconomic factors, drugs, and diet.

TABLE E-1	Historical Data Used in Nutrition Assessments
Type of History	**What It Identifies**
Health history	Current and previous health problems and family health history that affect nutrient needs, nutrition status, or the need for intervention to prevent or alleviate health problems
Socioeconomic history	Personal, cultural, financial, and environmental influences on food intake, nutrient needs, and diet therapy options
Drug history	Medications (prescription and over-the-counter), illicit drugs, dietary supplements, and alternative therapies that affect nutrition status
Diet history	Nutrient intake excesses or deficiencies and reasons for imbalances

nutrition screening: the use of preliminary nutrition assessment techniques to identify people who are malnourished or are at risk for malnutrition.

Appendix E

TABLE E-2   Risk Factors for Poor Nutrition Status

Health History

- Acquired immune deficiency syndrome (AIDS)
- Alcoholism
- Anorexia (lack of appetite)
- Anorexia nervosa
- Bulimia nervosa
- Burns
- Cancer
- Chewing or swallowing difficulties (including poorly fitted dentures, dental caries, missing teeth, and mouth ulcers)
- Chronic obstructive pulmonary disease
- Circulatory problems
- Constipation
- Crohn's disease
- Cystic fibrosis
- Decubitus ulcers (pressure sores)
- Dementia
- Depleted blood proteins
- Depression
- Diabetes mellitus

- Diarrhea, prolonged or severe
- Drug addiction
- Dysphagia
- Failure to thrive
- Feeding disabilities
- Fever
- GI tract disorders or surgery
- Heart disease
- HIV infection
- Hormonal imbalance
- Hyperlipidemia
- Hypertension
- Infections
- Kidney disease
- Liver disease
- Lung disease
- Malabsorption
- Mental illness
- Mental retardation
- Multiple pregnancies

- Nausea
- Neurologic disorders
- Organ failure
- Overweight
- Pancreatic insufficiency
- Paralysis
- Physical disability
- Pneumonia
- Pregnancy
- Radiation therapy
- Recent major illness
- Recent major surgery
- Recent weight loss or gain
- Tobacco use
- Trauma
- Ulcerative colitis
- Ulcers
- Underweight
- Vomiting, prolonged or severe

Socioeconomic History

- Access to groceries
- Activities
- Age
- Education

- Ethnic identity
- Income
- Kitchen facilities
- Number of people in household

- Occupation
- Religious affiliation

Drug History

- Amphetamines
- Analgesics
- Antacids
- Antibiotics
- Anticonvulsant agents
- Antidepressant agents
- Antidiabetic agents

- Antidiarrheals
- Antifungal agents
- Antihyperlipemics
- Antihypertensives
- Antineoplastics
- Antiulcer agents
- Antiviral agents

- Catabolic steroids
- Diuretics
- Hormonal agents
- Immunosuppressive agents
- Laxatives
- Oral contraceptives
- Vitamin and other dietary supplements

Diet History

- Deficient or excessive food intakes
- Frequently eating out
- Intravenous fluids (other than total parenteral nutrition) for 7 or more days

- Monotonous diet (lacking variety)
- No intake for 7 or more days
- Poor appetite
- Restricted or fad diets

- Unbalanced diet (omitting any food group)
- Recent weight gains or losses

Health History

The assessor can obtain a **health history** from records completed by the attending physician, nurse, or other health care professional. In addition, conversations with the client can uncover valuable information previously overlooked because no one thought to ask or because the client was not thinking clearly when asked.

An accurate, complete health history can reveal conditions that increase a client's risk for malnutrition (review Table E-2). Diseases and their therapies can have either immediate or long-term effects on nutrition status by interfering with ingestion, digestion, absorption, metabolism, or excretion of nutrients.

Socioeconomic History

A **socioeconomic history** reveals factors that profoundly affect nutrition status. The ethnic background and educational level of both the client and the other members of the household influence food availability and food choices. An understanding of the community environment is also important in assessing nutrition status. For example, the interviewer should be familiar with the food habits of the major ethnic groups within the locale, regional food preferences, and nutrition resources and programs available in the community. Local health departments and social agencies often can provide such information.

Level of income also influences the diet. In general, the quality of the diet declines as income falls. At some point, the ability to purchase the foods required to meet nutrient needs is lost; an inadequate income puts an adequate diet out of reach. Agencies use poverty indexes to identify people at risk for poor nutrition and to qualify people for government food assistance programs.

Low income affects not only the power to purchase foods but also the ability to shop for, store, and cook them. A skilled assessor will note whether a person has transportation to a grocery store that sells a sufficient variety of low-cost foods, and whether the person has access to a refrigerator and stove.

Drug History

The many interactions of foods and drugs require that health care professionals take a **drug history** and pay special attention to any client who takes drugs routinely. If a person is taking any drug, the assessor records the name of the drug; the dose, frequency, and duration of intake; the reason for taking the drug; and signs of any adverse effects.

The interactions of drugs and nutrients may take many forms:

- Drugs can alter food intake and the absorption, metabolism, and excretion of nutrients.
- Foods and nutrients can alter the absorption, metabolism, and excretion of drugs.

Highlight 17 discusses nutrient-drug interactions in more detail, and Table H17-1 (p. 616) summarizes the mechanisms by which these interactions occur and provides specific examples.

Diet History

A **diet history** provides a record of a person's eating habits and food intake and can help identify possible nutrient imbalances. Food choices are an important part of lifestyle and often reflect a person's philosophy. The assessor who asks nonjudgmental questions about eating habits and food intake encourages trust and enhances the likelihood of obtaining accurate information.

Assessors evaluate food intake using various tools such as the 24-hour recall, the usual intake record, the food record, and the food frequency questionnaire. Food models or photos and measuring devices can help clients identify the types of foods and quantities consumed. The assessor also needs to know how the foods are prepared and when they are eaten. In addition to asking about foods, assessors will ask about beverage consumption, including beverages containing alcohol or caffeine.

Besides identifying possible nutrient imbalances, diet histories provide valuable clues about how a person will accept diet changes should they be necessary. Information about what and how a person eats provides the background for realistic and attainable nutrition goals.

24-Hour Recall The **24-hour recall** provides data for one day only and is commonly used in nutrition surveys to obtain estimates of the typical food intakes for a population. The assessor asks the client to recount everything eaten or drunk in the past 24 hours or for the previous day.

---

socioeconomic history: a record of a person's social and economic background, including such factors as education, income, and ethnic identity.

drug history: a record of all the drugs, over-the-counter and prescribed, that a person takes routinely.

diet history: a record of eating behaviors and the foods a person eats.

24-hour recall: a record of foods eaten by a person for one 24-hour period.

E Appendix

An advantage of the 24-hour recall is that it is easy to obtain. It is also more likely to provide accurate data, at least about the past 24 hours, than estimates of average intakes over long periods. It does not, however, provide enough information to allow accurate generalizations about an individual's usual food intake. The previous day's intake may not be typical, for example, or the person may be unable to report portion sizes accurately or may conceal or forget information about foods eaten. This limitation is partially overcome when 24-hour recalls are collected on several nonconsecutive days.

Usual Intake To obtain data about a person's usual intake, an inquiry might begin with "What is the first thing you usually eat or drink during the day?" Similar questions follow until a typical daily intake pattern emerges. This method can be useful, especially in verifying food intake when the past 24 hours have been atypical. It also helps the assessor verify food habits. For example, one person may always eat an afternoon snack; another may never eat breakfast. A person whose intake varies widely from day to day, however, may find it difficult to answer such general questions, and in that case, another food intake tool should be used to estimate nutrient intake.

Food Record Another tool for history taking is the **food record,** in which the person records food eaten, including the quantity and method of preparation. Chapter 9 (p. 304) provides an example. A food record can help both the assessor and the client to determine factors associated with eating that may affect dietary balance and adequacy.

Food records work especially well with cooperative people but require considerable time and effort on their part. A prime advantage is that the record keeper assumes an active role and may for the first time become aware of personal food habits and assume responsibility for them. It also provides the assessor with an accurate picture of the person's lifestyle and factors that affect food intake. For these reasons, a food record can be particularly useful in outpatient counseling for such nutrition problems as overweight, underweight, or food allergy. The major disadvantages stem from poor compliance in recording the data and conscious or unconscious changes in eating habits that may occur while the person is keeping the record.

Food Frequency Questionnaire An assessor uses a **food frequency questionnaire** to compare a client's food intake with the Daily Food Guide. Clients may be asked how many servings of each of the following they eat in a typical day: breads, cereals, or grain products; vegetables; fruits; meat, poultry, fish, and alternatives; milk, cheese, and yogurt; and fats, oils, and sweets. This information helps pinpoint food groups, and therefore nutrients, that may be excessive or deficient in the diet. That a person ate no vegetables yesterday may not seem particularly significant, but never eating vegetables is a warning of possible nutrient deficiencies. When used with the usual intake or 24-hour recall approach, the food frequency questionnaire enables the assessor to double-check the accuracy of the information obtained.

Analysis of Food Intake Data After collecting food intake data, the assessor estimates nutrient intakes, either informally by using food guides or formally by using food composition tables. The assessor compares these intakes with standards, usually nutrient recommendations or dietary guidelines, to determine how closely the person's diet meets the standards. Are the types and amounts of proteins, carbohydrates (including fiber), and fats (including cholesterol) appropriate? Are all food groups included in appropriate amounts? Is caffeine or alcohol consumption excessive? Are intakes of any vitamins or minerals (including sodium and iron) excessive or deficient? An informal evaluation is possible only if the assessor has enough prior experience with formal calculations to "see" nutrient amounts in reported food intakes without calculations. Even then, such an informal analysis is best followed by a spot check for key nutrients by actual calculation.

food record: an extensive, accurate log of all foods eaten over a period of several days or weeks. A food record that includes associated information such as when, where, and with whom each food is eaten is sometimes called a **food diary.**

food frequency questionnaire: a checklist of foods on which a person can record the frequency with which he or she eats each food.

Formal calculations can be performed either manually (by looking up each food in a table of food composition, recording its nutrients, and adding them up) or by using a computer diet analysis program. The assessor then compares the intakes with standards such as the RDA.

Limitations of Food Intake Analysis Diet histories can be superbly informative, but the skillful assessor also keeps their limitations in mind. For example, a computer diet analysis tends to imply greater accuracy than is possible to obtain from data as uncertain as the starting information. Nutrient contents of foods listed in tables of food composition or stored in computer databases are averages and, for some nutrients, incomplete. In addition, the available data on nutrient contents of foods do not reflect the amounts of nutrients a person actually absorbs. Iron is a case in point: its availability from a given meal may vary depending on the person's iron status; the relative amounts of heme iron, nonheme iron, vitamin C, meat, fish, and poultry eaten at the meal; and the presence of inhibitors of iron absorption such as tea, coffee, and nuts. (Chapter 13 describes the many factors that influence iron absorption from a meal.)

Furthermore, reported portion sizes may not be correct. The person who reports eating "a serving" of greens may not distinguish between ¼ cup and 2 whole cups; only trained individuals can accurately report serving sizes. Children tend to remember the serving sizes of foods they like as being larger than serving sizes of foods they dislike.

An estimate of nutrient intakes from a diet history, combined with other sources of information, allows the assessor to confirm or eliminate the possibility of suspected food intake problems. The assessor must constantly remember that nutrient intakes in adequate amounts do not guarantee adequate nutrient status for an individual. Likewise, insufficient intakes do not always indicate deficiencies, but instead alert the assessor to possible problems. Each person digests, absorbs, metabolizes, and excretes nutrients in a unique way; individual needs vary. Intakes of nutrients identified by diet histories are only pieces of a puzzle that must be put together with other indicators of nutrition status in order to extract meaning.

Anthropometric Measurements

Anthropometrics are physical measurements that reflect body composition and development (see Table E-3). They serve three main purposes: first, to evaluate the progress of growth in pregnant women, infants, children, and adolescents; second, to detect undernutrition and overnutrition in all age groups; and third, to measure changes in body composition over time.

Health care professionals compare anthropometric measurements taken on an individual with population standards specific for gender and age or with previous measures of the individual. Measurements taken periodically and compared with previous measurements reveal changes in an individual's status.

TABLE E-3	Anthropometric Measurements Used in Nutrition Assessments
Type of Measurement	**What It Reflects**
Abdominal girth measurement	Abdominal fluid retention and abdominal organ size
Height-weight	Overnutrition and undernutrition; growth in children
Head circumference	Brain growth and development in infants and children under age two
Skinfold	Subcutaneous and total body fat
Waist circumference	Body fat distribution

anthropometrics: measurements of the physical characteristics of the body, such as height and weight.
• **anthropos** = human
• **metric** = measuring

FIGURE E-1 Length Measurement of an Infant

An infant is measured lying down on a measuring board with a fixed head-board and a movable footboard. Note that two people are needed to measure the infant's length.

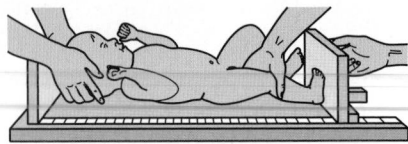

Mastering the techniques for taking anthropometric measurements requires proper instruction and practice to ensure reliability. Once the correct techniques are learned, taking measurements is easy and requires minimal equipment.

Height and weight are well-recognized anthropometrics; other anthropometrics include skinfold measurements and various measures of lean tissue. Other mea-sures are useful in specific situations. For example, a head circumference measurement may help to assess brain development in an infant, and an abdominal girth measurement supplies information about abdominal fluid retention in individuals with liver disease.

Measures of Growth and Development

Height and weight are among the most common and useful anthropometric measurements. Length measurements for infants and children up to age three and height measurements for children over three are particularly valuable in assessing growth and therefore nutrition status. For adults, height measurements alone are not critical, but help to estimate healthy weight and to interpret other assessment data. Once adult height has been reached, changes in body weight provide useful information in assessing overnutrition and undernutrition.

Height For infants and children younger than three, health care professionals may use special equipment to measure length. The assessor lays the barefoot infant on a measuring board that has a fixed headboard and movable footboard attached at right angles to the surface (see Figure E-1). Often two people are needed to obtain an accurate measurement: one to hold the infant's head against the headboard, and the other to keep the legs straight and do the measuring. This method provides the most accurate measure possible, but many health care professionals use a less exacting method. They may simply hold the infant straight with its head against the headboard or other vertical support, mark the blanket with a chalk or pen at the infant's heel, and then measure the distance from the headboard to the mark. Even more informally and less accurately, they may lay the infant on a flat surface and extend a nonstretchable measuring tape along the side of the infant from the top of the head to the heel of the foot.

The procedure for measuring a child who can stand erect and cooperate is the same as for an adult. The best way to measure standing height is with the person's back against a flat wall to which a nonstretchable measuring tape or stick has been fixed (see Figure E-2). The person stands erect, without shoes, with heels together. The person's line of sight should be horizontal, with the heels, buttocks, shoulders, and head touching the wall. The assessor places a ruler, book, or other inflexible object on top of the head at a right angle to the wall; carefully checks the height measurement; and records it immediately in either inches or centimeters so that the correct measurement will not be forgotten.

The measuring rod of a scale is commonly used, but is less accurate because it bends easily. The assessor follows the same general procedure, asking the person to face away from the scale and to take extra care to stand erect.

Unfortunately, many health care professionals merely ask clients how tall they are rather than measuring their height. Self-reported height is often inaccurate and should be used only as a last resort when measurement is impractical (in the case of an uncooperative client, an emergency admission, or the like).

Weight Valid weight measurements require scales that have been carefully maintained, calibrated, and checked for accuracy at regular intervals. Beam balance and electronic scales are the most accurate types of scales. To measure infants' weight, assessors use special scales that allow infants to lie or sit (see Figure E-3). Weighing infants naked, without diapers, is standard procedure. Children who can stand are weighed in the same way as adults (see Figure E-4). To make repeated measures useful, standardized conditions are necessary. Each weighing should take place at the same time of day (preferably before breakfast), in the same amount of clothing (with-

FIGURE E-2 Height Measurement of an Older Child or Adult

Height is measured most accurately when the person stands against a flat wall to which a measuring tape has been affixed.

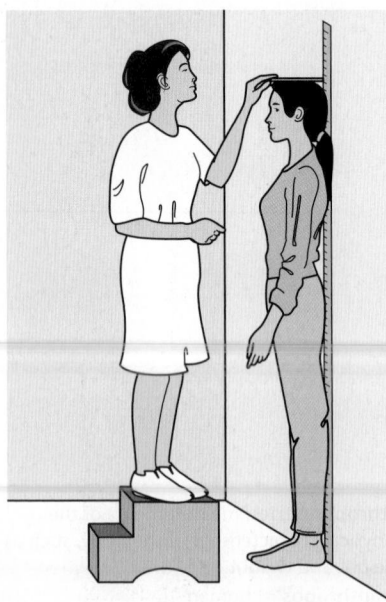

out shoes), after the person has voided, and on the same scale. Special scales and hospital beds with built-in scales are available for weighing people who are bedridden. Bathroom scales are inaccurate and inappropriate in a professional setting. As with all measurements, the assessor records the observed weight immediately in either pounds or kilograms.

Head Circumference Assessors may also measure head circumference to confirm that infant growth is proceeding normally or to help detect protein-energy malnutrition (PEM) and evaluate the extent of its impact on brain size. To measure head circumference, the assessor places a nonstretchable tape so that it encircles the largest part of the infant's or child's head: just above the eyebrow ridges, just above the point where the ears attach, and around the occipital prominence at the back of the head. To ensure accurate recording, the assessor immediately notes the measure in either inches or centimeters.

Analysis of Measures in Infants and Children Growth retardation is a sign of poor nutrition status. Obesity is also a sign that dietary intervention may be needed.

Health professionals generally evaluate physical development by monitoring the growth rate of a child and comparing this rate with standard charts. Standard charts compare weight to age, height to age, and weight to height; ideally, height and weight are in roughly the same percentile. Although individual growth patterns may vary, a child's growth curve will generally stay at about the same percentile throughout childhood. In children whose growth has been retarded, nutrition rehabilitation will ideally induce height and weight to increase to higher percentiles. In overweight children, the goal is for weight to remain stable as height increases, until weight becomes appropriate for height.

To evaluate growth in infants, an assessor uses charts such as those in Figures E-5 (A and B) through E-10 (A and B). ◆ The assessor follows these steps to plot a weight measurement on a percentile graph:

- Select the appropriate chart based on age and gender.
- Locate the child's age along the horizontal axis on the bottom of the chart.
- Locate the child's weight in pounds or kilograms along the vertical axis.
- Mark the chart where the age and weight lines intersect, and read off the percentile.

To assess length, height, or head circumference, the assessor follows the same procedure, using the appropriate chart. (When length is measured, use the chart for birth to 36 months; when height is measured, use the chart for 2 to 20 years.) Head circumference percentile should be similar to the child's height and weight percentiles. With height, weight, and head circumference measures plotted on growth percentile charts, a skilled clinician can begin to interpret the data.

Percentile charts divide the measures of a population into 100 equal divisions. Thus half of the population falls above the 50th percentile, and half falls below. The use of percentile measures allows for comparisons among people of the same age and gender. For example, a six-month-old female infant whose weight is at the 75 percentile weighs more than 75 percent of the female infants her age.

Head circumference is generally measured in children under two years of age. Since the brain grows rapidly before birth and during early infancy, extreme and chronic malnutrition during these times can impair brain development, curtailing the number of brain cells and the size of head circumference. Nonnutritional factors, such as certain disorders and genetic variation, can also influence head circumference.

Analysis of Measures in Adults For adults, health care professionals typically compare weights with weight-for-height standards. One such standard is the body mass index (BMI), ◆ described in Chapter 8 (pp. 259–260), which is useful for estimating the risk to health associated with overnutrition. The back cover shows BMI for various heights and weights.

FIGURE E-3 Weight Measurement of an Infant

Infants sit or lie down on scales that are designed to hold them while they are being weighed.

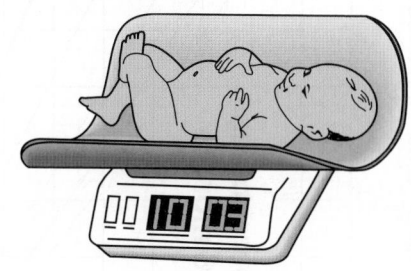

◆ Chapter 16 presents BMI charts for children and adolescents.

◆ Reminder: The *body mass index (BMI)* is an index of a person's weight in relation to height, determined by dividing the weight in kilograms by the square of the height in meters:

$$BMI = \frac{Weight\ (kg)}{Height\ (m)^2}$$

FIGURE E-4 Weight Measurement of an Older Child or Adult

Whenever possible, children and adults are measured on beam balance or electronic scales to ensure accuracy.

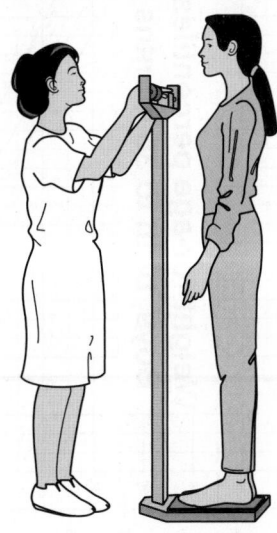

FIGURE E-5B   Weight-for-Age Percentiles: Girls, Birth to 36 Months

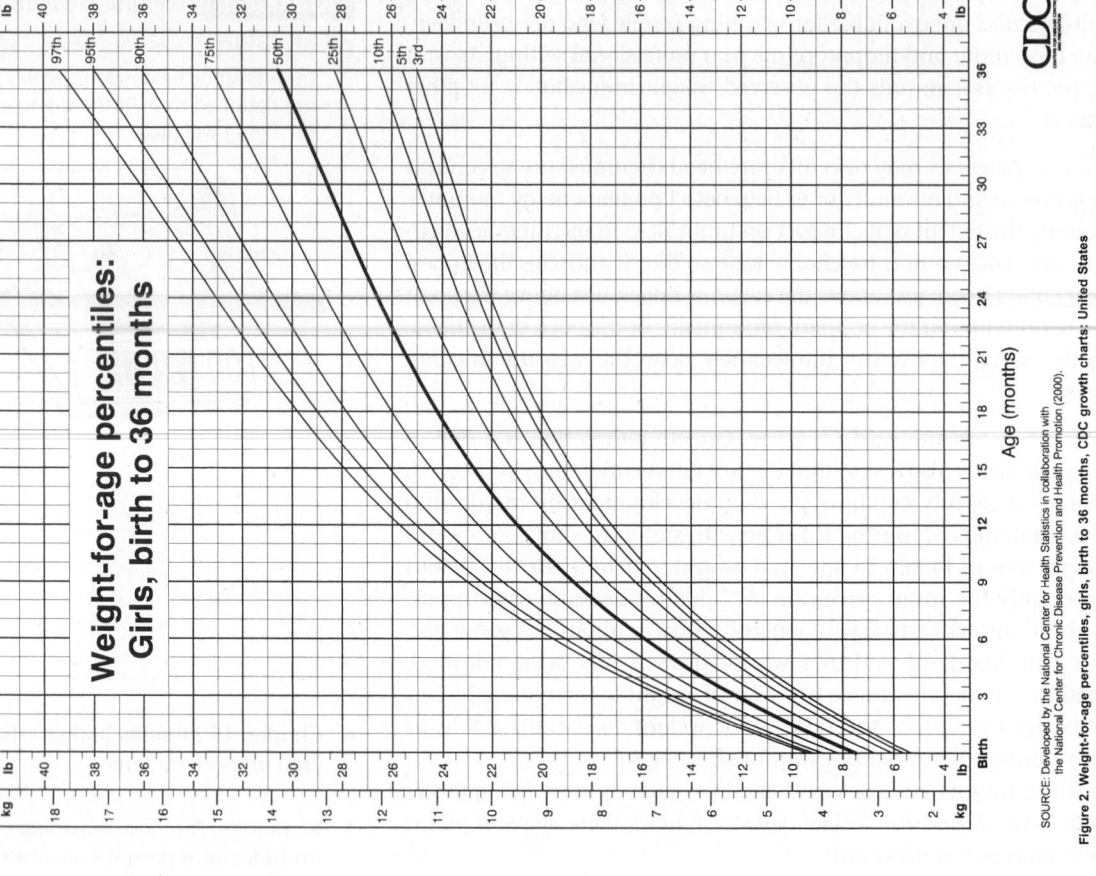

Weight-for-age percentiles: Girls, birth to 36 months

SOURCE: Developed by the National Center for Health Statistics in collaboration with the National Center for Chronic Disease Prevention and Health Promotion (2000).

Figure 2. Weight-for-age percentiles, girls, birth to 36 months, CDC growth charts: United States

FIGURE E-5A   Weight-for-Age Percentiles: Boys, Birth to 36 Months

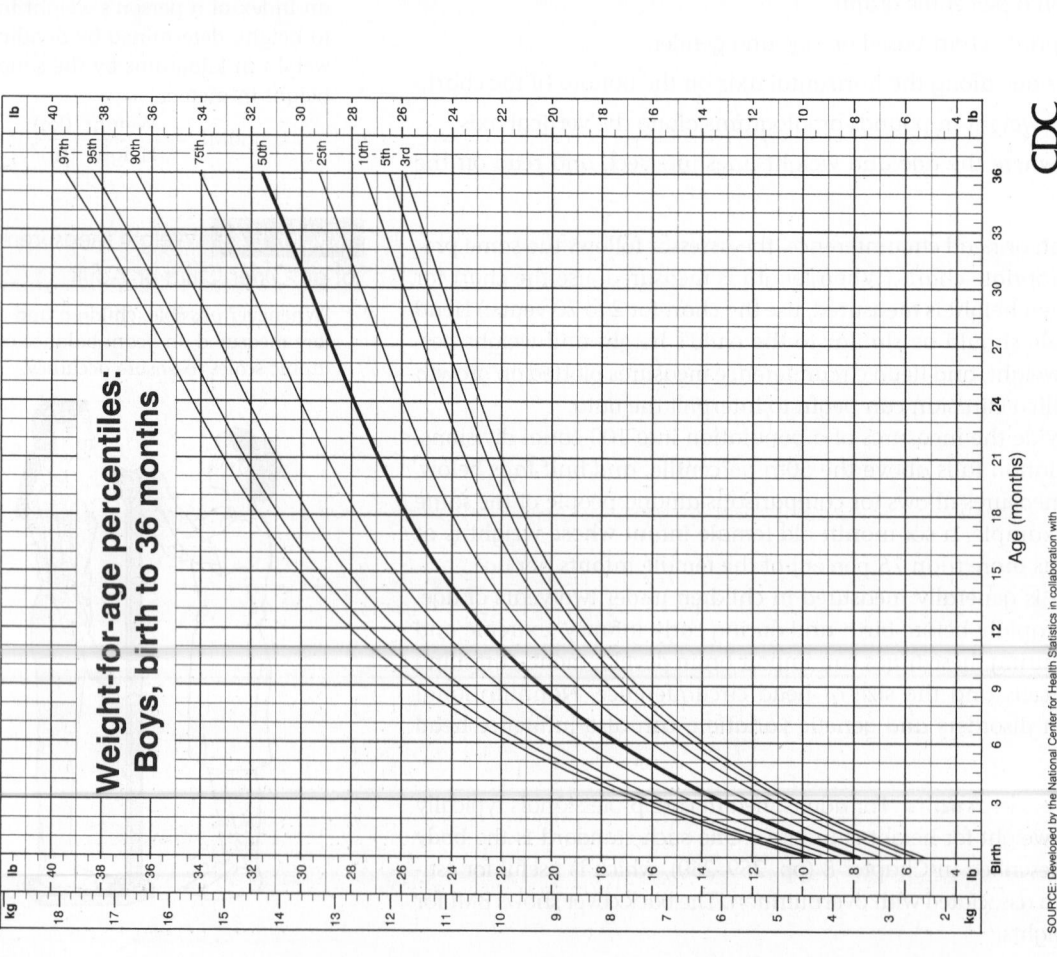

Weight-for-age percentiles: Boys, birth to 36 months

SOURCE: Developed by the National Center for Health Statistics in collaboration with the National Center for Chronic Disease Prevention and Health Promotion (2000).

Figure 1. Weight-for-age percentiles, boys, birth to 36 months, CDC growth charts: United States

FIGURE E-6B   Length-for-Age Percentiles: Girls, Birth to 36 Months

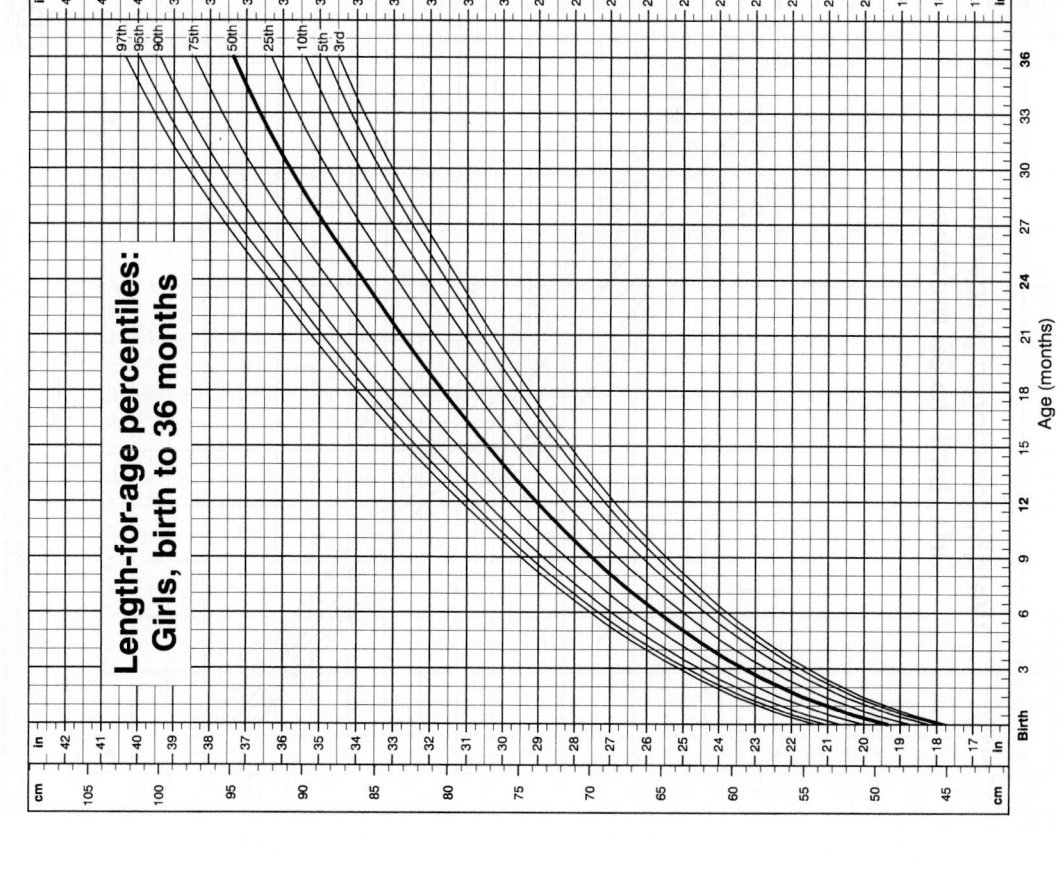

**Length-for-age percentiles:
Girls, birth to 36 months**

SOURCE: Developed by the National Center for Health Statistics in collaboration with
the National Center for Chronic Disease Prevention and Health Promotion (2000).

Figure 4. Length-for-age percentiles, girls, birth to 36 months, CDC growth charts: United States

FIGURE E-6A   Length-for-Age Percentiles: Boys, Birth to 36 Months

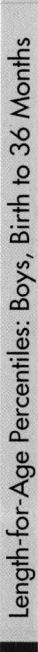
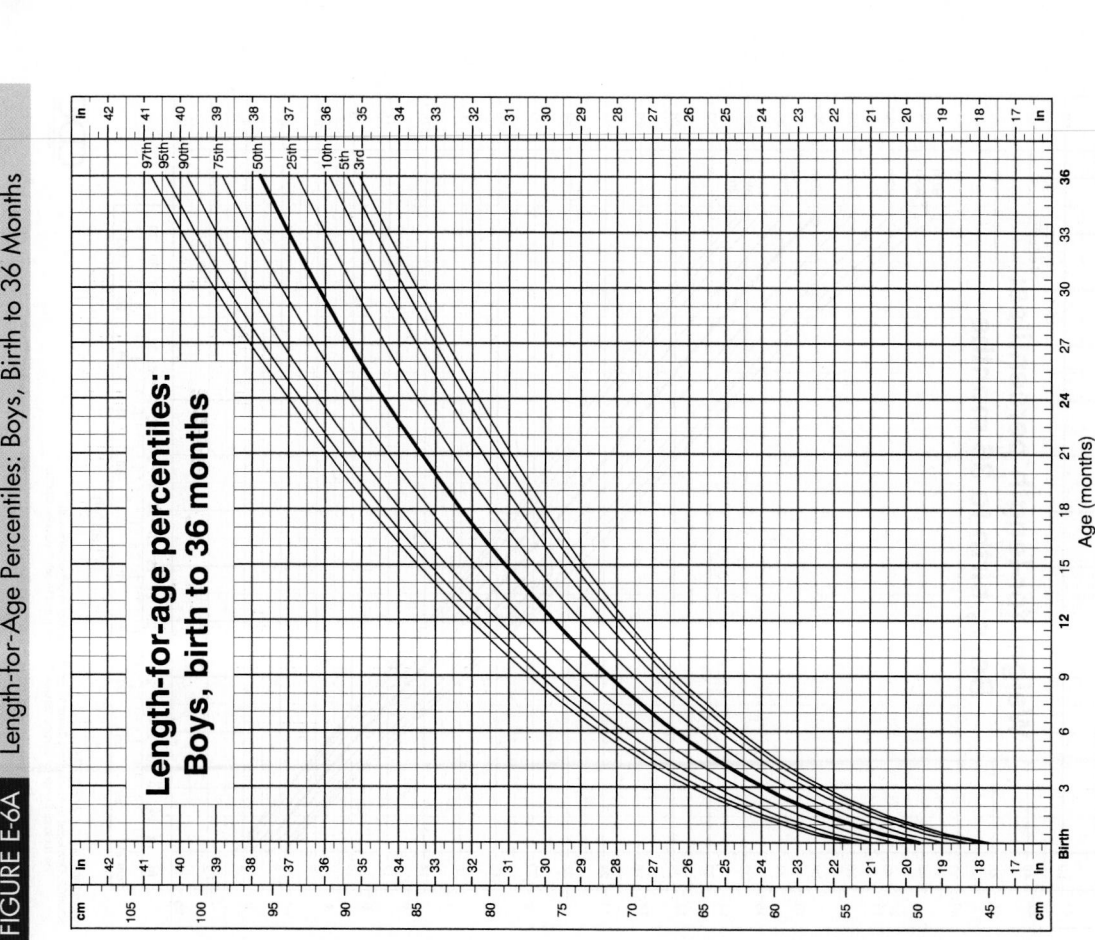

**Length-for-age percentiles:
Boys, birth to 36 months**

SOURCE: Developed by the National Center for Health Statistics in collaboration with
the National Center for Chronic Disease Prevention and Health Promotion (2000).

Figure 3. Length-for-age percentiles, boys, birth to 36 months, CDC growth charts: United States

Appendix
E

FIGURE E-7A Weight-for-Length Percentiles: Boys, Birth to 36 Months

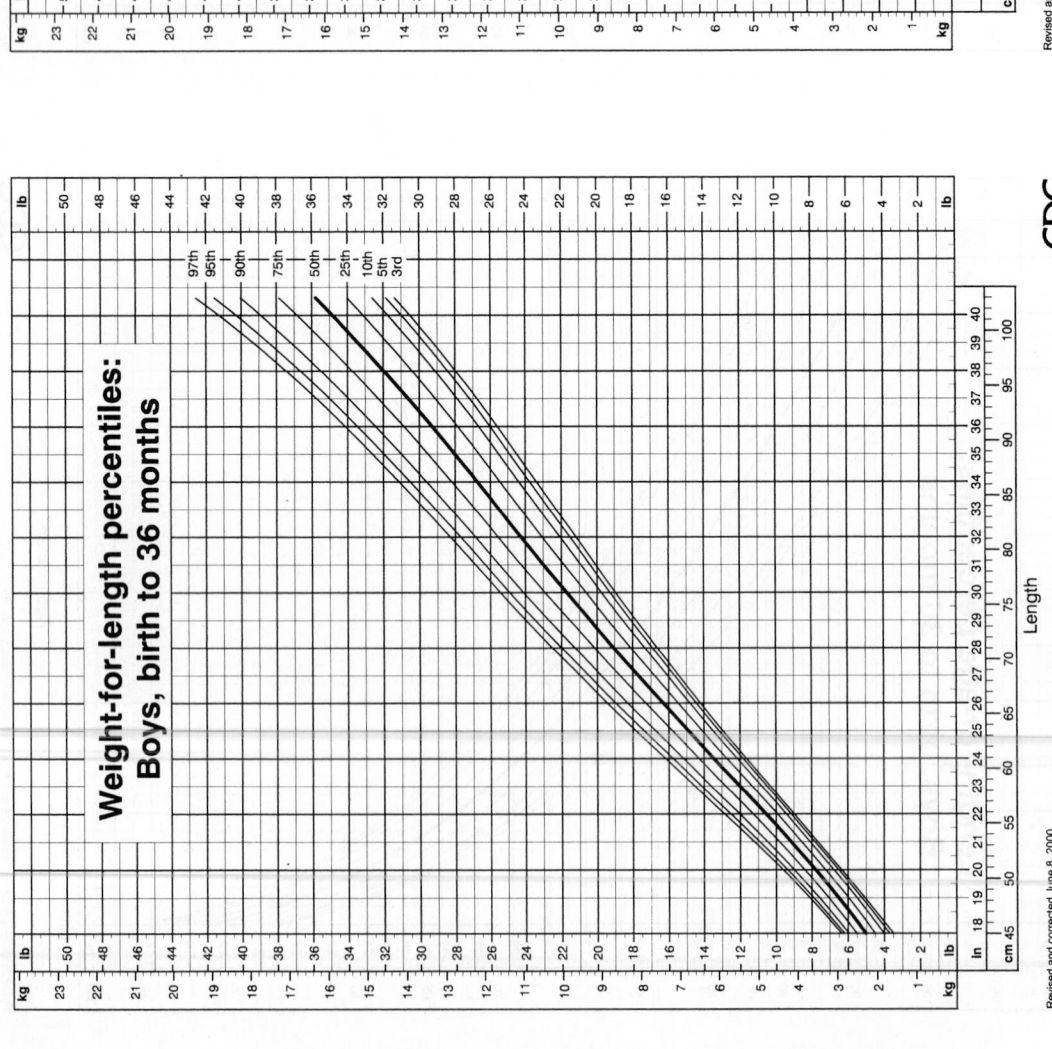

Figure 5. Weight-for-length percentiles, boys, birth to 36 months, CDC growth charts: United States

Revised and corrected June 8, 2000.
SOURCE: Developed by the National Center for Health Statistics in collaboration with the National Center for Chronic Disease Prevention and Health Promotion (2000).

FIGURE E-7B Weight-for-Length Percentiles: Girls, Birth to 36 Months

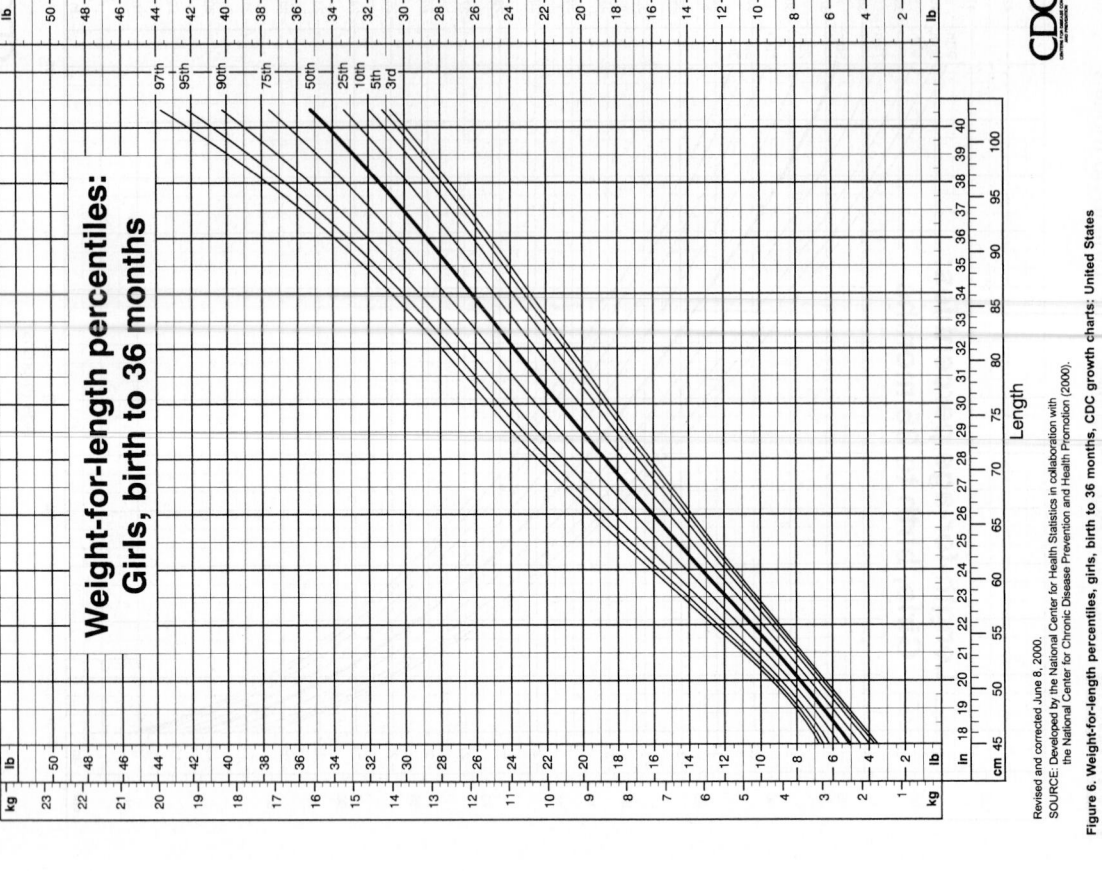

Figure 6. Weight-for-length percentiles, girls, birth to 36 months, CDC growth charts: United States

Revised and corrected June 8, 2000.
SOURCE: Developed by the National Center for Health Statistics in collaboration with the National Center for Chronic Disease Prevention and Health Promotion (2000).

FIGURE E-8A   Weight-for-Age Percentiles: Boys, 2 to 20 Years

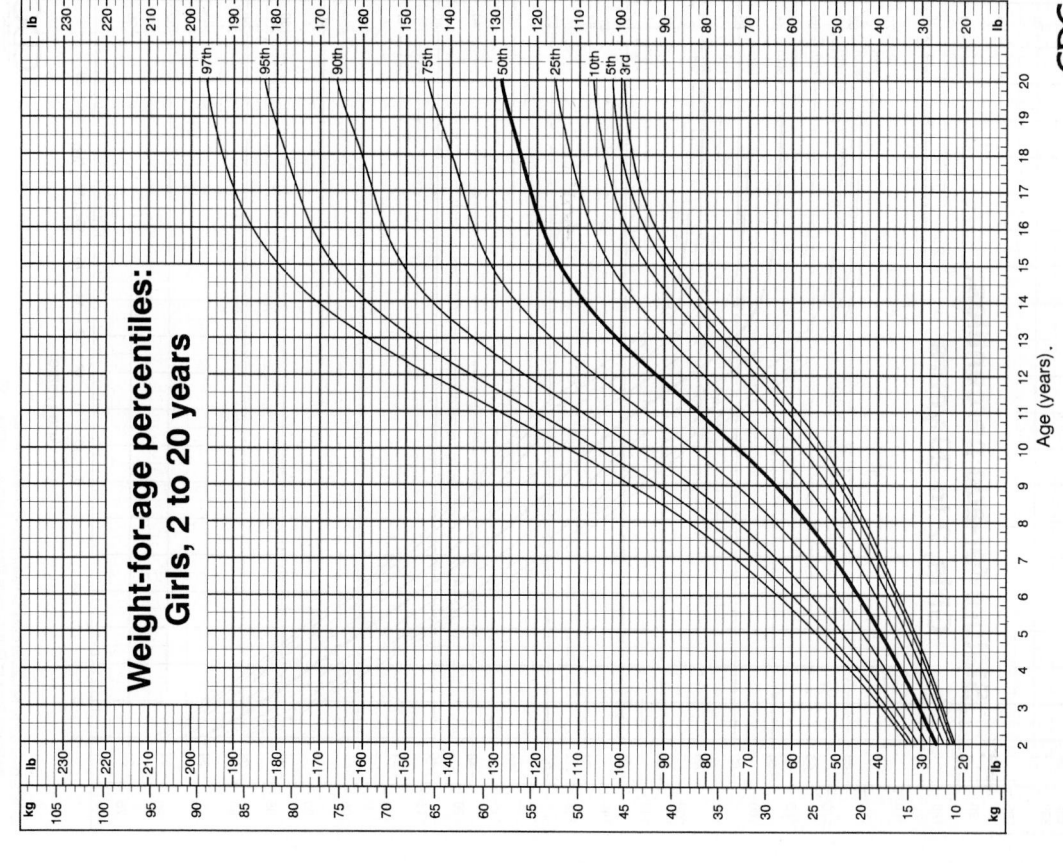

FIGURE E-8B   Weight-for-Age Percentiles: Girls, 2 to 20 Years

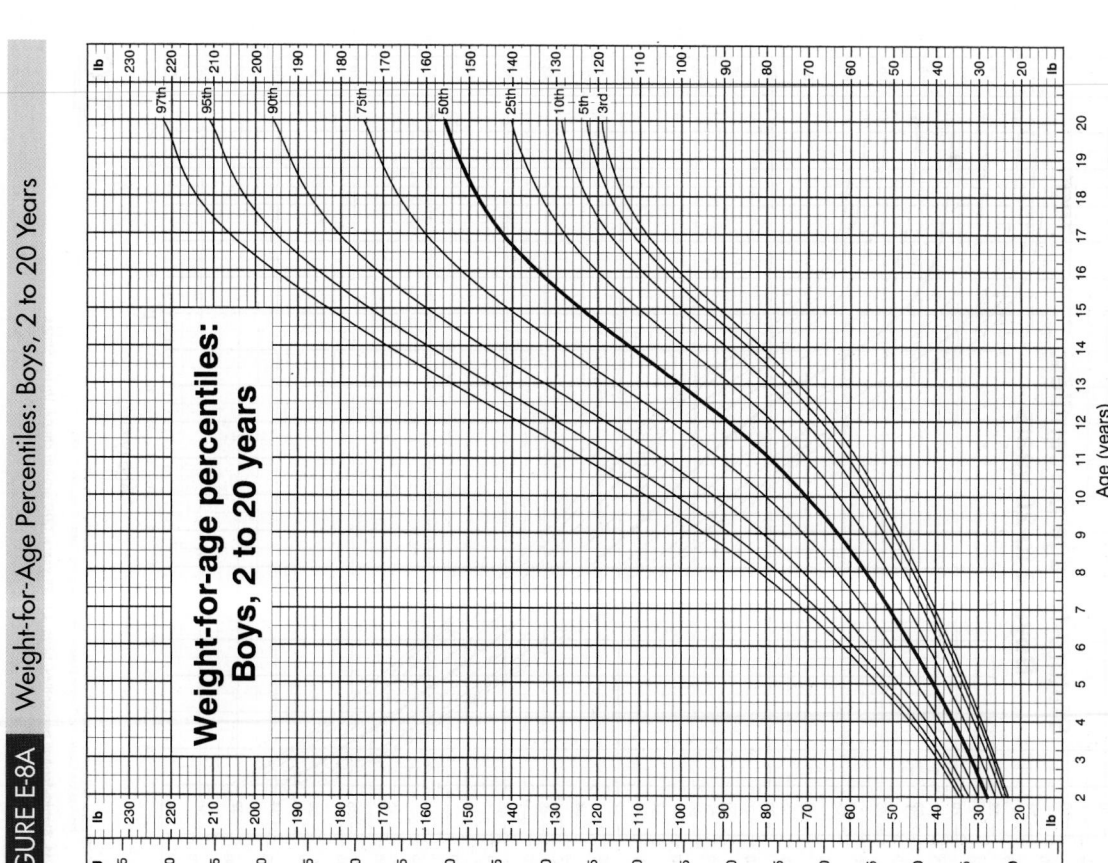

SOURCE: Developed by the National Center for Health Statistics in collaboration with the National Center for Chronic Disease Prevention and Health Promotion (2000).

Figure 9. Weight-for-age percentiles, boys, 2 to 20 years, CDC growth charts: United States

SOURCE: Developed by the National Center for Health Statistics in collaboration with the National Center for Chronic Disease Prevention and Health Promotion (2000).

Figure 10. Weight-for-age percentiles, girls, 2 to 20 years, CDC growth charts: United States

FIGURE E-9A   Stature-for-Age Percentiles: Boys, 2 to 20 Years

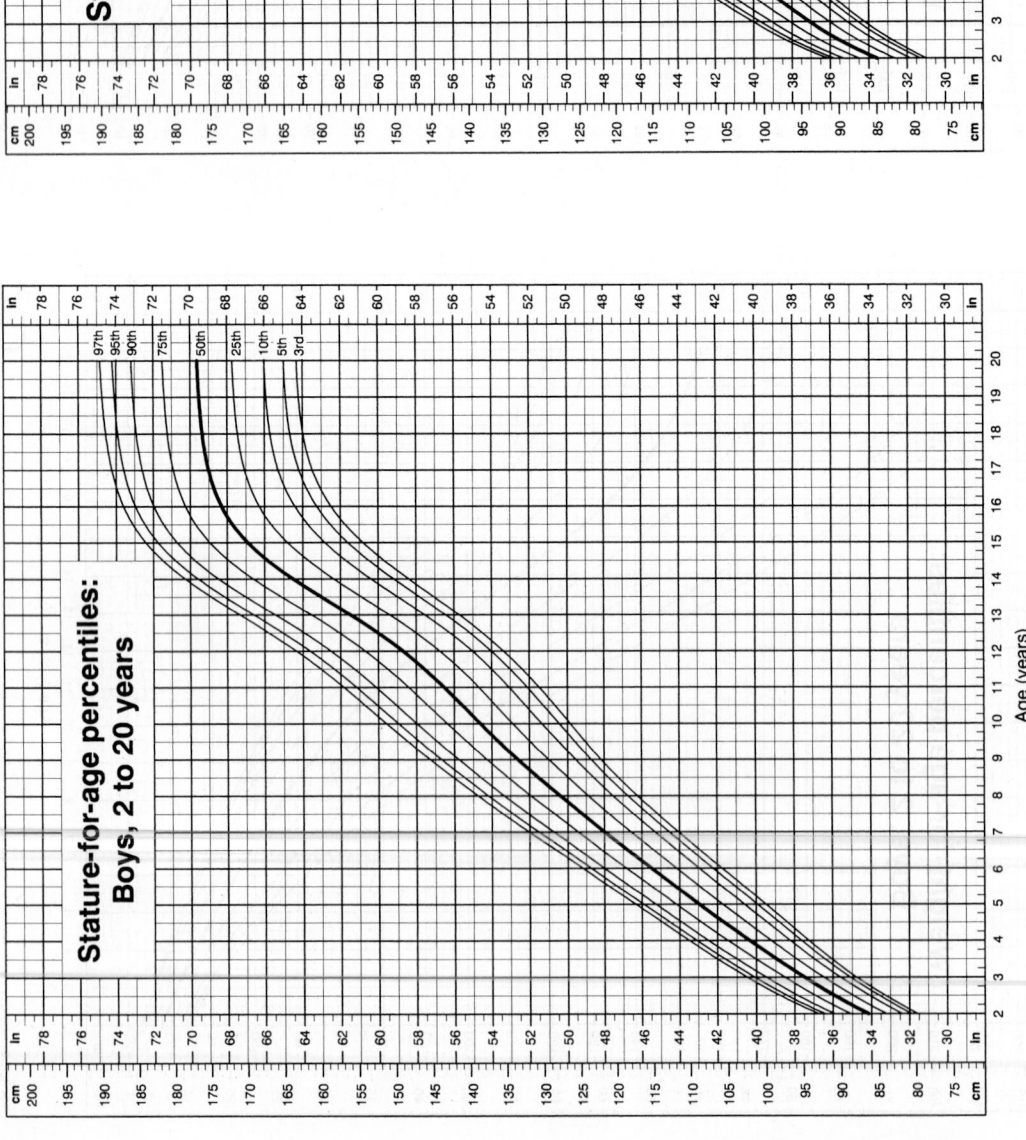

**Stature-for-age percentiles:
Boys, 2 to 20 years**

SOURCE: Developed by the National Center for Health Statistics in collaboration with
the National Center for Chronic Disease Prevention and Health Promotion (2000).

Figure 11. Stature-for-age percentiles, boys, 2 to 20 years, CDC growth charts: United States

FIGURE E-9B   Stature-for-Age Percentiles: Girls, 2 to 20 Years

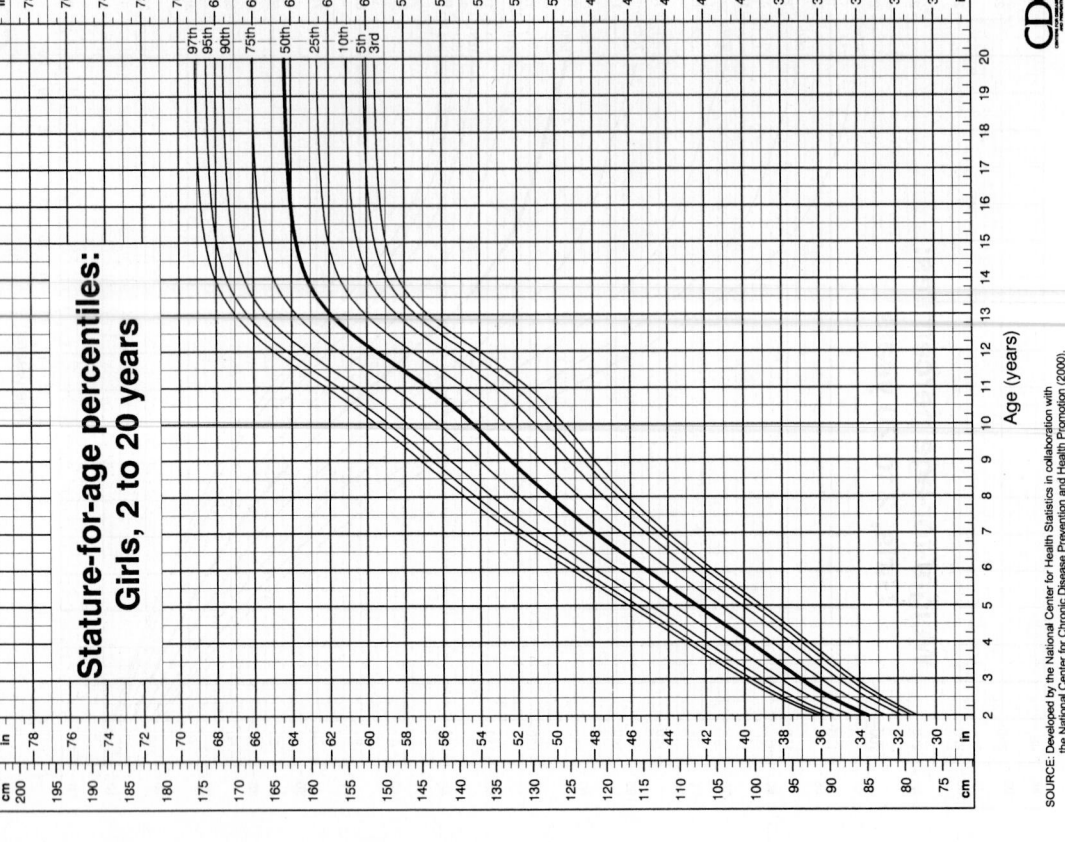

**Stature-for-age percentiles:
Girls, 2 to 20 years**

SOURCE: Developed by the National Center for Health Statistics in collaboration with
the National Center for Chronic Disease Prevention and Health Promotion (2000).

Figure 12. Stature-for-age percentiles, girls, 2 to 20 years, CDC growth charts: United States

FIGURE E-10B   Weight-for-Stature Percentiles: Girls, 2 to 20 Years

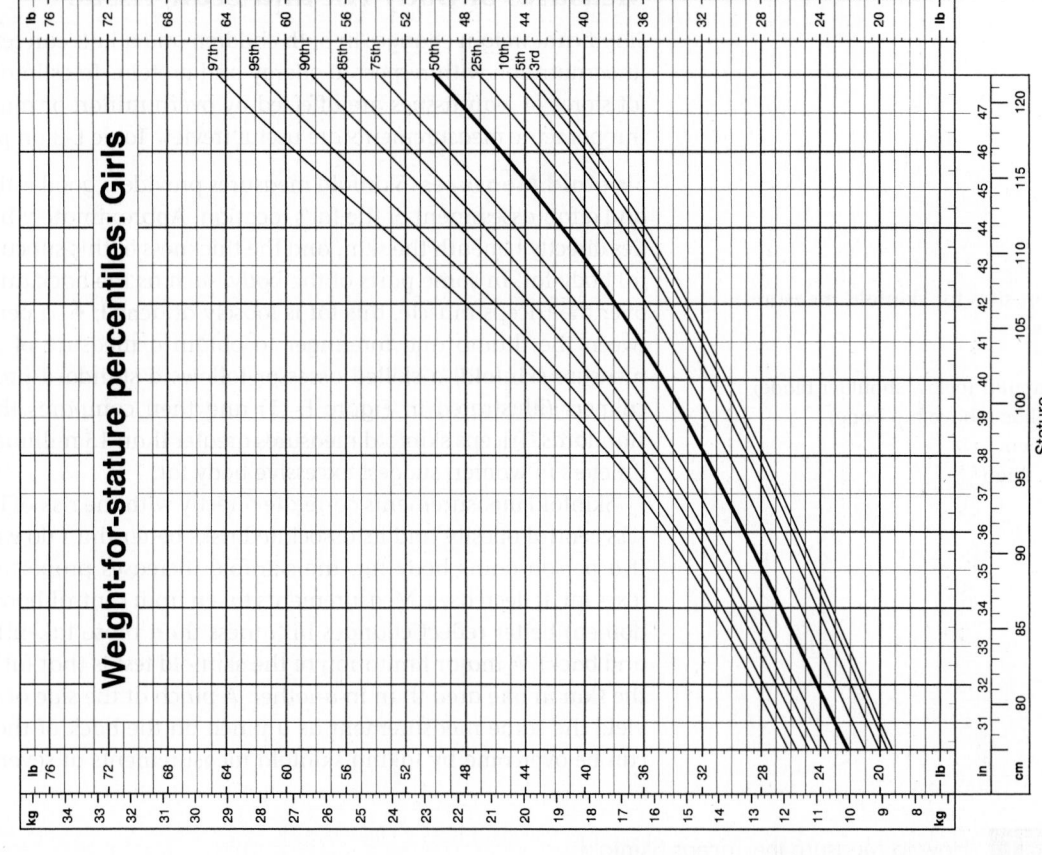

Weight-for-stature percentiles: Girls

SOURCE: Developed by the National Center for Health Statistics in collaboration with the National Center for Chronic Disease Prevention and Health Promotion (2000).

Figure 14. Weight-for-stature percentiles, girls, CDC growth charts: United States

FIGURE E-10A   Weight-for-Stature Percentiles: Boys, 2 to 20 Years

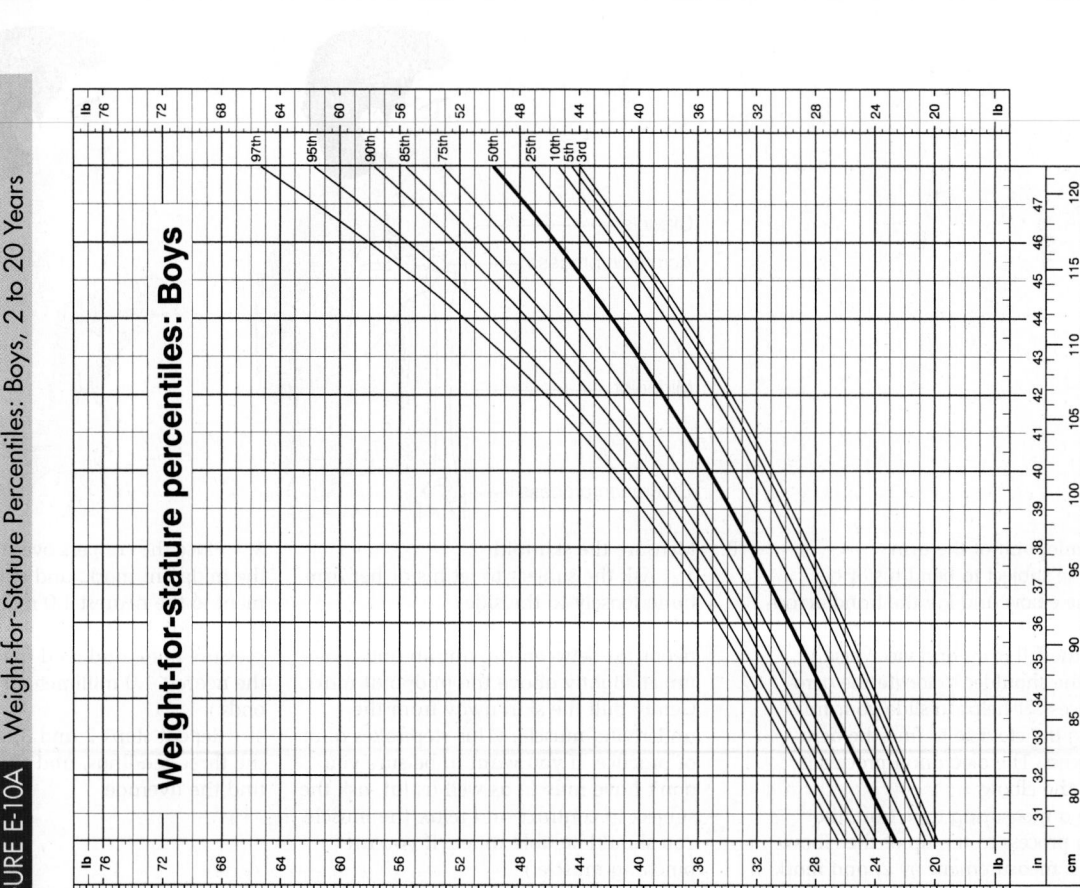

Weight-for-stature percentiles: Boys

SOURCE: Developed by the National Center for Health Statistics in collaboration with the National Center for Chronic Disease Prevention and Health Promotion (2000).

Figure 13. Weight-for-stature percentiles, boys, CDC growth charts: United States

◆ Common sites for skinfold measures:
- Triceps
- Biceps
- Subscapular (below shoulder blade)
- Suprailiac (above hip bone)
- Abdomen
- Upper thigh

Measures of Body Fat and Lean Tissue

Significant weight changes in both children and adults can reflect overnutrition and undernutrition with respect to energy and protein. To estimate the degree to which fat stores or lean tissues are affected by overnutrition or malnutrition, several anthropometric measurements are useful (review Table E-3 on p. E-5).

Skinfold Measures Skinfold measures provide a good estimate of total body fat and a fair assessment of the fat's location. Approximately half the fat in the body lies directly beneath the skin, and the thickness of this subcutaneous fat reflects total body fat. In some parts of the body, such as the back and the back of the arm over the triceps muscle, this fat is loosely attached; ◆ a person can pull it up between the thumb and forefinger to obtain a measure of skinfold thickness. To measure skinfold, a skilled assessor follows a standard procedure using reliable calipers (illustrated in Figure E-11) and then compares the measurement with standards. Triceps skinfold measures greater than 15 millimeters in men or 25 millimeters in women suggest excessive body fat.

Skinfold measurements correlate directly with the risk of heart disease. They assess central obesity and its associated risks better than do weight measures alone. If a person gains body fat, the skinfold increases proportionally; if the person loses fat, it decreases. Measurements taken from central-body sites (around the abdomen) better reflect changes in fatness than those taken from upper sites (arm and back). A major limitation of the skinfold test is that fat may be thicker under the skin in one area than in another. A pinch at the side of the waistline may not yield the same measurement as a pinch on the back of the arm. This limitation can be overcome by taking skinfold measurements at several (often three) differ-

---

FIGURE E-11 How to Measure the Triceps Skinfold

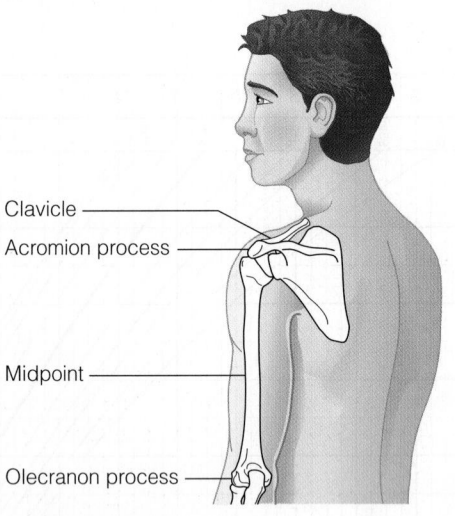
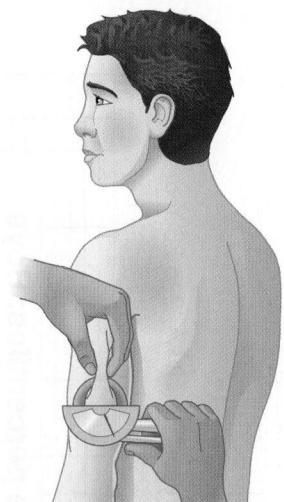

Clavicle
Acromion process
Midpoint
Olecranon process

A. Find the midpoint of the arm:
1. Ask the subject to bend his or her arm at the elbow and lay the hand across the stomach. (If he or she is right-handed, measure the left arm, and vice versa.)
2. Feel the shoulder to locate the acromion process. It helps to slide your fingers along the clavicle to find the acromion process. The olecranon process is the tip of the elbow.
3. Place a measuring tape from the acromion process to the tip of the elbow. Divide this measurement by 2, and mark the midpoint of the arm with a pen.

B. Measure the skinfold:
1. Ask the subject to let his or her arm hang loosely to the side.
2. Grasp a fold of skin and subcutaneous fat between the thumb and forefinger slightly above the midpoint mark. Gently pull the skin away from the underlying muscle. (This step takes a lot of practice. If you want to be sure you don't have muscle as well as fat, ask the subject to contract and relax the muscle. You should be able to feel if you are pinching muscle.)

3. Place the calipers over the skinfold at the midpoint mark, and read the measurement to the nearest 1.0 millimeter in two to three seconds. (If using plastic calipers, align pressure lines, and read the measurement to the nearest 1.0 millimeter in two to three seconds.)
4. Repeat steps 2 and 3 twice more. Add the three readings, and then divide by 3 to find the average.

FIGURE E-12 How to Measure Waist Circumference

Place the measuring tape around the waist just above the bony crest of the hip. The tape runs parallel to the floor and is snug (but does not compress the skin). The measurement is taken at the end of normal expiration.

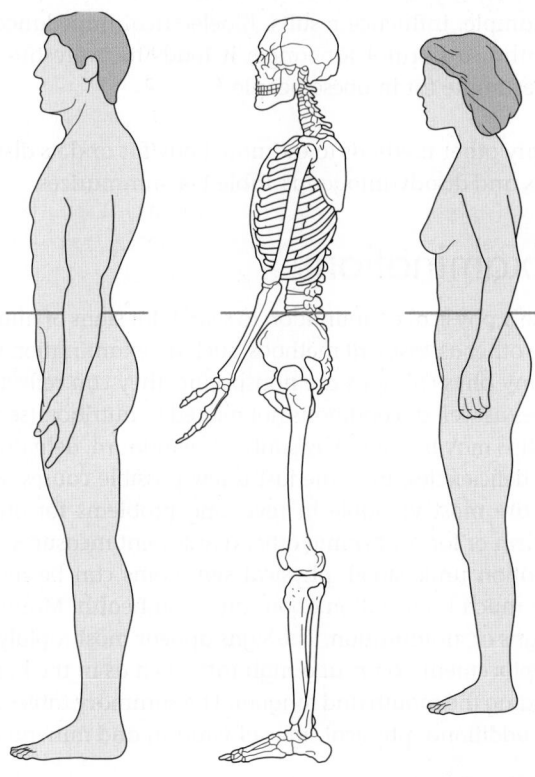

SOURCE: National Institutes of Health Obesity Education Initiative, *Clinical Guidelines on the Identification, Evaluation, and Treatment of Overweight and Obesity in Adults* (Washington, D.C.: U.S. Department of Health and Human Services, 1998), p. 59.

ent places on the body (including upper-, central-, and lower-body sites) and comparing each measurement with standards for that site. Multiple measures are not always practical in clinical settings, however, and most often, the triceps skinfold measurement alone is used because it is easily accessible. Skinfold measures are not useful in assessing changes in body fat over time.[1]

Waist Circumference Chapter 8 described how fat distribution correlates with health risks and mentioned that the waist circumference is a valuable indicator of fat distribution. To measure waist circumference, the assessor places a nonstretchable tape around the person's body, crossing just above the upper hip bones and making sure that the tape remains on a level horizontal plane on all sides (see Figure E-12). The tape is tightened slightly, but without compressing the skin.

Waist-to Hip Ratio Alternatively, some clinicians measure both the waist and the hips. The waist-to-hip ratio ♦ also assesses abdominal obesity, but provides no more information than using the waist circumference alone. In general, women with a waist-to-hip ratio of 0.80 or greater and men with a waist-to-hip ratio of 0.90 or greater have a high risk of health problems.

Hydrodensitometry To estimate body density using hydrodensitometry, the person is weighed twice—first on land and then again when submerged under water. Underwater weighing usually generates a good estimate of body fat and is useful in research, although the technique has drawbacks: it requires bulky, expensive, and nonportable equipment. Furthermore, submerging some people (especially those who are very young, very old, ill, or fearful) under water is not always practical.

♦ To calculate the waist-to-hip ratio, divide the waistline measurement by the hip measurement. For example, a woman with a 28-inch waist and 38-inch hips would have a ratio of 28 ÷ 38 = 0.74.

Bioelectric Impedance To measure body fat using the bioelectric impedance technique, a very-low-intensity electrical current is briefly sent through the body by way of electrodes placed on the wrist and ankle. As is true of other anthropometric techniques, bioelectrical impedance requires standardized procedures and calibrated instruments to provide reliable results. Recent food intake and hydration status, for example, influence results. Bioelectrical impedance is most accurate for people within a normal fat range; it tends to overestimate fat in lean people and underestimate fat in obese people.[2]

Clinicians use many other methods to estimate body fat and its distribution. Each has its advantages and disadvantages as Table E-4 summarizes.

Physical Examinations

An assessor can use a physical examination to search for signs of nutrient deficiency or toxicity. Like the other assessment methods, such an examination requires knowledge and skill. Many physical signs are nonspecific; they can reflect any of several nutrient deficiencies as well as conditions not related to nutrition (see Table E-5). For example, cracked lips may be caused by sunburn, windburn, dehydration, or any of several B vitamin deficiencies, to name just a few possible causes. For this reason, physical findings are most valuable in revealing problems for other assessment techniques to confirm or for confirming other assessment measures.

With this limitation understood, physical symptoms can be most informative and communicate much information about nutrition health. Many tissues and organs can reflect signs of malnutrition. The signs appear most rapidly in parts of the body where cell replacement occurs at a high rate, such as in the hair, skin, and digestive tract (including the mouth and tongue). The summary tables in Chapters 10, 11, 12, and 13 list additional physical signs of vitamin and mineral malnutrition.

Biochemical Analyses

All of the approaches to nutrition assessment discussed so far are external approaches. Biochemical analyses or laboratory tests help to determine what is happening to the body internally. Common tests are based on analysis of blood and

TABLE E-4	Methods of Estimating Body Fat and Its Distribution			
Method	Cost	Ease of Use	Accuracy	Measures Fat Distribution
Height and weight	Low	Easy	High	No
Skinfolds	Low	Easy	Low	Yes
Circumferences	Low	Easy	Moderate	Yes
Ultrasound	Moderate	Moderate	Moderate	Yes
Hydrodensitometry	Low	Moderate	High	No
Heavy water tritiated	Moderate	Moderate	High	No
Deuterium oxide, or heavy oxygen	High	Moderate	High	No
Potassium isotope (^{40}K)	Very high	Difficult	High	No
Total body electrical conductivity (TOBEC)	High	Moderate	High	No
Bioelectric impedance (BIA)	Moderate	Easy	High	No
Dual energy X-ray absorptiometry (DEXA)	High	Easy	High	No
Computed tomography (CT)	Very high	Difficult	High	Yes
Magnetic resonance imaging (MRI)	Very high	Difficult	High	Yes

SOURCE: Adapted with permisssion from G. A. Bray, a handout presented at the North American Association for the Study of Obesity and Emory University School of Medicine Conference on Obesity. Update: Pathophysiology, Clinical Consequences, and Therapeutic Options, Atlanta, Georgia, August 31-September 2, 1992.

TABLE E-5	Physical Findings Used in Nutrition Assessments		
Body System	Healthy Findings	Malnutrition Findings	What the Findings Reflect
Hair	Shiny, firm in the scalp	Dull, brittle, dry, loose; falls out	PEM
Eyes	Bright, clear pink membranes; adjust easily to light	Pale membranes; spots; redness; adjust slowly to darkness	Vitamin A, B vitamin, zinc, and iron status
Teeth and gums	No pain or caries, gums firm, teeth bright	Missing, discolored, decayed teeth; gums bleed easily and are swollen and spongy	Mineral and vitamin C status
Glands	No lumps	Swollen at front of neck	PEM and iodine status
Tongue	Red, bumpy, rough	Sore, smooth, purplish, swollen	B vitamin status
Skin	Smooth, firm, good color	Off-color, scaly, flaky, cracked, dry, rough, spotty; "sandpaper" feel or sores; lack of fat under skin	PEM, essential fatty acid, vitamin A, B vitamin, and vitamin C status
Nails	Firm, pink	Spoon-shaped, brittle, ridged, pale	Iron status
Internal systems	Regular heart rhythm, heart rate, and blood pressure; no impairment of digestive function, reflexes, or mental status	Abnormal heart rate, heart rhythm, or blood pressure; enlarged liver, spleen; abnormal digestion; burning, tingling of hands, feet; loss of balance, coordination; mental confusion, irritability, fatigue	PEM and mineral status
Muscles and bones	Muscle tone; posture, long bone development appropriate for age	"Wasted" appearance of muscles; swollen bumps on skull or ends of bones; small bumps on ribs; bowed legs or knock-knees	PEM, mineral, and vitamin D status

urine samples, which contain nutrients, enzymes, and metabolites that reflect nutrition status. Other tests, such as serum ◆ glucose, help pinpoint disease-related problems with nutrition implications. Tests that define fluid and electrolyte balance, acid-base balance, and organ function also have nutrition implications. Table E-6 (p. E-18) lists biochemical tests most useful for assessing vitamin and mineral status.

The interpretation of biochemical data requires skill. Long metabolic sequences lead to the production of the end products and metabolites seen in blood and urine. No single test can reveal nutrition status because many factors influence test results. The low blood concentration of a nutrient may reflect a primary deficiency of that nutrient, but it may also be secondary to the deficiency of one or several other nutrients or to a disease. Taken together with other assessment data, however, laboratory test results help to create a picture that becomes clear with careful interpretation. They are especially useful in helping to detect subclinical malnutrition by uncovering early signs of malnutrition before the clinical signs of a classic deficiency disease appear.

Laboratory tests used to assess vitamin and mineral status (review Table E-6) are particularly useful when combined with diet histories and physical findings. Vitamin and mineral levels present in the blood and urine sometimes reflect recent rather than long-term intakes. This makes detecting subclinical deficiencies ◆ difficult. Furthermore, many nutrients interact; therefore, the amounts of other nutrients in the body can affect a lab value for a particular nutrient. It is also important to remember that nonnutrient conditions such as diseases influence biochemical measures.

It is beyond the scope of this text to describe all lab tests and their relations to nutrition status. Instead, the emphasis is on lab tests used to detect protein-energy malnutrition (PEM) and nutritional anemias.

◆ The **serum** is the watery portion of the blood that remains after removal of the cells and clot-forming material; **plasma** is the fluid that remains when unclotted blood is centrifuged. In most cases, serum and plasma concentrations are similar, but plasma samples are more likely to clog mechanical blood analyzers, so serum samples are preferred.

◆ Reminder: A *subclinical deficiency* is a nutrient deficiency in the early stages before the outward signs have appeared.

Protein-Energy Malnutrition (PEM)

No single biochemical analysis can adequately evaluate PEM. Numerous procedures have been used over the years. This discussion focuses on the measures commonly used today—transthyretin, retinol-binding protein, serum transferrin, and

TABLE E-6 Biochemical Tests Useful for Assessing Vitamin and Mineral Status

Nutrient	Assessment Tests
Vitamins	
Vitamin A	Serum retinol, retinol-binding protein
Thiamin[a]	Erythrocyte (red blood cell) transketolase activity, erythrocyte thiamin pyrophosphate
Riboflavin[a]	Erythrocyte glutathione reductase activity
Vitamin B_6[a]	Urinary xanthurenic acid excretion after tryptophan load test, erythrocyte transaminase activity, plasma pyridoxal 5'-phosphate (PLP)
Niacin	Plasma or urinary metabolites NMN (N-methyl nicotinamide) or 2-pyridone, or preferably both expressed as a ratio
Folate[b]	Serum folate, erythrocyte folate (reflects liver stores)
Vitamin B_{12}[b]	Serum vitamin B_{12}, serum and urinary methylmalonic acid, Schilling test
Biotin	Urinary biotin, urinary 3-hydroxyisovaleric acid
Vitamin C	Plasma vitamin C[c], leukocyte vitamin C
Vitamin D	Serum vitamin D
Vitamin E	Serum α-tocopherol, erythrocyte hemolysis
Vitamin K	Serum vitamin K, plasma prothrombin; blood-clotting time (prothrombin time) is not an adequate indicator
Minerals	
Phosphorus	Serum phosphate
Sodium	Serum sodium
Chloride	Serum chloride
Potassium	Serum potassium
Magnesium	Serum magnesium, urinary magnesium
Iron	Hemoglobin, hematocrit, serum ferritin, total iron-binding capacity (TIBC), erythrocyte protoporphyrin, serum iron, transferrin saturation
Iodine	Serum thyroxine or thyroid-stimulating hormone (TSH), urinary iodine
Zinc	Plasma zinc, hair zinc
Copper	Erythrocyte superoxide dismutase, serum copper, serum ceruloplasmin
Selenium	Erythrocyte selenium, glutathione peroxidase activity

[a]Urinary measurements for these vitamins are common, but may be of limited use. Urinary measurements reflect recent dietary intakes and may not provide reliable information concerning the severity of a deficiency.
[b]Folate assessments should always be conducted in conjunction with vitamin B_{12} assessments (and vice versa) to help distinguish the cause of common deficiency symptoms.
[c]Vitamin C shifts between the plasma and the white blood cells known as leukocytes; thus a plasma determination may not accurately reflect the body's pool. A measurement of leukocyte vitamin C can provide information about the body's stores of vitamin C. A combination of both tests may be more reliable than either one alone.
SOURCE: Adapted from H. E. Sauberlich, *Laboratory Tests for the Assessment of Nutritional Status* (Boca Raton, Fla.: CRC Press, 1999).

IGF-1 (insulin-like growth factor 1). Table E-7 provides standards for these indicators. Although serum albumin is easily and routinely measured, it lacks the sensitivity to assess PEM because of its long turnover rate.[*]

Transthyretin and Retinol-Binding Protein Transthyretin ◆ and retinol-binding protein occur as a complex in the plasma. They have a rapid turnover and thus respond quickly to dietary protein inadequacy and therapy.[†] Conditions other than malnutrition that lower transthyretin include metabolic stress, hemodialysis, and hypothyroidism; those that raise transthyretin include kidney disease and corticosteroid use. Conditions other than protein malnutrition that lower retinol-binding protein include vitamin A deficiency, metabolic stress, hyperthyroidism, liver disease, and cystic fibrosis; kidney disease raises retinol-binding protein levels.

◆ Transthyretin is also known as *prealbumin* or *thyroxine-binding prealbumin.*

[*]The half-life of albumin is 18 days, an indication of a slow degradation rate.
[†]The half-lives of transthyretin and retinol-binding protein are 2 days and 12 hours, respectively.

TABLE E-7	Normal Values for Serum Proteins
Indicator	Normal
Albumin (g/dL)	3.5–5.4
Transferrin (mg/dL)	200–400
Transthyretin (mg/dL)	23–43
Retinol-binding protein (mg/dL)	3–7
IGF-1 (μg/L)	300

NOTE: Levels less than normal suggest compromised protein status.

Serum Transferrin Serum transferrin transports iron; consequently, its concentrations reflect both protein and iron status. Using transferrin as an indicator of protein status is complicated when an iron deficiency is present. Transferrin rises as iron deficiency grows worse and falls as iron status improves. Markedly reduced transferrin levels indicate severe PEM; in mild-to-moderate PEM, transferrin levels may vary, limiting their usefulness. Conditions other than protein malnutrition that lower transferrin include liver disease, kidney disease, and metabolic stress; those that raise transferrin include pregnancy, iron deficiency, hepatitis, blood loss, and oral contraceptive use. Although transferrin breaks down in the body more quickly than albumin, it is still relatively slow to respond to changes in protein intake and is not a sensitive indicator of the response to therapy.[*]

IGF-1 (Insulin-like Growth Factor 1) IGF-1 (insulin-like growth factor 1) declines in PEM. IGF-1 has a relatively short half-life and responds specifically to dietary protein rather than energy.[†] For these reasons, it is a sensitive indicator of protein status and response to therapy. Conditions that decrease IGF-1 include anorexia nervosa, inflammatory bowel disease, celiac disease, HIV infection, and fasting.

Nutritional Anemias

Anemia, a symptom of a wide variety of nutrition- and nonnutrition-related disorders, is characterized by a reduced number of red blood cells. Iron, folate, and vitamin B_{12} deficiencies caused by inadequate intake, poor absorption, or abnormal metabolism of these nutrients are the most common nutritional anemias. Some nonnutrition-related causes of anemia include massive blood loss, infections, hereditary blood disorders such as sickle-cell anemia, and chronic liver or kidney disease.

Assessment of Iron-Deficiency Anemia

Iron deficiency, a common mineral deficiency, develops in stages. ◆ Chapter 13 describes iron deficiency in detail. This section describes tests used to uncover iron deficiency as it progresses. Table E-8 (p. E-20) shows which laboratory tests detect various nutrition-related anemias, and Table E-9 (p. E-21) provides values used for assessing iron status. Although other tests are more specific in detecting early deficiencies, hemoglobin and hematocrit are the commonly available tests.

Hemoglobin Iron forms an integral part of the hemoglobin molecule that transports oxygen to the cells. In iron deficiency, the body cannot synthesize hemoglobin. Low hemoglobin values signal depleted iron stores. Table E-9 provides hemoglobin values used in nutrition assessment. Hemoglobin's usefulness in evaluating iron status is limited, however, because hemoglobin concentrations drop fairly late in the

◆ Stages of iron deficiency:
1. Iron stores diminish.
2. Transport iron decreases.
3. Hemoglobin production falls.

[*]The half-life of transferrin is 8 days.
[†]The half-life of IGF-1 is 12 to 15 hours.

TABLE E-8 Laboratory Tests Useful in Evaluating Nutrition-Related Anemias

Test or Test Result	What It Reflects
For Anemia (general)	
Hemoglobin (Hg)	Total amount of hemoglobin in the red blood cells (RBC)
Hematocrit (Hct)	Percentage of RBC in the total blood volume
Red blood cell (RBC) count	Number of RBC
Mean corpuscular volume (MCV)	RBC size; helps to determine if anemia is microcytic (iron deficiency) or macrocytic (folate or vitamin B_{12} deficiency)
Mean corpuscular hemoglobin concentration (MCHC)	Hemoglobin concentration within the average RBC; helps to determine if anemia is hypochromic (iron deficiency) or normochromic (folate or vitamin B_{12} deficiency)
Bone marrow aspiration	The manufacture of blood cells in different developmental states
For Iron-Deficiency Anemia	
↓ Serum ferritin	Early deficiency state with depleted iron stores
↓ Transferrin saturation	Progressing deficiency state with diminished transport iron
↑ Erythrocyte protoporphyrin	Later deficiency state with limited hemoglobin production
For Folate-Deficiency Anemia	
↓ Serum folate	Progressing deficiency state
↓ RBC folate	Later deficiency state
For Vitamin B_{12}–Deficiency Anemia	
↓ Serum vitamin B_{12}	Progressing deficiency state
Schilling test	Absorption of vitamin B_{12}

development of iron deficiency, and other nutrient deficiencies and medical conditions can also alter hemoglobin concentrations.

Hematocrit Hematocrit is commonly used to diagnose iron deficiency, even though it is an inconclusive measure of iron status. To measure the hematocrit, a clinician spins a volume of blood in a centrifuge to separate the red blood cells from the plasma. The hematocrit is the percentage of red blood cells in the total blood volume. Table E-9 includes values used to assess hematocrit status. Low values indicate incomplete hemoglobin formation, which is manifested by microcytic (abnormally small-celled), hypochromic (abnormally lacking in color) red blood cells.

Low hemoglobin and hematocrit values alert the assessor to the possibility of iron deficiency. However, many nutrients and other conditions can affect hemoglobin and hematocrit. The other tests of iron status help pinpoint true iron deficiency.

Serum Ferritin In the first stage of iron deficiency, iron stores diminish. Measures of serum ferritin provide an estimate of iron stores. Such information is most valuable to iron assessment. Table E-9 shows serum ferritin cutoff values that indicate iron store depletion in children and adults. Serum ferritin is not reliable for diagnosing iron deficiency in infants, since normal serum ferritin values are often present in conjunction with iron-responsive anemia.

A decrease in transport iron characterizes the second stage of iron deficiency. This is revealed by an increase in the iron-binding capacity of the protein transferrin and a decrease in serum iron. These changes are reflected by the transferrin saturation, which is calculated from the ratio of the other two values as described in the following paragraphs.

Total Iron-Binding Capacity (TIBC) Iron travels through the blood bound to the protein transferrin. TIBC is a measure of the total amount of iron that transferrin can

TABLE E-9	Criteria for Assessing Iron Status

Test	Age (yr)	Gender	Deficiency Value
Hemoglobin (g/dL)	0.5–10	M–F	<11
	11–15	M	<12
		F	<11.5
	>15	M	<13
		F	<12
	Pregnancy		<11
Hematocrit (%)	0.5–4	M–F	<32
	5–10	M–F	<33
	11–15	M	<35
		F	<34
	>15	M	<40
		F	<36
Serum ferritin (μg/L)	0.5–15	M–F	<10
	>15	M–F	<12
Total iron-binding capacity (μg/dL)	>15	M–F	>400
Serum iron (μg/dL)	>15	M–F	<60
Transferrin saturation (%)	0.5–4	M–F	<12
	5–10	M–F	<14
	>10	M–F	<16
Erythrocyte protoporphyrin (μg/dL RBC)	0.5–4	M–F	>80
	>4	M–F	>70

carry. Lab technicians measure iron-binding capacity directly. Table E-9 includes the cutoff for TIBC.

Serum Iron Lab technicians can also measure serum iron directly. Elevated values indicate iron overload; reduced values indicate iron deficiency. Table E-9 shows the deficient value for serum iron.

Transferrin Saturation The percentage of transferrin that is saturated with iron is an indirect measure that is derived from the serum iron and total iron-binding capacity measures as follows:

$$\%\text{Transferrin} = \frac{\text{serum iron}}{\text{total iron-binding capacity}} \times 100$$

Table E-9 shows deficient transferrin saturation values for various age groups.

The third stage of iron deficiency occurs when the supply of transport iron diminishes to the point that it limits hemoglobin production. It is characterized by increases in erythrocyte protoporphyrin, a decrease in mean corpuscular volume, and decreased hemoglobin and hematocrit.

Erythrocyte Protoporphyrin The iron-containing portion of the hemoglobin molecule is heme. Heme is a combination of iron and protoporphyrin. Protoporphyrin accumulates in the blood when iron supplies are inadequate for the formation of heme. Lab technicians can measure erythrocyte protoporphyrin directly in a blood sample. The cutoffs for abnormal values of erythrocyte protoporphyrin are shown in Table E 9.

Mean Corpuscular Volume (MCV) A direct or calculated measure of the mean corpuscular volume (MCV) determines the average size of a red blood cell. Such a measure helps to classify the type of nutrient anemia. In iron deficiency, the red blood cells are smaller than average.

Assessment of Folate and Vitamin B$_{12}$ Anemias

Folate deficiency and vitamin B$_{12}$ deficiency present a similar clinical picture—an anemia characterized by abnormally large red blood cell precursors (megaloblasts) in the bone marrow and abnormally large, mature red blood cells (macrocytic cells) in the blood. Distinguishing between these two deficiencies is particularly important because their treatments differ. Giving folate to a person with vitamin B$_{12}$ deficiency improves many of the lab test results indicative of vitamin B$_{12}$ deficiency, but this is a dangerous error because vitamin B$_{12}$ deficiency causes nerve damage that folate cannot correct. Thus inappropriate folate administration masks vitamin B$_{12}$– deficiency anemia, and nerve damage worsens. For this reason, it is critical to determine whether the anemia results from a folate deficiency or from a vitamin B$_{12}$ deficiency. The following biochemical assessment techniques help to make this distinction.

Mean Corpuscular Volume (MCV) As previously mentioned, the MCV is a measure of red blood cell size. In folate and vitamin B$_{12}$ deficiencies, the red blood cells are larger than average (macrocytic). Additional tests must be performed to differentiate folate from vitamin B$_{12}$ deficiency.

Folate Levels Serum folate levels fluctuate with changes in folate intake and metabolism. Thus serum folate concentrations reflect current status, but provide little information about folate stores. As folate deficiency progresses and low serum levels persist, folate stores decline, resulting in folate depletion. Folate depletion is characterized by a fall in the folate concentrations of red blood cells (erythrocytes). As erythrocyte folate levels diminish, folate-deficiency anemia develops. Because low erythrocyte folate concentrations also occur with vitamin B$_{12}$ deficiency, serum vitamin B$_{12}$ concentrations must also be measured. Table E-10 shows standards for folate assessment.

Vitamin B$_{12}$ Levels Serum and urinary methylmalonic acid are elevated in vitamin B$_{12}$ deficiency, but not in folate deficiency. Thus this measure is useful in distinguishing between the two. Vitamin B$_{12}$ deficiency usually arises from malabsorption. To determine whether malabsorption is the cause, a small oral dose of vitamin B$_{12}$ is given, and urinary excretion is measured. This procedure measures vitamin B$_{12}$ absorption and is called a Schilling test.

Early stages of vitamin B$_{12}$ deficiency can be detected by a low percentage saturation of its transport protein, a measure similar to iron's transferrin saturation. As the deficiency progresses, serum vitamin B$_{12}$ concentrations fall. Table E-10 shows standards for vitamin B$_{12}$ assessment.

Cautions about Nutrition Assessment

To give all the details of nutrition assessment procedures would entail writing another textbook. Nevertheless, any student of nutrition should know the basics of a proper nutrition assessment procedure for two reasons.

TABLE E-10	Criteria for Assessing Folate and Vitamin B$_{12}$		
	Deficient	Borderline	Acceptable
Serum folate (ng/mL)	<3.0	3.0–5.9	>6.0
Erythrocyte folate (ng/mL)	<140	140–159	>160
Serum vitamin B$_{12}$ (pg/mL)	<150	150–200	≥201
Serum methylmalonic acid (nmol/L)	<376	—	—

NOTE: A nanogram (ng) is one-billionth of a gram; a picogram (pg) is one-trillionth of a gram.

First, competent medical care includes attention to nutrition. Physicians should either employ a person skilled in nutrition assessment techniques or refer all clients to such a person to ensure the sound nutrition health of their clients. Health care facilities should make nutrition assessment a routine part of the initial workup on every client so that poor nutrition will not hinder the response to medical treatment and the recovery from illness.

Second, because nutrition is such a popular subject today, fraudulent practices are even more abundant than they have been in the past (and they have always been rampant). The knowledgeable consumer needs to know what procedures to expect in a nutrition assessment and what kinds of information they yield. This appendix has presented the basics of nutrition assessment for these reasons.

This caution is added: the tests outlined here yield information that becomes meaningful only when integrated into a whole picture by a skilled, experienced, and educated interpreter. Potential sources of error are many, from the taking of the initial data to their reporting and analysis. Each assessment method and measure is useful only as a part of the whole to confirm or eliminate the possibility of suspected nutrition problems. For example, the assessor must constantly remember that a sufficient intake of a nutrient does not guarantee adequate nutrient status for an individual. Conversely, the apparent inadequate intake of a nutrient does not, by itself, establish that a deficiency exists.

Similarly, many uncertainties, such as the calibration of the equipment, the skills of the measurer, and the perspective of the interpreter, limit the accuracy and value of anthropometric measures. This is also true of the results of the physical examination. Physical signs suggestive of malnutrition are nonspecific: they can reflect nutrient deficiencies or may be totally unrelated to nutrition. Assessors must interpret physical findings in light of other assessment findings. Finally, the usefulness of biochemical tests is also limited; the assessor must use caution in interpreting results. Vitamin and mineral blood concentrations may reflect disease processes, abnormal hormone levels, or other aberrations rather than dietary intake. Even if concentrations do reflect dietary intake, they may reflect what the person has been eating recently and not give a true picture of the person's nutrient status. Such complications sometimes make it difficult to detect a subclinical deficiency. Furthermore, many nutrients interact. The assessor has to keep in mind that an abnormal lab value for one nutrient may reflect abnormal status of other nutrients. The final diagnosis is therefore appropriately tentative, and its confirmation comes only after careful remedial steps successfully alleviate the observed problems.

REFERENCES

1. V. A. Hughes and coauthors, Anthropometric assessment of 10–y changes in body composition in the elderly, *American Journal of Clinical Nutrition* 80 (2004): 475–482.
2. G. Sun and coauthors, Comparison of multifrequency bioelectrical impedance analysis with dual-energy X-ray absorptiometry for assessment of percentage body fat in a large, healthy population, *American Journal of Clinical Nutrition* 81 (2005): 74–78.

Physical Activity and Energy Requirements

CONTENTS
Calculating Physical Activity Level
Estimating Physical Activity Level
Using a Shortcut to Estimate Total Energy Expenditure

Chapter 8 described how to calculate estimated energy requirements (EER) for adults by using an equation that accounts for gender, age, weight, height, and physical activity level. Table F-1 presents additional equations to determine the EER for infants, children, adolescents, and pregnant and lactating women.

This appendix helps you determine the correct physical activity (PA) factor to use in the equations, either by calculating the physical activity level or by estimating it. For those who prefer to bypass these steps, the appendix presents tables that provide a shortcut to estimating total energy expenditure.*

Calculating Physical Activity Level

To calculate your physical activity level, record all of your activities for a typical 24-hour day, noting the type of activity, the level of intensity, and the duration. Then, using a copy of Table F-2, find your activity in the first column (or an activity that is reasonably similar) and multiply the number of minutes spent on that activity by the factor in the third column. Put your answer in the last column and total the accumulated values for the day. Now add the subtotal of the last column to 1.1 (to account for basal energy and the thermic effect of food) as shown. This score indicates your physical activity level. Using Table F-3, find the PA factor for your age and gender that correlates with your physical activity level and use it in the energy equations presented in Table F-1.

Estimating Physical Activity Level

As an alternative to recording your activities for a day, you can use the third column of Table F-3 to decide if your daily activity is sedentary, low active, active, or very active. Find the PA factor for your age and gender that correlates with your typical physical activity level and use it in the energy equations presented in Table F-1.

Using a Shortcut to Estimate Total Energy Expenditure

The DRI Committee has developed estimates of total energy expenditure based on the equations for adults presented in Table F-1. These estimates are presented in Table F-4 for women and Table F-5 for men. You can use these tables to estimate your energy requirement—that is, the number of kcalories needed to maintain your current body weight. On the table appropriate for your gender, find your height in meters (or inches) in the left-hand column. Then follow the row across to find your weight in kilograms (or pounds). (If you can't find your exact height and weight, choose a value between the two closest ones.) Look down the column to find the number of kcalories that corresponds to your activity level.

Importantly, the values given in the tables are for 30-year-old people. Women 19 to 29 should add 7 kcalories per day for each year below age 30; older women should subtract 7 kcalories per day for each year above age 30. Similarly, men 19 to 29 should add 10 kcalories per day for each year below age 30; older men should subtract 10 kcalories per day for each year above age 30.

*This appendix, including the tables, is adapted from Committee on Dietary Reference Intakes, *Dietary Reference Intakes for Energy, Carbohydrate, Fiber, Fat, Fatty Acids, Cholesterol, Protein, and Amino Acids* (Washington, D.C.: National Academies Press, 2002/2005).

F Appendix

TABLE F-1   Equations to Determine Estimated Energy Requirement (EER)

Infants

0–3 months	EER = (89 × weight − 100) + 175
4–6 months	EER = (89 × weight − 100) + 56
7–12 months	EER = (89 × weight − 100) + 22
13–15 months	EER = (89 × weight − 100) + 20

Children and Adolescents

Boys

3–8 years	EER = 88.5 − (61.9 × age + PA × [(26.7 × weight) + (903 × height)] + 20
9–18 years	EER = 88.5 − (61.9 × age + PA × [(26.7 × weight) + (903 × height)] + 25

Girls

3–8 years	EER = 135.3 − (30.8 × age + PA × [(10.0 × weight) + (934 × height)] + 20
9–18 years	EER = 135.3 − (30.8 × age + PA × [(10.0 × weight) + (934 × height)] + 25

Adults

Men	EER = 662 − (9.53 × age + PA × [(15.91 × weight) + (539.6 × height)]
Women	EER = 354 − (6.91 × age + PA × [(9.36 × weight) + (726 × height)]

Pregnancy

1st trimester	EER = nonpregnant EER + 0
2nd trimester	EER = nonpregnant EER + 340
3rd trimester	EER = nonpregnant EER + 452

Lactation

0–6 months postpartum	EER = nonpregnant EER + 500 − 170
7–12 months postpartum	EER = nonpregnant EER + 400 − 0

NOTE: Select the appropriate equation for gender and age and insert weight in kilograms, height in meters, and age in years. See the text and Table F-3 to determine PA.

TABLE F-2   Physical Activities and Their Scores

If your activity was equivalent to this ...	Then list the number of minutes here and ...	Multiply by this factor ...	Add this column to get your physical activity level score:
Activities of Daily Living			
Gardening (no lifting)		0.0032	
Household tasks (moderate effort)		0.0024	
Lifting items continuously		0.0029	
Loading/unloading car		0.0019	
Lying quietly		0.0000	
Mopping		0.0024	
Mowing lawn (power mower)		0.0033	
Raking lawn		0.0029	
Riding in a vehicle		0.0000	
Sitting (idle)		0.0000	
Sitting (doing light activity)		0.0005	
Taking out trash		0.0019	
Vacuuming		0.0024	
Walking the dog		0.0019	
Walking from house to car or bus		0.0014	
Watering plants		0.0014	
Additional Activities			
Billiards		0.0013	
Calisthenics (no weight)		0.0029	
Canoeing (leisurely)		0.0014	
Chopping wood		0.0037	

continued

TABLE F-2	Physical Activities and Their Scores—continued		
If your activity was equivalent to this …	**Then list the number of minutes here and …**	**Multiply by this factor …**	**Add this column to get your physical activity level score:**
Additional Activities *continued*			
Climbing hills (carrying 11 lb load)		0.0061	
Climbing hills (no load)		0.0056	
Cycling (leisurely)		0.0024	
Cycling (moderately)		0.0045	
Dancing (aerobic or ballet)		0.0048	
Dancing (ballroom, leisurely)		0.0018	
Dancing (fast ballroom or square)		0.0043	
Golf (with cart)		0.0014	
Golf (without cart)		0.0032	
Horseback riding (walking)		0.0012	
Horseback riding (trotting)		0.0053	
Jogging (6 mph)		0.0088	
Music (playing accordion)		0.0008	
Music (playing cello)		0.0012	
Music (playing flute)		0.0010	
Music (playing piano)		0.0012	
Music (playing violin)		0.0014	
Rope skipping		0.0105	
Skating (ice)		0.0043	
Skating (roller)		0.0052	
Skiing (water or downhill)		0.0055	
Squash		0.0106	
Surfing		0.0048	
Swimming (slow)		0.0033	
Swimming (fast)		0.0057	
Tennis (doubles)		0.0038	
Tennis (singles)		0.0057	
Volleyball (noncompetitive)		0.0018	
Walking (2 mph)		0.0014	
Walking (3 mph)		0.0022	
Walking (4 mph)		0.0033	
Walking (5 mph)		0.0067	
Subtotal			
Factor for basal energy and the thermic effect of food			1.1
Your physical activity level score			

TABLE F-3	Physical Activity Equivalents and Their PA Factors					
Physical Activity Level	**Description**	**Physical Activity Equivalents**	**Men, 19+ yr PA Factor**	**Women, 19+ yr PA FActor**	**Boys, 3–18 yr PA Factor**	**Girls, 3–18 yr PA Factor**
1.0 to 1.39	Sedentary	Only those physical activities required for typical daily living	1.0	1.0	1.0	1.0
1.4 to 1.59	Low active	Daily living + 30–60 min moderate activity[a]	1.11	1.12	1.13	1.16
1.6 to 1.89	Active	Daily living + ≥ 60 min moderate activity	1.25	1.27	1.26	1.31
1.9 and above	Very active	Daily living + ≥ 60 min moderate activity *and* ≥ 60 min vigorous activity *or* ≥ 120 min moderate activity	1.48	1.45	1.42	1.56

[a]Moderate activity is equivalent to walking at a pace of 3 to 4^1/2 mph.

TABLE F-4 Total Energy Expenditure (TEE in kCalories per Day) for Women 30 Years of Age[a] at Various Levels of Activity and Various Heights and Weights

Heights m (in)	Physical Activity Level	Weight[b] kg (lb)					
1.45 (57)		38.9 (86)	45.2 (100)	52.6 (116)	63.1 (139)	73.6 (162)	84.1 (185)
		kCalories					
	Sedentary	1564	1623	1698	1813	1927	2042
	Low active	1734	1800	1912	2043	2174	2304
	Active	1946	2021	2112	2257	2403	2548
	Very active	2201	2287	2387	2553	2719	2886
1.50 (59)		41.6 (92)	48.4 (107)	56.3 (124)	67.5 (149)	78.8 (174)	90.0 (198)
		kCalories					
	Sedentary	1625	1689	1771	1894	2017	2139
	Low active	1803	1874	1996	2136	2276	2415
	Active	2025	2105	2205	2360	2516	2672
	Very active	2291	2382	2493	2671	2849	3027
1.55 (61)		44.4 (98)	51.7 (114)	60.1 (132)	72.1 (159)	84.1 (185)	96.1 (212)
		kCalories					
	Sedentary	1688	1756	1846	1977	2108	2239
	Low active	1873	1949	2081	2230	2380	2529
	Active	2104	2190	2299	2466	2632	2798
	Very active	2382	2480	2601	2791	2981	3171
1.60 (63)		47.4 (104)	55.0 (121)	64.0 (141)	76.8 (169)	89.6 (197)	102.4 (226)
		kCalories					
	Sedentary	1752	1824	1922	2061	2201	2340
	Low active	1944	2025	2168	2327	2486	2645
	Active	2185	2276	2396	2573	2750	2927
	Very active	2474	2578	2712	2914	3116	3318
1.65 (65)		50.4 (111)	58.5 (129)	68.1 (150)	81.7 (180)	95.3 (210)	108.9 (240)
		kCalories					
	Sedentary	1816	1893	1999	2148	2296	2444
	Low active	2016	2102	2556	2425	2594	2763
	Active	2267	2364	2494	2682	2871	3059
	Very active	2567	2678	2824	3039	3254	3469
1.70 (67)		53.5 (118)	62.1 (137)	72.3 (159)	86.7 (191)	101.2 (223)	115.6 (255)
		kCalories					
	Sedentary	1881	1963	2078	2235	2393	2550
	Low active	2090	2180	2345	2525	2705	2884
	Active	2350	2453	2594	2794	2994	3194
	Very active	2662	2780	2938	3166	3395	3623
1.75 (69)		56.7 (125)	65.8 (145)	76.6 (169)	91.9 (202)	107.2 (236)	122.5 (270)
		kCalories					
	Sedentary	1948	2034	2158	2325	2492	2659
	Low active	2164	2260	2437	2627	2817	3007
	Active	2434	2543	2695	2907	3119	3331
	Very active	2758	2883	3054	3296	3538	3780
1.80 (71)		59.9 (132)	69.7 (154)	81.0 (178)	97.2 (214)	113.4 (250)	129.6 (285)
		kCalories					
	Sedentary	2015	2106	2239	2416	2593	2769
	Low active	2239	2341	2529	2731	2932	3133
	Active	2519	2634	2799	3023	3247	3472
	Very active	2855	2987	3172	3428	3684	3940

continued

[a]For each year below 30, add 7 kcalories/day to TEE. For each year above 30, subtract 7 kcalories/day from TEE.
[b]These columns represent a BMI of 18.5, 22.5, 25, 30, 35, and 40, respectively.

| TABLE F-4 | Total Energy Expenditure (TEE in kCalories per Day) for Women 30 Years of Age[a] at Various Levels of Activity and Various Heights and Weights—continued |

Heights m (in)	Physical Activity Level	Weight[b] kg (lb)					
1.85 (73)		63.3 (139)	73.6 (162)	85.6 (189)	102.7 (226)	119.8 (264)	136.9 (302)
				kCalories			
	Sedentary	2083	2179	2322	2509	2695	2882
	Low active	2315	2422	2624	2836	3049	3262
	Active	2605	2727	2904	3141	3378	3615
	Very active	2954	3093	3292	3562	3833	4103
1.90 (75)		66.8 (147)	77.6 (171)	90.3 (199)	108.3 (239)	126.4 (278)	144.4 (318)
				kCalories			
	Sedentary	2151	2253	2406	2603	2800	2996
	Low active	2392	2505	2720	2944	3168	3393
	Active	2693	2821	3011	3261	3511	3760
	Very active	3053	3200	3414	3699	3984	4270
1.95 (77)		70.3 (155)	81.8 (180)	95.1 (209)	114.1 (251)	133.1 (293)	152.1 (335)
				kCalories			
	Sedentary	2221	2328	2492	2699	2906	3113
	Low active	2470	2589	2817	3053	3290	3526
	Active	2781	2917	3119	3383	3646	3909
	Very active	3154	3309	3538	3838	4139	4439

[a]For each year below 30, add 7 kcalories/day to TEE. For each year above 30, subtract 7 kcalories/day from TEE.
[b]These columns represent a BMI of 18.5, 22.5, 25, 30, 35, and 40, respectively.

| TABLE F-5 | Total Energy Expenditure (TEE in kCalories per Day) for Men 30 Years of Age[a] at Various Levels of Activity and Various Heights and Weights |

Heights m (in)	Physical Activity Level	Weight[b] kg (lb)					
1.45 (57)		38.9 (86)	47.3 (100)	52.6 (116)	63.1 (139)	73.6 (163)	84.1 (185)
				kCalories			
	Sedentary	1777	1911	2048	2198	2347	2496
	Low active	1931	2080	2225	2393	2560	2727
	Active	2127	2295	2447	2636	2826	3015
	Very active	2450	2648	2845	3075	3305	3535
1.50 (59)		41.6 (92)	50.6 (107)	56.3 (124)	67.5 (149)	78.8 (174)	90.0 (198)
				kCalories			
	Sedentary	1848	1991	2126	2286	2445	2605
	Low active	2009	2168	2312	2491	2670	2849
	Active	2215	2394	2545	2748	2951	3154
	Very active	2554	2766	2965	3211	3457	3703
1.55 (61)		44.4 (98)	54.1 (114)	60.1 (132)	72.1 (159)	84.1 (185)	96.1 (212)
				kCalories			
	Sedentary	1919	2072	2205	2376	2546	2717
	Low active	2089	2259	2401	2592	2783	2974
	Active	2305	2496	2646	2862	3079	3296
	Very active	2660	2887	3087	3349	3612	3875

continued

[a]For each year below 30, add 10 kcalories/day to TEE. For each year above 30, subtract 10 kcalories/day from TEE.
[b]These columns represent a BMI of 18.5, 22.5, 25, 30, 35, and 40, respectively.

F Appendix

TABLE F-5 Total Energy Expenditure (TEE in kCalories per Day) for Men 30 Years of Age[a] at Various Levels of Activity and Various Heights and Weights—continued

Heights m (in)	Physical Activity Level	Weight[b] kg (lb)					
1.60 (63)		47.4 (104)	57.6 (121)	64.0 (141)	76.8 (169)	89.6 (197)	102.4 (226)
				kCalories			
	Sedentary	1993	2156	2286	2468	2650	2831
	Low active	2171	2351	2492	2695	2899	3102
	Active	2397	2601	2749	2980	3210	3441
	Very active	2769	3010	3211	3491	3771	4051
1.65 (65)		50.4 (111)	61.3 (129)	68.1 (150)	81.7 (180)	95.3 (210)	108.9 (240)
				kCalories			
	Sedentary	2068	2241	2369	2562	2756	2949
	Low active	2254	2446	2585	2801	3017	3234
	Active	2490	2707	2854	3099	3345	3590
	Very active	2880	3136	3339	3637	3934	4232
1.70 (67)		53.5 (118)	65.0 (137)	72.3 (159)	86.7 (191)	101.2 (223)	115.6 (255)
				kCalories			
	Sedentary	2144	2328	2454	2659	2864	3069
	Low active	2338	2542	2679	2909	3139	3369
	Active	2586	2816	2961	3222	3483	3743
	Very active	2992	3265	3469	3785	4101	4417
1.75 (69)		56.7 (125)	68.9 (145)	76.6 (169)	91.9 (202)	107.2 (236)	122.5 (270)
				kCalories			
	Sedentary	2222	2416	2540	2757	2975	3192
	Low active	2425	2641	2776	3020	3263	3507
	Active	2683	2927	3071	3347	3623	3900
	Very active	3108	3396	3602	3937	4272	4607
1.80 (71)		59.9 (132)	72.9 (154)	81.0 (178)	97.2 (214)	113.4 (250)	129.6 (285)
				kCalories			
	Sedentary	2301	2507	2628	2858	3088	3318
	Low active	2513	2741	2875	3132	3390	3648
	Active	2782	3040	3183	3475	3767	4060
	Very active	3225	3530	3738	4092	4447	4801
1.85 (73)		63.3 (139)	77.0 (162)	85.6 (189)	102.7 (226)	119.8 (264)	136.9 (302)
				kCalories			
	Sedentary	2382	2599	2718	2961	3204	3447
	Low active	2602	2844	2976	3248	3520	3792
	Active	2883	3155	3297	3606	3915	4223
	Very active	3344	3667	3877	4251	4625	4999
1.90 (75)		66.8 (147)	81.2 (171)	90.3 (199)	108.3 (239)	126.4 (278)	144.4 (318)
				kCalories			
	Sedentary	2464	2693	2810	3066	3322	3579
	Low active	2693	2948	3078	3365	3652	3939
	Active	2986	3273	3414	3739	4065	4390
	Very active	3466	3806	4018	4413	4807	5202
1.95 (77)		70.3 (155)	85.6 (180)	95.1 (209)	114.1 (251)	133.1 (293)	152.1 (335)
				kCalories			
	Sedentary	2547	2789	2903	3173	3443	3713
	Low active	2786	3055	3183	3485	3788	4090
	Active	3090	3393	3533	3875	4218	4561
	Very active	3590	3948	4162	4578	4993	5409

[a]For each year below 30, add 10 kcalories/day to TEE. For each year above 30, subtract 10 kcalories/day from TEE.
[b]These columns represent a BMI of 18.5, 22.5, 25, 30, 35, and 40, respectively.

United States: Exchange Lists

Chapter 2 introduced the exchange system, and this appendix provides details from the 2003 edition. Appendix I presents Canada's meal planning system.

The Exchange Groups and Lists

The exchange system sorts foods into three main groups by their proportions of carbohydrate, fat, and protein. These three groups—the carbohydrate group, the fat group, and the meat and meat substitutes group (protein)—organize foods into several exchange lists (see Table G-1). Then any food on a list can be "exchanged" for any other on that same list. The carbohydrate group covers these exchange lists:

- Starch (cereals, grains, pasta, breads, crackers, snacks, starchy vegetables, and dried beans, peas, and lentils)
- Fruit
- Milk (fat-free, reduced fat, and whole)
- Other carbohydrates (desserts and snacks with added sugars and fats)
- Vegetables

The fat group covers this exchange list:

- Fats

The meat and meat substitutes group (protein) covers these exchange lists:

- Meat and meat substitutes (very lean, lean, medium-fat, and high-fat)

CONTENTS

The Exchange Groups and Lists
Combining Food Group Plans and Exchange Lists

TABLE G-1 The Exchange Groups and Lists

Group/Lists	Typical Item/Portion Size	Carbohydrate (g)	Protein (g)	Fat (g)	Energy[a] (kcal)
Carbohydrate Group					
Starch[b]	1 slice bread	15	3	0–1	80
Fruit	1 small apple	15	—	—	60
Milk					
Fat-free, low-fat	1 c fat-free milk	12	8	0–3	90
Reduced-fat	1 c reduced-fat milk	12	8	5	120
Whole	1 c whole milk	12	8	8	150
Other carbohydrates[c]	2 small cookies	15	varies	varies	varies
Vegetable (nonstarchy)	½ c cooked carrots	5	2	—	25
Meat and Meat Substitute Group [d]					
Meat					
Very lean	1 oz chicken (white meat, no skin)	—	7	0–1	35
Lean	1 oz lean beef	—	7	3	55
Medium-fat	1 oz ground beef	—	7	5	75
High-fat	1 oz pork sausage	—	7	8	100
Fat Group					
Fat	1 tsp butter	—	—	5	45

[a]The energy value for each exchange list represents an approximate average for the group and does not reflect the precise number of grams of carbohydrate, protein, and fat. For example, a slice of bread contains 15 grams of carbohydrate (that's 60 kcalories), 3 grams protein (that's another 12 kcalories), and a little fat—rounded to 80 kcalories for ease in calculating. A half-cup of vegetables (not including starchy vegetables) contains 5 grams carbohydrate (20 kcalories) and 2 grams protein (8 more), which has been rounded down to 25 kcalories.
[b]The starch list includes cereals, grains, breads, crackers, snacks, starchy vegetables (such as corn, peas, and potatoes), and legumes (dried beans, peas, and lentils).
[c]The other carbohydrates list includes foods that contain added sugars and fats such as cakes, cookies, doughnuts, ice cream, potato chips, pudding, syrup, and frozen yogurt.
[d]The meat and meat substitutes list includes legumes, cheeses, and peanut butter.

FIGURE G-1 Seeing Exchanges on a Food Label

Knowing that foods on the starch list provide 15 grams of carbohydrate and those on the vegetable list provide 5, you can count a lasagna dinner that provides 37 grams of carbohydrate as "2 starches and 1 vegetable"; knowing that foods on the meat list provide 7 grams of protein, you might count it as "3 meats"; the grams of fat suggest that the meat (and cheese) is probably medium-fat.

HOME TASTE
Lasagna Dinner
WITH MEAT SAUCE

Nutrition Facts
Serving size 10½ oz (298 g)
Servings per Package 1

Amount per serving

Calories 361	Calories from Fat 117

	% Daily Value
Total Fat 13 g	20%
Saturated Fat 8 g	40%
Cholesterol 87 mg	29%
Sodium 860 mg	36%
Total Carbohydrate 37 g	12%
Dietary fiber 0 g	
Sugars 8 g	
Protein 26 g	

Can you "see" these exchanges in the label above?

Exchange	Carbohydrate	Protein	Fat
2 starches	30 g	6 g	—
1 vegetable	5 g	2 g	—
3 medium-fat meats	—	21 g	15 g
Exchange totals	35	29	15
Label totals	37	26	13

Portion Sizes

The exchange system helps people control their energy intakes by paying close attention to portion sizes. The portion sizes have been carefully adjusted and defined so that a portion of any food on a given list provides roughly the same amount of carbohydrate, fat, and protein and, therefore, total kcalories. Any food on a list can then be exchanged, or traded, for any other food on that same list without significantly affecting the diet's balance or total kcalories. For example, a person may select either 17 small grapes or ½ large grapefruit as one fruit exchange, and either choice would provide roughly 60 kcalories. A whole grapefruit, however, would count as 2 exchanges.

To apply the system successfully, users must become familiar with portion sizes. A convenient way to remember the portion sizes and energy values is to keep in mind a typical item from each list (review Table G-1).

The Foods on the Lists

Foods do not always appear on the exchange list where you might first expect to find them. They are grouped according to their energy-nutrient contents rather than by their source (such as milks), their outward appearance, or their vitamin and mineral contents. Notice, for example, that cheeses are grouped with meats (not milk) because, like meats, cheeses contribute energy from protein and fat but provide negligible carbohydrate. Similarly, starchy vegetables such as potatoes are found on the starch list with breads and cereals, not with the vegetables, and bacon is with the fats and oils, not with the meats.

Diet planners learn to view mixtures of foods, such as casseroles and soups, as combinations of foods from different exchange lists. They also learn to interpret food labels with the exchange system in mind (see Figure G-1).

Controlling Energy and Fat

By assigning items like bacon to the fat list, the exchange system alerts consumers to foods that are unexpectedly high in fat. Even the starch list specifies which grain products contain added fat (such as biscuits, muffins, and waffles). In addition, the exchange system encourages users to think of fat-free milk as milk and of whole milk as milk with added fat, and to think of very lean meats as meats and of lean, medium-fat, and high-fat meats as meats with added fat. To that end, foods on the milk and meat lists are separated into categories based on their fat contents. The milk group is classed as fat-free, reduced-fat, and whole; the meat group as very lean, lean, medium-fat, and high-fat.

Control of food energy and fat intake can be highly successful with the exchange system. Exchange plans do not, however, guarantee adequate intakes of vitamins and minerals. Food group plans work better from that standpoint because the food groupings are based on similarities in vitamin-mineral content. In the exchange system, for example, meats are grouped with cheeses, yet the meats are iron-rich and calcium-poor, whereas the cheeses are iron-poor and calcium-rich. To take advantage of the strengths of both food group plans and exchange patterns, and to compensate for their weaknesses, diet planners often combine these two diet-planning tools.

Combining Food Group Plans and Exchange Lists

A person may find that using a food group plan together with the exchange lists eases the task of choosing foods that provide all the nutrients. The food group plan ensures that all classes of nutritious foods are included, thus promoting adequacy, balance, and variety. The exchange system classifies the food selections by their energy-yielding nutrients, thus controlling energy and fat intakes.

TABLE G-2 Diet Planning with the Exchange System Using the USDA Food Guide Pattern

2000-kCalorie Diet Plan Using USDA Food Guide	Selections Made Using the Exchange System	Energy (kcal)
Grains (breads and cereals)— 6 oz	Starch list—select 6 exchanges	480
Vegetables—2$\frac{1}{2}$ c	Vegetable list—select 5 exchanges	125
Fruits—2 c	Fruit list—select 4 exchanges	240
Meat—5$\frac{1}{2}$ oz	Meat list—select 5$\frac{1}{2}$ lean exchanges	300
Milk—3 c	Milk list—select 3 fat-free exchanges	270
Oils—6 tsp	Fat list—select 6 exchanges	270
Discretionary kcalories	—	267
Total		1955

Table G-2 shows how to use the USDA Food Guide plan together with the exchange lists to plan a diet. The USDA Food Guide ensures that a certain number of servings is chosen from each of the food groups (see the first column of the table). The second column translates the food groups into exchanges. With the addition of a few discretionary kcalories, this sample diet plan provides abut 1955 kcalories. Most people can meet their needs for all the nutrients within this reasonable energy allowance. The next step in diet planning is to assign the exchanges to meals and snacks. The final plan might look like the one in Table G-3.

Next, a person could begin to fill in the plan with real foods to create a menu (use Tables G-4 through G-12). For example, the breakfast plan calls for 1 starch exchange, 2 fruit exchanges, and 1 fat-free milk exchange. A person might select a bowl of shredded wheat with banana slices and milk and a small glass of orange juice:

¾ cup unsweetened, ready-to-eat cereal = 1 starch exchange

1 small banana = 1 fruit exchange

1 cup fat-free milk = 1 milk exchange

½ cup orange juice = 1 fruit exchange

Or half an English muffin and a bowl of fruit topped with yogurt:

½ English muffin = 1 starch exchange

⅓ cantaloupe melon = 1 fruit exchange

1¼ cup strawberries = 1 fruit exchange

⅔ cup fat-free plain yogurt = 1 milk exchange

TABLE G-3 A Sample Diet Plan and Menu

This diet plan is one of many possibilities. It follows the number of servings suggested by the Daily Food Guide and meets dietary recommendations to provide 45 to 65 percent of its kcalories from carbohydrate, 10 to 35 percent from protein, and 20 to 35 percent from fat.

Exchange	Breakfast	Lunch	Snack	Dinner	Snack
6 starch	1	2		2	1
5 vegetables				5	
4 fruit	2	1	1		
5$\frac{1}{2}$ lean meat		2		3$\frac{1}{2}$	
3 fat-free milk	1	1			1
6 fat		1		5	

❋ SAMPLE MENU ❋

Breakfast:	Cereal with banana and milk, orange juice
Lunch:	Turkey sandwich, milk, small bunch of grapes
Snack:	Apple
Dinner:	Spaghetti with meat sauce; salad with sunflower seeds and dressing; green beans; corn on the cob
Snack:	Graham crackers and milk

G Appendix

Then the person could move on to complete the menu for lunch, dinner, and snacks. (Table G-3 includes a sample menu.) As you can see, we all make countless food-related decisions daily—whether we have a plan or not. Following a plan, like the USDA Food Guide, that incorporates health recommendations and diet-planning principles helps a person to make wise decisions.

TABLE G-4 U.S. Exchange System: Starch List

1 starch exchange = 15 g carbohydrate, 3 g protein, 0–1 g fat, and 80 kcal
NOTE: In general, one starch exchange is ½ c cooked cereal, grain, or starchy vegetable; ⅓ c cooked rice or pasta; 1 oz of bread; ¾ to 1 oz snack food.

Serving Size	Food
Bread	
¼ (1 oz)	Bagel, 4 oz
2 slices (1½ oz)	Bread, reduced-kcalorie
1 slice (1 oz)	Bread, white (including French and Italian), whole-wheat, pumpernickel, rye
4 (⅔ oz)	Bread sticks, crisp, 4" x ½"
½	English muffin
½ (1 oz)	Hot dog or hamburger bun
¼	Naan, 8" x 2"
1	Pancake, 4" across, ¼"thick
½	Pita, 6" across
1 (1 oz)	Plain roll, small
1 slice (1 oz)	Raisin bread, unfrosted
1	Tortilla, corn, 6" across
1	Tortilla, flour, 6" across
⅓	Tortilla, flour, 10" across
1	Waffle, 4" square or across, reduced-fat
Cereals and Grains	
½ c	Bran cereals
½ c	Bulgur, cooked
½ c	Cereals, cooked
¾ c	Cereals, unsweetened, ready-to-eat
3 tbs	Cornmeal (dry)
⅓ c	Couscous
3 tbs	Flour (dry)
¼ c	Granola, low-fat
¼ c	Grape nuts
½ c	Grits, cooked
½ c	Kasha
⅓ c	Millet
¼ c	Muesli
½ c	Oats
⅓ c	Pasta, cooked
1½ c	Puffed cereals
⅓ c	Rice, white or brown, cooked
½ c	Shredded wheat
½ c	Sugar-frosted cereal
3 tbs	Wheat germ
Starchy Vegetables	
⅓ c	Baked beans
½ c	Corn
½ cob (5 oz)	Corn on cob, large
1 c	Mixed vegetables with corn, peas, or pasta

Serving Size	Food
½ c	Peas, green
½ c	Plantains
½ medium (3 oz) or ½ c	Potato, boiled
¼ large (3 oz)	Potato, baked with skin
½ c	Potatoes, mashed
1 c	Squash, winter (acorn, butternut, pumpkin)
½ c	Yams, sweet potatoes, plain
Crackers and Snacks	
8	Animal crackers
3	Graham crackers, 2½" square
¾ oz	Matzoh
4 slices	Melba toast
24	Oyster crackers
3 c	Popcorn (popped, no fat added or low-fat microwave)
¾ oz	Pretzels
2	Rice cakes, 4" across
6	Saltine-type crackers
15–20 (¾ oz)	Snack chips, fat-free or baked (tortilla, potato)
2–5 (¾ oz)	Whole-wheat crackers, no fat added
Beans, Peas, and Lentils (count as 1 starch + 1 very lean meat)	
½ c	Beans and peas, cooked (garbanzo, lentils, pinto, kidney, white, split, black-eyed)
⅔ c	Lima beans
3 tbs	Miso 🖉
Starchy Foods Prepared with Fat (count as 1 starch + 1 fat)	
1	Biscuit, 2½" across
½ c	Chow mein noodles
1 (2 oz)	Cornbread, 2" cube
6	Crackers, round butter type
1 c	Croutons
1 c (2 oz)	French-fried potatoes (oven baked)
¼ c	Granola
⅓ c	Hummus
⅛ (1 oz)	Muffin, 5 oz
3 c	Popcorn, microwave
3	Sandwich crackers, cheese or peanut butter filling
9–13 (¾ oz)	Snack chips (potato, tortilla)
⅓ c	Stuffing, bread (prepared)
2	Taco shells, 6" across
1	Waffle, 4½" square or across
4–6 (1 oz)	Whole-wheat crackers, fat added

🖉 = 400 mg or more of sodium per serving.

TABLE G-5 U.S. Exchange System: Fruit List

1 fruit exchange = 15 g carbohydrate and 60 kcal
NOTE: In general, one fruit exchange is 1 small fresh fruit; ½ c canned or fresh fruit or unsweetened fruit juice; ¼ c dried fruit.

Serving Size	Food
1 (4 oz)	Apple, unpeeled, small
½ c	Applesauce, unsweetened
4 rings	Apples, dried
4 whole (5½ oz)	Apricots, fresh
8 halves	Apricots, dried
½ c	Apricots, canned
1 (4 oz)	Banana, small
¾ c	Blackberries
¾ c	Blueberries
⅓ melon (11 oz) or 1 c cubes	Cantaloupe, small
12 (3 oz)	Cherries, sweet, fresh
½ c	Cherries, sweet, canned
3	Dates
1½ large or 2 medium (3½ oz)	Figs, fresh
1½	Figs, dried
½ c	Fruit cocktail
½ (11 oz)	Grapefruit, large
¾ c	Grapefruit sections, canned
17 (3 oz)	Grapes, small
1 slice (10 oz) or 1 c cubes	Honeydew melon
1 (3½ oz)	Kiwi
¾ c	Mandarin oranges, canned
½ (5½ oz) or ½ c	Mango, small
1 (5 oz)	Nectarine, small
1 (6½ oz)	Orange, small

Serving Size	Food
½ (8 oz) or 1 c cubes	Papaya
1 (4 oz)	Peach, medium, fresh
½ c	Peaches, canned
½ (4 oz)	Pear, large, fresh
½ c	Pears, canned
¾ c	Pineapple, fresh
½ c	Pineapple, canned
2 (5 oz)	Plums, small
½ c	Plums, canned
3	Plums, dried (prunes)
2 tbs	Raisins
1 c	Raspberries
1¼ c whole berries	Strawberries
2 (8 oz)	Tangerines, small
1 slice (13½ oz) or 1¼ c cubes	Watermelon

Fruit Juice, unsweetened

Serving Size	Food
½ c	Apple juice/cider
⅓ c	Cranberry juice cocktail
1 c	Cranberry juice cocktail, reduced-kcalorie
⅓ c	Fruit juice blends, 100% juice
⅓ c	Grape juice
½ c	Grapefruit juice
½ c	Orange juice
½ c	Pineapple juice
⅓ c	Prune juice

TABLE G-6 U.S. Exchange System: Milk List

NOTE: In general, one milk exchange is 1 c milk or yogurt.

Serving Size	Food
Fat-Free and Low-Fat Milk	
1 fat-free/low-fat milk exchange = 12 g carbohydrate, 8 g protein, 0–3 g fat, 90 kcal	
1 c	Fat-free milk
1 c	½% milk
1 c	1% milk
1 c	Fat-free or low-fat buttermilk
½ c	Evaporated fat-free milk
⅓ c dry	Fat-free dry milk
1 c	Soy milk, low-fat or fat-free
⅔ c (6 oz)	Yogurt, fat-free or low-fat, flavored, sweetened with nonnutritive sweetener and fructose
⅔ c (6 oz)	Yogurt, plain fat-free

Serving Size	Food
Reduced-Fat Milk	
1 reduced-fat milk exchange = 12 g carbohydrate, 8 g protein, 5 g fat, 120 kcal	
1 c	2% milk
1 c	Soy milk
1 c	Sweet acidophilus milk
¾ c	Yogurt, plain low-fat
Whole Milk	
1 whole milk exchange = 12 g carbohydrate, 8 g protein, 8 g fat, 150 kcal	
1 c	Whole milk
½ c	Evaporated whole milk
1 c	Goat's milk
1 c	Kefir
¾ c	Yogurt, plain (made from whole milk)

TABLE G-7 U.S. Exchange System: Sweets, Desserts, and Other Carbohydrates List

1 other carbohydrate exchange = 15 g carbohydrate, or 1 starch, or 1 fruit, or 1 milk exchange

Food	Serving Size	Exchanges per Serving
Angel food cake, unfrosted	1/12 cake (2 oz)	2 carbohydrates
Brownies, small, unfrosted	2″ square (1 oz)	1 carbohydrate, 1 fat
Cake, unfrosted	2″ square (1 oz)	1 carbohydrate, 1 fat
Cake, frosted	2″ square (2 oz)	2 carbohydrates, 1 fat
Cookies or sandwich cookies with creme filling	2 small (⅔ oz)	1 carbohydrate, 1 fat
Cookies, sugar-free	3 small or 1 large (¾–1 oz)	1 carbohydrate, 1–2 fats
Cranberry sauce, jellied	¼ c	1½ carbohydrates
Cupcake, frosted	1 small (2 oz)	2 carbohydrates, 1 fat
Doughnut, plain cake	1 medium (1½ oz)	1½ carbohydrates, 2 fats
Doughnut, glazed	3¾″ across (2 oz)	2 carbohydrates, 2 fats
Energy, sport, or breakfast bar	1 bar (1⅓ oz)	1½ carbohydrates, 0–1 fat
Energy, sport, or breakfast bar	1 bar (2 oz)	2 carbohydrates, 1 fat
Fruit cobbler	½ c (3½ oz)	3 carbohydrates, 1 fat
Fruit juice bar, frozen, 100% juice	1 bar (3 oz)	1 carbohydrate
Fruit snacks, chewy (pureed fruit concentrate)	1 roll (¾ oz)	1 carbohydrate
Fruit spreads, 100% fruit	1½ tbs	1 carbohydrate
Gelatin, regular	½ c	1 carbohydrate
Gingersnaps	3	1 carbohydrate
Granola or snack bar, regular or low-fat	1 bar (1 oz)	1½ carbohydrates
Honey	1 tbs	1 carbohydrate
Ice cream	½ c	1 carbohydrate, 2 fats
Ice cream, light	½ c	1 carbohydrate, 1 fat
Ice cream, low-fat	½ c	1½ carbohydrates
Ice cream, fat-free, no sugar added	½ c	1 carbohydrate
Jam or jelly, regular	1 tbs	1 carbohydrate
Milk, chocolate, whole	1 c	2 carbohydrates, 1 fat
Pie, fruit, 2 crusts	⅙ of 8″ commercially prepared pie	3 carbohydrates, 2 fats
Pie, pumpkin or custard	⅛ of 8″ commercially prepared pie	2 carbohydrates, 2 fats
Pudding, regular (made with reduced-fat milk)	½ c	2 carbohydrates
Pudding, sugar-free (made with fat-free milk)	½ c	1 carbohydrate
Reduced-calorie meal replacement (shake)	1 can (10–11 oz)	1½ carbohydrates, 0–1 fats
Rice milk, low-fat or fat-free, plain	1 c	1 carbohydrate
Rice milk, low-fat, flavored	1 c	1½ carbohydrates
Salad dressing, fat-free	¼ c	1 carbohydrate
Sherbet, sorbet	½ c	2 carbohydrates
Spaghetti or pasta sauce, canned	½ c	1 carbohydrate, 1 fat
Sports drinks	8 oz (1 c)	1 carbohydrate
Sugar	1 tbs	1 carbohydrate
Sweet roll or danish	1 (2½ oz)	2½ carbohydrates, 2 fats
Syrup, light	2 tbs	1 carbohydrate
Syrup, regular	1 tbs	1 carbohydrate
Syrup, regular	¼ c	4 carbohydrates
Vanilla wafers	5	1 carbohydrate, 1 fat
Yogurt, frozen	½ c	1 carbohydrate, 0–1 fat
Yogurt, frozen, fat-free	⅓ c	1 carbohydrate
Yogurt, low-fat with fruit	1 c	3 carbohydrates, 0–1 fat

= 400 mg or more sodium per exchange.

TABLE G-8 U.S. Exchange System: Nonstarchy Vegetable List

1 vegetable exchange = 5 g carbohydrate, 2 g protein, 0 g fat, and 25 kcal
NOTE: In general, one vegetable exchange is ½ c cooked vegetables or vegetable juice; 1 c raw vegetables. Starchy vegetables such as corn, peas, and potatoes are on the starch list (Table G-4).

Artichokes	Mushrooms
Artichoke hearts	Okra
Asparagus	Onions
Beans (green, wax, Italian)	Pea pods
Bean sprouts	Peppers (all varieties)
Beets	Radishes
Broccoli	Salad greens (endive, escarole, lettuce, romaine, spinach)
Brussels sprouts	
Cabbage	Sauerkraut
Carrots	Spinach
Cauliflower	Summer squash (crookneck)
Celery	Tomatoes
Cucumbers	Tomatoes, canned
Eggplant	Tomato sauce
Green onions or scallions	Tomato/vegetable juice
Greens (collard, kale, mustard, turnip)	Turnips
Kohlrabi	Water chestnuts
Leeks	Watercress
Mixed vegetables (without corn, peas, or pasta)	Zucchini

 = 400 mg or more sodium per exchange.

TABLE G-9 U.S. Exchange System: Meat and Meat Substitutes List

NOTE: In general, a meat exchange is 1 oz meat, poultry, or cheese; ½ c dried beans (weigh meat and poultry and measure beans after cooking).

Serving Size	Food
Very Lean Meat and Substitutes	
1 very lean meat exchange = 7 g protein, 0–1 g fat, 35 kcal	
1 oz	Poultry: Chicken or turkey (white meat, no skin), Cornish hen (no skin)
1 oz	Fish: Fresh or frozen cod, flounder, haddock, halibut, trout, lox (smoked salmon) ✒; tuna, fresh or canned in water
1 oz	Shellfish: Clams, crab, lobster, scallops, shrimp, imitation shellfish
1 oz	Game: Duck or pheasant (no skin), venison, buffalo, ostrich
	Cheese with ≤1g fat/oz:
¼ c	Fat-free or low-fat cottage cheese
1 oz	Fat-free cheese
1 oz	Processed sandwich meats with ≤1 g fat/oz (such as deli thin, shaved meats, chipped beef ✒, turkey ham)
2	Egg whites
¼ c	Egg substitutes, plain
1 oz	Hot dogs with ≤1 g fat/oz ✒
1 oz	Kidney (high in cholesterol)
1 oz	Sausage with ≤1 g fat/oz
Count as 1 very lean meat + 1 starch exchange:	
½ c	Beans, peas, lentils (cooked)
Lean Meat and Substitutes	
1 lean meat exchange = 7 g protein, 3 g fat, 55 kcal	
1 oz	Beef: USDA Select or Choice grades of lean beef trimmed of fat (round, sirloin, and flank steak); tenderloin; roast (rib, chuck, rump); steak (T-bone, porterhouse, cubed), ground round
1 oz	Pork: Lean pork (fresh ham); canned, cured, or boiled ham; Canadian bacon ✒; tenderloin, center loin chop
1 oz	Lamb: Roast, chop, leg
1 oz	Veal: Lean chop, roast
1 oz	Poultry: Chicken, turkey (dark meat, no skin), chicken (white meat, with skin), domestic duck or goose (well drained of fat, no skin)
	Fish:
1 oz	Herring (uncreamed or smoked)
6 medium	Oysters
1 oz	Salmon (fresh or canned), catfish
2 medium	Sardines (canned)
1 oz	Tuna (canned in oil, drained)
1 oz	Game: Goose (no skin), rabbit
	Cheese:
¼ c	4.5%-fat cottage cheese

Serving Size	Food
2 tbs	Grated Parmesan
1 oz	Cheeses with ≤3 g fat/oz
1½ oz	Hot dogs with ≤3 g fat/oz ✒
1 oz	Processed sandwich meat with ≤3 g fat/oz (turkey pastrami or kielbasa)
1 oz	Liver, heart (high in cholesterol)
Medium-Fat Meat and Substitutes	
1 medium-fat meat exchange = 7 g protein, 5 g fat, and 75 kcal	
1 oz	Beef: Most beef products (ground beef, meatloaf, corned beef, short ribs, Prime grades of meat trimmed of fat, such as prime rib)
1 oz	Pork: Top loin, chop, Boston butt, cutlet
1 oz	Lamb: Rib roast, ground
1 oz	Veal: Cutlet (ground or cubed, unbreaded)
1 oz	Poultry: Chicken (dark meat, with skin), ground turkey or ground chicken, fried chicken (with skin)
1 oz	Fish: Any fried fish product
	Cheese with ≤5 g fat/oz:
1 oz	Feta
1 oz	Mozzarella
¼ c (2 oz)	Ricotta
1	Egg (high in cholesterol, limit to 3/week)
1 oz	Sausage with ≤5 g fat/oz
1 c	Soy milk
¼ c	Tempeh
4 oz or ½ c	Tofu
High-Fat Meat and Substitutes	
1 high-fat meat exchange = 7 g protein, 8 g fat, 100 kcal	
1 oz	Pork: Spareribs, ground pork, pork sausage
1 oz	Cheese: All regular cheeses (American ✒, cheddar, Monterey Jack, swiss)
1 oz	Processed sandwich meats with ≤8 g fat/oz (bologna, pimento loaf, salami)
1 oz	Sausage (bratwurst, Italian, knockwurst, Polish, smoked)
1 (10/lb)	Hot dog (turkey or chicken) ✒
3 slices (20 slices/lb)	Bacon
1 tbs	Peanut butter (contains unsaturated fat)
Count as 1 high-fat meat + 1 fat exchange:	
1 (10/lb)	Hot dog (beef, pork, or combination) ✒

✒ = 400 mg or more of sodium per serving.

TABLE G-10 U.S. Exchange System: Fat List

1 fat exchange = 5 g fat and 45 kcal
NOTE: In general, one fat exchange is 1 tsp regular butter, margarine, or vegetable oil; 1 tbs regular salad dressing. Many fat-free and reduced fat foods are on the Free Foods List (Table G-11).

Serving Size	Food
Monounsaturated Fats	
2 tbs (1 oz)	Avocado
1 tsp	Oil (canola, olive, peanut)
8 large	Olives, ripe (black)
10 large	Olives, green, stuffed 🖊
6 nuts	Almonds, cashews
6 nuts	Mixed nuts (50% peanuts)
10 nuts	Peanuts
4 halves	Pecans
½ tbs	Peanut butter, smooth or crunchy
1 tbs	Sesame seeds
2 tsp	Tahini or sesame paste
Polyunsaturated Fats	
4 halves	English walnuts
1 tsp	Margarine, stick, tub, or squeeze
1 tbs	Margarine, lower-fat spread (30% to 50% vegetable oil)
1 tsp	Mayonnaise, regular
1 tbs	Mayonnaise, reduced-fat
1 tsp	Oil (corn, safflower, soybean)
1 tbs	Salad dressing, regular 🖊
2 tbs	Salad dressing, reduced-fat
2 tsp	Mayonnaise type salad dressing, regular
1 tbs	Mayonnaise type salad dressing, reduced-fat
1 tbs	Seeds (pumpkin, sunflower)
Saturated Fats*	
1 slice (20 slices/lb)	Bacon, cooked
1 tsp	Bacon, grease
1 tsp	Butter, stick
2 tsp	Butter, whipped
1 tbs	Butter, reduced-fat
2 tbs (½ oz)	Chitterlings, boiled
2 tbs	Coconut, sweetened, shredded
1 tbs	Coconut milk
2 tbs	Cream, half and half
1 tbs (½ oz)	Cream cheese, regular
1½ tbs (¾ oz)	Cream cheese, reduced-fat
	Fatback or salt pork† 🖊
1 tsp	Shortening or lard
2 tbs	Sour cream, regular
3 tbs	Sour cream, reduced-fat

🖊 = 400 mg or more sodium per exchange
*Saturated fats can raise blood cholesterol levels.
†Use a piece 1″ × 1″ × ¼″ if you plan to eat the fatback cooked with vegetables. Use a piece 2″ × 1″ × ½″ when eating only the vegetables with the fatback removed.

TABLE G-11 U.S. Exchange System: Free Foods List

NOTE: A serving of free food contains less than 20 kcalories or no more than 5 grams of carbohydrate; those with serving sizes should be limited to 3 servings a day whereas those without serving sizes can be eaten freely.

Serving Size	Food
Fat-Free or Reduced-Fat Foods	
1 tbs (½ oz)	Cream cheese, fat-free
1 tbs	Creamers, nondairy, liquid
2 tsp	Creamers, nondairy, powdered
4 tbs	Margarine spread, fat-free
1 tsp	Margarine spread, reduced-fat
1 tbs	Mayonnaise, fat-free
1 tsp	Mayonnaise, reduced-fat
1 tbs	Mayonnaise type salad dressing, fat-free
1 tsp	Mayonnaise type salad dressing, reduced-fat
	Nonstick cooking spray
1 tbs	Salad dressing, fat-free or low-fat
2 tbs	Salad dressing, fat-free, Italian
1 tbs	Sour cream, fat-free, reduced-fat
1 tbs	Whipped topping, regular
2 tbs	Whipped topping, light or fat-free
Sugar-Free Foods	
1 piece	Candy, hard, sugar-free
	Gelatin dessert, sugar-free
	Gelatin, unflavored
	Gum, sugar-free
2 tsp	Jam or jelly, light
	Sugar substitutes
2 tbs	Syrup, sugar-free
Drinks	
	Bouillon, broth, consommé ✐
	Bouillon or broth, low-sodium
	Carbonated or mineral water
	Club soda
1 tbs	Cocoa powder, unsweetened

Serving Size	Food
	Coffee
	Diet soft drinks, sugar-free
	Drink mixes, sugar-free
	Tea
	Tonic water, sugar-free
Condiments	
1 tbs	Catsup
	Horseradish
	Lemon juice
	Lime juice
	Mustard
1 tbs	Pickle relish
1½ medium	Pickles, dill ✐
2 slices	Pickles, sweet (bread and butter)
¾ oz	Pickles, sweet (gherkin)
¼ c	Salsa
1 tbs	Soy sauce, regular or light ✐
1 tbs	Taco sauce
	Vinegar
2 tbs	Yogurt
Seasonings	
	Flavoring extracts
	Garlic
	Herbs, fresh or dried
	Hot pepper sauces
	Pimento
	Spices
	Wine, used in cooking
	Worcestershire sauce

✐ = 400 mg or more of sodium per serving.

TABLE G-12 U.S. Exchange System: Combination Foods List

Food	Serving Size	Exchanges per Serving
Entrées		
Tuna noodle casserole, lasagna, spaghetti with meatballs, chili with beans, macaroni and cheese 🖊	1 c (8 oz)	2 carbohydrates, 2 medium-fat meats
Chow mein (without noodles or rice)	2 c (16 oz)	1 carbohydrate, 2 lean meats
Tuna or chicken salad	½ c (3½ oz)	½ carbohydrate, 2 lean meats, 1 fat
Frozen Entrées and Meals		
Dinner-type meal 🖊	Generally 14–17 oz	3 carbohydrates, 3 medium-fat meats, 3 fats
Entrée or meal with <340 kcal 🖊	About 8–11 oz	2–3 carbohydrates, 1–2 lean meats
Meatless burger, soy based	3 oz	½ carbohydrate, 2 lean meats
Meatless burger, vegetable and starch based	3 oz	1 carbohydrate, 1 lean meat
Pizza, cheese, thin crust 🖊	¼ of 12" (6 oz)	2 carbohydrates, 2 medium-fat meats, 1 fat
Pizza, meat topping, thin crust 🖊	¼ of 12" (6 oz)	2 carbohydrates, 2 medium-fat meats, 2 fats
Pot pie 🖊	1 (7 oz)	2½ carbohydrates, 1 medium-fat meat, 3 fats
Soups		
Bean 🖊	1 c	1 carbohydrate, 1 very lean meat
Cream (made with water) 🖊	1 c (8 oz)	1 carbohydrate, 1 fat
Instant 🖊	6 oz prepared	1 carbohydrate
Instant with beans/lentils 🖊	8 oz prepared	2½ carbohydrates, 1 very lean meat
Split pea (made with water) 🖊	½ c (4 oz)	1 carbohydrate
Tomato (made with water)	1 c (8 oz)	1 carbohydrate
Vegetable beef, chicken noodle, or other broth-type 🖊	1 c (8 oz)	1 carbohydrate
Fast Foods		
Burrito with beef 🖊	1 (5–7 oz)	3 carbohydrates, 1 medium-fat meat, 1 fat
Chicken nuggets 🖊	6	1 carbohydrate, 2 medium-fat meats, 1 fat
Chicken breast and wing, breaded and fried 🖊	1 each	1 carbohydrate, 4 medium-fat meats, 2 fats
Chicken sandwich, grilled 🖊	1	2 carbohydrates, 3 very lean meats
Chicken wings, hot	6 (5 oz)	1 carbohydrate, 3 medium-fat meats, 4 fats
Fish sandwich/tartar sauce 🖊	1	3 carbohydrates, 1 medium-fat meat, 3 fats
French fries 🖊	1 medium serving (5 oz)	4 carbohydrates, 4 fats
Hamburger, regular	1	2 carbohydrates, 2 medium-fat meats
Hamburger, large 🖊	1	2 carbohydrates, 3 medium-fat meats, 1 fat
Hot dog with bun 🖊	1	1 carbohydrate, 1 high-fat meat, 1 fat
Individual pan pizza 🖊	1	5 carbohydrates, 3 medium-fat meats, 3 fats
Pizza, cheese, thin crust 🖊	¼ of 12" (about 6 oz)	2½ carbohydrates, 2 medium-fat meats
Pizza, meat, thin crust 🖊	¼ of 12" (about 6 oz)	2½ carbohydrates, 2 medium-fat meats, 1 fat
Soft serve cone	1 small (5 oz)	2½ carbohydrates, 1 fat
Submarine sandwich 🖊	1 sub (6")	3 carbohydrates, 1 vegetable, 2 medium-fat meats, 1 fat
Submarine sandwich (<6 g fat) 🖊	1 sub (6")	2½ carbohydrates, 2 lean meats
Taco, hard or soft shell	1 (3–3½ oz)	1 carbohydrate, 1 medium-fat meat, 1 fat

🖊 = 400 mg or more sodium per exchange.

CONTENTS

Table of Food Composition

Table of Food Composition

This edition of the table of food composition includes a wide variety of foods. It is updated with each edition to reflect current nutrient data for foods, to remove outdated foods, and to add foods that are new to the marketplace.* The nutrient database for this appendix is compiled from a variety of sources, including the USDA Standard Release database and manufacturers' data. The USDA database provides data for a wider variety of foods and nutrients than other sources. Because laboratory analysis for each nutrient can be quite costly, manufacturers tend to provide data only for those nutrients mandated on food labels. Consequently, data for their foods are often incomplete; any missing information on this table is designated as a dash. Keep in mind that a dash means only that the information is unknown and should not be interpreted as a zero. A zero means that the nutrient is not present in the food.

Whenever using nutrient data, remember that many factors influence the nutrient contents of foods. These factors include the mineral content of the soil, the diet fed to the animal or the fertilizer used on the plant, the season of harvest, the method of processing, the length and method of storage, the method of cooking, the method of analysis, and the moisture content of the sample analyzed. With so many influencing factors, users should view nutrient data as a close approximation of the actual amount.

For updates, corrections, and a list of more than 8000 foods and codes found in the diet analysis software that accompanies this text, visit www.thomsonedu.com/nutrition and click on Diet Analysis Plus.

- **Fats** Total fats, as well as the breakdown of total fats to saturated, monounsaturated, polyunsaturated, and *trans* fats, are listed in the table. The fatty acids seldom add up to the total in part due to rounding but also because values are derived from a variety of laboratories.

- **Trans Fats** *Trans* fat data has been listed in the table. Because food manufacturers have only been required to report *trans* fats on food labels since January 2006, much of the data is incomplete. Missing *trans* fat data is designated with a dash. As additional *trans* fat data becomes available, the table will be updated.

- **Vitamin A and Vitamin E** In keeping with the 2001 RDA for vitamin A, this appendix presents data for vitamin A in micrograms (µg) RAE. Similarly, because the 2000 RDA for vitamin E is based only on the alpha-tocopherol form of vitamin E, this appendix reports vitamin E data in milligrams (mg) alpha-tocopherol, listed on the table as Vit E (mg α).

- **Bioavailability** Keep in mind that the availability of nutrients from foods depends not only on the quantity provided by a food, but also on the amount absorbed and used by the body—the bioavailability. The bioavailability of folate from fortified foods, for example, is greater than from naturally occurring sources. Similarly, the body can make niacin from the amino acid tryptophan, but niacin values in this table (and most databases) report preformed niacin only. Chapter 10 provides conversion factors and additional details.

- **Using the Table** The foods and beverages in this table are organized into several categories, which are listed at the head of each right-hand page. Page numbers are provided, and each group is color-coded to make it easier to find individual foods.

- **Caffeine Sources** Caffeine occurs in several plants, including the familiar coffee bean, the tea leaf, and the cocoa bean from which chocolate is made.

---

*This food composition table has been prepared by Wadsworth Publishing Company. The nutritional data are supplied by Axxya Systems.

Most human societies use caffeine regularly, most often in beverages, for its stimulant effect and flavor. Caffeine contents of beverages vary depending on the plants they are made from, the climates and soils where the plants are grown, the grind or cut size, the method and duration of brewing, and the amounts served. The accompanying table shows that, in general, a cup of coffee contains the most caffeine; a cup of tea, less than half as much; and cocoa or chocolate, less still. As for cola beverages, they are made from kola nuts, which contain caffeine, but most of their caffeine is added, using the purified compound obtained from decaffeinated coffee beans. The FDA lists caffeine as a multipurpose GRAS substance ◆ that may be added to foods and beverages. Drug manufacturers use caffeine in many products.

◆ Reminder: A GRAS substance is one that is "generally recognized as safe."

TABLE Caffeine Content of Selected Beverages, Foods, and Medications

Beverages and Foods	Serving Size	Average (mg)	Beverages and Foods	Serving Size	Average (mg)
Coffee			**Other beverages**		
Brewed	8 oz	95	Chocolate milk or hot cocoa	8 oz	5
Decaffeinated	8 oz	2	Starbucks Frappuccino Mocha	9.5 oz	72
Instant	8 oz	64	Starbucks Frappuccino Vanilla	9.5 oz	64
Tea			Yoohoo chocolate drink	9 oz	3
Brewed, green	8 oz	30	**Candies**		
Brewed, herbal	8 oz	0	Baker's chocolate	1 oz	26
Brewed, leaf or bag	8 oz	47	Dark chocolate covered coffee beans	1 oz	235
Instant	8 oz	26	Dark chocolate, semisweet	1 oz	18
Lipton Brisk iced tea	12 oz	7	Milk chocolate	1 oz	6
Nestea Cool iced tea	12 oz	12	Milk chocolate covered coffee beans	1 oz	224
Snapple iced tea (all flavors)	16 oz	42	White chocolate	1 oz	0
Soft drinks			**Foods**		
A & W Creme Soda	12 oz	29	Frozen yogurt, Ben & Jerry's coffee fudge	1 cup	85
Barq's Root Beer	12 oz	18	Frozen yogurt, Häagen-Dazs coffee	1 cup	40
Coca-Cola	12 oz	30	Ice cream, Starbucks coffee	1 cup	50
Dr. Pepper, Mr. Pibb, Sunkist Orange	12 oz	36	Ice cream, Starbucks Frappuccino bar	1 bar	15
A&W Root Beer, club soda, Fresca, ginger ale, 7-Up, Sierra Mist, Sprite, Squirt, tonic water, caffeine-free soft drinks	12 oz	0	Yogurt, Dannon coffee flavored	1 cup	45

			Drugs[a]	Serving Size	Average (mg)
Mello Yello	12 oz	51	**Cold remedies**		
Mountain Dew	12 oz	45	Coryban-D, Dristan	1 tablet	30
Pepsi	12 oz	32	**Diuretics**		
Energy drinks			Aqua-Ban	1 tablet	100
Amp	8.4 oz	70	Pre-Mens Forte	1 tablet	100
Aqua Blast	.5 L	90	**Pain relievers**		
Aqua Java	.5 L	55	Anacin, BC Fast Pain Reliever	1 tablet	32
E Maxx	8.4 oz	74	Excedrin, Midol, Midol Max Strength	1 tablet	65
Java Water	.5 L	125	**Stimulants**		
KMX	8.4 oz	33	Awake, NoDoz	1 tablet	100
Krank	.5 L	100	Awake Maximum Strength, Caffedrine, NoDoz Maximum Strength, Stay Awake, Vivarin	1 tablet	200
Red Bull	8.3 oz	67	**Weight-control aids**		
Red Devil	8.4 oz	42	Dexatrim	1 tablet	200
Sobe Adrenaline Rush	8.3 oz	77			
Sobe No Fear	16 oz	141			
Water Joe	.5 L	65			

[a]A pharmacologically active dose of caffeine is defined as 200 milligrams.

NOTE: The FDA suggests a maximum of 65 milligrams per 12-ounce cola beverage but does not regulate the caffeine contents of other beverages. Because products change, contact the manufacturer for an update on products you use regularly.

Source: Adapted from USDA database Release 18 (http://www.nal.usda.gov/fnic/foodcomp/Data/), Caffeine content of foods and drugs, Center for Science and the Public Interest (www.cspinet.org/new/cafchart.htm), and R. R. McCusker, B. A. Goldberger, and E. J. Cone, Caffeine content of energy drinks, carbonated sodas, and other beverages, *Journal of Analytical Toxicology* 30 (2006): 112–114.

H Appendix

TABLE H–1

Food Composition

(DA+ code is for Wadsworth Diet Analysis program)   (For purposes of calculations, use "0" for t, <1, <.1, <.01, etc.)

DA + Code	Food Description	Quantity	Measure	Wt (g)	H₂O (g)	Ener (kcal)	Prot (g)	Carb (g)	Fiber (g)	Fat (g)	Sat	Mono	Poly	Trans
												Fat Breakdown (g)		

BREADS, BAKED GOODS, CAKES, COOKIES, CRACKERS, CHIPS, PIES

Bagels

8534	Cinnamon & raisin	1	item(s)	71	23	195	7	39	2	1	0.19	0.12	0.48	—
4910	Enriched, all varieties	1	item(s)	71	23	195	7	38	2	1	0.16	0.09	0.49	0
4911	Plain, enriched, toasted	1	item(s)	66	18	195	7	38	2	1	0.16	0.09	0.49	0
8538	Oat bran	1	item(s)	71	23	181	8	38	3	1	0.14	0.18	0.35	—
12079	Whole grain	1	item(s)	85	—	170	9	35	6	2.5	0	—	—	0

Biscuits

25008	Biscuits	1	item(s)	41	16	121	3	16	1	5	1.40	1.41	1.82	0
16729	Scone	1	item(s)	42	11	149	4	19	1	6	2.01	2.55	1.26	—
25166	Wheat biscuits	1	item(s)	55	21	162	4	22	1	7	1.90	1.92	2.51	0

Bread

325	Boston brown, canned	1	slice(s)	45	21	88	2	19	2	1	0.13	0.09	0.25	—
8716	Bread sticks, plain	4	item(s)	24	1	99	3	16	1	2	0.34	0.86	0.87	—
25176	Cornbread	1	piece(s)	55	26	141	5	18	1	5	2.09	1.44	1.50	0
327	Cracked wheat	1	slice(s)	25	9	65	2	12	1	1	0.23	0.48	0.17	—
9079	Croutons, plain	¼	cup(s)	8	<1	31	1	6	<1	<1	0.11	0.23	0.10	—
8582	Egg	1	slice(s)	40	14	115	4	19	1	2	0.64	0.92	0.44	—
8585	Egg, toasted	1	slice(s)	37	10	117	4	19	1	2	0.60	1.11	0.43	—
329	French	1	slice(s)	25	9	69	2	13	1	1	0.16	0.30	0.17	—
8591	French, toasted	1	slice(s)	23	7	69	2	13	1	1	0.16	0.30	0.17	—
8597	Indian fry	1	item(s)	90	24	296	6	48	2	9	2.08	3.59	2.33	—
332	Italian	1	slice(s)	30	11	81	3	15	1	1	0.26	0.24	0.42	—
1393	Mixed grain	1	slice(s)	26	10	65	3	12	2	1	0.21	0.40	0.24	—
8604	Mixed grain, toasted	1	slice(s)	24	8	65	3	12	2	1	0.21	0.40	0.24	—
8605	Oat bran	1	slice(s)	30	13	71	3	12	1	1	0.21	0.48	0.51	—
8608	Oat bran, toasted	1	slice(s)	27	10	70	3	12	1	1	0.21	0.47	0.50	—
8609	Oatmeal	1	slice(s)	27	10	73	2	13	1	1	0.19	0.43	0.46	—
8613	Oatmeal, toasted	1	slice(s)	25	8	73	2	13	1	1	0.19	0.43	0.46	—
1409	Pita	1	item(s)	60	19	165	5	33	1	1	0.10	0.06	0.32	—
7905	Pita, whole wheat	1	item(s)	64	20	170	6	35	5	2	0.26	0.22	0.68	—
338	Pumpernickel	1	slice(s)	32	12	80	3	15	2	1	0.14	0.30	0.40	—
334	Raisin, enriched	1	slice(s)	26	9	71	2	14	1	1	0.28	0.60	0.18	—
8625	Raisin, toasted	1	slice(s)	24	7	71	2	14	1	1	0.28	0.60	0.18	—
10168	Rice, white	1	slice(s)	42	—	140	1	21	1	6	0.50	—	—	0
8653	Rye	1	slice(s)	32	12	83	3	15	2	1	0.20	0.42	0.26	—
8654	Rye, toasted	1	slice(s)	29	9	82	3	15	2	1	0.20	0.42	0.25	—
336	Rye, light	1	slice(s)	25	9	65	2	12	2	1	0.20	0.30	0.30	—
8588	Sourdough	1	slice(s)	25	9	69	2	13	1	1	0.16	0.30	0.17	—
8592	Sourdough, toasted	1	slice(s)	23	7	69	2	13	1	1	0.16	0.30	0.17	—
491	Submarine or hoagie roll	1	item(s)	135	41	400	11	72	4	8	1.80	3.00	2.20	—
8596	Vienna, toasted	1	slice(s)	23	7	69	2	13	1	1	0.16	0.30	0.17	—
8670	Wheat	1	slice(s)	25	9	65	2	12	1	1	0.22	0.43	0.23	—
8671	Wheat, toasted	1	slice(s)	23	7	65	2	12	1	1	0.22	0.43	0.23	—
340	White	1	Measure	25	9	67	2	13	1	1	0.18	0.17	0.34	—
1395	Whole wheat	1	slice(s)	46	15	128	4	24	3	2	0.37	0.53	1.35	—

Cakes

386	Angel food, from mix	1	slice(s)	50	16	129	3	29	<1	<1	0.02	0.01	0.06	—
8772	Butter pound, ready to eat, commercially prepared	1	slice(s)	75	18	291	4	37	<1	15	8.67	4.43	0.80	—
8737	Carrot, cream cheese frosting, from mix	1	slice(s)	111	23	484	5	52	1	29	5.43	7.24	15.10	—
4931	Chocolate, chocolate icing, commercially prepared	1	slice(s)	64	15	235	3	35	2	10	3.05	5.61	1.18	—
8756	Chocolate, from mix	1	slice(s)	95	23	340	5	51	2	14	5.16	5.74	2.62	—
393	Devil's food cupcake, chocolate frosting	1	item(s)	35	8	120	2	20	1	4	1.80	1.60	0.60	—
8757	Fruitcake, ready to eat, commercially prepared	1	piece(s)	43	11	139	1	26	2	4	0.45	1.81	1.43	—
1397	Pineapple upside down, from mix	1	slice(s)	115	37	367	4	58	1	14	3.35	5.97	3.77	—
411	Sponge, from mix	1	slice(s)	63	19	187	5	36	<1	3	0.82	0.99	0.41	—
8817	White, coconut frosting, from mix	1	slice(s)	112	23	399	5	71	1	12	4.36	4.14	2.42	—
8819	Yellow, chocolate frosting, ready to eat, commercially prepared	1	slice(s)	64	14	243	2	35	1	11	2.98	6.14	1.35	—
8822	Yellow, vanilla frosting, ready to eat, commercially prepared	1	slice(s)	64	14	239	2	38	<1	9	1.52	3.91	3.30	—

Snack cakes

8791	Chocolate snack cake, creme filled, w/frosting	1	item(s)	50	10	188	2	30	<1	7	1.43	2.85	2.62	—
25010	Cinnamon coffee cake	1	piece(s)	72	23	231	4	36	1	8	2.19	2.65	2.99	0

PAGE KEY: H–2 = Breads/Baked Goods   H–6 = Cereal/Rice/Pasta   H–10 = Fruit   H–14 = Vegetables/Legumes   H–24 = Nuts/Seeds   H–26 = Vegetarian
H–28 = Dairy   H–34 = Eggs   H–34 = Seafood   H–36 = Meats   H–40 = Poultry   H–40 = Processed meats   H–42 = Beverages   H–46 = Fats/Oils
H–48 = Sweets   H–50 = Spices/Condiments/Sauces   H–52 = Mixed foods/Soups/Sandwiches   H–58 = Fast food   H–74 = Convenience meals   H–76 = Baby foods

Chol (mg)	Calc (mg)	Iron (mg)	Magn (mg)	Pota (mg)	Sodi (mg)	Zinc (mg)	Vit A (µg)	Thia (mg)	Vit E (mg α)	Ribo (mg)	Niac (mg)	Vit B6 (mg)	Fola (µg)	Vit C (mg)	Vit B12 (µg)	Sele (µg)
0	13	2.70	20	105	229	0.80	15	0.27	0.22	0.20	2.19	0.04	79	<1	0	22
0	53	2.53	21	72	379	0.62	0	0.38	0.07	0.22	3.24	0.04	75	0	0	23
0	53	2.52	20	72	379	0.62	0	0.31	0.08	0.20	2.91	0.03	64	0	0	23
0	9	2.19	22	82	360	0.64	1	0.24	0.23	0.24	2.10	0.03	70	<1	0	24
0	200	1.08	120	0	200	4.5	0	0.44	—	0.5	8	0.6	—	0	1.79	0
<1	33	1.01	6	37	205	0.27	9	0.13	0.01	0.12	1.08	0.01	26	0	<.1	7
49	80	1.31	7	48	288	0.29	—	0.15	0.43	0.16	1.20	0.03	8	<.1	<1	—
<1	57	1.22	16	81	321	0.42	12	0.16	0.01	0.13	1.49	0.03	29	<.1	<.1	12
<1	32	0.95	28	143	284	0.23	11	0.01	0.14	0.05	0.50	0.04	5	0	<.1	10
0	5	1.03	8	30	158	0.21	0	0.14	0.24	0.13	1.27	0.02	39	0	0	9
21	88	1.01	10	59	209	0.57	38	0.13	0.33	0.16	0.98	0.04	36	2	<1	6
0	11	0.70	13	44	135	0.31	0	0.09	—	0.06	0.92	0.08	15	0	<.1	6
0	6	0.31	2	9	52	0.07	0	0.05	—	0.02	0.41	0.00	10	0	0	3
20	37	1.22	8	46	197	0.32	25	0.18	0.10	0.17	1.94	0.03	42	0	<.1	12
21	38	1.24	8	47	200	0.32	26	0.14	0.11	0.16	1.77	0.02	36	0	<.1	12
0	19	0.63	7	28	152	0.22	0	0.13	0.08	0.08	1.19	0.01	37	0	0	8
0	19	0.63	7	28	152	0.22	0	0.10	0.07	0.07	1.07	0.01	22	0	0	8
0	210	3.24	14	67	626	0.45	0	0.39	—	0.27	3.27	0.02	67	0	0	21
0	23	0.88	8	33	175	0.26	0	0.14	0.09	0.09	1.31	0.01	57	0	0	8
0	24	0.90	14	53	127	0.33	0	0.11	0.09	0.09	1.13	0.09	31	<.1	<.1	8
0	24	0.90	14	53	127	0.33	0	0.08	0.08	0.08	1.02	0.08	28	<.1	<.1	8
0	20	0.94	11	44	122	0.27	1	0.15	0.13	0.10	1.45	0.02	24	0	0	9
0	19	0.93	9	33	121	0.28	1	0.12	0.13	0.09	1.29	0.01	19	0	0	9
0	18	0.73	10	38	162	0.28	1	0.11	0.13	0.06	0.85	0.02	17	0	<.1	7
0	18	0.74	10	39	163	0.28	1	0.09	0.13	0.06	0.77	0.02	13	<.1	<.1	7
0	52	1.57	16	72	322	0.50	0	0.36	0.18	0.20	2.78	0.02	64	0	0	16
0	10	1.96	44	109	340	0.97	0	0.22	0.39	0.05	1.82	0.17	22	0	0	28
0	22	0.92	17	67	215	0.47	0	0.10	0.13	0.10	0.99	0.04	30	0	0	8
0	17	0.75	7	59	101	0.19	0	0.09	0.07	0.10	0.90	0.04	28	<.1	0	5
0	17	0.76	7	59	102	0.19	0	0.07	0.07	0.09	0.81	0.02	24	<.1	0	5
0	40	1.08	—	45	160	—	0	0.23	—	0.14	1.20	—	40	0	—	—
0	23	0.91	13	53	211	0.36	0	0.14	0.11	0.11	1.22	0.02	35	<1	0	10
0	23	0.90	12	53	210	0.36	0	0.11	0.11	0.10	1.09	0.02	30	<1	0	10
0	20	0.70	4	51	175	0.18	0	0.10	—	0.08	0.80	0.01	5	0	<.1	8
0	19	0.63	7	28	152	0.22	0	0.13	0.08	0.08	1.19	0.01	37	0	0	8
0	19	0.63	7	28	152	0.22	0	0.10	0.07	0.07	1.07	0.01	22	0	0	8
0	100	3.80	—	128	683	—	0	0.54	—	0.33	4.50	0.05	—	0	—	42
0	19	0.63	7	28	152	0.22	0	0.10	0.07	0.07	1.07	0.01	22	0	0	8
0	26	0.83	12	50	133	0.26	0	0.10	0.07	0.07	1.03	0.02	23	0	0	8
0	26	0.83	12	50	132	0.26	0	0.08	0.07	0.06	0.93	0.02	19	0	0	8
0	38	0.94	6	25	170	0.19	0	0.11	0.05	0.08	1.10	0.02	28	0	0	4
0	15	1.43	37	144	159	0.69	0	0.14	0.35	0.10	1.83	0.09	30	0	0	18
0	42	0.12	4	68	255	0.07	0	0.05	0.00	0.10	0.09	0.00	10	0	<.1	8
166	26	1.04	8	89	299	0.35	112	0.10	—	0.98		0.03	31	0	<1	7
60	28	1.39	20	124	273	0.54	—	0.15	—	0.17	1.13	0.08	13	1	<1	—
27	28	1.41	22	128	214	0.44	—	0.02	—	0.09	0.37	0.03	11	<.1	<.1	2
55	57	1.53	30	133	299	0.66	38	0.13	—	0.20	1.08	0.04	26	<1	<1	11
19	21	0.70	—	46	92	—	—	0.04	—	0.05	0.30	—	2	0	—	2
2	14	0.89	7	66	116	0.12	3	0.02	0.39	0.04	0.34	0.02	9	<1	<.1	1
25	138	1.70	15	129	367	0.36	71	0.18	—	0.18	1.37	0.04	30	1	<1	11
107	26	1.00	6	89	144	0.37	49	0.10	—	0.19	0.76	0.04	25	0	<1	12
1	101	1.30	13	111	318	0.37	13	0.14	0.13	0.21	1.19	0.03	35	<1	<.1	12
35	24	1.33	19	114	216	0.40	21	0.08	—	0.10	0.80	0.02	14	0	<1	2
35	40	0.68	4	34	220	0.16	12	0.06	—	0.04	0.32	0.02	17	0	<1	4
9	37	1.68	21	61	213	0.26	3	0.11	1.09	0.15	1.21	0.01	20	0	<.1	1
26	50	1.46	10	81	277	0.38	35	0.14	0.23	0.16	1.17	0.02	30	<.1	<1	10

TABLE H–1
Food Composition

(DA+ code is for Wadsworth Diet Analysis program) (For purposes of calculations, use "0" for t, <1, <.1, <.01, etc.)

DA + Code	Food Description	Quantity	Measure	Wt (g)	H₂O (g)	Ener (kcal)	Prot (g)	Carb (g)	Fiber (g)	Fat (g)	Sat	Mono	Poly	Trans
	BREADS, BAKED GOODS, CAKES, COOKIES, CRACKERS, CHIPS, PIES—Continued													
16777	Funnel cake	1	item(s)	90	37	278	7	29	1	14	2.77	4.46	6.33	—
8794	Sponge snack cake, creme filled	1	item(s)	43	9	155	1	27	<1	5	1.09	1.73	1.40	—
	Snacks, chips, pretzels													
29428	Bagel chips, plain	3	item(s)	29	—	130	3	19	1	5	0.50	—	—	—
29429	Bagel chips, toasted onion	3	item(s)	29	—	130	4	20	1	5	0.50	—	—	—
38192	Chex traditional snack mix	1	cup(s)	46	—	198	3	33	2	6	0.76	—	—	—
654	Potato chips, salted	20	item(s)	28	1	152	2	15	1	10	3.11	2.79	3.46	—
8816	Potato chips, unsalted	20	item(s)	28	1	152	2	15	1	10	3.11	2.79	3.46	—
4641	Tortilla chips, plain	6	item(s)	28	1	142	2	18	2	7	1.43	4.39	1.03	—
5096	Pretzels, plain, hard, twists	5	item(s)	30	1	114	3	24	1	1	0.23	0.41	0.37	—
4632	Pretzels, whole wheat	1	ounce(s)	28	1	103	3	23	2	1	0.16	0.29	0.24	—
	Cookies													
8859	Animal crackers	12	piece(s)	30	0	134	2	22	<1	4	1.03	2.29	0.56	—
8876	Brownie, prepared from mix	1	item(s)	24	3	112	1	12	1	7	1.76	2.60	2.26	—
25207	Chocolate chip cookies	1	item(s)	30	4	140	2	16	1	8	2.09	3.26	2.09	0
8915	Chocolate sandwich cookie, extra creme filling	1	item(s)	13	<1	65	<1	9	<1	3	0.50	1.39	1.22	1.10
14145	Fig Newtons	1	item(s)	16	—	55	1	10	1	1	0.50	0.50	0.00	0.50
8920	Fortune cookie	1	item(s)	8	1	30	<1	7	<1	<1	0.05	0.11	0.04	—
25208	Oatmeal cookies	1	item(s)	69	12	234	6	45	3	4	0.70	1.28	1.85	0
25213	Peanut butter cookies	1	item(s)	35	4	163	4	17	1	9	1.65	4.72	2.43	0
33095	Sugar cookies	1	item(s)	16	4	61	1	7	<1	3	0.63	1.27	0.87	0
9002	Vanilla sandwich cookie, creme filling	1	item(s)	10	<1	48	<1	7	<1	2	0.30	0.84	0.76	—
	Crackers													
9008	Cheese crackers (mini)	30	item(s)	30	1	151	3	17	1	8	2.81	3.63	0.74	—
9010	Cheese crackers (mini), low salt	30	item(s)	30	1	151	3	17	1	8	2.82	2.70	1.44	—
9012	Cheese cracker sandwich w/peanut butter	4	item(s)	28	1	139	3	16	1	7	1.23	3.64	1.43	—
8928	Honey graham crackers	4	item(s)	28	1	118	2	22	1	3	0.43	1.14	1.07	—
9016	Matzo crackers, plain	1	item(s)	28	1	112	3	24	1	<1	0.06	0.04	0.17	—
9024	Melba toast	3	item(s)	15	1	59	2	11	1	<1	0.07	0.12	0.19	—
14189	Ritz crackers	5	item(s)	16	<1	80	1	10	1	4	0.50	1.50	0.00	—
9014	Rye crispbread crackers	1	item(s)	10	1	37	1	8	2	<1	0.01	0.02	0.06	—
9028	Rye melba toast	3	item(s)	15	1	58	2	12	1	1	0.07	0.14	0.20	—
9040	Rye wafer	1	item(s)	11	1	37	1	9	3	<.1	0.01	0.02	0.04	—
432	Saltine crackers	5	item(s)	15	1	65	1	11	<1	2	0.44	0.96	0.25	0.54
9046	Saltine crackers, low salt	5	item(s)	15	1	65	1	11	<1	2	0.44	0.96	0.25	—
9048	Snack crackers, round	10	item(s)	30	1	151	2	18	<1	8	1.13	3.19	2.86	—
9050	Snack crackers, round, low salt	10	item(s)	30	1	151	2	18	<1	8	1.13	3.19	2.86	—
9052	Snack cracker sandwich, cheese filling	4	item(s)	28	1	134	3	17	1	6	1.72	3.15	0.72	—
9054	Snack cracker sandwich, peanut butter filling	4	item(s)	28	1	138	3	16	1	7	1.38	3.86	1.30	—
9044	Soda crackers	5	item(s)	15	1	65	1	11	<1	2	0.44	0.96	0.25	0.54
9055	Wheat crackers	10	item(s)	30	1	142	3	19	1	6	1.55	3.43	0.84	—
9057	Wheat crackers, low salt	10	item(s)	30	1	142	3	19	1	6	1.55	3.43	0.84	—
9059	Wheat cracker sandwich, cheese filling	4	item(s)	28	1	139	3	16	1	7	1.16	2.90	2.57	—
9061	Wheat cracker sandwich, peanut butter filling	4	item(s)	28	1	139	4	15	1	7	1.29	3.29	2.48	—
9022	Whole wheat crackers	7	item(s)	28	1	124	2	19	3	5	0.95	1.65	1.85	—
	Pastry													
16754	Apple fritter	1	item(s)	17	6	62	1	6	<1	4	0.87	1.69	1.13	—
5118	Cinnamon sweet roll w/icing, from refrigerator dough	1	item(s)	30	7	109	2	17	1	4	1.00	2.23	0.52	—
4945	Croissant, butter	1	item(s)	57	13	231	5	26	1	12	6.59	3.15	0.62	—
9096	Danish pastry, nut	1	item(s)	65	13	280	5	30	1	16	3.78	8.90	2.78	—
4947	Doughnut, cake	1	item(s)	47	10	198	2	23	1	11	1.70	4.37	3.70	—
9105	Doughnut, cake, chocolate glazed	1	item(s)	42	7	175	2	24	1	8	2.16	4.74	1.04	—
9115	Doughnut, creme filling	1	item(s)	85	32	307	5	26	1	21	4.62	10.27	2.62	—
437	Doughnut, glazed	1	item(s)	60	15	242	4	27	1	14	3.49	7.72	1.74	—
9117	Doughnut, jelly filling	1	item(s)	85	30	289	5	33	1	16	4.12	8.69	2.02	—
10617	Toaster pastry, brown sugar cinnamon	1	item(s)	50	5	210	3	35	1	6	1.00	4.00	1.00	—
30928	Toaster pastry, cream cheese	1	item(s)	54	—	200	3	23	1	11	3.50	—	—	—
	Muffins													
25015	Blueberry	1	item(s)	63	30	160	3	23	1	6	0.87	1.48	3.25	0
4997	Bran, from mix	1	item(s)	50	18	138	3	23	2	5	1.18	2.34	0.72	—
9189	Corn, ready to eat	1	item(s)	57	19	174	3	29	2	5	0.77	1.20	1.83	—

PAGE KEY: H–2 = Breads/Baked Goods   H–6 = Cereal/Rice/Pasta   H–10 = Fruit   H–14 = Vegetables/Legumes   H–24 = Nuts/Seeds   H–26 = Vegetarian
H–28 = Dairy   H–34 = Eggs   H–34 = Seafood   H–36 = Meats   H–40 = Poultry   H–40 = Processed meats   H–42 = Beverages   H–46 = Fats/Oils
H–48 = Sweets   H–50 = Spices/Condiments/Sauces   H–52 = Mixed foods/Soups/Sandwiches   H–58 = Fast food   H–74 = Convenience meals   H–76 = Baby foods

Chol (mg)	Calc (mg)	Iron (mg)	Magn (mg)	Pota (mg)	Sodi (mg)	Zinc (mg)	Vit A (µg)	Thia (mg)	Vit E (mg α)	Ribo (mg)	Niac (mg)	Vit B$_6$ (mg)	Fola (µg)	Vit C (mg)	Vit B$_{12}$ (µg)	Sele (µg)
63	128	1.86	18	154	273	0.64	—	0.24	1.55	0.32	1.86	0.05	14	<1	<1	—
7	19	0.55	3	37	155	0.12	2	0.07	0.50	0.06	0.52	0.01	17	<.1	<.1	1
0	0	0.72	—	45	70	—	0	—	—	—	—	—	—	0	0	—
0	0	0.72	—	50	300	—	0	—	—	—	—	—	—	0	0	—
0	0	0.55	0	76	623	0.00	0	0.09	—	0.05	1.22	0.00	12	0	—	—
0	7	0.46	19	362	169	0.31	0	0.05	1.91	0.06	1.09	0.19	13	9	0	2
0	7	0.46	19	362	2	0.31	0	0.05	2.59	0.06	1.09	0.19	13	9	0	2
0	44	0.43	25	56	150	0.43	1	0.02	1	0.05	0.36	0.08	3	0	0	2
0	11	1.30	11	44	515	0.26	0	0.14	—	0.19	1.58	0.03	51	0	0	2
0	8	0.76	9	122	58	0.18	0	0.12	—	0.08	1.86	0.04	15	<1	0	—
0	13	0.82	5	30	1118	0.19	—	0.10	0.04	0.09	1.04	0.00	50	0	<.1	—
18	14	0.44	13	42	82	0.23	42	0.03	—	0.05	0.24	0.02	7	<.1	<.1	3
13	11	0.70	12	62	109	0.24	27	0.07	0.54	0.06	0.82	0.02	16	<.1	<.1	4
0	3	0.37	4	16	64	0.08	0	0.01	0.25	0.02	0.20	0.00	6	0	<.1	<1
0	5	0.36	—	40	60	—	4	0.03	—	0.04	0.22	—	—	<1	—	<1
<1	1	0.12	1	3	22	0.01	<.1	0.01	0.00	0.01	0.15	0.00	5	0	<.1	<1
<.1	26	1.94	49	177	311	1.43	48	0.23	0.23	0.12	1.24	0.09	30	<1	<.1	17
13	28	0.67	22	104	157	0.46	51	0.08	0.74	0.09	1.81	0.05	21	<.1	<.1	5
18	5	0.32	2	13	50	0.08	31	0.04	0.28	0.04	0.28	0.01	8	<.1	<.1	3
0	3	0.22	1	9	35	0.04	0	0.03	0.16	0.02	0.27	0.00	5	0	0	<1
4	45	1.43	11	44	299	0.34	9	0.17	0.66	0.13	1.40	0.17	46	0	<1	3
4	45	1.44	11	32	137	0.33	—	0.18	—	0.12	1.41	0.18	8	0	<1	—
0	14	0.76	16	61	199	0.29	0	0.15	0.16	0.08	1.63	0.04	26	0	<.1	2
0	7	1.04	8	38	169	0.23	0	0.06	0.09	0.09	1.15	0.02	13	0	0	3
0	4	0.90	7	32	1	0.19	0	0.11	0.02	0.08	1.11	0.03	5	0	0	10
0	14	0.56	9	30	124	0.30	0	0.06	0.06	0.04	0.62	0.01	19	0	0	5
0	20	0.72	3	10	135	0.23	—	0.07	—	0.04	0.45	0.01	10	1	0	—
0	3	0.24	8	32	26	0.24	0	0.02	0.08	0.01	0.10	0.02	5	0	0	4
0	12	0.55	6	29	135	0.20	0	0.07	—	0.04	0.71	0.01	13	0	0	6
0	4	0.65	13	54	87	0.31	0	0.05	0.09	0.03	0.17	0.03	5	<.1	0	3
0	18	0.81	4	19	195	0.12	0	0.08	0.15	0.07	0.79	0.01	19	0	0	2
0	18	0.81	4	109	95	0.12	0	0.08	0.02	0.07	0.79	0.01	19	0	0	3
0	36	1.08	8	40	254	0.20	0	0.12	0.61	0.10	1.21	0.02	27	0	0	2
0	36	1.08	8	107	112	0.20	0	0.12	0.61	0.10	1.21	0.02	27	0	0	2
1	72	0.67	10	120	392	0.17	5	0.12	0.06	0.19	1.05	0.01	28	<.1	<.1	6
0	23	0.78	15	60	201	0.32	0	0.14	0.58	0.08	1.71	0.04	24	0	<.1	3
0	18	0.81	4	19	195	0.12	0	0.08	0.15	0.07	0.79	0.01	19	0	0	2
0	15	1.32	19	55	239	0.48	0	0.15	0.15	0.10	1.49	0.04	35	0	0	2
0	15	1.32	19	61	85	0.48	0	0.15	0.15	0.10	1.49	0.04	15	0	0	10
2	57	0.73	15	86	256	0.24	5	0.10	—	0.12	0.89	0.07	18	<.1	<.1	7
0	48	0.75	11	83	226	0.23	0	0.11	—	0.08	1.65	0.04	20	0	0	6
0	14	0.86	28	83	185	0.60	0	0.06	0.24	0.03	1.27	0.05	8	0	0	4
14	9	0.25	2	24	7	0.09	—	0.03	0.07	0.04	0.23	0.01	2	<1	<.1	—
0	10	0.80	4	19	250	0.10	—	0.12	—	0.07	1.09	0.01	14	<.1	<.1	—
38	21	1.16	9	67	424	0.43	101	0.22	—	0.14	1.25	0.03	35	<1	<.1	13
30	61	1.17	21	62	236	0.57	6	0.14	0.53	0.16	1.50	0.07	54	1	<1	9
17	21	0.92	9	60	257	0.26	—	0.10	—	0.11	0.87	0.03	22	<.1	<1	0
24	89	0.95	14	45	143	0.24	5	0.02	0.09	0.03	0.20	0.01	19	<.1	<.1	2
20	21	1.56	17	68	263	0.68	9	0.29	0.25	0.13	1.91	0.06	60	0	<1	9
4	26	0.36	13	65	205	0.46	2	0.53	—	0.04	0.39	0.03	13	<.1	<.1	5
22	21	1.50	17	67	249	0.64	14	0.27	0.37	0.12	1.82	0.09	58	0	<1	11
0	0	1.80	—	70	190	—	—	0.15	—	0.17	2.00	0.20	40	0	0	—
15	0	1.08	—	—	230	—	—	—	—	—	—	—	—	0	—	—
20	50	1.15	7	56	288	0.39	20	0.14	0.76	0.15	1.14	0.03	29	<1	<1	9
34	16	1.27	29	74	234	0.57	—	0.10	—	0.12	1.44	0.09	33	0	<.1	—
15	42	1.60	18	39	297	0.31	30	0.16	0.46	0.19	1.16	0.05	46	0	<.1	9

TABLE H–1
Food Composition

(DA+ code is for Wadsworth Diet Analysis program)   (For purposes of calculations, use "0" for t, <1, <.1, <.01, etc.)

DA + Code	Food Description	Quantity	Measure	Wt (g)	H₂O (g)	Ener (kcal)	Prot (g)	Carb (g)	Fiber (g)	Fat (g)	Sat	Mono	Poly	Trans
	BREADS, BAKED GOODS, CAKES, COOKIES, CRACKERS, CHIPS, PIES—Continued													
9121	English muffin, plain, enriched	1	item(s)	57	24	134	4	26	2	1	0.15	0.17	0.51	—
29582	English, toasted	1	item(s)	50	19	128	4	25	1	1	0.14	0.16	0.48	—
9145	English, wheat	1	item(s)	57	24	127	5	26	3	1	0.16	0.16	0.48	—
	Granola bars													
38161	Kudos milk chocolate w/fruit & nuts	1	item(s)	28	—	90	2	15	1	3	1.00	—	—	—
38196	Nature Valley banana nut crunchy	1	item(s)	21	—	95	2	14	1	4	0.50	—	—	—
38187	Nature Valley fruit n nut trail mix	1	item(s)	35	—	140	3	25	2	4	0.50	—	—	—
1383	Plain, hard	1	item(s)	25	1	115	2	16	1	5	0.58	1.07	2.95	—
4606	Plain, soft	1	item(s)	28	2	126	2	19	1	5	2.06	1.08	1.51	—
	Pies													
454	Apple pie, from home recipe	1	slice(s)	155	73	411	4	58	2	19	4.73	8.36	5.17	—
470	Pecan pie, from home recipe	1	slice(s)	122	24	503	6	64	0	27	4.87	13.64	6.97	—
472	Pumpkin pie, from home recipe	1	slice(s)	155	91	316	7	41	0	14	4.92	5.73	2.81	—
9007	Pie crust, frozen, ready to bake, enriched, baked	1	slice(s)	16	2	82	1	8	<1	5	1.69	2.51	0.65	—
5052	Pie crust, prepared w/water, baked	1	slice(s)	20	2	100	1	10	<1	6	1.54	3.46	0.77	—
	Rolls													
8555	Crescent dinner roll	1	item(s)	28	10	80	2	14	1	1	0.34	0.70	0.25	—
489	Hamburger roll or bun, plain	1	item(s)	43	15	120	4	21	1	2	0.47	0.48	0.85	—
490	Hard roll	1	item(s)	57	18	167	6	30	1	2	0.35	0.65	0.98	—
5127	Kaiser roll	1	item(s)	57	18	167	6	30	1	2	0.35	0.65	0.98	—
5130	Whole wheat roll or bun	1	item(s)	28	9	76	2	15	2	1	0.24	0.34	0.62	—
	Sport bars													
37026	Balance original chocolate	1	item(s)	50	—	200	14	22	1	6	3.50	—	—	—
37024	Balance original peanut butter	1	item(s)	50	—	200	14	22	1	6	2.50	—	—	—
36580	Clif Bar chocolate brownie energy bar	1	item(s)	68	—	240	10	41	6	4	1.00	—	—	—
36583	Clif Bar crunchy peanut butter energy bar	1	item(s)	68	—	240	12	39	5	5	0.50	—	—	—
36584	Clif Luna tropical crisp energy bar	1	item(s)	48	—	180	10	24	2	5	3.50	0.00	0.00	—
12005	Powerbar apple cinnamon	1	item(s)	65	—	230	10	45	3	3	0.50	1.50	0.50	—
16078	Powerbar banana	1	item(s)	65	—	230	9	45	3	2	0.50	1.00	0.50	—
16080	Powerbar chocolate	1	item(s)	65	—	230	10	45	3	2	0.50	0.50	1.00	—
16079	Powerbar mocha	1	item(s)	65	—	230	10	45	3	3	1.00	1.00	0.50	—
	Tortillas													
1391	Corn tortillas, soft	1	item(s)	26	11	58	1	12	1	1	0.09	0.17	0.29	—
1669	Flour tortilla	1	item(s)	32	9	104	3	18	1	2	0.56	1.21	0.34	—
1390	Taco shells, hard	1	item(s)	13	1	62	1	8	1	3	0.43	1.19	1.13	—
	Pancakes, waffles													
8926	Pancakes, blueberry, from recipe	3	item(s)	114	61	253	7	33	1	10	2.26	2.64	4.74	—
5037	Pancakes, from mix w/egg & milk	3	item(s)	114	60	249	9	33	2	9	2.33	2.36	3.33	—
9219	Waffle, plain, frozen, toasted	2	item(s)	66	28	174	4	27	2	5	0.95	2.12	1.84	—
500	Waffle, plain, from recipe	1	item(s)	75	<.1	218	6	25	2	11	2.14	2.64	5.08	—
30311	Waffle, 100% whole grain	1	item(s)	75	32	201	7	25	2	8	2.35	3.38	2.06	—
	CEREAL, FLOUR, GRAIN, PASTA, NOODLES, POPCORN													
	Grain													
2861	Amaranth, dry	½	cup(s)	98	10	365	14	65	15	6	1.62	1.40	2.82	—
1953	Barley, pearled, cooked	½	cup(s)	79	54	97	2	22	3	<1	0.07	0.04	0.17	—
1956	Buckwheat groats, cooked, roasted	½	cup(s)	84	64	77	3	17	2	1	0.11	0.16	0.16	—
1957	Bulgur, cooked	½	cup(s)	91	71	76	3	17	4	<1	0.04	0.03	0.09	—
1963	Couscous, cooked	½	cup(s)	79	57	88	3	18	1	<1	0.02	0.02	0.05	—
1967	Millet, cooked	½	cup(s)	120	86	143	4	28	2	1	0.21	0.22	0.61	—
1969	Oat bran, dry	½	cup(s)	47	3	116	8	31	7	3	0.62	1.12	1.30	—
1972	Quinoa, dry	½	cup(s)	85	8	318	11	59	5	5	0.50	1.30	1.99	—
	Rice													
129	Brown, long grain, cooked	½	cup(s)	98	71	108	3	22	2	1	0.18	0.32	0.31	—
2863	Brown, medium grain, cooked	½	cup(s)	97.5	0.07	109.19	2.26	22.92	1.75	0.8	0.16	0.29	0.28	—
37488	Jasmine, saffroned, cooked	½	cup(s)	280	—	340	8	78	0	0	0.00	—	—	0
30280	Pilaf, cooked	½	cup(s)	103	74	129	2	22	1	3	0.67	1.61	0.95	—
28066	Spanish, cooked	½	cup(s)	120	3	25	2	1	<1	<1	0.33	0.07	18.31	0
2867	White glutinous, cooked	½	cup(s)	87	67	84	2	18	1	<1	0.03	0.06	0.06	—
482	White, instant long grain, enriched, boiled	½	cup(s)	83	63	81	2	18	<1	<1	0.04	0.04	0.04	—
484	White, long grain, boiled	½	cup(s)	79	54	103	2	22	<1	<1	0.06	0.07	0.06	—
486	White, long grain, enriched, parboiled, cooked	½	cup(s)	88	63	100	2	22	<1	<1	0.06	0.07	0.06	—
1194	Wild brown, cooked	½	cup(s)	82	0.06	82.81	3.27	17.49	1.47	0.27	0.04	0.04	0.17	—

PAGE KEY: H–2 = Breads/Baked Goods H–6 = Cereal/Rice/Pasta H–10 = Fruit H–14 = Vegetables/Legumes H–24 = Nuts/Seeds H–26 = Vegetarian
H–28 = Dairy H–34 = Eggs H–34 = Seafood H–36 = Meats H–40 = Poultry H–40 = Processed meats H–42 = Beverages H–46 = Fats/Oils
H–48 = Sweets H–50 = Spices/Condiments/Sauces H–52 = Mixed foods/Soups/Sandwiches H–58 = Fast food H–74 = Convenience meals H–76 = Baby foods

Chol (mg)	Calc (mg)	Iron (mg)	Magn (mg)	Pota (mg)	Sodi (mg)	Zinc (mg)	Vit A (µg)	Thia (mg)	Vit E (mg α)	Ribo (mg)	Niac (mg)	Vit B_6 (mg)	Fola (µg)	Vit C (mg)	Vit B_{12} (µg)	Sele (µg)
0	30	1.43	12	75	264	0.40	0	0.25	—	0.16	2.21	0.02	42	0	<.1	—
0	95	1.36	11	72	252	0.38	0	0.19	0.17	0.14	1.90	0.02	15	<.1	<.1	—
0	101	1.64	21	106	218	0.61	0	0.25	0.26	0.17	1.91	0.05	36	0	0	17
0	200	0.36	—	—	60	—	0	—	—	—	—	—	—	0	0	—
0	10	0.54	—	60	80	—	0	—	—	—	—	—	—	0	—	—
0	0	0.00	—	—	95	—	0	—	—	—	—	—	—	0	—	—
0	15	0.72	24	82	72	0.50	2	0.06	—	0.03	0.39	0.02	6	<1	0	4
<1	30	0.73	21	92	79	0.43	0	0.08	—	0.05	0.15	0.03	7	0	<1	5
0	11	1.74	11	122	327	0.29	17	0.23	—	0.17	1.91	0.05	37	3	0	12
106	39	1.81	32	162	320	1.24	100	0.23	—	0.22	1.03	0.07	32	<1	<1	15
65	146	1.97	29	288	349	0.71	660	0.14	—	0.31	1.21	0.07	33	3	<1	11
0	3	0.36	3	18	104	0.05	0	0.04	0.42	0.06	0.39	0.01	9	0	<.1	<1
0	12	0.43	3	12	146	0.08	0	0.06	—	0.04	0.47	0.01	20	0	0	—
0	39	0.89	6	39	157	0.17	0	0.14	0.02	0.09	1.10	0.01	—	0	<.1	—
0	59	1.43	9	40	206	0.28	0	0.17	0.03	0.14	1.79	0.03	48	0	<.1	8
0	54	1.87	15	62	310	0.54	0	0.27	0.24	0.19	2.42	0.02	54	0	0	22
0	54	1.87	15	62	310	0.54	0	0.27	—	0.19	2.42	0.02	54	0	0	22
0	30	0.69	24	78	136	0.57	0	0.07	—	0.04	1.05	0.06	9	0	0	14
3	100	4.50	40	160	180	3.75	—	0.38	—	0.43	5.00	0.50	100	60	2	18
3	100	4.50	40	130	230	3.75	—	0.38	—	0.43	5.00	0.50	100	60	2	18
0	250	5.40	120	260	150	3.75	—	0.38	—	0.26	4.00	0.40	80	60	1	18
0	250	5.40	120	300	290	3.75	—	0.38	—	0.34	6.00	0.40	100	60	1	14
0	350	6.30	140	120	135	5.25	—	1.50	—	1.70	20.00	2.00	400	60	6	25
0	300	6.30	140	110	90	5.25	0	1.50	—	1.70	20.00	2.00	400	60	6	—
0	300	6.30	140	200	90	5.25	0	1.50	—	1.70	20.00	2.00	400	60	6	—
0	300	6.30	140	150	90	5.25	0	1.50	—	1.70	20.00	2.00	400	60	6	—
0	300	6.30	140	150	90	5.25	0	1.50	—	1.70	20.00	2.00	400	60	6	—
0	46	0.36	17	40	42	0.24	0	0.03	0.07	0.02	0.39	0.06	26	0	0	1
0	40	1.06	8	42	153	0.23	0	0.17	0.06	0.09	1.14	0.02	33	0	0	7
0	21	0.33	14	24	49	0.19	0	0.03	0.22	0.01	0.18	0.04	17	0	0	2
64	235	1.96	18	157	470	0.62	57	0.22	—	0.31	1.74	0.06	41	3	<1	16
81	245	1.48	25	227	576	0.86	82	0.23	—	0.36	1.40	0.12	105	1	<1	—
16	153	2.95	15	84	519	0.38	253	0.25	0.65	0.31	2.93	0.59	36	0	2	11
52	191	1.73	14	119	383	0.50	49	0.19	—	0.26	1.55	0.04	51	<1	<1	35
71	196	1.56	30	173	374	0.85	—	0.15	0.32	0.25	1.47	0.09	14	<1	<1	—
0	149	7.40	259	357	20	3.10	0	0.08	—	0.20	1.25	0.22	48	4	0	—
0	9	1.04	17	73	2	0.64	0	0.07	0.01	0.05	1.62	0.09	13	0	0	7
0	6	0.67	43	74	3	0.51	0	0.03	0.08	0.03	0.79	0.06	12	0	0	2
0	9	0.87	29	62	5	0.52	0	0.05	0.01	0.03	0.91	0.08	16	0	0	1
0	6	0.30	6	46	4	0.20	0	0.05	0.10	0.02	0.77	0.04	12	0	0	22
0	4	0.76	53	74	2	1.09	0	0.13	0.02	0.10	1.60	0.13	23	0	0	1
0	27	2.54	110	266	2	1.46	0	0.55	0.47	0.10	0.44	0.08	24	0	0	21
0	51	7.86	179	629	18	2.81	0	0.17	—	0.34	2.49	0.19	42	0	0	—
0	10	0.41	42	42	5	0.61	0	0.09	0.03	0.02	1.49	0.14	4	0	0	10
0	9.75	0.51	42.9	77.02	0.97	0.6	0	0.09	—	0.01	1.29	0.14	3.9	0	0	38
0	—	2.16	—	—	780	—	—	—	—	—	—	—	—	0	0	—
0	13	1.16	9	55	403	0.38	—	0.13	0.28	0.02	1.24	0.06	4	<1	<.1	—
1	47	0.78	48	1	13	0.13	<1	0.03	0.06	0.19	8.71	0.14	<.1	7	<.1	9
0	2	0.12	4	9	4	0.36	0	0.02	0.03	0.01	0.25	0.02	1	0	0	5
0	7	0.52	4	3	2	0.20	0	0.06	0.01	0.04	0.73	0.01	58	0	0	3
0	8	0.95	9	28	1	0.39	0	0.13	0.03	0.01	1.17	0.07	46	0	0	6
0	17	0.99	11	32	3	0.27	0	0.22	0.01	0.02	1.23	0.02	67	0	0	7
0	2.46	0.49	26.23	82.81	2.46	1.09	0	0.04	—	0.07	1.05	0.11	21.31	0	0	0.65

TABLE H–1
Food Composition

(DA+ code is for Wadsworth Diet Analysis program)   (For purposes of calculations, use "0" for t, <1, <.1, <.01, etc.)

DA + Code	Food Description	Quantity	Measure	Wt (g)	H₂O (g)	Ener (kcal)	Prot (g)	Carb (g)	Fiber (g)	Fat (g)	Sat	Mono	Poly	Trans

CEREAL, FLOUR, GRAIN, PASTA, NOODLES, POPCORN—Continued

Flour & grain fractions

DA + Code	Food Description	Quantity	Measure	Wt (g)	H₂O (g)	Ener (kcal)	Prot (g)	Carb (g)	Fiber (g)	Fat (g)	Sat	Mono	Poly	Trans
505	All purpose flour, self rising, enriched	½	cup(s)	63	7	221	6	46	2	1	0.10	0.05	0.26	—
503	All purpose flour, white, bleached, enriched	½	cup(s)	63	7	228	6	48	2	1	0.10	0.05	0.26	—
1643	Barley flour	½	cup(s)	56	6	198	4	45	2	1	0.16	0.10	0.38	—
383	Buckwheat flour, whole groat	½	cup(s)	60	7	201	8	42	6	2	0.41	0.57	0.57	—
504	Cake wheat flour, enriched	½	cup(s)	55	7	197	4	43	1	<1	0.07	0.04	0.21	—
426	Cornmeal, degermed, enriched	½	cup(s)	69	8	253	6	54	5	1	0.16	0.28	0.49	—
424	Cornmeal, yellow whole grain	½	cup(s)	61	6	221	5	47	4	2	0.31	0.58	1.00	—
1644	Masa corn flour, enriched	½	cup(s)	57	5	208	5	43	5	2	0.30	0.57	0.98	—
1976	Rice flour, brown	½	cup(s)	79	9	287	6	60	4	2	0.44	0.80	0.79	—
1645	Rice flour, white	½	cup(s)	79	9	289	5	63	2	1	0.30	0.35	0.30	—
1978	Rye flour, dark	½	cup(s)	64	7	207	9	44	14	2	0.20	0.21	0.77	—
1980	Semolina, enriched	½	cup(s)	84	11	301	11	61	3	1	0.13	0.10	0.36	—
2827	Soy flour, raw	½	cup(s)	43	2	186	15	15	4	9	1.27	1.94	4.96	—
1990	Wheat germ, crude	2	tablespoon(s)	14	2	52	3	7	2	1	0.24	0.20	0.86	—
506	Whole wheat flour	½	cup(s)	60	6	203	8	44	7	1	0.19	0.14	0.47	—

Breakfast bars

DA + Code	Food Description	Quantity	Measure	Wt (g)	H₂O (g)	Ener (kcal)	Prot (g)	Carb (g)	Fiber (g)	Fat (g)	Sat	Mono	Poly	Trans
39230	Atkins Morning Start apple crisp	1	item(s)	37	—	170	11	12	6	9	4.00	—	—	—
10574	Health Valley fat free apple	1	item(s)	38	—	110	2	26	3	0	0.00	0.00	0.00	0
10647	Nutri-Grain blueberry cereal bar	1	item(s)	37	5	140	2	27	1	3	0.50	2.00	0.50	—
10648	Nutri-Grain raspberry cereal bar	1	item(s)	37	5	140	2	27	1	3	0.50	2.00	0.50	—
10649	Nutri-Grain strawberry cereal bar	1	item(s)	37	5	140	2	27	1	3	0.50	2.00	0.50	—

Breakfast cereals, hot

DA + Code	Food Description	Quantity	Measure	Wt (g)	H₂O (g)	Ener (kcal)	Prot (g)	Carb (g)	Fiber (g)	Fat (g)	Sat	Mono	Poly	Trans
363	Corn grits, white, regular & quick, enriched, cooked w/water & salt	½	cup(s)	121	103	71	2	16	<1	<1	0.03	0.06	0.10	—
8636	Corn grits, yellow, regular & quick, enriched, cooked w/salt	½	cup(s)	121	103	71	2	16	<1	<1	0.03	0.06	0.10	—
1260	Cream of Wheat, instant, prepared	½	cup(s)	121	106	61	2	13	<1	<.1	0.01	0.01	0.04	0
365	Farina, enriched, cooked w/water & salt	½	cup(s)	117	102	56	2	12	<1	<.1	0.01	0.01	0.03	—
8657	Oatmeal, cooked w/water	½	cup(s)	117	100	74	3	13	2	1	0.19	0.37	0.44	—
5500	Oatmeal, maple & brown sugar, instant, prepared	1	item(s)	198	150	200	5	40	2	2	0.42	0.74	0.85	—
5510	Oatmeal, ready to serve, packet	1	item(s)	186	158	112	4	20	3	2	0.38	0.66	0.76	—

Breakfast cereals, ready to eat

DA + Code	Food Description	Quantity	Measure	Wt (g)	H₂O (g)	Ener (kcal)	Prot (g)	Carb (g)	Fiber (g)	Fat (g)	Sat	Mono	Poly	Trans
1197	All-Bran	1	cup(s)	62	2	160	8	46	20	2	0.00	0.00	1.00	0
1200	All-Bran Buds	1	cup(s)	91	3	212	6	73	42	3	—	—	—	0
1199	Apple Jacks	1	cup(s)	33	1	130	1	30	1	1	—	—	—	0
13633	Bran Flakes, Post	1	cup(s)	40	1	133	4	32	7	1	0.00	0.00	0.71	—
1204	Cap'n Crunch	1	cup(s)	36	1	144	2	30	1	2	0.53	0.39	0.27	—
1205	Cap'n Crunch Crunchberries w/wildberry colors	1	cup(s)	35	1	139	2	29	1	2	0.49	0.39	0.28	—
1206	Cheerios	1	cup(s)	30	1	110	3	22	3	2	0.00	0.50	0.50	—
3415	Cocoa Puffs	1	cup(s)	30	1	120	1	26	0	1	—	—	—	—
1207	Cocoa Rice Krispies	1	cup(s)	41	1	160	1	36	1	1	0.67	0.00	0.00	—
5522	Complete wheat bran flakes	1	cup(s)	39	1	120	4	31	7	1	—	—	—	0
1211	Corn Flakes	1	cup(s)	28	1	100	2	24	1	0	0.00	0.00	0.00	0
1247	Corn Pops	1	cup(s)	31	1	120	1	28	0	0	0.00	0.00	0.00	0
1937	Cracklin' Oat Bran	1	cup(s)	65	0	266	5	47	7	9	2.70	4.70	1.33	0
1220	Froot Loops	1	cup(s)	32	1	120	1	28	1	1	0.50	0.00	0.00	—
38214	Frosted Cheerios	1	cup(s)	30	—	120	2	25	1	1	0.00	0.00	0.00	—
372	Frosted Flakes	1	cup(s)	41	1	160	1	37	1	0	0.00	0.00	0.00	—
38215	Frosted Mini Chex	1	cup(s)	40	—	146	1	36	0	0	0.00	0.00	0.00	0
10268	Frosted Mini-Wheats	5	item(s)	51	3	180	5	41	5	1	0.00	0.00	0.50	0
38216	Frosted Wheaties	1	cup(s)	40	—	146	1	36	<1	0	0.00	0.00	0.00	—
1223	Granola, prepared	½	cup(s)	61	0	299	9	32	5	15	2.76	4.7	6.53	—
13334	Granola, Quaker 100% natural, oats & honey	½	cup(s)	48	0	219	5	31	3	9	3.83	4.0	1.19	—
13335	Granola, Quaker 100% natural, oats, honey & raisins	½	cup(s)	51	0	225	5	34	3	9	3.57	3.80	1.10	—
2415	Honey Bunches of Oats honey roasted	1	cup(s)	40	1	160	3	33	1	2	0.67	1.20	0.13	—
1227	Honey Nut Cheerios	1	cup(s)	30	1	120	3	24	2	2	0.00	0.50	0.00	—
2424	Honeycomb	1	cup(s)	22	<1	83	2	20	<1	<1	0.00			—
10286	Kashi puffed	1	cup(s)	25	—	70	3	13	2	1	0.00	—	—	—
1231	Kix	1	cup(s)	23	<1	90	2	20	1	<1	0.00	0.00	0.00	—
30569	Life	1	cup(s)	43	2	160	4	33	3	2	0.35	0.64	0.61	—
1233	Lucky Charms	1	cup(s)	30	1	120	2	25	1	1	0.00	0.00	0.00	—

PAGE KEY: H–2 = Breads/Baked Goods   H–6 = Cereal/Rice/Pasta   H–10 = Fruit   H–14 = Vegetables/Legumes   H–24 = Nuts/Seeds   H–26 = Vegetarian   H–28 = Dairy   H–34 = Eggs   H–34 = Seafood   H–36 = Meats   H–40 = Poultry   H–40 = Processed meats   H–42 = Beverages   H–46 = Fats/Oils   H–48 = Sweets   H–50 = Spices/Condiments/Sauces   H–52 = Mixed foods/Soups/Sandwiches   H–58 = Fast food   H–74 = Convenience meals   H–76 = Baby foods

Chol (mg)	Calc (mg)	Iron (mg)	Magn (mg)	Pota (mg)	Sodi (mg)	Zinc (mg)	Vit A (µg)	Thia (mg)	Vit E (mg α)	Ribo (mg)	Niac (mg)	Vit B_6 (mg)	Fola (µg)	Vit C (mg)	Vit B_{12} (µg)	Sele (µg)
0	211	2.92	12	78	794	0.39	0	0.42	0.03	0.26	3.65	0.03	123	0	0	22
0	9	2.90	14	67	1	0.44	0	0.49	0.04	0.31	3.69	0.03	114	0	0	21
0	16	0.71	45	186	4	1.05	0	0.07	—	0.03	2.57	0.16	13	0	0	2
0	25	2.44	151	346	7	1.87	0	0.25	0.19	0.11	3.69	0.35	32	0	0	3
0	8	3.99	9	57	1	0.34	0	0.49	0.01	0.23	3.70	0.02	101	0	0	3
0	3	2.85	28	112	2	0.50	8	0.49	0.10	0.28	3.47	0.18	161	0	0	5
0	4	2.10	77	175	21	1.11	7	0.23	0.26	0.12	2.22	0.19	15	0	0	9
0	80	4.11	63	170	3	1.01	0	0.81	0.09	0.43	5.61	0.21	133	0	0	9
0	9	1.56	88	228	6	1.94	0	0.35	0.95	0.06	5.01	0.58	13	0	0	—
0	8	0.28	28	60	0	0.63	0	0.11	0.09	0.02	2.05	0.34	3	0	0	12
0	36	4.13	159	467	1	3.60	1	0.20	0.90	0.16	2.73	0.28	38	0	0	23
0	14	3.64	39	155	1	0.88	0	0.68	0.22	0.48	5.00	0.09	153	0	0	75
0	88	2.71	183	1070	6	1.67	3	0.25	0.93	0.49	1.84	0.20	147	0	0	3
0	6	0.90	34	128	2	1.77	0	0.27	—	0.07	0.98	0.19	40	0	0	11
0	20	2.33	83	243	3	1.76	0	0.27	0.49	0.13	3.82	0.20	26	0	0	42
0	200	—	—	90	70	—	—	0.23	—	0.26	3.00	—	—	9	—	—
0	0	0.72	—	160	25	—	—	0.09	—	0.03	0.40	—	—	1	—	—
0	200	1.80	8	75	110	1.50	—	0.38	—	0.43	5.00	0.50	40	0	0	—
0	200	1.80	8	70	110	1.50	—	0.38	—	0.43	5.00	0.50	40	0	0	—
0	200	1.80	8	55	110	1.50	—	0.38	—	0.43	5.00	0.50	40	0	0	—
0	4	0.73	6	25	270	0.08	0	0.10	0.02	0.07	0.87	0.03	40	0	0	4
0	4	0.73	6	25	270	0.08	2	0.10	0.02	0.07	0.87	0.03	40	0	0	3
0	27	8.60	2	17	1	0.10	0	0.07	—	0.04	0.60	0.01	357	0	0	—
0	5	0.58	2	15	383	0.09	0	0.07	0.01	0.05	0.57	0.01	40	0	0	11
0	9	0.80	28	66	1	0.57	0	0.13	0.12	0.02	0.15	0.02	5	0	0	9
0	26	6.84	50	126	404	1.04	0	1.02	—	0.05	1.57	0.31	30	0	0	11
0	21	3.96	45	112	241	0.93	0	0.60	—	0.05	0.78	0.19	19	0	0	4
0	300	9.00	200	700	160	3.00	300	0.75	—	0.85	10.00	4.00	800	12	12	6
0	0	13.64	182	909	606	4.55	455	1.14	—	1.29	15.15	6.06	1212	18	18	26
0	0	4.50	8	35	150	1.50	150	0.38	—	0.43	5.00	0.50	100	15	2	2
0	0	10.77	80	253	293	2.00	—	0.50	—	0.57	6.65	0.67	133	0	2	—
0	5	6.00	20	72	269	4.99	3	0.51	—	0.57	6.66	0.67	133	0	0	7
<.1	7	6.14	19	71	242	5.12	2	0.51	—	0.57	6.66	0.67	133	<.1	0	7
0	100	8.10	40	95	280	3.75	150	0.38	—	0.43	5.00	0.50	200	6	2	11
0	100	4.50	8	50	170	3.75	0	0.38	—	0.43	5.00	0.50	100	6	2	2
0	53	5.99	11	67	253	2.00	200	0.50	—	0.57	6.65	0.67	133	20	2	6
0	0	23.94	53	226	279	19.95	299	2.00	—	2.26	26.60	2.66	532	80	8	4
0	0	8.10	3	25	200	0.17	150	0.38	—	0.43	5.00	0.50	100	6	2	1
0	0	1.80	2	25	120	1.50	150	0.38	—	0.43	5.00	0.50	100	6	2	2
0	27	2.38	80	293	186	2.00	299	0.49	—	0.56	6.65	0.67	218	20	2	14
0	0	4.50	8	35	150	1.50	150	0.38	—	0.43	5.00	0.50	100	15	2	2
0	100	4.50	16	55	210	3.75	—	0.38	—	0.43	5.00	0.50	100	6	2	—
0	0	5.99	4	27	200	0.21	200	0.50	—	0.57	6.65	0.67	133	8	2	2
0	133	11.97	—	33	266	3.99	—	0.50	—	0.57	6.65	0.67	266	8	2	—
0	0	15.30	60	170	5	1.50	0	0.38	—	0.43	5.00	0.50	100	0	2	2
0	133	10.77	0	47	266	9.98	—	1.00	—	1.13	13.30	1.33	532	8	4	—
0	48	2.59	107	328	13	2.5	2	0.44	3.59	0.17	1.29	0.18	51	1	0	16.95
1	61	1.21	51	225	20	1.04	1	0.12	—	0.11	0.81	0.07	17	<1	0.1	8.3
1	59	1.24	49	250	19	0.99	<1	0.12	—	0.11	0.8	0.07	16	<1	0.1	8.82
0	0	3.59	21	67	253	0.40	—	0.50	—	0.57	6.65	0.67	133	0	2	—
0	100	4.50	24	95	270	3.75	—	0.38	—	0.43	5.00	0.50	200	6	2	7
0	0	2.03	6	26	165	1.13	—	0.28	—	0.32	3.74	0.37	75	0	1	—
0	0	0.72	—	35	0	—	0	0.03	—	0.03	0.80	0.00	—	0	—	—
0	113	6.08	6	26	203	2.81	113	0.28	—	0.32	3.75	0.38	150	5	1	5
0	124	11.92	41	121	218	5.32	1	0.53	—	0.60	7.10	0.70	142	0	0	11
0	100	4.50	16	60	210	3.75	—	0.38	—	0.43	5.00	0.50	200	6	2	6

TABLE H–1
Food Composition

(DA+ code is for Wadsworth Diet Analysis program)   (For purposes of calculations, use "0" for t, <1, <.1, <.01, etc.)

DA + Code	Food Description	Quantity	Measure	Wt (g)	H₂O (g)	Ener (kcal)	Prot (g)	Carb (g)	Fiber (g)	Fat (g)	Sat	Mono	Poly	Trans

CEREAL, FLOUR, GRAIN, PASTA, NOODLES, POPCORN—Continued

DA + Code	Food Description	Quantity	Measure	Wt (g)	H₂O (g)	Ener (kcal)	Prot (g)	Carb (g)	Fiber (g)	Fat (g)	Sat	Mono	Poly	Trans
1201	Multi-Bran Chex	1	cup(s)	58	1	200	4	49	7	2	0.00	0.00	0.00	0
38220	Multi Grain Cheerios	1	cup(s)	30	—	110	3	24	3	1	0.00	0.00	0.00	—
1238	Nutri-Grain golden wheat	1	cup(s)	40	—	133	4	31	5	1	0.00	0.00	0.67	—
1241	Product 19	1	cup(s)	30	1	100	2	25	1	0	0.00	0.00	0.00	0
32432	Puffed rice, fortified	1	cup(s)	14	<1	56	1	13	<1	<.1	0.02	—	—	—
32433	Puffed wheat, fortified	1	cup(s)	12	0	43.68	1.76	9.55	0.52	0.14	0.02	—	—	—
2420	Raisin Bran	1	cup(s)	59	5	190	4	47	8	1	0.00	0.10	0.36	—
1244	Rice Chex	1	cup(s)	25	1	96	2	22	<1	0	0.00	0.00	0.00	0
1245	Rice Krispies	1	cup(s)	26	1	96	2	23	0	0	0.00	0.00	0.00	0
5593	Shredded Wheat	1	cup(s)	25	1	88	3	20	3	1	0.04	0.01	0.10	—
1248	Smacks	1	cup(s)	36	1	133	3	32	1	1	0.00	0.00	0.00	—
1246	Special K	1	cup(s)	31	1	110	7	22	1	0	0.00	0.00	0.00	0
3428	Total, corn flakes	1	cup(s)	23	1	83	2	18	1	0	0.00	0.00	0.00	0
1253	Total whole grain	1	cup(s)	40	1	146	3	31	4	1	0.00	0.00	0.00	—
1254	Trix	1	cup(s)	30	1	120	1	27	1	1	0.00	0.00	0.00	—
382	Wheat germ, toasted	2	tablespoon(s)	14	0	53.95	4.11	7	2.13	1.51	0.25	0.21	0.93	—
1257	Wheaties	1	cup(s)	30	1	110	3	24	3	1	0.00	0.00	0.00	—
	Pasta, noodles													
449	Chinese chow mein noodles, cooked	½	cup(s)	23	<1	119	2	13	1	7	0.99	1.73	3.90	—
1995	Corn pasta, cooked	½	cup(s)	70	48	88	2	20	3	1	0.07	0.13	0.23	—
448	Egg noodles, enriched, cooked	½	cup(s)	80	55	106	4	20	1	1	0.25	0.34	0.33	0.02
440	Macaroni, enriched, cooked	½	cup(s)	70	46	99	3	20	1	<1	0.07	0.06	0.19	—
1996	Pasta, plain, fresh-refrigerated, cooked	½	cup(s)	64	44	84	3	16	0	1	0.10	0.08	0.27	—
1725	Ramen noodles, cooked	½	cup(s)	114	95	104	3	15	1	4	0.19	0.22	0.21	—
2878	Soba noodles, cooked	½	cup(s)	95	69	94	5	20	0	<.1	0.02	0.02	0.03	—
2879	Somen noodles, cooked	½	cup(s)	88	60	115	4	24	0	<1	0.02	0.02	0.06	—
493	Spaghetti, al dente, cooked	½	cup(s)	65	42	95	4	20	1	1	0.05	0.05	0.15	—
2884	Spaghetti, whole wheat, cooked	½	cup(s)	70	47	87	4	19	3	<1	0.07	0.05	0.15	—
1563	Spinach egg noodles, enriched, cooked	½	cup(s)	80	55	105	4	19	2	1	0.29	0.39	0.28	—
2000	Tricolor vegetable macaroni, enriched, cooked	½	cup(s)	67	46	86	3	18	3	<.1	0.01	0.01	0.03	—
	Popcorn													
476	Air popped	1	cup(s)	8	<1	31	1	6	1	<1	0.05	0.09	0.15	—
4619	Caramel	1	cup(s)	35	1	152	1	28	2	5	1.27	1.01	1.58	—
4620	Cheese flavored	1	cup(s)	37	1	196	3	19	4	12	2.38	3.61	5.72	—
477	Popped in oil	1	cup(s)	33	1	165	3	19	3	9	1.61	2.70	4.43	—
	FRUIT AND FRUIT JUICES													
	Apples													
223	Raw medium, w/peel	1	item(s)	138	118	72	<1	19	3	<1	0.04	0.01	0.07	—
224	Slices	½	cup(s)	55	47	29	<1	8	1	<.1	0.02	0.00	0.03	—
946	Slices w/o skin, boiled	½	cup(s)	85	73	45	<1	12	2	<1	0.05	0.01	0.09	—
948	Dried, sulfured	½	cup(s)	22	7	52	<1	14	2	<.1	0.01	0.00	0.02	—
952	Juice, from frozen concentrate	½	cup(s)	120	105	56	<1	14	<1	<1	0.02	0.00	0.04	—
225	Juice, unsweetened, canned	½	cup(s)	124	109	58	<.1	14	<1	<1	0.02	0.01	0.04	—
226	Applesauce, sweetened, canned	½	cup(s)	128	101	97	<1	25	2	<1	0.04	0.01	0.07	—
227	Applesauce, unsweetened, canned	½	cup(s)	122	108	52	<1	14	1	<.1	0.01	0.00	0.02	—
38492	Crabapples	1	item(s)	35	28	27	<1	7	1	<1	0.02	0.00	0.03	—
	Apricot													
228	Fresh w/o pits	4	item(s)	140	121	67	2	16	3	1	0.04	0.24	0.11	—
230	Halves, dried, sulfured	¼	cup(s)	33	10	79	1	21	2	<1	0.01	0.02	0.02	—
229	Halves w/skin, canned in heavy syrup	½	cup(s)	129	100	107	1	28	2	<1	0.01	0.04	0.02	—
	Avocado													
233	California, whole, w/o skin or pit	1	item(s)	170	<1	284	3	15	12	26	3.59	16.61	3.42	—
234	Florida, whole, w/o skin or pit	1	item(s)	304	<1	365	7	24	17	31	5.90	16.70	5.00	—
2998	Pureed	⅛	cup(s)	29	21	46	1	2	2	4	0.61	2.82	0.52	—
	Banana													
235	Fresh whole, w/o peel	1	item(s)	118	88	105	1	27	3	<1	0.13	0.04	0.09	—
4580	Dried chips	¼	cup(s)	55	2	287	1	32	4	19	16.00	1.08	0.35	—
	Blackberries													
237	Raw	½	cup(s)	72	63	31	1	7	4	<1	0.01	0.03	0.20	—
958	Unsweetened, frozen	½	cup(s)	76	62	48	1	12	4	<1	0.01	0.03	0.18	—
	Blueberries													
238	Raw	½	cup(s)	72	61	41	1	10	2	<1	0.02	0.03	0.11	—
959	Canned in heavy syrup	½	cup(s)	128	98	113	1	28	2	<1	0.03	0.06	0.18	—
960	Unsweetened, frozen	½	cup(s)	78	67	40	1	10	2	1	0.04	0.07	0.22	—

PAGE KEY: H–2 = Breads/Baked Goods H–6 = Cereal/Rice/Pasta H–10 = Fruit H–14 = Vegetables/Legumes H–24 = Nuts/Seeds H–26 = Vegetarian H–28 = Dairy H–34 = Eggs H–34 = Seafood H–36 = Meats H–40 = Poultry H–40 = Processed meats H–42 = Beverages H–46 = Fats/Oils H–48 = Sweets H–50 = Spices/Condiments/Sauces H–52 = Mixed foods/Soups/Sandwiches H–58 = Fast food H–74 = Convenience meals H–76 = Baby foods

Chol (mg)	Calc (mg)	Iron (mg)	Magn (mg)	Pota (mg)	Sodi (mg)	Zinc (mg)	Vit A (µg)	Thia (mg)	Vit E (mg α)	Ribo (mg)	Niac (mg)	Vit B$_6$ (mg)	Fola (µg)	Vit C (mg)	Vit B$_{12}$ (µg)	Sele (µg)
0	100	16.20	60	220	390	3.75	158	0.38	—	0.03	5.00	0.50	100	6	2	5
0	100	18.00	24	85	200	15.00	—	1.50	—	1.70	20.00	2.00	400	15	6	—
0	0	1.46	32	146	279	4.99	0	0.50	—	0.57	6.65	0.67	133	20	2	9
0	0	18.00	16	50	210	15.00	225	1.50	—	1.70	20.00	2.00	400	60	6	4
0	1	4.44	4	16	<1	0.14	0	0.36	—	0.25	4.94	0.01	3	0	0	1
3.35	3.8	17.39	41.75	0.47	0.28	0		0.31	—	0.21	4.23	0.02	3.83	0	0	14.77
0	20	10.80	80	340	300	2.25	—	0.53	—	0.60	7.00	0.70	140	0	2	—
0	80	7.20	7	28	232	3.00	—	0.30	—	0.34	4.00	0.40	160	5	1	1
0	0	1.44	13	32	256	0.48	120	0.30	—	0.34	4.80	0.40	80	5	1	4
0	10	1.08	31	92	2	0.70	0	0.07	—	0.06	1.77	0.10	12	0	0	1
0	0	0.48	11	53	67	0.40	200	0.50	—	0.57	6.65	0.67	133	8	2	17
0	0	8.70	16	60	220	0.90	225	0.53	—	0.60	7.00	2.00	400	15	6	7
0	750	13.50	0	23	158	11.25	113	1.13	22.50	1.28	15.00	1.50	300	45	5	1
0	1330	23.94	32	120	253	19.95	200	2.00	31.24	2.26	26.60	2.66	532	80	8	2
0	100	4.50	0	15	190	3.75	150	0.38	—	0.43	5.00	0.50	100	6	2	6
0	6.35	1.28	45.2	133.76	0.56	2.35	0	0.23	—	0.11	0.78	0.13	49.72	0.84	0	9.18
0	0	8.10	32	110	220	7.50	150	0.75	2.26	0.85	10.00	1.00	200	6	3	1
0	5	1.06	12	27	99	0.32	0	0.13	—	0.09	1.34	0.02	20	0	0	10
0	1	0.18	25	22	0	0.44	2	0.04	0.78	0.02	0.39	0.04	4	0	0	2
26	10	1.27	15	22	6	0.49	5	0.15	0.14	0.07	1.19	0.03	51	0	<.1	17
0	5	0.98	13	22	1	0.37	0	0.14	0.04	0.07	1.17	0.02	54	0	0	15
21	4	0.73	12	15	4	0.36	4	0.13	—	0.10	0.63	0.02	41	0	<.1	—
18	9	0.89	9	34	415	0.31	—	0.08	—	0.05	0.71	0.03	4	<.1	<.1	—
0	4	0.45	9	33	57	0.11	0	0.09	—	0.02	0.48	0.04	7	0	0	—
0	7	0.46	2	25	141	0.19	0	0.02	—	0.03	0.09	0.01	2	0	0	—
0	7	1.00	12	52	1	0.35	0	0.12	0.04	0.07	0.90	0.04	8	0	0	40
0	11	0.74	21	31	2	0.57	0	0.08	0.21	0.03	0.49	0.06	4	0	0	18
26	15	0.87	19	30	10	0.50	4	0.20	0.46	0.10	1.18	0.09	51	0	<1	17
0	7	0.33	13	21	4	0.29	3	0.08	0.06	0.04	0.72	0.02	44	0	0	13
0	1	0.22	11	24	<1	0.28	1	0.02	0.02	0.02	0.16	0.02	2	0	0	1
2	15	0.61	12	38	73	0.20	1	0.02	0.42	0.02	0.77	0.01	2	0	<.1	1
4	42	0.83	34	97	331	0.75	14	0.05	—	0.09	0.54	0.09	4	<1	<1	4
0	3	0.92	36	74	292	0.87	3	0.04	—	0.04	0.51	0.07	6	<1	0	2
0	8	0.17	7	148	1	0.06	4	0.02	—	0.04	0.13	0.06	4	6	0	0
0	3	0.07	3	59	1	0.02	2	0.01	—	0.01	0.05	0.02	2	3	0	0
0	4	0.16	3	75	1	0.03	2	0.01	0.04	0.01	0.08	0.04	1	<1	0	<1
0	3	0.30	3	97	19	0.04	0	0.00	0.11	0.03	0.20	0.03	0	1	0	<1
0	7	0.31	6	151	8	0.05	0	0.00	0.01	0.02	0.05	0.04	0	1	0	<1
0	9	0.46	4	148	4	0.04	0	0.03	0.01	0.02	0.12	0.04	0	1	0	<1
0	5	0.45	4	78	4	0.05	1	0.02	0.27	0.04	0.24	0.03	1	2	0	<1
0	4	0.15	4	92	2	0.04	1	0.02	0.26	0.03	0.23	0.03	1	1	0	<1
0	6	0.13	2	68	<1	—	0	0.01	—	0.01	0.04	—	2	3	0	—
0	18	0.55	14	363	1	0.28	134	0.04	1.25	0.06	0.84	0.08	13	14	0	<1
0	18	0.88	11	383	3	0.13	59	0.00	1.43	0.02	0.85	0.05	3	<1	0	1
0	12	0.39	9	181	5	0.14	80	0.03	0.77	0.03	0.49	0.07	3	4	0	<1
0	22	1.00	49	861	14	1.12	104	0.12	3.35	0.24	3.24	0.47	105	15	0	1
0	30	0.50	73	1067	6	1.20	185	0.00	0.09	0.10	2.00	0.20	106	53	0	0
0	3	0.16	8	139	2	0.18	2	0.02	0.60	0.04	0.50	0.07	17	3	0	<1
0	6	0.31	32	422	1	0.18	4	0.04	0.12	0.09	0.78	0.43	24	10	0	1
0	10	0.69	42	296	3	0.41	2	0.05	0.13	0.01	0.39	0.14	8	3	0	1
0	21	0.45	14	117	1	0.38	8	0.01	0.84	0.02	0.47	0.02	18	15	0	<1
0	22	0.60	17	106	1	0.19	5	0.02	0.88	0.03	0.91	0.05	26	2	0	<1
0	4	0.20	4	55	1	0.12	2	0.03	0.41	0.03	0.30	0.04	4	7	0	<.1
0	6	0.42	5	51	4	0.09	3	0.04	0.49	0.07	0.14	0.05	3	1	0	<1
0	6	0.14	4	42	1	0.06	2	0.03	0.37	0.03	0.41	0.05	6	2	0	0

TABLE H–1
Food Composition

(DA+ code is for Wadsworth Diet Analysis program)   (For purposes of calculations, use "0" for t, <1, <.1, <.01, etc.)

DA + Code	Food Description	Quantity	Measure	Wt (g)	H₂O (g)	Ener (kcal)	Prot (g)	Carb (g)	Fiber (g)	Fat (g)	Sat	Mono	Poly	Trans
	FRUIT AND FRUIT JUICES—Continued													
	Boysenberries													
961	Canned in heavy syrup	½	cup(s)	128	98	113	1	29	3	<1	0.01	0.02	0.09	—
962	Unsweetened, frozen	½	cup(s)	66	57	33	1	8	3	<1	0.01	0.02	0.10	—
35576	**Breadfruit**	1	item(s)	384	271	396	4	104	17	1	0.00	0.00	0.00	—
	Cherries													
3000	Sour red, raw	½	cup(s)	78	67	39	1	9	1	<1	0.05	0.06	0.07	—
967	Sour red, canned in water	½	cup(s)	122	110	44	1	11	1	<1	0.03	0.03	0.04	—
240	Sweet, raw	½	cup(s)	73	60	46	1	12	2	<1	0.03	0.03	0.04	—
3004	Sweet, canned in heavy syrup	½	cup(s)	127	98	105	1	27	2	<1	0.04	0.05	0.06	—
969	Sweet, canned in water	½	cup(s)	124	108	57	1	15	2	<1	0.03	0.04	0.05	—
	Cranberries													
3007	Chopped, raw	½	cup(s)	55	48	25	<1	7	3	<.1	0.01	0.01	0.03	—
1638	Cranberry juice cocktail	½	cup(s)	127	108	72	0	18	<1	<1	0.01	0.02	0.06	—
241	Cranberry juice cocktail, low calorie, w/saccharin	½	cup(s)	127	120	24	<.1	6	0	<.1	0.00	0.00	0.00	—
1717	Cranberry apple juice drink	½	cup(s)	123	100	87	<.1	22	<1	<.1	0.00	0.00	0.00	—
242	Cranberry sauce, sweetened, canned	¼	cup(s)	69	42	105	<1	27	1	<1	0.01	0.01	0.05	—
	Dates													
244	Domestic, chopped	¼	cup(s)	44.5	0	126	1	33	4	<1	0.01	0.01	0	—
243	Domestic, whole	¼	cup(s)	44.5	0	126	1	33	4	<1	0.01	0.01	0	—
	Figs													
973	Raw, medium	2	item(s)	101	80	74	1	19	3	<1	0.06	0.07	0.14	—
975	Canned in heavy syrup	½	cup(s)	130	99	114	<1	30	3	<1	0.03	0.03	0.06	—
974	Canned in water	½	cup(s)	124	106	66	<1	17	3	<1	0.02	0.03	0.06	—
	Fruit cocktail & salad													
245	Fruit cocktail, canned in heavy syrup	½	cup(s)	124	100	91	<1	23	1	<.1	0.01	0.02	0.04	—
978	Fruit cocktail, canned in juice	½	cup(s)	119	104	55	1	14	1	<.1	0.00	0.00	0.00	—
977	Fruit cocktail, canned in water	½	cup(s)	119	108	38	<1	10	1	<.1	0.01	0.01	0.02	—
979	Fruit salad, canned in water	½	cup(s)	123	112	37	<1	10	1	<.1	0.01	0.02	0.03	—
	Gooseberries													
981	Raw	½	cup(s)	75	66	33	1	8	3	<1	0.03	0.04	0.24	—
982	Canned in light syrup	½	cup(s)	126	101	92	1	24	3	<1	0.02	0.02	0.14	—
	Grapefruit													
3022	Raw, pink or red	½	cup(s)	115	<.1	48	1	12	2	<1	0.02	0.02	0.04	—
247	Raw, white	½	item(s)	118	107	39	1	10	1	<1	0.02	0.02	0.03	—
251	Juice, pink, sweetened, canned	½	cup(s)	125	109	58	1	14	<1	<1	0.02	0.02	0.03	—
249	Juice, white	½	cup(s)	124	111	48	1	11	<1	<1	0.02	0.02	0.03	—
248	Sections, canned in light syrup	½	cup(s)	127	106	76	1	20	1	<1	0.02	0.02	0.03	—
983	Sections, canned in water	½	cup(s)	122	<.1	44	1	11	<1	<1	0.02	0.02	0.03	—
	Grapes													
255	American, slip skin	½	cup(s)	46	37	31	<1	8	<1	<1	0.05	0.01	0.05	—
256	European, red or green, adherent skin	½	cup(s)	80	<.1	55	1	14	1	<1	0.04	0.01	0.04	—
259	Juice, sweetened, added vitamin C, from frozen concentrate	½	cup(s)	125	109	64	<1	16	<1	<1	0.04	0.01	0.03	—
3159	Juice drink, canned	½	cup(s)	125	109	63	<1	16	0	0	0.00	0.00	0.00	—
3060	Raisins, seeded, packed	¼	cup(s)	41	7	122	1	32	3	<1	0.07	0.01	0.07	—
987	**Guava, raw**	1	item(s)	90	77	46	1	11	5	1	0.15	0.05	0.23	—
35593	**Guava, strawberry**	1	item(s)	6	5	4	<.1	1	<1	<.1	0.01	0.00	0.02	—
3027	**Jackfruit**	½	cup(s)	83	61	78	1	20	1	<1	0.05	0.04	0.07	—
8458	**Kiwi fruit**	1	item(s)	77	63	53	1	11	3	1	0.02	0.03	0.19	—
	Lemon													
992	Raw	1	item(s)	108	94	22	1	12	5	<1	0.04	0.01	0.10	—
262	Juice	1	tablespoon(s)	15	14	4	<.1	1	<.1	0	0.00	0.00	0.00	—
993	Peel	1	teaspoon(s)	2	2	1	<.1	<1	<1	<.1	0.00	0.00	0.00	—
	Lime													
994	Raw	1	item(s)	67	61	15	<1	6	2	<.1	0.01	0.01	0.02	—
269	Juice	1	tablespoon(s)	15	14	4	<.1	1	<.1	<.1	0.00	0.00	0.00	—
995	**Loganberries, frozen**	½	cup(s)	74	62	40	1	10	4	<1	0.01	0.02	0.13	—
	Mandarin orange													
1038	Canned in juice	½	cup(s)	125	111	46	1	12	1	<.1	0.00	0.01	0.01	—
1039	Canned in light syrup	½	cup(s)	126	105	77	1	20	1	<1	0.02	0.02	0.03	—
999	**Mango**	½	item(s)	104	85	67	1	18	2	<1	0.07	0.10	0.05	—
1005	**Nectarine, raw, sliced**	½	cup(s)	69	60	30	1	7	1	<1	0.02	0.06	0.08	—
	Melons													
271	Cantaloupe	½	cup(s)	80	72	27	1	7	1	<1	0.04	0.00	0.07	—
1000	Casaba melon	½	cup(s)	85	78	24	1	6	1	<.1	0.02	0.00	0.03	—

PAGE KEY: H–2 = Breads/Baked Goods   H–6 = Cereal/Rice/Pasta   H–10 = Fruit   H–14 = Vegetables/Legumes   H–24 = Nuts/Seeds   H–26 = Vegetarian
H–28 = Dairy   H–34 = Eggs   H–34 = Seafood   H–36 = Meats   H–40 = Poultry   H–40 = Processed meats   H–42 = Beverages   H–46 = Fats/Oils
H–48 = Sweets   H–50 = Spices/Condiments/Sauces   H–52 = Mixed foods/Soups/Sandwiches   H–58 = Fast food   H–74 = Convenience meals   H–76 = Baby foods

Chol (mg)	Calc (mg)	Iron (mg)	Magn (mg)	Pota (mg)	Sodi (mg)	Zinc (mg)	Vit A (µg)	Thia (mg)	Vit E (mg α)	Ribo (mg)	Niac (mg)	Vit B_6 (mg)	Fola (µg)	Vit C (mg)	Vit B_{12} (µg)	Sele (µg)
0	23	0.55	14	115	4	0.24	3	0.03	—	0.04	0.29	0.05	44	8	0	1
0	18	0.56	11	92	1	0.15	2	0.03	0.57	0.02	0.51	0.04	42	2	0	<1
0	65	2.07	96	1882	8	0.46	8	0.42	—	0.12	3.46	0.00	54	111	0	2
0	12	0.25	7	134	2	0.08	50	0.02	0.05	0.03	0.31	0.03	6	8	0	0
0	13	1.67	7	120	9	0.09	46	0.02	0.28	0.05	0.22	0.05	10	3	0	0
0	9	0.26	8	161	0	0.05	2	0.02	0.05	0.04	0.11	0.04	3	5	0	0
0	11	0.44	11	183	4	0.13	10	0.03	0.29	0.05	0.50	0.04	5	5	0	0
0	14	0.45	11	162	1	0.10	10	0.03	0.29	0.05	0.51	0.04	5	3	0	0
0	4	0.14	3	47	1	0.06	2	0.01	0.66	0.01	0.06	0.03	1	7	0	<.1
0	4	0.19	3	23	3	0.09	0	0.01	0.28	0.01	0.04	0.02	0	45	0	0
0	11	0.05	3	32	4	0.03	0	0.00	0.06	0.00	0.01	0.00	0	41	0	0
0	6	0.15	2	34	9	0.22	0	0.01	0.15	0.02	0.07	0.03	0	39	0	0
0	3	0.15	2	18	20	0.03	1	0.01	0.57	0.01	0.07	0.01	1	1	0	<1
0	17	0.45	19	292	1	0.12	1	0.02	0.02	0.02	0.56	0.07	9	<1	0	1
0	17	0.45	19	292	1	0.12	1	0.02	0.02	0.02	0.56	0.07	9	<1	0	1
0	35	0.37	17	233	1	0.15	7	0.06	0.11	0.05	0.40	0.11	6	2	0	<1
0	35	0.36	13	128	1	0.14	3	0.03	0.16	0.05	0.55	0.09	3	1	0	<1
0	35	0.36	12	128	1	0.15	2	0.03	0.10	0.05	0.55	0.09	2	1	0	<1
0	7	0.36	6	109	7	0.10	12	0.02	0.50	0.02	0.46	0.06	4	2	0	1
0	9	0.25	8	113	5	0.11	18	0.01	0.47	0.02	0.48	0.06	4	3	0	1
0	6	0.30	8	111	5	0.11	15	0.02	0.47	0.01	0.43	0.06	4	2	0	1
0	9	0.37	6	96	4	0.10	27	0.02	—	0.03	0.46	0.04	4	2	0	1
0	19	0.23	8	149	1	0.09	11	0.03	0.28	0.02	0.23	0.06	5	21	0	<1
0	20	0.42	8	97	3	0.14	9	0.03	—	0.07	0.19	0.02	4	13	0	1
0	25	0.09	10	155	0	0.08	30	0.05	0.15	0.03	0.23	0.06	15	36	0	<1
0	14	0.07	11	175	0	0.08	2	0.04	0.15	0.02	0.32	0.05	12	39	0	2
0	10	0.45	13	203	3	0.08	0	0.05	0.05	0.03	0.40	0.03	13	34	0	<1
0	11	0.25	15	200	1	0.06	2	0.05	0.27	0.02	0.25	0.05	12	47	0	<1
0	18	0.51	13	164	3	0.10	0	0.05	0.11	0.03	0.31	0.03	11	27	0	1
0	18	0.50	12	161	2	0.11	0	0.05	0.11	0.03	0.30	0.02	11	27	0	1
0	6	0.13	2	88	1	0.02	2	0.04	0.09	0.03	0.14	0.05	2	2	0	<.1
0	8	0.29	6	153	2	0.06	6	0.06	0.15	0.06	0.15	0.07	2	9	0	<.1
0	5	0.13	5	26	3	0.05	0	0.02	0.00	0.03	0.16	0.05	1	30	0	<1
0	4	0.13	4	41	1	0.03	0	0.01	0.00	0.02	0.09	0.02	1	20	0	<1
0	12	1.07	12	340	12	0.07	0	0.05	—	0.08	0.46	0.08	1	2	0	<1
0	18	0.28	9	256	3	0.21	28	0.05	0.66	0.05	1.08	0.13	13	165	0	1
0	1	0.01	1	18	2	—	—	0.00	—	0.00	0.04	0.00	—	2	0	—
0	28	0.50	31	251	2	0.35	12	0.02	—	0.09	0.33	0.09	12	6	0	<1
0	30	0.38	14	251	2	0.10	4	—	—	0.02	0.25	0.05	<.1	74	0	—
0	66	0.76	13	157	3	0.11	2	0.05	—	0.04	0.22	0.12	—	83	0	1
0	1	0.00	1	19	<1	0.01	<1	0.00	0.02	0.00	0.02	0.01	2	7	0	<.1
0	3	0.02	<1	3	<1	0.01	<.1	0.00	0.00	0.00	0.01	0.00	<1	3	0	<.1
0	9	0.06	5	78	1	0.05	1	0.02	0.15	0.01	0.10	0.03	7	20	0	<.1
0	1	0.00	1	17	<1	0.01	<1	0.00	0.03	0.00	0.02	0.01	1	5	0	<.1
0	19	0.47	15	107	1	0.25	1	0.04	0.64	0.02	0.62	0.05	19	11	0	<1
0	14	0.34	14	166	6	0.63	54	0.10	0.12	0.04	0.55	0.05	6	43	0	<1
0	9	0.47	10	98	8	0.30	53	0.07	0.13	0.06	0.56	0.05	6	25	0	1
0	10	0.13	9	161	2	0.04	39	0.06	1.16	0.06	0.60	0.14	14	29	0	1
0	4	0.19	6	139	0	0.12	12	0.02	0.53	0.02	0.78	0.02	3	4	0	0
0	7	0.17	10	215	13	0.14	136	0.03	0.04	0.02	0.59	0.06	17	30	0	<1
0	9	0.29	9	155	8	0.06	0	0.01	0.04	0.03	0.20	0.14	7	19	0	<1

TABLE H–1
Food Composition

(DA+ code is for Wadsworth Diet Analysis program)   (For purposes of calculations, use "0" for t, <1, <.1, <.01, etc.)

DA + Code	Food Description	Quantity	Measure	Wt (g)	H₂O (g)	Ener (kcal)	Prot (g)	Carb (g)	Fiber (g)	Fat (g)	Sat	Mono	Poly	Trans
	FRUIT AND FRUIT JUICES—Continued													
272	Honeydew	½	cup(s)	89	80	32	<1	8	1	<1	0.03	0.00	0.05	—
318	Watermelon	½	cup(s)	77	71	23	<1	6	<1	<1	0.01	0.03	0.04	—
	Orange													
273	Raw	1	item(s)	131	114	62	1	15	3	<1	0.02	0.03	0.03	—
3040	Peel	1	teaspoon(s)	2	1	2	<.1	1	<1	<.1	0.00	0.00	0.00	—
274	Sections	½	cup(s)	90	78	43	1	11	2	<1	0.01	0.02	0.02	—
275	Juice	½	cup(s)	124	109	56	1	13	<1	<1	0.03	0.04	0.05	—
29630	Juice, fresh squeezed	½	cup(s)	124	109	56	1	13	<1	<1	0.03	0.04	0.05	—
14414	Juice w/calcium & extra vitamin C	½	cup(s)	125	109	55	1	13	<1	0	0.00	0.00	0.00	—
278	Juice, unsweetened, from frozen concentrate	½	cup(s)	125	110	56	1	13	<1	<.1	0.01	0.01	0.01	—
	Papaya													
282	Raw	½	cup(s)	70	62	27	<1	7	1	<.1	0.03	0.03	0.02	—
16830	Dried, strips	2	item(s)	46	12	119	2	30	5	<1	0.13	0.12	0.09	—
35640	**Passion fruit, purple**	1	item(s)	18	13	17	<1	4	3	<1	0.00	0.00	0.00	—
	Peach													
283	Raw, medium	1	item(s)	98	87	38	1	9	1	<1	0.02	0.07	0.08	—
285	Halves, canned in heavy syrup	½	cup(s)	131	104	97	1	26	2	<1	0.01	0.05	0.06	—
286	Halves, canned in water	½	cup(s)	122	114	29	1	7	2	<.1	0.01	0.03	0.03	—
290	Slices, sweetened, frozen	½	cup(s)	125	93	118	1	30	2	<1	0.02	0.06	0.08	—
	Pear													
291	Raw	1	item(s)	166	139	96	1	26	5	<1	0.01	0.04	0.05	—
8672	Asian	1	item(s)	122	108	51	1	13	4	<1	0.01	0.06	0.07	—
293	Danjou	1	item(s)	200	168	120	1	30	5	1	0.00	0.20	0.20	—
294	Halves, canned in heavy syrup	½	cup(s)	133	107	98	<1	25	2	<1	0.01	0.04	0.04	—
1012	Halves, canned in juice	½	cup(s)	124	107	62	<1	16	2	<.1	0.00	0.02	0.02	—
1017	**Persimmon**	1	item(s)	25	16	32	<1	8	0	<1	0.01	0.02	0.02	—
	Pineapple													
295	Raw, diced	½	cup(s)	78	67	37	<1	10	1	<.1	0.01	0.01	0.03	—
3053	Canned in extra heavy syrup	½	cup(s)	130	101	108	<1	28	1	<1	0.01	0.02	0.05	—
1019	Canned in juice	½	cup(s)	125	104	75	1	20	1	<.1	0.01	0.01	0.04	—
296	Canned in light syrup	½	cup(s)	126	108	66	<1	17	1	<1	0.01	0.02	0.05	—
1018	Canned in water	½	cup(s)	123	112	39	1	10	1	<1	0.01	0.01	0.04	—
299	Juice, unsweetened, canned	½	cup(s)	125	107	70	<1	17	<1	<1	0.01	0.01	0.04	—
1024	**Plantain, cooked**	½	cup(s)	77	52	89	1	24	2	<1	0.05	0.01	0.03	—
300	**Plum, raw, large**	1	item(s)	83	72	38	1	9	1	<1	0.01	0.11	0.04	—
1027	**Pomegranate**	1	item(s)	154	125	105	1	26	1	<1	0.06	0.07	0.10	—
	Prunes													
5644	Dried	2	item(s)	17	5	40	<1	11	1	<.1	0.01	0.06	0.02	—
305	Dried, stewed	½	cup(s)	119	<.1	128	1	33	4	<1	0.00	0.15	0.04	—
306	Juice, canned	1	cup(s)	256	208	182	2	45	3	<.1	0.01	0.05	0.02	—
	Raisins, *see* grapes													
	Raspberries													
309	Raw	½	cup(s)	62	53	32	1	7	4	<1	0.01	0.04	0.23	—
310	Red, sweetened, frozen	½	cup(s)	125	91	129	1	33	6	<1	0.01	0.02	0.11	—
311	**Rhubarb, cooked with sugar**	½	cup(s)	120	82	140	1	38	3	<.1	0.00	0.00	0.05	—
	Strawberries													
313	Raw	½	cup(s)	72	65	23	<1	6	1	<1	0.01	0.03	0.11	—
315	Sweetened, frozen, thawed	½	cup(s)	128	100	99	1	27	2	<1	0.01	0.02	0.09	—
16828	**Tangelo**	1	item(s)	95	82	45	1	11	2	<1	0.01	0.02	0.02	—
	Tangerine													
316	Raw	1	item(s)	84	74	37	1	9	2	<1	0.02	0.03	0.03	—
1040	Juice	½	cup(s)	124	110	53	1	12	<1	<1	0.03	0.04	0.05	—
	VEGETABLES, LEGUMES													
	Amaranth													
1042	Leaves, raw	1	cup(s)	28	26	6	1	1	0	<.1	0.03	0.02	0.04	—
1043	Leaves, boiled, drained	½	cup(s)	66	60	14	1	3	0	<1	0.03	0.03	0.05	—
8683	**Arugula leaves, raw**	1	cup(s)	20	18	5	1	1	<1	<1	0.02	0.01	0.06	—
	Artichoke													
1044	Boiled, drained	1	item(s)	120	101	60	4	13	6	<1	0.04	0.01	0.08	—
2885	Hearts, boiled, drained	½	cup(s)	84	71	42	3	9	5	<1	0.03	0.00	0.06	—
	Asparagus													
566	Boiled, drained	½	cup(s)	90	0.08	20	2	4	2	0.19	0.06	0	0.12	—
568	Canned, drained	½	cup(s)	121	114	23	3	3	2	1	0.18	0.03	0.34	—
565	Tips, frozen, boiled, drained	½	cup(s)	90	82	25	3	4	1	<1	0.09	0.01	0.17	—

PAGE KEY: H–2 = Breads/Baked Goods H–6 = Cereal/Rice/Pasta H–10 = Fruit H–14 = Vegetables/Legumes H–24 = Nuts/Seeds H–26 = Vegetarian H–28 = Dairy H–34 = Eggs H–34 = Seafood H–36 = Meats H–40 = Poultry H–40 = Processed meats H–42 = Beverages H–46 = Fats/Oils H–48 = Sweets H–50 = Spices/Condiments/Sauces H–52 = Mixed foods/Soups/Sandwiches H–58 = Fast food H–74 = Convenience meals H–76 = Baby foods

Chol (mg)	Calc (mg)	Iron (mg)	Magn (mg)	Pota (mg)	Sodi (mg)	Zinc (mg)	Vit A (µg)	Thia (mg)	Vit E (mg α)	Ribo (mg)	Niac (mg)	Vit B_6 (mg)	Fola (µg)	Vit C (mg)	Vit B_{12} (µg)	Sele (µg)
0	5	0.15	9	203	16	0.08	3	0.03	0.02	0.01	0.37	0.08	17	16	0	1
0	5	0.19	8	86	1	0.08	22	0.03	0.04	0.02	0.14	0.03	2	6	0	<1
0	52	0.13	13	237	0	0.09	14	0.11	0.24	0.05	0.37	0.08	39	70	0	1
0	3	0.02	<1	4	<.1	0.01	<1	0.00	0.00	0.00	0.02	0.00	1	3	0	<.1
0	36	0.09	9	164	0	0.06	10	0.08	0.16	0.04	0.26	0.05	27	48	0	<1
0	14	0.25	14	248	1	0.06	12	0.11	0.05	0.04	0.50	0.05	37	62	0	<1
0	14	0.25	14	248	1	0.06	—	0.11	0.05	0.04	0.50	0.05	38	62	0	—
0	176	—	—	226	0	—	5	0.08	—	—	0.40	0.06	30	54	0	—
0	11	0.12	12	237	1	0.06	6	0.10	0.25	0.02	0.25	0.05	55	48	0	<1
0	17	0.07	7	180	2	0.05	39	0.02	0.51	0.02	0.24	0.01	27	43	0	<1
0	73	0.30	30	783	9	0.21	—	0.06	2.22	0.09	0.93	0.05	58	38	0	—
0	2	0.29	5	63	5	—	—	0.00	—	0.02	0.27	—	3	5	0	<1
0	6	0.25	9	186	0	0.17	16	0.02	0.72	0.03	0.79	0.02	4	6	0	<.1
0	4	0.35	7	121	8	0.12	22	0.01	0.64	0.03	0.80	0.02	4	4	0	<1
0	2	0.39	6	121	4	0.11	33	0.01	0.60	0.02	0.64	0.02	4	4	0	<1
0	4	0.46	6	163	8	0.06	18	0.02	0.77	0.04	0.82	0.02	4	118	0	1
0	15	0.28	12	198	2	0.17	2	0.06	0.20	0.04	0.26	0.05	12	7	0	<1
0	5	0.00	10	148	0	0.02	0	0.01	0.15	0.01	0.27	0.03	10	5	0	<1
0	22	0.50	12	250	0	0.24	—	0.04	1.00	0.08	0.20	0.04	15	8	0	1
0	7	0.29	5	86	7	0.11	0	0.01	0.11	0.03	0.32	0.02	1	1	0	0
0	11	0.36	9	119	5	0.11	0	0.01	0.10	0.01	0.25	0.02	1	2	0	0
0	7	0.63	—	78	<1	—	—	—	—	—	—	—	—	17	0	0
0	10	0.22	9	89	1	0.08	2	0.06	0.02	0.02	0.38	0.09	12	28	0	<.1
0	18	0.49	20	133	1	0.14	1	0.12	—	0.03	0.37	0.10	7	9	0	—
0	17	0.35	17	152	1	0.12	2	0.12	0.01	0.02	0.35	0.09	6	12	0	<1
0	18	0.49	20	132	1	0.15	3	0.11	0.01	0.03	0.37	0.09	6	9	0	1
0	18	0.49	22	156	1	0.15	2	0.11	0.01	0.03	0.37	0.09	6	9	0	<1
0	21	0.33	16	168	1	0.14	0	0.07	0.03	0.03	0.32	0.12	29	13	0	<1
0	2	0.45	25	358	4	0.10	35	0.04	0.10	0.04	0.58	0.18	20	8	0	1
0	5	0.14	6	130	0	0.08	14	0.02	0.21	0.02	0.34	0.02	4	8	0	0
0	5	0.46	5	399	5	0.18	8	0.05	0.92	0.05	0.46	0.16	9	9	0	1
0	9	0.42	8	125	1	0.09	17	0.01	0.00	0.03	0.33	0.04	1	1	0	<1
0	23	0.46	21	383	1	0.19	37	0.00	0.23	0.12	0.85	0.23	0	3	0	<1
0	31	3.02	36	707	10	0.54	0	0.04	0.31	0.18	2.01	0.56	0	10	0	2
0	15	0.42	14	93	1	0.26	1	0.02	0.54	0.02	0.37	0.03	13	16	0	<1
0	19	0.81	16	143	1	0.23	4	0.02	0.90	0.06	0.29	0.04	33	21	0	<1
0	174	0.25	16	115	1	—	—	0.02	—	0.03	0.25	—	—	4	0	—
0	12	0.30	9	110	1	0.10	1	0.02	0.21	0.02	0.28	0.03	17	42	0	<1
0	14	0.60	8	125	1	0.06	2	0.02	0.31	0.10	0.37	0.04	5	50	0	1
0	38	0.10	10	172	0	0.07	—	0.08	0.17	0.04	0.27	0.06	29	51	0	—
0	12	0.08	10	132	1	0.20	29	0.09	0.17	0.02	0.13	0.06	17	26	0	<1
0	22	0.25	10	220	1	0.04	16	0.07	0.16	0.02	0.12	0.05	6	38	0	<1
0	60	0.65	15	171	6	0.25	0	0.01	—	0.04	0.18	0.05	24	12	0	<1
0	138	1.49	36	423	14	0.58	92	0.01	—	0.09	0.37	0.12	38	27	0	1
0	32	0.29	9	74	5	0.09	24	0.01	0.09	0.02	0.06	0.01	19	3	0	<.1
0	54	1.55	72	425	114	0.59	11	0.08	0.23	0.08	1.20	0.13	61	12	0	<1
0	38	1.08	50	297	80	0.41	8	0.05	0.16	0.06	0.84	0.09	43	8	0	<1
0	20.7	0.81	12.6	201.6	12.6	0.54	48.59	0.14	1.35	0.12	0.97	0.07	134.1	6.92	0	5.48
0	19	0.73	12	208	347	0.48	50	0.07	0.38	0.12	1.15	0.13	116	22	0	2
0	21	0.58	12	196	4	0.50	—	0.06	1.08	0.09	0.93	0.02	121	22	0	4

TABLE H–1

Food Composition   (DA+ code is for Wadsworth Diet Analysis program)   (For purposes of calculations, use "0" for t, <1, <.1, <.01, etc.)

DA + Code	Food Description	Quantity	Measure	Wt (g)	H₂O (g)	Ener (kcal)	Prot (g)	Carb (g)	Fiber (g)	Fat (g)	Sat	Mono	Poly	Trans
	VEGETABLES, LEGUMES —Continued													
	Bamboo shoots													
1048	Boiled, drained	½	cup(s)	60	58	7	1	1	1	<1	0.03	0.00	0.06	—
1049	Canned, drained	½	cup(s)	65	62	12	1	2	1	<1	0.06	0.01	0.12	—
	Beans													
1801	Adzuki beans, boiled	½	cup(s)	115	76	147	9	28	8	<1	0.04	—	—	—
511	Baked beans w/franks, canned	½	cup(s)	129	89	182	9	20	9	8	3.02	3.64	1.07	—
512	Baked beans w/pork in tomato sauce, canned	½	cup(s)	127	92	124	7	25	6	1	0.50	0.56	0.17	—
513	Baked beans w/pork in sweet sauce, canned	½	cup(s)	127	89	140	7	27	7	2	0.71	0.80	0.24	0
1805	Black beans, boiled	½	cup(s)	86	57	114	8	20	7	<1	0.12	0.04	0.20	—
14597	Chickpeas, garbanzo beans, or bengal gram, boiled	½	cup(s)	82	49	134	7	22	6	2	0.22	0.48	0.95	—
569	Fordhook lima beans, frozen, boiled, drained	½	cup(s)	85	62	88	5	16	5	<1	0.07	0.02	0.14	—
1806	French beans, boiled	½	cup(s)	89	59	114	6	21	8	1	0.07	0.05	0.40	—
2773	Great northern beans, boiled	½	cup(s)	89	61	104	7	19	6	<1	0.12	0.02	0.17	—
2736	Hyacinth beans, boiled, drained	½	cup(s)	44	38	22	1	4	0	<1	0.05	0.06	0.00	—
515	Lima beans, boiled, drained	½	cup(s)	85	57	105	6	20	5	<1	0.06	0.02	0.13	—
570	Lima beans, baby, frozen, boiled, drained	½	cup(s)	90	65	95	6	18	5	<1	0.06	0.02	0.13	—
579	Mung beans, sprouted, boiled, drained	½	cup(s)	62	<.1	13	1	3	<1	<.1	0.02	0.00	0.02	—
510	Navy beans, boiled	½	cup(s)	91	57	129	8	24	6	1	0.13	0.05	0.22	0
32816	Pinto beans, boiled, drained, no salt added	½	cup(s)	114	106	25	2	5	0	<1	0.04	0.03	0.21	—
1052	Pinto beans, frozen, boiled, drained	½	cup(s)	47	27	76	4	15	4	<1	0.03	0.02	0.13	—
514	Red kidney beans, canned	½	cup(s)	128	99	109	7	20	8	<1	0.06	0.03	0.24	—
1810	Refried beans, canned	½	cup(s)	127	96	119	7	20	7	2	0.60	0.71	0.19	—
1053	Shell beans, canned	½	cup(s)	123	111	37	2	8	4	<1	0.03	0.02	0.13	—
1670	Soybeans, boiled	½	cup(s)	86	54	149	14	9	5	8	1.12	1.70	4.36	—
1108	Soybeans, green, boiled, drained	½	cup(s)	90	62	127	11	10	4	6	0.67	1.09	2.71	—
1807	White beans, small, boiled	½	cup(s)	90	57	127	8	23	9	1	0.15	0.05	0.25	—
574	Green string beans, canned, fat added in cooking	½	cup(s)	93	<.1	41	1	4	2	3	0.51	1.23	0.75	—
575	Yellow snap, string or wax beans, boiled, drained	½	cup(s)	62	<.1	22	1	5	2	<1	0.04	0.00	0.09	—
576	Yellow snap, string or wax beans, frozen, boiled, drained	½	cup(s)	68	<.1	19	1	4	2	<1	0.02	0.00	0.05	—
	Beets													
580	Whole, boiled, drained	2	item(s)	100	87	44	2	10	2	<1	0.03	0.04	0.06	—
581	Sliced, boiled, drained	½	cup(s)	85	74	37	1	8	2	<1	0.02	0.03	0.05	—
583	Sliced, canned, drained	½	cup(s)	85	77	26	1	6	1	<1	0.02	0.02	0.04	—
2730	Pickled, canned with liquid	½	cup(s)	114	93	74	1	18	3	<.1	0.01	0.02	0.03	—
584	Beet greens, boiled, drained	½	cup(s)	72	64	19	2	4	2	<1	0.02	0.03	0.05	—
585	**Cowpeas or black-eyed peas, boiled, drained**	½	cup(s)	83	0.06	80	2.61	16.76	4.12	0.31	0.07	0.02	0.13	—
	Broccoli													
587	Raw, chopped	½	cup(s)	44	39	15	1	3	1	<1	0.02	0.00	0.02	—
588	Chopped, boiled, drained	½	cup(s)	78	70	27	2	6	3	<1	0.06	0.03	0.13	—
590	Frozen, chopped, boiled, drained	½	cup(s)	92	83	26	3	5	3	<1	0.02	0.01	0.05	—
16848	**Broccoflower, raw, chopped**	½	cup(s)	32	29	10	1	2	1	<.1	0.01	0.01	0.04	—
	Brussels sprouts													
591	Boiled, drained	½	cup(s)	78	69	28	2	6	2	<1	0.08	0.03	0.20	—
592	Frozen, boiled, drained	½	cup(s)	78	67	33	3	6	3	<1	0.06	0.02	0.16	—
	Cabbage													
594	Raw, shredded	1	cup(s)	70	65	17	1	4	2	<.1	0.01	0.01	0.04	—
595	Boiled, drained, no salt added	1	cup(s)	150	140	33	2	7	3	1	0.08	0.05	0.29	—
35611	Chinese (pak choi or bok choy), boiled w/salt, drained	1	cup(s)	170	162	20	3	3	2	<1	0.04	0.02	0.13	—
16869	Kim chee	1	cup(s)	150	138	31	2	6	2	<1	0.04	0.02	0.15	—
596	Red, shredded, raw	1	cup(s)	70	63	22	1	5	1	<1	0.02	0.01	0.09	—
597	Savoy, shredded, raw	1	cup(s)	70	64	19	1	4	2	<.1	0.01	0.00	0.03	—
11710	**Capers**	1	teaspoon(s)	5	—	0	0	0	0	0	0.00	0.00	0.00	0
	Carrots													
600	Raw	½	cup(s)	61	54	25	1	6	2	<1	0.02	0.01	0.06	0
8691	Raw, baby	8	item(s)	80	72	28	1	7	1	<1	0.02	0.01	0.05	0
601	Grated	½	cup(s)	55	49	23	1	5	2	<1	0.02	0.01	0.06	0
602	Sliced, boiled, drained	½	cup(s)	78	0.07	27.29	0.59	6.41	2.33	0.14	0.02	0	0.08	—

PAGE KEY: H–2 = Breads/Baked Goods H–6 = Cereal/Rice/Pasta H–10 = Fruit H–14 = Vegetables/Legumes H–24 = Nuts/Seeds H–26 = Vegetarian
H–28 = Dairy H–34 = Eggs H–34 = Seafood H–36 = Meats H–40 = Poultry H–40 = Processed meats H–42 = Beverages H–46 = Fats/Oils
H–48 = Sweets H–50 = Spices/Condiments/Sauces H–52 = Mixed foods/Soups/Sandwiches H–58 = Fast food H–74 = Convenience meals H–76 = Baby foods

Chol (mg)	Calc (mg)	Iron (mg)	Magn (mg)	Pota (mg)	Sodi (mg)	Zinc (mg)	Vit A (µg)	Thia (mg)	Vit E (mg α)	Ribo (mg)	Niac (mg)	Vit B$_6$ (mg)	Fola (µg)	Vit C (mg)	Vit B$_{12}$ (µg)	Sele (µg)
0	7	0.14	2	320	2	0.28	0	0.01	—	0.03	0.18	0.06	1	0	0	<1
0	5	0.21	3	52	5	0.43	1	0.02	0.41	0.02	0.09	0.09	2	1	0	<1
0	32	2.30	60	612	9	2.04	0	0.13	—	0.07	0.82	0.11	139	0	0	1
8	62	2.22	36	302	553	2.40	5	0.07	0.59	0.07	1.16	0.06	39	3	0	8
9	71	4.15	44	380	557	7.41	5	0.07	0.13	0.06	0.63	0.09	29	4	0	6
9	77	2.10	43	336	425	1.90	1	0.06	0.04	0.08	0.44	0.11	47	4	0	6
0	23	1.81	60	305	1	0.96	0	0.21	—	0.05	0.43	0.06	128	0	0	1
0	40	2.37	39	239	6	1.25	1	0.10	0.29	0.05	0.43	0.11	141	1	0	3
0	26	1.55	36	258	59	0.63	9	0.06	0.25	0.05	0.91	0.10	18	11	0	1
0	56	0.96	50	327	5	0.57	0	0.12	—	0.05	0.48	0.09	66	1	0	1
0	60	1.89	44	346	2	0.78	0	0.14	—	0.05	0.60	0.10	90	1	0	4
0	18	0.33	18	114	1	0.17	3	0.02	—	0.04	0.21	0.01	20	2	0	1
0	27	2.08	63	485	14	0.67	16	0.12	0.12	0.06	0.88	0.16	22	9	0	2
0	25	1.76	50	370	26	0.50	7	0.06	0.58	0.05	0.69	0.10	14	5	0	2
0	7	0.40	9	63	6	0.29	1	0.03	0.04	0.06	0.50	0.03	18	7	0	<1
0	64	2.26	54	335	1	0.96	0	0.18	0.01	0.06	0.48	0.15	127	1	0	5
0	17	0.75	20	111	58	0.19	0	0.08	—	0.07	0.82	0.06	146	7	0	1
0	24	1.27	25	304	39	0.32	0	0.13	—	0.05	0.30	0.09	16	<1	0	1
0	31	1.61	36	329	436	0.70	0	0.13	0.77	0.11	0.58	0.03	65	1	0	2
10	44	2.10	42	338	378	1.48	0	0.03	0.00	0.02	0.40	0.18	14	8	0	2
0	36	1.21	18	134	409	0.33	13	0.04	0.04	0.07	0.25	0.06	22	4	0	1
0	88	4.42	74	443	1	0.99	0	0.13	0.30	0.25	0.34	0.20	46	1	0	6
0	131	2.25	54	485	13	0.82	7	0.23	—	0.14	1.13	0.05	100	15	0	1
0	65	2.54	61	414	2	0.98	0	0.21	—	0.05	0.24	0.11	123	0	0	1
0	24	0.81	12	100	266	0.26	129	0.01	0.40	0.05	0.18	0.03	—	4	0.00	—
0	29	0.80	16	187	2	0.22	5	0.05	0.28	0.06	0.38	0.03	21	6	0	<1
0	33	0.59	16	85	6	0.32	7	0.02	0.24	0.06	0.26	0.04	16	3	0	<1
0	16	0.79	23	305	77	0.35	2	0.03	0.04	0.04	0.33	0.07	80	4	0	1
0	14	0.67	20	259	65	0.30	2	0.02	0.03	0.03	0.28	0.06	68	3	0	1
0	13	1.55	14	126	165	0.18	1	0.01	0.03	0.03	0.13	0.05	26	3	0	<1
0	12	0.47	17	168	300	0.30	1	0.01	—	0.05	0.28	0.06	31	3	0	1
0	82	1.37	49	654	174	0.36	276	0.08	1.30	0.21	0.36	0.10	10	18	0	1
0	105.59	0.92	42.9	344.85	3.29	0.84	65.17	0.08	0.18	0.12	1.15	0.05	104.77	1.81	0	2.06
0	21	0.32	9	139	15	0.18	15	0.03	0.34	0.05	0.28	0.08	28	39	0	1
0	31	0.52	16	229	32	0.35	76	0.05	1.13	0.10	0.43	0.16	84	51	0	1
0	30	0.56	12	131	10	0.26	52	0.05	1.21	0.07	0.42	0.12	52	37	0	1
0	11	0.23	6	96	7	0.20	0	0.03	0.01	0.03	0.23	0.07	18	28	0	—
0	28	0.94	16	247	16	0.26	30	0.08	0.34	0.06	0.47	0.14	47	48	0	1
0	20	0.37	14	225	12	0.19	36	0.08	0.40	0.09	0.42	0.22	78	35	0	<1
0	33	0.41	11	172	13	0.13	6	0.04	0.10	0.03	0.21	0.07	30	23	0	1
0	47	0.26	12	146	12	0.14	11	0.09	0.18	0.08	0.42	0.17	30	30	0	1
0	158	1.77	19	631	459	0.29	360	0.05	0.15	0.11	0.73	0.28	70	44	0	1
0	145	1.28	27	375	995	0.36	—	0.07	0.08	0.10	0.75	0.34	88	80	0	—
0	32	0.56	11	170	19	0.15	39	0.04	0.12	0.05	0.29	0.15	13	40	0	<1
0	25	0.28	20	161	20	0.19	35	0.05	—	0.02	0.21	0.13	56	22	0	1
0	—	—	—	—	105	—	—	—	—	—	—	—	—	—	0	—
0	20	0.18	7	195	42	0.15	367	0.04	0.40	0.04	0.60	0.08	12	4	0	<.1
0	26	0.71	8	190	62	0.14	552	0.02	—	0.03	0.44	0.08	26	7	0	1
0	18	0.17	7	177	38	0.13	333	0.04	0.36	0.03	0.54	0.08	11	3	0	<.1
0	23.39	0.26	7.8	183.3	45.24	0.15	1914.9	0.05	0.80	0.03	0.5	0.11	10.92	2.8	0	0.54

TABLE H–1

Food Composition   (DA+ code is for Wadsworth Diet Analysis program)   (For purposes of calculations, use "0" for t, <1, <.1, <.01, etc.)

DA + Code	Food Description	Quantity	Measure	Wt (g)	H₂O (g)	Ener (kcal)	Prot (g)	Carb (g)	Fiber (g)	Fat (g)	Fat Breakdown (g)			
											Sat	Mono	Poly	*Trans*
	VEGETABLES, LEGUMES—Continued													
1055	Juice, canned	½	cup(s)	123	109	49	1	11	1	<1	0.03	0.01	0.09	—
32725	**Cassava or manioc**	½	cup(s)	103	61	165	1	39	2	<1	0.08	0.08	0.05	—
	Cauliflower													
605	Raw, chopped,	½	cup(s)	50	46	13	1	3	1	<1	0.02	0.01	0.05	—
606	Boiled, drained	½	cup(s)	62	58	14	1	3	2	<1	0.04	0.02	0.13	—
607	Frozen, boiled, drained	½	cup(s)	90	85	17	1	3	2	<1	0.03	0.01	0.09	—
	Celery													
609	Diced	½	cup(s)	60	58	8	<1	2	1	<1	0.03	0.02	0.05	—
608	Stalk	2	item(s)	80	76	11	1	2	1	<1	0.03	0.03	0.06	—
	Chard													
1056	Swiss chard, raw	1	cup(s)	36	33	7	1	1	1	<.1	0.01	0.01	0.03	—
1057	Swiss chard, boiled, drained	½	cup(s)	88	81	18	2	4	2	<.1	0.01	0.01	0.02	—
	Collard greens													
610	Boiled, drained	½	cup(s)	95	87	25	2	5	3	<1	0.04	0.02	0.16	—
611	Frozen, chopped, boiled, drained	½	cup(s)	85	75	31	3	6	2	<1	0.05	0.02	0.18	—
	Corn													
29614	Yellow corn, fresh, cooked	1	item(s)	100	0.06	107.37	3.3	24.96	2.78	1.27	0.19	0.37	0.59	—
612	Yellow sweet corn, boiled, drained	½	cup(s)	82	57	89	3	21	2	1	0.16	0.31	0.49	—
614	Yellow sweet corn, frozen, boiled, drained	½	cup(s)	82	63	66	2	16	2	1	0.08	0.16	0.26	—
615	Yellow creamed sweet corn, canned	½	cup(s)	128	101	92	2	23	2	1	0.08	0.16	0.25	—
618	**Cucumber**	¼	item(s)	75	72	11	<1	3	<1	<.1	0.03	0.00	0.04	—
16870	**Cucumber, kim chee**	½	cup(s)	75	68	16	1	4	1	<.1	0.02	0.00	0.03	—
	Dandelion greens													
2734	Raw	1	cup(s)	55	47	25	1	5	2	<1	0.09	0.01	0.17	—
620	Chopped, boiled, drained	½	cup(s)	53	47	17	1	3	2	<1	0.08	0.01	0.14	—
1066	**Eggplant, boiled, drained**	½	cup(s)	48	43	17	<1	4	1	<1	0.02	0.01	0.04	—
621	**Endive or escarole, chopped, raw**	1	cup(s)	53	49	9	1	2	2	<1	0.03	0.00	0.05	—
8784	**Jicama or yambean**	½	cup(s)	65	59	25	<1	6	3	<.1	0.01	0.00	0.03	—
	Kale													
29313	Raw	1	cup(s)	67	57	34	2	7	1	<1	0.06	0.03	0.23	—
623	Frozen, chopped, boiled, drained	½	cup(s)	65	59	20	2	3	1	<1	0.04	0.02	0.15	—
	Kohlrabi													
1071	Raw	1	cup(s)	135	123	36	2	8	5	<1	0.02	0.01	0.06	—
1072	Boiled, drained	½	cup(s)	83	74	24	1	6	1	<.1	0.01	0.01	0.04	—
	Leeks													
1073	Raw	1	cup(s)	89	74	54	1	13	2	<1	0.04	0.00	0.15	—
1074	Boiled, drained	½	cup(s)	52	47	16	<1	4	1	<1	0.01	0.00	0.06	—
	Lentils													
522	Boiled	½	cup(s)	99	69	115	9	20	8	<1	0.05	0.06	0.17	—
1075	Sprouted	1	cup(s)	77	52	82	7	17	0	<1	0.04	0.08	0.17	—
	Lettuce													
624	Butterhead, boston, or bibb	1	cup(s)	55	53	7	1	1	1	<1	0.02	0.00	0.06	—
625	Butterhead leaves	11	piece(s)	83	79	11	1	2	1	<1	0.02	0.01	0.10	—
626	Iceberg	1	cup(s)	55	53	6	<1	1	1	<.1	0.01	0.00	0.03	—
628	Iceberg, chopped	1	cup(s)	55	53	6	<1	1	1	<.1	0.01	0.00	0.03	—
629	Looseleaf	1	cup(s)	56	54	8	1	2	1	<.1	0.01	0.00	0.05	—
1665	Romaine, shredded	1	cup(s)	56	53	10	1	2	1	<1	0.02	0.01	0.09	—
	Mushrooms													
15585	Crimini (about 6)	3	ounce(s)	85	28	4	3	2	0	0.00	0.00	0.00	0	0
8700	Enoki	30	item(s)	90	80	31	2	6	2	<1	0.04	0.01	0.14	—
630	Mushrooms, raw	½	cup(s)	35	32	8	1	1	<1	<1	0.02	0.00	0.05	—
1079	Mushrooms, boiled, drained	½	cup(s)	78	71	22	2	4	2	<1	0.05	0.01	0.14	—
1080	Mushrooms, canned, drained	½	cup(s)	78	71	20	1	4	2	<1	0.03	0.00	0.09	—
15587	Portobello, raw	1	item(s)	85	30	3	4	3	0	0.00	0.00	0.00	0	0
2743	Shiitake, cooked	½	cup(s)	73	61	40	1	10	2	<1	0.04	0.05	0.02	—
	Mustard greens													
29319	Raw	1	cup(s)	56	51	15	2	3	2	<1	0.01	0.05	0.02	—
2744	Frozen, boiled, drained	½	cup(s)	75	70	14	2	2	2	<1	0.01	0.08	0.04	—
	Okra													
632	Sliced, boiled, drained	½	cup(s)	80	74	18	1	4	2	<1	0.04	0.02	0.04	—
32742	Frozen, boiled, drained, no salt added	½	cup(s)	92	84	26	2	5	3	<1	0.07	0.05	0.07	—
16866	Batter coated, fried	11	piece(s)	83	55	160	2	13	2	11	1.50	2.80	6.37	—
	Onions													
633	Raw, chopped	½	cup(s)	80	71	34	1	8	1	<.1	0.02	0.02	0.05	—
635	Chopped, boiled, drained	½	cup(s)	106	93	47	1	11	1	<1	0.03	0.03	0.08	—

PAGE KEY: H–2 = Breads/Baked Goods   H–6 = Cereal/Rice/Pasta   H–10 = Fruit   H–14 = Vegetables/Legumes   H–24 = Nuts/Seeds   H–26 = Vegetarian
H–28 = Dairy   H–34 = Eggs   H–34 = Seafood   H–36 = Meats   H–40 = Poultry   H–40 = Processed meats   H–42 = Beverages   H–46 = Fats/Oils
H–48 = Sweets   H–50 = Spices/Condiments/Sauces   H–52 = Mixed foods/Soups/Sandwiches   H–58 = Fast food   H–74 = Convenience meals   H–76 = Baby foods

Chol (mg)	Calc (mg)	Iron (mg)	Magn (mg)	Pota (mg)	Sodi (mg)	Zinc (mg)	Vit A (µg)	Thia (mg)	Vit E (mg α)	Ribo (mg)	Niac (mg)	Vit B$_6$ (mg)	Fola (µg)	Vit C (mg)	Vit B$_{12}$ (µg)	Sele (µg)
0	30	0.57	17	359	36	0.22	1176	0.11	1.43	0.07	0.47	0.27	5	10	0	1
0	16	0.28	22	279	14	0.35	1	0.09	0.20	0.05	0.88	0.09	28	21	0	1
0	11	0.22	8	152	15	0.14	1	0.03	0.04	0.03	0.26	0.11	29	23	0	<1
0	10	0.20	6	88	9	0.11	1	0.03	0.04	0.03	0.25	0.11	27	27	0	<1
0	15	0.37	8	125	16	0.12	0	0.03	0.05	0.05	0.28	0.08	37	28	0	1
0	24	0.12	7	157	48	0.08	13	0.01	0.16	0.03	0.19	0.04	22	2	0	<1
0	32	0.16	9	208	64	0.10	18	0.02	0.22	0.05	0.26	0.06	29	2	0	<1
0	18	0.65	29	136	77	0.13	110	0.01	0.68	0.03	0.14	0.04	5	11	0	<1
0	51	1.98	75	480	157	0.29	268	0.03	1.65	0.08	0.32	0.07	8	16	0	1
0	133	1.10	19	110	15	0.22	386	0.04	0.84	0.10	0.55	0.12	88	17	0	<1
0	179	0.95	26	213	43	0.23	489	0.04	1.06	0.10	0.54	0.10	65	22	0	1
0	2.12	0.6	31.81	247.59	242.45	0.47	21.87	0.21	0.09	0.07	1.6	0.05	—	6.16	0	—
0	2	0.50	26	204	14	0.39	11	0.18	0.07	0.06	1.32	0.05	38	5	0	<1
0	2	0.39	23	191	1	0.52	8	0.02	0.06	0.05	1.08	0.08	29	3	0	1
0	4	0.49	22	172	365	0.68	5	0.03	0.09	0.07	1.23	0.08	58	6	0	1
0	12	0.21	10	111	2	0.15	4	0.02	0.02	0.02	0.07	0.03	5	2	0	<1
0	7	3.62	6	88	766	0.38	—	0.02	0.36	0.02	0.35	0.08	17	3	0	—
0	103	1.71	20	219	42	0.23	137	0.11	2.65	0.14	0.45	0.14	15	19	0	<1
0	74	0.95	13	122	23	0.15	260	0.07	1.79	0.09	0.27	0.08	7	9	0	<1
0	3	0.12	5	59	<1	0.06	1	0.04	0.20	0.01	0.29	0.04	7	1	0	<.1
0	27	0.44	8	165	12	0.41	57	0.04	0.23	0.04	0.21	0.01	75	3	0	<1
0	8	0.39	8	98	3	0.10	1	0.01	0.30	0.02	0.13	0.03	8	13	0	<1
0	90	1.14	23	299	29	0.29	515	0.07	—	0.09	0.67	0.18	19	80	0	1
0	90	0.61	12	209	10	0.12	478	0.03	0.60	0.07	0.44	0.06	9	16	0	1
0	32	0.54	26	473	27	0.04	3	0.07	0.65	0.03	0.54	0.20	22	84	0	1
0	21	0.33	16	281	17	0.26	2	0.03	0.43	0.02	0.32	0.13	10	45	0	1
0	53	1.87	25	160	18	0.11	74	0.05	0.82	0.03	0.36	0.21	57	11	0	1
0	16	0.57	7	45	5	0.03	1	0.01	—	0.01	0.10	0.06	13	2	0	<1
0	19	3.30	36	365	2	1.26	0	0.17	0.11	0.07	1.05	0.18	179	1	0	3
0	19	2.47	28	248	8	1.16	2	0.18	—	0.10	0.87	0.15	77	13	0	<1
0	19	0.69	7	132	3	0.11	92	0.03	0.10	0.03	0.20	0.05	40	2	0	<1
0	29	1.02	11	196	4	0.17	137	0.05	0.15	0.05	0.29	0.07	60	3	0	<1
0	11	0.19	4	84	5	0.09	9	0.02	0.10	0.01	0.07	0.03	31	2	0	<1
0	11	0.19	4	84	5	0.09	9	0.02	0.10	0.01	0.07	0.03	31	2	0	<1
0	20	0.48	7	109	16	0.10	208	0.04	0.16	0.05	0.21	0.05	21	10	0	<1
0	19	0.55	8	139	5	0.13	163	0.04	0.07	0.04	0.18	0.04	77	14	0	<1
0	0.67	—	—	33	—	0	—	—	—	—	—	—	—	0	0	—
0	1	0.80	14	343	3	0.51	0	0.08	0.01	0.09	3.28	0.04	27	11	0	14
0	1	0.18	3	110	1	0.18	0	0.03	0.00	0.15	1.35	0.04	6	1	<.1	3
0	5	1.36	9	278	2	0.68	0	0.06	0.01	0.23	3.48	0.07	14	3	0	9
0	9	0.62	12	101	332	0.56	0	0.07	0.01	0.02	1.24	0.05	9	0	0	3
40	0.36	—	—	10	—	0	—	—	—	—	—	—	—	0	0	—
0	2	0.32	10	85	3	0.96	0	0.03	0.01	0.12	1.09	0.12	15	<1	0	18
0	58	0.82	18	199	14	0.11	295	0.05	1.13	0.06	0.45	0.10	105	39	0	1
0	76	0.84	10	104	19	0.15	266	0.03	1.01	0.04	0.19	0.08	53	10	0	<1
0	62	0.22	29	108	5	0.34	11	0.11	0.22	0.04	0.70	0.15	37	13	0	<1
0	88	0.62	47	215	3	0.57	16	0.09	0.29	0.11	0.72	0.04	134	11	0	1
2	54	1.13	32	170	110	0.44	—	0.16	1.51	0.13	1.29	0.11	34	9	<.1	—
0	18	0.15	8	115	2	0.13	0	0.04	0.02	0.02	0.07	0.12	15	5	0	<1
0	23	0.26	12	177	3	0.22	0	0.04	0.02	0.02	0.18	0.14	16	6	0	1

TABLE H-1
Food Composition

(DA+ code is for Wadsworth Diet Analysis program)   (For purposes of calculations, use "0" for t, <1, <.1, <.01, etc.)

DA + Code	Food Description	Quantity	Measure	Wt (g)	H₂O (g)	Ener (kcal)	Prot (g)	Carb (g)	Fiber (g)	Fat (g)	Sat	Mono	Poly	Trans
	VEGETABLES, LEGUMES—Continued													
2748	Frozen, boiled, drained	½	cup(s)	106	98	30	1	7	2	<1	0.02	0.01	0.04	—
16850	Red onions, sliced, raw	½	cup(s)	58	52	22	1	5	1	<.1	0.02	0.01	0.04	—
636	Scallions, green or spring onions	2	item(s)	30	27	10	1	2	1	<.1	0.01	0.01	0.02	—
1081	Onion rings, breaded & pan fried, frozen, heated	11	item(s)	78	22	318	4	30	1	21	6.70	8.49	3.99	—
16860	**Palm hearts, cooked**	½	cup(s)	73	51	75	2	19	1	<1	0.03	0.00	0.07	—
637	**Parsley, chopped**	1	tablespoon(s)	4	3	1	<1	<1	<1	<.1	0.01	0.01	0.00	—
638	**Parsnips, sliced, boiled, drained**	½	cup(s)	78	63	55	1	13	3	<1	0.04	0.09	0.04	—
	Peas													
639	Green peas, canned, drained	½	cup(s)	85	69	59	4	11	3	<1	0.05	0.03	0.14	—
641	Green peas, frozen, boiled, drained	½	cup(s)	80	64	62	4	11	4	<1	0.04	0.02	0.10	—
35694	Pea pods, boiled w/salt, drained	½	cup(s)	80	71	34	3	6	2	<1	0.04	0.02	0.08	—
1082	Peas & carrots, canned w/liquid	½	cup(s)	128	112	48	3	11	3	<1	0.06	0.03	0.16	—
1083	Peas & carrots, frozen, boiled, drained	½	cup(s)	80	69	38	2	8	2	<1	0.06	0.03	0.16	—
640	Snow or sugar peas, raw	½	cup(s)	32	28	13	1	2	1	<.1	0.01	0.01	0.03	—
2750	Snow or sugar peas, frozen, boiled, drained	½	cup(s)	80	69	42	3	7	2	<1	0.06	0.03	0.13	—
29324	Split peas, sprouted	½	cup(s)	60	37	77	5	17	0	<1	0.07	0.04	0.20	—
	Peppers													
643	Green bell or sweet, raw	½	cup(s)	75	70	15	1	3	1	<1	0.04	0.01	0.05	—
644	Green bell or sweet, boiled, drained	½	cup(s)	68	62	19	1	5	1	<1	0.02	0.01	0.07	—
1664	Green hot chili	1	item(s)	45	39	18	1	4	1	<.1	0.01	0.00	0.05	—
1663	Green hot chili, canned w/liquid	½	cup(s)	68	63	14	1	3	1	<.1	0.01	0.00	0.04	—
1086	Jalapeno, canned w/liquid	½	cup(s)	68	60	18	1	3	2	1	0.07	0.04	0.35	—
8703	Yellow bell or sweet	1	item(s)	186	171	50	2	12	2	<1	0.06	0.03	0.21	—
1087	**Poi**	½	cup(s)	122	87	136	<1	33	<1	<1	0.04	0.01	0.07	—
	Potatoes													
5791	Baked, flesh & skin	1	item(s)	202	144	220	5	51	4	<1	0.05	0.00	0.09	—
645	Baked, flesh only	½	cup(s)	61	46	57	1	13	1	<.1	0.02	0.00	0.03	—
1088	Baked, skin only	1	item(s)	58	27	115	2	27	5	<.1	0.02	0.00	0.02	—
5794	Boiled, drained, skin & flesh	1	item(s)	150	116	129	3	30	2	<1	0.04	0.00	0.06	—
647	Boiled, flesh only	½	cup(s)	78	60	67	1	16	1	<.1	0.02	0.00	0.03	—
5795	Boiled in skin, drained, flesh only	1	item(s)	136	105	118	3	27	2	<1	0.04	0.00	0.06	—
2759	Microwaved	1	item(s)	202	146	212	5	49	5	<1	0.05	0.00	0.09	—
5804	Microwaved, skin only	1	item(s)	58	37	77	3	17	4	<.1	0.02	0.00	0.02	—
2760	Microwaved in skin, flesh only	½	cup(s)	78	57	78	2	18	1	<.1	0.02	0.00	0.03	—
1089	Au gratin, prepared w/butter	½	cup(s)	123	91	162	6	14	2	9	5.80	2.63	0.34	—
1090	Au gratin mix, prepared w/water, whole milk, & butter	½	cup(s)	114	90	106	3	15	1	5	2.94	1.34	0.15	—
648	French fried, deep fried, prepared from raw	14	item(s)	70	32	190	3	24	2	10	1.93	4.21	2.97	—
649	French fried, frozen, heated	14	item(s)	70	40	140	2	22	2	5	0.88	3.33	0.55	—
1091	Hashed brown	½	cup(s)	78	37	207	2	27	2	10	1.11	3.13	2.78	—
653	Mashed, from dehydrated granules w/milk, water, & margarine	½	cup(s)	105	80	122	2	17	1	5	1.27	2.05	1.41	—
652	Mashed, w/margarine & whole milk	½	cup(s)	105	79	119	2	18	2	4	1.05	1.83	1.27	—
1097	Potato puffs, frozen, heated	½	cup(s)	64	34	142	2	20	2	7	3.26	2.79	0.51	—
1093	Scalloped, prepared w/butter	½	cup(s)	123	99	105	4	13	2	5	2.76	1.27	0.20	—
1094	Scalloped mix, prepared w/water, whole milk, & butter	½	cup(s)	114	90	106	2	15	1	5	2.99	1.38	0.22	—
	Pumpkin													
1773	Boiled, drained	½	cup(s)	123	115	25	1	6	1	<.1	0.05	0.01	0.00	—
656	Canned	½	cup(s)	123	110	42	1	10	4	<1	0.18	0.05	0.02	—
	Radicchio									<.1				
2498	Raw	1	cup(s)	40	37	9	1	2	<1	<1	0.02	0.00	0.04	—
8731	Raw, leaves	10	item(s)	80	75	18	1	4	1	<1	0.05	0.01	0.09	—
657	**Radishes**	6	item(s)	27	26	4	<1	1	<1	<1	0.01	0.00	0.01	—
1099	**Rutabaga, boiled, drained**	½	cup(s)	85	76	33	1	7	2	<1	0.02	0.02	0.08	—
658	**Sauerkraut, canned**	½	cup(s)	114	105	22	1	5	3	<1	0.04	0.01	0.07	—
	Seaweed													
1102	Kelp	½	cup(s)	41	33	17	1	4	1	<1	0.10	0.04	0.02	—
1104	Spirulina, dried	½	cup(s)	8	<1	22	4	2	<1	1	0.20	0.05	0.16	—
1106	**Shallots**	3	tablespoon(s)	30	24	22	1	5	0	<.1	0.01	0.00	0.01	—
	Soybeans													
1670	Boiled	½	cup(s)	86	0.05	148.77	14.31	8.53	5.15	7.71	1.11	1.7	4.35	—
2825	Dry roasted	½	cup(s)	86	1	388	34	28	7	19	2.69	4.11	10.50	—
2824	Roasted, salted	½	cup(s)	86	2	405	30	29	15	22	3.16	4.82	12.33	—

PAGE KEY: H–2 = Breads/Baked Goods   H–6 = Cereal/Rice/Pasta   H–10 = Fruit   H–14 = Vegetables/Legumes   H–24 = Nuts/Seeds   H–26 = Vegetarian
H–28 = Dairy   H–34 = Eggs   H–34 = Seafood   H–36 = Meats   H–40 = Poultry   H–40 = Processed meats   H–42 = Beverages   H–46 = Fats/Oils
H–48 = Sweets   H–50 = Spices/Condiments/Sauces   H–52 = Mixed foods/Soups/Sandwiches   H–58 = Fast food   H–74 = Convenience meals   H–76 = Baby foods

Chol (mg)	Calc (mg)	Iron (mg)	Magn (mg)	Pota (mg)	Sodi (mg)	Zinc (mg)	Vit A (µg)	Thia (mg)	Vit E (mg α)	Ribo (mg)	Niac (mg)	Vit B6 (mg)	Fola (µg)	Vit C (mg)	Vit B12 (µg)	Sele (µg)
0	17	0.32	6	115	13	0.07	0	0.02	0.01	0.03	0.15	0.07	14	3	0	<1
0	11	0.13	6	90	2	0.11	0	0.02	0.01	0.01	0.09	0.07	11	4	0	—
0	22	0.44	6	83	5	0.12	15	0.02	0.17	0.02	0.16	0.02	19	6	0	<1
0	24	1.32	15	101	293	0.33	9	0.22	—	0.11	2.82	0.06	52	1	0	3
0	13	1.23	7	1318	10	2.72	—	0.03	0.37	0.13	0.62	0.53	15	5	0	—
0	5	0.24	2	21	2	0.04	16	0.00	0.03	0.00	0.05	0.00	6	5	0	<.1
0	29	0.45	23	286	8	0.20	0	0.06	0.78	0.04	0.56	0.07	45	10	0	1
0	17	0.81	14	147	214	0.60	23	0.10	0.03	0.07	0.62	0.05	37	8	0	1
0	19	1.22	18	88	58	0.54	84	0.23	0.02	0.08	1.18	0.09	47	8	0	1
0	34	1.58	21	192	192	0.30	43	0.10	0.31	0.06	0.43	0.12	23	38	0	1
0	29	0.96	18	128	332	0.74	368	0.09	—	0.07	0.74	0.11	23	8	0	1
0	18	0.75	13	126	54	0.36	374	0.18	0.42	0.05	0.92	0.07	21	6	0	1
0	14	0.66	8	63	1	0.09	17	0.05	0.12	0.03	0.19	0.05	13	19	0	<1
0	47	1.92	22	174	4	0.39	53	0.05	0.38	0.10	0.45	0.14	28	18	0	1
0	22	1.36	34	229	12	0.63	5	0.14	—	0.09	1.85	0.16	86	6	0	<1
0	7	0.25	7	130	2	0.10	13	0.04	0.28	0.02	0.36	0.17	8	60	0	0
0	6	0.31	7	113	1	0.08	10	0.04	0.36	0.02	0.32	0.16	11	51	0	<1
0	8	0.54	11	153	3	0.14	27	0.04	0.31	0.04	0.43	0.13	10	109	0	<1
0	5	0.34	10	127	798	0.12	24	0.01	0.47	0.03	0.54	0.10	7	46	0	<1
0	16	1.28	10	131	1136	0.23	58	0.03	0.47	0.03	0.27	0.13	10	7	0	<1
0	20	0.86	22	394	4	0.32	19	0.05	—	0.05	1.66	0.31	48	341	0	1
0	19	1.07	29	223	15	0.27	4	0.16	2.80	0.05	1.34	0.33	26	5	0	1
0	20	2.75	55	844	16	0.65	0	0.22	—	0.07	3.32	0.70	22	26	0	2
0	3	0.21	15	239	3	0.18	0	0.06	0.02	0.01	0.85	0.18	5	8	0	<1
0	20	4.08	25	332	12	0.28	1	0.07	0.02	0.06	1.78	0.36	13	8	0	<1
0	13	1.27	34	572	7	0.47	0	0.15	—	0.03	2.13	0.44	15	18	0	—
0	6	0.24	16	256	4	0.21	0	0.08	0.01	0.01	1.02	0.21	7	6	0	<1
0	7	0.42	30	515	5	0.41	0	0.14	—	0.03	1.96	0.41	14	18	0	<1
0	22	2.50	55	903	16	0.73	0	0.24	—	0.06	3.46	0.69	24	31	0	1
0	27	3.45	21	377	9	0.30	0	0.04	—	0.04	1.29	0.29	10	9	0	<1
0	4	0.32	20	321	5	0.26	0	0.10	—	0.02	1.27	0.25	9	12	0	<1
28	146	0.78	25	485	530	0.85	78	0.08	—	0.14	1.22	0.21	13	12	0	3
17	94	0.36	17	249	499	0.27	59	0.02	—	0.09	1.07	0.05	8	4	0	3
0	9	1.02	28	731	8	0.53	0	0.10	0.09	0.05	1.90	0.33	13	21	0	—
0	6	0.87	15	293	21	0.28	0	0.08	0.08	0.02	1.46	0.22	8	7	0	<1
0	11	0.43	27	449	267	0.37	0	0.13	0.01	0.03	1.80	0.37	12	10	0	<1
2	34	0.22	21	163	181	0.25	49	0.09	0.54	0.09	0.91	0.17	8	7	<1	6
1	21	0.27	20	342	350	0.32	43	0.10	0.44	0.05	1.23	0.26	9	11	<.1	6
0	19	1.00	12	243	477	0.19	0	0.13	0.15	0.05	1.38	0.15	11	4	0	<1
15	70	0.70	23	463	410	0.49	39	0.08	—	0.11	1.29	0.22	13	13	0	2
13	41	0.43	16	231	388	0.28	40	0.02	—	0.06	1.17	0.05	11	4	0	2
0	18	0.70	11	282	1	0.28	306	0.04	0.98	0.10	0.51	0.05	11	6	0	<1
0	32	1.70	28	252	6	0.21	953	0.03	1.30	0.07	0.45	0.07	15	5	0	<1
0	8	0.23	5	121	9	0.25	<1	0.01	0.90	0.01	0.10	0.02	24	3	0	<1
0	15	0.46	10	242	18	0.50	1	0.01	1.81	0.02	0.20	0.05	48	6	0	1
0	7	0.09	3	63	11	0.08	0	0.00	0.00	0.01	0.07	0.02	7	4	0	<1
0	41	0.45	20	277	17	0.30	0	0.07	0.27	0.03	0.61	0.09	13	16	0	1
0	34	1.67	15	193	751	0.22	1	0.02	0.11	0.02	0.16	0.15	27	17	0	1
0	68	1.16	49	36	94	0.50	2	0.02	0.35	0.06	0.19	0.00	73	1	0	<1
0	9	2.14	15	102	79	0.15	2	0.18	0.38	0.28	0.96	0.03	7	1	0	1
0	11	0.36	6	100	4	0.12	18	0.02	—	0.01	0.06	0.10	10	2	0	<1
0	87.72	4.42	73.95	442.89	0.86	0.98	0.86	0.13	0.30	0.24	0.34	0.2	46.43	1.46	0	6.27
0	120	3.40	196	1173	2	4.10	0	0.37	—	0.65	0.91	0.19	176	4	0	17
0	119	3.35	125	1264	140	2.70	9	0.09	0.78	0.12	1.21	0.18	181	2	0	16

TABLE H–1
Food Composition

(DA+ code is for Wadsworth Diet Analysis program)   (For purposes of calculations, use "0" for t, <1, <.1, <.01, etc.)

DA + Code	Food Description	Quantity	Measure	Wt (g)	H₂O (g)	Ener (kcal)	Prot (g)	Carb (g)	Fiber (g)	Fat (g)	Sat	Mono	Poly	Trans
	VEGETABLES, LEGUMES—Continued													
30282	Soup (miso)	1	cup(s)	240	218	85	6	8	2	3	0.59	1.05	1.47	—
8739	Sprouted, stir fried	3	ounce(s)	85	57	106	11	8	1	6	0.84	1.37	3.41	—
	Soy products													
1813	Soy milk	1	cup(s)	240	214	118	9	11	3	5	0.51	0.78	2.00	—
2838	Tofu, dried, frozen (koyadofu)	3	ounce(s)	85	5	408	41	12	6	26	3.73	5.70	14.57	—
13844	Tofu, extra firm	3	ounce(s)	79	—	80	8	2	1	4	0.50	0.87	2.60	—
13843	Tofu, firm	3	ounce(s)	79	—	80	8	2	1	4	0.50	0.87	2.17	—
1816	Tofu, firm, w/calcium sulfate & magnesium chloride (nigari)	3	ounce(s)	85	0.07	65.48	6.83	2.52	0.34	3.79	0.54	0.83	2.14	—
1817	Tofu, fried	3	ounce(s)	85	43	230	15	9	3	17	2.48	3.79	9.69	—
13841	Tofu, silken	3	ounce(s)	91	—	30	6	0	1	1	0.50	0.51	1.52	—
13842	Tofu, soft	3	ounce(s)	91	—	30	6	1	1	1	0.50	1.00	2.00	—
1671	Tofu, soft, w/calcium sulfate & magnesium chloride (nigari)	3	ounce(s)	85	0.07	51.88	5.57	1.53	0.17	3.13	0.45	0.69	1.76	—
	Spinach													
659	Raw, chopped	1	cup(s)	30	27	7	1	1	1	<1	0.02	0.00	0.05	—
663	Canned, drained	½	cup(s)	108	100	25	3	4	3	1	0.09	0.02	0.23	—
660	Chopped, boiled, drained	½	cup(s)	90	82	21	3	3	2	<1	0.04	0.01	0.10	—
661	Chopped, frozen, boiled, drained	½	cup(s)	95	84	30	4	5	4	<1	0.09	0.00	0.20	—
662	Leaf, frozen, boiled, drained	½	cup(s)	95	84	30	4	5	4	<1	0.09	0.00	0.20	—
8470	Trimmed leaves	1	cup(s)	32	27	3	1	<.1	3	<.1	—	—	—	—
	Squash													
1662	Acorn, baked	½	cup(s)	103	85	57	1	15	5	<1	0.03	0.01	0.06	—
29702	Acorn, boiled, mashed	½	cup(s)	123	110	42	1	11	3	<.1	0.02	0.01	0.04	—
1661	Butternut, baked	½	cup(s)	103	90	41	1	11	3	<.1	0.02	0.01	0.04	—
29451	Butternut, frozen, boiled	½	cup(s)	132	116	51	2	13	2	<.1	0.02	0.01	0.04	—
32773	Butternut, frozen, boiled, mashed, no salt added	½	cup(s)	122	<1	47	1	12	0	<.1	0.02	0.00	0.03	—
29700	Crookneck & straightneck, boiled, drained	½	cup(s)	90	0.08	18	0.81	3.87	1.25	0.27	0.05	0.02	0.11	—
29703	Hubbard, baked	v	cup(s)	103	87	51	3	11	0	1	0.13	0.05	0.27	—
1660	Hubbard, boiled, mashed	½	cup(s)	118	107	35	2	8	3	<1	0.09	0.03	0.18	—
29704	Spaghetti, boiled, drained, or baked	½	cup(s)	78	72	21	1	5	1	<1	0.05	0.02	0.10	—
664	Summer, all varieties, sliced, boiled, drained	½	cup(s)	90	84	18	1	4	1	<1	0.06	0.02	0.12	—
665	Winter, all varieties, baked, mashed	½	cup(s)	103	91	38	1	9	3	<1	0.13	0.05	0.27	—
1112	Zucchini, boiled, drained	½	cup(s)	90	85	14	1	4	1	<.1	0.01	0.00	0.02	—
1113	Zucchini, frozen, boiled, drained	½	cup(s)	113	107	19	1	4	1	<1	0.03	0.01	0.06	—
	Sweet potatoes													
666	Baked, peeled	½	cup(s)	100	76	90	2	21	3	<1	0.03	0.00	0.06	—
667	Boiled, mashed	½	cup(s)	166	133	126	2	29	4	<1	0.05	0.00	0.10	—
668	Candied, home recipe	½	cup(s)	84	56	115	1	23	2	3	1.13	0.53	0.12	—
670	Canned, vacuum pack	½	cup(s)	100	76	91	2	21	2	<1	0.04	0.01	0.09	—
2765	Frozen, baked	½	cup(s)	88	65	88	2	21	2	<1	0.02	0.00	0.05	—
1136	Yams, baked or boiled, drained	½	cup(s)	68	48	79	1	19	3	<.1	0.02	0.00	0.04	—
32785	**Taro shoots, cooked, no salt added**	½	cup(s)	70	67	10	1	2	0	<.1	0.01	0.00	0.02	—
	Tomatillo													
8774	Raw	2	item(s)	68	62	22	1	4	1	1	0.09	0.11	0.28	—
8777	Raw, chopped	½	cup(s)	66	60	21	1	4	1	1	0.09	0.10	0.28	—
	Tomato													
671	Fresh, ripe, red	1	item(s)	123	0.11	22.13	1.08	4.82	1.47	0.24	0.05	0.06	0.16	—
16846	Fresh, cherry	5	item(s)	85	0.07	17.85	0.72	3.94	0.93	0.28	0.03	0.04	0.11	—
3952	Diced, red	½	cup(s)	90	85	16	1	4	1	<1	0.04	0.05	0.12	—
1118	Boiled, red	½	cup(s)	120	113	22	1	5	1	<1	0.02	0.02	0.05	—
675	Juice, canned	½	cup(s)	122	115	21	1	5	<1	<.1	0.01	0.01	0.03	—
75	Juice, no salt added	½	cup(s)	122	115	21	1	5	<1	<.1	0.01	0.01	0.03	—
1699	Paste, canned	2	tablespoon(s)	33	24	27	1	6	1	<1	0.04	0.03	0.07	—
1700	Puree, canned	¼	cup(s)	63	55	24	1	6	1	<1	0.02	0.02	0.05	—
1125	Sauce, canned	¼	cup(s)	61	55	20	1	5	1	<1	0.02	0.02	0.06	—
1120	Stewed, canned, red	½	cup(s)	128	117	33	1	8	1	<1	0.03	0.04	0.10	—
8778	Sun dried	½	cup(s)	27	4	70	4	15	3	1	0.12	0.13	0.30	—
8783	Sun dried in oil, drained	¼	cup(s)	28	15	59	1	6	2	4	0.52	2.38	0.57	—
	Turnips													
677	Turnips, cubed, boiled, drained	½	cup(s)	78	73	17	1	4	2	<.1	0.01	0.00	0.03	—
678	Turnip greens, chopped, boiled, drained	½	cup(s)	72	67	14	1	3	3	<1	0.04	0.01	0.07	—
679	Turnip greens, frozen, chopped, boiled, drained	½	cup(s)	82	74	24	3	4	3	<1	0.08	0.02	0.14	—

PAGE KEY: H–2 = Breads/Baked Goods   H–6 = Cereal/Rice/Pasta   H–10 = Fruit   H–14 = Vegetables/Legumes   H–24 = Nuts/Seeds   H–26 = Vegetarian
H–28 = Dairy   H–34 = Eggs   H–34 = Seafood   H–36 = Meats   H–40 = Poultry   H–40 = Processed meats   H–42 = Beverages   H–46 = Fats/Oils
H–48 = Sweets   H–50 = Spices/Condiments/Sauces   H–52 = Mixed foods/Soups/Sandwiches   H–58 = Fast food   H–74 = Convenience meals   H–76 = Baby foods

Chol (mg)	Calc (mg)	Iron (mg)	Magn (mg)	Pota (mg)	Sodi (mg)	Zinc (mg)	Vit A (µg)	Thia (mg)	Vit E (mg α)	Ribo (mg)	Niac (mg)	Vit B_6 (mg)	Fola (µg)	Vit C (mg)	Vit B_{12} (µg)	Sele (µg)
0	64	1.89	37	361	988	0.87	—	0.06	0.96	0.16	2.61	0.17	57	4	<1	—
0	70	0.34	82	482	12	1.79	1	0.36	—	0.16	0.94	0.14	108	10	0	1
0	10	1.39	46	338	29	0.55	5	0.39	3.24	0.17	0.35	0.10	5	0	0	3
0	310	8.28	50	17	5	4.17	22	0.42	—	0.27	1.01	0.24	78	1	0	46
0	60	1.08	78	—	0	—	0	—	0.03	—	—	—	—	0	0	—
0	60	1.08	52	—	0	—	0	—	—	—	—	—	—	0	0	—
0	137.78	1.23	39.12	149.68	6.8	0.85	0.85	0.07	—	0.08	0	0.05	28.06	0.17	0	7.99
0	316	4.14	51	124	14	1.69	1	0.14	0.03	0.04	0.09	0.08	23	0	0	24
0	300	0.73	35	—	65	—	0	—	—	—	—	—	—	0	2	—
0	300	0.72	33	—	65	—	0	—	—	—	—	—	—	0	2	—
0	94.4	0.94	22.96	102.05	6.8	0.54	0.85	0.03	0.01	0.03	0.45	0.04	37.42	0.17	0	7.56
0	30	0.81	24	167	24	0.16	141	0.02	0.61	0.06	0.22	0.06	58	8	0	<1
0	138	2.49	82	375	29	0.50	531	0.02	2.10	0.15	0.42	0.11	106	16	0	2
0	122	3.21	78	419	63	0.68	472	0.09	1.87	0.21	0.44	0.22	131	9	0	1
0	145	1.86	78	287	92	0.47	573	0.07	3.36	0.17	0.42	0.13	115	2	0	5
0	145	1.86	78	287	92	0.47	573	0.07	3.36	0.17	0.42	0.13	115	2	0	5
0	25	2.13	25	134	38	0.18	—	0.03	—	0.06	0.18	0.07	<.1	8	0	—
0	45	0.95	44	448	4	0.17	22	0.17	—	0.01	0.90	0.20	19	11	0	1
0	32	0.69	32	322	4	0.13	50	0.12	—	0.01	0.65	0.14	13	8	0	<1
0	42	0.62	30	291	4	0.13	572	0.07	1.32	0.02	0.99	0.13	19	15	0	1
0	25	0.77	12	176	3	0.16	—	0.07	—	0.05	0.61	0.09	22	5	0	1
0	23	0.70	11	162	2	0.14	406	0.05	—	0.05	0.56	0.08	19	4	0	1
0	18.2	0.41	18.2	183.73	1.73	0.25	29.46	0.04	—	0.03	0.39	0.09	19.93	7.28	0	0.17
0	17	0.48	23	367	8	0.15	310	0.08	—	0.05	0.57	0.18	16	10	0	1
0	12	0.33	15	253	6	0.12	236	0.05	0.14	0.03	0.39	0.12	12	8	0	<1
0	16	0.26	9	91	14	0.16	5	0.03	0.09	0.02	0.63	0.08	6	3	0	<1
0	24	0.32	22	173	1	0.35	10	0.04	0.13	0.04	0.46	0.06	18	5	0	<1
0	23	0.45	13	448	1	0.23	268	0.02	0.12	0.07	0.51	0.17	21	10	0	<1
0	12	0.32	20	228	3	0.16	50	0.04	0.11	0.04	0.39	0.07	15	4	0	<1
0	19	0.54	15	219	2	0.23	11	0.05	0.14	0.05	0.44	0.05	9	4	0	<1
0	38	0.69	27	475	36	0.32	961	1.45	0.71	0.11	1.49	0.29	6	20	0	<1
0	45	1.20	30	382	45	0.33	1310	0.09	1.56	0.08	0.89	0.27	10	21	0	<1
7	22	0.95	9	159	59	0.13	176	0.02	—	0.04	0.33	0.03	9	6	0	1
0	22	0.89	22	312	53	0.18	399	0.04	1.00	0.06	0.74	0.19	17	26	0	1
0	31	0.48	18	332	7	0.26	722	0.06	0.68	0.05	0.49	0.16	19	8	0	1
0	10	0.36	12	458	5	0.14	4	0.06	0.26	0.02	0.38	0.16	11	8	0	<1
0	10	0.29	6	241	1	0.38	2	0.03	—	0.04	0.57	0.08	2	13	0	1
0	5	0.42	14	182	1	0.15	4	0.03	0.26	0.02	1.26	0.04	5	8	0	<1
0	5	0.41	13	177	1	0.15	4	0.03	0.25	0.02	1.22	0.04	5	8	0	<1
0	12.3	0.33	13.52	291.51	6.15	0.2	76.26	0.04	0.66	0.02	0.73	0.09	18.45	15.62	0	0
0	4.25	0.37	9.35	188.69	7.65	0.07	52.7	0.05	0.46	0.03	0.53	0.07	—	16.23	0	—
0	9	0.24	10	213	5	0.15	38	0.03	0.49	0.02	0.53	0.07	14	11	0	0
0	13	0.82	11	262	13	0.17	29	0.04	0.67	0.03	0.64	0.09	16	27	0	1
0	12	0.52	13	279	328	0.18	28	0.06	0.39	0.04	0.82	0.14	24	22	0	<1
0	12	0.52	13	279	12	0.18	28	0.06	0.39	0.04	0.82	0.14	24	22	0	<1
0	12	0.98	14	333	259	0.21	25	0.02	1.41	0.05	1.01	0.07	4	7	0	2
0	11	1.11	14	274	249	0.23	16	0.02	1.23	0.05	0.92	0.08	7	7	0	3
0	8	0.62	10	203	321	0.12	10	0.01	1.27	0.04	0.60	0.06	6	4	0	<1
0	43	1.70	15	264	282	0.22	11	0.06	1.06	0.04	0.91	0.02	6	10	0	1
0	30	2.45	52	925	566	0.54	12	0.14	0.00	0.13	2.44	0.09	18	11	0	1
0	13	0.74	22	430	73	0.21	18	0.05	—	0.11	1.00	0.09	6	28	0	1
0	26	0.14	7	138	12	0.09	0	0.02	0.02	0.02	0.23	0.05	7	9	0	<1
0	99	0.58	16	146	21	0.10	274	0.03	1.35	0.05	0.30	0.13	85	20	0	1
0	125	1.59	21	184	12	0.34	441	0.04	2.18	0.06	0.38	0.05	32	18	0	1

TABLE H–1
Food Composition

(DA+ code is for Wadsworth Diet Analysis program)　　(For purposes of calculations, use "0" for t, <1, <.1, <.01, etc.)

DA+ Code	Food Description	Quantity	Measure	Wt (g)	H₂O (g)	Ener (kcal)	Prot (g)	Carb (g)	Fiber (g)	Fat (g)	Sat	Mono	Poly	Trans
	VEGETABLES, LEGUMES—Continued													
	Vegetables, mixed													
1132	Canned, drained	½	cup(s)	82	71	40	2	8	2	<1	0.04	0.01	0.10	—
680	Frozen, boiled, drained	½	cup(s)	91	76	59	3	12	4	<1	0.03	0.01	0.07	—
7489	Vegetable juice, V8 100%	½	cup(s)	120	113	25	1	5	1	0	0.00	0.00	0.00	0
7490	Vegetable juice, V8 low sodium	½	cup(s)	120	113	25	0	7	1	0	0.00	0.00	0.00	0
7491	Vegetable juice, V8 spicy hot	½	cup(s)	120	113	25	1	5	1	0	0.00	0.00	0.00	0
	Water chestnuts													
31073	Sliced, drained	½	cup(s)	75	70	20	<1	5	1	0	0.00	0.00	0.00	0
31087	Whole	½	cup(s)	75	70	20	<1	5	1	0	0.00	0.00	0.00	0
1135	**Watercress**	1	cup(s)	34	32	4	1	<1	<1	<.1	0.01	0.00	0.01	—
	NUTS, SEEDS, AND PRODUCTS													
	Almonds													
32886	Blanched	¼	cup(s)	36	2	211	8	7	4	18	1.41	11.70	4.37	—
32887	Dry roasted, no salt added	¼	cup(s)	35	1	206	8	7	4	18	1.40	11.61	4.36	—
29724	Dry roasted, salted	¼	cup(s)	35	1	206	8	7	4	18	1.40	11.61	4.36	—
29725	Oil roasted, salted	¼	cup(s)	39	1	238	8	7	4	22	1.65	13.66	5.31	—
508	Slivered	¼	cup(s)	34	2	195	7	7	4	17	1.31	10.85	4.12	—
1137	Almond butter, no salt added	1	tablespoon(s)	16	<1	101	2	3	1	9	0.90	6.14	1.98	—
32940	Almond butter, salt added	1	tablespoon(s)	16	<1	101	2	3	1	9	0.90	6.14	1.98	—
1138	**Beechnuts, dried**	¼	cup(s)	57	4	327	4	19	5	28	3.25	12.43	11.41	—
517	**Brazil nuts, unblanched, dried**	¼	cup(s)	35	1	230	5	4	3	23	5.30	8.59	7.20	—
1166	**Breadfruit seeds, roasted**	¼	cup(s)	57	28	118	4	23	3	2	0.41	0.20	0.82	—
1139	**Butternuts, dried**	¼	cup(s)	30	1	184	7	4	1	17	0.39	3.13	12.82	—
	Cashews													
1140	Dry roasted	¼	cup(s)	34	1	197	5	11	1	16	3.14	9.36	2.68	—
518	Oil roasted	¼	cup(s)	33	1	189	5	10	1	16	2.76	8.42	2.78	—
32889	Cashew butter, no salt added	1	tablespoon(s)	16	<1	94	3	4	<1	8	1.56	4.66	1.34	—
32931	Cashew butter, salt added	1	tablespoon(s)	16	<1	94	3	4	<1	8	1.56	4.66	1.34	—
	Coconut													
32896	Dried, not sweetened	¼	cup(s)	60	2	393	4	14	10	38	34.06	1.63	0.42	—
1153	Dried, shredded, sweetened	¼	cup(s)	24	3	122	1	12	1	9	7.68	0.37	0.09	—
520	Shredded	¼	cup(s)	21	10	75	1	3	2	7	6.27	0.30	0.08	—
	Chestnuts													
1152	Chinese, roasted	¼	cup(s)	57	23	136	3	30	0	1	0.10	0.35	0.17	—
32895	European, boiled & steamed	¼	cup(s)	57	39	74	1	16	0	1	0.15	0.27	0.31	—
32911	European, roasted	¼	cup(s)	57	23	139	2	30	3	1	0.23	0.43	0.49	—
32922	Japanese, boiled & steamed	¼	cup(s)	57	49	32	<1	7	0	<1	0.02	0.06	0.03	—
32923	Japanese, roasted	¼	cup(s)	57	28	114	2	26	0	<1	0.07	0.24	0.12	—
4958	**Flaxseeds or linseeds**	¼	cup(s)	57	5	276	11	19	16	19	1.79	3.85	12.54	—
32904	**Ginkgo nuts, dried**	¼	cup(s)	57	7	197	6	41	0	1	0.22	0.42	0.42	—
	Hazelnuts or filberts													
32901	Blanched	¼	cup(s)	57	3	357	8	10	6	35	2.65	27.32	3.15	—
32902	Dry roasted, no salt added	¼	Measure	57	1	366	9	10	5	35	2.56	26.43	4.80	—
1156	**Hickorynuts, dried**	¼	cup(s)	30	1	197	4	5	2	19	2.11	9.78	6.57	—
	Macadamias													
1157	Raw	¼	cup(s)	34	<1	241	3	5	3	25	4.04	19.72	0.50	—
32905	Dry roasted, no salt added	¼	cup(s)	34	1	241	3	4	3	25	4.00	19.86	0.50	—
32932	Dry roasted, salt added	¼	cup(s)	34	1	240	3	4	3	25	4.00	19.86	0.50	—
	Mixed nuts													
1159	With peanuts, dry roasted	¼	cup(s)	34	1	203	6	9	3	18	2.36	10.75	3.69	—
32933	With peanuts, dry roasted, salt added	¼	cup(s)	34	1	203	6	9	3	18	2.36	10.75	3.69	—
32906	Without peanuts, oil roasted, no salt added	¼	cup(s)	36	1	221	6	8	2	20	3.27	11.93	4.12	—
	Peanuts													
2807	Dry roasted	¼	cup(s)	37	0	214	9	8	3	18	2.51	8.99	5.72	—
2806	Dry roasted, salted	¼	cup(s)	37	0	214	9	8	3	18	2.51	8.99	5.72	—
1763	Oil roasted, salted	¼	cup(s)	36	0	216	10	5	3	19	3.12	9.33	5.49	—
2804	Raw	¼	cup(s)	37	2	207	9	6	3	18	2.49	8.92	5.68	—
1884	Peanut butter, chunky	1	tablespoon(s)	16	<1	94	4	3	1	8	1.53	3.77	2.27	—
30303	Peanut butter, low sodium	1	tablespoon(s)	16	<1	95	4	3	1	8	1.66	3.88	2.21	—
30305	Peanut butter, reduced fat	1	tablespoon(s)	18	<1	94	5	6	1	6	1.33	2.91	1.85	—
524	Peanut butter, smooth	1	tablespoon(s)	16	<1	96	4	3	1	8	1.60	3.96	2.38	—
	Pecans													
32907	Dry roasted, no salt added	¼	cup(s)	57	1	403	5	8	5	42	3.56	24.92	11.66	—

PAGE KEY: H–2 = Breads/Baked Goods   H–6 = Cereal/Rice/Pasta   H–10 = Fruit   H–14 = Vegetables/Legumes   H–24 = Nuts/Seeds   H–26 = Vegetarian
H–28 = Dairy   H–34 = Eggs   H–34 = Seafood   H–36 = Meats   H–40 = Poultry   H–40 = Processed meats   H–42 = Beverages   H–46 = Fats/Oils
H–48 = Sweets   H–50 = Spices/Condiments/Sauces   H–52 = Mixed foods/Soups/Sandwiches   H–58 = Fast food   H–74 = Convenience meals   H–76 = Baby foods

Chol (mg)	Calc (mg)	Iron (mg)	Magn (mg)	Pota (mg)	Sodi (mg)	Zinc (mg)	Vit A (µg)	Thia (mg)	Vit E (mg α)	Ribo (mg)	Niac (mg)	Vit B$_6$ (mg)	Fola (µg)	Vit C (mg)	Vit B$_{12}$ (µg)	Sele (µg)
0	22	0.86	13	237	121	0.33	474	0.04	0.28	0.04	0.47	0.06	20	4	0	<1
0	23	0.75	20	154	32	0.45	195	0.06	0.40	0.11	0.77	0.07	17	3	0	<1
0	20	0.54	13	270	310	0.24	50	0.05	—	0.03	0.87	0.17	—	30	0	—
0	20	0.36	—	420	70	—	63	0.02	—	0.02	0.75	—	—	30	0	—
0	20	0.36	13	255	370	0.24	50	0.05	—	0.03	0.88	0.17	—	18	0	—
0	7	0.23	—	—	6	—	0	—	—	—	—	—	—	2	—	—
0	7	0.23	—	—	6	—	0	—	—	—	—	—	—	2	—	—
0	41	0.07	7	112	14	0.04	80	0.03	0.34	0.04	0.07	0.04	3	15	0	<1
0	78	1.35	100	249	10	1.13	0	0.07	8.96	0.20	1.33	0.04	11	0	0	1
0	92	1.56	99	257	<1	1.22	0	0.03	8.97	0.30	1.33	0.04	11	0	0	1
0	92	1.56	99	257	117	1.22	0	0.03	8.97	0.30	1.33	0.04	11	0	0	1
0	114	1.44	108	274	133	1.20	0	0.04	10.19	0.31	1.44	0.05	11	0	0	1
0	84	1.45	93	246	<1	1.13	0	0.08	8.73	0.27	1.32	0.04	10	0	0	1
0	43	0.59	48	121	2	0.49	0	0.02	—	0.10	0.46	0.01	10	<1	0	—
0	43	0.59	48	121	72	0.49	0	0.02	—	0.10	0.46	0.01	10	<1	0	1
0	1	1.40	0	578	22	0.20	0	0.17	—	0.21	0.50	0.39	64	9	0	4
0	56	0.85	132	231	1	1.42	0	0.22	2.01	0.01	0.10	0.04	8	<1	0	671
0	49	0.51	35	615	16	0.59	9	0.23	—	0.14	4.20	0.24	34	4	0	8
0	16	1.21	71	126	<1	0.94	2	0.11	—	0.04	0.31	0.17	20	1	0	5
0	15	2.06	89	194	5	1.92	0	0.07	0.32	0.07	0.48	0.09	24	0	0	4
0	14	1.97	89	205	4	1.74	0	0.12	0.30	0.07	0.56	0.10	8	<.1	0	7
0	7	0.80	41	87	2	0.83	0	0.05	—	0.03	0.26	0.04	11	0	0	2
0	7	0.80	41	87	98	0.83	0	0.05	0.15	0.03	0.26	0.04	11	0	0	2
0	15	1.98	54	323	22	1.20	0	0.04	0.26	0.06	0.36	0.18	5	1	0	11
0	4	0.47	12	82	64	0.44	0	0.01	0.10	0.00	0.12	0.07	2	<1	0	4
0	3	0.51	7	75	4	0.23	0	0.01	0.05	0.00	0.11	0.01	5	1	0	2
0	11	0.85	51	271	2	0.53	0	0.09	—	0.05	0.85	0.25	41	22	0	4
0	26	0.98	31	405	15	0.14	1	0.08	—	0.06	0.41	0.13	22	15	0	—
0	16	0.52	19	336	1	0.32	1	0.14	0.28	0.10	0.76	0.28	40	15	0	1
0	6	0.30	10	67	3	0.23	1	0.07	—	0.03	0.31	0.06	10	5	0	—
0	20	1.19	36	242	11	0.81	2	0.26	—	—	0.40	0.24	33	16	0	—
0	111	3.48	203	381	19	2.34	0	0.10	—	0.09	0.78	0.52	156	1	0	3
0	11	0.91	30	566	7	0.38	31	0.24	—	0.10	6.65	0.36	60	17	0	—
0	84	1.87	91	373	0	1.25	1	0.27	9.92	0.06	0.88	0.33	44	1	0	2
0	70	2.48	98	428	0	1.42	2	0.19	8.66	0.07	1.16	0.35	50	2	0	2
0	18	0.64	52	131	<1	1.29	2	0.26	—	0.04	0.27	0.06	12	1	0	2
0	28	1.24	44	123	2	0.44	0	0.40	0.18	0.05	0.83	0.09	4	<1	0	1
0	23	0.89	40	122	1	0.43	0	0.24	0.19	0.03	0.76	0.12	3	<1	0	1
0	23	0.89	40	122	89	0.43	0	0.24	0.19	0.03	0.76	0.12	3	<1	0	4
0	24	1.27	77	204	4	1.30	<1	0.07	—	0.07	1.61	0.10	17	<1	0	1
0	24	1.27	77	204	229	1.30	0	0.07	3.75	0.07	1.61	0.10	17	<1	0	3
0	38	0.93	90	196	4	1.68	<1	0.18	—	0.17	0.71	0.06	20	<1	0	—
0	20	0.82	64	240	2	1.20	0	0.15	2.56	0.03	4.93	0.09	53	0	0	3
0	20	0.82	64	240	297	1.20	0	0.15	2.89	0.03	4.93	0.09	53	0	0	3
0	22	0.54	63	261	115	1.18	0	0.03	2.50	0.03	4.97	0.16	43	<1	0	1
0	34	1.67	61	257	7	1.19	0	0.23	3.04	0.05	4.40	0.13	88	0	0	3
0	8	0.33	31	101	75	0.52	0	0.02	1.01	0.02	2.19	0.07	15	0	0	1
0	6	0.29	25	107	3	0.47	0	0.01	1.23	0.02	2.14	0.07	12	0	0	—
0	6	0.34	31	120	97	0.50	0	0.05	1.20	0.01	2.63	0.06	11	0	0	—
0	8	0.30	28	88	80	0.47	0	0.01	1.44	0.02	2.14	0.07	12	0	0	1
0	41	1.59	75	240	1	2.87	4	0.26	0.74	0.06	0.66	0.11	9	<1	0	2

Appendix H

TABLE H–1
Food Composition

(DA+ code is for Wadsworth Diet Analysis program)   (For purposes of calculations, use "0" for t, <1, <.1, <.01, etc.)

DA + Code	Food Description	Quantity	Measure	Wt (g)	H₂O (g)	Ener (kcal)	Prot (g)	Carb (g)	Fiber (g)	Fat (g)	Fat Breakdown (g)			
											Sat	Mono	Poly	Trans
	NUTS, SEEDS, AND PRODUCTS—Continued													
32936	Dry roasted, salt added	¼	cup(s)	57	1	403	5	8	5	42	3.56	24.92	11.66	—
1162	Halves, oil roasted	¼	cup(s)	28	<1	197	3	4	3	21	1.99	11.27	6.49	—
526	Raw	¼	cup(s)	27	1	187	2	4	3	19	1.67	11.02	5.84	—
12973	**Pine nuts or pignolia, dried**	1	tablespoon(s)	9	<1	58	1	1	<1	6	0.42	1.61	2.93	—
	Pistachios													
1164	Dry roasted	¼	cup(s)	32	1	183	7	9	3	15	1.78	7.75	4.45	—
32938	Dry roasted, salt added	¼	cup(s)	32	1	182	7	9	3	15	1.78	7.75	4.45	—
1167	**Pumpkin or squash seeds, roasted**	¼	cup(s)	57	4	296	19	8	2	24	4.52	7.43	10.90	—
	Sesame													
1169	Sesame seeds, whole, roasted, toasted	3	teaspoon(s)	9	<1	51	2	2	1	4	0.60	1.63	1.89	—
32912	Sesame butter paste	1	tablespoon(s)	16	<1	95	3	4	1	8	1.14	3.07	3.57	—
32941	Tahini or sesame butter	1	tablespoon(s)	15	<1	89	3	3	1	8	1.11	3.00	3.48	—
	Soy nuts													
34173	Deep sea salted	¼	cup(s)	56	—	240	24	18	10	8	2.00	—	—	—
34174	Unsalted	¼	cup(s)	56	—	240	24	18	10	8	2.00	—	—	—
	Sunflower seeds													
528	Kernels, dried	¼	cup(s)	36	2	205	8	7	4	18	1.87	3.41	11.78	—
29721	Kernels, dry roasted, salted	¼	cup(s)	32	<1	186	6	8	3	16	1.67	3.04	10.52	—
29723	Kernels, toasted, salted	¼	cup(s)	34	<1	207	6	7	4	19	1.99	3.63	12.56	—
32928	Sunflower seed butter, salt added	1	tablespoon(s)	16	<1	93	3	4	0	8	0.80	1.46	5.04	—
	Trail mix													
4646	Trail mix	¼	cup(s)	38	3	173	5	17	2	11	2.08	4.70	3.62	—
4647	Trail mix with chocolate chips	¼	cup(s)	38	2	182	5	17	0	12	2.29	5.08	4.23	—
4648	Tropical trail mix	¼	cup(s)	35	3	142	2	23	0	6	2.97	0.87	1.81	—
	Walnuts													
529	Dried black, chopped	¼	cup(s)	31	1	193	8	3	2	18	1.05	4.69	10.96	—
531	English or persian	¼	cup(s)	30	1	196	5	4	2	20	1.84	2.68	14.15	—
	VEGETARIAN FOODS													
	Prepared													
34222	Brown rice & tofu stir-fry (vegan)	8	ounce(s)	227	183	228	12	13	3	16	1.25	4.03	9.54	0
34368	Cheese enchilada casserole (lacto)	8	ounce(s)	227	86	410	18	41	4	19	10.06	6.54	1.24	0
34247	Five bean casserole (vegan)	8	ounce(s)	228	178	178	6	26	5	6	1.11	2.49	1.96	0
34261	Lentil stew (vegan)	8	ounce(s)	228	152	125	8	24	7	<1	0.08	0.07	0.21	0
34397	Macaroni & cheese (lacto)	8	ounce(s)	226	163	181	8	17	<1	9	4.37	2.88	0.89	0
34238	Steamed rice & vegetables (vegan)	8	ounce(s)	228	100	265	5	40	3	10	1.84	3.91	4.07	0
34308	Tofu rice burgers (ovo-lacto)	1	piece(s)	218	78	435	22	68	6	8	1.69	2.39	3.52	—
34276	Vegan spinach enchiladas (vegan)	1	piece(s)	82	59	93	5	15	2	2	0.34	0.55	1.27	—
34243	Vegetable chow mein (vegan)	8	ounce(s)	227	163	166	6	22	2	6	0.65	2.66	2.47	0
34454	Vegetable lasagna (lacto)	8	ounce(s)	225	154	177	12	25	2	4	1.92	0.93	0.34	0
34339	Vegetable marinara (vegan)	8	ounce(s)	229	182	94	3	15	1	3	0.36	1.32	0.92	0
34356	Vegetable rice casserole (lacto)	8	ounce(s)	227	172	230	9	24	4	12	4.67	3.48	2.96	—
34311	Vegetable strudel (ovo-lacto)	8	ounce(s)	227	100	756	19	51	4	54	18.24	26.38	6.17	0
34371	Vegetable taco (lacto)	1	item(s)	227	147	365	13	43	9	17	6.45	5.81	4.02	—
34282	Vegetarian chili (vegan)	8	ounce(s)	227	196	116	6	21	7	2	0.24	0.29	0.74	0
34367	Vegetarian vegetable soup (vegan)	8	ounce(s)	226	204	92	3	14	2	4	0.77	1.67	1.30	0
	Boca burger													
32067	All American flamed grilled patty	1	item(s)	71	—	110	14	6	4	4	1.00	—	—	0
32070	Bigger chef max's favorite	1	item(s)	99	—	130	18	11	5	4	1.00	1.00	1.50	—
32069	Bigger vegan	1	item(s)	99	—	120	18	11	6	0	0.00	0.00	0.00	—
32074	Boca chik'n nuggets	4	item(s)	87	—	190	16	16	2	7	2.00	—	—	0
32075	Boca meatless ground burger	½	cup(s)	57	—	70	11	7	4	1	0.00	—	—	—
32073	Boca tenders	1	item(s)	85	—	140	20	9	3	3	0.00	2.00	1.00	—
32072	Breakfast links	2	item(s)	45	—	100	10	6	5	4	0.00	—	—	0
32071	Breakfast patties	1	item(s)	38	—	80	8	5	3	4	0.00	—	—	0
32068	Roasted garlic patty	1	item(s)	71	—	100	14	7	5	2	0.50	—	—	0
32066	Vegan original patty	1	item(s)	71	—	90	13	4	0	1	0.00	—	—	0
	Gardenburger													
37810	Bbq chik'n with sauce	1	item(s)	142	—	250	14	30	5	8	1.00	—	—	0
39661	Black bean burger	1	item(s)	71	—	80	8	11	4	2	0.00	—	—	0
39666	Buffalo chick'n wing	3	item(s)	95	—	180	9	8	5	12	1.50	—	—	0
37808	Chik'n grill	1	item(s)	71	—	100	13	5	3	3	0.00	—	—	0
39665	Country fried chicken w/creamy pepper gravy	1	item(s)	142	—	190	9	16	2	9	1.00	—	—	0
37805	Crispy nuggets	6	item(s)	82	—	180	4	22	3	9	1.50	—	—	0
39663	Homestyle classic burger	1	item(s)	71	—	110	12	6	4	5	0.50	—	—	0

PAGE KEY: H–2 = Breads/Baked Goods H–6 = Cereal/Rice/Pasta H–10 = Fruit H–14 = Vegetables/Legumes H–24 = Nuts/Seeds H–26 = Vegetarian
H–28 = Dairy H–34 = Eggs H–34 = Seafood H–36 = Meats H–40 = Poultry H–40 = Processed meats H–42 = Beverages H–46 = Fats/Oils
H–48 = Sweets H–50 = Spices/Condiments/Sauces H–52 = Mixed foods/Soups/Sandwiches H–58 = Fast food H–74 = Convenience meals H–76 = Baby foods

Chol (mg)	Calc (mg)	Iron (mg)	Magn (mg)	Pota (mg)	Sodi (mg)	Zinc (mg)	Vit A (µg)	Thia (mg)	Vit E (mg α)	Ribo (mg)	Niac (mg)	Vit B$_6$ (mg)	Fola (µg)	Vit C (mg)	Vit B$_{12}$ (µg)	Sele (µg)
0	41	1.59	75	240	217	2.87	4	0.26	0.74	0.06	0.66	0.11	9	<1	0	2
0	18	0.68	33	108	<1	1.23	1	0.13	0.70	0.03	0.33	0.05	4	<1	0	2
0	19	0.68	33	111	0	1.22	1	0.18	0.38	0.04	0.32	0.06	6	<1	0	1
0	1	0.48	22	51	<1	0.55	<.1	0.03	0.80	0.02	0.38	0.01	6	<.1	0	<.1
		<1														
0	35	1.34	38	333	<1	0.74	4	0.27	0.62	0.05	0.46	0.41	16	1	0	3
0	35	1.34	38	333	<1	0.74	4	0.27	0.62	0.05	0.46	0.41	16	1	0	3
0	24	8.48	303	457	10	4.22	11	0.12	0.00	0.18	0.99	0.05	32	1	0	3
0	89	1.33	32	43	1	0.64	0	0.07	—	0.02	0.41	0.07	9	0	0	1
0	154	3.07	58	93	2	1.17	<1	0.04	—	0.03	1.07	0.13	16	0	0	1
0	21	0.66	14	69	5	0.69	<1	0.24	—	0.02	0.85	0.02	15	1	0	<1
0	120	2.16	—	—	300	—	0	—	—	—	—	—	—	0	—	—
0	120	2.16	—	—	20	—	0	—	—	—	—	—	—	0	—	—
0	42	2.44	127	248	1	1.82	1	0.82	12.42	0.09	1.62	0.28	82	1	0	21
0	22	1.22	41	272	250	1.69	<1	0.03	8.35	0.08	2.25	0.26	76	<1	0	25
0	19	2.28	43	164	205	1.78	0	0.11	—	0.10	1.41	0.27	80	<1	0	21
0	20	0.76	59	12	83	0.85	<1	0.05	—	0.05	0.85	0.13	38	<1	0	—
0	29	1.14	59	257	86	1.21	<1	0.17	—	0.07	1.77	0.11	27	1	0	—
2	41	1.27	60	243	45	1.18	1	0.15	—	0.08	1.65	0.10	24	<1	0	—
0	20	0.92	34	248	4	0.41	1	0.16	—	0.04	0.52	0.11	15	3	0	—
0	19	0.98	63	163	1	1.05	1	0.02	0.56	0.04	0.15	0.18	10	1	0	5
0	29	0.87	47	132	1	0.93	<1	0.10	0.21	0.05	0.34	0.16	29	<1	0	1
0	266	4.73	88	375	112	1.51	121	0.14	0.07	0.12	1.08	0.28	32	18	0	11
42	468	2.58	37	204	1219	1.96	107	0.33	0.06	0.38	2.38	0.11	77	22	<1	22
0	48	1.71	42	367	618	0.60	54	0.09	0.53	0.08	0.93	0.11	33	8	<.1	4
0	23	2.35	31	380	289	0.87	18	0.14	0.14	0.10	1.50	0.16	61	13	0	9
22	187	0.77	20	120	768	1.11	82	0.15	0.29	0.24	1.02	0.04	39	<.1	<1	16
0	41	1.43	68	358	1403	0.91	86	0.16	3.05	0.12	2.76	0.30	28	13	<.1	8
51	468	4.78	90	455	2454	2.07	82	0.27	0.12	0.27	3.43	0.30	99	2	<1	43
0	117	1.13	40	168	134	0.68	26	0.07	—	0.07	0.54	0.11	46	1	0	5
0	190	3.65	28	302	371	0.74	8	0.13	0.06	0.12	1.43	0.15	47	7	0	6
10	144	1.91	33	393	637	1.06	31	0.20	0.05	0.27	2.07	0.21	64	15	<1	19
0	15	0.85	17	180	378	0.35	18	0.13	0.50	0.08	1.25	0.11	41	20	0	10
16	176	1.72	28	395	609	1.19	121	0.16	0.35	0.29	1.93	0.18	92	54	<1	6
46	318	3.36	39	299	813	1.98	288	0.45	0.21	0.50	4.52	0.16	123	27	<1	31
21	231	2.58	83	550	893	1.80	81	0.23	0.10	0.18	1.48	0.25	132	12	<1	10
<1	68	2.42	41	532	383	0.78	46	0.13	0.15	0.13	1.26	0.18	58	16	0	5
0	37	1.32	28	443	503	0.44	109	0.11	0.55	0.08	1.54	0.22	38	24	<.1	1
3	150	1.80	—	—	370	—	0	—	—	—	—	—	—	0	—	—
5	150	2.70	—	—	400	—	—	—	—	—	—	—	—	0	—	—
0	60	1.80	—	—	380	—	0	—	—	—	—	—	—	2	—	—
0	80	1.80	—	220	570	—	0	—	—	—	—	—	—	0	—	—
0	80	1.44	—	—	220	—	0	—	—	—	—	—	—	0	—	—
0	80	1.08	—	—	440	—	0	—	—	—	—	—	—	0	—	—
0	60	1.44	—	—	330	—	0	—	—	—	—	—	—	0	—	—
0	60	1.44	—	—	260	—	0	—	—	—	—	—	—	0	—	—
3	100	1.80	—	—	400	—	0	—	—	—	—	—	—	1	—	—
0	80	1.80	—	—	350	—	0	—	—	—	—	—	—	1	—	—
0	150	1.08	—	—	890	—	—	—	—	—	—	—	—	0	—	—
0	40	1.44	—	—	330	—	—	—	—	—	—	—	—	0	—	—
0	40	0.72	—	—	1000	—	—	—	—	—	—	—	—	0	—	—
0	60	3.60	—	—	360	—	—	—	—	—	—	—	—	0	—	—
5	40	1.44	—	—	550	—	—	—	—	—	—	—	—	0	—	—
5	60	0.72	—	—	570	—	—	—	—	—	—	—	—	5	—	—
0	80	1.44	—	—	380	—	—	—	—	—	—	—	—	0	—	—

TABLE H-1
Food Composition   (DA+ code is for Wadsworth Diet Analysis program)   (For purposes of calculations, use "0" for t, <1, <.1, <.01, etc.)

DA + Code	Food Description	Quantity	Measure	Wt (g)	H₂O (g)	Ener (kcal)	Prot (g)	Carb (g)	Fiber (g)	Fat (g)	Fat Breakdown (g) Sat	Mono	Poly	Trans
	VEGETARIAN FOODS—Continued													
37807	Meatless breakfast sausage	1	item(s)	43	—	50	5	2	2	4	0.00	—	—	0
37809	Meatless meatballs	6	item(s)	85	—	110	12	8	4	5	1.00	—	—	0
37806	Meatless riblets w/sauce	1	item(s)	142	—	210	17	11	4	5	0.00	—	—	0
29913	Original	3	ounce(s)	85	—	132	7	19	4	4	1.80	1.80	0.60	0
31707	Santa Fe	3	ounce(s)	85	—	156	—	24	5	3	1.20	—	—	—
29915	Veggie medley	3	ounce(s)	85	—	108	6	22	4	0	0.00	0.00	0.00	0
	Loma Linda													
9311	Big franks	1	item(s)	51	30	110	10	2	2	7	1.00	2.00	4.00	0
9315	Chik'n nuggets	5	item(s)	85	40	240	14	13	4	15	2.00	4.50	8.00	0
9317	Corn dogs	1	item(s)	71	31	150	7	22	3	4	0.50	1.00	2.50	0
9323	Fried chik'n with gravy	2	piece(s)	80	46	150	12	5	2	10	1.50	2.50	5.00	0
9326	Linketts, canned	1	item(s)	35	21	70	7	1	1	5	0.50	1.00	2.50	0
9336	Redi-Burger patties, canned	1	slice(s)	85	50	120	18	7	4	3	0.50	0.50	1.50	0
9354	Tender Rounds meatball substitute, canned in gravy	6	piece(s)	80	54	120	13	6	1	5	0.50	1.00	2.50	0
	Morningstar Farms													
33707	America's Original Veggie Dog links	1	item(s)	57	—	80	11	6	1	1	0.00	0.00	0.00	0
9362	Better n Eggs egg substitute	¼	cup(s)	57	50	20	5	0	0	0	0.00	0.00	0.00	0
9368	Breakfast links	2	item(s)	45	27	80	9	3	2	3	0.50	0.50	2.00	0
9371	Breakfast strips	2	item(s)	16	7	60	2	2	1	5	0.50	1.00	3.00	0
33705	Chik Nuggets	4	piece(s)	86	—	180	13	17	5	6	0.50	1.50	4.00	—
11587	Chik Patties	1	item(s)	71	36	150	9	16	2	6	1.00	1.50	2.50	—
2531	Garden veggie patties	1	item(s)	67	40	100	10	9	4	3	0.50	0.50	1.50	0
9412	Natural Touch low fat vegetarian chili, canned	1	cup(s)	230	173	170	18	21	11	1	—	—	—	0
33702	Spicy black bean veggie burger	1	item(s)	78	47	150	11	16	5	5	0.50	1.50	2.50	0
	Worthington													
9422	Chik Stiks	1	item(s)	47	27	110	10	4	2	6	1.00	1.00	3.00	0
9424	Chili, canned	1	cup(s)	230	167	290	19	21	9	15	2.50	3.50	9.00	0
9432	Crispychik patties	1	item(s)	71	37	150	9	16	2	6	1.00	1.50	3.50	0
9440	Dinner roast, frozen	1	slice(s)	85	53	180	12	5	3	12	1.50	5.00	5.00	0
9442	Fillets, frozen	2	piece(s)	85	48	180	16	8	4	9	1.00	3.50	4.50	0
9478	Meatless smoked beef, sliced	6	slice(s)	57	—	130	11	7	1	7	1.00	2.00	4.00	0
9480	Meatless smoked turkey, sliced	3	slice(s)	57	—	140	10	5	0	9	1.00	2.50	5.00	—
9462	Prosage links	2	item(s)	45	27	80	9	3	2	3	0.50	0.50	2.00	0
9486	Stripples bacon substitute	2	item(s)	16	7	60	2	2	1	5	0.50	1.00	2.50	0
9496	Vegetable Skallops	½	cup(s)	85	65	90	15	3	3	2	0.50	0.50	0.00	0
9434	Vegetarian cutlets	1	slice(s)	61	43	70	11	3	2	1	—	—	—	—
	DAIRY													
	Butter: *see Fats & Oils*													
	Cheese													
1433	Blue, crumbled	1	ounce(s)	28	12	100	6	1	0	8	5.29	2.21	0.23	—
884	Brick	1	ounce(s)	28	12	104	7	1	0	8	5.25	2.41	0.22	—
885	Brie	1	ounce(s)	28	14	94	6	<1	0	8	4.87	2.24	0.23	—
34821	Camembert	1	ounce(s)	29	15	87	6	<1	0	7	4.43	2.04	0.21	—
888	Cheddar or colby	1	ounce(s)	28	11	110	7	1	0	9	5.66	2.60	0.27	—
32096	Cheddar or colby, low fat	1	ounce(s)	28	18	49	7	1	0	2	1.23	0.59	0.06	—
5	Cheddar, shredded	¼	cup(s)	28	10	114	7	<1	0	9	5.96	2.65	0.27	—
889	Edam	1	ounce(s)	28	12	100	7	<1	0	8	4.92	2.28	0.19	—
890	Feta	1	ounce(s)	28	15	74	4	1	0	6	4.18	1.29	0.17	—
891	Fontina	1	ounce(s)	28	11	109	7	<1	0	9	5.37	2.43	0.46	—
8527	Goat, soft	1	ounce(s)	28	17	76	5	<1	0	6	4.14	1.37	0.14	—
893	Gouda	1	ounce(s)	28	12	100	7	1	0	8	4.93	2.17	0.18	—
894	Gruyere	1	ounce(s)	28	9	116	8	<1	0	9	5.30	2.81	0.49	—
895	Limburger	1	ounce(s)	28	14	92	6	<1	0	8	4.69	2.41	0.14	—
896	Monterey jack	1	ounce(s)	28	11	104	7	<1	0	8	5.34	2.45	0.25	—
13	Mozzarella, part skim milk	1	ounce(s)	28	15	71	7	1	0	4	2.83	1.26	0.13	—
12	Mozzarella, whole milk	1	ounce(s)	28	14	84	6	1	0	6	3.68	1.84	0.21	—
897	Muenster	1	ounce(s)	28	12	103	7	<1	0	8	5.35	2.44	0.19	—
898	Neufchatel	1	ounce(s)	28	17	73	3	1	0	7	4.14	1.90	0.18	—
14	Parmesan, grated	1	tablespoon(s)	5	1	22	2	<1	0	1	0.87	0.42	0.06	—
17	Provolone	1	ounce(s)	28	11	98	7	1	0	7	4.78	2.07	0.22	—
19	Ricotta, part skim milk	¼	cup(s)	62	46	85	7	3	0	5	3.03	1.42	0.16	—
18	Ricotta, whole milk	¼	cup(s)	62	44	107	7	2	0	8	5.10	2.23	0.24	—
20	Romano	1	tablespoon(s)	5	2	19	2	<1	0	1	0.86	0.39	0.03	—

PAGE KEY: H–2 = Breads/Baked Goods H–6 = Cereal/Rice/Pasta H–10 = Fruit H–14 = Vegetables/Legumes H–24 = Nuts/Seeds H–26 = Vegetarian
H–28 = Dairy H–34 = Eggs H–34 = Seafood H–36 = Meats H–40 = Poultry H–40 = Processed meats H–42 = Beverages H–46 = Fats/Oils
H–48 = Sweets H–50 = Spices/Condiments/Sauces H–52 = Mixed foods/Soups/Sandwiches H–58 = Fast food H–74 = Convenience meals H–76 = Baby foods

Chol (mg)	Calc (mg)	Iron (mg)	Magn (mg)	Pota (mg)	Sodi (mg)	Zinc (mg)	Vit A (µg)	Thia (mg)	Vit E (mg α)	Ribo (mg)	Niac (mg)	Vit B$_6$ (mg)	Fola (µg)	Vit C (mg)	Vit B$_{12}$ (µg)	Sele (µg)
0	20	0.72	—	—	120	—	—	—	—	—	—	—	—	0	—	—
0	60	1.80	—	—	400	—	—	—	—	—	—	—	—	0	—	—
0	60	1.80	—	—	720	—	—	—	—	—	—	—	—	4	—	—
24	72	0.00	37	232	672	1.07	0	0.12	—	0.18	1.30	0.10	12	0	<1	8
24	96	0.00	—	—	336	—	0	—	—	—	—	—	—	0	—	0
0	48	0.00	32	218	336	0.55	—	0.08	—	0.10	1.08	0.11	13	0	<.1	5
0	0	0.77	—	50	240	0.89	0	0.23	—	0.43	1.60	0.04	—	0	1	—
0	20	1.44	—	210	410	0.43	0	0.75	—	0.51	6.00	0.90	—	0	3	—
0	0	1.08	—	60	500	0.43	0	0.72	—	0.61	1.47	0.87	—	0	2	—
0	20	1.80	—	70	430	0.34	0	1.05	—	0.34	4.00	0.30	—	0	2	—
0	0	0.36	—	15	160	0.46	0	0.12	—	0.20	0.40	0.20	—	0	1	—
0	0	1.06	—	140	450	1.11	0	0.23	—	0.34	6.00	0.40	—	0	2	—
0	20	1.08	—	80	340	0.66	0	0.75	—	0.17	2.00	0.16	—	0	1	—
0	0	0.72	—	60	580	—	0	—	—	—	—	—	—	0	—	—
0	20	0.63	—	75	90	0.60	75	0.03	—	0.34	0.00	0.08	24	0	1	—
0	0	1.44	—	50	320	0.36	0	1.80	—	0.17	2.00	0.30	—	0	3	—
0	0	0.27	—	15	220	0.05	0	0.75	—	0.04	0.40	0.07	—	0	<1	—
0	40	3.60	—	330	590	—	0	1.20	—	0.26	5.00	0.40	—	0	3	—
0	0	1.80	—	210	540	0.31	0	1.80	—	0.17	2.00	0.20	—	0	1	—
0	40	0.72	—	180	350	0.58	—	6.47	—	0.10	0.00	0.00	—	0	0	—
0	40	1.80	—	480	870	1.36	—	0.60	—	0.21	0.00	0.30	—	0	0	—
0	40	1.80	44	320	470	0.93	0	—	—	0.14	0.00	0.21	—	0	<.1	—
0	20	1.80	—	100	300	0.31	0	0.60	—	0.17	6.00	0.40	—	0	2	—
0	40	3.60	—	420	1130	1.24	0	0.06	—	0.07	2.00	0.70	—	0	2	—
0	0	1.80	—	170	440	0.33	0	1.80	—	0.17	2.00	0.20	—	0	1	—
3	40	0.36	—	55	580	0.64	0	1.80	—	0.26	6.00	0.60	—	0	2	—
0	0	1.80	—	130	750	0.92	0	0.68	—	0.14	0.80	0.40	—	0	3	—
0	20	1.80	—	180	510	0.14	0	1.80	—	0.17	6.00	0.40	—	0	2	—
0	100	2.70	—	60	490	0.23	0	1.80	—	0.17	6.00	0.40	—	0	3	—
0	0	1.44	—	50	320	0.36	0	1.80	—	0.17	2.00	0.30	—	0	3	—
0	0	0.36	—	15	220	0.05	0	0.75	—	0.03	0.40	0.08	—	0	<1	—
0	0	0.72	—	10	410	0.67	0	0.03	—	0.03	0.00	0.01	—	0	0	—
0	0	0.00	—	30	340	0.43	0	0.03	—	0.04	0.00	0.04	—	0	0	—
21	150	0.09	7	73	395	0.75	56	0.01	0.07	0.11	0.29	0.05	10	0	<1	4
26	189	0.12	7	38	157	0.73	82	0.00	0.07	0.10	0.03	0.02	6	0	<1	4
28	52	0.14	6	43	176	0.67	49	0.02	0.07	0.15	0.11	0.07	18	0	<1	4
21	112	0.10	6	54	244	0.69	—	0.01	—	0.14	0.18	0.07	18	0	<1	4
27	192	0.21	7	36	169	0.86	74	0.00	0.08	0.11	0.03	0.02	5	0	<1	4
6	118	0.12	5	19	174	0.52	17	0.00	0.02	0.06	0.01	0.01	3	0	<1	4
30	204	0.19	8	28	175	0.88	75	0.01	0.08	0.11	0.02	0.02	5	0	<1	4
25	205	0.12	8	53	270	1.05	68	0.01	0.07	0.11	0.02	0.02	4	0	<1	4
25	138	0.18	5	17	312	0.81	35	0.04	0.05	0.24	0.28	0.12	9	0	<1	4
32	154	0.06	4	18	224	0.98	73	0.01	0.08	0.06	0.04	0.02	2	0	<1	4
13	40	0.54	5	7	105	0.26	82	0.02	0.05	0.11	0.12	0.07	3	0	<.1	1
32	196	0.07	8	34	229	1.09	46	0.01	0.07	0.09	0.03	0.02	6	0	<1	4
31	283	0.05	10	23	94	1.09	76	0.02	0.08	0.08	0.03	0.02	3	0	<1	4
25	139	0.04	6	36	224	0.59	95	0.02	0.06	0.14	0.04	0.02	16	0	<1	4
25	209	0.20	8	23	150	0.84	55	0.00	0.07	0.11	0.03	0.02	5	0	<1	4
18	219	0.06	6	24	173	0.77	36	0.01	0.04	0.08	0.03	0.02	3	0	<1	4
22	141	0.12	6	21	176	0.82	50	0.01	0.05	0.08	0.03	0.01	2	0	1	5
27	201	0.11	8	38	176	0.79	83	0.00	0.07	0.09	0.03	0.02	3	0	<1	4
21	21	0.08	2	32	112	0.15	83	0.00	—	0.05	0.04	0.04	3	0	<.1	1
4	55	0.05	2	6	76	0.19	6	0.00	0.01	0.02	0.01	0.00	1	0	<1	1
19	212	0.15	8	39	245	0.90	66	0.01	0.06	0.09	0.04	0.02	3	0	<1	4
19	167	0.27	9	77	77	0.82	66	0.01	0.04	0.11	0.05	0.01	8	0	<1	10
31	127	0.23	7	65	52	0.71	74	0.01	0.07	0.12	0.06	0.03	7	0	<1	9
5	53	0.04	2	4	60	0.13	5	0.00	0.01	0.02	0.00	0.00	<1	0	<.1	1

Appendix H

TABLE H-1

Food Composition   (DA+ code is for Wadsworth Diet Analysis program)   (For purposes of calculations, use "0" for t, <1, <.1, <.01, etc.)

DA + Code	Food Description	Quantity	Measure	Wt (g)	H₂O (g)	Ener (kcal)	Prot (g)	Carb (g)	Fiber (g)	Fat (g)	Sat	Mono	Poly	Trans
	DAIRY—Continued													
900	Roquefort	1	ounce(s)	28	11	103	6	1	0	9	5.39	2.37	0.37	—
21	Swiss	1	ounce(s)	28	10	106	8	2	0	8	4.98	2.04	0.27	—
	Imitation cheese													
7998	Shredded imitation cheddar	¼	cup(s)	28	—	90	5	2	0	7	1.50	—	—	—
8028	Shredded imitation mozzarella	¼	cup(s)	28	—	80	6	1	0	6	1.00	—	—	—
	Cottage Cheese													
9	Low fat, 1% fat	½	cup(s)	113	93	81	14	3	0	1	0.73	0.33	0.04	—
8	Low fat, 2% fat	½	cup(s)	113	90	102	16	4	0	2	1.38	0.62	0.07	—
	Cream cheese													
11	Cream cheese	2	tablespoon(s)	29	16	101	2	1	0	10	6.37	2.85	0.37	—
17366	Fat free cream cheese	2	tablespoon(s)	30	23	29	4	2	0	<1	0.27	0.10	0.02	—
10438	Tofutti Better Than Cream Cheese	2	tablespoon(s)	30	—	80	1	1	0	8	2.00	—	6.00	—
	Processed cheese													
22	American cheese, processed	1	ounce(s)	28	11	106	6	<1	0	9	5.58	2.54	0.28	—
24	American cheese food, processed	1	ounce(s)	28	12	94	5	2	0	7	4.23	2.05	0.31	—
25	American cheese spread, processed	1	ounce(s)	28	14	82	5	2	0	6	3.78	1.77	0.18	—
9110	Kraft deluxe singles pasteurized process American cheese	1	ounce(s)	28	—	110	5	1	0	9	6.00	—	—	—
23	Swiss cheese, processed	1	ounce(s)	28	12	95	7	1	0	7	4.55	2.00	0.18	—
	Soy cheese													
10430	Nu Tofu cheddar flavored cheese alternative	1	ounce(s)	28	—	70	6	1	0	4	0.50	2.50	1.00	—
10435	Nu Tofu mozzarella flavored cheese alternative	1	ounce(s)	28	—	70	6	2	0	4	0.50	2.50	1.00	—
	Cream													
26	Half & half	1	tablespoon(s)	15	12	20	<1	1	0	2	1.07	0.50	0.06	—
28	Light coffee or table, liquid	1	tablespoon(s)	15	11	29	<1	1	0	3	1.80	0.84	0.11	—
30	Light whipping cream, liquid	1	tablespoon(s)	15	10	44	<1	<1	0	5	2.90	1.36	0.13	—
32	Heavy whipping cream, liquid	1	tablespoon(s)	15	9	52	<1	<1	0	6	3.45	1.60	0.21	—
34	Whipped cream topping, pressurized	1	tablespoon(s)	4	2	10	<1	<1	0	1	0.52	0.24	0.03	—
	Sour cream													
36	Sour cream	2	tablespoon(s)	24	17	51	1	1	0	5	3.13	1.45	0.19	—
30556	Fat free sour cream	2	tablespoon(s)	32	26	24	1	5	0	0	0.00	0.00	0.00	0
	Imitation cream													
3659	Coffeemate nondairy creamer, liquid	1	tablespoon(s)	16	—	20	0	2	0	1	0.00	0.50	0.00	—
40	Cream substitute, powder	1	teaspoon(s)	2	<.1	11	<.1	1	0	1	0.65	0.02	0.00	—
35972	Nondairy coffee whitener, liquid, frozen	1	tablespoon(s)	16	12	22	<1	2	0	2	0.31	1.20	0.00	—
35975	Nondairy dessert topping, pressurized	1	tablespoon(s)	5	3	12	<.1	1	0	1	0.88	0.09	0.01	—
35976	Nondairy dessert topping, frozen	1	tablespoon(s)	5	3	16	<.1	1	0	1	1.09	0.08	0.03	—
904	Imitation sour cream	2	tablespoon(s)	24	17	50	1	2	0	5	4.27	0.14	0.01	—
	Fluid milk													
57	Fat free, nonfat, or skim	1	cup(s)	245	223	83	8	12	0	<1	0.29	0.12	0.02	—
58	Fat free, nonfat, or skim, w/nonfat milk solids	1	cup(s)	245	221	91	9	12	0	1	0.40	0.16	0.02	—
54	Low fat, 1%	1	cup(s)	244	219	102	8	12	0	2	1.54	0.68	0.09	—
55	Low fat, 1%, w/nonfat milk solids	1	cup(s)	245	220	105	9	12	0	2	1.48	0.69	0.09	—
60	Low fat buttermilk	1	cup(s)	245	221	98	8	12	0	2	1.34	0.62	0.08	—
51	Reduced fat, 2%	1	cup(s)	244	218	122	8	11	0	5	2.35	2.04	0.17	—
52	Reduced fat, 2%, w/nonfat milk solids	1	cup(s)	245	218	125	9	12	0	5	2.93	1.36	0.17	—
50	Whole, 3.3%	1	cup(s)	244	216	146	8	11	0	8	4.55	1.98	0.48	—
	Canned													
61	Whole evaporated	2	tablespoon(s)	32	23	42	2	3	0	2	1.45	0.74	0.08	—
62	Fat free, nonfat, or skim evaporated	2	tablespoon(s)	32	25	25	2	4	0	<.1	0.04	0.02	0.00	—
63	Sweetened condensed	2	tablespoon(s)	38	10	123	3	21	0	3	2.10	0.93	0.13	—
	Dried Milk													
64	Dried buttermilk	¼	cup(s)	30	1	118	10	15	0	2	1.09	0.51	0.07	—
65	Instant nonfat dry milk w/added vitamin A	¼	cup(s)	17	1	63	6	9	0	<1	0.08	0.03	0.00	—
5234	Skim milk powder	¼	cup(s)	18	1	64	6	9	0	<1	0.08	0.03	0.01	—
907	Whole dry milk	¼	cup(s)	32	1	161	9	12	0	9	5.43	2.57	0.22	—
909	**Goat milk**	1	cup(s)	244	212	168	9	11	0	10	6.51	2.71	0.36	—
	Chocolate milk													
69	Low fat	1	cup(s)	250	211	158	8	26	1	3	1.54	0.75	0.09	—
68	Reduced fat	1	cup(s)	250	209	180	8	26	1	5	3.10	1.47	0.18	—
67	Whole milk	1	cup(s)	250	206	208	8	26	2	8	5.26	2.48	0.31	—
33156	Chocolate syrup, fortified, prepared w/milk	1	cup(s)	263	220	197	8	24	<1	8	5.22	2.44	0.31	—

PAGE KEY: H–2 = Breads/Baked Goods H–6 = Cereal/Rice/Pasta H–10 = Fruit H–14 = Vegetables/Legumes H–24 = Nuts/Seeds H–26 = Vegetarian
H–28 = Dairy H–34 = Eggs H–34 = Seafood H–36 = Meats H–40 = Poultry H–40 = Processed meats H–42 = Beverages H–46 = Fats/Oils
H–48 = Sweets H–50 = Spices/Condiments/Sauces H–52 = Mixed foods/Soups/Sandwiches H–58 = Fast food H–74 = Convenience meals H–76 = Baby foods

Chol (mg)	Calc (mg)	Iron (mg)	Magn (mg)	Pota (mg)	Sodi (mg)	Zinc (mg)	Vit A (µg)	Thia (mg)	Vit E (mg α)	Ribo (mg)	Niac (mg)	Vit B6 (mg)	Fola (µg)	Vit C (mg)	Vit B12 (µg)	Sele (µg)
25	185	0.16	8	25	507	0.58	82	0.01	—	0.16	0.21	0.03	14	0	<1	4
26	221	0.06	11	22	54	1.22	62	0.02	0.11	0.08	0.03	0.02	2	0	1	5
0	150	0.00	—	—	420	—	—	—	—	—	—	—	—	0	—	—
0	150	0.00	8	—	320	1.20	—	0.00	—	0.26	0.00	0.00	40	0	<1	—
5	69	0.16	6	97	459	0.43	12	0.02	0.01	0.19	0.14	0.08	14	0	1	10
9	78	0.18	7	108	459	0.47	24	0.03	0.02	0.21	0.16	0.09	15	0	1	12
32	23	0.35	2	35	86	0.16	106	0.00	0.09	0.06	0.03	0.01	4	0	<1	1
2	56	0.05	4	49	164	0.26	84	0.02	0.00	0.05	0.05	0.02	11	0	<1	1
0	0	0.00	—	—	135	—	0	—	—	—	—	—	—	0	—	—
27	156	0.05	8	48	422	0.81	72	0.01	0.08	0.10	0.02	0.02	2	0	<1	4
23	162	0.16	9	83	359	0.91	57	0.02	0.06	0.15	0.05	0.02	2	0	<1	5
16	160	0.09	8	69	382	0.74	49	0.01	0.05	0.12	0.04	0.03	2	0	<1	3
25	150	0.00	0	25	450	0.90	84	—	—	0.10	—	—	—	0	<1	—
24	219	0.17	8	61	388	1.02	56	0.00	0.10	0.08	0.01	0.01	2	0	<1	5
0	200	0.36	—	—	190	—	—	—	—	—	—	—	—	0	—	—
0	150	0.36	—	—	190	—	—	—	—	—	—	—	—	0	—	—
6	16	0.01	2	20	6	0.08	15	0.01	0.05	0.02	0.01	0.01	<1	<1	<.1	<1
10	14	0.01	1	18	6	0.04	27	0.00	0.08	0.02	0.01	0.01	<1	<1	<.1	<.1
17	10	0.00	1	15	5	0.04	42	0.00	0.13	0.02	0.01	0.00	1	<.1	<.1	<.1
21	10	0.00	1	11	6	0.03	62	0.00	0.16	0.02	0.01	0.00	1	<.1	<.1	<.1
3	4	0.00	<1	6	5	0.01	7	0.00	0.02	0.00	0.00	0.00	<1	0	<.1	<.1
11	28	0.01	3	35	13	0.06	42	0.01	0.14	0.04	0.02	0.00	3	<1	<.1	1
3	40	0.00	3	41	45	0.16	—	0.01	0.00	0.05	0.02	0.01	4	0	<.1	—
0	0	0.00	—	30	0	—	0	0.02	—	0.02	0.20	—	—	0	—	—
0	<1	0.02	<.1	16	4	0.01	<.1	0.00	0.01	0.00	0.00	0.00	0	0	0	<.1
0	1	0.00	<.1	30	13	0.00	—	0.00	—	0.00	0.00	0.00	0	0	0	<1
0	<1	0.00	<.1	1	3	0.00	—	0.00	—	0.00	0.00	0.00	0	0	0	<.1
0	<1	0.01	<.1	1	1	0.00	—	0.00	—	0.00	0.00	0.00	0	0	0	<1
0	1	0.09	1	39	24	0.28	0	0.00	0.18	0.00	0.00	0.00	0	0	0	1
5	223	1.23	22	238	108	2.08	149	0.11	0.02	0.45	0.23	0.09	12	0	1	8
5	316	0.12	37	419	130	1.00	149	0.10	0.00	0.43	0.22	0.11	12	2	1	5
12	264	0.85	27	290	122	2.12	142	0.05	0.02	0.45	0.23	0.09	12	0	1	8
10	314	0.12	34	397	122	0.98	145	0.10	—	0.42	0.22	0.11	12	2	1	6
10	284	0.12	27	370	257	1.03	17	0.08	0.12	0.38	0.14	0.08	12	2	1	5
20	271	0.24	27	342	115	1.17	134	0.10	0.07	0.45	0.22	0.09	12	<1	1	6
20	314	0.12	34	397	127	0.98	137	0.10	—	0.42	0.22	0.11	12	2	1	6
24	246	0.07	24	325	105	0.93	68	0.11	0.15	0.45	0.26	0.09	12	0	1	9
9	82	0.06	8	95	33	0.24	20	0.01	0.04	0.10	0.06	0.02	3	1	<.1	1
1	93	0.09	9	106	37	0.29	38	0.01	0.00	0.10	0.06	0.02	3	<1	<.1	1
13	109	0.07	10	142	49	0.36	28	0.03	0.06	0.16	0.08	0.02	4	1	<1	6
21	360	0.09	33	484	157	1.22	15	0.12	0.03	0.48	0.27	0.10	14	2	1	6
3	215	0.05	20	298	96	0.77	124	0.07	0.00	0.30	0.16	0.06	9	1	1	5
3	222	0.06	21	307	99	0.79	0	0.07	—	0.31	0.16	0.06	9	1	1	5
31	296	0.15	28	431	120	1.08	83	0.09	0.16	0.39	0.21	0.10	12	3	1	5
27	327	0.12	34	498	122	0.73	139	0.12	0.17	0.34	0.68	0.11	2	3	<1	3
8	288	0.60	33	425	153	1.03	145	0.10	0.05	0.42	0.32	0.10	13	2	1	5
18	285	0.60	33	423	150	1.03	138	0.09	0.10	0.41	0.32	0.10	13	2	1	5
30	280	0.60	33	418	150	1.03	65	0.09	0.15	0.41	0.31	0.10	13	2	1	5
34	292	2.68	32	460	147	0.92	—	0.09	—	0.55	6.53	0.11	13	2	1	5

TABLE H–1

Food Composition

(DA+ code is for Wadsworth Diet Analysis program)   (For purposes of calculations, use "0" for t, <1, <.1, <.01, etc.)

DA + Code	Food Description	Quantity	Measure	Wt (g)	H₂O (g)	Ener (kcal)	Prot (g)	Carb (g)	Fiber (g)	Fat (g)	Sat	Mono	Poly	Trans
	DAIRY—Continued													
908	Cocoa, hot, prepared w/milk	1	cup(s)	250	206	193	9	27	3	6	3.58	1.69	0.09	0.18
33184	Cocoa mix with aspartame, added sodium & vitamin A, no added calcium or phosphorus, prepared with water	1	cup(s)	192	177	56	2	10	1	<1	0.00	0.15	0.01	—
70	**Eggnog**	1	cup(s)	254	189	343	10	34	0	19	11.29	5.67	0.86	—
	Breakfast drinks													
10093	Carnation Instant Breakfast classic chocolate malt, prepared w/skim milk, no sugar added	1	cup(s)	243	—	142	11	21	<1	1	0.89	—	—	—
10091	Carnation Instant Breakfast strawberry creme, prepared w/skim milk	1	cup(s)	273	—	220	13	39	0	<1	0.40	—	—	—
10094	Carnation Instant Breakfast strawberry creme, prepared w/skim milk, no sugar added	1	cup(s)	243	—	134	12	21	0	<1	0.45	—	—	—
10092	Carnation Instant Breakfast vanilla creme, prepared w/skim milk, no sugar added	1	cup(s)	273	—	220	13	39	0	<1	0.40	—	—	—
1417	Ovaltine rich chocolate flavor, prepared w/skim milk	1	cup(s)	243	—	134	12	21	0	<1	0.45	—	—	—
8539	**Malted milk, chocolate mix, fortified, prepared w/milk**	1	cup(s)	265	216	223	9	29	1	9	4.95	2.17	0.54	—
	Milkshakes													
73	Chocolate	1	cup(s)	227	164	270	7	48	1	6	3.81	1.77	0.23	—
74	Vanilla	1	cup(s)	227	169	254	9	40	0	7	4.28	1.98	0.26	—
	Ice cream													
4776	Chocolate	½	cup(s)	66	37	143	3	19	1	7	4.49	2.12	0.27	—
16514	Chocolate, soft serve	½	cup(s)	87	50	177	3	24	1	8	5.17	2.43	0.31	—
12137	Chocolate fudge, fat free no sugar added	½	cup(s)	71	—	100	4	22	0	0	0.00	0.00	0.00	0
82	Light vanilla	½	cup(s)	66	42	109	4	18	<1	3	1.71	0.57	0.10	—
78	Light vanilla, soft serve	½	cup(s)	86	60	108	4	19	0	2	1.40	0.65	0.09	—
16523	Sherbet, all flavors	½	cup(s)	97	64	133	1	29	<1	2	1.12	0.51	0.08	—
4778	Strawberry	½	cup(s)	66	40	127	2	18	1	6	3.43	—	—	—
76	Vanilla	½	cup(s)	66	40	133	2	16	<1	7	4.48	1.96	0.30	—
12146	Vanilla chocolate swirl, fat free, no sugar added	½	cup(s)	71	—	100	4	20	0	0	0.00	0.00	0.00	0
	Soy desserts													
10694	Tofutti low fat vanilla fudge nondairy frozen dessert	½	cup(s)	70	—	120	2	24	0	2	1.00	—	—	—
15721	Tofutti premium chocolate supreme nondairy frozen dessert	½	cup(s)	60	—	180	3	18	0	11	2.00	—	—	—
15720	Tofutti premium vanilla nondairy frozen dessert	½	cup(s)	60	—	190	2	20	0	11	2.00	—	—	—
	Ice milk													
16516	Flavored, not chocolate	½	cup(s)	66	45	91	2	15	0	3	1.72	0.81	0.11	—
16517	Chocolate	½	cup(s)	66	43	95	3	17	<1	2	1.29	0.61	0.08	—
	Pudding													
25032	Chocolate	½	cup(s)	144	110	154	5	23	1	5	2.78	1.94	0.23	0
1923	Chocolate, sugar free, prepared w/2% milk	½	cup(s)	133	—	100	5	14	<1	3	1.50	—	—	—
1722	Rice	½	cup(s)	113	73	175	6	26	1	6	1.99	2.14	0.88	—
4747	Tapioca, ready to eat	1	item(s)	142	105	169	3	28	<1	5	0.85	2.24	1.93	—
25031	Vanilla	½	cup(s)	136	110	116	5	17	<.1	3	1.31	1.21	0.16	0
1924	Vanilla, sugar free, prepared w/2% milk	½	cup(s)	133	90	4	12	<1	2	1.50	10	150	0.00	—
	Frozen yogurt													
4785	Chocolate, soft serve	½	cup(s)	72	46	115	3	18	2	4	2.61	1.26	0.16	—
1747	Fruit varieties	½	cup(s)	113	80	144	3	24	0	4	2.63	1.11	0.11	—
4786	Vanilla, soft serve	½	cup(s)	72	47	117	3	17	0	4	2.46	1.14	0.15	—
	Milk substitutes													
	Lactose free													
16081	Fat free calcium fortified milk	1	cup(s)	240	—	90	9	13	0	0	0.00	—	—	0
36486	Low fat milk	1	cup(s)	240	—	110	8	13	0	3	1.50	—	—	—
36487	Reduced fat milk	1	cup(s)	240	—	130	8	13	0	5	3.00	—	—	—
36488	Whole milk	1	cup(s)	240	—	160	8	12	0	9	5.00	—	—	—
	Rice													
10083	Rice Dream carob rice beverage	1	cup(s)	240	—	150	1	32	0	3	0.00	—	—	—
10087	Rice Dream vanilla enriched rice beverage	1	cup(s)	240	—	130	1	28	0	2	0.00	—	—	—
17089	Rice Dream original rice beverage, enriched	1	cup(s)	240	—	120	1	25	0	2	0.00	—	—	—

PAGE KEY: H–2 = Breads/Baked Goods   H–6 = Cereal/Rice/Pasta   H–10 = Fruit   H–14 = Vegetables/Legumes   H–24 = Nuts/Seeds   H–26 = Vegetarian
H–28 = Dairy   H–34 = Eggs   H–34 = Seafood   H–36 = Meats   H–40 = Poultry   H–40 = Processed meats   H–42 = Beverages   H–46 = Fats/Oils
H–48 = Sweets   H–50 = Spices/Condiments/Sauces   H–52 = Mixed foods/Soups/Sandwiches   H–58 = Fast food   H–74 = Convenience meals   H–76 = Baby foods

Chol (mg)	Calc (mg)	Iron (mg)	Magn (mg)	Pota (mg)	Sodi (mg)	Zinc (mg)	Vit A (µg)	Thia (mg)	Vit E (mg α)	Ribo (mg)	Niac (mg)	Vit B$_6$ (mg)	Fola (µg)	Vit C (mg)	Vit B$_{12}$ (µg)	Sele (µg)
20	263	1.20	58	493	110	1.58	128	0.10	0.08	0.46	0.33	0.10	13	1	1	7
<1	90	0.75	33	405	171	0.52	27	0.04	0.06	0.21	0.16	0.05	2	<1	<1	2
150	330	0.51	48	419	137	1.17	114	0.09	0.51	0.48	0.27	0.13	3	4	1	11
9	445	4.01	89	632	196	3.38	—	0.35	—	0.45	4.45	0.45	4	27	1	8
9	500	4.47	100	638	360	3.75	—	0.38	—	0.51	5.08	0.48	100	30	1	9
9	445	4.01	89	570	187	3.38	—	0.33	—	0.45	4.45	0.45	89	27	1	8
9	500	4.50	100	630	240	3.75	—	0.38	—	0.51	5.00	0.50	100	30	2	9
9	445	4.01	89	570	187	3.38	—	0.33	—	0.45	4.45	0.45	89	27	1	8
27	339	3.76	45	578	231	1.17	904	0.76	0.16	1.32	11.08	1.01	19	32	1	12
25	299	0.70	36	508	252	1.09	41	0.11	0.11	0.50	0.28	0.06	11	0	1	4
27	331	0.23	27	415	215	0.88	57	0.07	0.11	0.44	0.33	0.10	16	0	1	5
22	72	0.61	19	164	50	0.38	78	0.03	0.20	0.13	0.15	0.04	11	<1	<1	2
22	103	0.33	19	192	44	0.48	—	0.04	0.22	0.13	0.11	0.03	5	1	<1	—
0	80	0.36	—	—	60	—	—	—	—	—	—	—	—	0	—	—
17	77	0.05	9	137	49	0.48	91	0.02	0.08	0.11	0.06	0.02	3	<1	<1	1
10	135	0.05	12	190	60	0.46	25	0.04	0.05	0.17	0.10	0.04	5	1	<1	3
5	52	0.14	8	93	44	0.46	—	0.02	0.03	0.07	0.09	0.03	4	4	<1	—
19	79	0.14	9	124	40	0.22	63	0.03	—	0.17	0.11	0.03	8	5	<1	1
29	84	0.06	9	131	53	0.46	78	0.03	0.20	0.16	0.08	0.03	3	<1	<1	1
0	80	0.00	50	0					—					0		
0	0	0.00	—	8	90	—	0	—	—	—	—	—	—	0	—	—
0	0	0.00	—	7	180	—	0	—	—	—	—	—	—	0	—	—
0	0	0.00	—	2	210	—	0	—	—	—	—	—	—	0	—	—
9	91	0.07	10	138	56	0.29	—	0.04	0.06	0.17	0.06	0.04	4	1	<1	—
6	94	0.17	13	155	41	0.38	—	0.03	0.05	0.12	0.09	0.03	4	<1	<1	—
35	138	1.04	29	211	135	1.07	73	0.04	0.00	0.25	0.18	0.03	7	<1	<1	5
10	150	0.72	—	330	310	—	—	0.06	—	0.26	—	—	—	0	—	—
71	130	1.21	21	250	253	0.61	—	0.10	0.06	0.26	0.73	0.08	14	1	<1	—
1	119	0.33	11	136	226	0.38	0	0.03	0.43	0.14	0.44	0.03	4	1	<1	2
35	133	0.25	14	173	134	0.63	73	0.03	0.00	0.24	0.11	0.03	6	<1	<1	5
—	190	380	—	—	0.03	—	—	0.17	—	—	—	—	0	—	—	
4	106	0.90	19	188	71	0.35	32	0.03	—	0.15	0.22	0.05	8	<1	<1	2
15	113	0.52	11	176	71	0.32	—	0.05	0.10	0.20	0.08	0.05	5	1	<.1	—
1	103	0.22	10	152	63	0.30	42	0.03	0.08	0.16	0.21	0.06	4	1	<1	2
3	500	0.00	—	—	130	—	100	—	—	—	—	—	—	0	—	—
15	300	0.00	—	—	125	—	100	—	—	—	—	—	—	0	—	—
20	300	0.00	—	—	125	—	98	—	—	—	—	—	—	0	—	—
35	300	0.00	—	—	125	—	58	—	—	—	—	—	—	0	—	—
0	20	0.72	—	—	100	—	—	—	—	—	—	—	—	1	—	—
0	300	0.00	—	—	90	—	—	—	—	—	—	—	—	0	2	—
0	300	0.00	13	60	90	0.24	—	0.07	—	0.00	0.84	0.08	—	0	2	—

TABLE H–1
Food Composition

(DA+ code is for Wadsworth Diet Analysis program)   (For purposes of calculations, use "0" for t, <1, <.1, <.01, etc.)

DA + Code	Food Description	Quantity	Measure	Wt (g)	H₂O (g)	Ener (kcal)	Prot (g)	Carb (g)	Fiber (g)	Fat (g)	Sat	Mono	Poly	Trans
	DAIRY—Continued													
	Soy													
34750	Soy Dream chocolate enriched soy beverage	1	cup(s)	240	—	210	7	37	1	4	0.50	—	—	—
34749	Soy Dream vanilla enriched soy beverage	1	cup(s)	240	—	150	7	22	0	4	0.50	—	—	—
13840	Vitasoy light chocolate soymilk	1	cup(s)	237	—	100	4	17	0	2	0.50	0.50	1.00	—
13839	Vitasoy light vanilla soymilk	1	cup(s)	237	—	70	4	10	0	2	0.50	0.50	1.00	—
13836	Vitasoy rich chocolate soymilk	1	cup(s)	237	—	160	7	24	1	4	0.50	1.00	2.50	—
13835	Vitasoy vanilla delite soymilk	1	cup(s)	237	—	120	8	13	1	4	0.50	1.00	2.50	—
	Yogurt													
3615	Custard style, fruit flavors	6	ounce(s)	170	127	190	7	32	0	4	2.00	—	—	—
3617	Custard style, vanilla	6	ounce(s)	170	134	190	7	32	0	4	2.00	0.94	0.10	—
32101	Fruit, low fat	1	cup(s)	245	184	243	10	46	0	3	1.82	0.77	0.08	—
29638	Fruit, nonfat, sweetened w/low calorie sweetener	1	cup(s)	241	208	122	11	19	1	<1	0.21	0.10	0.04	—
93	Plain, low fat	1	cup(s)	245	208	154	13	17	0	4	2.45	1.04	0.11	—
94	Plain, nonfat	1	cup(s)	245	209	137	14	19	0	<1	0.28	0.12	0.01	—
32100	Vanilla, low fat	1	cup(s)	245	194	208	12	34	0	3	1.97	0.84	0.09	—
5242	Yogurt beverage	1	cup(s)	245	200	172	6	33	0	2	1.39	0.59	0.06	—
38202	Yogurt smoothie, nonfat, all flavors	1	item(s)	325	—	290	10	60	6	0	0.00	0.00	0.00	0
	Soy yogurt													
10453	White Wave plain silk cultured	8	ounce(s)	227	—	120	5	22	1	3	0.00	—	—	0
34616	Stonyfield Farm Osoy chocolate-vanilla pack organic cultured	1	serving(s)	113	—	90	4	15	3	2	0.00	—	—	—
34617	Stonyfield Farm Osoy strawberry-peach pack organic cultured	1	serving(s)	113	—	90	4	15	3	2	0.00	—	—	—
	EGGS													
96	Raw, whole	1	item(s)	50	38	74	6	<1	0	5	1.55	1.91	0.68	—
97	Raw, white	1	item(s)	33	29	17	4	<1	0	<.1	0.00	0.00	0.00	—
98	Raw, yolk	1	item(s)	17	9	53	3	1	0	4	1.59	1.95	0.70	—
99	Fried	1	item(s)	46	32	92	6	<1	0	7	1.98	2.92	1.22	—
100	Hard boiled	1	item(s)	50	37	78	6	1	0	5	1.63	2.04	0.71	—
101	Poached	1	item(s)	50	38	74	6	<1	0	5	1.54	1.90	0.68	—
102	Scrambled, prepared w/milk & butter	2	item(s)	122	89	203	14	3	0	15	4.49	5.82	2.62	—
	Egg Substitute													
920	Frozen	¼	cup(s)	60	44	96	7	2	0	7	1.16	1.46	3.74	—
918	Liquid	¼	cup(s)	63	52	53	8	<1	0	2	0.41	0.56	1.01	—
4028	Egg Beaters	¼	cup(s)	61	—	30	6	1	0	0	0.00	0.00	0.00	0
	SEAFOOD													
	Fish													
	Cod													
6040	Atlantic cod or scrod, baked or broiled	3	ounce(s)	44	34	46	10	0	0	<1	0.07	0.05	0.13	—
1573	Atlantic cod, cooked, dry heat	3	ounce(s)	85	65	89	19	0	0	1	0.14	0.11	0.25	—
2905	**Eel, raw**	3	ounce(s)	85	58	156	16	0	0	10	2.01	6.12	0.81	—
	Fish fillets													
25079	Baked	3	ounce(s)	84	80	99	22	0	0	1	0.08	0.07	0.26	—
8615	Batter coated or breaded, fried	3	ounce(s)	85	0.04	197.19	12.46	14.42	0.42	10.44	2.39	2.19	5.32	—
25082	Broiled fish steaks	3	ounce(s)	86	69	129	24	0	0	3	0.37	0.87	0.84	—
25083	Poached fish steaks	3	ounce(s)	86	68	112	21	0	0	2	0.33	0.76	0.74	—
25084	Steamed fish fillets	3	ounce(s)	86	73	80	17	0	0	1	0.12	0.08	0.22	—
25089	**Flounder, baked**	3	ounce(s)	85	65	114	15	<1	<.1	6	1.15	2.17	1.44	0
1825	**Grouper, cooked, dry heat**	3	ounce(s)	85	62	100	21	0	0	1	0.25	0.23	0.34	—
	Haddock													
6049	Baked or broiled	3	ounce(s)	44	33	50	11	0	0	<1	0.07	0.07	0.14	—
1578	Cooked, dry heat	3	ounce(s)	85	63	95	21	0	0	1	0.14	0.13	0.26	—
1886	**Halibut, Atlantic & Pacific, cooked, dry heat**	3	ounce(s)	85	61	119	23	0	0	2	0.35	0.82	0.80	—
1582	**Herring, Atlantic, pickled**	4	piece(s)	60	33	157	9	6	0	11	1.43	7.17	1.01	—
1587	**Jack mackerel, solids, canned, drained**	2	ounce(s)	57	39	88	13	0	0	4	1.05	1.26	0.94	—
8580	**Octopus, common, cooked, moist heat**	3	ounce(s)	85	51	139	25	4	0	2	0.39	0.28	0.41	—
1831	**Perch, mixed species, cooked, dry heat**	3	ounce(s)	85	62	99	21	0	0	1	0.20	0.17	0.40	—
1592	**Pacific rockfish, cooked, dry heat**	3	ounce(s)	85	62	103	20	0	0	2	0.40	0.38	0.50	—
	Salmon													
29727	Smoked chinook (lox)	2	ounce(s)	57	<.1	66	10	0	0	2	0.52	1.14	0.56	—

PAGE KEY: H–2 = Breads/Baked Goods   H–6 = Cereal/Rice/Pasta   H–10 = Fruit   H–14 = Vegetables/Legumes   H–24 = Nuts/Seeds   H–26 = Vegetarian
H–28 = Dairy   H–34 = Eggs   H–34 = Seafood   H–36 = Meats   H–40 = Poultry   H–40 = Processed meats   H–42 = Beverages   H–46 = Fats/Oils
H–48 = Sweets   H–50 = Spices/Condiments/Sauces   H–52 = Mixed foods/Soups/Sandwiches   H–58 = Fast food   H–74 = Convenience meals   H–76 = Baby foods

Chol (mg)	Calc (mg)	Iron (mg)	Magn (mg)	Pota (mg)	Sodi (mg)	Zinc (mg)	Vit A (µg)	Thia (mg)	Vit E (mg α)	Ribo (mg)	Niac (mg)	Vit B6 (mg)	Fola (µg)	Vit C (mg)	Vit B12 (µg)	Sele (µg)
0	300	1.80	60	350	160	0.60	33	0.15	—	0.07	0.80	0.12	60	0	3	—
0	300	1.80	40	260	140	0.60	33	0.15	—	0.07	0.80	0.12	60	0	3	—
0	300	0.72	24	200	140	0.90	0	0.09	—	0.34	—	—	24	0	1	—
0	300	0.72	24	200	110	0.90	0	0.09	—	0.34	—	—	24	0	1	—
0	300	1.08	40	320	150	0.90	0	0.15	—	0.34	—	—	60	0	1	—
0	40	0.72	—	320	115	—	0	—	—	—	—	—	—	0	—	—
15	200	0.00	16	310	90	—	0	—	—	0.26	—	—	—	0	—	—
15	200	0.00	16	300	90	—	0	—	—	0.26	—	—	—	0	—	—
12	338	0.15	32	434	130	1.64	27	0.08	0.05	0.40	0.21	0.09	22	1	1	7
3	370	0.62	41	550	139	1.83	—	0.10	0.17	0.50	0.11	0.09	26	1	—	—
15	448	0.20	42	573	172	2.18	34	0.11	0.05	0.52	0.28	0.12	27	2	1	8
5	488	0.22	47	625	189	2.38	5	0.12	0.07	0.57	0.30	0.13	29	2	1	9
12	419	0.17	39	537	162	2.03	29	0.10	0.00	0.49	0.26	0.11	27	2	1	12
13	260	0.22	39	399	98	1.10	—	0.11	0.05	0.51	0.30	0.15	29	2	2	—
5	300	2.70	100	580	290	2.25	—	0.38	—	0.43	5.00	0.50	100	15	2	—
0	700	0.90	—	—	30	—	—	—	—	—	—	—	—	0	0	—
0	100	0.72	—	—	20	—	0	—	—	—	—	—	—	0	—	—
0	100	0.72	—	—	20	—	0	—	—	—	—	—	—	0	—	—
212	27	0.92	6	67	70	0.56	70	0.03	0.49	0.24	0.04	0.07	24	0	1	16
0	2	0.03	4	54	55	0.01	0	0.00	0.00	0.00	0.15	0.04	0.00	1	0	<.1	7
205	21	0.45	1	18	8	0.38	63	0.03	0.43	0.09	0.00	0.06	24	0	<1	9
210	27	0.91	6	68	94	0.55	91	0.03	0.56	0.24	0.04	0.07	23	0	1	16
212	25	0.60	5	63	62	0.53	85	0.03	0.51	0.26	0.03	0.06	22	0	1	15
211	27	0.92	6	67	147	0.55	70	0.03	0.48	0.24	0.04	0.07	24	0	1	16
429	87	1.46	15	168	342	1.22	174	0.06	1.04	0.53	0.10	0.14	37	<1	1	27
1	44	1.19	9	128	119	0.59	7	0.07	0.95	0.23	0.08	0.08	10	<1	<1	25
1	33	1.32	6	207	111	0.82	11	0.07	0.17	0.19	0.07	0.00	9	0	<1	16
0	20	1.08	4	85	115	0.60	113	0.15	—	0.85	0.20	0.08	60	0	1	—
24	6	0.22	19	108	35	0.26	—	0.04	—	0.03	1.11	0.13	5	<1	<1	17
47	12	0.42	36	207	66	0.49	12	0.07	0.69	0.07	2.14	0.24	7	1	1	32
107	17	0.43	17	231	43	1.38	887	0.13	3.40	0.03	2.98	0.06	13	2	3	6
44	8	0.32	29	489	86	0.49	10	0.03	—	0.05	2.48	0.46	8	3	1	44
28.89	15.3	1.79	20.39	272	452.2	0.37	10.19	0.09	—	0.09	1.78	0.08	17	0	0.94	7.73
37	55	0.99	98	529	64	0.49	55	0.06	—	0.08	6.88	0.36	13	0	1	43
33	48	0.86	85	460	55	0.43	48	0.06	—	0.08	5.97	0.33	12	0	1	37
42	13	0.30	25	323	42	0.35	12	0.07	—	0.06	1.92	0.22	6	1	1	32
44	19	0.35	47	225	281	0.21	39	0.06	0.41	0.08	2.03	0.19	7	3	2	34
40	18	0.97	31	404	45	0.43	43	0.07	—	0.01	0.32	0.30	9	0	1	40
33	19	0.60	22	177	39	0.21	—	0.02	—	0.02	2.05	0.15	4	0	1	18
63	36	1.15	43	339	74	0.41	16	0.03	—	0.04	3.94	0.29	11	0	1	34
35	51	0.91	91	490	59	0.45	46	0.06	—	0.08	6.05	0.34	12	0	1	40
8	46	0.73	5	41	522	0.32	155	0.02	1.03	0.08	1.98	0.10	1	0	3	35
45	137	1.16	21	110	215	0.42	68	0.02	0.58	0.12	3.50	0.12	3	1	4	21
82	90	8.11	51	536	391	2.86	77	0.05	1.02	0.06	3.21	0.55	20	7	31	76
98	87	0.99	32	292	67	1.22	9	0.07	—	0.10	1.62	0.12	5	1	2	14
37	10	0.45	29	442	65	0.45	60	0.04	1.33	0.07	3.33	0.23	9	0	1	40
13	6	0.48	10	99	1134	0.17	15	0.01	—	0.05	2.67	0.15	1	0	2	22

TABLE H–1
Food Composition

(DA+ code is for Wadsworth Diet Analysis program)   (For purposes of calculations, use "0" for t, <1, <.1, <.01, etc.)

DA + Code	Food Description	Quantity	Measure	Wt (g)	H₂O (g)	Ener (kcal)	Prot (g)	Carb (g)	Fiber (g)	Fat (g)	Sat	Mono	Poly	Trans
	SEAFOOD—Continued													
1594	Broiled or baked w/butter	3	ounce(s)	85	54	155	23	0	0	6	1.16	2.29	2.33	—
2938	Coho, farmed, raw	3	ounce(s)	85	60	136	18	0	0	7	1.54	2.83	1.58	—
154	Sardines, Atlantic, with bones, canned in oil	2	item(s)	24	<.1	50	6	0	0	3	0.36	0.92	1.23	—
	Scallops													
155	Mixed species, breaded, fried	3	item(s)	47	<.1	100	8	5	0	5	1.24	2.09	1.32	—
1599	Steamed	3	ounce(s)	85	65	90	14	2	0	3	—	—	—	—
1839	Snapper, mixed species, cooked, dry heat	3	ounce(s)	85	60	109	22	0	0	1	0.31	0.27	0.50	—
	Squid													
1868	Mixed species, fried	3	ounce(s)	85	55	149	15	7	0	6	1.60	2.34	1.82	—
16617	Steamed or boiled	3	ounce(s)	85	63	90	15	3	0	1	0.35	0.11	0.51	—
1570	Striped bass, cooked, dry heat	3	ounce(s)	85	62	105	19	0	0	3	0.55	0.72	0.85	—
1601	Sturgeon, steamed	3	ounce(s)	85	59	111	17	0	0	4	0.97	2.04	0.73	—
1840	Surimi, formed	3	ounce(s)	85	65	84	13	6	0	1	0.16	0.13	0.38	—
1842	Swordfish, cooked, dry heat	3	ounce(s)	85	58	132	22	0	0	4	1.20	1.68	1.00	—
1846	Tuna, yellowfin or ahi, raw	3	ounce(s)	85	60	92	20	0	0	1	0.20	0.13	0.24	—
	Tuna, canned													
159	Light, canned in oil, drained	2	ounce(s)	57	34	113	17	0	0	5	0.87	1.68	1.64	—
355	Light, canned in water, drained	2	ounce(s)	57	42	66	14	0	0	<1	0.13	0.09	0.19	—
33211	Light, no salt, canned in oil, drained	2	ounce(s)	57	34	112	17	0	0	5	0.87	1.67	1.64	—
33212	Light, no salt, canned in water, drained	2	ounce(s)	57	43	66	14	0	0	<1	0.13	0.09	0.19	—
2961	White, canned in oil, drained	2	ounce(s)	57	36	105	15	0	0	5	0.73	1.85	1.69	—
351	White, canned in water, drained	2	ounce(s)	57	41	73	13	0	0	2	0.45	0.44	0.63	—
33213	White, no salt, canned in oil, drained	2	ounce(s)	57	36	105	15	0	0	5	0.94	1.41	1.92	—
33214	White, no salt, canned in water, drained	2	ounce(s)	57	42	73	13	0	0	2	0.45	0.44	0.63	—
	Yellowtail													
2970	Mixed species, raw	2	ounce(s)	57	42	83	13	0	0	3	0.73	1.13	0.81	—
8548	Mixed species, cooked, dry heat	3	ounce(s)	85	0.05	158.94	25.21	0	0	5.71	1.44	2.21	1.52	—
	Shellfish, meat only													
1857	Abalone, mixed species, fried	3	ounce(s)	85	51	161	17	9	0	6	1.40	2.33	1.42	—
16618	Abalone, steamed or poached	3	ounce(s)	85	41	177	29	10	0	1	0.25	0.18	0.18	—
	Crab													
1851	Blue crab, canned	2	ounce(s)	57	43	56	12	0	0	1	0.14	0.12	0.25	—
1852	Blue crab, cooked, moist heat	3	ounce(s)	85	66	87	17	0	0	2	0.19	0.24	0.58	—
8562	Dungeness crab, cooked, moist heat	3	ounce(s)	85	62	94	19	1	0	1	0.14	0.18	0.35	—
1860	Clams, cooked, moist heat	3	ounce(s)	85	54	126	22	4	0	2	0.16	0.15	0.47	—
1853	Crayfish, farmed, cooked, moist heat	3	ounce(s)	85	69	74	15	0	0	1	0.18	0.21	0.35	—
	Oysters													
8720	Baked or broiled	3	ounce(s)	85	69	90	6	3	0	6	1.38	2.18	1.88	—
152	Eastern, farmed, raw	3	ounce(s)	85	73	50	4	5	0	1	0.38	0.13	0.50	—
8715	Eastern, wild, cooked, moist heat	3	ounce(s)	85	60	116	12	7	0	4	1.31	0.53	1.65	—
8584	Pacific, cooked, moist heat	3	ounce(s)	85	55	139	16	8	0	4	0.87	0.66	1.52	—
1865	Pacific, raw	3	ounce(s)	85	70	69	8	4	0	2	0.43	0.30	0.76	—
1854	Lobster, northern, cooked, moist heat	3	ounce(s)	85	65	83	17	1	0	1	0.09	0.14	0.08	—
1862	Mussels, blue, cooked, moist heat	3	ounce(s)	85	52	146	20	6	0	4	0.72	0.86	1.03	—
	Shrimp													
1855	Mixed species, cooked, moist heat	3	ounce(s)	85	66	84	18	0	0	1	0.25	0.17	0.37	—
158	Mixed species, breaded, fried	3	ounce(s)	85	0.04	205.69	18.18	9.74	0.34	10.43	1.77	3.24	4.32	—
	BEEF, LAMB, PORK													
	Beef													
4450	Breakfast strips, cooked	2	slice(s)	23	0	101.47	7.07	0.31	0	7.77	3.24	3.8	0.35	—
174	Corned, canned	3	ounce(s)	85	49	213	23	0	0	13	5.25	5.07	0.54	—
33147	Cured, thin sliced	2	ounce(s)	57	31	87	18	2	0	1	0.54	0.48	0.04	—
4581	Jerky	1	ounce(s)	28	0	116.44	9.42	3.12	0.51	7.27	3.08	3.21	0.28	—
	Ground													
4411	Extra lean, broiled, well	3	ounce(s)	85	46	225	24	0	0	13	5.28	5.88	0.50	—
4417	Lean, broiled, medium	3	ounce(s)	85	47	231	21	0	0	16	6.16	6.87	0.59	—
4418	Lean, broiled, well	3	ounce(s)	85	45	238	24	0	0	15	5.89	6.56	0.56	—
4423	Regular, broiled, medium	3	ounce(s)	85	46	246	20	0	0	18	6.91	7.70	0.65	—
	Rib													
4183	Rib, whole, lean & fat, ¼" fat, roasted	3	ounce(s)	85	39	320	19	0	0	27	10.71	11.42	0.94	—
	Roast													
4264	Bottom round, lean & fat, ¼" fat, braised	3	ounce(s)	85	44	241	24	0	0	15	5.71	6.63	0.58	—

PAGE KEY: H–2 = Breads/Baked Goods H–6 = Cereal/Rice/Pasta H–10 = Fruit H–14 = Vegetables/Legumes H–24 = Nuts/Seeds H–26 = Vegetarian
H–28 = Dairy H–34 = Eggs H–34 = Seafood H–36 = Meats H–40 = Poultry H–40 = Processed meats H–42 = Beverages H–46 = Fats/Oils
H–48 = Sweets H–50 = Spices/Condiments/Sauces H–52 = Mixed foods/Soups/Sandwiches H–58 = Fast food H–74 = Convenience meals H–76 = Baby foods

Chol (mg)	Calc (mg)	Iron (mg)	Magn (mg)	Pota (mg)	Sodi (mg)	Zinc (mg)	Vit A (µg)	Thia (mg)	Vit E (mg α)	Ribo (mg)	Niac (mg)	Vit B$_6$ (mg)	Fola (µg)	Vit C (mg)	Vit B$_{12}$ (µg)	Sele (µg)
40	15	1.02	27	377	99	0.56	—	0.14	1.15	0.05	8.33	0.19	4	2	2	41
43	10	0.29	26	383	40	0.37	48	0.08	—	0.09	5.79	0.56	11	1	2	11
34	108	0.70	9	95	121	0.31	16	0.01	0.49	0.05	1.25	0.04	3	0	2	13
28	20	0.38	27	155	216	0.49	10	0.01	—	0.05	0.69	0.06	23	1	1	13
27	21	0.22	—	238	366	—	—	—	0.16	—	—	—	—	2	—	—
40	34	0.20	31	444	48	0.37	30	0.05	—	0.00	0.29	0.39	5	1	3	42
221	33	0.86	32	237	260	1.48	9	0.05	—	0.39	2.21	0.05	12	4	1	44
227	31	0.63	29	192	356	1.49	—	0.02	1.17	0.32	1.70	0.04	4	3	1	—
88	16	0.92	43	279	75	0.43	26	0.10	—	0.03	2.17	0.29	9	0	4	40
63	11	0.59	30	239	389	0.36	—	0.07	0.53	0.07	8.31	0.19	14	0	2	—
26	8	0.22	37	95	122	0.28	17	0.02	0.54	0.02	0.19	0.03	2	0	1	24
43	5	0.88	29	314	98	1.25	35	0.04	—	0.10	10.02	0.32	2	1	2	52
38	14	0.62	43	378	31	0.44	15	0.37	0.43	0.04	8.33	0.77	2	1	<1	31
10	7	0.79	18	118	202	0.51	13	0.02	0.50	0.07	7.06	0.06	3	0	1	43
17	6	0.87	15	134	192	0.44	10	0.02	0.19	0.04	7.53	0.20	2	0	2	46
10	7	0.79	18	117	28	0.51	13	0.02	—	0.07	7.03	0.06	3	0	1	43
17	6	0.87	15	134	28	0.44	10	0.02	—	0.04	7.53	0.20	2	0	2	46
18	2	0.37	19	189	225	0.27	3	0.01	1.30	0.04	6.63	0.24	3	0	1	34
24	8	0.55	19	134	214	0.27	3	0.00	0.48	0.02	3.29	0.12	1	0	1	37
18	2	0.37	19	189	28	0.27	14	0.01	—	0.04	6.63	0.24	3	0	1	34
24	8	0.55	19	134	28	0.27	3	0.00	—	0.02	3.29	0.12	1	0	1	37
31	13	0.28	17	238	22	0.29	16	0.08	—	0.02	3.86	0.09	2	2	1	21
60.34	24.64	0.53	32.29	457.29	42.5	0.56	26.35	0.14	—	0.04	7.41	0.15	3.4	2.46	1.06	39.77
80	31	3.23	48	241	502	0.81	2	0.19	—	0.11	1.62	0.13	12	2	1	44
143	50	4.85	69	295	980	1.38	—	0.29	6.74	0.13	1.90	0.22	6	3	1	—
50	57	0.48	22	212	189	2.28	1	0.05	1.04	0.05	0.78	0.09	24	2	<1	18
85	88	0.77	28	275	237	3.59	2	0.09	1.56	0.04	2.81	0.15	43	3	6	34
65	50	0.37	49	347	321	4.65	26	0.05	—	0.17	3.08	0.15	36	3	9	40
57	78	23.77	15	534	95	2.32	145	0.13	—	0.36	2.85	0.09	25	19	84	54
116	43	0.94	28	202	82	1.26	13	0.04	—	0.07	1.42	0.11	9	<1	3	29
42	37	5.30	38	126	418	72.22	60	0.07	0.99	0.06	1.04	0.05	8	3	15	—
21	37	4.91	28	105	151	32.23	7	0.09	—	0.06	1.08	0.05	15	4	14	54
89	77	10.19	81	239	359	154.37	46	0.16	—	0.15	2.11	0.10	12	5	30	61
85	14	7.82	37	257	180	28.25	124	0.11	0.72	0.38	3.08	0.08	13	11	24	131
43	7	4.35	19	143	90	14.14	69	0.06	—	0.20	1.71	0.04	9	7	14	65
61	52	0.33	30	299	323	2.48	22	0.01	0.85	0.06	0.91	0.07	9	0	3	36
48	28	5.71	31	228	314	2.27	77	0.26	—	0.36	2.55	0.09	65	12	20	76
166	33	2.63	29	155	190	1.33	58	0.03	1.17	0.03	2.20	0.11	3	2	1	34
150.44	56.95	1.07	34	191.25	292.39	1.17	47.59	0.1	—	0.11	2.6	0.08	20.39	1.27	1.58	35.44
26.89	2.03	0.7	6.1	93.11	509.17	1.43	0	0.02	0.07	0.05	1.46	0.07	1.8	0	0.77	6.05
73	10	1.77	12	116	855	3.03	0	0.02	0.13	0.12	2.07	0.11	8	0	1	36
45	3	1.58	11	140	1582	2.49	0	0.03	0.00	0.12	1.85	0.16	5	0	1	13
13.63	5.67	1.53	14.48	169.54	628.49	2.3	0	0.04	0.14	0.04	0.49	0.05	38.05	0	0.28	3.03
84	8	2.35	21	314	70	5.47	0	0.06	—	0.27	4.97	0.27	9	0	2	19
74	9	1.79	18	256	65	4.56	0	0.04	—	0.18	4.39	0.22	8	0	2	25
86	10	2.08	20	297	76	5.27	0	0.05	—	0.20	5.07	0.26	9	0	2	22
77	9	2.07	17	248	71	4.40	0	0.03	—	0.16	4.90	0.23	8	0	2	16
72	9	1.96	16	252	54	4.45	0	0.06	—	0.14	2.86	0.20	6	0	2	19
82	5	2.65	19	240	43	4.17	0	0.06	0.17	0.20	3.17	0.28	9	0	2	27

TABLE H–1
Food Composition

(DA+ code is for Wadsworth Diet Analysis program)   (For purposes of calculations, use "0" for t, <1, <.1, <.01, etc.)

DA + Code	Food Description	Quantity	Measure	Wt (g)	H₂O (g)	Ener (kcal)	Prot (g)	Carb (g)	Fiber (g)	Fat (g)	Sat	Mono	Poly	Trans
	BEEF, LAMB, PORK—Continued													
169	Bottom round, separable lean, ¼" fat, roasted	3	ounce(s)	85	0.05	160.64	24.45	0	0	6.26	2.13	2.83	0.24	—
4147	Chuck, arm pot roast, lean & fat, ¼" fat, braised	3	ounce(s)	85	41	282	23	0	0	20	7.97	8.68	0.77	—
4161	Chuck, blade roast, lean & fat, ¼" fat, braised	3	ounce(s)	85	40	293	23	0	0	22	8.70	9.44	0.78	—
5853	Chuck, blade roast, separable lean, ¼" trim, pot roasted	3	ounce(s)	85	0.04	209.1	27.45	0	0	10.15	3.94	4.37	0.33	—
4295	Eye of round, lean, ¼" fat, roasted	3	ounce(s)	85	55	149	25	0	0	5	1.76	2.06	0.15	—
4285	Eye of round, lean & fat, ¼" fat, roasted	3	ounce(s)	85	51	195	23	0	0	11	4.23	4.66	0.39	—
	Steak													
1757	Rib, small end, lean, ¼" fat, broiled	3	ounce(s)	85	49	188	24	0	0	10	3.84	4.01	0.27	—
4349	Short loin, T-bone steak, lean, ¼" fat, broiled	3	ounce(s)	85	52	174	23	0	0	9	3.05	4.23	0.26	—
4348	Short loin, T-bone steak, lean & fat, ¼" fat, broiled	3	ounce(s)	85	43	274	19	0	0	21	8.29	9.58	0.75	—
4360	Top loin, prime, lean & fat, ¼" fat, broiled	3	ounce(s)	85	43	275	22	0	0	20	8.16	8.61	0.73	—
	Variety													
188	Liver, pan fried	3	ounce(s)	85	53	149	23	4	0	4	1.27	0.56	0.49	0.17
4447	Tongue, simmered	3	ounce(s)	85	49	236	16	0	0	19	6.91	8.59	0.56	0.71
	Lamb													
	Chop													
3275	Loin, domestic, lean & fat, ¼" fat, broiled	3	ounce(s)	85	44	269	21	0	0	20	8.36	8.25	1.43	—
3287	Shoulder, arm, domestic, lean & fat, ¼" fat, braised	3	ounce(s)	85	38	294	26	0	0	20	8.39	8.65	1.45	—
3290	Shoulder, arm, domestic, lean, ¼" fat, braised	3	ounce(s)	85	42	237	30	0	0	12	4.28	5.24	0.78	—
	Leg													
3264	Domestic, lean & fat, ¼" fat, cooked	3	ounce(s)	85	46	250	21	0	0	18	7.51	7.50	1.28	—
	Rib													
183	Domestic, lean, ¼" fat, broiled	3	ounce(s)	85	50	200	24	0	0	11	3.95	4.43	1.00	—
182	Domestic, lean & fat, ¼" fat, broiled	3	ounce(s)	85	40	307	19	0	0	25	10.80	10.30	2.01	—
	Shoulder													
187	Arm & blade, domestic, choice, lean, ¼" fat, roasted	3	ounce(s)	85	54	173	21	0	0	9	3.47	3.71	0.81	—
186	Arm & blade, domestic, choice, lean & fat, ¼" fat, roasted	3	ounce(s)	85	48	235	19	0	0	17	7.17	6.94	1.38	—
	Variety													
3375	Brain, pan fried	3	ounce(s)	85	52	232	14	0	0	19	4.82	3.42	1.94	—
3406	Tongue, braised	3	ounce(s)	85	49	234	18	0	0	17	6.66	8.50	1.06	—
	Pork													
	Cured													
161	Bacon, cured, broiled, pan fried or roasted	2	slice(s)	13	2	68	5	<1	0	5	1.73	2.33	0.57	0
29229	Bacon, Canadian style, cured	2	ounce(s)	57	38	89	12	1	0	4	1.26	1.79	0.36	—
35422	Breakfast strips, cured, cooked	3	slice(s)	34	9	156	10	<1	0	12	4.34	5.58	1.92	—
16561	Ham, smoked or cured, lean, cooked	1	slice(s)	42	28	66	11	0	0	2	0.77	1.06	0.27	—
189	Ham, cured, boneless, 11% fat, roasted	3	ounce(s)	85	55	151	19	0	0	8	2.65	3.77	1.20	—
1316	Ham, cured, extra lean, 5% fat, roasted	3	ounce(s)	85	58	123	18	1	0	5	1.54	2.23	0.46	—
29215	Ham, cured, extra lean, 4% fat, canned	2	ounce(s)	57	42	68	10	0	0	3	0.86	1.25	0.22	—
	Chop													
32671	Loin, blade, lean & fat, pan fried	3	ounce(s)	85	42	291	18	0	0	24	8.65	9.97	2.64	—
32672	Loin, center cut, lean & fat, pan fried	3	ounce(s)	85	45	236	25	0	0	14	5.11	6.00	1.62	—
32682	Loin, center rib, boneless, lean & fat, braised	3	ounce(s)	85	49	217	22	0	0	13	5.21	6.13	1.12	—
32603	Loin, center rib, lean, broiled	3	ounce(s)	85	48	186	26	0	0	8	2.94	3.78	0.53	—
32481	Loin, whole, lean, braised	3	ounce(s)	85	52	174	24	0	0	8	2.87	3.54	0.60	—
32478	Loin, whole, lean & fat, braised	3	ounce(s)	85	50	203	23	0	0	12	4.35	5.15	1.00	—
	Leg or ham													
32471	Rump portion, lean & fat, roasted	3	ounce(s)	85	48	214	25	0	0	12	4.47	5.42	1.17	—
32468	Whole, lean & fat, roasted	3	ounce(s)	85	47	232	23	0	0	15	5.50	6.70	1.43	—
	Ribs													
32696	Loin, country style, lean, roasted	3	ounce(s)	85	49	210	23	0	0	13	4.52	5.49	0.94	—
32693	Loin, country style, lean & fat, roasted	3	ounce(s)	85	43	279	20	0	0	22	7.83	9.36	1.71	—
	Shoulder													
32629	Arm picnic, lean, roasted	3	ounce(s)	85	51	194	23	0	0	11	3.66	5.09	1.02	—

PAGE KEY: H–2 = Breads/Baked Goods   H–6 = Cereal/Rice/Pasta   H–10 = Fruit   H–14 = Vegetables/Legumes   H–24 = Nuts/Seeds   H–26 = Vegetarian
H–28 = Dairy   H–34 = Eggs   H–34 = Seafood   H–36 = Meats   H–40 = Poultry   H–40 = Processed meats   H–42 = Beverages   H–46 = Fats/Oils
H–48 = Sweets   H–50 = Spices/Condiments/Sauces   H–52 = Mixed foods/Soups/Sandwiches   H–58 = Fast food   H–74 = Convenience meals   H–76 = Baby foods

Chol (mg)	Calc (mg)	Iron (mg)	Magn (mg)	Pota (mg)	Sodi (mg)	Zinc (mg)	Vit A (µg)	Thia (mg)	Vit E (mg α)	Ribo (mg)	Niac (mg)	Vit B6 (mg)	Fola (µg)	Vit C (mg)	Vit B12 (µg)	Sele (µg)
66.3	4.25	2.66	23.79	332.35	56.09	3.92	0	0.06	—	0.2	3.45	0.31	10.19	0	2.29	23.29
84	9	2.64	16	209	51	5.81	0	0.06	0.19	0.20	2.70	0.24	8	0	3	21
88	11	2.64	16	196	54	7.07	0	0.06	0.15	0.20	2.06	0.22	4	0	2	21
73.94	11.05	3.12	19.54	223.55	60.34	8.72	0	0.06	—	0.23	0	0.24	—	0	2.09	22.69
59	4	1.66	23	336	53	4.03	0	0.08	—	0.14	3.19	0.32	6	0	2	23
61	5	1.56	20	308	50	3.69	0	0.07	0.15	0.14	2.97	0.30	6	0	2	22
68	11	2.18	23	335	59	5.94	0	0.09	0.12	0.19	4.08	0.34	7	0	3	19
50	5	3.11	22	278	65	4.34	0	0.09	0.12	0.21	3.94	0.33	7	0	2	9
58	7	2.56	18	234	58	3.56	0	0.08	0.19	0.18	3.29	0.28	6	0	2	10
67	8	1.89	20	294	54	3.85	0	0.07	—	0.15	3.96	0.31	6	0	2	19
324	5	5.24	19	298	65	4.45	6582	0.15	0.39	2.91	14.85	0.87	221	1	71	28
112	4	2.22	13	156	55	34.77	0	0.02	0.25	0.25	2.97	0.13	6	1	3	11
85	17	1.54	20	278	65	2.96	0	0.09	0.11	0.21	6.04	0.11	15	0	2	23
102	21	2.03	22	260	61	5.17	0	0.06	0.13	0.21	5.66	0.09	15	0	2	32
103	22	2.30	25	287	65	6.21	0	0.06	0.15	0.23	5.38	0.11	19	0	2	32
82	14	1.60	20	264	61	3.79	0	0.09	0.12	0.21	5.66	0.11	15	0	2	22
77	14	1.88	25	266	72	4.48	0	0.09	0.15	0.21	5.57	0.13	18	0	2	26
84	16	1.60	20	230	65	3.40	0	0.08	0.10	0.19	5.95	0.09	12	0	2	20
74	16	1.81	21	225	58	5.13	0	0.08	0.15	0.22	4.90	0.13	21	0	2	24
78	17	1.67	20	213	56	4.45	0	0.08	0.12	0.20	5.23	0.11	18	0	2	22
2128	18	1.73	19	304	133	1.70	0	0.14	—	0.31	3.87	0.20	6	20	20	10
161	9	2.24	14	134	57	2.54	0	0.07	—	0.36	3.14	0.14	3	6	5	24
14	1	0.18	4	71	291	0.44	1	0.05	0.04	0.03	1.40	0.04	<1	0	<1	8
28	5	0.39	10	195	799	0.79	0	0.43	0.12	0.10	3.53	0.22	2	0	<1	14
36	5	0.67	9	158	714	1.25	0	0.25	0.09	0.13	2.58	0.12	1	0	1	8
23	3	0.40	9	133	557	1.08	0	0.29	0.11	0.11	2.11	0.20	2	0	<1	—
50	7	1.14	19	348	1275	2.10	0	0.62	0.26	0.28	5.23	0.26	3	0	1	17
45	7	1.26	12	244	1023	2.45	0	0.64	0.21	0.17	3.42	0.34	3	0	1	17
22	3	0.53	10	206	712	1.09	0	0.47	0.10	0.13	3.01	0.26	3	0	<1	8
72	26	0.75	18	282	57	2.71	3	0.53	0.17	0.25	3.36	0.29	3	1	1	30
78	23	0.77	25	361	68	1.96	2	0.97	0.21	0.26	4.76	0.40	5	1	1	33
62	4	0.78	14	329	34	1.76	2	0.45	0.21	0.21	3.67	0.26	3	<1	<1	28
69	26	0.70	24	357	55	2.02	2	0.95	0.25	0.28	5.25	0.40	3	<1	1	40
67	15	0.96	17	329	43	2.11	2	0.56	0.18	0.23	3.90	0.33	3	1	<1	41
68	18	0.91	16	318	41	2.02	2	0.54	0.20	0.22	3.76	0.31	3	1	<1	39
82	10	0.89	23	318	53	2.40	3	0.64	0.19	0.28	3.96	0.27	3	<1	1	40
80	12	0.86	19	299	51	2.52	3	0.54	0.19	0.27	3.89	0.34	9	<1	1	39
79	25	1.10	20	297	25	3.24	2	0.49	—	0.29	3.97	0.37	4	<1	1	36
78	21	0.90	20	293	44	2.01	3	0.76	—	0.29	3.67	0.38	4	<1	1	32
81	8	1.21	17	299	68	3.46	2	0.49	—	0.30	3.67	0.35	4	<1	1	33

Appendix H

TABLE H–1
Food Composition

(DA+ code is for Wadsworth Diet Analysis program)   (For purposes of calculations, use "0" for t, <1, <.1, <.01, etc.)

DA + Code	Food Description	Quantity	Measure	Wt (g)	H₂O (g)	Ener (kcal)	Prot (g)	Carb (g)	Fiber (g)	Fat (g)	Sat	Mono	Poly	Trans
	BEEF, LAMB, PORK—Continued													
32626	Arm picnic, lean & fat, roasted	3	ounce(s)	85	44	270	20	0	0	20	7.47	9.12	2.00	—
	Rabbit													
3366	Domesticated, roasted	3	ounce(s)	85	52	167	25	0	0	7	2.04	1.84	1.33	—
3367	Domesticated, stewed	3	ounce(s)	85	50	175	26	0	0	7	2.13	1.93	1.39	—
	Veal													
3391	Liver, braised	3	ounce(s)	85	51	163	24	3	0	5	1.69	0.97	0.88	0.26
3319	Rib, lean only, roasted	3	ounce(s)	85	55	150	22	0	0	6	1.77	2.26	0.57	—
1732	**Deer or venison, roasted**	3	ounce(s)	85	55	134	26	0	0	3	1.06	0.75	0.53	—
	POULTRY													
	Chicken													
29562	Flaked, canned	2	ounce(s)	57	0.03	97.47	10.37	0.05	0	5.87	1.62	2.32	1.29	—
	Fried													
29632	Breast, meat only, breaded, baked or fried	3	ounce(s)	85	44	193	25	7	<1	7	1.62	2.66	1.73	—
35327	Broiler breast, meat only, fried	3	ounce(s)	85	51	159	28	<1	0	4	1.10	1.46	0.91	—
36413	Broiler breast, meat & skin, flour coated, fried	3	ounce(s)	85	48	189	27	1	<.1	8	2.08	2.98	1.67	—
35389	Broiler drumstick, meat only, fried	3	ounce(s)	85	53	166	24	0	0	7	1.81	2.50	1.68	—
36414	Broiler drumstick, meat & skin, flour coated, fried	3	ounce(s)	85	48	208	23	1	<.1	12	3.11	4.61	2.75	—
35406	Broiler leg, meat only, fried	3	ounce(s)	85	52	177	24	1	0	8	2.12	2.92	1.89	—
35484	Broiler wing, meat only, fried	3	ounce(s)	85	51	179	26	0	0	8	2.13	2.62	1.76	—
29580	Patty, fillet, or tenders, breaded, cooked	3	ounce(s)	85	42	241	14	13	<1	15	4.62	7.25	1.87	—
	Roasted, meat only													
35409	Broiler chicken leg	3	ounce(s)	85	55	162	23	0	0	7	1.95	2.59	1.68	—
35486	Broiler chicken wing	3	ounce(s)	85	53	173	26	0	0	7	1.92	2.22	1.51	—
35138	Roasting chicken, dark meat	3	ounce(s)	85	57	151	20	0	0	7	2.07	2.82	1.70	—
35136	Roasting chicken, light meat	3	ounce(s)	85	58	130	23	0	0	3	0.92	1.29	0.79	—
35132	Roasting chicken	3	ounce(s)	85	57	142	21	0	0	6	1.54	2.13	1.28	—
	Stewed													
3174	Meat only, stewed	3	ounce(s)	85	0.05	150.44	23.19	0	0	5.7	1.56	2.03	1.3	—
1268	Gizzard, simmered	3	ounce(s)	85	58	124	26	0	0	2	0.57	0.45	0.30	0.11
1270	Liver, simmered	3	ounce(s)	85	57	142	21	1	0	6	1.75	1.20	1.08	0.08
	Duck													
1286	Domesticated, meat & skin, roasted	3	ounce(s)	85	44	286	16	0	0	24	8.22	10.97	3.10	—
1287	Domesticated, meat only, roasted	3	ounce(s)	85	55	171	20	0	0	10	3.54	3.15	1.22	—
	Goose													
35507	Domesticated, meat & skin, roasted	3	ounce(s)	85	44	259	21	0	0	19	5.84	8.72	2.14	—
35524	Domesticated, meat only, roasted	3	ounce(s)	85	49	202	25	0	0	11	3.88	3.69	1.31	—
1297	Liver pâté, smoked, canned	4	tablespoon(s)	52	19	240	6	2	0	23	7.51	13.32	0.44	—
	Turkey													
3256	Ground turkey, cooked	3	ounce(s)	85	51	200	23	0	0	11	2.88	4.16	2.75	—
222	Roasted, fryer roaster breast, meat only	3	ounce(s)	85	58	115	26	0	0	1	0.20	0.11	0.17	—
219	Roasted, dark meat, meat only	3	ounce(s)	85	54	159	24	0	0	6	2.06	1.39	1.84	—
220	Roasted, light meat, meat only	3	ounce(s)	85	56	133	25	0	0	3	0.88	0.48	0.73	—
3263	Patty, batter coated, breaded, fried	1	item(s)	94	47	266	13	15	<1	17	4.41	7.02	4.43	—
1302	Turkey roll, light meat	2	slice(s)	57	41	83	11	<1	0	4	1.15	1.42	0.99	—
1303	Turkey roll, light & dark meat	2	slice(s)	57	40	84	10	1	0	4	1.16	1.30	1.01	—
	PROCESSED MEATS													
	Beef													
1331	Corned beef loaf, jellied, sliced	2	slice(s)	57	39	87	13	0	0	3	1.47	1.52	0.18	—
	Bologna													
13458	Made w/chicken, pork, & beef	1	slice(s)	28	15	90	3	1	0	8	3.00	4.05	1.10	—
13461	Light, made w/pork, chicken, & beef	1	slice(s)	28	18	60	3	2	0	4	1.50	2.04	0.43	—
13459	Beef	1	slice(s)	28	15	90	3	1	0	8	3.50	4.26	0.31	—
13565	Turkey	1	slice(s)	28	19	50	3	1	0	4	1.00	1.09	0.98	—
	Chicken													
13562	Oven roasted white chicken	1	slice(s)	28	20	40	4	1	0	3	0.50	—	—	—
	Ham													
13581	Honey glazed, traditional carved	2	slice(s)	45	—	50	8	1	0	2	0.50	0.68	0.18	—
13777	Deli sliced cooked	1	slice(s)	28	—	30	5	1	0	1	0.50	0.39	0.11	—
13778	Deli sliced honey	1	slice(s)	28	—	35	5	1	0	1	0.50	0.39	0.11	—
8614	**Pork & beef mortadella, sliced**	2	slice(s)	46	24	143	8	1	0	12	4.37	5.23	1.44	—

PAGE KEY: H–2 = Breads/Baked Goods   H–6 = Cereal/Rice/Pasta   H–10 = Fruit   H–14 = Vegetables/Legumes   H–24 = Nuts/Seeds   H–26 = Vegetarian
H–28 = Dairy   H–34 = Eggs   H–34 = Seafood   H–36 = Meats   H–40 = Poultry   H–40 = Processed meats   H–42 = Beverages   H–46 = Fats/Oils
H–48 = Sweets   H–50 = Spices/Condiments/Sauces   H–52 = Mixed foods/Soups/Sandwiches   H–58 = Fast food   H–74 = Convenience meals   H–76 = Baby foods

Chol (mg)	Calc (mg)	Iron (mg)	Magn (mg)	Pota (mg)	Sodi (mg)	Zinc (mg)	Vit A (µg)	Thia (mg)	Vit E (mg α)	Ribo (mg)	Niac (mg)	Vit B_6 (mg)	Fola (µg)	Vit C (mg)	Vit B_{12} (µg)	Sele (µg)
80	16	1.00	14	276	60	2.93	2	0.44	—	0.26	3.33	0.30	3	<1	1	29
70	16	1.93	18	326	40	1.93	0	0.08	—	0.18	7.17	0.40	9	0	7	33
73	17	2.01	17	255	31	2.01	0	0.05	0.37	0.14	6.09	0.29	8	0	6	33
434	5	4.34	17	280	66	9.55	17973	0.15	0.58	2.43	11.18	0.78	281	1	72	16
98	10	0.82	20	264	82	3.82	0	0.05	0.31	0.25	6.38	0.23	12	0	1	9
95	6	3.80	20	285	46	2.34	0	0.15	—	0.51	5.70	—	—	0	—	11
35.34	7.98	0.9	6.84	148.19	410.39	0.8	19.37	0	—	0.07	3.6	0.19	—	0	0.16	—
67	19	1.05	25	223	450	0.84	—	0.08	—	0.10	10.98	0.47	4	0	<1	—
77	14	0.97	26	235	67	0.92	—	0.07	—	0.11	12.57	0.54	3	0	<1	22
76	14	1.01	26	220	65	0.94	—	0.07	—	0.11	11.69	0.49	5	0	<1	20
80	10	1.12	20	212	82	2.74	—	0.07	—	0.20	5.23	0.33	8	0	<1	17
77	10	1.14	20	195	76	2.46	—	0.07	—	0.19	5.13	0.30	9	0	<1	16
84	11	1.19	21	216	82	2.53	—	0.07	—	0.21	5.69	0.33	8	0	<1	16
71	13	0.97	18	177	77	1.80	—	0.04	—	0.11	6.16	0.50	3	0	<1	22
51	14	1.06	17	209	452	0.88	—	0.08	—	0.12	5.71	0.26	9	<1	<1	—
80	10	1.11	20	206	77	2.43	—	0.06	—	0.20	5.37	0.32	7	0	<1	19
72	14	0.99	18	179	78	1.82	—	0.04	—	0.11	6.22	0.50	3	0	<1	21
64	9	1.13	17	191	81	1.81	14	0.05	—	0.16	4.88	0.26	6	0	<1	17
64	11	0.92	20	201	43	0.66	7	0.05	0.23	0.08	8.90	0.46	3	0	<1	22
64	10	1.03	18	195	64	1.29	10	0.05	—	0.13	6.70	0.35	4	0	<1	21
70.55	11.89	0.99	17.85	153	59.5	1.69	12.75	0.04	0.23	0.13	5.19	0.22	5.09	0	0.18	17.76
315	14	2.71	3	152	48	3.76	0	0.02	0.17	0.18	2.65	0.06	4	0	1	35
479	9	9.89	21	224	65	3.38	3384	0.25	0.70	1.69	9.39	0.64	491	24	14	70
71	9	2.30	14	173	50	1.58	54	0.15	0.59	0.23	4.10	0.15	5	0	<1	17
76	10	2.30	17	214	55	2.21	20	0.22	0.59	0.40	4.34	0.21	9	0	<1	19
77	11	2.41	19	280	60	2.23	18	0.07	—	0.28	3.55	0.32	2	0	<1	19
82	12	2.44	21	330	65	2.70	10	0.08	—	0.33	3.47	0.40	10	0	<1	22
78	36	2.86	7	72	362	0.48	521	0.05	—	0.16	1.31	0.03	31	0	5	23
87	21	1.64	20	230	91	2.43	0	0.05	0.29	0.14	4.10	0.33	6	0	<1	32
71	10	1.30	25	248	44	1.48	0	0.04	0.08	0.11	6.37	0.48	5	0	<1	27
72	27	1.98	20	247	67	3.79	0	0.05	0.54	0.21	3.10	0.31	8	0	<1	35
59	16	1.15	24	259	54	1.73	0	0.05	0.08	0.11	5.81	0.46	5	0	<1	27
58	13	2.07	14	259	752	1.35	10	0.09	1.18	0.18	2.16	0.19	26	0	<1	19
24	23	0.73	9	142	277	0.88	0	0.05	0.07	0.13	3.97	0.18	2	0	<1	13
31	18	0.77	10	153	332	1.13	0	0.05	0.19	0.16	2.72	0.15	3	0	<1	17
27	6	1.16	6	57	540	2.32	0	0.00	—	0.06	1.00	0.07	5	0	1	10
30	0	0.36	6	43	290	0.40	0	—	—	—	—	—	—	0	—	—
15	0	0.36	6	46	310	0.45	0	—	—	—	—	—	—	0	—	—
20	0	0.36	4	47	310	0.57	0	0.01	—	0.03	0.68	0.05	4	0	<1	—
20	40	0.36	6	43	270	0.52	0	—	—	—	—	—	—	0	—	—
15	0	0.36	7	85	350	0.32	0	—	—	—	—	—	—	0	—	—
25	0	0.72	—	—	560	—	0	—	—	—	—	—	—	0	—	—
15	0	0.00	—	—	240	—	0	—	—	—	—	—	—	0	—	—
15	0	0.00	—	—	240	—	0	—	—	—	—	—	—	0	—	—
26	8	0.64	5	75	573	0.97	0	0.05	0.10	0.07	1.23	0.06	1	0	1	10

TABLE H–1
Food Composition

(DA+ code is for Wadsworth Diet Analysis program)   (For purposes of calculations, use "0" for t, <1, <.1, <.01, etc.)

DA + Code	Food Description	Quantity	Measure	Wt (g)	H₂O (g)	Ener (kcal)	Prot (g)	Carb (g)	Fiber (g)	Fat (g)	Sat	Mono	Poly	Trans
	PROCESSED MEATS—Continued													
1323	**Pork olive loaf**	2	slice(s)	57	33	133	7	5	0	9	3.32	4.47	1.10	—
1324	**Pork pickle & pimento loaf**	2	slice(s)	57	32	149	7	3	0	12	4.45	5.45	1.47	—
	Sausages & frankfurters													
37296	Beerwurst beef beer salami (bierwurst)	1	slice(s)	29	17	74	4	1	0	6	2.50	2.69	0.21	—
37257	Beerwurst pork beer salami	1	slice(s)	21	13	50	3	<1	0	4	1.32	1.89	0.50	—
35338	Berliner, pork & beef	1	ounce(s)	28	17	65	4	1	0	5	1.72	2.27	0.45	—
37299	Braunschweiger pork liver sausage	1	slice(s)	15	0	51.34	1.97	0.34	0	4.48	1.52	2.08	0.52	—
37298	Bratwurst pork, cooked	1	piece(s)	74	42	181	10	2	0	14	5.15	6.73	1.51	—
1329	Cheesefurter or cheese smokie, beef & pork	1	item(s)	43	23	141	6	1	0	12	4.52	5.89	1.30	—
1330	Chorizo, beef & pork	2	ounce(s)	57	18	258	14	1	0	22	8.15	10.43	1.96	—
8600	Frankfurter, beef	1	item(s)	45	23	149	5	2	0	13	5.26	6.44	0.53	—
202	Frankfurter, beef & pork	1	item(s)	57	32	174	7	1	1	16	6.14	7.79	1.56	—
1293	Frankfurter, chicken	1	item(s)	45	26	116	6	3	0	9	2.49	3.82	1.82	—
3261	Frankfurter, turkey	1	item(s)	45	28	102	6	1	0	8	2.65	2.51	2.25	—
37275	Italian sausage, pork, cooked	1	item(s)	68	34	220	14	1	0	17	6.14	8.13	2.23	—
37307	Kielbasa, kolbassa, pork & beef	2⅛	ounce(s)	61	37	135	10	2	0	9	3.40	4.44	1.06	—
1333	Knockwurst or knackwurst, beef & pork	2	ounce(s)	57	31	174	6	2	0	16	5.79	7.26	1.66	—
37285	Pepperoni, beef & pork	1	slice(s)	11	3	55	2	<1	0	5	1.77	2.32	0.48	—
37313	Polish sausage, pork	2	slice(s)	57	31	163	8	2	—	14	4.91	6.42	1.46	—
206	Salami, beef, cooked, sliced	2	slice(s)	46	28	119	6	1	0	10	4.54	4.90	0.48	—
37272	Salami, pork, dry or hard	1	slice(s)	13	5	52	3	<1	0	4	1.52	2.05	0.48	—
3262	Salami, turkey	2	slice(s)	57	31	125	8	11	<.1	5	1.98	1.80	1.43	0
7162	Sausage, breakfast, turkey	2½	ounce(s)	100	67	190	17	<1	0	13	3.90	6.23	3.33	0
8620	Smoked sausage, beef & pork	2	ounce(s)	57	31	181	7	1	0	16	5.54	6.94	2.23	—
8619	Smoked, sausage, pork	2	ounce(s)	57	22	221	13	1	0	18	6.42	8.30	2.13	—
37273	Smoked, sausage, pork link	1	piece(s)	76	30	295	17	2	—	24	8.58	11.09	2.85	—
1336	Summer sausage, thuringer, or cervelat, beef & pork	2	ounce(s)	57	29	190	9	<1	0	17	6.82	7.35	0.68	—
37294	Vienna sausage, cocktail, beef & pork, canned	1	piece(s)	16	10	45	2	<1	0	4	1.49	2.01	0.27	—
	Spreads													
32419	Pork & beef sandwich spread	4	tablespoon(s)	60	36	141	5	7	<1	10	3.59	4.57	1.54	—
1318	Ham salad spread	¼	cup(s)	60	38	130	5	6	0	9	3.04	4.32	1.62	—
	Turkey													
16049	Breast, hickory smoked, slices	1	slice(s)	56	—	50	11	1	0	0	0.00	0.00	0.00	0
13606	Breast, hickory smoked fat free	1	slice(s)	28	—	25	4	1	0	0	0.00	0.00	0.00	0
16047	Breast, honey roasted, slices	1	slice(s)	56	—	60	11	2	0	0	0.00	0.00	0.00	0
16048	Breast, oven roasted, slices	1	slice(s)	56	—	50	11	1	0	0	0.00	0.00	0.00	0
13583	Breast, traditional carved	2	slice(s)	45	—	40	9	0	0	1	0.00	0.07	0.14	—
13604	Breast, oven roasted, fat free	1	slice(s)	28	—	25	4	1	0	0	0.00	0.00	0.00	0
13567	Turkey ham, 10% water added	1	slice(s)	28	20	35	5	0	0	1	0.00	0.22	0.31	—
13596	Turkey pastrami	2	ounce(s)	56	—	70	11	1	0	2	1.00	—	—	—
13597	Turkey salami	2	ounce(s)	56	—	120	8	1	0	9	2.50	2.92	2.30	—
	BEVERAGES													
	Alcoholic													
	Beer													
866	Ale, mild	12	fluid ounce(s)	360	332	148	1	13	1	0	0.00	0.00	0.00	—
686	Beer	12	fluid ounce(s)	356	336	118	1	6	<1	<1	0.00	0.00	0.00	0
869	Beer, light	12	fluid ounce(s)	354	337	99	1	5	0	0	0.00	0.00	0.00	0
16886	Beer, nonalcoholic	12	fluid ounce(s)	360	353	32	1	5	0	0	0.00	0.00	0.00	0
31608	Budweiser beer	12	fluid ounce(s)	355	328	143	1	11	0	0	0.00	0.00	0.00	0
31609	Bud Light beer	12	fluid ounce(s)	355	335	110	1	7	0	0	0.00	0.00	0.00	0
31613	Michelob Beer	12	fluid ounce(s)	355	323	155	1	13	0	0	0.00	0.00	0.00	0
31614	Michelob Light beer	12	fluid ounce(s)	355	330	134	1	12	0	0	0.00	0.00	0.00	0
	Gin, rum, vodka, whiskey													
687	Distilled alcohol, 80 proof	1	fluid ounce(s)	28	19	64	0	0	0	0	0.00	0.00	0.00	0
688	Distilled alcohol, 86 proof	1	fluid ounce(s)	28	18	70	0	<.1	0	0	0.00	0.00	0.00	0
689	Distilled alcohol, 90 proof	1	fluid ounce(s)	28	17	73	0	0	0	0	0.00	0.00	0.00	0
856	Distilled alcohol, 94 proof	1	fluid ounce(s)	28	17	76	0	0	0	0	0.00	0.00	0.00	0
857	Distilled alcohol, 100 proof	1	fluid ounce(s)	28	16	82	0	0	0	0	0.00	0.00	0.00	0
	Liqueurs													
3142	Coffee liqueur, 63 proof	1	fluid ounce(s)	35	14	107	<.1	11	0	<1	0.04	0.01	0.04	—
33187	Coffee liqueur, 53 proof	1	fluid ounce(s)	35	11	117	<.1	16	0	<1	0.04	0.01	0.04	—

PAGE KEY: H–2 = Breads/Baked Goods H–6 = Cereal/Rice/Pasta H–10 = Fruit H–14 = Vegetables/Legumes H–24 = Nuts/Seeds H–26 = Vegetarian
H–28 = Dairy H–34 = Eggs H–34 = Seafood H–36 = Meats H–40 = Poultry H–40 = Processed meats H–42 = Beverages H–46 = Fats/Oils
H–48 = Sweets H–50 = Spices/Condiments/Sauces H–52 = Mixed foods/Soups/Sandwiches H–58 = Fast food H–74 = Convenience meals H–76 = Baby foods

Chol (mg)	Calc (mg)	Iron (mg)	Magn (mg)	Pota (mg)	Sodi (mg)	Zinc (mg)	Vit A (µg)	Thia (mg)	Vit E (mg α)	Ribo (mg)	Niac (mg)	Vit B$_6$ (mg)	Fola (µg)	Vit C (mg)	Vit B$_{12}$ (µg)	Sele (µg)
22	62	0.31	11	169	843	0.78	34	0.17	0.14	0.15	1.04	0.13	1	0	1	9
21	54	0.58	10	193	789	0.80	12	0.17	0.24	0.14	1.17	0.11	3	0	1	8
18	3	0.44	4	67	265	0.71	0	0.02	—	0.04	0.99	0.05	1	0	1	5
12	2	0.16	3	53	261	0.36	0	0.12	—	0.04	0.69	0.07	1	0	<1	—
13	3	0.33	4	80	368	0.70	0	0.11	—	0.06	0.88	0.06	1	0	1	4
23.69	1.36	1.42	1.67	27.49	131.54	0.42	641.01	0.03	—	0.23	1.27	0.05	—	0	3.05	8.81
44	33	0.96	11	157	412	1.70	0	0.37	—	0.14	2.37	0.16	1	1	1	16
29	25	0.46	6	89	465	0.97	20	0.11	0.00	0.07	1.25	0.06	1	0	1	7
50	5	0.90	10	226	700	1.93	0	0.36	0.12	0.17	2.91	0.30	1	0	1	12
24	6	0.68	6	70	513	1.11	0	0.02	0.09	0.07	1.07	0.04	2	0	1	4
29	6	0.66	6	95	638	1.05	10	0.11	0.14	0.07	1.50	0.07	2	0	1	8
45	43	0.90	5	38	617	0.47	18	0.03	0.10	0.05	1.39	0.14	2	0	<1	8
48	48	0.83	6	81	642	1.40	0	0.02	0.28	0.08	1.86	0.10	4	0	<1	7
53	16	1.02	12	207	627	1.62	0	0.42	—	0.16	2.83	0.22	3	1	1	15
41	27	0.88	10	169	566	1.23	0	0.14	—	0.13	1.75	0.11	3	0	1	11
34	6	0.37	6	113	527	0.94	0	0.19	—	0.08	1.55	0.10	1	0	1	8
9	1	0.15	2	38	224	0.28	0	0.04	—	0.03	0.55	0.03	<1	0	<1	—
40	7	0.82	8	102	546	1.10	0	0.29	—	0.08	1.96	0.11	1	1	1	10
33	3	1.01	6	86	524	0.81	0	0.05	0.09	0.09	1.49	0.08	1	0	1	7
10	2	0.17	3	48	289	0.54	0	0.12	—	0.04	0.72	0.07	<1	0	<1	3
45	42	0.87	15	225	616	1.76	1	0.24	0.14	0.17	2.26	0.24	6	12	1	11
92	57	2.20	18	188	665	2.07	0	0.04	0.00	0.12	3.55	0.29	5	1	<1	—
33	7	0.43	7	101	517	0.71	7	0.11	0.07	0.06	1.67	0.09	1	0	<1	0
39	17	0.66	11	191	851	1.60	0	0.40	0.14	0.15	2.57	0.20	3	1	1	12
52	23	0.88	14	255	1137	2.14	0	0.53	—	0.20	3.43	0.27	4	0	1	16
43	7	1.44	8	154	704	1.45	0	0.09	0.12	0.19	2.44	0.15	1	0	3	12
8	2	0.14	1	16	152	0.26	0	0.01	—	0.02	0.26	0.02	1	0	<1	3
23	7	0.47	5	66	608	0.61	16	0.10	1.04	0.08	1.04	0.07	1	0	1	6
22	5	0.35	6	90	547	0.66	0	0.26	1.04	0.07	1.26	0.09	1	0	<1	11
25	0	0.72	—	—	730	—	0	—	—	—	—	—	—	—	0	—
10	0	0.00	—	—	300	—	0	—	—	—	—	—	—	—	0	—
20	0	0.72	—	—	640	—	0	—	—	—	—	—	—	—	0	—
20	0	0.72	—	—	620	—	0	—	—	—	—	—	—	—	0	—
20	0	0.72	—	—	540	—	0	—	—	—	—	—	—	—	0	—
10	0	0.00	—	—	330	—	0	—	—	—	—	—	—	—	0	—
20	0	0.36	6	81	310	0.73	0	—	—	—	—	—	—	—	0	—
40	0	0.72	—	—	590	—	0	—	—	—	—	—	—	—	0	—
50	40	0.72	—	—	500	—	0	—	—	—	—	—	—	—	0	—
0	18	0.11	—	—	18	—	0	0.02	0.00	0.10	1.63	—	—	0	<.1	—
0	18	0.07	21	89	14	0.04	0	0.02	0.00	0.09	1.61	0.18	21	0	<.1	2
0	18	0.14	18	64	11	0.11	0	0.03	0.00	0.11	1.39	0.12	14	0	<.1	2
0	25	0.04	32	90	18	0.04	—	0.02	0.00	0.10	1.63	0.18	22	0	<.1	—
0	18	0.11	21	89	9	0.07	0	0.02	0.00	0.09	1.61	0.18	21	0	<.1	4
0	18	0.14	18	64	9	0.11	0	0.03	0.00	0.11	1.39	0.12	15	0	<.1	4
0	18	0.11	21	89	9	0.07	0	0.02	0.00	0.09	1.61	0.18	21	0	<.1	4
0	18	0.14	18	64	9	0.11	0	0.03	0.00	0.11	1.39	0.12	15	0	<.1	4
0	0	0.01	0	1	<1	0.01	0	0.00	0.00	0.00	0.00	0.00	0	0	0	0
0	0	0.01	0	1	<1	0.01	0	0.00	0.00	0.00	0.00	0.00	0	0	0	0
0	0	0.01	0	1	<1	0.01	0	0.00	0.00	0.00	0.00	0.00	0	0	0	0
0	0	0.01	0	1	<1	0.01	0	0.00	0.00	0.00	0.00	0.00	0	0	0	0
0	0	0.01	0	1	<1	0.01	0	0.00	0.00	0.00	0.00	0.00	0	0	0	0
0	<1	0.02	1	10	3	0.01	0	0.00	—	0.00	0.05	0.00	0	0	0	<1
0	<1	0.02	1	10	3	0.01	0	0.00	0.00	0.00	0.05	0.00	0	0	0	<1

TABLE H–1
Food Composition

(DA+ code is for Wadsworth Diet Analysis program)   (For purposes of calculations, use "0" for t, <1, <.1, <.01, etc.)

DA + Code	Food Description	Quantity	Measure	Wt (g)	H₂O (g)	Ener (kcal)	Prot (g)	Carb (g)	Fiber (g)	Fat (g)	Sat	Mono	Poly	Trans
	BEVERAGES—Continued													
736	Cordials, 54 proof	1	fluid ounce(s)	30	9	106	<.1	13	0	<.1	0.02	0.01	0.04	—
	Wine													
858	Champagne, domestic	5	fluid ounce(s)	150	—	105	<1	4	0	0	0.00	0.00	0.00	0
861	Red wine, California	5	fluid ounce(s)	150	133	125	<1	4	0	0	0.00	0.00	0.00	0
690	Sweet dessert wine	5	fluid ounce(s)	150	106	240	<1	21	0	0	0.00	0.00	0.00	0
1481	White wine	5	fluid ounce(s)	148	132	100	<1	1	0	0	0.00	0.00	0.00	0
1811	Wine cooler	10	fluid ounce(s)	300	270	150	<1	18	<.1	<.1	0.01	0.00	0.02	—
	Carbonated													
692	Club soda	12	fluid ounce(s)	355	355	0	0	0	0	0	0.00	0.00	0.00	0
12010	Coca-Cola Classic cola soda	12	fluid ounce(s)	360	—	146	0	41	0	0	0.00	0.00	0.00	0
12031	Coke diet cola soda	12	fluid ounce(s)	360	—	2	0	<1	0	0	0.00	0.00	0.00	0
693	Cola	12	fluid ounce(s)	426	380	179	<1	46	0	0	0.00	0.00	0.00	—
9522	Cola soda, decaffeinated	12	fluid ounce(s)	372	331	156	<1	40	0	0	0.00	0.00	0.00	0
1415	Cola, low calorie w/aspartame	12	fluid ounce(s)	355	354	4	<1	<1	0	0	0.00	0.00	0.00	0
9524	Cola, decaffeinated, low calorie w/aspartame	12	fluid ounce(s)	355	354	4	<1	<1	0	0	0.00	0.00	0.00	0
1412	Cream soda	12	fluid ounce(s)	371	321	189	0	49	0	0	0.00	0.00	0.00	0
31899	Diet 7 Up	12	fluid ounce(s)	360	—	0	0	0	0	0	0.00	0.00	0.00	0
695	Ginger ale	12	fluid ounce(s)	366	334	124	0	32	0	0	0.00	0.00	0.00	0
694	Grape soda	12	fluid ounce(s)	372	330	160	0	42	0	0	0.00	0.00	0.00	0
1876	Lemon lime soda	12	fluid ounce(s)	368	330	147	0	38	0	0	0.00	0.00	0.00	—
29392	Mountain Dew diet soda	12	fluid ounce(s)	360	—	0	0	0	0	0	0.00	0.00	0.00	0
29391	Mountain Dew soda	12	fluid ounce(s)	360	—	170	0	46	0	0	0.00	0.00	0.00	0
3145	Orange soda	12	fluid ounce(s)	372	326	179	0	46	0	0	0.00	0.00	0.00	0
1414	Pepper-type soda	12	fluid ounce(s)	368	329	151	0	38	0	<1	0.26	0.00	0.00	—
2391	Pepper-type or cola soda, low calorie w/saccharin	12	fluid ounce(s)	355	354	0	0	<1	0	0	0.00	0.00	0.00	0
29389	Pepsi diet cola soda	12	fluid ounce(s)	360	—	0	0	0	0	0	0.00	0.00	0.00	0
29388	Pepsi regular cola soda	12	fluid ounce(s)	360	—	150	0	41	0	0	0.00	0.00	0.00	0
696	Root beer	12	fluid ounce(s)	370	330	152	0	39	0	0	0.00	0.00	0.00	0
31898	7 Up	12	fluid ounce(s)	360	—	240	0	59	0	0	0.00	0.00	0.00	0
12034	Sprite diet soda	12	fluid ounce(s)	360	—	4	0	0	0	0	0.00	0.00	0.00	0
12044	Sprite soda	12	fluid ounce(s)	360	—	144	0	39	0	0	0.00	0.00	0.00	0
	Coffee													
731	Brewed	8	fluid ounce(s)	237	236	9	<1	0	0	0	0.00	0.00	0.00	0
9520	Brewed, decaffeinated	8	fluid ounce(s)	237	235	5	<1	1	0	0	0.00	0.00	0.00	0
16882	Cappuccino	8	fluid ounce(s)	240	224	78	4	6	<1	4	2.53	1.18	0.15	—
16883	Cappuccino, decaffeinated	8	fluid ounce(s)	240	224	78	4	6	<1	4	2.53	1.18	0.15	—
16880	Espresso	8	fluid ounce(s)	237	235	5	<1	1	0	0	0.00	0.00	0.00	0
16881	Espresso, decaffeinated	8	fluid ounce(s)	237	235	5	<1	1	0	0	0.00	0.00	0.00	0
732	Instant, prepared	8	fluid ounce(s)	239	237	5	<1	1	0	0	0.00	0.00	0.00	0
	Fruit drinks													
29357	Crystal Light low calorie lemonade drink	8	fluid ounce(s)	240	—	5	0	0	0	0	0.00	0.00	0.00	0
6012	Fruit punch drink w/added vitamin C, canned	8	fluid ounce(s)	276	242	129	0	33	<1	<.1	0.01	0.01	0.01	0
260	Grape drink, canned	8	fluid ounce(s)	250	221	113	<.1	29	0	0	0.00	0.00	0.00	0
266	Lemonade, from frozen concentrate	8	fluid ounce(s)	248	213	131	<1	34	<1	<1	0.02	0.00	0.04	—
268	Limeade, from frozen concentrate	8	fluid ounce(s)	247	220	104	<.1	26	0	<.1	0.00	0.00	0.00	—
31143	Gatorade Thirst Quencher, all flavors	8	fluid ounce(s)	240	—	50	0	14	0	0	0.00	0.00	0.00	0
17372	Kool-Aid (lemonade/punch/fruit drink)	8	fluid ounce(s)	248	220	108	<1	28	<1	<.1	0.01	0.01	0.02	—
17225	Kool-Aid sugar free, low calorie tropical punch mix, prepared	8	fluid ounce(s)	240	—	5	0	0	0	0	0.00	0.00	0.00	0
14266	Odwalla strawberry 'c' monster fruit drink	8	fluid ounce(s)	240	—	150	2	34	1	1	0.00	—	—	0
10080	Odwalla strawberry lemonade quencher	8	fluid ounce(s)	240	—	120	1	28	1	0	0.00	0.00	0.00	0
10099	Snapple fruit punch	8	fluid ounce(s)	240	—	110	0	29	0	0	0.00	0.00	0.00	0
10096	Snapple kiwi strawberry	8	fluid ounce(s)	240	211	110	0	28	0	0	0.00	0.00	0.00	0
	Slim Fast ready to drink shake													
16056	Dark chocolate fudge	11	fluid ounce(s)	325	—	220	10	42	5	3	1.00	1.50	0.50	—
16054	French vanilla	11	fluid ounce(s)	325	—	220	10	40	5	3	0.50	1.50	0.50	—
16055	Strawberries n cream	11	fluid ounce(s)	325	—	220	10	40	5	3	0.50	1.50	0.50	—
	Tea													
733	Tea, prepared	8	fluid ounce(s)	237	236	2	0	1	0	0	0.00	0.00	0.01	0
33179	Decaffeinated, prepared	8	fluid ounce(s)	237	236	2	0	1	0	0	0.00	0.00	0.01	0
1877	Herbal, prepared	8	fluid ounce(s)	237	236	2	0	<1	0	0	0.00	0.00	0.01	0
734	Instant tea mix, unsweetened, prepared	8	fluid ounce(s)	237	236	2	<.1	<1	0	0	0.00	0.00	0.00	0

PAGE KEY: H–2 = Breads/Baked Goods   H–6 = Cereal/Rice/Pasta   H–10 = Fruit   H–14 = Vegetables/Legumes   H–24 = Nuts/Seeds   H–26 = Vegetarian
H–28 = Dairy   H–34 = Eggs   H–34 = Seafood   H–36 = Meats   H–40 = Poultry   H–40 = Processed meats   H–42 = Beverages   H–46 = Fats/Oils
H–48 = Sweets   H–50 = Spices/Condiments/Sauces   H–52 = Mixed foods/Soups/Sandwiches   H–58 = Fast food   H–74 = Convenience meals   H–76 = Baby foods

Chol (mg)	Calc (mg)	Iron (mg)	Magn (mg)	Pota (mg)	Sodi (mg)	Zinc (mg)	Vit A (µg)	Thia (mg)	Vit E (mg α)	Ribo (mg)	Niac (mg)	Vit B6 (mg)	Fola (µg)	Vit C (mg)	Vit B12 (µg)	Sele (µg)
0	<1	0.02	<1	5	2	0.01	0	0.00	0.00	0.00	0.02	0.00	0	0	0	—
0	—	—	—	—	—	—	—	—	—	—	0.00	—	—		0	—
0	12	1.43	16	171	15	0.15	0	0.02	0.00	0.04	0.12	0.05	1	0	<.1	—
0	12	0.36	14	138	14	0.11	0	0.03	0.00	0.03	0.32	0.00	0	0	0	1
0	13	0.47	15	118	7	0.10	0	0.01	—	0.01	0.10	0.02	0	0	0	<1
0	17	0.81	16	135	25	0.17		0.01	0.03	0.02	0.13	0.04	4	5	<.1	—
0	18	0.04	4	7	75	0.36	0	0.00	0.00	0.00	0.00	0.00	0	0	0	0
0	—	—	—	0	50	—	0	—	—	—	—	—	—	0	—	—
0	—	—	—	18	42	—	0	—	—	—	—	—	—	0	—	—
0	13	0.09	4	4	17	0.04	0	0.00	0.00	0.00	0.00	0.00	0	0	0	<1
0	11	0.07	4	4	15	0.04	0	0.00	0.00	0.00	0.00	0.00	0	0	0	<1
0	11	0.11	4	21	18	0.00	0	0.02	0.00	0.08	0.00	0.00	0	0	0	0
0	14	0.11	4	0	21	0.28	0	0.02	0.00	0.08	0.00	0.00	0	0	0	<1
0	19	0.19	4	4	44	0.26	0	0.00	0.00	0.00	0.00	0.00	0	0	0	0
0	—	—	—	116	53	—	—	—	0.00	—	—	—	—	—	—	—
0	11	0.66	4	4	26	0.18	0	0.00	0.00	0.00	0.00	0.00	0	0	0	<1
0	11	0.30	4	4	56	0.26	0	0.00	0.00	0.00	0.00	0.00	0	0	0	0
0	7	0.26	4	4	41	0.18	0	0.00	0.00	0.00	0.06	0.00	0	0	0	0
0	—	—	—	70	35	—	—	—	—	—	—	—	—	—	—	—
0	—	—	—	0	70	—	—	—	—	—	—	—	—	—	—	—
0	19	0.22	4	7	45	0.37	0	0.00	—	0.00	0.00	0.00	0	0	0	0
0	11	0.15	0	4	37	0.15	0	0.00	—	0.00	0.00	0	0	0	<1	
0	14	0.07	4	14	57	0.11	0	0.00	0.00	0.00	0.00	0.00	0	0	0	<1
0	—	—	—	30	35	—	—	—	—	—	—	—	—	—	—	—
0	—	—	—	0	35	—	—	—	—	—	—	—	—	—	—	—
0	18	0.18	4	4	48	0.26	0	0.00	0.00	0.00	0.00	0.00	0	0	0	<1
0	—	—	—	0	113	—	—	—	—	—	—	—	—	—	—	—
0	—	—	—	110	36	—	0	—	—	—	—	—	—	0	—	—
0	—	—	—	0	71	—	0	—	—	—	—	—	—	0	—	—
0	2	0.02	5	114	2	0.02	0	0.00	0.02	0.12	0.00	0.00	5	0	0	0
0	5	0.12	12	128	5	0.05	0	0.00	0.00	0.00	0.53	0.00	<1	0	0	0
17	152	0.26	22	250	62	0.50	—	0.04	0.10	0.20	0.37	0.05	5	1	<1	—
17	152	0.26	22	250	62	0.50	—	0.04	0.10	0.20	0.37	0.05	5	1	<1	—
0	5	0.12	12	128	5	0.05	0	0.00	0.05	0.00	0.53	0.00	<1	0	0	—
0	5	0.12	12	128	5	0.05	0	0.00	0.05	0.00	0.53	0.00	<1	0	0	—
0	10	0.10	7	72	5	0.02	0	0.00	0.00	0.00	0.56	0.00	0	0	0	<1
0	0	0.00	—	160	20	—	0	—	—	—	—	—	—	0	—	—
0	22	0.58	6	69	61	0.33	—	0.06	0.00	0.06	0.06	0.00	4	99	0	0
0	5	0.45	3	30	15	0.30	0	0.00	0.00	0.01	0.03	0.01	0	85	0	<1
0	10	0.52	5	50	7	0.07	0	0.02	0.02	0.07	0.05	0.02	2	13	0	<1
0	7	0.02	2	22	5	0.02	0	0.00	0.00	0.01	0.02	0.01	2	6	0	<1
0	10	0.18	—	30	110	—	—	—	—	—	—	—	—	1	—	—
0	14	0.46	5	50	31	0.20	—	0.04	—	0.05	0.05	0.01	4	42	0	1
0	0	0.00	—	10	10	—	0	—	—	—	—	—	—	6	—	—
0	20	1.44	—	330	40	—	—	—	—	—	—	—	—	600	0	—
0	20	0.00	—	70	30	—	0	—	—	—	—	—	—	60	0	—
0	0	0.00	—	20	10	—	0	—	—	—	—	—	—	0	0	—
0	0	0.00	—	40	10	—	0	—	—	—	—	—	—	0	0	—
5	400	2.70	140	600	220	2.25	—	0.53	—	0.60	7.00	0.70	120	60	2	18
5	400	2.70	140	600	220	2.25	—	0.53	—	0.60	7.00	0.70	120	60	2	18
5	400	2.70	140	600	220	2.25	—	0.53	—	0.60	7.00	0.70	120	60	2	18
0	0	0.05	7	88	7	0.05	0	0.00	0.00	0.03	0.00	0.00	12	0	0	0
0	0	0.05	7	88	7	0.05	0	0.00	0.00	0.03	0.00	0.00	12	0	0	0
0	5	0.19	2	21	2	0.09	0	0.02	0.00	0.01	0.00	0.00	2	0	0	0
0	7	0.05	5	47	7	0.02	0	0.00	0.00	0.00	0.09	0.00	0	0	0	0

TABLE H–1
Food Composition

(DA+ code is for Wadsworth Diet Analysis program)   (For purposes of calculations, use "0" for t, <1, <.1, <.01, etc.)

DA + Code	Food Description	Quantity	Measure	Wt (g)	H₂O (g)	Ener (kcal)	Prot (g)	Carb (g)	Fiber (g)	Fat (g)	Fat Breakdown (g)			
											Sat	Mono	Poly	Trans
	BEVERAGES—Continued													
735	Instant lemon flavored tea mix w/sugar, prepared	8	fluid ounce(s)	259	236	88	<1	22	0	<.1	0.01	0.00	0.02	—
	Water													
1413	Mineral water, carbonated	8	fluid ounce(s)	237	237	0	0	0	0	0	0.00	0.00	0.00	0
33183	Poland spring water, bottled	8	fluid ounce(s)	237	237	0	0	0	0	0	0.00	0.00	0.00	0
1	Tap water	8	fluid ounce(s)	237	237	0	0	0	0	0	0.00	0.00	0.00	—
1879	Tonic water	8	fluid ounce(s)	244	222	83	0	21	0	0	0.00	0.00	0.00	0
	FATS AND OILS													
	Butter													
104	Butter	1	tablespoon(s)	15	2	108	<1	<.1	0	12	6.13	5.00	0.43	—
921	Unsalted	1	tablespoon(s)	15	3	108	<1	<.1	0	12	7.71	3.15	0.46	—
107	Whipped	1	tablespoon(s)	11	2	82	<.1	<.1	0	9	5.76	2.67	0.34	—
944	Whipped, unsalted	1	tablespoon(s)	11	2	82	<.1	<.1	0	9	5.76	2.67	0.34	—
2522	Butter Buds, dry butter substitute	1	teaspoon(s)	2	—	8	0	2	0	0	0.00	0.00	0.00	—
	Fats, cooking													
2671	Beef tallow, semisolid	1	tablespoon(s)	13	0	115	0	0	0	13	6.37	5.35	0.51	—
922	Chicken fat	1	tablespoon(s)	13	<.1	115	0	0	0	13	3.81	5.72	2.68	—
5454	Household shortening w/vegetable oil	1	tablespoon(s)	13	0	115	0	0	0	13	3.39	5.56	2.75	2.20
111	Lard	1	tablespoon(s)	13	0	114	0	0	0	13	4.94	5.68	1.41	—
	Margarine													
114	Margarine	1	tablespoon(s)	14	2	101	<1	<1	0	11	2.23	5.05	3.58	—
116	Soft	1	tablespoon(s)	14	2	101	<1	<.1	0	11	1.95	4.02	4.88	—
117	Soft, unsalted	1	tablespoon(s)	14	3	101	<1	<1	0	11	1.95	5.26	3.62	—
928	Unsalted	1	tablespoon(s)	14	3	101	<.1	<.1	0	11	2.12	5.17	3.53	—
119	Whipped	1	tablespoon(s)	9	1	64	<.1	<.1	0	7	1.17	3.25	2.51	—
	Spreads													
16164	I Can't Believe It's Not Butter! whipped spread	1	tablespoon(s)	14	4	60	0	0	0	7	1.50	1.50	2.50	—
16157	Promise vegetable oil spread, stick	1	tablespoon(s)	14	4	90	0	0	0	10	2.50	2.00	4.00	—
	Oils													
2681	Canola	1	tablespoon(s)	14	0	120	0	0	0	14	0.97	8.01	4.03	—
120	Corn	1	tablespoon(s)	14	0	120	0	0	0	14	1.73	3.29	7.98	0.04
122	Olive	1	tablespoon(s)	14	0	119	0	0	0	14	1.82	9.98	1.35	—
124	Peanut	1	tablespoon(s)	14	0	119	0	0	0	14	2.28	6.24	4.32	—
2693	Safflower	1	tablespoon(s)	14	0	120	0	0	0	14	0.84	10.15	1.95	—
923	Sesame	1	tablespoon(s)	14	0	120	0	0	0	14	1.93	5.40	5.67	—
130	Soybean w/cottonseed oil	1	tablespoon(s)	14	0	120	0	0	0	14	2.45	4.01	6.54	—
128	Soybean, hydrogenated	1	tablespoon(s)	14	0	120	0	0	0	14	2.03	5.85	5.11	—
2700	Sunflower	1	tablespoon(s)	14	0	120	0	0	0	14	1.77	6.28	4.95	—
357	**Pam original no stick cooking spray**	1	serving(s)	0	—	0	0	0	0	0	0.00	0.00	0.00	
	Salad dressing													
132	Blue cheese	2	tablespoon(s)	31	10	154	1	2	0	16	3.03	3.76	8.51	—
133	Blue cheese, low calorie	2	tablespoon(s)	32	25	32	2	1	0	2	0.82	0.57	0.78	—
1764	Caesar	2	tablespoon(s)	30	10	158	<1	1	<.1	17	2.64	4.05	9.86	—
29654	Creamy, reduced calorie, fat free, cholesterol free, sour cream and/or buttermilk & oil	2	tablespoon(s)	32	24	34	<1	6	0	1	0.16	0.21	0.46	—
29617	Creamy, reduced calorie, sour cream and/or buttermilk & oil	2	tablespoon(s)	30	22	48	<1	2	0	4	0.63	0.98	2.40	—
134	French	2	tablespoon(s)	31	11	143	<1	5	0	14	1.76	2.63	6.56	—
135	French, low fat	2	tablespoon(s)	33	18	76	<1	10	<1	4	0.36	1.92	1.64	—
136	Italian	2	tablespoon(s)	29	17	86	<1	3	0	8	1.32	1.86	3.80	—
137	Italian, diet	2	tablespoon(s)	30	25	23	<1	1	0	2	0.14	0.66	0.51	—
139	Mayonnaise type	2	tablespoon(s)	29	12	115	<1	7	0	10	1.44	2.65	5.29	—
942	Oil & vinegar	2	tablespoon(s)	31	15	140	0	1	0	16	2.84	4.62	7.52	—
1765	Ranch	2	tablespoon(s)	30	12	146	<1	2	<.1	16	2.32	3.85	8.92	—
3666	Ranch, reduced calorie	2	tablespoon(s)	30	21	62	<1	2	<.1	6	1.13	1.79	2.89	—
940	Russian	2	tablespoon(s)	31	11	151	<1	3	0	16	2.23	3.61	9.00	—
939	Russian, low calorie	2	tablespoon(s)	33	21	46	<1	9	<.1	1	0.20	0.29	0.75	—
941	Sesame seed	2	tablespoon(s)	31	12	136	1	3	<1	14	1.90	3.64	7.68	—
142	Thousand island	2	tablespoon(s)	31	15	115	<1	5	<1	11	1.59	2.46	5.68	—
143	Thousand island, low calorie	2	tablespoon(s)	31	19	62	<1	7	<1	4	0.23	1.98	0.82	—
	Sandwich spreads													
138	Mayonnaise w/soybean oil	1	tablespoon(s)	14	2	99	<1	1	0	11	1.64	2.70	5.89	0.04

PAGE KEY: H–2 = Breads/Baked Goods   H–6 = Cereal/Rice/Pasta   H–10 = Fruit   H–14 = Vegetables/Legumes   H–24 = Nuts/Seeds   H–26 = Vegetarian
H–28 = Dairy   H–34 = Eggs   H–34 = Seafood   H–36 = Meats   H–40 = Poultry   H–40 = Processed meats   H–42 = Beverages   H–46 = Fats/Oils
H–48 = Sweets   H–50 = Spices/Condiments/Sauces   H–52 = Mixed foods/Soups/Sandwiches   H–58 = Fast food   H–74 = Convenience meals   H–76 = Baby foods

Chol (mg)	Calc (mg)	Iron (mg)	Magn (mg)	Pota (mg)	Sodi (mg)	Zinc (mg)	Vit A (µg)	Thia (mg)	Vit E (mg α)	Ribo (mg)	Niac (mg)	Vit B$_6$ (mg)	Fola (µg)	Vit C (mg)	Vit B$_{12}$ (µg)	Sele (µg)
0	5	0.05	5	49	8	0.03	0	0.00	0.00	0.04	0.09	0.01	0	<1	0	<1
0	33	0.00	0	0	2	0.00	0	0.00	—	0.00	0.00	0.00	0	0	0	0
0	2	0.02	2	0	2	0.00	0	0.00	—	0.00	0.00	0.00	0	0	0	0
0	4.74	0.00	2.37	0	4.74	0	0	0	0.57	0	0	0	0	0	0	0
0	2	0.02	0	0	10	0.24	0	0.00	0.00	0.00	0.00	0.00	0	0	0	0
32	4	0.00	<1	4	86	0.01	103	0.00	0.35	0.01	0.01	0.00	<1	0	<.1	<1
32	4	0.00	<1	4	2	0.01	103	0.00	0.35	0.01	0.01	0.00	<1	0	<.1	<1
25	3	0.02	<1	3	94	0.01	78	0.00	0.26	0.00	0.00	0.00	<1	0	<.1	<1
25	3	0.02	<1	3	1	0.01	—	0.00	0.26	0.01	0.00	0.00	<1	0	<.1	—
0	0	0.00	0	2	70	0.00	0	0.00	0.00	0.00	0.00	0.00	<1	0	0	—
14	0	0.00	0	0	0	0.00	0	0.00	0.35	0.00	0.00	0.00	0	0	0	<.1
11	0	0.00	0	0	0	0.00	0	0.00	0.35	0.00	0.00	0.00	0	0	0	<.1
0	0	0.00	0	0	0	0.00	0	0.00	—	0.00	0.00	0.00	0	0	0	—
12	0	0.00	0	0	0	0.01	0	0.00	0.08	0.00	0.00	0.00	0	0	0	<.1
0	4	0.01	<1	6	133	0.00	115	0.00	1.27	0.01	0.00	0.00	<1	<.1	<.1	0
0	4	0.00	<1	5	152	0.00	103	0.00	0.99	0.00	0.00	0.00	<1	<.1	<.1	0
0	4	0.00	<1	5	4	0.00	103	0.00	1.23	0.00	0.00	0.00	<1	<.1	<.1	0
0	2	0.00	<1	4	<1	0.00	115	0.00	1.80	0.00	0.00	0.00	<1	<.1	<.1	0
0	2	0.00	<1	3	97	0.00	—	0.00	0.45	0.00	0.00	0.00	<.1	<.1	<.1	—
0	10	0.18	—	4	70	—	—	1.65	0.00	0.00	0.00	—	—	1	—	—
0	10	0.18	—	9	90	—	—	0.00	—	0.00	0.00	—	—	1	—	—
0	0	0.00	0	0	0	0.00	0	0.00	2.33	0.00	0.00	0.00	0	0	0	0
0	0	0.00	0	0	0	0.00	0	0.00	1.94	0.00	0.00	0.00	0	0	0	0
0	<1	0.09	0	<1	<1	0.00	0	0.00	1.94	0.00	0.00	0.00	0	0	0	0
0	0	0.00	0	0	0	0.00	0	0.00	2.12	0.00	0.00	0.00	0	0	0	0
0	0	0.00	0	0	0	0.00	0	0.00	4.64	0.00	0.00	0.00	0	0	0	0
0	0	0.00	0	0	0	0.00	0	0.00	0.19	0.00	0.00	0.00	0	0	0	0
0	0	0.00	0	0	0	0.00	0	0.00	1.65	0.00	0.00	0.00	0	0	0	0
0	0	0.00	0	0	0	0.00	0	0.00	1.10	0.00	0.00	0.00	0	0	0	0
0	0	0.00	0	0	0	0.00	0	0.00	—	0.00	0.00	0.00	0	0	0	0
0	0	0.00	—	0	0	—	0	—	0.00	—	—	—	—	0	0	—
5	25	0.06	0	11	335	0.08	21	0.00	1.84	0.03	0.03	0.01	9	1	<.1	<1
<1	28	0.16	2	2	384	0.08	—	0.01	0.08	0.03	0.02	0.01	1	<.1	<.1	—
1	7	0.05	1	9	323	0.03	—	0.00	1.57	0.00	0.01	0.00	1	0	<.1	—
0	12	0.08	2	43	320	0.06	0	0.00	0.21	0.02	0.01	0.01	1	0	0	—
0	2	0.04	1	11	307	0.01	—	0.00	0.72	0.00	0.01	0.01	4	<1	<.1	—
0	7	0.25	2	21	261	0.09	7	0.01	1.56	0.02	0.06	0.00	0	0	<.1	0
0	4	0.28	3	35	262	0.07	9	0.01	0.10	0.02	0.15	0.02	1	0	0	1
0	2	0.19	1	14	486	0.04	1	0.00	1.47	0.01	0.00	0.02	0	0	0	1
2	3	0.20	1	26	410	0.06	<1	0.00	0.06	0.00	0.00	0.02	0	0	0	2
8	4	0.06	1	3	209	0.05	19	0.00	0.61	0.01	0.00	0.00	2	0	<.1	<1
0	0	0.00	0	2	<1	0.00	0	0.00	1.44	0.00	0.00	0.00	0	0	0	0
1	4	0.03	1	8	354	0.01	—	0.00	1.85	0.00	0.00	0.00	<1	<.1	<.1	—
<1	5	0.01	1	8	414	0.02	—	0.00	0.73	0.01	0.01	0.00	<1	<1	<.1	—
6	6	0.18	1	48	266	0.13	5	0.02	1.02	0.02	0.18	0.01	3	2	<.1	<1
2	6	0.20	0	51	283	0.03	1	0.00	0.13	0.00	0.00	0.00	1	2	<.1	1
0	6	0.18	0	48	306	0.03	1	0.00	1.53	0.00	0.00	0.00	0	0	0	<1
8	5	0.37	2	33	269	0.08	3	0.45	1.25	0.02	0.13	0.00	0	0	0	<1
<1	5	0.28	2	62	254	0.06	5	0.01	0.31	0.01	0.13	0.00	0	0	0	0
5	2	0.07	<1	5	78	0.02	12	0.00	0.72	0.00	0.00	0.08	1	0	<.1	<1

TABLE H–1
Food Composition

(DA+ code is for Wadsworth Diet Analysis program)   (For purposes of calculations, use "0" for t, <1, <.1, <.01, etc.)

DA+ Code	Food Description	Quantity	Measure	Wt (g)	H₂O (g)	Ener (kcal)	Prot (g)	Carb (g)	Fiber (g)	Fat (g)	Sat	Mono	Poly	Trans
	FATS AND OILS—Continued													
2708	Mayonnaise w/soybean & safflower oils	1	tablespoon(s)	14	0	98.94	0.15	0.37	0	10.95	1.18	1.79	7.59	—
140	Mayonnaise, low calorie	1	tablespoon(s)	16	10	37	<.1	3	0	3	0.53	0.72	1.70	—
141	Tartar sauce	2	tablespoon(s)	28	9	144	<1	4	<.1	14	2.14	4.13	7.57	—
	SWEETS													
4799	**Butterscotch or caramel topping**	2	tablespoon(s)	41	13	103	1	27	<1	<.1	0.05	0.01	0.00	—
	Candy													
1786	Almond Joy candy bar	1	item(s)	49	5	240	2	29	2	13	9.00	3.63	0.74	0
1785	Bit-o-Honey candy	6	item(s)	40	2	170	1	34	0	3	2.00	0	20	—
33375	Butterscotch candy	2	piece(s)	12	1	47	<.1	11	0	<1	0.25	0.10	0.01	—
1701	Chewing gum, stick	1	item(s)	3	<.1	7	0	2	<.1	<.1	0.00	0.00	0.00	—
33378	Chocolate fudge w/nuts, prepared	2	piece(s)	38	3	175	2	26	1	7	2.29	1.41	2.81	—
1787	Jelly beans	15	item(s)	43	3	159	0	40	<.1	<.1	0.00	0.00	0.00	—
1784	Kit Kat wafer bar	1	item(s)	42	1	220	3	27	1	11	7.00	3.53	0.34	0
4674	Krackel candy bar	1	item(s)	41	1	220	3	26	1	11	6.00	3.94	0.37	0
4934	Licorice	4	piece(s)	44	7	147	1	34	1	1	0.18	0.07	0.01	—
1780	Life Savers candy	1	item(s)	2	—	8	0	2	0	<.1	0.00	—	—	0
1790	Lollipop	1	item(s)	28	—	108	0	28	0	0	0.00	0.00	0.00	0
4679	M & Ms peanut chocolate candy, small bag	1	item(s)	49	1	250	5	30	2	13	5.00	5.42	2.07	—
1781	M & Ms plain chocolate candy, small bag	1	item(s)	48	1	240	2	34	1	10	6.00	3.30	0.30	—
4673	Milk chocolate bar	1	item(s)	91	1	483	8	53	2	28	16.69	7.20	0.63	—
1783	Milky Way bar	1	item(s)	58	4	270	2	41	1	10	5.00	3.50	0.35	—
1788	Peanut brittle	1½	ounce(s)	43	<1	206	3	30	1	8	1.76	3.43	1.94	—
1789	Reese's peanut butter cups	2	piece(s)	45	1	250	5	25	1	14	5.00	6.17	2.34	0
4689	Reese's pieces candy, small bag	1	item(s)	46	1	230	6	26	1	11	7.00	0.97	0.46	0
33399	Semisweet chocolate candy, made w/butter	½	ounce(s)	14	<.1	68	1	9	1	4	2.49	1.41	0.13	—
1782	Snickers bar	1	item(s)	59	3	280	4	35	1	14	5.00	6.13	2.89	—
4694	Special Dark chocolate bar	1	item(s)	41	<1	220	2	24	3	13	8.00	4.59	0.41	0
4695	Starburst fruit chews, original fruits	1	package	59	4	240	0	48	0	5	1.00	2.10	1.83	—
4698	Taffy	3	piece(s)	45	2	169	<.1	41	0	1	0.92	0.43	0.05	—
4699	Three Musketeers bar	1	item(s)	60	4	260	2	46	1	8	4.50	2.59	0.27	—
4702	Twix caramel cookie bars	2	item(s)	58	2	280	3	37	1	14	5.00	7.75	0.49	—
4705	York peppermint pattie	1	item(s)	42	4	170	1	34	1	3	2.00	1.32	0.12	0
	Frosting, icing													
4760	Chocolate frosting, ready to eat	2	tablespoon(s)	28	5	112	<1	18	<1	5	1.55	2.54	0.60	—
4771	Creamy vanilla frosting, ready to eat	2	tablespoon(s)	28	4	118	0	19	<.1	5	0.84	1.37	2.24	—
17291	Dec-a-Cake variety pack candy decoration	1	teaspoon(s)	4	—	15	0	3	0	1	0.00	—	—	—
536	White icing	2	tablespoon(s)	40	3	163	<1	32	0	4	0.86	2.07	1.19	—
	Gelatin													
13697	Gelatin snack, all flavors	1	item(s)	99	97	70	1	17	0	0	0.00	0.00	0.00	—
2616	Mixed fruit gelatin mix, sugar free, low calorie, prepared	½	cup(s)	121	—	10	1	0	0	0	0.00	0.00	0.00	0
548	**Honey**	1	tablespoon(s)	21	4	64	<.1	17	<.1	0	0.00	0.00	0.00	0
	Jams, Jellies													
23054	Jams, jellies, preserves, all flavors	1	tablespoon(s)	20	<.1	56	<.1	14	<1	<.1	0.00	0.01	0.00	—
23278	Jams, jellies, preserves, all flavors, low sugar	1	tablespoon(s)	18	<.1	25	<.1	6	<1	<.1	0.00	0.01	0.02	—
545	**Marshmallows**	4	item(s)	29	5	92	1	23	<.1	<.1	0.02	0.02	0.01	—
4800	**Marshmallow cream topping**	2	tablespoon(s)	28	6	91	<1	22	<.1	<.1	0.02	0.02	0.01	—
555	**Molasses**	1	tablespoon(s)	20	4	58	0	15	0	<.1	0.00	0.01	0.01	—
4780	**Popsicle or ice pop**	1	item(s)	59	47	42	0	11	0	0	0.00	0.00	0.00	—
	Sugar													
559	Brown, packed	1	teaspoon(s)	5	<.1	17	0	4	0	0	0.00	0.00	0.00	0
563	Powdered, sifted	⅓	cup(s)	33	<.1	130	0	33	0	<.1	0.01	0.01	0.02	—
561	White granulated	1	teaspoon(s)	4	<.1	15	0	4	0	0	0.00	0.00	0.00	—
	Sugar Substitute													
1760	Equal sweetener, packet	1	item(s)	1	<.1	4	<.1	1	0	0	0.00	0.00	0.00	0
13029	Splenda granular no calorie sweetener	1	teaspoon(s)	1	—	2	0	1	0	0	0.00	0.00	0.00	0
1759	Sweet n Low sugar substitute, packet	1	item(s)	1	<.1	4	0	1	0	0	0.00	0.00	0.00	0
	Syrup													
3148	Chocolate	2	tablespoon(s)	38	12	105	1	24	1	<1	0.19	0.11	0.01	—
29676	Maple	¼	cup(s)	80	26	209	0	54	0	<1	0.03	0.05	0.08	—
4795	Pancake	¼	cup(s)	80	30	187	0	49	1	0	0.00	0.00	0.00	0

PAGE KEY: H–2 = Breads/Baked Goods   H–6 = Cereal/Rice/Pasta   H–10 = Fruit   H–14 = Vegetables/Legumes   H–24 = Nuts/Seeds   H–26 = Vegetarian
H–28 = Dairy   H–34 = Eggs   H–34 = Seafood   H–36 = Meats   H–40 = Poultry   H–40 = Processed meats   H–42 = Beverages   H–46 = Fats/Oils
H–48 = Sweets   H–50 = Spices/Condiments/Sauces   H–52 = Mixed foods/Soups/Sandwiches   H–58 = Fast food   H–74 = Convenience meals   H–76 = Baby foods

Chol (mg)	Calc (mg)	Iron (mg)	Magn (mg)	Pota (mg)	Sodi (mg)	Zinc (mg)	Vit A (µg)	Thia (mg)	Vit E (mg α)	Ribo (mg)	Niac (mg)	Vit B_6 (mg)	Fola (µg)	Vit C (mg)	Vit B_{12} (µg)	Sele (µg)
8.14	2.48	0.06	0.13	4.69	78.38	0.01	11.59	0	3.04	0	0	0.07	1.1	0	0.03	0.22
4	<.1	0.00	<.1	2	80	0.02	0	0.00	0.32	0.00	0.00	0.00	0	0	0	—
11	6	0.21	1	10	200	0.05	—	0.00	0.97	0.00	0.01	0.08	2	<1	<.1	—
<1	22	0.08	3	34	143	0.08	11	0.00	—	0.04	0.02	0.01	1	<1	<.1	0
3	20	0.36	33	138	70	0.40	0	0.02	—	0.08	0.24	—	—	0	—	—
0.00	—	—	85	—	0	—	—	—	—	—	—	0	—	0	—	—
1	<1	0.00	<1	<1	47	0.00	3	0.00	0.01	0.00	0.00	0.00	0	0	0	<.1
0	0	0.00	0	<.1	<.1	0.00	0	0.00	0.00	0.00	0.00	0.00	0	0	0	<.1
5	21	0.75	21	68	16	0.54	14	0.03	0.10	0.04	0.12	0.03	6	<.1	<.1	1
0	1	0.06	1	16	21	0.02	0	0.00	0.00	0.00	0.00	0.00	0	0	0	<1
3	40	0.36	16	126	25	0.52	8	0.07	—	0.23	1.07	0.05	60	0	<.1	2
3	60	0.37	—	169	80	—	0	—	—	—	—	—	—	0	—	—
0	3	0.13	3	28	109	0.07	0	0.01	0.08	0.02	0.04	0.04	0	0	0	—
0	<1	0.04	—	0	1	—	0	0.00	—	0.00	0.00	—	—	0	—	0
0	0	0.00	—	—	11	—	0	0.00	—	0.00	0.00	—	—	0	—	1
5	40	0.36	36	171	25	1.13	15	0.03	—	0.07	1.60	0.04	17	1	<.1	2
5	40	0.36	20	127	30	0.46	15	0.03	—	0.07	0.11	0.01	3	1	<1	1
22	228	0.83	61	399	92	1.00	20	0.06	—	0.26	0.15	0.10	11	2	<1	—
5	60	0.18	20	140	95	0.41	15	0.02	—	0.07	0.20	0.03	6	1	<1	3
5	11	0.52	18	71	189	0.37	17	0.06	1.09	0.02	1.13	0.03	20	0	<.1	1
3	20	0.36	40	233	140	0.82	7	0.11	—	0.08	2.08	0.07	25	0	<.1	2
0	40	0.00	20	182	90	0.35	25	0.04	—	0.07	1.31	0.03	13	0	<.1	1
3	5	0.44	16	52	2	0.23	<1	0.01	—	0.01	0.06	0.01	<1	0	0	<1
5	40	0.36	42	—	140	1.38	15	0.03	—	0.07	1.60	0.05	23	1	<.1	3
3	0	0.72	46	136	0	0.60	0	0.01	—	0.03	0.16	0.01	1	0	0	1
0	10	0.18	1	1	0	0.00	—	0.00	—	0.00	0.00	0.00	0	30	0	<1
4	1	0.03	<1	2	40	0.02	—	0.00	—	0.01	0.01	0.00	0	0	<.1	—
5	20	0.36	18	80	110	0.33	14	0.02	—	0.03	0.20	0.01	0	1	<1	2
5	40	0.36	18	117	115	0.45	15	0.09	—	0.13	0.69	0.02	14	1	<1	1
0	0	0.36	25	71	10	0.31	0	0.01	—	0.04	0.34	0.01	2	0	<.1	—
0	2	0.40	6	55	51	0.08	0	0.00	0.44	0.00	0.03	0.00	<1	0	0	<1
0	1	0.04	<1	10	52	0.02	0	0.00	0.43	0.08	0.06	0.00	2	0	0	<.1
0	0	0.00	—	—	15	—	0	—	—	—	—	—	—	0	—	—
<1	5	0.02	—	7	92	—	—	0.00	0.33	0.01	0.00	—	—	<.1	—	—
0	0	0.00	—	0	40	—	0	—	—	—	—	—	—	0	—	—
0	0	0.00	0	0	50	0.00	0	0.00	0.00	0.00	0.00	0.00	0	0	0	—
0	1	0.09	<1	11	1	0.05	0	0.00	0.00	0.01	0.03	0.01	<1	<1	0	<1
0	4	0.10	1	15	6	0.01	0.00	0.00	0.00	0.02	0.01	0.00	2.20	1.76	0.00	—
0	2	0.05	1	19	<1	0.02	0.76	0.01	0.01	0.03	0.01		—	4.93	0.00	—
0	1	0.07	1	1	23	0.01	0	0.00	0.00	0.00	0.02	0.00	<1	0	0	<1
0	1	0.06	1	1	23	0.01	0	0.00	0.00	0.00	0.02	0.00	<1	0	0	1
0	41	0.94	48	293	7	0.06	0	0.01	0.00	0.00	0.19	0.13	0	0	0	4
0	0	0.00	1	2	7	0.01	0	0.00	0.00	0.00	0.00	0.00	0	0	0	0
0	4	0.09	1	16	2	0.01	0	0.00	0.00	0.00	0.00	0.00	<.1	0	0	<.1
0	<1	0.01	0	1	<1	0.00	0	0.00	0.00	0.01	0.00	0.00	0	0	0	<.1
0	<.1	0.00	0	<.1	0	0.00	0	0.00	0.00	0.00	0.00	0.00	0	0	0	<.1
0	0	0.00	0	0	0	0.00	0	0.00	0.00	0.00	0.00	0.00	0	0	0	0
0	10	0.18	—	—	<1	—	—	0.02	0.00	0.02	0.20	—	—	1	0	—
0	0	0.00	0	—	0	0.00	0	0.00	0.00	0.00	0.00	0.00	0	0	0	0
0	5	0.79	24	84	27	0.27	0	0.00	0.00	0.02	0.12	0.00	1	<.1	0	1
0	54	0.96	11	163	7	3.33	0	0.00	0.00	0.01	0.02	0.00	0	0	0	<1
0	2	0.02	2	12	66	0.06	0	0.00	0.00	0.01	0.01	0.00	0	0	0	0

TABLE H–1

Food Composition (DA+ code is for Wadsworth Diet Analysis program) (For purposes of calculations, use "0" for t, <1, <.1, <.01, etc.)

DA + Code	Food Description	Quantity	Measure	Wt (g)	H₂O (g)	Ener (kcal)	Prot (g)	Carb (g)	Fiber (g)	Fat (g)	Sat	Mono	Poly	Trans
	SPICES, CONDIMENTS, SAUCES													
	Spices													
807	Allspice, ground	1	teaspoon(s)	2	<1	5	<1	1	<1	<1	0.05	0.01	0.04	—
1171	Anise seeds	1	teaspoon(s)	2	<1	7	<1	1	<1	<1	0.01	0.21	0.07	—
729	Baker's yeast active	1	teaspoon(s)	4	<1	12	2	2	1	<1	0.02	0.10	0.00	—
683	Baking powder, double acting, w/phosphate	1	teaspoon(s)	5	<1	2	<.1	1	<.1	0	0.00	0.00	0.00	0
1611	Baking soda	1	teaspoon(s)	5	<.1	0	0	0	0	0	0.00	0.00	0.00	0
8552	Basil	1	teaspoon(s)	1	1	<1	<.1	<.1	<.1	<.1	0.00	0.00	0.00	—
34959	Basil, fresh	1	piece(s)	1	<1	<1	<.1	<.1	<.1	<.1	0.00	0.00	0.00	—
808	Basil, ground	1	teaspoon(s)	1	<.1	4	<1	1	1	<.1	0.00	0.01	0.03	—
809	Bay leaf	1	teaspoon(s)	1	<.1	2	<.1	<1	<1	<.1	0.01	0.01	0.01	—
11720	Betel leaves	1	ounce(s)	28	—	17	2	2	0	<.1	—	—	—	—
818	Black pepper	1	teaspoon(s)	2	<1	5	<1	1	1	<.1	0.02	0.02	0.02	—
730	Brewer's yeast	1	teaspoon(s)	3	<1	8	1	1	1	0	0.00	0.00	0.00	0
35417	Capers	1	teaspoon(s)	4	—	2	0	0	0	0	0.00	0.00	0.00	—
1172	Caraway seeds	1	teaspoon(s)	2	<1	7	<1	1	1	<1	0.01	0.15	0.07	—
819	Cayenne pepper	1	teaspoon(s)	2	<1	6	<1	1	<1	<1	0.06	0.05	0.15	—
1173	Celery seeds	1	teaspoon(s)	2	<1	8	<1	1	<1	1	0.04	0.32	0.07	—
1174	Chervil, dried	1	teaspoon(s)	1	<.1	1	<1	<1	<.1	<.1	0.00	0.01	0.01	—
810	Chili powder	1	teaspoon(s)	3	<1	8	<1	1	1	<1	0.08	0.09	0.19	—
8553	Chives, chopped	1	teaspoon(s)	1	1	<1	<.1	<.1	<.1	<.1	0.00	0.00	0.00	—
8556	Cilantro	1	teaspoon(s)	2	1	<1	<.1	<.1	<.1	<.1	0.00	0.00	0.00	—
811	Cinnamon, ground	1	teaspoon(s)	2	<1	6	<.1	2	1	<1	0.01	0.01	0.01	—
812	Cloves, ground	1	teaspoon(s)	2	<1	7	<1	1	1	<1	0.11	0.03	0.15	—
1175	Coriander leaf, dried	1	teaspoon(s)	1	<.1	2	<1	<1	<.1	<.1	0.00	0.01	0.00	—
1176	Coriander seeds	1	teaspoon(s)	2	<1	5	<1	1	1	<1	0.02	0.24	0.03	—
1706	Cornstarch	1	tablespoon(s)	8	1	30	<.1	7	<.1	<.1	0.00	0.00	0.00	—
11729	Cumin, ground	1	teaspoon(s)	5	—	11	<1	1	1	<1	—	—	—	—
1177	Cumin seeds	1	teaspoon(s)	2	<1	8	<1	1	<1	<1	0.03	0.29	0.07	—
1178	Curry powder	1	teaspoon(s)	2	<1	7	<1	1	1	<1	0.04	0.11	0.05	—
1179	Dill seeds	1	teaspoon(s)	2	<1	6	<1	1	<1	<1	0.02	0.20	0.02	—
1180	Dill weed, dried	1	teaspoon(s)	1	<.1	3	<1	1	<1	<.1	0.00	0.01	0.00	—
34949	Dill weed, fresh	5	piece(s)	1	1	<1	<.1	<.1	<.1	<.1	0.00	0.01	0.00	—
4949	Fennel leaves, fresh	1	teaspoon(s)	1	1	<1	<.1	<.1	0	<.1	0.00	0.00	0.00	—
1181	Fennel seeds	1	teaspoon(s)	2	<1	7	<1	1	1	<1	0.01	0.20	0.03	—
1182	Fenugreek seeds	1	teaspoon(s)	4	<1	12	1	2	1	<1	0.05	—	—	—
11733	Garam masala, powder	1	ounce(s)	28	—	107	4	13	0	4	—	—	—	—
1067	Garlic clove	1	item(s)	3	2	4	<1	1	<.1	<.1	0.00	0.00	0.01	—
813	Garlic powder	1	teaspoon(s)	3	<1	9	<1	2	<1	<.1	0.00	0.00	0.01	—
1183	Ginger, ground	1	teaspoon(s)	2	<1	6	<1	1	<1	<1	0.03	0.02	0.02	—
1068	Ginger root	2	teaspoon(s)	4	3	3	<.1	1	<.1	<.1	0.01	0.01	0.01	—
35497	Leeks, bulb & lower leaf, freeze-dried	¼	cup(s)	1	<.1	3	<1	1	<.1	<.1	0.00	0.00	0.01	—
1184	Mace, ground	1	teaspoon(s)	2	<1	8	<1	1	1	1	0.16	0.19	0.07	—
1185	Marjoram, dried	1	teaspoon(s)	1	<.1	2	<.1	<1	<1	<.1	0.00	0.01	0.03	—
1186	Mustard seeds, yellow	1	teaspoon(s)	3	<1	15	1	1	<1	1	0.05	0.65	0.18	—
814	Nutmeg, ground	1	teaspoon(s)	2	<1	12	<1	1	<1	1	0.57	0.07	0.01	—
2747	Onion flakes, dehydrated	1	teaspoon(s)	2	<.1	6	<1	1	<1	<.1	0.00	0.00	0.00	—
1187	Onion powder	1	teaspoon(s)	2	<1	7	<1	2	<1	<.1	0.00	0.00	0.01	—
815	Oregano, ground	1	teaspoon(s)	2	<1	5	<1	1	1	<1	0.04	0.01	0.08	—
816	Paprika	1	teaspoon(s)	2	<1	6	<1	1	1	<1	0.04	0.03	0.17	—
817	Parsley, dried	1	teaspoon(s)	0	<.1	1	<.1	<1	<.1	<.1	0.00	0.01	0.00	—
1189	Poppy seeds	1	teaspoon(s)	3	<1	15	1	1	<1	1	0.14	0.18	0.86	—
1190	Poultry seasoning	1	teaspoon(s)	2	<1	5	<1	1	<1	<1	0.05	0.02	0.03	—
1191	Pumpkin pie spice, powder	1	teaspoon(s)	2	<1	6	<.1	1	<1	<1	0.11	0.02	0.01	—
1192	Rosemary, dried	1	teaspoon(s)	1	<1	4	<.1	1	1	<1	0.09	0.04	0.03	—
11723	Rosemary, fresh	1	teaspoon(s)	1	<1	1	<.1	<1	<.1	<.1	0.02	0.01	0.01	—
2722	Saffron powder	1	teaspoon(s)	1	<.1	2	<1	<1	<.1	<.1	0.01	0.00	0.01	—
11724	Sage	1	ounce(s)	28	—	34	1	4	0	1	—	—	—	—
1193	Sage, ground	1	teaspoon(s)	1	<.1	2	<.1	<1	<1	<.1	0.05	0.01	0.01	—
822	Salt, table	¼	teaspoon(s)	2	<.1	0	0	0	0	0	0.00	0.00	0.00	0
30189	Salt substitute	¼	teaspoon(s)	1	—	<.1	0	<.1	0	0	0.00	0.00	0.00	0
30190	Salt substitute, seasoned	¼	teaspoon(s)	1	—	1	<.1	<1	0	<.1	0.00	—	—	—
1194	Savory, ground	1	teaspoon(s)	1	<1	4	<.1	1	1	<.1	0.05	—	—	—
820	Sesame seed kernels, toasted	1	teaspoon(s)	3	<1	15	<1	1	<1	1	0.18	0.49	0.57	—
11725	Sorrel	1	tablespoon(s)	9	—	2	<1	<1	<.1	<.1	0.00			

PAGE KEY: H–2 = Breads/Baked Goods   H–6 = Cereal/Rice/Pasta   H–10 = Fruit   H–14 = Vegetables/Legumes   H–24 = Nuts/Seeds   H–26 = Vegetarian
H–28 = Dairy   H–34 = Eggs   H–34 = Seafood   H–36 = Meats   H–40 = Poultry   H–40 = Processed meats   H–42 = Beverages   H–46 = Fats/Oils
H–48 = Sweets   H–50 = Spices/Condiments/Sauces   H–52 = Mixed foods/Soups/Sandwiches   H–58 = Fast food   H–74 = Convenience meals   H–76 = Baby foods

Chol (mg)	Calc (mg)	Iron (mg)	Magn (mg)	Pota (mg)	Sodi (mg)	Zinc (mg)	Vit A (μg)	Thia (mg)	Vit E (mg α)	Ribo (mg)	Niac (mg)	Vit B$_6$ (mg)	Fola (μg)	Vit C (mg)	Vit B$_{12}$ (μg)	Sele (μg)
0	13	0.13	3	20	1	0.02	1	0.00	—	0.00	0.05	0.00	1	1	0	<.1
0	14	0.78	4	30	<1	0.11	<1	0.01	—	0.01	0.06	0.01	<1	<1	0	<1
0	3	0.66	4	80	2	0.26	0	0.09	0.00	0.22	1.59	0.06	94	<.1	<.1	1
0	339	0.52	2	<1	363	0.00	0	0.00	0.00	0.00	0.00	0.00	0	0	0	<.1
0	0	0.00	0	0	1259	0.00	0	0.00	0.00	0.00	0.00	0.00	0	0	0	<.1
0	1	0.03	1	4	<.1	0.01	2	0.00	—	0.00	0.01	0.00	1	<1	0	<.1
0	1	—	<1	2	<.1	0.00	—	0.00	—	0.00	0.01	0.00	<1	—	0	<.1
0	30	0.59	6	48	<1	0.08	7	0.00	0.10	0.00	0.10	0.03	4	1	0	<.1
0	5	0.26	1	3	<1	0.02	2	0.00	—	0.00	0.01	0.01	1	<1	0	<.1
0	110	2.29	—	156	2	—	—	0.04	—	0.07	0.20	—	—	1	0	—
0	9	0.61	4	26	1	0.03	<1	0.00	0.02	0.01	0.02	0.01	<1	<1	0	<.1
0	6	0.47	6	51	3	0.21	0	0.42	—	0.11	1.00	0.07	104	0	0	0
0	0	0.00	—	—	140	—	0	—	—	—	—	—	—	0	—	—
0	14	0.34	5	28	<1	0.12	<1	0.01	0.05	0.01	0.08	0.01	<1	<1	0	<1
0	3	0.14	3	36	1	0.04	37	0.01	0.54	0.02	0.16	0.04	2	1	0	<1
0	35	0.90	9	28	3	0.14	<.1	0.01	0.02	0.01	0.06	0.02	<1	<1	0	<1
0	8	0.19	1	28	<1	0.05	2	0.00	—	0.00	0.03	0.01	2	<1	0	<1
0	7	0.37	4	50	26	0.07	39	0.01	—	0.02	0.21	0.10	3	2	0	<1
0	1	0.02	<1	3	<.1	0.01	2	0.00	0.76	0.00	0.01	0.00	1	1	0	<.1
0	1	0.03	<1	8	1	0.00	—	0.00	—	0.00	0.02	0.00	1	1	0	<.1
0	28	0.88	1	12	1	0.05	<1	0.00	0.02	0.00	0.03	0.01	1	1	0	<.1
0	14	0.18	6	23	5	0.02	1	0.00	0.18	0.01	0.03	0.01	2	2	0	<1
0	7	0.25	4	27	1	0.03	2	0.01	—	0.01	0.06	0.02	2	3	0	<1
0	13	0.29	6	23	1	0.08	0	0.00	—	0.01	0.04	—	0	<1	0	<1
0	<1	0.04	<1	<1	1	0.00	0	0.00	0.00	0.00	0.00	0.00	0	0	0	<1
0	20	—	—	44	5	—	—	—	—	—	—	—	—	—	—	—
0	20	1.39	8	38	4	0.10	1	0.01	0.07	0.01	0.10	0.01	<1	<1	0	<1
0	10	0.59	5	31	1	0.08	1	0.01	0.44	0.01	0.07	0.02	3	<1	0	<1
0	32	0.34	5	25	<1	0.11	<.1	0.01	—	0.01	0.06	0.01	<1	<1	0	<1
0	18	0.49	5	33	2	0.03	3	0.00	—	0.00	0.03	0.02	2	1	0	0
0	2	—	1	7	1	0.01	—	0.00	—	0.00	0.02	0.02	2	—	0	—
0	1	0.03	—	4	<.1	—	—	0.00	—	0.00	0.01	0.00	—	<1	0	—
0	24	0.37	8	34	2	0.07	<1	0.01	—	0.01	0.12	0.01	—	<1	0	0
0	7	1.24	7	28	2	0.09	<1	0.01	—	0.01	0.06	0.02	2	<1	0	<1
0	215	9.25	94	411	28	1.07	—	0.10	—	0.09	0.71	—	0	0	0	—
0	5	0.05	1	12	1	0.03	0	0.01	0.00	0.00	0.02	0.04	<.1	1	0	<1
0	2	0.08	2	31	1	0.07	0	0.01	0.02	0.00	0.02	0.08	<.1	1	0	1
0	2	0.21	3	24	1	0.08	<1	0.00	0.32	0.00	0.09	0.02	1	<1	0	1
0	1	0.02	2	17	1	0.01	0	0.00	0.01	0.00	0.03	0.01	<1	<1	0	<.1
0	3	0.06	1	19	<1	0.01	<1	0.01	—	0.00	0.03	0.01	3	1	0	<.1
0	4	0.24	3	8	1	0.04	1	0.00	0.01	0.00	0.02	0.01	2	<1	0	<.1
0	12	0.50	2	9	<1	0.02	2	0.00	0.01	0.00	0.02	0.01	2	<1	0	<.1
0	17	0.33	10	23	<1	0.19	<.1	0.02	0.10	0.01	0.26	0.01	3	<.1	0	4
0	4	0.07	4	8	<1	0.05	<1	0.01	—	0.00	0.03	0.00	2	<.1	0	<.1
0	4	0.03	2	27	<1	0.03	<.1	0.01	—	0.00	0.02	0.03	3	1	0	<.1
0	8	0.05	3	20	1	0.05	0	0.01	0.01	0.00	0.01	0.03	3	<1	0	<.1
0	24	0.66	4	25	<1	0.07	5	0.01	0.28	0.00	0.09	0.02	4	1	0	<1
0	4	0.50	4	49	1	0.09	55	0.01	0.63	0.04	0.32	0.08	2	1	0	<1
0	4	0.29	1	11	<1	0.01	2	0.00	0.02	0.00	0.02	0.00	1	<1	0	<1
0	41	0.26	9	20	1	0.29	0	0.02	0.03	0.00	0.03	0.01	2	<.1	0	<1
0	15	0.53	3	10	<1	0.05	2	0.00	0.03	0.00	0.04	0.02	2	<1	0	<1
0	12	0.34	2	11	1	0.04	<1	0.00	0.02	0.00	0.04	0.01	1	<1	0	<1
0	15	0.35	3	11	1	0.04	2	0.01	—	0.01	0.01	0.02	4	1	0	<.1
0	2	0.05	1	5	<1	0.01	1	0.00	—	0.00	0.01	0.00	1	<1	0	—
0	1	0.08	2	12	1	0.01	<1	0.00	—	0.00	0.01	0.01	1	1	0	<.1
0	170	—	45	110	1	0.48	—	0.03	—	—	—	—	—	—	—	—
0	12	0.20	3	7	<.1	0.03	2	0.01	0.05	0.00	0.04	0.02	2	<1	0	<.1
0	<1	0.00	<.1	<1	581	0.00	0	0.00	0.00	0.00	0.00	0.00	0	0	0	<.1
0	7	0.00	<.1	604	<.1	—	0	—	—	—	—	—	—	0	—	—
0	0	0	476	<1	—	0	—	—	—	—	—	—	—	0	—	—
0	30	0.53	5	15	<1	0.06	4	0.01	—	—	0.06	0.03	—	1	0	<.1
0	4	0.21	9	11	1	0.28	<.1	0.03	0.01	0.01	0.15	0.00	3	0	0	<.1
0				<1												

TABLE H–1
Food Composition

(DA+ code is for Wadsworth Diet Analysis program)   (For purposes of calculations, use "0" for t, <1, <.1, <.01, etc.)

DA + Code	Food Description	Quantity	Measure	Wt (g)	H₂O (g)	Ener (kcal)	Prot (g)	Carb (g)	Fiber (g)	Fat (g)	Sat	Mono	Poly	Trans
	SPICES, CONDIMENTS, SAUCES—Continued													
11721	Spearmint	1	teaspoon(s)	2	2	1	<.1	<1	<1	<.1	0.00	0.00	0.01	—
35498	Sweet green peppers, freeze-dried	¼	cup(s)	2	<.1	5	<1	1	<1	<.1	0.01	0.00	0.03	—
11726	Tamarind leaves	1	ounce(s)	28	—	33	2	5	0	1	—	—	—	—
11727	Tarragon	1	ounce(s)	28	—	14	1	2	0	<1	—	—	—	—
1195	Tarragon, ground	2	teaspoon(s)	2	<1	5	<1	1	<1	<1	0.03	0.01	0.06	—
11728	Thyme, fresh	1	teaspoon(s)	1	1	1	<.1	<1	<1	<.1	0.00	0.00	0.00	—
821	Thyme, ground	1	teaspoon(s)	1	<1	4	<1	1	1	<1	0.04	0.01	0.02	—
1196	Turmeric, ground	1	teaspoon(s)	2	<1	8	<1	1	<1	<1	0.07	0.04	0.05	—
11995	Wasabi	1	tablespoon(s)	14	11	11	1	2	<1	<.1	—	—	—	—
1188	White pepper	1	teaspoon(s)	2	<1	7	<1	2	1	<.1	0.02	0.02	0.01	—
	Condiments													
674	Catsup or ketchup	1	tablespoon(s)	15	11	14	<1	4	<1	<.1	0.01	0.01	0.04	—
703	Dill pickle	1	ounce(s)	28	26	5	<1	1	<1	<.1	0.01	0.00	0.02	—
1641	Horseradish sauce, prepared	1	teaspoon(s)	5	3	10	<1	<1	<.1	1	0.59	0.28	0.04	—
140	Mayonnaise, low calorie	1	tablespoon(s)	16	10	37	<.1	3	0	3	0.53	0.72	1.70	—
138	Mayonnaise w/soybean oil	1	tablespoon(s)	14	2	99	<1	1	0	11	1.64	2.70	5.89	0.04
1682	Mustard, brown	1	teaspoon(s)	5	4	5	<1	<1	<.1	<1	—	—	—	—
700	Mustard, yellow	1	teaspoon(s)	5	4	3	<1	<1	<1	<1	0.01	0.11	0.03	—
706	Sweet pickle relish	1	tablespoon(s)	15	9	20	<.1	5	<1	<.1	0.01	0.03	0.02	—
141	Tartar sauce	2	tablespoon(s)	28	9	144	<1	4	<.1	14	2.14	4.13	7.57	—
	Sauces													
685	Barbecue sauce	2	tablespoon(s)	31	25	23	1	4	<1	1	0.08	0.24	0.21	—
834	Cheese sauce	¼	cup(s)	70	49	121	5	5	<1	9	4.19	2.67	1.81	—
32123	Chili enchilada sauce, green	2	tablespoon(s)	57	53	15	1	3	1	<1	0.04	0.04	0.13	0
32122	Chili enchilada sauce, red	2	tablespoon(s)	32	24	27	1	5	2	1	0.08	0.05	0.43	0
29688	Hoisin sauce	1	tablespoon(s)	16	7	35	1	7	<1	1	0.09	0.15	0.27	—
16670	Mole poblano sauce	½	cup(s)	133	103	155	5	11	2	11	2.67	5.15	2.91	—
29689	Oyster sauce	1	tablespoon(s)	16	13	8	<1	2	<.1	<.1	0.01	0.01	0.01	—
1655	Pepper sauce or tabasco	1	teaspoon(s)	5	5	1	<.1	<.1	<.1	<.1	0.01	0.00	0.02	—
347	Salsa	2	tablespoon(s)	16	14	4	<1	1	<1	<.1	0.00	0.00	0.02	—
841	Soy sauce	1	tablespoon(s)	18	13	10	1	2	0	<.1	0.00	0.00	0.01	—
839	Sweet & sour sauce	2	tablespoon(s)	39	30	37	<.1	9	<.1	<.1	0.00	0.00	0.00	—
1613	Teriyaki sauce	1	tablespoon(s)	18	12	15	1	3	<.1	0	0.00	0.00	0.00	0
25294	Tomato sauce	½	cup(s)	112	100	46	2	8	2	1	0.18	0.29	0.72	0
728	White sauce, medium	¼	cup(s)	63	47	92	2	6	<1	7	1.78	2.78	1.79	—
1654	Worcestershire sauce	1	teaspoon(s)	6	4	4	0	1	0	0	0.00	0.00	0.00	0
	Vinegar													
30853	Balsamic	1	tablespoon(s)	15	—	10	0	2	0	0	0.00	0.00	0.00	0
727	Cider	1	tablespoon(s)	15	14	2	0	1	0	0	0.00	0.00	0.00	0
1673	Distilled	1	tablespoon(s)	15	14	2	0	1	0	0	0.00	0.00	0.00	0
15439	Tarragon	1	tablespoon(s)	16	—	0	0	0	0	0	0.00	0.00	0.00	0
	MIXED FOODS, SOUPS, SANDWICHES													
	Mixed Dishes													
16652	Almond chicken	1	cup(s)	242	186	280	22	16	3	15	1.91	6.07	5.62	—
25224	Barbecued chicken	2	piece(s)	177	100	325	27	15	<1	17	4.63	6.78	3.71	0
25227	Bean burrito	1	item(s)	149	82	327	17	33	6	15	8.30	4.73	0.85	0
9516	Beef & vegetable fajita	1	item(s)	223	144	397	23	35	3	18	5.50	7.53	3.45	—
16796	Beef or pork egg roll	2	item(s)	128	85	227	10	19	1	12	2.88	5.96	2.64	—
177	Beef stew w/vegetables, prepared	1	cup(s)	245	201	220	16	15	3	11	4.40	4.50	0.50	—
30233	Beef stroganoff w/noodles	1	cup(s)	256	190	343	20	23	2	19	7.37	5.62	4.47	—
16651	Cashew chicken	1	cup(s)	242	131	644	43	17	3	46	7.75	20.83	14.47	—
475	Cheese pizza	2	slice(s)	126	60	281	15	41	0	6	3.08	1.98	0.98	—
30330	Cheese quesadilla	1	item(s)	54	19	183	6	18	1	10	3.49	3.42	2.16	—
215	Chicken & noodles, prepared	1	cup(s)	240	170	365	22	26	1	18	5.10	7.10	3.90	—
30239	Chicken & vegetables w/broccoli, onion, bamboo shoots in soy based sauce	1	cup(s)	162	112	287	22	6	1	19	5.13	7.65	4.68	—
25093	Chicken cacciatore	1	cup(s)	230	166	266	28	5	1	14	3.98	5.78	3.11	0
28020	Chicken fried turkey steak	3	ounce(s)	85	48	122	13	12	1	2	0.59	0.37	0.78	—
218	Chicken pot pie	1	cup(s)	252	154	542	23	42	3	31	9.79	12.52	7.03	—
30240	Chicken teriyaki	1	cup(s)	244	163	339	51	13	1	7	1.78	2.03	1.71	—
25119	Chicken waldorf salad	½	cup(s)	100	68	178	14	6	1	11	1.76	3.18	5.05	0
25099	Chili con carne	¾	cup(s)	215	175	197	14	21	7	7	2.55	2.83	0.54	0
1062	Coleslaw	¾	cup(s)	90	73	62	1	11	1	2	0.35	0.64	1.22	—
1896	Combination pizza, w/meat & vegetables	2	slice(s)	158	75	368	26	43	5	11	3.07	5.09	1.83	—

PAGE KEY: H–2 = Breads/Baked Goods   H–6 = Cereal/Rice/Pasta   H–10 = Fruit   H–14 = Vegetables/Legumes   H–24 = Nuts/Seeds   H–26 = Vegetarian
H–28 = Dairy   H–34 = Eggs   H–34 = Seafood   H–36 = Meats   H–40 = Poultry   H–40 = Processed meats   H–42 = Beverages   H–46 = Fats/Oils
H–48 = Sweets   H–50 = Spices/Condiments/Sauces   H–52 = Mixed foods/Soups/Sandwiches   H–58 = Fast food   H–74 = Convenience meals   H–76 = Baby foods

Chol (mg)	Calc (mg)	Iron (mg)	Magn (mg)	Pota (mg)	Sodi (mg)	Zinc (mg)	Vit A (µg)	Thia (mg)	Vit E (mg α)	Ribo (mg)	Niac (mg)	Vit B_6 (mg)	Fola (µg)	Vit C (mg)	Vit B_{12} (µg)	Sele (µg)
0	4	0.23	1	9	1	0.02	4	0.00	—	0.00	0.02	0.00	2	<1	0	—
0	2	0.17	3	51	3	0.04	3	0.02	0.06	0.02	0.12	0.04	4	30	0	<.1
0	85	1.48	20	—	—	—	—	0.07	—	0.03	1.16	—	—	1	0	—
0	48	—	14	128	3	0.17	—	0.04	—	—	—	—	—	1	0	—
0	18	0.52	6	48	1	0.06	3	0.00	0.10	0.02	0.14	0.04	4	1	0	<.1
0	3	0.14	1	5	<.1	0.01	2	0.00	—	0.00	0.01	0.00	<1	1	0	<.1
0	26	1.73	3	11	1	0.09	3	0.01	—	0.01	0.07	0.01	4	1	0	<.1
0	4	0.91	4	56	1	0.10	0	0.00	—	0.01	0.11	0.04	1	1	0	<.1
0	13	0.11	—	—	—	—	—	0.02	—	0.01	0.07	—	—	11	0	—
0	6	0.34	2	2	<1	0.03	0	0.00	0.10	0.00	0.01	0.00	<1	1	0	<.1
0	3	0.08	3	57	167	0.04	7	0.00	0.22	0.07	0.23	0.02	2	2	0	<.1
0	3	0.15	3	33	363	0.04	3	0.00	0.03	0.01	0.02	0.00	<1	1	0	0
2	5	0.00	1	7	15	0.01	—	0.00	0.03	0.01	0.00	0.00	1	<.1	<.1	—
4	<.1	0.00	<.1	2	80	0.02	0	0.00	0.32	0.00	0.00	0.00	0	0	0	—
5	2	0.07	<1	5	78	0.02	12	0.00	0.72	0.00	0.00	0.08	1	0	<.1	<1
0	6	0.09	1	7	68	0.02	0	0.00	0.09	0.00	0.01	0.00	<1	<.1	0	<.1
0	4	0.09	2	8	56	0.03	<1	0.00	0.01	0.00	0.02	0.00	<1	<1	0	2
0	<1	0.13	1	4	122	0.02	1	0.00	0.06	0.00	0.03	0.00	<1	<1	0	0
11	6	0.21	1	10	200	0.05	—	0.00	0.97	0.00	0.01	0.08	2	<1	<.1	—
0	6	0.28	6	54	255	0.06	<1	0.01	0.01	0.01	0.28	0.02	1	2	0	<1
20	128	0.15	6	21	578	0.68	56	0.00	—	0.08	0.02	0.01	3	<1	<.1	2
0	5	0.36	9	126	62	0.11	—	0.03	0.00	0.02	0.63	0.06	6	44	0	0
0	7	1.05	11	231	114	0.15	—	0.02	0.22	0.22	0.61	0.34	7	<1	0	<1
<1	5	0.16	4	19	258	0.05	0	0.00	0.04	0.03	0.19	0.01	4	<.1	0	<1
1	37	1.51	57	283	305	0.95	—	0.07	1.72	0.09	1.82	0.09	14	5	<.1	—
0	5	0.03	1	9	437	0.01	0	0.00	0.00	0.02	0.24	0.00	2	<.1	<.1	1
0	1	0.06	1	6	32	0.01	4	0.00	—	0.00	0.01	0.01	<.1	<1	0	—
0	5	0.16	2	34	69	0.04	5	0.01	0.19	0.01	0.13	0.02	3	2	0	<.1
0	3	0.36	6	32	1029	0.07	0	0.01	0.00	0.02	0.61	0.03	3	0	0	—
0	5	0.20	1	8	98	0.01	0	0.00	—	0.01	0.12	0.04	<1	0	0	—
0	5	0.31	11	41	690	0.02	0	0.01	0.00	0.01	0.23	0.02	4	0	0	<1
0	21	1.08	19	431	199	0.30	48	0.05	0.39	0.05	1.18	0.13	15	15	0	1
4	74	0.21	9	98	221	0.26	—	0.04	—	0.12	0.25	0.03	3	1	<1	—
0	6	0.30	1	45	56	0.01	—	0.00	0.00	0.01	0.04	0.00	0	1	0	—
0	0	0.00	—	—	0	—	0	—	—	—	—	—	—	—	0	—
0	1	0.09	3	15	<1	0.00	0	0.00	0.00	0.00	0.00	0.00	0	0	0	<.1
0	1	0.09	0	2	<1	0.00	0	0.00	0.00	0.00	0.00	0.00	0	0	0	5
0	0	0.00	—	0	0	—	0	—	—	—	—	—	—	—	0	0
40	69	1.97	60	549	526	1.62	—	0.09	4.11	0.20	9.48	0.44	26	7	<1	—
120	26	1.64	31	387	477	2.69	69	0.07	0.01	0.37	6.92	0.39	15	5	<1	19
38	331	2.95	45	384	514	1.92	119	0.24	0.01	0.29	1.82	0.15	115	4	<1	18
45	84	3.74	37	476	757	3.51	—	0.39	0.80	0.30	5.37	0.38	23	27	2	—
74	30	1.66	20	248	547	0.91	—	0.32	1.28	0.25	2.55	0.19	20	4	<1	—
71	29	2.90	—	613	292	—	—	0.15	0.51	0.17	4.70	—	—	17	<.1	15
74	70	3.26	37	393	818	3.66	—	0.21	1.25	0.31	3.80	0.21	17	1	2	—
96	74	2.92	94	640	1355	2.24	—	0.23	4.11	0.22	19.76	0.88	64	11	<1	—
19	233	1.16	32	219	672	1.63	147	0.37	—	0.33	4.96	0.09	69	3	1	27
13	132	1.21	13	77	230	0.64	—	0.13	0.43	0.14	1.09	0.04	6	15	<.1	—
103	26	2.20	—	149	600	—	—	0.05	—	0.17	4.30	—	—	0	—	29
84	22	1.38	29	344	962	1.70	—	0.08	1.12	0.17	7.90	0.32	13	8	<1	—
103	45	2.21	37	444	451	2.01	53	0.10	0.00	0.21	9.20	0.54	15	8	<1	22
27	69	1.34	19	197	139	1.08	5	0.15	0.00	0.18	3.46	0.22	21	<1	<1	16
69	64	3.38	38	393	651	1.93	607	0.40	1.06	0.40	7.24	0.24	31	11	<1	—
157	52	3.27	67	589	3209	3.75	—	0.15	0.59	0.37	16.69	0.89	23	6	1	—
42	20	0.78	24	197	246	1.13	21	0.04	0.62	0.10	4.05	0.25	15	2	<1	11
27	43	3.16	50	646	865	2.44	25	0.13	0.02	0.23	3.01	0.18	56	10	1	10
7	41	0.53	9	163	21	0.18	48	0.06	—	0.06	0.24	0.11	24	29	0	1
41	202	3.07	36	357	765	2.23	117	0.43	—	0.35	3.92	0.19	65	3	1	22

TABLE H–1
Food Composition

(DA+ code is for Wadsworth Diet Analysis program) (For purposes of calculations, use "0" for t, <1, <.1, <.01, etc.)

DA+ Code	Food Description	Quantity	Measure	Wt (g)	H₂O (g)	Ener (kcal)	Prot (g)	Carb (g)	Fiber (g)	Fat (g)	Sat	Mono	Poly	Trans
	MIXED FOODS, SOUPS, SANDWICHES—Continued													
1574	Crab cakes, from blue crab	1	item(s)	60	43	93	12	<1	0	5	0.89	1.69	1.36	—
32144	Enchiladas w/green chili sauce (enchiladas verdes)	1	item(s)	144	104	207	9	18	3	12	6.35	3.65	0.96	0
2793	Falafel patty	3	item(s)	51	18	170	7	16	0	9	1.22	5.19	2.12	—
28546	Fettuccine alfredo	1	cup(s)	222	81	247	11	42	1	3	1.61	0.79	0.43	0
32146	Flautas	3	item(s)	162	78	438	25	36	4	22	8.22	8.80	2.29	—
29629	Fried rice w/meat or poultry	1	cup(s)	198	129	329	12	41	1	12	2.27	3.53	5.69	—
16649	General tso chicken	1	cup(s)	146	91	293	19	16	1	17	3.98	6.27	5.27	—
1826	Green salad	¾	cup(s)	104	99	17	1	3	2	<.1	0.01	0.00	0.04	—
1814	Hummus	½	cup(s)	123	80	218	6	25	5	11	1.38	6.04	2.56	—
16650	Kung pao chicken	1	cup(s)	162	88	431	29	11	2	31	5.19	13.95	9.69	—
16622	Lamb curry	1	cup(s)	236	188	256	28	3	1	14	3.93	4.92	3.35	—
25253	Lasagna w/ground beef	1	cup(s)	237	157	288	18	22	2	15	7.47	4.84	0.84	0
442	Macaroni & cheese	1	cup(s)	200	122	393	15	40	1	19	8.18	6.72	2.66	—
25105	Meat loaf	1	slice(s)	115	85	244	17	7	<1	16	6.15	6.89	0.83	0
16646	Moo shi pork	1	cup(s)	151	77	512	19	5	1	46	6.84	14.80	22.07	—
16788	Nachos w/beef, beans, cheese, tomatoes, & onions	7	item(s)	551	284	1496	40	119	19	99	22.34	40.19	30.69	—
1668	Pepperoni pizza	2	slice(s)	142	66	362	20	40	1	14	4.47	6.28	2.33	—
655	Potato salad	½	cup(s)	125	95	179	3	14	2	10	1.79	3.10	4.67	—
29637	Ravioli, meat filled, w/tomato or meat sauce, canned	1	cup(s)	251	196	220	9	38	2	4	1.58	1.49	0.41	—
25109	Salisbury steaks w/mushroom sauce	1	serving(s)	135	102	251	17	9	1	15	5.98	6.67	0.76	0
16637	Shrimp creole w/rice	1	cup(s)	243	176	311	27	28	1	9	1.83	3.79	2.88	—
497	Spaghetti & meat balls w/tomato sauce, prepared	1	cup(s)	248	174	330	19	39	3	12	3.90	4.40	2.20	—
28585	Spicy thai noodles (pad thai)	8	ounce(s)	231	74	222	9	36	3	6	0.83	3.33	1.83	0
33073	Stir fried pork & vegetables w/rice	1	cup(s)	235	173	349	15	34	2	16	5.55	6.87	2.62	0
28588	Stuffed shells	2½	item(s)	299	189	292	18	33	3	10	3.81	3.57	1.62	0
16821	Sushi w/egg in seaweed	6	piece(s)	156	117	190	9	20	<1	8	2.09	3.02	1.55	—
16819	Sushi w/vegetables & fish	6	piece(s)	156	102	217	8	44	2	1	0.16	0.14	0.20	—
16820	Sushi w/vegetables in seaweed	6	piece(s)	156	110	182	3	41	1	<1	0.10	0.11	0.11	—
25266	Sweet & sour pork	¾	cup(s)	249	206	264	29	17	1	8	2.59	3.51	1.48	0
16824	Tabouli, tabbouleh, or tabuli	1	cup(s)	160	124	199	3	16	4	15	2.04	10.83	1.37	—
25276	Three bean salad	½	cup(s)	99	82	95	2	10	3	6	0.76	1.41	3.48	0
160	Tuna salad	½	cup(s)	103	65	192	16	10	0	9	1.58	2.96	4.23	0
25241	Turkey & noodles	1	cup(s)	319	228	271	24	21	1	9	2.39	3.48	2.27	0
16794	Vegetable egg roll	2	item(s)	128	90	202	5	20	2	12	2.46	5.71	2.65	—
16818	Vegetable sushi, no fish	6	piece(s)	156	99	225	5	50	2	<1	0.11	0.10	0.14	—
	Sandwiches													
1744	Bacon, lettuce & tomato w/mayonnaise	1	item(s)	164	97	349	11	34	2	19	4.54	7.22	6.07	—
30287	Bologna & cheese w/margarine	1	item(s)	111	46	350	13	28	1	20	8.55	8.40	2.28	—
30286	Bologna w/margarine	1	item(s)	83	34	256	7	26	1	13	4.08	6.31	2.07	—
16546	Cheese	1	item(s)	83	31	262	10	27	1	13	5.59	4.77	1.67	—
8789	Cheeseburger, large, plain	1	item(s)	185	72	609	30	47	0	33	14.84	12.74	2.44	—
8624	Cheeseburger, large, w/bacon, vegetables, & condiments	1	item(s)	195	85	608	32	37	2	37	16.24	14.49	2.71	—
1745	Club w/bacon, chicken, tomato, lettuce, & mayonnaise	1	item(s)	246	137	555	31	48	3	26	5.94	—	—	—
1908	Cold cut submarine w/cheese & vegetables	1	item(s)	228	132	456	22	51	2	19	6.81	8.23	2.28	—
30247	Corned beef	1	item(s)	130	75	268	19	25	2	10	3.75	3.96	0.80	—
25283	Egg salad	1	item(s)	126	72	278	10	29	1	13	2.96	3.97	4.79	—
16686	Fried egg	1	item(s)	96	50	226	10	26	1	9	2.29	3.51	1.64	—
16547	Grilled cheese	1	item(s)	83	27	292	10	27	1	16	6.22	6.29	2.54	—
16659	Gyro w/onion & tomato	1	item(s)	105	67	170	12	21	1	4	1.53	1.41	0.43	—
1906	Ham & cheese	1	item(s)	146	74	352	21	33	2	15	6.44	6.74	1.38	—
31890	Ham w/mayonnaise	1	item(s)	112	55	282	14	27	1	13	3.06	5.04	3.79	—
756	Hamburger, double patty, large, w/condiments & vegetables	1	item(s)	226	121	540	34	40	0	27	10.52	10.33	2.80	—
8793	Hamburger, large, plain	1	item(s)	137	58	426	23	32	2	23	8.38	9.88	2.14	—
8795	Hamburger, large, w/vegetables & condiments	1	item(s)	218	121	512	26	40	3	27	10.42	11.42	2.20	—
25134	Hot chicken salad	1	item(s)	98	49	239	16	23	1	9	2.83	2.61	2.76	0
1411	Hot dog w/bun, plain	1	item(s)	98	53	242	10	18	2	15	5.11	6.85	1.71	—
25133	Hot turkey salad	1	item(s)	98	50	221	16	23	1	7	2.23	1.76	2.28	0
30249	Pastrami	1	item(s)	134	71	331	14	27	2	18	6.18	8.74	1.02	—

PAGE KEY: H–2 = Breads/Baked Goods   H–6 = Cereal/Rice/Pasta   H–10 = Fruit   H–14 = Vegetables/Legumes   H–24 = Nuts/Seeds   H–26 = Vegetarian
H–28 = Dairy   H–34 = Eggs   H–34 = Seafood   H–36 = Meats   H–40 = Poultry   H–40 = Processed meats   H–42 = Beverages   H–46 = Fats/Oils
H–48 = Sweets   H–50 = Spices/Condiments/Sauces   H–52 = Mixed foods/Soups/Sandwiches   H–58 = Fast food   H–74 = Convenience meals   H–76 = Baby foods

Chol (mg)	Calc (mg)	Iron (mg)	Magn (mg)	Pota (mg)	Sodi (mg)	Zinc (mg)	Vit A (µg)	Thia (mg)	Vit E (mg α)	Ribo (mg)	Niac (mg)	Vit B$_6$ (mg)	Fola (µg)	Vit C (mg)	Vit B$_{12}$ (µg)	Sele (µg)
90	63	0.65	20	194	198	2.45	34	0.05	—	0.05	1.74	0.10	32	2	4	24
27	266	1.08	38	251	276	1.27	—	0.07	0.03	0.16	1.28	0.18	45	59	<1	6
0	28	1.74	42	298	150	0.77	1	0.07	—	0.08	0.53	0.06	47	1	0	1
9	153	1.88	32	123	386	1.48	51	0.35	0.00	0.34	2.60	0.06	103	1	<1	35
73	146	2.66	61	223	886	3.44	0	0.10	0.10	0.17	3.00	0.27	96	0	1	37
102	36	2.66	31	182	821	1.42	—	0.30	1.60	0.19	3.51	0.24	24	3	<1	—
65	27	1.49	24	250	906	1.40	—	0.10	1.62	0.19	6.28	0.28	17	12	<1	—
0	13	0.65	11	178	27	0.22	59	0.03	—	0.05	0.57	0.08	38	24	0	<1
0	60	1.93	36	213	298	1.34	0	0.11	0.92	0.06	0.49	0.49	73	10	0	3
64	49	1.96	63	428	907	1.50	—	0.15	4.32	0.15	13.23	0.59	43	8	<1	—
89	36	2.97	40	495	495	6.62	—	0.09	1.30	0.28	8.05	0.20	27	1	3	—
68	222	2.33	40	437	493	2.81	108	0.19	0.22	0.29	3.02	0.20	50	10	1	22
30	323	2.26	42	263	800	1.95	327	0.25	0.72	0.40	2.18	0.10	12	<1	<1	—
85	54	2.09	21	278	423	3.55	27	0.08	0.00	0.29	3.77	0.13	20	<1	2	17
172	30	1.45	26	330	1078	1.83	—	0.50	5.39	0.38	2.90	0.31	22	8	1	—
82	699	6.71	205	1067	1611	7.55	—	0.31	7.71	0.50	5.62	0.85	59	14	1	—
28	129	1.87	17	305	534	1.04	105	0.27	—	0.47	6.09	0.11	74	3	<1	26
85	24	0.81	19	318	661	0.39	40	0.10	—	0.08	1.11	0.18	9	13	0	5
17	28	2.04	23	337	1354	1.19	—	0.22	0.70	0.20	2.88	0.14	17	22	<1	—
60	64	2.21	23	282	370	3.66	27	0.11	0.00	0.30	4.00	0.13	22	<1	2	17
181	101	4.44	64	439	381	1.73	—	0.29	2.07	0.10	4.77	0.22	12	18	1	—
89	124	3.70	—	665	1009	—	82	0.25	—	0.30	4.00	—	—	22	—	22
37	32	1.58	50	187	598	1.08	38	0.18	0.36	0.13	1.88	0.17	44	22	<.1	3
46	39	2.65	32	394	574	2.07	80	0.51	0.38	0.20	5.07	0.30	102	18	<1	23
35	241	3.18	63	462	543	1.68	280	0.32	0.00	0.36	4.64	0.30	109	15	<1	36
217	42	1.63	18	128	527	0.98	—	0.12	0.67	0.29	1.33	0.13	29	2	<1	—
11	24	2.18	25	204	340	0.79	—	0.26	0.25	0.07	2.77	0.15	14	4	<1	—
0	20	1.54	20	99	153	0.70	—	0.20	0.12	0.04	1.86	0.14	10	2	0	—
74	41	1.78	35	622	624	2.53	64	0.80	0.20	0.37	6.69	0.65	14	10	1	50
0	29	1.25	36	246	799	0.48	—	0.08	2.43	0.05	1.14	0.11	31	29	0	—
0	26	0.96	15	144	224	0.31	12	0.04	0.89	0.06	0.26	0.06	31	9	0	3
13	17	1.03	19	182	412	0.57	25	0.03	0.00	0.07	6.87	0.08	8	2	1	42
77	60	2.69	33	379	576	2.64	108	0.23	0.29	0.32	6.40	0.30	60	1	1	34
60	29	1.61	18	193	548	0.51	—	0.16	1.28	0.21	1.59	0.10	27	6	<1	—
0	23	2.40	23	158	369	0.84	—	0.28	0.16	0.06	2.44	0.13	15	4	0	—
20	76	2.54	27	328	837	0.98	—	0.39	1.16	0.27	3.81	0.20	31	15	<1	—
35	221	2.18	24	185	940	1.68	—	0.30	0.56	0.33	2.77	0.12	21	<.1	1	—
16	60	1.96	15	112	598	0.85	—	0.29	0.50	0.21	2.73	0.08	19	<.1	<1	—
19	216	1.75	20	135	655	1.14	—	0.25	0.47	0.29	2.04	0.07	19	<.1	<1	—
96	91	5.46	39	644	1589	5.55	185	0.48	—	0.57	11.17	0.28	74	0	3	39
111	162	4.74	45	332	1043	6.83	82	0.31	—	0.41	6.63	0.31	86	2	2	33
72	116	4.05	47	463	855	1.65	—	0.61	1.53	0.44	11.92	0.59	48	9	1	—
36	189	2.51	68	394	1651	2.58	71	1.00	—	0.80	5.49	0.14	87	12	1	31
46	67	2.67	20	187	1177	2.24	—	0.24	0.21	0.25	3.23	0.10	22	2	1	—
217	107	2.60	18	147	494	0.94	94	0.26	0.13	0.43	2.27	0.16	82	1	1	24
207	80	2.25	17	120	433	0.85	—	0.27	0.66	0.41	2.06	0.10	34	0	<1	—
19	219	1.76	21	137	696	1.15	—	0.19	0.72	0.28	1.86	0.06	13	<.1	<1	—
34	46	1.85	21	209	272	2.30	—	0.24	0.26	0.21	3.14	0.13	18	4	1	—
58	130	3.24	16	291	771	1.37	96	0.31	0.29	0.48	2.69	0.20	76	3	1	23
36	59	2.10	23	245	1033	1.50	—	0.71	0.50	0.31	4.89	0.26	19	0	<1	—
122	102	5.85	50	570	791	5.67	5	0.36	—	0.38	7.57	0.54	77	1	4	26
71	74	3.58	27	267	474	4.11	0	0.29	—	0.29	6.25	0.23	60	0	2	27
87	96	4.93	44	480	824	4.88	24	0.41	—	0.37	7.28	0.33	83	3	2	34
39	114	1.93	20	150	470	1.22	28	0.20	0.28	0.23	4.93	0.20	54	<1	<1	17
44	24	2.31	13	143	670	1.98	0	0.24	—	0.27	3.65	0.05	48	<.1	1	26
37	113	2.04	22	167	459	1.09	23	0.19	0.29	0.21	4.36	0.23	54	<1	<1	20
51	68	2.64	23	243	1335	2.69	—	0.29	0.27	0.27	4.77	0.13	21	2	1	—

TABLE H–1
Food Composition

(DA+ code is for Wadsworth Diet Analysis program)   (For purposes of calculations, use "0" for t, <1, <.1, <.01, etc.)

DA + Code	Food Description	Quantity	Measure	Wt (g)	H₂O (g)	Ener (kcal)	Prot (g)	Carb (g)	Fiber (g)	Fat (g)	Sat	Mono	Poly	Trans
	MIXED FOODS, SOUPS, SANDWICHES—Continued													
16701	Peanut butter	1	item(s)	93	24	344	13	37	3	17	3.55	8.16	4.58	—
30306	Peanut butter & jelly	1	item(s)	93	24	330	11	42	3	15	3.00	6.87	3.82	—
1910	Roast beef, plain	1	item(s)	139	68	346	22	33	1	14	3.61	6.80	1.71	—
1909	Roast beef submarine w/mayonnaise & vegetables	1	item(s)	216	127	410	29	44	—	13	7.09	1.84	2.61	—
1907	Steak w/mayonnaise & vegetables	1	item(s)	204	104	459	30	52	2	14	3.81	5.34	3.35	—
25288	Tuna salad	1	item(s)	179	102	414	24	29	2	22	3.61	5.46	11.43	—
31891	Turkey w/mayonnaise	1	item(s)	143	75	330	29	26	1	11	2.61	3.25	4.40	—
30283	Turkey submarine w/cheese, lettuce, tomato, & mayonnaise	1	item(s)	277	156	583	37	51	3	25	7.15	8.03	7.81	—
	Soups													
25296	Bean	1	cup(s)	301	253	191	14	29	6	2	0.67	0.83	0.53	0
711	Bean with pork, condensed, prepared w/water	1	cup(s)	265	223	180	8	24	9	6	1.59	2.28	1.91	—
713	Beef noodle, condensed, prepared w/water	1	cup(s)	244	224	83	5	9	1	3	1.15	1.24	0.49	—
825	Cheese, condensed, prepared w/milk	1	cup(s)	251	207	231	9	16	1	15	9.11	4.09	0.45	—
826	Chicken broth, condensed, prepared w/water	1	cup(s)	244	234	39	5	1	0	1	0.39	0.59	0.27	—
25297	Chicken noodle	1	cup(s)	286	258	117	11	11	1	3	0.78	1.10	0.66	—
827	Chicken noodle, condensed, prepared w/water	1	cup(s)	241	222	75	4	9	1	2	0.65	1.11	0.55	—
724	Chicken noodle, dehydrated, prepared w/water	1	cup(s)	252	237	58	2	9	<1	1	0.31	0.52	0.39	—
823	Cream of asparagus, condensed, prepared w/milk	1	cup(s)	248	213	161	6	16	1	8	3.32	2.08	2.23	—
824	Cream of celery, condensed, prepared w/milk	1	cup(s)	248	214	164	6	15	1	10	3.94	2.46	2.65	—
708	Cream of chicken, condensed, prepared w/milk	1	cup(s)	248	210	191	7	15	<1	11	4.64	4.46	1.64	—
715	Cream of chicken, condensed, prepared w/water	1	cup(s)	244	221	117	3	9	<1	7	2.07	3.27	1.49	—
709	Cream of mushroom, condensed, prepared w/milk	1	cup(s)	248	210	203	6	15	<1	14	5.13	2.98	4.61	—
716	Cream of mushroom, condensed, prepared w/water	1	cup(s)	244	220	129	2	9	<1	9	2.44	1.71	4.22	—
25298	Cream of vegetable	1	cup(s)	285	251	165	7	15	2	9	1.56	4.62	1.92	—
16689	Egg drop	1	cup(s)	244	229	73	8	1	0	4	1.15	1.52	0.59	—
25138	Golden squash	1	cup(s)	258	224	144	8	21	2	4	0.84	2.18	0.88	0
16663	Hot & sour	1	cup(s)	244	210	161	15	5	1	8	2.72	3.40	1.20	—
28054	Lentil chowder	1	cup(s)	229	188	150	11	27	12	<1	0.09	0.08	0.22	0
28560	Macaroni & bean	1	cup(s)	229	129	136	6	21	5	3	0.48	2.06	0.59	0
714	Manhattan clam chowder, condensed, prepared w/water	1	cup(s)	244	224	78	2	12	1	2	0.38	0.38	1.29	—
28561	Minestrone	1	cup(s)	230	177	99	4	16	5	2	0.32	1.30	0.43	0
717	Minestrone, condensed, prepared w/water	1	cup(s)	241	220	82	4	11	1	3	0.55	0.70	1.11	—
28038	Mushroom & wild rice	1	cup(s)	230	188	81	4	12	2	<1	0.05	0.02	0.15	0
828	New England clam chowder, condensed, prepared w/milk	1	cup(s)	248	211	164	9	17	1	7	2.95	2.26	1.09	—
28036	New England style clam chowder	1	cup(s)	229	207	83	3	15	2	<1	0.08	0.03	0.05	0
28566	Old country pasta	1	cup(s)	228	164	135	6	20	3	3	1.17	1.60	0.63	0
725	Onion, dehydrated, prepared w/water	1	cup(s)	246	237	27	1	5	1	1	0.12	0.32	0.07	—
16667	Shrimp gumbo	1	cup(s)	244	206	171	10	19	3	7	1.34	3.02	2.05	—
28037	Southwestern corn chowder	1	cup(s)	229	202	102	5	18	2	<1	0.12	0.12	0.20	0
25140	Split pea	1	cup(s)	165	117	85	4	19	2	<1	0.07	0.03	0.18	0
718	Split pea with ham, condensed, prepared w/water	1	cup(s)	253	207	190	10	28	2	4	1.77	1.80	0.63	—
710	Tomato, condensed, prepared w/milk	1	cup(s)	248	210	161	6	22	3	6	2.90	1.61	1.12	—
719	Tomato, condensed, prepared w/water	1	cup(s)	244	220	85	2	17	<1	2	0.37	0.44	0.95	—
726	Tomato vegetable, dehydrated, prepared w/water	1	cup(s)	253	237	56	2	10	1	1	0.38	0.30	0.08	—
28595	Turkey noodle	1	cup(s)	228	203	106	8	14	2	2	0.27	1.06	0.67	0
28051	Turkey vegetable	1	cup(s)	227	203	98	11	8	2	1	0.32	0.17	0.30	0
720	Vegetable beef, condensed, prepared w/water	1	cup(s)	244	224	78	6	10	<1	2	0.85	0.81	0.12	—
28598	Vegetable gumbo	1	cup(s)	229	168	153	4	26	3	4	0.61	2.93	0.56	0
25141	Vegetable	1	cup(s)	252	225	96	5	20	4	—	0.06	0.04	0.16	0
721	Vegetarian vegetable, condensed, prepared w/water	1	cup(s)	241	223	72	2	12	—	2	0.29	0.82	0.72	—

PAGE KEY: H–2 = Breads/Baked Goods   H–6 = Cereal/Rice/Pasta   H–10 = Fruit   H–14 = Vegetables/Legumes   H–24 = Nuts/Seeds   H–26 = Vegetarian
H–28 = Dairy   H–34 = Eggs   H–34 = Seafood   H–36 = Meats   H–40 = Poultry   H–40 = Processed meats   H–42 = Beverages   H–46 = Fats/Oils
H–48 = Sweets   H–50 = Spices/Condiments/Sauces   H–52 = Mixed foods/Soups/Sandwiches   H–58 = Fast food   H–74 = Convenience meals   H–76 = Baby foods

Chol (mg)	Calc (mg)	Iron (mg)	Magn (mg)	Pota (mg)	Sodi (mg)	Zinc (mg)	Vit A (µg)	Thia (mg)	Vit E (mg α)	Ribo (mg)	Niac (mg)	Vit B_6 (mg)	Fola (µg)	Vit C (mg)	Vit B_{12} (µg)	Sele (µg)
1	80	2.47	62	272	479	1.25	0	0.33	2.39	0.25	6.46	0.17	43	0	<.1	—
1	68	2.11	53	239	409	1.06	—	0.27	2.02	0.21	5.45	0.15	37	<1	<.1	—
51	54	4.23	31	316	792	3.39	11	0.38	—	0.31	5.87	0.26	57	2	1	29
73	41	2.81	67	330	845	4.38	30	0.41	—	0.41	5.96	0.32	71	6	2	26
73	92	5.16	49	524	798	4.53	20	0.41	—	0.37	7.30	0.37	90	6	2	42
53	100	3.29	35	302	795	1.08	46	0.26	0.35	0.26	12.29	0.48	70	1	2	71
69	78	3.10	34	315	490	2.94	—	0.30	0.74	0.33	6.64	0.46	24	0	<1	—
70	324	3.88	51	552	2408	2.66	—	0.53	1.19	0.49	12.50	0.54	46	5	2	—
5	80	3.08	61	590	690	1.41	26	0.27	0.03	0.15	3.61	0.23	139	3	<1	8
3	85	2.15	48	421	996	1.09	48	0.09	0.80	0.03	0.59	0.04	34	2	<.1	8
5	15	1.10	5	100	952	1.54	7	0.07	0.68	0.06	1.07	0.04	20	<1	<1	7
48	289	0.80	20	341	1019	0.68	359	0.06	—	0.33	0.50	0.08	10	1	<1	7
0	10	0.51	2	210	776	0.24	0	0.01	0.05	0.07	3.35	0.02	5	0	<1	0
24	26	1.34	16	335	776	0.77	49	0.15	0.02	0.16	5.57	0.13	40	1	<1	10
7	17	0.77	5	55	1106	0.39	36	0.05	0.10	0.06	1.39	0.03	22	<1	<1	6
10	5	0.50	8	33	577	0.20	3	0.20	0.13	0.08	1.09	0.03	18	0	<.1	10
22	174	0.87	20	360	1042	0.92	62	0.10	—	0.28	0.88	0.06	30	4	<1	8
32	186	0.69	22	310	1009	0.20	114	0.07	—	0.25	0.44	0.06	7	1	<1	5
27	181	0.67	17	273	1047	0.67	179	0.07	—	0.26	0.92	0.07	7	1	1	8
10	34	0.61	2	88	986	0.63	163	0.03	—	0.06	0.82	0.02	2	<1	<.1	7
20	179	0.60	20	270	918	0.64	35	0.08	1.24	0.28	0.91	0.06	10	2	<1	4
2	46	0.51	5	100	881	0.59	15	0.05	0.95	0.09	0.72	0.01	5	1	<.1	1
1	68	1.38	17	312	784	0.74	100	0.12	1.06	0.20	3.27	0.12	37	10	<1	5
103	21	0.75	5	220	729	0.48	—	0.02	0.29	0.19	3.03	0.05	15	0	<1	—
4	203	1.63	39	412	500	1.72	454	0.17	0.53	0.38	1.15	0.15	32	10	1	8
34	29	1.89	29	382	1561	1.51	—	0.27	0.12	0.25	4.97	0.20	13	1	<1	—
<1	47	4.07	55	590	26	1.44	163	0.21	0.06	0.12	1.69	0.30	164	13	0	3
<1	64	1.86	32	254	489	0.46	174	0.15	0.35	0.13	1.36	0.09	59	7	0	9
2	27	1.63	12	188	578	0.98	56	0.03	0.34	0.04	0.82	0.10	10	4	4	9
0	68	1.76	31	273	423	0.38	138	0.10	0.23	0.10	0.69	0.07	47	12	0	4
2	34	0.92	7	313	911	0.75	118	0.05	—	0.04	0.94	0.10	36	1	0	8
0	27	1.08	26	332	267	0.87	4	0.06	0.07	0.21	2.97	0.14	18	4	<.1	4
22	186	1.49	22	300	992	0.79	57	0.07	0.45	0.24	1.03	0.13	10	3	10	13
2	69	1.29	26	430	236	0.66	34	0.07	0.02	0.12	1.02	0.20	17	12	3	4
6	51	2.32	47	434	319	0.69	114	0.20	0.01	0.15	2.42	0.23	65	17	<.1	9
0	12	0.15	5	64	849	0.05	0	0.03	0.00	0.06	0.48	0.00	2	<1	0	2
51	99	2.34	51	515	515	0.93	—	0.19	1.90	0.10	2.54	0.19	59	26	<1	—
1	65	1.10	24	374	200	0.73	46	0.08	0.09	0.14	1.65	0.22	27	37	<1	2
0	30	1.25	33	352	608	0.57	112	0.12	0.00	0.09	1.67	0.21	61	9	0	<1
8	23	2.28	48	400	1007	1.32	23	0.15	—	0.08	1.47	0.07	3	2	<1	8
17	159	1.81	22	449	744	0.30	64	0.13	1.24	0.25	1.52	0.16	17	68	<1	2
0	12	1.76	7	264	695	0.24	29	0.09	2.32	0.05	1.42	0.11	15	66	0	<1
0	8	0.63	20	104	1146	0.18	10	0.06	0.35	0.05	0.79	0.05	10	6	0	5
24	27	1.40	22	200	372	0.67	81	0.20	0.02	0.11	2.68	0.15	45	5	<1	13
20	36	1.30	22	383	328	0.90	110	0.08	0.01	0.09	3.33	0.27	21	10	<1	9
5	17	1.12	5	173	791	1.54	95	0.04	0.37	0.05	1.03	0.08	10	2	<1	4
0	52	1.90	35	313	471	0.56	15	0.17	0.58	0.07	1.59	0.16	51	18	0	4
0	41	2.45	38	688	674	0.78	118	0.12	0.00	0.13	2.37	0.27	33	23	0	5
0	22	1.08	7	210	822	0.46	116	0.05	—	0.05	0.92	0.06	10	1	0	4

TABLE H–1
Food Composition

(DA+ code is for Wadsworth Diet Analysis program)   (For purposes of calculations, use "0" for t, <1, <.1, <.01, etc.)

DA + Code	Food Description	Quantity	Measure	Wt (g)	H₂O (g)	Ener (kcal)	Prot (g)	Carb (g)	Fiber (g)	Fat (g)	Sat	Mono	Poly	Trans
	FAST FOOD													
	Arby's													
36094	Au jus sauce	1	serving(s)	85	—	5	<1	1	<.1	<.1	0.02	—	—	—
751	Beef 'n cheddar sandwich	1	item(s)	198	—	480	23	43	2	24	8.00	—	—	—
9279	Cheddar curly fries	1	serving(s)	170	—	460	6	54	4	24	6.00	—	—	—
36131	Chocolate shake	1	serving(s)	397	—	480	10	84	0	16	8.00	—	—	—
36045	Curly fries, large	1	serving(s)	198	—	620	8	78	7	30	7.00	—	—	—
36044	Curly fries, medium	1	serving(s)	128	—	400	5	50	4	20	5.00	—	—	—
9265	Fish fillet sandwich	1	item(s)	220	—	529	23	50	2	27	7.00	9.20	10.60	—
752	Ham 'n cheese sandwich	1	item(s)	170	—	340	23	35	1	13	4.50	—	—	—
36048	Homestyle fries, large	1	serving(s)	213	—	560	6	79	6	24	6.00	—	—	—
36047	Homestyle fries, medium	1	serving(s)	142	—	370	4	53	4	16	4.00	—	—	—
33465	Homestyle fries, small	1	serving(s)	113	—	300	3	42	3	13	3.50	—	—	—
9267	Italian sub sandwich	1	item(s)	312	—	780	29	49	3	53	15.00	—	—	—
36041	Market Fresh grilled chicken caesar salad w/o dressing	1	serving(s)	338	—	230	33	8	3	8	3.50	—	—	—
9291	Roast beef deluxe sandwich, light	1	item(s)	182	—	296	18	33	6	10	3.00	5.00	2.00	—
9251	Roast beef sandwich, giant	1	item(s)	228	—	480	32	41	3	23	10.00	—	—	—
9249	Roast beef sandwich, junior	1	item(s)	129	—	310	16	34	2	13	4.50	—	—	—
750	Roast beef sandwich, regular	1	item(s)	157	—	350	21	34	2	16	6.00	—	—	—
2009	Roast beef sandwich, super	1	item(s)	245	—	470	22	47	3	23	7.00	—	—	—
9269	Roast beef sub sandwich	1	item(s)	334	—	760	35	47	3	48	16.00	—	—	—
9295	Roast chicken deluxe sandwich, light	1	item(s)	194	—	260	23	33	3	5	1.00	—	—	—
9293	Roast turkey deluxe sandwich, light	1	item(s)	194	—	260	23	33	3	5	0.50	—	—	—
36132	Strawberry shake	1	serving(s)	397	—	500	11	87	0	13	8.00	—	—	—
9273	Turkey sub sandwich	1	item(s)	306	—	630	26	51	2	37	9.00	—	—	—
36130	Vanilla shake	1	serving(s)	397	—	470	10	83	0	15	7.00	—	—	—
	Auntie Anne's													
35371	Cheese dipping sauce	1	serving(s)	35	—	100	3	4	0	8	4.00	—	—	—
35353	Cinnamon sugar soft pretzel	1	item(s)	120	—	350	9	74	2	2	0.00	—	—	—
35354	Cinnamon sugar soft pretzel w/butter	1	item(s)	120	—	450	8	83	3	9	5.00	—	—	—
35372	Marinara dipping sauce	1	serving(s)	35	—	10	0	4	0	0	0.00	0.00	0.00	0
35357	Original soft pretzel	1	item(s)	120	—	340	10	72	3	1	0.00	—	—	—
35358	Original soft pretzel w/butter	1	item(s)	120	—	370	10	72	3	4	2.00	—	—	—
35359	Parmesan herb soft pretzel	1	item(s)	120	—	390	11	74	4	5	2.50	—	—	—
35360	Parmesan herb soft pretzel w/butter	1	item(s)	120	—	440	10	72	9	13	7.00	—	—	—
35361	Sesame soft pretzel	1	item(s)	120	—	350	11	63	3	6	1.00	—	—	—
35362	Sesame soft pretzel w/butter	1	item(s)	120	—	410	12	64	7	12	4.00	—	—	—
35364	Sour cream & onion soft pretzel	1	item(s)	120	—	310	9	66	2	1	0.00	—	—	—
35366	Sour cream & onion soft pretzel w/butter	1	item(s)	120	—	340	9	66	2	5	3.00	—	—	—
35373	Sweet mustard dipping sauce	1	serving(s)	35	—	60	1	8	0	2	1.00	—	—	—
35367	Whole wheat soft pretzel	1	item(s)	120	—	350	11	72	7	2	0.00	—	—	—
35368	Whole wheat soft pretzel w/butter	1	item(s)	120	—	370	11	72	7	5	1.50	—	—	—
	Boston Market													
34975	Bbq baked beans	¾	cup(s)	201	—	270	8	48	12	5	2.00	—	—	—
34976	Black beans & rice	1	cup(s)	227	—	300	8	45	5	10	1.50	—	—	—
34978	Butternut squash	¾	cup(s)	193	—	150	2	25	6	6	4.00	—	—	—
35006	Caesar side salad	1	serving(s)	119	—	300	5	13	1	26	4.50	—	—	—
34979	Chicken gravy	1	ounce(s)	28	—	15	0	2	0	1	0.00	—	—	—
34973	Chicken pot pie	1	item(s)	425	—	750	26	57	2	46	14.00	—	—	—
35007	Cole slaw	¾	cup(s)	184	—	300	2	30	3	19	3.00	—	—	—
35057	Cornbread	1	item(s)	68	—	200	3	33	1	6	1.50	—	—	—
35008	Cranberry walnut relish	¾	cup(s)	210	—	350	3	75	3	5	0.00	—	—	—
34980	Creamed spinach	¾	cup(s)	181	—	260	9	11	2	20	13.00	—	—	—
34981	Glazed carrots	¾	cup(s)	153	—	280	1	35	4	15	3.00	—	—	—
34983	Green bean casserole	¾	cup(s)	170	—	80	1	9	2	5	1.50	—	—	—
34982	Green beans	¾	cup(s)	85	—	70	1	6	2	4	0.50	—	—	—
34967	Half chicken, w/skin	1	item(s)	277	—	590	70	4	0	33	10.00	—	—	—
34984	Homestyle mashed potatoes	¾	cup(s)	173	—	210	4	30	2	9	5.00	—	—	—
34985	Homestyle mashed potatoes & gravy	1	cup(s)	201	—	230	4	32	3	9	5.00	—	—	—
34969	Honey glazed ham	5	ounce(s)	142	—	210	24	10	0	8	3.00	—	—	—
34988	Hot cinnamon apples	¾	cup(s)	181	—	250	0	56	3	5	0.50	—	—	—
34989	Macaroni & cheese	¾	cup(s)	192	—	280	13	33	1	11	6.00	—	—	—
34970	Meatloaf	5	ounce(s)	142	—	282	20	15	1	17	7.28	—	—	—
35012	Old-fashioned potato salad	¾	cup(s)	150	—	200	3	22	2	12	2.00	—	—	—

PAGE KEY: H–2 = Breads/Baked Goods   H–6 = Cereal/Rice/Pasta   H–10 = Fruit   H–14 = Vegetables/Legumes   H–24 = Nuts/Seeds   H–26 = Vegetarian
H–28 = Dairy   H–34 = Eggs   H–34 = Seafood   H–36 = Meats   H–40 = Poultry   H–40 = Processed meats   H–42 = Beverages   H–46 = Fats/Oils
H–48 = Sweets   H–50 = Spices/Condiments/Sauces   H–52 = Mixed foods/Soups/Sandwiches   H–58 = Fast food   H–74 = Convenience meals   H–76 = Baby foods

Chol (mg)	Calc (mg)	Iron (mg)	Magn (mg)	Pota (mg)	Sodi (mg)	Zinc (mg)	Vit A (µg)	Thia (mg)	Vit E (mg α)	Ribo (mg)	Niac (mg)	Vit B$_6$ (mg)	Fola (µg)	Vit C (mg)	Vit B$_{12}$ (µg)	Sele (µg)
0	0	0.00	—	—	386	—	0	—	—	—	—	—	—	0	—	—
90	100	3.60	—	—	1240	—	0	—	—	—	—	—	—	1	—	—
5	60	1.80	—	—	1290	—	0	—	—	—	—	—	—	15	—	—
45	500	0.72	—	—	370	—	38	—	—	—	—	—	—	2	—	—
0	0	2.70	—	—	1540	—	0	—	—	—	—	—	—	21	—	—
0	0	1.80	—	—	990	—	0	—	—	—	—	—	—	15	—	—
43	90	3.78	—	450	864	—	10	0.35	—	0.31	5.60	—	—	1	—	—
90	150	2.70	—	—	1450	—	20	—	—	—	—	—	—	1	—	—
0	0	1.80	—	—	1070	—	0	—	—	—	—	—	—	30	—	—
0	0	1.08	—	—	710	—	0	—	—	—	—	—	—	21	—	—
0	0	0.72	—	—	570	—	0	—	—	—	—	—	—	15	—	—
120	250	2.70	—	—	2440	—	—	—	—	—	—	—	—	2	—	—
80	200	1.80	—	—	920	—	—	—	—	—	—	—	—	42	—	—
42	130	4.50	—	392	826	—	40	0.27	—	0.49	8.40	—	—	8	—	—
110	60	5.40	—	—	1440	—	0	—	—	—	—	—	—	0	—	—
70	60	2.70	—	—	740	—	0	—	—	—	—	—	—	0	—	—
85	60	3.60	—	—	950	—	0	—	—	—	—	—	—	0	—	—
85	80	3.60	—	—	1130	—	40	—	—	—	—	—	—	1	—	—
130	300	4.50	—	—	2230	—	40	—	—	—	—	—	—	4	—	—
40	100	2.70	—	—	1010	—	—	—	—	—	—	—	—	2	—	—
40	80	1.80	—	—	980	—	—	—	—	—	—	—	—	1	—	—
15	350	0.36	—	—	340	—	36	—	—	—	—	—	—	1	—	—
100	200	0.36	—	—	2170	—	—	—	—	—	—	—	—	2	—	—
45	500	1.08	—	—	360	—	39	—	—	—	—	—	—	2	—	—
10	100	0.00	—	—	510	—	—	—	—	—	—	—	—	0	—	—
0	20	1.98	—	—	410	—	0	—	—	—	—	—	—	0	—	—
25	30	2.34	—	—	430	—	—	—	—	—	—	—	—	0	—	—
0	0	0.00	—	—	180	—	0	—	—	—	—	—	—	0	—	—
0	30	2.34	—	—	900	—	0	—	—	—	—	—	—	0	—	—
10	30	2.16	—	—	930	—	—	—	—	—	—	—	—	0	—	—
10	80	1.80	—	—	780	—	—	—	—	—	—	—	—	1	—	—
30	60	1.80	—	—	660	—	—	—	—	—	—	—	—	1	—	—
0	20	2.88	—	—	840	—	0	—	—	—	—	—	—	0	—	—
15	20	2.70	—	—	860	—	—	—	—	—	—	—	—	0	—	—
0	30	1.98	—	—	920	—	—	—	—	—	—	—	—	0	—	—
10	40	2.16	—	—	930	—	—	—	—	—	—	—	—	0	—	—
40	0	0.00	—	—	120	—	0	—	—	—	—	—	—	0	—	—
0	30	1.98	—	—	1100	—	0	—	—	—	—	—	—	0	—	—
10	30	2.34	—	—	1120	—	—	—	—	—	—	—	—	0	—	—
0	100	3.60	—	—	540	—	42	—	—	—	—	—	—	6	—	—
0	40	1.80	—	—	1050	—	0	—	—	—	—	—	—	4	—	—
20	80	1.08	—	—	560	—	1150	—	—	—	—	—	—	30	—	—
15	100	0.72	—	—	690	—	—	—	—	—	—	—	—	9	—	—
0	0	0.00	—	—	180	—	0	—	—	—	—	—	—	0	—	—
110	40	4.50	—	—	1530	—	—	—	—	—	—	—	—	1	—	—
20	60	0.72	—	—	540	—	108	—	—	—	—	—	—	36	—	—
25	0	1.08	—	—	390	—	0	—	—	—	—	—	—	0	—	—
0	0	5.40	—	—	0	—	0	—	—	—	—	—	—	0	—	—
55	250	2.70	—	—	740	—	—	—	—	—	—	—	—	9	—	—
0	40	1.08	—	—	80	—	1000	—	—	—	—	—	—	1	—	—
5	20	0.72	—	—	670	—	—	—	—	—	—	—	—	2	—	—
0	40	0.36	—	—	250	—	30	—	—	—	—	—	—	5	—	—
290	0	2.70	—	—	1010	—	0	—	—	—	—	—	—	0	—	—
25	40	0.36	—	—	590	—	53	—	—	—	—	—	—	15	—	—
25	60	0.36	—	—	780	—	—	—	—	—	—	—	—	15	—	—
75	0	1.08	—	—	1460	—	0	—	—	—	—	—	—	0	—	—
0	20	0.36	—	—	45	—	—	—	—	—	—	—	—	0	—	—
30	300	1.44	—	—	890	—	—	—	—	—	—	—	—	0	—	—
68	91	2.46	—	—	592	—	—	—	—	—	—	—	—	1	—	—
15	60	1.08	—	—	450	—	0	—	—	—	—	—	—	6	—	—

H Appendix

TABLE H–1

Food Composition

(DA+ code is for Wadsworth Diet Analysis program)   (For purposes of calculations, use "0" for t, <1, <.1, <.01, etc.)

DA + Code	Food Description	Quantity	Measure	Wt (g)	H₂O (g)	Ener (kcal)	Prot (g)	Carb (g)	Fiber (g)	Fat (g)	Sat	Mono	Poly	Trans
	FAST FOOD—Continued													
34965	Quarter chicken, dark meat, no skin	1	item(s)	95	—	190	22	1	0	10	3.00	—	—	—
34966	Quarter chicken, dark meat, w/skin	1	item(s)	125	—	320	30	2	0	21	6.00	—	—	—
34963	Quarter chicken, white meat, no skin or wing	1	item(s)	140	—	170	33	2	0	4	1.00	—	—	—
34964	Quarter chicken, white meat, w/skin & wing	1	item(s)	152	—	280	40	2	0	12	3.50	—	—	—
34993	Rice pilaf	1	cup(s)	137	—	140	2	24	1	4	0.50	—	—	—
34968	Rotisserie turkey breast, skinless	5	ounce(s)	142	—	170	36	3	0	1	0.00	—	—	—
34998	Savory stuffing	1	cup(s)	132	—	190	4	27	2	8	1.50	—	—	—
34999	Squash casserole	¾	cup(s)	187	—	330	7	20	3	24	13.00	—	—	—
35003	Steamed vegetables	1	cup(s)	102	—	30	2	6	2	0	0.00	—	—	0
35004	Sweet potato casserole	¾	cup(s)	181	—	280	3	39	2	13	4.50	—	—	—
35005	Whole kernel corn	¾	cup(s)	146	—	180	5	30	2	4	0.50	—	—	—
	Burger King													
29731	Biscuit with sausage, egg, & cheese	1	item(s)	189	—	650	20	38	1	46	14.00	—	—	1
3739	BK Broiler chicken sandwich	1	item(s)	258	—	550	30	52	3	25	5.00	—	—	—
14249	Cheeseburger	1	item(s)	133	—	360	19	31	2	17	8.00	—	—	0.50
14251	Chicken sandwich	1	item(s)	224	—	660	25	53	3	39	8.00	—	—	2.20
3808	Chicken Tenders, 8 pieces	1	serving(s)	123	—	340	22	20	1	19	5.00	—	—	3.50
14259	Chocolate shake, small	1	item(s)	333	—	620	12	72	2	32	21.00	—	—	0
29732	Croissanwich w/sausage & cheese	1	item(s)	107	—	420	14	23	1	31	11.00	—	—	2
14261	Croissanwich w/sausage, egg, & cheese	1	item(s)	157	—	520	19	24	1	39	14.00	—	—	1.93
3809	Double cheeseburger	1	item(s)	189	—	540	32	32	2	31	15.00	—	—	1.50
14244	Double Whopper	1	item(s)	374	—	980	52	52	4	62	22.00	—	—	2
14245	Double Whopper w/cheese	1	item(s)	399	—	1070	57	53	4	70	27.00	—	—	2.50
14250	Fish Fillet sandwich	1	item(s)	185	—	520	18	44	2	30	8.00	—	—	1.12
14255	French fries, medium, salted	1	item(s)	117	—	360	4	46	4	18	5.00	—	—	4.50
14262	French toast sticks	1	serving(s)	112	—	390	6	46	2	20	4.50	—	—	4.50
14248	Hamburger	1	item(s)	121	—	310	17	31	2	13	5.00	—	—	0.50
14263	Hash brown rounds, small	1	serving(s)	75	—	230	2	23	2	15	4.00	—	—	5.0
14256	Onion rings, medium	1	serving(s)	91	—	320	4	40	3	16	4.00	—	—	3.50
39000	Tendercrisp chicken sandwich	1	item(s)	310	—	810	28	72	6	47	8.00	—	—	4.28
14258	Vanilla shake, small	1	item(s)	305	—	560	11	56	1	32	21.00	—	—	0
1736	Whopper	1	item(s)	291	—	710	31	52	4	43	13.00	—	—	1
14243	Whopper w/cheese	1	item(s)	316	—	800	36	53	4	50	18.00	—	—	2
	Carl's Jr													
10801	Carl's Catch fish sandwich	1	item(s)	201	—	530	18	55	2	28	7.00	—	1.89	—
10862	Carl's Famous Star hamburger	1	item(s)	254	—	590	24	50	3	32	9.00	—	—	—
10866	Charboiled chicken salad-to-go	1	item(s)	350	—	200	25	12	4	7	3.00	—	1.02	—
10855	Charboiled Sante Fe chicken sandwich	1	item(s)	220	—	540	28	37	2	31	8.00	—	—	—
10790	Chicken stars (6 pieces)	6	item(s)	90	—	260	13	14	1	16	4.50	—	1.71	—
34864	Chocolate shake, small	1	item(s)	595	—	530	14	96	0	10	7.00	—	—	—
10797	Crisscut fries	1	serving(s)	139	—	410	5	43	4	24	5.00	—	—	—
10799	Double western bacon cheeseburger	1	item(s)	308	—	920	51	65	3	50	21.00	—	6.55	—
34855	Famous bacon cheeseburger	1	item(s)	279	—	700	31	51	3	41	13.00	—	—	—
14238	French fries, small	1	serving(s)	92	—	290	5	37	3	14	3.00	—	—	—
10798	French toast dips w/o syrup	1	serving(s)	105	—	370	6	42	1	20	2.50	—	1.35	—
34856	Hamburger	1	item(s)	119	—	280	14	36	1	9	3.50	—	—	—
10802	Onion rings	1	serving(s)	127	—	430	7	53	3	22	5.00	—	0.84	—
38925	Six Dollar burger	1	item(s)	539	—	1000	39	72	6	82	25.00	—	—	—
34858	Spicy chicken sandwich	1	item(s)	198	—	480	14	47	2	26	5.00	—	—	—
34867	Strawberry shake, small	1	item(s)	595	—	510	14	91	0	10	7.00	—	—	—
10865	Super Star hamburger	1	item(s)	345	—	790	41	51	3	47	15.00	—	—	—
10818	Vanilla shake, small	1	item(s)	595	—	470	15	78	0	11	7.00	—	—	—
10770	Western bacon cheeseburger	1	item(s)	225	—	660	31	64	3	30	12.00	—	4.85	—
	Chick Fil-A													
38746	Biscuit w/bacon, egg, & cheese	1	item(s)	155	—	430	16	38	1	24	9.00	—	—	2.85
38747	Biscuit w/egg	1	item(s)	135	—	340	11	38	1	16	4.50	—	—	3
38748	Biscuit w/egg & cheese	1	item(s)	148	—	390	13	38	1	21	7.00	—	—	2.98
38753	Biscuit w/gravy	1	item(s)	191	—	310	5	44	1	13	3.50	—	—	3.98
38752	Biscuit w/sausage, egg, & cheese	1	item(s)	189	—	540	18	43	1	33	13.00	—	—	2.67
38741	Biscuit, plain	1	item(s)	78	—	260	4	38	1	11	2.50	—	—	2.97
38771	Carrot & raisin salad	1	item(s)	91	—	130	1	22	2	5	1.00	—	—	0
38761	Chargrilled chicken cool wrap	1	item(s)	245	—	380	29	54	3	6	3.00	—	—	0
38766	Chargrilled chicken garden salad	1	item(s)	275	—	180	22	9	3	6	3.00	—	—	0
38758	Chargrilled chicken sandwich	1	item(s)	157	—	280	26	30	1	7	1.50	—	—	0

Appendix H

PAGE KEY: H–2 = Breads/Baked Goods   H–6 = Cereal/Rice/Pasta   H–10 = Fruit   H–14 = Vegetables/Legumes   H–24 = Nuts/Seeds   H–26 = Vegetarian
H–28 = Dairy   H–34 = Eggs   H–34 = Seafood   H–36 = Meats   H–40 = Poultry   H–40 = Processed meats   H–42 = Beverages   H–46 = Fats/Oils
H–48 = Sweets   H–50 = Spices/Condiments/Sauces   H–52 = Mixed foods/Soups/Sandwiches   H–58 = Fast food   H–74 = Convenience meals   H–76 = Baby foods

Chol (mg)	Calc (mg)	Iron (mg)	Magn (mg)	Pota (mg)	Sodi (mg)	Zinc (mg)	Vit A (µg)	Thia (mg)	Vit E (mg α)	Ribo (mg)	Niac (mg)	Vit B6 (mg)	Fola (µg)	Vit C (mg)	Vit B12 (µg)	Sele (µg)
115	0	1.08	—	—	440	—	0	—	—	—	—	—	—	0	—	—
155	0	1.80	—	—	500	—	0	—	—	—	—	—	—	0	—	—
85	0	0.72	—	—	480	—	0	—	—	—	—	—	—	0	—	—
135	0	1.08	—	—	510	—	0	—	—	—	—	—	—	0	—	—
0	20	1.08	—	—	520	—	—	—	—	—	—	—	—	4	—	—
100	20	1.80	—	—	850	—	0	—	—	—	—	—	—	2	—	—
5	40	1.44	—	—	620	—	—	—	—	—	—	—	—	2	—	—
70	200	0.72	—	—	1110	—	—	—	—	—	—	—	—	5	—	—
0	40	0.35	—	—	135	—	389	—	—	—	—	—	—	18	—	—
10	40	1.08	—	—	190	—	—	—	—	—	—	—	—	9	—	—
0	0	0.36	—	—	170	—	20	—	—	—	—	—	—	5	—	—
190	150	2.70	—	—	1600	—	90	—	—	—	—	—	—	0	—	—
105	60	3.60	—	—	1110	—	—	0.46	—	0.23	10.50	—	—	6	—	—
50	150	3.60	—	—	790	—	63	0.25	—	0.32	4.18	—	—	1	—	—
70	80	2.70	—	—	1330	—	—	0.47	—	0.30	9.59	—	—	0	—	—
50	20	0.72	—	—	840	—	—	0.14	—	0.12	10.93	—	—	0	—	—
95	350	1.08	—	—	310	—	42	0.11	—	0.56	0.24	—	—	0	—	—
45	100	3.60	—	—	840	—	—	—	—	—	—	—	—	0	—	—
210	300	4.50	—	—	1090	—	140	0.36	—	0.42	4.35	—	—	0	—	—
100	250	4.50	—	—	1050	—	100	0.26	—	0.45	6.37	—	—	1	—	—
160	150	9.00	—	—	1070	—	—	0.40	—	0.60	11.08	—	—	9	—	—
185	300	9.00	—	—	1500	—	—	0.40	—	0.67	11.07	—	—	9	—	—
55	150	2.70	—	—	840	—	14	—	—	—	—	—	—	1	—	—
0	20	0.72	—	—	640	—	0	0.16	—	0.48	2.32	—	—	9	—	—
0	60	1.80	—	—	440	—	0	0.19	—	0.22	2.86	—	—	0	—	—
40	76	3.60	—	—	580	—	9	0.25	—	0.29	4.26	—	—	1	—	—
0	0	0.36	—	—	450	—	0	0.11	—	0.07	2.11	—	—	1	—	—
0	97	0.00	—	—	460	—	0	0.14	—	0.09	2.33	—	—	0	—	—
60	80	4.50	—	—	1800	—	—	—	—	—	—	—	—	9	—	—
95	300	0.36	—	—	220	—	39	0.11	—	0.64	0.22	—	—	0	—	—
85	150	6.30	—	—	980	—	52	0.39	—	0.44	7.33	—	—	9	—	—
110	250	6.30	—	—	1420	—	157	0.39	—	0.51	7.31	—	—	9	—	—
80	150	1.80	—	—	1030	—	60	—	—	—	—	—	—	2	—	—
70	100	4.50	—	—	910	—	—	—	—	—	—	—	—	6	—	—
75	150	1.80	—	—	440	—	—	—	—	—	—	—	—	5	—	—
95	200	2.70	—	—	1210	—	—	—	—	—	—	—	—	6	—	—
40	20	1.08	—	—	480	—	0	—	—	—	—	—	—	0	—	—
45	600	1.08	—	—	350	—	0	—	—	—	—	—	—	0	—	—
0	20	1.80	—	—	950	—	0	—	—	—	—	—	—	12	—	—
155	300	7.20	—	—	1770	—	—	—	—	—	—	—	—	1	—	—
95	200	5.40	—	—	1310	—	102	—	—	—	—	—	—	6	—	—
0	0	1.08	—	—	180	—	0	—	—	—	—	—	—	21	—	—
0	40	1.08	—	—	430	—	0	0.26	—	0.24	2.00	—	—	0	—	—
35	80	2.70	—	—	480	—	0	—	—	—	—	—	—	1	—	—
0	20	0.72	—	—	700	—	0	—	—	—	—	—	—	4	—	—
135	350	5.40	—	—	1690	—	—	—	—	—	—	—	—	21	—	—
40	100	2.70	—	—	1220	—	—	—	—	—	—	—	—	6	—	—
45	600	0.00	—	—	330	—	0	—	—	—	—	—	—	0	—	—
130	100	7.20	—	—	980	—	—	—	—	—	—	—	—	9	—	—
50	600	0.00	—	—	350	—	0	—	—	—	—	—	—	0	—	—
85	200	5.40	—	—	1410	—	40	—	—	—	—	—	—	1	—	—
265	150	3.60	—	—	1070	—	—	—	—	—	—	—	—	0	—	—
245	80	2.70	—	—	740	—	—	—	—	—	—	—	—	0	—	—
260	150	2.70	—	—	960	—	—	—	—	—	—	—	—	0	—	—
5	60	1.80	—	—	930	—	0	—	—	—	—	—	—	0	—	—
280	150	3.60	—	—	1030	—	—	—	—	—	—	—	—	0	—	—
0	60	1.80	—	—	670	—	0	—	—	—	—	—	—	0	—	—
0	20	0.36	—	—	90	—	—	—	—	—	—	—	—	4	—	—
70	200	2.70	—	—	1060	—	—	—	—	—	—	—	—	6	—	—
70	150	0.72	—	—	660	—	—	—	—	—	—	—	—	30	—	—
70	80	1.80	—	—	980	—	0	—	—	—	—	—	—	2	—	—

TABLE H–1
Food Composition

(DA+ code is for Wadsworth Diet Analysis program)   (For purposes of calculations, use "0" for t, <1, <.1, <.01, etc.)

DA + Code	Food Description	Quantity	Measure	Wt (g)	H₂O (g)	Ener (kcal)	Prot (g)	Carb (g)	Fiber (g)	Fat (g)	Sat	Mono	Poly	Trans
	FAST FOOD—Continued													
38759	Chargrilled deluxe chicken sandwich	1	item(s)	195	—	290	27	31	2	7	1.50	—	—	0
38742	Chicken biscuit	1	item(s)	137	—	400	16	43	2	18	4.50	—	—	2.83
38743	Chicken biscuit w/cheese	1	item(s)	151	—	450	19	43	2	23	7.00	—	—	2.85
38762	Chicken caesar wrap	1	item(s)	227	—	460	36	52	2	10	6.00	—	—	0
38757	Chicken deluxe sandwich	1	item(s)	208	—	420	28	39	2	16	3.50	—	—	0
38764	Chicken salad sandwich	1	item(s)	153	—	350	20	32	5	15	3.00	—	—	0
38756	Chicken sandwich	1	item(s)	170	—	410	28	38	1	15	3.50	—	—	0
38768	Chick-n-Strip salad	1	item(s)	331	—	390	34	22	4	18	5.00	—	—	0
38763	Chick-n-Strips	4	item(s)	127	—	290	29	14	1	13	2.50	—	—	0
38770	Coleslaw	1	item(s)	105	—	210	1	14	2	17	2.50	—	—	0
38755	Hash browns	1	serving(s)	84	—	170	2	20	2	9	4.50	—	—	1
38765	Hearty breast of soup	1	cup(s)	241	—	140	8	18	1	4	1.00	—	—	0
38778	Icedream, small cone	1	item(s)	135	—	160	4	28	0	4	2.00	—	—	0
38774	Icedream, small cup	1	serving(s)	213	—	230	5	38	0	6	3.50	—	—	0
38775	Lemonade	1	cup(s)	255	—	170	0	41	0	1	0.00	—	—	0
38776	Lemonade, diet	1	cup(s)	255	—	25	0	5	0	0	0.00	0.00	0.00	0
38777	Nuggets	8	item(s)	113	—	260	26	12	1	12	2.50	—	—	0
38769	Side salad	1	item(s)	108	—	60	3	4	2	3	1.50	—	—	0
38767	Southwest chargrilled salad	1	item(s)	303	—	240	22	17	5	8	3.50	—	—	0
38772	Waffle potato fries, small, salted	1	serving(s)	85	—	280	3	37	5	14	5.00	—	—	1.50
	Cinnabon													
39569	Caramel Pecanbon	1	item(s)	272	—	1100	16	141	8	56	10.00	—	—	5
39572	Caramellata Chill w/whipped cream	16	fluid ounce(s)	480	—	406	10	61	0	14	8.00	—	—	1
39571	Cinnapoppers	1	serving(s)	74	—	368	4	41	2	21	11.00	—	—	1
39567	Classic roll	1	item(s)	221	—	813	15	117	4	32	8.00	—	—	5
39568	Minibon	1	item(s)	92	—	339	6	49	2	13	3.00	—	—	2
39573	Mochalatta chill w/whipped cream	16	fluid ounce(s)	480	—	362	9	55	0	13	8.00	—	—	—
39570	Stix	5	item(s)	85	—	379	6	41	1	21	6.00	—	—	4
	Dairy Queen													
1466	Banana split	1	item(s)	369	—	510	8	96	3	12	8.00	3.00	0.50	0
38552	Brownie Earthquake	1	serving(s)	304	—	740	10	112	0	27	16.00	—	—	3
38561	Chocolate chip cookie dough blizzard, small	1	item(s)	319	—	720	12	105	0	28	14.00	—	—	2.50
1464	Chocolate malt, small	1	item(s)	418	—	650	15	111	0	16	10.00	—	—	0.50
38541	Chocolate shake, small	1	item(s)	397	—	560	13	93	1	15	10.00	—	—	0.50
17257	Chocolate soft serve	½	cup(s)	94	—	150	4	22	0	5	3.50	—	—	0
1463	Chocolate sundae, small	1	item(s)	163	—	280	5	49	0	7	4.50	1.00	1.00	0
1462	Dipped cone, small	1	item(s)	156	—	340	6	42	1	17	9.00	4.00	3.00	1
38555	Oreo cookies blizzard, small	1	item(s)	283	—	570	11	83	1	21	10.00	—	—	2.50
38547	Royal Treats Peanut Buster parfait	1	item(s)	305	—	730	16	99	2	31	17.00	—	—	0
17256	Vanilla soft serve	½	cup(s)	94	—	140	3	22	0	5	3.00	—	—	0
	Domino's													
31606	Barbeque wings	1	item(s)	25	—	50	6	2	<1	2	0.65	—	—	—
31604	Breadsticks	1	item(s)	37	—	116	3	18	1	4	0.79	—	—	—
37551	Buffalo chicken kickers	1	item(s)	24	14	47	4	3	<1	2	0.39	—	—	—
37548	Cinnastix	1	item(s)	32	8	122	2	15	1	6	1.15	—	—	—
	Classic hand tossed pizza													
31573	America's favorite feast, 12"	2	slice(s)	205	99	508	22	57	4	22	9.20	—	—	—
31574	America's favorite feast, 14"	2	slice(s)	283	138	697	30	79	5	30	12.70	—	—	—
37543	Bacon cheeseburger feast, 12"	2	slice(s)	198	60	549	25	55	3	26	11.62	—	—	—
37545	Bacon cheeseburger feast, 14"	2	slice(s)	275	121	762	35	75	4	36	16.10	—	—	—
37546	Barbeque feast, 12"	2	slice(s)	192	85	506	22	62	3	20	9.08	—	—	—
37547	Barbeque feast, 14"	2	slice(s)	262	115	691	30	85	4	27	12.24	—	—	—
31569	Cheese, 12"	2	slice(s)	159	—	375	15	55	3	11	4.81	—	—	—
31570	Cheese, 14"	2	slice(s)	219	—	516	21	75	4	15	6.72	—	—	—
37538	Deluxe feast, 12"	2	slice(s)	201	102	465	20	57	3	18	7.66	—	—	—
37540	Deluxe feast, 14"	2	slice(s)	273	138	627	26	78	5	24	10.20	—	—	—
31685	Deluxe, 12"	2	slice(s)	213	—	465	20	57	3	18	7.65	—	—	—
31694	Deluxe, 14"	2	slice(s)	273	—	627	26	78	5	24	10.20	—	—	—
31686	Extravaganzza, 12"	2	slice(s)	245	127	576	27	59	4	27	11.56	—	—	—
31695	Extravaganzza, 14"	2	slice(s)	329	171	773	36	88	5	36	15.42	—	—	—
31575	Hawaiian feast, 12"	2	slice(s)	204	105	450	21	58	3	16	7.20	—	—	—
31576	Hawaiian feast, 14"	2	slice(s)	283	147	623	29	80	5	22	10.09	—	—	—
31687	Meatzza, 12"	2	slice(s)	213	—	560	26	57	3	26	11.40	—	—	—
31696	Meatzza, 14"	2	slice(s)	293	139	753	35	78	5	34	15.24	—	—	—

PAGE KEY: H–2 = Breads/Baked Goods H–6 = Cereal/Rice/Pasta H–10 = Fruit H–14 = Vegetables/Legumes H–24 = Nuts/Seeds H–26 = Vegetarian
H–28 = Dairy H–34 = Eggs H–34 = Seafood H–36 = Meats H–40 = Poultry H–40 = Processed meats H–42 = Beverages H–46 = Fats/Oils
H–48 = Sweets H–50 = Spices/Condiments/Sauces H–52 = Mixed foods/Soups/Sandwiches H–58 = Fast food H–74 = Convenience meals H–76 = Baby foods

Chol (mg)	Calc (mg)	Iron (mg)	Magn (mg)	Pota (mg)	Sodi (mg)	Zinc (mg)	Vit A (µg)	Thia (mg)	Vit E (mg α)	Ribo (mg)	Niac (mg)	Vit B$_6$ (mg)	Fola (µg)	Vit C (mg)	Vit B$_{12}$ (µg)	Sele (µg)
70	80	1.80	—	—	990	—	—	—	—	—	—	—	—	5	—	—
30	60	2.70	—	—	1200	—	0	—	—	—	—	—	—	0	—	—
45	150	2.70	—	—	1430	—	—	—	—	—	—	—	—	0	—	—
80	500	2.70	—	—	1390	—	—	—	—	—	—	—	—	1	—	—
60	100	2.70	—	—	1300	—	—	—	—	—	—	—	—	2	—	—
65	150	1.80	—	—	880	—	—	—	—	—	—	—	—	0	—	—
60	100	2.70	—	—	1300	—	—	—	—	—	—	—	—	0	—	—
80	200	0.36	—	—	860	—	—	—	—	—	—	—	—	30	—	—
65	20	0.36	—	—	730	—	—	—	—	—	—	—	—	1	—	—
20	40	0.36	—	—	180	—	—	—	—	—	—	—	—	27	—	—
10	0	0.72	—	—	350	—	—	—	—	—	—	—	—	0	—	—
25	40	1.08	—	—	900	—	—	—	—	—	—	—	—	0	—	—
15	100	0.36	—	—	80	—	—	—	—	—	—	—	—	0	—	—
25	150	0.00	—	—	100	—	—	—	—	—	—	—	—	0	—	—
0	0	0.36	—	—	10	—	0	—	—	—	—	—	—	15	—	—
0	0	0.36	—	—	5	—	0	—	—	—	—	—	—	15	—	—
70	40	1.08	—	—	1090	—	0	—	—	—	—	—	—	0	—	—
10	100	0.00	—	—	75	—	—	—	—	—	—	—	—	15	—	—
60	200	1.08	—	—	770	—	—	—	—	—	—	—	—	24	—	—
15	20	0.00	—	—	105	—	0	—	—	—	—	—	—	21	—	—
63	—	—	—	—	600	—	—	—	—	—	—	—	—	—	—	—
46	—	—	—	—	187	—	—	—	—	—	—	—	—	—	—	—
62	—	—	—	—	104	—	—	—	—	—	—	—	—	—	—	—
67	—	—	—	—	801	—	—	—	—	—	—	—	—	—	—	—
27	—	—	—	—	337	—	—	—	—	—	—	—	—	—	—	—
46	100	0.00	—	—	252	—	—	—	—	—	—	—	—	0	—	—
16	—	—	—	—	413	—	—	—	—	—	—	—	—	—	—	—
30	250	1.80	—	860	180	—	—	0.15	—	0.60	0.20	—	—	15	—	—
50	250	1.80	—	—	350	—	—	—	—	—	—	—	—	0	—	—
50	350	2.70	—	—	370	—	—	—	—	—	—	—	—	1	—	—
55	450	1.80	—	—	370	—	—	—	—	—	—	—	—	2	—	—
50	450	1.44	—	—	280	—	—	0.12	—	—	—	—	—	2	—	—
15	100	0.72	—	—	75	—	—	—	—	—	—	—	—	0	—	—
20	200	1.08	—	278	140	—	—	0.06	—	0.24	0.20	—	—	0	—	—
20	200	1.08	—	290	130	—	—	0.06	—	0.26	0.20	—	—	1	—	—
40	350	2.70	—	—	430	—	—	—	—	—	—	—	—	1	—	—
35	300	1.80	—	—	400	—	—	—	—	—	—	—	—	1	—	—
15	150	0.72	—	—	70	—	150	—	—	—	—	—	—	0	—	—
26	6	0.32	—	—	175	—	—	—	—	—	—	—	—	<.1	—	—
0	<.1	0.87	—	—	152	—	—	—	—	—	—	—	—	6	—	—
9	3	0.00	—	—	163	—	—	—	—	—	—	—	—	0	—	—
0	6	0.70	—	—	110	—	—	—	—	—	—	—	—	<.1	—	—
49	202	3.70	—	—	1221	—	—	—	—	—	—	—	—	1	—	—
68	281	5.10	—	—	1685	—	—	—	—	—	—	—	—	1	—	—
60	293	3.56	—	—	1274	—	—	—	—	—	—	—	—	0	—	—
84	395	4.96	—	—	1809	—	—	—	—	—	—	—	—	0	—	—
46	—	—	—	—	1206	—	—	—	—	—	—	—	—	—	—	—
63	393	4.42	—	—	1672	—	—	—	—	—	—	—	—	2	—	—
23	187	2.99	—	—	776	—	131	—	—	—	—	—	—	0	—	—
32	261	4.13	—	—	1080	—	184	—	—	—	—	—	—	0	—	—
40	199	3.56	—	—	1063	—	—	—	—	—	—	—	—	1	—	—
53	276	4.84	—	—	1432	—	—	—	—	—	—	—	—	2	—	—
40	199	3.56	—	—	1063	—	—	—	—	—	—	—	—	1	—	—
53	276	4.85	—	—	1432	—	—	—	—	—	—	—	—	2	—	—
60	290	4.08	—	—	1348	—	—	—	—	—	—	—	—	1	—	—
89	403	5.48	—	—	1780	—	—	—	—	—	—	—	—	2	—	—
41	274	3.30	—	—	1102	—	—	—	—	—	—	—	—	2	—	—
57	384	4.57	—	—	1544	—	—	—	—	—	—	—	—	3	—	—
344	282	3.71	—	—	1463	—	—	—	—	—	—	—	—	<1	—	—
85	393	5.04	—	—	1947	—	—	—	—	—	—	—	—	<1	—	—

H Appendix

TABLE H–1
Food Composition

(DA+ code is for Wadsworth Diet Analysis program)   (For purposes of calculations, use "0" for t, <1, <.1, <.01, etc.)

DA + Code	Food Description	Quantity	Measure	Wt (g)	H₂O (g)	Ener (kcal)	Prot (g)	Carb (g)	Fiber (g)	Fat (g)	Sat	Mono	Poly	Trans
	FAST FOOD—Continued													
31571	Pepperoni feast, extra pepperoni & cheese, 12"	2	slice(s)	196	87	534	24	56	3	25	10.92	—	—	—
31572	Pepperoni feast, extra pepperoni & cheese, 14"	2	slice(s)	270	121	732	33	77	4	34	15.00	—	—	—
31577	Vegi feast, 12"	2	slice(s)	203	107	439	19	57	4	16	7.09	—	—	—
31578	Vegi feast, 14"	2	slice(s)	278	147	304	27	78	5	22	9.89	—	—	—
37549	Dot cinnamon	1	item(s)	28	8	99	2	15	1	4	0.68	—	—	—
31605	Double cheesy bread	1	item(s)	35	11	123	4	13	1	6	2.06	—	—	—
31607	Hot wings	1	item(s)	25	—	45	5	1	<1	2	0.65	—	—	—
	Thin crust pizza													
31583	America's favorite, 12"	¼	item(s)	159	—	408	19	34	2	23	9.77	—	—	—
31584	America's favorite, 14"	¼	item(s)	202	—	557	26	47	3	31	13.19	—	—	—
31579	Cheese, 12"	¼	item(s)	106	—	273	12	31	2	12	9.37	—	—	—
31580	Cheese, 14"	¼	item(s)	148	—	382	17	43	2	17	6.72	—	—	—
31688	Deluxe, 12"	¼	item(s)	159	—	363	16	34	2	19	7.64	—	—	—
31697	Deluxe, 14"	¼	item(s)	202	—	494	22	47	3	25	10.20	—	—	—
31689	Extravaganzza, 12"	¼	item(s)	159	—	425	20	34	3	24	9.41	—	—	—
31698	Extravaganzza, 14"	¼	item(s)	202	—	571	27	48	4	31	12.44	—	—	—
31585	Hawaiian, 12"	¼	item(s)	159	—	349	18	35	2	16	7.20	—	—	—
31586	Hawaiian, 14"	¼	item(s)	202	—	489	25	48	3	23	10.09	—	—	—
31690	Meatzza, 12"	¼	item(s)	159	—	458	23	33	2	27	11.39	—	—	—
31699	Meatzza, 14"	¼	item(s)	202	—	619	31	46	3	36	15.24	—	—	—
31581	Pepperoni, extra pepperoni & cheese 12"	¼	item(s)	159	—	420	20	32	2	24	10.46	—	—	—
31582	Pepperoni, extra pepperoni & cheese 14"	¼	item(s)	202	—	586	28	45	3	34	14.55	—	—	—
31587	Vegi, 12"	¼	item(s)	159	—	338	16	34	3	17	7.08	—	—	—
31588	Vegi, 14"	¼	item(s)	202	—	471	22	47	3	23	9.89	—	—	—
	Ultimate deep dish pizza													
31596	America's favorite, 12"	2	slice(s)	235	—	617	26	59	4	33	12.88	—	—	—
31702	America's favorite, 14"	2	slice(s)	311	—	851	36	84	5	44	17.35	—	—	—
31590	Cheese, 12"	2	slice(s)	181	—	482	19	56	3	22	7.91	—	—	—
31591	Cheese, 14"	2	slice(s)	257	—	677	26	80	5	30	10.88	—	—	—
31589	Cheese, 6"	1	item(s)	215	—	598	23	68	4	28	9.94	—	—	—
31591	Deluxe, 12"	2	slice(s)	235	—	527	23	59	4	29	10.75	—	—	—
31700	Deluxe, 14"	2	slice(s)	311	—	788	31	84	5	38	14.36	—	—	—
31692	Extravaganzza, 12"	2	slice(s)	235	—	635	27	59	4	34	12.52	—	—	—
31701	Extravaganzza, 14"	2	slice(s)	311	—	866	36	85	6	45	16.60	—	—	—
31599	Hawaiian, 12"	2	slice(s)	235	—	558	24	60	4	26	10.31	—	—	—
31600	Hawaiian, 14"	2	slice(s)	311	—	784	35	85	5	36	14.25	—	—	—
31693	Meatzza, 12"	2	slice(s)	235	—	667	30	58	4	37	14.50	—	—	—
31703	Meatzza, 14"	2	slice(s)	311	—	914	40	83	5	49	19.40	—	—	—
31593	Pepperoni, extra pepperoni & cheese 12"	2	slice(s)	235	—	629	26	57	4	34	13.57	—	—	—
31594	Pepperoni, extra pepperoni & cheese 14"	2	slice(s)	311	—	880	37	82	5	47	18.71	—	—	—
31602	Vegi, 12"	2	slice(s)	235	—	547	22	59	4	26	10.19	—	—	—
31603	Vegi, 14"	2	slice(s)	311	—	765	32	84	6	36	14.05	—	—	—
31598	With ham & pineapple tidbits, 6"	1	item(s)	430	—	619	25	70	4	28	10.19	—	—	—
31595	With Italian sausage, 6"	1	item(s)	430	—	642	25	70	4	31	11.33	—	—	—
31592	With pepperoni, 6"	1	item(s)	430	—	647	25	69	4	32	11.70	—	—	—
31601	With vegetables, 6"	1	item(s)	430	—	619	23	71	5	29	10.11	—	—	—
	In-n-Out Burger													
34374	Cheeseburger	1	item(s)	268	—	480	22	39	3	27	10.00	—	—	—
34391	Cheeseburger w/mustard & ketchup	1	item(s)	268	—	400	22	41	3	18	9.00	—	—	—
34390	Cheeseburger, lettuce leaves instead of buns	1	item(s)	300	—	330	18	11	2	25	9.00	—	—	—
34377	Chocolate shake	1	item(s)	425	—	690	9	83	0	36	24.00	—	—	—
34375	Double-Double cheeseburger	1	item(s)	328	—	670	37	40	3	41	18.00	—	—	—
34393	Double-Double cheeseburger w/mustard & ketchup	1	item(s)	328	—	590	37	42	3	32	17.00	—	—	—
34392	Double-Double cheeseburger, lettuce leaves instead of buns	1	item(s)	361	—	520	33	11	2	39	17.00	—	—	—
34376	French fries	1	item(s)	125	—	400	7	54	2	18	5.00	—	—	—
34373	Hamburger	1	item(s)	243	—	390	16	39	3	19	5.00	—	—	—
34389	Hamburger w/mustard & ketchup	1	item(s)	243	—	310	16	41	3	10	4.00	—	—	—
34388	Hamburger, lettuce leaves instead of buns	1	item(s)	275	—	240	12	10	2	17	4.50	—	—	—

PAGE KEY: H–2 = Breads/Baked Goods   H–6 = Cereal/Rice/Pasta   H–10 = Fruit   H–14 = Vegetables/Legumes   H–24 = Nuts/Seeds   H–26 = Vegetarian
H–28 = Dairy   H–34 = Eggs   H–34 = Seafood   H–36 = Meats   H–40 = Poultry   H–40 = Processed meats   H–42 = Beverages   H–46 = Fats/Oils
H–48 = Sweets   H–50 = Spices/Condiments/Sauces   H–52 = Mixed foods/Soups/Sandwiches   H–58 = Fast food   H–74 = Convenience meals   H–76 = Baby foods

Chol (mg)	Calc (mg)	Iron (mg)	Magn (mg)	Pota (mg)	Sodi (mg)	Zinc (mg)	Vit A (µg)	Thia (mg)	Vit E (mg α)	Ribo (mg)	Niac (mg)	Vit B_6 (mg)	Fola (µg)	Vit C (mg)	Vit B_{12} (µg)	Sele (µg)
57	279	3.36	—	—	1349	—	155	—	—	—	—	—	—	<1	—	—
78	390	4.66	—	—	1855	—	233	—	—	—	—	—	—	<1	—	—
34	279	3.44	—	—	987	—	—	—	—	—	—	—	—	1	—	—
47	389	4.71	—	—	1369	—	—	—	—	—	—	—	—	2	—	—
0	6	0.59	—	—	86	—	—	—	—	—	—	—	—	<.1	—	—
6	47	0.66	—	—	164	—	—	—	—	—	—	—	—	<1	—	—
26	5	0.30	—	—	354	—	—	—	—	—	—	—	—	1	—	—
51	318	1.52	—	—	1285	—	—	—	—	—	—	—	—	<1	—	—
69	444	2.07	—	—	1751	—	—	—	—	—	—	—	—	1	—	—
23	225	0.97	—	—	835	—	125	—	—	—	—	—	—	0	—	—
32	315	1.36	—	—	1172	—	175	—	—	—	—	—	—	0	—	—
40	237	1.54	—	—	1123	—	—	—	—	—	—	—	—	1	—	—
53	330	2.08	—	—	1523	—	—	—	—	—	—	—	—	2	—	—
53	245	1.95	—	—	1408	—	—	—	—	—	—	—	—	1	—	—
69	340	2.59	—	—	1871	—	—	—	—	—	—	—	—	2	—	—
41	312	1.28	—	—	1162	—	—	—	—	—	—	—	—	2	—	—
57	437	1.80	—	—	1635	—	—	—	—	—	—	—	—	3	—	—
64	320	1.69	—	—	1523	—	—	—	—	—	—	—	—	<1	—	—
454	446	2.27	—	—	2039	—	—	—	—	—	—	—	—	<1	—	—
54	316	1.34	—	—	1362	—	162	—	—	—	—	—	—	<1	—	—
76	442	1.87	—	—	1900	—	227	—	—	—	—	—	—	<1	—	—
34	317	1.42	—	—	1047	—	—	—	—	—	—	—	—	1	—	—
47	442	1.94	—	—	1460	—	—	—	—	—	—	—	—	2	—	—
58	334	4.43	—	—	1573	—	—	—	—	—	—	—	—	1	—	—
78	464	6.24	—	—	2155	—	—	—	—	—	—	—	—	1	—	—
30	241	3.88	—	—	1123	—	151	—	—	—	—	—	—	<1	—	—
41	335	5.53	—	—	1575	—	210	—	—	—	—	—	—	1	—	—
36	295	4.67	—	—	1341	—	174	—	—	—	—	—	—	1	—	—
47	253	4.45	—	—	1410	—	—	—	—	—	—	—	—	2	—	—
62	349	6.25	—	—	1927	—	—	—	—	—	—	—	—	2	—	—
60	261	4.86	—	—	1696	—	—	—	—	—	—	—	—	2	—	—
78	359	6.76	—	—	2275	—	—	—	—	—	—	—	—	2	—	—
48	328	4.19	—	—	1449	—	—	—	—	—	—	—	—	2	—	—
67	457	5.97	—	—	2039	—	—	—	—	—	—	—	—	3	—	—
379	336	4.60	—	—	1810	—	—	—	—	—	—	—	—	1	—	—
501	466	6.44	—	—	2443	—	—	—	—	—	—	—	—	1	—	—
61	332	4.25	—	—	1650	—	187	—	—	—	—	—	—	1	—	—
85	462	6.04	—	—	2304	—	260	—	—	—	—	—	—	1	—	—
41	333	4.33	—	—	1334	—	—	—	—	—	—	—	—	2	—	—
57	462	6.11	—	—	1864	—	—	—	—	—	—	—	—	2	—	—
43	298	4.84	—	—	1498	—	—	—	—	—	—	—	—	1	—	—
45	302	4.89	—	—	1478	—	—	—	—	—	—	—	—	1	—	—
47	299	4.81	—	—	1524	—	168	—	—	—	—	—	—	1	—	—
36	307	5.10	—	—	1472	—	—	—	—	—	—	—	—	5	—	—
60	200	3.60	—	—	1000	—	188	—	—	—	—	—	—	15	—	—
55	200	3.60	—	—	1080	—	182	—	—	—	—	—	—	15	—	—
60	200	1.08	—	—	720	—	—	—	—	—	—	—	—	18	—	—
95	300	0.72	—	—	350	—	143	—	—	—	—	—	—	0	—	—
120	350	5.40	—	—	1430	—	184	—	—	—	—	—	—	15	—	—
115	350	5.40	—	—	1510	—	229	—	—	—	—	—	—	15	—	—
120	350	1.08	—	—	1160	—	275	—	—	—	—	—	—	18	—	—
0	20	1.80	—	—	245	—	0	—	—	—	—	—	—	0	—	—
40	40	3.60	—	—	640	—	50	—	—	—	—	—	—	15	—	—
35	40	3.60	—	—	720	—	75	—	—	—	—	—	—	15	—	—
40	40	1.08	—	—	370	—	—	—	—	—	—	—	—	18	—	—

Appendix H

TABLE H–1
Food Composition

(DA+ code is for Wadsworth Diet Analysis program)   (For purposes of calculations, use "0" for t, <1, <.1, <.01, etc.)

DA + Code	Food Description	Quantity	Measure	Wt (g)	H₂O (g)	Ener (kcal)	Prot (g)	Carb (g)	Fiber (g)	Fat (g)	Sat	Mono	Poly	Trans
	FAST FOOD—Continued													
34379	Strawberry shake	1	item(s)	425	—	690	8	91	2	33	22.00	—	—	—
34378	Vanilla shake	1	item(s)	425	—	680	9	78	2	37	25.00	—	—	—
	Jack in the Box													
30392	Bacon ultimate cheeseburger	1	item(s)	353	—	1120	52	59	2	55	28.00	—	—	3.13
1740	Breakfast Jack	1	item(s)	133	—	310	14	34	1	14	5.00	—	—	0
14074	Cheeseburger	1	item(s)	116	—	300	14	31	2	13	6.00	—	—	0.89
14106	Chicken breast pieces	5	piece(s)	150	—	360	27	24	1	17	3.00	—	—	4.48
37241	Chicken club salad	1	item(s)	535	—	310	28	15	5	16	6.00	—	—	0
14111	Chocolate ice cream shake	1	item(s)	315	—	660	11	89	1	29	18.00	—	—	1
14075	Double cheeseburger	1	item(s)	155	—	410	20	32	1	22	11.00	—	—	—
14098	French fries, jumbo	1	serving(s)	142	—	410	4	55	4	20	4.50	—	—	5.34
14099	French fries, super scoop	1	serving(s)	198	—	580	6	77	6	28	6.00	—	—	7.07
14073	Hamburger	1	item(s)	104	—	250	12	30	2	9	3.50	—	—	0.88
14090	Hash browns	1	serving(s)	57	—	150	1	13	2	10	2.50	—	—	3
14072	Jack's Spicy Chicken sandwich	1	item(s)	253	—	580	24	53	3	31	6.00	—	—	2.81
1468	Jumbo Jack hamburger	1	item(s)	269	—	600	22	58	3	31	11.00	—	—	1.55
1469	Jumbo Jack hamburger w/cheese	1	item(s)	294	—	690	26	60	3	38	16.00	—	—	1.55
1470	Onion rings	1	serving(s)	119	—	500	6	51	3	30	5.00	—	—	10
33141	Sausage, egg, & cheese biscuit	1	item(s)	223	—	760	25	33	2	60	20.00	—	—	5.72
14095	Seasoned curly fries	1	serving(s)	125	—	400	6	45	5	23	5.00	—	—	7
14077	Sourdough Jack	1	item(s)	244	—	700	30	36	3	49	16.00	—	—	2.98
37249	Southwest chicken salad	1	serving(s)	598	—	340	28	31	9	13	6.00	—	—	0
14112	Strawberry ice cream shake	1	item(s)	313	—	640	10	84	0	28	18.00	—	—	1
14078	Ultimate cheeseburger	1	item(s)	328	—	990	41	59	2	66	28.00	—	—	3.05
14110	Vanilla ice cream shake	1	item(s)	285	—	570	12	65	0	29	18.00	—	—	1
	Jamba Juice													
31646	Banana berry smoothie	24	fluid ounce(s)	719	—	470	5	112	5	2	0.50	—	—	—
31647	Caribbean passion smoothie	24	fluid ounce(s)	730	—	440	4	102	4	2	1.00	—	—	—
38422	Carrot juice	16	fluid ounce(s)	472	—	100	3	23	0	1	0.00	—	—	—
31648	Chocolate mood smoothie	24	fluid ounce(s)	612	—	690	16	142	2	8	4.50	—	—	—
31649	Citrus squeeze smoothie	24	fluid ounce(s)	729	—	450	4	105	5	2	1.00	—	—	—
31650	Coffee mood smoothie	24	fluid ounce(s)	560	—	596	13	121	1	6	4.00	—	—	—
31651	Coldbuster smoothie	24	fluid ounce(s)	724	—	430	5	100	5	3	1.00	—	—	—
31652	Cranberry craze smoothie	24	fluid ounce(s)	731	—	420	6	97	4	2	1.00	—	—	—
31654	Jamba powerboost smoothie	24	fluid ounce(s)	730	—	440	6	103	7	2	0.00	—	—	—
38423	Lemonade	16	fluid ounce(s)	483	—	300	1	75	0	0	0.00	0.00	0.00	0
31656	Lime sublime smoothie	24	fluid ounce(s)	721	—	450	3	104	6	2	1.00	—	—	—
31657	Mango-a-go-go smoothie	24	fluid ounce(s)	739	—	500	4	117	4	2	1.00	—	—	—
38424	Orange juice, freshly squeezed	16	fluid ounce(s)	496	—	220	3	52	1	1	0.00	—	—	—
38426	Orange/carrot juice	16	fluid ounce(s)	484	—	160	3	37	0	1	0.00	—	—	—
31660	Orange-a-peel smoothie	24	fluid ounce(s)	726	—	440	9	102	5	1	0.00	—	—	—
31665	Protein berry pizzaz smoothie	24	fluid ounce(s)	710	—	440	20	92	6	2	0.00	—	—	—
31667	Raspberry refresher smoothie	24	fluid ounce(s)	636	—	442	3	101	8	3	0.90	—	—	—
31668	Razzmatazz smoothie	24	fluid ounce(s)	730	—	480	3	112	4	2	1.00	—	—	—
31669	Strawberries wild smoothie	24	fluid ounce(s)	725	—	450	6	105	4	0	0.00	—	—	—
38421	Strawberry tsunami smoothie	24	fluid ounce(s)	740	—	530	4	128	4	2	1.00	—	—	—
38427	Vibrant C juice	16	fluid ounce(s)	448	—	210	2	50	1	0	0.00	0.00	0.00	0
38428	Wheatgrass juice, freshly squeezed	1	ounce(s)	32	—	5	1	1	0	0	0.00	0.00	0.00	0
	Kentucky Fried Chicken (KFC)													
31850	BBQ baked beans	1	serving(s)	156	—	190	6	33	6	3	1.00	—	—	0.29
31853	Biscuit	1	item(s)	56	—	180	4	20	1	10	2.50	—	—	3.44
31851	Coleslaw	1	serving(s)	142	—	232	2	26	3	14	2.00	—	—	0.27
31842	Colonel's Crispy Strips	3	item(s)	150	—	340	28	20	0	16	4.50	—	—	4.47
31849	Corn on the cob	1	item(s)	162	—	150	5	35	2	2	0.00	—	—	0
3761	Extra Crispy chicken, breast	1	item(s)	162	—	470	34	19	0	28	8.00	—	—	4.50
3762	Extra Crispy chicken, drumstick	1	item(s)	60	—	160	12	5	0	10	2.50	—	—	1.50
3763	Extra Crispy chicken, thigh	1	item(s)	114	—	370	21	12	0	26	7.00	—	—	3
3764	Extra Crispy chicken, whole wing	1	item(s)	52	—	190	10	10	0	12	3.50	—	—	2
31833	Honey BBQ wing pieces	6	item(s)	189	—	607	33	33	1	38	10.00	—	—	5.42
10810	Hot & spicy chicken, breast	1	item(s)	179	—	450	33	20	0	27	8.00	—	—	0
10813	Hot & spicy chicken, drumstick	1	item(s)	60	—	140	13	4	0	9	2.50	—	—	0
10811	Hot & spicy chicken, thigh	1	item(s)	128	—	390	22	14	0	28	8.00	—	—	0
10812	Hot & spicy chicken, whole wing	1	item(s)	55	—	180	11	9	0	11	3.00	—	—	0
10859	Hot wings pieces	6	piece(s)	135	—	471	27	18	2	33	8.00	—	—	4.03
31848	Macaroni & cheese	1	serving(s)	153	—	180	7	21	2	8	3.00	—	—	2.81

PAGE KEY: H–2 = Breads/Baked Goods H–6 = Cereal/Rice/Pasta H–10 = Fruit H–14 = Vegetables/Legumes H–24 = Nuts/Seeds H–26 = Vegetarian H–28 = Dairy H–34 = Eggs H–34 = Seafood H–36 = Meats H–40 = Poultry H–40 = Processed meats H–42 = Beverages H–46 = Fats/Oils H–48 = Sweets H–50 = Spices/Condiments/Sauces H–52 = Mixed foods/Soups/Sandwiches H–58 = Fast food H–74 = Convenience meals H–76 = Baby foods

Chol (mg)	Calc (mg)	Iron (mg)	Magn (mg)	Pota (mg)	Sodi (mg)	Zinc (mg)	Vit A (µg)	Thia (mg)	Vit E (mg α)	Ribo (mg)	Niac (mg)	Vit B6 (mg)	Fola (µg)	Vit C (mg)	Vit B12 (µg)	Sele (µg)
85	250	0.00	—	—	280	—	134	—	—	—	—	—	—	0	—	—
90	300	0.00	—	—	390	—	145	—	—	—	—	—	—	0	—	—
160	300	7.20	—	600	2260	—	—	—	—	—	—	—	—	1	—	—
210	150	3.60	—	210	770	—	—	—	—	—	—	—	—	4	—	—
40	150	3.60	—	180	840	—	40	—	—	—	—	—	—	0	—	—
80	20	1.80	—	430	970	—	—	—	—	—	—	—	—	1	—	—
65	300	3.60	—	1010	890	—	—	—	—	—	—	—	—	54	—	—
110	350	0.36	—	720	270	—	215	—	—	—	—	—	—	0	—	—
70	250	4.50	—	280	920	—	—	—	—	—	—	—	—	1	—	—
0	20	1.08	—	550	690	—	0	—	—	—	—	—	—	6	—	—
0	20	1.44	—	770	960	—	0	—	—	—	—	—	—	9	—	—
30	100	3.60	—	155	610	—	0	—	—	—	—	—	—	0	—	—
0	10	0.18	—	190	230	—	0	—	—	—	—	—	—	0	—	—
60	150	1.80	—	470	950	—	—	—	—	—	—	—	—	9	—	—
45	164	4.92	—	390	980	—	—	—	—	—	—	—	—	10	—	—
75	250	4.50	—	420	1360	—	—	—	—	—	—	—	—	9	—	—
0	40	2.70	—	140	420	—	40	—	—	—	—	—	—	18	—	—
280	100	2.70	—	240	1390	—	—	—	—	—	—	—	—	0	—	—
0	40	1.80	—	580	890	—	—	—	—	—	—	—	—	0	—	—
80	200	4.50	—	450	1220	—	—	—	—	—	—	—	—	9	—	—
60	300	4.50	—	1020	920	—	—	—	—	—	—	—	—	48	—	—
110	350	0.00	—	610	220	—	202	—	—	—	—	—	—	0	—	—
130	300	7.20	—	480	1670	—	—	—	—	—	—	—	—	1	—	—
115	400	0.00	—	630	220	—	218	—	—	—	—	—	—	0	—	—
5	200	1.08	32	1000	85	0.30	—	0.06	0.32	0.26	1.20	0.40	33	15	0	0
5	100	1.80	24	810	60	0.30	—	0.09	0.64	0.26	5.00	0.50	100	78	0	1
0	150	2.70	80	1030	250	0.90	0	0.53	—	0.26	5.00	0.70	80	18	0	6
25	500	1.08	32	760	280	0.60	0	0.09	0.00	0.85	0.40	0.08	9	6	1	4
5	150	1.80	60	1150	50	0.30	—	0.30	0.40	0.26	1.90	0.40	100	168	0	1
28	455	0.30	49	634	429	1.50	—	0.10	0.16	0.60	0.30	0.10	18	7	1	3
5	100	1.08	60	1240	35	15.00	—	0.38	17.71	0.34	3.00	0.40	122	1302	0	1
5	250	1.44	16	500	90	0.30	—	0.03	0.64	0.26	5.00	0.50	100	54	0	1
0	1100	1.44	480	1110	40	15.00	—	5.25	17.71	5.78	66.00	6.80	640	294	10	70
0	20	0.00	8	200	10	0.00	0	0.03	0.00	0.17	14.00	1.80	320	36	0	0
5	150	1.80	32	660	75	0.60	—	0.12	0.32	0.26	7.00	0.80	160	66	<1	1
5	100	1.08	24	800	60	0.30	—	0.15	1.61	0.26	5.00	0.70	120	72	0	1
0	60	1.08	60	990	0	0.30	0	0.45	—	0.14	2.00	0.20	160	246	0	0
0	100	1.80	60	1010	125	0.60	0	0.45	—	0.26	3.00	0.50	120	132	0	3
0	250	1.80	60	1350	100	0.30	—	0.38	0.64	0.43	3.00	0.40	140	240	0	1
0	1100	2.62	39	650	240	0.58	0	0.09	0.31	0.10	1.55	0.40	58	60	0	4
3	104	2.20	56	806	47	0.80	—	0.10	0.40	0.30	1.60	0.40	43	35	<1	1
5	150	1.80	32	790	70	0.60	—	0.09	0.32	0.26	6.00	0.90	160	60	0	1
0	250	1.80	32	1020	115	0.30	—	0.03	0.32	0.34	1.20	0.20	32	60	0	1
5	100	1.08	24	480	10	0.30	0	0.06	—	0.34	14.00	1.80	320	90	0	1
0	20	1.08	40	720	0	0.30	0	0.30	—	0.10	1.60	0.40	80	678	0	0
0	0	1.80	8	80	0	0.00	0	0.03	—	0.03	0.40	0.04	16	4	0	3
5	80	1.80	—	—	760	—	—	—	—	—	—	—	—	1	—	—
0	20	1.08	—	—	560	—	—	—	—	—	—	—	—	1	—	—
8	30	0.18	—	—	284	—	65	—	—	—	—	—	—	34	—	—
70	10	0.72	—	—	1140	—	—	—	—	—	—	—	—	1	—	—
0	10	0.18	—	—	20	—	10	—	—	—	—	—	—	4	—	—
135	19	1.44	—	—	1230	—	—	—	—	—	—	—	—	1	—	—
70	9	0.65	—	—	415	—	—	—	—	—	—	—	—	1	—	—
120	19	1.04	—	—	710	—	—	—	—	—	—	—	—	1	—	—
55	9	0.34	—	—	390	—	—	—	—	—	—	—	—	1	—	—
193	40	1.44	—	—	1145	—	—	—	—	—	—	—	—	5	—	—
130	10	1.07	—	—	1450	—	—	—	—	—	—	—	—	1	—	—
65	20	0.68	—	—	380	—	—	—	—	—	—	—	—	1	—	—
125	10	1.44	—	—	1240	—	—	—	—	—	—	—	—	1	—	—
60	10	0.72	—	—	420	—	—	—	—	—	—	—	—	1	—	—
150	40	1.44	—	—	1230	—	—	—	—	—	—	—	—	1	—	—
10	150	0.18	—	—	860	—	350	—	—	—	—	—	—	1	—	—

Appendix H

TABLE H–1
Food Composition
(DA+ code is for Wadsworth Diet Analysis program)   (For purposes of calculations, use "0" for t, <1, <.1, <.01, etc.)

DA + Code	Food Description	Quantity	Measure	Wt (g)	H₂O (g)	Ener (kcal)	Prot (g)	Carb (g)	Fiber (g)	Fat (g)	Sat	Mono	Poly	Trans
	FAST FOOD—Continued													
31847	Mashed potatoes with gravy	1	serving(s)	136	—	120	1	17	2	6	1.00	—	—	0.50
10825	Original Recipe chicken, breast	1	item(s)	161	—	370	40	11	0	19	6.00	—	—	2.50
10826	Original Recipe chicken, drumstick	1	item(s)	59	—	140	14	4	0	8	2.00	—	—	1
10827	Original Recipe chicken, thigh	1	item(s)	126	—	360	22	12	0	25	7.00	—	—	1.50
10828	Original Recipe chicken, whole wing	1	item(s)	47	—	145	11	5	0	9	2.50	—	—	1
3760	Original Recipe chicken sandwich w/sauce	1	item(s)	200	—	450	29	33	2	22	5.00	—	—	—
31834	Original Recipe chicken sandwich w/o sauce	1	item(s)	187	—	360	29	21	1	13	3.50	—	—	—
31852	Potato salad	1	serving(s)	160	—	230	4	23	3	14	2.00	—	—	0.31
10845	Potato wedges	1	serving(s)	156	—	376	6	53	5	15	4.20	—	—	6.12
10853	Rotisserie Gold chicken, breast & wing w/skin	4	ounce(s)	114	—	218	26	1	0	12	3.51	—	—	—
10851	Rotisserie Gold chicken, thigh & leg w/skin	4	ounce(s)	114	—	260	23	1	0	18	5.15	—	—	—
10852	Rotisserie Gold chicken, thigh & leg w/o skin	4	ounce(s)	117	—	217	27	0	0	12	3.50	—	—	—
31843	Spicy Crispy Strips	3	item(s)	115	—	335	25	23	1	15	4.00	—	—	—
10854	Tender Roast chicken, breast w/o skin	1	item(s)	118	—	169	31	1	0	4	1.20	—	—	—
	Long John Silver													
39392	Baked cod	1	serving(s)	101	—	120	22	1	0	5	1.00	—	—	—
3777	Batter dipped fish sandwich	1	item(s)	177	—	440	17	48	3	20	5.00	—	—	—
37568	Battered fish	1	item(s)	92	—	230	11	16	0	13	4.00	—	—	—
37569	Breaded clams	1	serving(s)	85	—	240	8	22	1	13	2.00	—	—	—
39404	Clam chowder	1	item(s)	227	—	220	9	23	0	10	4.00	—	—	—
39398	Cocktail sauce	1	ounce(s)	28	—	25	0	6	0	0	0.00	0.00	0.00	0
3770	Coleslaw	1	serving(s)	113	—	200	1	15	4	15	2.50	1.76	4.10	—
39394	Crunchy shrimp basket	21	item(s)	114	—	340	12	32	2	19	5.00	—	—	—
39400	French fries, large	1	item(s)	142	—	390	4	56	5	17	4.00	—	—	—
3774	Fries regular	1	serving(s)	85	—	230	3	34	3	10	2.50	7.40	5.10	—
3779	Hushpuppy	1	piece(s)	23	—	60	1	9	1	3	0.50	—	—	—
3781	Shrimp batter-dipped	1	piece(s)	14	—	45	2	3	0	3	1.00	—	—	—
39399	Tartar sauce	1	ounce(s)	28	—	100	0	4	0	9	1.50	—	—	—
39395	Ultimate fish sandwich	1	item(s)	199	—	500	20	48	3	25	8.00	—	—	—
	McDonald's													
2247	Barbecue sauce	1	serving(s)	28	—	45	0	10	0	0	0.00	0.00	0.00	0
737	Big Mac hamburger	1	item(s)	216	—	590	24	47	3	34	11.00	—	—	1.48
738	Cheeseburger	1	item(s)	121	—	330	15	36	2	14	6.00	—	—	1.02
29775	Chicken McGrill sandwich	1	item(s)	213	—	400	25	37	2	17	3.00	—	—	0
3792	Chicken McNuggets	4	item(s)	72	—	210	10	12	1	13	2.50	—	—	1.13
1873	Chicken McNuggets	6	item(s)	108	—	310	15	18	2	20	4.00	—	—	1.69
73	Chocolate milkshake	8	fluid ounce(s)	227	164	270	7	48	1	6	3.81	1.77	0.23	—
29774	Crispy chicken sandwich	1	item(s)	219	—	500	22	46	2	26	4.50	—	—	1.50
743	Egg McMuffin	1	item(s)	138	—	300	18	29	2	12	4.50	—	—	0.42
742	Filet-o-fish sandwich	1	item(s)	156	—	470	15	45	1	26	5.00	—	—	1.11
2257	French fries, large	1	serving(s)	176	—	540	8	68	6	26	4.50	—	—	6.18
1872	French fries, small	1	serving(s)	68	—	210	3	26	2	10	1.50	—	—	2.30
2244	French fries, super size	1	serving(s)	198	—	610	9	77	7	29	5.00	—	—	—
33822	Fruit n' yogurt parfait	1	item(s)	338	—	380	10	76	2	5	2.00	—	—	0.18
2251	Garden salad	1	item(s)	177	—	35	2	7	3	0	0.00	0.00	0.00	0
739	Hamburger	1	item(s)	107	—	280	12	35	2	10	4.00	—	—	0.51
2003	Hash browns	1	item(s)	53	—	130	1	14	1	8	1.50	—	—	2
2249	Honey sauce	1	item(s)	14	—	45	0	12	0	0	0.00	0.00	0.00	—
33816	McSalad Shaker chef salad	1	item(s)	206	—	150	17	5	2	8	3.50	—	—	—
33817	McSalad Shaker garden salad	1	item(s)	149	—	100	7	4	2	6	3.00	—	—	—
33818	McSalad Shaker grilled chicken caesar salad	1	item(s)	163	—	100	17	3	2	3	1.50	—	—	—
38396	Newman's Own cobb salad dressing	1	item(s)	59	—	120	1	9	0	9	1.50	—	—	0.01
38397	Newman's Own creamy caesar salad dressing	1	item(s)	59	—	190	2	4	0	18	3.50	—	—	0.29
38398	Newman's Own low fat balsamic vinaigrette salad dressing	1	item(s)	44	—	40	0	4	0	3	0.00	—	—	0.01
38399	Newman's Own ranch salad dressing	1	item(s)	59	—	290	1	4	0	30	4.50	—	—	0.22
1874	Plain hotcakes w/syrup & margarine	3	item(s)	228	—	600	9	104	0	17	3.00	—	—	4
740	Quarter Pounder hamburger	1	item(s)	172	—	430	23	37	2	21	8.00	—	—	1.01
741	Quarter Pounder hamburger w/cheese	1	item(s)	200	—	530	28	38	2	30	13.00	—	—	1.51
2005	Sausage McMuffin w/egg	1	item(s)	164	—	450	20	29	2	28	10.00	—	—	0.59

Appendix H

PAGE KEY: H–2 = Breads/Baked Goods H–6 = Cereal/Rice/Pasta H–10 = Fruit H–14 = Vegetables/Legumes H–24 = Nuts/Seeds H–26 = Vegetarian H–28 = Dairy H–34 = Eggs H–34 = Seafood H–36 = Meats H–40 = Poultry H–40 = Processed meats H–42 = Beverages H–46 = Fats/Oils H–48 = Sweets H–50 = Spices/Condiments/Sauces H–52 = Mixed foods/Soups/Sandwiches H–58 = Fast food H–74 = Convenience meals H–76 = Baby foods

Chol (mg)	Calc (mg)	Iron (mg)	Magn (mg)	Pota (mg)	Sodi (mg)	Zinc (mg)	Vit A (µg)	Thia (mg)	Vit E (mg α)	Ribo (mg)	Niac (mg)	Vit B$_6$ (mg)	Fola (µg)	Vit C (mg)	Vit B$_{12}$ (µg)	Sele (µg)
1	10	0.36	—	—	440	—	—	—	—	—	—	—	—	1	—	—
145	20	1.14	—	—	1145	—	—	—	—	—	—	—	—	1	—	—
75	10	0.70	—	—	440	—	—	—	—	—	—	—	—	1	—	—
165	10	1.00	—	—	1060	—	—	—	—	—	—	—	—	1	—	—
60	10	0.36	—	—	370	—	—	—	—	—	—	—	—	1	—	—
70	40	1.80	—	—	940	—	—	—	—	—	—	—	—	1	—	—
60	40	1.80	—	—	890	—	—	—	—	—	—	—	—	1	—	—
15	20	2.70	—	—	540	—	100	—	—	—	—	—	—	1	—	—
4	36	1.55	—	—	1323	—	—	—	—	—	—	—	—	8	—	—
102	7	0.12	—	—	718	—	—	—	—	—	—	—	—	1	—	—
127	8	0.14	—	—	764	—	—	—	—	—	—	—	—	1	—	—
128	10	0.18	—	—	772	—	—	—	—	—	—	—	—	1	—	—
70	20	0.90	—	—	1140	—	—	—	—	—	—	—	—	1	—	—
112	10	0.18	—	—	797	—	—	—	—	—	—	—	—	1	—	—
90	20	0.72	—	—	240	—	—	—	—	—	—	—	—	0	—	—
35	60	3.60	—	—	1120	—	—	—	—	—	—	—	—	9	—	—
30	20	1.80	—	—	700	—	—	—	—	—	—	—	—	5	—	—
10	20	1.08	—	—	1110	—	—	—	—	—	—	—	—	0	—	—
25	150	0.72	—	—	810	—	—	—	—	—	—	—	—	0	—	—
0	0	0.00	—	—	250	—	—	—	—	—	—	—	—	0	—	—
20	40	0.36	—	223	340	0.70	34	0.07	—	0.08	2.35	—	—	18	—	—
105	500	1.80	—	—	720	—	—	—	—	—	—	—	—	1	—	—
0	0	0.00	—	—	580	—	—	—	—	—	—	—	—	24	—	—
0	0	0.00	—	370	350	0.30	—	0.09	—	0.02	1.60	—	—	15	—	—
0	20	0.36	—	—	200	—	—	—	—	—	—	—	—	0	—	—
15	0	0.00	—	—	125	—	—	—	—	—	—	—	—	1	—	—
15	0	0.00	—	—	250	—	—	—	—	—	—	—	—	0	—	—
50	150	3.60	—	—	1310	—	—	—	—	—	—	—	—	9	—	—
0	10	0.18	—	45	250	—	3	—	—	—	—	—	—	4	—	—
85	300	4.50	—	430	1090	—	60	—	—	—	—	—	—	4	—	—
45	250	2.70	—	250	830	—	60	—	—	—	—	—	—	2	—	—
60	200	2.70	—	440	890	—	—	—	—	—	—	—	—	6	—	—
35	20	0.72	—	180	460	—	—	—	—	—	—	—	—	1	—	—
50	20	0.72	—	260	680	—	—	—	—	—	—	—	—	1	—	—
25	299	0.70	36	508	252	1.09	41	0.11	0.11	0.50	0.28	0.06	11	0	1	4
50	200	2.70	—	400	1100	—	—	—	—	—	—	—	—	6	—	—
235	300	2.70	—	210	830	—	—	—	0.72	—	—	—	—	1	—	—
50	200	1.80	—	280	890	—	40	—	—	—	—	—	—	1	—	—
0	20	1.44	—	1210	350	—	—	—	—	—	—	—	—	21	—	—
0	10	0.36	—	470	135	—	—	—	—	—	—	—	—	9	—	—
0	20	1.44	—	1370	390	—	—	—	—	—	—	—	—	24	—	—
15	300	1.80	—	550	240	—	—	—	—	—	—	—	—	24	—	—
0	40	1.09	—	410	20	—	—	—	—	—	—	—	—	24	—	—
30	200	2.70	—	230	590	—	5	—	—	—	—	—	—	2	—	—
0	10	0.36	—	210	330	—	—	—	—	—	—	—	—	2	—	—
0	10	0.18	—	7	0	—	—	—	—	—	—	—	—	1	—	—
95	150	1.44	—	360	740	—	323	—	—	—	—	—	—	15	—	—
75	150	1.08	—	290	120	—	273	—	—	—	—	—	—	15	—	—
40	100	1.08	—	420	240	—	—	—	—	—	—	—	—	12	—	—
10	40	0.18	—	13	440	—	—	—	0.00	—	—	—	—	1	—	—
20	60	0.18	—	16	500	—	—	—	15.40	—	—	—	—	1	—	—
0	10	0.18	—	9	730	—	—	—	0.00	—	—	—	—	2	—	—
20	40	0.18	—	64	530	—	—	—	—	—	—	—	—	1	—	—
20	100	4.50	—	280	770	—	—	—	—	—	—	—	—	1	—	—
70	200	4.50	—	370	840	—	10	—	—	—	—	—	—	2	—	—
95	350	4.50	—	420	1310	—	100	—	—	—	—	—	—	2	—	—
255	300	2.70	—	260	930	—	115	—	0.72	—	—	—	—	1	—	—

TABLE H–1
Food Composition

(DA+ code is for Wadsworth Diet Analysis program)   (For purposes of calculations, use "0" for t, <1, <.1, <.01, etc.)

DA + Code	Food Description	Quantity	Measure	Wt (g)	H₂O (g)	Ener (kcal)	Prot (g)	Carb (g)	Fiber (g)	Fat (g)	Sat	Mono	Poly	Trans
	FAST FOOD—Continued													
3163	Strawberry milkshake	8	fluid ounce(s)	226	168	256	8	43	1	6	3.93	—	—	—
74	Vanilla milkshake	8	fluid ounce(s)	227	169	254	9	40	0	7	4.28	1.98	0.26	—
	Pizza Hut													
39009	Hot chicken wings	2	item(s)	57	—	110	11	1	0	6	2.00	—	—	0.25
14025	Meat Lovers hand tossed pizza	1	slice(s)	125	—	320	16	30	2	15	7.00	—	—	0.53
14026	Meat Lovers pan pizza	1	slice(s)	130	—	360	16	29	2	20	7.00	—	—	0.53
31009	Meat Lovers stuffed crust pizza	1	slice(s)	188	—	500	25	44	3	25	11.00	—	—	1.11
14024	Meat Lovers thin 'n crispy pizza	1	slice(s)	112	—	310	15	22	2	18	8.00	—	—	0.57
14031	Pepperoni Lovers hand tossed pizza	1	slice(s)	114	—	300	15	30	2	14	7.00	—	—	0.50
14032	Pepperoni Lovers pan pizza	1	slice(s)	119	—	350	15	29	2	19	8.00	—	—	0.50
31011	Pepperoni Lovers stuffed crust pizza	1	slice(s)	171	—	480	23	44	3	24	11.00	—	—	1.05
14030	Pepperoni Lovers thin 'n crispy pizza	1	slice(s)	94	—	270	13	22	2	14	7.00	—	—	0.51
10834	Personal Pan pepperoni pizza	1	slice(s)	59	—	150	7	18	—	6	2.50	—	—	0.97
10842	Personal Pan supreme pizza	1	slice(s)	73	—	170	8	19	1	7	3.00	—	—	0.95
39013	Personal Pan Veggie Lovers pizza	1	slice(s)	69	—	150	6	19	1	6	2.00	—	—	0.50
14028	Veggie Lovers hand tossed pizza	1	slice(s)	120	—	220	10	31	2	6	3.00	—	—	0.25
14029	Veggie Lovers pan pizza	1	slice(s)	125	—	260	10	31	2	12	4.00	—	—	0.26
31010	Veggie Lovers stuffed crust pizza	1	slice(s)	181	—	370	17	45	3	14	7.00	—	—	0.53
14027	Veggie Lovers thin 'n crispy pizza	1	slice(s)	110	—	190	8	23	2	7	3.00	—	—	0.54
39012	Wing blue cheese dipping sauce	1	item(s)	43	—	230	2	2	0	24	5.00	—	—	1
39011	Wing ranch dipping sauce	1	item(s)	43	—	210	1	4	0	22	3.50	—	—	0.50
	Starbucks													
38042	Apple cider, tall steamed	12	fluid ounce(s)	360	—	180	0	45	0	0	0.00	0.00	0.00	0
38052	Cappuccino, tall	12	fluid ounce(s)	360	—	120	7	10	0	6	4.00	—	—	—
38053	Cappuccino, tall nonfat	12	fluid ounce(s)	360	—	80	7	11	0	0	0.00	0.00	0.00	0
38054	Cappuccino, tall soy milk	12	fluid ounce(s)	360	—	100	5	13	1	3	0.00	—	—	—
38059	Cinnamon spice mocha, tall nonfat w/o whipped cream	12	fluid ounce(s)	360	—	170	11	32	0	0	0.50	0.00	0.00	0
38057	Cinnamon spice mocha, tall w/whipped cream	12	fluid ounce(s)	360	—	320	10	31	0	17	11.00	—	—	—
38051	Espresso, single shot	1	fluid ounce(s)	30	—	5	0	1	0	0	0.00	0.00	0.00	—
38088	Flavored syrup, 1 pump	1	serving(s)	10	—	20	0	5	0	0	0.00	0.00	0.00	0
32562	Frappuccino coffee drink, lite mocha	9½	fluid ounce(s)	281	—	100	7	12	3	3	2.00	—	—	0
38079	Frappuccino, grande chocolate malt	16	fluid ounce(s)	480	—	470	15	87	2	10	3.50	—	—	—
38075	Frappuccino, grande mocha malt	12	fluid ounce(s)	360	—	430	14	91	1	7	4.00	—	—	—
32561	Frappuccino low fat coffee drink, all flavors	9½	fluid ounce(s)	281	—	190	6	39	0	3	2.00	—	—	—
38067	Frappuccino, tall caramel	12	fluid ounce(s)	360	—	210	4	43	0	3	1.50	—	—	—
38078	Frappuccino, tall chocolate	12	fluid ounce(s)	360	—	290	13	52	1	5	1.00	—	—	—
38069	Frappuccino, tall chocolate brownie	12	fluid ounce(s)	360	—	270	5	51	1	7	4.50	—	—	—
38070	Frappuccino, tall coffee	12	fluid ounce(s)	360	—	190	4	38	0	3	1.50	—	—	—
38071	Frappuccino, tall espresso	12	fluid ounce(s)	360	—	160	4	33	0	2	1.50	—	—	—
38073	Frappuccino, mocha	12	fluid ounce(s)	360	—	220	5	44	0	3	1.50	—	—	—
38072	Frappuccino, tall mocha coconut	12	fluid ounce(s)	360	—	300	5	58	2	7	5.00	—	—	—
38080	Frappuccino, tall vanilla	12	fluid ounce(s)	360	—	260	11	47	0	4	1.00	—	—	—
38074	Frappuccino, tall white chocolate	12	fluid ounce(s)	360	—	240	5	48	0	4	2.50	—	—	—
33111	Latte, tall w/nonfat milk	12	fluid ounce(s)	360	335	123	12	17	0	1	0.40	0.16	0.02	0
33112	Latte, tall w/whole milk	12	fluid ounce(s)	360	325	212	11	17	0	11	6.90	3.24	0.42	—
33109	Macchiato, tall caramel w/nonfat milk	12	fluid ounce(s)	360	—	140	7	27	0	1	0.40	—	—	—
33110	Macchiato, tall caramel w/whole milk	12	fluid ounce(s)	360	—	190	6	27	0	7	4.00	—	—	—
33107	Mocha coffee drink, tall nonfat, w/o whipped cream	12	fluid ounce(s)	360	—	180	12	33	1	2	1.50	0.68	0.08	—
38089	Mocha syrup	1	serving(s)	17	—	25	1	6	0	1	0.00	—	—	—
33108	Mocha, tall w/whole milk	12	fluid ounce(s)	360	—	340	12	33	1	20	12.00	3.48	0.44	—
38084	Tazo chai black tea, tall	12	fluid ounce(s)	360	—	210	6	36	0	5	3.50	—	—	—
38083	Tazo chai black tea, tall nonfat	12	fluid ounce(s)	360	—	170	6	37	0	0	0.00	0.00	0.00	0
38087	Tazo chai black tea, tall soy milk	12	fluid ounce(s)	360	—	190	4	39	1	2	0.00	—	—	—
38063	Tazo chai creme frappuccino, tall	12	fluid ounce(s)	360	—	280	11	51	0	4	1.00	—	—	—
38076	Tazo iced tea, tall	12	fluid ounce(s)	360	—	60	0	16	0	0	0.00	0.00	0.00	0
38077	Tazo tea, grande lemonade	16	fluid ounce(s)	480	—	120	0	31	0	0	0.00	0.00	0.00	0
38065	Tazoberry creme frappuccino, tall	12	fluid ounce(s)	360	—	240	4	54	1	1	0.00	—	—	—
38066	Tazoberry frappuccino, tall	12	fluid ounce(s)	360	—	140	1	36	1	0	0.00	0.00	0.00	0
38045	Vanilla creme steamed nonfat milk, tall w/whipped cream	12	fluid ounce(s)	360	—	180	12	32	0	0	0.00	0.00	0.00	—
38046	Vanilla creme steamed soy milk, tall w/whipped cream	12	fluid ounce(s)	360	—	300	8	37	1	12	6.00	—	—	—

Chol (mg)	Calc (mg)	Iron (mg)	Magn (mg)	Pota (mg)	Sodi (mg)	Zinc (mg)	Vit A (µg)	Thia (mg)	Vit E (mg α)	Ribo (mg)	Niac (mg)	Vit B$_6$ (mg)	Fola (µg)	Vit C (mg)	Vit B$_{12}$ (µg)	Sele (µg)
25	256	0.25	29	412	188	0.82	59	0.10	—	0.44	0.40	0.10	7	2	1	5
27	331	0.23	27	415	215	0.88	57	0.07	0.11	0.44	0.33	0.10	16	0	1	5
70	0	0.36	—	—	450	—	—	—	—	—	—	—	—	0	—	—
40	150	1.80	—	—	830	—	—	—	—	—	—	—	—	6	—	—
40	150	2.70	—	—	810	—	—	—	—	—	—	—	—	6	—	—
65	250	2.70	—	—	1450	—	—	—	—	—	—	—	—	9	—	—
45	150	1.80	—	—	880	—	—	—	—	—	—	—	—	9	—	—
40	200	1.80	—	—	730	—	58	—	—	—	—	—	—	2	—	—
40	200	2.70	—	—	710	—	58	—	—	—	—	—	—	2	—	—
65	300	2.70	—	—	1300	—	—	—	—	—	—	—	—	4	—	—
40	200	1.44	—	—	700	—	58	—	—	—	—	—	—	2	—	—
15	80	1.44	—	—	340	—	38	—	—	—	—	—	—	1	—	—
15	80	1.86	—	—	400	—	—	—	—	—	—	—	—	4	—	—
10	80	1.80	—	—	280	—	—	—	—	—	—	—	—	4	—	—
15	150	1.80	—	—	490	—	—	—	—	—	—	—	—	9	—	—
15	150	2.70	—	—	470	—	—	—	—	—	—	—	—	9	—	—
35	250	2.70	—	—	980	—	—	—	—	—	—	—	—	12	—	—
15	150	1.44	—	—	480	—	—	—	—	—	—	—	—	12	—	—
25	20	0.00	—	—	550	0	—	—	—	—	—	—	—	0	—	—
10	0	0.00	—	—	340	0	—	—	—	—	—	—	—	0	—	—
0	0	1.08	—	—	15	—	0	—	—	—	—	—	—	0	0	—
25	250	0.00	—	—	95	—	0	—	—	—	—	—	—	1	0	—
3	200	0.00	—	—	100	—	0	—	—	—	—	—	—	0	0	—
0	250	0.72	—	—	75	—	0	—	—	—	—	—	—	0	0	—
5	300	0.72	—	—	150	—	0	—	—	—	—	—	—	0	0	—
70	350	1.08	—	—	140	—	0	—	—	—	—	—	—	2	0	—
0	0	0.00	—	—	0	—	0	—	—	—	—	—	—	0	0	—
0	0	0.00	—	—	0	—	0	—	—	—	—	—	—	0	0	—
13	200	1.08	—	—	80	—	0	—	—	—	—	—	—	0	—	—
15	250	2.70	—	—	420	—	0	—	—	—	—	—	—	12	0	—
20	250	1.08	—	—	390	—	0	—	—	—	—	—	—	0	0	—
12	220	0.00	—	—	110	—	—	—	—	—	—	—	—	0	—	—
10	150	0.00	—	—	180	—	0	—	—	—	—	—	—	0	0	—
3	400	1.80	—	—	300	—	0	—	—	—	—	—	—	5	0	—
10	150	1.44	—	—	220	—	0	—	—	—	—	—	—	0	0	—
10	150	0.00	—	—	180	—	0	—	—	—	—	—	—	0	0	—
10	100	0.00	—	—	160	—	0	—	—	—	—	—	—	0	0	—
10	150	0.72	—	—	180	—	0	—	—	—	—	—	—	0	0	—
10	150	1.08	—	—	220	—	0	—	—	—	—	—	—	0	0	—
3	400	0.00	—	—	280	—	0	—	—	—	—	—	—	4	0	—
10	150	0.00	—	—	210	—	0	—	—	—	—	—	—	0	0	—
6	420	0.18	40	—	174	1.35	—	0.12	—	0.47	0.36	0.14	18	4	1	—
46	400	0.18	47	254	165	1.28	—	0.13	—	0.54	0.35	0.14	17	3	1	—
25	250	0.36	—	—	110	—	—	—	—	—	—	—	—	2	—	—
25	200	0.36	—	—	105	—	—	—	—	—	—	—	—	1	—	—
5	350	2.70	—	—	150	—	—	—	—	—	—	—	—	2	—	—
0	0	0.72	—	—	0	—	0	—	—	—	—	—	—	0	0	—
47	300	0.18	—	—	169	—	—	—	—	—	—	—	—	2	—	—
20	200	0.36	—	—	85	—	0	—	—	—	—	—	—	1	0	—
5	200	0.36	—	—	95	—	0	—	—	—	—	—	—	0	0	—
0	200	0.72	—	—	70	—	0	—	—	—	—	—	—	0	0	—
3	400	0.00	—	—	280	—	0	—	—	—	—	—	—	4	0	—
0	0	0.00	—	—	0	—	0	—	—	—	—	—	—	0	0	—
0	0	0.00	—	—	15	—	0	—	—	—	—	—	—	5	0	—
0	150	0.00	—	—	125	—	0	—	—	—	—	—	—	1	0	—
0	0	0.00	—	—	30	—	0	—	—	—	—	—	—	0	0	—
5	350	0.00	—	—	170	—	0	—	—	—	—	—	—	0	0	—
30	400	1.44	—	—	130	—	0	—	—	—	—	—	—	0	0	—

TABLE H–1
Food Composition

(DA+ code is for Wadsworth Diet Analysis program)   (For purposes of calculations, use "0" for t, <1, <.1, <.01, etc.)

DA + Code	Food Description	Quantity	Measure	Wt (g)	H₂O (g)	Ener (kcal)	Prot (g)	Carb (g)	Fiber (g)	Fat (g)	Sat	Fat Breakdown (g) Mono	Poly	Trans
	FAST FOOD—Continued													
38044	Vanilla creme steamed whole milk, tall w/whipped cream	12	fluid ounce(s)	360	—	340	10	31	0	18	12.00	—	—	—
38090	Whipped cream	1	serving(s)	27	—	100	0	2	0	9	6.00	—	—	—
38062	White chocolate mocha, tall nonfat w/o whipped cream	12	fluid ounce(s)	360	—	260	12	45	0	4	3.00	—	—	—
38061	White chocolate mocha, tall w/whipped cream	12	fluid ounce(s)	360	—	410	11	44	0	20	13.00	—	—	—
38048	White hot chocolate, tall w/o whipped cream	12	fluid ounce(s)	360	—	300	15	51	0	5	3.50	—	—	—
38047	White hot chocolate, tall w/whipped cream	12	fluid ounce(s)	360	—	460	13	50	0	22	15.00	—	—	—
38050	White hot chocolate soy milk, tall w/whipped cream	12	fluid ounce(s)	360	—	420	11	56	1	16	9.00	—	—	—
	Subway													
34023	Asiago caesar chicken wrap	1	item(s)	244	—	413	22	47	2	15	3.00	—	—	0
38622	Atkins-friendly chicken bacon ranch wrap	1	item(s)	213	—	480	40	19	11	27	9.00	—	—	0
38623	Atkins-friendly turkey bacon melt wrap	1	item(s)	199	—	430	32	22	12	25	9.00	—	—	0
34029	Bacon & egg breakfast sandwich	1	item(s)	127	—	302	14	29	1	15	4.00	—	—	0
32045	Chocolate chip cookie	1	item(s)	48	—	209	3	29	1	10	3.50	—	—	1.07
32048	Chocolate chip M&M cookie	1	item(s)	48	—	210	2	29	1	10	3.00	—	—	2.67
32049	Chocolate chunk cookie	1	item(s)	48	—	210	2	30	1	10	3.00	—	—	2.67
4024	Classic Italian B.M.T. sandwich, 6", white bread	1	item(s)	250	—	453	21	40	3	24	8.00	—	—	0
16397	Club salad	1	item(s)	323	—	145	17	12	3	4	1.00	—	—	0
3422	Club sandwich, 6", white bread	1	item(s)	253	—	294	22	40	3	5	1.50	—	—	0
4030	Cold cut trio sandwich, 6", white bread	1	item(s)	254	—	415	19	40	3	20	7.00	—	—	0
34030	Ham & egg breakfast sandwich	1	item(s)	147	—	291	15	30	1	12	3.00	—	—	0
3885	Ham sandwich, 6", white bread	1	item(s)	219	—	261	17	39	3	5	1.50	—	—	0
34026	Honey mustard melt sandwich, 6", Italian bread	1	item(s)	258	—	373	23	47	3	11	5.00	—	—	—
34027	Horseradish roast beef sandwich, 6", Italian bread	1	item(s)	230	—	401	18	42	3	17	3.00	—	—	—
4651	Meatball sandwich, 6", white bread	1	item(s)	284	—	501	23	46	4	25	10.00	—	—	0.75
15839	Melt sandwich, 6", white bread	1	item(s)	256	—	380	23	41	3	15	5.00	—	—	—
32046	Oatmeal raisin cookie	1	item(s)	48	—	197	3	29	1	8	2.00	—	—	2.67
32047	Peanut butter cookie	1	item(s)	48	—	220	3	26	1	12	3.00	—	—	1.07
3957	Roast beef sandwich, 6", white bread	1	item(s)	220	—	264	18	39	3	5	1.00	—	—	0
16403	Roasted chicken breast salad	1	item(s)	304	—	137	16	12	3	3	0.50	—	—	—
16378	Roasted chicken breast sandwich, 6", white bread	1	item(s)	234	—	311	25	40	3	6	1.50	—	—	0
34028	Southwest steak & cheese sandwich, 6", Italian bread	1	item(s)	255	—	412	23	42	4	18	6.00	—	—	—
4032	Spicy italian sandwich, 6", white bread	1	item(s)	213	—	458	19	42	2	24	9.00	—	—	0
4031	Steak & cheese sandwich, 6", white bread	1	item(s)	253	—	362	23	41	4	13	4.50	—	—	0
34024	Steak & cheese wrap	1	item(s)	245	—	353	22	46	3	9	4.00	—	—	—
32050	Sugar cookie	1	item(s)	48	—	222	2	28	1	12	3.00	—	—	3.73
16402	Tuna salad	1	item(s)	314	—	238	13	11	3	16	4.00	—	—	—
15844	Tuna sandwich, 6", white bread	1	item(s)	252	—	419	18	39	3	21	5.00	—	—	—
15834	Turkey breast & ham sandwich, 6", white bread	1	item(s)	229	—	267	18	40	3	5	1.00	—	—	0
34025	Turkey breast & bacon wrap	1	item(s)	228	—	318	19	45	2	7	2.50	—	—	—
16376	Turkey breast sandwich, 6", white bread	1	item(s)	220	—	254	16	39	3	4	1.00	—	—	0
16375	Veggie delite, 6", white bread	1	item(s)	163	—	200	7	37	3	3	0.50	—	—	0
32051	White macadamia nut cookie	1	item(s)	48	—	221	2	27	1	12	3.00	—	—	1.07
	Taco Bell													
29906	7-layer burrito	1	item(s)	283	—	530	18	67	10	22	8.00	—	—	3
744	Bean burrito	1	item(s)	198	—	370	14	55	8	10	3.50	—	—	2
749	Beef burrito supreme	1	item(s)	248	—	440	18	51	7	18	8.00	—	—	2
33417	Beef chalupa supreme	1	item(s)	153	—	390	14	31	3	24	10.00	—	—	3
29910	Beef gordita supreme	1	item(s)	153	—	310	14	30	3	16	7.00	—	—	0.50
2014	Beef soft taco	1	item(s)	99	—	210	10	21	2	10	4.50	—	—	1
10860	Beef soft taco supreme	1	item(s)	134	—	260	11	22	3	14	7.00	—	—	1
2018	Big beef burrito supreme	1	item(s)	291	—	510	23	52	11	23	9.00	6.55	1.61	—
14467	Big chicken burrito supreme	1	item(s)	255	—	460	27	50	3	17	6.00	—	—	—
34472	Chicken burrito supreme	1	item(s)	248	—	410	21	50	5	14	6.00	—	—	2
33418	Chicken chalupa supreme	1	item(s)	153	—	370	17	30	1	20	8.00	—	—	3

PAGE KEY: H–2 = Breads/Baked Goods   H–6 = Cereal/Rice/Pasta   H–10 = Fruit   H–14 = Vegetables/Legumes   H–24 = Nuts/Seeds   H–26 = Vegetarian
H–28 = Dairy   H–34 = Eggs   H–34 = Seafood   H–36 = Meats   H–40 = Poultry   H–40 = Processed meats   H–42 = Beverages   H–46 = Fats/Oils
H–48 = Sweets   H–50 = Spices/Condiments/Sauces   H–52 = Mixed foods/Soups/Sandwiches   H–58 = Fast food   H–74 = Convenience meals   H–76 = Baby foods

Chol (mg)	Calc (mg)	Iron (mg)	Magn (mg)	Pota (mg)	Sodi (mg)	Zinc (mg)	Vit A (µg)	Thia (mg)	Vit E (mg α)	Ribo (mg)	Niac (mg)	Vit B$_6$ (mg)	Fola (µg)	Vit C (mg)	Vit B$_{12}$ (µg)	Sele (µg)
75	40	0.00	—	—	160	—	0	—	—	—	—	—	—	2	0	—
40	0	0.00	—	—	10	—	0	—	—	—	—	—	—	0	0	—
5	400	0.00	—	—	210	—	0	—	—	—	—	—	—	0	0	—
70	400	0.00	—	—	210	—	0	—	—	—	—	—	—	2	0	—
10	450	0.00	—	—	250	—	0	—	—	—	—	—	—	0	0	—
75	500	0.00	—	—	250	—	0	—	—	—	—	—	—	4	0	—
35	500	1.44	—	—	210	—	0	—	—	—	—	—	—	0	0	—
46	40	2.70	—	—	1320	—	—	—	—	—	—	—	—	15	—	—
90	350	2.70	—	—	1340	—	—	—	—	—	—	—	—	7	—	—
65	300	2.70	—	—	1650	—	—	—	—	—	—	—	—	5	—	—
185	60	1.80	—	—	480	—	—	—	—	—	—	—	—	15	—	—
12	0	1.00	—	—	135	—	0	—	—	—	—	—	—	0	—	—
13	0	1.00	—	—	135	—	0	—	—	—	—	—	—	0	—	—
12	0	1.00	—	—	150	—	0	—	—	—	—	—	—	0	—	—
56	100	2.70	—	—	1740	—	—	—	—	—	—	—	—	24	—	—
30	40	1.80	—	—	1070	—	—	—	—	—	—	—	—	30	—	—
30	40	3.60	—	—	1250	—	60	—	—	—	—	—	—	24	—	—
57	150	3.60	—	—	1670	—	100	—	—	—	—	—	—	24	—	—
189	60	2.70	—	—	700	—	67	—	—	—	—	—	—	15	—	—
25	40	2.70	—	—	1260	—	—	—	—	—	—	—	—	24	—	—
41	100	2.70	—	—	1570	—	—	—	—	—	—	—	—	24	—	—
27	40	3.60	—	—	880	—	—	—	—	—	—	—	—	24	—	—
56	100	3.60	—	—	1350	—	—	—	—	—	—	—	—	24	—	—
41	100	2.70	—	—	1690	—	—	—	—	—	—	—	—	24	—	—
14	0	1.00	—	—	180	—	0	—	—	—	—	—	—	0	—	—
0	0	1.00	—	—	200	—	0	—	—	—	—	—	—	0	—	—
20	40	3.60	—	—	840	—	60	—	—	—	—	—	—	24	—	—
36	40	1.08	—	—	730	—	—	—	—	—	—	—	—	30	—	—
48	60	3.60	—	—	880	—	—	—	—	—	—	—	—	24	—	—
44	100	6.30	—	—	1120	—	—	—	—	—	—	—	—	24	—	—
57	30	3.00	—	—	1498	—	—	—	—	—	—	—	—	13	—	—
37	100	6.30	—	—	1200	—	—	—	—	—	—	—	—	24	—	—
37	150	7.20	—	—	1400	—	—	—	—	—	—	—	—	15	—	—
18	0	1.00	—	—	170	—	0	—	—	—	—	—	—	0	—	—
42	100	1.08	—	—	880	—	177	—	—	—	—	—	—	30	—	—
42	100	2.70	—	—	1180	—	100	—	—	—	—	—	—	24	—	—
23	40	2.70	—	—	1210	—	—	—	—	—	—	—	—	24	—	—
24	60	2.70	—	—	1490	—	—	—	—	—	—	—	—	15	—	—
15	40	2.70	—	—	1000	—	—	—	—	—	—	—	—	24	—	—
0	40	1.80	—	—	500	—	—	—	—	—	—	—	—	24	—	—
13	0	1.00	—	—	140	—	0	—	—	—	—	—	—	—	—	—
25	300	3.59	—	—	1360	—	—	—	—	—	—	—	—	5	—	—
10	200	2.69	—	—	1200	—	53	—	—	—	—	—	—	5	—	—
40	200	2.70	—	—	1330	—	351	—	—	—	—	—	—	9	—	—
40	150	1.80	—	—	600	—	—	—	—	—	—	—	—	5	—	—
35	150	2.70	—	—	590	—	—	—	—	—	—	—	—	5	—	—
25	100	1.80	—	—	620	—	44	—	—	—	—	—	—	2	—	—
40	150	1.80	—	—	630	—	73	—	—	—	—	—	—	5	—	—
60	150	2.70	—	493	1500	—	877	—	—	0.07	—	—	—	5	—	—
70	101	1.46	—	—	1200	—	—	—	—	—	—	—	—	2	—	—
45	200	2.70	—	—	1270	—	—	—	—	—	—	—	—	9	—	—
45	100	1.08	—	—	530	—	—	—	—	—	—	—	—	5	—	—

TABLE H–1
Food Composition

(DA+ code is for Wadsworth Diet Analysis program)   (For purposes of calculations, use "0" for t, <1, <.1, <.01, etc.)

DA + Code	Food Description	Quantity	Measure	Wt (g)	H₂O (g)	Ener (kcal)	Prot (g)	Carb (g)	Fiber (g)	Fat (g)	Sat	Mono	Poly	Trans
	FAST FOOD—Continued													
29900	Chicken fajita wrap supreme	1	item(s)	255	—	510	20	53	3	24	7.76	—	—	—
29895	Choco taco ice cream dessert	1	item(s)	113	—	310	3	37	1	17	10.00	—	—	—
10794	Cinnamon twists	1	serving(s)	35	—	160	0	28	0	5	1.00	—	—	1.50
14465	Grilled chicken burrito	1	item(s)	198	—	390	19	49	3	13	4.00	—	—	—
29911	Grilled chicken gordita supreme	1	item(s)	153	—	290	17	28	2	12	5.00	—	—	0
14463	Grilled chicken soft taco	1	item(s)	99	—	190	14	19	0	6	2.50	—	—	—
29912	Grilled steak gordita supreme	1	item(s)	153	—	290	16	28	2	13	6.00	—	—	0.50
29904	Grilled steak soft taco	1	item(s)	127	—	280	12	21	1	17	4.50	—	—	1
29905	Grilled steak soft taco supreme	1	item(s)	135	—	240	15	20	2	11	5.00	—	—	—
2021	Mexican pizza	1	serving(s)	216	—	550	21	46	7	31	11.00	—	—	5
2011	Nachos	1	serving(s)	99	—	320	5	33	2	19	4.50	—	—	5
2012	Nachos bellgrande	1	serving(s)	308	—	780	20	80	12	43	13.00	—	—	10
34473	Steak burrito supreme	1	item(s)	248	—	420	19	50	6	16	7.00	—	—	2
33419	Steak chalupa supreme	1	item(s)	153	—	370	15	29	2	22	8.00	—	—	3
29899	Steak fajita wrap supreme	1	item(s)	255	—	510	21	52	3	25	8.00	—	—	—
747	Taco	1	item(s)	78	—	170	8	13	3	10	4.00	—	—	0.50
2015	Taco salad w/salsa, with shell	1	serving(s)	533	—	790	31	73	13	42	15.00	—	—	8.75
14459	Taco supreme	1	item(s)	113	—	220	9	14	3	14	7.00	—	—	1
748	Tostada	1	item(s)	170	—	250	11	29	7	10	4.00	—	—	1.50
29901	Veggie fajita wrap supreme	1	item(s)	255	—	470	11	55	3	22	7.00	—	—	—
	CONVENIENCE MEALS													
	Banquet													
29961	Barbeque chicken meal	1	item(s)	281	—	330	16	37	2	13	3.00	—	—	—
14788	Boneless white fried chicken meal	1	item(s)	234	—	490	14	49	2	27	7.00	—	—	—
29960	Fish sticks meal	1	item(s)	187	—	270	13	31	3	10	3.00	—	—	—
29957	Lasagna with meat sauce meal	1	item(s)	312	—	320	15	46	7	9	4.00	—	—	—
14777	Macaroni & cheese meal	1	item(s)	340	—	420	15	57	5	14	8.00	—	—	—
1741	Meatloaf meal	1	item(s)	269	—	240	14	20	4	11	4.00	—	—	—
39418	Pepperoni pizza meal	1	item(s)	191	—	480	11	56	5	23	8.00	—	—	—
33759	Roasted white turkey meal	1	item(s)	255	—	230	14	30	5	6	2.00	—	—	—
1743	Salisbury steak meal	1	item(s)	269	197	380	12	28	3	24	12.00	—	—	—
	Budget Gourmet													
1914	Cheese manicotti w/meat sauce	1	item(s)	284	194	420	18	38	4	22	11.00	6.00	1.34	—
1915	Chicken w/fettucini	1	item(s)	284	—	380	20	33	3	19	10.00	—	—	—
3986	Light beef stroganoff	1	item(s)	248	177	290	20	32	3	7	4.00	—	—	—
3996	Light sirloin of beef in herb sauce	1	item(s)	269	214	260	19	30	5	7	4.00	2.30	0.31	—
3987	Light vegetable lasagna	1	item(s)	298	227	290	15	36	5	9	1.79	0.89	0.60	—
	Healthy Choice													
36979	Bowls chicken teriyaki with rice	1	item(s)	298	—	330	19	50	5	6	2.00	2.00	2.00	—
9425	Cheese French bread pizza	1	item(s)	170	—	360	20	57	5	5	1.50	—	—	—
9306	Chicken enchilada suprema meal	1	item(s)	320	252	360	13	59	8	7	3.00	2.00	2.00	—
9316	Lemon pepper fish meal	1	item(s)	303	—	280	11	49	5	5	2.00	1.00	2.00	—
9322	Traditional salisbury steak meal	1	item(s)	354	250	360	23	45	5	9	3.50	4.00	1.00	—
9359	Traditional turkey breasts meal	1	item(s)	298	—	330	21	50	4	5	2.00	1.50	1.50	—
9451	Zucchini lasagna	1	item(s)	383	—	280	13	47	5	4	2.50	—	—	—
	Stouffers													
2363	Cheese enchiladas with mexican rice	1	serving(s)	276	—	370	12	48	5	14	5.00	—	—	—
2313	Cheese French bread pizza	1	serving(s)	294	—	370	14	43	3	16	6.00	—	—	—
11138	Cheese manicotti w/tomato sauce	1	item(s)	255	—	330	17	35	3	13	8.00	—	—	—
2366	Chicken pot pie	1	item(s)	284	—	740	23	56	4	47	18.00	12.41	10.48	—
11116	Homestyle baked chicken breast w/mashed potatoes & gravy	1	item(s)	252	—	260	19	21	1	11	3.00	—	—	—
11146	Homestyle beef pot roast & potatoes	1	item(s)	252	—	270	16	25	3	12	4.50	—	—	—
11152	Homestyle roast turkey breast w/stuffing & mashed potatoes	1	item(s)	273	—	300	16	34	2	11	3.00	—	—	—
11043	Lean Cuisine Cafe Classics baked chicken & whipped potatoes w/stuffing	1	item(s)	227	—	240	17	33	3	5	1.50	1.50	1.00	0
11046	Lean Cuisine Cafe Classics honey mustard chicken	1	item(s)	213	—	260	18	37	1	4	1.50	1.00	1.00	0
360	Lean Cuisine Everyday Favorites chicken chow mein w/rice	1	item(s)	255	—	210	12	33	2	3	1.00	1.00	0.50	0
9467	Lean Cuisine Everyday Favorites fettucini alfredo	1	item(s)	262	—	280	13	40	2	7	3.50	2.00	1.00	0
11055	Lean Cuisine Everyday Favorites lasagna w/meat sauce	1	item(s)	291	—	300	19	41	3	8	4.00	2.00	0.50	0
9479	Lean Cuisine French bread deluxe pizza	1	item(s)	174	—	330	18	44	3	9	3.50	1.50	1.00	0

PAGE KEY: H–2 = Breads/Baked Goods   H–6 = Cereal/Rice/Pasta   H–10 = Fruit   H–14 = Vegetables/Legumes   H–24 = Nuts/Seeds   H–26 = Vegetarian
H–28 = Dairy   H–34 = Eggs   H–34 = Seafood   H–36 = Meats   H–40 = Poultry   H–40 = Processed meats   H–42 = Beverages   H–46 = Fats/Oils
H–48 = Sweets   H–50 = Spices/Condiments/Sauces   H–52 = Mixed foods/Soups/Sandwiches   H–58 = Fast food   H–74 = Convenience meals   H–76 = Baby foods

Chol (mg)	Calc (mg)	Iron (mg)	Magn (mg)	Pota (mg)	Sodi (mg)	Zinc (mg)	Vit A (µg)	Thia (mg)	Vit E (mg α)	Ribo (mg)	Niac (mg)	Vit B_6 (mg)	Fola (µg)	Vit C (mg)	Vit B_{12} (µg)	Sele (µg)
57	165	1.52	—	—	1182	—	—	—	—	—	—	—	—	7	—	—
20	60	0.72	—	—	100	—	—	—	—	—	—	—	—	0	—	—
0	0	0.37	—	—	150	—	0	—	—	—	—	—	—	0	—	—
40	151	1.44	—	—	1240	—	—	—	—	—	—	—	—	2	—	—
45	100	1.80	—	—	530	—	—	—	—	—	—	—	—	5	—	—
30	100	1.08	—	—	550	—	15	—	—	—	—	—	—	1	—	—
35	100	2.70	—	—	520	—	—	—	—	—	—	—	—	4	—	—
30	100	1.44	—	—	650	—	29	—	—	—	—	—	—	4	—	—
35	100	1.08	—	—	510	—	29	—	—	—	—	—	—	4	—	—
45	350	3.60	—	—	1030	—	—	—	—	—	—	—	—	6	—	—
4	80	0.72	—	—	530	—	0	—	—	—	—	—	—	0	—	—
35	200	2.70	—	—	1300	—	162	—	—	—	—	—	—	6	—	—
35	200	2.70	—	—	1260	—	789	—	—	—	—	—	—	9	—	—
35	100	1.44	—	—	520	—	—	—	—	—	—	—	—	4	—	—
50	150	1.80	—	—	1200	—	—	—	—	—	—	—	—	6	—	—
25	60	1.08	—	—	350	—	44	—	—	—	—	—	—	2	—	—
65	400	6.23	—	—	1670	—	—	—	—	—	—	—	—	21	—	—
40	80	1.44	—	—	360	—	73	—	—	—	—	—	—	5	—	—
15	150	1.44	—	—	710	—	281	—	—	—	—	—	—	5	—	—
30	150	1.44	—	—	990	—	—	—	—	—	—	—	—	6	—	—
50	40	1.08	—	—	1210	—	0	—	—	—	—	—	—	5	—	—
65	60	1.08	—	—	1150	—	—	—	—	—	—	—	—	0	—	—
30	60	1.44	—	—	690	—	—	—	—	—	—	—	—	2	—	—
20	100	2.70	—	—	1170	—	—	—	—	—	—	—	—	0	—	—
20	150	1.44	—	—	1330	—	0	—	—	—	—	—	—	0	—	—
30	0	1.80	—	—	1040	—	0	—	—	—	—	—	—	0	—	—
35	150	1.80	—	—	870	—	0	—	—	—	—	—	—	0	—	—
25	60	1.80	—	—	1070	—	—	—	—	—	—	—	—	4	—	—
60	40	1.44	—	—	1140	—	0	—	—	—	—	—	—	0	—	—
85	300	2.70	45	484	810	2.29	—	0.45	—	0.51	4.00	0.23	31	0	1	—
85	100	2.70	—	—	810	—	—	0.15	—	0.43	6.00	—	—	0	0	—
35	40	1.80	39	280	580	4.71	—	0.17	—	0.37	4.28	0.27	19	2	3	—
30	40	1.80	58	540	850	4.81	—	0.16	—	0.29	5.53	0.37	38	6	2	—
15	283	3.03	79	420	780	1.39	—	0.22	—	0.45	3.13	0.32	75	59	<1	—
40	20	0.72	—	—	600	—	—	—	—	—	—	—	—	15	—	—
10	350	3.60	—	—	600	—	—	—	—	—	—	—	—	12	—	—
30	40	1.44	—	—	580	—	—	—	—	—	—	—	—	4	—	—
30	40	0.36	—	—	580	—	—	—	—	—	—	—	—	30	—	—
45	80	2.70	—	—	580	—	—	—	—	—	—	—	—	21	—	—
35	40	1.44	—	—	600	—	—	—	—	—	—	—	—	0	—	—
10	200	1.80	—	—	310	—	—	—	—	—	—	—	—	0	—	—
25	200	1.44	—	360	890	—	—	—	—	—	—	—	—	12	—	—
15	200	1.80	—	240	880	—	—	—	—	—	—	—	—	0	—	—
40	350	1.08	—	430	810	—	—	—	—	—	—	—	—	1	—	—
65	150	2.70	—	—	1170	—	—	—	—	—	—	—	—	2	—	—
50	20	0.72	—	500	760	—	0	—	—	—	—	—	—	0	—	—
35	20	1.80	—	790	820	—	—	—	—	—	—	—	—	6	—	—
35	40	0.72	—	450	1190	—	0	—	—	—	—	—	—	0	—	—
30	80	0.72	—	480	690	—	—	—	—	—	—	—	—	0	—	—
35	60	0.36	—	370	640	—	—	—	—	—	—	—	—	0	—	—
30	20	0.36	—	310	620	—	—	—	—	—	—	—	—	0	—	—
20	200	0.36	—	260	670	—	0	—	—	—	—	—	—	0	—	—
30	200	1.08	—	590	650	—	—	—	—	—	—	—	—	5	—	—
20	100	1.80	—	390	630	—	—	—	—	—	—	—	—	9	—	—

TABLE H–1

Food Composition (DA+ code is for Wadsworth Diet Analysis program) (For purposes of calculations, use "0" for t, <1, <.1, <.01, etc.)

DA + Code	Food Description	Quantity	Measure	Wt (g)	H₂O (g)	Ener (kcal)	Prot (g)	Carb (g)	Fiber (g)	Fat (g)	Fat Breakdown (g) Sat	Mono	Poly	Trans
	CONVENIENCE MEALS—Continued													
	Weight Watchers													
11164	Smart Ones chicken enchiladas suiza entree	1	serving(s)	255	—	270	15	33	2	9	3.50	—	—	—
11155	Smart Ones garden lasagna entree	1	item(s)	312	—	270	14	36	5	7	3.50	—	—	—
11187	Smart Ones pepperoni pizza	1	item(s)	158	—	390	23	46	4	12	4.00	—	—	—
31514	Smart Ones spicy penne pasta & ricotta	1	item(s)	289	—	280	11	45	4	6	2.00	—	—	—
31512	Smart Ones spicy szechuan style vegetables & chicken	1	item(s)	255	—	220	11	39	3	2	0.50	—	—	—
	BABY FOODS													
787	Apple juice	4	fluid ounce(s)	127	112	60	0	15	<1	<1	0.02	0.00	0.04	—
778	Applesauce, strained	4	tablespoon(s)	64	55	31	<1	8	1	<1	0.02	0.01	0.04	—
779	Bananas w/tapioca, strained	4	tablespoon(s)	60	50	34	<1	9	1	<.1	0.02	0.01	0.01	—
604	Carrots, strained	4	tablespoon(s)	56	52	15	<1	3	1	<.1	0.01	0.00	0.03	—
770	Chicken noodle dinner, strained	4	tablespoon(s)	64	55	42	2	6	1	1	0.38	0.55	0.30	—
801	Green beans, strained	4	tablespoon(s)	60	0.05	15	0.77	3.53	1.13	0.05	0.01	0	0.03	—
910	Human milk, mature	2	fluid ounce(s)	62	54	43	1	4	0	3	1.24	1.02	0.31	—
760	Mixed cereal, prepared w/whole milk	4	ounce(s)	114	85	128	5	18	1	4	2.19	1.25	0.43	—
772	Mixed vegetable dinner, strained	2	ounce(s)	57	50	23	1	5	1	<.1	0.00	0.00	0.06	—
762	Rice cereal, prepared w/whole milk	4	ounce(s)	114	85	131	4	19	<1	4	2.64	1.02	0.16	—
758	Teething biscuits	1	item(s)	11	1	43	1	8	<1	<1	0.17	0.16	0.09	—

PAGE KEY: H–2 = Breads/Baked Goods H–6 = Cereal/Rice/Pasta H–10 = Fruit H–14 = Vegetables/Legumes H–24 = Nuts/Seeds H–26 = Vegetarian
H–28 = Dairy H–34 = Eggs H–34 = Seafood H–36 = Meats H–40 = Poultry H–40 = Processed meats H–42 = Beverages H–46 = Fats/Oils
H–48 = Sweets H–50 = Spices/Condiments/Sauces H–52 = Mixed foods/Soups/Sandwiches H–58 = Fast food H–74 = Convenience meals H–76 = Baby foods

Chol (mg)	Calc (mg)	Iron (mg)	Magn (mg)	Pota (mg)	Sodi (mg)	Zinc (mg)	Vit A (µg)	Thia (mg)	Vit E (mg α)	Ribo (mg)	Niac (mg)	Vit B_6 (mg)	Fola (µg)	Vit C (mg)	Vit B_{12} (µg)	Sele (µg)
50	250	1.08	—	—	660	—	—	—	—	—	—	—	—	4	—	—
30	350	1.80	—	—	610	—	—	—	—	—	—	—	—	6	—	—
45	450	1.80	—	320	650	—	55	—	—	—	—	—	—	5	—	—
5	150	2.70	—	250	400	—	—	—	—	—	—	—	—	6	—	—
10	150	1.80	—	—	730	—	—	—	—	—	—	—	—	2	—	—
0	5	0.72	4	115	4	0.04	1	0.01	0.76	0.02	0.11	0.04	0	73	0	<1
0	3	0.14	2	45	1	0.01	1	0.01	0.38	0.02	0.04	0.02	1	25	0	<1
0	3	0.12	6	53	5	0.04	1	0.01	0.36	0.02	0.11	0.07	4	10	0	<1
0	12	0.21	5	110	21	0.08	321	0.01	0.29	0.02	0.26	0.04	8	3	0	<1
10	17	0.41	9	89	15	0.35	70	0.03	0.13	0.04	0.46	0.04	7	<.1	<.1	2
0	23.39	0.44	14.39	94.8	1.2	0.12	27	0.01	0.31	0.05	0.2	0.02	21	3.11	0	0.18
9	20	0.02	2	31	10	0.10	38	0.01	0.05	0.02	0.11	0.01	3	3	<.1	1
12	250	11.85	31	226	53	0.81	28	0.49	—	0.66	6.56	0.07	12	1	<.1	—
0	12	0.19	6	69	5	0.09	77	0.01	—	0.02	0.29	0.04	5	2	0	<1
12	272	13.85	51	216	52	0.73	25	0.53	—	0.57	5.91	0.13	9	1	<.1	4
0	29	0.39	4	36	40	0.10	3	0.03	0.03	0.06	0.48	0.01	5	1	<.1	3

WHO: Nutrition Recommendations
Canada: Guidelines and Meal Planning

CONTENTS

Nutrition Recommendations from WHO
Eating Well with Canada's Food Guide
Canada's Meal Planning for Healthy Eating

This appendix presents nutrition recommendations from the World Health Organization (WHO) and details for Canadians on the *Eating Well with Canada's Food Guide* and the *Beyond the Basics* meal planning system.

Nutrition Recommendations from WHO

The World Health Organization (WHO) has assessed the relationships between diet and the development of chronic diseases. Its recommendations include:

- Energy: sufficient to support growth, physical activity, and a healthy body weight (BMI between 18.5 and 24.9) and to avoid weight gain greater than 11 pounds (5 kilograms) during adult life

- Total fat: 15 to 30 percent of total energy

- Saturated fatty acids: <10 percent of total energy

- Polyunsaturated fatty acids: 6 to 10 percent of total energy

- Omega-6 polyunsaturated fatty acids: 5 to 8 percent of total energy

- Omega-3 polyunsaturated fatty acids: 1 to 2 percent of total energy

- *Trans* fatty acids: <1 percent of total energy

- Total carbohydrate: 55 to 75 percent of total energy

- Sugars: <10 percent of total energy

- Protein: 10 to 15 percent of total energy

- Cholesterol: <300 mg per day

- Salt (sodium): <5 g salt per day (<2 g sodium per day), appropriately iodized

- Fruits and vegetables: ≥400 g per day (about 1 pound)

- Total dietary fiber: >25 g per day from foods

- Physical activity: one hour of moderate-intensity activity, such as walking, on most days of the week

Eating Well with Canada's Food Guide

Figure I-1 presents the 2007 *Eating Well with Canada's Food Guide,* which interprets Canada's *Guidelines for Healthy Eating* (see Table 2-2 on p. 40) for consumers and recommends a range of servings to consume daily from each of the four food groups. Additional publications, which are available from Health Canada ◆ through its website, provide many more details.

◆ Search for "Canada's food guide" at Health Canada: **www.hc-sc.gc.ca**

FIGURE I-1   *Eating Well with Canada's Food Guide*

 Health Canada   Santé Canada   *Your health and safety... our priority.*   *Votre santé et votre sécurité... notre priorité.*

Eating Well with Canada's Food Guide

Canada

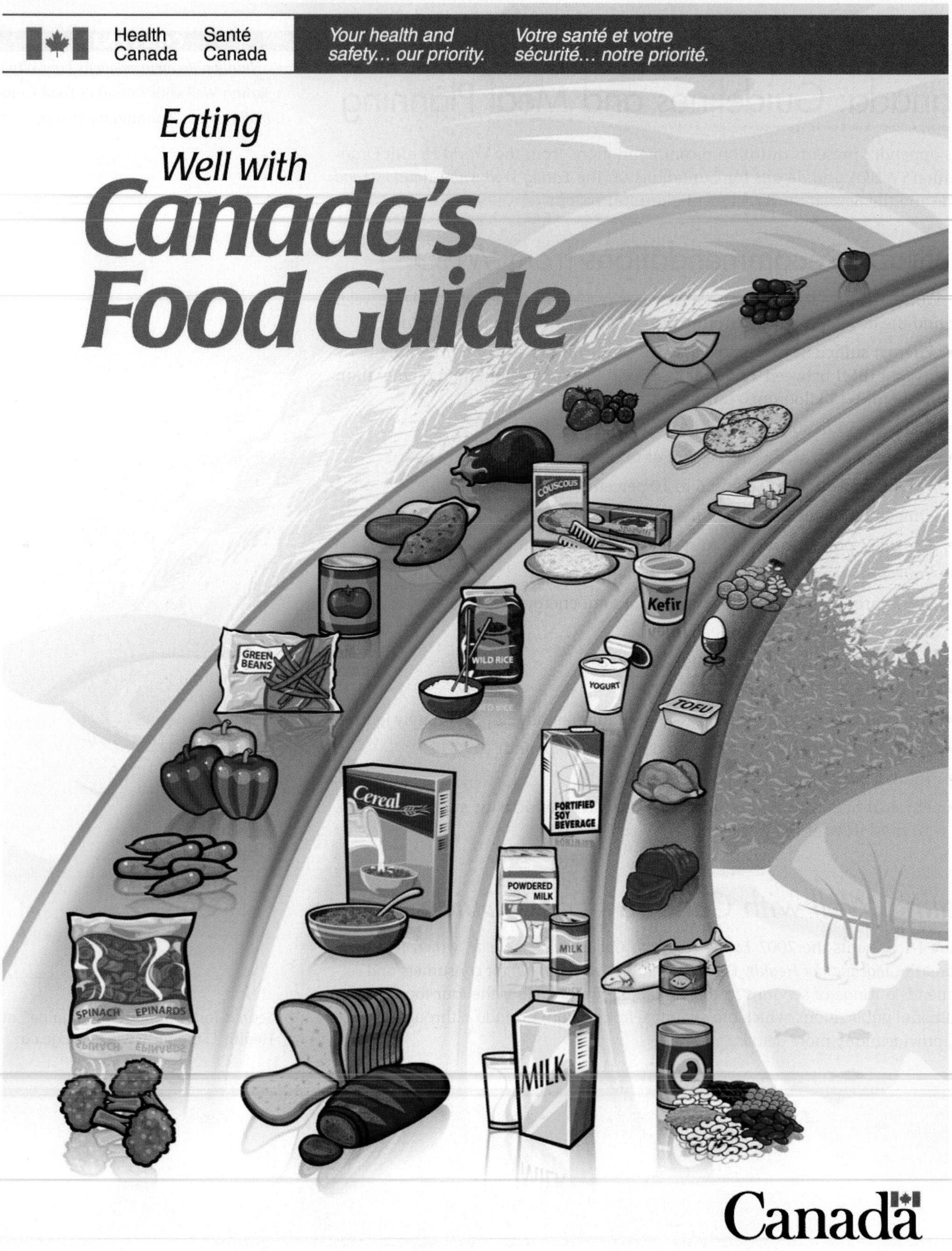

FIGURE I-1   *Eating Well with Canada's Food Guide—continued*

Recommended Number of *Food Guide Servings* per Day

	Children			Teens		Adults			
Age in Years	2-3	4-8	9-13	14-18		19-50		51+	
Sex	Girls and Boys			Females	Males	Females	Males	Females	Males
Vegetables and Fruit	4	5	6	7	8	7-8	8-10	7	7
Grain Products	3	4	6	6	7	6-7	8	6	7
Milk and Alternatives	2	2	3-4	3-4	3-4	2	2	3	3
Meat and Alternatives	1	1	1-2	2	3	2	3	2	3

The chart above shows how many Food Guide Servings you need from each of the four food groups every day.

Having the amount and type of food recommended and following the tips in *Canada's Food Guide* will help:

• Meet your needs for vitamins, minerals and other nutrients.

• Reduce your risk of obesity, type 2 diabetes, heart disease, certain types of cancer and osteoporosis.

• Contribute to your overall health and vitality.

FIGURE I-1 | *Eating Well with Canada's Food Guide*—continued

What is One Food Guide Serving?
Look at the examples below.

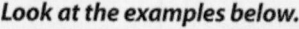

Fresh, frozen or canned vegetables
125 mL (½ cup)

Leafy vegetables
Cooked: 125 mL (½ cup)
Raw: 250 mL (1 cup)

Fresh, frozen or canned fruits
1 fruit or 125 mL (½ cup)

100% Juice
125 mL (½ cup)

Bread
1 slice (35 g)

Bagel
½ bagel (45 g)

Flat breads
½ pita or ½ tortilla (35 g)

Cooked rice, bulgur or quinoa
125 mL (½ cup)

Cereal
Cold: 30 g
Hot: 175 mL (¾ cup)

Cooked pasta or couscous
125 mL (½ cup)

Milk or powdered milk (reconstituted)
250 mL (1 cup)

Canned milk (evaporated)
125 mL (½ cup)

Fortified soy beverage
250 mL (1 cup)

Yogurt
175 g
(¾ cup)

Kefir
175 g
(¾ cup)

Cheese
50 g (1 ½ oz.)

Cooked fish, shellfish, poultry, lean meat
75 g (2 ½ oz.)/125 mL (½ cup)

Cooked legumes
175 mL (¾ cup)

Tofu
150 g or
175 mL (¾ cup)

Eggs
2 eggs

Peanut or nut butters
30 mL (2 Tbsp)

Shelled nuts and seeds
60 mL (¼ cup)

Oils and Fats
- Include a small amount – 30 to 45 mL (2 to 3 Tbsp) – of unsaturated fat each day. This includes oil used for cooking, salad dressings, margarine and mayonnaise.
- Use vegetable oils such as canola, olive and soybean.
- Choose soft margarines that are low in saturated and trans fats.
- Limit butter, hard margarine, lard and shortening.

FIGURE I-1 *Eating Well with Canada's Food Guide—continued*

Make each Food Guide Serving count...
wherever you are – at home, at school, at work or when eating out!

▶ **Eat at least one dark green and one orange vegetable each day.**
- Go for dark green vegetables such as broccoli, romaine lettuce and spinach.
- Go for orange vegetables such as carrots, sweet potatoes and winter squash.

▶ **Choose vegetables and fruit prepared with little or no added fat, sugar or salt.**
- Enjoy vegetables steamed, baked or stir-fried instead of deep-fried.

▶ **Have vegetables and fruit more often than juice.**

▶ **Make at least half of your grain products whole grain each day.**
- Eat a variety of whole grains such as barley, brown rice, oats, quinoa and wild rice.
- Enjoy whole grain breads, oatmeal or whole wheat pasta.

▶ **Choose grain products that are lower in fat, sugar or salt.**
- Compare the Nutrition Facts table on labels to make wise choices.
- Enjoy the true taste of grain products. When adding sauces or spreads, use small amounts.

▶ **Drink skim, 1%, or 2% milk each day.**
- Have 500 mL (2 cups) of milk every day for adequate vitamin D.
- Drink fortified soy beverages if you do not drink milk.

▶ **Select lower fat milk alternatives.**
- Compare the Nutrition Facts table on yogurts or cheeses to make wise choices.

▶ **Have meat alternatives such as beans, lentils and tofu often.**

▶ **Eat at least two Food Guide Servings of fish each week.***
- Choose fish such as char, herring, mackerel, salmon, sardines and trout.

▶ **Select lean meat and alternatives prepared with little or no added fat or salt.**
- Trim the visible fat from meats. Remove the skin on poultry.
- Use cooking methods such as roasting, baking or poaching that require little or no added fat.
- If you eat luncheon meats, sausages or prepackaged meats, choose those lower in salt (sodium) and fat.

Enjoy a variety of foods from the four food groups.

Satisfy your thirst with water!

Drink water regularly. It's a calorie-free way to quench your thirst. Drink more water in hot weather or when you are very active.

* Health Canada provides advice for limiting exposure to mercury from certain types of fish. Refer to www.healthcanada.gc.ca for the latest information.

Appendix

I

FIGURE I-1 | *Eating Well with Canada's Food Guide—continued*

Advice for different ages and stages...

Children

Following *Canada's Food Guide* helps children grow and thrive.

Young children have small appetites and need calories for growth and development.

• Serve small nutritious meals and snacks each day.

• Do not restrict nutritious foods because of their fat content. Offer a variety of foods from the four food groups.

• Most of all... be a good role model.

Women of childbearing age

All women who could become pregnant and those who are pregnant or breastfeeding need a multivitamin containing **folic acid** every day. Pregnant women need to ensure that their multivitamin also contains **iron**. A health care professional can help you find the multivitamin that's right for you.

Pregnant and breastfeeding women need more calories. Include an extra 2 to 3 Food Guide Servings each day.

Here are two examples:
• Have fruit and yogurt for a snack, or

• Have an extra slice of toast at breakfast and an extra glass of milk at supper.

Men and women over 50

The need for **vitamin D** increases after the age of 50.

In addition to following *Canada's Food Guide*, everyone over the age of 50 should take a daily vitamin D supplement of 10 μg (400 IU).

How do I count Food Guide Servings in a meal?

Here is an example:

Vegetable and beef stir-fry with rice, a glass of milk and an apple for dessert		
250 mL (1 cup) mixed broccoli, carrot and sweet red pepper	=	2 **Vegetables and Fruit** Food Guide Servings
75 g (2 ½ oz.) lean beef	=	1 **Meat and Alternatives** Food Guide Serving
250 mL (1 cup) brown rice	=	2 **Grain Products** Food Guide Servings
5 mL (1 tsp) canola oil	=	part of your **Oils and Fats** intake for the day
250 mL (1 cup) 1% milk	=	1 **Milk and Alternatives** Food Guide Serving
1 apple	=	1 **Vegetables and Fruit** Food Guide Serving

FIGURE I-1   *Eating Well with Canada's Food Guide—continued*

Eat well and be active today and every day!

The benefits of eating well and being active include:

- Better overall health.
- Lower risk of disease.
- A healthy body weight.
- Feeling and looking better.
- More energy.
- Stronger muscles and bones.

Be active

To be active every day is a step towards better health and a healthy body weight.

Canada's Physical Activity Guide recommends building 30 to 60 minutes of moderate physical activity into daily life for adults and at least 90 minutes a day for children and youth. You don't have to do it all at once. Add it up in periods of at least 10 minutes at a time for adults and five minutes at a time for children and youth.

Start slowly and build up.

Eat well

Another important step towards better health and a healthy body weight is to follow *Canada's Food Guide* by:

- Eating the recommended amount and type of food each day.
- Limiting foods and beverages high in calories, fat, sugar or salt (sodium) such as cakes and pastries, chocolate and candies, cookies and granola bars, doughnuts and muffins, ice cream and frozen desserts, french fries, potato chips, nachos and other salty snacks, alcohol, fruit flavoured drinks, soft drinks, sports and energy drinks, and sweetened hot or cold drinks.

Read the label

- Compare the Nutrition Facts table on food labels to choose products that contain less fat, saturated fat, trans fat, sugar and sodium.
- Keep in mind that the calories and nutrients listed are for the amount of food found at the top of the Nutrition Facts table.

Nutrition Facts

Per 0 mL (0 g)

Amount	% Daily Value
Calories 0	
Fat 0 g	0 %
Saturates 0 g	0 %
+ Trans 0 g	
Cholesterol 0 mg	
Sodium 0 mg	0 %
Carbohydrate 0 g	0 %
Fibre 0 g	0 %
Sugars 0 g	
Protein 0 g	

Vitamin A	0 %	Vitamin C	0 %
Calcium	0 %	Iron	0 %

Limit trans fat

When a Nutrition Facts table is not available, ask for nutrition information to choose foods lower in trans and saturated fats.

Take a step today...

✓ Have breakfast every day. It may help control your hunger later in the day.

✓ Walk wherever you can – get off the bus early, use the stairs.

✓ Benefit from eating vegetables and fruit at all meals and as snacks.

✓ Spend less time being inactive such as watching TV or playing computer games.

✓ Request nutrition information about menu items when eating out to help you make healthier choices.

✓ Enjoy eating with family and friends!

✓ Take time to eat and savour every bite!

For more information, interactive tools, or additional copies visit Canada's Food Guide on-line at:
www.healthcanada.gc.ca/foodguide

or contact:

Publications
Health Canada
Ottawa, Ontario K1A 0K9
E-Mail: publications@hc-sc.gc.ca
Tel.: 1-866-225-0709
Fax: (613) 941-5366
TTY: 1-800-267-1245

Également disponible en français sous le titre :
Bien manger avec le Guide alimentaire canadien

This publication can be made available on request on diskette, large print, audio-cassette and braille.

Appendix

I

Canada's Meal Planning for Healthy Eating

Beyond the Basics: Meal Planning for Healthy Eating, Diabetes Prevention and Management is Canada's system of meal planning.[1] Similar to the U.S. exchange system, *Beyond the Basics* sorts foods into groups and defines portion sizes to help people manage their blood glucose and maintain a healthy weight. Because foods that contain carbohydrate raise blood glucose, the food groups are organized into two sections—those that contain carbohydrate (presented in Table I-1) and those that contain little or no carbohydrate (shown in Table I-2). One portion from any of the food groups listed in Table I-1 provides about 15 grams of available carbohydrate (total carbohydrate minus fiber) and counts as one carbohydrate choice. Within each group, foods are identified as those to "choose more often" (generally higher in vitamins, minerals, and fiber) and those to "choose less often" (generally higher in sugar, saturated fat, or *trans* fat).

[1]The tables for the Canadian meal planning system are adapted from *Beyond the Basics: Meal Planning for Healthy Eating, Diabetes Prevention and Management,* copyright 2005, with permission of the Canadian Diabetes Association. Additional information is available from **www.diabetes.ca**.

Key:
- ● Choose more often
- ▲ Choose less often

TABLE I-1 Food Groups that Contain Carbohydrate

1 serving = 15 g carbohydrate or 1 carbohydrate choice

Food	Measure
Grains and starches: 15 g carbohydrate, 2 g protein, 0 g fat, 286 kJ (68 kcal)	
▲ Bagel, large	¼
▲ Bagel, small	½
▲ Bannock, fried	1.5″ × 2.5″
● Bannock, whole grain baked	1.5″ × 2.5″
● Barley, cooked	125 mL (½ c)
▲ Bread, white	30 g (1 oz)
● Bread, whole grain	30 g (1 oz)
● Bulgur, cooked	125 mL (½ c)
▲ Bun, hamburger or hotdog	½
▲ Cereal, flaked unsweetened	125 mL (½ c)
● Cereal, hot	¾ c
● Chapati, whole wheat (6″)	1
● Corn	125 mL (½ c)
● Couscous, cooked	125 mL (½ c)
▲ Crackers, soda type	7
▲ Croutons	⅔ c
● English muffin, whole grain	½
▲ French fries	10
● Millet, cooked	⅓ c
▲ Naan bread (6″)	¼
▲ Pancake (4″)	1
● Pasta, cooked	125 mL (½ c)
▲ Pita bread, white (6″)	1
● Pita bread, whole wheat (6″)	1
▲ Pizza crust (12″)	¹⁄₁₂
● Plantain, mashed	⅓ c
● Potatoes, boiled or baked	½ medium

(continued on the next page)

TABLE I-1   Food Groups that Contain Carbohydrate—continued

1 serving = 15 g carbohydrate or 1 carbohydrate choice

Food	Measure
Grains and starches: 15 g carbohydrate, 2 g protein, 0 g fat, 286 kJ (68 kcal)	
● Rice, cooked	⅓ c
● Roti, whole wheat (6″)	1
● Soup, thick type	250 mL (1 c)
● Sweet potato, mashed	⅓ c
▲ Taco shells (5″)	2
● Tortilla, whole wheat (6″)	1
▲ Waffle (4″)	1
Fruits:15 g carbohydrate, 1 g protein, 0 g fat, 269 kJ (64 kcal)	
● Apple	1 medium
● Apple sauce, unsweetened	125 mL (½ c)
● Banana	1 small
● Blackberries	500 mL (2 c)
● Cherries	15
● Fruit, canned in juice	125 mL (½ c)
▲ Fruit, dried	50 mL (¼ c)
● Grapefruit	1 small
● Grapes	15
● Kiwi	2 medium
▲ Juice	125 mL (½ c)
● Mango	½ medium
● Melon	250 mL (1 c)
● Orange	1 medium
● Other berries	250 mL (1 c)
● Pear	1 medium
● Pineapple	¾ c
● Plum	2 medium
● Raspberries	500 mL (2 c)
● Strawberries	500 mL (2 c)
Milk and alternatives: 15 g carbohydrate, 8 g protein, variable fat, 386–651 kJ (92–155 kcal)	
● Chocolate milk, 1%	125 mL (½ c)
● Evaporated milk, canned	125 mL (½ c)
● Milk, fluid	250 mL (1 c)
● Milk powder, skim	30 mL (2 tbs)
● Soy beverage, flavored	125 mL (½ c)
● Soy beverage, plain	250 mL (1 c)
● Soy yogurt, flavored	⅓ c
● Yogurt, nonfat, plain	¾ c
● Yogurt, skim, artificially sweetened	250 mL (1 c)
Other choices (sweet foods and snacks): 15 g carbohydrate, variable protein and fat	
▲ Brownies, unfrosted	2″ × 2″
▲ Cake, unfrosted	2″ × 2″
▲ Cookies, arrowroot or gingersnap	3–4
▲ Jam, jelly, marmalade	15 mL (1 tbs)
● Milk pudding, skim, no sugar added	125 mL (½ c)
▲ Muffin	1 small (2″)
▲ Oatmeal granola bar	1 (28 g)
● Popcorn, low fat	750 mL (3 c)
▲ Pretzels, low fat, large	7
▲ Pretzels, low fat, sticks	30
▲ Sugar, white	15 mL (3 tsp or packets)

TABLE I-2   Food Groups that Contain Little or No Carbohydrate

Food	Measure
Vegetables: To encourage consumption, most vegetables are considered "free"	
● Asparagus	
● Beans, yellow or green	
● Bean sprouts	
● Beets	
● Broccoli	
● Cabbage	
● Carrots	
● Cauliflower	
● Celery	
● Cucumber	
● Eggplant	
● Greens	
● Leeks	
● Mushrooms	
● Okra	
▲ Parsnips[a]	
▲ Peas[a]	
● Peppers	
▲ Rutabagas (turnips)[a]	
● Salad vegetables	
● Snow peas	
▲ Squash, winter[a]	
● Tomatoes	
Meat and alternatives: 0 g carbohydrate, 7 g protein, 3–5 g fat, 307 kJ (73 kcal)	
● Cheese, skim (<7% milk fat)	30 g (1 oz)
● Cheese, light (<17% milk fat)	30 g (1 oz)
▲ Cheese, regular (17–33% milk fat)	30 g (1 oz)
● Cottage cheese (1–2% milk fat)	50 mL (¼ c)
● Egg	1 large
▲ Fish, canned in oil	50 mL (¼ c)
● Fish, canned in water	50 mL (¼ c)
● Fish, fresh, cooked	30 g (1 oz)
● Hummus[b]	⅓ c
● Legumes, cooked[b]	125 mL (½ c)
● Meat, game, cooked	30 g (1 oz)

[a] These vegetables provide significant carbohydrate when more than 125 mL (½ c) is eaten.
[b] Legumes contain 15 g carbohydrate in a 125 mL (½ c) serving.

(continued on the next page)

TABLE I-2　Food Groups that Contain Little or No Carbohydrate—continued

Food	Measure
Meat and alternatives: 0 g carbohydrate, 7 g protein, 3–5 g fat, 307 kJ (73 kcal)	
● Meat, ground, lean, cooked	30 g (1 oz)
▲ Meat, ground, medium-regular, cooked	30 g (1 oz)
● Meat, lean, cooked	30 g (1 oz)
● Meat, organ or tripe, cooked	30 g (1 oz)
● Meat, prepared, low fat	30 g (1 oz)
▲ Meat, prepared, regular fat	30 g (1 oz)
▲ Meat, regular, cooked	30 g (1 oz)
● Peameal/back bacon, cooked	30 g (1 oz)
● Poultry, ground, lean, cooked	30 g (1 oz)
● Poultry, skinless, cooked	30 g (1 oz)
▲ Poultry/wings, skin on, cooked	30 g (1 oz)
● Shellfish, cooked	30 g (1 oz)
● Tofu (soybean)	½ block (100 g)
● Vegetarian meat alternatives	30 g (1 oz)
Fats: 0 g carbohydrate, 0 g protein, 5 g fat, 189 kJ (45 kcal)	
● Avocado	⅛
▲ Bacon	30 g (1 oz)
● Butter	5 mL (1 tsp)
▲ Cheese, spreadable	15 mL (1 tbs)
● Margarine, non-hydrogenated	5 mL (1 tsp)
▲ Mayonnaise, light	30 mL (2 tbs)
● Nuts	15 mL (1 tbs)
● Oil, canola or olive	5 mL (1 tsp)
● Salad dressing, regular	15 mL (1 tbs)
● Seeds	15 mL (1 tbs)
● Tahini	7.5 mL (½ tbs)
Extras: <5 g carbohydrate, 84 kJ (20 kcal)	
Broth	
Coffee	
Herbs and spices	
Ketchup	
Mustard	
Sugar-free soft drinks	
Sugar-free gelatin	
Tea	

Appendix

I

Healthy People 2010

Table 1-4 (p. 23) lists the objectives from the Nutrition and Overweight focus area of the Healthy People 2010 initiative. This table presents additional nutrition-related objectives from other focus areas.

TABLE J-1 Nutrition-Related Objectives from Other Focus Areas

Access to Quality Health Services

- Increase the proportion of persons appropriately counseled about health behaviors.

Arthritis, Osteoporosis, and Chronic Back Conditions

- Reduce the proportion of adults with osteoporosis.

Cancer

- Reduce the overall cancer death rate.
- Reduce the breast cancer death rate.
- Reduce the colorectal cancer death rate.
- Increase the proportion of physicians and dentists who counsel their at-risk patients about tobacco-use cessation, physical activity, and cancer screening.

Chronic Kidney Disease

- Increase the proportion of treated chronic kidney failure patients who have received counseling on nutrition, treatment choices, and cardiovascular care 12 months before the start of renal replacement therapy.

Diabetes

- Increase the proportion of persons with diabetes who receive formal diabetes education.
- Prevent diabetes.
- Reduce diabetes-related deaths among persons with diabetes.

Educational and Community-Based Programs

- Increase the proportion of middle, junior high, and senior high schools that provide school health education to prevent health problems in the following areas: unintentional injury; violence; suicide; tobacco use and addiction; alcohol and other drug use; unintended pregnancy, HIV/AIDS, and STD infection; unhealthy dietary patterns; inadequate physical activity; and environmental health.
- Increase the proportion of worksites that offer a comprehensive employee health promotion program to their employees.
- Increase the proportion of employees who participate in employer-sponsored health promotion activities.
- Increase the proportion of community health promotion programs that address multiple Healthy People 2010 focus areas.
- Increase the proportion of local health departments that have established culturally appropriate and linguistically competent community health promotion and disease prevention programs.

Health Communication

- Increase the proportion of health-related World Wide Web sites that disclose information that can be used to assess the quality of the site.

Heart Disease and Stroke

- Reduce coronary heart disease deaths.
- Reduce stroke deaths.
- Reduce the proportion of adults with high blood pressure.

(continued)

TABLE J-1 Nutrition-Related Objectives from Other Focus Areas—continued

Heart Disease and Stroke, *continued*

- Increase the proportion of adults with high blood pressure who are taking action (for example, losing weight, increasing physical activity, or reducing sodium intake) to help control their blood pressure.
- Reduce the mean total blood cholesterol levels among adults.
- Reduce the proportion of adults with high total blood cholesterol levels.

Maternal, Infant, and Child Health

- Reduce low birth weight (LBW) and very low birthweight (VLBW).
- Increase the proportion of mothers who achieve a recommended weight gain during pregnancy.
- Reduce the occurrence of spina bifida and other neural tube defects.
- Increase the proportion of pregnancies begun with an optimum folate level.
- Increase abstinence from alcohol, cigarettes, and illicit drugs among pregnant women.
- Reduce the occurrence of fetal alcohol syndrome (FAS).
- Increase the proportion of mothers who breastfeed their babies.

Mental Health and Mental Disorders

- Reduce the relapse rates for persons with eating disorders, including anorexia nervosa and bulimia nervosa.

Physical Activity and Fitness

- Reduce the proportion of adults who engage in no leisure-time physical activity.
- Increase the proportion of adults who engage regularly, preferably daily, in moderate physical activity for at least 30 minutes per day.
- Increase the proportion of adults who engage in vigorous physical activity that promotes the development and maintenance of cardiorespiratory fitness 3 or more days per week for 20 or more minutes per occasion.
- Increase the proportion of adolescents who engage in moderate physical activity for at least 30 minutes on 5 or more of the previous 7 days.
- Increase the proportion of adolescents who engage in vigorous physical activity that promotes cardiorespiratory fitness 3 or more days per week for 20 or more minutes per occasion.
- Increase the proportion of adolescents who participate in daily school physical education.
- Increase the proportion of worksites offering employer-sponsored physical activity and fitness programs.

Substance Abuse

- Reduce average annual alcohol consumption.

SOURCE: Adapted from Healthy People 2010: **www.healthypeople.gov**

Glossary

Many medical terms have their origins in Latin or Greek. By learning a few common derivations, you can glean the meaning of words you have never heard of before. For example, once you know that "hyper" means above normal, "glyc" means glucose, and "emia" means blood, you can easily determine that "hyperglycemia" means high blood glucose. The derivations at left will help you to learn many terms presented in this glossary.

GENERAL

a- or *an-* = not or without
ana- = up
ant- or *anti-* = against
ante- or *pre-* or *pro-* = before
cata- = down
co- = with or together
bi- or *di-* = two, twice
dys- or *mal-* = bad, difficult, painful
endo- = inner or within
epi- = upon
exo- = outside of or without
extra- = outside of, beyond, or in addition
gen- or *-gen* = gives rise to, producing
homeo- = like, similar, constant unchanging state
hyper- = over, above, excessive
hypo- = below, under, beneath
in- = not
inter- = between, in the midst
intra- = within
-itis = infection or inflammation
-lysis = break
macro- = large or long
micro- = small
mono- = one, single
neo- = new, recent
oligo- = few or small
-osis or *-asis* = condition
para- = near
peri- = around, about
poly- = many or much
semi- = half
-stat or *-stasis-* = stationary
tri- = three

BODY

angi- or *vaso-* = vessel
arterio- = artery
cardiac or *cardio-* = heart
-cyte = cell
enteron = intestine
gastro- = stomach
hema- or *-emia* = blood
hepatic = liver
myo- or *sarco-* = muscle
nephr- or *renal* = kidney
neuro- = nerve
osteo- = bone
pulmo- = lung
ure- or *-uria* = urine
vena = vein

CHEMISTRY

-al = aldehyde
-ase = enzyme
-ate = salt
glyc- or *gluc-* = sweet (glucose)
hydro- or *hydrate* = water
lipo- = lipid
-ol = alcohol
-ose = carbohydrate
saccha- = sugar

A

24-hour recall: a record of foods eaten by a person for one 24-hour period.

absorption: the uptake of nutrients by the cells of the small intestine for transport into either the blood or the lymph.

Acceptable Daily Intake (ADI): the estimated amount of a sweetener that individuals can safely consume each day over the course of a lifetime without adverse effect.

Acceptable Macronutrient Distribution Ranges (AMDR): ranges of intakes for the energy nutrients that provide adequate energy and nutrients and reduce the risk of chronic diseases.

accredited: approved; in the case of medical centers or universities, certified by an agency recognized by the U.S. Department of Education.

acesulfame (AY-sul-fame) **potassium:** an artificial sweetener composed of an organic salt that has been approved for use in both the United States and Canada; also known as **acesulfame-K** because K is the chemical symbol for potassium.

acetaldehyde (ass-et-AL-duh-hide): an intermediate in alcohol metabolism.

acetyl CoA (ASS-eh-teel, or ah-SEET-il, coh-AY): a 2-carbon compound (acetate, or acetic acid) to which a molecule of CoA is attached.

acid controllers: medications used to prevent or relieve indigestion by suppressing production of acid in the stomach; also called **H2 blockers.**

acid-base balance: the equilibrium in the body between acid and base concentrations (see Chapter 12).

acidosis (assi-DOE-sis): above-normal acidity in the blood and body fluids.

acids: compounds that release hydrogen ions in a solution.

acne: a chronic inflammation of the skin's follicles and oil-producing glands, which leads to an accumulation of oils inside the ducts that surround hairs; usually associated with the maturation of young adults.

acupuncture (AK-you-PUNK-cher): a technique that involves piercing the skin with long thin needles at specific anatomical points to relieve pain or illness.

acute PEM: protein-energy malnutrition caused by recent severe food restriction; characterized in children by thinness for height (wasting).

added sugars: sugars and syrups used as an ingredient in the processing and preparation of foods such as breads, cakes, beverages, jellies, and ice cream as well as sugars eaten separately or added to foods at the table.

adaptive thermogenesis: adjustments in energy expenditure related to changes in environment such as extreme cold and to physiological events such as overfeeding, trauma, and changes in hormone status.

additives: substances not normally consumed as foods but added to food either intentionally or by accident.

adequacy (dietary): providing all the essential nutrients, fiber, and energy in amounts sufficient to maintain health.

Adequate Intake (AI): the average daily amount of a nutrient that appears sufficient to maintain a specified criterion; a value used as a guide for nutrient intake when an RDA cannot be determined.

adipose (ADD-ih-poce) **tissue:** the body's fat tissue; consists of masses of triglyceride-storing cells.

adolescence: the period from the beginning of puberty until maturity.

adrenal glands: glands adjacent to, and just above, each kidney.

adrenocorticotropin (ad-REE-noh-KORE-teeoh-TROP-in) **ATCH:** a hormone, so named because it stimulates *(trope)* the adrenal cortex. The adrenal gland, like the pituitary, has two parts, in this case the outer portion *(cortex)* and an inner core *(medulla)*. The release of ACTH is mediated by **corticotropin-releasing hormone (CRH).**

adverse reactions: unusual responses to food (including intolerances and allergies).

aerobic (air-ROE-bic): requiring oxygen.

agribusinesses: agriculture practiced on a massive scale by large corporations owning vast acreages and employing intensive technological, fuel, and chemical inputs.

AIDS (acquired immune deficiency syndrome): the late stage of HIV infection, in which severe complications develop.

alcohol: a class of organic compounds containing hydroxyl (OH) groups.

alcohol abuse: a pattern of drinking that includes failure to fulfill work, school, or home responsibilities; drinking in situations that are physically dangerous (as in driving while intoxicated); recurring alcohol-related legal problems (as in aggravated assault charges); or continued drinking despite ongoing social problems that are caused by or worsened by alcohol.

alcohol dehydrogenase (dee-high-DROJ-eh-nayz): an enzyme active in the stomach and the liver that converts ethanol to acetaldehyde.

alcoholism: a pattern of drinking that includes a strong craving for alcohol, a loss of control and an inability to stop drinking once begun, withdrawal symptoms (nausea, sweating, shakiness, and anxiety) after heavy drinking, and the need for increasing amounts of alcohol to feel "high."

alcohol-related birth defects (ARBD): malformations in the skeletal and organ systems (heart, kidneys, eyes, ears) associated with prenatal alcohol exposure.

alcohol-related neurodevelopmental disorder (ARND): abnormalities in the central nervous system and cognitive development associated with prenatal alcohol exposure.

aldosterone (al-DOS-ter-own): a hormone secreted by the adrenal glands that regulates blood pressure by increasing the reabsorption of sodium by the kidneys. Aldosterone also regulates chloride and potassium concentrations.

alitame (AL-ih-tame): an artificial sweetener composed of two amino acids (alanine and aspartic acid); FDA approval pending.

alkalosis (alka-LOE-sis): above-normal alkalinity (base) in the blood and body fluids.

alpha-lactalbumin (lact-AL-byoo-min): a major protein in human breast milk, as opposed to **casein** (CAY-seen), a major protein in cow's milk.

alpha-tocopherol: the active vitamin E compound.

Alzheimer's disease: a degenerative disease of the brain involving memory loss and major structural changes in neuron networks; also known as **senile dementia of the Alzheimer's type (SDAT), primary degenerative dementia of senile onset,** or **chronic brain syndrome**.

amenorrhea (ay-MEN-oh-REE-ah): the absence of or cessation of menstruation. *Primary amenorrhea* is menarche delayed beyond 16 years of age. *Secondary amenorrhea* is the absence of three to six consecutive menstrual cycles.

American Dietetic Association (ADA): the professional organization of dietitians in the United States. The Canadian equivalent is Dietitians of Canada, which operates similarly.

amino (a-MEEN-oh) **acids:** building blocks of proteins. Each contains an amino group, an acid group, a hydrogen atom, and a distinctive side group, all attached to a central carbon atom.

amino acid pool: the supply of amino acids derived from either food proteins or body proteins that collect in the cells and circulating blood and stand ready to be incorporated in proteins and other compounds or used for energy.

amino acid scoring: a measure of protein quality assessed by comparing a protein's amino acid pattern with that of a reference protein; sometimes called chemical scoring.

ammonia: a compound with the chemical formula NH_3; produced during the deamination of amino acids.

amniotic (am-nee-OTT-ic) **sac:** the "bag of waters" in the uterus, in which the fetus floats.

amylase (AM-ih-lace): an enzyme that hydrolyzes amylose (a form of starch). Amylase is a carbohydrase, an enzyme that breaks down carbohydrates.

anabolic steroids: drugs related to the male sex hormone, testosterone, that stimulate the development of lean body mass.

anabolism (an-AB-o-lism): reactions in which small molecules are put together to build larger ones. Anabolic reactions require energy.

anaerobic (AN-air-ROE-bic): not requiring oxygen.

anaphylactic (ana- fill-LAC-tic) **shock:** a life-threatening, whole-body allergic reaction to an offending substance.

anemia (ah-NEE-me-ah): literally, "too little blood." Anemia is any condition in which too few red blood cells are present, or the red blood cells are immature (and therefore large) or too small or contain too little hemoglobin to carry the normal amount of oxygen to the tissues. It is not a disease itself but can be a symptom of many different disease conditions, including many nutrient deficiencies, bleeding, excessive red blood cell destruction, and defective red blood cell formation.

anencephaly (AN-en-SEF-a-lee): an uncommon and always fatal type of neural tube defect; characterized by the absence of a brain.

aneurysm (AN-you-rizm): an abnormal enlargement or bulging of a blood vessel (usually an artery) caused by damage to or weakness in the blood vessel wall.

angina (an-JYE-nah or AN-ji-nah): a painful feeling of tightness or pressure in and around the heart, often radiating to the back, neck, and arms; caused by a lack of oxygen to an area of heart muscle.

angiotensin (AN-gee-oh-TEN-sin): a hormone involved in blood pressure regulation. Its precursor protein is called angiotensinogen; it is activated by renin, an enzyme from the kidneys.

anions (AN-eye-uns): negatively charged ions.

anorexia (an-oh-RECK-see-ah) **nervosa:** an eating disorder characterized by a refusal to maintain a minimally normal body weight and a distortion in perception of body shape and weight.

antacids: medications used to relieve indigestion by neutralizing acid in the stomach.

antagonist: a competing factor that counteracts the action of another factor.

anthropometric (AN-throw-poe-MET-rick): relating to measurement of the physical characteristics of the body, such as height and weight.

antibodies: large proteins of the blood and body fluids, produced by the immune system in response to the invasion of the body by foreign molecules (usually proteins called antigens).

antidiuretic hormone (ADH): a hormone produced by the pituitary gland in response to dehydration (or a high sodium concentration in the blood). It stimulates the kidneys to reabsorb more water and therefore prevents water loss in urine (also called **vasopressin**).

antigens: substances that elicit the formation of antibodies or an inflammation reaction from the immune system.

antioxidant: in the human body, a substance that significantly decreases the adverse effects of free radicals on normal physiological functions.

antioxidants: as a food additive, preservatives that delay or prevent rancidity of fats in foods and other damage to food caused by oxygen.

antipromoters: factors that oppose the development of cancer.

antiscorbutic (AN-tee-skor-BUE-tik) **factor:** the original name for vitamin C.

anus (AY-nus): the terminal outlet of the GI tract.

aorta (ay-OR-tuh): the large, primary artery that conducts blood from the heart to the body's smaller arteries.

appendix: a narrow blind sac extending from the beginning of the colon that stores lymph cells.

appetite: the integrated response to the sight, smell, thought, or taste of food that initiates or delays eating.

arachidonic (a-RACK-ih-DON-ic) **acid:** an omega-6 polyunsaturated fatty acid with 20 carbons and four double bonds; present in small amounts in meat and other animal products and synthesized in the body from linoleic acid.

arginine: a nonessential amino acid falsely promoted as enhancing the secretion of human growth hormone, the breakdown of fat, and the development of muscle.

aroma therapy: a technique that uses oil extracts from plants and flowers (usually applied by massage or baths) to enhance physical, psychological, and spiritual health.

arteries: vessels that carry blood from the heart to the tissues.

artesian water: water drawn from a well that taps a confined aquifer in which the water is under pressure.

arthritis: inflammation of a joint, usually accompanied by pain, swelling, and structural changes.

artificial fats: zero-energy fat replacers that are chemically synthesized to mimic the sensory and cooking qualities of naturally occurring fats but are totally or partially resistant to digestion.

artificial sweeteners: sugar substitutes that provide negligible, if any, energy; sometimes called **nonnutritive sweeteners**.

ascorbic acid: one of the two active forms of vitamin C.

-ase (ACE): a word ending denoting an enzyme. The word beginning often identifies the compounds the enzyme works on.

aspartame (ah-SPAR-tame or ASS-par-tame): an artificial sweetener composed of two amino acids (phenylalanine and aspartic acid); approved for use in both the United States and Canada.

atherosclerosis (ATH-er-oh-scler-OH-sis): a type of artery disease characterized by placques (accumulations of lipid-containing material) on the inner walls of the arteries (see Chapter 18).

atoms: the smallest components of an element that have all of the properties of the element.

ATP or **adenosine** (ah-DEN-oh-seen) **triphosphate** (try-FOS-fate): a common high-energy compound composed of a purine (adenine), a sugar (ribose), and three phosphate groups.

atrophic (a-TRO-fik) **gastritis** (gas-TRY-tis): chronic inflammation of the stomach accompanied by a diminished size and functioning of the mucous membrane and glands.

atrophy (AT-ro-fee): becoming smaller; with regard to muscles, a decrease in size (and strength) because of disuse, undernutrition, or wasting diseases.

autoimmune disorder: a condition in which the body develops antibodies to its own proteins and then proceeds to destroy cells containing these proteins. In type 1 diabetes, the body develops antibodies to its insulin and destroys the pancreatic cells that produce the insulin, creating an insulin deficiency.

autonomic nervous system: the division of the nervous system that controls the body's automatic responses. Its two branches are the sympathetic branch, which helps the body respond to stressors from the outside environment, and the parasympathetic branch, which regulates normal body activities between stressful times.

ayurveda (AH-your-VAY-dah): a traditional Hindu system of improving health by using herbs, diet, meditation, massage, and yoga to stimulate the body, mind, and spirit to prevent and treat disease.

B

balance (dietary): providing foods in proportion to each other and in proportion to the body's needs.

basal metabolic rate (BMR): the rate of energy use for metabolism under specified conditions: after a 12-hour fast and restful sleep, without any physical activity or emotional excitement, and in a comfortable setting. It is usually expressed as kcalories per kilogram body weight per hour.

basal metabolism: the energy needed to maintain life when a body is at complete digestive, physical, and emotional rest.

bases: compounds that accept hydrogen ions in a solution.

B-cells: lymphocytes that produce antibodies. B stands for bone marrow where the B-cells develop and mature.

beer: an alcoholic beverage brewed by fermenting malt and hops.

behavior modification: the changing of behavior by the manipulation of antecedents (cues or environmental factors that trigger behavior), the behavior itself, and consequences (the penalties or rewards attached to behavior).

belching: the expulsion of gas from the stomach through the mouth.

beriberi: the thiamin-deficiency disease.

beta-carotene (BAY-tah KARE-oh-teen): one of the carotenoids; an orange pigment and vitamin A precursor found in plants.

BHA and **BHT:** preservatives commonly used to slow the development of off-flavors, odors, and color changes caused by oxidation.

bicarbonate: an alkaline compound with the formula HCO_3 that is secreted from the pancreas as part of the pancreatic juice. (Bicarbonate is also produced in all cell fluids from the dissociation of cabonic acid to help maintain the body's acid-base balance.)

bifidus (BIFF-id-us, by-FEED-us) **factors:** factors in colostrum and breast milk that favor the growth of the "friendly" bacterium *Lactobacillus* (lack-toh-ba-SILL-us) *bifidus* in the infant's intestinal tract, so that other, less desirable intestinal inhabitants will not flourish.

bile: an emulsifier that prepares fats and oils for digestion; an exocrine secretion made by the liver, stored in the gallbladder, and released into the small intestine when needed.

binders: chemical compounds in foods that combine with nutrients (especially minerals) to form complexes the body cannot absorb. Examples include phytates (FYE-tates) and oxalates (OCK-sa-lates).

binge-eating disorder: an eating disorder with criteria similar to those of bulimia nervosa, excluding purging or other compensatory behaviors.

bioaccumulation: the accumulation of contaminants in the flesh of animals high on the food chain.

bioavailability: the rate at and the extent to which a nutrient is absorbed and used.

bioelectromagnetic medical applications: the use of electrical energy, magnetic energy, or both to stimulate bone repair, wound healing, and tissue regeneration.

biofeedback: the use of special devices to convey information about heart rate, blood pressure, skin temperature, muscle relaxation, and the like to enable a person to learn how to consciously control these medically important functions.

biofield therapeutics: a manual healing method that directs a healing force from an outside source (commonly God or another supernatural being) through the practitioner and into the client's body; commonly known as "laying on of hands."

biological value (BV): a measure of protein quality assessed by measuring the amount of protein nitrogen that is retained from a given amount of protein nitrogen absorbed.

biotechnology: the use of biological systems or organisms to create or modify products. Examples include the use of bacteria to make yogurt, yeast to make beer, and cross-breeding to enhance crop production.

bioterrorism: the intentional spreading of disease-causing microorganisms or toxins.

biotin (BY-oh-tin): a B vitamin that functions as a coenzyme in metabolism.

blind experiment: an experiment in which the subjects do not know whether they are members of the experimental group or the control group.

blood lipid profile: results of blood tests that reveal a person's total cholesterol, triglycerides, and various lipoproteins.

body composition: the proportions of muscle, bone, fat, and other tissue that make up a person's total body weight.

body mass index (BMI): an index of a person's weight in relation to height; determined by dividing the weight (in kilograms) by the square of the height (in meters).

bolus (BOH-lus): a portion; with respect to food, the amount swallowed at one time.

bomb calorimeter (KAL-oh-RIM-eh-ter): an instrument that measures the heat energy released when foods are burned, thus providing an estimate of the potential energy of the foods.

bone density: a measure of bone strength. When minerals fill the bone matrix (making it dense), they give it strength.

bone meal or powdered bone: crushed or ground bone preparations intended to supply calcium to the diet. Calcium from bone is not well absorbed and is often contaminated with toxic minerals such as arsenic, mercury, lead, and cadmium.

boron: a nonessential mineral that is promoted to increase muscle mass.

bottled water: drinking water sold in bottles.

botulism (BOT-chew-lism): an often fatal foodborne illness caused by the ingestion of foods containing a toxin produced by bacteria that grow without oxygen.

bovine growth hormone (BGH): a hormone produced naturally in the pituitary gland of a cow that promotes growth and milk production; now produced for agricultural use by bacteria.

branched-chain amino acids: the essential amino acids leucine, isoleucine, and valine, which are present in large amounts in skeletal muscle tissue; falsely promoted as fuel for exercising muscles.

breast milk bank: a service that collects, screens, processes, and distributes donated human milk.

brown adipose tissue: masses of specialized fat cells packed with pigmented mitochondria that produce heat instead of ATP.

brown sugar: refined white sugar crystals to which manufacturers have added molasses syrup with natural flavor and color; 91 to 96% pure sucrose.

bulimia (byoo-LEEM-ee-ah) **nervosa:** an eating disorder characterized by repeated episodes of binge eating usually followed by self-induced vomiting, misuse of laxatives or diuretics, fasting, or excessive exercise.

C

caffeine: a natural stimulant found in many common foods and beverages, including coffee, tea, and chocolate; may enhance endurance by stimulating fatty acid release. High doses cause headaches, trembling, rapid heart rate, and other undesirable side effects.

calcitonin (KAL-seh-TOE-nin): a hormone secreted by the thyroid gland that regulates blood calcium by lowering it when levels rise too high.

calcium: the most abundant mineral in the body; found primarily in the body's bones and teeth.

calcium rigor: hardness or stiffness of the muscles caused by high blood calcium concentrations.

calcium tetany (TET-ah-nee): intermittent spasm of the extremities due to nervous and muscular excitability caused by low blood calcium concentrations.

calcium-binding protein: a protein in the intestinal cells, made with the help of vitamin D, that facilitates calcium absorption.

calories: units by which energy is measured. Food energy is measured in kilocalories (1000 calories equal 1 kilocalorie), abbreviated kcalories or kcal. One kcalorie is the amount of heat necessary to raise the temperature of 1 kilogram (kg) of water 1°C.

cancers: malignant growths or tumors that result from abnormal and uncontrolled cell division.

capillaries (CAP-ill-aries): small vessels that branch from an artery. Capillaries connect arteries to veins. Exchange of oxygen, nutrients, and waste materials takes place across capillary walls.

carbohydrate loading: a regimen of moderate exercise followed by the consumption of a high-carbohydrate diet that enables muscles to store glycogen beyond their normal capacities; also called **glycogen loading** or **glycogen super compensation.**

carbohydrates: compounds composed of carbon, oxygen, and hydrogen arranged as monosaccharides or multiples of monosaccharides. Most, but not all, carbohydrates have a ratio of one carbon molecule to one water molecule: $(CH_2O)_n$.

carbonated water: water that contains carbon dioxide gas, either naturally occurring or added, that causes bubbles to form in it; also called bubbling or sparkling water.

carbonic acid: a compound with the formula H_2CO_3 that results from the combination of carbon dioxide (CO_2) and water (H_2O); of particular importance in maintaining the body's acid-base balance.

carcinogenesis (CAR-sin-oh-JEN-eh-sis): the process of cancer development.

carcinogens (CAR-sin-oh-jenz or car-SIN-oh-jenz): substances that can cause cancer (the adjective is *carcinogenic*).

cardiac output: the volume of blood discharged by the heart each minute; determined by multiplying the stroke volume by the heart rate. The stroke volume is the amount of oxygenated blood the heart ejects toward the tissues at each beat.

cardiorespiratory conditioning: improvements in heart and lung function and increased blood volume, brought about by aerobic training.

cardiorespiratory endurance: the ability to perform large-muscle, dynamic exercise of moderate-to-high intensity for prolonged periods.

cardiovascular disease (CVD): a general term for all diseases of the heart and blood vessels. Atherosclerosis is the main cause of CVD. When the arteries that carry blood to the heart muscle become blocked, the heart suffers damage known as **coronary heart disease (CHD).**

carnitine (CAR-neh-teen): a nonessential, nonprotein amino acid made in the body from lysine that helps transport fatty acids across the mitochondrial membrane.

carotenoids (kah-ROT-eh-noyds): pigments commonly found in plants and animals, some of which have vitamin A activity. The carotenoid with the greatest vitamin A activity is beta-carotene.

carpal tunnel syndrome: a pinched nerve at the wrist, causing pain or numbness in the hand. It is often caused by repetitive motion of the wrist.

cartilage therapy: the use of cleaned and powdered connective tissue, such as collagen, to improve health.

catabolism (ca-TAB-o-lism): reactions in which large molecules are broken down to smaller ones. Catabolic reactions release energy.

catalyst (CAT-uh-list): a compound that facilitates chemical reactions without itself being changed in the process.

cataracts (KAT-ah-rakts): thickenings of the eye lenses that impair vision and can lead to blindness.

cathartic (ka-THAR-tik): a strong laxative.

cations (CAT-eye-uns): positively charged ions.

CDC (Centers for Disease Control): a branch of the Department of Health and Human Services that is responsible for, among other things, monitoring foodborne diseases.

cell: the basic structural unit of all living things.

cell differentiation (DIF-er-EN-she-AY-shun): the process by which immature cells develop specific functions different from those of the original that are characteristic of their mature cell type.

cell membrane: the thin layer of tissue that surrounds the cell and encloses its contents; made primarily of lipid and protein.

cellulite (SELL-you-light or SELL-you-leet): supposedly, a lumpy form of fat; actually, a fraud. Fatty areas of the body may appear lumpy when the strands of connective tissue that attach the skin to underlying muscles pull tight where the fat is thick. The fat itself is the same as fat anywhere else in the body. If the fat in these areas is lost, the lumpy appearance disappears.

central nervous system: the central part of the nervous system; the brain and spinal cord.

central obesity: excess fat around the trunk of the body; also called **abdominal fat** or **upper-body fat.**

certification: the process in which a private laboratory inspects shipments of a product for selected chemicals and then, if the product is free of violative levels of those chemicals, issues a guarantee to that effect.

certified nutritionists or **certified nutritional consultants** or **certified nutrition therapists:** a person who has been granted a document declaring his or her authority as a nutrition professional.

cesarean section: a surgically assisted birth involving removal of the fetus by an incision into the uterus, usually by way of the abdominal wall.

CHD risk equivalents: disorders that raise the risk of heart attacks, strokes, and other complications associated with cardiovascular disease to the same degree as existing CHD. These disorders include symptomatic carotid artery disease, peripheral arterial disease, abdominal aortic aneurysm, and diabetes mellitus.

chelate (KEY-late): a substance that can grasp the positive ions of a mineral.

chelation (kee-LAY-shun) **therapy:** the use of ethylene diamine tetraacetic acid (EDTA) to bind with metallic ions, thus healing the body by removing toxic metals.

chiropractic (KYE-roh-PRAK-tik): a manual healing method of manipulating the spine to restore health.

chloride (KLO-ride): the major anion in the extracellular fluids of the body. Chloride is the ionic form of chlorine, Cl⁻.

chlorophyll (KLO-row-fil): the green pigment of plants, which absorbs light and transfers the energy to other molecules, thereby initiating photosynthesis.

cholecystokinin (COAL-ee-SIS-toe-KINE-in), or **CCK:** a hormone produced by cells of the intestinal wall. Target organ: the gallbladder. Response: release of bile and slowing of GI motility.

cholesterol (koh-LESS-ter-ol): one of the sterols containing a four ring carbon structure with a carbon side chain.

cholesterol-free: less than 2 mg cholesterol per serving and 2 g or less saturated fat and trans fat combined per serving.

choline (KOH-leen): a nitrogen-containing compound found in foods and made in the body from the amino acid methionine. Choline is part of the phospholipid lecithin and the neurotransmitter acetylcholine.

chromium picolinate (CROW-mee-um pick-oh-LYN-ate): a trace mineral supplement; falsely promoted as building muscle, enhancing energy, and burning fat. Picolinate is a derivative of the amino acid tryptophan that seems to enhance chromium absorption.

chromosomes: structures within the nucleus of a cell made of DNA and associated proteins. Human beings have 46 chromosomes in 23 pairs. Each chromosome has many genes.

chronic diseases: diseases characterized by a slow progression and long duration.

chronic PEM: protein-energy malnutrition caused by long-term food deprivation; characterized in children by short height for age (stunting).

chronological age: a person's age in years from his or her date of birth.

chylomicrons (kye-lo-MY-cronz): the class of lipoproteins that transport lipids from the intestinal cells to the rest of the body.

chyme (KIME): the semiliquid mass of partly digested food expelled by the stomach into the duodenum.

cirrhosis (seer-OH-sis): advanced liver disease in which liver cells turn orange, die, and harden, permanently losing their function; often associated with alcoholism.

clinically severe obesity: a BMI of 40 or greater or a BMI of 35 or greater with additional medical problems. A less preferred term used to describe the same condition is **morbid obesity.**

CoA (coh-AY): coenzyme A; the coenzyme derived from the B vitamin pantothenic acid and central to energy metabolism.

coenzyme Q10: a lipid found in cells (mitochondria) shown to improve exercise performance in heart disease patients, but not effective in improving the performance of healthy athletes.

coenzymes: complex organic molecules that work with enzymes to facilitate the enzymes' activity. Many coenzymes have B vitamins as part of their structures.

colitis (ko-LYE-tis): inflammation of the colon.

collagen (KOL-ah-jen): the protein from which connective tissues such as scars, tendons, ligaments, and the foundations of bones and teeth are made.

colonic irrigation: the popular, but potentially harmful practice of "washing" the large intestine with a powerful enema machine.

colostrum (ko-LAHS-trum): a milklike secretion from the breast, present during the first day or so after delivery before milk appears; rich in protective factors.

complementary and alternative medicine (CAM): diverse medical and health care systems, practices, and products that are not currently considered part of conventional medicine; also called adjunctive, unconventional, or unorthodox therapies.

complementary medicine: an approach that uses alternative therapies as an adjunct to, and not simply a replacement for, conventional medicine.

complementary proteins: two or more dietary proteins whose amino acid assortments complement each other in such a way that the essential amino acids missing from one are supplied by the other.

complex carbohydrates (starches and fibers): polysaccharides composed of straight or branched chains of monosaccharides.

compound: a substance composed of two or more different atoms—for example, water (H_2O).

conception: the union of the male sperm and the female ovum; fertilization.

condensation: a chemical reaction in which two reactants combine to yield a larger product.

conditionally essential amino acid: an amino acid that is normally nonessential, but must be supplied by the diet in special circumstances when the need for it exceeds the body's ability to produce it.

conditioning: the physical effect of training; improved flexibility, strength, and endurance.

confectioners' sugar: finely powdered sucrose, 99.9% pure.

congregate meals: nutrition programs that provide food for the elderly in conveniently located settings such as community centers.

conjugated linoleic acid: a collective term for several fatty acids that have the same chemical formula as linoleic acid (18 carbons, two double bonds) but with different configurations.

constipation: the condition of having infrequent or difficult bowel movements.

contaminants: substances that make a food impure and unsuitable for ingestion.

contamination iron: iron found in foods as the result of contamination by inorganic iron salts from iron cookware, iron-containing soils, and the like.

control group: a group of individuals similar in all possible respects to the experimental group except for the treatment. Ideally, the control group receives a placebo while the experimental group receives a real treatment.

conventional medicine: diagnosis and treatment of diseases as practiced by medical doctors (M.D.) and doctors of osteopathy (D.O.) and allied health professionals such as physical therapists and registered nurses; also called allopathy; Western, mainstream, orthodox, or regular medicine; and biomedicine.

cool-down: 5 to 10 minutes of light activity, such as walking or stretching, following a vigorous workout to gradually return the body's core to near-normal temperature.

Cori cycle: the path from muscle glycogen to glucose to pyruvate to lactate (which travels to the liver) to glucose (which can travel back to the muscle) to glycogen; named after the scientist who elucidated this pathway.

corn sweeteners: corn syrup and sugars derived from corn.

corn syrup: a syrup made from cornstarch that has been treated with acid, high temperatures, and enzymes that produce glucose, maltose, and dextrins. See also **high-fructose corn syrup (HFCS).**

cornea (KOR-nee-uh): the transparent membrane covering the outside of the eye.

coronary arteries: blood vessels that supply blood to the heart.

coronary heart disease (CHD): the damage that occurs when the blood vessels carrying blood to the heart (the coronary arteries) become narrow and occluded.

correlation (CORE-ee-LAY-shun): the simultaneous increase, decrease, or change in two variables. If A increases as B increases, or if A decreases as B decreases, the correlation is positive. (This does not mean that A causes B or vice versa.) If A increases as B decreases, or if A decreases as B increases, the correlation is negative. (This does not mean that A prevents B or vice versa.) Some third factor may account for both A and B.

correspondence schools: schools that offer courses and degrees by mail. Some correspondence schools are accredited; others are not.

cortical bone: the very dense bone tissue that forms the outer shell surrounding trabecular bone and comprises the shaft of a long bone.

coupled reactions: pairs of chemical reactions in which some of the energy released from the breakdown of one compound is used to create a bond in the formation of another compound.

covert (KOH-vert): hidden, as if under covers.

CP, creatine phosphate (also called **phosphocreatine**): a high-energy compound in muscle cells that acts as a reservoir of energy that can maintain a steady supply of ATP. CP provides the energy for short bursts of activity.

C-reactive protein (CRP): a protein released during the acute phase of infection or inflammation that enhances immunity by promoting phagocytosis and activating platelets. Its presence may be used to assess a person's risk of an impending heart attack or stroke.

creatine (KREE-ah-tin): a nitrogen-containing compound that combines with phosphate to form the high-energy compound creatine phosphate (or phosphocreatine) in muscles. Claims that creatine enhances energy use and muscle strength need further confirmation.

cretinism (CREE-tin-ism): a congenital disease characterized by mental and physical retardation and commonly caused by maternal iodine deficiency during pregnancy.

critical periods: finite periods during development in which certain events occur that will have irreversible effects on later developmental stages; usually a period of rapid cell division.

cross-contamination: the contamination of food by bacteria that occurs when the food comes into contact with surfaces previously touched by raw meat, poultry, or seafood.

cruciferous vegetables: vegetables of the cabbage family, including cauliflower, broccoli, and brussels sprouts.

crypts (KRIPTS): tubular glands that lie between the intestinal villi and secrete intestinal juices into the small intestine.

cyclamate (SIGH-kla-mate): an artificial sweetener that is being considered for approval in the United States and is available in Canada as a tabletop sweetener, but not as an additive.

cytokines (SIGH-toe-kines): special proteins that direct immune and inflammatory responses.

cytoplasm (SIGH-toh-plazm): the cell contents, except for the nucleus.

cytosol: the fluid of cytoplasm; contains water, ions, nutrients, and enzymes.

D

Daily Values (DV): reference values developed by the FDA specifically for use on food labels.

deamination (dee-AM-ih-NAY-shun): removal of the amino (NH_2) group from a compound such as an amino acid.

defecate (DEF-uh-cate): to move the bowels and eliminate waste.

deficient: the amount of a nutrient below which almost all healthy people can be expected, over time, to experience deficiency symptoms.

dehydration: the condition in which body water output exceeds water input. Symptoms include thirst, dry skin and mucous membranes, rapid heartbeat, low blood pressure, and weakness.

Delaney Clause: a clause in the Food Additive Amendment to the Food, Drug, and Cosmetic Act that states that no substance that is known to cause cancer in animals or human beings at any dose level shall be added to foods.

denaturation (dee-NAY-chur-AY-shun): the change in a protein's shape and consequent loss of its function brought about by heat, agitation, acid, base, alcohol, heavy metals, or other agents.

dental caries: decay of teeth.

dental plaque: a gummy mass of bacteria that grows on teeth and can lead to dental caries and gum disease.

dextrose: an older name for glucose.

DHEA (dehydroepiandrosterone) and androstenedione: hormones made in the adrenal glands that serve as precursors to the male hormone testosterone; falsely promoted as burning fat, building muscle, and slowing aging. Side effects include acne, aggressiveness, and liver enlargement.

diabetes (DYE-uh-BEET-eez): a chronic disorder of carbohydrate metabolism, usually resulting from insufficient or ineffective insulin.

diarrhea: the frequent passage of watery bowel movements.

diet: the foods and beverages a person eats and drinks.

diet history: a record of eating behaviors and the foods a person eats.

dietary fibers: in plant foods, the nonstarch polysaccharides that are not digested by human digestive enzymes, although some are digested by GI tract bacteria. Dietary fibers include cellulose, hemicelluloses, pectins, gums, and mucilages and the nonpolysaccharides lignins, cutins, and tannins.

dietary folate equivalents (DFE): the amount of folate available to the body from naturally occurring sources, fortified foods, and supplements, accounting for differences in the bioavailability from each source.

Dietary Reference Intakes (DRI): a set of nutrient intake values for healthy people in the United States and Canada. These values are used for planning and assessing diets and include:
- Estimated Average Requirements (EAR)
- Recommended Dietary Allowances (RDA)
- Adequate Intakes (AI)
- Tolerable Upper Intake Levels (UL)

dietetic technician: a person who has completed a minimum of an associate's degree from an accredited university or college and an approved dietetic technician program that includes a supervised practice experience. See also *dietetic technician, registered (DTR).*

dietetic technician, registered (DTR): a dietetic technician who has passed a national examination and maintains registration through continuing professional education.

dietitian: a person trained in nutrition, food science, and diet planning. See also *registered dietitian.*

digestion: the process by which food is broken down into absorbable units.

digestive enzymes: proteins found in digestive juices that act on food substances, causing them to break down into simpler compounds.

digestive system: all the organs and glands associated with the ingestion and digestion of food.

dioxins (dye-OCK-sins): a class of chemical pollutants created as by-products of chemical manufacturing, incineration, chlorine bleaching of paper pulp, and other industrial processes. Dioxins persist in the environment and accumulate in the food chain.

dipeptide (dye-PEP-tide): two amino acids bonded together.

disaccharides (dye-SACK-uh-rides): pairs of monosaccharides linked together.

discretionary kcalorie allowance: the kcalories remaining in a person's energy allowance after consuming enough nutrient-dense foods to meet all nutrient needs for a day.

disordered eating: eating behaviors that are neither normal nor healthy, including restrained eating, fasting, binge eating, and purging.

dissociates (dis-SO-see-aites): physically separates.

distilled liquor or **hard liquor:** an alcoholic beverage made by fermenting and distilling grains; sometimes called **distilled spirits.**

distilled water: water that has been vaporized and recondensed, leaving it free of dissolved minerals.

diverticula (dye-ver-TIC-you-la): sacs or pouches that develop in the weakened areas of the intestinal wall (like bulges in an inner tube where the tire wall is weak).

diverticulitis (DYE-ver-tic-you-LYE-tis): infected or inflamed diverticula.

diverticulosis (DYE-ver-tic-you-LOH-sis): the condition of having diverticula.

DNA (deoxyribonucleic acid): the double helix molecules of which genes are made.

docosahexaenoic (DOE-cossa-HEXA-ee-NO-ick) **acid** (DHA): an omega-3 polyunsaturated fatty acid with 22 carbons and six double bonds; present in fish and synthesized in limited amounts in the body from linolenic acid.

dolomite: a compound of minerals (calcium magnesium carbonate) found in limestone and marble. Dolomite is powdered and is sold as a calcium-magnesium supplement. However, it may be contaminated with toxic minerals, is not well absorbed, and interacts adversely with absorption of other essential minerals.

double-blind experiment: an experiment in which neither the subjects nor the researchers know which subjects are members of the experimental group and which are serving as control subjects, until after the experiment is over.

Down syndrome: a genetic abnormality that causes mental retardation, short stature, and flattened facial features.

drink: a dose of any alcoholic beverage that delivers 1/2 oz of pure ethanol:
- 5 oz of wine
- 10 oz of wine cooler
- 12 oz of beer

drug: a substance that can modify one or more of the body's functions.

drug history: a record of all the drugs, over-the-counter and prescribed, that a person takes routinely.

DTR: see *dietetic technician, registered.*

duodenum (doo-oh-DEEN-um, doo-ODD-num): the top portion of the small intestine (about "12 fingers' breadth" long in ancient terminology).

duration: length of time (for example, the time spent in each activity session).

dysentery (DISS-en-terry): an infection of the digestive tract that causes diarrhea.

dysphagia (dis-FAY-jah): difficulty in swallowing.

E

eating disorders: disturbances in eating behavior that jeopardize a person's physical or psychological health.

eclampsia (eh-KLAMP-see-ah): a severe stage of preeclampsia characterized by convulsions.

edema (eh-DEEM-uh): the swelling of body tissue caused by excessive amounts of fluid in the interstitial spaces; seen in protein deficiency (among other conditions).

eicosanoids (eye-COSS-uh-noyds): derivatives of 20-carbon fatty acids; biologically active compounds that help to regulate blood pressure, blood clotting, and other body functions. They include prostaglandins (PROS-tah-GLAND-ins), thromboxanes (throm-BOX-ains), and leukotrienes (LOO-ko-TRY-eens).

eicosapentaenoic (EYE-cossa-PENTA-ee-NO-ick) **acid (EPA):** an omega-3 polyunsaturated fatty acid with 20 carbons and five double bonds; present in fish and synthesized in limited amounts in the body from linolenic acid.

electrolyte solutions: solutions that can conduct electricity.

electrolytes: salts that dissolve in water and dissociate into charged particles called ions.

electron transport chain: the final pathway in energy metabolism that transports electrons from hydrogen to oxygen and captures the energy released in the bonds of ATP.

element: a substance composed of atoms that are alike—for example, iron (Fe).

embolism (EM-boh-lizm): the obstruction of a blood vessel by an **embolus** (EM-boh-luss), or traveling clot, causing sudden tissue death.

embryo (EM-bree-oh): the developing infant from two to eight weeks after conception.

emergency shelters: facilities that are used to provide temporary housing.

emerging risk factors: recently identified factors that enhance the ability to predict disease risk in an individual.

emetic (em-ETT-ic): an agent that causes vomiting.

empty-kcalorie foods: a popular term used to denote foods that contribute energy but lack protein, vitamins, and minerals.

emulsifier (ee-MUL-sih-fire): a substance with both water-soluble and fat-soluble portions that promotes the mixing of oils and fats in a watery solution.

endoplasmic reticulum (en-doh-PLAZ-mic reh-TIC-you-lum): a complex network of intracellular membranes. The rough endoplasmic reticulum is dotted with ribosomes, where protein synthesis takes place. The smooth endoplasmic reticulum bears no ribosomes.

enemas: solutions inserted into the rectum and colon to stimulate a bowel movement and empty the lower large intestine.

energy: the capacity to do work. The energy in food is chemical energy. The body can convert this chemical energy to mechanical, electrical, or heat energy.

energy density: a measure of the energy a food provides relative to the amount of food (kcalories per gram).

energy-yielding nutrients: the nutrients that break down to yield energy the body can use.

enriched: the addition to a food of nutrients that were lost during processing so that the food will meet a specified standard.

enteropancreatic (EN-ter-oh-PAN-kree-AT-ik) **circulation:** the circulatory route from the pancreas to the intestine and back to the pancreas.

enzymes: proteins that facilitate chemical reactions without being changed in the process; protein catalysts.

EPA (Environmental Protection Agency): a federal agency that is responsible for, among other things, regulating pesticides and establishing water quality standards.

epidemic (ep-ih-DEM-ick): the appearance of a disease (usually infectious) or condition that attacks many people at the same time in the same region.

epigenetics: the study of heritable changes in gene function that occur without a change in the DNA sequence.

epiglottis (epp-ih-GLOTT-iss): cartilage in the throat that guards the entrance to the trachea and prevents fluid or food from entering it when a person swallows.

epinephrine (EP-ih-NEFF-rin): a hormone of the adrenal gland that modulates the stress response; formerly called adrenaline. When administered by injection, epinephrine counteracts anaphylactic shock by opening the airways and maintaining heartbeat and blood pressure.

epithelial (ep-i-THEE-lee-ul) **cells:** cells on the surface of the skin and mucous membranes.

epithelial tissue: the layer of the body that serves as a selective barrier between the body's interior and the environment. (Examples are the cornea of the eyes, the skin, the respiratory lining of the lungs, and the lining of the digestive tract.)

ergogenic (ER-go-JEN-ick) **aids:** substances or techniques used in an attempt to enhance physical performance.

erythrocyte (eh-RITH-ro-cite) **hemolysis** (he-MOLL-uh-sis): the breaking open of red blood cells (erythrocytes); a symptom of vitamin E–deficiency disease in human beings.

erythrocyte protoporphyrin (PRO-toe-PORE-fe-rin): a precursor to hemoglobin.

erythropoietin (eh-RITH-ro-POY-eh-tin): a hormone that stimulates red blood cell production.

esophageal (ee-SOF-ah-GEE-al) **sphincter:** a sphincter muscle at the upper or lower end of the esophagus. The lower esophageal sphincter is also called the **cardiac sphincter.**

esophagus (ee-SOFF-ah-gus): the food pipe; the conduit from the mouth to the stomach.

essential amino acids: amino acids that the body cannot synthesize in amounts sufficient to meet physiological needs (see Table 6-1 on p. 182).

essential fatty acids: fatty acids needed by the body but not made by it in amounts sufficient to meet physiological needs.

essential nutrients: nutrients a person must obtain from food because the body cannot make them for itself in sufficient quantity to meet physiological needs; also called indispensable nutrients. About 40 nutrients are currently known to be essential for human beings.

Estimated Average Requirement (EAR): the average daily amount of a nutrient that will maintain a specific biochemical or physiological function in half the healthy people of a given age and gender group.

Estimated Energy Requirement (EER): the average dietary energy intake that maintains energy balance and good health in a person of a given age, gender, weight, height, and level of physical activity.

estrogens: hormones responsible for the menstrual cycle and other female characteristics.

ethanol: a particular type of alcohol found in beer, wine, and distilled liquor; also called **ethyl alcohol.**

exchange lists: diet-planning tools that organize foods by their proportions of carbohydrate, fat, and protein. Foods on any single list can be used interchangeably.

exercise: planned, structured, and repetitive body movements that promote or maintain physical fitness.

experimental group: a group of individuals similar in all possible respects to the control group except for the treatment. The experimental group receives the real treatment.

extra lean: less than 5 g of fat, 2 g of saturated fat and trans fat combined, and 95 mg of cholesterol per serving and per 100 g of meat, poultry, and seafood.

extracellular fluid: fluid outside the cells. Extracellular fluid includes two main components—the interstitial fluid and plasma. Extracellular fluid accounts for approximately one-third of the body's water.

F

fad diets: popular eating plans that promise quick weight loss. Most fad diets severely limit certain foods or overemphasize others (for example, never eat potatoes or pasta or eat cabbage soup daily).

faith healing: healing by invoking divine intervention without the use of medical, surgical, or other traditional therapy.

false negative: a test result indicating that a condition is not present (negative) when in fact it is present (therefore false).

false positive: a test result indicating that a condition is present (positive) when in fact it is not (therefore false).

famine: widespread and extreme scarcity of food in an area that causes starvation and death in a large portion of the population.

FAO (Food and Agriculture Organization): an international agency (part of the United Nations) that has adopted standards to regulate pesticide use among other responsibilities.

fat replacers: ingredients that replace some or all of the functions of fat and may or may not provide energy.

fat-free: less than 0.5 g of fat per serving (and no added fat or oil); synonyms include "zero-fat," "no-fat," and "nonfat."

fats: lipids that are solid at room temperature (77°F or 25°C).

fatty acid: an organic compound composed of a carbon chain with hydrogens attached and an acid group (COOH) at one end and a methyl group (CH_3) at the other end.

fatty acid oxidation: the metabolic breakdown of fatty acids to acetyl CoA; also called **beta oxidation.**

fatty liver: an early stage of liver deterioration seen in several diseases, including kwashiorkor and alcoholic liver disease. Fatty liver is characterized by an accumulation of fat in the liver cells.

fatty streaks: accumulations of cholesterol and other lipids along the walls of the arteries.

FDA (Food and Drug Administration): a part of the Department of Health and Human Services' Public Health Service that is responsible for ensuring the safety and wholesomeness of all dietary supplements and food processed and sold in interstate commerce except meat, poultry, and eggs (which are under the jurisdiction of the USDA); inspecting food plants and imported foods; and setting standards for food composition and product labeling.

female athlete triad: a potentially fatal combination of three medical problems— disordered eating, amenorrhea, and osteoporosis.

fermentable: the extent to which bacteria in the GI tract can break down fibers to fragments that the body can use.

ferritin (FAIR-ih-tin): the iron storage protein.

fertility: the capacity of a woman to produce a normal ovum periodically and of a man to produce normal sperm; the ability to reproduce.

fetal alcohol spectrum disorder: a range of physical, behavioral, and cognitive abnormalities caused by prenatal alcohol exposure.

fetal alcohol syndrome (FAS): a cluster of physical, behavioral, and cognitive abnormalities associated with prenatal alcohol exposure, including facial malformations, growth retardation, and central nervous disorders.

fetal programming: the influence of substances during fetal growth on the development of diseases in later life.

fetus (FEET-us): the developing infant from eight weeks after conception until term.

fibrocystic (FYE-bro-SIS-tik) **breast disease:** a harmless condition in which the breasts develop lumps, sometimes associated with caffeine consumption. In some, it responds to abstinence from caffeine; in others, it can be treated with vitamin E.

fibrosis (fye-BROH-sis): an intermediate stage of liver deterioration seen in several diseases, including viral hepatitis and alcoholic liver disease. In fibrosis, the liver cells lose their function and assume the characteristics of connective tissue cells (fibers).

filtered water: water treated by filtration, usually through activated carbon filters that reduce the lead in tap water, or by reverse osmosis units that force pressurized water across a membrane removing lead, arsenic, and some microorganisms from tap water.

fitness: the characteristics that enable the body to perform physical activity; more broadly, the ability to meet routine physical demands with enough reserve energy to rise to a physical challenge; or the body's ability to withstand stress of all kinds.

flavonoids (FLAY-von-oyds): yellow pigments in foods; phytochemicals that may exert physiological effects on the body.

flaxseeds: the small brown seeds of the flax plant; valued as a source of linseed oil, fiber, and omega-3 fatty acids.

flexibility: the capacity of the joints to move through a full range of motion; the ability to bend and recover without injury.

fluid balance: maintenance of the proper types and amounts of fluid in each compartment of the body fluids (see also Chapter 12).

fluorapatite (floor-APP-uh-tite): the stabilized form of bone and tooth crystal, in which fluoride has replaced the hydroxyl groups of hydroxyapatite.

fluorosis (floor-OH-sis): discoloration and pitting of tooth enamel caused by excess fluoride during tooth development.

folate (FOLE-ate): a B vitamin; also known as folic acid, folacin, or pteroylglutamic (tare-o-EEL-glue-TAM-ick) acid (PGA). The coenzyme forms are DHF (dihydrofolate) and THF (tetrahydrofolate).

follicle-stimulating hormone (FSH): a hormone that stimulates maturation of the ovarian follicles in females and the production of sperm in males. (The ovarian follicles are part of the female reproductive system where the eggs are produced.) The release of FSH is mediated by follicle-stimulating hormone releasing hormone (FSH–RH).

food allergy: an adverse reaction to food that involves an immune response; also called **food-hypersensitivity reaction.**

food aversions: strong desires to avoid particular foods.

food bank: a facility that collects and distributes food donations to authorized organizations feeding the hungry.

food chain: the sequence in which living things depend on other living things for food.

food cravings: strong desires to eat particular foods.

food frequency questionnaire: a checklist of foods on which a person can record the frequency with which he or she eats each food.

food group plans: diet-planning tools that sort foods into groups based on nutrient content and then specify that people should eat certain amounts of foods from each group.

food insecurity: limited or uncertain access to foods of sufficient quality or quantity to sustain a healthy and active life.

food insufficiency: an inadequate amount of food due to a lack of resources.

food intolerances: adverse reactions to foods that do not involve the immune system.

food pantries: programs that provide groceries to be prepared and eaten at home.

food poverty: hunger resulting from inadequate access to available food for various reasons, including inadequate resources, political obstacles, social disruptions, poor weather conditions, and lack of transportation.

food record: an extensive, accurate log of all foods eaten over a period of several days or weeks. A food record that includes associated information such as when, where, and with whom each food is eaten is sometimes called a food diary.

food recovery: collecting wholesome food for distribution to low-income people who are hungry.

food security: access to enough food to sustain a healthy and active life.

food substitutes: foods that are designed to replace other foods.

foodborne illness: illness transmitted to human beings through food and water, caused by either an infectious agent (foodborne infection) or a poisonous substance (food intoxication); commonly known as **food poisoning.**

foods: products derived from plants or animals that can be taken into the body to yield energy and nutrients for the maintenance of life and the growth and repair of tissues.

fortified: the addition to a food of nutrients that were either not originally present or present in insignificant amounts. Fortification can be used to correct or prevent a widespread nutrient deficiency or to balance the total nutrient profile of a food.

fossil fuels: coal, oil, and natural gas.

fraudulent: the promotion, for financial gain, of devices, treatments, services, plans, or products (including diets and supplements) that alter or claim to alter a human condition without proof of safety or effectiveness.

free: "nutritionally trivial" and unlikely to have a physiological consequence; synonyms include "without," "no," and "zero." A food that does not contain a nutrient naturally may make such a claim, but only as it applies to all similar foods (for example, "applesauce, a fat-free food").

free radicals: unstable and highly reactive atoms or molecules that have one or more unpaired electrons in the outer orbital.

frequency: the number of occurrences per unit of time (for example, the number of activity sessions per week).

fructose (FRUK-tose or FROOK-tose): a monosaccharide; sometimes known as fruit sugar or levulose. Fructose is found abundantly in fruits, honey, and saps.

fuel: compounds that cells can use for energy. The major fuels include glucose, fatty acids, and amino acids; other fuels include ketone bodies, lactate, glycerol, and alcohol.

functional foods: foods that contain physiologically active compounds that provide health benefits beyond their nutrient contributions; sometimes called designer foods or nutraceuticals.

G

g: grams; a unit of weight equivalent to about 0.03 ounces.

galactose (ga-LAK-tose): a monosaccharide; part of the disaccharide lactose.

gallbladder: the organ that stores and concentrates bile. When it receives the signal that fat is present in the duodenum, the gallbladder contracts and squirts bile through the bile duct into the duodenum.

gamma-oryzanol: a plant sterol that supposedly provides the same physical responses as anabolic steroids without the adverse side effects; also known as ferulic acid, ferulate, or FRAC.

gastric glands: exocrine glands in the stomach wall that secrete gastric juice into the stomach.

gastric juice: the digestive secretion of the gastric glands of the stomach.

gastrin: a hormone secreted by cells in the stomach wall. Target organ: the glands of the stomach. Response: secretion of gastric acid.

gastroesophageal reflux: the backflow of stomach acid into the esophagus, causing damage to the cells of the esophagus and the sensation of heartburn.

gastrointestinal (GI) tract: the digestive tract. The principal organs are the stomach and intestines.

gatekeepers: with respect to nutrition, key people who control other people's access to foods and thereby exert profound impacts on their nutrition.

gene expression: the process by which a cell converts the genetic code into RNA and protein.

gene pool: all the genetic information of a population at a given time.

generally recognized as safe (GRAS): food additives that have long been in use and are believed safe.

genes: sections of chromosomes that contain the instructions needed to make one or more proteins.

genetic engineering: the use of biotechnology to modify the genetic material of living cells so that they will produce new substances or perform new functions. Foods produced via this technology are called **genetically modified (GM)** or **genetically engineered (GE) foods.**

genetics: the study of genes and inheritance.

genome (GEE-nome): the full complement of genetic material (DNA) in the chromosomes of a cell. In human beings, the genome consists of 46 chromosomes.

genomics: the study of all the genes in an organism and their interactions with environmental factors.

gestation (jes-TAY-shun): the period from conception to birth. For human beings, the average length of a healthy gestation is 40 weeks. Pregnancy is often divided into three-month periods, called **trimesters.**

gestational diabetes: abnormal glucose tolerance during pregnancy.

ghrelin (GRELL-in): a protein produced by the stomach cells that enhances appetite and decreases energy expenditure.

ginseng: a plant whose extract supposedly boosts energy. Side effects of chronic use include nervousness, confusion, and depression.

glands: cells or groups of cells that secrete materials for special uses in the body. Glands may be exocrine (EKS-oh-crin) glands, secreting their materials "out" (into the digestive tract or onto the surface of the skin), or endocrine (EN-doe-crin) glands, secreting their materials "in" (into the blood).

glucagon (GLOO-ka-gon): a hormone that is secreted by special cells in the pancreas in response to low blood glucose concentration and elicits release of glucose from liver glycogen stores.

glucocorticoids: hormones from the adrenal cortex that affect the body's management of glucose.

gluconeogenesis (gloo-ko-nee-oh-JEN-ih-sis): the making of glucose from a noncarbohydrate source.

glucose (GLOO-kose): a monosaccharide; sometimes known as *blood sugar* or *dextrose.*

glucose polymers: compounds that supply glucose, not as single molecules, but linked in chains somewhat like starch. The objective is to attract less water from the body into the digestive tract (osmotic attraction depends on the number, not the size, of particles).

glycemic index: a method of classifying foods according to their potential for raising blood glucose.

glycemic (gly-SEEM-ic) **response:** the extent to which a food raises the blood glucose concentration and elicits an insulin response.

glycerol (GLISS-er-ol): an alcohol composed of a three-carbon chain, which can serve as the backbone for a triglyceride.

glycogen (GLY-ko-jen): an animal polysaccharide composed of glucose; manufactured and stored in the liver and muscles as a storage form of glucose. Glycogen is not a significant food source of carbohydrate and is not counted as one of the complex carbohydrates in foods.

glycolysis (gly-COLL-ih-sis): the metabolic breakdown of glucose to pyruvate. Glycolysis does not require oxygen (anaerobic).

goblet cells: cells of the GI tract (and lungs) that secrete mucus.

goiter (GOY-ter): an enlargement of the thyroid gland due to an iodine deficiency, malfunction of the gland, or overconsumption of a goitrogen. Goiter caused by iodine deficiency is **simple goiter.**

goitrogen (GOY-troh-jen): a substance that enlarges the thyroid gland and causes **toxic goiter.** Goitrogens occur naturally in such foods as cabbage, kale, brussels sprouts, cauliflower, broccoli, and kohlrabi.

Golgi (GOAL-gee) **apparatus:** a set of membranes within the cell where secretory materials are packaged for export.

good source of: the product provides between 10 and 19% of the Daily Value for a given nutrient per serving.

gout (GOWT): a common form of arthritis characterized by deposits of uric acid crystals in the joints.

granulated sugar: crystalline sucrose; 99.9% pure.

growth hormone (GH): a hormone secreted by the pituitary that regulates the cell division and protein synthesis needed for normal growth. The release of GH is mediated by GH-releasing hormone (GHRH).

H

hard water: water with a high calcium and magnesium content.

hazard: a source of danger; used to refer to circumstances in which harm is possible under normal conditions of use.

Hazard Analysis Critical Control Points (HACCP): a systematic plan to identify and correct potential microbial hazards in the manufacturing, distribution, and commercial use of food products; commonly referred to as "HASS-ip."

HDL (high-density lipoprotein): the type of lipoprotein that transports cholesterol back to the liver from the cells; composed primarily of protein.

health claims: statements that characterize the relationship between a nutrient or other substance in a food and a disease or health-related condition.

health history: an account of a client's current and past health status and disease risks.

healthy: a food that is low in fat, saturated fat, cholesterol, and sodium and that contains at least 10% of the Daily Values for vitamin A, vitamin C, iron, calcium, protein, or fiber.

Healthy People: a national public health initiative under the jurisdiction of the U.S. Department of Health and Human Services (DHHS) that identifies the most significant preventable threats to health and focuses efforts toward eliminating them.

heart attack: sudden tissue death caused by blockages of vessels that feed the heart muscle; also called **myocardial** (my-oh-KAR-dee-al) **infarction** (in-FARK-shun) or **cardiac arrest.**

heartburn: a burning sensation in the chest area caused by backflow of stomach acid into the esophagus.

heat stroke: a dangerous accumulation of body heat with accompanying loss of body fluid.

heavy metals: mineral ions such as mercury and lead, so called because they are of relatively high atomic weight. Many heavy metals are poisonous.

Heimlich (HIME-lick) **maneuver** (abdominal thrust maneuver): a technique for dislodging an object from the trachea of a choking person.

hematocrit (hee-MAT-oh-krit): measurement of the volume of the red blood cells packed by centrifuge in a given volume of blood.

heme (HEEM): the iron-holding part of the hemoglobin and myoglobin proteins. About 40% of the iron in meat, fish, and poultry is bound into heme; the other 60% is nonheme iron.

hemochromatosis (HE-moh-KRO-ma-toe-sis): a genetically determined failure to prevent absorption of unneeded dietary iron that is characterized by iron overload and tissue damage.

hemoglobin (HE-moh-GLO-bin): the globular protein of the red blood cells that carries oxygen from the lungs to the cells throughout the body.

hemolytic (HE-moh-LIT-ick) **anemia:** the condition of having too few red blood cells as a result of erythrocyte hemolysis.

hemophilia (HE-moh-FEEL-ee-ah): a hereditary disease in which the blood is unable to clot because it lacks the ability to synthesize certain clotting factors.

hemorrhagic (hem-oh-RAJ-ik) **disease:** a disease characterized by excessive bleeding.

hemorrhoids (HEM-oh-royds): painful swelling of the veins surrounding the rectum.

hemosiderin (heem-oh-SID-er-in): an iron-storage protein primarily made in times of iron overload.

hemosiderosis (HE-moh-sid-er-OH-sis): a condition characterized by the deposition of hemosiderin in the liver and other tissues.

hepatic portal vein: the vein that collects blood from the GI tract and conducts it to capillaries in the liver.

hepatic vein: the vein that collects blood from the liver capillaries and returns it to the heart.

hepcidin: a hormone produced by the liver that regulates iron balance.

herbal (ERB-al) **medicine:** the use of plants to treat disease or improve health; also known as *botanical medicine* or *phytotherapy*.

hGH (human growth hormone): a hormone produced by the brain's pituitary gland that regulates normal growth and development; also called **somatotropin.** Some athletes misuse this hormone to increase their height and strength.

hiccups (HICK-ups): repeated cough-like sounds and jerks that are produced when an involuntary spasm of the diaphragm muscle sucks air down the windpipe; also spelled hiccoughs.

high: 20% or more of the Daily Value for a given nutrient per serving; synonyms include "rich in" or "excellent source."

high fiber: 5 g or more fiber per serving. A high-fiber claim made on a food that contains more than 3 g fat per serving and per 100 g of food must also declare total fat.

high potency: 100% or more of the Daily Value for the nutrient in a single supplement and for at least two-thirds of the nutrients in a multinutrient supplement.

high-fructose corn syrup (HFCS): a syrup made from cornstarch that has been treated with an enzyme that converts some of the glucose to the sweeter fructose; made especially for use in processed foods and beverages, where it is the predominant sweetener.

high-quality proteins: dietary proteins containing all the essential amino acids in relatively the same amounts that human beings require. They may also contain nonessential amino acids.

high-risk pregnancy: a pregnancy characterized by indicators that make it likely the birth will be surrounded by problems such as premature delivery, difficult birth, retarded growth, birth defects, and early infant death.

histamine (HISS-tah-mean or HISS-tah-men): a substance produced by cells of the immune system as part of a local immune reaction to an antigen; participates in causing inflammation.

HIV (human immunodeficiency virus): the virus that causes AIDS. The infection progresses to become an immune system disorder that leaves its victims defenseless against numerous infections.

HMB (beta-hydroxy-beta-methylbutyrate): a metabolite of the branched-chain amino acid leucine. Claims that HMB increases muscle mass and strength are based on the results of two studies from the lab that developed HMB as a supplement.

homeopathy (hoh-me-OP-ah-thee): a practice based on the theory that "like cures like," that is, that substances that cause symptoms in healthy people can cure those symptoms when given in very dilute amounts.

homeostasis (HOME-ee-oh-STAY-sis): the maintenance of constant internal conditions (such as blood chemistry, temperature, and blood pressure) by the body's control systems. A homeostatic system is constantly reacting to external forces to maintain limits set by the body's needs.

honey: sugar (mostly sucrose) formed from nectar gathered by bees. An enzyme splits the sucrose into glucose and fructose. Composition and flavor vary, but honey always contains a mixture of sucrose, fructose, and glucose.

hormones: chemical messengers. Hormones are secreted by a variety of glands in response to altered conditions in the body. Each hormone travels to one or more specific target tissues or organs, where it elicits a specific response to maintain homeostasis.

hormone-sensitive lipase: an enzyme inside adipose cells that responds to the body's need for fuel by hydrolyzing triglycerides so that their parts (glycerol and fatty acids) escape into the general circulation and thus become available to other cells for fuel. The signals to which this enzyme responds include epinephrine and glucagon, which oppose insulin.

hourly sweat rate: the amount of weight lost plus fluid consumed during exercise per hour.

human genome (GEE-nome): the full complement of genetic material in the chromosomes of a person's cells.

hunger: the painful sensation caused by a lack of food that initiates food-seeking behavior; a consequence of food insecurity that, because of prolonged, involuntary lack of food, results in discomfort, illness, weakness, or pain that goes beyond the usual uneasy sensation.

hydrochloric acid: an acid composed of hydrogen and chloride atoms (HCl) that is normally produced by the gastric glands.

hydrogenation (HIGH-dro-jen-AY-shun or high-DROJ-eh-NAY-shun): a chemical process by which hydrogens are added to monounsaturated or polyunsaturated fatty acids to reduce the number of double bonds, making the fats more saturated (solid) and more resistant to oxidation (protecting against rancidity). Hydrogenation produces *trans*-fatty acids.

hydrolysis (high-DROL-ih-sis): a chemical reaction in which a major reactant is split into two products, with the addition of a hydrogen atom (H) to one and a hydroxyl group (OH) to the other (from water, H_2O). (The noun is *hydrolysis;* the verb is *hydrolyze.*)

hydrophilic (high-dro-FIL-ick): a term referring to water-loving, or water-soluble, substances.

hydrophobic (high-dro-FOE-bick): a term referring to water-fearing, or non-water-soluble, substances; also known as lipophilic (fat loving).

hydrotherapy: the use of water (in whirlpools, as douches, or packed as ice, for example) to promote relaxation and healing.

hydroxyapatite (high-drox-ee-APP-ah-tite): crystals made of calcium and phosphorus.

hyperactivity: inattentive and impulsive behavior that is more frequent and severe than is typical of others a similar age; professionally called **attention-deficit/hyperactivity disorder (ADHD).**

hyperglycemia: elevated blood glucose concentrations.

hypertension: higher-than-normal blood pressure. Hypertension that develops without an identifiable cause is known as **essential** or **primary hypertension;** hypertension that is caused by a specific disorder such as kidney disease is known as **secondary hypertension.**

hyperthermia: an above-normal body temperature.

hypertrophy (high-PER-tro-fee): growing larger; with regard to muscles, an increase in size (and strength) in response to use.

hypnotherapy: a technique that uses hypnosis and the power of suggestion to improve health behaviors, relieve pain, and heal.

hypoallergenic formulas: clinically tested infant formulas that support infant growth and development but do not provoke reactions in 90% of infants or children with confirmed cow's milk allergy.

hypoglycemia (HIGH-po-gly-SEE-me-ah): an abnormally low blood glucose concentration.

hyponatremia (HIGH-poe-na-TREE-mee-ah): a decreased concentration of sodium in the blood.

hypothalamus (high-po-THAL-ah-mus): a brain center that controls activities such as maintenance of water balance, regulation of body temperature, and control of appetite.

hypothermia: a below-normal body temperature.

hypothesis (hi-POTH-eh-sis): an unproven statement that tentatively explains the relationships between two or more variables.

I

ileocecal (ill-ee-oh-SEEK-ul) **valve:** the sphincter separating the small and large intestines.

ileum (ILL-ee-um): the last segment of the small intestine.

imagery: a technique that guides clients to achieve a desired physical, emotional, or spiritual state by visualizing themselves in that state.

imitation foods: foods that substitute for and resemble another food, but are nutritionally inferior to it with respect to vitamin, mineral, or protein content. If the substitute is not inferior to the food it resembles and if its name provides an accurate description of the product, it need not be labeled "imitation."

immune system: the body's natural defense against foreign materials that have penetrated the skin or mucous membranes.

immunity: the body's ability to defend itself against diseases (see also Chapter 18).

immunoglobulins (IM-you-noh-GLOB-you-linz): proteins capable of acting as antibodies.

implantation: the stage of development in which the zygote embeds itself in the wall of the uterus and begins to develop; occurs during the first two weeks after conception.

indigestion: incomplete or uncomfortable digestion, usually accompanied by pain, nausea, vomiting, heartburn, intestinal gas, or belching.

indirect or **incidental additives:** substances that can get into food as a result of contact during growing, processing, packaging, storing, cooking, or some other stage before the foods are consumed; sometimes called **accidental additives.**

infectious diseases: diseases caused by bacteria, viruses, parasites, or other microorganisms that can be transmitted from one person to another through air, water, or food; by contact; or through vector organisms such as mosquitoes.

inflammation: an immunological response to cellular injury characterized by an increase in white blood cells.

initiators: factors that cause mutations that give rise to cancer, such as radiation and carcinogens.

inorganic: not containing carbon or pertaining to living things.

inositol (in-OSS-ih-tall): a nonessential nutrient that can be made in the body from glucose. Inositol is a part of cell membrane structures.

insoluble fibers: indigestible food components that do not dissolve in water. Examples include the tough, fibrous structures found in the strings of celery and the skins of corn kernels.

insulin (IN-suh-lin): a hormone secreted by special cells in the pancreas in response to (among other things) increased blood glucose concentration. The primary role of insulin is to control the transport of glucose from the bloodstream into the muscle and fat cells.

insulin resistance: the condition in which a normal amount of insulin produces a subnormal effect in muscle, adipose, and liver cells, resulting in an elevated fasting glucose; a metabolic consequence of obesity that precedes type 2 diabetes.

integrative medicine: an approach that incorporates alternative therapies into the practice of conventional medicine (similar to complementary medicine, but a closer relationship is implied).

intensity: the degree of exertion while exercising (for example, the amount of weight lifted or the speed of running).

intentional food additives: additives intentionally added to foods, such as nutrients, colors, and preservatives.

intermittent claudication (klaw-dih-KAY-shun): severe calf pain caused by inadequate blood supply. It occurs when walking and subsides during rest.

Internet (the net): a worldwide network of millions of computers linked together to share information.

interstitial (IN-ter-STISH-al) **fluid:** fluid between the cells (intercellular), usually high in sodium and chloride. Interstitial fluid is a large component of extracellular fluid.

intra-abdominal fat: fat stored within the abdominal cavity in association with the internal abdominal organs, as opposed to the fat stored directly under the skin (subcutaneous fat).

intracellular fluid: fluid within the cells, usually high in potassium and phosphate. Intracellular fluid accounts for approximately two-thirds of the body's water.

intrinsic factor: a glycoprotein (a protein with short polysaccharide chains attached) secreted by the stomach cells that binds with vitamin B_{12} in the small intestine to aid in the absorption of vitamin B_{12}.

invert sugar: a mixture of glucose and fructose formed by the hydrolysis of sucrose in a chemical process; sold only in liquid form and sweeter than sucrose. Invert sugar is used as a food additive to help preserve freshness and prevent shrinkage.

ions (EYE-uns): atoms or molecules that have gained or lost electrons and therefore have electrical charges. Examples include the positively charged sodium ion (Na+) and the negatively charged chloride ion (Cl-).

iridology: the study of changes in the iris of the eye and their relationships to disease.

iron deficiency: the state of having depleted iron stores.

iron overload: toxicity from excess iron.

iron-deficiency anemia: severe depletion of iron stores that results in low hemoglobin and small, pale red blood cells. Anemias that impair hemoglobin synthesis are **microcytic** (small cell).

irradiation: sterilizing a food by exposure to energy waves, similar to ultraviolet light and microwaves.

irritable bowel syndrome: an intestinal disorder of unknown cause. Symptoms include abdominal discomfort and cramping, diarrhea, constipation, or alternating diarrhea and constipation.

IU: international units; an old measure of vitamin activity determined by biological methods (as opposed to new measures that are determined by direct chemical analyses). Many fortified foods and supplements use IU on their labels.

J

jejunum (je-JOON-um): the first two-fifths of the small intestine beyond the duodenum.

K

kcal: kcalories; a unit by which energy is measured.

kcalorie (energy) **control:** management of food energy intake.

kcalorie-free: fewer than 5 kcal per serving.

kefir (keh-FUR): a fermented milk created by adding *Lactobacillus acidophilus* and other bacteria that break down lactose to glucose and galactose, producing a sweet, lactose-free product.

keratin (KARE-uh-tin): a water-insoluble protein; the normal protein of hair and nails.

keratinization: accumulation of keratin in a tissue; a sign of vitamin A deficiency.

keratomalacia (KARE-ah-toe-ma-LAY-shuh): softening of the cornea that leads to irreversible blindness; seen in severe vitamin A deficiency.

keto (KEY-toe) **acid:** an organic acid that contains a carbonyl group (C=O).

ketone (KEE-tone) **bodies:** the product of the incomplete breakdown of fat when glucose is not available in the cells.

ketosis (kee-TOE-sis): an undesirably high concentration of ketone bodies in the blood and urine.

kwashiorkor (kwash-ee-OR-core, kwash-ee-or-CORE): a form of PEM that results either from inadequate protein intake or, more commonly, from infections.

L

lactadherin (lack-tad-HAIR-in): a protein in breast milk that attacks diarrhea-causing viruses.

lactase: an enzyme that hydrolyzes lactose.

lactase deficiency: a lack of the enzyme required to digest the disaccharide lactose into its component monosaccharides (glucose and galactose).

lactate: a 3-carbon compound produced from pyruvate during anaerobic metabolism.

lactation: production and secretion of breast milk for the purpose of nourishing an infant.

lactoferrin (lack-toh-FERR-in): a protein in breast milk that binds iron and keeps it from supporting the growth of the infant's intestinal bacteria.

lacto-ovo-vegetarians: people who include milk, milk products, and eggs, but exclude meat, poultry, fish, and seafood from their diets.

lactose (LAK-tose): a disaccharide composed of glucose and galactose; commonly known as *milk sugar.*

lactose intolerance: a condition that results from inability to digest the milk sugar lactose; characterized by bloating, gas, abdominal discomfort, and diarrhea.

lactovegetarians: people who include milk and milk products, but exclude meat, poultry, fish, seafood, and eggs from their diets.

large intestine or **colon** (COAL-un): the lower portion of intestine that completes the digestive process. Its segments are the ascending colon, the transverse colon, the descending colon, and the sigmoid colon.

larynx: the upper part of the air passageway that contains the vocal cords; also called the *voice box.*

laxatives: substances that loosen the bowels and thereby prevent or treat constipation.

LDL (low-density lipoprotein): the type of lipoprotein derived from very-low-density lipoproteins (VLDL) as VLDL triglycerides are removed and broken down; composed primarily of cholesterol.

lean: less than 10 g of fat, 4.5 g of saturated fat and trans fat combined, and 95 mg of cholesterol per serving and per 100 g of meat, poultry, and seafood.

lean body mass: the body minus its fat.

lecithin (LESS-uh-thin): one of the phospholipids. Both nature and the food industry use lecithin as an emulsifier to combine water-soluble and fat-soluble ingredients that do not ordinarily mix, such as water and oil.

legumes (lay-GYOOMS, LEG-yooms): plants of the bean and pea family, with seeds that are rich in protein compared with other plant-derived foods.

leptin: a protein produced by fat cells under direction of the ob gene that decreases appetite and increases energy expenditure; sometimes called the *ob protein.*

less: at least 25% less of a given nutrient or kcalories than the comparison food (see individual nutrients); synonyms include "fewer" and "reduced."

less cholesterol: 25% or less cholesterol than the comparison food (reflecting a reduction of at least 20 mg per serving), and 2 g or less saturated fat and trans fat combined per serving.

less fat: 25% or less fat than the comparison food.

less saturated fat: 25% or less saturated fat and *trans* fat combined than the comparison food.

let-down reflex: the reflex that forces milk to the front of the breast when the infant begins to nurse.

levulose: an older name for fructose.

license to practice: permission under state or federal law, granted on meeting specified criteria, to use a certain title (such as dietitian) and offer certain services. Licensed dietitians may use the initials LD after their names.

life expectancy: the average number of years lived by people in a given society.

life span: the maximum number of years of life attainable by a member of a species.

light or lite: one-third fewer kcalories than the comparison food; 50% or less of the fat or sodium than the comparison food; any use of the term other than as defined must specify what it is referring to (for example, "light in color" or "light in texture").

lignans: phytochemicals present in flaxseed, but not in flax oil, that are converted to phytosterols by intestinal bacteria and are under study as possible anticancer agents.

limiting amino acid: the essential amino acid found in the shortest supply relative to the amounts needed for protein synthesis in the body.

linoleic (lin-oh-LAY-ick) acid: an essential fatty acid with 18 carbons and two double bonds.

linolenic (lin-oh-LEN-ick) acid: an essential fatty acid with 18 carbons and three double bonds.

lipids: a family of compounds that includes triglycerides, phospholipids, and sterols. Lipids are characterized by their insolubility in water. (Lipids also include the fat-soluble vitamins, described in Chapter 11.)

lipoprotein lipase (LPL): an enzyme that hydrolyzes triglycerides passing by in the bloodstream and directs their parts into the cells, where they can be metabolized for energy or reassembled for storage.

lipoproteins (LIP-oh-PRO-teenz): clusters of lipids associated with proteins that serve as transport vehicles for lipids in the lymph and blood.

listeriosis: an infection caused by eating food contaminated with the bacterium *Listeria monocytogenes,* which can be killed by pasteurization and cooking but can survive at refrigerated temperatures; certain ready-to-eat foods, such as hot dogs and deli meats, may become contaminated after cooking or processing, but before packaging.

liver: the organ that manufactures bile. (The liver's many other functions are described in Chapter 7.)

longevity: long duration of life.

low: an amount that would allow frequent consumption of a food without exceeding the Daily Value for the nutrient. A food that is naturally low in a nutrient may make such a claim, but only as it applies to all similar foods (for example, "fresh cauliflower, a low-sodium food"); synonyms include "little," "few," and "low source of."

low birthweight (LBW): a birthweight of 5½ lb (2500 g) or less; indicates probable poor health in the newborn and poor nutrition status in the mother during pregnancy, before pregnancy, or both. Normal birthweight for a full-term baby is 6½ to 8¾ lb (about 3000 to 4000 g).

low cholesterol: 20 mg or less cholesterol per serving and 2 g or less saturated fat and trans fat combined per serving.

low fat: 3 g or less fat per serving.

low kcalorie: 40 kcal or less per serving.

low saturated fat: 1 g or less saturated fat and less than 0.5 g of trans fat per serving.

low sodium: 140 mg or less per serving.

low-risk pregnancy: a pregnancy characterized by indicators that make a normal outcome likely.

lumen (LOO-men): the space within a vessel, such as the intestine.

lutein (LOO-teen): a plant pigment of yellow hue; a phytochemical believed to play roles in eye functioning and health.

luteinizing (LOO-tee-in-EYE-zing) hormone (LH): a hormone that stimulates ovulation and the development of the corpus luteum (the small tissue that develops from a ruptured ovarian follicle and secretes hormones); so called because the follicle turns yellow as it matures. In men, LH stimulates testosterone secretion. The release of LH is mediated by luteinizing hormone–releasing hormone (LH–RH).

lycopene (LYE-koh-peen): a pigment responsible for the red color of tomatoes and other red-hued vegetables; a phytochemical that may act as an antioxidant in the body.

lymph (LIMF): a clear yellowish fluid that is similar to blood except that it contains no red blood cells or platelets. Lymph from the GI tract transports fat and fat-soluble vitamins to the bloodstream via lymphatic vessels.

lymphatic (lim-FAT-ic) system: a loosely organized system of vessels and ducts that convey fluids toward the heart. The GI part of the lymphatic system carries the products of fat digestion into the bloodstream.

lymphocytes (LIM-foh-sites): white blood cells that participate in acquired immunity; B-cells and T-cells.

lysosomes (LYE-so-zomes): cellular organelles; membrane-enclosed sacs of degradative enzymes.

M

macrobiotic diets: extremely restrictive diets limited to a few grains and vegetables; based on metaphysical beliefs and not on nutrition. A macrobiotic diet might consist of brown rice, miso soup, and sea vegetables, for example.

macular (MACK-you-lar) degeneration: deterioration of the macular area of the eye that can lead to loss of central vision and eventual blindness. The **macula** is a small, oval, yellowish region in the center of the retina that provides the sharp, straight-ahead vision so critical to reading and driving.

magnesium: a cation within the body's cells, active in many enzyme systems.

major minerals: essential mineral nutrients found in the human body in amounts larger than 5 g; sometimes called **macrominerals.**

malignant (ma-LIG-nant): describes a cancerous cell or tumor, which can injure healthy tissue and spread cancer to other regions of the body.

malnutrition: any condition caused by excess or deficient food energy or nutrient intake or by an imbalance of nutrients.

maltose (MAWL-tose): a disaccharide composed of two glucose units; sometimes known as malt sugar.

maltase: an enzyme that hydrolyzes maltose.

mammary glands: glands of the female breast that secrete milk.

maple sugar: a sugar (mostly sucrose) purified from the concentrated sap of the sugar maple tree.

marasmus (ma-RAZ-mus): a form of PEM that results from a severe deprivation, or impaired absorption, of energy, protein, vitamins, and minerals.

margin of safety: when speaking of food additives, a zone between the concentration normally used and that at which a hazard exists. For common table salt, for example, the margin of safety is 1/5 (five times the amount normally used would be hazardous).

massage therapy: a healing method in which the therapist manually kneads muscles to reduce tension, increase blood circulation, improve joint mobility, and promote healing of injuries.

matrix (MAY-tricks): the basic substance that gives form to a developing structure; in the body, the formative cells from which teeth and bones grow.

matter: anything that takes up space and has mass.

Meals on Wheels: a nutrition program that delivers food for the elderly to their homes.

meat replacements: products formulated to look and taste like meat, fish, or poultry; usually made of textured vegetable protein.

meditation: a self-directed technique of relaxing the body and calming the mind.

MEOS or microsomal (my-krow-SO-mal) ethanol-oxidizing system: a system of enzymes in the liver that oxidize not only alcohol but also several classes of drugs.

metabolic syndrome: a combination of risk factors—insulin resistance, hypertension, abnormal blood lipids, and abdominal obesity—that greatly increase a person's risk of developing coronary heart disease; also called **Syndrome X, insulin resistance syndrome,** or **dysmetabolic syndrome.**

metabolism: the sum total of all the chemical reactions that go on in living cells. Energy metabolism includes all the reactions by which the body obtains and expends the energy from food.

metalloenzymes (meh-TAL-oh-EN-zimes): enzymes that contain one or more minerals as part of their structures.

metallothionein (meh-TAL-oh-THIGH-oh-neen): a sulfur-rich protein that avidly binds with and transports metals such as zinc.

metastasize (me-TAS-tah-size): the spread of cancer from one part of the body to another.

MFP factor: a peptide released during the digestion of meat, fish, and poultry that enhances nonheme iron absorption.

micelles (MY-cells): tiny spherical complexes of emulsified fat that arise during digestion; most contain bile salts and the products of lipid digestion, including fatty acids, monoglycerides, and cholesterol.

μg: micrograms; one-millionth of a gram.

µg DFE: micrograms dietary folate equivalents; a measure of folate activity.

µg RAE: micrograms retinol activity equivalents; a measure of vitamin A activity.

microarray technology: research tools that analyze the expression of thousands of genes simultaneously and search for particular gene changes associated with a disease. DNA microarrays are also called DNA chips.

microvilli (MY-cro-VILL-ee, MY-cro-VILL-eye): tiny, hairlike projections on each cell of every villus that can trap nutrient particles and transport them into the cells; singular *microvillus.*

milk anemia: iron-deficiency anemia that develops when an excessive milk intake displaces iron-rich foods from the diet.

milliequivalents (mEq): the concentration of electrolytes in a volume of solution. Milliequivalents are a useful measure when considering ions because the number of charges reveals characteristics about the solution that are not evident when the concentration is expressed in terms of weight.

mg: milligrams; one-thousandth of a gram.

mg NE: milligrams niacin equivalents; a measure of niacin activity.

mmol: millimoles; one thousandth of a mole, the molecular weight of a substance. To convert mmol to mg, multiply by the atomic weight of the substance.

mineral oil: a purified liquid derived from petroleum and used to treat constipation.

mineral water: water from a spring or well that typically contains 250 to 500 parts per million (ppm) of minerals.

mineralization: the process in which calcium, phosphorus, and other minerals crystallize on the collagen matrix of a growing bone, hardening the bone.

minerals: inorganic elements. Some minerals are essential nutrients required in small amounts by the body for health.

misinformation: false or misleading information.

mitochondria (my-toh-KON-dree-uh); singular **mitochondrion:** the cellular organelles responsible for producing ATP aerobically; made of membranes (lipid and protein) with enzymes mounted on them.

moderate exercise: activity equivalent to the rate of exertion reached when walking at a speed of 4 miles per hour (15 minutes to walk one mile).

moderation: in relation to alcohol consumption, not more than two drinks a day for the average-size man and not more than one drink a day for the average-size woman.

moderation (dietary): providing enough but not too much of a substance.

molasses: the thick brown syrup produced during sugar refining. Molasses retains residual sugar and other by-products and a few minerals; blackstrap molasses contains significant amounts of calcium and iron.

molecule: two or more atoms of the same or different elements joined by chemical bonds. Examples are molecules of the element oxygen, composed of two oxygen atoms (O_2), and molecules of the compound water, composed of two hydrogen atoms and one oxygen atom (H_2O).

molybdenum (mo-LIB-duh-num): a trace element.

monoglycerides: molecules of glycerol with one fatty acid attached. A molecule of glycerol with two fatty acids attached is a **diglyceride.**

monosaccharides (mon-oh-SACK-uh-rides): carbohydrates of the general formula $CnH2nOn$ that typically form a single ring.

monosodium glutamate (MSG): a sodium salt of the amino acid glutamic acid commonly used as a flavor enhancer. The FDA classifies MSG as a

"generally recognized as safe" ingredient.

monounsaturated fatty acid (MUFA): a fatty acid that lacks two hydrogen atoms and has one double bond between carbons—for example, oleic acid. A **monounsaturated fat** is composed of triglycerides in which most of the fatty acids are monounsaturated.

more: at least 10% more of the Daily Value for a given nutrient than the comparison food; synonyms include "added" and "extra."

mouth: the oral cavity containing the tongue and teeth.

MSG symptom complex: an acute, temporary intolerance reaction that may occur after the ingestion of the additive MSG (monosodium glutamate). Symptoms include burning sensations, chest and facial flushing and pain, and throbbing headaches.

mucous (MYOO-kus) **membranes:** the membranes, composed of mucus-secreting cells, that line the surfaces of body tissues.

mucus (MYOO-kus): a slippery substance secreted by cells of the GI lining (and other body linings) that protects the cells from exposure to digestive juices (and other destructive agents).

muscle dysmorphia (dis-MORE-fee-ah): a psychiatric disorder characterized by a preoccupation with building body mass.

muscle endurance: the ability of a muscle to contract repeatedly without becoming exhausted.

muscle strength: the ability of muscles to work against resistance.

muscular dystrophy (DIS-tro-fee): a hereditary disease in which the muscles gradually weaken. Its most debilitating effects arise in the lungs.

mutations: a permanent change in the DNA that can be inherited.

myoglobin: the oxygen-holding protein of the muscle cells.

N

NAD (nicotinamide adenine dinucleotide): the main coenzyme form of the vitamin niacin. Its reduced form is NADH.

narcotic (nar-KOT-ic): a drug that dulls the senses, induces sleep, and becomes addictive with prolonged use.

natural water: water obtained from a spring or well that is certified to be safe and sanitary. The mineral content may not be changed, but the water may be treated in other ways such as with ozone or by filtration.

naturopathic (nay-chur-oh-PATH-ick) **medicine:** a system that taps the natural healing forces within the body by integrating several practices, including traditional medicine, herbal medicine, clinical nutrition, homeopathy, acupuncture, East Asian medicine, hydrotherapy, and manipulative therapy.

neotame (NEE-oh-tame): an artificial sweetener composed of two amino acids (phenylalanine and aspartic acid); approved for use in the United States.

net protein utilization (NPU): a measure of protein quality assessed by measuring the amount of protein nitrogen that is retained from a given amount of protein nitrogen eaten.

neural tube: the embryonic tissue that forms the brain and spinal cord.

neural tube defects: malformations of the brain, spinal cord, or both during embryonic development that often result in lifelong disability or death.

neurofibrillary tangles: snarls of the threadlike strands that extend from the nerve cells, commonly found in the brains of people with Alzheimer's dementia.

neurons: nerve cells; the structural and functional units of the nervous system. Neurons initiate and conduct nerve impulse transmissions.

neuropeptide Y: a chemical produced in the brain that stimulates appetite, diminishes energy expenditure, and increases fat storage.

neurotransmitters: chemicals that are released at the end of a nerve cell when a nerve impulse arrives there. They diffuse across the gap to the next cell and alter the membrane of that second cell to either inhibit or excite it.

niacin (NIGH-a-sin): a B vitamin. The coenzyme forms are NAD (nicotinamide adenine dinucleotide) and NADP (the phosphate form of NAD). Niacin can be eaten preformed or made in the body from its precursor, tryptophan, one of the amino acids.

niacin equivalents (NE): the amount of niacin present in food, including the niacin that can theoretically be made from its precursor, tryptophan, present in the food.

niacin flush: a temporary burning, tingling, and itching sensation that occurs when a person takes a large dose of nicotinic acid; often accompanied by a headache and reddened face, arms, and chest.

night blindness: slow recovery of vision after flashes of bright light at night or an inability to see in dim light; an early symptom of vitamin A deficiency.

nitrites (NYE-trites): salts added to food to prevent botulism. One example is sodium nitrite, which is used to preserve meats.

nitrogen balance: the amount of nitrogen consumed (N in) as compared with the amount of nitrogen excreted (N out) in a given period of time.

nitrosamines (nye-TROHS-uh-meens): derivatives of nitrites that may be formed in the stomach when nitrites combine with amines. Nitrosamines are carcinogenic in animals.

nonessential amino acids: amino acids that the body can synthesize (see Table 6-1).

nonnutritive sweeteners: sweeteners that yield no energy (or insignificant energy in the case of aspartame).

nonpoint water pollution: water pollution caused by runoff from all over an area rather than from discrete "point" sources. An example is the pollution caused by runoff from agricultural fields.

nucleotide bases: the nitrogen-containing building blocks of DNA and RNA—cytosine (C), thymine (T), uracil (U), guanine (G), and adenine (A). In DNA, the base pairs are A–T and C–G and in RNA, the base pairs are A–U and C–G.

nucleotides: the subunits of DNA and RNA molecules, composed of a phosphate group, a 5-carbon sugar (deoxyribose for DNA and ribose for RNA), and a nitrogen-containing base.

nucleus: a major membrane-enclosed body within every cell, which contains the cell's genetic material, DNA, embedded in chromosomes.

nursing bottle tooth decay: extensive tooth decay due to prolonged tooth contact with formula, milk, fruit juice, or other carbohydrate-rich liquid offered to an infant in a bottle.

nutrient claims: statements that characterize the quantity of a nutrient in a food.

nutrient density: a measure of the nutrients a food provides relative to the energy it provides. The more nutrients and the fewer kcalories, the higher the nutrient density.

nutrients: chemical substances obtained from food and used in the body to provide energy, structural materials, and regulating agents to support growth, maintenance, and repair of the body's tissues. Nutrients may also reduce the risks of some diseases.

nutrition: the science of foods and the nutrients and other substances they contain, and of their actions within the body (including ingestion, digestion, absorption, transport, metabolism, and excretion). A broader definition includes the social, economic, cultural, and psychological implications of food and eating.

nutrition assessment: a comprehensive analysis of a person's nutrition status that uses health, socioeconomic, drug, and diet histories; anthropometric measurements; physical examinations; and laboratory tests.

nutrition screening: the use of preliminary nutrition assessment techniques to identify people who are malnourished or are at risk for malnutrition.

nutritional genomics: the science of how nutrients affect the activities of genes (nutrigenomics) and how genes affect the interactions between diet and disease (nutrigenetics).

nutritionist: a person who specializes in the study of nutrition. Note that this definition does not specify qualifications and may apply not only to registered dietitians but also to self-described experts whose training is questionable. Most states have licensing laws that define the scope of practice for those calling themselves nutritionists.

nutritive sweeteners: sweeteners that yield energy, including both sugars and sugar replacers.

O

obese: overweight with adverse health effects; BMI 30 or higher.

oils: lipids that are liquid at room temperature (77°F or 25°C).

olestra: a synthetic fat made from sucrose and fatty acids that provides 0 kcalories per gram; also known as **sucrose polyester.**

omega: the last letter of the Greek alphabet (ω), used by chemists to refer to the position of the first double bond from the methyl (CH_3) end of a fatty acid.

omega-3 fatty acid: a polyunsaturated fatty acid in which the first double bond is three carbons away from the methyl (CH_3) end of the carbon chain.

omega-6 fatty acid: a polyunsaturated fatty acid in which the first double bond is six carbons from the methyl (CH_3) end of the carbon chain.

omnivores: people who have no formal restriction on the eating of any foods.

opsin (OP-sin): the protein portion of the visual pigment molecule.

oral rehydration therapy (ORT): the administration of a simple solution of sugar, salt, and water, taken by mouth, to treat dehydration caused by diarrhea.

organelles: subcellular structures such as ribosomes, mitochondria, and lysosomes.

organic: in agriculture, crops grown and processed according to USDA regulations defining the use of fertilizers, herbicides, insecticides, fungicides, preservatives, and other chemical ingredients.

organic: in chemistry, a substance or molecule containing carbon-carbon bonds or carbon-hydrogen bonds. This definition excludes coal, diamonds, and a few carbon-containing compounds that contain only a single carbon and no hydrogen, such as carbon dioxide (CO_2), calcium carbonate ($CaCO_3$), magnesium carbonate ($MgCO_3$), and sodium cyanide (NaCN).

organic: on food labels, that at least 95% of the product's ingredients have been grown and processed according to USDA regulations defining the use of fertilizers, herbicides, insecticides, fungicides, preservatives, and other chemical ingredients (see Chapter 19).

organic halogens: an organic compound containing one or more atoms of a halogen—fluorine, chlorine, iodine, or bromine.

orlistat (OR-leh-stat): a drug used in the treatment of obesity that inhibits the absorption of fat in the GI tract, thus limiting kcaloric intake.

orthomolecular medicine: the use of large doses of vitamins to treat chronic disease.

osmosis: the movement of water across a membrane toward the side where the solutes are more concentrated.

osmotic pressure: the amount of pressure needed to prevent the movement of water across a membrane.

osteoarthritis: a painful, degenerative disease of the joints that occurs when the cartilage in a joint deteriorates; joint structure is damaged, with loss of function; also called **degenerative arthritis.**

osteomalacia (OS-tee-oh-ma-LAY-shuh): a bone disease characterized by softening of the bones. Symptoms include bending of the spine and bowing of the legs. The disease occurs most often in adult women.

osteoporosis (OS-tee-oh-pore-OH-sis): a disease in which the bones become porous and fragile due to a loss of minerals; also called **adult bone loss.**

overnutrition: excess energy or nutrients.

overt (oh-VERT): out in the open and easy to observe.

overweight: body weight above some standard of acceptable weight that is usually defined in relation to height (such as BMI); BMI 25 to 29.9.

ovum (OH-vum): the female reproductive cell, capable of developing into a new organism upon fertilization; commonly referred to as an *egg.*

oxaloacetate (OKS-ah-low-AS-eh-tate): a carbohydrate intermediate of the TCA cycle.

oxidants (OKS-ih-dants): compounds (such as oxygen itself) that oxidize other compounds. Compounds that prevent oxidation are called *antioxidants,* whereas those that promote it are called *prooxidants.*

oxidation (OKS-ee-day-shun): the process of a substance combining with oxygen; oxidation reactions involve the loss of electrons.

oxidative stress: a condition in which the production of oxidants and free radicals exceeds the body's ability to handle them and prevent damage.

oxytocin (OCK-see-TOH-sin): a hormone that stimulates the mammary glands to eject milk during lactation and the uterus to contract during childbirth.

oyster shell: a product made from the powdered shells of oysters that is sold as a calcium supplement, but it is not well absorbed by the digestive system.

ozone therapy: the use of ozone gas to enhance the body's immune system.

P

pancreas: a gland that secretes digestive enzymes and juices into the duodenum. (The pancreas also secretes hormones into the blood that help to maintain glucose homeostasis.)

pancreatic (pank-ree-AT-ic) **juice:** the exocrine secretion of the pancreas, containing enzymes for the digestion of carbohydrate, fat, and protein as well as bicarbonate, a neutralizing agent. The juice flows from the pancreas into the small intestine through the pancreatic duct. (The pancreas also has an endocrine function, the secretion of insulin and other hormones.)

pantothenic (PAN-toe-THEN-ick) **acid:** a B vitamin. The principal active form is part of coenzyme A, called "CoA" throughout Chapter 7.

parathyroid hormone: a hormone from the parathyroid glands that regulates blood calcium by raising it when levels fall too low; also known as **parathormone** (PAIR-ah-THOR-moan).

pasteurization: heat processing of food that inactivates some, but not all, microorganisms in the food; not a sterilization process. Bacteria that cause spoilage are still present.

pathogen (PATH-oh-jen): a microorganism capable of producing disease.

PBB (polybrominated biphenyl) and **PCB (polychlorinated biphenyl):** toxic organic compounds used in pesticides, paints, and flame retardants.

PDCAAS (protein digestibility–corrected amino acid score): a measure of protein quality assessed by comparing the amino acid score of a food protein with the amino acid requirements of preschool-age children and then correcting for the true digestibility of the protein; recommended by the FAO/WHO and used to establish protein quality of foods for Daily Value percentages on food labels.

peak bone mass: the highest attainable bone density for an individual, developed during the first three decades of life.

peer review: a process in which a panel of scientists rigorously evaluates a research study to assure that the scientific method was followed.

pellagra (pell-AY-gra): the niacin-deficiency disease.

pepsin: a gastric enzyme that hydrolyzes protein. Pepsin is secreted in an inactive form, pepsinogen, which is activated by hydrochloric acid in the stomach.

peptic ulcer: a lesion in the mucous membrane of either the stomach (a gastric ulcer) or the duodenum (a duodenal ulcer).

peptidase: a digestive enzyme that hydrolyzes peptide bonds.

peptide bond: a bond that connects the acid end of one amino acid with the amino end of another, forming a link in a protein chain.

percent fat-free: may be used only if the product meets the definition of low fat or fat-free and must reflect the amount of fat in 100 g (for example, a food that contains 2.5 g of fat per 50 g can claim to be "95 percent fat free").

peripheral (puh-RIFF-er-ul) **nervous system:** the peripheral (outermost) part of the nervous system; the vast complex of wiring that extends from the central nervous system to the body's outermost areas. It contains both somatic and autonomic components.

peripheral resistance: the resistance to pumped blood in the small arterial branches (arterioles) that carry blood to tissues.

peristalsis (per-ih-STALL-sis): wavelike muscular contractions of the GI tract that push its contents along.

pernicious (per-NISH-us) **anemia:** a blood disorder that reflects a vitamin B_{12} deficiency caused by lack of intrinsic factor and characterized by abnormally large and immature red blood cells. Other symptoms include muscle weakness and irreversible neurological damage.

persistence: stubborn or enduring continuance; with respect to food contaminants, the quality of persisting, rather than breaking down, in the bodies of animals and human beings.

pesticides: chemicals used to control insects, weeds, fungi, and other pests on plants, vegetables, fruits, and animals. Used broadly, the term includes herbicides (to kill weeds), insecticides (to kill insects), and fungicides (to kill fungi).

pH: the unit of measure expressing a substance's acidity or alkalinity.

phagocytes (FAG-oh-sites): white blood cells (neutrophils and macrophages) that have the ability to ingest and destroy foreign substances.

phagocytosis (FAG-oh-sigh-TOH-sis): the process by which phagocytes engulf and destroy foreign materials.

pharynx (FAIR-inks): the passageway leading from the nose and mouth to the larynx and esophagus, respectively.

phenylketonuria (FEN-il-KEY-toe-NEW-ree-ah) or **PKU**: an inherited disorder characterized by failure to metabolize the amino acid phenylalanine to tyrosine.

phospholipid (FOS-foe-LIP-id): a compound similar to a triglyceride but having a phosphate group (a phosphorus-containing salt) and choline (or another nitrogen-containing compound) in place of one of the fatty acids.

phosphorus: a major mineral found mostly in the body's bones and teeth.

photosynthesis: the process by which green plants use the sun's energy to make carbohydrates from carbon dioxide and water.

physical activity: bodily movement produced by muscle contractions that substantially increase energy expenditure.

physiological age: a person's age as estimated from her or his body's health and probable life expectancy.

phytic (FYE-tick) **acid**: a nonnutrient component of plant seeds; also called **phytate** (FYE-tate). Phytic acid occurs in the husks of grains, legumes, and seeds and is capable of binding minerals such as zinc, iron, calcium, magnesium, and copper in insoluble complexes in the intestine, which the body excretes unused.

phytochemicals (FIE-toe-KEM-ih-cals): nonnutrient compounds found in plant-derived foods that have biological activity in the body.

phytoestrogens: plant-derived compounds that have structural and functional similarities to human estrogen. Phytoestrogens include the isoflavones genistein, daidzein, and glycitein.

phytosterols: plant-derived compounds that have structural similarities to cholesterol and lower blood cholesterol by competing with cholesterol for absorption. Phytosterols include sterol esters and stanol esters.

pica (PIE-ka): a craving for nonfood substances. Also known as **geophagia** (gee-oh-FAY-gee-uh) when referring to clay eating and **pagophagia** (pag-oh-FAY-gee-uh) when referring to ice craving.

pigment: a molecule capable of absorbing certain wavelengths of light so that it reflects only those that we perceive as a certain color.

placebo (pla-see-bo): an inert, harmless medication given to provide comfort and hope; a sham treatment used in controlled research studies.

placebo effect: a change that occurs in reponse to expectations in the effectiveness of a treatment that actually has no pharmaceutical effects.

placenta (plah-SEN-tuh): the organ that develops inside the uterus early in pregnancy, through which the fetus receives nutrients and oxygen and returns carbon dioxide and other waste products to be excreted.

plant-pesticides: pesticides made by the plants themselves.

plaque (PLACK): an accumulation of fatty deposits, smooth muscle cells, and fibrous connective tissue that develops in the artery walls in atherosclerosis. Plaque associated with atherosclerosis is known as **atheromatous** (ATH-er-OH-ma-tus) **plaque.**

platelets: tiny, disc-shaped bodies in the blood, important in blood clot formation.

point of unsaturation: the double bond of a fatty acid, where hydrogen atoms can easily be added to the structure.

polypeptide: many (ten or more) amino acids bonded together.

polysaccharides: compounds composed of many monosaccharides linked together. An intermediate string of three to ten monosaccharides is an **oligosaccharide.**

polyunsaturated fatty acid (PUFA): a fatty acid that lacks four or more hydrogen atoms and has two or more double bonds between carbons—for example, linoleic acid (two double bonds) and linolenic acid (three double bonds). A **polyunsaturated fat** is composed of triglycerides in which most of the fatty acids are polyunsaturated.

post term (infant): an infant born after the 42nd week of pregnancy.

postpartum amenorrhea: the normal temporary absence of menstrual periods immediately following childbirth.

potassium: the principal cation within the body's cells; critical to the maintenance of fluid balance, nerve impulse transmissions, and muscle contractions.

precursors: substances that precede others; with regard to vitamins, compounds that can be converted into active vitamins; also known as **provitamins.**

prediabetes: condition in which blood glucose levels are higher than normal but not high enough to be diagnosed as diabetes; considered a major risk factor for future diabetes and cardiovascular diseases; formerly called **impaired glucose tolerance.**

preeclampsia (PRE-ee-KLAMP-see-ah): a condition characterized by hypertension, fluid retention, and protein in the urine; formerly known as *pregnancy-induced hypertension.*

preformed vitamin A: dietary vitamin A in its active form.

prehypertension: slightly higher-than-normal blood pressure, but not as high as hypertension (Table 18-4).

prenatal alcohol exposure: subjecting a fetus to a pattern of excessive alcohol intake characterized by substantial regular use or heavy episodic drinking.

preservatives: antimicrobial agents, antioxidants, and other additives that retard spoilage or maintain desired qualities, such as softness in baked goods.

pressure ulcers: damage to the skin and underlying tissues as a result of compression and poor circulation; commonly seen in people who are bedridden or chairbound.

preterm (infant): an infant born prior to the 38th week of pregnancy; also called a **premature infant.** A **term** infant is born between the 38th and 42nd week of pregnancy.

primary deficiency: a nutrient deficiency caused by inadequate dietary intake of a nutrient.

probiotics: living microorganisms found in foods that, when consumed in sufficient quantities, are beneficial to health.

processed foods: foods that have been treated to change their physical, chemical, microbiological, or sensory properties.

progesterone: the hormone of gestation (pregnancy).

progressive overload principle: the training principle that a body system, in order to improve, must be worked at frequencies, durations, or intensities that gradually increase physical demands.

prolactin (pro-LAK-tin): a hormone secreted from the anterior pituitary gland that acts on the mammary glands to promote the production of milk. The release of prolactin is mediated by **prolactin-inhibiting hormone (PIH).**

promoters: factors that favor the development of cancers once they have begun.

proof: a way of stating the percentage of alcohol in distilled liquor. Liquor that is 100 proof is 50% alcohol; 90 proof is 45%, and so forth.

prooxidants: substances that significantly induce oxidative stress.

proteases (PRO-tee-aces): enzymes that hydrolyze protein.

protein digestibility: a measure of the amount of amino acids absorbed from a given protein intake.

protein efficiency ratio (PER): a measure of protein quality assessed by determining how well a given protein supports weight gain in growing rats; used to establish the protein quality for infant formulas and baby foods.

protein turnover: the degradation and synthesis of protein.

protein-energy malnutrition (PEM), also called **protein-kcalorie malnutrition (PCM)**: a deficiency of protein, energy, or both, including kwashiorkor, marasmus, and instances in which they overlap.

proteins: compounds composed of carbon, hydrogen, oxygen, and nitrogen atoms, arranged into amino acids linked in a chain. Some amino acids also contain sulfur atoms.

protein-sparing action: the action of carbohydrate (and fat) in providing energy that allows protein to be used for other purposes.

puberty: the period in life in which a person becomes physically capable of reproduction.

public health dietitians: dietitians who specialize in providing nutrition services through organized community efforts.

public water: water from a municipal or county water system that has been treated and disinfected.

purified water: water that has been treated by distillation or other physical or chemical processes that remove dissolved solids. Because purified water contains no minerals or contaminants, it is useful for medical and research purposes.

purines: compounds of nitrogen-containing bases such as adenine, guanine, and caffeine.

pyloric (pie-LORE-ic) **sphincter**: the circular muscle that separates the stomach from the small intestine and regulates the flow of partially digested food into the small intestine; also called **pylorus** or **pyloric valve.**

pyruvate (PIE-roo-vate): a 3-carbon compound that plays a key role in energy metabolism.

Q

qi gong (chée GUNG): a Chinese system that combines movement, meditation, and breathing techniques to enhance the flow of qi (vital energy) in the body.

quality of life: a person's perceived physical and mental well-being.

R

randomization (ran-dom-ih-zay-shun): a process of choosing the members of the experimental and control groups without bias.

raw sugar: the first crop of crystals harvested during sugar processing. Raw sugar cannot be sold in the United States because it contains too much filth (dirt, insect fragments, and the like). Sugar sold as "raw sugar" domestically has actually gone through over half of the refining steps.

RD: see *registered dietitian.*

Recommended Dietary Allowance (RDA): the average daily amount of a nutrient considered adequate to meet the known nutrient needs of practically all healthy people; a goal for dietary intake by individuals.

rectum: the muscular terminal part of the intestine, extending from the sigmoid colon to the anus.

reduced kcalorie: at least 25% fewer kcalories per serving than the comparison food.

reference protein: a standard against which to measure the quality of other proteins.

refined: the process by which the coarse parts of a food are removed. When wheat is refined into flour, the bran, germ, and husk are removed, leaving only the endosperm.

reflux: a backward flow.

registered dietitian (RD): a person who has completed a minimum of a bachelor's degree from an accredited university or college, has completed approved course work and a supervised practice program, has passed a national examination, and maintains registration through continuing professional education.

registration: listing; with respect to health professionals, listing with a professional organization that requires specific course work, experience, and passing of an examination.

relaxin: the hormone of late pregnancy.

remodeling: the dismantling and re-formation of a structure.

renin (REN-in): an enzyme from the kidneys that activates angiotensin.

rennin: an enzyme that coagulates milk; found in the gastric juice of cows, but not human beings.

replication (REP-lih-KAY-shun): repeating an experiment and getting the same results.

requirement: the lowest continuing intake of a nutrient that will maintain a specified criterion of adequacy.

residues: whatever remains. In the case of pesticides, those amounts that remain on or in foods when people buy and use them.

resistant starches: starches that escape digestion and absorption in the small intestine of healthy people.

resting metabolic rate (RMR): similar to the basal metabolic rate (BMR), a measure of the energy use of a person at rest in a comfortable setting, but with less stringent criteria for recent food intake and physical activity. Consequently, the RMR is slightly higher than the BMR.

retina (RET-in-uh): the layer of light-sensitive nerve cells lining the back of the inside of the eye; consists of rods and cones.

retinoids (RET-ih-noyds): chemically related compounds with biological activity similar to that of retinol; metabolites of retinol.

retinol activity equivalents (RAE): a measure of vitamin A activity; the amount of retinol that the body will derive from a food containing preformed retinol or its precursor beta-carotene.

retinol-binding protein (RBP): the specific protein responsible for transporting retinol.

rheumatoid (ROO-ma-toyd) arthritis: a disease of the immune system involving painful inflammation of the joints and related structures.

rhodopsin (ro-DOP-sin): a light-sensitive pigment of the retina; contains the retinal form of vitamin A and the protein opsin.

riboflavin (RYE-boh-flay-vin): a B vitamin. The coenzyme forms are FMN (flavin mononucleotide) and FAD (flavin adenine dinucleotide).

ribose: a 5-carbon sugar falsely promoted as improving the regeneration of ATP and thereby the speed of recovery after high-power exercise.

ribosomes (RYE-boh-zomes): protein-making organelles in cells; composed of RNA and protein.

rickets: the vitamin D–deficiency disease in children characterized by inadequate mineralization of bone (manifested in bowed legs or knock-knees, outward-bowed chest, and knobs on ribs). A rare type of rickets, not caused by vitamin D deficiency, is known as vitamin D–refractory rickets.

risk: a measure of the probability and severity of harm.

risk factor: a condition or behavior associated with an elevated frequency of a disease but not proved to be causal. Leading risk factors for chronic diseases include obesity, cigarette smoking, high blood pressure, high blood cholesterol, physical inactivity, and a diet high in saturated fats and low in vegetables, fruits, and whole grains.

RNA (ribonucleic acid): a compound similar to DNA, but RNA is a single strand with a ribose sugar instead of a deoxyribose sugar and uracil instead of thymine as one of its bases.

royal jelly: the substance produced by worker bees and fed to the queen bee; falsely promoted as increasing strength and enhancing performance.

S

saccharin (SAK-ah-ren): an artificial sweetener that has been approved for use in the United States. In Canada, approval for use in foods and beverages is pending; currently available only in pharmacies and only as a tabletop sweetener, not as an additive.

safety: the condition of being free from harm or danger.

saliva: the secretion of the salivary glands. Its principal enzyme begins carbohydrate digestion.

salivary glands: exocrine glands that secrete saliva into the mouth.

salt: a compound composed of a positive ion other than H^+ and a negative ion other than OH^-. An example is sodium chloride ($Na^+ Cl^-$).

salt sensitivity: a characteristic of individuals who respond to a high salt intake with an increase in blood pressure or to a low salt intake with a decrease in blood pressure.

sarcopenia (SAR-koh-PEE-nee-ah): loss of skeletal muscle mass, strength, and quality.

satiating: having the power to suppress hunger and inhibit eating.

satiation (say-she-AY-shun): the feeling of satisfaction and fullness that occurs during a meal and halts eating. Satiation determines how much food is consumed during a meal.

satiety (sah-TIE-eh-tee): the feeling of fullness and satisfaction that occurs after a meal and inhibits eating until the next meal. Satiety determines how much time passes between meals.

saturated fat-free: less than 0.5 g of saturated fat and 0.5 g of trans fat per serving.

saturated fatty acid: a fatty acid carrying the maximum possible number of hydrogen atoms—for example, stearic acid. A saturated fat is composed of triglycerides in which most of the fatty acids are saturated.

scurvy: the vitamin C–deficiency disease.

secondary deficiency: a nutrient deficiency caused by something other than an inadequate intake such as a disease condition or drug interaction that reduces absorption, accelerates use, hastens excretion, or destroys the nutrient.

secretin (see-CREET-in): a hormone produced by cells in the duodenum wall. Target organ: the pancreas. Response: secretion of bicarbonate-rich pancreatic juice.

sedentary: physically inactive (literally, "sitting down a lot").

segmentation (SEG-men-TAY-shun): a periodic squeezing or partitioning of the intestine at intervals along its length by its circular muscles.

selenium (se-LEEN-ee-um): a trace element.

senile dementia: the loss of brain function beyond the normal loss of physical adeptness and memory that occurs with aging.

senile plaques: clumps of the protein fragment beta-amyloid on the nerve cells, commonly found in the brains of people with Alzheimer's dementia.

serotonin (SER-oh-TONE-in): a neurotransmitter important in sleep regulation, appetite control, intestinal motility, obsessive-compulsive behaviors, and mood disorders.

set point: the point at which controls are set (for example, on a thermostat). The set-point theory that relates to body weight proposes that the body tends to maintain a certain weight by means of its own internal controls.

sibutramine (sigh-BYOO-tra-mean): a drug used in the treatment of obesity that slows the reabsorption of serotonin in the brain, thus suppressing appetite and creating a feeling of fullness.

sickle-cell anemia: a hereditary form of anemia characterized by abnormal sickle- or crescent-shaped red blood cells. Sickled cells interfere with oxygen transport and blood flow. Symptoms are precipitated by dehydration and insufficient oxygen (as may occur at high altitudes) and include hemolytic anemia (red blood cells burst), fever, and severe pain in the joints and abdomen.

simple carbohydrates (sugars): monosaccharides and disaccharides.

small intestine: a 10-foot length of small-diameter intestine that is the major site of digestion of food and absorption of nutrients. Its segments are the duodenum, jejunum, and ileum.

socioeconomic history: a record of a person's social and economic background, including such factors as education, income, and ethnic identity.

sodium: the principal cation in the extracellular fluids of the body; critical to the maintenance of fluid balance, nerve impulse transmissions, and muscle contractions.

sodium bicarbonate: baking soda; an alkaline salt believed to neutralize blood lactic acid and thereby to reduce pain and enhance possible workload. "Soda loading" may cause intestinal bloating and diarrhea.

sodium-free and **salt-free:** less than 5 mg of sodium per serving.

soft water: water with a high sodium or potassium content.

solanine (SOH-lah-neen): a poisonous narcotic-like substance present in potato peels and sprouts.

soluble fibers: indigestible food components that dissolve in water to form a gel. An example is pectin from fruit, which is used to thicken jellies.

solutes (SOLL-yutes): the substances that are dissolved in a solution. The number of molecules in a given volume of fluid is the solute concentration.

somatic (so-MAT-ick) nervous system: the division of the nervous system that controls the voluntary muscles, as distinguished from the autonomic nervous system, which controls involuntary functions.

somatostatin (GHIH): a hormone that inhibits the release of growth hormone; the opposite of somatotropin (GH).

soup kitchens: programs that provide prepared meals to be eaten on site.

sperm: the male reproductive cell, capable of fertilizing an ovum.

sphincter (SFINK-ter): a circular muscle surrounding, and able to close, a body opening. Sphincters are found at specific points along the GI tract and regulate the flow of food particles.

spina (SPY-nah) bifida (BIFF-ih-dah): one of the most common types of neural tube defects; characterized by the incomplete closure of the spinal cord and its bony encasement.

spirulina: a kind of alga ("blue-green manna") that supposedly contains large amounts of protein and vitamin B_{12}, suppresses appetite, and improves athletic performance. It does none of these things and is potentially toxic.

sports anemia: a transient condition of low hemoglobin in the blood, associated with the early stages of sports training or other strenuous activity.

spring water: water originating from an underground spring or well. It may be bubbly (carbonated), or "flat" or "still," meaning not carbonated. Brand names such as "Spring Pure" do not necessarily mean that the water comes from a spring.

starches: plant polysaccharides composed of glucose.

sterile: free of microorganisms, such as bacteria.

sterols (STARE-ols or STEER-ols): compounds containing a four ring carbon structure with any of a variety of side chains attached.

stevia (STEE-vee-ah): a South American shrub whose leaves are used as a sweetener; sold in the United States as a dietary supplement that provides sweetness without kcalories.

stomach: a muscular, elastic, saclike portion of the digestive tract that grinds and churns swallowed food, mixing it with acid and enzymes to form chyme.

stools: waste matter discharged from the colon; also called **feces** (FEE-seez).

stress: any threat to a person's well-being; a demand placed on the body to adapt.

stress fractures: bone damage or breaks caused by stress on bone surfaces during exercise.

stress response: the body's response to stress, mediated by both nerves and hormones.

stressors: environmental elements, physical or psychological, that cause stress.

stroke: an event in which the blood flow to a part of the brain is cut off; also called **cerebrovascular accident (CVA).**

structure-function claims: statements that characterize the relationship between a nutrient or other substance in a food and its role in the body.

subclavian (sub-KLAY-vee-an) **vein:** the vein that provides passageway from the lymphatic system to the vascular system.

subclinical deficiency: a deficiency in the early stages, before the outward signs have appeared.

subjects: the people or animals participating in a research project.

successful weight-loss maintenance: achieving a weight loss of at least 10 percent of initial body weight and maintaining the loss for at least one year.

sucralose (SUE-kra-lose): an artificial sweetener approved for use in the United States and Canada.

sucrase: an enzyme that hydrolyzes sucrose.

sucrose (SUE-krose): a disaccharide composed of glucose and fructose; commonly known as *table sugar, beet sugar,* or *cane sugar.* Sucrose also occurs in many fruits and some vegetables and grains.

sudden infant death syndrome (SIDS): the unexpected and unexplained death of an apparently well infant; the most common cause of death of infants between the second week and the end of the first year of life; also called *crib death.*

sugar replacers: sugarlike compounds that can be derived from fruits or commercially produced from dextrose; also called sugar alcohols or polyols. Sugar alcohols are absorbed more slowly than other sugars and metabolized differently in the human body; they are not readily utilized by ordinary mouth bacteria. Examples are maltitol, mannitol, sorbitol, xylitol, isomalt, and lactitol.

sugar-free: less than 0.5 g of sugar per serving.

sulfate: the oxidized form of sulfur.

sulfites: salts containing sulfur that are added to foods to prevent spoilage.

sulfur: a mineral present in the body as part of some proteins.

supplement: any pill, capsule, tablet, liquid, or powder that contains vitamins, minerals, herbs, or amino acids; intended to increase dietary intake of these substances.

sushi: vinegar-flavored rice and seafood, typically wrapped in seaweed and stuffed with colorful vegetables. Some sushi is stuffed with raw fish; other varieties contain cooked seafood.

sustainable: able to continue indefinitely; using resources at such a rate that the earth can keep on replacing them and producing pollutants at a rate with which the environment and human cleanup efforts can keep pace, so that no net accumulation of pollution occurs.

sustainable agriculture: agricultural practices that use individualized approaches appropriate to local conditions so as to minimize technological, fuel, and chemical inputs.

synergistic (SIN-er-JIS-tick): multiple factors operating together in such a way that their combined effects are greater than the sum of their individual effects.

T

tagatose (TAG-ah-tose): a monosaccharide structurally similar to fructose that is incompletely absorbed and thus provides only 1.5 kcalories per gram; approved for use as a "generally recognized as safe" ingredient.

TCA cycle or **tricarboxylic** (try-car-box-ILL-ick) **acid cycle:** a series of metabolic reactions that break down molecules of acetyl CoA to carbon dioxide and hydrogen atoms; also called the **Kreb's cycle** after the biochemist who elucidated its reactions.

T-cells: lymphocytes that attack antigens. T stands for the thymus gland, where the T-cells mature.

tempeh (TEM-pay): a fermented soybean food, rich in protein and fiber.

teratogenic (ter-AT-oh-jen-ik): causing abnormal fetal development and birth defects.

testosterone: a steroid hormone from the testicles, or testes. The steroids, as explained in Chapter 5, are chemically related to, and some are derived from, the lipid cholesterol.

textured vegetable protein: processed soybean protein used in vegetarian products such as soy burgers; see also *meat replacements.*

theory: a tentative explanation that integrates many and diverse findings to further the understanding of a defined topic.

thermic effect of food (TEF): an estimation of the energy required to process food (digest, absorb, transport, metabolize, and store ingested nutrients); also called the *specific dynamic effect (SDE) of food* or the *specific dynamic activity (SDA) of food.*

thermogenesis: the generation of heat; used in physiology and nutrition studies as an index of how much energy the body is expending.

thiamin (THIGH-ah-min): a B vitamin. The coenzyme form is TPP (thiamin pyrophosphate).

thirst: a conscious desire to drink.

thoracic (thor-ASS-ic) **duct:** the main lymphatic vessel that collects lymph and drains into the left subclavian vein.

thrombosis (throm-BOH-sis): the formation of a **thrombus** (THROM-bus), or a blood clot, that may obstruct a blood vessel, causing gradual tissue death.

thyroid-stimulating hormone (TSH): a hormone secreted by the pituitary that stimulates the thyroid gland to secrete its hormones—thyroxine and triiodothyronine. The release of TSH is mediated by TSH-releasing hormone (TRH).

tocopherol (tuh-KOFF-er-ol): a general term for several chemically related compounds, one of which has vitamin E activity.

tofu (TOE-foo): a curd made from soybeans, rich in protein and often fortified with calcium; used in many Asian and vegetarian dishes in place of meat.

Tolerable Upper Intake Level (UL): the maximum daily amount of a nutrient that appears safe for most healthy people and beyond which there is an increased risk of adverse health effects.

tolerance level: the maximum amount of residue permitted in a food when a pesticide is used according to the label directions.

toxicity: the ability of a substance to harm living organisms. All substances are toxic if high enough concentrations are used.

trabecular (tra-BECK-you-lar) **bone:** the lacy inner structure of calcium crystals that supports the bone's structure and provides a calcium storage bank.

trace minerals: essential mineral nutrients found in the human body in amounts smaller than 5 g; sometimes called **microminerals.**

trachea (TRAKE-ee-uh): the air passageway from the larynx to the lungs; also called the *windpipe.*

training: practicing an activity regularly, which leads to conditioning. (Training is what you do; conditioning is what you get.)

trans **fat-free:** less than 0.5 g of trans fat and less than 0.5 g of saturated fat per serving.

transamination (TRANS-am-ih-NAY-shun): the transfer of an amino group from one amino acid to a keto acid, producing a new nonessential amino acid and a new keto acid.

trans-**fatty acids:** fatty acids with hydrogens on opposite sides of the double bond.

transferrin (trans-FAIR-in): the iron transport protein.

transient hypertension of pregnancy: high blood pressure that develops in the second half of pregnancy and resolves after childbirth, usually without affecting the outcome of the pregnancy.

transient ischemic (is-KEY-mik) **attack (TIA):** a temporary reduction in blood flow to the brain, which causes temporary symptoms that vary depending on the part of the brain affected. Common symptoms include light-headedness, visual disturbances, paralysis, staggering, numbness, and inability to swallow.

travelers' diarrhea: nausea, vomiting, and diarrhea caused by consuming food or water contaminated by any of several organisms, most commonly, *E. coli, Shigella, Campylobacter jejuni,* and *Salmonella.*

triglycerides (try-GLISS-er-rides): the chief form of fat in the diet and the major storage form of fat in the body; composed of a molecule of glycerol with three fatty acids attached; also called **triacylglycerols** (try-ay-seel-GLISS-er-ols).

tripeptide: three amino acids bonded together.

tumor: an abnormal tissue mass with no physiological function; also called a **neoplasm** (NEE-oh-plazm).

turbinado (ter-bih-NOD-oh) **sugar:** sugar produced using the same refining process as white sugar, but without the bleaching and anti-caking treatment. Traces of molasses give turbinado its sandy color.

type 1 diabetes: the type of diabetes that accounts for 5 to 10% of diabetes cases and usually results from autoimmune destruction of pancreatic beta cells. In this type of diabetes, the pancreas produces little or no insulin.

type 2 diabetes: the type of diabetes that accounts for 90 to 95% of diabetes cases and usually results from insulin resistance coupled with insufficient insulin secretion. Obesity is present in 80 to 90% of cases.

type I osteoporosis: osteoporosis characterized by rapid bone losses, primarily of trabecular bone.

type II osteoporosis: osteoporosis characterized by gradual losses of both trabecular and cortical bone.

U

ulcer: a lesion of the skin or mucous membranes characterized by inflammation and damaged tissues.

ultrahigh temperature (UHT) treatment: sterilizing a food by brief exposure to temperatures above those normally used.

umbilical (um-BILL-ih-cul) **cord:** the ropelike structure through which the fetus's veins and arteries reach the placenta; the route of nourishment and oxygen to the fetus and the route of waste disposal from the fetus. The scar in the middle of the abdomen that marks the former attachment of the umbilical cord is the **umbilicus** (um-BILL-ih-cus), commonly known as the "belly button."

undernutrition: deficient energy or nutrients.

underweight: body weight below some standard of acceptable weight that is usually defined in relation to height (such as BMI); BMI below 18.5.

unsaturated fatty acid: a fatty acid that lacks hydrogen atoms and has at least one double bond between carbons (includes monounsaturated and polyunsaturated fatty acids). An **unsaturated fat** is composed of triglycerides in which most of the fatty acids are unsaturated.

unspecified eating disorders: eating disorders that do not meet the defined criteria for specific eating disorders.

urea (you-REE-uh): the principal nitrogen-excretion product of protein metabolism. Two ammonia fragments are combined with carbon dioxide to form urea.

USDA (U.S. Department of Agriculture): the federal agency responsible for enforcing standards for the wholesomeness and quality of meat, poultry, and eggs produced in the United States; conducting nutrition research; and educating the public about nutrition.

uterus (YOU-ter-us): the muscular organ within which the infant develops before birth.

V

validity (va-lid-ih-tee): having the quality of being founded on fact or evidence.

variables: factors that change. A variable may depend on another variable (for example, a child's height depends on his age), or it may be independent (for example, a child's height does not depend on the color of her eyes). Sometimes both variables correlate with a third variable (a child's height and eye color both depend on genetics).

variety (dietary): eating a wide selection of foods within and among the major food groups.

vasoconstrictor (VAS-oh-kon-STRIK-tor): a substance that constricts or narrows the blood vessels.

vegans (VEE-gans): people who exclude all animal-derived foods (including meat, poultry, fish, eggs, and dairy products) from their diets; also called **pure vegetarians, strict vegetarians,** or **total vegetarians.**

vegetarians: a general term used to describe people who exclude meat, poultry, fish, or other animal-derived foods from their diets.

veins (VANES): vessels that carry blood to the heart.

very low sodium: 35 mg or less per serving.

villi (VILL-ee, VILL-eye): fingerlike projections from the folds of the small intestine; singular **villus.**

viscous: a gel-like consistency.

vitamin A: all naturally occurring compounds with the biological activity of retinol (RET-ih-nol), the alcohol form of vitamin A.

vitamin A activity: a term referring to both the active forms of vitamin A and the precursor forms in foods without distinguishing between them.

vitamin B$_{12}$: a B vitamin characterized by the presence of cobalt. The active forms of coenzyme B$_{12}$ are methylcobalamin and deoxyadenosylcobalamin.

vitamin B$_6$: a family of compounds—pyridoxal, pyridoxine, and pyridoxamine. The primary active coenzyme form is PLP (pyridoxal phosphate).

vitamins: organic, essential nutrients required in small amounts by the body for health.

VLDL (very-low-density lipoprotein): the type of lipoprotein made primarily by liver cells to transport lipids to various tissues in the body; composed primarily of triglycerides.

VO$_2$max: the maximum rate of oxygen consumption by an individual at sea level.

vomiting: expulsion of the contents of the stomach up through the esophagus to the mouth.

W

waist circumference: an anthropometric measurement used to assess a person's abdominal fat.

warm-up: 5 to 10 minutes of light activity, such as easy jogging or cycling, prior to a workout to prepare the body for more vigorous activity.

water balance: the balance between water intake and output (losses).

water intoxication: the rare condition in which body water contents are too high in all body fluid compartments.

wean: to gradually replace breast milk with infant formula or other foods appropriate to an infant's diet.

websites: Internet resources composed of text and graphic files, each with a unique URL (Uniform Resource Locator) that names the site (for example, www.usda.gov).

weight management: maintaining body weight in a healthy range by preventing gradual weight gain over time and losing weight if overweight.

weight training (also called resistance training): the use of free weights or weight machines to provide resistance for developing muscle strength and endurance. A person's own body weight may also be used to provide resistance as when a person does push-ups, pull-ups, or abdominal crunches.

well water: water drawn from ground water by tapping into an aquifer.

Wernicke-Korsakoff (VER-nee-key KORE-sah-kof) **syndrome:** a neurological disorder typically associated with chronic alcoholism and caused by a deficiency of the B vitamin thiamin; also called *alcohol-related dementia.*

whey protein: a by-product of cheese production; falsely promoted as increasing muscle mass. Whey is the watery part of milk that separates from the curds.

white sugar: pure sucrose or "table sugar," produced by dissolving, concentrating, and recrystallizing raw sugar.

whole grain: a grain milled in its entirety (all but the husk), not refined.

wine: an alcoholic beverage made by fermenting grape juice.

WHO (World Health Organization): an international agency concerned with promoting health and eradicating disease.

World Wide Web (the web, commonly abbreviated www): a graphical subset of the Internet.

X

xanthophylls (ZAN-tho-fills): pigments found in plants; responsible for the color changes seen in autumn leaves.

xerophthalmia (zer-off-THAL-mee-uh): progressive blindness caused by severe vitamin A deficiency.

xerosis (zee-ROW-sis): abnormal drying of the skin and mucous membranes; a sign of vitamin A deficiency.

Y

yogurt: milk product that results from the fermentation of lactic acid in milk by *Lactobacillus bulgaricus* and *Streptococcus thermophilus.*

Z

zygote (ZY-goat): the product of the union of ovum and sperm; so-called for the first two weeks after fertilization.

Index

Page references in bold indicate definitions of terms. (See also Glossary, GL-1 to GL-18)

Page references followed by the letter "f" indicate figures or photographs.

Page references followed by the letter "t" indicate tables.

Page references followed by the letter "n" indicate footnotes.

Page references with combined letter and number (A-1) refer to the appendixes.

A

Abdominal fat, **262**–263
  See also Central obesity
Abortion, spontaneous, 544
Absorption, **71**, 80–83
  by active transport, 81f, 108
  of alcohol, 240
  by facilitated diffusion, 81f, 108
  GI anatomy and, 79f, 80–83, 81f, 82f
  of medications, 616
  medications and, 616, 616t
  olestra and, 165
  regulation of, 86–88
  by simple diffusion, 81f
  vascular system and, 82f
  See also Digestion; Glycemic index; Transport (nutrient); *specific nutrients*
Acceptable Daily Intake (ADI), **132**, 133t, 135
Acceptable Macronutrient Distribution Ranges (AMDR), **18**
Accidental additives, **685**
Accredited (schools), **32**, 33, 33n
Accutane, 374
Acesulfame potassium (acesulfame-K), **132**, 133t, 134
Acetaldehyde, **239**, 240, 240f, 244, 336
Acetaldehyde dehydrogenase, 240f, 241, 241f
Acetic acid, 108n, 140f, B-6
Acetone, 235, 235f
Acetylcholine, 345, 606
Acetyl CoA, **218**
  amino acid metabolism and, 225, 225f
  B vitamins and, 334, 335, 347f, 348
  fat metabolism and, 222, 223f, 224f
  fatty liver and, 241
  glucose metabolism and, 221–222, 221f
  TCA cycle and, 227–228, 227n, 228f, 231f
Acid-base balance, **113**, 406–408
  alcohol and, 241
  ammonia and, 225
  hydrochloric acid, 413
  ketosis and, 113
  pH scale and, 407f
  regulation of, 191, 406–408, 408f, 410n
  vomiting and, 412, 413n
  See also pH
Acid controllers, **94**, 96–97
"Acid indigestion", 96–97, 97t
Acidosis, **191**, 407f
Acids, **191**, B-6
  See also pH
Acne (and vitamin A), **374**
Acrodermatitis enteropathica, 455n
Acrylamide, 644–645, 685–686

ACTH (adrenocorticotropin), **A-3**, A-4, A-5
Active transport, 81f, 108, 192f
Acupuncture, **653**, 656t
Acute disease, **3**
Acute PEM, **197**
ADA. *See* American Dietetic Association (ADA)
Adaptive thermogenesis, 254, **256**, 307
Addictions. *See* Cravings
Additives, **682**–687
  antioxidants, 143, 143n, 684
  cancer risk, 643
  indirect or incidental, **685**–687
  intentional food additives, **683**–685, 683t
  nutrient additives, 354, 685
  regulation of, 136, 682–683
  sodium in, 412
  sugar alternatives, 132–137, 133t, 134f, 136t, 137f
  sugar as, 117–121
  See also Food industry
Adenomas, **642**
Adenosine diphosphate (ADP), 217f, C-9f
Adenosine triphosphate. *See* ATP
Adequacy (dietary), **37**, 39, 673–674
Adequate Intake (AI), **17**–18, 18f, 19, inside front cover
ADH (antidiuretic hormone), **239**, A-3
  alcohol and, 243
  blood volume regulation, 403f, A-5
  function of, 191t
  water retention and, 401
ADHD (attention-deficit/hyperactivity disorder), **564**
Adipokines, **265**
Adipose tissue, **155**
  cell structure, 155f
  composition of, 250
  estrogen synthesis, 266
  exercise and, 301
  lipoprotein lipase, **155**, 282–283
  metabolism in, 282–283
  number and size of cells, 282, 283f, 284
  white *vs.* brown, 286
  See also Fats (body)
Adolescence, **575**–580
  alcohol/drug use, 245, 579
  bone density and, 435
  calcium needs, 418
  diabetes in, 115
  eating disorders, 271, 276
  iron deficiency and, 446
  nutrition during, 575–580
  obesity surgery, 292–293
  overweight, 115, 120, 281
  pregnancy during, 529
  smoking/tobacco use, 579–580, 589
  soft drinks, 568
  websites on, 580–581
ADP (adenosine diphosphate), 217f, C-9f
Adrenal glands, 352, **401**, 406, A-5, A-6
Adrenaline. *See* Epinephrine
Adrenocorticotropin (ACTH), **A-3**, A-4, A-5
Adult bone loss, **421**
Adverse reactions, **566**
  to drugs. *See* Nutrient-drug interactions
  to foods, 566, 684, 685, 690
  to herbs, 658

Advertising
  of antioxidants, 390
  of chromium supplements, 461
  food industry, 287, 569
  FTC policies, 365
  laxatives, 95
  obesity and, 569
  signs of quackery, 33, 34f
  of supplements, 203, 362, 363–364, 365, 503, 504
Aerobic, defined, **220**
Aerobic activity
  carbohydrate use and, 221, 486, 490
  cardiorespiratory training, 480t, 482–483, 483f
  fat use and, 489
  protein use and, 490
African Americans/Blacks
  bone density, 260
  eclampsia/preeclampsia, 528, 529
  life expectancy, 593
  nonfood cravings and, 525
  osteoporosis and, 435
  vitamin D and, 380
Age, chronological, **595**
Age, physiological, **595**
Aging (older adults), **593**–611
  arthritis, 605–606
  bone mass, 379, 421f, 433–434, 433f, 434f, 603. *See also* Osteoporosis
  cognitive function and, 606–607
  constipation, 602
  energy needs, 256
  exercise and, 478, 484, 595–596, 596t
  fiber and, 602
  food choices/eating habits, 607–611
  health strategies for, 608t
  heart disease risk, 628, 631
  hypertension and, 634
  longevity and nutrition, 593–597
  medications and, 615
  National Institute on Aging, 437
  nutrient concerns, 601–604, 604t, 606t
  physiological changes, 598–600
  population statistics, 593, 594f
  setting DRI for, 601
  vision problems, 604–605
  vitamin D deficiency, 378–379
  water needs of, 398, 601
  websites on, 611–612
Agribusiness, **716**, 720
Agriculture, 716–720
  antibiotic resistance, 687
  biopharming, 695
  biotechnology, **693**–697, 697t
  bovine growth hormone (BGH), **686**–687
  energy use, 717–718, 718f, 718t, 719f
  environmental degradation, 710, 716–717
  genetic diversity, loss of, 710, 717
  genetic engineering, 693–697, 694f, 697t
  limitations to food production, 710
  livestock, 668–669, 676, 710, 716, 717f, 718, 719, 719f
  livestock, grass-fed, 162, 177, 718, 719
  organically grown crops, 7, **680**–681, 681f
  overpopulation and, 710
  PBB contaminated meat, 676
  pesticides, **678**–681, 695, 716, 718t

Agriculture, *continued*
 pesticides, alternatives to, 680
 sustainable, **716**, 717–720, 718t, 719f
 websites on, 697
 See also USDA (U.S. Department of
  Agriculture)
AI. *See* Adequate Intake (AI)
AIDS (acquired immune deficiency syndrome),
  536–537, **623**–624, 624t
Air displacement plethysmography, **264f**
Alanine, 182f
Albumin, serum, E-19n, E-19t
Alcohol, 238–247, **239**
 absorption of, 240
 amount in beverages, 238–240, 244t
 blood levels, 242, 243t
 blood sugar and, 246t
 brain, effects on, 242–243, 242f, 243t, 543
 cancer and, 244, 246t, 643, 644t
 death associated with, 25t, 242, 244, 245
 diabetes and, 641
 Dietary Guidelines and, 40t, 43f
 as diuretic, 400
 drugs and, 242
 effects, long-term, 245, 246t
 effects, short-term, 244, 400, 496
 ethanol, defined, **239**
 exercise and, 496
 fertility and, 545
 fetal development/pregnancy, 530, 543–545,
  543f, 545f
 health benefits of, 238
 heart disease and, 244, 246t, 632t
 hypertension and, 635
 intake appropriate, 40t, 43f, 238–240, 245, 247
 kcalories in, 8, 9t, 243, 244t
 lactation and, 537
 liver and, 240–242, 246t
 malnutrition and, 243–244, 246t
 metabolism of, 240–242, 241f, 242f
 myths concerning, 245, 246t
 nutrient imbalances and, 579
 obesity and, 243, 246t
 personal strategies for, 245, 247
 serotonin and, 120
 structure of, 102f, 238f
 TCA cycle and, C-15
 tolerance for, 239, 240
 vitamin deficiencies and, 244, 327, 336
 websites on, 247, 545
 weight control and, 298
Alcohol abuse, **239**
 by adolescents, 245, 579
 binge drinking, 244–245
 deficiencies and, 327, 336, 338
 disease risks and, 246t
 effects overview, 244–245
 fetal alcohol syndrome, 543–545, 543f, 545f
 Healthy People 2010 goals, J-2t
 heart disease and, 244, 246t
 iron overload and, 448
 malnutrition and, 243–244, 246t
 osteoporosis and, 435
 paternal, and low birthweight, 545
 tissue damage from, 240
 websites on, 247
Alcohol dehydrogenase, **239**, 240, 240f, 241f
Alcoholism, **239**
 health effects of, 246t
 malnutrition and, 243–244, 246t
 signs of, 245t
 websites on, 247
Alcohol-related birth defects (ARBD), 543, **544**
Alcohol-related neurodevelopmental disorder
  (ARND), 543, **544**
Aldosterone, **401**, A-3

blood volume regulation, 401–402, 403f
 fluids and electrolyte balance, 406
 functions of, A-6
Alendronate, 434n
Alitame, **132**, 133n, 133t, 135
Alkaline phosphatase, 452n
Alkalosis, **191**, 407f, 413, 413n
Alkylresorcinols, 470t
Allergies, **565**–567
 asymptomatic *vs.* symptomatic, **565**
 breast milk and, 536, 552
 food allergies, defined, **565**
 formulas for infants with, 553
 GM foods and, 696
 prevention of, in infants, 555–556
 vs. adverse reactions to foods, 566–567
 websites on, 581
 See also Adverse reactions
Almonds, 173
Aloe vera, 654f, 657t
Alpha-carotene, 370n, 470n
Alpha cells (pancreas), 113n
Alpha-lactalbumin, **550**
Alpha-linolenic acid, 154n
Alpha-tocopherol, **380**, 383, 393, C-9f
 See also Vitamin E
Alternative agriculture, 680–681
Alternative medicine, **652**–659
 See also Complementary and alternative
  medicine
Alzheimer's disease, **606**–607, 606n, 612
AMDR (Acceptable Macronutrient Distribution
  Ranges), **18**
Amenorrhea, **270**
 bone loss and, 434
 in eating disorders, 271, 271f, 273
 postpartum, **537**
 primary and secondary, **270**
American Dietetic Association (ADA), 31, **32**,
  573, 696, 703, 711
American Heart Association, 33
American Journal of Clinical Nutrition, 33
Amino acid pool, **193**
Amino acids, **181**–183
 absorption of, 185, 186f
 alcohol's effect on, 241
 body protein breakdown and, 193–194
 branched-chain, **203**
 conditionally essential, **183**
 deamination of, **194**
 endogenous *vs.* exogenous, **193**
 energy metabolism, 193, 194, 224–226, 225f,
  226f, 347f, C-11 to C-13f
 essential, 182t, **183**, 195, 196, 343n, D-1t
 fat synthesis, 194
 functions of, 188f, 193–194
 glucogenic, 194n, 221f, 225, 225f
 hydrophilic *vs.* hydrophobic, 184
 indispensable/dispensable, **183**
 ketogenic, 194n, 221f, 225, 225f, 226f
 limiting, **195**
 listed, 182t
 melanin synthesis, 194
 neurotransmitter synthesis, 194
 niacin synthesis, 194
 nonessential, **182**, 182t, 194, 225, 225f, 226, 226f
 PDCAAS, **D-1** to D-2, D-2t
 protein-sparing action of carbohydrate, 193n
 in protein synthesis, 183–184, 183f, 184f,
  194, 195
 structure of, 181–182, 182f, 183f, C-4f
 sulfur and, 425, 427
 supplements, 185, 202–203, 202n
 synthesis of, 194, 225, 225f, 226, 226f, 336
 thyroxin synthesis, 194
 See also specific amino acids

Amino acid scoring, **D-1**, D-1t
Aminopeptidases, in protein digestion, 186f
Ammonia, **225**, B-3 to B-4, B-6
Amniotic fluid, 518f
Amniotic sac, **510**, 511f
Amphetamines, 616
Amylases, **108**
Amylopectin, 106f, C-2f
Amylose, 106f, C-2f
Anabolic steroids, **503**, 505, 506t
Anabolism, **214**, 215f
Anaerobic, defined, **220**
Anaerobic metabolism, 220, 220f, 221,
  485, 485t
Anaphylactic shock, **566**
Androstenedione, 506
Anecdotes, **11**
Anemia, **189**, 341
 assessment of, E-19 to E-22, E-20t, E-21t
 causes of, 341, 348
 in children, 560, 563
 folate and, 341, E-20t, E-22, E-22t
 "goat's milk," 341, 553
 hemolytic, **382**
 iron-deficiency. *See* Iron-deficiency anemia
 lead poisoning and, 564
 macrocytic (megaloblastic), **341**
 microcytic, 337n, 355n
 microcytic hypochromic, **446**
 milk anemia, **557**
 pernicious, **343**, 344f
 red blood cells in, 189, 189f, 344f, 446, 447f
 sickle-cell, **189**, 189f
 "sports anemia," **493**
 vitamin B_{12} deficiency, 343–344, 344f, E-20t,
  E-22, E-22t
Anencephaly, **513**
Aneurysms, **626**, 627
Angina, **626**, 627
Angiotensin, **401**, 403f, **A-3**, A-6
Angiotensinogen, 401
Angular stomatitis, 330n
Animal foods *vs.* plant foods
 agriculture and, 717t, 718–719, 719f
 bone health and, 200
 fossil fuel use, 717, 719f
 heart disease and, 65, 144f, 157, 199
Animal studies, 13f, 285f, 596–597
Anions, **403**, 404t, 405f
Anorexia nervosa, **270**
 overview of, 307
 binge eating and, 276
 bone loss and, 434
 diagnosis/intervention, 272–274, 273t
 ghrelin and, 285
 malnutrition and, 197, 273
 overriding hunger, 251–252
 websites on, 277
 See also Eating disorders
Antacids, **94, 431**
 calcium and, 436
 criteria for use, 96–97
 folate and, 341
 nutrient absorption and, 616
Antagonists, **336**
Anthropometric measurements, **21**, 264f, 548,
  E-5 to E-16, E-5t, E-6f to E-15f, E-16t
Antibiotics
 as incidental food additives, 687
 nutrient-drug interactions, 616
 for older adults, 599
 resistance to, 687
 sodium in, 618
 vitamin K and, 383
Antibodies, **192, 622**
 See also Immune system

Anticoagulants, 354, 383
Antidiuretic hormone. *See* ADH
Antigens, **192, 622**
Antimicrobial agents, 683–684, 683t
Antioxidants, **143, 351,** 390–393
  Alzheimer's disease and, 607
  for athletes, 492
  beta-carotene, 372, 391
  cancer risk and, 391–392, 645
  as food additives, 143, 683t, 684
  food sources, 393
  free radicals and, 351f
  in fruits/vegetables, 391–392
  heart disease and, 392, 393
  mechanism of action, 351, 351f, 391, 391f
  in Mediterranean diet, 597
  older adults and, 605, 607
  phytochemicals as, 391, 469–470, 470t, 471
  as prooxidants, 393
  rheumatoid arthritis and, 605
  selenium as, 457
  slowing aging, 597, 598
  smokers and, 580
  supplements and, 364, 390, 392–393
  vitamin C, 351, 351f, 352, 354, 391, 391f
  vitamin E, 382, 391
Antipromoters (cancer), **642,** 645
Antiscorbutic factor, **351**
Anus, **72,** 73f, 76
Appendicitis and fiber, 122
Appendix, **72,** 73f, 74
Appetite, **251**
  alcohol and, 243
  artificial sweeteners and, 135
  drugs/herbs and, 292, 579, 615–616
  exercise and, 301
  factors affecting, 251–253
  fasting/starvation and, 235
  fruit *vs.* juice, 53
  ghrelin and, 285, 286
  leptin and, 284
  smoking and, 579
  See also Hunger (sensation); Satiety
Appropriate for gestational age (AGA), **526**
Arabinose, C-3f
Arachidonic acid, **154,** 154f, 155, 159t, 550
ARBD (alcohol-related birth defects), 543, **544**
Arginine, 199–200, **504**
Ariboflavinosis, **329**
Aristolochia fangchi, 658
ARND (alcohol-related neurodevelopmental
  disorder), 543, **544**
Aroma therapy, **653**
Arsenic, 462
Arteries, **83,** 84f
  See also Atherosclerosis; Vascular system
Artesian water, **400**
Arthritis, 246t, **605**–606, 612
Artificial colors, 683t, 684–685
Artificial fats, **164**–165
Artificial flavors, 685
Artificial sweeteners, **132**–138, 133t, 134f, 135t,
  137f, 532
Ascorbic acid. *See* Vitamin C
-ase (word ending), **77,** 108
Asian Americans, ethnic cuisine of, 46t
Aspartame, **132,** 133–134, 133n, 133t, 134f,
  135, 135t
Aspartic acid, 182f
Aspirin, 154, 341, 615, 616
Assessment of nutrition status. *See* Nutrition
  assessment
-ate (word ending), 218n, 404
Atheromatous plaques, **587, 626**
Atherosclerosis, **147,** 586–**587, 626**
  antioxidants and, 392

atherogenic diet, 629–630
  cholesterol and, 147
  development of, 586–587, 587f, 626–628
  in diabetics, 640
  risk factors for, 629–630
  See also Cardiovascular disease (CVD);
    Cholesterol; Coronary heart disease (CHD)
Athletes, 477–507
  amenorrhea in, 271, 271f
  body composition, 258, 259, 261–262,
    310–311
  body image, 272
  calcium for, 271
  carbohydrate intake, 486–488, 499
  carbohydrate loading, **487**
  diet planning for, 496–499, 498f
  eating disorders in, 271f, 310–311
  energy expenditure, 255t, 257t
  fat intake, 161, 488–489
  female athlete triad, **270,** 271f
  fluids and electrolytes for, 271–272,
    493–496, 494t
  food/fluid restriction, 271–272, 398, 492
  glucose supply, maximizing, 487–488, 488t
  iron and, 492–493
  osteoporosis in, 271, 271f
  pregame/postgame meals, 497–499, 498f
  protein needs, 201, 490–491, 491t, 497
  sodium and, 398, 412
  steroid use by, 505–506, 506t
  stress fractures in, **270,** 271
  supplements for, 202, 492, 497, 503–506, 506t
  vegetarians, 492
  vitamin/mineral needs, 491–493
  weight standards, 271–272, 492
  weight training, 481
  See also Physical activity
Atkins Diet, 317t
Atoms, properties of, 102, 102f, **B-1** to B-3, B-2t
ATP (adenosine triphosphate), **216**
  coupled reactions, 216, 217f
  energy for exercise, 484–485, 485t
  energy metabolism central pathways, 231f
  energy transfer and, 216
  glucose metabolism and, 219f–222f, 220,
    220n, C-15n, C-15t
  structure of, 216f, C-9f
  See also TCA (Krebs) cycle
Atrophic gastritis, **343,** 599
Atrophy (muscle), **481**
Attention-deficit/hyperactivity disorder
  (ADHD), **564**
Autoimmune disorders, **638**
Autonomic nervous system, **A-7** to A-8, A-8f
Available carbohydrates, **108**
Avian influenza, 669
Avidin, **334**
Ayurveda, **653,** 656

B

Bacteria
  antimicrobial agents, 683–684, 683t
  dental caries and, 119
  E. coli infection, 665t, 666
  gastrointestinal. *See* Intestinal bacteria
  Helicobacter pylori, 97, 343
  Lactobacillus bifidus, 86, 551–552
  probiotics, 86
  ulcers and, 13f, 97, 343
  vitamins produced by, 86
  water contamination, 672
  See also Foodborne illnesses; Infections/
    infectious disease
Balance (dietary), **38**
Bariatrics, **292**
Barrett's esophagus, 97

Basal metabolic rate (BMR), **254**
  exercise and, 255t, 300
  factors affecting, 254–256, 255t
  infants, 254
  obesity and uncoupling proteins, 286
  in older adults, 601
  thyroid hormones and, 455
  websites on, 266
Basal metabolism, **254,** 254f, 255t
Bases, **191,** B-6
B-cells, **622**
Beans, 43f, 47f, 52f, 677
  See also Legumes; Soy products
Beauty. *See* Body image
Beer, 238, **239,** 244, 244t, 496, 684
Behavior
  of children, 120, 562, 563, 564–565
  fetal alcohol syndrome and, 543
  hunger and, 562–564
  hyperactivity, **564**–565
  nutrient deficiencies and, 447, 562, 563
  sugar and, 120
  violence and alcohol, 245
  See also Lifestyle choices
Behavior modification, for weight loss, **303,** 571
Beikost, **555**
Belching, **94,** 95–96, 97t
Benzopyrene, 644n
Beriberi, **327,** 328f
Beta-carotene, **369**–377
  as antioxidant, 372, 391
  cancer and, 372, 580
  overconsumption of, 374, 375f, 377n
  as prooxidant, 374
  retinol activity equivalents (RAE), **374**
  structure of, 370f, C-5f
  supplements, 274, 392–393
  vitamin A precursors, 369, 370f, 372
  vitamin E and, 363
  See also Carotenoids
Beta cells (pancreas), 113n, 515
Beta-cryptoxanthin, 370n, 470n
Beta oxidation, **222**
Beverages
  coffee, 97, 199, 686
  fluid balance and, 400
  fruit "drinks," 53
  "health drinks" for children, 379, 557
  "health food" and malnutrition, 197
  healthy choices, 400
  kcalories in, 121, 400
  liquid diets, 504, 602
  soy "milk," 53, 65
  sports drinks, 121, 487, 495, 507
  sugar content, 117–118, 121, 568
  teas, 472f, 655, 656, 658t
  tooth decay and, 119
  for weight gain, 308
  weight loss and, 297
  See also Alcohol; Caffeine; Fruit juices; Milk
    and milk products; Soft drinks; Water
BGH (bovine growth hormone), **686**–687
BHA, 143n, **684,** 684n
BHT, 143n, **684,** 684n
Bicarbonate, 77, **78,** 87, 407, 408, 408f, 413n
Bifidus factors, 551–552
Bile, **78**
  cholesterol and, 149, 150f
  components of, 149
  emulsification/digestion of fat, 78, 80t, 88,
    148f, 149, 150f
  enterohepatic circulation, 149, 151f
  vitamin absorption and, 369
Bile acids, 122, 149, 150f
Bile ducts, 73f
Binders, **409**

Binge drinking, 244–245
Binge eating, 274, 275f, 285
Binge-eating disorder, **270**, 276, 277t
Bioaccumulation, **675**, 675f, 676
Bioavailability, **324**
  of calcium, 418, 419, 420, 420f
  factors affecting, H-0
  of folate, 338, 340
  of iron, 444, 444f, 450, 551, 554
  of magnesium, 424
  oxalates/phytates and, 409
  of supplements, 363
  of vitamin B₁₂, 603
  of vitamins, 324
  of zinc, 452–453
Bioelectrical impedance, **264f**, E-16, E-16t
Bioelectromagnetic medical applications, **653**
Biofeedback, **653**
Biofield therapeutics, **653**
Bioflavonoids, 346
Biological value of proteins, **D-1**, D-2, D-2t
Biopharming, 695
Biotechnology, **693**–697, 694f, 697t
  See also Genetically engineered (GE) foods
Bioterrorism, **621**, 663
Biotin, **333**–335, 335t, 347f, 356t, C-8f
Bird flu, 669
Birth defects
  anencephaly, **513**
  cretinism and iodine deficiency, 456
  diabetes and, 527, 528
  Down syndrome, 340, **530**
  father's alcohol intake and, 545
  fetal alcohol syndrome (FAS), 543–545, 543f, **544**, 545f
  folate and, 338, 340, 340f
  older women and, 530
  vitamin A and, 374
  websites on, 539
  See also Neural tube defects
Birthweight
  factors affecting, 515–517, 527, 528, 530
  low (LBW), 515, 516, **525**–526, 530
  paternal alcohol intake, 545
  prematurity and, 554
Bitter orange, 291t
Black cohosh, 657t
Bladder cancer, 133, 135, 644t
Blind experiments, 12–13, **14**
Blindness, 371, 373, 373f
  See also Vision
Blood
  calcium levels, 417f, 418f, 431
  iron and, 445, 445f, 446
  pH of, 407f
  plasma, **E-17**
  serum, **E-17**
  white blood cells, 622–623
  See also Red blood cells
Blood alcohol levels, 242, 243t
Blood cholesterol. *See* Blood lipid profiles;
  Cholesterol (blood)
Blood circulation. *See* Vascular system
Blood clotting
  aspirin and, 615
  in atherosclerosis, 627
  fibrin and, 192, 384f
  Ginkgo biloba and, 658
  mechanism of, 384f
  vitamin E and, 382
  vitamin K and, 382, 383–384, 384f
  vitamin K and warfarin, 617
Blood glucose levels, 113–117
  chromium and, 461
  fiber and, 106, 115–116
  glycogen and, 112

hyperglycemia, 246t, **637**, 638
hypoglycemia, **115**, 246t, 641
normal range, 113
regulation of, 112, 113–117, 114f, 190, 461
starches and, 108
sugar and, 120
See also Glucagon; Glycemic index; Insulin
Blood lipid profiles, **156**–157
  in children, 587, 588t
  components of, 156, 630
  desirable levels, 156, 588t, 631t
  diet *vs.* medications, 589
  fish/fish oil and, 159
  genetics and, 210
  glycemic index and, 115
  heart disease risk and, 157, 588t, 628t, 629, 630, 631t
  inflammation and, 265–266
  in obese children, 569
  strategies for improving, 157, 162, 173, 633
  test method, 151n
  vegetarian diets and, 65
  See also Cholesterol (blood); HDL; LDL;
    Triglycerides
Blood pressure
  atherosclerosis and, 627
  determinants of, 634f
  heart disease risk, 628t, 631
  minerals and, 412, 414, 416, 424
  normal/abnormal levels, 528n, 635
  regulation of, 401–402, 403f, 412, A-6
  in vegetarians, 65
  See also Hypertension
Blood sugar. *See* Blood glucose levels
Blood transferrin, 443, 443f, 445
Blood volume, 401–402, 402f, 403f
Blueberries, flavonoids in, 472f
BMI. *See* Body mass index (BMI)
BMR. *See* Basal metabolic rate (BMR)
Body composition, **258**–266
  overview of, 6, 6f
  BMR and, 254, 255t, 256
  exercise and, 258, 300–301, 478, 599
  fat, percentage, 6, 6f, 260, 261f
  fat distribution, 259, 260–263, 262f, 263f
  fat *vs.* muscle, 254, 258, 259, 261f, 397
  gender differences, 6f, 260, 261f, 262, 263f, 576
  lean body mass, 194, **254**, 258, 484
  measuring, 258–263, 263f, 264f, E-14f, E-14 to E-15, E-15f, E-16t
  minerals, 7t, 404t, 409f, B-4, B-4t
  older adults, 598–599
  overweight *vs.* overfat, 258, 259
  skinfold measures, **264f**, E-14f
  water, 6f, 397, 399f
  during weight loss/gain, 250
Body fat. *See* Fats (body)
Body image
  accepting body weight, 259t
  of athletes, 272
  in eating disorders, 272, 276
  fashion and BMI, 258–260, 258f
  sound nutrition and, 5
Body mass index (BMI), **259**–260, inside back
  cover
  calculation of, 259
  children, 567, 568f
  fashion and, 258–260, 258f
  heart disease risk, 628t
  mortality and disease, 259, 263–266, 264f
  protein intake and, 318, 319
  weight and height, 288, 289
  weight assessment, 260f, 261
Body weight. *See* Weight (body)
Bolus, 73, **74**

Bomb calorimeter, **250**, 250f
Bone, powdered, **431**
Bone density, **431**–437
  body weight and, 260
  breastfeeding and, 535
  calcium and, 416, 417, 417f, 418, 418f, 419, 431–437, 523, 535, 577
  exercise and, 478, 484
  fluoride and, 460
  hormones and, 434–435, 434n, A-6
  maximizing, 434
  measuring, 432
  milk and, 577, 578
  peak bone mass, 378, **418**, 421f, 577
  race and, 260
  soft drinks and, 578
  vitamins and, 377, 378, 384, 434, 436
  See also Osteoporosis
Bone fractures
  milk/calcium and, 419
  osteoporosis and, 431, 432
  protein and, 436
  stress fractures in athletes, **270**, 271
  underweight and, 264
  vitamin A excess, 374
  vitamin D and, 379
Bone marrow, 445–446, 445f
Bone mass. *See* Bone density; Osteoporosis
Bone meal, **431**, 436
Bones, 431–437
  calcium and, 416, 417, 417f, 418, 418f, 419, 431–437, 523, 535, 577
  colas and, 422
  cortical, **431**, 432
  as dietary calcium source, 419f, 420
  fetal development of, 522–523
  growth/remodeling of, 372, 416, 435–436
  hormones and, 416, 417, 417f
  magnesium and, 423–424
  minimizing loss, 434
  osteoarthritis, **605**
  silicon and, 462
  structure of, 190, 432f
  trabecular, **431**–432, 432f
  vanadium and, 462
  vitamin A and, 372, 374, 436
  vitamin C and, 353
  vitamin D and, 377, 378, 434, 436, 522–523
  See also Rickets
  websites on, 437
  See also Osteoporosis
Boron, 462, **504**
Bottled water, **400**, 401, 689
Botulism, 118n, **556**, 556n, 665t, 666, 671
Bovine growth hormone (BGH), **686**–687
Bovine spongiform encephalopathy, 668n
Bowel movements, 78, 93–95
  See also Constipation; Diarrhea
Brain
  aging and, 606–607, 606t, 607t
  alcohol and, 242–243, 242f, 243t, 544
  blood volume regulation, 403f
  deficiencies/malnutrition and, 563, 606, E-7
  development of, 209, 550, 552
  in eating disorders, 272
  energy source for, 112, 156, 223, 234
  fetal nutrient needs, 520, 532
  hunger and, 251, 253, 562, 563
  lead toxicity and, 463
  nutrient relationships, 606t
  omega-3 fatty acids and, 155
  PCB/mercury and, 676
  zinc deficiency and, 453
  See also Hypothalamus
Bran, 50, **50f**
Branched-chain amino acids, **203**

Breads, 50–51
 calcium in, 419
 in Canadian food groups, I-8t
 enriched/fortified, **50**–51, 51f, 450
 in exchange lists, G-1t, G-4t
 fiber in, 51f, 51, 126f
 folate fortification, 51, 340, 340n, 342f
 heart disease and, 633
 labels, 126f
 nutrients in, 42f, 50–51, 51f
 phytates in, 453n
 in USDA Food Guide, 42f
 whole grain, 42f, 50, 51f, 126f
 See also Grains
Breakfast, 574, 577
Breakfast cereals, 51–52, 412, 412f, 555–556
Breast cancer
 breastfeeding and, 537
 dietary fat and, 160
 estrogen and, 266, 643
 exercise/weight and, 643
 folate and, 341
 risk summary, 644t
Breast disease, fibrocystic, **382**
Breastfeeding, 532–540
 alcohol and, 537
 benefits of, 531, 533t, 537, 550–552, 554
 caffeine and, 538
 cancer risk and, 537
 certified lactation consultants, 534
 drug use, illicit, 537
 duration of, 550, 555
 energy needs during, 521f, 534–535
 fish consumption and, 531, 676
 frequency of, 550
 iron needs and, 536
 lactation, defined, **533**
 maternal health and, 536–537
 medications and, 537
 nutrient needs during, 521f, 534–536, inside front cover
 physiological process of, 533
 smoking and, 537
 support for success, 534, 534t
 websites on, 539
Breast milk
 composition of, 535, 550–551, 550f, 553f
 environmental contaminants in, 174, 531, 538, 676
 foods flavoring, 536
 hormones affecting, A-5
 preterm, 554
Breast milk banks, **552**
Brown adipose tissue, **286**
Buffalo meat, 719
Buffers, 407, 408f
Bulimia nervosa, 93, **270**, 274–276, 274t, 275f, 275t
 See also Eating disorders
Butter, 144f
Butter vs. margarine, 157, 166f, 471
Butyric acid, 108n
B vitamins, 326–350
 overview, 326, 356t
 coenzymes and, 216, 220, 326, 327, 327f, 347–348, 347f
 deficiencies, 244, 348–349, 349f, 356t
 DRI, RDA and AI, 326
 energy metabolism and, 326, 347–348, 347f
 food sources, 349, 356t
 functions of, 347–348, 356t
 heart disease and, 199, 200
 interdependence, 346
 list of, 10n
 "non-B vitamins," 345–346
 toxicities, 349, 356t
 See also specific B vitamins

C

Cabbage family, 456, 645, 677
Caffeine, **503**
 adolescents' intake, 578
 athletic activity and, 496, 505
 decaffeinated coffee, 686
 diuretic effects, 400
 in foods/drinks/drugs, H-0 to H-1t
 iron bioavailability, 538
 lactation and, 538
 pharmacologically active dose, H-1n
 pregnancy and, 532
 websites on, 581
Calcitonin, 191t, **416, 417**, 417f, 434n, **A-3**, A-6
Calcium, **416**–422
 overview of, 422t, 426t
 absorption of, 409, 417f, 418, 434, 436, A-6
 antibiotics and, 616
 for athletes, 271
 bioavailability, 418, 419, 420, 420f
 blood clotting and, 384f
 blood levels, 416, 417f, 418f, A-6
 blood pressure and, 416
 in bones, 416, 417, 417f, 418f, 431–432, A-6
  See also Osteoporosis
 breast milk and, 550, 551
 children's/adolescents' needs, 418, 577
 deficiency, 241, 378, 417–418, 422t
 food sources, 38, 65, 66–67, 418–421, 419f, 420f
 functions of, 416–418, 422t
 hormones and, 417f, 432, 434–436, 434n, A-6
 intake recommendations, 418, 420, 422t, 435–436
 lead toxicity and, 436, 463, 531
 for older adults, 603
 osteoporosis and, 200, 361, 411, 421, 433–434, 435–436
 pregnancy/lactation, 521f, 523, 524, 535
 proteins (dietary) and, 200
 storage of, 416, 417, 431–432
 supplements, 361, 363, 416, 436
 in tooth formation, 416
 toxicity, 422t
 vegetarian diets, 65, 66–67, 67n
 vitamin D and, 377, 378, 417f, 434, 436, A-6
 websites on, 427
 women's intakes of, 200
Calcium-binding protein, **418**
Calcium rigor, **417**
Calcium tetany, **417**
Calculation, aids to, inside back cover
 See also Measurements
Calmodulin, **416**
Calories, **7**
 See also kCalories (kcal)
Calorimetry, **250**, 250f
Campylobacter jejuni, 664, 665t
Canada
 aspartame, 133n
 dietitians in, 34
 DRI and, 16n
 Eating Well with Canada's Food Guide, I-1, I-2f to I-7f
 Food and Nutrition website, 26
 guidelines for healthy eating, 40t
 labeling website, 61
 ma huang, 290n
 Meal Planning for Healthy Eating, I-8t to I-11t
 milk fortification, 375n, 379n
 nutrition websites, 33, 61
 physical activity guidelines, I-7f
 supplements, 159n, 202n, 442n
Canadian Council of Sports Medicine, 500
Cancer, **642**–646
 acrylamide and, 686
 alcohol and, 244, 246t, 644t, 646t
 alternative therapies, 656t
 antioxidants and, 391–392, 645
 artificial sweeteners and, 133, 134, 135
 body weight and, 266, 643, 646t
 breastfeeding and, 537
 carotenoids and, 372
 chlorinated water and, 688
 classifications of, 642
 Delaney Clause and, 682
 environmental/lifestyle factors, 642–643, 644t, 646t
 exercise and, 478, 646t
 fat (dietary) and, 159–160
 fiber and, 122–123, 448, 645
 folate and, 341
 food additives and, 682, 684
 free radicals and, 448
 gastroesophageal reflux and, 97
 genetic factors, 642
 H. pylori and, 97
 Healthy People 2010 goals, J-1t
 initiators/promoters/antipromoters, **642**, 643–645, 643f
 iron and, 448
 lung: smoking and supplements, 580
 meat and, 160, 392
 obesity and, 266
 phytochemicals and, 469–470, 472f, 645, 655
 proteins (dietary) and, 200
 risk reduction, 644t, 645, 646t
 saturated fats and, 160, 645
 selenium and, 457
 skin, 379–380
 soy products, 469–470, 472f
 sugars on cell membranes, 112
 trans fats and, 645
 vegetable/fruit intake, 65, 372, 391–392, 470, 643, 644t, 645
 vegetarian diets and, 65
 vitamin intake and, 392, 656t
 websites on, 648
 whole grains and, 645, 646t
 See also specific types
Candy. See Sweets
Capillaries, 82f, **83**, 84f
Capsaicin, 470t
Carbohydrase, **77**, 108
Carbohydrate loading, **487**, 488
Carbohydrates, defined, **101**
Carbohydrates, unavailable, **108**
 See also Fiber
Carbohydrates (body). See Blood glucose levels; Glucose; Glycogen
Carbohydrates (chemistry), **101**–107
 elements in, 7t
 metabolism of, 114f, 115–116, 215t, 219–222, 219f–222f, 233, C-10 to C-11
 structure of, 102–107, 102f–107f, C-1 to C-3f
 types of, 102–107, 107t
 See also Energy metabolism
Carbohydrates (dietary), **101**–129
 absorption of, 108–110, 110f
 available, **108**
 body's use of, 227t
 in breast milk, 550, 550f
 in breast milk vs. formula, 553f
 in Canadian food groups, I-8t to I-9t, I-9t
 for children, 559
 complex, **101**, 105–107, 297
 cravings for, 120–121
 diabetes and, 640–641
 Dietary Guidelines and, 40t
 digestion of, 77, 79f, 80t, 107–108
 energy (kcal) in, 9t
 in exchange lists, 48, G-1t, G-3t, G-4t

Carbohydrates (dietary), *continued*
  for exercise, 485–488, 485t, 486f, 488t,
    490, 497
  fat made from, 113, 156, 222, 227t, 232, 233
  fat metabolism and, 226, 228n
  in food group plans, 41t, 42f–43f, 44t, 48t
  glycemic effect, 488
  glycemic index, **115**–116, 116f, 316, 488
  glycogen, effects on, 487–488
  glycogen depletion, 319–320
  "high-impact *vs.* low-impact," 488
  importance of, 227
  on labels, 58, 126–127, 126f
  for older adults, 602
  overeating and, 232, 233, 234f
  as percent of energy intake, 487n
  protein-sparing action of, **112**, 194
  recommended intake of, 18, 124–127,
    125t, 126f
  serotonin and, 120
  simple, **101**–105. *See also* Sugars
  types of, 102–107, 107t
  unavailable, **108**
  in weight control, 101, 113, 120, 233,
    296t, 298
  for weight loss, 295t, 315, 318
  See also Diets, high-carbohydrate; Diets,
    low-carbohydrate; Starch; Sugars; Sweets
Carbon, 7t, 218, B-3
Carbonated water, **400**
Carbon bonds, 102, 102f, 140–142, 145f, B-3
Carbon dioxide, 221, 227n, 407, 408f, 483f
Carbonic acid, **407**, 408f
Carbonic anhydrase, 452n
Carboxypeptidases, 186f
Carcinogenesis, **642**
Carcinogens, **642**, 644, 644n, 645, 686
Carcinomas, **642**
Cardiac arrest, **626**, 627
Cardiac output, **482**, 634f
Cardiac sphincter. *See* Esophageal sphincter
Cardiorespiratory conditioning, **482**, 483f
Cardiorespiratory endurance, **480**, 482–483
Cardiorespiratory fitness, 266, 480t
Cardiovascular disease (CVD), **157**, **587**,
  626–632
  alcohol and, 244, 246t, 336, 632t
  antioxidants and, 392
  arginine and, 199–200
  breastfeeding and, 552
  B vitamins and, 199, 200
  cholesterol (blood), 13f, 152, 157, 392, 587,
    628t, 629
  cholesterol (dietary), 157–158, 175f, 632t
  copper deficiency, 458
  coronary heart disease (CHD), **157**, **587**, **626**,
    628–632, 628t, 632t
  death rates, 24t, 157, 628
  in diabetics, 629, 640
  early development of, 586–588
  exercise and, 478, 489, 629, 632t
  fats: fish/fish oils, 159, 174, 632t
  fats: healthy choices, 157, 176t, 633
  fats: high-fat diets, 172–177
  fats: monounsaturated, 65, 158, 173, 633
  fats: omega-3 fatty acids, 158, 159, 174, 632t
  fats: plant *vs.* animal, 65, 144f, 157, 199
  fats: polyunsaturated, 65, 158, 392
  fats: saturated, 157, 158, 173, 175, 175f, 632t
  fats: *trans*, 143–144, 157, 632t, 633
  fetal development and, 515
  fiber and, 106, 122, 123t, 632t
  folate and, 340–341
  genetic factors, 120, 210, 586
  glycemic index and, 115
  Healthy People 2010 goals, J-1t to J-2t
  high-protein, low-carbohydrate diets, 319

  homocysteine and, 199, 340–341
  hypertension and, 627, 628t, 629
  iron stores and, 448
  lifestyle and, 24, 586–589, 628t, 629–630
  magnesium and, 424
  meat and, 319
  Mediterranean diet and, 13f, 173, 175,
    177, 471
  metabolic syndrome and, 630
  niacin and, 332
  nuts and, 173–174
  orange juice and, 13f
  phytochemicals and, 163, 470t, 471, 472f
  plant sterols/stanols and, 632t
  potassium and, 632t
  proteins (dietary) and, 199–200
  risk assessment, 631
  risk factors, emerging, **630**
  risk factors: major, 481, 628–632, 628t
  risk reduction strategies, 392, 630–632,
    632t, 633
  selenium deficiency and, 457
  smoking/tobacco use, 589, 629, 632t
  sodium and, 400, 632t
  soy products and, 65, 472f, 632t
  statistics on, 589
  sugar and, 120, 632t
  vegetable/fruit intake, 392, 471, 630, 633
  vegetarian diets and, 65
  vitamin deficiencies and, 336
  vitamins and, 13f, 382, 392
  websites on, 168
  weight/obesity and, 265, 629, 630, 632t
  whole grains and, 630, 633
  See also Atherosclerosis; Hypertension; Strokes
Careers in nutrition. *See* Health care professionals
Carnitine, **346**, 352, 364, 503, 504
Carotene, C-5f
Carotenoids, **369**
  bioavailability of, 375
  cancer and, 372, 392
  effects of, 470, 470t, 471
  food sources of, 375–376, 470t, 472f
  hypercarotenemia, 377n
  types of, 370n
  vision and, 605
  as vitamin A precursors, 370f, 375–376
  See also Beta-carotene
Carpal tunnel syndrome, **336**
Carrying capacity, **707**
Cartilage therapy, **653**
Case-control studies, 13f
Casein, **550**
Catabolism, 215f, **216**
  See also Energy metabolism
Catalase, 391n
Catalysts, **76**
Cataracts, **604**–605
Cathartics, **270**, 274–275
Cations, **403**, 404t, 405f
Causation *vs.* correlation, 15
CCK (cholecystokinin), **88**, 88t, 149, 251,
  252, A-6
CDC (Centers for Disease Control), 499, **664**
Cell differentiation, **371**
Cell membranes, **A-2**
  cell structure and, 214f
  free radicals and, 452
  phospholipids in, 145, 146f, 422
  selective permeability, 404–405
  structure of, 81f, 146f, A-3f
  sugars and, 112
  transport proteins in, 191, 192f
Cells, **A-2** to A-3
  in absorptive process, 80–81, 82f
  adipose cells, 155–156, 155f, 266, 282, 283f,
    284, 286

  alpha cells (pancreas), 113n
  beta cells (pancreas), 113n, 515
  composition of, B-4, B-4f
  electrolytes and, 403, 404–405, 405f
  epithelial, 371
  fluids associated with, 399f
  of immune system, 622–623
  metabolism within, 214, 214f
  red blood cells, 447f. *See* Red blood cells
  structure of, 214f, A-2 to A-3, A-3f
  vitamin A and differentiation of, 371
  white blood cells, 622–623
Cellulite, **291**
Cellulose, 106, 106n, 107f, 122, **C-2**
Centers for Disease Control (CDC), 499, **664**
Central nervous system, **A-7** to A-8, A-8f
  See also Brain; Nerves/nervous system
Central obesity, **262**–263, 262f, 263f
  alcohol and, 243
  disease/mortality, 265, 630
  exercise and, 301–302
  smoking and, 262
Cereals. *See* Breads; Grains
Cereals, breakfast, 51–52, 412, 412f, 555–556
Cerebral thrombosis, **627**
Cerebrovascular accident (CVA), **626**
Certification (pesticide inspections), **682**
Certified nutritionists, **32**
Ceruloplasmin, 458n
Cervical cancer, 644t
Cesarean section, **516**, 522, 522n, 529–530
Chaff, **50f**
Chamomile, 657t
Chaparral, 657t
CHD risk equivalents, **626**, 629, 631
Cheese, 47, 111, 126
  See also Milk and milk products
Cheilosis, 330n, 349f
Chelates, **451**
Chelation therapy, **653**
Chemistry, B-1 to C-17
  acids/bases. *See* pH
  of amino acids, 181–183, 182f, 182t
  atoms, properties of, 102, 102f, B-1 to B-3, B-2t
  basic concepts of, B-1 to B-8
  biochemical structures/pathways, C-1 to C-17
  bonds, 140–142, 145f, B-3, B-3 to B-4, B-4f
  of carbohydrates, 101–107. *See also*
    Carbohydrates (chemistry)
  carbon "backbones," 218
  chemical reactions overview, B-6 to B-8
  composition of foods, 6, 7t, 9
  electrolytes, 402–404, 404f, 404t, 405f
  elemental composition of body, 409f, B-4t
  elements, table of, B-2t
  enzymes/coenzymes, 76–78, 327f
  of fats, 139–144. *See also* Fats (chemistry)
  free radicals. *See* Free radicals
  ion formation, B-5, B-5 to B-6
  minerals, 408
  of nutrients, 5–11, 7t
  oxidation-reduction reactions, B-7f, B-7 to B-8
  of proteins, 181–185. *See also* Proteins
    (chemistry)
  vitamins, C-5 to C-9f
  See also Energy metabolism; Laboratory tests;
    Metabolism
Chewing, 599–600
Chicken. *See* Poultry
Child, Julia, 177
Children, 558–575
  overview of nutrient needs, 559–562, 562f
  aspartame, 135
  behavior of, 120, 562, 563, 564–565
  body mass index, 567, 568f
  body shape of, 559f
  bone mass, 435–436

calcium, 418, 435–436
choking in, 92, 557, 572
cholesterol levels, 587, 588t
chronic diseases, early development of, 586–589, 588t
deficiencies and health beverages, 379
diabetes and obesity, 115, 569, 586
Dietary Guidelines for, 40t
energy needs, 558–559, 560, 562t
exercise for, 567, 569, 571
fat cell development in, 282
fats (dietary), 155, 560, 588
fish consumption, 174, 676
food allergy/intolerance, 565–567
growth assessment, E-6 to E-7, E-11f to E-13f
Healthy People 2010 goals, J-2t
hypertension in, 587–588
infectious diseases and, 372–373, 453
iodine deficiency in, 456
iron deficiency, 446, 447
iron-deficiency anemia, 560, 563
iron toxicity, 361–362, 448
lead toxicity, 463, 463t, 564
learning and nutrition, 562, 563
malnutrition in, 197–199, 562–564, 563t, 705, 707, E-7
mealtime guidelines, 571–573
milk for, 379, 418–419, 554, 557
overweight, 115, 281, 558, 567–571, 567f, 568f, 586, E-7
pesticides and, 678, 681
protein-energy malnutrition (PEM), 196–199, 197t, 198f, 199f
protein needs, 560
school nutrition programs, 573–575
supplement overdoses, 361–362, 448
supplements for, 560
toddlers, 557–558, 571t
vegetable/fruit intake, 561–562, 569, 571, 573t
vegetarian diets and, 559
vitamin A and, 372–373
vitamin D and, 37f, 378. *See also* Rickets
websites on, 580–581
of women with anorexia nervosa, 273
zinc deficiency, 453
See also Adolescence; Infants
China, 457
Chiropractic, **653**
Chitosan, 291t
Chloride, **413**–414, 414t, 426t
deficiency and toxicity, 413–414, 414t
functions of, 413, 414t
intake recommendations, 413, 414t
losses of, 406, 413
Chlorine, atomic structure of, B-5
Chlorophyll, **376**
Chocolate, 120–121, 472f
Choking
in infants/children, 92, 557, 572
prevention of, 92, 93f, 97t
vs. normal swallowing, 92f
Cholecalciferol, **377**, 379n, C-8f
See also Vitamin D
Cholecystokinin (CCK), **88**, 88t, 149, 251, 252, A-6
Cholesterol, **146**, 147f
Cholesterol, endogenous *vs.* exogenous, **146**
Cholesterol (blood)
in childhood, 587, 588t
dietary cholesterol and, 157
diet *vs.* medications, 589, 632
fiber and, 106, 122
"good" *vs.* "bad," 152
heart disease and, 13f, 152, 157, 587, 628t, 629, 631
levels. *See* Blood lipid profiles
lipoprotein composition, 151–152, 153f

margarine and, 157, 164n, 471, 472
mycoprotein and, 471
niacin and, 332
saturated fats and, 157, 158, 175, 175f
soy products and, 65, 162, 471, 472f
synthesis of, 122, 147, 162
trans-fatty acids and, 157
weight loss and, 294
See also HDL; LDL; VLDL
Cholesterol (body), functions of, 147, 147f, 149
Cholesterol (dietary)
blood cholesterol and, 157
Daily Value for, 147
exogenous, **146**
food sources, 146, 157, 158f
heart disease and, 157–158, 173, 175f
on labels, **58**, 58n
reducing, 157–158
scavenger pathway, 152
U.S. intake of, 157f, 161
websites on, 168
Choline, **145**, 146f, 345, 345t, 346, 607
Chondroitin, 606
Chromium, 461–462, 462t, 464t
Chromium picolinate, 461, **503**, 504
Chromosomes, **207**, 208, 208f, A-2, A-3f
See also DNA; Genetics/genes
Chronic diseases, **3**, **24**, 624–660
overview of risk factors, 24–25, 25t, 624–625, 625f
alcohol and, 244, 246t
antioxidants and, 392
body fat and, 262, 263f, 265–266
calcium and, 414
diet recommendations, 632t, 633, 646–647, 647f
diet recommendations: fat, 159–160, 172–177
early development of, 586–589
energy intake restriction and, 597
exercise and. *See* Physical activity, benefits of
fetal development and, 515
folate and, 340–341
genetics and, 210, 625, 625f, 647
lifestyle and, 586–589, 625, 625f, 629–630
Mediterranean diet and, 13f, 173, 177, 471
obesity and, 115, 262, 263f, 289, 586, 625f, 646
obesity as, 292
proteins (dietary) and, 199–200, 319
supplements and, 361
vegetarian diets and, 65, 67
websites on, 648
weight loss and, 294
See also Cancer; Cardiovascular disease (CVD); Diabetes; Hypertension
Chronic PEM, **197**
Chronological age, **595**
Chylomicrons, 83, **149**, 151, 152f, 153f
Chyme, 74, **74**, 75, 87
Chymotrypsin, in protein digestion, 186f
Ciguatera poisoning, 670n
Ciprofloxacin, 616
Circulatory systems. *See* Lymphatic system; Vascular system
Cirrhosis, **239**, 241
Cis-fatty acids, 143, 145f
Clay eating. *See* Pica
Climate change, 709
Clinically severe obesity, **292**
Clinical trials, 13f, 14t
Clostridium perfringens, 665t
CoA. *See* Coenzyme A (CoA)
Cobalamin. *See* Vitamin B_{12}
Cobalt, 462, 462f
Cocaine, 579
Coconut oil, 142, 144f, 157, 175
Coenzyme A (CoA), **218**

formation of, 347f, 348
function of, 221f, 334, 347f
structure of, C-7f
Coenzyme Q_{10} (ubiquinone), 346, **504**
Coenzymes, **216**
B vitamin deficiencies and, 326
B vitamins and, 216, 220, 326, 328, 330f, 336
folate and, 338
in glucose metabolism, 219f–222f
mechanism of action, 327f
pantothenic acid and, C-7f
pyridoxal phosphate (PLP), **336**
vitamin B_6 and, C-7f
vitamins and TCA cycle, 228f, 328, 330f, 347f, 348
vitamins/structures of, C-5 to C-9f
Cofactors, **216**
Coffee, 97, 199, 686
Cognitive function. *See* Brain; Intelligence
Cohort studies, 13f
Cola beverages, 39, 422, H-1t
Colds, 12–15, 352, 455, 478
Colitis, **94**
Collagen, **190**, 192, 351–352
Collagenase, 186f
Colon/colorectal cancer
alcohol and, 244
fiber and, 122–123
meat and, 644
risk summary, 644t
vegetarian diet and, 65
Colonic irrigation, **94**, 95
Colon (large intestine), **72**, 73f
anatomy of, 74, 78f
bacteria in. *See* Intestinal bacteria
carbohydrate/fiber digestion in, 106, 108, 109f
diverticular disease, **94**, 94f, 95, 122
fiber and, 78, 79f, 122
function of, 73f, 74, 78f, 79f
vegetarian diets and, 65
Colostrum, **551**
"Combining foods" myth, 81–82
Comfrey, 657t
Complementary and alternative medicine, **652**–659
herbal remedies, 654f, 655–658, 656t–658t
for hyperactivity, 564
nutrition-related, 654–658
risk-benefit relationships, 652, 655f, 656–658, 656t–658t
websites on, 659
Complementary proteins, **195**–196, 196f
Complex carbohydrates. *See under* Carbohydrates (dietary)
Composition of foods, H-0 to H-77t
See also Chemistry
Composition of the body. *See* Body composition
Compound, defined, **B-1**
Conception, **510**
fertility/infertility, 264, 526
See also Fertility/infertility
Condensation, **104**, 104f, 143f
Conditionally essential nutrients, 156, 183, 345
Conditioning, **480**
Cones (of retina), 371f
Congregate meals programs, **609**
Constipation, **94**
fiber and, 95, 106, 122
iron supplements and, 451
in older adults, 602
during pregnancy, 524t, 525
prevention of, 95, 97t
treatment of, 95
Consumers, 663–698
alternative medicine, 657–658
energy and food production, 717–720, 719f

Consumers, *continued*
environmental contaminants, 676–677
food additives, **682**–687
foodborne illnesses, **664**–673, 665t
GM food concerns, 695–696, 697t
pesticides, 567, **678**–681
water, 687–689
websites for, 33, 34, 690–691
weight-loss bill of rights, 290t
See also Grocery shopping
Contaminants, **674**
dietary variety and, 39
in seafood, 159, 174, 531
in supplements, 203, 436
in water, 401, 553, 565
See also Environmental contaminants;
Foodborne illnesses; Lead
Contamination, cross-, 566, **667,** 670
Contamination iron, **450**–451
Continuing Survey of Food Intakes by
Individuals (CSFII), 22n
Contraceptives, 341, 537
Control groups, 12, **14**
Convenience and food choices, 4, 567
Conventional medicine, **652**
Cooking/food preparation
acrylamide and, 644–645, 685–686
for children, 571–573
environmental considerations, 712
fat recommendations, 173–177
foodborne illnesses, preventing, 665t,
667–671, 669f, 671t
grilled meats and cancer risk, 644–645, 644n
iron from cookware, 450–451
lead poisoning, preventing, 565
low-fat tips, 53, 161–167
microwave, 344, 686
minerals, 10, 408, 420, 450–451
niacin, 332
nutrient loss, minimizing, 10, 324t, 674
for older adults, 600, 608, 609–610
pesticide residues, minimizing, 680
salt, reducing, 411
thiamin, 324, 328
trans-fats, 159
vitamin B_6, 336
vitamin B_{12} 344–345
vitamin C, 354
vitamin E, 383
vitamins and, 10, 324t
websites on, 427, 713
See also Diet planning; Grocery shopping;
Processed foods
Cool-down, **481**
Copper, 458–459, 464t
overview of, 459t
absorption of, and zinc, 453, 458
deficiency, 458, 459t
functions of, 458, 458n, 459t
intake recommendations, 459, 459t
toxicity, 459, 459t
Cori cycle, 220f, **221,** 487
Corn and niacin, 332
Corn breeding, 693
Cornea, **371**
Corn syrup, **118,** 556
Coronary arteries, **626**
Coronary heart disease (CHD), **157, 587, 626,**
628–632, 628t, 632t
See also Atherosclerosis; Cardiovascular
disease (CVD)
Coronary thrombosis, **627**
Correlation (research), **14,** 15
Correspondence schools, **32,** 33
Cortical bone, **431,** 432
Corticotropin-releasing hormone (CRH), **A-3,**
A-4, A-5

Costs
breastfeeding *vs.* formula, 533t
food choices and, 4
of functional foods, 472
low-budget meals, 610, 704
of physical inactivity, 478
of pregnancy in adolescents, 529
of supplements, 364
of weight loss treatments, 288
See also Food assistance programs
Coupled reactions, **216,** 217f
Covert, defined, **22**
CP (creatine phosphate), 484–**485,** 485t
Cravings
for nonfood substances, 447, 525
during pregnancy, **525**
for sugar/carbohydrates, 120–121
C-reactive protein, **627**
Creatine, 485, **503,** 504–505
Creatine phosphate (CP), 484–**485,** 485t
Credentials, fake, 33
Cretinism, **456**
Creutzfeldt-Jakob Disease, 668n
Crib death. *See* Sudden infant death
syndrome (SIDS)
Critical periods (fetal development),
512–515, 512f
Cross-contamination, 566, **667,** 670
Cross-sectional studies, 13f
Cruciferous vegetables, 456, **645,** 677
Cryptosporidiosis, 665t
Crypts, **80,** 82f
Curcumin, 470t
Cutins, 106n
Cyanocobalamin. *See* Vitamin B_{12}
Cyclamate, **132,** 133t, 135
Cyclosporiasis, 665t
Cysteine, 184f, 425
Cytochrome C oxidase, 458n
Cytochromes, 443n
Cytokines, **622**
Cytoplasm, 214f, **A-2,** A-3f
Cytosol, **A-2**

D

Daidzein, 470t
Daily Values (DV), **55**
calculating personal values, 57, 165
carbohydrate recommendations, 124
fat recommendations, 160–161, 165–167
for food labels, inside back cover
on labels of foods, 54f, 55–57, 56t, 166f
proteins (dietary), 196, 197n
Dairy products. *See* Milk and milk products
DASH eating plan, 411, 416, 635t, 636, 636t
DDT, in breast milk, 538
Deamination, 225, 226f
Death
from AIDS, 624t
alcohol and, 25t, 242, 244, 245, 624f
BMI and, 264f, 265
from cancer, 24t
causes of, in U.S., 24, 24t, 25t, 624f
from choking, 92
from chronic diseases, 624f
from dehydration, 398, 398t
from diabetes, 24t, 637
from diarrhea, 707
from drugs, illicit, 25t, 290, 579
from eating disorders, 273, 274
from foodborne illnesses, 664, 665t, 666, 670
from heart disease, 24t, 157, 628
from heat stroke, 494
from infant formulas in developing countries,
536–537
from infections, 24t, 199
iron supplements and, 361–362, 448

from malnutrition, 199, 701, 707
obesity and, 263, 264f, 265
during pregnancy, 529, 530
from scurvy, 350
from SIDS, 531
smoking and, 25, 25t
from strokes, 24t, 628
vitamin A deficiency and, 562
from water intoxication, **398**
Defecate/defecation, **94,** 95
See also Constipation; Diarrhea; Feces
Deficiencies, **17, 22**
alcohol and, 241, 243–244, 327, 336, 338
assessment of. *See* Nutrition assessment
behavior and, 447, 562, 563
brain function and, 606
causes of, 348
covert, **22**
development of, 19, 22, 22f
dietary adequacy and, 37
disease, distinguishing from, 348–349, 350
exercise and, 478, 492
immune system and, 599
in infants, 557
as interrelated, 346, 348
laboratory tests and, 21–22
lactose intolerance and, 111
minerals, summary of, 426t
obesity surgery and, 293
in older adults, 599, 606
overt, **22**
in preterm infants, 554
primary, **22**
protein-energy malnutrition (PEM), **196**–199,
197t, 198f, 199f
proteins (dietary), 196, 241
rice milk/drinks, 197
role of DRI/RDA/AI, 17, 18f
secondary, **22**
subclinical, **22,** 360–361, E-17
sugar intake and, 117–119
supplements for correcting, 360
symptoms of, 20, 22, 348–349, 350. *See also*
under specific nutrients
See also Malnutrition; Nutrition assessment;
specific nutrients
Degenerative arthritis, **605**
Dehydration, **398**
alcohol use and, 243
athletes "making weight," 272
chloride and, 413–414
exercise and, 493–496, 494t
high-protein diets, 226
in infants, 549
in older adults, 601
oral rehydration therapy (ORT), **406, 707**
rehydration, 406, 494–495, 494t
salt tablets and, 412, 495
signs/effects of, 398, 398t, 400, 493, 494
vomiting and, 93
Dehydroepiandrosterone (DHEA), **503,** 506
Delaney Clause, **682**
Dementia, senile, **606,** 607t
Denaturation, **184**–185
Dental caries, **119,** 119f
children and, 572
fluoride and, 460–461
infant bottle feeding, 553, 554f
lead and, 463
sugar and, 119
sugar replacers and, 136
websites, 127
See also Teeth
Dental plaque, **119**
Deoxyadenosylcobalamin, **342**
Deoxyribonucleic acid. *See* DNA
Deoxythymidine kinase, 452n

Depression, 155, 275, 478, 600, 607, 654f
Dermatitis of pellagra, 332f
Designer foods. *See* Functional foods
Development, sustainable, 708, 711
DEXA (dual energy X-ray absorptiometry, **264f,** 432, E-16t
Dextrins, **108**
Dextrose, **102, 118**
    See also Glucose
DHA (docosahexaenoic acid), **154,** 159n, 159t, 174, 550
DHEA (dehydroepiandrosterone), **503,** 506
DHF (dihydrofolate), **338**
Diabetes, **115, 637**–641
    complications of, 639–640, 639f
    development of, 637–638
    exercise and, 478, 638, 641
    fetal development and, 515, 527–528
    fiber and carbohydrates, 106, 123t
    glycemic index and, 115
    Healthy People 2010 goals, J-1t
    heart disease risk, 629, 640
    hyperglycemia and, 637
    hypoglycemia and, 115
    laboratory tests for, 354
    nutrient-gene interactions, 515
    obesity and, 115, 265, 289, 569, 586, 638
    in pregnancy (gestational), **528**
    race/ethnicity and, 638
    statistics on, 586, 637f
    websites on, 127, 539, 648
    weight loss and, 265, 641
Diabetes type 1, **115, 637**
    overview of, 638, 638t
    causes of, 115, 638
    diet and, 641
    lactation and, 537
    metabolic consequences of, 639f
    pregnancy and, 527
    vs. type 2, 638t
Diabetes type 2, **115, 637**
    overview of, 638, 638t
    causes of, 115, 638
    in children, 569
    fiber and carbohydrates, 122
    insulin resistance and, 638
    metabolic consequences of, 639f
    obesity and, 289, 569, 586
    vs. type 1, 638t
    weight loss/exercise, 641
Diarrhea, **94**
    cause/treatment, 93–94, 665n
    deaths from, 707
    dysentery, **198**
    electrolyte balance and, 93, 406, 413
    in infants, 552, 556
    malnutrition and, 198, 199
    oral rehydration therapy, **707**
    prevention of, 97t
    travelers', **672,** 673
Dietary folate equivalents (DFE), **338,** 339
Dietary Guidelines for Americans, 39–41, 40t
    alcohol, 45, 238
    breastfeeding, 535
    children/teens, 554, 557, 559, 560, 570, 576, 577
    chronic disease reduction, 636, 646, 647, 647t
    dental caries, 119
    eating patterns, 41
    exercise/physical activity, 300, 305, 306, 479, 483, 519, 535, 576, 595, 647
    fat intake, 45, 160–161, 162, 164, 560
    fiber intake, 124
    folate intake, 510, 514
    foodborne illnesses, 531, 557, 610, 667, 668, 671
    fruits/vegetables, 52, 53, 124
    iron intake, 449, 510
    key recommendations, 40t

milk, 53, 554, 577
    nutrient-dense foods, 45
    older adults, 597, 605, 612
    overweight children, 570
    potassium-rich foods, 412, 636
    pregnancy, 510, 514, 516, 519, 531
    salt/sodium intake, 45, 411, 412, 636
    sugar intake, 45, 121
    vitamin B$_{12}$, 603
    vitamin D, 380, 603
    vs. MyPyramid and labels, 60t
    websites on, 40, 61
    weight and health, 250, 294, 300, 305, 306, 570
    whole grains, 51, 124, 559
Dietary Reference Intakes. *See* DRI (Dietary Reference Intakes)
Dietary Supplement Health and Education Act of 1994, 365, 442
Dieter's tea, 290
Dietetic technician, registered (DTR), **32**
Dietetic technicians, **32**
Diet history, 20–21, 287, E-2t, **E-3** to E-5
Dietitians, **32**
    duties of, 32
    education of, 32, 33, 33n
    hunger activism, 711
    public health, **32**
    registered, **19, 32**
    websites for finding, 34
Dietitians of Canada, 33, 34
Diet planning, 37–67
    blood glucose and balanced meals, 114–116
    Canadian food group system, I-1, I-2f to I-7f, I-8t to I-11t
    carbohydrate intake, 121, 124–127, 125t, 126f, 497
    for cardiovascular health, 632t, 633
    for children, 557f, 558–562, 561f, 570, 571–573, 571t, 573t, 588–589
    environmental concerns, 712
    evaluating foods, 329
    exchange lists, 47–48, G-3t to G-11t
    for exercise, 496–499, 498f
    fat intake and, 161–167, 172–177
    food group plans, **41**–53, 42f–43f, 44t, 48t, G-3t, G-3 to G-4
    food pyramids, 47, 47f, 65–66, 66f
    functional foods/phytochemicals, 471
    glycemic index and, 115–116
    grocery shopping, 48–53, 608, 704
    for infants, 555–557, 555t, 557f
    during lactation, 534–536
    low-cost meals, 704
    for obesity. *See* Obesity treatment
    for older adults, 600, 607–611
    during pregnancy, 519–525, 521f, 522f, 524t
    principles of, 37–39, 60t
    protein intake, 66, 199–203, 497
    sample menus, 48, 48t, 49f, 498f
    for single people, 609–610
    sugar guidelines, 121
    for toddlers, 556
    variety, importance of, 67, 89, 329
    vegetarian, 44, 46, 64–68, 66f
    websites on, 61
    for weight gain, 307–308
    for weight loss, 295–298, 295t, 296f, 299t
    See also Diet therapy
Diets, **3**
    dangers of, 289–290, 291t
    DASH eating plan, 411, 416, 635t, 636, 636t
    fad diets, **290,** 315–321, 316t, 317t, 320t
    hypoglycemia and, 115
    kcalories and. *See* Diets, low-kcalorie
    ketogenic, 113, 156, 235, 319–320, 320t
    for lactose intolerance, 111
    macrobiotic, **64,** 67, **653,** 656t

during pregnancy, 532
    tyramine-controlled, 617, 618t
    See also Diet therapy; Mediterranean diet; Obesity treatment; Vegetarian diets; Weight loss
Diets, carbohydrate-modified, 317t
Diets, high-carbohydrate
    for athletes, 486, 486f, 487, 488, 497, 498f, 499
    glycogen and, 486, 487, 488
    heart disease and, 122
    protein use and, 490
    weight management and, 123
Diets, high-carbohydrate, low-fat, 317t
Diets, high-fat, 13f, 39, 172–177, 488–489
Diets, high-fiber, 122–124, 448
Diets, high-protein
    cancer and, 200
    chronic disease and, 199–200, 319
    dehydration and, 226
    effectiveness claims, 316t
    heart disease and, 319
    kcalories in, 200, 318
    kidney disease and, 200
    osteoporosis and, 200
    risks/benefits, 200, 317t
    thermic effect of, 256, 318
Diets, high-protein, low-carbohydrate, 317t, 318, 319
Diets, low-carbohydrate
    energy metabolism and, 227
    fat *vs.* lean loss, 319, 320
    glycogen and, 319–320
    health effect of, 319–320, 320t
    myths of, 316t, 318
    during pregnancy, 532
    protein use and, 490
    saturated fats and, 318–319
    side effects of, 317t, 320t
Diets, low-fat
    for children, 560
    diet planning for, 161–167, 162f, 166f
    fatty acid deficiencies and, 155
    guidelines, 172
    LDL and, 210
    meats in, 53, 162, 163
    satiating hormones and, 286
    for weight loss, 298
    weight loss claims, 316t, 317t
Diets, low-kcalorie, 235, 295–296, 295t, 296f, 361
    See also Fasting
Diets, metabolic type, 317t
Diets, weight-loss, 315–321, 316t, 317t, 320t
Diet therapy
    for constipation, 95
    for diabetes, 115, 640–641
    for eating disorders, 273, 275–276, 275t, 277t
    for heart disease, 632t, 633
    for hypertension, 410–411, 416, 635t, 636, 636t
    for irritable bowel syndrome, 94
    for kidney disease, 200
    for PKU, 133–134, 209
    See also Obesity treatment
Differentiation (cell), **371**
Diffusion, facilitated, 81f, 108
Diffusion, simple, 81f
Digestibility of protein, **195**
Digestion, **71**–80
    overview of, 71–72
    of carbohydrates, 77, 79f, 107–108, 109f
    of fats, 79f, 147–149, 148f, 151f
    of fiber by intestinal flora, 78, 79f, 106, 108, 108n, 109f
    hormones and, 87, 149, 151, A-6 to A-7
    in intestines, 73f, 74, 75f, 77, 82f, 87–88, 148f, 149
    in mouth, 72–73, 74, 76f, 147–148, 148f

Digestion, *continued*
  muscles involved in, 74–76, 75f, 76f
  nervous system and, 87–88
  organs involved in, 72–76, 73f, 79f
  of protein, 77, 79f, 185, 186f
  secretions of, 76–78, 76f, 77f, 80t, 87–88
  in stomach, 73f, 74, 75, 75f, 148–149, 148f
  vitamin A deficiency and, 373
  websites on, 90, 98
  See also Absorption; Digestive system; GI (gastrointestinal) tract
Digestive enzymes, 76–78, **77**
  carbohydrates, 77, 108, 109f, 110
  fats. *See* Lipases
  lecithinase, 145
  protein, 185, 186f
  in saliva, 76f, 77
  See also Pancreatic enzymes
Digestive juices. *See* Gastric juices; Pancreatic juice
Digestive system, **72**, 73f
  See also Digestion; GI (gastrointestinal) tract
Diglycerides, **147**
Digoxin, 655f, 657
Dihydrofolate (DHF), **338**
Dihydroxyphenyl isatin, 95n
DiOGenes project, 319
Dioxins, 538, **686**
Dipeptidases, 185, 186f
Dipeptides, **183**, 183f
Direct calorimetry, **250**
Disaccharides, **103**
  chemistry of, 103–105, 104f
  digestion/absorption of, 108, 109f, 110–111
  structure of, 104f, C-1
  See also Lactose intolerance
Discretionary kcalorie allowance, **45**
  energy intake and, 41t, 45f
  exercise and, 300f
  fats and, 45, 161
  in food group plans, 48t
  sugar and, 121
Disease
  chronic. *See* Chronic diseases
  deficiencies/malnutrition *vs.*, 20, 348–349, 350
  exercise and. *See* Physical activity, benefits of
  free radicals and, 390–392
  genetic. *See* Genetic disorders
  genetic engineering and, 696
  infectious. *See* Infections/infectious disease
  iron overload and, 448
  lifestyle and. *See* Lifestyle choices
  obesity/overweight and, 115, 265–266, 288–289, 569, 586, 587, 605, 646
  risk/prevention overview, 24–25, 24t, 25t, 624–625, 625f
  smoking and. *See* Smoking/tobacco use
  strategies for health, 646–647, 647f
  underweight and, 264–265
  vegetarian diets and, 65, 175
  See also specific diseases
Disordered eating, **270**–272
Dissociate, defined, **403**
Distance Education and Training Council, 34
Distilled liquor, 238, **239**, 244t
Distilled water, **400**
Disulfide bridges, 184f
Dithiothiones, 470n
Diuretics
  alcohol, caffeine and water balance, 400, 496
  caffeine content of, H-1t
  hypertension and, 636–637
  potassium and, 636–637
Diverticula, **94**, 95, 95f, 122
Diverticulitis, **94**, 95
Diverticulosis, **94**, 95
DNA (deoxyribonucleic acid), **207**

antioxidants and cancer, 392
chromosomes, **207**, 208, 208f, **A-2**, A-3f
folate and, 338, 339f, 341
free radicals and, 391f, 392
fruits and vegetables, 391–392
Human Genome Project, 207
nitrogen in, 193n
in nucleus, 208, 208f, 214f
phosphorus and, 422
protein synthesis and, 187, 188f, 490
vitamin B$_{12}$ and, 343, 344
See also Genetics/genes; Genomics, nutritional
DNA polymerase, 452n
Docosahexaenoic acid (DHA), **154**, 159t, 174, 550
Dolomite, **431**, 436
Double-blind experiment, 13–14, **14**
"Dowager's hump," 433f
Down syndrome, 340, **530**
DRI (Dietary Reference Intakes), **16**–20, inside front cover
  for assessing dietary intake, 21f
  component categories, 16–18, 19
  for exercise, 288
  for fats, 160–161, 172
  high doses of nutrients and, 18f, 325–326
  international recommendations, 19
  nutritional genomics and, 16
  for older adults, 601
  purpose/uses of, 16, 18–19
  reference adults used, 18
  safe *vs.* toxic nutrient intakes, 18, 18f
  source of, 16n
  sugars, 121
  websites, 28
Drink, defined, 238, **239**
Driving, alcohol and, 243t, 245
Drug, **239**
Drug history, 20, E-2t, **E-3**
Drug-nutrient interactions. *See* Nutrient-drug interactions
Drugs, actions of, 615
Drugs, therapeutic. *See* Medications
Drug use/abuse
  adolescents and, 579
  alcohol and, 238
  lactation and, 537
  nutrition problems and, 579
  pregnancy and, 530
  websites on, 247
  See also Alcohol abuse
DTR (dietetic technician registered), **32**
Dual energy X-ray absorptiometry, **264f**, 432, E-16t
Duodenum, **72**, 73f, 74, 77
Duration (of exercise), defined, **480**
DV. *See* Daily Values (DV)
Dwarfism, 453f
Dysentery, **198**
Dysmetabolic syndrome, **630**
Dysphagia, **599**

E

E. coli infection, 665t, 666
EAR (Estimated Average Requirement), 16–**17**, 17f, 18f, 19, 21f
Eating behaviors, 302–303
Eating disorders, **270**–277
  anorexia nervosa, 251–252, **270**, 272–274, 273t, 307
  in athletes, 270–271, 271f, 272
  binge eating, **270**, 274, 275f, 276, 277t
  bulimia nervosa, 93, **270**, 274–276, 274t, 275f, 275t
  Healthy People 2010 goals, J-2t
  preventing, 272, 272t
  risk factors for, 271
  society's role in, 276

unspecified, **270**, 276, 277t
websites on, 277
Eat Right 4 Your Type diet, 317t
Echinacea, 656–657, 657t, 658t
Eclampsia, **528**–529
Economic factors. *See* Costs; Socioeconomic status
Ecstasy, 579
Edema, **191**
  beriberi and, 327, 328f
  causes of, 191
  malnutrition and, 198, 199f
  pregnancy/preeclampsia, 528
Education
  in alternative medicine, 652
  of consumers, 60
  correspondence schools, **32**, 33
  fake credentials, 33
  of health care professionals, 31, 33, 33n
  Healthy People 2010 goals, J-1t
  hunger activism, 711
  hungry children and, 562, 563
  lead contamination and, 564
  of nutrition professionals, 31, 32, 33, 33n
  population growth and, 709
  school nutrition and learning, 562, 573–575
  websites on, 34
EER (Estimated Energy Requirement), **18**, 257, F-2t, inside front cover
Eggs
  avidin in, **334**
  cholesterol in, 158
  enriched with omega-3 fatty acids, 158, 159
  recommended intake of, 158
  as reference protein, 195
  safe handling of, 671
Eicosanoids, **154**–155, 627
Eicosapentaenoic acid (EPA), **154**, 159n, 159t, 174
Elastase, 186f
Eldercare Locator, 609n
Elderly people. *See* Aging (older adults)
Electrolytes, **403**
  for athletes, 271–272, 494–495, 495
  balance/imbalance, 93, 402–406, 404f, 404t, 405f
  chemistry of, 402–406, 404f, 404t, 405f
  chloride, 404t, 406, 413–414
  in eating disorders, 275
  minerals, 404t
  potassium, 403, 404t, 406, 414–415
  replacing losses, 406
  sodium, 403, 404t, 406, 410–413
  in sports drinks, 495
  See also Fluid balance
Electrolyte solutions, **403**–405
Electrons, B-1 to B-3, B-2t
Electron transport chain (ETC), **218**
  alcohol and, 241
  ATP synthesis, 229f, 231f
  B vitamins and, 347f
  cytochromes, 443n
  functions of, 220, 222, 229
  iron in, 443
  reactions of, C-14f, C-14 to C-15, C-15t
Elements, 408, **B-1**, B-2t, B-3
Ellagic acid, 470n, 472f
Elvjhem, Conrad, 332n
Embolism, **626**, 627
Embolus, **626**
Embryo, 511f, **512**, 512f
Emergency shelters, **704**
Emerging Infections Program (EIP), 666n
Emerging risk factors, **630**
Emetics, **270**, 274–275
Emotions, food choices and, 4–5
  See also Psychological problems

Empty-kcalorie foods, **39**, 298
See also Nutrient density
EMS (eosinophilia myalgia syndrome), 203
Emulsification
    bile acids and, 78, 149, 150f
    fat digestion and, 78, 88, 148f, 149, 150f
    phospholipids and, 145
Emulsifiers, **78**, 685
Endocrine glands, **78**
See also Hormones
Endocrine system, A-3 to A-5, A-4f
Endocrinology, **A-3**
Endogenous protein, **193**
Endopeptidases, 185
Endoplasmic reticulum, **A-2**, A-3f
Endosperm, **50f**
Endurance, muscle, 480, **480**, 481, 484
Enemas, **94**, 95
Energy, **6**, 7–10, **B-1**
    amino acids and, 226f
    brain and glucose, 234
    carbohydrates, simple, **101**–105
    deficiency vs. excess, 20
    in exchange list portions, 47–48
    from fiber, 108, 108n, 109
    from glucose vs. fat, 101
    kcalories (kcal) as measure of, **7**–9
    ketone bodies, 113
    on labels, 56–57
    photosynthesis, **213**
    protein intake vs., 201
    requirements. See kCalories (kcal) needs
    from short-chain fatty acids, 108, 108n, 109f
    USDA Food Guide servings, 41, 41t, 44t, 49f
    See also Energy metabolism; kCalories (kcal);
        Metabolism
Energy balance, 249–257
    overview of, 249–250
    appetite and, 251–253, 252f, 253f
    components of energy expenditure, 253–256,
        254f, 255t
    estimating energy requirements, 256–257
    leptin and ghrelin, 284–286
Energy density, **8**–9
    comparing foods, 9f
    obesity and, 287, 569
    for weight gain, 308
    for weight loss, 296–297, 297f, 298
Energy metabolism, 213–236
    overview of, 214–218
    acetyl CoA. See Acetyl CoA
    aerobic vs. anaerobic, **220**, 485, 485t, 490
    alcohol and, C-15, C-16f
    amino acids, 194, 224–226, 225f, 226f, 231f,
        347f, C-11, C-12f
    ATP. See ATP (adenosine triphosphate)
    basal metabolism and, 254–256, 254f, 255t
    B vitamins and, 326, 327, 328, 333–334, 335,
        347–348, 347f
    carbohydrates, 114f, 115–116, 219–222, C-10
        to C-11, C-14f, C-15t
    central pathways, 231f
    copper and, 458n
    electron transport chain. See Electron transport
        chain (ETC)
    energy balance and, 230, 232–236
    exercise: ATP and CP, 484–485, 485t
    exercise: fat, 485t, 489
    exercise: gender and EER, 257
    exercise: glucose/glycogen, 485–488,
        485t, 486f
    exercise: protein, 486f, 490–491, 491t
    exercise: specific activities, 255t, F-1 to F-6t
    exercise: weight loss, 300
    fasting, effects of, 233–236, 234f, 235f
    fats. See Fat metabolism; Oxidation (of fats)
    feasting, effects of, 232–233

final steps of, 227–230
    glucose, 112, 114f, 115–116, 219–222,
        219f–222f, 228n, 231f
    glycerol, 222, 224f, C-10
    hormonal regulation of, A-5 to A-6
    iron-deficiency anemia, 447
    of lean tissue, 254
    magnesium and, 424
    metabolic water, 398–399, 399t
    nutrient use summary, 226, 227t
    oxidation-reduction reactions, B-7f, B-7 to B-8
    phosphorus and, 422
    proteins, 192, 201, 490, 491t
    pyruvate. See Pyruvate
    TCA cycle. See TCA (Krebs) cycle
    thyroid hormones and, 455
    uncoupling proteins, 286
    vitamins and, 347–348, 347f
    weight changes and, 283, 300, 305
    white vs. brown adipose tissue, 286
    See also kCalories (kcal)
Energy restriction (and longevity), 596–597
Energy-yielding nutrients, **7**–11, 9t, 18,
    217–218
See also specific nutrients
Enriched (foods), **50**–52
See also Fortified (enriched) foods
Enterogastrones, **87**
Enterohepatic circulation
    of bile, 149, 151f
    of folate, 338
    of vitamin B₁₂, 343
Enterokinase, 186n
Enteropancreatic circulation, **452**, 453f
Enteropeptidase, 186f
Environmental consciousness
    "ecological footprint," 719, 719f
    energy and food production, 717–720, 719f
    food choices and, 4–5, 711–713
    genetic engineering, 695–696, 697t
    global vs. local food, 719–720
    websites on, 697, 720
Environmental contaminants, 674–677
    agriculture and, 716–717
    bioaccumulation, 675f, 676
    cancer risk and, 642–643, 644t
    dioxins, 538, **686**
    heavy metals, **463**. See also specific metals
    hunger and overpopulation, 708f, 709–710
    infant formulas and, 536
    manganese, 459–460
    mercury, 159, 174, 531, 675–676, 675f,
        676–677
    PBB and PCB, 676
    pregnancy and, 531
    See also Lead
Environmental Protection Agency (EPA), **664**,
    676, 678, 680, 688
Enzymes, **190**
    alcohol/drug metabolism, 240, 241, 242
    in breast milk, 552
    carbohydrate digestion, 77, 108, 109f, 110
    coenzymes and, 216, 327f
    copper-requiring, 458, 458n
    digestion of, 77, 185
    fat digestion. See Lipases
    free radicals and, 391, 391n
    functions of, 190, 191t, 216, 216
    gastric, 77, 149
    of intestinal cells, 77, 81
    lactose intolerance and, 110–111
    lecithinase, 145
    mechanism of action, 190f
    metalloenzymes, **452**, 452n, 462
    pancreatic. See Pancreatic enzymes
    protein digestion and, 77, 185, 186f
    renin, **401**

salivary, 76f, 77
    in supplements, 364
    zinc-requiring, 452
    See also Coenzymes
Eosinophilia myalgia syndrome (EMS), 203
EPA. See Eicosapentaenoic acid; Environmental
    Protection Agency
Ephedra, 290, 657t, 658
Ephedrine, 290, 291t
Epidemic, 282, **283**
Epidemiological studies, 13f, 14t
Epigenetics, **189**, **207**, 208–209
Epiglottis, **72**, 73, 73f
Epinephrine, **114**
    exercise and, 489
    functions of, A-5
    as a medication, 566
    stress, reaction to, 114, 114f
    synthesis of, 194
Epithelial cells, **371**
Epithelial tissues, **371**, 373–374
Ergocalciferol, **377**
See also Vitamin D
Ergogenic aids, **503**–507
Erythrocyte hemolysis, **382**, 383n
Erythrocyte protoporphyrin, **446**, E-20t, E-21t
Erythrocytes. See Red blood cells
Erythropoietin, **A-3**, A-6
Escherichia coli, 665t, 666
Esophageal sphincter, **72**, 73f, 74, 76, 76f
Esophagus, **72**, 73f, 74
Essential nutrients, **7**
    conditionally essential nutrients, 156,
        183, 345
    essential amino acids, 182t, **183**, 195,
        196, D-1t
    essential fatty acids, **154**–155, 154f, 520
    water as, 397
Estimated Average Requirement (EAR), 16–**17**,
    17f, 18f, 19, 21f
Estimated Energy Requirement (EER), **18**, 257,
    F-2t, inside front cover
Estrogen replacement therapy, 434
Estrogens, **A-3**, A-7
    adipose tissue and, 266
    breast cancer and, 266, 643
    contraceptives and lactation, 537
    fat cell metabolism, 282
    grapefruit juice and, 617t
    heart disease risk, 628
    osteoporosis and, 434
    phytoestrogens, 434, **469**–470, 470t, 472f
    selective estrogen-receptor modulator
        (SERM), 434n
Ethanol (ethyl alcohol). See Alcohol
Ethnic foods, 4, 46, 46t, 61
Ethyl alcohol. See Alcohol
Evening primrose oil, 658t
Exchange lists, **47**–48, G-1 to G-11
    Canadian system, I-1, I-8t to I-11t
    carbohydrates and, 48, G-1t, G-6t
    combination foods, G-11t
    controlling energy and fat, G-2
    diet planning, 48, G-3t
    fat, 48, G-1t, G-2, G-8t, G-9t
    food group plans and, 47–48
    free foods, G-10t
    fruit, G-1t, G-3t, G-5t
    labels and, G-2f
    meat/meat substitutes, 47, G-1t, G-3t, G-8t
    milk, 47, G-1t, G-3t, G-5t
    protein and, 47
    starch, 48, G-1, G-1t, G-4t
    vegetables, 48, G-1t, G-3t, G-7t
    websites on, 61
Exercise, defined, **477**
See also Athletes; Physical activity

Exocrine glands, **78**, A-4f
Exogenous protein, **193**
Experimental groups, 12, **14**
Experiments. *See* Research
Extracellular fluid, **398**, 399f
Eyes. *See* Vision

F

Facilitated diffusion, 81f, 108
Fad diets, **290**, 315–321, 316t, 317t, 320t
   See also Quackery/quacks
FAD (flavin adenine dinucleotide), 328, **329**,
   330f, 347f, 348, C-5f
Faith healing, **653**
Falling, 431, 595
False negative, **354**
False positive, **354**
Famine, **705**–706, 706f
   See also Hunger, chronic/world
FAO (Food and Agricultural Organization), 19,
   26, 121, **664**
   See also WHO
Farming. *See* Agriculture
FAS. *See* Fetal alcohol syndrome
Fast foods
   adolescents and, 578
   nutrient composition of, H-58 to H-77
   overeating, 287
   salt/sodium in, 456
   trans fats in, 159, 177
   vitamin A and, 376
Fasting
   alcohol metabolism and, 240
   carbohydrates and, 234, 234f
   effects of, 233–236, 234f
   fat metabolism during, 156, 234f, 235
   health and, 597
   ketosis and, 156, 235, 235f
   proteins (body) and, 234–235, 234f, 240
   See also Anorexia nervosa; Eating disorders;
      Malnutrition; Starvation
Fat cells. *See* Adipose tissue
Fat-free foods, 296
Fat-free milk, **53**
Fatigue, causes of, 348, 447, 448
Fat metabolism
   overview of, 155–156, 222–223, 223f, 224f
   acid-base balance, 113
   carbohydrates and, 226, 228n
   fasting and, 156
   genetics and, 210
   ketone bodies and, 113
   lipoprotein lipase, **155**, 282–283
   liver and, 215t
   on low-kcalorie diet, 235
   oxidation/TCA cycle, 228n, 231f
   synthesis of fatty acids, 222
   See also Fats (chemistry); Oxidation (of fats)
Fat replacers, **164**–165
Fats, artificial, **164**–165
Fats, defined, **139**
Fats (blood lipids). *See* Atherosclerosis; Blood
   lipid profiles; Cholesterol (blood);
   Chylomicrons; HDL; LDL; Lipoproteins;
   Triglycerides; VLDL
Fats (body), 153–155
   abdominal fat/central obesity, 243, **262**–263,
      262f, 263f, 265, 301–302, 630
   adipose tissue, **155**–156, 155f, 266, 282–283,
      283f, 284, 286
   alcohol and, 240, 241, 241f, 243
   from amino acids/protein, 194, 225, 227t
   in athletes, 258, 259, 261–262
   calcium and, 416
   from carbohydrates/glucose, 113, 120, 156,
      222, 227t, 232, 233
   chronic diseases and, 262, 263f, 265–266

dietary fat and, 150, 155, 227t
distribution of, 260–263, 260f, 262f, 263f, E-16t
energy, using for, 156, 156n, 489
energy balance and, 249–250
estrogen and, 266
exercise and, 301–302, 489
fasting, effects of, 234f, 235
functions of, 145, 153–155, 262
glycolipids, 112
health risks, 263–266, 263n
kcalories (kcal) in, 156, 156n, 249–250, 489
longevity and, 597
measurement of, 261, 263, 264f, E-14 to
   E-16, E-16t
storage of, 139, 150, 155–156, 232, 282, 283f
upper-body, **262**–263, 263f
white *vs.* brown adipose tissue, 286
   See also Body composition; Body mass index
      (BMI); Obesity; Overweight
Fats (chemistry), 139–144
   diglycerides, **147**
   elements in, 7t
   firmness of, 142
   glucose produced from, 156
   hydrogenation of, **143**, 144f
   kcalories (kcal) in, 9t
   monoglycerides, **147**, 151f
   oxidation of. *See* Oxidation (of fats)
   phospholipids, **145**–146, 146f
   stability/rancidity, 143
   sterols, **146**–147, 146n, 147f
   structure of, 139–144, 140f–146f, 141t, C-3t
   synthesis from protein, 194
   terminology of, **141**
   types of, listed, 147
   See also Fat metabolism; Fatty acids
Fats (dietary), **139**, 141–177
   absorption of, 83, 149–150, 152f
   alternatives to, 164–165
   body's use of, 227t
   in breast milk, 550, 550f
   in breast milk *vs.* formula, 553f
   calculation of personal allowance, 165
   in Canadian food groups, I-11t
   cancer and, 159–160, 645
   for children, 554, 560, 588–589
   cooking with, 157, 163
   degree of saturation in foods, 141t, 144f
   diabetes and, 641
   Dietary Guidelines and, 40t
   digestion of, 78, 79f, 80t, 88, 147–149,
      148f, 151f
   discretionary kcalories and, 45, 161
   emulsification by bile, 78, 88, 148f, 149, 150f
   energy (kcal) in, 9t, 156, 156n, 160, 165–167,
      229–230
   in exchange lists, 48, G-1t, G-3t, G-9t
   for exercise, 488–489
   in fad diets, 315–316
   in fast foods, 159, 177, 287
   in fish, 158–159, 158f, 159t, 174
   food sources, 157f, 161–167, 162f, 166f
   in formulas, 553f
   fried foods and carcinogens, 644–645
   health benefits from, 158–159, 172–175
   heart disease and, 633. *See under*
      Cardiovascular disease (CVD)
   in high-protein diets, 319
   hydrogenated, 166f, 175
   for infants/toddlers, 548, 554, 556
   intake recommendations, 18, 160–167,
      172–177, 175f, 176t, 489
   intestinal motility and, 88
   "invisible," 163
   on labels, 57, 58, **58**, 58n, 165–167, 166f
   in low-carbohydrate diets, 318–319
   in meats, 53, 65, 162, 162f, 175, 177, G-8t

in milk and milk products, 53, 162, 162f, G-5t
monounsaturated. *See* Monounsaturated fats
   obesity and, 160, 315–316
   for older adults, 602
   overeating and, 232, 233, 234f
   phospholipids, **145**–146, 146f, 149
   polyunsaturated. *See* Polyunsaturated fats
   protein-sparing action of, **112**
   rancidity, 143
   recommendations for reducing, 161–167
   satiating effect of, 252, 253f
   saturated. *See* Saturated fats
   sterols, **146**
   storage of, 155–156, 230
   trans-. *See* Fatty acids, *trans*-
   transport of, 83, 149–150, 150–153, 152f, 153f
   unsaturated fatty acids, 141t, 142f, 144f,
      176t, C-3t
   in USDA Food Guide, 43f, 44, 47f
   in vegetarian diets, 65, 66, 67
   websites on, 168
   weight gain and low-fat foods, 296
   for weight gain plans, 308
   for weight loss plans, 295t, 296, 296t, 297f, 298
   See also Diets, high-fat; Fatty acids
Fat-soluble vitamins. *See* Vitamins, fat-soluble
Fat substitutes, 164–165
Fatty acids, **140**–142
   arachidonic acid, **154**, 154f, 155, 550
   in breast milk, 550
   chemistry of, 154–155, 154f, C-3t
   cis-, 143, 145f
   deficiencies, 154, 155
   DHA (docosahexaenoic acid), **154**, 159t,
      174, 550
   effect of alcohol on, 240, 241, 241f
   EPA (eicosapentaenoic acid), **154**, 159n,
      159t, 174
   essential, **154**–155, 154f, 520. *See also* Linoleic
      acid; Linolenic acid
   exercise and, 489
   fish oil, 158–159, 174, 605
   medium-chain, 140, 152f
   metabolism of. *See* Fat metabolism
   monounsaturated. *See* Monounsaturated fats
   oxidation of. *See* Oxidation of fats
   polyunsaturated. *See* Polyunsaturated fatty
      acids (PUFA)
   saturated. *See* Saturated fats
   structure of, 140–144, 140f–146f, 141t, 230f
   synthesis of, 154, 222
   trans-. *See* Fatty acids, *trans*-
   unsaturated, **141**, 142–144, 144f
Fatty acids, omega-3, **142**
   bone density and, 436
   cancer risk and, 160, 645
   chemistry of, 154
   deficiency of, 155
   eggs enriched with, 158
   fetal development and, 520
   in fish, 174, 676, 677
   food sources, 67, 141t, 144f, 158, 159t, 176t
   health benefits from, 158–159, 174
   health risks from, 159
   heart disease and, 158, 627, 632t, 677
   intake recommendations, 158–159
   macular degeneration and, 605
   in Mediterranean diet, 177
   in range-fed meat, 162, 177, 719
   rheumatoid arthritis, 605
   structure of, 141t, 142, 142f
   in vegetarian diets, 67
Fatty acids, omega-6, **142**
   chemistry of, 154, 154f
   fetal development and, 520
   food sources, 141t, 144f, 154, 159t, 176t
   heart disease and, 159

intake recommendations, 159
structure of, 141t, 142, 142f, 154f
Fatty acids, short-chain
absorption of, 152f
cholesterol synthesis and, 162
fiber fermented by bacteria, 108, 108n, 109f, 123
structure of, 140
types of, 108n
Fatty acids, trans-, **143**–144
Daily Values and, 165
in dairy products, 143n
food industry and, 175
food sources, 157, 159, 175, 176t, 633, H-0
health risks of, 143–144, 157, 633, 645
intake in U.S., 157
intake recommendations, 159
on labels, 58, 166f
structure of, 143, 145f
Fatty liver, 198, **239**, 240, 241
Fatty streaks, 586–**587**
FDA (Food and Drug Administration), **360, 664**
additive regulations, 682–683
artificial sweeteners approved, 132, 135, 136
food labeling, 55, 59, 59t
functions of, 663, 664, 666
genetic engineering, 696
herbal supplements and, 656
infant formula regulation, 553
MedWatch program, 690
olestra on labels, 165
pesticide regulations, 678, 679
protein labeling regulations, 196
supplements, 364, 365, 442
water safety, 689
websites/address, 33, 61
weight loss products and, 291n
Feasting, 232–233, 234f
Feces, **78**
See also Constipation; Diarrhea
Feedback mechanisms, 87
Feeding Infants and Toddlers Study (FITS), 561–562
Female athlete triad, **270**, 271f
Fermentable, defined, **106**
Ferritin, **443**, 445, 446, 448
Fertility/infertility, 246t, 264, **509**, 526, 545, 676
Ferulic acid, 470n
Fetal alcohol spectrum disorder, 543, **544**
Fetal alcohol syndrome (FAS), 530, 543–545, 543f, **544**, 545f
Fetal development, 510–515
overview of, 511f
alcohol's effects on, 543–545, 543f, 545f
caffeine and, 532
choline and, 345
critical periods, **512**–515, 512f, 544
drugs, illicit and, 530
folate and, 338, 340, 340f
infant birthweight. See Birthweight
iodine and, 456
lead exposure, 531
malnutrition and, 515, 526–527
maternal weight and, 515–518, 518f
mercury exposure, 531
nutrients influencing, 514–515, 520, 522, 524
vitamin A and, 372, 532
See also Birth defects
Fetal programming, **515**
Fetus, 511f, **512**
Feverfew, 657t, 658t
Fiber, **101**
overview of, 123t
antidepressants and, 616
blood glucose levels and, 115–116
in breads/grains, 50f, 51, 51f, 122, 123, 125t
calcium absorption, 418
cancer and, 122–123, 448, 645
chemistry of, 106, 107f, C-2, C-2f to C-3f

in children's diets, 560
cholesterol and, 106, 122
constipation and, 95, 106, 122
diabetes and, 122, 123t, 640
dietary, **106**–107
digestion/fermentation of, 78, 79f, 106, 108, 108n, 109f
energy from, 108, 108n, 109
excess intake of, 123–124
food sources, 106–108, 123t, 124–127, 125t
in fruit/fruit juices, 53
functional, 106–107
functions of, 78, 106, 109f, 123t
gastrointestinal health, 122, 123, 123t
heart disease and, 122, 123t
insoluble, **106**, 123t
iron absorption, 444, 448
on labels, **58**, 126–127, 126f
mineral absorption and, 124, 444, 448
for older adults, 602
quantities in foods, 125t
recommended intake of, 124–127, 125t, 126f
satiety and, 108, 252, 286
soluble/viscous, **106**, 122, 123t, 622t
supplements, 106–107, 123
total, 107
types of, 106–107
websites on, 127
in weight control, 123
for weight loss, 295t, 297–298
Fibrin, 192, 384f
Fibrocystic breast disease, **382**
Fibrosis, **239**, 241
"Fight-or-flight," 598, A-5
See also Epinephrine
Filtered water, **400**
Fish oils
health benefits of, 159, 160
heart disease and, 159, 622t, 632t
macular degeneration and, 605
rheumatoid arthritis and, 605
supplements, 159, 159n, 531
ulcers and, 13f
Fish/seafood
bioaccumulation of toxins, 675f, 676–677
as calcium source, 417f, 420
cancer and, 644, 645
cholesterol in, 158f
environmental issues, 670, 710, 717
essential fatty acids, 158–159
fat intake and, 159
heart disease and, 158–159, 174, 622t
iodine in, 456
lipids in, 158–159, 158f, 159t, 174
mercury contamination of, 159, 174, 531, 675–676, 676–677
during pregnancy/lactation, 174, 531
regulation of, 676
safe cooking/handling of, 670–671, 670n, 671t
trans fats and, 159
tuna, 676
USDA Food Guide, 43f
"Fit and fat," 266
Fitness, **477**–501
benefits of, 478–480
guidelines for, 480–484, 480t
overweight and, 266, 288–289
program sample, 483t
websites on, 499–500
See also Athletes; Physical activity
"5 to 9 a day" campaign, 52, 52f, 61
Flavin adenine dinucleotide (FAD), 328, **329**, 330f, 347f, 348, C-5f
Flavin mononucleotide (FMN), 328, **329**, C-5f
Flavonoids, **469**, 470t, 471, 472f
Flavor enhancers, 685
Flaxseed, **469**, 470t, 472f

Flaxseed oil, 144f
Flexibility, **480**, 480t
Flora, **86**
Flours, 50f
See also Grains
Fluid balance, **190**–191
alcohol use and, 243
athletes and, 271–272, 496
diarrhea and, 93
disruption of, 406
in eating disorders, 275
exercise and, 493–496, 494t
maintaining, 190–191, 402–406, 402f, 404f, 404t, 405f
minerals/electrolytes, 404–405, 404f, 404t, 409, 413
regulation of, 409, 410
replacing losses, 406
water balance, **398**–401, 399f, 399t
See also Electrolytes
Fluorapatite, **460**
Fluoridated water, 460–461, 461f, 689
Fluoride, 460–461, 461f, 461t, 464t, 551, 551t
Fluorosis, **460**–461, 461f
Fluoxetine (Prozac) for bulimia nervosa, 276
FMN (flavin mononucleotide), 328, **329**, C-5f
Folate, **338**–342, 356t
overview of, 342t
absorption/activation, 338, 339f
alcohol abuse and, 243–244
bioavailability, 338, 340
birth defects and, 338, 340, 340f, 514–515
cancer and, 341
deficiency, 338–341, 342t, 553, 617
dietary folate equivalents (DFE), **338**, 339
enterohepatic circulation of, 338
food sources, 341, 342f, 342t
in fortified foods, 51, 51f, 340, 340f, 340n, 514–515
functions of, 338, 340–341
gene expression and, 208, 209f
heart disease and, 340–341
medication antagonists, 617, 617n
methotrexate and, 617, 617f
pregnancy and, 338, 340, 514–515, 520, 521f
RDA/recommendations, 338, 342f, 514
serum levels, E-22, E-22t
structure of, 339f, 617f, C-7f
supplements, 338, 340, 514
vitamin B_{12} and, 340, 341, 343–344, 344f
Folate deficiency anemia, 341, E-20t, E-22, E-22t
Folic acid. See Folate
Follicle-stimulating hormone (FSH), **A-4**
Follicle-stimulating hormone releasing hormone (FSH-RH), **A-4**, A-5
Follicular hyperkeratosis, 373f
Fontanel, **381f**
Food allergies. See Allergies
Food and Agricultural Organization. See FAO
Food and Drug Administration (FDA). See FDA (Food and Drug Administration)
Food and Nutrition Board, 16n
Food assistance programs
for older adults, 608–609
in schools, 573–575, 574t
in the U.S., 703–704
websites/addresses, 712t, 713
WIC, 527, 529, 536, 539
Food aversion (during pregnancy), **525**
Food banks, **704**
Food biotechnology, **693**–697
Foodborne Diseases Active Surveillance Network (FoodNet), 666n
Foodborne illnesses, **664**–673
botulism, 118n, **556**, 556n, 665t, 666, 671
Dietary Guidelines and, 40t
food industry and, 666, 667f

Foodborne illnesses, *continued*
  in infants, 556, 557
  in older adults, 610
  during pregnancy, 531
  preventing, 531, 665t, 666, 667–671, 667f, 669t, 671t
  safety hotlines, 670
  symptoms of, 664, 665t
  travelers and, 672, 673
  types/sources of, 665t
  viruses, 665t, 669
  websites on, 667f, 690
Food chain, **675,** 676
Food choices
  hunger and environmentalism, 711–713
  motivations for, 3–5
  for older adults, 607–611
  See also Diet planning
"Food combining" myth, 81–82
Food composition, 6, 7t, 9, 250–251
Food composition data, 266, H-0 to H-77t
Food craving (during pregnancy), **525**
Food frequency questionnaire, **E-4**
Food group plans, **41**–53
  Canadian, I-2f to I-7f
  for children, 561f
  energy and, 41, 41t, 44, 44t
  ethnic foods in, 46, 46t
  exchange lists and, 47–48
  exchange lists combined with, G-3t, G-3 to G-4
  miscellaneous foods in, 43f
  mixtures of foods in, 46
  MyPyramid, 47, 47f, 65–66, 66f, 561f
  nutrient density and, 42f–43f, 45
  USDA Food Guide, 42f–43f
Food Guide Pyramid. *See* MyPyramid
Food-hypersensitivity reactions, **565**
  See also Allergies
Food industry
  added sugars, 117–121
  additives, **682**–687
  advertising, 287, 569
  antioxidants, 143, 354, 684
  artificial sweeteners, 132–135, 133t, 134f, 135t
  emulsifiers, 145
  energy use by, 717
  fat replacers, **164**–165
  fiber supplements, 106–107
  foodborne illnesses, 666, 667f
  functional foods, **5,** 471, 472
  genetic engineering, **693**–697, 697t
  health claims on labels, 59, 59t
  healthy choices, 5, 164, 177
  hydrogenation of fats, 143, 175
  irradiation of foods, 672–673
  sugar replacers used, 136, 136t, 137f
  supplements, 203, 364, 390, 461, 503
  trans-fatty acids, 175, 177
  tropical oils, 142, 175
  See also Fast foods; Processed foods
Food insecurity, **702,** 703
Food insufficiency, **702**
Food intake. *See* Appetite; Diet history; Hunger
Food intolerances, **566**
  See also Allergies
Food intoxications, 665t, 666
Food labeling. *See* Labeling
Food pantries, **704**
Food poisoning, **664**
  See also Foodborne illnesses
Food poverty, **702**
Food production. *See* Agriculture
Food records, 304f, **E-4**
Food recovery, **704**
Foods, **3**
  as alternative medicines, 655

"healing powers" of, 469–473
  vs. supplements, 19, 349, 363, 365, 392–393, 471, 604
Foods, functional, **5, 469,** 471–473
Food safety concerns. *See* Environmental contaminants; Foodborne illnesses; Safety; Toxicity
Food Safety Inspection Service (FSIS), 666n
Food security, **702**
Food Stamp Program, 703–704
Food substitutes, **53**
Food Surveys Research Group website, 26
Formaldehyde, 134
Formulas. *See* Infant formulas
Fortified (enriched) foods, **50**–52
  baby foods, 556
  "biofortification," 694
  bread/grains, 50–51, 51f, 340, 340n, 450, 514
  breakfast cereals, 51–52
  calcium, 420
  eggs/omega-3 fatty acids, 159
  folate, 51, 51f, 340, 340f, 340n, 514–515
  for infants, 67
  iodized salt, 456
  iron, 50, 51f, 448, 450, 556
  margarine, 471, 472, 472n, 633
  milk: vitamin A, 53, 375, 375n
  milk: vitamin D, 53, 330, 330n, 379, 379n
  nutrient additives, 685
  soy "milk," 53
  for vegans, 67
  vitamin B₁₂, 67
  vitamin D, 418
  See also Functional foods
Fosamax, 434n
Fossil fuels, **709,** 717, 719f
Foxglove, 655f, 657, 658
Fraud, 30, **32,** 33, 34, 34f
  See also Information on nutrition, validity of; Quackery/quacks
Free radicals, **351, 390**
  in aging, 597
  Alzheimer's disease and, 606–607
  atherosclerosis, 627
  cancer and, 444
  chemical reactions of, 390–392, 391f, B-8
  copper and, 458
  disease and, 390–392
  iron and, 444, 445
  oxygen-derived, 390, 390n, 391
  vitamin C and, 351, 351f, 352, 391, 392
  vitamin E and, 382, 391, 392
  zinc and, 452
  See also Antioxidants; Oxidative stress
Frequency (of exercise), **480**
Fructose, **103**
  absorption of, 108, 110f
  body fat and, 120
  metabolism of, C-10
  structure of, 102n, 103f
  sweetness of, 103, 116
Fruit juices, 617
  in exchange lists, G-5t
  grapefruit, 617, 617t
  for infants/children, 553, 556
  intake recommendations, 42f, 53
  tooth decay and, 553
Fruits
  antioxidants in, 391–392, 393
  in Canadian food groups, I-9t
  cancer and, 392, 470, 643, 644t, 645, 646t
  carbohydrate content of, 126
  dental caries and, 119
  discretionary kcalories and, 45
  dried, 65, 119
  in exchange lists, G-1t, G-3t, G-5t
  fat intake and, 162–163

fiber content of, 125t
  "5 to 9 a day" campaign, 52f
  in food group plans, 41t, 42f, 46t, 47f, 48t, 52–53, I-4f
  glycemic index of, 116f
  heart disease and, 392, 471, 630, 633
  nutrient density, 39, 119
  nutrients in, 42f, 65
  phytochemicals in, 471, 472f
  sugar content, 119, 126
  websites on, 52f, 61
FSH (follicle-stimulating hormone), **A-4**
FSH/LH-releasing hormone (FSH/LH-RH), A-5
FTC (Federal Trade Commission), 365
Fuel, **213**
Functional foods, **5, 469,** 471–473
  See also Fortified (enriched) foods; Phytochemicals

G

Galactose, **103**
  absorption of, 108–109, 110f
  metabolism of, 219f, C-10
  structure of, 103f, 104f, C-2f, C-3f
Gallbladder, **72**
  anatomy of GI tract, 73f, 74
  fat digestion and, 78, 88, 148f, 149
  See also Bile
Gallbladder disease, 478
Gamma-linolenic acid, 154n
Gamma-oryzanol, **504**
Gangrene, **640**
Gardening, 712
Garlic, 472f, 657t, 658t
Gas, intestinal, 95–96, 97t
Gastric acidity, 77, 87, 97, 413, A-6
Gastric glands, 77, **78**
Gastric juices, 75, 77, **78**
Gastric lipase, 148f, 149
Gastrin, **87,** 88t, A-6
Gastritis, atrophic, **343,** 599
Gastroenteritis, 665t
Gastrointestinal reflux, **94,** 96–97, 96f, 97t
Gastrointestinal reflux disease (GERD), **94**
Gastrointestinal tract. *See* GI (gastrointestinal) tract
Gatekeepers, **571,** 578
Gelatin, 195
Gender differences
  alcohol intoxication, 240
  blood alcohol levels, 243t
  BMR and, 255t, 256, 257
  body composition, 6f, 260, 262, 263f, 576
  eating disorders, 271, 272, 274
  energy needs, 44t, 254, 255t, 256, 257, 577
  fat cells and LPL, 282
  heart disease risk, 628
  iron needs, 449, 576–577, 603
  iron status, 446, 448
  osteoporosis risk, 432, 433t, 436
Gene expression, **189, 207,** 208, 452
Gene pool, **286**
Generally recognized as safe (GRAS) list, **682,** 696, H-0
Genes, **207**
  See also Genetics/genes
Genetic abnormalities. *See* Birth defects; Genetic disorders
Genetically engineered (GE) foods, 566, **693**–697
Genetically modified (GM) foods, **693**–697
Genetic disorders
  disease and, 209–210
  Down syndrome, 340, **530**
  hemophilia, **384**
  intrinsic factor and, 343
  iron overload, 448
  Menkes disease, 459

phenylketonuria (PKU), 134–135, 183, **207**, 209
Prader-Willi syndrome, 284, 285
sickle-cell anemia, **189**, 189f
Wilson's disease, 459
Genetic engineering, 687, **693**–697, 694f, 697t
Genetics/genes, **207**
cancer risk and, 642
chromosomes, **A-2**
chronic disease risks, 625, 625f, 647
diabetes, type 1, 115
diabetes, type 2, 638
energy restriction and, 596
epigenetics, **189**
fetal programming, **515**
gene expression, **189, 207**, 208
health history and, 20
heart disease risk, 210, 586, 628
hypertension and, 634–635
lifestyle, synergistic with, 625
lipoproteins and, 152
loss of diversity in food crops, 710, 717
obesity and, 284–285, 316t, 567, 597
ob gene (obesity), 283, 285f
osteoporosis risk, 435
protein synthesis and, 189
sequencing errors, 187, 189
single nucleotide polymorphisms, 210
See also DNA
Genetic test kits, 207
Genistein, 470t
Genome/genomics, **11, 207**, 208–209, **647**
Genomics, nutritional, **11, 207**–211
DRI and, 16
during fetal development, 515
genetic variation and disease, 209–210
health care ramifications, 210, 647
lipoproteins, 152, 210
protein synthesis and, 189
"slow-aging" and energy intake, 597
See also Genetics/genes
Genotoxicants, 686
Geophagia, **447**, 525, 653
Germanium, 656
Germ (of grains), 50, **50f**
Gestation, **512**
Gestational diabetes, **528**, 539
GHIH (somatostatin), **A-5**
GH-releasing hormone (GRH), **A-4**
Ghrelin, **285**–286, 292
GH (somatotropin), **A-5**
Giardiasis, 665t
GI (gastrointestinal) tract, **72**–89
alcohol abuse and, 244
anatomy of, 72–76, 73f, 75f, 76f, 78f, 79f, 81–83, 82f
carbohydrate digestion in, 87, 108, 109f
cell replacement, 6, 190
in eating disorders, 273, 275
fat digestion in, 148f
fiber and, 78, 122–123
fiber and carbohydrates, 107–108, 109f, 122
fluids and electrolyte balance, 406
folate and, 339f
hormones produced in, 86–88, 88t, A-6 to A-7
hunger and, 251
in infants, 552
lymphatic system and, 82, 83, 84–85, 84f
in older adults, 599
problems with, 92–98, 97t, 123, 123t, 165, 343. *See also* Constipation; Diarrhea; Foodborne illnesses; Heartburn; Vomiting
promoting health of, 86, 88–89, 123t
protective factors, 77, 78
protein digestion in, 186f
regulation of, 86–89, 88t

secretions of, 76–78, 76f, 86–88
vitamin A and, 371, 373–374
websites on, 90, 98
See also Absorption; Colon (large intestine); Digestion; Intestinal bacteria; Small intestines
Ginger, 657t, 658t
Ginkgo biloba, 654f, 657t, 658
Ginseng, 654f, 657t, 658t
Glands, **78**, 80t, A-3 to A-7, A-4f
See also specific glands
Gliomas, **642**
Glossitis, 330n, 333n, 349f
Glucagon, **113**
function of, 113, 114, 191t, A-5
secretion of, 113n, 114f
Glucocorticoids, **A-4**, A-5
Glucogenic amino acids, 194n, 221f, 225, 225f
Gluconeogenesis, **112**
biotin and, 334
glycerol and, 156, 222, 223
proteins/amino acids and, 112, 192, 194, 225, 225f, 234–235
Glucosamine, 606
Glucose, **102**, 111–117
absorption of, 108–109, 110f, 122. *See also* Glycemic index; Glycemic response
chemistry of, 102–103
conversion to fat, 113, 222, 227t
depletion of, 487
in diabetes, 639–640, 639f
energy content of, 230
exercise and, 485–488, 485t, 486f
fasting, effects of, 232–233, 234f
function of, 111–112
liver and, 105n, 107, 110f, 113, 114, 215t, 221
metabolism of, 114f, 115–116, 219–222, 219f–222f, 233, C-15t
in polysaccharides, 106f
produced from fat/glycerol, 156, 222
produced from lactate, 220f, 221, 487
produced from proteins/amino acids, 112, 192, 194, 225, 225f, 234–235
produced from pyruvate, 220
in sports drinks, 495
storage of. *See* Glycogen
structure of, 102f–104f, 230f, C-1f
See also Blood glucose levels; Carbohydrates; Gluconeogenesis
Glucose polymers, **495**
Glucose tolerance, impaired, **637**
Glucose tolerance factor (GTF), **461**
Glucuronic acid, C-3f
Glutamate, folate and, 338, 339f
Glutathione peroxidase, 391n
Glycemic index, **115**–116, 116f, 316, 488
Glycemic response, **115**–116, 136, 640
Glycerol, **142**
absorption of, 152f
glucose from, 222, 223
metabolism of, 222–223, 224f, C-10
structure of, 142f, 143f
Glycine, 182f
Glycobiology, 112
Glycogen, **105**
as energy storage, 105, 112, 114f, 486–488
exercise and, 485–488, 488t
glucagon and, 113, 114f
liver and, 105n, 112, 114f
low-carbohydrate diets and, 319
metabolism of, 215f, 347f
structure of, 105, 106f, C-2
Glycogen depletion, 319, 487, 490
Glycogen loading, **487**
Glycogen super compensation, **487**
Glycolipids, 112

Glycolysis, **219**–222
ATP produced, 219f–222f, 222, C-15n, C-15t
location of reactions, A-2n
pathways, 219f–222f, C-10f
Glycoproteins, 112, 639
GM foods, **693**–697, 694f, 697t
Goat's milk, 341, 553
Goblet cells, **80**, 82f, 371, 373
Goiters, 13f, **456**, 456f
Goitrogens, **456**, 677
Goldberger, Joseph, 332n, 357
Goldenseal, 657t
Golgi apparatus, **A-2**, A-3, A-3f
Gout, 354, **606**
Government policies, hunger and, 703–704, 711
Government resources
safety hotlines, 670, 680
websites, 26, 33, 61, 499–500
WIC, 527, 529, 539
See also FDA; USDA
Grains, 50–51
breakfast cereals, 51–52, 412, 412f, 555–556
in Canadian food groups, I-8t, I-9t
carbohydrate content of, 125, 126f
corn, 332, 693
discretionary kcalories and, 45
in exchange lists, G-4t
fat intake and, 162–163
fiber content, 50f, 51f, 51, 125t, 126f
flours, types of, 50f
folate fortification, 51, 51f, 340, 340n, 514
in food group plans, 41t, 42f, 47f, 48t, 49f
glycemic index of, 116f
iron content, 449, 450
meat production and, 717f, 718
nutrients in, 42f, 50–51, 50f, 51f
phytates in, 409
proteins, complementary, 196f
refined/enriched, **50**–51, 50f, 51f, 449, 450
in USDA Food Guide, 41t, 46t, 48t
wheat, 50–51, 50f
whole. *See* Grains, whole
See also Breads
Grains, whole, **50**, 51f
cancer and, 645, 646t
for children, 559
diabetes and, 122, 640
fiber content, 50f, 51f, 123, 125t, 126f
heart disease and, 630, 633
nutrients in, 50, 51f
in USDA Food Guide, 42f, 47f
wheat plant, 50f
Grapefruit juice, 617, 617t
Grapes, 472f
GRAS (generally recognized as safe) list, **682**, 696, H-0
Grocery shopping
diet planning and, 48–53
environmental issues, 712, 717–720, 717f, 718t, 719f
fat intake and, 161–167, 166f
food labels and, 54–61, 54f, 60t, 166f
for older adults, 600, 608, 609–611
thrifty meals, 610, 704
See also Cooking/food preparation
Growth
during adolescence, 575–576, 577
bone development, 372, 421f, 435–436
energy needs during, 256, 547–549, 558–559, 576
of infants, 547–549, 547f
iron deficiency and, 446
malnutrition and, 198, 453f, 562
measurement of, E-6 to E-7, E-6f to E-13f
obesity and, 569
phosphorus and, 422
protein and, 190, 548–549

Growth, *continued*
  vitamin A and, 372
  vitamin D and, 37f, 377
  zinc deficiency, 453, 453f
  See also Fetal development
Growth charts, 548f, E-8f to E-13f
Growth hormone (GH), 191t, **A-4**
GTF (glucose tolerance factor), **461**
Guidelines for Healthy Eating (Canada), 40t
Gums (fiber), 106n, 685

H

Habit and food choice, 4, 304
  See also Lifestyle choices
Hair, E-17t
Hard liquor, 238, **239**, 244t
Hard water, **400**
Hazard Analysis Critical Control Points
  (HACCP), **666**
Hazards, **663**
  See also Safety
HCl. *See* Hydrochloric acid (HCl)
HDL (high-density lipoprotein), **152**
  blood levels, 156, 157, 628t
  composition of, 151n, 153f
  DASH eating plan, 636
  function of, 152
  heart disease risk, 152, 628t, 629, 631
  LDL ratio to, 152, 629
  in obese children, 587
  size and density of, 153f
  trans-fatty acids and, 157
Head circumference, E-7
Health
  overview of, 24–25
  body composition and, 258–266, 260f, 263f,
    264f. *See also under* Obesity
  food choices for, 5
  status. *See* Nutrition assessment; Nutrition
    status
  strategies for older adults, 608t
  websites, 648
  See also Disease
Health Canada website, 33
Health care professionals
  in alternative health, 652, 659
  certified lactation consultants, 534
  dietetic technicians, **32**
  dietitian career descriptions, 32
  nutrition education of, 31, 32
  nutritionists, **32**
  physicians, 31
  public health dietitians, **32**
  registered dietitians, **19, 32**
  websites for, 33, 34
Health claims, **59**
  food choices and, 5
  on food labels, 59, 59t
  on supplement labels, 364
  See also Information on nutrition, validity of
Health history, 20–21, 22f, **E-2**, E-2t
Healthy People 2010, **23**, 23t, 26, 532, J-1t to J-2t
Heart attacks, **626**
  blood cholesterol and, 13f, 157
  C-reactive protein and, 627
  death rate, 628
  mechanism of, 627–628
  obesity and, 265
  plaque and, 629
  See also Cardiovascular disease (CVD)
Heartburn, **94**
  causes of, 77, 96–97
  during pregnancy, 524t, 525
  preventing, 97t
Heart disease. *See* Cardiovascular disease (CVD)
Heart rate, 482
Heat cramps, 495

Heat energy
  ATP and, 216
  generation of, 253–254
  kcalorie as unit of, **7**–9, 250
  white *vs.* brown adipose tissue, 286
Heat stroke, **493**–494
Heavy metals, **463**
  See also specific metals
Height measurement, E-6, E-6f
Heimlich maneuver, 92, 93f, **94**
Helicobacter pylori, 97, 98, 343
Hematocrit, **446**, E-20, E-20t, E-21f
Heme iron, **443**–444, 444f
Hemicelluloses, 106n, C-2f to C-3f
Hemochromatosis, **448**
Hemoglobin, **184**
  copper and, 458
  function of, 184
  in iron deficiency, 446, E-19 to E-20, E-20t, E-21t
  iron in, 184f, 443–444
  in sickle-cell anemia, 189, 189f
  structure of, 184f
Hemolytic anemia, **382**
Hemophilia, **384**
Hemorrhagic disease, **384**
Hemorrhoids, 94, **94**, 122, 525
Hemosiderin, **445**, 448
Hemosiderosis, **448**
Hepatic portal vein, **83**, 85f
Hepatic vein, **83**, 85f
Hepatitis, 665t
Hepatitis A virus, 670
Hepcidin, **445**, 448
Herbal medicines/supplements, 655–659
  for athletes, 505
  dosage, 657
  herbal medicines, **653**
  herb-drug interactions, 657–658, 658t
  labeling of, 657, 658
  lactation and, 537
  "natural" *vs.* safe, 34f, 656
  obesity treatment, 290, 291t
  precautions, 656t, 657t, 658t
  during pregnancy, 530
  websites on, 659
Herbal sterols, 505
Heredity. *See* Genetics/genes
Herpes, 203
Hesperidin, 346
Heterocyclicamines, 644n
Hexoses, **102**
hGH (human growth hormone), **503**, 506
Hiccups, 94, 96
High blood pressure. *See* Hypertension
High-carbohydrate diets. *See* Diets, high-
  carbohydrate
High-density lipoprotein. *See* HDL
High potency, **360**, 361, 364
High-quality protein, **195**
High-risk pregnancy, **525**–532, 526t
Histamine, **352**
Historical data (in nutrition assessment), 20–21,
  22f, E-1 to E-5, E-2t
HIV (human immunodeficiency virus), 536–537,
  623–624, 624t
HMB (beta-hydroxy-beta-methylbutyrate), **504**
Homeopathy, **653**
Homeostasis, **86**
  blood glucose, 113, 114f
  calcium, 417–418, 417f
  nervous system and, A-7 to A-8
  potassium, 414
  set-point theory and, 283
  water balance, 398, 401
  See also Acid-base balance; Electrolytes
Homocysteine
  alcohol abuse and, 244

  folate and, 340–341
  heart disease risk, 199, 340–341, 628–629
Honey, **118**
  botulism risk, 118n, 556, 671
  fructose in, 102
  nutrients in, 118–119, 118t
Hormonal athletic supplements, 505–506, 506t
Hormones, **87, A-4**
  overview of, A-3 to A-7, A-4f
  blood glucose levels and, 113–114, 114f
  blood pressure and, 401–402, A-6
  bone remodeling, 416, 417, 417f, 432
  calcium balance and, 416, 417f, A-6
  changes with age, 598n
  cholesterol in synthesis of, 147
  energy metabolism and, A-5 to A-6
  fat storage and, 416
  functions of, 190, 191n, 191t
  gastrointestinal, 86–88, 88t, 149, A-6 to A-7
  as incidental food additives, 686–687
  iron balance, 445, 448
  lactation and, 533, A-5
  nervous system and, 86–88
  obesity/appetite, 284–286
  osteoporosis and, 434–435, 434n
  pregnancy and, A-6
  proteins as, 190
  regulation of, A-4
  satiety and, 251, 252, 284–286
  sex, A-7. *See also* Estrogens; Testosterone
  stress and, A-4, A-5
  synthesis of, 147, 194
  vitamin C and, 352
  vitamin D, 377, A-6
  weight control and, 284–286
  See also Phytosterols; *specific hormones*
Hormone-sensitive lipase, **156**
Hourly sweat rate, **494**
Human genome, **207**, 211
  See also Genome/genomics
Human Genome Project, 207
Human growth hormone. *See* hGH (human
  growth hormone)
Human intervention research, 13f, 14t
Human milk. *See* Breast milk
Hunger, chronic/world, **701**–714
  in children, 197–199, 197t, 562–564, 563t
  environmental degradation and, 709–710
  food supply and, 709–710
  malnutrition, 197–199, 197t, 706–707
  overpopulation and, 707–709, 708f
  reasons for famines, 705–706, 706f
  relief organizations, 712t
  solutions, 199, 701, 703–704, 710–713
  statistics, 701, 702, 702f, 704, 706, 706f, 707
  United States, 702–705, 702f
  websites on, 713
Hunger (sensation), **251**–253
  academic performance and, 562, 563
  factors affecting, 251–253, 252f, 253f
  fiber and, 123
  protein and, 318
  smoking and, 579
  See also Appetite; Satiety
Husk, **50f**
Hydration. *See* Dehydration
Hydrochloric acid (HCl), **78**
  acid-base balance, 413, 413n
  functions of, 77, 185, 186f
  metabolic alkalosis and vomiting, 413n
Hydrodensitometry, **264f**, E-15, E-16t
Hydrogenation (of fats), **143**
  in convenience foods, 175
  on labels, 166f
  in margarine *vs.* butter, 166f
  structure change, 144f
  trans fats and, 157

Hydrogen peroxide, B-8, B-8f
Hydrolysis, **77**
  of ATP, 216, 217f
  by digestive enzymes, 76
  of disaccharides, 104, 104f
  of triglycerides, 148f, 149, 151f, 155
Hydrophilic, **147**
Hydrophobic, **147**
Hydrotherapy, **653**
Hydroxyapatite, **416**
Hydroxycitric acid, 291t
Hydroxylysine, 352
Hydroxyproline, 182n, 352
Hyperactivity, 120, **564**–565, 581
Hypercarotenemia, 377n
Hyperglycemia, 246t, **637**, 638
Hyperkeratinization, 373f
Hyperplastic obesity, **283**
Hypertension, **626**, 632–637
  calcium and, 416
  in children, 569, 587–588
  development of, 632–634
  drug therapy, 636–637
  essential, **626**
  exercise and, 636
  guidelines for, 628t
  heart disease risk, 627, 628t, 629, 632
  magnesium and, 424
  MAO inhibitors and, 617
  nutrient-gene interactions, 515
  obesity and, 265, 569, 635
  omega-3 fatty acids and, 158
  potassium and, 414
  pregnancy and, 528, 528n
  prehypertension, **626**, 628, 628t
  primary *vs.* secondary, **626**
  risk factor summary, 634–635
  salt sensitivity and, **410**
  sodium and, 400, 410–411, 635t, 636, 636t
  treatment of, 635–637, 635t
  in vegetarians, 65
Hyperthermia, **493**–494, 579
Hypertrophic obesity, **283**
Hypertrophy (muscle), **481**
Hypnotherapy, **653**
Hypoallergenic formulas, **553**
Hypoglycemia, **115**, 246t, 641
Hyponatremia, 398, 412, **495**–496
Hypothalamus, **251**
  hormones produced by, A-4 to A-5
  hunger and, 251
  location of, A-4f
  water balance and, 398, 403f
Hypothermia, **494**
Hypothesis, 11, 12f, **14**
Hypothyroidism, 456

I

IGF-1 (insulin-like growth factor 1), E-19, E-19n
Ileocecal valve, **72**, 73f, 74, 76
Ileum, **72**, 73f, 74
Imagery, **653**
Imitation foods, **53**
Immune system, **622**
  alcohol and, 241
  allergies and, 565–566
  antibodies, **192**, **622**
  antigens, **192**
  breastfeeding and, 551–552
  components of, 622–623
  deficiencies, effects of, 599
  eicosanoids and, 154, 159n
  exercise and, 478n
  free radicals and, 390
  heart disease and, 627
  malnutrition and, 623, 623f, 623t
  in older adults, 599

overweight and, 265
rheumatoid arthritis and, 605
vitamin C and, 352
  See also Allergies
Immunity, **192**
Immunoglobulins, **622**
Implantation (of zygote), **510**
Imported foods, 666, 678–679
Incidental additives, **685**–687
Indigestion, **94**, 96–97, 97t
Indirect additives, **685**–687
Indirect calorimetry, **250**
Indispensable nutrients, **7**
Indoles, 470t
Infant formulas, 552–553
  allergies and, 553
  fatty acids in, 550
  health and, 533t, 536, 553
  "health beverages" replacing, 379
  soy, 67, 553, 557
  vision and mental development, 550–551
Infants, 547–558
  basal metabolic rate, 254
  birth defects. *See* Birth defects
  birthweight, 515–516, 545, 554
  blood calcium, 417n
  botulism in, 556, 556n, 671
  of drug users, 530
  energy needs of, 547–548, 549f
  fat-free diets, 155
  fat needs, 548, 554, 556
  feeding skills of, 555t
  goat's milk anemia, 341
  growth rate, 547–548, 547f, E-6 to E-7,
    E-6f to E-10f
  Healthy People 2010 goals, J-2t
  honey and botulism, 556
  iron needs, 551, 551t, 556
  low birthweight, **525**–526
  malnutrition, 379, 706, E-7
  mental development, 550
  milk, 554, 557, 557f
  mineral needs, 549, 549f, 551, 551t
  pesticides and, 678, 681
  post term, **516**
  premature, **516**
  preterm, **516**, 525–526, 530, 554
  protein needs, 548–549, 549f, 550, 550f, 553f
  solid foods for, 555–557, 555t, 557f
  supplements, 384–385, 551, 551t
  term, **516**
  vegetable/fruit intake, 561–562
  vegetarian diets, 557
  vitamin K, 384–385
  vitamin needs, 549, 549f, 551t, 556
  vomiting in, 93
  water intake, 549
  websites on, 580–581
  See also Breastfeeding; Children; Fetal development; Pregnancy; Rickets
Infections/infectious disease, **621**–624
  botulism, 118n, **556**, 556n, 665t, 666, 671
  breastfeeding and, 536–537, 551
  children and, 372–373, 455
  colds, 12–15, 352, 455, 478
  from contaminated water, 553
  deaths from, 24t, 199
  in diabetics, 639–640
  dysentery, **198**–199
  E. coli infection, 665t, 666
  exercise and, 478
  Helicobacter pylori, 97, 343
  HIV/AIDS, 536–537, **623**–624, 624t
  in infants, 551, 556, 671
  iron overload and, 448
  lead toxicity and, 463
  malnutrition and, 197, 198–199, 453–454, 707

measles, 199, 372–373
  in older adults, 599
  tuberculosis, 336
  vitamin A and, 372–373
  zinc and, 453, 455
  See also Foodborne illnesses
Infertility/fertility, 246t, 264, 509, 526, 545, 676
Inflammation, **265**
  cancer and, 642
  heart disease and, 626–627
  rheumatoid arthritis, 605
  vitamin E and, 382
Information on nutrition, validity of, 30–34
  alternative medicine, 652–659
  ergogenic aids, 503
  experts/professionals, 31–33
  fad diets, 315–321, 316t, 317t, 320t
  functional foods/phytochemicals, 473
  herbal medicines, 656t, 657t, 658, 658t
  Internet sites, 30, 31f, 33, 34
  naive *vs.* accurate view of needs, 18f
  news reports, 30–31
  red flags of quackery, 33, 34f
  scientific research, 15–16
  supplements, 362, 363–364, 503
  vitamin impostors, 346
  websites on, 33, 34, 659
  weight loss, 289–291, 290t, 291t
  See also Myths
INH (isonicotinic acid hydrazide), 336, 336n
Initiators (cancer), **642**, 643–645, 643f
Inorganic, **7**
Inorganic nutrients, 7t
Inositol, **346**, 364
Insensible water losses, 399n
Insoluble fibers, **106**, 123t
  See also Fiber.
Insulin, **113**
  chromium and blood glucose, 461
  diabetes and, 115, 637, 638, 639f, 641
  fad diet claims, 316, 316t
  functions of, 113, 114, 114f, 190, 191t,
    316t, 637
  hormones effected by, A-4
  impaired glucose tolerance, **637**
  structure of, 184f
  sugar intake and, 120
  zinc and, 452
  See also Blood glucose levels
Insulin-like growth factor 1 (IGF-1), E-19, E-19n
Insulin resistance, **265**, 630
  body weight and, 265–266, 316
  mechanism of, 638
  trans-fatty acids and, 157
Integrative medicine, **652**
Intelligence, 552, 562, 563, 564, 565
Intensity (of exercise), **480**
Intentional food additives, **683**–685, 683t
Intermediate-density lipoprotein (IDL), 151n
Intermittent claudication, **382**
International Food Information Council, 33
International System of Units (SI), 8
Internet, **32**, 364, 659
Internet sites. *See* Websites
Interstitial fluid, **398**, 399f
Intestinal bacteria
  biotin and, 334
  cholesterol synthesis and, 162
  fiber digestion, 78, 79f, 86, 106, 108, 108n,
    109f, 122, 123
  lactose intolerance and, 110, 111
  as protective, 86
  vitamin K and, 86, 383, 385n
  yogurt and, 86, 162
Intestinal lipase, 148f
Intestines. *See* Colon (large intestine); GI
  (gastrointestinal) tract; Small intestines

Intra-abdominal fat, 262–263, 262f, 263f
Intracellular fluid, **398**
Intrinsic factor, **343**
In vitro studies, 13f
Iodine, 455–457, 464t
  overview of, 457t
  deficiency, 13f, 456, 456f, 457t
  food sources, 456, 457t
  functions of, 455, 457t
  intake recommendations, 456, 457t
  selenium and, 442
  toxicity, 67, 456, 457t
  websites on, 465
Ions, **403**, 404f, 404t, B-5, B-5 to B-6
  See also Electrolytes
Iridology, **653**
Iron, 442–451, 464t
  overview of, 451t
  adolescent needs, 576–577
  for athletes, 492–493
  blood losses and, 443n, 445, 446, 522
  in breast milk, 551, 552
  in cookware, 450–451
  copper and, 458
  ferrous/ferric, 442, 451, 458, B-7
  food sources, 65, 66, 449–450, 450f, 451t
  functions of, 442–443, 445f, 451t
  heme *vs.* nonheme, **443**–444, 444f
  for infants, 551, 551t, 556
  intake recommendations, 449, 450f, 451t, 577
  lactoferrin, 552
  lead toxicity and, 463
  losses of, 445, 445n, 446
  manganese absorption and, 442
  menstruation and, 360, 577
  in milk, 554
  during pregnancy/lactation, 446, 521f, 522, 529, 536
  recycling, 445, 445f
  regulation/balance, 444, 445
  storage, 443, 445, 445f
  supplements, 360, 361–362, 446, 448, 450–451
  total iron-binding capacity (TIBC), E-20 to E-21, E-21t
  toxicity, 361–362, 447–448, 451t
  transport of, 191, 443f, 444–445, 445f
  vegetarian diets, 65, 66
  in whole grains, 51f
  zinc absorption and, 453, 522
Iron absorption
  bioavailability, 450, 551, 554
  caffeine and, 538
  calcium and, 436
  enhancing, 444, 446, 449, 450, 451, 522, 556
  inhibition of, 444, 448, 449, 451, 525
  mechanism of, 443–444, 443f, 444f, 445
  MFP factor, **444**, 450
  from plant foods, 66
  from supplements, 450–451, 522
  vitamin C and, 66, 351, 354, 444, 448, 522
  vitamin C and iron supplements, 451
  See also Iron overload
Iron cookware, 450–451
Iron deficiency, **445**–447
  assessment of, 22, 446
  in athletes, 492
  atrophic gastritis, 343
  in children/teens, 563, 577
  lead absorption and, 564
  in malnutrition, 198
  statistics on, 445–446
  symptoms of, 446, 447, 451t
Iron-deficiency anemia, **446**
  assessment of, E-19 to E-21, E-20t, E-21t
  in children, 560, 563
  development of, 22, 446–447

  exercise and, 492–493
  in older adults, 603
  during pregnancy, 529
  red blood cells in, 446, 447f
  symptoms of, 37, 348, 446–447
Iron overload, 354, **447**–448, 450, 465
Irradiation (of foods), 330, 330n, **672**–673
Irritable bowel syndrome, 93, **94**
Isoflavones, 470t
Isoleucine, 196f
Isomalt, 132, 136t
Isonicotinic acid hydrazide (INH), 336n, 618
Isothiocyanates, 470n, 470t

J

Jejunum, **72**, 73f, 74
Joule, **7**
Journals, 31f, 33
Jun bu huan, 656

K

Kava, 657t, 658, 658t
kCalorie (energy) control, **38**, 596–597
kCalories (kcal), **7**
  in alcohol, 8, 9n, 243, 244t
  available from food, 8–9, 9t
  in beverages, 400
  calculating, 9, 9f, 257
  in carbohydrates, 9t
  discretionary. *See* Discretionary kcalorie allowance
  "empty," **39**, 298
  as energy measurement, 7–9, 9f
  fad diets and, 318
  in fast food, 287
  from fat, reducing, 161–167, 162f, 166f
  in fat (body), 156, 156n, 249–250, 489
  in fat (dietary), 9t, 156, 156n, 160, 165–167
  in fat replacers, 164
  in foods, measuring, 250–251, 250f, 251n
  in fruit juices, 556
  on labels of foods, 54f, 56–57, 56t, **58**
  in lecithin, 146
  in low-fat foods, 164
  in mixers for alcohol, 244t
  nutrient density and, **38**, 42–43f, 118–119, 118t
  in protein, 9t
  sugar intake and, 117–118, 118t, 120, 121
  sugar replacers and, 132, 135
  See also Energy; Energy density; Energy metabolism; Nutrient density
kCalories (kcal) needs
  adolescents, 576
  carbohydrate recommendations, 124–127
  of children, 558–559, 560, 562t
  estimating requirements, 41, 41t, 44, 44t, 255t, 256–257
  for exercise, 254, 254f, 255t, 257t, 300, 487, 497
  for exercise: calculating, 44t, 257, F-1, F-2 to F-6t
  fat, intake recommendations, 160–161
  gender differences, 44t, 254, 256, 577
  of infants, 547–548, 549f
  during lactation, 534–535
  of older adults, 44t, 601–602
  during pregnancy, 520, 521f, 521n
  protein intake, as percentage, 201
  recommendations (EER, AMDR), **18**
  sugar intake and, 121
  weight gain plans, 299t, 308
  weight loss plans, 295–296, 295t, 299t
Kefir, **111**
Keratin, **373**
Keratinization, 373–**374**, 373f
Keratomalacia, **373**
Keshan disease, **457**
Keto acids, **225**, 226f, 235

Ketogenic amino acids, 194n, 221f, 225, 225f, 226f
Ketogenic diets. *See* Ketosis
Ketone bodies, **113**
  brain/nerves and, 156
  in diabetes, 639f
  fat metabolism and, 113, 156
  formation of, 235f, C-16 to C-17, C-17f
Ketosis, **113**
  adverse effects of, 235, 319–320, 320t
  alcohol use and, 241
  dieting and, 319–320, 320t
  fasting/starvation, 156, 235
  inadequate carbohydrate and, 113, 156
Kidney disease
  alcohol as risk for, 246t
  cancer and, 644t
  diabetes and, 586, 640
  Healthy People 2010 goals, J-1t
  herbal medicine risk, 656
  proteins (dietary) and, 200
  water intoxication and, 398
  See also Kidney stones
Kidneys, functions of
  acid-base balance and, 407, 408, 410n
  amino acid metabolism, 194
  blood pressure regulation, 401–402, 634
  blood volume regulation, 401–402, 403f
  calcium balance in bone, 416, 417f
  fluids and electrolyte balance, 402–406, 402f, 404f, 404t, 405f
  hormones and, 401, 406, A-5, A-6
  medications and, 617, 618
  nephron function, 402f
  sodium/potassium, 406, 410
  urea excretion, 226, 227f
  vitamin D activation, 377, 377f
  water balance, 399
Kidney stones
  calcium and vitamin D, 379, 418
  proteins (dietary) and, 200
  vitamin C and, 354, 354n, 355n
  water intake and, 400
Kilocalories. *See* kCalories (kcal)
Kilograms (kg), 8, inside back cover
Kilojoule (kJ), 7, 8, 9n, inside back cover
Kombucha tea, 656
Krebs cycle. *See* TCA (Krebs) cycle
Kwashiorkor, 197t, **199**, 199f
  See also Protein-energy malnutrition (PEM)

L

Labeling, 54–61
  of allergens, 566
  artificial sweeteners, 137f
  carbohydrate content, 125t, 126–127, 126f
  Daily Values, 54f, **55**–57, 56t, 165–167, inside back cover
  exchange lists and, G-2f
  fat content, 165–167, 166f
  fiber content, 126–127, 126f
  glossary of terms, **58**
  GM foods, 696
  health claims, **59**, 59t, 363–364
  herbal supplements, 657, 658
  ingredient list, 54f, 55
  Nutrition Facts, 54f, 55–56
  organically grown crops, 681f
  phytochemicals, 473
  protein content, 196
  regulations for, 59, 59t, 60t, 196
  serving sizes, 55
  structure-function claims, **59**, 60t, 364
  sugar content, 58, 117, 118, 121
  of supplements, 360, 364–365, 365f
  websites on, 61

Laboratory studies, 13f, 14t
Laboratory tests, E-16 to E-22
    blood glucose, 113
    bone density, 432
    cholesterol, 156–157, 587, 588t. *See also* Blood
        lipid profiles
    diabetes, 354
    false positive/negative results, **354**
    iron deficiency, 446, E-19 to E-21, E-20t, E-21t
    nutrition assessment, 21–22, 22f, E-16
        to E-22, E-18t
Lactadherin, **552**
Lactase, 108, 110–111
Lactase deficiency, **110**
Lactate (lactic acid), **220**
    alcohol and, 241
    in breast milk, 535
    exercise and, 221, 458t, 486–487, 535
    metabolic pathways, 220–221, 220f, 221f
Lactation, 533–540
    See also Breastfeeding
Lactation consultants, certified, 534
Lacteals, **85**
Lactitol, 132, 136t
Lactobacillus bifidus, 86, 551–552
Lactoferrin, **552**
Lacto-ovo-vegetarians, **64**, 66
Lactose, **105**
    in breast milk and formula, 550
    foods containing, 105, 111
    in medications, 111, 618
    structure of, 105, C-1f
Lactose intolerance, **110**–111
    ethnic differences, 111
    formulas for infants with, 553
    websites on, 127
Lactovegetarians, **64**
Laetrile, 346, 653, 677
LaLeche League International, 539
Large intestine, **72**, 73f
    See also Colon (large intestine)
Larynx, 92, 92f, **94**
Laxatives, **94**, 95, 290–291
LDL (low-density lipoprotein), **151**
    blood levels, 156, 157, 588t, 628t
    composition of, 151n, 153f
    DASH eating plan, 636
    free radical damage, 627
    function of, 152
    genetics and, 210
    to HDL ratio, 152, 629
    heart disease risk, 152, 175, 175f, 628t, 629
    levels, improving, 173, 633
    in obese children, 587
    oxidation of, 382
    plaque formation and, 627
    saturated fat and, 157, 175, 175f
    size and density of, 153f
    trans-fatty acids and, 157
Lead
    anemia and, 564
    in calcium supplements, 436
    fetal exposure to, 531
    in herbal medicines, 656
    malnutrition and, 564
    protection against, 565
    toxicity, 463, 463t, 560, 563
    in water, 401, 553, 565
    websites on, 581
Lean body mass, 194, **254**, 261f, 484
Lecithin, **145**–146, 146f, 345
Lecithinase, 145
Legumes, **44**
    amino acid profile, 195
    carbohydrates/fiber in, 125t, 126
    diet planning and, 44, 163

exchange lists, G-4t, I-10t
    in food group plans, 41t, 43f, 44, 46t, 47f,
        52, 52f, I-4f
    glycemic index of, 116f
    nutrients in, 43f, 44
    proteins, complementary, 196f
    in recipes, 52f
    types of, 52
    for vegetarians, 65, 66
    See also Plant foods; Soy products
Length measurements, E-6, E-6f, E-9f, E-10f
Leptin, **284**–285, 285f
Less-fat (milk), **53**
Let-down reflex, **533**
Leukemias, 462, **642**
Levulose, **103**
Licensed dietitians, 32
License to practice, **32**
Life expectancy, **593**
    body weight and, 263, 264f
    exercise and, 478
    lifestyle and, 594
Life span, **593**
Lifestyle choices
    chronic disease risk, 25, 210, 586–589, 625,
        625f, 629–630
    death rates and, 25t
    environmental considerations, 710–713
    food choices, 3–5
    genes interacting with, 210
    heart disease risk, 629–630, 631–632, 632t
    hypertension and, 65, 635t
    life expectancy and, 263, 264f, 594
    obesity and, 286–288, 299–302, 567–568,
        569, 588
    for older adults, 608t
    pregnancy and, 530–531
    sedentary, and health, 266, 287–288, 299–302,
        478, 567–568, 587, 588. *See also* Physical
        activity, benefits of
    vegetarians and health, 65
Light, defined, **58**
Lignans, **469**, 470t, 471, 472f
Lignin, 106n
Lima beans, 677
Limiting amino acids, **195**
Limonene, 470t
Lind, James, 350
Lingual lipase, 147–148, 148f
Linoleic acid, **141**
    AI for, 160, inside front cover
    in breast milk and formula, 550
    chemistry of, 154, 154f
    conjugated, **144**, 291t, 503, 505
    deficiency of, 154
    food sources, 141t, 154, 159t
    structure of, 141f, 141t, 142f, C-3t
    See also Fatty acids, omega-6
Linolenic acid, **141**
    AI for, 160, inside front cover
    in breast milk and formula, 550
    chemistry of, 154, 154f, 154n
    food sources, 141t, 154, 159t
    functions of, 154
    structure of, 141t, 142f, C-3t
    See also Fatty acids, omega-3
Lipases, **77**
    gastric, 80n, 148f, 149
    hormone-sensitive, **156**
    intestinal, 148f, 149
    lingual, 147–148, 148f
    lipoprotein (LPL), **155**, 282–283
    pancreatic, 87, 148f, 149
Lipectomy, 293
Lipids, **139**
    See also Blood lipid profiles; Fats

Lipophilic, **147**
Lipoprotein lipase (LPL), **155**, 282–283
Lipoproteins, **150**–152, 151n, 153f
    See also Blood lipid profiles; Cholesterol;
        Chylomicrons; HDL; LDL; VLDL
Liposuction, 293
Lipotoxicity, **283**
Liquid nutritional formulas, 504, 602
Listeriosis, **531**, 665t, 666
"Lite," defined, **58**
Liver (body), 73f, **78**, 85f
    absorbed nutrients in, 83–84, 84f, 85f
    alcohol and, 240–242, 246t
    amino acid metabolism, 194
    bile and, 78, 149, 151f
    blood glucose regulation, 112, 113, 114, 114f
    cholesterol synthesis, 122, 147
    cirrhosis, **239**, 241
    fatty, 198, **239**, 240, 241
    glucose and, 105n, 107, 110f, 112, 221, 487
    glycogen storage and use, 105n, 112, 114f
    iron storage and recycling, 445, 445f
    lactate acid, 220f, 221, 487
    lipids/lipoproteins, 151
    metabolic functions of, 215t
    protective functions, 84
    urea and, 226, 226f, 227f
    vitamin A storage, 370, 372, 376, 376n
    vitamin D activation, 377, 377f
    zinc storage, 453f
Liver cancer, 643, 644t
Liver disease, 240, 241, 246t, 657t, 665t
Liver (food), 376
Longevity, **593**–597
    See also Life expectancy
Low birthweight (LBW), 515, 516, **525**–526, 530
Low-carbohydrate diets. *See* Diets, low-
    carbohydrate
Low-density lipoprotein. *See* LDL
Low-fat diets. *See* Diets, low-fat
Low-fat foods, 296, 298
Low-risk pregnancy, **525**
LPL. *See* Lipoprotein lipase
Lumen, **72**
Lung cancer, 580, 644t
Lungs
    acid-base balance and, 407
    exercise and, 478
    free radicals and, B-8
    functions of, 83, 84f, 483f
    vascular system and, 84f
Lutein, 370n, **469**, 471, 472f
Luteinizing hormone (LH), **A-4**
Luteinizing hormone-releasing hormone
    (LH-RH), **A-4**
Lycopene, 370n, **469**, 470, 470t, 472f
Lymph, 83, **85**
Lymphatic system, 82, 82f, 83, **84**–85, 149
Lymphocytes, **622**–623
Lymphomas, **642**
Lymph tissues, 623t
Lysine, 196f, 203
Lysosomes, **372**, **A-2**, A-3f
Lysyl oxidase, 458n

M

Macrobiotic diets, **64**, 67, **653**, 656t
Macrocytic (megaloblastic) anemia, **341**
Macrominerals, **408**
    See also Minerals, major
Macronutrients, **7**
    See also specific nutrients
Macrophages, **622**, 627
Macrosomia, **516**
Macula, **605**
Macular degeneration, **605**

Mad cow disease, 668
Magnesium, **423**–425
  overview of, 425t, 426t
  absorption of, 409
  deficiency, 424, 425t
  food sources, 424, 425f, 425t
  functions of, 424, 425t, 436
  intake recommendations, 424, 424t, 425f
  phosphorus and, 409
  toxicity, 424, 425t
Ma huang, 290, 291t, 658
Malignant, **642**, 643f
Malnutrition, **20**, 197–199
  alcohol and, 243–244, 246t
  causes of, 197–198, 705–706
  in children, 197–199, 557, 562–564, 563t, 705, 707, E-7
  cocaine and, 579
  in eating disorders, 273, 275
  fertility and, 509, 526–527
  immune system and, 623, 623f, 623t
  in infants, 557
  infectious disease and, 197, 198–199, 453–454, 707
  kwashiorkor, 197t, **198**
  lead contamination and, 564
  marasmus, **197**, 197t
  in older adults, 600
  pregnancy/fetal development and, 509, 515, 526–527
  protein-energy. *See* Protein-energy malnutrition (PEM)
  recovering from, 199
  risk factors in older adults, 609t
  symptoms/signs, 20, 197t, 563t, E-17t
  types of, 197, 197t
  vitamin A deficiency and, 373–374
  websites on, 204
  world hunger, 705–707, 706f
  zinc and, 453–454
  See also Deficiencies; Eating disorders; Hunger, chronic/world; Nutrition assessment; Nutrition status
Maltase, **108**
Maltitol, 132, 136t
Maltose, **104**, 104f, C-1f
Mammary glands, **533**
Manganese, 442, 459–460, 460t, 464t
Mannitol, 132, 136t
Mannose, C-2f
Marasmus, **197**, 197t, 198f
  See also Protein-energy malnutrition (PEM)
Marasmus-kwashiorkor mix, 198
Margarine
  butter *vs.*, 157, 166f, 471
  as functional food, 471, 472
  heart health and, 633
  to lower cholesterol, 164, 164n
  phytosterol source, 472n, 633
  trans-fatty acids, 157
Margin of safety (additives), **683**
Marijuana, 579, 654
Massage therapy, **653**, 656t
Mastication, **72**
Matrix, **190**
Matter, **B-1** to B-3, B-2t
Mayo Clinic website, 26
Meal planning. *See* Diet planning
Meals on Wheels, **609**
Mean corpuscular volume (MCV), E-20t, E-22
Measles, 199, 372–373
Measurements
  anthropometric. *See* Anthropometric measurements
  glossary of nutrient measures, inside back cover

growth charts, 548f, E-8f to E-13f
  household, 55t
  of kcalories (kcal), 7–9, 250–251, 250f, 251n
  metric, inside back cover
  metric units, 8, 55t
Meat alternates/substitutes, 41t, 43f, 44, 53, 66, 126
  See also Soy products
Meat replacements, **64**, 66
Meats
  bovine growth hormone (BGH), **686**–687
  buffalo, 719
  in Canadian food groups, I-4f
  cancer and, 65, 160, 392, 644, 644n, 646t
  cholesterol in, 158f
  cooking: low-fat tips, 53
  cooking/handling safely, 644, 668, 669f, 670, 671t
  dioxins, 686
  discretionary kcalories and, 45
  in exchange lists, 47, G-1t, G-3t, G-8t, I-10t to I-11t
  farming and, 716, 717f, 718, 719, 719f
  fat and heart disease, 65, 175
  fat in, 53, 157, 157f, 162, 162f, 163, G-8t
  "free-range," 162, 177
  heart disease and, 65, 175, 319
  as iron source, 444, 444f, 450, 450f
  limiting consumption of, 201–202
  in low-fat diets, 53, 162, 162f, 163
  mad cow disease, 668
  niacin in, 332, 334f
  nitrosamines in, 684
  nutrients in, 43f, 53
  PBB contamination of, 676
  portion sizes, 53
  protein in, 195, 201, 202
  range-fed beef, 718, 719
  saving money on, 704
  serving sizes, 43, 201
  thiamin in, 329f
Medical exams. *See* Physical examinations
Medical terms, GL-1 to GL-18
Medical tests. *See* Laboratory tests
Medications
  absorption and, 616, 616t
  for acne, 374
  alcohol and, 242
  anticoagulants, 354
  aspirin, 341, 615, 616
  for bulimia nervosa, 276
  caffeine in, H-1t
  for cholesterol (blood), 589
  diuretics. *See* Diuretics
  drug excretion, 616t, 618
  drug history, E-2t, **E-3**
  genetic engineering of, 695
  heartburn and, 96–97
  herbal. *See* Herbal medicines/supplements
  herb-drug interactions, 657–658, 658t
  for hypertension, 636–637
  lactation and, 537
  lactose in, 111, 618
  laxatives, 96
  marijuana as, 654
  metabolism and, 616, 616t
  metabolism of, 242
  methotrexate, 617, 617f
  nutrient absorption and, 616, 616t
  nutrient excretion and, 616t, 617–618
  nutrient interactions with. *See* Nutrient-drug interactions
  for obesity treatment, 290, 291t, 292, 616
  older adults use of, 615
  for osteoporosis, 434, 434n

peptic ulcer and, 97
  pharmacological effects of vitamins, 332, 360
  pregnancy and, 530
  single amino acid supplements as, 203
  sodium in, 618
  sorbitol in, 618
  sugar in, 618
  vitamin B$_6$ and, 336
  vitamin K and, 384
  vs. functional foods, 473
  See also specific medications
Meditation, **653**
Mediterranean diet
  composition of, 177
  food groups, 46t
  health and, 177
  heart disease and, 13f, 173, 177, 471
  oxidative stress and, 597
  phytochemicals and, 471
Megaloblastic anemia, **341**
Megestrol acetate, 615
Melanin, 194
Melanomas, **642**
Memory loss, 606–607
Men
  fathers, 545
  fertility of, 509, 545, 676
  prostate cancer, 160, 644t
  See also Gender differences
Menadione, **385**, C-9f
  See also Vitamin K
Menaquinone. *See* Vitamin K
Menkes disease, 459
Menopause, 434, 434f, 435
Menstruation/menstrual period
  amenorrhea, **270**, 271, 271f, 273, 434, **537**
  iron and, 360, 445n, 446, 492, 577
Mental health. *See* Brain; Psychological problems
Mental retardation. *See* Retardation
MEOS (microsomal ethanol-oxidizing system), **239**, 242
Mercury contamination, 159, 174, 531, 675–676, 675f
Meridia, 292n
Messenger RNA, protein synthesis and, 187, 188f, 208
Metabolic alkalosis, 413n
Metabolic rate, basal. *See* Basal metabolic rate (BMR)
Metabolic rate, resting (RMR), **254**
Metabolic syndrome, 265–266, **630**
Metabolic-type diets, 317t
Metabolism, **10**, 213–236
  in adipose tissue, 155–156
  of alcohol, 240–242, 240f, 241f
  of amino acids/proteins, 192, 193–194, 215f, 241, C-11 to C-13f
  anabolism and catabolism, **214**, 215f, **216**
  basal, **254**, 254f, 255t
  basic chemical reactions, 214–217, 215f
  of carbohydrates, 115–116, 219–222, 219f–222f
  diabetes, consequences of, 639, 639f
  fad diet claims, 316, 319
  of fats. *See* Fat metabolism
  of glucose in diabetes, 639, 639f
  inflammation and, 265
  liver's function in, 215t
  low-carbohydrate diets and, 319
  manganese and, 459
  medications and, 616–617, 616t
  oxygen in, 221
  zinc, 452–453, 453f
  See also Basal metabolic rate; Energy metabolism
Metalloenzymes, **452**, 452n, 462
Metallothionein, **452**, 453f

Metastasize, **642**, 643f
Methamphetamines, 579
Methane, B-3
Methanol, 134
Methionine, 196f, 343, 343n, 345, 425
Methotrexate, 617, 617f
Methoxatin, 346
Methylcobalamin, **342**
Methylmercury, 675–676, 675f
Metric measurement units, 8, 55t, inside back cover
Mexican cuisine, 46t
MFP factor, **444**, 450
Micelles, **149**, 152f
Microangiopathies, **640**
Microarray technology, **207**, 208
Microcytic anemia, 337n, 355n
Microcytic hypochromic anemia, **446**
Microflora, **86**
Microminerals. *See* Minerals, trace
Micronutrients, **7**
Microsomal ethanol-oxidizing system (MEOS), **239**, 242
Microvillus/microvilli, **80**, 82f
Microwave cooking, 344–345, 686
Middle East, zinc deficiency in, 453, 453f
Milk, low-fat, **53**, 554
Milk, no-fat, **53**
Milk, nonfat, **53**, 155, 554
Milk, reduced fat, **53**
Milk, skim, **53**
Milk, soy, 53, 65
Milk, zero-fat, **53**
Milk and milk products
    alternatives to, 53, 65, 197
    bovine growth hormone (BGH), **686**–687
    calcium, 416, 418–419, 419f, 420
    in Canadian food groups, I-4f
    carbohydrate content of, 126
    cheese, 47, 111, 126
    for children/teens, 562f, 573t, 577
    cholesterol in, 158f
    dental health and, 119
    discretionary kcalories and, 45
    in exchange lists, 47, G-1t, G-3t, G-5t, I-9t
    fat, *trans,* 143n
    fat intake and, 53, 157f, 162, 163, 175
    folate and, 341
    fortification of, 53, 330
    glycemic index of, 116f
    goat's milk, 341, 553
    heart disease and, 633
    for infants, 554, 557, 557f. *See also* Breast milk; Infant formulas
    intake recommendations, 418–419, 420, 523
    kefir, **111**
    lactose intolerance and, **110**–111
    in low-fat diets, 162, 163
    nutrient density, 38
    nutrients in, 43f, 53, 330
    for older adults, 603
    protein content, 201–202
    riboflavin in, 330, 331f
    safety, 671
    ultrahigh temperature (UHT) treatment, **610**
    in USDA Food Guide, 41t, 43f, 45, 46t, 47f, 48t, 49f
    in vegetarian diets, 65
    vitamin A fortification, 375, 375n
    vitamin D fortification, 330, 330n, 379, 379n, 418
    websites on, 427, 581
    weight control and, 416
Milk anemia, **557**
Milk sugar. *See* Lactose
Milliequivalents (mEq), **403**

Mind-body therapies, 656t
Mineralization, **416**
Mineral oil, **94**, 95
Minerals, **10**, 408–427
    overview of, 408–410, 409f, 426t, 464t
    absorption and fiber, 107, 124
    absorption and phytates, 107, 409
    absorption of, 79f, 363, 409. *See also* Iron absorption
    adolescent needs, 576–577
    alcohol use and, 243
    as alternative medicines, 655
    assessment tests, E-18t
    bioavailability of, 363, 409
    body composition, 7t, 404t, 409f, B-4t
    chemistry of, 408
    for children, 560
    cooking/food preparation, 10, 408, 450–451
    evaluating foods for, 329
    for exercise, 491–493
    fluids and electrolyte balance, 402–406, 404f, 404t, 405f
    functions of, 10
    infant needs, 549, 549f
    listed, 10n, 402, 409f
    nutrient-drug interactions, 616, 617
    nutrient interactions, 409
    for older adults, 603
    during pregnancy/lactation, 521f, 522, 523, 531, 535
    RDA and AI for, inside front cover
    recommendations: establishing DRI, 18f
    supplements, **360**, 362t, 363, 365f
    Tolerable Upper Intake Level, 362t, inside front cover
    transport of, 409
    in water, 400–401, 420, 424, 688
    websites on, 365, 427, 465
    in whole grains, 51f
    See also Electrolytes; Nutrient interactions; *specific minerals*
Minerals, major, **408**–427
    overview of, 408–410, 426t
    body composition, 404t, 409f
    listed, 10n, 402
    See also specific minerals
Minerals, trace, **441**–465
    overview of, 441–442, 464t
    body composition, 409f, B-4t
    deficiencies, 441, 442, 464t
    food sources, 441, 464t
    listed, 10n
    nutrient interactions, 442
    supplements of, 442, 442n
    toxicity, 441–442, 464t
    websites on, 465
    See also specific minerals
Mineral tablets. *See* Supplements
Mineral water, **400**, 420, 424
Misinformation, **32**
    See also Information on nutrition, validity of; Myths
Miss America, 258f
Mitochondria, **220**, A-2
    in cell structure, A-3f
    exercise and, 221, 488, 489
    functions of, 214f, 220, 229f, A-2
    oxidation of fatty acids, 222n
    structure of, 214f
Moderate exercise, **481**
Moderation (alcohol), 238–240, **239**
Moderation (dietary), **39**
Molasses, **118**, 118t
Mole, B-6n
Molecules, **B-1**
Molybdenum, **462**, 462t, 464t

Monoamine oxidase (MAO) inhibitors, 617, 618t
Monoglycerides, **147**, 151f
Monosaccharides, **102**
    absorption of, 108–109, 110f
    chemistry of, 102–103, 104f
    in hemicelluloses, C-2f to C-3f
    structure of, 102f–103f, C-1f, C-2f
Monosodium glutamate (MSG), **685**
Monoterpenes, 470t, 472f
Monounsaturated fats, **141**
    in exchange lists, G-9t
    food sources, 141t, 144f, 158, 176t
    heart disease risk, 65, 158, 173, 633
Monounsaturated fatty acids (MUFA), **141**
Mortality. *See* Death; Life expectancy
Motility, **74**, 88, 94
Mouth, **72**
    B vitamin deficiency, 330n, 333n, 349f
    cancer of, 644t
    carbohydrate digestion, 79f, 108, 109f
    chewing, 599–600
    digestive functions, 72–73, 73f, 74, 76f
    fat digestion, 147–148, 148f
    fiber digestion, 79f
    protein digestion, 186f
    See also Dental caries; Teeth
MSG symptom complex, **685**
Mucilages, 106n
Mucosal ferritin, 443, 443f
Mucosal transferrin, 443, **443**, 443f, 444
Mucosa/mucosal, **443**
Mucous, 373
Mucous membranes, **78, 371**, 373f
Mucus, 77, **78**
Muscle conditioning
    cardiorespiratory training and, 482, 483f
    hypertrophy/atrophy, **481**
    protein remodeling, 490
    training, **480**
    weight training, 480t, **484**
Muscle dysmorphia, **270**, 272
Muscle endurance, 480, **480**, 481
Muscles/muscular system
    atrophy, **481**
    body composition, 261f
    creatine and, 504–505
    digestion and, 74–76, 75f, 76f
    energy/fuel for, 484–489, 485t, 486f, 490, 491
    energy metabolism, 220f, 221, 482
    exercise and, 221, 482, 485–488, 490
    exercise for weight gain, 308
    fasting/starvation and, 234–235
    glycogen and, 105n, 112, 485–488
    intestinal, 82f
    myoglobin, **443**
    potassium and, 414
    protein intake and, 202
    of stomach, 75, 75f
    vitamin E and, 382
    See also Body composition; Weight training
Muscle strength, **480**
    chromium picolinate and, 461
    older adults and, 484, 595–596
    training and, 184, 480, 481
Muscular dystrophy, **382**
Mushrooms, 677
Mutations, **207**, 209
    See also Genetic disorders
Mycoprotein, 471, 471n
Myocardial infarction, **626**
    See also Heart attacks
Myoglobin, **443**
MyPyramid, 47, 47f, 66f
Myths
    about alcohol, 245, 246t
    about amino acid supplements, 185

Myths, *continued*
cellulite, **291**
"food combining," 81–82
about lecithin, 145–146
"spot reducing," 301–302, 489
vitamin impostors, 346
about weight loss, 315–320, 316t
See also Information on nutrition, validity of;
Quackery/quacks

N

NADH, **239**, 241, C-6f, C-11 to C-15,
C-13f, C-16f
NAD (nicotinamide adenine dinucleotide),
239, C-6f
in alcohol metabolism, 241, 241f, C-15
function of, **331**
TCA cycle and vitamins, 347–348, 347f
TCA cycle reactions, C-12f, C-12 to C-14, C-
13f, C-15t
NADP, **331**, C-6f
Naphthoquinone. *See* Vitamin K
Narcotic, alcohol as, **239**, 242
National Health and Nutrition Examination
Survey (NHANES), 22n, 26
National Library of Medicine, 31f
National Nutrition Monitoring program, 22–23
"Natural" *vs.* safe, 34f, 349, 656
Natural water, **400**
Naturopathic medicine, **653**
Nausea during pregnancy, 524–525, 524t
Negative correlation (research), **14**, 15
Negative feedback, **A-4**
Neotame, **132**, 133t, 134
Nephrons, 402f
Nerves/nervous system
alcohol and, 242–243
in Alzheimer's disease, 607
central nervous system, **A-7** to A-8, A-8f
in diabetes, 640
diagram of, A-8f
energy source for, 112, 234, 235
functions of, A-7 to A-8
GI hormones and, 86–88
lead toxicity and, 463, 564
magnesium deficiency, 424
neural tube, **338**
neural tube development, 512–515, 513f. *See
also* Neural tube defects
potassium and, 414
thiamin and, 327
vitamin B₁₂, 341, 344
vitamin B₆ and, 336
vitamin E and, 382
See also Brain
Net protein utilization (NPU), **D-1**
Neural tube, **338**, 513f
Neural tube defects, **338**, 513–515
anencephaly, **513**
critical periods, **512**, 512f, 513–515
folate and, 338, 340, 340f
incidence of, 513n
maternal obesity and, 516
spina bifida, 340f, 341f, **513**, 514f
websites on, 357, 539
Neurofibrillary tangles, **607**
Neurons, **606**
Neuropeptide Y, **253**
Neurotransmitters, **194**
acetylcholine, 345, 606
epinephrine. *See* Epinephrine
norepinephrine, 194
serotonin. *See* Serotonin
synthesis of, 194, 606
tyrosine and, 194
vitamin C and, 352

Neutrophils, **622**
News media, 30–31
NHANES (National Health and Nutrition
Examination Survey), 22n, 26
Niacin, **331**–333, 356t
overview of, 333t
cooking and, 332
deficiency, 331–332, 332f, 332n, 333n,
333t, 348
food sources, 332, 333t, 334f
functions of, 220, 331, 333t
precursor of, 194
RDA/recommendations, 331, 333t, 334f
structure of, C-6f
toxicity, 332, 333t
tryptophan, 194, 331, 332, 336
Niacin equivalents (NE), **331**, 333
Niacin flush, **332**
Nickel, 462
Nicotinamide. *See* Niacin
Nicotinamide adenine dinucleotide. *See* NAD
Nicotinic acid. *See* Niacin
Night blindness, **373**, 373f
See also Vision
Nitrites, **684**
Nitrogen
atomic structure, B-3
in organic compounds, B-3
in proteins, 193n
protein utilization and, D-2
urea and, 226, 226f, C-15 to C-16, C-16f
Nitrogen balance, **193**–194
Nitrosamines, **684**
Non-B vitamins, 345–346
Nonnutrients. *See* Phytochemicals
Nonnutritive sweeteners, **132**
See also Artificial sweeteners
Nonpoint water pollution, **716**, 717
Nonstarch polysaccharides, 106
Noradrenalin. *See* Norepinephrine
Norepinephrine, 194, 617, A-5
NPU (net protein utilization), **D-1**
Nucleotide bases, **207**, 208
Nucleotides, **207**, 208
Nucleus, 208f, 214f, **A-2**, A-3f
Nursing bottle tooth decay, **553**, 554f
Nutraceuticals. *See* Functional foods
Nutrient additives, 685
Nutrient claims (on labels), **57**
Nutrient density, **38**–39
comparing foods, 38
evaluating foods for, 329
exercise, diets and, 497
food labels and, 55
of fruits, 39, 119
for older adults, 602
of snack foods, 39
of sugary foods, 118t, 119
USDA Food Guide and, 42f–43f, 45
of vegetables, 329, 330
weight management and, 39, 45
See also Energy density
Nutrient-drug interactions, 615–618, 616t
anticoagulants and vitamin K, 384, 617
fat-soluble vitamins and mineral oil, 95
folate and, 341, 617, 617f
grapefruit juice and, 617, 617t
metabolism and, 616–617
minerals and antibiotics, 616
tyramine and MAO inhibitors, 617, 618t
Nutrient-gene interactions. *See* Genomics,
nutritional
Nutrient interactions
overview of, 463–464
beta-carotene and vitamin E, 363
B vitamins, 340, 341, 346

calcium, potassium, sodium, 411
calcium and iron, 436
calcium and magnesium, 424
calcium and manganese, 459
calcium and protein, 418
calcium and sodium, 409, 411, 418
calcium and vitamin D, 378, 417f, 418,
434, 436
copper and vitamin C, 442
copper and zinc, 453, 459
fat-soluble vitamins, 386
fiber and minerals, 124, 444
folate and vitamin B₁₂, 340, 341, 342–344,
344f, 514
iodine and selenium, 442
iron and manganese, 442, 459
iron and vitamin C, 66, 351, 354, 444,
448, 556
iron and zinc, 453, 522
magnesium and phosphorus, 409
minerals (overview), 409, 442
riboflavin and vitamin B₆, 346
soy and zinc, 66
supplements and, 363
vitamin A and zinc, 453
vitamin E and vitamin K, 363, 382
See also Nutrient-drug interactions
Nutrient measures (glossary of), inside back
cover
Nutrients, **6**
chemistry of, 5–11, C-1 to C-17
classes of, 7t
conditionally essential, 156, 345
energy-yielding, **7**–10, 7t, 9t, 18, 215f, 216,
217–218, 227
essential, **7**, 154–155, 195, 397
indispensable, **7**
interdependence of, 89
macro- *vs.* micronutrients, **7**
naive *vs.* accurate view of needs, 18f
physiological *vs.* pharmacological effects of,
332, 360
recommendations. *See* DRI; RDA
See also specific nutrients
Nutrigenetics, **11**, 207
Nutrigenomics, **11**, 207
Nutrition, **3**
food choices and, 5
Healthy People 2010 goals, 23, 23t, J-1t to J-2t
national trends in, 23
recommendations. *See* DRI; RDA
research methods, 11–16
websites/resources, 26, 33, 34
See also Dietitians; Information on nutrition,
validity of
Nutritional genomics. *See* Genomics, nutritional
Nutrition assessment, **20**–24, E-1 to E-23
anthropometrics overview, 21, **E-5** to E-6, E-5t
biochemical analyses. *See* Laboratory tests
cautions, E-22 to E-23
data analysis, E-4 to E-5
fat *vs.* lean tissue, 262–263, 264f, E-14 to
E-16, E-16t
growth/growth charts, 548f, E-6 to E-7,
E-6f to E-13f
Healthy People 2010 goals, 23, 23t
historical information, 20–21, 22f, 287, E-1 to
E-5, E-2t
of individuals, 20–22, 21f
iron deficiency, 22, 446
physical examinations, 21, 22f, E-16, E-17t
of populations, 22–24
protein-energy malnutrition, E-17t, E-17 to
E-19, E-19t, E-22t
Nutrition Facts, 55–56, G-2f
Nutritionists, **32**

Nutrition screening, **E-1** to E-23
Nutrition status
  medications and, 615–618, 616t
  national surveys, 22–23, 22n
  of older adults, 598–601, 615
  risk factors, E-2t
  supplements and, 360–361
  vitamins and minerals, E-18t
  See also Deficiencies; Nutrition assessment
Nutrition support. *See* Diet therapy
Nutritive sweeteners, **132,** 136, 136t
Nuts, 43f, 126, 173–174, 393, 566

O

Obesity, 281–310
  in adolescence, 115, 120, 576
  alcohol and, 243, 246t
  animal studies on, 13f, 285f
  BMI and, 260f
  BMR and, 254
  body composition and, 262–263, 262f, 263f
  calcium and, 416
  cancer risk, 266, 643, 646t
  causes of, 283–288
  central obesity, 243, **262**–263, 262f, 263f, 265, 301–302, 630
  in children, 115, 120, 567–571, 567f, 568f, 586
  cholesterol, blood levels, 587, 588
  as chronic disease, 292
  clinically severe, **292**
  diabetes and, 115, 265, 586, 638
  environmental influences on, 302–303
  exercise and, 287–288, 299–302, 569
  fast food/restaurant portions, 287
  fat and energy intake, 160, 315–316
  fat cell number and, 282, 283f
  genetic basis of, 284–285, 316t
  health risks overview, 263–266, 288–289, 625f
  heart disease risk, 265, 629, 630
  hunger/poverty and, 702–703
  hyperplastic/hypertrophic, **283**
  hypertension and, 265, 635
  lifestyle choices and, 285–287, 299–303
  lipoprotein lipase (LPL) and, 282–283
  mortality rates, 264f, 265
  in older adults, 598
  overeating and, 285–286
  overnutrition and, **20**
  during pregnancy, 516
  prevention of, 569–570
  psychological/social factors, 289, 289f
  smoking and, 262, 264
  statistics on, 281, 282f
  sugar and, 120
  types of, 262f, 263f, 283
  websites on, 309
  See also Obesity treatment; Overweight; Weight loss; Weight management
Obesity gene, 283, 285f
Obesity treatment, 294–305
  aggressive treatments, 292–293, 293f
  behavior modification, 571
  for children, 569–571
  dangers of, 289–291, 291t
  drugs, 290, 291t, 292, 616
  exercise, 299–302
  expectations and goals, 294–295, 294f
  herbal products, 291t
  safe rate of weight loss, 295
  strategies, successful, 294–298, 295t, 296t, 297f, 299t
  support groups, 304
  surgery, 286, 292–293, 293f
  websites on, 309
  See also Diet planning; Diets; Weight loss; Weight management

Ob gene, 283, 285f
Obligatory water excretion, **399**
Ob protein, **284**
Oils, **139**
  heart health and, 633
  saturation, degree of, 142, 144f, 164
  tropical, 142, 144f, 175, 633
  in USDA Food Guide, 41t, 44, 47f
  See also Fats; Fish oils; Monounsaturated fats; Polyunsaturated fats
Older adults. *See* Aging (older adults)
Oldways Preservation and Exchange Trust, 61, 67
Olean. *See* Olestra
Oleic acid, 141t, 145f
Olestra, 93, **164**–165
Oligosaccharides, **105**
Olive oil, 144f, 158, 173
Omega, defined, **141**
Omega-3 fatty acids. *See* Fatty acids, omega-3
Omega-6 fatty acids. *See* Fatty acids, omega-6
Omnivores, **64**
Opsin, 192, **371,** 371f
Oral rehydration therapy (ORT), **406, 707**
Organelles, **A-2**
Organic, **7, 58,** 680
Organically grown crops, 7, 680, 681f, 691
Organic halogen, **675**
Organic nutrients, 7, 7t
Organosulfur compounds, 470t
Orlistat, **292**
Ornish Diet, 317t
Ornithine, 182n
Orotic acid, 346
Orthomolecular medicine, **653**
Osmosis, **405,** 405f
Osmotic pressure, **405**
Osteoarthritis, **605**
Osteoblasts, **372,** 417f
Osteoclasts, **372,** 377n, 417f
Osteomalacia, **378,** 381t, 522
Osteopenia, 434f
Osteoporosis, **421,** 431–437
  age and bone mass, 433–434, 433f, 434f, 603
  in athletes, 271, 271f
  body weight and, 264, 435
  calcium and, 200, 361, 411, 421, 433–434, 435–436
  eating disorders and, 271
  estrogen replacement therapy, 434
  exercise and, 435, 478
  gender and, 434–435, 436
  height loss, 433f
  hip fractures, 431, 433, 436
  hormones and, 434–435, 434n
  potassium and, 411
  proteins (dietary) and, 200
  risk factors, 432–433, 433t
  sodium and, 411
  therapy for, 361, 434, 434n
  type I, **431,** 432, 433t
  type II, **431,** 432, 433t
  types of bone, 431–432, 432f
  vitamin A and, 374
  vitamin D and, 378, 434, 436
  websites on, 437
Ovarian cancer, 644t
Overeating
  binge eating, **270,** 274, 275f, 276, 277t
  cognitive influences, 251
  compulsive, 276
  energy metabolism and, 232–233, 234f
  factors affecting, 251–252, 252f, 253f, 302–303
  obesity due to, 287, 304
Overfat *vs.* overweight, 258, 259
Overload principle, 480–481

Overnutrition, **20**
  See also Feasting; Obesity
Overpopulation, 707–709
Overt, defined, **22**
Overweight, **259,** 281–310
  arthritis and, 605
  BMI and, 260f
  breastfeeding and, 552
  cataracts and, 605
  causes of, 283–288
  in children, 558, 567–571, 567f, 568f, E-7
  cholesterol, blood levels, 588
  fertility and, 509
  fitness and, 266, 288–289
  health risks overview, 265–266
  Healthy People 2010 goals, 23t
  older adults, 598
  during pregnancy, 516, 517f, 517t
  prevalence of, 282f, 282
  salt sensitivity, 410
  vs. overfat, 258, 259
  websites on, 309
  See also Obesity; Weight gain; Weight loss
Ovum, **510,** 511f
Oxalate/oxalic acid, **409**
  calcium absorption, 418
  iron absorption, 444
  kidney stones, 354n, 355n
  mineral absorption, 409
Oxaloacetate, **227,** 228f
Oxidants, **390,** 391
  See also Antioxidants; Prooxidants
Oxidation (of energy nutrients), 223
Oxidation (of fats), **143, 222**
  carbohydrate intake and, 228n
  carnitine and, 346
  exercise and, 489
  fatty acid metabolism, 222–223, 223f, 231f
  genetics and, 210
  in mitochondria, 222n
  rancidity, 143
  reaction sequence, C-11, C-11f
  vitamin E and, 382, 383
  See also Ketone bodies
Oxidation-reduction reactions, 442, B-7f, B-7 to B-8
Oxidative burst, 352, 390
Oxidative stress, **351, 390**
  aging process and, 597, 606–607
  cataracts and, 605
  diet and, 597
  effects of, 391
  exercise and, 492
  iron and, 448
  vegetable intake and, 598
  vitamin C and, 351, 353
  vitamin E, 492
  See also Antioxidants; Free radicals
Oxygen
  atomic structure of, B-3
  circulatory system and exercise, 482, 483f
  energy metabolism and, 229, 486
  free radicals, 390, 390n, 391
  in glucose metabolism, 221
  lead toxicity and, 463
  molecular structure of, B-4f
  oxygenated water, 505
  VO_2 max, **482,** 483f
  See also Aerobic activity; Hemoglobin
Oxygen-derived free radicals, 390, 390n, 391
Oxytocin, **533, A-5**
Oysters, 670
Oyster shell, **431,** 436
Ozone therapy, **653**

P

PABA (para-aminobenzoic acid), 346
Pagophagia, **447**
Pain, tryptophan and, 203
Palm oil, 142, 144f, 157, 175
Pancreas, **72**, 73f, 74, 515
Pancreatic cancer, 341, 644t
Pancreatic duct, 73f
Pancreatic enzymes
  amylase, **108**
  carbohydrases, 87, 109f
  functions of, 77, 80t
  lipases, 87, 148f, 149
  protein digestion, 186f
  secretion of, 87–88, 109f
  zinc and, 452, 453f
Pancreatic hormones. *See* Glucagon; Insulin
Pancreatic juice, 77, 77f, **78**
Pancreatitis, 88
Pangamic acid, 346
Pantothenic acid, **335**, 335t, 347f, 348, 356t, C-7f
Para-aminobenzoic acid (PABA), 346
Paraguay tea, 656
Paralytic and neurotoxic shellfish poisoning, 670n
Parasympathetic (nervous system), A-7 to A-8, A-8f
Parathormone (PTH), 191t, **416**, 434, 434n, A-6
Parathyroid gland, 416, 417f, A-6
Parathyroid hormone, **417**, 417f, A-6
Pasteurization, **666**, 673
Pathogens, **664**
PBB (polybrominated biphenyl), **676**
PCBs (polychlorinated biphenyls), **676**
PDCAAS (protein-digestibility-corrected amino acid score), **D-1** to D-2, D-2t
Peak bone mass, **418**, 421f
Peanuts, 566
Peas. *See* Legumes
Pectins, 106n
Peer review, **14**, 15
Pellagra, **331**, 332f, 332n, 348;p
PEM. *See* Protein-energy malnutrition
Pepsin, **185**, 186f
Pepsinogen, **185**
Peptic ulcer, **94**, 97, 97t
Peptidase, **185**
Peptide bond, **183**, 183f
Perfringens food poisoning, 665t
Peripheral nervous system, **A-7** to A-8, A-8f
Peripheral resistance, **633**, 634f
Peristalsis, **74**–75, 75f, 86, 92–93, 95
Pernicious anemia, **343**, 344f, 514
Peroxides, B-8
PER (protein efficiency ratio), **D-1**, D-3 to D-4, D-4t
Persistence (of contaminants), **674**–675
Pesticides, **678**–681
  adverse reactions, 567
  cancer risk, 643
  effects of, 716
  EPA hotline for, 680
  imported foods and, 678–679
  plant-pesticides, **693**, 695
  sustainable agriculture, 718t
  tolerance levels, **567**
pH, **77**
  acid-base balance, 406–407, 407f
  of digestive secretions, 77f
  explanation of scale, 77f, 407f, B-6
  in intestines, 77, 87
  ketosis and, 235
  in stomach, 77
  See also Acid-base balance
Phagocytes, **622**

Phagocytosis, **622**
Pharmacological effect of nutrients, 332, 360
Pharynx, **72**, 73, 73f
Phenolic acids, 470t
Phenylalanine, 133–134, 134f, 182f, 183, 209
Phenylketonuria (PKU), 133–134, 183, **207**, 209
Phospholipids, **145**–146, 146f, 149, 422
  See also Lecithin
Phosphoproteins, 422
Phosphorus, **422**–423
  overview of, 423t, 426t
  absorption of, 409
  deficiency, 422, 423t
  food sources, 422, 423f, 423t
  functions of, 422, 423t
  intake recommendations, 422, 423f, 423t
  magnesium and, 409
  toxicity, 423t
Photosynthesis, **213**, B-7
Phylloquinone, **385**
  See also Vitamin K
Physical activity, **477**–501
  alcohol and, 496
  appetite and, 301
  basal metabolic rate and, 254, 254f, 255t, 256
  body's response to, 481
  caffeine and, 496
  children, 567–568, 569, 570, 588
  discretionary kcalories and, 300, 300f
  duration, 485, 485t, 487, 489, 490
  endurance, 484, 486f, 487, 489
  energy (kcal) expenditure, 254, 254f, 255t, 257t, 300, 482, 489
  energy (kcal) expenditure: calculating, 257, F-1, F-2 to F-6t
  energy metabolism: carbohydrates, 221, 485–488, 485t, 486f, 488t
  energy metabolism: fats, 486f, 489
  energy metabolism: proteins, 486f, 490–491, 491t
  exercise, defined, **477**
  free radicals and, 492
  Healthy People 2010 goals, J-2t
  intensity, 482, 485t, 486, 489, 490
  during lactation, 534–535
  minerals for, 491–493
  moderate exercise, **481**
  pregnancy and, 509, 518–519, 519f, 529
  "spot reducing," 301, 489
  vitamins for, 491–493
  websites on, 499–500, 648
  See also Aerobic activity; Athletes; Fitness
Physical activity, benefits of
  overview of, 301, 478–480
  arthritis and, 605
  blood lipids and, 588
  body composition and, 300–301
  cancer and, 478, 643, 646t
  constipation and, 94
  diabetes and, 638, 641
  heart disease risks, 478, 489, 629, 632t
  hypertension reduction, 636
  longevity, 595–596
  muscle mass, 599f
  obesity and, 266, 569, 570
  for older adults, 478, 595–596, 596t
  osteoporosis and, 435, 478, 484
  psychological, 301
  for weight control, 287–288, 299–302, 305, 484
  for weight gain, 308
Physical activity guidelines
  overview of, 479f, 480–484, 480t
  Canadian recommendations, I-7f
  carbohydrate intake, 486f, 487–488, 497
  cardiorespiratory endurance, **480**, 482–483, 483f

  choosing types of, 479, 479f
  in daily routines, 479f
  Dietary Guidelines and, 39, 40t, 479
  diet planning for, 496–499, 498f
  duration, **480**, 480t, 483t, 576
  fat intake, 489
  fluids and electrolytes, 493–497, 494t
  frequency, 479, 479f, **480**, 480t, 483t
  for heart disease reduction, 632t
  for hypertension reduction, 635t, 636
  intensity, **480**, 480t, 482
  moderate exercise, **481**
  for older adults, 596, 596t, 603
  progressive overload principle, **480**
  protein intake, 490–491, 491t, 497
  pyramid, 479f
  safety, 481, 484, 493–495
  sample schedule, 483t
  snacks, 487, 498f
  warm-up/cool-down, **481**
  websites on, 581
  for weight management, 288, 299–302, 495
  weight training, 481, **484**
Physical examinations, 21, 22f, E-16, E-17t
  See also Laboratory tests
Physical fitness. *See* Fitness
Physicians, nutrition information from, 31
Physiological age, **595**
Physiological fuel value, **250**
Phytates (phytic acid), **107**, **409**
  calcium absorption, 418
  digoxin and, 616
  iron absorption, 444, 448
  manganese and, 459
  minerals and, 107, 409, 470t
  yeast and, 453n
  zinc and, 452
Phytochemicals, **6**, 469–471
  as antioxidants, 391, 469–470, 470t, 471
  cancer and, 469–470, 470t, 645, 655
  carotene. *See* Beta-carotene; Carotenoids
  disease prevention, 469–471, 470t, 472f
  effects of, 470t
  food sources, 158, 469–471, 470t, 472f
  in green tea, 655
  heart disease and, 471, 472f
  macular degeneration and, 472f
  in nuts, 173
  osteoporosis and, 434
  types of, 470t, 472f
  See also Functional foods
Phytoestrogens, 434, **469**, 470t, 472f
Phytosterols, **469**, 471, 472, 472f, 633
Pica, **447**, 525, 564
Picolinate, **503**
"Pigeon breast," 381n
Pigment, **371**
Pituitary gland, 403f, **A-3** to A-4, A-4f
PKU (phenylketonuria), 133–134, 183, **207**, 209
Placebo effect, 12, **14**, 653
Placebos, 12–13, **14**, 352
Placenta, **510**, 511f
Plant foods
  cancer risk and, 123, 643, 644t, 646t
  fats and health, 65, 144f, 157
  in food group plans, 41t, 42f–43f, 44, 44t
  protein and bone health, 200
  protein and heart disease, 199
  protein quality, 195
  vs. animal foods: sustainable agriculture, 717, 717f, 718–719, 718t, 719f
  See also Fruits; Grains; Legumes; Nuts; Phytochemicals; Vegetables
Plant-pesticides, **693**, 695
Plant sterols, 470t
  See also Phytosterols

Plaque, dental, **119**
Plaques, atheromatous, **626,** 627, 629
Plaques, fibrous, 586–**587,** 587f
  See also Atherosclerosis
Plaques, senile, **607**
Plasma, **E-17**
Platelets, **627**
PLP (pyridoxal phosphate), **336,** 347f, 348
  See also Vitamin B₆
Point of unsaturation, **141**
Poisoning. *See* Foodborne illnesses; Lead;
  Toxicity; *specific toxins*
Polar, **403**
Polar bear liver, 376
Pollution. *See* Contaminants; Environmental
  contaminants
Polybrominated biphenyl (PBB), **676**
Polychlorinated biphenyls (PCBs), **676**
Polyglutamate, 338, 339f
Polyols, **132**
Polypeptide, **183**
Polysaccharides, **105**–107
  nonstarch, 106
  structure of, 106f, C-2f to C-3f
  See also Glycogen; Starch
Polyunsaturated fats, **141**
  in exchange lists, G-9t
  food sources, 141t, 144f, 158, 173, 174,
    176f, 176t
  free radicals and, 390, 391f
  genetics and, 210
  heart disease and, 158, 392
  LDL cholesterol and, 210
  in range fed beef, 162, 719
  replacing saturated fats, 162, 162f, 163, 164,
    164t, 166f
  structure, 141–142, 141f–144f, 141t, C-3t
  vitamin E and, 382, 383
Polyunsaturated fatty acids (PUFA), **141**
  See also Fatty acids, omega-3; Fatty acids,
    omega-6
Population
  growth, hunger, environmental degradation,
    708f, 709–710
  older adults in U.S., 593, 594f
  world, increase in, 707–709
Populations, nutrition assessment of, 22–24
Pork, thiamin in, 328f, 329
Portal vein, **83,** 85f
Portion sizes. *See* Serving sizes/portion sizes
Positive correlation (research), **14,** 15
Postpartum amenorrhea, **537**
Post term (infant), **516**
Potable water, **688**
Potassium, **414**–415
  overview of, 415t, 426t
  deficiency, 414, 415t, 636–637
  Dietary Guidelines and, 40t, 412, 640
  diuretics and, 636–637
  food sources, 414, 415f
  functions of, 412, 414, 415t, 436
  hypertension and, 414
  intake recommendations, 414, 415t
  osteoporosis and, 411
  in processed foods, 412, 412f, 414
  sodium-potassium pump, 406
  toxicity, 414–415, 415t
  transport proteins and, 192f
Potatoes, 116, 354, 644–645, 677, 685, 695
Poultry, 163, 668, 669, 669f, 670
  See also Meats
Poverty. *See* Food assistance programs; Hunger,
  chronic/world; Socioeconomic status
Prader-Willi syndrome, 284, 285
Prealbumin. *See* Transthyretin
Prebiotics, **86**

Precursors (vitamin), **324**
Prediabetes, **637**
Preeclampsia, 517, **528**
Pregnancy, 509–545
  in adolescence, 529
  alcohol use during, 245, 530, 543–545,
    543f, 545f
  body changes during, 519
  body composition and, 262
  caffeine use during, 532
  calcium, 418
  critical periods, **512**–515, 512f
  diabetes and, 527–528
  drugs (illicit) and, 530
  drugs (medications) and, 530
  eating disorders and, 273
  energy needs, 520, 521f
  environmental contaminants, 531
  exercise and, 509, 518–519, 519f, 529
  father's alcohol intake and, 545
  fish consumption, 174, 531, 675, 676
  folate and, 338, 340, 514–515, 520, 521f
  foodborne illnesses, 531
  Healthy People 2010 goals, J-2t
  herbal supplements and, 657n
  high-risk, **525**–532, 526t
  hormones, A-6
  hypertension and, 528, 528n
  illness, maternal, and, 509
  iodine in, 456
  iron, 446, 521f, 522
  low-risk, **525**
  malnutrition and, 526–527
  maternal discomfort, alleviating, 524t
  nutrition before, 509–510, 526–527
  nutrition during, 519–525, 521f, 522f, 523f,
    524t, inside front cover
  nutrition-related concerns, 524–525, 524t
  in older women, 529–530
  placental development, 510, 511f
  smoking/tobacco use, 530–531
  supplements during, 374, 514, 520, 521f, 522,
    523, 524, 530, 531–532
  underweight and, 264–265
  vitamin A and, 374
  vitamin B₁₂ needs, 520, 521f, 524
  websites on, 539, 545
  weight gain during, 516–517, 517f, 517t, 518f,
    528, 529
  zinc needs, 521f, 522
  See also Birth defects; Fertility/infertility; Fetal
    development
Prehypertension, **626,** 628, 628t
Prejudice and body weight, 289
Premature (infant), **516**
Prenatal alcohol exposure, 543, **544**
Prepared foods, 4, 175, 177
Preservatives, **682**
  See also Additives
Pressure ulcers, **602**
Preterm (infant), **516,** 525–526, 530, 554
Primary amenorrhea, **270**
Primary deficiency, **22**
Pritikin Program, 317t
Probiotics, **86**
Processed foods, **50**
  calcium, potassium, sodium, 412f
  fried, and cancer, 644–645
  functional foods, 471–473
  obesity and, 569
  potassium, 412, 412f, 414
  prepared foods, 4, 175, 177
  salt/sodium in, 411–412, 412f, 456
  vitamin E in, 383
Progesterone, **A-5,** A-7
Progressive overload principle, **480**

Prolactin, **533,** A-4, **A-5**
Prolactin-inhibiting hormone (PIH), **A-5**
Proline, 182n
Promoters (cancer), **642,** 643f, 645
Proof (alcohol), 238, **239**
Prooxidants, 354, 374, **390,** 393, 448
Propionic acid, 108n
Prostaglandins, 615, 627
Prostate cancer, 160, 644t
Prostate gland, 654f
Protease inhibitors, 470t
Proteases, **77,** 185, 186f
Protein deficiency. *See* Protein-energy
  malnutrition (PEM)
Protein digestibility-corrected amino acid score
  (PDCAAS), **D-1** to D-2, D-2t
Protein efficiency ratio (PER), **D-1,** D-3
  to D-4, D-4t
Protein-energy malnutrition (PEM), **196**–199,
  197t, 198f
  acute, **197**
  in anorexia nervosa, 273
  assessment of, E-17 to E-19, E-17t, E-19t
  chronic, **197**
  immune system and, 623, 623t
  indicators of, 273n
  kwashiorkor, 197t, **198,** 199f
  marasmus, **197,** 197t, 198f
  websites for, 204
  See also Malnutrition
Protein-kcalorie malnutrition (PCM). *See*
  Protein-energy malnutrition (PEM)
Proteins, defined, **181**
Proteins (body), 187–194
  alcohol's effect on, 241
  building muscles, 202
  endogenous, defined, **193**
  exercise and, 490–491
  fasting/low-kcal diets, 201, 234–235, 234f
  fluid balance and, 405–406
  free radicals and, 391f
  functions of, 10, 184, 189–193, 190f,
    191t, 192f
  gene expression and, 189, **207,** 208
  glycoproteins, 112
  low-carbohydrate diets and, 319
  metabolism overview, 192, 193–194
  nitrogen balance, **193**
  phospholipids in, 422
  sulfur and, 425, 427
  vitamin A and, 372
Proteins (chemistry), 181–185
  amino acids in, 182t, C-4f
  denaturation, **184**–185
  elements in, 7t
  estimation/measurement of, 193n
  gluconeogenesis, **112,** 192, 225, 225f, 334
  liver metabolism of, 215t
  metabolism overview, 193–194, 215f, 241,
    C-11 to C-13f
  structure of, 181–185, 183f, 184f
  synthesis of, 187–189, 188f, 194, 195, 208,
    351–352, 371, 490
  See also Amino acids
Proteins (dietary), 195–203
  amino acid scoring, **D-1,** D-1t
  biological value of, **D-1,** D-2, D-2t
  BMI and, 318, 319
  body's use of, 227t
  in breast milk, 550, 550f, 554
  in breast milk *vs.* formula, 553f
  calcium and bones, 436
  calcium loss and, 418
  in Canadian food groups, I-12t to I-11t
  cancer and, 200
  for children, 560

Proteins (dietary), *continued*
complementary, **195**–196, 196f
Daily Values, 196, 197n
deficiencies, 196
digestibility of, **195**
digestion of, 77, 79f, 80t, 88, 185, 186f
energy (kcal) in, 9t, 10, 230
in exchange lists, 47, G-1t, G-3t, G-8t
for exercise, 491, 491t, 497
exogenous, defined, **193**
fat made from, 232
fats (dietary) and, 319
health effects of, 199–200
heart disease and, 199–200, 319
high-protein diets. *See* Diets, high-protein
high-quality, **195**
hunger and, 252
for infant growth, 201, 548–549
intestinal motility and, 88
labeling regulations, 196
net protein utilization (NPU), **D-1**
niacin and, 332
nitrogen balance, **193**
for older adults, 602
osteoporosis and, 200
overconsumption of, 199, 201–202, 319
overeating and, 232, 234f
plant *vs.* animal sources, 65, 157, 195, 199, 200
during pregnancy/lactation, 520, 521f
protein digestibility-corrected amino acid score (PDCAAS), **D-1** to D-2, D-2t
protein efficiency ratio (PER), **D-1**, D-3 to D-4, D-4t
quality of, 194–196, D-1t, D-1 to D-4, D-2t, D-4t
RDA/intake recommendations, 18, 201–202
reference protein (standard), **195**
supplements, 202–203, 202n, 520
textured vegetable protein, **53, 64,** 66
thermic effect of food, 256, 318
USDA Food Guide, 41t, 43f, 44
in vegetarian diets, 66, 66f, 196
for weight loss, 295t
See also Amino acids; Protein-energy malnutrition (PEM)
Protein-sparing action, **112,** 194
Protein turnover, **193**
Proteomics, **187**
Prothrombin, 384f
Protons, B-1 to B-3, B-2t
Provitamins, **324**
Prozac (fluoxetine), 276n
Prune juice, 95
Psychological problems
alcohol as risk for, 246t
from being overweight, 289f, 569
dementia, 606–607, 607t
depression, 155, 275, 478, 600, 654f
eating disorders and, 272, 274, 275, J-2t
exercise and, 478
muscle dysmorphia, **270,** 272
in older adults, 600
weight loss and, 301, 304
PTH (parathormone), 191t, **416,** 434, 434n, A-6
Puberty, **576**
Public health dietitian, **32**
Public water, **400**
PubMed, 30, 31f
PUFA. *See* Polyunsaturated fatty acids
Pulmonary circulation, 84f
Purging, 274–275, 275f
Purified water, **400**
⋯⋯⋯⋯ **606**
⋯⋯⋯⋯ hincter, **72,** 73f, 74, 75, 76, 87

Pyramids
children, 561f
MyPyramid, 47, 47f, 60t, 65–66, 66f
physical activity, 479f
vegetarian diets, 65, 66f, 67
websites on, 67, 580
See also Diet planning
Pyridoxal, C-6f
See also Vitamin B$_6$
Pyridoxal phosphate (PLP), **336,** 347f, 348, C-7f
See also Vitamin B$_6$
Pyridoxamine, C-6f
See also Vitamin B$_6$
Pyridoxamine phosphate, C-7f
See also Vitamin B$_6$
Pyridoxine, C-6f
See also Vitamin B$_6$
Pyrroloquinoline quinone, 346
Pyruvate (pyruvic acid), **218,** 218n
amino acid metabolism, 225, 225f, C-11 to C-13f
B vitamins and, 347, 347f
glucose metabolism, 219–222, 219f–222f
glycerol metabolism, 222, 224f
supplements, 291t, **504**
in TCA cycle, 228f, A-2n, C-11 to C-13f
PYY, 285

Q

Qi gong, **653**
Quackery/quacks, 30, **32,** 33, 34, 34f
fad diets, 315–321
See also Fad diets; Information on nutrition, validity of; Myths
Quality of life, **594**
Quorn, 471n

R

Race/ethnicity
bone density and, 260
diabetes and, 638
ethnic foods, 4, 46, 46t, 61
lactose intolerance and, 111
obesity and, 576
osteoporosis and, 435
See also African Americans/Blacks
Rachitic rosary, **378,** 381n
RAE (retinol activity equivalents), **374**
Raloxifene, 434n
Randomization (in research), 12, **14**
RBP (retinol-binding protein), **370,** E-18, E-19t
RDA (Recommended Dietary Allowances), **17,** inside front cover
for assessing dietary intake, 21f
for protein, setting of, 201
purpose of, 17, 19
safe *vs.* toxic nutrient intakes, 18f
vs. Estimated Average Requirement (EAR), 16–17, 17f
See also DRI (Dietary Reference Intakes); specific nutrients
Reactive oxygen species (ROS), 390n
Recommended Dietary Allowances (RDA). *See* RDA
Rectum, **72,** 73f, 76
Red blood cells
in anemia, 189, 189f, 344f, 446, 447f
erythrocyte hemolysis, **382,** 383n
erythrocyte protoporphyrin, **446,** E-20t, E-21t
erythropoietin, **A-3,** A-6
glucose needs of, 223, 234
iron and, 445
lead toxicity and, 463
life span of, 6, 445
normal, 189f

in "sports anemia," **493**
See also Hemoglobin
Reduction reactions, B-7
Reference protein, **195**
Refined (foods), **50**–52, 50f, 51f
Reflux, **76, 94,** 96–97, 96f, 97t
Registered dietitians (RD), **19, 32**
Registration, **32**
Regulations. *See under* FDA (Food and Drug Administration)
Relaxin, **A-5,** A-6
Religious dietary traditions, 5
Remodeling (bone), **372,** 416
Renin, **401,** 403f, 410n, **A-3,** A-6
Rennin, **693,** 694
Replication (research), **14,** 15
Reproductive system, vitamin A and, 372
Requirements (for nutrients), **16,** inside front cover
See also DRI; RDA
Research, 11–16
on alternative medicine, 652–654
analysis/interpretation of, 14–15
approaches to, 11–15
on colds (example), 12–15
correlation, **14,** 15
evaluating validity of, 15–16, 30–31, 33, 34
hypotheses and theories, 11–12, 12f, **14**
journal articles, 31t, 33
on obesity, 285f
publishing of, 15–16
PubMed searches, 31t
sample size, 13
study designs, 11–15, 12f, 13f, 14t
terminology, 11–14
Residues (pesticide), **678**
Resistance training, 480t, **484**
Resistant starch, **107**
Resource use, 717–720, 719f
Restaurants
fast food, 159, 376, 578, H-58 to H-77
obesity and, 287, 303
salt/sodium, 456
serving sizes, 54, 303
trans fats in, 159, 177
Resting metabolic rate (RMR), **254**
Resveratrol, 470t, 472f
Retardation, mental
cretinism and iodine deficiency, 456
Down syndrome, 340, **530**
fetal alcohol syndrome, 530, 543–545
malnutrition and, 706
PKU (phenylketonuria), 133, 209
Retina, **371,** 373
Retin-A, 374
Retinal, 369–370, 370f, 371, 371f, 373, C-5f
Retinoic acid, 244, 370–371, 370f, C-5f
Retinoids, **369**
Retinol, 369–370, 370f, 372, C-5f
Retinol activity equivalents (RAE), **374**
Retinol-binding protein (RBP), **370,** 452, E-18, E-19t
Retinyl esters, 369
Rheumatoid arthritis, **605**
Rhodopsin, **371,** 371f
Riboflavin, 328–330, **329**
overview of, 330t, 356t
deficiency, 329, 330t
destruction of, 324
food sources, 329–330, 330t, 331f
functions of, 328, 330t
RDA/recommendations, 329, 330t, 331f
in structure of coenzymes, 330f, C-5f
vitamin B$_6$ and, 346
Ribose, **504**
Ribosomes, 187, 188f, 214f, **A-3,** A-3f

Rice, beriberi and, 327
Rice milk/drinks, 197, 557
Rickets, **378**
  bones of skull, 381f
  described, 378f, 381t
  osteomalacia, **378**, 381t
  sunshine and, 379
  in vegans, 67
  vitamin D and, 522–523, 551
Risedronate, 434n
Risk, **663**
  See also Safety
Risk factors, **24**–25
RNA polymerase, 452n
RNA (ribonucleic acid), 187, 188f, 193n, **207**, 208
Rods (of retina), 371f
Rough endoplasmic reticulum, **A-2**, A-3f
Royal jelly, **504**

S

Saccharin, **132**–133, 133t
Safety, **663**–689
  alternative therapies and, 652, 655f, 656t–658t
  of artificial sweeteners, 132–136
  choking, 92, 92f, 93f, 572
  ergogenic aids, 503–507, 506t
  exercise and, 481, 484, 493–495
  of fat replacers, 165
  food additives, 683
  of functional foods, 472–473
  genetic engineering (GM foods), **693**–697, 697t
  herbal remedies, 652–658, 655f, 657t, 658t
  herbal weight loss products, 291, 291t
  margin of safety (additives), **683**
  "natural" *vs.* safe herbs, 656
  pesticide exposure, 678–681
  public health strategies, 306–307, 306t
  of supplements, 392–393, 436, 656–659, 656t–658t
  See also Contaminants; Foodborne illnesses; Quackery/quacks; Toxicity
Salicylates, 655
Saliva, 76–77, **78**, 109f
Salivary amylase, 108
Salivary glands, **78**
  carbohydrate digestion, 77, 80t, 108
  fat digestion, 80n, 147–148, 148f
  functions of, 76–77
  location of, 76f, 109f
  protein digestion, 186f
Salmonella, 664, 665t
Salts, **403**, 404f
  See also Electrolytes
Salt sensitivity, **410**, 410n, 635
Salt (table). *See* Sodium; Sodium chloride
Saponins, 470t
Sarcomas, **642**
Sarcopenia, **598**, 599f
Satiating, **251**
Satiation, **251**, 252f, 253f
Satiety, **108**
  factors affecting, 251–253, 252f, 253f
  fat and, 252, 298
  fiber and, 108, 252
  ghrelin and, 285, 286
  leptin and, 284
  overriding signals, 251–252
  protein and, 252
  PYY and, 285
Saturated fats, **141**
  blood cholesterol and, 157, 158, 175, 175f
  cancer and, 160, 645
  chemistry of, 140, C-3t
  diabetes and, 641
  in exchange lists, G-9t

food sources, 141t, 144f, 157, 157f, 175, 176t
heart disease risk, 65, 157, 158, 173, 175f, 626, 632t, 633
intake, lowering, 162, 162f, 163, 164, 164t, 166f, 167, 176f
intake recommendations, 157
on labels, **58**
in meats, 162f
in milk and milk products, 162f
structure of, 140, 141t, C-3t
in U.S. diet, 157f
vegetarian diets and, 65
Saturated fatty acids, **141**
Saw palmetto, 654f, 657t, 658t
School nutrition programs, 573–575, 574t, 702
Science of nutrition. *See* Research
Scientific method, 11, 12f
Scombroid poisoning, 670n
Scurvy, **350**, 353, 353f, 354
Seafood. *See* Fish/seafood
Seaweed, 67
Secondary amenorrhea, **270**
Secondary deficiency, **22**
Second Harvest, 704
Secretin, **87**, 88t, A-6
Sedentary, defined, **477**
  See also Lifestyle choices
Segmentation (intestinal), **75**–76, 75f
Selective estrogen-receptor modulator (SERM), 434n
Selenium, **457**, 464t
  overview of, 458t
  deficiency, 457, 458t
  food sources, 457–458, 458t
  intake recommendations, 458, 458t
  iodine and, 442
  toxicity, 458, 458t
Self-image/self-esteem, 276, 289, 301, 478, 569
  See also Body image
Senile dementia, **606**
Senile plaques, **607**
Senna, 655
Serotonin, **120**, **290**
  drug use and, 579
  functions of, 194
  precursor of, 194
  vitamin B$_6$, 336
Serum, **E-17**
Serum ferritin, E-20, E-20t, E-21t
Serum iron, E-21, E-21t
Serum transferrin, E-20t, E-21t
Serving sizes/portion sizes
  in Canada's *Food Guide*, I-3t to I-6t
  in Canadian food groups, I-8t to I-11t
  energy intake and, 41t, 44t
  estimating, 46
  in exchange lists, G-1 to G-11, G-1t, G-4t to G-11t
  fast food, 287
  fat and, 252, 253f
  on labels, 54f, 55
  meats/protein, 43f, 53
  nutritional assessment and, E-5
  overeating and, 303
  in restaurants, 54, 303
  satiety and, 252–253, 253f
  USDA Food Guide and, 41, 42f–43f, 44, 46
  for weight gain, 308
  for weight loss, 296
Set-point theory, **283**
Seven Countries Study, 173
Sex. *See* Gender differences
Sex hormones. *See* Estrogens; Progesterone; Testosterone
Shape Up America, 266
Shigellosis, 665t

Shopping. *See* Grocery shopping
Sibutramine, **292**
Sickle-cell anemia, **189**, 189f, 204
SIDS. *See* Sudden infant death syndrome
Silicon, 462
Simple carbohydrates. *See under* Carbohydrates (dietary)
Skin
  acne, 374
  beta-carotene and, 373f, 374, 375f, 377n
  epithelial cells, **371**
  finding cause of problems, 350
  keratinization of, 373f, **374**
  vitamin A and, 373–374
  vitamin C and, 353, 353f
  vitamin D and, 377, 380, 380f
Skin cancer, 379–380
Skin cells, 190
Skinfold body fat test, 264f
Skinfold measures, **264f**, E-14f, E-14 to E-15, E-16t
Sleep, 203, 286, 478
Small for gestational age (SGA), **526**
Small intestines, **72**
  absorptive functions, 79f, 81–83, 81f, 82f, 110f
  anatomy of, 73f, 74, 74n, 80, 82f
  bacteria in. *See* Intestinal bacteria
  calcium balance and, 417f
  carbohydrates digestion in, 79f, 108, 109f
  digestive functions, 75f, 79f, 109f
  enzymes of, 77, 81, 109f, 186f
  fat absorption, 149–150, 152f
  fat digestion, 79f, 148f, 149
  motility, **74**, 88, 94
  muscles of, 75–76, 75f
  peristalsis, **74**–75, 75f, 86
  pH of, 87
  protein digestion, 79f, 185, 186f
Smell, sense of, 72
Smoking/tobacco use
  adolescents and, 579–580, 589
  antioxidants and, 580
  atherosclerosis and, 587
  beta-carotene and, 374
  body fat and, 262, 264
  cancer and, 643, 644t
  chronic disease risk, 25, 25t
  deaths from, 25, 25t
  folate and, 341
  heart disease risk, 589, 629, 631
  lactation and, 538
  nutrient intakes and, 579
  osteoporosis and, 435
  pregnancy and, 530–531
  smokeless tobacco, 580
  supplements and cancer risk, 580
  vitamin C and, 353
  vitamin E and, 383
  websites on, 581, 648
Smooth endoplasmic reticulum, **A-2**, A-3f
Snacks
  for adolescents, 578
  for children, 569, 572, 573t
  in exchange lists, G-4t
  for exercise, 487, 498f
  heart health and, 633
  for older adults, 602
  portion sizes, 303
  for weight gain, 308
Social interactions, food choices and, 4, 302, 600, 609
Societal attitudes
  adolescent body weight, 576
  athletes' body weight, 271
  eating disorders and, 272, 276
  prejudice and body weight, 289
  See also Body image

Socioeconomic history, E-2t, **E-3**
Socioeconomic status
  birthweight and, 526
  environmental degradation and, 709–710
  hunger and, 702–704, 702f, 705, 707–709
  lead poisoning and, 564
  malnutrition and, 197, 562
  of older adults, 600
  overpopulation and, 707–709
  See also Food assistance programs
Sodium, **410**–413
  overview of, 413t, 426t
  in antacids, 618
  atomic structure of, B-5
  calcium and potassium, 411, 412f
  calcium loss and, 418
  DASH eating plan, 411, 416, 636
  deficiency, 412, 413t
  Dietary Guidelines and, 40t, 45, 411, 412, 636
  food sources, 411–412, 412f, 413t
  functions of, 410, 413t
  heart disease and, 633
  high-sodium diets, 402–403
  hypertension and, 400, 410–411, 635t, 636, 636t
  hyponatremia, **495**–496
  intake recommendations, 410, 411, 412f, 413t
  on labels, 58
  losses of, 406, 412
  osteoporosis, 411
  in processed foods, 411–412, 412f
  reducing intake, 411
  retention/regulation, 401–402, 403f, 406, A-6
  salt sensitivity, **410**, 410n, 635
  in sports drinks, 495
  toxicity, 413, 413t
  transport proteins and, 192f
  in water, 400
  websites on, 427
Sodium bicarbonate, **504**
Sodium chloride
  in fast foods, 456
  intake recommendations, 410, 411
  iodine in, 456
  ion formation, B-5
  salt tablets, 412, 495
  sodium content of, 411
  See also Chloride
Sodium-potassium pump, 406
Soft drinks
  caffeine content of, 496, 578, H-1t
  cola beverages, 39, 422, H-1t
  diet, 135t
  displacing nutrients, 422
  quantities consumed, 568, 578
  sugar content of, 117–118, 118t, 120, 568
Soft water, **400**–401
Solanine (in potatoes), **677**
Soluble fibers, **106**
  See also Fiber
Solute concentration, **405**
Solutes, **405**
Somatic nervous system, **A-7**, A-8f
Somatostatin (GHIH), **A-5**
Somatotropin (GH), **A-5**
  See also Growth hormone (GH)
Sorbitol, 93, 132, 136t, 618
Soup kitchens, **704**
South Beach Diet, 317t
Soy formulas, 67, 553, 557
Soy "milk," 53, 65
Soy products
  blood cholesterol and, 65, 162, 471, 472f
  cancer and, 469–470, 472f
  heart disease and, 632t
  osteoporosis and, 434
  phytochemicals and, 434, 469–470, 472f

  precautions, 656t
  protein quality, 195
  textured vegetable protein, **53**, **64**, 66
  tofu, **64**, 65, 67n
  vitamin B$_{12}$ and, 344
  zinc absorption, 66
Specific dynamic activity (SDA), **256**
Specific dynamic effect (SDE), **256**
Sperm, **510**
Sphincters, **72**, 73f, 74, 76, 76f
Spina bifida, 340f, 341f, **513**, 514f, 539
  See also Neural tube defects
Spirulina, **504**
Sports. *See* Athletes
"Sports anemia," **493**
Sports drinks, 121, 487, 495, 507
"Spot reducing," 301, 489
Spring water, **400**
St. John's wort, 290, 654f, 657t, 658, 658t
Stanol esters, 472n
Staphylococcus aureus, 665t, 666
Starch, **101**
  in Canadian food groups, I-8t to I-9t
  chemistry/structure of, 105–106, 106f, 107f, **C-2**, C-2f
  digestion and absorption, 79f, 108–109, 109f
  in exchange lists, 48, G-1, G-1t, G-4t
  food sources, 105–106
  glucose and, 105
  health effects of, 122–124
  on labels, 126–127
  recommended intake of, 124–127, 125t
  resistant, **107**
  See also Carbohydrates
Starvation
  BMR and, 255n
  fat and lean tissue losses, 194, 234–235, 250
  ketosis, 156, 235, 235f
  physical consequences of, 272–273
  symptoms of, 236
  See also Eating disorders; Fasting; Malnutrition
Stature-for-age percentiles, E-12f
Stearic acid, 140, 140f, 141t, 157
Sterile, defined, **384**
Steroids, 146n
Steroids, anabolic, **503**, 505, 506t
Sterols, **146**–147, 146n, 147f, 149, 164
Stevia, **132**, 136
Stomach, **72**, 73f
  atrophic gastritis, 343
  carbohydrate digestion, 108, 109f
  fat digestion, 148–149, 148f
  function of, 74, 75, 77, 79f
  gastric juice, **78**
  gastrin and, 87
  hunger sensation and, 251
  muscles of, 75, 75f
  obesity surgery, 292–293, 293f
  peptic ulcers, 97, 97t
  pH of, 77, 77f, 87
  protein digestion, 77, 79f, 185, 186f
Stomach cancer, 65, 97, 644t
Stools, 78
Strength training, 302, 480t, 481, 484
Stress, **597**
  aging process and, 597–598
  epinephrine and, 114
  exercise and, 301
  hormonal response to, A-4, A-5
  overeating and, 252, 304
  supplements and, 364
  vitamin C and, 352
  See also Oxidative stress
Stress eating, **251**
Stress fractures, **270**, 271
Stressors, **597**

Stress response, **598**
Strokes, **626**
  alcohol and, 635
  atherosclerosis and, 627
  blood cholesterol and, 157
  omega-3 fatty acids and, 158
  potassium and, 414
  websites on, 648
Structure-function claims, **59**, 60t, 364
Studies. *See* Research
Subclavian vein, **85**
Subclinical deficiency, **22**
Subjects (of research), 12, **14**
Successful weight-loss maintenance, **305**
Sucralose, **132**, 133t, 134
Sucrase, 108
Sucrose, 104, **104**, C-1f
  See also Sugars
Sucrose polyester, **164**
Sudden infant death syndrome (SIDS), **531**, 556n
Sugar alcohols, **132**, 136, 136n, 136t
Sugar-free (on labels), **58**, 136, 137f
Sugar replacers, **132**, 136, 136t
Sugars, **101**–105, 118
  absorption of, 79f
  alternatives to, 132–137, 133t
  behavior and, 120, 564
  in blood. *See* Blood glucose levels
  chemistry of, 102–105
  dental caries and, 119
  diabetes and, 640–641
  disaccharides. *See* Disaccharides
  discretionary kcalories and, 45
  energy (kcal) in, 117–118, 118t, 120, 121
  in foods, 121
  glycemic index of, 116
  health effects of, 117–121
  heart disease and, 120
  honey *vs.*, 118, 118t, 556
  intake guidelines, 121
  on labels, 58, 117, 118, 121
  monosaccharides. *See* Monosaccharides
  obesity and, 120
  structure of, 102f–104f, C-1 to C-3f
  types of (glossary), **118**
  websites on, 127
  See also Sweets; *specific sugars*
Sugars, added, **117**–121, 568
Sulfate, **425**, 426t, 427
Sulfites, **684**
Sulforaphane, 472f
Sulfur, **425**
Sunlight in synthesis of vitamin D, 377, 379–380, 380f
Superoxide dismutase (SOD), 391n, 458n
Supplements, **360**–365
  amino acids, 185, 202–203, 202n
  antioxidants, 390, 392
  arguments for and against, 360–363
  for arthritis, 606
  for athletes, 202, 492, 497, 503–507, 506t
  average doses, 362t
  beta-carotene, 363, 374, 580
  bioavailability of, 363
  breakfast cereals as, 51
  B vitamins, toxicity of, 349
  caffeine, **503**
  calcium, 361, 363, 416, 436
  carnitine, 346, 503
  for children, 373, 560
  choline, 346, 607
  chromium picolinate, 461, **503**, 504
  "complete" nutrition, 504
  contaminants in, 206, 436
  creatine, **503**, 504–505
  enzymes, 364

ergogenic aids, **503**–507, 506t
fad diets and, 319
fiber, 106–107, 123
fish oil, 159, 531
folate, 338, 340, 514
foods vs., 19, 349, 363, 365, 392–393, 471, 604
herbal. See Herbal medicines/supplements
high potency, **360**, 361, 364
hormonal, 505–506, 506t
for infants, 384–385, 551, 551t
inositol, 346
iron, 360, 361–362, 446, 448, 450–451, 521f, 522, 536
iron overload, 448
iron toxicity, 448
labeling of, 364–365, 365f
during lactation, 536
lecithin as, 145–146
liquid diets, 504, 602
MedWatch (FDA program), 365
minerals, 362t, 655
misinformation on, 34f, 362, 363–364, 503–507
"natural," 34f, 349
need for, determining, 361, 362
nutrient interactions and, 409
for older adults, 603–604
omega-3 fatty acids, 159
potassium, 414–415
during pregnancy, 514, 520, 521f, 522, 523, 523f, 524, 530, 531–532
protein/amino acids, 520
protein powders, 202
quackery and, 34f
regulation of, 136, 363, 364–365, 442
risks associated with, 392–393, 436, 656–659, 656t–658t
salt tablets, 412
selection of, 34f, 363–364, 436, 442
smokers and, 580
statistics on use, 360
stevia, 136
structure-function claims, 364
Tolerable Upper Intake Level, 362t
toxicity, 325–326, 325f, 349, 361–362
trace minerals, 442, 442n
for vegetarians, 67
vitamin A, 373, 374
vitamin B₁₂, 344
vitamin C, 352, 352f, 354, 392, 448
vitamin D, 361, 379, 380
vitamin E, 392–393
vitamin K, 384–385
vitamins, 362t, 655, 656t
websites on, 365, 659
for weight loss, 290, 291t, 296
zinc, 455, 459
See also Functional foods
Support groups, 304
Surgery
in obesity treatment, 285, 292–293, 293f
vitamin C and, 353
Sushi, **670**
Sustainable, defined, **711**
Sustainable agriculture. See under Agriculture
Sustainable development, 708, 711
Swallowing, 72–73, 92, 92f, 599
See also Choking
Sweat, fluid and electrolytes, 398, 412, 493, 494
Sweeteners, artificial. See Artificial sweeteners
Sweets
caffeine content of, H-1t
in Canadian food groups, I-9t
children and, 572
in exchange lists, G-6t
in food group plans, 43f, 45

glycemic index of, 116f
infants and toddlers, 556
nutrient deficiencies and, 117–119
See also Sugars
Sympathetic (nervous system), A-7 to A-8, A-8f
Syndrome X, **630**
Synergistic, defined, **623**

T

Tagatose, **132**, 133t, 134–135
Tannic acid and iron absorption, 444
Tanning lamps, 380
Tannins, 106n, 470t
Taste preferences, 4–5
Taste sensations, 72, 410, 600
Taurine, 182n
Taxol, 655
TCA (Krebs) cycle, **218**
alcohol and, 241, 241f, C-15
biotin and, 333–334
B vitamins and, 35, 347–348, 347f
diagram of, 228f, 231f, C-11f to C-13f
mitochondria's role, A-2, A-2n
niacin and, 331
reactions of, 227–230, 228f, C-11 to C-14, C-15t, C-16f
riboflavin and, 328, 330f
thiamin and, 327
T-cells, **622**–623
Teas, 472f, 655, 656, 658t
See also Caffeine
Technology
food safety, 672–673
genetic engineering, **693**–697, 694f, 697t
See also Food industry
Teenagers. See Adolescence
Teeth
calcium and, 416
dioxins and, 538
fluoride and, 460–461, 461f, 551
loss with age, 599–600
malnutrition and, E-17t
smoking and, 580
structure of, 119f
vitamin C and, 353, 363
See also Dental caries
Television
obesity and, 288, 569
validity of information on, 30–31
Tempeh, **64**, 65
Temperature regulation, 579, A-7 to A-8
See also Hyperthermia; Hypothermia
Teosinte, 693, 693f
Teratogenic, defined, **374**
Term (infant), **516**
Terrorism, 621, 663
Testosterone, 282, 434–435, A-5, A-7
Tetracycline, 616
Tetrahydrofolate (THF), **338**
Tetrahydrofolic acid, C-7f
Textured vegetable protein, 53, **64**, 66
Thermic effect of food, 254, 254f, **256**, 318
Thermogenesis, 253–256, 256, 307
THF (tetrahydrofolate), **338**
Thiamin, **327**–328
overview of, 329t
alcohol abuse and, 327
cooking and, 324, 328
deficiency, 244, 327, 328f
food sources, 328, 328f, 329
functions of, 327, 328f, 347f
RDA/recommendations, 327, 328f
structure of, C-5f
sulfites and, 684
Wernicke-Korsakoff syndrome and, **239**, 244, **328**

Thiamin pyrophosphate (TPP), **327**, 347f, C-5f
Thioredoxin reductase, 391n
Thirst, **398**, 401, 410, 601
Thoracic duct, **85**
Thrombin, 384f
Thrombosis, **626**, 627
Thromboxanes, 627
Thrombus, **626**
Thyroid disease website, 465
Thyroid gland, 417f, 456, 456f, 677
Thyroid hormone, 255n, 455–456, A-4, **A-5**
Thyroid-stimulating hormone (TSH), 456, A-4, **A-5**
Thyroxin, 191t, 194, **455**, A-5
Tobacco. See Smoking/tobacco use
Tocopherol equivalents (TE), 383
Tocopherols, **381**, 393, C-9f
See also Vitamin E
Tofu, **64**, 65, 67n
Tolerable Upper Intake Level, **18**, inside front cover
high doses of nutrients and, 325–326, 325f
preventing toxicity, 18, 18f
supplement doses, 362t
Tolerance level (pesticide residue), **567**, **678**
Tomatoes, 470, 472f, 694
Tongue: glossitis, 330n, 333n, 349f
Tooth decay. See Dental caries
Total iron-binding capacity (TIBC), E-20 to E-21, E-21t
Toxemia, **528**
Toxicants, natural, 677–678
Toxicity, **663**
alcohol, 238, 244, 543–545
amino acid supplements and, 203
aspartame metabolites, 134
beta-carotene supplements, 374
B vitamin supplements, 349
food intoxications, 666
herbal remedies, 657t, 658
laboratory tests and, 21
laetrile and, 346, 653
lead, 463, 463t, 531, 553, 564, 565
liver's function and, 84
naturally occurring in foods, 677–678
nutrient-drug interactions, 617
safe vs. toxic nutrient intakes, 18, 18f
solanine in potatoes, **677**
supplement dosage, 325–326, 325f, 349, 361–362
vitamin A in liver, 376
See also Contaminants; Environmental contaminants; Foodborne illnesses; Pesticides; specific nutrients
TPP (thiamin pyrophosphate), **327**, 347f, C-5f
Trabecular bone, **431**–432, 432f
Trace minerals. See Minerals, trace
Trachea, 73f, 92, 92f, **94**
Training (physical), **480**
See also Physical activity
Transamination, **225**, 226f
Transcription, **187**
Trans-fatty acids. See Fatty acids, trans-
Transferrin, **443**
half-life of, E-19n
in iron absorption, 443, 443f, 444
in iron deficiency, 446
in iron transport, 443, 445, 445f
normal serum value, E-19t
in PEM, E-19
in zinc absorption, 452–453
Transferrin saturation, E-21, E-21t
Transfer RNA, protein synthesis and, 187, 188f
Transient hypertension of pregnancy, **528**
Transient ischemic attack (TIA), **626**, 627
Translation, **187**

Transport (nutrient), 83–85
  active, 81f, 108
  diffusion, 81f, 108
  of electrolytes, 405–406
  of lipids, 149–150, 150–153, 152f, 153f
  liver and, 83–84, 85f
  lymphatic system, 82, 83, 84–85, 149–150
  vascular system and, 83–84, 84f, 85f
  See also specific nutrients
Transport proteins, 191, 192f
Transthyretin, E-18, E-19t
Travelers' diarrhea, 672, 673
Triacylglycerols. See Triglycerides
Tricarboxylic acid cycle. See TCA (Krebs) cycle
Triglycerides, 142
  blood levels, 156, 628t
  body vs. food composition, 139
  functions of, 153–154
  heart disease and, 628t, 630
  hydrolysis of, 149, 151f, 155
  metabolism of, 215f
  structure of, 142, 143f, 224f
  transport of, 150–152
  See also Fats; Fatty acids
Trimesters, 512
Tripeptidases, 185, 186f
Tripeptide, 183
Trypsin, in protein digestion, 186f
Tryptophan
  in complementary proteins, 196f
  gelatin lacking, 195
  niacin and, 194, 331, 332, 336
  for pain/sleep, 203
  serotonin and, 194
  supplements, 203
TSH-releasing hormone (TRH), A-5
TSH (thyroid-stimulating hormone), A-4, A-5
Tuberculosis and vitamin B₆, 336
Tumors, 642, 643f
24-hour recall, E-3 to E-4
Tyramine, MAO inhibitors and, 617, 618t
Tyrosine, 183, 194, 209

U

Ubiquinone (coenzyme Q₁₀), 346
Ulcers, gastrointestinal, 13f, 94, 97, 97t
Ulcers, pressure, 602
Ultimate Weight Solution Diet, 317t
Ultrahigh temperature (UHT) treatment, 610, 672
Umbilical cord, 510, 511f
Umbilicus, 510
Unavailable carbohydrates, 108
  See also Fiber
Uncoupling proteins, 286
Undernutrition, 20
Underweight, 259
  bone density and, 435
  fashion and BMI, 258–259, 258f
  ghrelin and, 285
  health risks of, 262, 264–265, 264f, 307
  older adults, 602
  pregnancy and, 264–265, 509, 516, 517f, 517t
  strategies for weight gain, 299t, 307–308
  See also Eating disorders; Weight gain;
    Weight loss
UNICEF (United Nations International
  Children's Emergency Fund), 562
United States
  body weight statistics, 260f, 282f
  death, causes of, 24, 24t, 25t, 624f
  Dietary Guidelines for Americans, 39–41, 40t
  hunger in, 702–705, 702f
  population of older adults, 593, 594f
Unsaturated fats, 141
  replacing saturated fats, 162, 162f, 163, 164,
    164t, 166f, 176f

See also Monounsaturated fats;
    Polyunsaturated fats
Unsaturated fatty acids, 140f–142f, 141–142,
    141t, 142–144, C-3t
Unsaturation, point of, 141
Upper-body fat, 262–263, 262f, 263f
Urea, 226
  excretion of, 194, 226, 227f
  synthesis of, 226, 226f
Urea cycle, C-15 to C-16, C-16f
Urine, 399, 400, 402f
  See also Urea
U.S. Pharmacopoeia (USP), 363
USDA Food Guide, 41–47
  exchange system and, 47–48
  food groups, choices within, 42f–43f
  sample menus, 48t, 49f
  serving sizes, 42f–43f, 46
  vegetarian diets and, 44, 46
  See also Discretionary kcalorie allowance; Food
    group plans
USDA (U.S. Department of Agriculture), 664,
    668, 669f, 697, 703–704
Uterus, 510, 511f
UV light, 380, 380n

V

Valerian, 655, 657t, 658t
Validity (research), 14, 15
Values (beliefs) and food choices, 4–5
Vanadium, 462
Variables (research), 12, 14
Variety (dietary), 39
  absorption and, 89
  overeating and, 303
  in vegetarian diets, 67
  for vitamins and minerals, 329
Vascular system, 83–84
  angiotensin and, 400
  in diabetes, 640
  in intestinal villi, 82f
  nutrient absorption and, 83–84, 84f, 85f
  nutrient transport and, 83–84
  oxygen delivery, 84f, 483f
  renin and, 400
  vitamin C and, 353f
  vitamin E and, 382
  See also Atherosclerosis; Cardiovascular dis-
    ease (CVD); Hypertension
Vasoconstrictor, 401
Vasopressin, 401, A-3
  See also ADH (antidiuretic hormone)
Vegans, 64
  adequacy of diet, 67
  children's diets, 559
  fiber and, 123
  fossil fuel use in farming, 719f
  infants' diets, 379, 557
  during pregnancy, 520, 524
  riboflavin and, 330
  vitamin B₁₂ and, 343, 344, 520, 524
  vitamin D and, 379, 524
  See also Vegetarian diets
Vegetables
  antioxidants in, 391–392, 393, 470
  calcium and, 65, 419, 419f, 420f
  in Canadian food groups, I-10t
  cancer and, 65, 391–392, 470, 643, 644t,
    645, 646t
  carbohydrate content of, 126
  cooking of, 674
  cruciferous, 456, 645, 677
  discretionary kcalories and, 45
  DNA and, 391–392
  in exchange lists, 48, G-1t, G-3t, G-4t, G-7t
  fat intake and, 162–163

fiber content of, 125t
  "5 to 9 a day" campaign, 52f
  flavonoids in, 471, 472f
  in food group plans, 41t, 42f, 44, 44t, 46t, 47f,
    48f, 49f, 52
  glycemic index of, 116f
  goitrogen-containing, 677
  heart disease and, 392, 471, 630, 633
  intake recommendations, 41t, 44
  intake statistics, 561–562, 569
  nutrient density, 329, 330
  nutrients in, 42f, 44, 393
  starchy, 48
  vitamin A in, 375–376, 375f
  websites on, 52f, 61, 357
  See also Phytochemicals; Plant foods
Vegetarian, 64
Vegetarian diets, 64–68
  athletes, 492
  calcium and, 65, 66–67, 67n
  cancer and, 65
  environmental impact of, 719, 719f
  food pyramids for, 65–66, 66f
  health benefits of, 65, 175
  for infants and children, 379, 557
  iron and, 65–66, 444, 449, 492
  omega-3 fatty acids, 67
  pregnancy/lactation, 520
  protein and, 65, 66, 196
  supplements for, 67, 361
  USDA Food Guide and, 44, 46
  vitamin B₁₂ and, 66, 67, 343, 344
  vitamin D and, 66, 67, 379
  websites for, 67
  zinc and, 66
  See also Vegans
Veins, 83, 84f
  See also Vascular system
Vertebrae, collapse of, 432, 433f
Very-low-density lipoprotein. See VLDL
Vibrio bacteria, 665n, 665t, 670n
Villus/villi, 80–81, 82f
Violence and alcohol, 245
Viscous, defined, 106
Viscous fibers, 123t
Vision
  blindness, 371, 373, 373f
  cataracts, 604–605
  in diabetes, 640
  infant diet and, 550–551
  leptin and, 285
  macular degeneration, 605
  night blindness, 373, 373f
  in older adults, 600, 604–605
  opsin, 192
  retina, structure of, 371f
  vitamin A and, 244, 370–371, 371f, 373, 373f
  vitamin E and, 382
  websites on, 611
  See also Blindness
Vitamin A, 369–377
  overview of, 376t–377t, 386t
  absorption/transport, 370
  activity, 369, H-0
  cancer and, 656t
  deficiency, 372–374, 373f, 376t, 562, 706
  food sources, 346t, 374–376, 375f
  forms of, 369, 370f, C-5f
  functions of, 369–372, 371f, 373f, 436
  genetically engineered foods, 694
  megadoses in pregnancy, 532
  precursors, 369, 370f, 375
  preformed, 374
  pregnancy and, 374
  RDA/recommendations, 374, 375f, 376t
  storage of, 372, 376n

structure of, C-5f
supplements, 372–373, 374
toxicity, 374, 376, 377t
zinc and, 452, 453
See also Beta-carotene
Vitamin A activity, **369**
Vitamin B$_1$. *See* Thiamin
Vitamin B$_2$. *See* Riboflavin
Vitamin B$_3$. *See* Niacin
Vitamin B$_5$, 346
Vitamin B$_6$, **336**–337
  overview of, 337t, 356t
  alcohol use and, 244
  antagonists of, 336
  cooking and, 336
  deficiency, 244, 336, 337t, 618
  food sources, 336–337, 337f, 339f
  functions of, 336, 337t
  isoniazid (INH) and, 618
  RDA/recommendations, 336, 337f, 339f
  riboflavin and, 346
  structure/forms of, C-6f, C-7f
  toxicity, 336, 337t
Vitamin B$_{12}$, **343**–345
  overview of, 345t, 356t
  cobalt and, 462, 462f
  cooking and, 344–345
  deficiency, 342–344, 344f, 345t, E-20t, E-22, E-22t
  enterohepatic circulation, 343
  folate and, 340, 342–343, 343–344, 344f, 514
  food sources, 344–345, 345t
  functions of, 342–343, 345t
  gene expression and, 208, 209f
  intrinsic factor and absorption of, 343
  for older adults, 602–603, 604
  during pregnancy, 520, 521f, 524
  RDA/recommendations, 343, 345t
  serum levels, E-22, E-22t
  structure of, C-7f
  supplements, 344
  vegetarian diets, 66, 67
Vitamin B$_{15}$, 346
Vitamin B$_{17}$, 346
Vitamin C, 350–355
  overview of, 355t, 356t
  active forms of, 351f
  anticoagulant, 656t
  as antioxidant, 351, 351f, 352, 354, 391, 392
  cancer and, 392
  cataracts and, 605
  cooking and, 324, 354
  deficiency, 350, 353, 353f, 355t, 356t
  food sources, 354, 355f, 355t, 356t
  functions of, 351–352, 355t
  heart disease and, 13f, 392, 393
  for infants, 556
  iron absorption and, 66, 351, 354, 444, 448, 522
  iron absorption from supplements, 451
  overview, 355t, 356t
  during pregnancy, 522
  as prooxidant, 354, 448
  RDA/recommendations, 352–353, 352f, 355t
  research example, 12–15
  in smokers, 580
  stress and, 352
  structure of, C-8f
  supplements, 352, 352f, 354
  tooth enamel and, 363
  toxicity, 353–354, 356t
Vitamin D, 377–379
  overview of, 381t, 386t
  activation of, 377, 377f
  adolescent needs, 576
  AI/recommendations, 379–380, 381t

bone growth, 377, 378
calcium absorption, 377, 378, A-6
calcium and, 417, 417f, 418
calcium in bone, 434, 436
deficiency, 377f, 378–379, 381t, 551
food sources, 379, 381t
forms of, 377, 381t, C-8f
functions of, 377, A-6
infant needs, 551, 551t
milk fortification with, 330, 330n
for older adults, 603
pregnancy and, 521f, 522–523
skin color and, 380
structure of, 147f, C-8f
supplements, 361, 379, 380
synthesis of, 147f, 377, 377f, 379–380, 380f, 380n, C-8f
toxicity, 379, 381t
vegetarian diets, 66, 67
Vitamin D$_2$, **377**
Vitamin D$_3$, **377**, C-8f
Vitamin E, 381–383
  overview of, 383t, 386t
  activity, H-0
  as antioxidant, 382, 391
  for athletes, 492
  beta-carotene and, 363
  cancer and, 392, 656t
  cataracts and, 605
  cooking and, 383
  deficiency, 382, 383t
  food sources, 383, 383t
  functions of, 382, 383t
  heart disease and, 392
  lungs, protection of, B-8
  RDA/recommendations, 382–383, 383t
  structure of, C-9f
  supplements, 392, 393
  tocopherols, 381–382, 393, C-9f
  toxicity, 382, 393
  vitamin K and, 363
Vitamin impostors, 346
Vitamin K, 383–385
  overview of, 385t, 386t
  AI/recommendations, 385, 385t
  anticoagulants and, 617
  deficiency, 383–384, 385t
  food sources, 385, 385t
  functions of, 383–384, 384f, 436
  medications and, 384
  structure of, C-9f
  synthesis of, 86, 383, 385n, 385t
  toxicity, 385, 385t
  vitamin E and, 363, 382
Vitamin P, 346
Vitamins, **10**, 323–357, 369–388
  overview of, 323–326, 326t
  absorption of, 79f, 325, 363
  as additives, 684
  adolescent needs, 576
  as alternative medicines, 655
  assessment tests, E-18t
  bioavailability of, **324**, 363
  brain function and, 606t
  for children, 560
  coenzymes and, 327f
  cooking/losses, 324, 324t
  destruction of, 324t
  dose levels, effects of, 325–326, 325f
  elements in, 7t
  evaluating foods for, 329
  for exercise, 491–493
  fat-soluble. *See* Vitamins, fat-soluble
  functions of, 10, 323
  "impostors," 346
  infant needs, 549, 549f, 556

lactation and, 521f, 535
minimizing loss of, 674
non-B vitamins, 345–346
for older adults, 602–603
physiological *vs.* pharmacological effects of, 332
precursors, **324**
pregnancy and, 520, 521f, 522–523, 531–532
RDA and AI for, inside front cover
solubility of, 324–325
storage of, 325, 336
structure of, 323, C-5f to C-9f
supplement overview, **360**–365, 362t, 365f
Tolerable Upper Intake Level, 325–326, 362t, inside front cover
toxicity of, 325–326, 325f
water-soluble. *See* Vitamins, water-soluble
websites on, 357, 365, 387
in whole grains, 51f
See also B vitamins; Deficiencies; DRI; Nutrient interactions; Toxicity; *specific vitamins*
Vitamins, fat-soluble, 369–388
  overview of, 324–325, 326t, 369, 385–386, 386t
  absorption of, 165, 369
  food sources, 324
  listed, 10n, 324, 369
  mineral oil and, 95
  olestra and, 165
  storage of, 325, 369
  transport of, 325, 369
  websites on, 387
  See also specific vitamins
Vitamins, water-soluble, 323–357
  overview of, 324–325, 326t, 356t
  food sources, 325
  listed, 10n, 324
  websites on, 357
  See also specific vitamins
Vitamin tablets. *See* Supplements
VLDL (very-low-density lipoprotein), **151**, 151n, 153f
Volume, metric units, 8
Volunteer health agencies, websites, 33
VO$_2$ max, **482**, 483f
Vomiting, 92–93, **94**
  acid-base balance, 413, 413n
  in bulimia nervosa, 274–275, 274t
  fluids and electrolyte imbalance, 406
  by infants, 93
  metabolic alkalosis and, 413n
  during pregnancy, 524, 524t
  projectile vomiting, 93
  sodium and electrolyte balance, 412

W

Wadsworth website, 26
Waist circumference, **263**, 263n, E-15, E-15f
Waist-to-hip ratio, 263n, E-15
Walnuts, 173
War and famine, 705–706
Warfarin (Coumadin), 617
Warm-up, **481**
Water, 397–405
  ADH and retention of, 401
  alcohol use and, 243
  for athletes, 493–496, 494t, 496–497
  blood pressure and, 401–402
  blood volume and, 401–402, 403f
  body composition, 6, 6f
  bottled, **400**, 401, 689
  contamination of, 687–689
  disinfection of, 690
  electrolytes and, 404f
  exercise and, 496
  fluoridation of, 460, 461f, 689
  food composition, 6, 399t

Water, *continued*
functions of, 11, 397, 404f
hard *vs.* soft, **400**–401, 424
health effects summary, 400–401
home treatment systems, 688–689
infant needs, 549
intake recommendations, 399–401
during lactation, 535–536
losses, routes of, 399, 399n, 399t
minerals in, 400–401, 420, 424
molecular structure of, 7t, B-4f, B-6, B-7f
obligatory water excretion, **399**
for older adults, 602
oxygenated, 505
protein intake and, 226
regulation of, 688–689
sources of, 398–399, 399t
sources of drinking water, 688
thirst *vs.* need, 398
for travelers, 673
types of, **400**–401
websites on, 691
weight loss and, 250, 297
See also Beverages; Dehydration; Fluid balance
Water balance, **398**–401, 399f, 399t
See also Electrolytes; Fluid balance
Water intoxication, **398**
Water pollution/contamination
bacterial, 687, 688
effects on food production, 709
groundwater, 688
infants formulas and, 553
lead poisoning, 565
nonpoint water pollution, **716,** 717
safety, 687–689
seafood and, 670, 675–676, 675f
soft water and, 401
Water scarcity, 709, 716
Water-soluble vitamins. *See* Vitamins, water-soluble
Wean, defined, **552**
Websites, **32**
for this book, 26
assessing validity of, 30, 31, 33, 503
accredited schools, 34
adolescence, 581
aging, 611–612
agriculture, 720
AIDS/HIV, 648
alcohol/alcoholism, 247
allergies/adverse reactions to foods, 581
alternative therapies, 659
Alzheimer's disease, 612
anorexia nervosa, 277
arthritis, 612
artificial sweeteners, 137
birth defects, 539
body weight, 266
breastfeeding, 539
bulimia nervosa, 277
caffeine, 581
calcium, 427
Canadian, 26, 33, 34
cancer, 648
child nutrition, 580–581
cholesterol, 168
chronic diseases, 648
consumer groups, 33
consumer health, 648
DASH diet, 648
dental caries, 127
diabetes, 33, 127, 589, 648
Dietary Guidelines, 40t
dietitians, 33, 34
diet planning, 61

digestion and absorption, 90
digestive problems, 98
DRI (Dietary Reference Intakes), 26
drug abuse, 247
eating disorders, 277
exchange lists, 61
exercise, 499–500, 581, 648
fad diets, 321
FAO, 26
fat intake, 168
fetal alcohol syndrome, 545
fiber, 127
Fight Bac!, 667f
fitness, 499–500
"5 to 9 a day" campaign, 52f, 61
foodborne illnesses, 667f, 690
food pyramids, 67, 580
food safety, 690–691
Food Surveys Research Group, 26
fraud/quackery, 34
functional foods, 473
genetic engineering, 697
gestational diabetes, 539
government health agencies, 26, 33, 61, 499–500
Healthy People 2010, 26
heart disease, 168
herbal supplements, 659
hunger, world, 704, 712t, 713
hyperactivity, 581
infants, 580–581
iodine, 465
iron overload, 465
irradiation, 690
journals, 33
labeling of foods, 61
lactose intolerance, 127
lead poisoning, 581
malnutrition, 204
Mayo Clinic, 26
MedWatch (FDA), 690
milk, 427, 581
minerals, 365, 427, 465
neural tube defects, 357
NHANES, 26
nutrition, overviews of, 26
nutritional genomics, 211
organic foods, 691
osteoporosis, 437
pregnancy, 539
professional organizations, 33
sickle-cell anemia, 204
smoking/tobacco use, 581, 648
sodium, 427
spina bifida, 357
stroke, 648
sugars, 127
supplements, 365, 659
thyroid disease, 465
vegetables, 357
vegetarian diets, 67
vitamins, 357, 365
volunteer health agencies, 33
water, 691
weight control, 581, 589
WHO, 26
WIC program, 539
Weight, metric units, 8, inside back cover
Weight (body), 258–267
accepting yourself, 259t
of adults in U.S., 260f, 282f
Alzheimer's disease and, 607
of athletes, 258, 259, 261–262, 270, 271–272, 271f
body image and, 258–260, 258f, 272, 276, 289
cardiorespiratory fitness and, 266

energy consumption and, 10
food choices and, 5
ghrelin and, **285**–286
for healthy adults, 258–260, 259t, 260–263, 260f, 260t
of infants, 547f, 548f. *See also* Birthweight
measurement of, E-6 to E-7, E-7f, E-8f to E-15f, E-14 to E-15
mortality and, 263, 264f
osteoporosis risk and, 264
overweight *vs.* overfat, 258, 259
smoking and, 579
See also Body composition; Fats (body); Obesity; Obesity treatment; Overweight; Underweight; Weight gain; Weight loss; Weight management
Weight cycling, 274, 289f
Weight-for-age percentiles, 548f, E-8f, E-11f
Weight-for-length percentiles, E-10f
Weight-for-stature percentiles, E-13f
Weight gain, 307–308
alcohol and, 243
by athletes, 272
cognitive influences, 251
exercise and, 254, 308
fat *vs.* muscle, 308
health and, 263–266
of infants, 547–548, 547f, 548f
leptin and, 284–285, 285f
lipoprotein lipase (LPL), 282–283
marijuana and, 579
medications and, 615
overnutrition, **20,** 232–233
during pregnancy, 515–518, 517f, 517t, 518f, 528, 529
preventing, 306
proteins (dietary) and, 194
set-point theory of, **283**
strategies for, 299t, 307–308
Weight loss, 294–299
behavior modification, **303**
benefits of, 294
bill of rights, 290t
body composition and, 250
bone density and, 435
carbohydrates and, 120
for children, 569–571
cocaine use, 579
dangers of, 289–291
in diabetes, 641
eating plans, 295–298, 295t, 296t, 297f, 299t
exercise and, 254, 299–301, 305, 495
expectations and goals, 294–295, 294f
fad diets, **290,** 315–321, 316t, 317t, 320t
fat and, 156, 295t, 296t, 297f, 299t
fat *vs.* lean tissue, 250, 296
fish and, 159
gimmicks, 291
hypertension and, 635
kcalories and, 295–296, 295t
ketosis-producing diets, 113, 235, 319–320, 320t
leptin and, 284–285, 285f
low-fat foods, 296
maintaining, 283, 285
metabolism and, 283, 300, 305
myths *vs.* facts, 315–320, 316t
need for, judging, 288–289
in older adults, 598, 602
pregnancy, after, 518, 535
pregnancy, during 516, 532
proteins (dietary) and, 200
regaining weight, 282–283, 298
safe rate of, 295
set-point theory of, **283**
"spot reducing," 301–302, 489

statistics on, 288
strategies for, 299–302, 299t
successful weight-loss maintenance, **305**
supplements for, 291t, 296
support groups, 304
undernutrition, **20**
vs. fat loss, 320
websites on, 581, 589
See also Diets; Eating disorders; Obesity treatment
Weight management, **281**–310
artificial sweeteners and, 135
attitude and, 303–304
calcium and, 416
carbohydrates, 101, 113, 297, 298
Dietary Guidelines and, 40t, 570
exchange groups and, G-2
exercise and, 299–302, 479, 482, 489
fiber and, 123
food records for, 304f
glycemic index and, 115–116
health and, 294–295
Healthy People 2010 goals, 23t
heart disease and, 630
nutrient density and, 39, 45
during pregnancy, 515–518, 517f, 517t
proteins (dietary) and, 200
public health strategies, 306–307, 306t
strategies for, 299t
successful weight-loss maintenance, **305**
sugar and, 120
vegetarian diets and, 65
water and, 297
weight cycling and, 289f
See also Diet planning
Weight training, 435, 480t, **484**

Well water, **400**
Wernicke-Korsakoff syndrome, **239**, 244, **328**
Wheat, 50–51, 50f
    See also Breads; Grains
Wheat germ, 50f
Whey protein (supplement), **202**
White blood cells, 622–623
White flour. *See* Grains
Whole grain. *See* Grains, whole
WHO (World Health Organization), **664**
    nutrition standards, 19, 121, I-1
    vitamin A and, 372–373
    website/address, 26
    See also FAO
WIC (Special Supplemental Food Program for Women, Infants, and Children), 527, 529, 536, 539
Wilson's disease, 459
Wine, 238, **239**, 239f, 244t
Women
    calcium intake, 421, 436
    iron intake, 449
    iron losses, 443n, 446, 577
    See also Gender differences
World Health Organization. *See* WHO
World Wide Web, **32**
    See also Websites

X

Xanthophylls, **376**
Xenical, 292n
Xerophthalmia, **373**
Xerosis, **373**
Xylitol, 132, 136t
Xylose, C-2f

Y

Yeast, 344, 453n
Yersiniosis, 665t
Yogurt, **86**, 111, 162
Yohimbe, 657t
Yohimbine, 291t

Z

Zeaxanthin, 370n, 470n, 472f
Zinc, 452–455, 464t
    overview of, 455t
    absorption of, 66, 452, 453f, 455n, 522
    in breast milk, 551
    copper absorption and, 453, 459
    deficiency, 452, 453, 453f, 455t, 562
    enteropancreatic circulation, **452**, 453f
    food sources, 66, 454, 454f
    functions of, 452, 453, 455t, 522
    iron and, 453, 522
    metabolism, 452–453, 453f
    nutrient interactions, 453
    phytates and, 452
    in pregnancy, 521f, 522
    RDA/intake recommendations, 454, 454f, 455t
    storage in liver, 453f
    supplements, 455, 459
    toxicity, 454, 455t
    transport of, 452–453
    vegetarian diets, 66
Zinc gluconate, 455
Zone Diet, 317t
Zygote, **510**, 511f, 512f

Aids to Calculation

Many mathematical problems have been worked out in the "How to" sections of the text and practice problems have been provided in the "Nutrition Calculations" sections at the end of some chapters. These pages offer additional help and examples.

Conversions

A conversion factor is a fraction that converts a measurement expressed in one unit to another unit—for example, from pounds to kilograms or from feet to meters. To create a conversion factor, an equality (such as 1 kilogram = 2.2 pounds) is expressed as a fraction:

$$\frac{1\ kg}{2.2\ lb}\ \text{and}\ \frac{2.2\ lb}{1\ kg}$$

To convert the units of a measurement, use the fraction with the desired unit in the numerator.

Example 1: Convert a weight of 130 pounds to kilograms. Multiply 130 pounds by the conversion factor that includes both pounds and kilograms, with the desired unit (kilograms) in the numerator:

$$130\ lb \times \frac{1\ kg}{2.2\ lb} = \frac{130\ kg}{2.2} = 59\ kg$$

Alternatively, to convert a measurement from one unit of measure to another, multiply the given measurement by the appropriate equivalent found in the accompanying table of weights and measures.

Example 2: Convert 64 fluid ounces to liters. Locate the equivalent measure from the table (1 ounce = 0.03 liter) and multiply the number of ounces by 0.03:

$$64\ oz \times 0.03\ oz/L = 1.9\ L$$

Percentages

A percentage is a fraction whose denominator is 100. For example:

$$50\% = \frac{50}{100}$$

Like other fractions, percentages are used to express a portion of a quantity. Fractions whose denominators are numbers other than 100 can be converted to percentages by first dividing the numerator by the denominator and then multiplying the result by 100.

Example 3: Express $5/8$ as a percent.

$$\frac{5}{8} = 5 \div 8 = 0.625$$

$$0.625 \times 100 = 62.5\%$$

The following examples show how to calculate specific percentages.

Example 4: Suppose your energy intake for the day is 2000 kcalories (kcal) and your recommended energy intake is 2400 kcalories. What percent of the recommended energy intake did you consume?

Divide your intake by the recommended intake.
   2000 kcal (intake) ÷ 2400 kcal (recommended) = 0.83

Multiply by 100 to express the decimal as a percent.
   0.83 × 100 = 83%

Example 5: Suppose a man's intake of vitamin C is 120 milligrams and his RDA is 90 milligrams. What percent of the RDA for vitamin C did he consume?

Divide the intake by the recommended intake.
   120 mg (intake) ÷ 90 mg (RDA) = 1.33

Multiply by 100 to express the decimal as a percent.
   1.33 × 100 = 133%

Example 6: Dietary recommendations suggest that carbohydrates provide 45 to 65 percent of the day's energy intake. If your energy intake is 2000 kcalories, how much carbohydrate should you eat?

Because this question has a range of acceptable answers, work the problem twice. First, use 45% to find the least amount you should eat.

Divide 45 by 100 to convert to a decimal.
   45 ÷ 100 = 0.45

Multiply kcalories by 0.45.
   2000 kcal × 0.45 = 900 kcal

Divide kcalories by 4 to convert carbohydrate kcal to grams.
   900 kcal ÷ 4 kcal/g = 225 g

Now repeat the process using 65% to find the maximum number of grams of carbohydrates you should eat.

Divide 65 by 100 to convert it to a decimal.
   65 ÷ 100 = 0.65

Multiply kcalories by 0.65.
   2000 kcal × 0.65 = 1300 kcal

Divide kcalories by 4 to convert carbohydrate kcal to grams.
   1300 kcal ÷ 4 kcal/g = 325 g

If you plan for between 45% and 65% of your 2000-kcalorie intake to be from carbohydrates, you should eat between 225 grams and 325 grams of carbohydrates.